Proceedings of the
XXVII International Conference on

High Energy Physics

20–27 July 1994, Glasgow, Scotland, UK

Proceedings of the XXVII International Conference on

High Energy Physics

Volume II: Parallel Sessions

20–27 July 1994, Glasgow, Scotland, UK

Edited by

P J Bussey and I G Knowles

Department of Physics and Astronomy
University of Glasgow

Institute of Physics Publishing, Bristol and Philadelphia

British Library Cataloguing in Publication Data

A catalogue record for this book is available from the British Library

ISBN 0-7503-0123-6   Vol. I
     0-7503-0124-4   Vol. II
     0-7503-0125-2   (2 vol. set)

Library of Congress Cataloging-in-Publication Data are available

Published by Institute of Physics Publishing, wholly owned by The Institute of Physics, London
Techno House, Redcliffe Way, Bristol BS1 6NX, UK
US Editorial Office: Institute of Physics Publishing, The Public Ledger Building, Suite 1035,
Independence Square, Philadelphia, PA 19106, USA

Printed in the UK by Galliard (Printers) Ltd, Great Yarmouth, Norfolk

Contents

VOLUME I

PLENARY SESSIONS

Pl-1 Top Quark Searches

Pl-2 Precision Tests of the Electroweak Interaction

Pl-3 Electroweak Theory at the Z^0 and above

Pl-4 Low x Physics, Deep Inelastic Scattering and Structure Functions

Pl-5 Beyond the Standard Model

Pl-6 Searches for New Particles

Pl-7 Non-Perturbative Methods

Pl-22 Conference Summary

VOLUME II

PARALLEL SESSIONS
Pa-1 Electroweak Interactions

Pa-2 Heavy Quark Physics

Pa-3 Heavy Ion Collisions

Pa-4 Beyond the Standard Model

Pa-5 Low x Physics

Pa-6 DIS and Structure Functions

Pa-7 Neutrino Masses, Mixing and Oscillations

Pa-11 QCD and Jet Physics

Pa-14 Flavour Production on Hadronic Targets

Pa-15 Non-Perturbative Methods

Pa-16 Weak Decays

Pa-17 Experimental Techniques

Pa-18 Top Quark Searches

Pa-19 Field Theory and String Theory

Pa-20 Low Q^2 and Soft Phenomena

Pa-21 Rare Decays

Pa-22 New Detectors and their Physics Aims

Pa-23 Light Quark and Gluonium Spectroscopy

Pa-24 Future Accelerators

Electroweak Interactions

Conveners: W. D. Schlatter (CERN)
T. Riemann (DESY-IFH Zeuthen)

Scientific secretaries: J. Skullerud
G. Jenkins

Energy Calibration with Resonant Depolarization at LEP

R. Assmann[†], A. Blondel[§], B. Dehning[‡], A. Dress[‡], P. Grosse-Wiesmann[‡], R. Jacobsen[‡],
M. Jonker[‡], J.P. Koutchouk[‡], J. Miles[‡], M. Placidi[‡], R. Schmidt[‡], J. Wenninger[‡]

‡ CERN, Geneva, Switzerland
† Max-Planck-Institut für Physik, Werner-Heisenberg-Institut, München, Germany
§ Ecole Polytechnique, Paris, France

Abstract

The 1993 LEP running was devoted to an improved measurement of the mass and the resonance width of the Z boson. The achieved precision depends crucially on an accurate calibration of the LEP beam energy. The determination of the spin precession frequency by resonant depolarization is the most powerful technique to perform such an energy calibration. During 1993 the understanding of polarization build up and preservation was improved and regular energy calibrations were done at the end of luminosity fills distributed over all three operational beam energies. A well tested model for the energy variations could be developed and detailed investigations on the systematic uncertainty of the energy scale were performed. New values of the Z boson mass and width with an uncertainty in the MeV range can be expected.

1. Introduction

A measurement of the spin precession frequency of a transverse polarized electron beam by controlled resonant depolarization is a unique tool for an accurate measurement of the average beam energy. The determination of the absolute energy scale is reduced to a frequency measurement. The technique had been pioneered in Novosibirsk and was subsequently applied to the accurate measurement of several particle masses [1]. For an accurate energy calibration at LEP the attainable precision is more than an order of magnitude better as provided by other available techniques and the error in the determination of the electroweak mass and width parameter is dominated by the error on the beam energy.

The delicate procedures to establish and measure polarization for energy calibration in LEP are described in two Ph.D. theses [2, 3] and the results presented in this proceedings are discussed in more detail in two forthcoming papers [5, 6].

2. Resonant Depolarization Principle

The motion of a classical spin vector of a relativistic electron in electromagnetic fields is described by the Thomas-BMT equation. For electrons that only see the vertical bending field of the storage ring it precesses $a\gamma$ times during one machine turn. a is the magnetic anomaly and γ the Lorentz factor of the electron. The spin tune is defined as $a\gamma$. Its average value ν_0 for electrons is proportional to the average beam energy E:

$$\nu_0 = a\gamma = \frac{E[\text{MeV}]}{440.6486(1)}$$

The vertical component of the spin vector is conserved in an e^+e^- storage ring with purely vertical magnetic fields. Due to the Sokolov-Ternov effect vertical polarization can build up to a maximum of 92.4%. Any non-vertical magnetic fields can perturb the spin precession and subsequently reduce the attainable level of transverse polarization; therefore great care has to be taken to the vertical alignment of the LEP quadrupoles. After applying refined spin matching techniques high

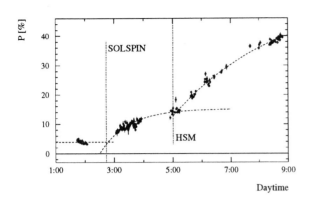

Figure 1. LEP polarization build up during a machine development period after applying refined methods of spin handling. SOLSPIN is a procedure to correct for the solenoids of the LEP experiments. HSM stands for Harmonic Spin Matching, a method to correct the depolarizing kicks from vertical quadrupol misalignments.

levels of transverse polarization could be routinely obtained. Fig. 1 illustrates the recent progress from a dedicated machine study; on another occasion a record polarization of 57% was achieved.

An oscillating horizontal field from an RF-magnet is used for the resonant measurement of the spin precession frequency at LEP. Fig. 2 illustrates the principal. If the kicks from the RF-magnet are in phase with the spin precession then the spin rotations about the horizontal direction add up coherently from turn to turn; about 10^4 turns ($\approx$ 1 second) are needed to bring the polarization vector into the horizontal plane, or twice as much to flip its sign. With $f_{\rm dep}$ being the frequency of the RF-magnet the resonance condition between the kicker and the nominal spin precession reads $f_{\rm dep} = [\nu] \cdot f_{\rm rev}$, where $f_{\rm rev}$ is the revolution frequency of the particles which is well determined by the frequency of the accelerating cavities. $[\nu]$ denotes the non-integer part of the spin tune. Its integer part n is known from the setting of the bending field.

By changing the frequency $f_{\rm dep}$ of the kicker field and by measuring the beam polarization one can look for a resonance condition. At LEP the frequency of the RF field is slowly varied with time over a given range. The difference $\Delta\nu_{\rm scan}$ in frequency between start and end of the "sweep" in practice determines the resolution of the spin tune measurement. For standard energy calibrations $\Delta\nu_{\rm scan}$ was set to .002, which corresponds to 0.9 MeV in beam energy. However, on some occasions the beam energy was measured with a better resolution, down to 0.22 MeV. Fig. 3 shows an example. After observation of a drop in polarization the spin tune and the beam energy can be calculated

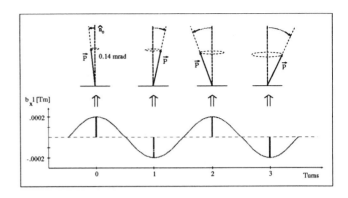

Figure 2. Resonance condition between the nominal spin precession with $[\nu] = 0.5$ and the radial perturbation $b_x l$ from the LEP RF-magnet. After being tilted the polarization vector precesses with $[\nu]$ about its initial direction and is resonantly rotated away from the vertical direction.

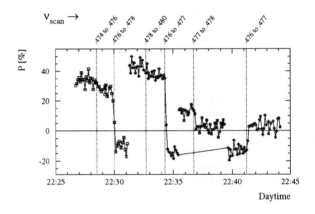

Figure 3. Example of an energy calibration. Vertical dashed lines indicate an active radial RF-magnet with the scan range (ν_{scan}) indicated above. Several scans over different bunches are used to measure the non-integer part of the spin tune. Spin flip to negative polarization was observed and checked by flipping it again when the right spin tune was chosen.

from the measured $f_{\rm dep}$ and the known $f_{\rm rev}$ and n. The quantity which is measured is the average precession frequency taken over a time period much longer than betatron and synchrotron oscillations of the individual particles. Its accuracy is therefore not limited by the beam energy spread (30 MeV in LEP). This was verified in a measurement of the FWHM of the depolarizing resonance which was as small as 200 keV for the standard LEP energy calibrations (see fig. 4).

3. Calibration Accuracy

We observed an excellent short-term reproducibility and stability of the measured beam energy. This is shown in fig. 5 where the spin tune from several

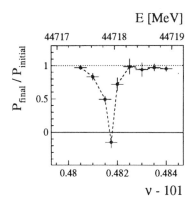

Figure 4. A measurement of the artificially excited spin resonance for a standard energy calibration at LEP is shown.

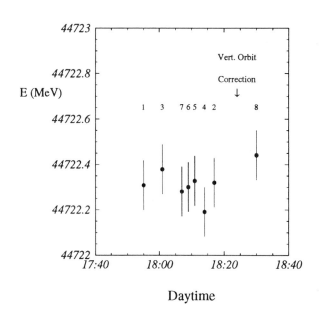

Figure 5. Comparison of the energies of different electron bunches (indicated by the labels above the points). The errors plotted here correspond frequency scan width (note the the tiny energy scale).

bunches over a period of half an hour are compared. Possible sources of systematic errors on the LEP energy calibration by resonant depolarization were theoretically evaluated [3, 6, 7]: The total systematic error on a single energy measurement is theoretically estimated to be about 200 keV for LEP at 45.6 GeV. The main uncertainties come from residual horizontal magnetic fields and interference of resonances. In several dedicated experiments an upper bound for the systematic error of 1.1 MeV was estimated.

During several investigations the LEP beam energy was continuously monitored over many hours to study effects like moon and sun tides or energy variations with dipole temperatures. In fig. 6 the medium term stability is well demonstrated by three observations of tide cycles. Occasional jumps or deviations of the order of 0.5 to two MeV are observed when the energy is tracked for some hours (see also [6]). The origin of those jumps is not fully understood.

4. LEP Energy during 1993

During the 1993 luminosity run the beam energy of LEP was accurately measured 24 times in regular intervals. The beam energies E were corrected to a common reference, taking into account changes of the magnet temperature, tidal changes of the LEP circumference, changes of the magnetic field and a few other parameters [6] . The corrected beam energy showed unexpected variations over the year of up to 20 MeV. This indicated that the model of energy variations had not been complete. A detailed investigation of the horizontal beam orbit relative to the the quadrupoles [8] possible with the precise beam orbit monitoring system revealed changes in the LEP radius by more than hundred μm. In a strong focusing lattice as used in LEP small changes in the machine radius have large

effects in the contribution of the quadrupols to the net magnetic bending field. A change by 12 μm in radius correspondes to a change of energy by 1 MeV at a beam energy of 45 GeV; this had been well checked by the tide studies. Over th whole running period Fig. 7 shows a distinct shape in the horizontal orbit larger than the tide variation, but with a time scale of weeks.

Fig. 8 shows the measured beam energy for the two off-peak center of mass energies relative to the magnetic measurement system (NMR) after those horizontal orbit informations were included into the standard correction procedures.

For the energy below the Z peak the remaining scatter is 7.2 MeV for E_{cm} and 5.0 MeV for the corresponding point above. Upto now the origin of the remaining scatter could not be understood quantitatively. For the final analysis of the electroweak parameter it would be sufficient to understand that the measurements are an unbiassed sample in order to match the statistical precision in Z mass and width.

5. Conclusions

The LEP beam energy was measured in 1993 regularly with a precision of better than 1 MeV. Unexpected variations of up to 20 MeV were found and explained by tiny quadrupole movements. The absolute energy

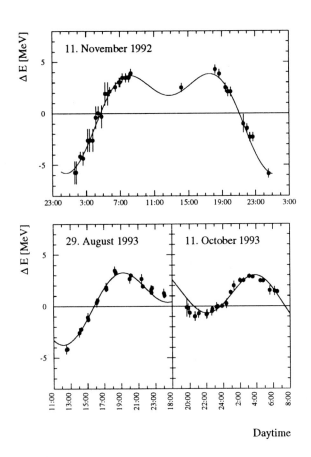

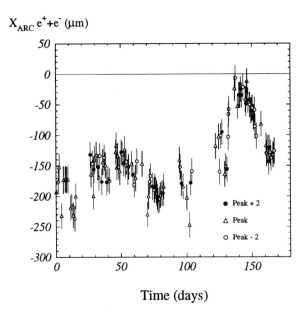

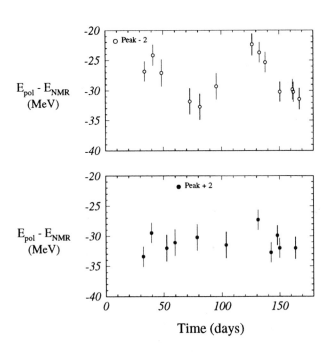

Figure 7. The measured LEP orbit seen by the quadrupole beam orbit monitors in its variation over the year. The shape correlates with the unexpected variations of the LEP beam energy as observed by the resonant depolarization technique.

Figure 6. The measured change of beam energy ΔE is shown as a function of time for three experiments. The observed variation of beam energy fits very well with the expected change due to tidal deformations of the LEP circumference.

scale of LEP was controlled at the MeV level and a high precision measurement of the mass and width of the Z boson at LEP is possible.

6.   References

[1] Y.M. Shatunov and A.N. Skrinsky,
     Particle World 1,2(1989)35.
[2] B. Dehning, PhD thesis at the University Munich 1994.
[3] R. Assmann, PhD thesis at the University Munich 1994.
[4] M. Placidi and R. Rossmanith,
     Nucl. Instr. Meth. A274(1989)79.
[5] R. Assmann et al.: "Polarization Studies at LEP in 1993".
     Divisional report CERN SL/94-08 (AP). To be published.
[6] L. Arnaudon et al.:   "Energy Calibration by Resonant
     Depolarization in LEP 1993".
     Divisional report CERN SL/94-71. To be published.
[7] R. Assmann and J.P. Koutchouk: "Spin Tune Shifts due to
     Optics Imperfections".
     Divisional report CERN SL/94-13 (AP).
[8] J. Wenninger: "Study of the LEP Beam Energy with Beam
     Orbits and Tunes". Divisional report CERN SL/94-14 (BI).

Figure 8. The measured beam energy variation $E - E_{NMR}$ in LEP is shown as a function of time in 1993.

LEP energy error for Z^0 mass and width measurement

M. Koratzinos

CERN, Geneva

On behalf of the LEP Energy Working Group

Abstract

An important aspect of the 1993 LEP scan, set to measure accurately the mass and the width of the Z^0, is the accuracy of the knowledge of the LEP energy. The statistical error of the Z^0 lineshape quantities defines the desirable level of this accuracy, which is of the order of 2 MeV in the centre-of-mass energy. Quantities affecting the energy of LEP induce variations which are an order of magnitude higher than this. A comprehensive strategy is therefore required to limit the error to these low levels. This paper describes the strategy and the preliminary errors obtained for the mass and the width of the Z^0 due to the LEP energy uncertainty.

1. Introduction

The analysis presented here is the work of the LEP Energy Working Group, an inter-disciplinary body comprising scientists from the LEP experiments as well as from the LEP machine. The results presented here are preliminary.

1.1. Motivation and required accuracy

The 1993 scan at LEP was performed at three energy points around the Z^0 peak: $20\,\mathrm{pb}^{-1}$ per experiment were delivered at an energy of about 91.2 GeV, close to the Z^0 peak cross section, (referred to as the *peak* point) and $10\,\mathrm{pb}^{-1}$ were delivered at each of two energy points about 1.8 GeV above and below the peak energy. (referred to as *peak+2* and *peak-2* points). The resulting statistical error on the mass and the width of the Z^0 when combining the four LEP experiments together is 1.8 MeV and 2.5 MeV respectively. The error resulting from the uncertainty in the LEP energy, which is common to all experiments and needs to be added in quadrature to the above numbers, needs to at least match these figures for efficient use of the available statistics.

To a good approximation, the errors on M_Z and Γ_Z due to the energy scale uncertainty are given by

$$\Delta M_Z \approx 0.5\Delta(E_{P+2} + E_{P-2})$$
$$\Delta \Gamma_Z \approx 0.71\Delta(E_{P+2} - E_{P-2}) \tag{1}$$

The knowledge of the peak energy is less critical to the determination of the Z^0 mass and width.

2. Quantities affecting the LEP energy

The mean energy of electrons and positrons circulating in the LEP ring is a function of the magnetic fields they encounter in their path.

The circulating beams move on a central orbit whose length is defined by the RF frequency, which is known to adequate precision and does not change during physics running; particles moving out of the orbit will see different RF accelerating fields than the average, which will put them back to the central orbit.

There are two categories of magnetic fields, which affect the energy of circulating beams in a different way: dipole fields and higher order fields.

Dipole fields define the bending strength of the magnets that deflect the electrons around the ring. Since the electrons are constrained to move in the orbit defined by the RF frequency, the higher the $\int Bdl$ seen by the electrons, the higher their energy should be. The quantities affecting the total dipole field seen by the electrons is the current of the main bend magnets, the hysteresis properties of these magnets, their length and the permeability constant of the material between the magnets and the beam. The last two are affected by the temperature and humidity of the LEP ring. Studies have shown that if the humidity is kept at reasonable levels, its effect on the magnetic field can be neglected.

For the higher order fields (effectively quadruple fields in our case) the situation is different; the electrons see a different field depending on the beam position with respect to the centre of the quadruples, and this effect dominates over small quadruple current variations. This effect produces a beam orbit - beam energy relationship, where by 'beam orbit' we denote the relative position of the beam with respect to the LEP ring. As we have seen, in absolute scale the beam orbit is constant and defined by the RF frequency, whereas the size of the LEP ring itself is influenced by geological factors, like terrestrial tides [1] and other long term variations [2] that have sizeable effects on its total length.

The centre of mass energy at each interaction point is further influenced by the RF system which is not symmetric with respect to the four LEP experiments resulting in small, calculable, differences [3].

The influence of all above factors on the LEP energy results in typical changes in the centre of mass energy of the order of 1 MeV per hour. This is of about the same magnitude as the error we are aiming to achieve, therefore the LEP energy should be monitored with a frequency larger than once per hour.

3.   The strategy for minimizing the errors

The strategy for measuring the LEP energy can be summarized as follows: we are using a *model* to follow relative changes to the LEP energy, taking into account all known factors that affect the energy of the beams. For this model to be accurate, we need careful and reliable monitoring of all quantities affecting the energy, as well as their exact relationship to energy changes.

However, we are still left with two questions: We do not know the absolute scale of the energy, and we also do not know the effect of quantities that are not taken into account in our model. To solve both problems, we need an energy measurement that relies on different principles than magnetic field calculations and which is also rather accurate. A method that satisfies both criteria is the energy measurement using the technique of resonant depolarization [4]. This method measures the instantaneous energy of the machine with an accuracy better than 1 MeV. It could be performed on all three energy points in 1993, it was however expensive in

terms of delivered luminosity since a measurement took about four hours with no physics data-taking possible during that time. This rather long time needed for a measurement prohibited frequent energy calibrations, and hence defined the overall strategy. A resonant depolarization measurement was routinely performed approximately twice a week during the scanning period: Out of 38 fills at peak-2 and 31 at peak+2, 13 and 11 fills respectively were successfully calibrated.

Apart from the direct energy measurement, the resonant depolarization method also allows the determination of the error of our model of the LEP energy for the first time: Since the calibrated fills are an unbiased sample of all physics fills, the scatter of the difference of the energy given by the model and the energy measured with the resonant depolarization method gives the total fill to fill error due to all sources, known and unknown. We then only need to rely on assumptions and indirect measurements for the small uncertainty of the energy of LEP within a fill.

4.   The model of energy evolution

The energy of LEP at some specific time t and fill is given by

$$
\begin{aligned}
E_{LEP}(t) = C_{norm}&(fill) \\
&\times (dipole\ current)(i) \\
&\times (magnet\ temp\ correction)(t) \\
&\times (tide\ correction)(t) \\
&\times (orbit\ correction)(fill) \\
&\times (RF\ correction)(fill)
\end{aligned}
\tag{2}
$$

E_{LEP} is given at 15 minute intervals for all physics fills for each experiment, since the RF correction is different for every experiment.

C_{norm} is the normalization factor determined from the resonant depolarization measurements. The dipole current and magnet temperature correction define the relative dipole field, whereas the tide and orbit corrections the quadruple field. The tide correction takes care of the short term variations of the LEP ring due to the tides whereas the orbit correction, applied once per fill, takes care of the long term geological trends that affect the LEP circumference.

The fills with a resonant depolarization measurement are treated differently than the rest of the fills and C_{norm} is replaced by the energy measured for that fill.

5.   The errors

The total uncertainty in the LEP energy has contributions due to three sources: The LEP energy reproducibility error on a fill to fill basis; the LEP energy uncertainty within a fill; and finally the uncertainty due to any further assumptions made.

5.1. The LEP energy reproducibility error

This error is estimated from the scatter of the difference between the LEP energy of the model and the LEP energy measured with the resonant depolarization technique, which gives a measurement of the total reproducibility error due to all sources. The plot of this difference versus time for all calibrated fills in 1993 can be seen in figure 1.

The model has greatly benefited from the use of beam orbit information that monitors the long term evolution of the size of the LEP ring. Without using this information, the scatter is a factor of two larger.

The scatter of this plot is (6.3 ± 1.3) MeV in the LEP centre of mass energy. Provided that calibrated fills are an unbiased sample of all fills, the error on the LEP energy due to the reproducibility of LEP for uncalibrated fills would be $6.3/\sqrt{N_{uncal}}$ MeV where N_{uncal} is the number of uncalibrated fills. This error is uncorrelated between energy points. For calibrated fills this error does not apply.

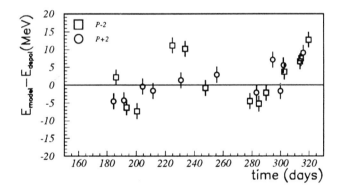

Figure 1. E_{model} compared to E_{LEP}. The scatter of this plot is a measurement of the LEP energy reproducibility error. The scatter is 6.3 MeV per fill in the centre of mass energy.

5.2. Energy uncertainty during a fill

For the LEP energy uncertainty during a fill we need to examine all the factors in the model of the evolution of the LEP energy. The calculated errors for the two off-peak points can be seen in table 1.

The uncertainty in C_{norm} for the case of uncalibrated fills is the scatter of figure 1 divided by the square root of the number of calibrated fills this time, and is uncorrelated between the two energy points. Again, for calibrated fills this error does not apply. Combining the error due to C_{norm} and the reproducibility error of LEP

source	peak - 2	peak+2	correlation
C_{norm}	1.1	1.2	uncorrelated
dipole current	0.0	0.0	
magnet temperature	0.1	0.3	correlated
tide correction	0.0	0.0	
RF correction	0.2	0.2	correlated

Table 1. Factors contributing to the LEP energy error during a fill.

(since they both have to do with the calibration procedure) for all fills, we end up with errors of 1.6 and 1.4 MeV respectively for peak+2 and peak-2.

There is negligible uncertainty due to the dipole currents, since they are almost constant during a physics fill. The magnet temperature error comes from the fact that the LEP ring warms up during a fill (by +0.12°C on average between the mean temperature and the temperature at the end of a fill for peak+2) and the temperature coefficient is known with a 25% uncertainty. This error is correlated between the two energy points. The tide correction has a negligible effect due to the fact that the phenomenon is periodic and rather well understood. The RF correction error, due to the anticorrelated nature of the effect between opposite interaction points, is much smaller when combining all experiments. Again, it is mostly correlated between energy points.

Note that the effect of hysteresis and the orbit measurement error are absorbed in the reproducibility error.

5.3. Uncertainties due to assumptions

Two further points need to be assigned an error, due to some implicit assumptions made:

The energy of positrons has been assumed to be the same as the energy of electrons, whose energy was routinely measured during calibrations. However, the energy of positrons has not been measured to the same accuracy up to now. According to simulations, the positron energy can at most differ from that of the electrons by 0.5 MeV, but until an accurate positron energy measurement is available, we are (conservatively) assuming an error of 2.0 MeV, 50% correlated between the two off peak energy points. †

The dipole magnetic field during a fill at constant dipole current and temperature is taken to be constant. To validate this assumption, a system to directly measure the dipole field in the LEP ring (using a nuclear magnetic resonance (NMR) probe) was in operation in

† A recent measurement not available at the time of the conference indicates that the difference between the electron and positron energies is smaller than 0.2 MeV.

1993. This system showed drifts and jumps for the magnetic field, which could not be attributed to changes in current or temperature, and it is believed that at least part of these drifts and jumps is an artifact of the NMR monitoring system. A series of experiments has been scheduled to clarify this point. In the current analysis the NMR information is not used in our model, but we have conservatively taken the total energy increase seen by the NMR as an additional error, which will hopefully be reduced when the NMR experiments have been carried out. This gives an extra uncertainty of 2.1 MeV at peak+2 and 2.9 MeV at peak-2, correlated between energy points.

5.4. Errors on M_Z and Γ_Z

An error matrix of (number of energy points) × (number of experiments) for the two cases of calibrated/uncalibrated fills is used for calculating the total errors due to the LEP energy on the mass and width of the Z^0. (The numbers presented in the previous chapter are approximate projections to get a feeling for these errors.) This covariance matrix corresponds to

$$\Delta M_Z(E_{LEP}) = 3.3 \, MeV \, [3.1 \, MeV \, preliminary]$$
$$\Delta \Gamma_Z(E_{LEP}) = 2.2 \, MeV \, [1.5 \, MeV \, preliminary] \quad (3)$$

where in brackets I denote the part of this error which is due to preliminary sources and which will hopefully be reduced when the final error estimates are available.

6. Conclusions

The high statistics of the 1993 scan call for a low error due to the uncertainty in the LEP energy for an accurate determination of the mass and the width of the Z^0. The extensive use of the resonant depolarization technique together with the beam orbit measurement information and extensive monitoring of all quantities that affect the LEP energy have helped to be thoroughly on-course for achieving this goal.

One should mention the impressive progress that has been achieved in this field over the last few years. The preliminary errors quoted now are nearly a factor of ten better that what was hoped to be achieved before LEP started running; Only a few years ago in 1990 the error on M_Z was 20 MeV. This impressive progress would not have been possible without the efficient and inspired work of the LEP machine scientists and the close collaboration with the physicists of the LEP experiments.

References

[1] L. Arnaudon *et al.*, *Effects of Terrestrial Tides on the LEP Beam Energy*, CERN SL/94-07 (1994).

[2] J. Wenninger, *Study of the LEP Beam Energy with Beam Orbits and Tunes*, CERN SL/94-14 (1994).

[3] G. Quast, *Uncertainties on the Energy Correction due to RF effects in 1993*, memo to the LEP Energy Group, 1993.

[4] L. Arnaudon *et al.*, *Accurate Determination of the LEP Beam Energy by Resonant Depolarization*, CERN SL/94-71 (1994).

Measurement of Z Lineshape and Electroweak Parameters

Martin W. Grünewald [*‡]

CERN Division PPE, CH-1211 Geneva 23, Switzerland

On behalf of the LEP Collaborations

Abstract

LEP, the Large Electron Positron collider located at CERN, provides e^+e^- interactions at center-of-mass energies, $\sqrt{s}$, around 91 GeV. Four large experiments, ALEPH, DELPHI, L3 and OPAL, take data since 1989. This article concentrates on the results derived from the data taken during the 1993 LEP run, which combined high luminosity with a three-point scan in center-of-mass energy. As the data analysis is still in progress, all experimental results presented in the following are preliminary.

1. Introduction

To lowest order, two Feynman diagramms contribute to the e^+e^- annihilation into a pair of fermions, $f\bar{f}(\gamma)$, the s-channel exchange of the photon and the s-channel exchange of the Z boson. The total cross section thus contains three contributions, arising from photon, Z exchange and their interference, $\sigma^0 = \sigma_Z^0 + \sigma_\gamma^0 + \sigma_{int}^0$, where:

$$\sigma_Z^0 = \frac{12\pi}{m_Z^2}\frac{\Gamma_e}{\Gamma_Z}\frac{\Gamma_f}{\Gamma_Z}\frac{s\Gamma_Z^2}{(s-m_Z^2)^2 + s^2\Gamma_Z^2/m_Z^2} \quad (1)$$

$$\sigma_\gamma^0 = \frac{4\pi\alpha^2}{3s}q_e^2 q_f^2 N_f^c \quad (2)$$

$$\sigma_{int}^0 = \frac{4\pi\alpha^2}{3}J_f\frac{s-m_Z^2}{(s-m_Z^2)^2 + s^2\Gamma_Z^2/m_Z^2}. \quad (3)$$

A Breit-Wigner with s-dependent total width is used to describe the Z boson. For $\sqrt{s}$ close to m_Z, $\sigma_Z^0 \gg \sigma_\gamma^0$, $|\sigma_{int}^0|$. QED corrections are included by convolution, $\sigma(s) = \int_0^1 dz\, R(z,s)\sigma^0(zs)$, which reduces the peak cross section by $\approx 25\%$.

The Z lineshape (cross section as function of center-of-mass energy) therefore yields the properties of the Z boson: its position determines the mass, m_Z, its width the total Z width, Γ_Z, and its height the product of the Z branching fractions into initial and final state, $B_e B_f = \frac{\Gamma_e}{\Gamma_Z}\frac{\Gamma_f}{\Gamma_Z}$.

2. Measurement of Luminosity

The measurement of luminosity used for normalization is crucial for every cross-section measurement. At e^+e^- colliders, the reaction typically used in the measurement of luminosity is that of Bhabha scattering, $e^+e^- \to e^+e^-(\gamma)$. As the initial state is identical to the final state, two additional Feynman-diagramms contribute to this process (besides the s-channel ones introduced earlier), the t-channel exchange of the photon and the Z boson. At small scattering angles, θ, the process is dominated by the t-channel γ exchange, which is a known QED process. Therefore the luminosity is nearly independent of the Z boson under study. Since $\frac{d\sigma}{d\theta} \propto \frac{1}{\theta^3} + higher\ orders$, the Bhabha cross section is large, thus yielding a small statistical error.

The schematic view of the luminosity measurement is shown in figure 1. Luminosity Bhabha events are accepted, if the scattered lepton is within the angular range from θ_{min} to θ_{max}. Because of the steeply varying cross section with the scattering angle, the dominant experimental systematic errors are due to the geometry of the luminosity monitors and the definition of the fiducial volume. In order to exploit the high-luminosity LEP data, all four LEP experiments have installed new luminosity monitors for the 1993 run.

ALEPH and OPAL have installed new silicon-tungsten calorimeters, and L3 has placed planes of silicon in front of their BGO monitor. Typical ranges of scattering angles for these detectors are 25 to 60 mrad, which translates into a visible Bhabha cross section of about 100 nb. This is larger than the largest Z peak cross section of 30 nb for the inclusive hadronic

* Now at Humboldt-University, Berlin, Germany; current adress: CERN-PPE

‡ E-mail: gruenew@hpl3.cern.ch

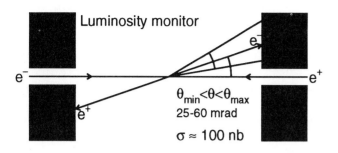

Figure 1. Luminosity Measurement

final state. DELPHI has installed a very small angle tagger, which has an accepted Bhabha cross section in excess of 200 nb, and is used for the relative luminosity measurement. Table 2 summarizes the progress in the experimental precision of the luminosity measurement achieved by the new generation of luminosity monitors.

Experiment	old	preliminary
ALEPH	0.45	0.09
DELPHI	0.46	0.28
L3	0.51	0.16
OPAL	0.41	0.07
$\oplus$ **Theory**		**0.25**

Table 1. Systematic error (%) in luminosity measurement

It is obvious, that the theoretical error on the Bhabha cross section, arising from missing higher-order corrections in the cross-section calculations, is by far the dominant systematic error in the luminosity determination. Its size of 0.25% has been estimated by the authors of the event generator BHLUMI V2.01 [1], which is used by all LEP experiments, and has recently been verified [2]. Prompted by the progress on the experimental side, a considerable effort is currently under way in order to reach a theoretical uncertinaty of less than 0.1%. Although analytical calculations have recently reached this goal, the experiments need a full event generator which is in preparation [3].

3. Data Sample

The LEP data used for the determination of electroweak parameters includes the data collected from 1990 up to the end of 1993. Scans in center-of-mass energy were performed in 1990 and 1991, with seven energy points (including the peak) each year. During 1992, LEP ran at the peak only. In 1993, the energy scan contained three center-of-mass energy points, labelled peak and peak plus/minus 2 GeV. Together with the improved calibration of the LEP center-of-mass energy [4], the 1993 data is especially valuable to measure the mass and total width of the Z boson, as the luminosity collected

off the peak is increased by a factor of 3.5 (see table 3).

[pb^{-1}]	1990-1992	1993	all
on peak	135	61	196
off peak	29	72	101
Totals	164	133	297

Table 2. Total luminosity collected by the four LEP experiments together up to the end of 1993

All visible Z decays are investigated. In terms of partial deacy widths, the reactions $e^+e^- \to$ hadrons(γ), $e^+e^- \to e^+e^-(\gamma)$, $e^+e^- \to \mu^+\mu^-(\gamma)$, $e^+e^- \to \tau^+\tau^-(\gamma)$ determine $\Gamma_e\Gamma_{had}$, Γ_e^2, $\Gamma_e\Gamma_\mu$, $\Gamma_e\Gamma_\tau$, respectively. Since $\sigma_{had} \approx 20\sigma_\ell$ for each lepton species ℓ ($\ell = e, \mu, \tau$), the hadronic lineshape essentially determines m_Z and Γ_Z. The number of selected events is listed in table 3. Each LEP experiment has collected about 1.8M hadronic and 0.2M leptonic events.

Experiment	hadrons	leptons
ALEPH	1.8M	0.22M
DELPHI	1.7M	0.18M
L3	1.8M	0.16M
OPAL	1.8M	0.23M
Totals	7.1M	0.78M

Table 3. Number of events collected by the four LEP experiments up to the end of 1993

4. Fitting Procedure

The electroweak parameters are determined using a χ^2 fit to the measured cross sections, including the correlations between the measurements. These correlations include the errors arising from the calibration of the LEP beam energy, which are 4 and 3 MeV on m_Z and Γ_Z, respectively, for the preliminary 1993 LEP energy calibration. They also include the correlated luminosity theory error of $\Delta\sigma/\sigma = \pm 0.25\%$.

In order to avoid correlations between the fitted parameters, the following set of parameters is used: m_Z, Γ_Z, $\sigma_{had}^\circ = \frac{12\pi}{m_Z^2}\frac{\Gamma_e}{\Gamma_Z}\frac{\Gamma_{had}}{\Gamma_Z}$, and $R_\ell = \frac{\sigma_{had}^\circ(Z)}{\sigma_\ell^\circ(Z)} = \frac{\Gamma_{had}}{\Gamma_\ell}$. The above parameter set isolates the different LEP energy errors (absolute energy scale, relative energy scale) in m_Z, Γ_Z, and the luminosity theory error in σ_{had}°. The parameters R_ℓ, being ratios of cross sections, are free of this normalization uncertainty.

Two types of fits are performed to extract electroweak parameters. The so-called "model-independent" fits unfold the measured cross sections for QED radiative effects. From the Z exchange contribution to the total cross section, the mass, total and partial widths are determined as free and independent parameters (equation 1). The photon exchange is fixed by QED. Its validity has to be assumed in order to be able to calculate QED radiative corrections. Also the γZ-interference term, J_f, is usually fixed to its Standard-Model value, although this is not strictly necessary and reduces artificially the error on the mass of the Z boson (see the correlation contours in figure 2a) [5].

The second type of fits are called Standard-Model fits, as they take place completely within the Standrd-Model framework. The main unknowns of the Standad Model are m_Z, m_W, m_H, m_t, and α_S. The mass of the W boson, m_W, is replaced by the precisely measured Fermi coupling constant G_F. As the sensitivity of the data to m_H is marginal, three fits are performed, fixing m_H to 300 GeV to get the central values, and then to 60 and 1000 GeV in order to study m_H effects on the fitted parameters. With this procedure, the main parameters in the SM fits are m_Z, α_S and m_t.

Several analytical programs are used to calculate the measured quantities, such as cross sections, as a function of the electroweak parameters. Most commonly used are the programs ALIBABA [6] for the e^+e^- final state with its complications due to the t-channel contributions, and MIZA [7] and ZFITTER [8] for the s-channel processes.

5. Electroweak Parameters

The results of the "model-independent" fits are shown in figures 2 and 3, respectively. Note, that the errors on m_Z given in figure 2b correspond to the case where the hadronic γZ-interference term is fixed to its SM prediction. If instead it is determined from the data, the error on m_Z increases by ± 8 MeV per LEP experiment. Other parameters are only marginally affected. The data support the hypothesis of lepton universality. The LEP combined "model-independent" fit results [9] are:

$$m_Z = 91188.8 \pm 4.4 \pm 4(J_f) \text{ MeV} \qquad (4)$$
$$\Gamma_Z = 2497.4 \pm 3.8 \text{ MeV} \qquad (5)$$
$$\sigma^0_{\text{had}} = 41.49 \pm 0.12 \text{ nb} \qquad (6)$$
$$R_\ell = 20.795 \pm 0.040 \qquad (7)$$

In figures 2 and 3, the fitted parameters are compared to the predictions of the Standard Model for the corresponding Z Mass, showing the sensitivity of the measurements to m_t, m_H, and α_S. As figure 3c shows, $R_\ell = \Gamma_{\text{had}}/\Gamma_\ell$ is especially sensitive to the strong coupling constant α_S (via Γ_{had}) and rather insensitive to top and and Higgs effects (as it is a ratio of partial widths). It thus allows to determine the strong coupling constant with the result: $\alpha_S = 0.126 \pm 0.006^{+0.005}_{-0.004}$, where the first error is experimental and the second due to theory [10].

The partial widths are given by: $\Gamma_{\text{had}} = 1745.9 \pm 4.0$ MeV and $\Gamma_\ell = 83.96 \pm 0.18$ MeV, where Γ_ℓ is defined as the partial decay width into a pair of massless charged leptons. The invisible width of the Z boson,

corresponding to the decay of the Z into invisible final states, is given by: $\Gamma_{\text{inv}} = 499.8 \pm 3.5$ MeV. Within the SM, the invisible width of the Z is solely given by the decay into $\nu\bar{\nu}$ pairs. Hence it is possible to determine the number of light neutrino species: $N_\nu = (\Gamma_{\text{inv}}/\Gamma_\ell)\cdot(\Gamma_\ell/\Gamma_\nu)_{\text{SM}} = 2.988 \pm 0.023$. The error on N_ν is dominated by the 0.25% theory error on the luminosity measurement ($\Delta N_\nu(\text{luminosity}) = 0.019$).

The results of the LEP combined SM fits [9] are:

$$m_Z = 91188.7 \pm 4.4 \text{ MeV} \qquad (8)$$
$$\alpha_S = 0.126 \pm 0.005 \pm 0.002(\text{Higgs}) \qquad (9)$$
$$m_t = 173^{+12+18}_{-13-20}(\text{Higgs}) \text{ GeV} \qquad (10)$$

where the first error is experimental, and the second due to the variation of m_H from 60 to 1000 GeV around the central value of 300 GeV. In this fit, the error on the Z mass is reduced, as the (hadronic) interference term is restricted to the range allowed within the SM. Note, that this fit includes *all* electroweak measurements from LEP, not only cross sections.

6. Conclusions

From the lineshape point of view, the 1993 LEP run is a success, combining improved calibration of the LEP beam energies [4] with a large increase in the off-peak luminosity and an improved measurement of the total luminosity. Preliminary results from cross sections are:
$$m_Z = 91188.8 \pm 1.8 \pm 4(\sqrt{s}) \pm 4(J_f) \text{ MeV}$$
$$\Gamma_Z = 2497.4 \pm 2.7 \pm 2.7(\sqrt{s}) \text{ MeV}$$
The contribution of the LEP energy calibration($\sqrt{s}$) will be reduced below the 2–3 MeV level for Δm_Z and $\Delta \Gamma_Z$ [4]. In order to remove the J_f contribution to Δm_Z, a short run at $\sqrt{s} \approx 80$ GeV is needed.

Acknowledgement: It is a pleasure to thank my colleagues of the LEP electroweak working group which provides consistent averages of the results of the four LEP experiments; as well as M.Martinez, J.Rander (ALEPH); G.Myatt, M.Winter (DELPHI); S.Ganguli, J.Mnich (L3); M.Mannelli, D.Schaile (OPAL) for detailed informations on the individual analyses.

References

[1] S. Jadach *et al.*, Phys. Lett. **B268** (1991) 253;
    S. Jadach *et al.*, Computer Phys. Comm. **70** (1992) 305.
[2] W. Beenakker and B. Pietrzyk, Preprint CERN-TH.6760/92.
[3] B.Ward, *these proceedings*.
[4] P.Grosse-Wiesmann; M. Koratzinos, *these proceedings*.
[5] M. Grünewald, S. Kirsch, Preprint CERN-PPE/93-188.
[6] W. Beenakker *et al.*, Nucl. Phys. **B349** (1991) 323.
[7] M.Martinez *et al.*, Zeit. Phys. **C49** (1991) 645.
[8] D.Bardin *et al.*, Preprint CERN-TH. 6443/92.
[9] The LEP Collaborations and the LEP Electroweak Working Group, Preprint CERN-PPE *in preparation*.
[10] T. Hebbeker *et al.*, Phys. Lett. **B331** (1994) 165.

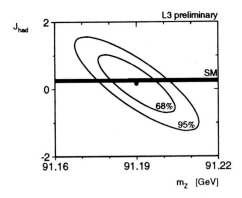

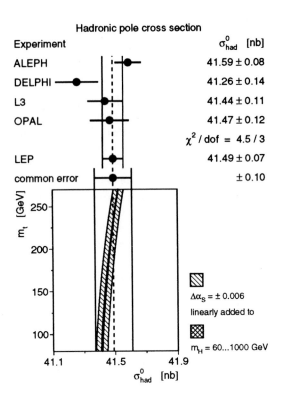

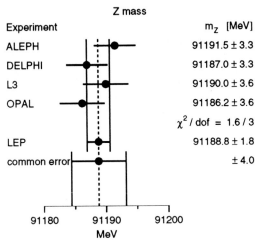

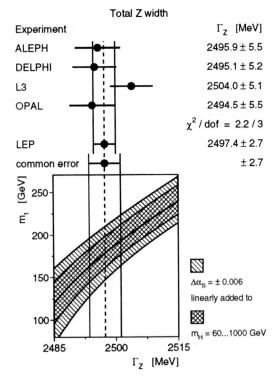

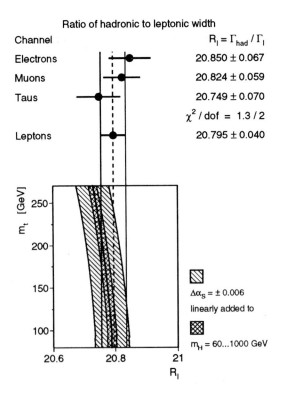

Figure 2. a) Correlation of γZ interference term with Z mass; b) Z mass; c) total Z width.

Figure 3. a) Hadronic pole cross section (σ^0_{had}); b) ratio of hadronic to leptonic partial width (R_ℓ).

Determination of the electroweak mixing angle from forward-backward asymmetries with quarks and leptons

Klaus Mönig

CERN

on behalf of the LEP collaborations

Abstract

A measurement of the forward-backward asymmetries with quarks and leptons at LEP is presented. For each number a LEP average is given and a value of the effective electroweak mixing angle $\sin^2 \theta_{eff}^{lept}$ is derived. Averaging over all LEP measurements including the τ-polarization and its asymmetry yields $\sin^2 \theta_{eff}^{lept} (LEP) = 0.2321 \pm 0.0004$

1. Introduction

Generally the forward-backward asymmetry is defined as

$$A_{FB} = \frac{N_F - N_B}{N_F + N_B}, \qquad (1)$$

where $N_{F/B}$ is the number of events where the fermion is produced forward/backward with respect to the incident electron direction. For pure s-channel vector boson exchange A_{FB} can be expressed also via the angular distributions of the events as

$$\frac{1}{\sigma} \frac{\partial \sigma}{\partial \cos \theta} = \frac{3}{8}(1 + \cos^2 \theta) + A_{FB} \cos \theta. \qquad (2)$$

For pure Z exchange the forward-backward asymmetry for the fermion f is given by

$$A_{FB}^0 = \frac{3}{4} \mathcal{A}_e \mathcal{A}_f \qquad (3)$$

$$\mathcal{A}_f = \frac{2 a_f v_f}{a_f^2 + v_f^2} \qquad (4)$$

$$\frac{v_f}{a_f} = 1 - 4|Q_f| \sin^2 \theta_{eff}^f. \qquad (5)$$

To obtain A_{FB}^0 from the measured asymmetry few corrections have to be applied:

1) The centre of mass energy at which LEP was running deviates somewhat from the Z mass.
2) QED corrections, mostly due to initial state radiation, have to be applied.
3) A small correction due to photon exchange and $\gamma - Z$-interference has to be applied.
4) For quark final states QCD corrections have to be taken into account.

Corrections 1)-3) were calculated using ZFITTER [1]. They are generally small for quarks but quite sizable for leptons. The QCD correction has been recently calculated by Lampe for conditions close to the experimental procedure [2]. It is about 3% of the asymmetry for hadronic final states. An error of a quarter of the correction is assigned to it due to uncertainties in the mass dependent part and also because the change in the correction due to implicit cuts in the analyses is not fully studied. $\alpha_s = 0.12$ has been used for all numbers presented.

2. Lepton asymmetries

All lepton asymmetries presented here are based on the data taken from 1990 to 1993 where all 1993 data are preliminary. This corresponds to a data sample of about 200000 leptonic events per experiment.

The analytical lineshape programs are able to calculate the lepton asymmetries within experimental cuts. So the asymmetries within cuts measured at the different centre of mass energies are fitted together with the cross section measurements for the Z lineshape parameters and A_{FB}^0 [4, 5]. Details of the analyses can be found in [6, 7, 8, 9]. Figure 1 summarizes the measurements of the different experiments and the different lepton species. Also the average for each lepton species and the global average are given. The full fit results including the covariance matrices can be found in [5].

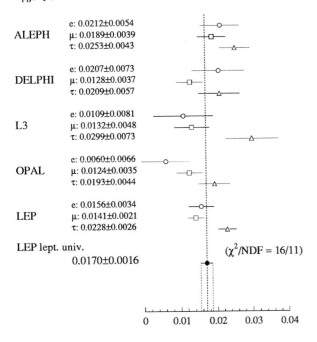

Figure 1. Measurements of $A_{FB}^0(lept)$ by the LEP collaborations

3. Quark asymmetries

For this conference new results on b-, c- and s-quarks are presented. Since the s-quark asymmetry is presented for the first time it is not yet included in the global averages. There also exist measurements of the inclusive charge asymmetry, however they have not been updated within the last year.

Several methods have been used to extract the asymmetries:

1) inclusive leptons (b,c),
2) jet charge + lifetime tag (b),
3) D^*-mesons (c,(b)),
4) fast charged Kaons and Λ-baryons.

The data presented are generally a mixture of published and preliminary data. Since no easily definable cuts are possible for hadronic final states and sizable backgrounds from other quarks are present the fragmentation + detector Monte Carlo is always used to correct to A_{FB}^{meas} with full acceptance and the corrections to A_{FB}^0 are applied analytically.

3.1. Inclusive leptons

Prompt leptons from b decays are separated from other sources (cascade-, charm-decays, fakes) using their momentum (p) and transverse momentum relative to the jet axis (p_t). Either A_{FB}^b and A_{FB}^c are extracted from the data using the full (p, p_t) spectrum or only A_{FB}^b is extracted after a cut on p_t. ALEPH [10], DELPHI [11] and L3 [12] present both asymmetries on old well understood datasets and A_{FB}^b on the more recent data. OPAL [13] has already managed to obtain A_{FB}^b and A_{FB}^c from their full data set. The $b\bar{b}$-mixing was always measured in a coherent analysis, so that no further systematics due to this correction are induced.

3.2. Lifetime tag + jet charge

Large progress has been achieved in measuring the b-asymmetry with a combination of a lifetime tag with a jet charge technique. Using a lifetime tag b events are enriched to more than 90% purity. A jet charge per hemisphere is defined by

$$Q_h = \frac{\sum_i q_i p_i^\kappa}{\sum_i p_i^\kappa}, \qquad (6)$$

where κ is a tunable parameter that turns out to be optimal around $\kappa \approx 0.5$. ALEPH [14] and OPAL [15] present analyses where A_{FB}^b is extracted from the difference and the sum or the product of the two hemisphere charges per event. DELPHI [16] presents a method where the Q_h distribution for b and $\bar{b}$ hemispheres is measured from jets opposite to a high p_t lepton. The asymmetry is then extracted using a counting method. Both methods only need the background correction and the hemisphere correlations (first method) from Monte Carlo. The $b\bar{b}$-mixing correction and the bulk of the QCD correction are included automatically in this measurements.

3.3. D^*-mesons

D^{*+} mesons are reconstructed via the decay $D^{*+} \to \pi^+ D^0$ where the D^0 is reconstructed in $D^0 \to K^+\pi^-, K^+\pi^-\pi^+\pi^-, K^+\pi^-(\pi^0)$. D^* mesons originating from b and c quark events are separated using their energy and, in the case of DELPHI, additional lifetime information. ALEPH [17] presents a measurement of A_{FB}^c based on high energy D^*'s. DELPHI [18] and

fermion	A_{FB}^{meas}	A_{FB}^0
leptons	–	0.0170 ± 0.0016
b-quarks	0.0915 ± 0.0037	0.0967 ± 0.0038
c-quarks	0.0675 ± 0.0091	0.0760 ± 0.0091
s-quarks	0.140 ± 0.043	0.146 ± 0.043

Table 1. Measured and corrected peak asymmetries for the different fermions

OPAL [19] measure both asymmetries using the full spectrum.

3.4. s-asymmetry

DELPHI [20] has presented a first measurement of the s-asymmetry. They select fast $K^\pm$ using their RICH detectors and fast Λ's using the p, π mass spectrum. 20000 (1200) Kaons (Λ's) are selected with an s-quark purity of 40% (55%). With these candidates the raw asymmetry is measured and corrected for backgrounds using a Monte Carlo predicted sample composition and measured b- and c-asymmetries. A final result of

$$A_{FB}^s = (14.0 \pm 3.9(stat) \pm 1.8(syst))\% \qquad (7)$$

is obtained ($\sqrt{s} = 91.28 GeV$).

3.5. Combination of results

In order to combine the different analyses from different experiments the LEP collaborations have agreed on a common set of external parameters and their errors. All single sources of errors are made public. This allows a meaningful average of the different results with a correct treatment of common systematics. All numbers shown here are from a combined fit to the b and c partial width [21], the $b \to l$ and $b \to c \to l$ branching ratios, the $b\bar{b}$ mixing parameter and the quark asymmetries. Details of the fit and the results can be found in [5]. Figure 2 shows all presented measurements of $A_{FB}^b(peak)$ and $A_{FB}^c(peak)$ together with the averages. Figure 3 shows the off-peak asymmetries.

4. Interpretation of results

Table 1 summarizes the measured and corrected asymmetries for the different fermions.

Due to vertex corrections $\sin^2 \theta_{eff}$ is in principle flavour dependent. Using the notation $\sin^2 \theta_{eff}^{b/c} = \sin^2 \theta_{eff}^{lept} + \delta^{b/c}$ one finds $\delta^c = -0.0001$ independent of the standard model parameters and $\delta^b = 0.0012 \pm 0.0006$ for $m_t = 170 \pm 30 GeV$ and $M_H = 300^{+700}_{-240} GeV$. Due to the low sensitivity of A_{FB}^b to δ^b ($\partial A_{FB}^b / \partial \delta^b = -0.07$) $\sin^2 \theta_{eff}^{lept}$ can be extracted safely from the quark asymmetries. Figure 4 summarizes all LEP

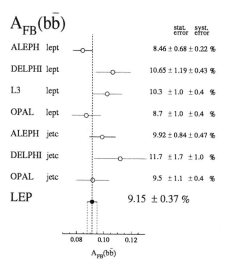

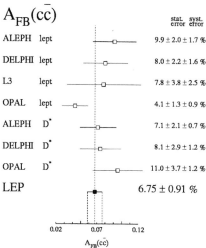

Figure 2. Measurements of $A_{FB}^b(peak)$ and $A_{FB}^c(peak)$ by the LEP collaborations. The numbers are as given in the references. The points and the error bars are transported to the agreed standard ($\sqrt{s} = 91.26 GeV$).

measurements of $\sin^2 \theta_{eff}^{lept}$ including the τ-polarization and its asymmetry [22] and compares them with the standard model prediction. A total LEP average of $\sin^2 \theta_{eff}^{lept} (LEP) = 0.2321 \pm 0.0004$ is found.

From the lepton asymmetries and the τ-polarization measurements $\mathcal{A}_e$ can be derived and from this and the b/c-asymmetries $\mathcal{A}_{b/c}$ can be calculated. Assuming lepton universality one obtains:

$$\mathcal{A}_e = 0.1453 \pm 0.0051 \qquad (8)$$
$$\mathcal{A}_c = 0.698 \pm 0.087 \qquad (9)$$
$$\mathcal{A}_b = 0.888 \pm 0.047, \qquad (10)$$

and not assuming lepton universality:

$$\mathcal{A}_e = 0.1469 \pm 0.0083 \qquad (11)$$
$$\mathcal{A}_c = 0.690 \pm 0.091 \qquad (12)$$

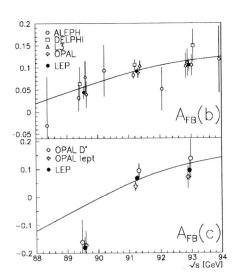

Figure 3. Measurements of $A^b_{FB}(\sqrt{s})$ and $A^c_{FB}(\sqrt{s})$ by the LEP collaborations compared to the theoretical prediction. Only analyses that provide also off-peak points are shown.

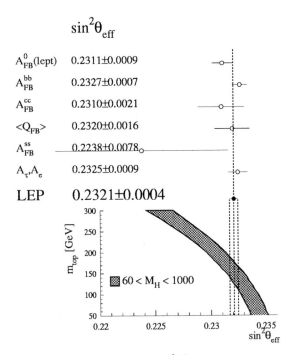

Figure 4. Measurements of $\sin^2\theta^{lept}_{eff}$ at LEP compared to the standard model prediction

$$\mathcal{A}_b = 0.878 \pm 0.060. \tag{13}$$

The lepton couplings are discussed in more detail in [23]. For the quark couplings the standard model predicts

$$\mathcal{A}_c = 0.665 \pm 0.006 \tag{14}$$

$$\mathcal{A}_b = 0.934 \pm 0.001, \tag{15}$$

in perfect agreement with the data.

Acknowledgments

I would like to thank D. Bardine, I. Brock, B. Clare, M. Girone, R. Jones, R. Lindner, J. Mnich, S. Olchevski, B. Pietrzyk, D. Schaile and R. Tenchini for their help in preparing the talk. Also it is a pleasure to thank the LEP electroweak working group for the work combining the data. Especially I like to thank P. Wells for her work on the heavy flavour averages.

References

[1] D. Bardine et al., CERN-TH 6443/92 (May 1992).

[2] B. Lampe, *A note on QCD corrections to A^b_{FB} using thrust to determine the b-quark direction*, MPI-Ph/93-74.

[3] G. Altarelli, B.Lampe, Nucl. Phys. **B391** (1993) 3.

[4] M. Grünewald, these proceedings

[5] The LEP Collaborations, *Combined Preliminary Data on Z^0 Parameters from the LEP Experiments and Constraints on the Standard Model*, note in preparation

[6] ALEPH Collaboration, *Preliminary Results on Z Production Cross-Sections and Lepton Forward-Backward Asymmetries using the 1993 Data*, ICHEP94 Ref. GSL-0557,GSL-0558

[7] DELPHI Collaboration, *Precision Determination of the Z^0 Resonance Parameters*, DELPHI 94-102 PHYS 419, July 1994.

[8] L3 Collaboration, *Results on Electroweak Parameters from L3*, July 1994, L3 Note 1620.

[9] OPAL Collaboration, *A Preliminary Update of the Z^0 Line Shape and Lepton Asymmetry Measurements with the 1993 Data*, OPAL Internal Physics Note PN121, 8 March 1994.

[10] $B^0\overline{B^0}$ *mixing and $b\overline{b}$ asymmetry from high p_t leptons*, ALEPH 94-036; ALEPH Collaboration: D. Buskulic et al., Zeit. Phys. **C62** (1994) 179.

[11] DELPHI Collaboration, *DELPHI Results on Electroweak Physics with Quarks*, DELPHI 94-111 PHYS 428, and references therein.

[12] L3 Collaboration, *L3 Results on $A^{b\overline{b}}_{FB}$, $A^{c\overline{c}}_{FB}$ and χ for the Glasgow Conference* L3 Note 1624

[13] OPAL Collaboration, *The forward-backward asymmetry of $e^+e^- \to Z^0 \to b\overline{b}$ and $e^+e^- \to Z^0 \to c\overline{c}$ from events tagged by a lepton*, OPAL Physics Note PN118, March 4 1994

[14] ALEPH Collaboration: D. Buskulic et al., CERN-PPE/94-84, Submitted to Phys. Lett. B

[15] OPAL Collaboration, *A Measurement of the Forward-Backward asymmetry of $e^+e^- \to b\overline{b}$ using a jet charge algorithm and lifetime tagged events*, OPAL physics note PN127, March 2 1994.

[16] *Measurement of the Forward-Backward asymmetry of $e^+e^- \to Z^0 \to b\overline{b}$ using prompt leptons and a microvertex tag*, DELPHI 94-62 PHYS 383

[17] ALEPH Collaboration: D. Buskulic et al., Zeit. Phys. **C62** (1994) 1791.

[18] DELPHI Collaboration, *Measurement of the Forward-backward asymmetry of charm and bottom quarks at the Z^0 pole using $D^{*\pm}$ mesons*, DELPHI 94-95 PHYS 412.

[19] OPAL Collaboration, *Updated Measurement of the Forward-Backward Asymmetry of $e^+e^- \to b\overline{b}$ and $e^+e^- \to c\overline{c}$ on and near the Z^0 peak using $D^{*\pm}$ Mesons*, OPAL Physics Note, PN125, 10 March 1994.

[20] DELPHI Collaboration, *First measurement of the Strange Quark Asymmetry at the Z^0 pole*, DELPHI 94-96 PHYS 413.

[21] R.W.L. Jones, these proceedings

[22] J.C. Brient, these proceedings

[23] D. Schaile, these proceedings

Measuring The Left-Right Cross Section Asymmetry in Z Boson Production by e^+e^- Collisions at the SLC

Michael J. Fero

Massachusetts Institute of Technology, Cambridge, Massachusetts 0213
and
Stanford Linear Accelerator Center, Stanford University, Stanford, CA 94309

Representing the SLD Collaboration

Abstract

We present a precise measurement of the left-right cross section asymmetry (A_{LR}) for Z boson production by e^+e^- collisions. The measurement was performed at a center-of-mass energy of 91.26 GeV with the SLD detector at the SLAC Linear Collider (SLC). The luminosity-weighted average polarization of the SLC electron beam was $(63.0\pm1.1)\%$. Using a sample of 49,392 Z decays, we measure A_{LR} to be 0.1628 ± 0.0071(stat)±0.0028(syst) which determines the effective weak mixing angle to be $\sin^2\theta_W^{\text{eff}} = 0.2292 \pm 0.0009$(stat) ± 0.0004(syst).

1. Introduction

In 1992, the SLD Collaboration performed the first measurement of the left-right cross section asymmetry (A_{LR}) in the production of Z bosons by e^+e^- collisions [?]. In this talk, we present a substantially more precise result based upon data recorded during the 1993 run of the SLAC Linear Collider (SLC).

The left-right asymmetry is defined as $A_{LR} \equiv (\sigma_L - \sigma_R)/(\sigma_L + \sigma_R)$, where σ_L and σ_R are the e^+e^- production cross sections for Z bosons (at the Z pole) with left-handed and right-handed electrons, respectively. To leading order, the Standard Model predicts that this quantity depends upon the vector (v_e) and axial-vector (a_e) couplings of the Z boson to the electron current,

$$A_{LR} = \frac{2v_e a_e}{v_e^2 + a_e^2} = \frac{2\left[1 - 4\sin^2\theta_W^{\text{eff}}\right]}{1 + \left[1 - 4\sin^2\theta_W^{\text{eff}}\right]^2}, \quad (1)$$

where the effective electroweak mixing parameter is defined as $\sin^2\theta_W^{\text{eff}} \equiv (1 - v_e/a_e)/4$. Note that A_{LR} a sensitive function of $\sin^2\theta_W^{\text{eff}}$, and therefore depends upon electroweak radiative corrections—including those which involve the top quark and Higgs boson, and those arising from new phenomena.

We measure A_{LR} by counting hadronic (and $\tau^+\tau^-$) decays of the Z boson for each of the two longitudinal polarization states of the electron beam. These measurements require knowledge of the absolute beam polarization, but do not require knowledge of the absolute luminosity, detector acceptance, or efficiency.

2. Polarized SLC

The 1993 run of the SLC featured enhanced beam polarization and luminosity. The beam polarization at the SLC source was increased by the use of a strained-lattice GaAs photocathode [?] illuminated by a Ti-Sapphire laser operating at 865 nm [?]. As in 1992, the circular polarization of each laser pulse (and hence, the helicity of each electron pulse) was chosen randomly.

The maximum luminosity of the collider was increased to 5×10^{29} cm^2/sec by the use of flat (elliptical) beams which had transverse aspect ratios of 3/1 [?]. The flat-beam mode of operation precluded the use of the two solenoidal spin rotator magnets (located downstream of the electron damping ring) that had previously been used to orient the electron spin direction prior to acceleration in the linac. To maintain the vertical spin orientation of the beam in the north damping ring during acceleration and launch into the SLC North Arc, a pair of large amplitude betatron oscillations in the arc was used to adjust the spin direction [5] to achieve longitudinal polarization at the SLC interaction point (IP). Due to energy-spread-induced spin diffusion and imperfect spin orientation, the longitudinal polarization of the electron beam at the IP was typically 95-96% of the polarization in the linac. The luminosity-weighted mean e^+e^- center-of-mass energy $(E_{c.m.})$ was measured with precision energy spectrometers [6] to be 91.26±0.02 GeV.

2.1. Beam Polarization Measurements

The longitudinal beam polarization $(\mathcal{P}_e)$ was measured by a Compton scattering polarimeter [7] located 33 m downstream of the IP. After passing through the IP and before it is deflected by dipole magnets, the electron beam collides with a circularly polarized photon beam produced by a frequency-doubled Nd:YAG laser of wavelength 532 nm. The scattered and unscattered electron beams remain unseparated until they pass through a pair of dipole magnets. The scattered electrons are dispersed horizontally and exit the vacuum system through a thin window. Multichannel Cherenkov and proportional tube detectors measure the momentum spectrum of the electrons in the interval from 17 to 30 GeV/c.

The counting rates in each detector channel are measured for parallel and antiparallel combinations of the photon and electron beam helicities. The asymmetry formed from these rates is equal to the product $\mathcal{P}_e\mathcal{P}_\gamma A(E)$ where $\mathcal{P}_\gamma$ is the circular polarization of the of the laser beam at the electron-photon crossing point and $A(E)$ is the theoretical asymmetry function at the accepted energy E of the scattered electrons [8].

Polarimeter data are acquired continually during the operation of the SLC. We obtain $\mathcal{P}_e$ from the observed asymmetry using the measured value of $\mathcal{P}_\gamma$ and the theoretical asymmetry function (including $\sim 1\%$ corrections for detector effects). The absolute statistical precision obtained in a three-minute interval is typically $\delta\mathcal{P}_e = 1\%$. The systematic uncertainties that affect the polarization measurement are summarized in Table 1. After the uncertainty on the laser polarization, the largest contributions are due to the linearity of the Cherenkov detector and the analyzing power calibration, which includes energy scale and response function uncertainties. The total relative systematic uncertainty is estimated to be $\delta\mathcal{P}_e/\mathcal{P}_e = 1.3\%$.

2.2. The Chromatic Effect

The Compton polarimeter measures $\mathcal{P}_e^C$, which can differ slightly from the polarization of the beam that actually annihilates on the positrons to produce Z bosons.

Systematic Uncertainty	$\frac{\delta\mathcal{P}_e}{\mathcal{P}_e}$ (%)	$\frac{\delta A_{LR}}{A_{LR}}$ (%)
Laser polarization	1.0	
Detector calibration	0.4	
Detector linearity	0.6	
Interchannel consistency	0.5	
Electronic moise	0.2	
Total polarization uncertainty	1.3	1.3
Chromaticity correction (ξ)		1.1
Total small corrections		0.1
Total systematic uncertainty		1.7

Table 1. Systematic uncertainties on the A_{LR} measurement

Effects due to beam disruption of the electron bunch by the positron bunch, or spin rotation due to quadrupoles between the SLC interaction point and the Compton interaction point, have been shown to be negligible. However, a chromatic effect at the SLC interaction point is not. Because of the electron energy-dependent rate of spin precession in the SLC Arc, the off-nominal energy tails of the beam have a different net longitudinal polarization at the SLC interaction point than does the core of the beam. In the chromatic effect, off-energy electrons are not well focused at the SLC interaction point and thus cannot contribute to luminosity. Thus, the polarization of the beam that produces luminosity is different than the total beam polarization. This implies that the instantaneous polarization at the SLC interaction point will be a weighted average over number density, luminosity, and polarization as functions of energy,

$$\mathcal{P}_e = \int n(E)\mathcal{P}(E)\mathcal{L}(E)\,dE \left/ \int n(E)\mathcal{L}(E)\,dE \right. . \quad (2)$$

The Compton polarimeter, with its interaction point at a place of low-dispersion downstream of the SLC interaction point, measures the total beam polarization, which is the same as the SLC interaction point polarization in the case where the luminosity is constant with energy,

$$\mathcal{P}_e^C = \int n(E)\mathcal{P}(E)\,dE \left/ \int n(E)\,dE \right. . \quad (3)$$

we characterize the difference between the SLC interaction point and Compton interaction point polarizations with a single parameter ξ, refered to as the *chromaticity correction*,

$$\mathcal{P}_e = (1 + \xi)\,\mathcal{P}_e^C . \quad (4)$$

The size of the chromaticity effect can be estimated from a simple chromaticity model. With the luminosity given by,

$$\mathcal{L}(E) = N^+(E)N^-(E)/4\pi\sigma_x(E)\sigma_y(E) , \quad (5)$$

we see that calculation of the size of the effect requires some knowlege of the spot-size dependence on energy. This is taken from a simple model of the chromatic effects in the SLC final focus [9]. The other required inputs are the intensity versus energy profile $n(E)$

(found by measuring scattered radiation as a thin wire is scanned across the SLC electron beam at a high dispersion point) and the polarization $\mathcal{P}(E)$ versus energy profile (measured directly by varying the beam energy and monitoring polarization). For the Gaussian core of the beam $\Delta E/E = 0.2\%$, the model predicts a small effect $\xi < 0.002$. However, $n(E)$ has a low-energy tail extending to $\Delta E/E = 1\%$, with correspondingly low polarization and large beam size. With this effect, the size of the chromaticity correction is estimated to be $\xi = 0.019 \pm 0.005$.

A more rigorous bound on the size of the chromaticity effect can be made using a conservative, essentially model-independent estimate based on experimental observations. The chromaticity correction is rigorously limited by the following relation:

$$(1 - \xi) \leq \left[\frac{\mathcal{P}_e^C \left(\frac{\Delta E}{E} = 0\right)}{\mathcal{P}_e^C}\right]_{\max} \left[\frac{\mathcal{P}_e}{\mathcal{P}_e^C \left(\frac{\Delta E}{E} = 0\right)}\right]_{\max} \quad (6)$$

where the upper limit on ξ is determined by finding the upper limit on the two polarization ratios defined in this equation. Comparision of the polarization of a monochromatic beam, $\mathcal{P}_e^C(\Delta E/E = 0)$, versus a normal energy spread beam, $\mathcal{P}_e^C$, comes from direct measurement. In special tests, the core width of the electron beam energy distribution was reduced to less than 0.1%, and the low-energy tail was removed by overcompressing the beam in the damping ring. In this configuration, the spin diffusion due to the SLC North Arc has been made negligible, since the energy spread of the beam has been made negligible. When compared to the measured polarization during normal beam running the upper limit on the first of the two ratios is,

$$\left[\mathcal{P}_e^C(\Delta E/E = 0)/\mathcal{P}_e^C\right] < 1.0628(95\%\text{C.L.}) \ . \quad (7)$$

A bound on the second ratio is found by noting that $\mathcal{P}_e$ must be less than $\mathcal{P}_e(\Delta E/E = 0)$, and the ratio is at most unity. We make a conservative estimate, assuming that the energy tail of the beam does not contribute to the luminosity weighted polarization, and that all of the polarization comes from the core of the beam. The upper bound on this ratio is determined by a TURTLE transport simulation of the arc and final focus region, with the conservative (that is, tending to maximize the ratio) beam parameters listed in Table 2. This gives the upper limit,

$$\left[\mathcal{P}_e/\mathcal{P}_e^C(\Delta E/E = 0)\right] < 0.986(95\%\text{C.L.}) \quad (8)$$

for the ratio of normal polarization to that which would be seen with a monocromatic beam. The limit on the chromaticity correction is thus $0 \leq \xi \leq 0.048$. The central value is taken as the correction, and the width as the error, $\xi = 0.024 \pm 0.016$ [7].

Parameter	Assumed Limit
θ_y^{rms}	< 200 μrad
θ_x^{rms}	< 300 μrad
ϵ_y	> 650 μm-rad
ϵ_x	> 100 μm-rad
σ_E	$> 0.15\%$
$\mathcal{P}_e/\mathcal{P}_e(\Delta E/E = 0)$	< 0.986

Table 2. Beam parameters used in chromatic effect estimate.

3. Event Selection

The e^+e^- collisions are measured by the SLD detector with a trigger that relies on a combination of calorimeter and tracking information. In order to maximize the number of events avaiible for the A_{LR} measurement in the sometimes harsh background environment of the SLC the event selection is entirely based on the liquid argon calorimeter [1]. The combined efficiency of the trigger and selection criteria is $(93\pm1)\%$ for hadronic Z decays. Less than 1% of the sample consists of tau pairs. Muon pair events deposit only small energy in the calorimeter; they are not included in the sample. The residual background in the sample is due primarily to beam-related backgrounds and e^+e^- final state events. From the data, we estimate the background fraction due to these sources to be $(0.23 \pm 0.10)\%$. The background fraction due to cosmic rays and two-photon processes is $(0.02\pm0.01)\%$.

Using the detector, the number (N_L, N_R) of hadronic and $\tau^+\tau^-$ decays of the Z boson for each of the two longitudinal polarization states (L,R) of the electron beam is counted. The electron beam polarization is precisely measured with the polarimeter.

Applying the selection criteria, we count 27,225 (N_L) events produced with the left-polarized electron beam and 22,167 (N_R) produced with the right-polarized beam. The measured left-right cross section asymmetry for Z production is

$$A_m \equiv (N_L - N_R)/(N_L + N_R) = 0.1024 \pm 0.0045 \ . \quad (9)$$

The measured asymmetry A_m does not vary significantly as more restrictive criteria (calorimetric and tracking based) are applied to the sample, and A_m is uniform when binned by the azimuth and polar angle of the thrust axis.

The measured asymmetry A_m is related to A_{LR} by the following expression, which incorporates a number of small correction terms in lowest-order approximation,

$$A_{LR} = \frac{A_m}{\langle \mathcal{P}_e \rangle} + \frac{1}{\langle \mathcal{P}_e \rangle} \left\{ f_b(A_m - A_b) - A_{\mathcal{L}} + A_m^2 A_{\mathcal{P}} \right.$$

$$\left. -E_{c.m.} [\sigma'(E_{c.m.})/\sigma(E_{c.m.})] A_E - A_\epsilon + \langle \mathcal{P}_e \rangle \mathcal{P}_{e+} \right\}, \quad (10)$$

where $\langle \mathcal{P}_e \rangle$ is the mean luminosity-weighted polarization for the 1993 run; f_b is the background fraction; $\sigma(E)$ is the unpolarized Z cross section at energy E; $\sigma'(E)$ is the derivative of the cross section with respect to E; $\mathcal{P}_{e^+}$ is any longitudinal positron polarization assumed to have constant helicity [11]; and A_b, $A_{\mathcal{L}}$, $A_{\mathcal{P}}$, A_E, and A_ε are the left-right asymmetries of the residual background, the integrated luminosity, the beam polarization, the center-of-mass energy, and the product of detector acceptance and efficiency, respectively.

The luminosity-weighted average polarization $\langle \mathcal{P}_e \rangle$ is estimated from measurements of $\mathcal{P}_e$ made when Z events were recorded,

$$\langle \mathcal{P}_e \rangle = (1+\xi) \, \frac{1}{N_Z} \sum_{i=1}^{N_Z} \mathcal{P}_i = (0.630 \pm 0.011) \, , \quad (11)$$

where N_Z is the total number of Z events and $\mathcal{P}_i$ is the polarization measurement associated in time with the ith event. The error on $\langle \mathcal{P}_e \rangle$ is dominated by the systematic uncertainties on the polarization measurement and the chromaticity correction, ξ.

The corrections defined in square brackets in Eq. 10 are very small but for completeness they are shown in Table 3. Of these corrections, the most significant one is that due to background contamination. The correction for this is moderated by a nonzero left-right background asymmetry ($A_b = 0.031 \pm 0.010$) arising from e^+e^- final states which remain in the sample. Backgrounds give a net fractional correction to A_{LR} of $(+0.17 \pm 0.07)\%$.

The corrections in Eq. 10 give a net correction to A_{LR} of only $(+0.10 \pm 0.08)\%$ of the uncorrected value. The contributions to the systematic error are summarized in Table 1.

4.   Results

Using Eq. 10, we find the left-right asymmetry to be

$$A_{LR}(91.26 \text{ GeV}) = 0.1628 \pm 0.0071(\text{stat}) \pm 0.0028(\text{syst}) \, .$$
$$(12)$$

This result is corrected to account for photon exchange and for electroweak interference which arises from the deviation of the effective e^+e^- center-of-mass energy from the Z-pole energy (including the effect of initial-state radiation). The result for pole asymmetry A_{LR}^0 and the effective weak mixing angle is

$$A_{LR}^0 = 0.1656 \pm 0.0071(\text{stat}) \pm 0.0028(\text{syst}) \, ,$$
$$\sin^2 \theta_W^{\text{eff}} = 0.2292 \pm 0.0009(\text{stat}) \pm 0.0004(\text{syst}) \, . \quad (13)$$

We also cite the measurement combined with our previous measurement [1] with 10,000 Z bosons at 20% polarization (statistically weak by comparison) for a value of $\sin^2 \theta_W^{\text{eff}} = 0.2294 \pm 0.0010$, which corresponds to the pole asymmetry, $A_{LR}^0 = 0.1637 \pm 0.0075$.

Correction	Value (10^{-4})	$\Delta A_{LR}/A_{LR}$ (%)
f_b	23 ± 10	0.17 ± 0.07
A_b	310 ± 100	
A_ε	≈ 0	≈ 0
$A_{\mathcal{L}}$	0.38 ± 0.50	-0.037 ± 0.049
$A_{\mathcal{P}}$	-33 ± 1	-0.034 ± 0.001
A_E	0.0044	0.00085 ± 0.00002
$\mathcal{P}_{e^+}$	< 0.15	< 0.0009
Total correction		0.10 ± 0.08

Table 3. A list of possible sources of error on the A_{LR} measurement. None are significant.

5.   Conclusions

We note that with this measurement we have made the most precise single determination of $\sin^2 \theta_W^{\text{eff}}$ to date. When considered within the Minimal Standard Model framework, this result predicts the top mass to be $m_t = 240^{+30+18}_{-45-20}$ GeV where the first errors are experimental and the second reflect a range of possible Higgs mass values from 60 to 1000 GeV. This $\sin^2 \theta_W^{\text{eff}}$ determination is smaller by 2.5 standard deviations than a recent LEP average value 0.2322 ± 0.0004 extracted from measurements of the forward-backward asymmetries of leptonic, hadronic, b-quark, and c-quark final states, and those of the polarization of tau lepton final states (assuming universality of the weak neutral current couplings) [10]. With the SLC now providing 80% polarized electron beam, and with on the order of 100,000 Z bosons next year, we should be able to reduce the error on $\sin^2 \theta_W^{\text{eff}}$ as determined by the A_{LR} measurement by a factor of two.

Acknowledgments

We thank the personnel of the SLAC accelerator department and the technical staffs of our collaborating institutions for their outstanding efforts on our behalf. This work was supported by Department of Energy contract DE–AC03–76SF00515 (SLAC); the National Science Foundation; the Istituto Nazionale di Fisica Nucleare of Italy; the Japan-US Cooperative Research Project on High Energy Physics; and the Science and Engineering Research Council of the United Kingdom.

References

[1] K. Abe *et al.*, *Phys. Rev. Lett.* **70**, 2515 (1993).
[2] T. Maruyama *et al.*, *Phys. Rev.* /bf B46, 4261 1992.
[3] J. Frisch *et al.*, SLAC-PUB-6165, April 1993.
[4] C. Adolphsen *et al.*, SLAC-PUB-6118, May 1993.
[5] T. Limberg, P. Emma, and R. Rossmanith, SLAC-PUB-6210, May 1993.
[6] J. Kent *et al.*, SLAC-PUB-4922, March 1989.
[7] D. Calloway *et al.*, SLAC-PUB-6423, June 1994.
[8] See S.B. Gunst and L.A. Page, *Phys. Rev.* **92**, 970 (1953).
[9] F.J. Decker, private communication.
[10] A. Blondel *et al.*, Constraints on Standard Model Parameters from Combined Preliminary Data of the LEP Experiments, LEPEWWG/94-02, July 1994.
[11] See Michael J. Fero, SLAC–PUB–6678 (Oct 1994).

The Measurement of $R_b = \Gamma(Z^0 \to b\bar{b})/\Gamma(Z^0 \to \text{hadrons})$

Roger W L Jones[‡]

CERN,
1211 Geneva, Switzerland

Abstract

The current experimental status with regard to measurements of the ratio of partial widths R_b and R_c is reviewed. The results of averaging the measurements from the four LEP experiments, and also of a combined fit to all of the LEP measurements in the heavy-flavour electroweak sector are presented, where the correlations between the experiment and internal to the experiments have been accounted for. The fit gives $R_b = 0.2202 \pm 0.0020$ and $R_c = 0.1583 \pm 0.0098$, and $R_b = 0.2192 \pm 0.0018$ if R_c is constrained to its Standard Model prediction. A preliminary SLD result is also presented.

1. Introduction

The partial width ratio $R_b = \Gamma(Z^0 \to b\bar{b})/\Gamma(Z^0 \to \text{hadrons})$ is of particular theoretical interest because it is subject to virtual top quark corrections to the $Zb\bar{b}$ vertex, which are Cabibbo suppressed in the case of non-b quarks. Propagator corrections occur for all $Z^0 \to q\bar{q}$ decays, and so effectively cancel in the ratio, which is correspondingly insensitive to the Higgs mass, m_{Higgs}. Hence, the Standard Model predicts a decrease in R_b of $\sim 2.5\%$ as the top mass m_{top} is increased from $100\,\text{GeV}/c^2$ to $250\,\text{GeV}/c^2$ (for reasonable Higgs masses); in contrast, the ratio $R_c = \Gamma(Z^0 \to c\bar{c})/\Gamma(Z^0 \to \text{hadrons})$ is nearly constant for the same variation of m_{top}.

The ratio R_b is obtained from the ratios of cross-sections $\sigma(e^+e^- \to b\bar{b})/\sigma(e^+e^- \to \text{hadrons})$ around the Z^0 peak§. The procedure used in making the measurement is to count the number of $e^+e^- \to \text{hadrons}$ events observed, and then to tag the $e^+e^- \to b\bar{b}$ events by some means with a known efficiency, thereby determining the fraction of $e^+e^- \to b\bar{b}$ events in the sample, and hence the desired ratio of cross-sections.

‡ E-mail: rwlj@cernvm.cern.ch
§ The ratio thus obtained should be corrected to the true ratio of partial widths using a program such as ZFITTER[1].

The same procedure is used for R_c.

With $\sim 7 \times 10^6$ multihadronic events recorded in the combined LEP datasets by the end on 1993, the relative error on the measurement of R_b is now $< 1\%$. This accuracy is achieved partly due to the ability of the high spatial resolution silicon microvertex detectors to identify ('tag') $Z^0 \to b\bar{b}$ decays by means of the relatively long b-hadron lifetime ('lifetime tagging'), and partly due to the high statistics allowing the efficiency for b-tagging to be determined directly from the data. However, as the results obtained change by $\sim 1\%$ given a $\sim 10\%$ variation in the assumed value of R_c, the accurate measurement on R_c is of renewed interest.

2. Heavy-quark tagging

The measurement of the partial widths R_b and R_c require a method by which $e^+e^- \to b\bar{b}$ (or $e^+e^- \to c\bar{c}$) may be tagged, with a known efficiency. Various methods are available.

The relatively long lifetimes of b-hadrons, combined with the boost provided in Z^0 decays, give rise to decay lengths of a few millimetres. This lifetime information may be used to select a sample of b-quark events. Typically, either several tracks with impact parameters with respect to the primary vertex that are significantly larger than the measurement errors are required, or else a secondary vertex is sought with a significant decay length. The tagging efficiencies achieved for b-quarks are $\sim 25\%$ for 95% purity.

The tagging of heavy flavour decays by the identification of a lepton in the decay products is well established. The high mass of the heavy quarks and their hard fragmentation lead to the leptons having a hard momentum (p) spectrum, and the large mass leads to a large momentum component transverse to the parent jet axis (p_t). The p_t is typically smaller for c-decays than for b-decays, allowing the two to be separated. The disadvantage of the lepton tag is the small ($\sim 10\%$) semileptonic branching ratio for b- and c-quarks, compounded by identification inefficiencies for $e^\pm$ and $\mu^\pm$ and the inability to identify cleanly $\tau^\pm$ in semileptonic decays, leading to b-quark tagging efficiencies of about 10% for 90% purities. Despite this statistical limitation, the lepton tags still provide competitive electroweak measurements.

Neither lepton tagging nor lifetime tagging allow a clean sample of charm events to be isolated. However, while both b- and c-events may give rise to $D^{*\pm}$, by selecting $D^{*\pm}$ carrying a large fraction of the beam energy a relatively pure charm sample is obtained, as the $D^{*\pm}$ may be a first rank hadron in charm events. In b-events, the $D^{*\pm}$ are mainly produced in the decay chain, and so have a softer spectrum. Lifetime, lepton and event-shape information may also be used to separate the b- and c-sources. Alternatively, $D^\pm$ and D^0 may be used, which avoids the need to assume the probability of a c-quark giving rise to a $D^{*\pm}$ at the price of a a higher combinatorial background.

Event shape variables have been used to tag heavy flavour events. Unfortunately, heavy flavour events are not very dissimilar to light quark events in these variables. To improve the accuracy of these methods, multivariate discriminants and neural nets based on several shape variables are often used, but the resulting purities still remain low with respect to the other heavy flavour tags. The statistical precision when using such taggers is good, however.

3. Measurements of R_b

The decay $Z^0 \rightarrow q\bar{q}$ is typically back-to-back, and so the quark and anti-quark are usually produced in opposite hemispheres as defined by a plane normal to the thrust axis. The tagging probabilities when considering each hemisphere are therefore essentially independent. The high event statistics now available at LEP allow measurements of R_b using the double tagging technique whereby the b quark tagging efficiency is determined from the data themselves rather than from Monte Carlo,

essentially eliminating all systematic errors associated with uncertainties in B hadron production and decay. For a total sample of N_{tot} hadronic Z^0 decays, if the number of hemispheres tagged is N_t and the number of events with both hemispheres tagged is N_{tt}, then in the absence of background and correlations in the tagging efficiency between the hemispheres, the efficiency to tag a hemisphere in a b-event, $\eta_b = 2N_{tt}/N_t$ while $R_b = N_t^2/(4N_{tt}N_{tot})$.

Backgrounds complicate this picture, and their level must still be inferred by other means. The value of R_c assumed (which determines the level of the dominant background) is an important common systematic uncertainty in the R_b measurements.

The correlations in tagging efficiencies between the hemispheres are small for the acceptances considered, but are an important source of systematic uncertainty. They arise through physical processes such as hard gluon radiation, detector effects such as the angular dependences of the tagging efficiency and experimental errors such as the mis-estimation of the primary vertex resolution.

The assumptions about fragmentation and heavy flavour production in u, d, s and c-events are also common to the measurements; charm production and decay properties are also important sources of uncertainty. Gluon splitting giving rise to heavy flavours in light-quark events is accounted for; there is now good agreement between the various Monte Carlo predictions and analytical calculations, and an error of half the predicted production rate is typically assumed.

The lifetime tags give the most precise determination of R_b; ALEPH use the lifetime tagging alone in their double-tagging analysis[2], while DELPHI[3] and OPAL[4] have use a combination of lifetime and lepton tagging to increase their statistical precision. The analyses are optimised to give a minimum total error, leading to comparable statistical and systematic errors on the measurements; both will be reduced as increased statistics become available.

SLD also have a preliminary R_b measurement using lifetime tagging [5]. They do not as yet employ a double-tagging method, relying on Monte Carlo predictions of the tagging efficiency. Their Monte Carlo provides an excellent description of the detector, but must still rely on physical inputs such as the b-lifetime and mean decay multiplicity.

As described above, event shape variables may be used to tag $Z^0 \rightarrow b\bar{b}$ events. ALEPH have combined an event shape tag in one hemisphere with a lepton tag in the other hemisphere[6], and so it is in one sense a double tag analysis, but does not have the feature of two independent estimates of the same efficiency. The event shape tag is calibrated against the known efficiency of the lepton tag, introducing a

~ 20% statistical correlation with the ALEPH lepton fit measurement (see below). L3 have also used event shapes to measure R_b[7]; in this case a lepton tag in the opposite hemisphere was used to select samples whereby the Monte Carlo modelling may be compared with the data. The typical purities obtained are ~ 65% for a ~ 35% efficiency. It should also be remarked that the DELPHI double-tagging result[3] includes some event shape information.

The results of analyses where only the single parameter R_b is measured are shown in figure 1, along with an average of the LEP single parameter results.

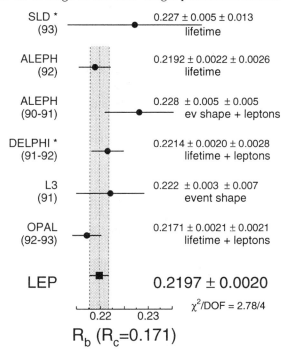

$$R_b \ (R_c=0.171)$$

Figure 1. Summary of measurements of R_b, excluding lepton fits. An asterisk indicates that the result is preliminary. The errors are statistical and systematic but with the contribution from R_c removed. The SLD result is not included in the average.

The oldest-established method for b-tagging is the use of leptons. While the selection of events with a lepton with a p and p_t will select a reasonably pure b-sample†, in general an inclusive lepton sample is used in fit to the two-dimensional p and p_t spectra for single and dilepton ($\ell^\pm\ell^\pm$, $\ell^\pm\ell^\mp$) events[9, 3, 10]. These fits are *not* optimised for R_b measurements, but are used for the simultaneous determination of some subset of the quantities R_b, R_c, the forward-backward asymmetries $A_{\rm FB}^{b\bar{b}}$, $A_{\rm FB}^{c\bar{c}}$, the mixing parameter χ, the fragmentation parameters $\langle x_{\rm E}\rangle_b$, $\langle x_{\rm E}\rangle_c$ and the branching fractions $B(b\to\ell)$ and $B(c\to\ell)$. The fitted values are correlated with each other, and the common Model assumptions lead to correlations between the results from the different experiments. The multi-parameter approach

† This approach is used by L3[8].

leads to a reduction in the systematic uncertainties due to the b- and c-fragmentation and decay.

The R_b determinations from multiparameter lepton fits are shown in figure 2, along with the results of a fit to all the LEP inclusive lepton data.

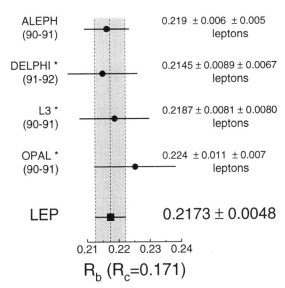

$$R_b \ (R_c=0.171)$$

Figure 2. Summary of measurements of R_b from fits to inclusive lepton spectra. An asterisk indicates that the result is preliminary. The errors are statistical and systematic but with the contribution from R_c removed (in cases where it was not fitted).

4. Measurements of R_c

The multi-parameter fits to the inclusive lepton spectra performed by ALEPH and DELPHI included R_c as a free parameter. They thereby provide a measurement of R_c, though correlated with the R_b measurements from the same fits.

More precise measurements of R_c may be obtained by tagging charm events with a fast, charmed hadron. OPAL have used $D^{*\pm}$ mesons[11], while DELPHI have used D^0 and $D^\pm$ mesons in their analysis[12].

Table 1 summarises current LEP measurements of R_c from fits to inclusive leptons and from tagging with charmed mesons.

5. Averaging procedure

Averages of the LEP R_b values have been produced with the collaboration of the individual experiments through the LEP Electroweak Working Group, and in particular the Heavy Flavour subgroup[13]. Common sources of systematic error have been identified and standard variations in these sources agreed, allowing the correlation between the systematic uncertainties to be calculated. The interdependencies on the other fitted

Expt	Data	Tag	Result	ref.
R_c from global fits to leptons				
ALEPH	90-91	ℓ	$0.1646 \pm 0.0054 \pm 0.0203$	[9]
DELPHI*	91-92	ℓ	$0.1623 \pm 0.0085 \pm 0.0209$	[3]
R_c from D and D*$^\pm$ mesons				
DELPHI*	91-92	D	$0.209 \pm 0.019 \pm 0.026$	[12]
OPAL*	90-92	D*$^\pm$	$0.141 \pm 0.008 \pm 0.014$	[11]
LEP av.			0.1583 ± 0.0098	[13]

Table 1. Summary of LEP measurements of R_c. An asterisk indicates that the result is preliminary.

electroweak quantities (*e.g.* that of R_b on R_c) have been provided accounted for. All results have therefore been corrected to a common set of assumptions and input values before averaging. As the SLD R_b cannot as yet be treated with this level of detail, it has been omitted from the fits, but would anyway have comparatively little weight.

A full fit was performed to the various heavy-flavour electroweak parameters. The fit was performed by minimising the quantity:

$$\chi^2 = \sum_{ij} \left(r_i(\mu) - x^\mu\right) \mathcal{C}_{ij}^{-1} \left(r_j(\nu) - x^\nu\right)$$

where r_i is the ith corrected measured quantity, x^μ the corresponding fitted value and $\mathcal{C}$ is the covariance matrix for all the heavy flavour results. The result of the global fit was:

$$R_b = 0.2202 \pm 0.0020$$
$$R_c = 0.1583 \pm 0.0098$$

It will be noted that the R_b result has a -0.4 correlation with the R_c result. If R_c is fixed to its Standard Model prediction of 0.171 then the fit gives:

$$R_b = 0.2192 \pm 0.0018 \text{ (Full fit, } R_c \text{ fixed)}.$$

As a cross-check, the same procedure was also used on the lepton multi-parameter results alone with $R_c = 0.171$ and all other parameters free, and also on the subset of five results where R_b was measured alone:

$$R_b = 0.2173 \pm 0.0048 \text{ (Lepton fits only)}$$
$$R_b = 0.2197 \pm 0.0020 \text{ (Single measurements only)},$$

The weighted average of these sub-averages is in good agreement with the R_b from the full fit with R_c similarly fixed:

$$R_b = 0.2194 \pm 0.0018 \text{ (Double tag plus lepton fits)},$$

6. Conclusions

The high statistics and excellent tracking now available now allow R_b to be measured with a combined uncertainty of $< 1\%$. The measurement of R_c is becoming increasingly important in the R_b measurement, as well as being a test of the Standard Model predictions in its own right, and deserves renewed study. Figure 3 compares the average of the LEP R_b measurements (with R_c fixed to the Standard Model prediction) with the predictions of the Standard Model for varying $m_{\rm top}$. The agreement with the Standard Model is reasonable for $m_{\rm top} \sim 170 {\rm GeV}/c^2$, as implied by a global fit to the available electroweak data[14]; the measured values of R_b (with R_c fixed to its Standard Model prediction) and of R_c (with R_b fixed) agree at the 1.8σ and 1.4σ levels, respectively.

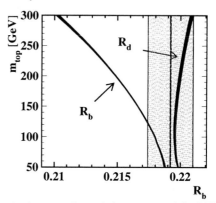

Figure 3. A comparison of the average of the LEP measurements of R_b (shaded area) with the Standard Model predictions as a function of $m_{\rm top}$. The predictions for R_d are also given for comparison.

References

[1] D. Bardin *et al.*, Zeit. Phys. **C44** (1989) 493; Nucl. Phys. **B351** (1991) 1; Phys. Lett. **B255** (1991) 290; and CERN-TH 6443/92.
[2] ALEPH Collaboration:D. Buskulic *et al.*, Phys. Lett. **B313** (1993) 535.
[3] DELPHI Collaboration: DELPHI 94-111 PHYS 428, and references therein.
[4] OPAL Collaboration: R. Akers *et al.*, CERN PPE/94-106.
[5] H. A. Neal Jr., private communication;
SLD Collaboration: SLAC PUB/6569, in preparation.
[6] ALEPH Collaboration: D. Buskulic *et al.*, Phys. Lett. **B313** (1993) 549.
[7] L3 Collaboration: O. Adriani *et al.*, Phys. Lett. **B307** (1993) 237.
[8] L3 Collaboration: L3 Note: 1625.
[9] ALEPH Collaboration: D. Buskulic *et al.*, Zeit. Phys. **C62** (1994) 179.
[10] OPAL Collaboration: R. Akers *et al.*, Zeit. Phys. **C60** (1993) 199; and OPAL Physics Note PN118, March 1994.
[11] OPAL Collaboration: OPAL Physics Note: PN148.
[12] DELPHI Collaboration: DELPHI 94-103 PHYS 420.
[13] Heavy Flavour Subgroup of the LEP Electroweak Working Group Internal Note: D. Abbaneo *et al.*, LEPHF/94-03; ALEPH 94-119; DELPHI 94-108; L3 Note 1627; and OPAL TN242.
[14] D. Schaile, these proceedings.

Precision Calculation of the Small Angle Bhabha Cross Section*

B. F. L. Ward[†¶] , S. Jadach[§‖] , E. Richter-Wąs[‡‖] and Z. Wąs[§‖]

† Dept. of Physics, Univeristy of Tennessee, Knoxville, TN 37996-1200, USA
¶ SLAC, P. O. Box 4349, Stanford University, Stanford, CA 94309, USA
§ Institute of Nuclear Physics, ul. Kawiory 26a, PL–30–055 Cracow, Poland
‖ Theory Division, CERN, CH–1211 Geneva 23, Switzerland
‡ Chair of Computer Science, Jagellonian University, ul. Reymonta 4, PL-30-059 Cracow, Poland

Abstract

We present the theoretical basis and sample Monte Carlo data for the YFS exponentiated second order (LL) calculation of low angle Bhabha scattering in the LEP/SLC luminosity regime. Tests for below .1% combined physical and technical precision are discussed. We conclude that the current error on the luminosity as calculated using BHLUMI4.00 is $^{+.16\%}_{-.089\%}$, where the upper(lower) error corresponds to the symmetric narrow(asymmetric) ALEPH SICAL-type acceptance.

1. Introduction

The uncertainty on the LEP/SLC luminosity process, low angle bhabha scattering eneters all cross sections measured therein. As Pietrzyk [1] has emphasized, for example, each .1% uncertainty in the respective luminosity cross section corresponds to .0075 uncertainty in the number N_ν of massless neutrino generations. Thus, it is important to keep the theoretical contribution to the luminosity cross section uncertainty at the level of $\sim \frac{1}{2} - \frac{1}{3}$ of the corresponding experimental error so that it does not affect the accuracy of the precision tests of the Standard Model in Z^0 physics in an unacceptable way. In this paper, we present the initial results on our new YFS Monte Carlo BHLUMI4.00 in which we show that we have achieved below .1% precision on the low angle bhabha scattering cross section in the new ALEPH SICAL[1] detector acceptance. In this way, we illustrate that the desired regime of below .1% precision theoretical predictions for this cross section is indeed feasible.

* Partly supported by the Polish Government KBN grants 203809101, 22-3729102 and by the US Department of Energy Contracts DE-FG05-91ER40627 and DE-AC03-76ER00515. Invited talk presented by BFLW.

More specifically, in reference [2] we showed that our YFS methods as realized in the Monte Carlo event generator BHLUMI2.00 were able to achieve 0.25% precision on the LEP/SLC luminosity process. If we recall that error budget from table 3 of this latter reference, in view of the result for the Z exchange contribution given in reference [3], we see that the dominant error in the budget is that of the of the $\mathcal{O}(\alpha^2)$ bremsstrahlung effects and that these should be our focus in improving on the precision of BHLUMI2.00. In the 1992 time frame of the publication of BHLUMI2.00 in reference [4], the typical experimental precision on the respective cross section was $\sim$ 0.5% [5] so that indeed the theoretical precision of 0.25% was acceptable. Recently, the LEP Collaborations have introduced more precise luminometers [1] and two of them, ALEPH and OPAL [6, 7] , have broken the 0.1% barrier on the experimental error, with results of .09% and .07% respectively. Accordingly, it is now important to reduce the theoretical error on the luminosity cross section to the respective below 0.1% regime as well. Here, we show how we achieve this precision in the acceptance of the new ALEPH SICAL luminometer in the LEP energy regime. Similar results for the other LEP Collaborations' new luminometers will appear elsewhere

[8].

Our discussion is organized as follows. In the next section, we present our analysis of the key issues necessary to improve the precision of BHLUMI2.00 to the below .1% regime. We give explicit Monte Carlo data which shows that we have achieved this precision for the ALEPH SICAL luminometer. Our final section contains our summary remarks.

2. Analysis

Our analysis for achieving the below .1% regime for the theoretical error on $\sigma_{\mathcal{L}}$, the small angle bhabha cross section in the LEP/SLC luminosity regime, proceeds according to our general strategy [2] in which we establish a baseline calculational framework on which we can anchor the new level of precision to known semi-analytical and MC results with known technical and physical precisions. In this section, we present the respective analysis.

The fundamental point is that we need to control both the physical and the technical precision to below .1% precision. To this end, we construct a series of triggers $TR_i, i = 0, \cdots, n$, in which we pass smoothly from an academic trigger, TR_0, which is not exactly the ALEPH SICAL acceptance but which allows us to compute the cross section analytically to the trigger TR_n which corresponds to the ALEPH SICAL. For each trigger, we control the corresponding technical and physical errors in BHLUMI4.00 by comparing with the appropriate analytical and/or $OLBIS \oplus LUMLOG$[9] known exact $\mathcal{O}(\alpha) + \mathcal{O}(\alpha^m)_{LL}, m = 2, 3$, results, for example, where LL denotes leading logs and we will refer to the case $m = 2$ as $\mathcal{O}(\alpha^2)_{prag}$. For our academic trigger, we define the cuts as follows: $|t_{min}| < |t| < |t_{max}|$ and $V < V_{max}$, where t is the four-momentum transfer squared transmitted through t-channel photon exchange, and the variable V represents a measure of the total energy carried away by all emitted real photons; we take $V = 1 - \frac{2(p_1 p_2)|t|}{(2(p_1 p_2) + 2(p_1 K_p))^2} \frac{2(q_1 q_2)|t|}{(2(q_1 q_2) + 2(q_1 K_q))^2}$, where $p_i = 1, 2$ are the four-momenta of incoming and outgoing electron, $q_i = 1, 2$ are four-momenta of incoming and outgoing positron, and K_p and K_q are the total four-momenta of all photons emitted from electron and positron lines respectively. With the above definition of the phase-space window, it is possible to integrate the $\mathcal{O}(\alpha^2)_{prag}$ matrix element keeping all terms within the $\mathcal{O}(\alpha^2)_{prag}$ approximation, where our big logarithm variable is taken as $L = \ln |t|/m_e^2$, for definiteness. In order to establish the technical precision at the 0.03% level, we actually followed the integration to the third order $\mathcal{O}(\alpha^3)_{prag}$ approximation, which includes terms up to NLL at $\mathcal{O}(\alpha^2)$ and up to LL at $\mathcal{O}(\alpha^3)$ in addition to the exact $\mathcal{O}(\alpha)$ cross section.

The resulting integrated cross section is recorded in Eq.(2) of reference [10]; we do not record it here due to lack of space. Using results such as figures 3 and 4 in reference [10], respectively, we have checked that the technical precision of BHLUMI4.00 is indeed .03% for the academic trigger(based on comparison with our Eq.(2) in reference [10]) and that the missing $\mathcal{O}(\alpha^2 L^2)$ correction in BHLUMI2.00 for the original LEP luminosity-type of trigger analyzed in reference [2] is below 0.04%. Continuing in this way, if we repeat the check of the old solution $OLDBIS \oplus LUMLOG$ vs BHLUMI as we did in reference [2] but for version 4.00 for the new ALEPH SICAL acceptance instead of version 2.00 for the old LEP-type luminometer acceptance, we get the results in figure 1.

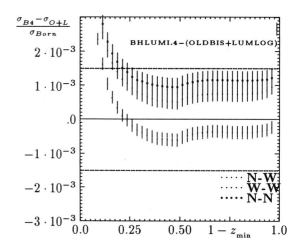

Figure 1. Trigger and angular range of ALEPH luminosity detector SICAL. MC results from the new BHLUMI version 4.0 (unpublished). Dotted lines mark the usual 0.15% limit.

Accordingly, already, we can improve significantly over the .25% precision estimate given in reference [2] using the results given herein and others derived from the same theoretical apparatus. Specifically, if we recall the error budget given in table 3 of the latter reference, we may use the results in reference [10] together with those in figure 1 to conclude that the total error, physical + technical, on the bremsstrahlung contribution to the BHLUMI4.0 differential cross section is now $^{+.15\%}_{-.065\%}$ for the standard calorimetric energy cut between 0.5 and 0.9. Further, from reference [3] we have that the error on the QED vacuum polarization contribution is now $\pm.05\%$ and from reference [11], we have confirmed our original estimate that the missing pairs contribution gives an error of $\pm.025\%$. Here, we may advocate taking this pairs effect from references [2, 11] with a corresonding reduction in the error associated with it to $\pm.01\%$. In this way, we may now quote the error budget for BHLUMI4.00 in the ALEPH SICAL-type angular

BHLUMI 4.00 precision		
Type of contribution	Physical	Technical
{1} Vacuum polarization hadronic	0.05%	
{2} Missing part of $\left(\frac{\alpha}{\pi}\right)^2 L$ brems.	$\begin{array}{c}+.15\%\\-.065\%\end{array}$	
{3} Missing part of $\left(\frac{\alpha}{\pi}\right)^3 L^3$ brems.	0.000%	0.008%
{4} Up-down interference	+0.004%	0.001%
{5} e^+e^- pairs LL non-singlet	0.007%	0.002%
{6} e^+e^- pairs LL singlet	< 0.002%	
{7} pairs NLL, quarks, μ	< 0.007%	
{8} Z exchange	0.033%	
{9} γ exchange s-channel	< 0.0002%	
Total	$\begin{array}{c}+.16\%\\-.089\%\end{array}$	

Table 1. The precision on the cross section at $\sqrt{s} = 92.5$ GeV for the SICAL-type acceptance. The precision listed is for BHLUMI4.00, with the understanding that the Z exchange correction is taken from reference [5] and pairs effects are taken from references [1,9]. The program calculates, for the SICAL-type trigger, the LL $\mathcal{O}(\alpha^2)$ exponentiated differential cross section (this latter differential cross section , upon integration, leads to Eq.(2) in reference [10] for an academic trigger). We list here the theoretical uncertainties of the corrections which are included in BHLUMI 4.00, e.g. {1,9}, which are known from other sources , e.g. {5-8}, but are still left-out and are to be taken there from [1,5,9] or corrections which are left-out , e.g. {2-4}, but are calculated {3-4} or estimated {2} by us. Total theoretical error is indicated, where the upper error corresponds to the symmetric narrow SICAL acceptance and the lower error to the asymmetric SICAL acceptance.

regime as shown in table 1, where the total theoretical error on respective luminosity calculation is now $^{+.16\%}_{-.089\%}$ for the respective $^{narrow}_{asymmetric}$ SICAL acceptance.

3. Conclusions

We conclude that the way to below .1% precision LEP/SLC luminosity calculations is open and we already have begun to peer into its beckoning horizon. This is exciting indeed!

Specifically, the main $\mathcal{O}(\alpha^2 L^2)$ part of the missing 2nd order bremsstrahlung correction in BHLUMI2.0) is now realized in BHLUMI4.00. Work on the remaining $\mathcal{O}(\alpha^2 L)$ is in progress[8].(See also the work of Fadin *et al.* [12].) The missing part of the $\mathcal{O}(\alpha^3 L^3)$ correction in BHLUMI4.00 is known and is small in the relevant LEP luminosity acceptance. Our current error on the ALEPH SICAL accepted cross section is now .089% in the relevant asymmetric case. We look forward to further reduction in this theoretical precision tag in the not-too-distant future.

Acknowledgments

Useful discussions with Drs. S. Arcelli, M. Dallavalle, B. Pietrzyk, and W.D. Schlatter are acknowledged. We acknowledge the support and kind hospitality of Dr. J. Ellis, of the CERN Theory Division. Two of us (SJ and BFLW) are grateful for the support of the ALEPH Collaboration; one of us (SJ) was supported in part by the IN2P3 French-Polish Collaboration through LAPP Annecy and by the Italian INFN through the University of Bologna, Bologna, Italy.

References

[1] B. Pietrzyk, Proc. of the Tennessee International Symp. on Radiative Corrections 1994, in press; Ed. B.F.L. Ward (World Scientific 1994); and references therein.

[2] S. Jadach, E. Richter-Wąs, B.F.L. Ward and Z. Wąs, Phys. Lett. **B268** (1991) 253.

[3] B. Pietrzyk and W. Beenakker, Phys. Lett. **B304** (1993) 366.

[4] S. Jadach, E. Richter-Wąs, B.F.L. Ward and Z. Wąs, Computer Phys. Comm. **70** (1992) 305.

[5] H. Meinhard, Proc. of the Rochester Conf. on High Energy Phys. 1992, p. 687; Ed. J. Sanford (World Scientific 1992).

[6] M. Gruenwald, these proceedings.

[7] D. Schaile, these proceedings.

[8] S. Jadach *et al.*, to appear.

[9] S. Jadach, E. Richter-Wąs, B.F.L. Ward and Z. Wąs, Phys. Lett. **B260** (1991) 438.

[10] S. Jadach *et al.*, Proc. of the Rencontre de Moriond 1994, in press; Ed. J. T. Thanh Van(Frontieres 1994).

[11] S. Jadach, M. Skrzypek and B. F. L. Ward, Phys. Rev. **D47** (1993) 3733.

[12] V. Fadin *et al.*, Proc. of the Tennessee International Symp. on Radiative Corrections 1994, in press; Ed. B.F.L. Ward (World Scientific 1994).

Precision Calculations for the Z

Giampiero Passarino

Dipartimento di Fisica Teorica, Università di Torino and
INFN, Sezione di Torino

Abstract

The present status of precision calculations for LEP 1 physics is briefly discussed with particular emphasis to the possibility of estimating the theoretical error for the various observables.

The '89 Yellow Report [1] laid the foundation stone for LEP 1 physics but now the '94 Precision Calculation Working Group (PCWG) is formulating a completely revised analysis with the goal of updating the theoretical predictions for pseudo-observables and for realistic observables and of discussing an estimate of their theoretical error. The PCWG is based on 5 Collaborations (BHM [2], LEPTOP [3], TOPAZ0 [4], WOH [2], ZFITTER [5]) plus a small angle Bhabha sub-group and a certain number of individual contributors. The complete project concerns precision calculations and comparisons for pseudo-observables (widths $\Gamma_f, \Gamma_h, \Gamma_z$ their ratios R, R_b, and other peak quantity as $\sigma_{had}, A_{FB}(\mu), A_{FB}(b), A_{LR}, \sin^2\theta_e$ and $\sin^2\theta_b$) and for realistic observables ($\sigma(\mu)$ and $A_{FB}(\mu)$, $\sigma(had)$, $\sigma(e)$ and $A_{FB}(e)$).

An important fact to realize is that we had several new calculations of radiative corrections since '89 and their effect must be understood, classified descriptively, systematized and codified. Here it will only be possible to present a brief summary list of some of these effects:

- Two-loop heavy top effects in $\rho, g_{V,A}(b)$ for arbitrary values of m_H [6].
- $\mathcal{O}(\alpha\alpha_s)$ final state radiation [7].
- $\mathcal{O}(\alpha\alpha_s)$ corrections to vector boson self-energies [8].
- Complete $\mathcal{O}(\alpha_s^2 \frac{m_b^2}{M_Z^2})$ corrections to Γ_A, including NNLO terms for the running b-quark mass [9].
- Complete $\mathcal{O}(\alpha_s^2)$ corrections to Γ_z and $\mathcal{O}(\alpha_s^3)$ corrections to Γ_h [9].

The last three points give all that we know about final state QCD radiation and here we only mention the fact that the singlet QCD contribution is ambiguous, starting at $\mathcal{O}(\alpha_s^2)$, for partial $\bar{q}q$ channels, although perfectly defined for the total hadronic rate. As a consequence those events with primary light q and secondary b must be subtracted experimentally and the proper definition of $\Gamma_{\bar{q}q}(q \neq b)$ must be clarified with the experimentalists. The status of final state QCD corrections can be summarized by the following QCD and mass correction factors for the vector and axial-vector part of each partial decay rate

$$
\begin{aligned}
R_q^V(s) &= 1 + \delta_e + \delta_v a_s^2 - 12.76706 a_s^3 \\
&\quad + 12 \frac{\bar{m}_q^2(s)}{s} a_s \delta_{vm},
\end{aligned}
\tag{1}
$$

$$
\begin{aligned}
R_q^A(s) &= 1 + \delta_e + \left[\delta_v - (2I_q^{(3)})\mathcal{I}^{(2)}\right] a_s^2 \\
&\quad + \left[-12.76706 - (2I_q^{(3)})\mathcal{I}^{(3)}\right] a_s^3 \\
&\quad - 6 \frac{\bar{m}_q^2(s)}{s} \delta_{am}^1 - 10 \frac{\bar{m}_q^2(s)}{m_t^2} a_s^2 \delta_{am}^2,
\end{aligned}
\tag{2}
$$

$$
R_h^V(s) = -0.41318 \left(\sum_q v_q\right)^2 a_s^3
\tag{3}
$$

where

$$
\delta_e = \frac{3}{4} Q_q^2 a + a_s - \frac{1}{4} Q_q^2 a a_s
$$

$$\delta_v = 1.40923 + \left(\frac{44}{675} - \frac{2}{135}\ln\frac{s}{m_t^2}\right)\frac{s}{m_t^2}$$

$$\delta_{vm} = 1 + 8.7a_s + 45.15a_s^2$$

$$\delta_{am}^1 = 1 + \frac{11}{3}a_s + \left(11.286 + \ln\frac{s}{m_t^2}\right)a_s^2$$

$$\delta_{am}^2 = \frac{8}{81} - \frac{1}{54}\ln\frac{s}{m_t^2} \tag{4}$$

and

$$a_s = \frac{\alpha_s(s)}{\pi}, \qquad a = \frac{\alpha(s)}{\pi}$$

$$\mathcal{I}^{(2)}(x) = -\frac{37}{12} + \ln x + \frac{7}{81}x + 0.0132x^2,$$

$$\mathcal{I}^{(3)}(x) = -\frac{5651}{216} + \frac{8}{3} + \frac{23}{36}\pi^2 + \zeta(3) + \frac{67}{18}\ln x,$$
$$+ \frac{23}{12}\ln^2 x, \tag{5}$$

and $x = s/m_t^2$, $m_t = m_{t(pole)}$.

To complete our summary list we add

- $\mathcal{O}(\alpha_s G_F m_t^2)$ corrections to Γ_b, the FJRT effect [10].
- The $\bar{t}t$ threshold effects [11].
- The $\mathcal{O}(\alpha\alpha_s^2)$ correction to ρ [12].

All these effects have been implemented into the various codes since the road to potentially new discoveries must proceed through a full control of the standard effects.

Next we shortly discuss the archetype of numerical comparisons. All the ingredients should be ideally the same for all codes but their practical implementation could differ with respect to missing higher order corrections. Clearly an effort is needed in order to show that all codes under a similar setting actually give an answer where $\Delta_{th} \ll \Delta_{exp}$. The difference in predictions among codes in their default setting is a first estimate of the theoretical uncertainty but, in the end, each code, by adapting different choices related to the implementation of radiative corrections, should be able to produce predictions accompanied by an *internal* estimate of the uncertainty. We must create an isomorphism between theoretical and experimental Collaborations. The final objective is strictly dictated by the projected experimental error.

Till now all the numbers produced should be considered as preliminary and the final results will be available in a couple of months. The present bulk of the comparisons is represented by 21 tables ($7m_t \times 3m_H \times 4\alpha_s$) for pseudo-observables produced by BHM/LEPTOP/TOPAZ0/WOH/ZFITTER for input parameters $M_z = 91.190\,\text{GeV}$, $\alpha = 1/128.87$, $m_c = 1.5\,\text{GeV}$ and $m_b = 4.7\,\text{GeV}$. The $\bar{t}t$ threshold effect and the $\mathcal{O}(\alpha\alpha_s^2)$ corrections to the ρ-parameter have not yet been included. To illustrate the present situation we

show in figure 1 the relative deviations for $\Gamma_z, \Gamma_e, \Gamma_b$ from the average among the five codes, i.e. we plot $dO_i = O_i/<O>-1$, i =codes.

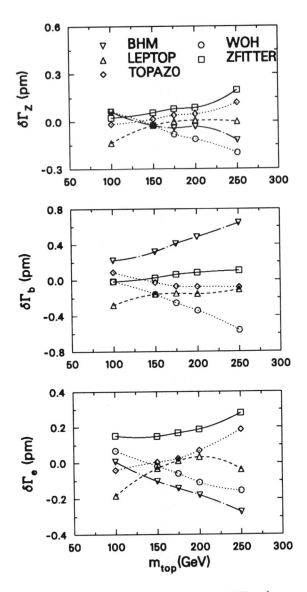

Figure 1. Relative deviation from average, $\alpha_s = 0.125$ and $m_H = 300\,\text{GeV}$.

The general comment is that we are well below the 0.1% wall and that $R_b(m_t \downarrow)$ and $A_{LR}(m_t \uparrow)$ do not seem open to question or debate from a theoretical point of view.

However forcing all codes to give the same answer is not our final goal since there are different options for radiative corrections, all (almost) equally plausible. Among several different options we would like to quote the so-called expansion-problem and factorization-problem. Whenever a quantity q is computed in perturbation theory as $q = q_0 + \frac{\alpha}{\pi}q_1$, with q_0 containing all leading higher order terms, and q^2 is needed we have a non-expanded solution, $q^2 = (q_0 + \frac{\alpha}{\pi}q_1)^2$, and an expanded solution, $q^2 = q_0^2 + 2\frac{\alpha}{\pi}q_0 q_1$. Also a given observables O which receives EW and QCD corrections can be given by a factorized expression, $O = O_B(1 + \delta_W)(1 + \delta_{QED} + \delta_{QCD})$ or by a non-factorized expression, $O = O_B(1 + \delta_{QED} + \delta_{QCD}) + O_W$. The last option merely reflects our ignorance on the two loop mixed (EW/QCD) corrections. To illustrate this point we make use of the theoretical uncertainty as predicted by TOPAZ0 and compare it with the results of BHM/LEPTOP/ZFITTER. This is shown in figure 2 for Γ_z, Γ_e and Γ_b. Notice that on top of the uncertainty associated with missing higher orders we still have to add the variations induced by $60\,\text{GeV} < m_H < 1\,\text{TeV}$ (quite arbitrary), $0.118 < \alpha_s(M_z) < 0.132$ (or your preferred version), by the error in the hadronic contribution to the running of α and by the scale at which α_s is computed in QCD corrections. Connected to the last point there is the question of how to include the $\bar{t}t$ threshold effects. A pragmatic and convenient solution consists in absorbing the additional corrections into the $\mathcal{O}(\alpha_s)$ term by evaluating it with an adjusted scale $\mu = \xi m_t$. Using some recent estimate [13] we find that at $m_t = 175\,\text{GeV}$ the change in scale is equivalent to a shift $\Delta\Gamma_e \approx 0.02\,\text{MeV}$, $\Delta\Gamma_z \approx 0.4 \div 0.5\,\text{MeV}$, $\Delta A_{FB}(\mu) \approx 1.1 \times 10^{-4}$ and $\Delta A_{LR} \approx 4 \div 5 \times 10^{-4}$.

The fact that we can give an estimate of the theoretical error also opens the possibility of performing fits to the LEP data which return $m_t, \alpha_s \dots$ with a theoretical error [14]. For instance from LEP+SLD+CDF data we can derive

$$m_t = 174.0^{+9.3}_{-9.6}(stat)^{+12.0}_{-12.5}(m_H)^{+0.2}_{-3.4}(th)\,\text{GeV} \qquad (6)$$

Finally for the realistic observables we can anticipate 3-4 steps. First a comparison with no angular cuts, no initial state pair production and no initial-final QED interference. Successively a full comparison will be performed, including s' cut, angular cuts and acollinearity cuts. As an example we show in figure 3 the comparison for the fully extrapolated muon cross section and the forward-backward asymmetry. For σ we have reported the relative deviation from average and for A_{FB} the absolute one. The error bars refer to the projected statistical error [15].

In conclusion we are almost convinced that we can do without a full two loop calculation in the standard model, but perhaps we cannot. Certainly in few years from now, when LEP will not exist anymore, only archived data will be available and the systematized effort to accomplish a comprehensive comparison of independent theoretical predictions will show its importance. With great effort we can keep $\Delta_{th} \ll \Delta_{exp}$ to learn something unmistakable new from the experiments.

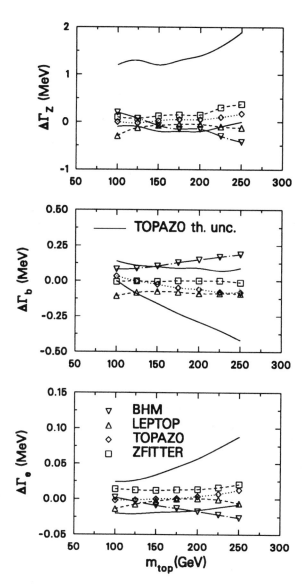

Figure 2. Absolute deviation from average, $\alpha_s = 0.125$ and $m_H = 300\,\text{GeV}$.

I am grateful to Dima Bardin, Wolfgang Hollik, Manel Martinez and Sasha Rozanov for their help and for stimulating discussions.

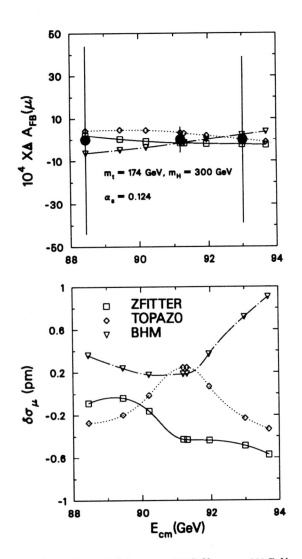

Figure 3. $\sigma(\mu)$ and $A_{FB}(\mu)$ for $m_t = 174\,\mathrm{GeV}$, $m_H = 300\,\mathrm{GeV}$ and $\alpha_s = 0.124$.

References

[1] *Z Physics at LEP* 1, Eds. G. Altarelli, R. Kleiss and C. Verzegnassi, CERN Report 89-08, Vol.I (1989) 235.

[2] G. Burgers, W. Hollik and M. Martinez, program BHM; W. Hollik, Fortschr. Phys. **38** (1990) 3, 165; M. Consoli, W. Hollik and F. Jegerlehner: CERN Report 89-08 Vol.I (1989) 7; G. Burgers, F. Jegerlehner, B. Kniehl and J.H. Kühn: CERN Report 89-08, Vol.I (1989) 55.

[3] V. A. Novikov, L. B. Okun, A. N. Rozanov and M. I. Vysotsky, CERN preprint: CERN-TH.7217/94.

[4] G. Montagna, O. Nicrosini, G. Passarino, F. Piccinini and R. Pittau, Nucl. Phys. **B401** (1993) 3 and Comp.Phys. Comm. **76** (1993) 328.

[5] D. Bardin et al., program ZFITTER 4.0; Nucl. Phys. **B351** (1991) 1; Zeit. Phys.**C44** (1989) 493 and Phys. Lett. **B255** (1991) 290.

[6] R. Barbieri et al., Phys. Lett. **B288** (1992) 95.

[7] A. L. Kataev, Phys. Lett. **B287** (1992) 209.

[8] B. A. Kniehl, Nucl. Phys. **B347** (1990) 86; A. Djouadi, Nuovo Cim. **100A** (1988) 357.

[9] K. G. Chetyrkin, Phys. Lett. **B307** (1993) 169; K. G. Chetyrkin and A. Kwiatkowski, Phys. Lett. **B305** (1993) 285; S. A. Larin, T. van Ritbergen and J. A. M. Vermaseren, Phys. Lett. **B320** (1994) 159; K. G. Chetyrkin and J. H. Kühn, Phys. Lett. **B308** (1993) 127.

[10] J. Fleischer, O. V. Tarasov, F. Jegerlehner and P. Raczka, Phys. Lett. **B293** (1992) 437.

[11] V. S. Fadin and V. A. Khoze, JETP Lett. **46** (1987) 525; B. A. Kniehl and A. Sirlin, Phys. Rev. **D47** (1993) 883; F. J. Yndurain, Phys. Lett. **B321** (1994) 400; B. A. Kniehl and A. Sirlin, DESY-preprint: DESY 93-194; B. H. Smith and M. B. Voloshin, UMN-TH-1241/94, TPI-MINN-94/5-T.

[12] L. Avdeev, J. Fleischer, S. Mikhailov and O. Tarasov, BI-TP-93-60.

[13] B. A. Kniehl, private communication

[14] G. Montagna, O. Nicrosini, G. Passarino and F. Piccinini, *The Top-Quark and the Higgs-Boson Masses from LEP, SLC and CDF Data*, CERN-TH.7322/94.

[15] M. Martinez, private communication.

Tau polarization at LEP

Jean-Claude Brient

L.P.N.H.E.
Ecole Polytechnique
IN2P3 , C.N.R.S.

Abstract

The tau polarization in Z decays has been measured in the four LEP experiments and is presented here. Substantial improvements have been obtained since the 1993 ECHEP conference, leading to an accurate test of e-τ universality in neutral currents. In the framework of the standard model, combining the results of the 4 experiments, the effective weak mixing angle is measured to be 0.2325 ± 0.0009. This value is one of the most precise measurements of this parameter. The measurements of the tau polarization mean value $< P_\tau >$ and the polarization forward backward asymmetry P_τ^{FB} are expected to improve, specially P_τ^{FB} where the error is dominated by the statistics.

1. Introduction

The polarization of the tau lepton in the Z decay to a tau pair, is given by :

$$P_\tau(cos\theta) = -\frac{\mathcal{A}_\tau(1 + cos^2\theta) + \mathcal{A}_e 2cos\theta}{(1 + cos^2\theta) + \mathcal{A}_e \mathcal{A}_\tau cos\theta} \quad (1)$$

where θ is the polar angle between the electron beam and the produced τ^-,

$$\mathcal{A}_\tau = \frac{2g_v^\tau g_a^\tau}{g_v^{\tau\,2} + g_a^{\tau\,2}} \quad (2)$$

$$\mathcal{A}_e = \frac{2g_v^e g_a^e}{g_v^{e\,2} + g_a^{e\,2}} \quad (3)$$

g_v^l (g_a^l) being the vector coupling (axial coupling) of the lepton. The parameter $\mathcal{A}_\tau$ is equal to $- < P_\tau >$, the mean polarization of the tau lepton (integrated over polar angle), and $\mathcal{A}_e$ is equal to $-\frac{4}{3} P_\tau^{FB}$, the forward-backward asymmetry of tau polarization. In the framework of the Standard Model, the coupling constants are related to $sin^2 \theta_W$, by :

$$\frac{g_v}{g_a} = 1 - 4 sin^2 \theta_W^{eff.} \quad (4)$$

The most recent measurements of the τ polarization are reviewed here. Compared to the Marseille conference, the main improvements are:
• the forward-backward asymmetry of tau polarization is now measured by the 4 experiments
• the full sensitivity of the a1 channel has been obtained (this channel is used only by ALEPH and DELPHI)
• the data taken from 1990 to 1992 have been analyzed (data 1993 are included in L3 results)

2. The measurement of the τ polarization

The τ polarization is measured through the τ decay products. In the 2-body hadronic final state ($\pi\nu^\dagger$, $\rho\nu$ and $a_1\nu$), a high sensitivity can be reached, which is not the case in leptonic decays ($e\nu\nu$ and $\mu\nu\nu$) [1].

For $\pi\nu$ and leptonic decays, the pion (lepton) energy provides the information on the final state, while three and six kinematic variables are needed in the $\rho\nu$ and $a_1\nu$ respectively.

Common systematics between the 4 experiments have been found negligible, except in a1ν, where the

† τ decay to $\pi\nu$ and Kν are not distinguished and just called $\pi\nu$

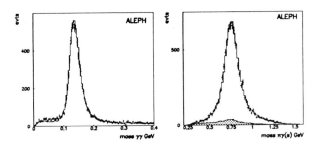

Figure 1. mass $\gamma\gamma$ and mass $\pi\gamma$'s in tau events in ALEPH. The histogram is the prediction of KORAL Monte Carlo and ALEPH simulation, the shaded histogram shows the background coming from others τ decays

model dependence of the a_1 decay used in Monte Carlo generator [2] is common to the 4 experiments[3]. However, since the weight in the measurement of the $a_1\nu$ channel is not large, the correlation effect can be neglected.

In each experiment, the systematics are related to the channel selection and to the energy/direction measurement of the decay product of the tau. Therefore, understanding the agreement between Monte Carlo and data relates directly to the systematic errors.However, it must be noted that Monte Carlo statistics is now one of the largest contributions to the total systematic error.

The reconstruction of the photon(s) and the estimation of their energies is the tricky part in the largest weigth channel, the $\rho\nu$ channel. It appears that transverse granularity of the electromagnetic calorimeter, is the key point in that field. The figure 1 shows the mass $\gamma\gamma$ measured in ALEPH. The Monte Carlo/data agreement is reasonable, as well as for the mass $\pi\gamma$'s, in figure 1. The L3 experiment used a different approach, based on the calorimetric energy response [4], the numbers of photons and theirs energies are estimated from the BGO response after subtraction of the average charged pion shower in the crystal, estimated using GEANT simulation [5].

For the other channels, the systematic errors are essentially related to the charged track identification. Control samples to test the relative efficiencies Monte Carlo/data are made with kinematicaly selected leptons (Z decays and 2-photons reactions), while the pion case is harder, and usually solved by using $\rho\nu$ channel (tagging π^0) and/or by using one part of the detector information to tag the charged pion and the rest ot perform the checks.

The non-tau background is important only in the lepton channels, with the 2-photons to lepton pairs and Z decays to lepton pairs process (e^+e^- t-channel pro-

OPAL

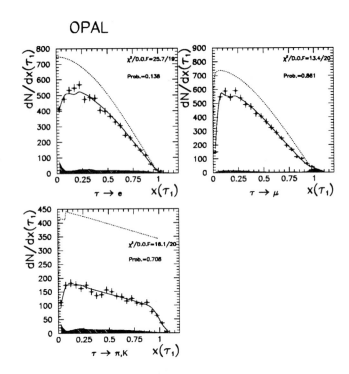

Figure 2. leptonic and $\pi\nu$ channels distributions in OPAL. Shaded histogram are the backgrounds.

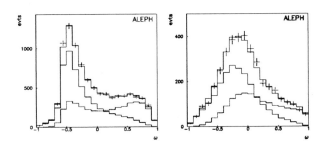

Figure 3. ω distribution in $\rho\nu$ and $a_1\nu$ channel measured in ALEPH. dashed and point-line histograms are the 2 helicities distributions

duction contributes also to the $e\nu\nu$ channel).

In addition to the "standard" tau decay channels, DELPHI defines a class of "inclusive pion", with one charged pion and any number of photon(s). This class of events recovers tau decays not classified in the "standard" channels.

The figure 2 shows the energy distributions for the leptonic channnels and $\pi\nu$ channels measured by OPAL. The shaded histograms are the background, the curves are the result of the fits.

In the $\rho\nu$ and $a_1\nu$ channels, the polarization information contained in the kinematic variables of the decay products, are summarized into a single variable, called here ω [6].

The ω distributions obtained in ALEPH for the

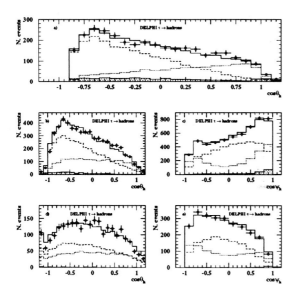

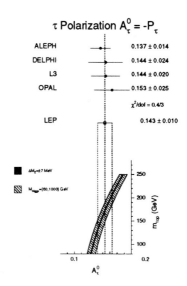

Figure 4. the distributions used in the "inclusive pion" channel in DELPHI. the two variables $\cos\theta_h$ and $\cos\psi_h$ are similar to the two angles describing the $\rho\nu$ channel

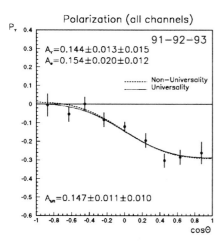

Figure 5. $P_\tau(\cos\theta)$ as measured by L3

$\rho\nu$ and $a_1\nu$ channels are shown in figure 3, while figure 4 shows the distributions of the inclusive pion distributions obtained by DELPHI.

The measurement of the polarization as a function of the polar angle is illustrated by the results of L3, shown in figure 5. The curves are the results of the fit of $\mathcal{A}_\tau$ and $\mathcal{A}_e$ and with universality, the fit of $\mathcal{A}_{lepton}$.

The figure 6 shows the measured values of $\mathcal{A}_\tau$ and $\mathcal{A}_e$ respectively, for the 4 experiments. Combining them together :

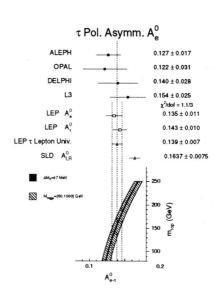

Figure 6. Values of $\mathcal{A}_\tau$ and $\mathcal{A}_e$ measured by the four LEP experiments

$$\mathcal{A}_\tau = 0.143 \pm 0.010 \qquad (5)$$

and

$$\mathcal{A}_e = 0.135 \pm 0.011 \qquad (6)$$

It must be noted that the systematic errors on $\mathcal{A}_\tau$ are about the same order of magnitude than the statistical ones, while for $\mathcal{A}_e$ the systematic errors represent 30% or less of the statistical ones. These measurements lead to a test of lepton universality in neutral currents. In term of the ratio g_v/g_a, the result can be written as :

$$\frac{(g_v^\tau/g_a^\tau)}{(g_v^e/g_a^e)} = 1.06 \pm 0.11 \qquad (7)$$

Now, using e-τ universality in neutral currents, we can write

$$g_v^{e-\tau}/g_a^{e-\tau} = 0.070 \pm 0.0037 \qquad (8)$$

and the effective weak mixing angle is measured to be :

$$\sin^2 \theta_W^{eff.} = 0.2325 \pm 0.0009 \qquad (9)$$

3.   Conclusions

LEP experiments have measured the ratio g_v^τ/g_a^τ from $< P_\tau >$ with a precision of 7% (it was 10% at 1993 ECHEP). This measurement has statistical and systematic errors of the same order and systematic errors are dominated by the errors coming from the statistic of the Monte Carlo sample.

Since the 1993 ECHEP conference, an important improvement in accuracy has been obtained on the forward backward asymmetry of tau polarization, leading to a measurement of the ratio g_v^e/g_a^e with a precision of 7% (it was 20% at 1993 ECHEP).

The e-τ universality in neutral currents is now checked within 10%. The $\sin^2 \theta_W^{eff.}$ measured by the τ polarization analyser, reached 0.4% of precision, which is one of the most precise measurement. Moreover, systematic errors between the 4 LEP experiments are essentially uncorrelated.

In the near future, the 1993 and 1994 data will improve the precision, at least in the forward backward asymmetry of tau polarization, which is still limited by the statistics.

References

[1] A. Rouge, Zeit. Phys. **C48** (1990) 75.
[2] S. Jadach *et al.*, The KORALZ Monte Carlo, CERN yellow report: 89-03, vol. 3 (1989) 69.
[3] P. Renton *et al.*, CERN preprint: CERN LEPTAU/94-02;
    ALEPH Collaboration: J. Harton and H. Videau, submitted paper GLS0551;
    DELPHI Collaboration: P. Abreu *et al.*, submitted paper GLS0207;
    L3 Collaboration, submitted abstract GLS0643;
    OPAL Collaboration: R. Akers *et al.*, submitted paper GLS0585.
[4] L3 collaboration, O.Adriani et al, Phys. Lett. B294(1992),466
[5] R. Brun *et al.*, GEANT 3, CERN report: CERN DD/EE/44-1 (revised).
[6] A. Rouge *et al.*, Ecole Polytechnique preprint: X-LPHNE 92-22;
    M. Davier *et al.*, Orsay preprint: LAL 92-73.

Preliminary results on high precision measurements of hadron production in electron-positron annihilation

B.I.Khazin

Institute of Nuclear Physics, Novosibirsk, Russia

On behalf of the CMD-2 collaboration

Abstract

A new level in precise knowledge of hadron production in e^+e^- annihilation is needed to interpret the high precision measurements of Standard Model parameters and the future muon g-2 experiment in preparation at Brookhaven.

The general purpose detector CMD-2 at the VEPP-2M electron-positron collider at Novosibirsk has collected todate about $1.8\ pb^{-1}$ of integrated luminosity in the energy range from ϕ to ρ mesons. The preliminary analysis of this data is presented.

1. Introduction

The precise measurements of the cross section $e^+e^- \to \pi^+\pi^-$ described in this paper were performed with the CMD-2 [1,2] detector at VEPP-2M collider [3] at the Budker Institute of Nuclear Physics in Novosibirsk. The data obtainable in the VEPP-2M energy region from the threshold of pion pair production up to 2x740 MeV is valuable both for further study of light vector mesons and for the evaluation of a dispersion integral which relates the ratio R of $e^+e^- \to hadrons$ cross section over that for $e^+e^- \to \mu^+\mu^-$ with the hadronic vacuum polarization. The knowledge of R is required for interpretation of the precise measurements of the basic parameters of the Standard Model and the anomalous magnetic moments of particles [4,5]. The new BNL E821 experiment which will measure the muon g-2 with 0.35 ppm accuracy requires the knowledge of R with a systematic error less than 0.5%. The main contribution to the dispersion integral in this case comes from the energy region available with VEPP-2M.

The CMD-2 experiment will scan the energy region of VEPP-2M with a 10 MeV c.m. energy step collecting about 1000 pion pairs in each point.

2. Data and analysis

In 1994 the c.m. energy range from 2x505 MeV down to 2x405 MeV has been scanned with 230 nb^{-1} of integrated luminosity. To keep the systematic error of the hadronic contribution to the muon g-2 below 0.5% one has to know the c.m. energy with about 10^{-4} accuracy. The energy of the beams were measured in each point by means of resonance depolarization technique [6]. The organization of the detector trigger is described in [7,8]. In this experiment the existence of at least one charged track in the drift chamber and energy deposition greater than 20 MeV in the calorimeter were required and about 13 millions of this type events were recorded.

For further analysis the two track events satisfying the conditions of proximity to the interaction point and collinearity were selected. The distributions of the events on mentioned above parameters and imposed cuts are shown in figure 1. It is seen from the picture that those cuts removes the most of the background. To determine the ratio R the distributions of the thus selected events on longitudinal coordinate of the vertex, polar angle and scatter plot of energy deposited in calorimeter by the negative and positive particles were

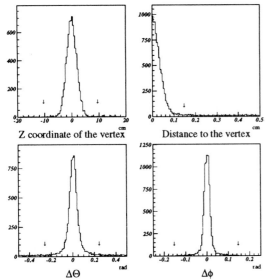

Figure 1. The cuts imposed for selection of collinear events.

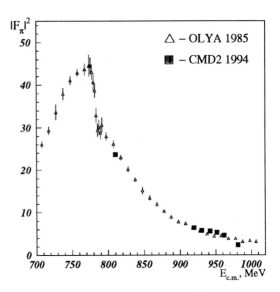

Figure 3. The experimental data on $|F_\pi|^2$.

used.The results of maximal likelihood fit are shown on figure2.

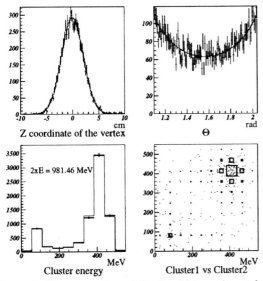

Figure 2. The comparison of the fit with experimental data.

The basic fitted parameters were number of electrons N_e, the ratio $(N_{muons} + N_{pions})/N_e$, number of background events N_b. The ratio of N_{muons}/N_e were taken from QED. It is seen from the picture that the experimental data are fitted pretty well.

The ratio N_{pions}/N_e simply relates to the value of pion formfactor which is represented on figure 3 together with the most detailed measurements from OLYA detector [9]. As it follows from the picture our new results are in a good agreement with the previous experiments.

The statistical error of the hadronic cross section is about 3%. The systematic error at present is estimated to be about 2%. The main contributions to this value comes from the determination of the fiducial volume - 1.5% and from present theoretical calculations of the radiative corrections for Bhabha events - 0.9%. The calibration of Z-chamber and improvement of the radiative corrections calculations will decrease the systematic uncertainty to the level of 0.5%.

3. Summary

One third of the data obtained during a scan of the c.m. energy region from 2x505 MeV down to 2x405 MeV were analysed. The systematic error is well under control and will be made less than 0.5% after final calibration of the Z-chamber and the development of the new approach to the calculation of radiative corrections to Bhabha events. The experiment will be prolonged in 1995.

References

[1] G.A Aksenov *et al.*, Novosibirsk preprint: INP 85-118.
[2] B.I.Khazin *et al.*, Proc. of the XXVI Int.Conf. on High Energy Physics,1992, vol.2, p.1876; Ed. J.R.Sanford (AIP 1993).
[3] V.V.Anashin *et al.*, Novosibirsk preprint: INP 84-114.
[4] M.Vysotski, these proceedings.
[5] Muon g-2 Design Report AGS 821, Brookhaven National Laboratory, July 1992.
[6] Ya.S.Derbenev *et al.*, Part. Acc. **10** (1980) 177.
[7] V.M.Aulchenko *et al.*, Novosibisrk preprint: INP 88-43.
[8] E.V.Anashkin *et al.*,Nucl. Instr. Meth. **A323** (1992) 178.
[9] L.M.Barkov *et al.*, Nucl. Phys. **B256** (1985) 365.

Flavour Universality of Neutrino Couplings with the Z

B. Akkus°, E. Arik°, R. Beyer‡, F.W. Büsser§, A. Capone♯, A.G. Cocco*, D. DePedis♯
E.Di Capua††, U. Dore♯, A. Ereditato*, D. Favart‖, G. Fiorillo*, W. Flegel‡, C. Foos§,
A.Frenkel-Rambaldi♯, L. Gerland§, P. Gorbunov¶, G. Grégoire‖, E. Grigoriev¶, H. Grote‡, K.Hiller
♭, V. Khovansky¶, E. Knoops‖, V. Laimaître‖, T. Layda§, W. Lippich+, D. Macina♯,
F.Marchetti-Stasi*, A. Maslennikov¶, T. Mouthuy‡, R. Nahnhauer♭, A. Nathaniel+, F. Niebergall§,
H. Øverås‡, V. Palladino*, J. Panman‡, G. Piredda♯, G. Rädel§, S. Ricciardi††, H.E. Roloff♭,
A.Rozanov‡, B. Saitti††, R. Santacesaria♯, M. Serin-Zeyrek°, R. Sever°, P. Stähelin§,A. Straude+,
P.Strolin*, P. Tolun°, P. Vilain†, J. Vogt+, T. Voss§, G. Wilquet†, K. Winter‡, G. Zacek‡, V. Zacek‡

† Inter-University Institute for High Energy Physics, Brussels, Belgium
‡ CERN, Geneva, Switzerland
§ II. Institute für Experimentalphysik, Universität Hamburg, Hamburg, Germany
‖ Université Catholique de Louvain, Louvain–la–Neuve, Belgium
¶ ITEP, Moscow, Russian Federation
+ Sektion Physik der Universität München, München, Germany
* Università "Frederico II" and INFN, Naples, Italy
♯ Università "La Sapienza" and INFN, Rome, Italy
†† Universitá di Ferrara and INFN, Ferrara, Italy
◇ High Energy Physics Research Centre, YEFAM, Ankara, Turkey
♭ DESY–IFH, Zeuthen, Germany

Presented by Alfredo G. Cocco on behalf of the CHARM II Collaboration

Abstract

The final results on electroweak parameters derived from neutrino electron scattering events collected by the CHARM II detector are reported. Results are based on data taken from 1987 to 1991 during the exposure of the detector to the wide band neutrino beam at CERN. From the absolute neutrino-electron scattering event rate we determined the effective vector and axial-vector neutral current coupling constants to be $g_V^{\nu e} = -0.035 \pm 0.017$ and $g_A^{\nu e} = -0.503 \pm 0.017$. This measurements lead the CHARM II Collaboration to obtain the first experimental evidence of the universality of muon neutrino couplings with the Z.

1. Introduction

The importance of measuring the electroweak parameters in purely leptonic processes is well described in modern literature. The CHARM II detector [1] built for the study of neutrino–electron elastic scattering provide a unique tool to test the validity of the Standard Model predictions in the low-Q^2 region of the neutral current interactions.

We will summarise here the most recent outcomes of the analysis performed by the CHARM II Collaboration on the largest sample of neutrino–electron scattering events actually avalaible. The data used are selected from the whole sample recorded over five years

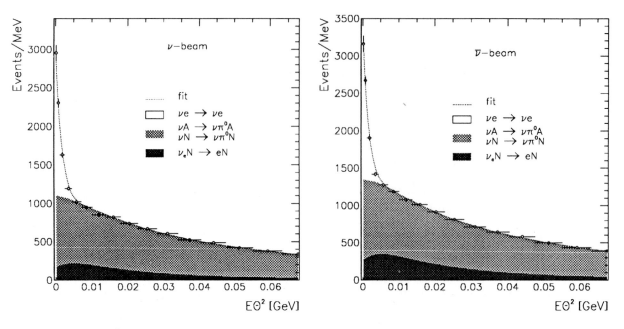

Figure 1. $E_e\theta_e^2$ distributions of the experimental data for neutrino and antineutrino beam exposures. Contributions of different processes are shown according to the fit results.

(1987–1991) of detector exposure to the neutrino and antineutrino wide band beams at CERN.

2. Electroweak parameters

A detailed description of the CHARM II detector and of the analysis method user in order to determine the coupling constants $g_V^{\nu_\mu e}$ and $g_A^{\nu_\mu e}$ can be found in references [1,2]. The proceedure makes full use of the information contained in the differential form of the neutrino–electron scattering cross–section. High precition absolute neutrino flux measurements were performed in order to achieve the final result.

As shown in figure 1, a total of

$$2677 \pm 82 \quad and \quad 2752 \pm 88$$

event were found in the neutrino and antineutrino data sample, respectively [3].

The fourfold ambiguity in the determination of $g_V^{\nu_\mu e}$ and $g_A^{\nu_\mu e}$ which is expected from the quadratic dependence of the cross sections on the couplings, is reduced to a two-fold one owing to the presence of ν_e and $\bar\nu_e$ components in the beam.

About 10% of the neutrino–electron scattering events are induced by electron-neutrinos, which select two solutions. Results from electron–positron collider experiments [4] resolve the remaining ambiguity as shown in figure 2.

The results for the effective vector and axial-vector

coupling constants from neutrino–electron scattering are

$$g_V^{\nu_\mu e} = -0.035 \pm 0.012(stat.) \pm 0.012(syst.)$$
$$g_A^{\nu_\mu e} = -0.503 \pm 0.006(stat.) \pm 0.016(syst.) \ .$$

The systematic errors are dominated by uncertainties of the background determination, of the neutrino flux measurement and of the selection efficiency.

CHARM II result can be directly compared with the measurements at LEP. The Z^o exchange diagram for neutrino electron scattering is infact related by crossing symmetry to the electron–positron annihilation process via Z^o exchange. Even if the two measurements refer to different Q^2 scales ($Q^2 = 0.01$ GeV^2 and $Q^2 = m_Z^2$) contributions that are expected to arise from the running of the fine structure constant and from the effect of the neutrino charge radius cancel almost completely, resulting in a difference of $g_V^{\nu_\mu e} - g_V^e(LEP) = -0.002$. Individual terms are larger by an order of magnitude.

Figure 3 shows that results from neutrino-electron scattering have reached comparable precision in g_V^e. The agreement of the measurement performed at $Q^2 \approx 0.01$ GeV^2 with those performed at $Q^2 = M_Z^2$ is remarkable.

3. Neutrino flavour universality

The high precision measurements of $g_V^{\nu_\mu e}$ and $g_A^{\nu_\mu e}$ obtained by the CHARM II experiment allow the determination of the coupling g^{ν_μ} without assuming neutrino flavour universality.

Following infact arguments expressed in ref. [6], the coupling constants determined in neutrino–electron scattering experiments $g_V^{\nu_\mu e}$ and $g_A^{\nu_\mu e}$ can be expressed in the form

$$g_{V,A}^{\nu_\mu e}(0.01\ GeV^2) = 2 \cdot g^{\nu_\mu}(M_Z^2) \cdot g_{V,A}^e(M_Z^2)$$

This is mainly due to the coincidence of two fact: the first is that, as mentiond before, large contributions in radiative corrections arising from $\gamma - Z$ mixing and from the neutrino charge radius in neutrino–electron scattering nearly cancel each other; the second is that fermion couplings to the Z boson do not run unless $|Q^2| \gg M_Z^2$. All these terms can thus be safely neglected compared with the experimental uncertainties of the CHARM II results.

We can use, in this way, the values for the vector and axial-vector electron couplings derived from the LEP experiments [4] to determine

$$2g^{\nu_\mu} = 1.004 \pm 0.033 \ . \tag{1}$$

This result has to be compared with the LEP result on the average value of the neutrino coupling to the Z obtained from Γ_{inv} assuming the total number of neutrinos to be three and neutrino flavour universality.

As described in reference [5] the value obtained in equation (1) can be combined with results from other experiments to obtain

$$
\begin{aligned}
2g^{\nu_e} &= 1.019 \pm 0.142 \\
2g^{\nu_\tau} &= 0.98 \pm 0.15
\end{aligned}
$$

assuming $N_\nu = 3$, or

$$N_\nu = 2.98 \pm 0.20 \tag{2}$$

assuming flavour universality. This last result is in good agreement with that one obtained at LEP from

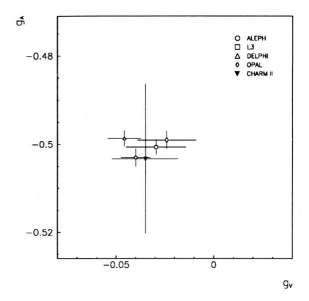

Figure 3. Comaprison of CHARM II results with LEP ones. In e^+e^- annihilation g_V^e and g_A^e are measured from lepton partial widths and forward-backward asymmetries assuming leptonic universality [4].

Γ_{inv} based on the assumption of both neutrino flavour universality and Standard Model couplings ($2g^\nu = 1$); however, the error in equation (2) reflects the status of our present knowledge.

In conclusion, because the CHARM II results on neutrino electron scattering have been obtained without assumptions about neutrino flavour universality, the coupling g^{ν_μ} can be determined from this experiment. Earlier experiments had established the equality of g^{ν_e} and g^{ν_μ} at the 15% level. Combining these results with LEP data, neutrino flavour universality in neutral current coupling is demonstrated for the first time and the assumption $2g^\nu = 1$ is not required anymore for evaluating the number of neutrino families.

References

[1] CHARM II Collaboration, K. De Winter *et al.*, Nucl. Instr. Meth. **A278** (1989) 670;
CHARM II Collaboration, D. Geiregat *et al.*, Nucl. Instr. Meth. **A325** (1993) 92.
[2] CHARM II Collaboration, P. Vilain et al., Phys. Lett. **B281** (1992) 159.
[3] CHARM II Collaboration, P. Vilain *et al.*, *Precision measurement of Electroweak parameters in neutrino–electron scattering*, to be published in Physics Letters **B**
[4] The LEP Collaborations and the LEP Electroweak working group, CERN-PPE/93-157 August 26, 1993.
[5] CHARM II Collaboration, P. Vilain *et al.*, Phys. Lett. **B320** (1994) 203.
[6] V.A. Novikov, L.B. Okun and M.I. Vysotsky, Phys. Lett. **B298** (1993) 453.

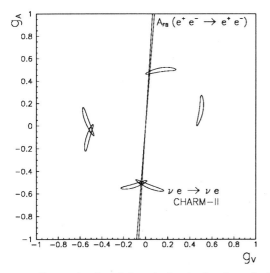

Figure 2. Determination of the solution in the $g_V^e - g_A^e$ plane. The forward backward asymmetry from LEP and the CHARM II results combine to resolve their intrinsic ambiguity.

Four-fermion production at LEP2 and beyond

F.A. Berends[†], R. Kleiss[§] and R. Pittau[†‡]

† Insituut-Lorentz, Leiden University, Leiden, The Netherlands
§ NIKHEF-H, Amsterdam, The Netherlands

1. Introduction

Four-fermion production will provide much of the interesting physics at LEP2 and beyond, whereas two-fermion production plays that rôle at LEP1. Key reactions are double-gauge boson production processes, and some single-gauge boson ones with sizeable cross sections:

$$e^+e^- \rightarrow W^+W^-, ZZ, We\nu_e, Ze^+e^-, Z\nu_e\bar{\nu}_e, \tag{1}$$

all leading to four fermions in the final state. Other processes that might be crucial are those related to Higgs boson production,

$$e^+e^- \rightarrow ZH, He^+e^-, H\nu_e\bar{\nu}_e. \tag{2}$$

When the Higgs boson mass is below 110 GeV, it decays predominantly into $b\bar{b}$ ($> 80\%$) and therefore these reactions also lead to four fermions.

In the study of the signals of the above processes one has to consider specific four-fermion final states. However, there are also other channels that can contribute to a given final state. These we shall call *background processes*, and their cross section is typically much smaller than that for the signal processes.

Thus, one issue consists of studying the interplay between the electroweak signal and the background, for a given final state. For some final states, *i.e.* the four-quark final state, even this is insufficient since QCD provides yet another background channel. One the one hand, there is QCD production of four quarks/antiquarks, that interferes with their

electroweak production. On the other hand, also the $q\bar{q}gg$ final state forms a 4-jet background to the 4-jet state orginating from four quarks.

Another issue is the effect of radiative corrections, in particular to the signal, and to some extent, also for the background.

It is the purpose of this paper to review the status of theoretical studies of four-ferimion production. First, we focus on signal-and-background questions for gauge-boson production, then we discuss the present strategy for radiative corrections, and, finally, we turn to Higgs boson production.

2. Signal and background in gauge-boson production

2.1. The final states and Feynman diagrams

To get an idea of the complexity of gauge-boson production, we compare W and Z pair production with single-Z production at LEP1. To this end, table 1 collects some properties of the three processes. The

signal	number of final states			number of diagrams	
	lept.	semil.	hadr.	signal	bckgr.
Z	6	0	5	1	0,1,3
WW	9	12	4	3	6 (for a) to 53 (b)
ZZ	21	30	15	2(4)	4 (c) to 140 (d)

Table 1. Comparison of numbers of distinct final states and numbers of diagrams between single- and double-gauge boson production. The final states referred to are: (a) $\mu\bar{\nu}_\mu\nu_\tau\tau^+$, (b) $e^+e^-\nu_e\bar{\nu}_e$, (c) $\nu_\mu\bar{\nu}_\mu\nu_\tau\bar{\nu}_\tau$, and (d) $e^+e^+e^-e^-$.

number of different final states increases substantially from LEP1 to LEP2. Whereas single-Z production

‡ present address: FNAL, Batavia Ill., USA. Research supported by EU under contract number CHRX-CT-92-0004.

leads to 11 distinct final states, WW or ZZ production yield 25 and 66 different final states, respectively, even assuming a diagonal CKM matrix.

For these final states, the number of background diagrams varies significantly. For LEP1, the background is usually just single-photon exchange in the s channel, with the exception of $\nu_i \bar{\nu}_i$ $(i = \mu, \tau)$ (no background), $\nu_e \bar{\nu}_e$ (t-channel W exchange) and $e^+ e^-$ (γ, Z exhange also in the t channel). For the processes (1), a complete inventory of background diagrams can be found in [1]. Here, we just mention that the number ranges between 6 and 53 for WW production, and between 4 and 140 for ZZ production. In this counting, we have omitted QCD processes and Higgs production-decay diagrams; if we keep these restrictions in mind these numbers agree with those of reference [2].

The large number of background diagrams, and its variation over specific final states, make the computation of four-fermion production far from trivial even at the Born level. Therefore, the availability of independent calculations, preferably using different techniques, is mandatory. Recently, results have been published that are based on two different approaches.

One such approach is semi-analytical [2, 3]. Here, the integration over phase space is performed analytically, as far as humanly possible. The remaining integrations are then done numerically. The other approach is completely based on Monte Carlo techniques, and generates weighted events [1, 4, 5]. In the next subsections, we discuss the methods and some results.

2.2. Semi-analytical method

This approach is currently being applied to W-pair and Z-pair [2], and Higgs boson production [3]. Turning specifically to W-pair production, the four-fermion cross section is written as an integral over the sum of the contributions of the signal, the background, and their interference:

$$
\sigma^{4f} = \int_0^s ds_1 \, \rho_W(s_1) \int_0^s ds_2 \, \rho_W(s_2) \left[\sigma^{WW}(s; s_1, s_2) \right.
$$
$$
\left. + \sigma^B(s; s_1, s_2) + \sigma^I(s; s_1, s_2) \right] \, . \quad (3)
$$

The Breit-Wigner shape of the vector bosons is extracted as and overall factor:

$$
\rho_W(t) = t \, \Gamma_W \, \mathrm{Br} / \left(\pi M_W \left| t - M_W^2 + it\Gamma_W/M_W \right|^2 \right) \, ,
$$
$$
(4)
$$

where Br is the branching ratio to the chosen final state. The expression for σ^{WW} has been known for some time [6], but the background and interference ones were not. They have been derived for the following final states: $\tau^+ \nu_\tau \mu^- \bar{\nu}_\mu$, $d\bar{u}\mu^+\nu_\mu$, $u\bar{d}s\bar{c}$, which have, respectively, 6, 7,

and 8 background diagrams. These have in common the annihilation into a photon or Z which then decays into the four fermions. The advantage of the method is that it requires only a twofold numerical integration, giving high accuracy with little CPU time. A disadvantage is that only experimental cuts in s_1 and s_2 can be imposed naturally. Also, quite an amount of analytical work is still needed to obtain σ^B and σ^I for the remaining interesting final states.

2.3. Eevent-generator approach

When one wants to apply Monte Carlo techniques to evaluate the four-fermion cross sections with good accuracy in a reasonable amount of CPU time, two requirements must be met. One is a fast evaluation of the matrix elements, the other an efficient sampling of phase space.

A fast evaluation of the matrix elements is achieved by neglecting the fermion masses, since then fewer helicity amplitudes have to be considered. A disadvantage is that singulariries arise which have to be removed by kinematical cuts. For an efficient treatment of the phase space, the choice of phase space variables has to be adapted to the specific final state.

Two recent studies [4, 5] use a general package for Monte Carlo integration and the computation of the matrix element squared. In principle, any nonzero value for the fermion masses can be taken. Thus, the calculation is general, but time-consuming. Another recent study [1] aims at a fast and efficient calculation of any chosen four-fermion final state. It employs one, general, subroutine to calculate any specific matrix element. This specification also yields an automatic choice of the optimal phase-space variables used in the event generation, adapted to the peaking structure of the contributing Feynman diagrams. The evaluation of the matrix elements is based on a spinorial calculation of the helicity amplitudes, the phase-space generation relies on a so-called multichannel approach [7, 8]. The advantage of Monte Carlo is that any experimental cut on the phase space can actually be implemented. For the treatment of reference [1] there is the additional advantage that the cross section for any massless final state is evaluated very efficiently. The cuts required to avoid the collinear singularities are usually the same as those used in experiments which separate the particle tracks.

2.4. Numerical results

In this paragraph, results are given for the W-pair signal diagrams and the complete calculation of signal-cum-background, for leptonic and semi-leptonic final states (for four quarks, we refer to section 3.2). In

process	$\sqrt{s}$ (GeV)			
	150	175	200	500
W-pair	.3600 E-2	.1181	.1304	.2130 E-1
	.0011	.0002	.0003	.0011
$e^+e^-\nu_e\bar{\nu}_e$	.2949 E-2	.1208	.1466	.6111 E-1
	.0008	.0002	.0003	.0028
$\mu^+\mu^-\nu_\mu\bar{\nu}_\mu$	.4350 E-2	.1196	.1364	.2209 E-1
	.0012	.0002	.0003	.0011
$e^+e^-\nu_\mu\bar{\nu}_\mu$	.8379 E-3	.1906 E-2	.6226 E-2	.2342 E-2
	.0026	.0004	.0008	.0006
$\nu_\tau\bar{\nu}_\tau\mu^+\mu^-$	.7927 E-3	.1342 E-2	.5457 E-2	.1054 E-2
	.0031	.0003	.0007	.0003
$\nu_e\bar{\nu}_e\mu^+\mu^-$	.1002 E-2	.1842 E-2	.6004 E-2	.7660 E-2
	.0004	.0005	.0009	.0079
W-pair	.3598 E-2	.1187	.1315	.2130 E-1
	.0011	.0002	.0003	.0011
$e^-\bar{\nu}_e\nu_\mu\mu^+$	.2912 E-2	.1192	.1359	.3598 E-1
	.0008	.0002	.0003	.0014
$\mu^-\bar{\nu}_\mu\nu_\tau\tau^+$	.3649 E-2	.1193	.1307	.2101 E-1
	.0010	.0002	.0003	.0010

Table 2. Leptonic cross sections in picobarns. The second line of each entry is the Monte Carlo error. In the first six entries $m(e^+e^-), m(\mu^+\mu^-) > 10$ GeV, $|\cos\theta_{e\pm,\;\mu\pm}| < 0.9$ (θ is the scattering angle), $E_{e\pm,\;\mu\pm} > 20$ GeV. In the last three ones $E_{e-,\;\mu\pm,\;\tau+} > 20$ GeV, $|\cos\theta_{e-,\;\mu\pm,\;\tau+}| < 0.9$.

proces hline	$\sqrt{s}$ (GeV)			
	150	175	200	500
W-pair	.9605 E-2	.3342	.3601	.4682 E-1
	.0030	.0007	.0008	.0028
$e^-\bar{\nu}_e u\bar{d}$	.7563 E-2	.3345	.3745	.8293 E-1
	.0021	.0007	.0009	.0035
$\mu^-\bar{\nu}_\mu u\bar{d}$	.9728 E-2	.3337	.3610	.4599 E-1
	.0028	.0007	.0008	.0024

Table 3. Semileptonic cross sections (in pb). $E_{e-,\;\mu-,\;u,\;\bar{d}} > 20$ GeV, $|\cos\theta_{e-,\;\mu-,\;u,\;\bar{d}}| < 0.9$, $|\cos\angle(u,\bar{d})| < 0.9$, $m(u\bar{d}) > 10$ GeV.

		$\sqrt{s}$ (GeV)		
		190	200	500
W-pair		.3532	.3419	.2498 E-1
		.0009	.0008	.0018
1 cut		.3612	.3550	.3522 E-1
		.0009	.0009	.0020
W-pair		.3392	.3259	.2236 E-1
		.0009	.0009	.0014
2 cuts		.3407	.3292	.2228 E-1
		.0009	.0009	.0014

Table 4. $e^-\bar{\nu}_e u\bar{d}$ cross section in picobarns. The 1st entry is a comparison between the WW signal and the full result with a cut $70 < m_{(u\bar{d})} < 90$ GeV. In the 2nd entry $70 < m_{(e\nu_e)}, m_{(u\bar{d})} < 90$ GeV. All the other cuts are as in table 3, except that an energy cut $E_{e-,\;u,\;\bar{d}} > 50$ GeV is required at $\sqrt{s} = 500\,GeV$.

table 2, the cross sections for leptonic states are given.

Some of these cannot arise from the signal, but are experimentally indistinguishable from it: these are so-called *non-interfering* backgrounds. From the table, it is clear that at LEP2 energies the complete and the restricted signal cross section generally differ by several per cent, except for $\mu^-\bar{\nu}_\mu\tau^+\nu_\tau$ where the difference is negligible. For 500 GeV, the differences become more dramatic for final states containing $e\nu_e$. For the semi-leptonic final states, again the one with $e^-\bar{\nu}_e u\bar{d}$ shows the largest difference (table 3). This difference can be removed by making two invariant-mass cuts (table 4). Further details can be found in reference [1]. Where available, the semi-analytical results agree with the Monte Carlo ones.

3. Radiative corrections

Higher-order QED corrections can be written as an expansion in α, but (in the case of initial-state radiation) also as a convolution with two structure functions Φ, or a single flux function G:

$$
\begin{aligned}
\sigma(s) &= \sigma_0(s)\left[1 + \mathcal{O}(\alpha) + \mathcal{O}(\alpha^2) + \cdots\right] \\
&= \int_0^1 dx_1 \int_0^1 dx_2\, \Phi(x_1)\,\Phi(x_2)\,\hat{\sigma}(sx_1x_2) \\
&= \int_0^1 dz\, G(z)\,\hat{\sigma}(zs) \ . \qquad (5)
\end{aligned}
$$

For the s-channel processes at LEP1, the flux function is known up to and including $\mathcal{O}(\alpha^2)$. Its leading logarithmic terms are universal (independent of the particular process) but its subleading ones are not. Also, $\hat{\sigma}$ is known including non-photonic electroweak corrections: it is sometimes called the *dressed* Born term. Precise knowledge of $\sigma(s)$ is crucial for an accurate determination of M_Z and Γ_Z.

For LEP2, much less is known about the precise radiative corrections, for a review see [9]. For on-shell W pair production, the $\mathcal{O}(\alpha)$ correction is known. In $G(z)$, the subleading terms are lacking, although conjectures have been made, on the basis of a current splitting technique [10]. Moreover, there is no simple form for a dressed Born term. For an explcitly four-fermion final state even less is known, although an ambitious project is under way [11]. At the moment, the safest strategy is to take into account the leading logarithmic terms in $\Phi(x)$ or $G(z)$, thus incorporating the dominant part of initial-state radiation. This has been done for four fermions originating from W's in [10, 12], and for the complete matrix element in [13, 14]. As an example, results for four-jet final states are given in table 5. Reference [10] employs the semi-analtyical approach, calling for a three-dimensional numerical integration, the other studies use Monte Carlo techniques.

The measurement of M_W will mainly come from a reconstruction of the jet momenta in semi-leptonic or hadronic decays [15]. To this end, a good knowledge of the energy lost to initial-state radiation is indispensable. In the literature, it has been investigated how various assumptions on $G(z)$ and $\hat{\sigma}(s)$ affect the average energy loss in the semileptonic [10, 13] and hadronic channels [14]. In particular, for the latter the theoretical predictions depend strongly on what is taken into account in the four-quark cross section. As we can see

$\sqrt{s}$ (GeV)		175		190
		σ	ϵ	σ
WW signal		3.0674	–	3.5136
		0.0074		0.0090
WW signal + ISR		2.5622	1.091	3.1416
		0.0071	0.005	0.0089
All EW diagrams + ISR		2.5922	1.104	3.3553
		0.0075	0.005	0.0097
All EW diagrams + interf. QCD + ISR		2.6202	1.188	3.3789
		0.0079	0.017	0.0100
All EW diagrams + all QCD + ISR		3.1155	2.513	3.8688
		0.0123	0.065	0.0146

Table 5. Cross section in picobarn and average energy loss (ϵ) in GeV for $e^+e^- \to 4$ jets. $E_{(all\ particles)} > 20\ GeV$, $|\cos\theta_{(all\ particles)}| < 0.9$, $m(ij) > 10\ GeV$ and $|\cos(i,j)| < 0.9$ between all possible final state pairs. The second line in each entry is the estimated Monte Carlo error.

in table 5, the inclusion of QCD backgrounds increases the energy loss considerably. This is due to a different energy dependence of the backgrounds.

4.   Backgrounds to the Higgs boson signal

Whereas very precise calculations are needed for W-pair production, this is not the case for Higgs boson production reactions. The distinction between signal and background is, in the latter case, also much more pronounced due to the narrowness of the Higgs boson peak. In a number of papers, the signal and backgrounds for the reactions (2) have been studied, in particular for the final states $b\bar{b}\mu^+\mu^-$ [3, 4], $b\bar{b}\nu_\mu\bar{\nu}_\mu$ [3, 4, 5], and $b\bar{b}\nu_e\bar{\nu}_e$ [4, 5]. These backgrounds can also be calculated (in the approximation of massless b quarks) in the approach of reference [1], and form a test case where one has 24,10, and 19 diagrams respectively, excluding the Higgs signal itself.

In table 6, comparisons between the semi-analytical and Monte Carlo calculations of various Higgs boson background processes are presented. The input parameters are $M_Z = 91.173$ GeV, $\Gamma_Z = 2.4971$ GeV, $M_W = 80.22$ GeV, $\Gamma_W = 2.033$ GeV, $1/\alpha = 131.0485$, $\sin^2\theta_w = 0.225836$. These values reproduce the correct

		$\sqrt{s} = 200$ GeV		$\sqrt{s} = 500$ GeV	
		$e^+e^- \to b\bar{b}\mu^+\mu^-$			
M_{bb}	$M_{\mu\mu}$	[1]	[3]	[1]	[3]
20	2	29.82±.03	29.850	8.75±.01	8.736
50	2	29.44±.03	29.440	8.61±.01	8.631
20	10	19.41±.02	19.425	6.79±.01	6.774
50	10	19.08±.02	19.107	6.69±.01	6.689
		$e^+e^- \to b\bar{b}\nu_\mu\bar{\nu}_\mu$			
M_{bb}		[1]	[3]	[1]	[3]
20		23.70±.02	23.683	8.72±.01	8.720
50		23.25±.02	23.251	8.61±.01	8.619

Table 6. Comparison between references [1] and [3] for two backgrounds to Higgs production. The cross sections are in fb, and M_{bb} and $M_{\mu\mu}$ refer to cuts (in GeV) on the invariant masses of the quark and muon pairs. All fermions are taken to be massless.

Fermi constant. Although we could not yet compare with the results of reference [4] with exactly the same input parameters, their results seem to be compatible with those of table 6.

Acknowledgement

We are grateful to the authors of references [3] and [4] for supplying us with detailed results of their calculations.

References

[1] F.A. Berends, R. Kleiss and R. Pittau, Nucl. Phys. **B424** (1994) 308.
[2] D. Bardin, M. Bilenky, D. Lehner, A. Olchevski and T. Riemann, CERN-TH.7295/94, DESY 94-093.
[3] D. Bardin, A. Leike and T. Riemann, CERN-TH.7305/94.
[4] E. Boos, M. Sachwitz, H.J. Schreiber, and S. Sichanin, Zeit. Phys. **C61** (1994) 675; DESY 93-183; and DESY 94-91.
[5] M. Dubinin, V. Edneral, Y. Kurihara, and Y. Shimizu, Phys. Lett. **B329** (1994) 379.
[6] T. Muta, R. Najima, and S. Wakaizumi, Mod. Phys. Lett. **A1** (1986) 203.
[7] F.A. Berends, P.H. Daverveldt and R. Kleiss, Nucl. Phys. **B253** (1985) 441; and Computer Phys. Comm. **40** (1986) 285.
[8] J. Hilgart, R. Kleiss and F. le Diberder, Computer Phys. Comm. **75** (1993) 191.
[9] W. Beenakker and A. Denner, DESY 94-51.
[10] D. Bardin, M. Bilenky, A. Olchevski and T. Riemann, Phys. Lett. **B308** (1993) 403.
[11] A. Aeppli, G.J. van Oldenborgh and D. Wyler, PSI-PR-93-22.
[12] H. Anlauf, P. Manakos, T. Mannel and H.D. Dahmen, Darmstadt/Siegen preprint: IKDA-93-28 and SI-93-4.
[13] F.A. Berends, R. Kleiss and R. Pittau, INLO-PUB-6/94 and NIKHEF-H/94-20 (to appear in Nucl. Phys. **B**).
[14] R. Pittau, Phys. Lett. **B335** (1994) 490.
[15] S. Katsanevas *et al.*, DELPHI internal report 92-166 Phys 250.

W Mass Measurements from DØ and CDF Experiments at TeVatron

Chang Kee Jung

State University of New York at Stony Brook

For the DØ and the CDF Collaborations

Abstract

We present preliminary measurements of the W boson mass made by the DØ and CDF experiments using data collected at the Fermilab TeVatron $\bar{p}p$ collider operating at $\sqrt{s} = 1.8$ TeV. The result from the CDF $W \rightarrow e\nu$ data analysis is $M_W = 80.47 \pm 0.15(\text{stat}) \pm 0.25(\text{sys})$ GeV/c^2 and the result from the CDF $W \rightarrow \mu\nu$ data analysis is $M_W = 80.29 \pm 0.20(\text{stat}) \pm 0.24(\text{sys})$ GeV/c^2. The result from the DØ $W \rightarrow e\nu$ data analysis is $M_W = 79.86 \pm 0.16(\text{stat}) \pm 0.31(\text{sys})$ GeV/c^2. When combined with the previous measurements, these results yield a world average value of M_W, 80.23 ± 0.18 GeV/c^2.

1. Introduction

The W boson mass M_W is one of the fundamental parameters of the Standard Model. With already precisely measured the Z boson mass (better than 0.01%), α and G_μ, a precision measurement of M_W provides a stringent test of the SM. The W mass is also sensitive to the top quark mass (quadratically) and the Higgs boson mass (logarithmically) through radiative loop correction. Thus, a precision measurement of M_W can provide constraint to the top quark mass and eventually to the Higgs mass. Furthermore M_W provides a constraint on S and T parameters[1] which are introduced to study heavy physics effects on the gauge boson self-energies.[2]

To date, the direct measurements of M_W have been made only at the hadronic colliders and it will remain so until the LEP II collider starts its operation. In this paper, we present the most recent measurements of the W boson mass made by the DØ and CDF experiments using data collected at the Fermilab TeVatron $\bar{p}p$ collider operating at $\sqrt{s} = 1.8$ TeV. The analyses are based on about 20 pb^{-1} (CDF) and about 13 pb^{-1} (DØ) of data collected during the 1992-93 collider run. The CDF[3] and DØ[4] detectors are described in detail elsewhere.

2. Overview of the M_W measurement Techniques

Measuring M_W using the leptonic decays of the W boson requires a measurement of neutrino momentum. The neutrino momentum, however, cannot be measured directly and inferred by the visible energy in the event. Since energy along the beam line is not well known, we define the transverse mass of the W as following:

$$M_T^W = \sqrt{2p_T^l p_T^\nu (1 - \cos\phi_{l,\nu})},$$

where $\phi_{l,\nu}$ is the azimuthal angle between the lepton and the neutrino direction. The basic techniques of measuring M_W, then, involve fitting the transverse mass spectra of the Ws to spectra generated with fast Monte Carlo (MC) simulations. The fast MC simulation is necessary since it is extremely hard to generate sufficient number of full detector simulated events for a desired statistical accuracy.

The p_T spectrum of the W boson in the fast MC is generated with the next to leading order calculation[5] in DØ and with the data p_T spectrum of the Z boson in CDF. DØ uses the HMRSb structure function and CDF uses the MRS D_' structure function. The MC's are further tuned using the information from data as much as possible including effects of acceptance, resolution, underlying events, multiple interactions, missing p_T resolution, etc. The same set of event selection cuts are applied to the data and the simulated MC event samples. The MC events are corrected for final state radiations and relevant background contributions are included. M_T^W spectra for various M_W values are generated and compared to the M_T^W spectra of the data. The best fit M_W values are obtained using the maximum likelihood method.

3.   Event Selection

For M_W measurements, DØ uses only $W \rightarrow e\nu$ channel events while CDF uses both $W \rightarrow e\nu$ and $W \rightarrow \mu\nu$ channels. The event selection criteria for both experiments are quite similar to each other. The minimum lepton p_T and the missing p_T for the W candidates are required to be 25 GeV. The minimum and maximum of M_T^W are required to be 60 GeV and 90 GeV for DØ, 60 GeV and 100 GeV for CDF. DØ requires the p_T of W to be less than 30 GeV. CDF requires there are no other jets with E_T greater than 20 GeV and no other tracks with p_T greater than 10 GeV. Both experiments require the leptons to be in the central rapidity region and apply various lepton quality cuts. After these requirements DØ has 4817 events, and CDF has 6421 $W \rightarrow e\nu$ and 4090 $W \rightarrow \mu\nu$ events for W mass fitting.

4.   Energy Scale and Underlying Event Corrections

In order to make a precision measurement of M_W, calibration of a detector for its momentum-energy scale is an absolute necessity. DØ determines the calorimeter energy scale and its uncertainties by comparing mass fits of $Z \rightarrow ee$ events to the LEP Z mass. The linearity of the calibration between the W and Z masses is also determined from the $Z \rightarrow ee$ events, making use of the fact that the electrons from these decays cover a wide range of energies in the lab frame, depending on the momentum of the Z and the decay angle. The Z mass is fit as a function of the factor $f = 2(E_1 + E_2)\sin^2(\gamma/2)/M$, where E_1 and E_2 are the energies of the two electrons in the lab frame, γ is the opening angle in that frame, and M is the invariant mass. This is shown in figure 1. A linear fit to this plot determines an offset which is consistent with zero and a slope. The energy scale contribution to the uncertainty in the W mass measurement is estimated to be ±260 MeV. CDF calibrates their detector for its momentum scale by using $\psi \rightarrow \mu\mu$ events in their central tracking chambers. From a comparison of their reconstructed ψ mass with the Particle Data Group value, they obtain a correction

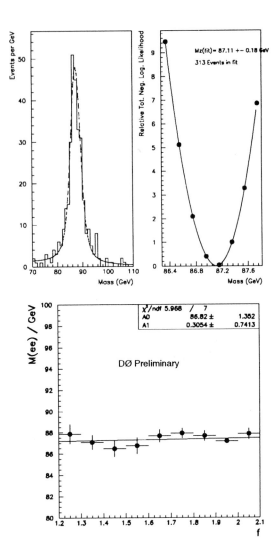

Figure 1. DØ calorimeter calibration data: the $M(ee)$ spectrum and $\langle M(ee) \rangle$ vs. f (see text) for the $Z \rightarrow ee$ sample.

factor to the momentum scale of 1.00076 ± 0.00071. The result is checked with the Υ and Z resonances, as shown in figure 2. CDF then transfers the momentum scale correction to the calorimeter energy scale determination by using a sample of W electrons. The energy scale is determined by fitting the ratio of the measured electron energy in the calorimeter to the measured momentum in the tracking chamber to a simulated lineshape which includes the effects of radiative W decays and external bremsstrahlung in the detector material.

The response of the detector to the low energy hadrons from recoiling soft jets against the W or from underlying events is poorly known. Both DØ and CDF utilize the information from Z data samples to correct for the uncertainty in the response. Detailed descriptions of the correction methods can be found elsewhere.[6]

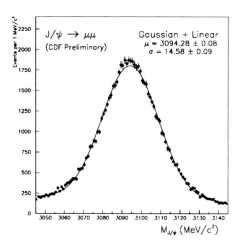

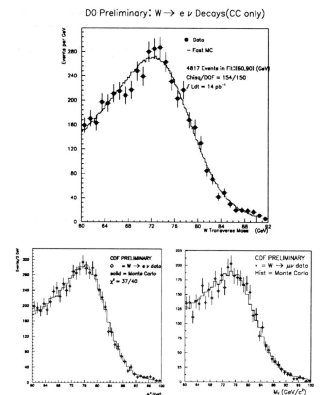

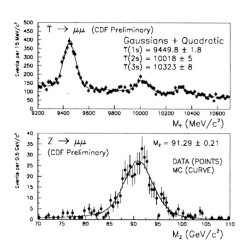

Figure 2. CDF spectrometer calibration data: $\psi \to \mu\mu$, $\Upsilon \to \mu\mu$ and $Z \to \mu\mu$. The ψ sample sets the calibration scale, and the other resonances serve as checks.

5. Backgrounds and Radiative Corrections

The major backgrounds to the $W \to e\nu$ events are $W \to \tau\nu$ and QCD events. These backgrounds are included in the MC's. CDF finds a shift of +80 MeV in the W mass when the backgrounds are included in the fit. The major backgrounds to the $W \to \mu\nu$ events are $W \to \tau\nu$, $Z \to \mu\mu$, $Z \to \tau\tau$, cosmic ray and QCD events. CDF finds a shift of +232 MeV in the W mass when these backgrounds are included.

CDF also corrects their results for radiative decays of Ws, while DØ does not yet correct for the radiation. CDF finds a shift of +80 MeV in the W mass for the $W \to e\nu$ analysis and a shift of +154 MeV for the $W \to \mu\nu$ analysis when the correction is applied. Neither experiment has yet included an uncertainty on this correction to the systematic errors in the W mass measurements.

Figure 3. Fits to the W transverse mass spectra for DØ electrons, CDF electrons and CDF muons. Note that the scale on the DØ spectrum is 60-92 GeV, while the CDF spectra go from 60-100 GeV.

6. Results

The final transverse mass spectra, after calibration corrections, are shown in figure 3 along with the best fits. In each case the agreement between the data and the MC fit is excellent. The results of the mass fits are (in GeV/c^2):

$$M(W) = \begin{cases} 80.47 \pm 0.15(\text{stat}) \pm 0.25(\text{sys}) & \text{CDF(e)} \\ 80.29 \pm 0.20(\text{stat}) \pm 0.24(\text{sys}) & \text{CDF}(\mu) \\ 79.86 \pm 0.16(\text{stat}) \pm 0.31(\text{sys}) & \text{DØ(e)}. \end{cases}$$

The sources of systematic uncertainties are summarized in table 1. The results from both experiments are still preliminary, and several of the systematic uncertainties are expected to improve in the final result, including the DØ energy scale contribution and the CDF resolution uncertainty. The CDF and DØ groups have together produced a world average which combines these three new results with the earlier CDF[7] and UA2[8] measurements of $M(W)$. The new average accounts for errors (100 MeV in PDF) that are assumed to be common to the measurements. The result is

$$M(W) = 80.23 \pm 0.18 \text{ GeV (1994 World Average)}$$

The individual measurements and the average are compared in figure 4 to the standard model predictions

Table 1. Uncertainties in the W mass measurements, in MeV.

	CDF (e)	CDF (μ)	DØ(e)
Energy Scale	130	60	260
Resolution	140	120	70
Background	50	50	30
Fitting	20	20	30
PDF	100	100	70
p_T^W and und. evt.	120	145	120
Width	-	-	20
Total Sys.	250	240	307
Statistical	150	200	160
Total (Stat + Sys)	290	300	346

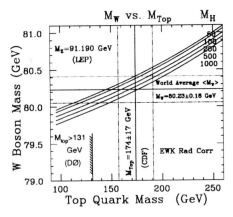

Figure 5. Minimal Standard Model predictions for mass relations. The curves show $M(W)$ as a function of $M(top)$ for various values of $M(Higgs)$. The horizontal band is the world average of $M(W)$ from hadron colliders, and the vertical band is the $M(top)$ range suggested by recent evidence from CDF[13], while the region at the left is excluded by the DØ top search[14].

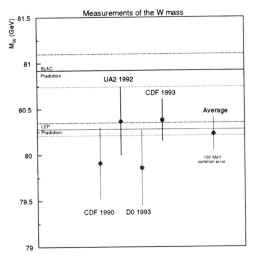

Figure 4. Comparison of hadron collider $M(W)$ measurements and indirect $M(W)$ predictions.

extrapolated from LEP measurements[9] and from SLAC left-right asymmetry measurements[10]. The direct $M(W)$ measurements are in good agreement with one another and with the LEP prediction, but are about 2σ from the SLAC prediction. In fig. 5, the relationship among the top quark, the W and the Higgs masses in the minimal Standard Model[11] is shown along with the current measurements. Although the present uncertainties in the measured W and top masses are now large, it is feasible to obtain a significant constraint on the Higgs mass in the future, if the uncertainty in the top quark mass becomes about 5 GeV and the uncertainty in the W mass becomes about 50 MeV. Studies indicate these precisions should be attainable with the expected increase in statistics of about 1 fb^{-1}.[12]

7. Conclusion

The DØ and the CDF experiments at the Fermilab TeVatron have measured the W mass with the 1993-1994 collider data. The new measurements result in a new world average value of the W mass $M(W) =$

80.23 ± 0.18 GeV/c^2 when combined with the previous statistically independent measurements. No significant deviation from the SM predictions have been observed.

The W mass measurements have already reached the systematic limit of precision. However, the systematic uncertainties are expected to decrease as more data are accumulated. Both CDF and DØ are also continuously improving their analysis methods to better estimate the systematic uncertainties. Currently the Tevatron is running at a luminosity greater than 10^{31} cm^{-2}s^{-1} and is expected to run untill the end of 1995 yielding more than 100 pb^{-1} of accumulated data for both experiments. This work is supported in part by the U.S. Department of Energy under contract No. DE-FG02-92ER40697.

References

[1] M. Peskin. and T. Takeuchi, Phys. Rev. Lett. **65** (1990) 964; and Phys. Rev. **D46** (1992) 381.
[2] W. Marciano, Brookhaven report: BNL-60177.
[3] CDF: F. Abe *et al.*, Nucl. Instr. Meth. **A271** (1988) 387.
[4] DØ: S. Abachi *et al.*, Nucl. Instr. Meth. **A338** (1994) 185.
[5] P. Arnold and R. Kauffman, ANL-HEP-PR-90-70.
[6] Q. Zhu, *Measurement of the W Boson Mass in Proton-Antiproton Collisions at* $\sqrt{S} = 1.8$ *Tev* Ph.D. Thesis, New York University (1994);
    D. Saltzberg, FERMILAB-CONF-93/355-E.
[7] CDF: F. Abe *et al.*, Phys. Rev. **D43** (1991) 2070.
[8] UA2: J. Alitti *et al.*, Phys. Lett. **B276** (1992) 354.
[9] K. Moenig, these proceedings.
[10] M. Fero, these proceedings.
[11] F. halzen and B. Kniehl, Nucl. Phys. **B353** (1991) 567.
[12] *Test of the Electroweak Theory* DPF Long-Range Planning Study (1994).
[13] CDF: F. abe *et al.* Phys. Rev. Lett. **73** (1994) 225.
[14] DØ: S. Abachi *et al.*, Phys. Rev. Lett. **72** (1994) 2138.

Electroweak Boson Pair Production at the Tevatron

Steven M. Errede*†

Loomis Laboratory of Physics, The University of Illinois at Urbana-Champaign, Urbana, IL 61801 USA

Abstract

Preliminary results from CDF and DØ on $W\gamma$, $Z\gamma$ and WW, WZ, ZZ boson pair production in $\sqrt{s} = 1.8$ TeV p̄-p collisions from the 1992-93 collider run are presented. Direct limits on $\mathcal{CP}$-conserving and $\mathcal{CP}$-violating $WW\gamma$, WWZ, $ZZ\gamma$ and $Z\gamma\gamma$ anomalous couplings have been obtained. The results are consistent with Standard Model expectations. In the static limit, the direct experimental limits on $WW\gamma$ and $ZZ\gamma$ anomalous couplings are related to bounds on the higher-order static (transition) EM moments of the W (Z) bosons. Expectations from the on-going and future Tevatron collider runs are discussed.

1. Introduction

During the 1992-93 Tevatron collider run, CDF (DØ) accumulated ~ 20 (13) pb^{-1} integrated luminosity. The inclusive W/Z data samples obtained during this run are sufficiently large that studies of rare and/or semi-rare exclusive processes such as $W\gamma$, $Z\gamma$, WW, WZ and ZZ-pair production are now becoming feasible.

The observation and detailed study of these processes provide important new tests of the Standard Model (SM) of electroweak (EWK) interactions through the investigation and study of tri-linear gauge boson couplings of the W, Z and γ. Strong gauge cancellations are predicted to occur in the $W\gamma$, WW and WZ processes, while no such cancellations are expected for the $Z\gamma$ or ZZ processes. The tri-linear gauge boson couplings associated with the $WW\gamma$ and WWZ vertices (s-channel Feynman diagrams) are a consequence of the non-Abelian $SU_L(2) \times U_Y(1)$ symmetry of the EWK theory [1]. They are the *only* non-zero tree-level tri-vector boson vertices allowed in the SM. The corresponding u and t-channel diboson processes depend only on the coupling between quarks and EWK bosons. However, the fermion-gauge boson couplings are now well-tested in the production and decay of single bosons, and are considered as known. Diboson production is therefore primarily a test of the strength and nature of the tri-linear gauge boson couplings.

In various non-standard models of the electroweak interactions, the $V = W$, Z and γ are viewed as composite, rather than fundamental particles [2]. In such scenarios, non-standard $WW\gamma$, WWZ, $ZZ\gamma$, $Z\gamma\gamma$ and ZZZ anomalous couplings may exist.

New physics must be introduced at large $\hat{s}$ [3] in order to avoid violation of tree-level S-matrix unitarity [4]. The anomalous couplings are modified via the introduction of generalized dipole form factors [5, 6] $a(\hat{s}) = a_o/(1 + \hat{s}/\Lambda_V^2)^n$ where $a_o = \Delta\kappa, \lambda...$ which force the anomalous boson couplings to approach their SM values at large $\hat{s}$. The form factor scale Λ_V is presumed to be significantly larger than the typical $\hat{s}$ values seen at the Tevatron. A signature of the existence of non-zero anomalous couplings is an excess rate of production of diboson pairs, particularly at high transverse energies. The absence of an excess of such events can therefore be used to obtain *direct* experimental limits on such anomalous couplings for each diboson process.

2. Diboson Pair Production at the Tevatron

CDF (DØ) extract $W\gamma/Z\gamma$ data samples from inclusive e/μ channel W/Z samples by requiring an isolated photon in a fiducial region of their central (central + endcap) EM calorimeters with $E_T^\gamma \geq 7$ (10) GeV. A minimum lepton $-$ photon angular separation of $\Delta R_{\ell\gamma} = \sqrt{\Delta\eta^2 + \Delta\phi^2} > 0.7$ suppresses final-state QED bremsstrahlung. Background from W/Z+jets is suppressed by requiring isolated photons and transverse/longitudinal EM shower development consistent with a single photon. The level of W/Z+jet background in each of the $W\gamma/Z\gamma$ data samples is determined by use of QCD jet data samples to obtain a jet fragmentation probability $\mathcal{P}_{J\to\gamma}(E_T)$ which is then convoluted with the jet E_T spectrum in each of the inclusive W/Z data samples. The $Z\gamma$ background in the $W\gamma$ data arising from non-observation of one of the Z decay leptons is estimated from MC simulations. The contributions to $W\gamma$ and $Z\gamma$ from tau W/Z decay channels are also estimated from MC simulations and found to be small.

* Supported in part by the U.S. Department of Energy, Division of High Energy Physics, Grant No. DE-FG02-91ER40677.
† E-mail: serrede@uihepa.hep.uiuc.edu

WW, WZ and ZZ data samples are also extracted from inclusive e/μ W/Z data. CDF has analyzed the $WW, WZ \to \ell\bar{\nu}\,jj$ and $ZW, ZZ \to \ell^+\ell^-\,jj$ ($\ell = e$ or μ) channels using standard W/Z lepton selection cuts, and requiring $60 < M_{jj} < 110$ GeV/c^2. For leptonic W (Z) events, CDF eliminates W/Z+jets background by requiring $P_T^{jj} > 130$ (100) GeV/c, which also eliminates the SM signal but retains good sensitivity for non-zero $WW\gamma/WWZ$ anomalous couplings. DØ has analyzed the $WW \to e\nu_e\,\ell\nu_\ell$ channel using standard lepton cuts for selection of W pairs. The Z mass region in the ee channel is excluded and $M_T(ee, \not{E}_T) > 100$ GeV/c^2 is required. Backgrounds from Z decay and fake electrons are estimated from data and MC simulations.

SM and anomalous coupling predictions for the $W\gamma$ and $Z\gamma$ processes are obtained via use of the Baur/Berger MC event generators [5, 6] and detailed MC detector simulations. MRSD$-'$ structure functions are used for event generation as they best match the recent W lepton asymmetry measurements from CDF [7]. SM and anomalous coupling predictions for the WW, WZ and ZW processes are obtained via use of the Zeppenfeld MC event generator [8] and MC detector simulations.

Preliminary CDF and DØ results from the 1992-93 collider run for event yields and SM predictions for $W\gamma$, $Z\gamma$, WW, WZ and ZZ production are summarized in Table 1, along with UA2 $W\gamma$ [9] and preliminary CDF $W\gamma$, $Z\gamma$ results from the 1988-89 collider run [10]. All results are in good agreement with SM expectations.

3.   Direct Limits on W/Z Anomalous Couplings

Direct experimental limits on $WW\gamma$, $ZZ\gamma$ and $Z\gamma\gamma$ anomalous couplings for the $W\gamma/Z\gamma$ processes are obtained via binned maximum likelihood fits to the E_T^γ distribution. The observed E_T^γ distribution is compared to the sum of expected signal plus background(s) prediction, calculating the Poisson likelihood that this sum would fluctuate to the observed number of events in each E_T bin, and convoluting with a Gaussian distribution to take into account systematic uncertainties associated with backgrounds, luminosity normalization, structure function choice, Q^2-scale and uncertainties in the shape of the $P_T(W\gamma/Z\gamma)$ distribution, efficiencies, *etc.*

CDF extracts direct experimental limits on $WW\gamma$ and WWZ anomalous couplings for the WW/WZ processes via comparison of observed events to the expected signal, including systematic uncertainties due to luminosity normalization, jet energy scale and resolution, structure function choice and higher order QCD corrections, *etc.* DØ extracts direct experimental limits on $WW\gamma/WWZ$ anomalous couplings via

Table 1. Diboson pair event yields and SM comparison. UA2 and DØ (CDF) quote SS (DS) $\pm 1\sigma$ stat+syst uncertainties.

	N_{obs}	ΣN_{bkgnd}	N_{signal}	N_{pred}^{SM}
UA2 '90 $W\gamma_e$	16	6.8 ± 1.0	$9.2^{+5.2}_{-3.2}$	11.9 ± 1.1
CDF '88 $W\gamma_{e+\mu}$	13	6.2 ± 1.7	6.8 ± 4.0	7.0 ± 1.0
CDF '92 $W\gamma_{e+\mu}$	25	8.5 ± 2.4	16.5 ± 5.5	23.3 ± 3.4
DØ '92 $W\gamma_{e+\mu}$	19	$5.5^{+3.0}_{-2.3}$	$13.5^{+5.3}_{-3.0}$	13.8 ± 2.1
CDF '88 $Z\gamma_{e+\mu}$	4	0.4 ± 0.1	3.6 ± 2.0	2.0 ± 0.2
CDF '92 $Z\gamma_{e+\mu}$	8	0.5 ± 0.2	7.5 ± 2.8	7.1 ± 0.8
DØ '92 $Z\gamma_{e+\mu}$	6	0.2 ± 0.1	$5.8^{+3.6}_{-2.4}$	4.2 ± 0.9
CDF '92 WW/WZ	1	—	1	0.08
CDF '92 ZW/ZZ	0	—	0	0.01
DØ '92 WW	2	2.2 ± 1.0	2	0.55

Table 2. 95% CL limits on $WW\gamma$ anomalous couplings. Only one coupling is allowed to deviate from its SM value at a time.

$\mathcal{CP}$-conserving	$\Delta\kappa^\gamma$	λ^γ
UA2 '90 $W\gamma_e$	$-4.5 < \Delta\kappa^\gamma < 4.9$	$-3.6 < \lambda^\gamma < 3.9$
CDF '88 $W\gamma_{e+\mu}$	$-6.0 < \Delta\kappa^\gamma < 6.4$	$-2.4 < \lambda^\gamma < 2.3$
CDF '92 $W\gamma_{e+\mu}$	$-2.3 < \Delta\kappa^\gamma < 2.2$	$-0.7 < \lambda^\gamma < 0.7$
DØ '92 $W\gamma_{e+\mu}$	$-2.3 < \Delta\kappa^\gamma < 2.3$	$-0.7 < \lambda^\gamma < 0.7$
CDF '92 WW/WZ	$-1.0 < \Delta\kappa^\gamma < 1.1$	$-0.8 < \lambda^\gamma < 0.8$
DØ '92 WW	$-3.3 < \Delta\kappa^\gamma < 3.5$	$-2.6 < \lambda^\gamma < 2.7$
$\mathcal{CP}$-violating	$\tilde{\kappa}^\gamma$	$\tilde{\lambda}^\gamma$
UA2 '90 $W\gamma_e$	$-4.7 < \tilde{\kappa}^\gamma < 4.7$	$-3.7 < \tilde{\lambda}^\gamma < 3.7$
CDF '88 $W\gamma_{e+\mu}$	$-6.2 < \tilde{\kappa}^\gamma < 6.2$	$-2.4 < \tilde{\lambda}^\gamma < 2.4$
CDF '92 $W\gamma_{e+\mu}$	$-2.2 < \tilde{\kappa}^\gamma < 2.2$	$-0.7 < \tilde{\lambda}^\gamma < 0.7$
DØ '92 $W\gamma_{e+\mu}$	$-2.3 < \tilde{\kappa}^\gamma < 2.3$	$-0.7 < \tilde{\lambda}^\gamma < 0.7$
CDF '92 WW/WZ	$-3.4 < \tilde{\kappa}^\gamma < 3.4$	$-0.8 < \tilde{\lambda}^\gamma < 0.8$

comparison of their background non-subtracted 95% CL upper limit on $\sigma \cdot B(WW)_{expt} < 133$ pb with $\sigma \cdot B(WW)_{pred}$ as a function of anomalous couplings.

Table 2 summarizes the results from hadron colliders on 95% CL, direct limits on $WW\gamma$ anomalous couplings. Figure 1 shows the 95% CL limit contours for $\mathcal{CP}$-conserving $WW\gamma$ anomalous couplings. The limit contours for $\mathcal{CP}$-violating $WW\gamma$ anomalous couplings (not shown) are similar. For the WW/WZ boson pair processes, $\Delta\kappa^\gamma = \Delta\kappa^Z$ and $\lambda^\gamma = \lambda^Z$ have been assumed. The maximum value of the form factor scale Λ_W where the combined $W\gamma+WW$ unitarity constraint contour lies outside the anomalous couplings limit contour for each experiment is indicated. Table 3 summarizes the results on 95% CL, direct limits on $ZZ\gamma$ and $Z\gamma\gamma$ anomalous couplings from CDF, DØ and L3 at LEP [11]. The Tevatron limits on $Z\gamma\gamma$ anomalous couplings are the first *direct* test of these couplings. Figure 2 shows the 95% CL limit contours for $\mathcal{CP}$-conserving/violating $ZZ\gamma$ anomalous couplings. The Tevatron limit contours for $Z\gamma\gamma$ anomalous couplings (not shown) are similar. The different orientation of limit contours in each figure is due to the $\hat{s}$-dependencies of the anomalous couplings.

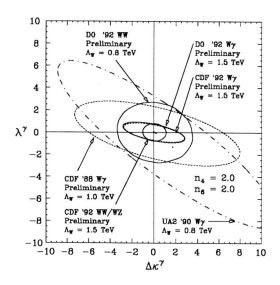

Figure 1. 95% CL limits on $\mathcal{CP}$-conserving $WW\gamma$ anomalous couplings.

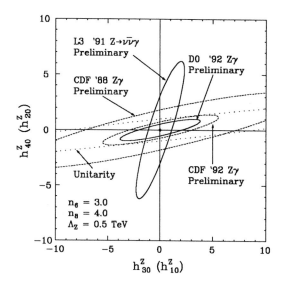

Figure 2. 95% CL limits on $\mathcal{CP}$-conserving ($\mathcal{CP}$-violating) $ZZ\gamma$ anomalous couplings.

Table 3. 95% CL limits on $ZZ\gamma/Z\gamma\gamma$ anomalous couplings for $\Lambda_Z = 500$ GeV. Only one coupling is allowed to deviate from its SM value at a time.

$\mathcal{CP}$-conserving	$h_{30}^{Z,\gamma}$	$h_{40}^{Z,\gamma}$
CDF '88 $Z\gamma_{e+\mu}$	$-7.1 < h_{30}^{Z} < 7.1$	$-1.8 < h_{40}^{Z} < 1.8$
CDF '92 $Z\gamma_{e+\mu}$	$-3.0 < h_{30}^{Z} < 2.9$	$-0.7 < h_{40}^{Z} < 0.7$
DØ '92 $Z\gamma_{e+\mu}$	$-2.1 < h_{30}^{Z} < 2.1$	$-0.5 < h_{40}^{Z} < 0.5$
L3 '91 $Z \to \nu\bar{\nu}\gamma$	$-1.1 < h_{30}^{Z} < 1.1$	$-3.0 < h_{40}^{Z} < 3.0$
CDF '88 $Z\gamma_{e+\mu}$	$-7.4 < h_{30}^{\gamma} < 7.4$	$-1.9 < h_{40}^{\gamma} < 1.9$
CDF '92 $Z\gamma_{e+\mu}$	$-3.1 < h_{30}^{\gamma} < 3.1$	$-0.8 < h_{40}^{\gamma} < 0.8$
DØ '92 $Z\gamma_{e+\mu}$	$-2.2 < h_{30}^{\gamma} < 2.1$	$-0.5 < h_{40}^{\gamma} < 0.5$
$\mathcal{CP}$-violating	$h_{10}^{Z,\gamma}$	$h_{20}^{Z,\gamma}$
CDF '88 $Z\gamma_{e+\mu}$	$-7.1 < h_{10}^{Z} < 7.1$	$-1.8 < h_{20}^{Z} < 1.8$
CDF '92 $Z\gamma_{e+\mu}$	$-2.9 < h_{10}^{Z} < 2.9$	$-0.7 < h_{20}^{Z} < 0.7$
DØ '92 $Z\gamma_{e+\mu}$	$-2.1 < h_{10}^{Z} < 2.1$	$-0.5 < h_{20}^{Z} < 0.5$
L3 '91 $Z \to \nu\bar{\nu}\gamma$	$-1.1 < h_{10}^{Z} < 1.1$	$-3.0 < h_{20}^{Z} < 3.0$
CDF '88 $Z\gamma_{e+\mu}$	$-7.4 < h_{10}^{\gamma} < 7.4$	$-1.9 < h_{20}^{\gamma} < 1.9$
CDF '92 $Z\gamma_{e+\mu}$	$-3.1 < h_{10}^{\gamma} < 3.1$	$-0.8 < h_{20}^{\gamma} < 0.8$
DØ '92 $Z\gamma_{e+\mu}$	$-2.2 < h_{10}^{\gamma} < 2.2$	$-0.5 < h_{20}^{\gamma} < 0.5$

Table 4. 95% CL limits on W boson EM moments. Only one EM moment is allowed to deviate from its SM value at a time.

$\mathcal{CP}$-conserving	$g_W-2 = \Delta\kappa^\gamma + \lambda^\gamma$	$q_W^e - 1 = \Delta\kappa^\gamma - \lambda^\gamma$
UA2 '90 $W\gamma_e$	$-4.4 < g_W-2 < 4.0$	$-12.3 < q_W^e-1 < 16.3$
CDF '88 $W\gamma_{e+\mu}$	$-3.7 < g_W-2 < 3.7$	$-5.5 < q_W^e-1 < 5.8$
CDF '92 $W\gamma_{e+\mu}$	$-1.2 < g_W-2 < 1.1$	$-1.6 < q_W^e-1 < 1.7$
DØ '92 $W\gamma_{e+\mu}$	$-1.2 < g_W-2 < 1.1$	$-1.6 < q_W^e-1 < 1.7$
CDF '92 WW/WZ	$-1.2 < g_W-2 < 1.3$	$-1.3 < q_W^e-1 < 1.3$
DØ '92 WW	$-3.5 < g_W-2 < 3.7$	$-3.8 < q_W^e-1 < 4.2$
$\mathcal{CP}$-violating	$d_W = \tilde{\kappa}^\gamma + \tilde{\lambda}$	$q_W^m = \tilde{\kappa}^\gamma - \tilde{\lambda}$
UA2 '90 $W\gamma_e$	$-4.2 < d_W < 4.2$	$-14.3 < q_W^m < 14.3$
CDF '88 $W\gamma_{e+\mu}$	$-3.7 < d_W < 3.7$	$-5.6 < q_W^m < 5.6$
CDF '92 $W\gamma_{e+\mu}$	$-1.1 < d_W < 1.1$	$-1.6 < q_W^m < 1.6$
DØ '92 $W\gamma_{e+\mu}$	$-1.1 < d_W < 1.1$	$-1.6 < q_W^m < 1.6$
CDF '92 WW/WZ	$-1.6 < d_W < 1.6$	$-1.4 < q_W^m < 1.4$

related to the higher-order EM transition moments of the Z boson in the static limit via [13]:

$$
\begin{aligned}
d_{Z_T} &= -\frac{e}{M_Z}\frac{1}{\sqrt{2}}\frac{k^2}{M_Z^2}(h_{30}^Z - h_{40}^Z) &\equiv& -\frac{e}{2M_Z}\frac{k^2}{M_Z^2}\delta_{Z_T}^* \\
Q_{Z_T}^m &= \frac{e}{M_Z^2}\sqrt{10}\,(2h_{30}^Z) &\equiv& \frac{e}{M_Z^2}q_{Z_T}^m \\
\mu_{Z_T} &= -\frac{e}{M_Z}\frac{1}{\sqrt{2}}\frac{k^2}{M_Z^2}(h_{10}^Z - h_{20}^Z) &\equiv& -\frac{e}{2M_Z}\frac{k^2}{M_Z^2}g_{Z_T}^* \\
Q_{Z_T}^e &= \frac{e}{M_Z^2}\sqrt{10}\,(2h_{10}^Z) &\equiv& \frac{e}{M_Z^2}q_{Z_T}^e
\end{aligned}
$$

The 95% CL limits on W (Z) boson EM static (transition) moments are summarized in Tables 4 (5), and shown in Figures 3 (4). The 95% CL limit contours for $\mathcal{CP}$-violating W boson EM moments (not shown) are similar to the $\mathcal{CP}$-conserving moments. Note that the relative signs of μ_W and Q_W^e are now known to >95% CL, in agreement with the SM prediction.

4. Direct Limits on W/Z Boson EM Moments

In the static limit (photon energy $k \to 0$), the $WW\gamma$ anomalous couplings, which are relativistic quantities, are related to the higher-order classical EM moments of the W boson (with $\hbar = c = 1$) via [12]:

$$
\begin{aligned}
\mu_W &= \frac{e}{2M_W}(2 + \Delta\kappa_\gamma + \lambda_\gamma) &\equiv& \frac{e}{2M_W}g_W \\
Q_W^e &= -\frac{e}{M_W^2}(1 + \Delta\kappa_\gamma - \lambda_\gamma) &\equiv& -\frac{e}{M_W^2}q_W^e \\
d_W &= \frac{e}{2M_W}(\tilde{\kappa}_\gamma + \tilde{\lambda}_\gamma) &\equiv& \frac{e}{2M_W}\delta_W \\
Q_W^m &= -\frac{e}{M_W^2}(\tilde{\kappa}_\gamma - \tilde{\lambda}_\gamma) &\equiv& -\frac{e}{M_W^2}q_W^m \\
\langle R_W^2 \rangle &= \frac{1}{M_W^2}(1 + \Delta\kappa_\gamma + \lambda_\gamma) &\equiv& \frac{1}{M_W^2}r_W^2
\end{aligned}
$$

The sign associated with each of these quantities indicates their orientation relative to the spin direction of the W^+ boson. The $ZZ\gamma$ anomalous couplings are

5. Summary and Future Prospects

CDF and DØ have obtained preliminary results on $W\gamma$, $Z\gamma$ and WW, WZ and ZZ boson pair production,

Table 5. 95% CL limits on Z boson EM transition moments for $\Lambda_Z = 500$ GeV. Only one EM moment is allowed to deviate from its SM value at a time.

$\mathcal{CP}$-conserving	$\delta^*_{Z_T} = \sqrt{2}(h^Z_{30} - h^Z_{40})$	$q^m_{Z_T} = \sqrt{10}(2h^Z_{30})$
CDF '88 $Z\gamma_{e+\mu}$	$-2.6 < \delta^*_{Z_T} < 2.6$	$-14.5 < q^m_{Z_T} < 14.4$
CDF '92 $Z\gamma_{e+\mu}$	$-1.1 < \delta^*_{Z_T} < 1.1$	$-6.0 < q^m_{Z_T} < 6.0$
DØ '92 $Z\gamma_{e+\mu}$	$-0.7 < \delta^*_{Z_T} < 0.7$	$-4.6 < q^m_{Z_T} < 4.6$
L3 '91 $Z \to \nu\bar{\nu}\gamma$	$-4.6 < \delta^*_{Z_T} < 4.6$	$-10.3 < q^m_{Z_T} < 10.3$
$\mathcal{CP}$-violating	$g^*_{Z_T} = \sqrt{2}(h^Z_{10} - h^Z_{20})$	$q^e_{Z_T} = \sqrt{10}(2h^Z_{10})$
CDF '88 $Z\gamma_{e+\mu}$	$-2.6 < g^*_{Z_T} < 2.6$	$-14.4 < q^e_{Z_T} < 14.4$
CDF '92 $Z\gamma_{e+\mu}$	$-1.1 < g^*_{Z_T} < 1.1$	$-6.0 < q^e_{Z_T} < 6.0$
DØ '92 $Z\gamma_{e+\mu}$	$-0.7 < g^*_{Z_T} < 0.7$	$-4.6 < q^e_{Z_T} < 4.6$
L3 '91 $Z \to \nu\bar{\nu}\gamma$	$-4.6 < g^*_{Z_T} < 4.6$	$-10.3 < q^e_{Z_T} < 10.3$

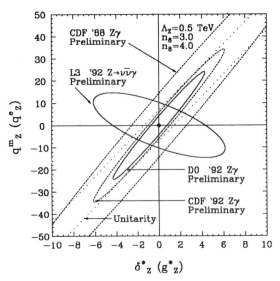

Figure 4. 95% CL limits on $\mathcal{CP}$-conserving ($\mathcal{CP}$-violating) Z boson EM transition moments for $\Lambda_Z = 500$ GeV.

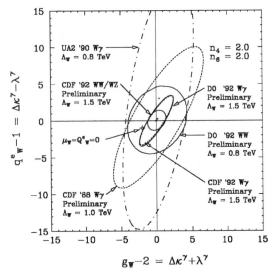

Figure 3. 95% CL limits on $\mathcal{CP}$-conserving W boson EM moments. The point where $\mu_W = Q^e_W = 0$ is indicated.

direct limits on $WW\gamma$, WWZ, $ZZ\gamma$ and $Z\gamma\gamma$ anomalous couplings and higher-order static (transition) EM moments of the W (Z) bosons. All results are in good agreement with SM expectations. An increase of $\sim 10\times$ more data is anticipated from the present collider run. With the commissioning of the Main Injector by the end of the decade, ~ 1 fb^{-1} data samples are envisioned. Detailed studies of EWK boson pair production at the Tevatron will continue throughout this era, providing evermore stringent tests of the SM on the nature of the mutual interactions of the W, Z and γ at each stage.

I thank the members of the CDF and DØ collaborations for their help and cooperation. In particular I thank H. Aihara, D. Benjamin, B. Choudhary, M. Demarteau, T. Diehl, J. Ellison, T.A. Fuess, H. Johari, G. Landsberg, M. Lindgren, T. Müller, D. Neuberger, A. Spadafora, M. Vondracek, R.G. Wagner and C. Wendt. I also thank U. Baur, F. Boudjema, J. Busenitz, R. Szalapszki and D. Zeppenfeld for their help, advice and many stimulating conversations.

References

[1] K. Hagiwara, *et al.*, Nucl. Phys. **B382** (1987) 253. We adopt the conventions of this paper. See also: R.W. Brown and K.O. Mikaelian, Phys. Rev. **D19** (1979) 922; K. Gaemers and G. Gounaris, Zeit. Phys. **C1** (1979) 259; K. Hagiwara, *et al.*, Phys. Rev. **D41** (1990) 2113.

[2] F.M. Renard, Nucl. Phys. **B196** (1982) 93; R. Barbieri, *et al.*, Phys. Lett. **B141** (1985) 455; J.P. Eboli and A.V. Olinto, Phys. Rev. **D38** (1988) 3461.

[3] A. DeRujula, *et al.*, Nucl. Phys. **B384** (1992) 3; A. Falk, *et al.*, Nucl. Phys. **B365** (1991) 523; J. Bagger, *et al.*, Nucl. Phys. **B399** (1993) 364; K. Hagiwara, *et al.*, Phys. Rev. **D48** (1993) 2182; C. Burgess and D. London, Phys. Rev. **D48** (1993) 4337; C. Artz, *et al.*, Phys. Rev. **D49** (1994) 1370.

[4] J.M. Cornwall, *et al.*, Phys. Rev. Lett. **30** (1973) 1268; Phys. Rev. **D10** (1974) 1145; C.H. Llewellyn Smith, Phys. Lett. **B46** (1973) 233; S.D. Joglekar, Ann. Phys. (NY) **83** (1974) 427.

[5] U. Baur and E.L. Berger, Phys. Rev. **D41** (1990) 1476.

[6] U. Baur and E.L. Berger, Phys. Rev. **D47** (1993) 4889.

[7] H. Budd, these proceedings and ICHEP-94 gls0415.

[8] Weak boson pair production event generator program provided by D. Zeppenfeld, private communication (1993).

[9] J. Alitti, *et al.*, Phys. Lett. **B241** (1990) 150.

[10] F. Abe, *et al.*, FERMILAB-PUB-94/244-E, submitted to Phys. Rev. D (1994).

[11] J. Busenitz, private communication, (1994) and J. Busenitz, proceedings of the DPF'94 conference, Aug. 2-6, 1994, Alberquerque, NM, USA.

[12] H. Aronson, Phys. Rev. **186** (1969) 1434; K.J. Kim and Y.-S. Tsai, Phys. Rev. **D7** (1973) 3710.

[13] F. Boudjema, private communication (1993).

Parallel Session Pa-2

Heavy Quark Physics

Conveners: M. Neubert (CERN)
D. MacFarlane (SLAC/McGill)

Scientific secretaries: H. Hoeber
A. Lidsey (reserve)

Review of Charmed Particle Lifetimes

Sergio P. Ratti[‡]

Dept. of Nuclear and Theoretical Physics
University of Pavia and INFN
via A.Bassi 6, I-27100, Pavia, Italy

1. Introduction

In the history of the Rochester Conferences, the issue of the charm lifetimes has never been specifically addressed (while it was in topical workshops [1]); at Singapore (1990), B. Gittelmann [2] briefly discussed the τ_{D^+}, τ_{D^0} difference, assuming a substantial identity of the lifetimes of τ_{D^0} and $\tau_{D^\pm}$ and mentioned that both τ_{D^0} and $\tau_{\Lambda_c^+}$ were known at a 10% level. At Dallas (1992) P.Drell [3] concentrated on b lifetimes and I.Bigi [3] speculated theoretically on the D^+/D^0 lifetime ratio. At the European I.C.H.E.P. (Marseille, 1993), the E687 collaboration [4] contributed the measurement of the lifetimes of the lightest charmed Baryons: Λ_c^+, Ξ_c^+ and Ξ_c^0. More recently, E687 provided precise lifetime measurements for charged mesons [5, 6]. In this short review, after briefly discussing the issue and the measurement methods, I'll essentially compare the charmed lifetime values as known in 1994 to their knowledge in 1992.

2. The Issue

It is known that $\tau = 1/\Gamma_{tot}$ and that to Γ_{tot} all channels: purely leptonic Γ_l, semileptonic Γ_{sl} and non leptonic, hadron decays Γ_h contribute ($\Gamma_{tot} = \Gamma_l + \Gamma_{sl} + \Gamma_h$). However, the purely leptonic branching ratios are very small, therefore the two major contributions are Γ_{sl} and Γ_h. The total semileptonic decay rates of D^+ and D^0 are expected to be equal within errors. From the Data Particle Review, $\Gamma(D^0 \to eX)/\Gamma(D^+ \to eX) = 1.13 \pm 0.22$ - no new experimental measurements of this ratio have been made available since the 1992 Conference. The ratio $R = \tau_{D^+}/\tau_{D^0}$ is well known since several years [7] and the value is: $R = 2.538 \pm 0.043 \pm 0.025$. Thus the

difference in the lifetimes must come from the hadronic sector of the decay, namely from the QCD corrections -color and helicity suppression, as an example- to the different diagrams. For the $q\bar{q}$ states, outer and inner decay diagrams are different, the inner decay being color suppressed; the weak exchange diagram can contribute to the neutral meson but not to the charged ones and it is helicity suppressed; the weak annihilation diagram can contribute to the $D_s^\pm$ decay but is Cabibbo suppressed for the D^+ and cannot contribute to the D^0 decay as it would lead to a flavour changing neutral current. This is qualitatively known and thus the question is to what extent the weak exchange diagram contribution to the D^0 decay may be different from the contribution of the weak annihilation to the $D_s^\pm$ decay. The charmed baryons are more complex 3-body systems; the annihilation diagram is totally absent, no antiquarks are present but the role of the 3 quarks may be more intriguing, while the possible presence of two identical quarks may lead to interference effects -depending upon particular situations.

Several theorists [8, 9, 10, 11]- have done non-perturbative QCD *relative* estimates of lifetimes; i.e. the hierarchy of $\tau_{\Lambda_c^+}$, $\tau_{\Xi_c^+}$, $\tau_{\Xi_c^0}$ and $\tau_{\Omega_c^0}$, on the basis of the different contributions to the full width. The hadron sector contributes with an outer decay spectator diagram to all lifetimes; the weak exchange diagram contributes to the decays of Λ_c^+ and Ξ_c^0. The weak exchange among valence quarks is neither helicity nor color suppressed, therefore its contribution may be substantial. To this, one may add possible interferences generated by the presence of light quarks, u or s, other then those participating into the decay process and the *collective* effects of identical quarks -the presence of 3 s quarks in the Ω_c^0 final state introduces a significant spin wave function factor [9]. Charmed baryons are thus a good laboratory to investigate non perturbative QCD.

‡ Due to the short advance notice, this review would have been impossible without the invaluable help of L.Viola and P.Vitulo in preparing data, tables and figures for the oral presentation. The author gratefully acknowledges their contribution.

3.   The methods

Measuring the lifetime is conceptually very trivial: one measures the flight path l, the momentum p of a particle of mass m; then the proper time is $t = lm/pc$. However: $\tau_c = 1/\Gamma_c \sim (m_\mu/m_c)^5/\Gamma_\mu \sim 10^{-12 \div 13}$ s; thus lifetime measurements crucially depend upon the spatial resolution of the detectors more than on the momentum resolution (usually [12] few percents). Only the progress in the development of sofisticated vertex detectors have made the measurements of proper times less than hundred femtoseconds possible. Parameters like detachment-ratio d between measured flight path l and its error σ_l- helps in selecting events, however, the confusion around the production vertex might make it difficult to disintangle the vertices when τ is particularly small (the case of the baryons) and the values of the proper time t become comparable to the experimental time resolution σ_t. The detailed charm particle production processes are far for being understood (how many *nearby* decay vertices may be around that may cause rejecting charm decays; the more so, the shorter are the proper times, when the decay and production vertices are really very close one to the other). Given this warning, the lifetime is measured by fitting the exponential decay law to the experimental data. One has a *peak* region around the mass of the charmed particle and a *side-band* background region to be properly subtracted. The experimental proper time distribution is severely distorted by both acceptance and selection criteria; when the l/σ_l cut is used -say $l/\sigma_l \geq \alpha$- the *reduced* proper time $t' = (l - \alpha\sigma_l)/\beta\gamma c$ is used. Monte-Carlo simulations provide the correction of the raw data for acceptance, efficiency, analysis cuts and all the like. As a matter of principle, the comparison of the *theoretical* distribution $d\sigma/dt = (1/\tau)e^{-t/\tau}$ to the experimental distribution dn/dt can be performed at any intermediate stage, from a full deformation of the *theoretical* shape, to a full deformation of the *raw* data. If and when $t' \gg \sigma_t$ and to extent that σ_l is small compared to τ and independent of l, the overall correction function is independent of the lifetime and the *effective* reduced time distribution becomes a factorized function $S(t') = f(t')e^{-t'/\tau}$. If and when the measured proper times are definitely comparable to the resolution and the lifetime is very short, the *effective* time distribution cannot be factorized and is:

$$F(t',\tau,\sigma_\tau) = \int \frac{1}{\sigma_t\sqrt{2\pi}} e^{\frac{-(t'-t)^2}{2\sigma_t^2}} \, dt = g(t',\tau,\sigma_t)e^{-\frac{t'}{\tau}}$$

(1)

thus the Monte-Carlo correction function is very delicate for small t's; it depends on both the proper time uncertainty and the lifetime itself; in addition, for small τ, the detachment cut is least effective ($t' \approx t$) in selecting the reduced time range (this is the case of the Ω_c^0). The fitting of the lifetime is achieved either via a full Maximum Likelihood Method (MLM) or via a *binned likelihood* (BLM) [13] fitting a Poisson probability of observing s_i signal events in bin i centered around t_i , when n_i are predicted, in the presence of b_i background events. MLM uses all the statistical information available and, as is well known, it doesn't differ much from the χ^2 method for large statistics. MLM requires to determine the *fake* background lifetime, while BLM introduces as a parameter the amount of background under the peak not necessarily coincident with that given by the mass distribution.

4.   The Data

4.1.   Mesons

The new measurements of the lifetimes for the three charmed mesons -since the Dallas Conference and the 1992 edition of the Particle Data Book (PDB) [7]- are compared to the values in the PDB in the first part of Table 1, together with the new calculated world average. New precise measurements of the light mesons D^+ and D^0 have been published by E687 [5]. The relatively large lifetimes and the abundant statistics make life relatively simple: one can select on very safe detachments and be drastic on background rejection; the fitting gives no specific problems; the method used is BLM. They selected over 16,000 events D^0 into $K^-\pi^+$ and $K^-\pi^-2\pi^+$ (a factor ~ 4 larger than the statistics provided by other experiments) for detachments d larger than 5.0 and more than 9,000 events $D^+ \to k^-2\pi^+$ for $d \geq 15.0$ (a statistics ~ 30 times larger than the previous ones). Statistical and systematic (which is set equal to $\sim 1\%$) errors are now comparable and thus difficult to improve. Recently, the same collaboration also measured the $\tau_{D^\pm}$ with more than 900 $D_s^\pm \to \phi\pi^+$ events [6], a factor ~ 3.5 better than the previous experiments. The method used is again BLM; $\tau_{D^\pm}$ is measured for d from 3.0 to 20.0. From these precise values, the ratios have been measured:

$$\frac{\tau_{D^+}}{\tau_{D^0}} = 2.54 \pm 0.04;$$

(2)

$$\frac{\tau_{D_s}}{\tau_{D^0}} = 1.15 \pm 0.05.$$

(3)

The D^+/D^0 lifetime ratio is well consistent with the PDB value, while, for the first time, there is good evidence that the lifetimes of D^0 and $D_s^\pm$ are different.

4.2.   Baryons

Charmed baryons are known to have shorter lifetimes; being heavier particles, they are expected to be

D MESON LIFETIMES (ps)					
	Ref	PDB Average[7]	New Data	N. Events	New Average
$D^+ \to K^- 2\pi^+$	[5]	$1.066 \pm .023$	$1.048 \pm .015 \pm .011$	9200	$1.053 \pm .013$
$D^0 \to (K^-\pi^+/K(3\pi))$	[5]	0.420 ± 0.008	$0.413 \pm 0.004 \pm 0.003$	16700	0.414 ± 0.004
$D_s \to \phi\pi$	[6]	$0.450 ^{+0.030}_{-0.026}$	$0.475 \pm 0.020 \pm 0.007$	900	0.467 ± 0.017
BARYON LIFETIMES (ps)					
	Ref.	PDB Average[7]	New Data	N. Events	New Average
$\Lambda_c^+ \to pK^-\pi^+$	[16]	$0.191 ^{+0.015}_{-0.012}$	$0.215 \pm 0.016 \pm 0.008$	691	0.202 ± 0.012
$\Xi_c^+ \to \Xi^- 2\pi^+$	[16]	$0.30 ^{+0.10}_{-0.06}$	$0.41 ^{+0.11}_{-0.08} \pm 0.02$	30	$0.34 ^{+0.05}_{-0.04}$
$\Xi_c^+ \to \Lambda^0 K^- 2\pi^+$	[15]		$0.32 ^{+0.08}_{-0.06} \pm 0.05$	$30 \div 40$	
$\Xi_c^0 \to \Xi^- \pi^+$	[16]	$0.082 ^{+0.059}_{-0.030}$	$0.101 ^{+0.025}_{-0.017} \pm 0.005$	42	$0.098 ^{+0.023}_{-0.015}$

Table 1. Charmed Meson and Baryon Lifetimes

produced to relatively smaller momenta and therefore to have shorter path lengths. Their production cross section is also smaller, so that the measurement of their lifetime is expected to be more problematic. The most recent new information on charmed baryon lifetimes has been contributed to this Conference by the Cleo [14] and the WA89 [15] collaborations. Since Dallas, E687 has provided the measurement of $\tau_{\Lambda_c^+}$, $\tau_{\Xi_c^+}$, $\tau_{\Xi_c^0}$ and anticipated the measurement of $\tau_{\Omega_c^0}$ [16] Cleo has measured the semileptonic decays $\Xi_c^+ \to \Xi^0 e^+ \nu_e$ and $\Xi_c^0 \to \Xi^- e^+ \nu_e$. That collaboration relates the ratio of the branching ratios to the lifetime ratio, i.e.:

$$R = \frac{BR(\Xi_c^+ \to \Xi^0 e^+ \nu_e)}{BR(\Xi_c^0 \to \Xi^- e^+ \nu_e)} = \frac{\Gamma_{sl}(\Xi_c^+)\tau_{\Xi_c^+}}{\Gamma_{sl}(\Xi_c^0)\tau_{\Xi_c^0}}. \quad (4)$$

They make three assumptions; i.e. that the semileptonic decay width of Ξ_c^+ and Ξ_c^0 be equal; that $\Gamma_{sl}(\Xi_c^+)$ and $\Gamma_{sl}(\Xi_c^0)$ be equal and that Ξ_c^+ and Ξ_c^0 be equally produced in $e^+ e_-$ annihilations at 10 GeV, to find: $R = 2.46 \pm 0.70 ^{+.33}_{-.23}$. This is consistent with the known ratios $R = 4.06 \pm 1.26$ measured by E687 [16] and $R = 2.44 \pm 1.68$ measured by NA32 [17].

The WA89 collaboration has selected excellent signals of strange-charmed baryons produced by a 300 GeV hyperon beam at CERN on a 4% interaction length nuclear target made of copper and carbon and found signals for Λ_c^+, Σ_c^0, Ξ_c^+ and Ω_c^0. They provide a lifetime measurement for the Ξ_c^+ based on a starting sample of 124 events in the decay mode $\Xi_c^+ \to \Lambda k^- 2\pi^+$. The fit used is BLM and the result is $\tau_{\Xi_c^+} = 0.32 ^{+.08}_{-.06}(stat.) \pm .05(syst.)$ ps. The new measurements of the baryon lifetimes are compared to the PDB in the bottom part of Table 1. The new world average is also reported.

5. Conclusions

The scenario of the charmed particles lifetimes is greatly improved in the past two years and will make progress with the contributions from E687, WA89/WA92 and the

new experiments in preparation. The statistical errors on the meson lifetimes have improved by $\sim$ a factor 2; furthermore -apart from the $D_s^\pm$ meson- the statistical errors have reached the level of systematics. The new *physics* information here is that D^0 and $D_s^\pm$ have different lifetimes. In the baryon sector, the lifetimes are now at least *measured* with errors around or better than 5% compared to previous estimates with errors of $\sim$ 20%. In addition, $\tau_{\Omega_c^0}$ will come soon. Charm studies are providing theorists with very useful information on non perturbative QCD effects. The experiments are challenging $\tau \leq 100$ fs. Theorists are then challenged to do calculations rather than *estimates*: of the lifetimes, of their hierarchy, as well as of several other quantities of charm decays.

References

[1] see e.g. L.M. Cremaldi, Heavy Quarks at Fixed Target 1993, p. 245; Ed.s S. Bianco, F.L. Fabbri (INFN, Frascati Physics Series, 1993).

[2] B. Gittelmann, Proc. 25th I.C.H.E.P. 1990, p. 227; Ed.s K.K. Phua and Y. Yamaguchi (S. East Asia Th. Phys. Ass. and Phys. Soc. of Japan 1991).

[3] a)- P. Drell, Proc. 26th I.C.H.E.P. 1992, p. 3; Ed. J.R. Sanford (A.I.P. Conf. Proc. No. 272); b)- I.I. Bigi, p. 402.

[4] S.P. Ratti Proc. of The European I.C.H.E.P. 1993, p. 47; Ed.s J. Carr, M. Perrottet (Edition Frontieres, 1994).

[5] P.L. Frabetti *et al.*, Phys. Lett. **B323** (1994) 459.

[6] P.L. Frabetti *et al.*, Phys. Rev. Lett. **71** (1993) 827.

[7] K. Hisaka *et al.*, Phys. Rev. **D45** (1992) n.11, Part II.

[8] B. Blok, M.A. Shifman, pre. TPI-MINN-93/55-T (1993).

[9] B. Guberina, *et al.*, Zeit. Phys. **C33** (1986) 297.

[10] M.B. Voloshin *et al.*, JETP Lett. **64** (1986) 698.

[11] V. Gupta *et al.*, Int. J. Mod. Phys. **5** (1990) 879.

[12] *see:* P.L. Frabetti *et al.*, Nucl. Instr. Meth. **A320** (1992) 519.

[13] P.L. Frabetti *et al.*, Phys. Lett. **B263** (1991) 584.

[14] Cleo Collaboration: J.P. Alexander *et al.* CLNS 94/1288 CLEO 94-14 (1994); contribution GLS0245 to this Conf.

[15] WA89 Collaboration: R. Werding *et al.*, contribution GLS0046 to this Conf.

[16] P.L. Frabetti, *et al.* Phys. Rev. Lett. **70** (1993) 1381; *ibid.* **70** (1993) 1755; *ibid.* **70** (1993) 2058.

[17] S. Barlag, *et al.*, Phys. Lett. **B233** (1989) 522; *ibid.* **B236** (1990) 495.

Theory of Weak Inclusive Decays and Lifetimes of Heavy Hadrons

Mikhail Shifman

Theoretical Physics Institute, University of Minnesota, Minneapolis, MN 55455, USA

Abstract

The theory of preasymptotic effects in inclusive decays of heavy flavors is briefly reviewed.

1. Introduction

Heavy flavor hadrons H_Q contain a heavy quark Q plus a cloud built from light quarks (antiquarks) and gluons. The heavy quark Q experiences a weak transition. The nature of this transition is of no concern to me here. It can be a radiative transition, like $b \to s\gamma$, semileptonic decay like $b \to cl\nu_l$ or a non-leptonic decay to lighter quarks, e.g. $b \to c\bar{u}d$. It is assumed that at short distances the amplitude is known from the electroweak theory. The task of the QCD-based theory is to calculate preasymptotic effects in the decay rate of the hadron H_Q. These effects are due to interactions with the soft degrees of freedom in the light cloud.

The foundation of the theory was laid in the eighties [1] when it was realized that the operator product expansion [2] could be used in application to the so called transition operator of the type

$$\hat{T}(Q \to f \to Q) = i \int d^4x \{\mathcal{L}_W(x), \mathcal{L}_W^\dagger(0)\}_T, \quad (1)$$

where $\mathcal{L}_W$ is the short-distance weak Lagrangian governing the transition $Q \to f$ under consideration. The momentum operator $\mathcal{P}_\mu$ of the heavy quark Q is written as a sum of two terms, $\mathcal{P}_\mu = m_Q v_\mu + \pi_\mu$ where v_μ is the four-velocity of the heavy *hadron* H_Q, π_μ is the residual momentum operator, responsible for the interaction with the "background" gluon field in the light cloud. The large mechanical part $m_Q v_\mu$ in the heavy quark momentum guarantees that the transition operator (1) can be found as a sum of *local* operators (with some reservations to be discussed below). These operators are ordered according to their dimensions. At

the level of $1/m_Q^2$ we have only two operators; extra four-fermion operators are added at the level of $1/m_Q^3$. A few of these were calculated 8 years ago [1].

At the next stage each term in the expansion must be averaged over the hadronic state H_Q. At this stage the bound state dynamics is accounted for.

After the initial excitement the OPE-based theory of the inclusive heavy flavor decays was in a rather dormant state until recently. The revival it experiences now is due to a combination of several factors. First, a very concise and convenient language was created, the heavy quark effective theory (HQET) [3]. Calculations of the non-perturbative effects were translated in this language and developed in Refs. [4, 5, 6]. Second, all relevant operators appearing at the level up to $1/m_Q^3$ were catalogued and our understanding of their matrix elements (I mean the numerical values) was significantly advanced. Finally, the issue of convergence of the non-perturbative series was clarified. In the beauty family one expects that the first two or three terms in the expansion ensure reasonable accuracy of the predicted lifetimes. As for the charmed quark we will see that it is, perhaps, too light for duality to set in. Since OPE is used in the Minkowski domain the validity of duality is crucial for the whole approach. Theoretically the onset of duality is correlated with the behavior of high-order terms in the non-perturbative series.

2. Master equation

The OPE-based approach is applicable in a very wide range of problems. Here we will concentrate on the total inclusive widths. Generically the m_Q^{-1} expansion for the width has the form (for definiteness I will speak about the beauty family)

$$\Gamma(H_b \to f) = \frac{G_F^2 m_b^5}{192\pi^3}|CKM|^2 \times$$

$$\left\{ c_3(f)\frac{\langle H_b|\bar{b}b|H_b\rangle}{2M_{H_B}} + \frac{c_5(f)}{m_b^2}\frac{\langle H_b|\bar{b}(i/2)\sigma Gb|H_b\rangle}{2M_{H_B}} + \right.$$

$$\left. \sum_i \frac{c_6^{(i)}(f)}{m_b^3}\frac{\langle H_b|(\bar{b}\Gamma_i q)(\bar{q}\Gamma_i b)|H_b\rangle}{2M_{H_B}} + \mathcal{O}(m_b^{-4}) \right\}. \quad (2)$$

The coefficient functions $c_i(f)$ depend on the particular inclusive transition considered and are calculable. They are determined by short-distance QCD provided that the energy release is large enough. On the other hand, the matrix elements on the *rhs* reflect the large-distance dynamics and are essentially non-perturbative. But they are universal, and, as seen from Eq. (2), there are only a few of them.

The matrix element of the chromomagnetic operator σG is expressible through spin splittings, say $M_{B^*} - M_B$. The four-fermion dim-6 operators can be evaluated, in the case of mesons, within factorization. For baryons a reliable calculation of the corresponding matrix elements is a problem essentially unsolved so far. As for the scalar density, $\bar{b}b$, it is this term that exactly reproduces the parton model (asymptotic) result, plus preasymptotic corrections. This operator also can be written as an expansion,

$$\bar{b}b = \bar{b}\gamma_0 b - \frac{1}{2m_Q^2}\bar{b}(\vec{\pi}^2 - (i/2)\sigma G)b +$$

$$\frac{1}{4m_Q^3}g^2\bar{b}\gamma_0 T^a b \sum_q \bar{q}\gamma_0 T^a q + \mathcal{O}(1/m_b^4) \quad (3)$$

where the sum runs over the light quarks. A new operator appearing here is $\bar{b}\vec{\pi}^2 b$, the square of the spatial momentum of the b-quark. The matrix element of this operator in the B meson can be limited from below, for a detailed discussion see Ref. [7]. The average spatial momentum turns out to be surprisingly large, larger than 0.6 GeV! The QCD sum rule calculations [8] yield even a larger value, ~ 0.7 GeV. The expectation value of $\vec{\pi}^2$ in baryons is expected to be close to that in mesons.

Time/space limitations do not allow me to go into further details. Let me point out only the most remarkable features of the overall picture.

(i) The total rates do not contain non-perturbative corrections of order $1/m_b$, the so called CGG/BUV theorem [4, 5]. The corrections start at the level $1/m_b^2$. This sets the scale of preasymptotic effects in the beauty family at the level of several per cent since $\langle B|\bar{b}i\sigma Gb|B\rangle/2m_b^3 \sim 0.03$. In particular, deviations of the lifetime ratios from unity are expected to be of this order of magnitude. At the level $1/m_b^2$ all B mesons

have the same lifetimes (disregarding some small $SU(3)_{fl}$ breaking effects).

(ii) The difference in the lifetimes of baryons and mesons is due to the fact that the expectation values of the operators in Eq. (2) are different for mesons and baryons. This difference arises at the level $1/m_b^2$.

(iii) Four-fermion dim-6 operators produce effects formally scaling like $1/m_b^3$, although numerically they seem to be enhanced since the corresponding coefficients have one loop less and, additionally, a key constant f_B turns out to be rather large. This enhancement may lead to the fact that dimension 5 and 6 operators are competitive in the beauty family. The four-fermion operators shift the lifetimes of mesons versus baryons and split the meson lifetimes from each other.

(iv) Situation with B_s is exceptional. The lifetime difference $\tau(B_{s,\text{short}}) - \tau(B_{s,\text{long}})$ is due to a mechanism not exhibited in Eq. (2), namely $B\bar{B}$ oscillations. The corresponding estimates were done in [9].

3. Phenomenological implications

Assembling all theoretical elements discussed above (and those which are discussed in the original literature) we arrive at the following pattern. The lifetime of a charged B meson is predicted to exceed that of a neutral B meson,

$$\frac{\tau(B^-)}{\tau(B_d)} - 1 \approx 0.05(f_B/200\text{MeV})^2 \sim 0.05. \quad (4)$$

At this level it is expected that $\bar{\tau}(B_d) \approx \bar{\tau}(B_s)$ where $\bar{\tau}$ denotes the average lifetime of the two mass eigenstates in the B^0–$\bar{B}^0$ system. It is curious that B_s oscillations will seemingly produce the largest lifetime difference,

$$\frac{\Delta\Gamma(B_s)}{\bar{\Gamma}(B_s)} \approx 0.18(f_B/200\text{MeV})^2 \sim 0.18. \quad (5)$$

The baryon matrix elements are always most difficult for consistent analysis; therefore, the baryon-to-meson lifetime ratios should be taken with caution. Still, plausible estimates indicate that one can expect $\tau(\Lambda_b)/\tau(B_d) \sim 0.9$.

4. A grain of salt: $\text{Br}_{\text{sl}}(B)$

The theory of preasymptotic effects which I have just sketched, being applied to the problem of the semileptonic branching ratio in the B mesons, leads to a paradox. In this case the heavy quark expansion can be readily carried out up to terms of order $1/m_b^3$. One obtains a formula very similar to Eq. (2), with the same structure and the same operators [10]. The leading non-perturbative correction $\mathcal{O}(m_b^{-2})$ tends to diminish the branching ratio while the term $\mathcal{O}(m_b^{-3})$ tends to increase it. Both effects, however, are far too small to produce a noticeable impact on the branching ratio. At best they shift the prediction for the branching ratio by 0.5% or less. Thus we are forced to conclude that the prediction for $\mathrm{Br}_{sl}(B)$ is controlled by perturbative QCD. People believe that perturbative QCD typically yields $\mathrm{Br}_{sl}(B) \approx 13\%$; twisting arms allows one to go down to 12.5% [11]. At the same time experimentalists, both CLEO and ARGUS, seem to be firm in their conclusion that $\mathrm{Br}_{sl}(B) < 11\%$. What went wrong?

I leave aside the possibility that the experimental numbers are wrong. There is no visible loophole in the OPE-based theory of preasymptotic effects either. Then the remaining logical options are as follows: (i) something is missing in the perturbative analysis; (ii) new physics shows up in the B meson decays. Both options must be investigated. In a recent paper [12] a new contribution in the perturbative calculation is identified, not included in the analysis of Ref. [11], which seemingly works in the right direction – diminishes $\mathrm{Br}_{sl}(B)_{\mathrm{pert}}$ by $\sim 0.5\%$. It remains to be seen whether the perturbative number can reach the 11% mark under realistic choice of relevant theoretical parameters (the quark masses, α_s, etc.). (Let me make a side remark: I do not believe that $\alpha_s(M_Z)$ can be as large as 0.126, as is allegedly implied by the so called global fits at the Z peak at present. A wealth of low-energy data point to a significantly lower value of α_s, something like 0.114 or even lower. In terms of Λ_{QCD} the difference is drastic. I urge to take this discrepancy very seriously.)

5. The family of charm

It might seem to be a trivial exercise to substitute m_b by m_c in the master equation. Yes, technically this is easy, and formally all $1/m_c^2$ and $1/m_c^3$ corrections have been written down and classified. They are much larger, of course, than in the beauty family; typically of order of 0.5. I refer those interested to a very detailed recent update [13]. Qualitatively the pattern of the lifetimes in the charm family emerging in the heavy quark expansion agrees with experiment. Namely, those particles that live longer are predicted to live longer, etc. However, quantitatively the $\mathcal{O}(m_c^{-2})$ and $\mathcal{O}(m_c^{-3})$ preasymptotic terms are smaller than what one needs in order to reproduce, say, $\tau(D^+)/\tau(\Xi_c^0)_{\mathrm{exp}} \sim 12$. Since arithmetically the calculation is certainly correct one may start suspecting that something went wrong in the basics.

The operator product expansion, the foundation of the whole approach, is a well defined procedure in the Euclidean domain. A specific feature of the transition operator (1) is its essentially Minkowski character. Therefore, in justifying the short-distance calculation of the coefficient functions one must always keep in mind a kind of analytic continuation, through a dispersion relation. Thus, strictly speaking, theoretical predictions for $c_i(f)$ in Eq. (2) refer to quantities integrated over energy in some energy range.

If the energy release is large enough so that duality is valid and the integrand is smooth, this smearing is unimportant; one can predict the coefficient functions for the given energy release, locally. It is always tacitly assumed that this is the case. The onset of duality is governed by exponential terms, not visible to any finite order in $1/m_Q$ expansion. Due to this reason the onset must be abrupt.

We are inclined to think that the c quark is not heavy enough to warrant duality. The strongest argument comes from consideration of $\Gamma_{sl}(D)$. Indeed, with the reasonable value of m_c ($m_c(m_c) \sim 1.3$ GeV) the parton-model prediction is close to the experimental number. The first perturbative correction is negative [11] and the second seems to be negative as well [14]. The non-perturbative corrections follow the same pattern. The leading $1/m_c^2$ term is known from Ref. [5] while the $1/m_c^3$ correction has been estimated recently [15]; both are negative. The combined effect of the leading corrections amounts to reducing $\Gamma_{sl}(D)$ by 50%, and the next-to-leading terms only worsen the situation!

This work was supported in part by DOE under the grant number DE-FG02-94ER40823.

References

[1] M. Shifman and M. Voloshin, 1982, see in V. Khoze and M. Shifman, Sov. Phys. Uspekhi **26** (1983) 387; N. Bilić, B. Guberina and J. Trampetić, Nucl. Phys. **B248** (1984) 261; M. Voloshin and M. Shifman, Sov. Journ. Nucl. Phys. **41** (1985) 120; JETP **64** (1986) 698.

[2] K. Wilson, Phys. Rev. **179** (1969) 1499; K. Wilson and J. Kogut, Phys. Rep. **12** (1974) 75.

[3] E. Eichten and B. Hill, Phys. Lett. **B234** (1990) 511; H. Georgi, Phys. Lett. **B240** (1990) 447.

[4] J. Chay, H. Georgi and B. Grinstein, Phys. Lett. **B247** (1990) 399.

[5] I. Bigi, N. Uraltsev and A. Vainshtein, Phys. Lett. **B293** (1992) 430; (E) *ibid.* **B297** (1993) 477.

[6] B. Blok and M. Shifman, Nucl. Phys. **B399** (1993) 441; 459.

[7] I. Bigi, N. Uraltsev, A. Vainshtein and M. Shifman, Minnesota Preprint TPI-MINN-94/12-T.

[8] P. Ball and V. Braun, Phys. Rev. **D49** (1994) 2472.

[9] M. Voloshin, N. Uraltsev, V. Khoze and M. Shifman, Yad. Fiz. **46** (1987) 181 [Sov. Journ. Nucl. Phys. **46** (1987) 112].

[10] I. Bigi, B. Blok, A. Vainshtein and M. Shifman, Phys. Lett. **B323** (1994) 408.

[11] G. Altarelli and S. Petrarca, Phys. Lett. **B261** (1991) 303.

[12] P. Ball and U. Nierste, Munich Preprint TUM-T31-56/94/R.

[13] B. Blok and M. Shifman, Preprint TPI-MINN-93/55-T.

[14] M. Luke, M. Savage and M. Wise, Preprint UTPT 94-24.

[15] B. Blok, R. Dikeman and M. Shifman, Minnesota Preprint TPI-MINN-94/23-T.

A preliminary measurement of the average B hadron lifetime

Steven L. Manly

Yale University, New Haven, CT 06511, USA

Representing the SLD collaboration

Abstract

The average B hadron lifetime was measured using data collected with the SLD detector at the SLC in 1993. From a sample of $\sim$50,000 Z^0 events, a sample enriched in $Z^0 \rightarrow b\bar{b}$ was selected by applying an impact parameter tag. The lifetime was extracted from the decay length distribution of inclusive vertices reconstructed in three dimensions. A binned maximum likelihood method yielded an average B hadron lifetime of $\tau_B = 1.577 \pm 0.032(\text{stat.}) \pm 0.046(\text{syst.})$ ps.

1. Introduction and Experimental Technique

Precision measurements of the average B hadron lifetime, τ_B, are important for the study of the b quark and its weak couplings to u and c quarks. Results of τ_B measurements presented in 1993[1] differed substantially from the 1992 world average[2]. Reports of additional independent precision measurements of τ_B are interesting and timely.

In this paper, results are presented on a measurement of τ_B using data taken with the SLD detector at the Stanford Linear Collider (SLC). This analysis was performed on $\sim$50,000 Z^0 decays recorded during the 1993 run of SLC.

Charged particle tracking was done using the central drift chamber (CDC) and the vertex detector (VXD)[3]. The liquid argon calorimeter (LAC) was used in the event trigger and in the determination of event shape quantities[4]. The angular errors of the CDC combined with local $\sigma(r\phi)$ and $\sigma(rz)$ of 6μm for the VXD clusters lead to an rϕ (plane perpendicular to the beams) impact parameter resolution of $(\alpha, \beta)_{r\phi} = (11\mu\text{m}, 70\mu\text{m})$†. The rz (plane containing the beam axis) impact parameter resolution is $(\alpha, \beta)_{rz} = (38\mu\text{m}, 70\mu\text{m})$. During the 1993 SLD run the $\langle \text{rms} \rangle_{xyz}$ profile of the SLC beams was $2.4 \times 0.8 \times 700\ \mu\text{m}^3$ at the interaction point (IP). The IP x and y positions were tracked by SLD using reconstructed tracks from hadronic Z^0 events. Muon pairs (not used in the average IP determination) were used to check the IP xy position, giving $\sigma_{xy}^{IP} = 7 \pm 2\ \mu\text{m}$. The z position of the IP was measured on an event-by-event basis with $\sigma_z \simeq 35\ \mu\text{m}$ as determined by simulation.

The Monte Carlo (MC) physics simulation modeled Z^0 and heavy flavor decays with the LUND JETSET (version 6.3) Monte Carlo generator[5], which was adjusted to reflect current knowledge of the B and D decay spectra. The MC detector simulation was based on GEANT (version 3.15)[6] and produced raw hits that were superimposed on randomly triggered events from the data to simulate SLC backgrounds.

Standard hadronic event and track selection cuts[7] were applied, resulting in a sample of 29,400 Z^0 events. The JADE jet finding algorithm[8] with y_{cut}=0.02 was used to determine the jet axes in the event from calorimetry clusters. For each track passing selection criteria, an impact parameter relative to the interaction point was determined. It was signed with respect to the nearest jet axis using standard conventions[7]. A normalized impact parameter was formed by dividing the signed 2d track impact parameter by the error on the extrapolated track added in quadrature with the beam position error. Events were tagged as potentially

† The impact parameter resolution function is parametrized as $\alpha \oplus \beta / P\sqrt{sin^3\theta}$.

containing a B hadron by requiring at least three quality tracks in the event with positive normalized 2d impact parameter greater than 3. With this tag a $Z^\circ \rightarrow b\bar{b}$ efficiency of 69% and purity of 82% was obtained according to Monte Carlo studies. From the data sample passing the hadronic event selection described above, 4294 events were tagged.

2. Vertex Selection

Candidate secondary vertices were formed from all pairs of charged tracks in the same hemisphere with at least one hit in the VXD. A vertex-constrained fit was performed on all such pairs that extrapolated to within three standard deviations of a common point having their common point in the same hemisphere as the two tracks. To reduce background from tracks originating from the interaction point, the distance from the interaction point to the secondary vertex was required to be at least 1mm. Furthermore, two-prong vertices consistent with arising from γ conversions, K° or Λ° decays were removed from the sample.

Next, the two-prong vertices that shared common tracks were combined to form multi-prong vertices using a similar procedure. Tracks from multi-prong candidates were required to extrapolate to within 10 standard deviations of a common point. A total vertex fit χ^2 less than 27(35) was required for three(four)-prong candidates. No candidates with more than four prongs were kept.

Events with more than 100 vertices remaining were removed. This was done to reduce the computer time consumed in the succeeding stages of the analysis. This cut removed 122 events. There were 22 events which had no secondary vertices. At this point, some vertex quality cuts were imposed on the sample. Vertices were removed if the vertex fit probability was less than 5% or if all tracks in the vertex had a normalized 2d impact parameter to the IP less than 2.5. These cuts removed poor vertex fits and vertices with a high probability of containing a track originating from the IP, i.e., not from a secondary vertex. There were approximately 84,000 vertices (not all independent) in 4172 events remaining at this stage of the analysis.

The first column of table 1 shows the percentage of remaining vertices broken down by vertex type according to a Monte Carlo study. A vertex is in the 'b' category if all its tracks originate from the weak decay of a b quark. The other categories are similarly defined.

In most events, the remaining vertices were not independent. Some tracks were shared by more than one vertex. In addition, finding a multi-pronged vertex meant that lower multiplicity vertices containing a subset of the tracks were found as well. An algorithm was developed to reduce these remaining

Vertex type	Before Partition Selection (%)	After Partition Selection (%)	Final Sample (%)
b	16	19	22
cascade c	12	21	23
b+(cascade c)	44	33	35
b+other	12	7	4
(cascade c)+other	7	7	4
primary c	2	5	9
ip	1	3	1
Other	6	5	2

Table 1. Vertex type in sample according to Monte Carlo study.

vertices to a set of independent vertices. All possible unique sets of independent vertices (partitions) were found. The unique set used in the analysis was chosen by maximizing the joint fit probability of the event (product of the fit probabilities for each of the vertices in the partition, $P(\chi^2, d.o.f.)$). Table 1, column 2 shows the constitution of the remaining vertex sample according to a Monte Carlo study.

The primary background to real secondary vertices in the remaining sample were vertices made up entirely, or in part, of tracks originating from the IP. This background was substantially reduced by the decay length cut implemented earlier in the analysis. An additional cut was made to further reduce this background. Vertices were removed if the angle between the vertex line-of-flight and the nearest jet axis was greater than 150 mrad. Two other cuts were made to enhance the track quality, and thus the vertex quality, as well as to reduce the number of vertices arising from IP tracks. Vertices were removed if any track in the vertex had momentum less than 0.7 GeV/c or if any track had a transverse momentum with respect to the vertex line-of-flight less than 0.07 GeV/c.

The final cut in the vertex selection was to demand no more than one vertex per event hemisphere by selecting the vertex closest to the IP. This simplified the statistical and systematic error calculations. Table 1, column 3 shows the constitution of the final vertex sample used in the analysis according to a Monte Carlo study. The final sample consisted of 5427 vertices, made up of 4104 two-prong vertices, 1068 three-prong vertices and 255 four-prong vertices. Note that 63% of the event hemispheres in selected, heavy quark tagged events have at least one vertex at the end of vertex selection. Of these, 88% contain B hadron lifetime information according to a Monte Carlo study, i.e., they contain tracks associated with a weak b quark decay or the decay of the cascade c quark from the b quark.

3. Lifetime Analysis

The lifetime was extracted from the decay length distribution by using a binned likelihood function. The

Monte Carlo was generated with a fixed value of τ_B. The τ_B dependence was introduced by a weighting procedure. Decay length distributions were produced for τ_B values ranging from 0.7 to 2.3 ps, in steps of 0.02 ps. The likelihood was then computed for each value of τ_B. The maximum likelihood fits to the decay length distribution yielded an average B hadron lifetime of $\tau_B = 1.577 \pm 0.032$ ps where the error is statistical only. Figure 1 shows the vertex decay length distribution compared to the Monte Carlo distribution giving the best lifetime fit. The $\chi^2/d.o.f.$ for this fit was ~2.

A number of checks were made to increase confidence in this analysis. In one check, the Monte Carlo events were divided into five independent samples, each containing events scattered throughout the entire sample. Each of the five sets was successively analyzed as if it was the data and the other four subsets were Monte Carlo events. The five lifetime measurements yielded 1.528 ± 0.036 ps, 1.539 ± 0.037 ps, 1.449 ± 0.036 ps, 1.563 ± 0.039 ps, and 1.524 ± 0.037 ps, respectively, all in good agreement with the generated value. In another check of the analysis method and weighting scheme, Monte Carlo events were generated with an average B hadron lifetime of 2.0 ps. If these events were used (instead of the 1.515 ps sample) in the lifetime analysis, a measurement of 1.573 ± 0.030 ps resulted. A final check was performed to verify that no significant bias resulted from using events which passed the heavy quark tag. An impact parameter based heavy quark jet tag was used on the data. The lifetime analysis was done using only hemispheres opposite a tagged jet. The lifetime resulting from this study was 1.596 ± 0.039 ps, consistent with the result found above.

The systematic errors associated with this measurement are listed in table 2. A detailed description of how the systematic errors were determined can be found elsewhere[7]. The dominant systematic error is that due to b quark fragmentation. Refinements in the analysis are expected to reduce this error. Other significant contributions arise from a lack of knowledge of the charm content of B hadron decays and from some uncertainty in the SLD charged particle tracking efficiency. Added in quadrature, the net systematic error is 0.046 ps. This yields a (preliminary) result of $\tau_B = 1.577 \pm 0.032(\text{stat.}) \pm 0.046(\text{syst.})$ ps for the average B hadron lifetime.

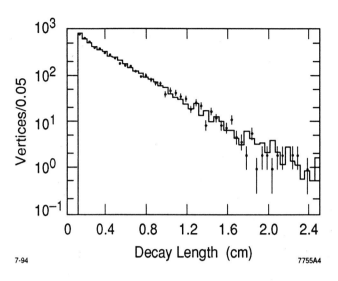

Figure 1. Decay length distribution for vertices passing all selection criteria in data (points) and Monte Carlo (histogram) events. The Monte Carlo distribution corresponds to that with the best-fit lifetime.

Systematic error	$\sigma\tau_B$ in ps
b fragmentation	0.038
c fragmentation	0.004
charm content	0.018
B baryon fraction	0.002
R_b	0.001
R_c	0.003
b multiplicity	0.006
detector effects	0.013
fit and binsize	0.010
TOTAL	0.046 ps

Table 2. Summary of systematic errors in this lifetime analysis

References

[1] W. Venus, Proc. of the 16th Symp. on Lepton and Photon Interactions, Cornell University, 1993, p.274; Eds. P. Drell and D. Rubin (AIP 1993).
[2] Particle Data Group, Phys. Rev. **D45**, Part II (1992).
[3] G.Agnew et al., SLAC preprint: SLAC-PUB-5906; Also in the Proc. of the 26th International Conf. on High Energy Phys., Dallas, 1992, p. 1862; Ed. J. Sanford (AIP 1992).
[4] D. Axen et al., Nucl. Instr. and Meth. **A238** (1993) 472.
[5] T. Sjöstrand, and M. Bengtsson, Comp. Phys. Comm. **43** (1987) 367.
[6] R. Brun et al., CERN DD/EE/84-1, 1987.
[7] SLD Collaboration: K. Abe et al., SLAC preprint: SLAC-PUB-6586.
[8] JADE Collaboration: W. Bartel et al., Z. Phys. **C33** (1986) 23.

Acknowledgments

We would like to thank the personnel of the SLAC accelerator department and the technical staffs of our collaborating institutions for their outstanding efforts on our behalf.

B^+ and B^0 Mean Lifetime Measurements

Fritz DeJongh[†]

Fermilab
P.O. Box 500, Batavia IL 60510, USA

Abstract

We review B^+ and B^0 mean lifetime measurements, including direct measurements and determination of the lifetime ratio via measurements of the ratio of branching ratios. We present world averages.

1. Introduction

The most precise determination of the CKM matrix element V_{cb} is obtained by comparing measurements [1] of the rate of exclusive $b \to cl\nu$ decays, extrapolated to a particular kinematic point, with theoretical predictions [2]. The mean lifetime of the particular B hadron for the exclusive decay is needed to convert experimental measurements of branching ratios into decay rates.

The mean lifetime of the D^+ is 2.5 times that of the D^0. The difference in the B system is expected to be smaller, with the mean B^+ lifetime as much as 7% larger than that of the B^0 [3].

We present herein results from direct measurements, as well as results from measurements of ratios of branching ratios. The numerical values of all results, and the world averages, are presented in Fig. 1. References to a specific charge state imply the charge-conjugate state as well. For the direct measurements, the decay length L of the B meson is measured with a silicon vertex detector, and the boost $\beta\gamma$ is measured with tracking in a magnetic field, and calorimetry. The proper lifetime $c\tau$ is simply the ratio $L/\beta\gamma$. We present results from CDF, from the reaction $p\bar{p}(\sqrt{s} = 1.8~\text{TeV}) \to b\bar{b} + X$, and results from ALEPH, DELPHI, and OPAL, from the reaction $e^+e^- \to Z \to b\bar{b}$.

If a B^+ decay mode is related to a B^0 decay mode

by a single isospin amplitude, the ratio of branching ratios is equivalent to the ratio of mean lifetimes. We present such results using inclusive semileptonic decays from CLEO, and $J/\psi K$ decays from CDF.

2. Fully reconstructed decays

In the case where the B hadron is fully reconstructed, the B hadron type, $\beta\gamma$, and L are all unambiguously measured, and the systematic uncertainties are minimal. CDF has reconstructed [4]:

- $B^+ \to J/\psi K^+, J/\psi K^{*+}, \psi(2S)K^+, \psi(2S)K^{*+}$
- $B^0 \to J/\psi K_S, J/\psi K^{*0}, \psi(2S)K_S, \psi(2S)K^{*0}$

The decay $J/\psi \to \mu^+\mu^-$ triggers the event. Without the trigger restriction, ALEPH has reconstructed [5]:

- $B^+ \to J/\psi K^+, \bar{D}^0\pi^+, \bar{D}^0\rho^+, \bar{D}^0 a_1^+$
- $B^0 \to D^-\pi^+, D^{*-}\pi^+$

3. Partial reconstruction of $B \to \bar{D}^{(*)}l\nu X$

In this method, one reconstructs the charmed meson and the lepton from a semileptonic decay. Events with $D^{*-} \to \bar{D}^0\pi^-$ are dominantly from B^0 decay, events with $\bar{D}^0$, excluding D^{*-} candidates, are dominantly from B^+ decay, and events with D^- are dominantly from B^0 decay since $\bar{D}^{*0}$ does not decay to D^-.

Some complications are that the decay is not fully reconstructed, so it is necessary to estimate the boost of the B based on the boost of the lepton and charm.

† E-mail: fritzd@fnald.fnal.gov

This can be done with about 15% resolution. Systematic uncertainties in the average boost lead to systematic uncertainties in the mean lifetime. Also, approximately 30% of semileptonic decays are through the chain $B \to \bar{D}^{**} l\nu, \bar{D}^{**} \to \bar{D}^*\pi$ or $\bar{D}\pi$. This, along with an imperfect efficiency for reconstructing the soft pion from the D^{*-} decay chain, mixes the B^+/B^0 composition of the samples. This mix needs to be understood in order to obtain individual B lifetimes.

There are results from ALEPH [6], DELPHI [7], OPAL [8], and CDF [9]. For the purposes of the world average, we assume that systematic uncertainties in background shape and sample composition are correlated among all experiments. The boost estimate depends on the B production and decay spectra, therefore we assume that systematic uncertainties from this source are correlated among the LEP experiments only.

4.   Topological Reconstruction

The DELPHI collaboration has selected 1816 secondary vertex candidates [10] for which all tracks in a jet are unambiguously assigned to either the primary or secondary vertex. The charge of the B hadron candidate is simply the sum of the charges of the tracks assigned to the secondary vertex. The B purity is 99%, and the charged/neutral assignment is 80% correct for the charged sample, and 57% correct for the neutral sample. The proper lifetime for an event is taken relative to the minimum value for which the event would have passed the cuts.

The B^+ and B^0 lifetimes are extracted using independent measurements of the Λ_b and B_s fractions and lifetimes, which lead to the dominant systematic uncertainty.

5.   Ratios of Branching Ratios

CLEO produces B mesons in the reaction $e^+e^- \to \Upsilon(4S) \to B^+B^-, B^0\bar{B}^0$. Therefore, tagging the charge of one B determines the charge of the other B, and by counting leptons opposite the tag sample, one determines the semileptonic branching ratios of the charged and neutral B mesons. This method of using tags has the advantage over previous methods that it does not rely on the assumption that the branching ratios of the $\Upsilon(4S)$ to charged and neutral B mesons are equal. CLEO has used 3 tagging techniques [11]:

- Fully reconstruct $B \to \bar{D}^{(*)}\pi/\rho/a_1, \psi K, \psi K^*$.
- Observe only the lepton and "slow" pion in the decay chain $B^0 \to D^{*-}l\nu, D^{*-} \to \bar{D}^0\pi^-_{slow}$. Contributions from $\bar{D}^{**}$ are suppressed with lepton momentum cuts. This provides most of the tags for the neutral sample.
- Reconstruct only the "fast" and "slow" pions in the decay chain $B^0 \to D^{*-}\pi^+_{fast}, D^{*-} \to \bar{D}^0\pi^-_{slow}$.

The major systematic uncertainties are from the uncertainty in the lepton spectrum, and from a dependence of the efficiency of the tag selection on the multiplicity of the untagged B.

CDF has reconstructed $B^+ \to \psi K^+$ and $B^0 \to \psi K_s$ [12]. Assuming the production cross-section for B^+ and B^0 are equal, CDF derives the ratio of branching ratios.

6.   Conclusions

The world average is calculated grouping systematic uncertainties into correlated sets as stated above. The results are shown in Fig. 1. We conclude that the B^+ lifetime is consistent with being the same as the B^0 lifetime. The uncertainty on the world average is similar to the largest theoretically expected difference. Many experiments can add additional channels, and all experiments cited herein continue to take data, so we can expect continued improvements in precision in the near future.

7.   Acknowledgements

Thanks to Kay Kinoshita, Robert Kowalewski, Vivek Sharma, Fumi Ukegawa, and Wilbur Venus for providing information on the latest results. Thanks to Tim Hessing for the use of a program to calculate averages with correlated systematic uncertainties.

References

[1] CLEO collaboration, contribution to this conference, ICHEP94 Ref. 0251; ALEPH collaboration, contribution to this conference, ICHEP94 Ref. 0605.

[2] M. Shifman, contribution to this conference, ICHEP94 Ref. 0823; M. Neubert, contribution to this conference, ICHEP94 Ref. 0935.

[3] I.I. Bigi and N.G. Uraltsev, Phys. Lett. **B280** (1992) 271.

[4] F. Abe *et al.*, Phys. Rev. Lett. **71** (1994) 3456.

[5] ALEPH collaboration, contribution to this conference, ICHEP94 Ref. 0602.

[6] ALEPH collaboration, contribution to this conference, ICHEP94 Ref. 0579.

[7] P. Abreu *et al.*, Zeit. Phys. **C57** (1993) 181.

[8] OPAL collaboration, contribution to this conference, ICHEP94 Ref. 0533.

[9] CDF collaboration, contribution to this conference, ICHEP94 Ref. 0655.

[10] DELPHI collaboration, contribution to this conference, ICHEP94 Ref. 0165.

[11] M. Athanas *et al.*, CLEO 94-16.

[12] J. Gonzalez, Proc. of the Workshop on *B* Phys. at Hadron Accelerators 1993, p. 285; Eds. P. McBride and C.S. Mishra.

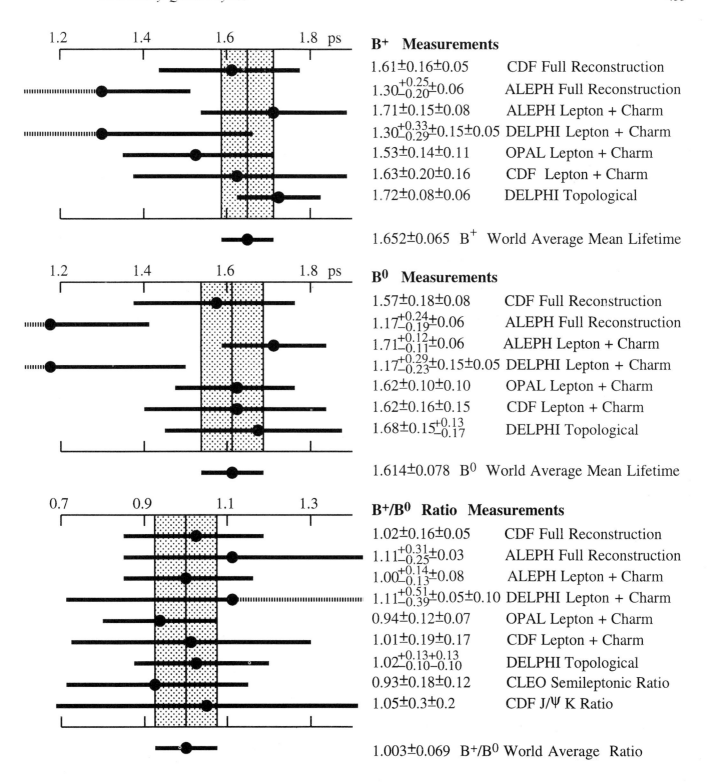

B⁺ Measurements

$1.61\pm0.16\pm0.05$	CDF Full Reconstruction
$1.30^{+0.25}_{-0.20}\pm0.06$	ALEPH Full Reconstruction
$1.71\pm0.15\pm0.08$	ALEPH Lepton + Charm
$1.30^{+0.33}_{-0.29}\pm0.15\pm0.05$	DELPHI Lepton + Charm
$1.53\pm0.14\pm0.11$	OPAL Lepton + Charm
$1.63\pm0.20\pm0.16$	CDF Lepton + Charm
$1.72\pm0.08\pm0.06$	DELPHI Topological

1.652 ± 0.065 B⁺ World Average Mean Lifetime

B⁰ Measurements

$1.57\pm0.18\pm0.08$	CDF Full Reconstruction
$1.17^{+0.24}_{-0.19}\pm0.06$	ALEPH Full Reconstruction
$1.71^{+0.12}_{-0.11}\pm0.06$	ALEPH Lepton + Charm
$1.17^{+0.29}_{-0.23}\pm0.15\pm0.05$	DELPHI Lepton + Charm
$1.62\pm0.10\pm0.10$	OPAL Lepton + Charm
$1.62\pm0.16\pm0.15$	CDF Lepton + Charm
$1.68\pm0.15^{+0.13}_{-0.17}$	DELPHI Topological

1.614 ± 0.078 B⁰ World Average Mean Lifetime

B⁺/B⁰ Ratio Measurements

$1.02\pm0.16\pm0.05$	CDF Full Reconstruction
$1.11^{+0.31}_{-0.25}\pm0.03$	ALEPH Full Reconstruction
$1.00^{+0.14}_{-0.13}\pm0.08$	ALEPH Lepton + Charm
$1.11^{+0.51}_{-0.39}\pm0.05\pm0.10$	DELPHI Lepton + Charm
$0.94\pm0.12\pm0.07$	OPAL Lepton + Charm
$1.01\pm0.19\pm0.17$	CDF Lepton + Charm
$1.02^{+0.13+0.13}_{-0.10-0.10}$	DELPHI Topological
$0.93\pm0.18\pm0.12$	CLEO Semileptonic Ratio
$1.05\pm0.3\pm0.2$	CDF J/$^{\psi}$ K Ratio

1.003 ± 0.069 B⁺/B⁰ World Average Ratio

Figure 1. Summary of B^+ and B^0 mean lifetime measurements.

Paper presented at XXVII Int. Conf. on High Energy Physics: Session Pa-2 Glasgow, UK, 20–27 July 1994

Review of B_s Lifetimes

Claire H. Shepherd-Themistocleous

Centre for Research in Particle Physics,
Carleton University, Ottawa, Canada K1S 5B6

Abstract

This paper reviews the current measurements of the B_s lifetime. Results from the ALEPH, DELPHI, CDF and OPAL collaborations are presented. The B_s decay is either fully or partially reconstructed and the lifetime extracted from the measured decay lengths. A world average lifetime of 1.56 ± 0.14 ps is found.

1. Introduction

In the spectator model the only process that determines the lifetime of the B hadrons is the decay of the b quark. The B baryons are therefore all predicted to have the same lifetime in this model. Non-spectator effects such as quark interference, W exchange and W annihilation will tend, as in the charm system, to cause differences in the lifetimes and following hierarchy $\tau(B^+) > \tau(B_s^0) \geq \tau(B_d^0) > \tau(\Lambda_b)$ is expected [1]. The maximum difference is expected to be of the order of 10%. The determination of exclusive lifetimes therefore is a test of heavy quark effective theory. If this is understood then a determination of the CKM matrix element V_{cb} is possible.

2. Measurements of B_s

A number of different methods have been used to determine τ_{B_s}. The measurements discussed here are from the ALEPH [2], DELPHI [3] and OPAL [4] experiments at LEP and the CDF [5] experiment at the Tevatron collider. All these experiments utilize high resolution Si microvertex detectors, which alow impact parameter resolutions of the order of $15\mu m$. When used in conjunction with large gas tracking chambers, decay length resolutions of $\sim 300\mu m$ on decay lengths of $\sim 2mm$ (LEP) $\sim 0.8mm$ (CDF) are obtained.

2.1. $D_s \ell$ Correlations

The decays considered are:-

$$
\begin{array}{ll}
B_s \rightarrow D_s^- \, \ell^+ \, \nu \, X & \qquad B_s \rightarrow D_s^- \, \ell^+ \, \nu \, X \\
\quad \hookrightarrow K^{*0} \, K^- & \qquad \quad \hookrightarrow \phi \, \pi^- \\
\quad \hookrightarrow K^+ \, \pi^- & \qquad \quad \hookrightarrow K^+ \, K^- \, .
\end{array}
$$

All four experiments have determined τ_{B_s} using $D_s \ell$ correlations.

The D_s^- is reconstructed by looking for $K^+ K^- \pi^-$ correlations. The measurement of the rate of energy loss, dE/dx, is used by most experiments to identify and separate the kaons and pions. Good quality D_s vertices are also required. The reconstructed D_s is then associated with a lepton of the right sign i.e. $D_s^+ \ell^-$ or $D_s^- \ell^+$. To increase the b purity of the sample the leptons are required to have high p and/or p_t. The requirement of a large invariant mass suppresses combinatorial and physics background. A plot of the mass of the $KK\pi$ combination for $KK\pi\ell$ correlations is shown in figure 1.

The decay length is then determined by forming a vertex between the D_s candidate and the ℓ and determining the distance from the primary to the secondary vertex. All experiments except ALEPH perform this operation in the x-y plane†. ALEPH uses 3D vertexing.

† The z axis is in the beam direction.

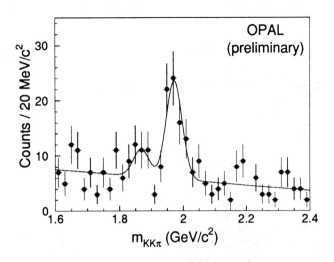

Figure 1. An example of the KKπ invariant mass distribution for $K^+K^-\pi^-\ell^+$ combinations. The statelite peak is due to D^- decays to KKπ.

by including a term in the log likelihood fits or as a systematic error. The function used to parameterize the combinatorial background is only required to provide a good representation of its shape and several functions are used in the different analyses. An example of a fit is shown in figure 2.

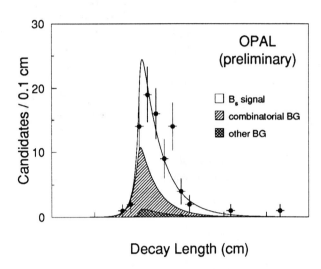

Figure 2. The decay length distribution for $D_s\ell$ correlations for events with a KKπ mass within a region of $\pm50\,\text{MeV}/c^2$ around the D_s fitted mass. The solid curve represents the total fit.

The conversion of the decay length into a decay time requires a knowledge of the B_s momentum. This decay is only partially reconstructed since at least the ν is not detected and hence p_{B_s} cannot be directly measured. A number of methods for estimating the boost are used. Most experiments use some variation of converting the $p_{D_s\ell}$ to p_{B_s} using the ratio $p_{B_s}/p_{D_s\ell}$ obtained from Monte Carlo simulations. ALEPH uses a missing energy method to estimate the energy of the ν and is hence able to determine p_{B_s}.

Unbinned log likelihood fits are performed over signal and sideband regions defined in the KKπ mass spectrum to extract the B_s lifetime. The signal is parameterized by a gaussian convoluted with an exponential, $G(t,\sigma_t) \otimes \text{Exp}(\tau_{B_s}) \otimes B$, where B represents the boost estimate. Its form differs between experiments. DELPHI measure a decay length from the primary vertex to the D_s vertex hence their signal is parameterized by a function of the form, $\text{Exp}(\tau_B) \otimes \text{Exp}(\tau_{D_s}) \otimes G(t,\sigma_t)$. The boost is estimated using Monte Carlo simulations to derive a relation between the B momentum and the D_s momentum.

The background consists of a combinatorial part and a "physics" part due to decays of B hadrons other than B_s that can lead to final states which contain KKπℓ. The main sources of such physics backgrounds are the decays $B_{u,d} \rightarrow D_s^+\bar{D}X$, $\bar{D} \rightarrow \ell^-\bar{\nu}X'$ and $B_{u,d} \rightarrow D_s^-K\ell^+\nu X$. The magnitudes of the backgrounds due to both of these are reduced by the high p and p_t requirements on the ℓ and the high $m_{D_s\ell}$ requirement. The expected fractions of these sources are estimated from selection efficiencies determined from Monte Carlo simulations and known branching ratios. They are allowed for either

The systematic errors in these measurements come mainly from the estimation of background levels, the estimate of the boost and possible fit biases. With the currently avaliable data the statistical error dominates. The values of τ_{B_s} obtained by the various experiments are shown in table 1.

Exp.	$D_s\ell$ cands	BG frac.	τ_{B_s} (ps)
ALEPH	35 ± 7	0.25	$1.92^{+0.45}_{-0.35} \pm 0.04$
CDF	76 ± 8	0.45	$1.42^{+0.27}_{-0.23} \pm 0.11$
DELPHI	37 ± 8	0.30	$1.32^{+0.41}_{-0.32} \pm 0.18$
OPAL	55 ± 10	0.35	$1.33^{+0.26}_{-0.21} \pm 0.06$

Table 1. Table of B_s lifetimes determined using $D_s\ell$ correlations.

2.2. D_s-hadron correlations and inclusive D_s

More inclusive methods have been used by ALEPH and DELPHI. The D_s is identified in the same way as in the $D_s\ell$ methods.

ALEPH correlates the D_s with a high p_t hadron of the opposite sign to the D_s and requires a high p_{D_sh}. A decay length from the primary vertex to the D_sh vertex is determined and converted to a proper time using the jet mass and momentum to estimate p_{B_s}/m_{B_s}.

Residual differences are corrected for using information from Monte Carlo simulations.

In this method the physics backgrounds are large. The following sources of D_s are allowed for in the fits $b \to \bar{B}_s^0 \to D_s^+$, $b \to B_{u,d}, B_s, \Lambda_b \to D_s^-$ (via a W^-) and $c \to D_s^+$. Figure 3 shows ALEPHs fit to the proper time distribution. The fractions of the various sources of D_s are partly determined by obtaining an estimate of the fractions of D_s from $b\bar{b}$ or $c\bar{c}$ events. A probability for a D_s originating in a $b\bar{b}$ event can be defined by using a quark tag in the hemisphere opposite to that in which the D_s is identified. By using efficiencies determined from Monte Carlo simulations and fitting to the probability spectrum the branching fractions for $b \to B_s \to D_s$ and $c \to D_s$ can be determined. Using this information in combination with known branching fractions for the decay of the D_s the fractions of D_s from each of the sources mentioned above can be determined.

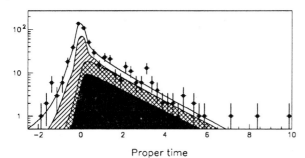

Proper time

Figure 3. This shows the fit to the proper time distribution in the signal region. The black area is the contribution from the signal ($\tau = \tau_{B_s}$), the cross hatched area is that due to the B hadron background ($\tau = \tau_b$), the hatched area is due to events where the hadron originates from the primary vertex ($\tau = 0$) and the white space is due to combinatorial background. The solid curve is the total fit.

DELPHI uses inclusive D_s ($\to \phi\pi$ only) and determines the decay length from the primary vertex to the D_s vertex. The sources of D_s considered are the same as in the previous case. The fraction of D_s from $c\bar{c}$ events is estimated from known branching rations and efficiencies determined from Monte Carlo simulation samples. The purity of B_s in the sample of B is also estimated from known production rates and branching ratios. The boost is estimated from the D_s momenta and a relation between p_{B_s} and $p_{D_s\ell}$ is derived from Monte Carlo simulations. The combinatorial background is estimated from sidebands and an "anti" signal region defined to be events that do not pass a particular selection cut. An unbinned log likelihood fit is performed to extract τ_B and then the B_s lifetime is extracted using the average B hadron lifetime and the fraction of candidates that are B_s.

The systematic errors in these methods are large compared to those in the $D_s\ell$ case. The main source is the estimation of backgrounds. The lifetimes are shown

in table 2.

Exp.	Cand. in peak	τ_{B_s} (ps)
ALEPH	~ 320	$1.75^{+0.30+0.18}_{-0.28-0.23}$
DELPHI	~ 210	$1.56^{+0.38}_{-0.32} \pm 0.23$

Table 2. Table of B_s lifetimes determined using $D_s h$ correlations and inclusive D_s.

2.3. $B_s \to J/\psi\phi$

CDF have determined a lifetime from $B_s \to J/\psi\phi$. This has the advantage of being a fully reconstructed mode and therefore no boost estimate is required. It may also eventually be possible to see differences in the B_s long and short lifetimes by comparing the τ_{B_s} from this decay mode to that from $B_s \to D_s\ell\nu$, for example. Current statistics however are too low to observe any possible differences.

The B_s are reconstructed by looking for $\mu^+\mu^-K^+K^-$ correlations and a signal of 10 ± 3 events is seen. A fit to signal and sideband regions gives $\tau_{B_s} = 1.74^{+0.90}_{-0.60} \pm 0.07$ ps

3. Conclusion

A weighted average, using fractional errors, of all of the above numbers except the $J/\psi\phi$ number gives a value of 1.54 ± 0.14 ps. The correlations in the systematic errors between these measurements were considered, but found to be negligible and so have been ignored. This average has an error of $< 10\%$ and difference between this lifetime and the lifetime of the Λ_b is expected to be of this order. Exclusive b hadron lifetimes are therefore reaching a precision where one might expect to start to be able to see differences between the species. The B_s lifetime is currently statistics limited. Any differences in the B hadron lifetimes should therefore become observable in the near future.

References

[1] G. Altarelli and S. Petrarca, Phys. Lett. **B261** (1991) 303; I.I. Bigi, Phys. Lett. **B 169** (1986) 101; J.H. Kühn *et al* , *Heavy Flavours at LEP*, MPI-PAE/PTh 49/89, August 1989, contribution by R. Rückl, p. 59.
[2] ALEPH Collaboration: Contribution to this conference, gls0578: ALEPH Collaboration: Phys. Lett. **B322** (1994) 275
[3] DELPHI Collaboration: Contribution to this conference, gls0233
[4] OPAL Collaboration: Internal Physics Note PN150
[5] CDF Collaboration: Contribution to this conference gls0609

Measurements of the b Baryon Lifetime at LEP

L. Moneta

ALEPH Collaboration

Imperial College, London SW7 2BZ, UK

Abstract

Recent measurements of the b baryon lifetime obtained at LEP are reviewed. The combined LEP average of these measurements has been computed, taking into account correlated systematic errors between different analyses. The average lifetime of the b baryons is found to be significantly shorter than the B meson lifetimes.

1. Introduction

The measurement of the b baryon lifetime is of particular interest because it can provide a test of b hadron decay theory. In the spectator model the lifetimes of all the b hadrons are expected to be equal. However, as it has been observed in the charm system, the presence of non-spectator effects, like W-exchange or the quark interference, may cause different lifetimes. These effects are expected to produce only a difference of a few percent in the B meson's lifetimes due to the heavy mass of the b quark. In contrast, a lifetime difference between baryon and meson decays may arise from non-perturbative QCD corrections of order $1/m_b^2$ and also from the W exchange decay diagram which, in the b baryon case, is not helicity suppressed. Present theoretical expectations for the lifetime ratio are $\tau_{\Lambda_b}/\tau_{B^0} \approx 0.9$ [1]. Precise measurements of the b baryon lifetime can test these theoretical predictions and add more information to the understanding of b decay.

The experimental conditions at LEP are quite favourable for performing measurements of the individual b hadron lifetimes, thanks to a long b hadron decay path (≈ 3 mm) and a copious production rate. Each of the four LEP experiments has recorded between 1991 and 1993 about 1.8 million Z^0 decays of which about 400,000 are $Z^0 \rightarrow b\bar{b}$ events. Each experiment is now equipped with a silicon vertex detector which allows pre-

cise tracking reconstruction. This, with good lepton and baryon identification, enables the b baryon signal to be isolated.

2. Event selection and measurement techniques

The isolation of b baryon events is quite complex due to a relatively low production rate, between 8 and 12% of all the b hadrons. First, generic b hadrons are selected through their semileptonic decays by requiring the presence in the event of a lepton with high momentum. Then the b baryons are isolated from the B mesons by looking for light quark baryons, like Λ's or protons, with the right sign, produced in the decay chain. Of all the b baryons produced at LEP, the Λ_b^0 is expected to be the most important component, at least 70%, with respect to other b baryons such as Ξ_b or Ω_b which contain at least one s quark. In the following, the symbol Λ_b will be used to denote the generic b baryons produced at LEP.

Three different methods have been employed by the LEP collaborations to isolate b baryons. They are based on a right sign correlation between a lepton and a baryon, such as Λ or p or Λ_c, produced in the Λ_b decay chain. ALEPH and OPAL use both electrons and muons while DELPHI uses only muons.

Once the b baryons are selected, the lifetime is

measured using standard techniques based on the reconstruction of the b baryon decay length or of the lepton impact parameter.

2.1. *Selection using $\Lambda - \ell$ correlations*

This first method is the most common and was the first used by ALEPH, DELPHI and OPAL, as evidence of b baryon production in Z^0 decays [2]. The signal results from the decay† $\Lambda_b \to \Lambda_c^+ \ell^- \overline{\nu}$ followed by the decay $\Lambda_c^+ \to \Lambda X$, with the Λ decaying to pπ^-. The same side $\Lambda\ell^-$ correlation, as opposed to $\Lambda\ell^+$, is a distinctive signature of a semileptonic b baryon decay. This selection procedure is efficient and provides the highest statistics, thanks to the large branching ratio $\Lambda_c \to \Lambda X$. Physics background processes, such as B meson decay $\overline{B} \to \Lambda_c^+ X \ell^- \overline{\nu}$, are suppressed by simply requiring a high lepton transverse momentum (p_t) with respect to the jet axis. Processes like $\Lambda_c^+ \to \Lambda X \ell^+ \nu$, where the Λ_c can arise either from a B meson decay or directly from $Z^0 \to c\overline{c}$ events contribute only in the wrong sign and they are also suppressed with the p_t cut. The main background results from accidental combinations of real Λ's produced during fragmentation or fake Λ's due to combinatorial pπ, associated with real or fake leptons. Due to the high p_t cut the leptons come mostly from b decay. The excess in the yield of $\Lambda\ell^-$ over $\Lambda\ell^+$ combinations observed in the data, represents the contribution due to the semileptonic Λ_b decays. However, a correction, taken from a study of Monte Carlo events, is applied for a production asymmetry between the $\Lambda\ell^-$ and $\Lambda\ell^+$ background candidates. For example, ALEPH uses a correction factor for the ratio $\Lambda\ell^-$ to $\Lambda\ell^+$ of 0.8 ± 0.2, which also includes the contribution of semileptonic Λ_c decay in the wrong sign peak. This selection procedure has been used by ALEPH, DELPHI and OPAL to yield a b baryon purity of about 60%. Each collaboration has then used its own technique to determine the lifetime.

OPAL [3] measures the Λ_b decay length by vertexing the lepton and the reconstructed Λ direction vector. Although the Λ's do not come directly from the Λ_b, the short lifetime of the Λ_c does not bias the measurement. Nevertheless the decay length has a large error due to the long Λ lifetime, which decays mostly inside the tracking detectors. The analysis employed by DELPHI [4], includes an additional π consistent with the b baryon decay chain, to improve the resolution in the Λ_b vertex. But this has the disadvantage of decreasing the efficiency and of reducing the statistical precision of the measurement. The b baryon lifetime is then extracted by a maximum likelihood fit to the proper time distribution of the $\Lambda\ell^-$ candidates. The proper time is obtained by estimating the boost from

† Charge conjugate decays are implied throughout this paper.

the measured Λ and ℓ momenta, in the OPAL case, or, by DELPHI, from the measured missing energy in the hemisphere. To parametrize the background shape, OPAL fits also the wrong sign candidates, while DELPHI fits $\Lambda\ell^-$ candidates resulting from a loosening of the Λ selection.

ALEPH [5] performs a fit to the lepton impact parameter distribution to extract the b baryon lifetime. This procedure is similar to that used for the inclusive b hadron lifetime [6]. The shape of the signal and of the background are parametrized using physics functions obtained from Monte Carlo events for each single component which contributes to the $\Lambda\ell^-$ combinations. Fig. 1 shows the ALEPH impact parameter distribution together with the signal and the background functions divided into the various components. The impact parameter is a lifetime estimator with less statistical power than the decay length, but it has a better resolution, is insensitive to the Λ_b boost and is very efficient. A disadvantage of the impact parameter technique is due to a sensitivity to the $\Lambda_b \to \ell$ decay model and to the Λ_b polarization. OPAL [3] has also measured the lifetime by fitting the impact parameter distribution for those events where the lepton has at least one associated hit in the silicon vertex detector. The OPAL decay length and the impact parameter measurements are combined taking into account the statistical correlation.

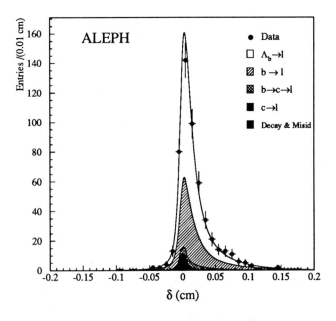

Figure 1. ALEPH impact parameter distribution

The $\Lambda\ell^-$ correlation method gives the highest number of candidates and currently yields the most precise measurement of the b baryon lifetime. The systematic error is at present between 6 and 10% and is mainly due to the level and shape of the background and to the unknown Λ_b polarization.

2.2. Selection using $\Lambda_c - \ell$ correlations

A different method to select b baryon events and to measure their lifetime is by tagging events with a same side $\Lambda_c^+ \ell^-$ correlation, where the Λ_c^+ is fully reconstructed in the $pK^+\pi^-$ channel. This method is inefficient due to the low branching ratio $\Lambda_c^+ \to pK^+\pi^-$ but results in a signal with a purity of more than 70%. Moreover, this procedure allows a measurement with high precision of the Λ_b decay length by vertexing the lepton and the Λ_c vector obtained from the $pK\pi$ vertex. By estimating the Λ_b boost from the ℓ and Λ_c momenta, ALEPH and DELPHI have performed a fit to the proper time distribution of the $\Lambda_c^+\ell^-$ candidates to determine τ_{Λ_b}. These measurements have a low systematic error but require much greater statistics to become competitive with the measurements based on $\Lambda\ell^-$ correlations.

2.3. Selection using $p - \mu$ correlations

A new method has been employed by DELPHI [4], using the proton identification capabilities at high momentum provided by the gas RICH. High momentum protons ($p > 8$ GeV) associated with high p_t muons are a signature of a b baryon decay. Although the protons are mostly produced by secondary c baryon decays, they follow the original direction. Therefore, due to the low c baryon lifetime, the protons can be used together with the μ to find the Λ_b decay length. A global fit to the selected candidates yield the b baryon lifetime and the sample composition. The background level is rather high and is dominated by misidentified protons such as K's resulting from c hadron decays. In addition the shape of the background shape is determined by the Monte Carlo, and it is found to be the dominant systematic error. This analysis has been performed so far only on the data collected during 1992 when the gas RICH was operational, therefore the statistics are presently quite low.

3. Summary

The results of the different analyses performed by the LEP experiments are summarized in fig. 2. The numbers are corrected for a Λ_b polarization of $47\pm47\%$. The LEP average is computed taking into account common systematic errors, while the statistical errors are assumed to be uncorrelated. The average LEP b baryon lifetime is $\tau_{\Lambda_b} = 1.17 \pm 0.11$ ps. Assuming

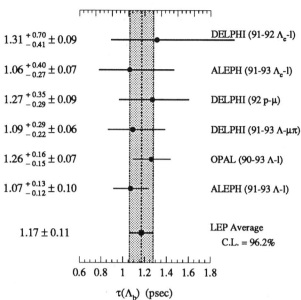

Figure 2. Summary of the b baryon lifetime measurements.

that the measurements of the b baryon and of the B^0 lifetime [8] are uncorrelated, the resulting ratio is $\tau_{\Lambda_b}/\tau_{B^0} = 0.72 \pm 0.08$.

4. Conclusions

Based on 3 years of running at LEP the b baryon lifetime has been measured with an overall precision of about 9%. The result is significantly lower than the B meson lifetimes, and the difference is at present greater than theoretically expected. However, by the end of LEP100 the expected increase of statistics by a factor of 3, will allow a measurement of the lifetime with a precision of 5-6%, which will increase the statistical significance of the test of the theoretical predictions.

References

[1] I. Bigi *et al.*, "Non-leptonic decays of beauty hadrons - from phenomenology to theory", in *B Decays* (second edition); Editor S. Stone (World Scientific Publishers 1994).

[2] ALEPH Coll., D. Decamp *et al.*, Phys. Lett. **B278** (1992) 209; DELPHI Coll., P. Abreu *et al.*, Phys. Lett. **B311** (1993) 379; OPAL Coll., P.D. Acton *et al.*, Phys. Lett. **B281** (1992) 394.

[3] OPAL Coll., Contribution #0534 to this conference.

[4] DELPHI Coll., Contribution #0162 to this conference.

[5] ALEPH Coll., Contribution #0603 to this conference.

[6] ALEPH Coll., D. Buskulic *et al.*, Phys. Lett. **B295** (1992) 174.

[7] ALEPH Coll., Contribution #0596 to this conference.

[8] F. DeJongh, talk given in this conference in PA02.

New Results on J/ψ and ψ' Decays from BES

Li Jin[‡]

IHEP, CAS, Beijing 100039, China

Representing the BES Collaboration

Abstract

This paper describes new results from BES. (1) The branching ratio for $\psi' \to \tau^+\tau^-$ has been measured for the first time. (2) The decay width of the J/ψ and the branching ratio for leptonic decay have been given in two independent ways. (3) The ξ does exist in the J/ψ radiative decays $J/\psi \to \gamma K^+ K^-$ and $J/\psi \to \gamma K_s^0 K_s^0$, and a new decay mode $\xi \to p\bar{p}$ has been found.

1. BEPC and BES.

The BEijing Spectrometer (BES) [1] is a large general-purpose solenoidal detector at Beijing Electron Positron Collider (BEPC). Since September 1989, BES has collected 9×10^6 J/ψ events, 1.4×10^6 ψ' events and 25 pb^{-1} of D$_s$(4.03 GeV) events, and has a very successful τ mass measurement. On the basis of these data, BES have studied the charm particles J/ψ and ψ': some new results are presented in the following sections.

2. Measurement of the branching ratio for $\psi' \to \tau^+\tau^-$.

The τ is a conventional lepton, which behaves like the other two charged leptons, the electron and muon – a hypothesis called e-μ-τ universality. In the $c\bar{c}$ system, the ψ' provides a unique opportunity to compare the three generations of leptons by studying its leptonic decays. The branching ratios for ψ' into e, μ and τ pairs, B_{ee}, $B_{\mu\mu}$ and $B_{\tau\tau}$, are related by:

$$\frac{B_{\tau\tau}}{\left(1 + \frac{4m_\tau^2}{M^2}\right)\left(1 - \frac{4m_\tau^2}{M^2}\right)^{\frac{1}{2}}} = \frac{B_{\mu\mu}}{\left(1 + \frac{4m_\mu^2}{M^2}\right)\left(1 - \frac{4m_\mu^2}{M^2}\right)^{\frac{1}{2}}}$$

$$= \frac{B_{ee}}{\left(1 + \frac{4m_e^2}{M^2}\right)\left(1 - \frac{4m_e^2}{M^2}\right)^{\frac{1}{2}}}.$$

Previous experiments have yielded measurements of B_{ee} and $B_{\mu\mu}$ for the ψ', but no data for $B_{\tau\tau}$ [2]. We present here the first measurement of $B_{\tau\tau}$ for the ψ', based on 1.83 pb^{-1} of ψ' data collected at BEPC with BES.

The branching ratio for $\psi' \to \tau^+\tau^-$ is given by

$$B_{\tau\tau} = \frac{N_{\tau\tau} - \sigma_{QED}\, L}{N_{\psi'}}.$$

Here $N_{\tau\tau}$ is the total number of $\tau^+\tau^-$ events, σ_{QED} is the cross section for QED τ-pair production, and L is the integrated luminisity at the ψ' resonance, which has been measured by observing large angle dimuon events in the BES detector.

2.1. Total cross section for τ-pair production near the ψ' resonance region.

Because of the two processes occurring in the region, the QED process $e^+e^- \to \tau^+\tau^-$ and the ψ' decay $e^+e^- \to \psi' \to \tau^+\tau^-$, the total cross section is:

$$\sigma_0(s) = \frac{4\pi\alpha^2}{3s}\beta\frac{(3-\beta^2)}{2} \times$$

‡ E-mail: lij@bepc2.ihep.ac.cn

$$\times \left\{ 1 + \frac{3M^3}{\alpha s}\Gamma_{ll}.F\frac{2(s-M^2)}{(s-M^2)^2 + M^2\Gamma^2} \right.$$

$$\left. + \left(\frac{3M^3}{\alpha s}\right)^2 \Gamma_{ll}^2.F^2\frac{1}{(s-M^2)^2 + M^2\Gamma^2} \right\}.$$

The first term is the cross section for the QED process, the second term is the interference term between the two processes, and the third term is the ψ' resonance;

$$F \equiv \frac{1}{\left(1 + \frac{2m_l^2}{M^2}\right)\left(1 - \frac{4m_l^2}{M^2}\right)^{\frac{1}{2}}}.$$

We also need to consider corrections from initial and final state radiation, vacuum polarization, Coulomb effects, and the energy spread of the beam.

2.2.   *The total number of $\tau^+\tau^-$ events, $N_{\tau\tau}$.*

The $\tau^+\tau^-$ events are identified by means of the $e\mu$ and $e\pi$ decay topologies:

$$
\begin{array}{ll}
\psi' \rightarrow \tau^{\pm}\tau^{\mp} & \psi' \rightarrow \tau^{\pm}\tau^{\mp} \\
\quad\hookrightarrow e^{\mp}\nu \quad \text{and} & \quad\hookrightarrow e^{\mp}\nu \\
\quad\hookrightarrow \mu^{\pm}\nu & \quad\hookrightarrow \pi^{\mp}\nu
\end{array}
$$

To estimate the background, the same event selection requirements are applied to 5×10^6 J/ψ data events; only 5–8 events meet the criteria for $e\mu$ and $e\pi$ respectively, corresponding to a ratio $R_{bg} < 10^{-3}$. A Monte-Carlo study on the two-photon process has been performed, and no background events were found.

In order to translate observed $e\mu$ ($e\pi$) events into total $\tau^+\tau^-$ event numbers, it is necessary to make substantial corrections:

$$N_{\tau\tau} = \frac{n_{e\mu(e\pi)}}{B.\varepsilon_{det}.\varepsilon_{trig}.\varepsilon_{filt}},$$

where $n_{e\mu}, n_{e\pi}$ are the observed numbers of $\pi\mu$ and $e\pi$ events, ε_{trig} is the trigger efficiency, ε_{filt} is the filter efficiency, ε_{det} is the detection efficiency, and B the branching ratio for $\tau^+\tau^- \rightarrow e\mu$ or $\tau^+\tau^- \rightarrow e\pi$.

After Monte-Carlo studies, the data analysis gave, from the observed numbers $n_{e\mu} = 70$ and $n_{e\pi} = 43$, the value $N_{\tau\tau} = 7560 \pm 915 \pm 380$.

2.3.   *Determination of the number of ψ' events.*

The number of ψ' events was determined from the inclusive decay $\psi' \rightarrow \pi^+\pi^- J/\psi$:

$$N_{\psi'} = \frac{n_{J\psi}^{obs}/\varepsilon_{J/\psi}}{Br(\psi' \rightarrow \pi^+\pi^- J/\psi)}.$$

where $n_{J\psi}^{obs}$ is the number of observed $\psi' \rightarrow \pi^+\pi^- J/\psi$ events, and $\varepsilon_{J/\psi}$ is the detection efficiency. We use $Br(\psi' \rightarrow \pi^+\pi^- J/\psi) = (32.4 \pm 2.6)\%$ [2].

2.4.   *Branching ratio for $\psi' \rightarrow \tau^+\tau^-$.*

From the total number of $\tau^+\tau^-$ pairs produced, the integrated luminosity and the total number of ψ' events, we get for the branching ratio of $\psi' \rightarrow \tau^+\tau^-$:

$$B_{\tau\tau} = (3.19 \pm 0.86 \pm 0.45\,{}^{+0.48}_{-0.59}) \times 10^{-3},$$

where the first error is statistical, the second is systematic, and the third is a systematic error which comes from uncertainty in the beam energy and energy spread.

3.   A measurement of the J/ψ decay widths and branching ratios from BES.

Most of the data on J/ψ decay widths are determined from e^+e^- collisions before 1980 by measuring the cross section curves for $e^+e^- \rightarrow e^+e^-, \mu^+\mu^-$ and hadrons in the vicinity of the J/ψ resonance. The Particle Data Group tables for 1990 reflect the typical values up to that time. MARK III then measured B_e and B_μ with higher accuracy through the decay channels of $\psi' \rightarrow \pi^+\pi^- J/\psi$, with $J/\psi \rightarrow l^+l^-$; anything. These data were combined with the old data to give the PDG 1992 values [2], which are quite different from the old values of the total and leptonic widths. Hence it still seems of interest to measure the J/ψ decay widths and branching ratios through these two methods using BES, to see if consistent results can be obtained.

We have determined the J/ψ decay widths and branching ratios in two different ways: by measuring the cross sections for $e^+e^- \rightarrow e^+e^-, \mu^+\mu^-$ and hadrons in the vicinity of the J/ψ resonance, and measuring the ratio of the numbers of events of $\psi' \rightarrow \pi^+\pi^- J/\psi$, $J/\psi \rightarrow l^+l^-$ and $J/\psi \rightarrow$ anything.

3.1.   *J/ψ decay widths by cross section measurement.*

In this section we describe the determination of the J/ψ decay widths by measuring the cross sections for $J/\psi \rightarrow e^+e^-, \mu^+\mu^-$ and hadrons as a function of energy near the J/ψ resonance using BES.

The luminosity of BEPC is measured by a luminosity monitor sitting in the small polar angle region. At 25 beam energy points in the vicinity of the J/ψ resonance we measured the observed cross section for $e^+e^- \rightarrow e^+e^-, \mu^+\mu^-$ and hadrons, obtained by dividing the numbers of selected $e^+e^-, \mu^+\mu^-$ and hadron events by the integrated luminosity at each beam energy point. To fit the observed cross sections, we need to know the acceptance for these processes. The acceptance A is equal to the product of the trigger efficiency ε_{trig}, and the reconstruction and event selection efficiency ε_{rs} for each process.

The data were fitted simultaneously to obtain the mass and the partial widths to electrons, muons and

partial width to leptons	5.14 ± 0.38 keV
partial width to hadrons	74.9 ± 12.5 keV
total width	85.2 ± 13.2 keV
branching fraction to leptons	6.04 ± 0.50 keV

Table 1. Results of the fit.

hadrons; the total width is the sum of these three partial widths. The fit folded the Gaussian beam resolution function with radiative effects and a Breit-Wigner cross section. The results are listed in table 1. Here we assume $e - \mu$ universality. The errors principally reflect the systematic uncertainties, which include overall normalization errors, and energy setting errors of ± 25 keV. It can be seen that compared with the old data, our preliminary results for the partial and total widths are much closer to the 1992 PDG values.

3.2. Measurement of the branching ratios for $J/\psi \to l^+l^-$.

In addition to the motivations mentioned above, the determination of the J/ψ branching ratios via $\psi' \to \pi^+\pi^- J/\psi$, $J/\psi \to l^+l^-$ can test $e - \mu$ universality, since here we are free of QED background. Using:

$$\psi' \to \pi^+\pi^- J/\psi$$
$$\hookrightarrow l^+l^- \quad (I)$$
$$\hookrightarrow \text{anything} \quad (II)$$

we can express the J/ψ branching ratios as:

$$B(J/\psi \to l^+l^-) = \frac{N_l^{prod}}{N_J^{prod}} = \frac{N_l^{obs}/(\varepsilon_l^{MC} A_l^{fit})}{N_J^{obs}/(\varepsilon_J^{MC} A_J^{fit})}.$$

The number of observed events N^{obs}, the acceptance ε^{MC}, the efficiency of the filter A^{filt} and the number of events produced in the different channels are shown in table 2.

	$J/\psi \to e^+e^-$	$\to \mu^+\mu^-$	$\to$ anything
N^{obs}	1127	1020	35704
ε^{MC}	25.35%	27.26 %	48.77%
A^{filt}	100.0%	84.7%	98.5%
N^{prod}	4446	4418	74324

Table 2.

So the branching ratios for $J/\psi \to \mu^+\mu^-$ and $J/\psi \to e^+e^-$ are:

$$Br(J/\psi \to \mu^+\mu^-) = (5.94 \pm 0.19 \pm 0.18)\%$$
$$Br(J/\psi \to e^+e^-) = (5.98 \pm 0.18 \pm 0.20)\%$$

Decay channel	M_ξ MeV/c^2	Γ_ξ MeV/c^2	$Br(J/\psi \to \gamma\xi)\times$ $Br(\xi \to$ final state$)$
$\xi \to K^+K^-$	2228 ± 9	27^{+23}_{-20}	$(3.5^{+1.4}_{-1.3}) \times 10^{-5}$
$\xi \to K_s^0 K_s^0$	2229 ± 8	21^{+30}_{-18}	$(2.3^{+1.1}_{-0.9}) \times 10^{-5}$
$\xi \to p\bar{p}$	2236 ± 4	18^{+12}_{-10}	$(1.9 \pm 0.6) \times 10^{-5}$

Table 3. $\xi(2230)$ results.

We can see that B_e and B_μ are within errors the same. Assuming $e - \mu$ universality,

$$Br(J/\psi \to l^+l^-) = (5.96 \pm 0.14 \pm 0.20)\%.$$

The results of these two measurements are in agreement and have already been given. These values for B_e and B_μ are in good agreement with the MARK III measurement, and the partial and total widths are much closer to the 1992 PDG data than to the old measurements. The present results significantly lower the uncertainties on these quantities.

4. Study of the $\xi(2230)$.

Although fixed target experiments found the struction at 2.2 GeV, only MARK III has observed the $\xi(2.2)$ and measured its mass and width and the branching ratios $\xi(2.2) \to K_s^0 K_s^0$ and $\xi(2.2) \to K^+K^-$ [3]; no other group in e^+e^- collision experiments have found such a narrow *resonance*. We have observed the $\xi(2.2)$ in the decay channels $J/\psi \to \gamma K^+K^-$, $\gamma K_s^0 K_s^0$ and $\gamma p\bar{p}$.

From the distributions of the invariant mass of K^+K^-, $K_s^0 K_s^0$ and $p\bar{p}$ in J/ψ radiative decays, we can see a very clear signal near 2.2 GeV. The mass m_ξ, decay width Γ_ξ, and the product of the branching ratios for $(J/\psi \to \gamma\xi)$ and $(\xi \to$ final state$)$ are given by fits and shown in Table 3:

It is easy to understand that (1) the ξ does exist in J/ψ radiative decays $J/\psi \to \gamma\xi$, $\xi \to K^+K^-$ and $J/\psi \to \gamma\xi$, $\xi \to K_s^0 K_s^0$; (2) the mass and width of the ξ that we measured are consistent with the MARK III results; (3) we have found a new decay mode $\xi \to p\bar{p}$. What is the ξ? $s\bar{s}$? A 4-quark state? A glueball? These exciting questions need further study.

References

[1] BES Collaboration; J. Z. Bai et al, Nucl. Instr. Meth. **A344** (1994) 319
[2] Particle Data Group; K. Hikasa et al, Phys. Rev. **D45** (1992)
[3] R. M. Baltrusaitis et al, Phys. Rev. Lett. **56** (1986) 107
[4] J. Augustin et al, Phys. Rev. Lett. **60** (1988) 2238

Direct Measurement of the Pseudoscalar Decay Constant f_{D_s} from BES

Changchun Zhang[†‡]

† Institute of High Energy Physics, Chinese Academy of Sciences, Beijing

Representing the BES collaboration

Abstract

The Beijing Spectrometer (BES) experiment has collected a data sample corresponding to about $22.3\,pb^{-1}$ at center of mass energy 4.03 GeV, which is just above the threshold for $D_s \overline{D}_s$ production. This permits D_s reconstruction with excellent mass resolution by applying the beam-energy constraint to the D_s system. By investigating the system recoiling against a reconstructed D_s, a few candidates for D_s leptonic decay are identified. From these events, the value of the Pseudoscalar Decay Constant, f_{D_s}, is estimated.

1. Introduction

The pseudoscalar decay constants, f_p, for mesons containing heavy quark c or b are sensitive in testing the quark content and its behaviour in the meson[1]. Estimates of mixing and CP violation in B meson system require knowledge of f_B, and f_B may be estimated from Lattice Gauge calculations[2] if f_D or f_{Ds} is known. For many years, theorists have made strong efforts to calculate these decay constants, but large discrepencies remain between various approaches[3]. Previous measurements of f_{Ds} were made with some theoretical or experimental assumptions[4].

The partial leptonic decay width of D_s is written as[5]

$$\Gamma(D_s^+ \rightarrow \ell^+ \nu) = \frac{G_F^2 |V_{cs}|^2}{8\pi} f_{D_s}^2 m_{D_s} m_\ell^2 (1 - \frac{m_\ell^2}{m_{D_s}^2})^2. \tag{1}$$

where m_{D_s} is the D_s mass, m_ℓ the lepton mass, the CKM matrix element $V_{cs} = 0.974$, G_F the Fermi constant.

* Work supported in part by the National Natural Science Foundation of China

‡ E-mail: zhangcc@bepc5.ihep.ac.cn

The Beijing Spectrometer (BES) experiment has collected a data sample corresponding to about 22.3 pb^{-1} at 4.03 GeV, which is just above the threshold for $D_s \overline{D}_s$ production.[6] The BES detector is designed to identify electrons, photons, pions, kaons and muons[7].

2. D_s signal at $E_{cm} = 4.03$ GeV

Beam-constraint is imposed on momentum of D_s daughter tracks in a kinematic fitting in order to improve measured D_s mass resolution. One constraint, requiring missing mass equal to the reconstructed D_s tag mass, is used in this analysis.

The D_s signal is searched for in its three D_s decay modes as $D_s^+ \rightarrow \phi\pi^+, \overline{K}^{*0} K^+$ and $\overline{K}^0 K^+$, with $\phi \rightarrow K^+ K^-$, $\overline{K}^{*0} \rightarrow K^-\pi^+$ and $\overline{K}^0 \rightarrow \pi^+\pi^-$. A requirement on the difference between the D_s measured energy and the beam energy effectively suppresses the background from D decays. Mass cuts of ϕ, K^{*0} or K_s^0 further suppress the background.

The polar angle, $\theta_{\pi+}$ in the $\overline{K}^{*0}$ helicity frame, are calculated. Background is suppresed by the helicity angle cuts $|\cos\theta_{\pi+}| > 0.4$. In the K_s^0 case, a decay length ≥ 0.5 cm, decay alignment $cos\theta \geq 0.9$ in xy

BES RECORD: 14523,RUN: 3273,CM ENERGY: 4.03GeV

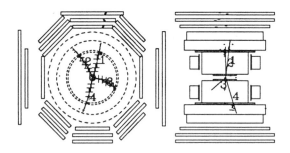

Figure 1. One candidate event for D_s muonic decay, where $D_s^+ \rightarrow \overline{K}^{*0}K^+$ with $\overline{K}^{*0} \rightarrow K^-\pi^+$ and $D_s^- \rightarrow \mu^-\nu$

plane and pion vertex in z direction $|\delta Z_{\pi^+\pi^-}| < 5cm$ are required. D_s signals for $\phi\pi$, $K^{*0}K$ and K^0K decay modes are clearly seen individually.

From the kinematic fit mass distribution, a Gaussian signal plus polynomial background and an enhancement near 1.94 GeV/c^2 from $D\overline{D}^*$ events is fitted. The total number of observed D_s tags, N_{tag}, from $\phi\pi$, $K^{*0}K$ and K^0K decay modes is found to be

$$N_{tag} = \sum_i N_i = 95.1 \pm 13.5. \qquad (2)$$

3. Search for D_s leptonic decays

The topology of $e^+e^- \rightarrow D_s^+ D_s^-$ events, searched as D_s leptonic decays, is $D_s^+ \rightarrow 3$ charged particles and $D_s^- \rightarrow \mu^- +$ missing ν, or $e^- +$ missing ν. Three D_s final states are reconstructed with tracks that are identified as consistent pions or kaons. Rejecting events that contain one or more identified photons would effectively suppress background to a considerable level. The recoil to reconstructed D_s tag must contain only one track with opposite charge, and must have an identification consistent with a muon or electron hypothesis. This procedure results in 2 candidates having muon tracks, and 1 candidate having an electron track. These 3 events sit right at D_s mass region and are accepted as D_s leptonic decay candidates. The missing momentum for these events points to the barrel part of the detector. No photon and extra charged track can be found in the detector.

Monte Carlo study shows that contamination from D production is negligible and the backgrounds mostly come from processes $D_s^+ \rightarrow \overline{K}_l^0 K^+$ and $D_s^+ \rightarrow \tau^+\nu$ with $\tau^+ \rightarrow \pi^+\nu$. Estimation of 0.04 and 0.6 background events for $D_s^+ \rightarrow \mu^+\nu$ and $D_s^+ \rightarrow \tau^+\nu$ with $\tau^+ \rightarrow \mu^+\nu\nu, e^+\nu\nu$, obtained from the tagged sample data with a single recoiling hadron and the lepton identificant fake rates, is used in this analysis.

4. Results and Discussion

Using maximum likelihood method and taking both branching fractions, $B_{\mu\nu}$ and $B_{\tau\nu}$, as the free parameters, we find that $B_r(D_s \rightarrow \mu\nu) = (1.8^{+5.2}_{-0.5})\%$ and $B_r(D_s \rightarrow \tau\nu) = (14^{+20}_{-5})\%$. If we imvoke the universality of $e-\mu-\tau$ and use the theoretical prediction of the ratio $B_{\tau\nu}/B_{\tau\nu}$, we find $B_r(D_s \rightarrow \mu\nu) = (1.4^{+1.2}_{-0.7})\%$ and the result of

$$f_{D_s} = (434^{+153+35}_{-133-33}) \; MeV.$$

The first error is statistical determined from fitting procedure, and the second error is the systematic caused by the uncertainties of tag efficiency, background estimation, and the D_s life time. Our measurement is model−independent and absolute, i.e. not affected by the branching fraction of $D_s^+ \rightarrow \phi\pi^+$. We do not make use of L_{int} and $\sigma(D_s\overline{D}_s)$.

5. Conclusion

From our D_s tag sample, a few D_s leptonic decay events with low level background are observed. The first measurement on $D_s^+ \rightarrow \tau^+\nu$, $\tau^+ \rightarrow \mu^+\nu\nu$ and it's branching fraction is made. Our value of f_{D_s}, from a direct measurement, is higher than the current theoretical expectations ranging from 150 to 360 MeV.[2,3]

We acknowledge the excellent support of BEPC machine physicists and the efforts of all the engineers and technicians who have participated in the construction and maintenance of BEPC machine and BES detector.

References

[1] J.L.Rosner, presented at Snowmass 90, Nov. 1990; C.H.Chang and Y.Q.Chen, Phys. Rev. D46 (1992) 3845 and Phys. Rev. D49 (1994) 3399;

[2] M.Witherell,talk at XVI inter. Symp., Cornell Univ., Aug. 1993; C Bernard et al., Phys.Rev. D38 (1988),3540; M.B.Gavela et al., Phys.Lett. B206 (1988); D.S. Du, Phys.Rev. D34 (1986) 3428;

[3] J.G. Bian and T.Huang, Modern Phys.Lett 8 (1993), 635; P.Cea et al., Phys.Lett. B 206 (1988) 691; P.Colangelo et.al, Phys.Rev.D43(1991), 3002.; D.Bortoletto and S.Stone, Phys.Rev.Lett. 65(1990) 2951; J.L.Rosner, Phys.Rev. D42 (1990) 3732; R.R.Mendel and H.D.Trottier, Phys.Lett. B231 (1989), 312;

[4] Y.Kubota et al.,talk at XVI inter. Symp., Aug. 1993, Cornell Univ.; S.Aoki et al., Prog. of Theor.Phys. 89(1993),131;

[5] K.Hikasa et al., Phys. Rev. D45(1992),1.

[6] C.H. Chang, talk at BES Meeting, Feb. 1990; C.C. Zhang and C.H. Chang, talk at the National workshop on Charm Physics (Beijing),Oct. 1990; M.Fero and W.Toki, Internal report, Jan. 1991.

[7] J.Z. Bai et al., NIM A344 (1994), 319; Phys.Rev.Lett., 69 (1992), 3021.; Zhipeng Zheng, invited talk at XVI inter. Symp. Cornell Univ., Aug. 1993.

*Paper presented at XXVII Int. Conf. on High Energy Physics: Session Pa-2
Glasgow, UK, 20–27 July 1994*

Direct Measurement of $B(D_S \to \phi\pi)$

Joseph M. Izen*

University of Texas at Dallas, Box 830688, Richardson, Texas   75083-0688, U.S.A

Representing the Beijing Spectrometer Collaboration†

Abstract

The Beijing Spectrometer (BES) has observed production of D_s mesons produced at $\sqrt{s}$ = 4.03 GeV at the Beijing Electron Collider (BEPC). BES reconstructs D_s mesons in the $\phi\pi$, $\overline{K}^{*0}K$, and $K_S^0 K$ final states. Two fully reconstructed $e^+e^- \to D_s^+ D_s^-$ events are used to determine $B(D_s \to \phi\pi)$ = 0.042 $^{+0.090}_{-0.015}$ $^{+0.017}_{-0.000}$ $\pm$ 0.005 (preliminary). This is the first direct, model-independent measurement of $B(D_s \to \phi\pi)$.

1 . Introduction

Many fixed target and e^+e^- experiments have observed inclusive production of D_s mesons, and the branching fractions of many decays are known relative to $D_s^+ \to \phi\pi^+$ [1]. Determining the D_s absolute branching fraction scale from these measurements has required theoretical input. Either the number of observed decays is normalized by an *estimate* of the D_s production, or a *theoretical estimate* of the ratio $\Gamma(D_s^+ \to \phi e^+ v)/\Gamma(D^+ \to K^{*0}e^+ v)$ plus the measured D_s and D^+ lifetimes are used to relate $B(D_s^+ \to \phi\pi^+)$ to $B(D^+ \to K^-\pi^+\pi^+)$. Published $B_{\phi\pi}$ results range from 0.031–0.051, despite the agreement for $B(D_s^+ \to \phi e^+ v)/B(D_s^+ \to \phi\pi^+)$ (0.49–0.61) from which they are derived.

In this measurement, $D_s^+ D_s^-$ pairs were produced exclusively in e^+e^- annihilation just above threshold. Reconstructing a D_s^+ (a *single tag*) insures the presence of a D_s^-. The frequency with which the second D_s is reconstructed (*double tagged*) was used to obtain a direct measurement of $B(D_s^+ \to \phi\pi^+)$

2 . Data Set

This analysis is based on 21.6 pb^{-1} recorded by the BES detector [2]. The BEPC was operated at $\sqrt{s}$ = 4.03 GeV where the coupled-channel model predicts a $\sigma(e^+e^- \to D_s^+ D_s^-)$ maximum of ~750 pb [3].

*E-mail: joe@utdallas.edu
†Collaborating Institutions: Institute of High Energy Physics, Beijing, Boston Univ., California Inst. of Technology, Colorado State University, Massachusetts Inst. of Technology, Stanford Linear Accelerator Center, Univ. of Hawaii, Univ. California at Irvine, Univ. of Texas at Dallas, Univ. of Washington at Seattle.
‡Reference to a state also implies its charge conjugate.

3 . Measurement of $\sigma_{D_s^+ D_s^-} \cdot B_{\phi\pi}$

BES reconstructs $\phi\pi$, $\overline{K}^{*0}K$, and $K_S^0 K$ single tags; however, just the first was used to estimate $\sigma \cdot B$ because this channel has the lowest background. Candidates were selected by applying event vertex, track quality, and fiducial cuts ($cos\theta$ < 0.85). Kaons were identified by time of flight and/or dE/dx ($\chi_K^2 < \chi_\pi^2$). A resonance cut $|M_{KK} - M_\phi|$ < 18 MeV and an energy cut, $|E_{KK\pi} - E_{beam}|$ < 50 MeV were applied. The beam constrained mass ($\sqrt{E_{beam}^2 - p_{KK\pi}^2}$) distribution in Fig. 1 shows an excess of 47 $\pm$ 12 events at the D_s mass. The relation $\sigma_{D_s^+ D_s^-} \cdot B_{\phi\pi} = N_{\phi\pi} / 2\varepsilon_{\phi\pi}\int Ldt$ gives $\sigma_{D_s^+ D_s^-} \cdot B_{\phi\pi}$ =

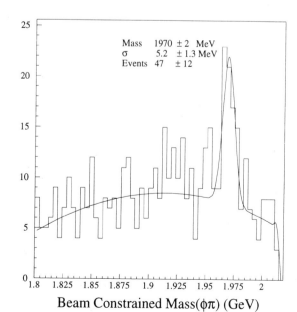

Mass	1970	± 2 MeV
σ	5.2	± 1.3 MeV
Events	47	± 12

Beam Constrained Mass($\phi\pi$) (GeV)

Figure 1. Beam constrained mass of $D_s^+ \to \phi\pi^+$ single tag candidates.

$(9.6 \pm 2.4 \pm 1.0)\ pb$ (preliminary).

4. Measurement of $B_{\phi\pi}$

Double tags were reconstructed using the $\phi\pi$, $\overline{K}^{*0}K$, and $K_s^0 K$ channels. Tracks were required to be consistent (>1% probability) with their assigned hypotheses. Resonance mass cuts of ± 18, ± 50, and $\pm 20\ MeV$ were used for the ϕ, $\overline{K}^{*0}$, and K_s^0 respectively, and a helicity angle cut $|cos\theta_{K^*\to K\pi}| > 0.4$ was required for $\overline{K}^{*0}$s. Candidate events were kinematically constrained to $(E, \vec{p})=(\sqrt{s}, \vec{0})$, and an equal-mass constraint was applied to the tags. The 5-C fit mass distribution in Fig 2. has two candidates in the signal region. Fig. 3 shows a display of one of the candidates. The same two events were selected in confirming analyses without kinematic fits. Low mass regions from the 5-C fit and confirming analyses and from Monte Carlo studies led to a background estimate of 0.2 ± 0.1 events. Using:

$$B_{\phi\pi} = 2(N_{double} / \sum_{modes\ i,j} b_i b_j \varepsilon_{ij}) / (N_{single} / \varepsilon_{single})$$

with $b_i \equiv B_{D_s\to mode\ i} / B_{\phi\pi}$ gives the likelihood function shown in Fig. 4 and the preliminary result:

$$B_{\phi\pi} = \ 0.042 \ {}^{+0.090}_{-0.015} \ {}^{+0.017}_{-0.000} \ \pm 0.005$$
$$\text{stat.} \quad \text{vary cuts} \quad \text{vary b.g.}$$

5. Discussion

This first direct measurement of $B_{\phi\pi}$ is consistent with previous indirect measurements. The large statistical errors reflect a cross section 2-3 times lower than expected. Uncertainties may be reduced by the use of more decay channels; however, further running at $\sqrt{s} = 4.03$ GeV or

above $D_s^* D_s$ threshold is needed to better the precision reported for indirect methods.

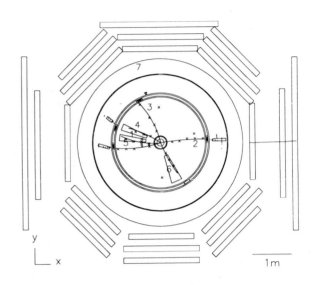

Figure 3. Double tag candidate. $D_S \to \phi\pi$: 4 K^-, 1 K^+, 6 π^- vs. $D_S \to K^{*0}K$: 3 K^-, 2 K^+, 5 π^+

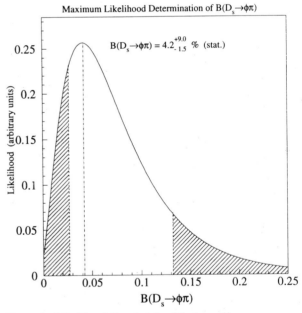

Figure 4. Likelihood function for B($D_s^+ \to \phi\pi^+$)

References

[1] Particle Data Group,Phys. Rev. **D**50, (1994)
[2] M.H.Ye, Z.P. Zheng, Proc. of the 1989 Intl. Symp. on Lepton and Photon Int. at High Energies, p. 122
[3] W.S. Lockman, "*D* and D_S Production in the Range $3.8 < \sqrt{s} < 4.5$ GeV", Mark III memo, March 30, 1987 E. Eichten, *et al.*, Phys. Rev. **D**21, 203 (1980)

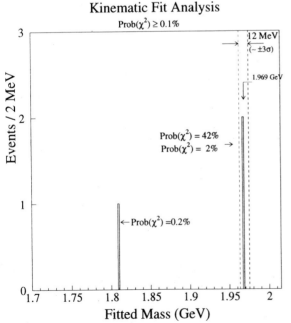

Figure 2. Fit (5-C) mass distribution of double-tag candidates.

Paper presented at XXVII Int. Conf. on High Energy Physics: Session Pa-2
Glasgow, UK, 20–27 July 1994

Recent Results in Charm Semileptonic Decays

R K Kutschke

Department of Physics, University of California
Santa Barbara, CA 93016, USA

Representing the CLEO Collaboration

Abstract

New results in the field of charm semileptonic decays will be surveyed. Most importantly, there is a preliminary, new measurement of the absolute branching fraction for the decay $D^0 \rightarrow X e^+ \nu_e$.

1. Introduction

The measurements reviewed in this paper were made using the CLEO II and ARGUS detectors, 4π sollenoidal spectrometers which operate at $e^+ e^-$ storage rings with $E_{CM} \approx 10.58$ GeV. The charm hadrons studied here were created by the process $e^+ e^- \rightarrow c\bar{c}$ followed by fragmentation (continuum production).

The signature of charm continuum production is that events have a two jet topology and that charm hadrons are produced with high momentum. Typically the charm hadron direction is almost parallel to the thrust axis of the event. Also, many of the charm mesons come from the decay chains, $D^* \rightarrow D\pi$ and $D_s^{*+} \rightarrow D_s^+ \gamma$. In these cases, one can use a variant of the well known D^*-trick to dramatically improve the signal to background ratio. To illustrate this, consider the decay chain $D_s^{*+} \rightarrow D_s^+ \gamma$, $D_s^+ \rightarrow \eta \ell^+ \nu$, for which one can define the mass difference $M(\eta \ell^+ \gamma) - M(\eta \ell)$. Although the unobserved ν is included in neither combination, the spectrum of this mass difference remains peaked, albeit less strongly peaked than for a fully reconstructed mode of the D_s^+.

Taken together these properties allow one to select efficiently, and with a good signal to background ratio, events which contain charm hadrons. Moreover they provide constraints from which one can recover some of the information carried away by the unobserved neutrino. Some of the CLEO analyses, for example,

estimate the direction of the charm hadron by assuming that it is parallel to the thrust axis of the event. Up to a quadratic ambiguity, this allows one to reconstruct q^2, the invariant mass squared of the $\ell\nu$ system. Similarly, one can measure all of the decay angles in a decay chain such as $\Lambda_c \rightarrow \Lambda e^+ \nu$, $\Lambda \rightarrow p\pi^-$. Given measurements of q^2 and of all of the decay angles, one can fit a multi-dimensional distribution (in q^2 and the decay angles) to obtain information about the form factors in the Λ_c decay. It is important to emphasize that none of the data presented here is sensitive to the shape of the form factors: the best that one can do, at present, is to assume a q^2 dependence for the form factors and then to measure the relative strength of the different form factors in a decay.

The form factor measurements presented here were made using a method, pioneered by E691, to fit observed (not efficiency corrected) multi-dimensional distributions. In this method, the observed distribution is described by the convolution of the physics function with the full detector response. The convolution is done by re-weighting Monte Carlo events, a method which deals both with large smearing of kinematic variables and with sharp changes in efficiency.

Because of space constraints, some information, either from previous experiments or from theory, has been quoted or alluded to without a proper reference. All of the proper references can be found in the papers in the bibliography.

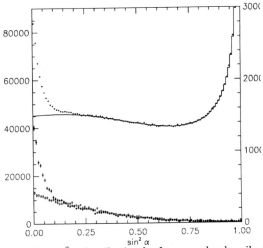

Figure 1. The $\sin^2 \alpha$ distribution for four samples described in the text. The scale on the left hand side of the figure is for the upper two distributions while that on the right hand side is for the lower two distributions.

2. $\mathbf{B(D^0 \rightarrow Xe^+ \nu_e)}$

In recent years there have been significant improvements in the measurements of branching fractions for exclusive charm semileptonic decays. Measurements of inclusive charm semileptonic branching fractions, however, have not kept pace: the 1994 PDG averages are still dominated by 1985 Mark III results with 10 to 15% uncertainties.

Recently, the CLEO collaboration has measured $B(D^0 \rightarrow Xe^+ \nu_e)$ using a method pioneered by HRS. When a D^* is created via continuum production, its momentum is nearly parallel to the thrust axis of the event. Because the Q value of the decay $D^{*+} \rightarrow D^0 \pi^+$ is small, the lab frame angle between the π^+ and the thrust axis, α, is also small. The upper points in Fig. 1 show the distribution of $\sin^2 \alpha$ for π^+ mesons with $0.225 \leq p_{\pi^+} < 0.450$ GeV. The shape of the distribution for π^+ mesons which do not come from the decay $D^{*+} \rightarrow D^0 \pi^+$ is shown as the solid outline histogram [1]. The excess near $\sin^2 \alpha = 0$ is due to the decay $D^{*+} \rightarrow D^0 \pi^+$ and provides a measure of the number of D^0 mesons produced. The solid data points in the lower part of the figure show the distribution of $\sin^2 \alpha$ when there is also a positron within a $37°$ cone around the π^+. The positron must have momentum above 0.7 GeV. The hollow data points show the shape of the $\sin^2 \alpha$ distribution for background processes. The excess near $\sin^2 \alpha = 0$ is due to the decay chain $D^{*+} \rightarrow D^0 \pi^+$, $D^0 \rightarrow Xe^+ \nu$. The branching fraction $B(D^0 \rightarrow Xe^+ \nu_e)$ is found by taking the the area between the lower two curves, dividing by the area between the upper two curves and then correcting for backgrounds and efficiency. This gives a preliminary result of,

$$B(D^0 \rightarrow X^- e^+ \nu_e) = (6.97 \pm 0.18 \pm 0.30)\%. \quad (1)$$

The uncertainties in this measurement represent a significant improvement over those in the 1994 PDG value, $(7.7 \pm 1.2)\%$.

3. $\mathbf{B(D_s^+ \rightarrow \eta \ell^+ \nu)}$ and $\mathbf{B(D_s^+ \rightarrow \eta' \ell^+ \nu)}$

Last year E653 obtained the first evidence for the decay $D_s^+ \rightarrow (\eta, \eta')\ell^+ \nu$. They were, however, unable to separate the contributions from the η and the η'. This year CLEO has observed each of these decays separately [2]. They present preliminary results of,

$$R_\eta = \frac{B(D_s^+ \rightarrow \eta \, \ell^+ \nu)}{B(D_s^+ \rightarrow \phi \, \ell^+ \nu)} = 1.74 \pm 0.34 \pm 0.24$$

$$R_{\eta'} = \frac{B(D_s^+ \rightarrow \eta' \ell^+ \nu)}{B(D_s^+ \rightarrow \phi \, \ell^+ \nu)} = 0.71^{+0.19}_{-0.18}{}^{+0.08}_{-0.10}. \quad (2)$$

They also report the pseudoscalar to vector ratio for D_s^+ semileptonic decay,

$$\frac{B(D_s^+ \rightarrow (\eta + \eta') \, \ell^+ \nu)}{B(D_s^+ \rightarrow \phi \ell^+ \nu)} = 2.46 \pm 0.39 \pm 0.26. \quad (3)$$

In the non-strange sector the corresponding ratio is,

$$\frac{B(D \rightarrow K \ell^+ \nu)}{B(D \rightarrow K^* \ell^+ \nu)} = 1.75 \pm 0.15. \quad (4)$$

Up to phase space corrections these two numbers should be equal to each other, which they are to within 1.5 standard deviations.

In the past, CLEO has reported an estimate for the scale of the D_s^+ branching fractions by making the assumption $\Gamma(D_s^+ \rightarrow \phi e^+ \nu) = \Gamma(D \rightarrow K^* e^+ \nu)$. This gave [3] $B(D_s^+ \rightarrow \phi e^+ \nu) = (2.74 \pm 0.36)\%$ and $B(D_s^+ \rightarrow \phi \pi) = (5.1 \pm 0.4 \pm 0.4 \pm 0.7)\%$. A theoretically more robust assumption is that $\Gamma(D_s^+ \rightarrow Xe^+ \nu) = \Gamma(D^0 \rightarrow Xe^+ \nu)$, from which one obtains,

$$B(D_s^+ \rightarrow \phi e^+ \nu) =$$
$$\frac{(1 - f_{cs} - f_{misc})}{1 + R_\eta + R_{\eta'}} B(D^0 \rightarrow Xe^+ \nu)\frac{\tau_{D_s^+}}{\tau_{D^0}}. \quad (5)$$

Here $f_{cs}(\approx 0.05 \pm 0.01)$ is an estimate for the the fraction of Cabibbo suppressed D_s^+ decay modes and $f_{misc}(\approx 0.06 \pm 0.04)$ is an estimate for the fraction of miscellaneous modes, such as $f_0(975)$. Combining the above results with previous CLEO results and with E687 lifetime measurements gives,

$$B(D_s^+ \rightarrow \phi e^+ \nu) = (2.06 \pm 0.33)\%$$
$$B(D_s^+ \rightarrow \phi \pi^+) = (3.82 \pm 0.74)\%. \quad (6)$$

Finally, CLEO reports,

$$\frac{B(D_s^+ \rightarrow \eta' e^+ \nu)}{B(D_s^+ \rightarrow \eta e^+ \nu)} = 0.41 \pm 0.13 \pm 0.05. \quad (7)$$

This can be compared with the previously measured ratio,

$$\frac{B(D_s^+ \to \eta'\rho^+)}{B(D_s^+ \to \eta\rho^+)} = 1.20 \pm 0.33, \qquad (8)$$

which is far from the prediction of factorization, ≈ 0.3.

4. Form Factors Ratios for $\mathbf{D_s^+ \to \phi\ell^+\nu}$

The decay $D_s^+ \to \phi e^+\nu$ is described by three form factors, denoted by $A_1(q^2)$, $A_2(q^2)$, and $V(q^2)$. Using the method sketched in the introduction, the CLEO collaboration has measured the following ratios of the form factors [4],

$$R_2 = \frac{A_2(0)}{A_1(0)} = 1.5 \pm 0.5 \pm 0.3$$

$$R_V = \frac{V(0)}{A_1(0)} = 0.9 \pm 0.6 \pm 0.3. \qquad (9)$$

From this they compute, $\Gamma_L/\Gamma_T = 1.0 \pm 0.3 \pm 0.2$. Within these relatively large errors, the above results and previous measurements of the same quantities are consistent with each other. Factorization arguments suggest that R_2 and R_V should be the same for this decay as they are for the decay $D \to K^*\ell^+\nu$. However the experimental results do not provide strong support for this argument — the values only agree at about the two standard deviation level.

5. First Observation of $\mathbf{\Xi_c^+ \to \Xi^0 e^+\nu_e}$

CLEO has reported the first observation of the decay, $\Xi_c^+ \to \Xi^0 e^+\nu_e$. In the same paper they also report on the previously observed decay $\Xi_c^0 \to \Xi^- e^+\nu_e$. Their preliminary results are [5],

$$\sigma(\Xi_c^0) \cdot B(\Xi_c^0 \to \Xi^- e^+\nu_e) = (0.63 \pm 0.12 \pm 0.10) \text{ pb}$$

$$\sigma(\Xi_c^+) \cdot B(\Xi_c^+ \to \Xi^0 e^+\nu_e) = (1.55 \pm 0.33 \pm 0.25) \text{ pb},$$

where $\sigma(\Xi_c^0)$ is a shorthand for $\sigma(e^+e^- \to \Xi_c^0 X)$. If one assumes that $\Gamma(\Xi_c^+ \to \Xi^0 e^+\nu) = \Gamma(\Xi_c^0 \to \Xi^- e^+\nu)$ and $\sigma(\Xi_c^+) = \sigma(\Xi_c^0)$, then the above results can be used to determine the ratio of the lifetimes,

$$\frac{\tau(\Xi_c^+)}{\tau(\Xi_c^0)} = \frac{B(\Xi_c^+ \to \Xi^0 e^+\nu)}{B(\Xi_c^0 \to \Xi^- e^+\nu)} = 2.46 \pm 0.70^{+0.33}_{-0.23}.$$

This measurement is in agreement with previous, direct measurements of the lifetime ratio by E687 (4.06 ± 1.26) and NA32 (2.44 ± 1.68).

6. $\mathbf{\Lambda_c^+ \to \Lambda e^+\nu_e}$

In the limit that the mass of the electron can be neglected and that the charm quark is heavy compared

with Λ_{QCD}, the decay $\Lambda_c^+ \to \Lambda e^+\nu_e$ is described by two form factors, denoted by $f_1(q^2)$ and $f_2(q^2)$. Körner and Krämer suggest that the q^2 dependence of both of these form factors should be given by a dipole form and that $f_2(q^2) < f_1(q^2)$. Using the method sketched in the introduction, the CLEO collaboration has made the first measurement of the ratio of these two form factors [6],

$$f_2/f_1 = -0.33 \pm 0.16 \pm 0.15. \qquad (10)$$

An alternative method for analyzing this decay is to measure various asymmetries in the decay angle distributions. The ARGUS collaboration selects Λ candidates which come from the decay chain $\Lambda_c^+ \to \Lambda\ell^+\nu$, $\Lambda \to p\pi^-$, and then looks at the distribution of $\cos\theta_\Lambda$, where θ_Λ is the angle between the p direction in the Λ rest frame and the Λ momentum in the Λ_c^+ rest frame. This distribution has the form, $\frac{d\Gamma}{d\cos\theta_\Lambda} \propto (1 + \alpha_{\Lambda_c}\alpha_\Lambda\cos\theta_\Lambda)$, where α_Λ is the well known Λ asymmetry parameter and where α_{Λ_c} is the asymmetry parameter for the decay, $\Lambda_c^+ \to \Lambda\ell^+\nu$. They obtain [7] $\alpha_{\Lambda_c} = -0.91 \pm 0.42 \pm 0.25$, which is in agreement with a previous CLEO result of $-0.89^{+0.17+0.09}_{-0.11-0.05}$. In principle one can infer the form factor ratio from this measurement but the sensitivity is very poor.

7. Conclusions

In the past year there has been an important improvement in the precision of the measurement of of the branching fraction $B(D^0 \to Xe^+\nu)$. There have also been several first observations, $D_s^+ \to \eta\ell^+\nu$, $D_s^+ \to \eta'\ell^+\nu$ and $\Xi_c^+ \to \Xi^0 e^+\nu$. In addition, there has been a first measurement of the form factor ratio in the decay $\Lambda_c \to \Lambda e^+\nu$. All of the main semileptonic decay modes in the D_s^+ sector have now been observed and one can ask if the patterns observed in the non-strange sector are reproduced in the decays of the D_s^+.

References

[1] D. S. Akerib et. al. (CLEO Collab.), Phys. Rev. Lett. **71** (1993) 3070.

[2] M. Battle et. al. (CLEO Collab.), "Measurement of the Ratios $\mathcal{B}(D_s^+ \to \eta\ell^+\nu)/\mathcal{B}(D_s^+ \to \phi\ell^+\nu)$ and $\mathcal{B}(D_s^+ \to \eta'\ell^+\nu)/\mathcal{B}(D_s^+ \to \phi\ell^+\nu)$", CLEO CONF 94-18. Also GLS0381.

[3] F. Butler et. al. (CLEO Collab.), Phys. Lett. **B324** (1994) 255.

[4] P. Avery et. al. (CLEO Collab.), Preprint CLNS 94/1290. Also GLS0250.

[5] J. P. Alexander et. al. (CLEO Collab.), Preprint CLNS 94/1288. Also GLS0245.

[6] J. Dominick et. al. (CLEO Collab), "Form Factor Ratio Measurement in $\Lambda_c^+ \to \Lambda e^+\nu_e$", CLEO CONF 94-19. Also GLS0253.

[7] H. Albrecht et. al. (ARGUS Collab.), Phys. Lett. **B326** (1994) 320. Also GLS0194.

A Lattice Study of Decays of Heavy-light Mesons

D G Richards[‡]

Department of Physics and Astronomy, The University of Edinburgh,
The King's Buildings, Mayfield Road, Edinburgh EH9 3JZ, UK

On behalf of the UKQCD Collaboration

Abstract

We present results for the leptonic and semi-leptonic decay matrix elements of heavy-light mesons obtained in quenched QCD, using an $O(a)$-improved fermion action. We find our best results for the decay constants of the B and D mesons are $f_D = 185 \; ^{+\;3}_{-\;4}(\text{stat}) \; ^{+\;42}_{-\;7}(\text{syst})$ MeV and $f_B = 160 \; ^{+\;6}_{-\;6} \; ^{+\;53}_{-\;19}$ MeV respectively. The non-scaling corrections are substantial; of order 30 % for f_D and of order 10 % for f_B.

We compute the Isgur-Wise function by studying semi-leptonic decays of the form $P \rightarrow P' l \bar{\nu}$, where P and P' are heavy-light pseudoscalar mesons. We find a value for the slope parameter of $\rho^2 = 0.9 \; ^{+\;2}_{-\;2} \; ^{+\;4}_{-\;2}$. Finally, we present results for the leading-order matrix element for the decay $B \rightarrow K^* \gamma$. We find results for the on-shell form factor $T_1(q^2{=}0)$ to be consistent (in the Standard Model) with the recent CLEO experimental branching ratio.

1. Introduction

The leptonic and semi-leptonic decays of heavy-light pseudoscalar mesons provide a crucial laboratory for the determination of the parameters of the Standard Model. However, a necessary prerequisite is a quantitative understanding of strong-interaction effects, characterised by the pseudoscalar decay constants, f_P, in the case of leptonic decays, and by the semi-leptonic form factors in the case of the semi-leptonic decays. Lattice QCD enables an *ab initio* investigation of these effects. This paper provides a compendium of the results of the *UKQCD Collaboration* on heavy-light physics.

The paper is arranged as follows. Section 2 contains our results for the determination of f_B and f_D. Section 3 contains our results for the semi-leptonic decays of the B and D mesons. Finally, in section 4 we discuss the rare decay $B \rightarrow K^* \gamma$, which does not occur at tree-level, and thus provides an extremely subtle test of the

Standard Model. We end this introduction with a brief description of the simulation.

1.1. Simulation details

Our principal results are obtained from a simulation in the quenched approximation on a $24^3 \times 48$ lattice at $\beta = 6.2$, using 60 gauge field configurations. The quark propagators are computed using an $O(a)$-improved Wilson fermion action [1], with "rotated" operators [2]. We find an inverse lattice spacing $a^{-1} = 2.73(5)$GeV, obtained by measuring the string tension. Full details of the simulation are contained in ref. [3].

2. Leptonic Decays

The finite lattice spacing employed in our simulations precludes the study of the B-meson directly, since it would be subject to uncontrolled discretisation errors. Instead, we chose to investigate the decays of heavy-

‡ E-mail: dgr@th.ph.ed.ac.uk

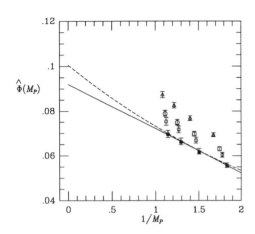

Figure 1. The data for $\hat{\Phi}(M_P)$ plotted against the inverse meson mass. The open symbols denote points with $\kappa_l < \kappa_{\rm crit}$, whereas full symbols denote those extrapolated to $\kappa_{\rm crit}$. The solid line represents the linear fit using the three heaviest meson masses, whereas the dashed curve results from a quadratic fit to all four.

light mesons containing a quark with a mass around that of the charm quark, and to extrapolate our results to the physical b-quark mass. In this study we have used four values of the heavy-quark mass. To perform the extrapolation, we appeal to the Heavy-Quark Effective Theory; in the heavy-quark limit, the quantity $f_P\sqrt{M_P}$ scales like

$$f_P\sqrt{M_P} = {\rm const.} \times [\alpha_s(M_P)]^{-2/\beta_0} , \quad M_P \longrightarrow \infty. \quad (1)$$

where f_P is the pseudoscalar decay constant, and M_P the corresponding pseudoscalar mass. Thus in figure 1 we plot the quantity

$$\hat{\Phi}(M_P) \equiv (\alpha_s(M_P)/\alpha_s(M_B))^{2/\beta_0} Z_A^{-1} f_P\sqrt{M_P}, \quad (2)$$

where Z_A is the matching coefficient. To quantify the non-scaling effects in f_P, we fit (2) to linear and quadratic functions of $1/M_P$. The fit reveals $O(1/M_P)$ corrections to f_P of approximately 10% at M_B and 30% at M_D, in agreement with previous analyses, and we obtain for our best results:

$$f_D = 185 \; ^{+\,4}_{-\,3}({\rm stat}) \; ^{+\,42}_{-\,7}({\rm syst}) \; {\rm MeV}$$

$$f_B = 160 \; ^{+\,6}_{-\,6} \; ^{+\,53}_{-\,19} \; {\rm MeV}$$

$$\frac{f_{D_s}}{f_D} = 1.18 \; ^{+\,2}_{-\,2}; \frac{f_{B_s}}{f_B} = 1.22 \; ^{+\,4}_{-\,3}. \quad (3)$$

Full details of our study are contained in ref. [4].

3. Semi-leptonic Decays

We have studied the matrix elements appropriate both to the semi-leptonic decays $D \to K$ and $D \to K^*$,

and to the decays $B \to D(D^*)$. The former decays involve CKM matrix elements that are well constrained in the Standard Model by experiment, and provide a "benchmark" for our lattice calculation. Full details of this study are provided in ref. [5]. In this paper we will concentrate on the decays $B \to D(D^*)$.

In the limit of exact heavy-quark symmetry, the six form factors for the decays $B \to D$ and $B \to D^*$ are given by the universal Isgur-Wise function $\xi(\omega = v \cdot v')$, where v and v' are the four-velocities of the ingoing and outgoing mesons. This function is absolutely normalised: $\xi(1) = 1$. We obtain $\xi(\omega)$ by studying decays of the form $P \to P'l\bar{\nu}$ where P and P' are heavy-light pseudoscalar mesons. These processes are described by matrix elements of the heavy-quark vector current $\bar{Q}'\gamma^\mu Q$, which can be decomposed in terms of two form factors, $h^+_{Q\to Q'}(\omega)$ and $h^-_{Q\to Q'}(\omega)$,

$$\frac{\langle P'(\vec{p}')|\bar{Q}'\gamma^\mu Q|P(\vec{p})\rangle}{\sqrt{M_P M_{P'}}} =$$
$$(v + v')^\mu h^+_{Q\to Q'}(\omega) + (v - v')^\mu h^-_{Q\to Q'}(\omega). \quad (4)$$

For heavy quarks of finite mass, there are corrections relating the form factors to $\xi(\omega)$. For the case of $h^+(\omega)$ they are parametrised as

$$h^+(\omega) = (1 + \beta^+(\omega) + \gamma^+(\omega))\xi(\omega) , \quad (5)$$

where $\beta^+(\omega)$ and $\gamma^+(\omega)$ contain the radiative and non-scaling corrections respectively. We employ the same values of the heavy-quark mass as those used in the study of leptonic decays. We obtain the Isgur-Wise function from $h^+(\omega)$, correcting for $\beta^+(\omega)$ [6]. We combine data at different values of the heavy-quark mass in our analysis; we find no evidence for non-scaling effects in our data.

We fit the measured $\xi(\omega)$ to $s\xi_{NR}(\omega)$ where

$$\xi_{NR}(\omega) \equiv \frac{2}{\omega + 1} \exp\left(-(2\rho^2 - 1)\frac{\omega - 1}{\omega + 1}\right) \quad (6)$$

and s accounts for the uncertainty in the normalisation of our data. ρ^2 is the slope of the Isgur-Wise function at zero recoil, for which we obtain

$$\rho^2_{u,d} = 0.9 \; ^{+\,2}_{-\,2}({\rm stat}) \; ^{+\,4}_{-\,2}({\rm syst}) \quad (7)$$

$$\rho^2_s = 1.2 \; ^{+\,2}_{-\,2}({\rm stat}) \; ^{+\,2}_{-\,1}({\rm syst}), \quad (8)$$

where u, d and s are the light-quark flavours.

The experimentally-measured decay rate is $dB(\bar{B} \to D^*l\bar{\nu})/d\omega$; we can use our determination of the Isgur-Wise function to perform a single-parameter fit to the data to extract V_{cb}. This is illustrated for CLEO-II data [7] in figure 2. Note that, though radiative corrections at $\omega = 1$ have been taken into account in the data, we otherwise assume exact heavy-quark symmetry

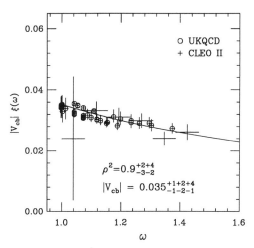

Figure 2. Least-χ^2 fits to CLEO II experimental data for $|V_{cb}| \, \xi(\omega)$, using the parametrisation $\xi_{NR}(\omega)$ with ρ^2 given by equation (7). The first error on $|V_{cb}|$ is experimental, the second from lattice statistical uncertainties, and the third from the lattice systematic errors on ρ^2.

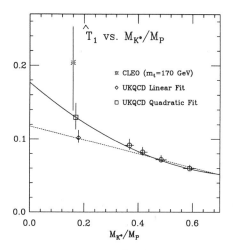

Figure 3. The scaling quantity $\hat{T}_1(q^2 = 0)$ as defined in the text. The dashed and solid lines are linear and quadratic fits in $1/M_P$ respectively. Also shown is the "experimental" determination using the CLEO data.

Acknowledgments

This research was supported by the UK Science and Engineering Research Council under grants GR/G 32779 and GR/J 21347, by the University of Edinburgh and by Meiko Limited. We are grateful to Edinburgh University Computing Service and, in particular, to Mike Brown for maintenance of service on the Meiko i860 Computing Surface. DGR acknowledges the support of the Particle Physics and Astronomy Research Council through an Advanced Fellowship.

in relating $\xi(\omega)$ to the experimentally measured form factors. The lattice determination of the $\bar{B} \to D^* l \bar{\nu}$ form factors is in progress.

4. Rare Decays

Excluding QCD contributions, the free quark decay $b \to s\gamma$ in the SM proceeds via the "penguin" diagrams. The charm and top quarks dominate, because the up quark contribution to the loop is suppressed by the small CKM factor $|V_{ub}V_{us}^*|$. The exclusive decay $B \to K^*\gamma$ has recently been measured by CLEO [8], who obtained $BR(B \to K^*\gamma) = (4.5 \pm 1.5 \pm 0.9) \times 10^{-5}$. The phenomenological importance of this process has encouraged the lattice study of the decay matrix elements [9, 10, 11]. The hadronisation ratio may be related to a single on-shell form factor: $T_1(q^2 = 0)$. In figure 3 we show $\hat{T}_1(q^2 = 0)$, defined by

$$\hat{T}_1 \equiv T_1(q^2 = 0) \left(\frac{M_P}{M_B} \right)^{3/2} \left(\frac{\alpha_s(M_P)}{\alpha_s(M_B)} \right)^{2/\beta_0} \quad (9)$$

which, assuming pole-dominance, scales in the limit of exact heavy-quark symmetry, together with linear and quadratic fits in $1/M_P$. Also shown is the "experimental" determination of the form-factor, using $m_t = 170$ GeV and $\tau_B = 1.5$ ps. Alternatively, using our determination of $T_1(0)$, we obtain

$$BR(B \to K^*\gamma) = \left(1.5 \pm 0.6 \, (\text{stat.}) \, {}^{+9}_{-8} \, (\text{sys.}) \right) \times 10^{-5} \quad (10)$$

consistent with the experimental branching ratio above.

References

[1] B. Sheikholeslami and R. Wohlert, Nucl. Phys. **B259** (1985) 572.

[2] G. Heatlie *et al.*, Nucl. Phys. **B352** (1991) 266.

[3] UKQCD Collaboration, C. Allton *et al.*, Nucl. Phys. **B407** (1993) 331; and Phys. Rev. **D49** (1994) 474.

[4] UKQCD Collaboration, R. M. Baxter *et al.*, Phys. Rev. **D49** (1994) 1594.

[5] UKQCD Collaboration, L. Lellouch *et al.*,, Edinburgh Preprint: 94/546, Southampton Preprint: 93/94-32.

[6] M. Neubert, Phys. Rev. **D46** (1992) 2212.

[7] "Semi-leptonic B Decays", S. Stone, in "B Decays", ed. S. Stone, 2nd Edition (World Scientific 1994).

[8] CLEO Collaboration, R. Ammar *et al.*, Phys. Rev. Lett. **71** (1993) 674.

[9] UKQCD Collaboration, K. C. Bowler *et al.*, Phys. Rev. Lett. **72** (1994) 1398; and Edinburgh Preprint 94/544, Southampton Preprint 93/94-29.

[10] C. Bernard, P. Hsieh, and A. Soni, Phys. Rev. Lett. **72** (1994) 1402.

[11] see talk by A. Abada, APE Collaboration, this conference.

Review of Hadronic Decays of Charm Hadrons

Milind V. Purohit

Princeton University
Princeton, NJ 08544
U. S. A.

Abstract

Recent results on the hadronic decays of charm are summarized. We begin with observations of charm baryon decays by EXCHARM and CLEO II and charm baryon and meson decays by E687. Next we discuss a search for wrong sign $D^0 \to K^+\pi^-\pi^0$ decays by CLEO II. Finally, we summarize the new limits on $D^0 - \overline{D}^0$ mixing and an observation of Doubly Cabibbo Suppressed Decays by E791.

1. Charm Baryon Decays

1.1. EXCHARM results on charm baryons

Traditionally charm baryons have been harder to observe and study because of their lower production rates. Experiment EXCHARM [1] overcomes this by using a baryon beam (neutrons) with a mean energy of 37 GeV incident on a carbon target. This is followed by a magnetic spectrometer (26 planes of PWC's) and Čerenkov counters for kaon and proton identification. In order to further reduce combinatoric backgrounds, decays with Λ and K_s^0 particles were selected where the subsequent $\Lambda \to p\pi$ and $K_s^0 \to \pi^+\pi^-$ decays serve as clean identifiers.

Significant peaks were seen in four different modes: 41 events over a background of 75 events in the decay $\Lambda_c^+ \to \Lambda\pi^+\pi^+\pi^-$ and 35 events over a background of 48 events in the decay $\Lambda_c^+ \to \overline{K}^0 p\pi^+\pi^-$ thus yielding the ratio

$$\frac{\Gamma(\Lambda_c^+ \to \overline{K}^0 p\pi^+\pi^-)}{\Gamma(\Lambda_c^+ \to \Lambda\pi^+\pi^+\pi^-)} = 2.4 \pm 1.0$$

Also, 27 events of the decay $\Xi_c^+ \to \overline{K}^0 pK^-\pi^+$ were seen over a background of 16 events and 27 events of the decay $\Xi_c^+ \to \Lambda K^-\pi^+\pi^+$ were seen over a background of

14 events leading to the ratio

$$\frac{\Gamma(\Xi_c^+ \to \overline{K}^0 pK^-\pi^+)}{\Gamma(\Xi_c^+ \to \Lambda K^-\pi^+\pi^+)} = 2.3 \pm 1.1$$

This is the first reported observation of the decay $\Xi_c^+ \to \overline{K}^0 pK^-\pi^+$. Of these decays, $(40\pm20)\%$ appear to come from the resonant mode $\Lambda \overline{K}^{*0}\pi^+$.

1.2. CLEO II results on charm baryons

Using their powerful electromagnetic detector to identify η decays CLEO II has observed [2] several Λ_c^+ decays into η and other particles: 109 ± 16 $\Lambda_c^+ \to \Lambda\eta\pi^+$ events, 53 ± 10 $\Lambda_c^+ \to p\overline{K}^0\eta$ events, 15 ± 5 $\Lambda_c^+ \to \Sigma^+\eta$ events and 46 ± 8 $\Lambda_c^+ \to K_s^0 K^+$ events. They obtain the branching ratios

$$\frac{\Gamma(\Lambda_c^+ \to \Lambda\eta\pi^+)}{\Gamma(\Lambda_c^+ \to pK^-\pi^+)} = 0.36 \pm 0.06 \pm 0.05$$

and

$$\frac{\Gamma(\Lambda_c^+ \to p\overline{K}^0\eta)}{\Gamma(\Lambda_c^+ \to pK^-\pi^+)} = 0.25 \pm 0.05 \pm 0.04$$

1.3. E687 results on charm baryons

The Ω_c^0 remains elusive because of its short lifetime (at least for most vertex-based experiments). E687 has succeeded in isolating Σ^+ decays of the Ω_c^0 using both the $p\pi^0$ and the $n\pi^+$ decays of the Σ^+ ([3]). In both cases, the neutral is not detected but confirmation of the neutron is sometimes possible. Using weighting to avoid double-counting solutions when the Σ^+ momentum is not known, E687 finds 40.7±8.5 events in the $\Omega_c^0 \rightarrow \Sigma^+ K^- K^- \pi^+$ mode at a mass of $(2699.6\pm1.2\pm1.5)$ MeV/c^2. This is lower than the mass measured by ARGUS $(2716\pm3\pm2$ MeV/c$^2)$ [4] but consistent with an earlier E687 measurement $(2705\pm3\pm2$ MeV/c$^2)$ [5].

2. Charm Meson Decays

2.1. E687 results

E687 have improved the precision of some charm decay measurements e.g., they find that

$$\frac{\Gamma(D^0 \rightarrow K^+ K^-)}{\Gamma(D^0 \rightarrow \pi^- \pi^+)} = 2.53 \pm 0.46 \pm 0.19$$

(see [6]). Among their many interesting results of this kind is a clean observation of 59±12 events in the $D_s^+ \rightarrow \pi^+\pi^-\pi^+$ decay mode. Similarly, they find that there are 40±7 and 24±5 signal events respectively in the D^+ and D_s^+ regions of the 5π mass plot. A preliminary Dalitz plot analysis of their 3π signal indicates that the f_0 component is dominant. Of course, they have to isolate the non-resonant component from the background due to the many possible broad resonances in order to conclude whether there is a significant contribution from the annihilation diagram. They can aid this analysis by using their 409±26 events in the $D_s^+ \rightarrow K^+ K^- \pi^+$ decay mode to establish the $f_0\pi^+$ branching fraction.

3. $D^0 - \overline{D}^0$ mixing

D^0-$\overline{D}^0$ mixing is expected to be very small in the standard model, with mixing rates predicted in the range 10^{-10} to 10^{-7}. This provides us with a large window to study effects beyond the standard model. For instance, recently Lawrence Hall and Steven Weinberg [7] have explored the consequences of an extension of the standard model involving charged Higgs bosons. They predict an extremely small amount of direct CP violation in neutral kaon decays and also very small CP violating effects in decays of B mesons. However, one testable prediction is a large amount ($\sim$ 0.2%) of $D^0 - \overline{D}^0$ mixing. Other models [8], [9] also predict large (relative to the standard model) $D^0 - \overline{D}^0$ mixing. These include supersymmetric models, models involving a fourth generation and models with left-right symmetry.

3.1. *Results of wrong-sign searches by CLEO II*

Experiments CLEO II and E791 have recently made significant progress towards obtaining limits on $D^0 - \overline{D}^0$ mixing. CLEO II has previously published a wrong sign signal in the $K\pi$ mode. (The result was a wrong sign signal with strength $(0.77\pm0.25\pm0.25)$% of the right sign signal [10]). However, they were unable to resolve this as mixing or Doubly Cabibbo Suppressed Decays (DCSD's) due to lack of lifetime information. More recently CLEO II has searched for a wrong-sign signal in the $D^0 \rightarrow K^+\pi^-\pi^0$ channel. In this mode they find no evidence of a signal ([11]):

$$\frac{\Gamma(D^0 \rightarrow K^+\pi^-\pi^0)}{\Gamma(D^0 \rightarrow K^-\pi^+\pi^0)} < 0.68\% \qquad \text{at the 90\% C.L.}$$

3.2. *E791 result on $D^0 - \overline{D}^0$ mixing*

The E791 detector has excellent lifetime sensitivity and the experiment has collected the largest reconstructed sample of charm decays. This allows them to separate a mixing signal, if any, from the doubly Cabibbo-suppressed decay which has the same final state particles by utilizing the different time dependence of the signal. Therefore the E791 collaboration has begun a determination of the amount of $D^0 - \overline{D}^0$ mixing, if any, using 1/3 of the E791 data sample. The detailed analysis is written up as an E791 internal memo [12]. The highlights are presented below.

In order to search for $D^0 - \overline{D}^0$ mixing, E791 use only D^0 mesons from D^{*+} decays in which case the charge of the pion from the D^{*+} decay identifies the charm quantum number of the D^0 at birth. When the D^0 decays, the charge of the kaon identifies the charm quantum number and this way one can tell if mixing has occured. The experiment fits their right- and wrong-sign data in three dimensions: $K\pi$ mass, the q-value in the D^* decays and measured decay lifetime using a maximum likelihood fit. The wrong-sign decay fit includes a mixing term and a Doubly Cabibbo Suppressed Decay term, with different lifetime dependences as well as an interference term. The q-value is a mass difference defined by

$$q = m_{K\pi\pi} - m_{K\pi} - m_\pi$$

The results below come from the fit. However, it is easier to illustrate the search by the lifetime distribution of the wrong-sign sample after background subtraction and correction for acceptance which is shown in Figure 1. No peak is seen at two D^0 lifetimes, indicating no evidence for mixing. Of course, this may also come about from negative interference with DCSD decays. (See limits below).

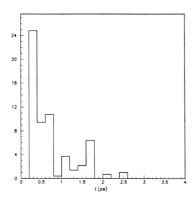

Figure 1. The time distribution of wrong sign $D^0 \to K^-\pi^+$ decays in the signal region. The distribution is background subtracted and acceptance corrected.

The rate r e.g., for mixing is defined by

$$r_{\text{mix}} \equiv \frac{\Gamma(D^0 \to \overline{D}^0 \to K^+\pi^-)}{\Gamma(D^0 \to K^-\pi^+)}$$

The results are:

$$r_{\text{mix}} < 0.47\% \qquad \text{at the 90\% C.L.}$$

and

$$r_{\text{DCSD}} < 2.7\% \qquad \text{at the 90\% C.L.}$$

or

$$r_{\text{DCSD}} = 1.9^{+0.6}_{-0.8}\%$$

Already, with only 1/3 of E791's data, these limits equal the best limit on mixing. For comparison, E691 obtained a limit [13] of $r_{\text{mix}} < 0.50\%$ in the $K\pi$ mode and $r_{\text{mix}} < 0.37\%$ combining the $K\pi$ and $K\pi\pi$ decay modes of the D^0. If the E791 limit is obtained in the same fashion as E691's limit, i.e., using parabolic errors, the E791 limit is 0.37%, better than E691's limit of 0.50%. Since the E791 limit comes from 1/3 of their data set and from only one of the two important D^0 hadronic decay modes, they expect that with the full data set, both modes and further analysis improvements, the sensitivity will improve by around a factor of 3. Already, a preliminary analysis in the $D^0 \to K\pi\pi$ mode [14] indicates that

$$r_{\text{mix}} < 3.0\% \qquad \text{at the 90\% C.L.}$$

(Assuming maximal interference from DCSD). Further, they find that

$$r_{\text{mix}} < 0.3\% \qquad \text{at the 90\% C.L.}$$

(Assuming no interference from DCSD).

E691 also obtained $r_{\text{DCSD}} < 1.5\%$. The E791 limit appears to be a little worse than one might project from this simply because E791 may have begun to see the signal that CLEO II sees, while the statistics for E691 were quite low.

4. Observation of DCSD D^+ decays by E791

Doubly Cabibbo Suppressed Decays of the D^+ are interesting both because they have never been observed and because definite predictions have been made about their rates, based on models of D mesons and their decay mechanisms. Most D-meson decay models explain the larger D^+ lifetime (relative to the D^0, D^+ lifetimes) as being due to interference of the color-allowed and color-suppressed spectator diagrams. This interference does not occur in the rarer DCSD decays, thereby enhancing their branching ratio relative to the Cabibbo-favored decays (naively this ratio is expected to be $\tan^4\theta_C$). Preliminary analyses of ~40% of E791's data set have now been completed. Figure 2 shows the Cabibbo-favored signal $D^+ \to K^-\pi^+\pi^+$ and the next figure shows the signal in the doubly Cabibbo-suppressed mode $D^+ \to K^+\pi^-\pi^-$. There is a clear signal which leads to the ratio [15]

$$\frac{\Gamma(D^+ \to K^+\pi^-\pi^+)}{\Gamma(D^+ \to K^-\pi^+\pi^+)} = (3.9 \pm 0.9 \pm 0.5) \times \tan^4\theta_c$$

This is already a much better limit/signal than the Particle Data booklet [16] limit of $20 \times \tan^4\theta_c$. A preliminary examination of the resonant subcomponents has been done and E791 find that

$$\frac{\Gamma(D^+ \to K^{*0}\pi^+)}{\Gamma(D^+ \to K^-\pi^+\pi^+)} < 2.9 \times \tan^4\theta_c$$

If this is considered to be a signal, E791 obtains

$$\frac{\Gamma(D^+ \to K^{*0}\pi^+)}{\Gamma(D^+ \to K^-\pi^+\pi^+)} = (1.9 \pm 0.6) \times \tan^4\theta_c$$

(statistical error only).

Similarly, an examination of decays to three charged kaons has revealed that

$$\frac{\Gamma(D^+ \to K^+K^-K^+)}{\Gamma(D^+ \to K^-\pi^+\pi^+)} < 1.7 \times \tan^4\theta_c$$

and the resonant decay can be compared to the $\phi\pi^+$ decay mode giving

$$\frac{\Gamma(D^+ \to \phi K^+)}{\Gamma(D^+ \to \phi\pi^+)} < 20.3 \times \tan^4\theta_c$$

These limits are lower than and inconsistent with the level at which WA82 has claimed a signal (in the

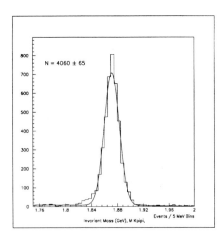

Figure 2. Invariant mass distribution for the Cabibbo-favored decay $D^+ \to K^-\pi^+\pi^+$ from 1/3 of the E791 data sample. This is used as normalization for the doubly Cabibbo-suppressed signal.

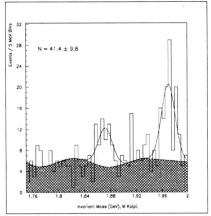

Figure 3. Invariant mass distribution for the doubly Cabibbo-suppressed decay $D^+ \to K^+\pi^+\pi^-$ from 1/3 of the E791 data sample.

$K^+K^-K^+$ mode, see [17]) and a little lower than but consistent with a signal observed by E691 (see [18]). E791 plans to continue using their very large charm data set for analyses of $D^0 - \overline{D}^0$ mixing, doubly Cabibbo-suppressed decays, charm baryons, flavor-changing neutral currents, semileptonic decays etc.

References

[1] V. D. Kekelidze "Study of the Decays of Charmed Baryons Λ_c^+ and Ξ_c^+ Produced by Neutrons at the Serpukhov Accelerator", in the Proceedings of the XXVII International Conference on High Energy Physics, Glasgow, Scotland (1994).

[2] D. Fujino, private communication, for the CLEO II collaboration.

[3] S. P. Ratti "Observation of the Ω_c^0 in Experiment E687 at Fermilab", in the Proceedings of the XXVII International Conference on High Energy Physics, Glasgow, Scotland (1994).

[4] H. Albrecht et al., Phys. Lett. **B288** (1992) 367.

[5] P. L. Frabetti et al., Phys. Lett. **B300**, (1993) 190.

[6] G. Bellini, "Study of Charmed Meson States Photoproduced at High Energy at Fermilab", in the Proceedings of the XXVII International Conference on High Energy Physics, Glasgow, Scotland (1994).

[7] L. Hall and S. Weinberg, Phys. Rev. **D48**, (1993) 979.

[8] K. S. Babu et al., Phys. Lett. **B205**, (1988) 540.

[9] E. Ma, Mod. Phys. Lett. **A3**, (1988) 319.

[10] D. Cinabro et al., Phys. Rev. Lett. **72**, (1994) 1406.

[11] G. Crawford et al., "Search for $D^0 \to K^+\pi^-\pi^0$", in the Proceedings of the XXVII International Conference on High Energy Physics, Glasgow, Scotland (1994).

[12] M. V. Purohit "A $D^0 - \overline{D}^0$ mixing and DCSD Analysis of E791 data", E791 internal memo #142, (1994) 1.

[13] J. C. Anjos et al., Phys. Rev. Lett. **60**, (1988) 1239.

[14] G. Blaylock, private communication (1994).

[15] J. S. Wiener "Doubly Cabibbo Suppressed Decays of the Charged D Meson", Princeton University Ph. D. thesis, unpublished (1994).

[16] The Particle Data Group in the "Review of Particle Properties", Phys. Rev. **D45**, (1992) 1.

[17] M. Adamovich et al., Phys. Lett. **B305** (1993) 177.

[18] J. C. Anjos et al., Phys. Rev. Lett. **69** (1992) 2892.

Paper presented at XXVII Int. Conf. on High Energy Physics: Session Pa-2
Glasgow, UK, 20–27 July 1994

Υ and J/Ψ Physics and Standard Model Parameters from Non-Relativistic Lattice QCD

John H. Sloan*

SCRI, Florida State University, Tallahassee, FL 32306

for the NRQCD Collaboration

Abstract

We report on precision lattice simulations of the Υ and J/Ψ systems, using an NRQCD lattice action for the heavy quark fields. We calculate the bound state spectrum for S, P, and D states, obtaining good agreement with experimental results for observed states and predictions for unobserved states. We use the results of our spectrum simulations to determine $\alpha_{\overline{\text{MS}}}(M_Z)$ and M_b, two parameters of the standard model.

In this talk we report on results from accurate numerical simulations of the spectra of the Υ and J/Ψ families of mesons. The J/Ψ results reported here are preliminary, as are the dynamical Υ results. A more detailed description of the Υ results can be found in [1, 2, 3]. Our simulations use the NRQCD [4] action for the quarks, including all relativistic effects through $\mathcal{O}(M_b v^4)$ where M_b is the b-quark's mass and v its average velocity. In our simulations, we have utilized a variety of important lattice techniques, including the perturbative improvement of actions, tadpole improvement, and multicorrelated fits for extracting the spectrum of excited states. These techniques give us excellent control over systematic uncertainties in the simulations, at relatively large values of the lattice spacing. Furthermore, the high statistics and small systematic errors of our results allow us to extract accurate values for two of the fundamental parameters of the Standard Model: the mass of the b-quark, and the strong coupling constant $\alpha_{\overline{\text{MS}}}(M_Z)$.

In Figure 1, we present our simulation results for the

Υ system's $^3S_1$, $^1P_1$, and $^1D_2$ spectra, together with the corresponding experimental values from [5].

As can be seen, our calculation of the Υ spectrum matches quite well with experiment. An interesting effect is a slight indication (2σ) in the quenched results that the 2S-1S and 1P-1S splittings are inconsistent, the first being too large and the second too small. This is precisely what is expected due to quenching, and appears to be reduced by the inclusion of dynamical fermions. It will be interesting to see if this effect survives when higher statistics results are analyzed; if so it will be one of the first lattice spectrum calculations in which the effects of quenching are observed and subsequently removed by the inclusion of dynamical fermions.

Figure 2 presents our results for the spin splittings of the S and P-wave ground states of the Υ system. We expect systematic uncertainties in all energies of about 5 MeV, as indicated in the plot. For the χ_b states, this is comparable to the statistical errors shown, while for the h_b and η_b, systematic errors dominate. Comparing the quenched and $n_f = 2$ hyperfine splittings, we see a fairly strong dependence on dynamical fermion content. Extrapolating to $n_f = 4$ (the amount of vacuum polarization at hyperfine momentum transfers),

---

* Members of the collaboration who contributed to the work presented here are C.T.H. Davies and A. Lidsey, Univ. of Glasgow; K. Hornbostel, Southern Methodist Univ.; T. Klassen, A. Langnau and G.P. Lepage, Cornell Univ.; C. Morningstar, Univ. of Edinburgh; J. Shigemitsu, Ohio State Univ.; and J. Sloan, SCRI

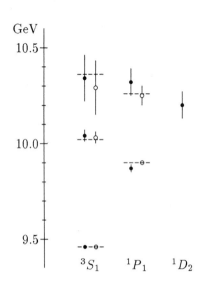

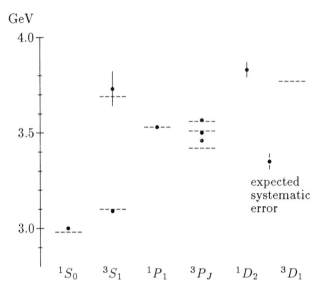

Figure 1. NRQCD simulation results for the spectrum of the Υ system including radial excitations, using an inverse lattice spacing of 2.4 GeV. Experimental values (dashed lines) are indicated for the triplet S-states, and for the spin-average of the triplet P-states. The energy zero from simulation results is adjusted to give the correct mass to the $\Upsilon(1S)$, while the $\Upsilon(2S)$ and $\chi_b(1P)$ both contributed to the choice of a^{-1}. Error bars indicate statistical uncertainties only. Results are shown for $n_f = 0$ (filled circles) and $n_f = 2$ (open circles).

splittings are very sensitive to the quark mass and to the coefficients in the NRQCD lagrangian, this agreement with experiment is a strong result.

Figure 3. Quenched NRQCD simulation results for the spectrum of the J/Ψ system including radial excitations, using an inverse lattice spacing of 1.23 GeV. Experimental values are indicated by dashed lines. The spin-weighted average of the $J/\Psi(1S)$ and $\eta_c(1S)$ was used to set the zero of energy for simulation results, while its splitting with the $h_b(1P)$ was used to set a^{-1}. Error bars are shown where visible, and only indicate statistical uncertainties.

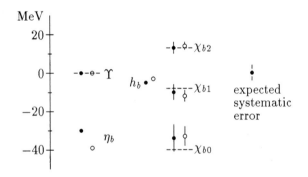

Figure 2. Simulation results for the spin structure of the lowest lying S-wave and P-wave states in the Υ family, using an inverse lattice spacing of 2.4 GeV. The dashed lines are experimental values. Energies are measured relative to the center of mass of observed states. Error bars indicate statistical uncertainties only. Results are shown for $n_f = 0$ (filled circles) and $n_f = 2$ (open circles).

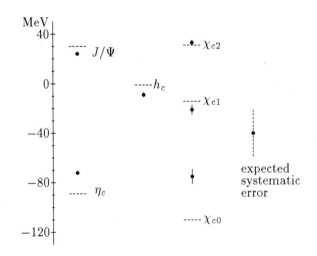

Figure 4. Quenched Simulation results for the spin structure of the J/Ψ family, using an inverse lattice spacing of 1.23 GeV. Energies for $J/\Psi/\eta_c$ and h_c/χ_c groups are measured relative to their center of mass. Error bars for points are statistical; expected systematic errors are shown at the side.

we expect the $\Upsilon(1S) - \eta_b(1S)$ splitting to be 48(5) MeV.

Our values for the χ_b splittings show good agreement with the data. Note that the lattice spacing and bare quark mass used to obtain Figure 2 were fixed by the spin-averaged spectrum. In other words, the splittings in Figure 2 are predictions of the theory, generated by terms in the action which have no significant effect on the tuning of the theory's free parameters. Since these

In Figure 3, we present preliminary results for

the spectrum of the J/Ψ system, together with the corresponding experimental values from [5]. Figure 4 presents a higher resolution view of the charmonium spin splittings.

Examining the figures, we see that systematic errors are much more important relative to statistical errors in the J/Ψ system. For almost all the states displayed, expected lattice spacing and relativistic errors dominate the statistical errors. An interesting inconsistency in the spin splittings (within the expected systematic errors, however) is in the ratio of the $\chi_{c2}(1P)$ - $\chi_{c1}(1P)$ splitting to the $\chi_{c1}(1P)$ - $\chi_{c0}(1P)$ splitting; in our simulation it is very close to 1. It will be interesting to determine whether or not this discrepancy is due to relativistic corrections. The fact that we have the statistics to resolve our systematic errors in the J/Ψ system actually has some advantages; if going to a higher order in our calculation removes the systematic errors, it will be a very strong indication that we really do have these errors under control. Such calculations are underway.

The extraction of $\alpha_{\overline{MS}}$ from a lattice calculation of the Υ or J/Ψ spectrum is a standard technique, described in [6]. There are two subtleties in the procedure. The first involves going from bare to renormalized lattice perturbation theory[7]; this is necessary both to remove large logarithms and large tadpole contributions. The second is a direct result of the quenched approximation; because vacuum polarization effects are not included properly, α_s will run with an incorrect beta function. In the past, these quenching errors have been removed through a perturbative estimate; our access to unquenched configurations allows us to remove these errors directly[3]. The typical momentum transfer by gluons in bottomonium is about 500-1000 MeV, which means that the screening effects of three light quarks should be felt in the spin-averaged spectrum. We have used our quenched and $n_f = 2$ Υ calculations to extract $\alpha_{\overline{MS}}^{(0)}$ and $\alpha_{\overline{MS}}^{(2)}$ at a scale, 3.56 GeV, near the inverse lattice spacing. We then linearly extrapolate the inverse coupling to obtain $\alpha_{\overline{MS}}^{(3)}(3.56\,\mathrm{GeV}) = .220(8)$. Running this to the Z mass yields $\alpha_{\overline{MS}}^{(5)}(M_Z) = .115(2)$. The dominant error in this new determination of α_s is due to the perturbative formula translating the lattice coupling into the $\overline{MS}$ scheme.

We have determined the bare lattice b quark mass by requiring the mass of the Υ to match its experimental value of 9.46 GeV. From this bare mass, $M_b^0 = 4.0(1)$ GeV, the pole mass can be computed using lattice perturbation theory, resulting in $M_b = 5.0(2)$ GeV[2]. The dominant error here is perturbative; the scale at which the perturbative coupling must be evaluated is fairly soft, giving it a large value in the calculation. For this reason,

we have also performed a perturbative matching calculation (in which these soft gluonic effects cancel) to find the corresponding value of the $\overline{MS}$ mass, $M_b^{\overline{MS}}(M_b) = 4.0(1)$ GeV[2]. Because of these scale problems, we are as yet unable to obtain pole or $\overline{MS}$ masses for the c quark.

We have presented results from our program of high-precision analyses of heavy-quark mesons using NRQCD. We have shown that lattice simulations can accurately account for the structure of the Υ spectrum up through the $\Upsilon(3S)$. We have seen indications of quenching in the Υ spectrum and removed the effect by including dynamical fermions. For the J/Ψ system, our preliminary results are also quite good; all spin splittings examined were consistent with experiment, up to expected systematic effects. A higher order NRQCD action[8] will reduce these expected uncertainties, providing an even more stringent test of our methods.

We have used these spectrum calculations to make new determinations of the strong coupling constant and the b-quark's mass. The quality of our results indicates that NRQCD can be a powerful tool to calculate nonperturbative, physically interesting, quantities in QCD.

This work was supported in part by grants from the DOE, NSF, and SERC. The computer simulations were performed at the Ohio Supercomputer Center and at the Atlas centre RAL, UK. We thank the HEMCGC, UKQCD, and Staggered collaborations for generously providing us with the gauge field ensembles necessary for these calculations[9, 10].

References

[1] "Precision Υ Spectroscopy from Nonrelativistic Lattice QCD", NRQCD Collaboration: C.T.H. Davies *et al*, FSU-SCRI-94-57, to appear in Phys. Rev. **D**.

[2] "A New Determination of M_b using Lattice QCD", NRQCD Collaboration: C.T.H. Davies *et al*, FSU-SCRI-94-39, to appear in Phys. Rev. Lett.

[3] "A Precise Determination of α_s from Lattice QCD", NRQCD Collaboration: C.T.H. Davies *et al*, FSU-SCRI-94-79, submitted to Phys. Lett. **B**.

[4] G. P. Lepage and B. A. Thacker, Nucl. Phys. **B** (Proc. Suppl.) **4** (1988) 199; B. A. Thacker and G. P. Lepage, Phys. Rev. **D43** (1991) 196.

[5] Particle Data Group: K. Hikasa *et al*, Phys. Rev. **D45** (1992).

[6] A. El-Khadra, G. Hockney, A. Kronfeld, and P. Mackenzie, Phys. Rev. Lett. **69** (1992) 729; G. P. Lepage, Nucl. Phys. B (Proc. Suppl.) **26** (1992) 45, and references therein; A. El-Khadra, Nucl. Phys. B (Proc. Suppl.) **34** (1994) 141, and references therein.

[7] G.P. Lepage and P.B. Mackenzie, Phys. Rev. **D48** (1993) 2250.

[8] G. P. Lepage, L. Magnea, C. Nakhleh, U. Magnea and K. Hornbostel, Phys. Rev. **D46** (1992) 4052.

[9] R. Gupta *et al*, Phys. Rev. **D43** (1991) 2003.

[10] K. Bitar *et al.*, Nucl. Phys. **B** (Proc. Suppl.) **26**, (1992) 259; Phys. Rev. **D46** (1992) 2169.

Paper presented at XXVII Int. Conf. on High Energy Physics: Session Pa-2
Glasgow, UK, 20–27 July 1994

Selected ARGUS results on hadronic charm decays

Yu. M. Zaitsev

Institute of Theoretical and Experimental Physics,
B.Cheremushkinskaya 25, 117259, Moscow, Russia

Abstract

Using the ARGUS detector at the e^+e^- storage ring DORIS II, we have studied Cabibbo-suppressed D^0 decay modes resulting in the $K^+K^-\pi^+\pi^-$ final state and two-body D^0 decay modes with a ϕ meson in the final state. We also present a measurement of the $D^+ \to K_S^0 K_S^0 K^+$ branching ratio.

In this paper we briefly report on a study of Cabibbo-suppressed D^0 decays. Complete results and discussion on the details of analysis can be found in ref. [1]. The decays under consideration include the $D^0 \to K^+K^-\pi^+\pi^-$ and the $D^0 \to K_S^0 K_S^0 \pi^+\pi^-$ decay modes as well as a number of two-body channels with a ϕ meson in the final state.

The data used for the analysis were taken using the ARGUS detector [2] at the e^+e^- storage ring DORIS II at DESY. The integrated luminosity of the sample is equal to 476 pb^{-1}, corresponding to more than $500,000$ D^0 and about $300,000$ D^+ mesons from continuum production. Particle identification was based on specific ionization, time of flight, energy deposition in the shower counters and hits in the muon chambers. A K_S^0 candidate was defined as a $\pi^+\pi^-$ pair forming a secondary vertex with an invariant mass within ± 30 MeV/c^2 of the K_S^0 mass.

D^0 decay modes were analysed either from $D^{*+} \to D^0\pi^+$ † decay or without D^{*+} reconstruction. All $D^0(D^{*+})$ and D^+ meson candidates were required to satisfy $x_p \geq 0.5$, where the scaled momentum of the D meson candidate is defined by $x_p = p_D/p_D^{max}$. The invariant mass resolutions, the efficiencies for particle reconstruction and for the kinematical cuts for all channels were obtained from Monte Carlo simulation. The mass spectra for the D^0, D^+ and D^{*+} signals were fitted

with the sum of a Gaussian, to parametrize the signal, and a polynomial, to parametrize background.

The $D^0 \to K_S^0 \pi^+\pi^-$ channel was used for normalization of the $D^0 \to K_S^0 K_S^0 \pi^+\pi^-$ mode, while the $D^0 \to K^-\pi^+\pi^-\pi^+$ channel was chosen for other D^0 decays. To normalize $D^+ \to K_S^0 K_S^0 K^+$ we used the $D^+ \to K^-\pi^+\pi^+$ mode. Systematic errors were determined by varying the cuts, the background parametrization, the single track reconstruction efficiency and the widths of the signals.

To study the $D^0 \to K^+K^-\pi^+\pi^-$ resonance structure, D^0 candidates were accepted if their reconstructed masses differed by less than 20 MeV/c^2 from the nom-

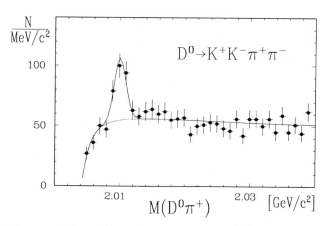

Figure 1. $D^0 \to K^+K^-\pi^+\pi^-$ decay mode. $D^0\pi^+$ invariant mass distribution

---

† References to a specific particle state should be interpreted as implying the charge-conjugate state also.

Decay mode	N_{ev}	ε_{rel}	BR_i/BR_{norm}	$BR_i\%$
$D^0 \to K^-\pi^+\pi^-\pi^+$	3226 ± 65	1.00		7.5 ± 0.5
$D^0 \to K^+K^-\pi^+\pi^-$	114 ± 20	0.86	$0.041 \pm 0.007 \pm 0.005$	$0.31 \pm 0.05 \pm 0.04$
$D^0 \to \phi\pi^+\pi^-$	28 ± 8	0.43	$0.020 \pm 0.006 \pm 0.005$	$0.15 \pm 0.04 \pm 0.03$
$D^0 \to K^{*0}K^-\pi^+$	55 ± 18	0.40	$0.043 \pm 0.014 \pm 0.009$	$0.32 \pm 0.10 \pm 0.07$
$D^0 \to \overline{K^{*0}}K^+\pi^-$	30 ± 17	0.40	$0.023 \pm 0.013 \pm 0.009$	$0.17 \pm 0.10 \pm 0.07$
$D^0 \to \phi\pi^0$	< 5.3 @90%CL	0.10	< 0.018 @90%CL	< 0.14 @90%CL
$D^0 \to \phi\omega$	< 4.4 @90%CL	0.06	< 0.027 @90%CL	< 0.21 @90%CL
$D^0 \to \phi\eta$	< 5.7 @90%CL	0.06	< 0.035 @90%CL	< 0.28 @90%CL
$D^0 \to K_S^0\pi^+\pi^-$	521 ± 26 2110 ± 86	1.00		2.7 ± 0.3
$D^0 \to K_S^0K_S^0\pi^+\pi^-$	8.6 ± 3.1 24.6 ± 9.7	0.22	$0.063 \pm 0.019 \pm 0.015$	$0.17 \pm 0.05 \pm 0.04$

Table 1. Summary of studied D^0 decay modes.

inal D^0 mass. Figure 1 shows a clear signal at the D^{*+} mass in the $D^0\pi^+$ invariant mass distribution for the $D^0 \to K^+K^-\pi^+\pi^-$ channel. A contribution of 6 events from $D^0 \to K^-\pi^+\pi^-\pi^+$ due to $\pi \to$ "K" mis-identification was subtracted, giving a signal of 114 ± 20 events. Corresponding numbers of events, relative efficiencies and branching ratios are shown in Table 1.

ϕ, η and ω candidates were accepted if they had a measured mass within two standard deviations of the known masses. Narrow intermediate resonances (η,ω) were kinematically fitted, constraining their masses to the nominal values. D^0 candidates from reconstructed D^{*+} mesons were also treated in this way. Taking into account the π meson charge from the $D^0\pi$ combination in the D^{*+} signal we can distinguish D^0 from $\overline{D^0}$ and thus the decay modes $D^0 \to K^{*0}K^-\pi^+$ and $D^0 \to \overline{K^{*0}}K^+\pi^-$ from each other. We fit the $K\pi$ invariant mass distributions with a relativistic Breit-Wigner function to describe the $K^{*0}(\overline{K^{*0}})$ signal, and a polynomial to parametrize non-K^* contributions.

The value obtained for $BR(D^0 \to \phi\pi^+\pi^-) \cdot BR(\phi \to K^+K^-) + BR(D^0 \to K^{*0}K^-\pi^+) \cdot BR(K^{*0} \to K^+\pi^-) = (0.29 \pm 0.07 \pm 0.05)\%$ is close to the $BR(D^0 \to K^+K^-\pi^+\pi^-) = (0.31 \pm 0.05 \pm 0.04)\%$. Therefore, we conclude that this final state is realized either via a ϕ or a K^{*0} meson, although our accuracy allows a contribution from other intermediate states with smaller partial widths.

The good K_S^0 mass resolution and secondary vertex requirement provide us with a clean event sample of D decays with K_S^0 mesons in the final state. The D^0 resolution for the $K_S^0K_S^0\pi^+\pi^-$ mode was found to be 9.2 MeV/c^2 from Monte Carlo. The fit of the $D^0\pi^+$ invariant mass spectrum yields a signal of 8.6 ± 3.1 events at the D^{*+} mass. A signal is also observed in the $K_S^0K_S^0\pi^+\pi^-$ invariant mass spectrum without D^{*+} reconstruction at the level of 24.6 ± 9.7 events.

The $D^+ \to K_S^0K_S^0K^+$ decay is so far the only

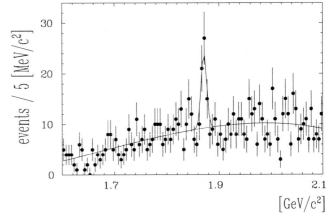

Figure 2. $K_S^0K_S^0K^+$ invariant mass distribution

observed decay mode of the D^+ into three kaons, which involves the popping of an $s\bar{s}$ pair. Unlike most charm meson decays it seems to proceed as a three-body decay. The $K_S^0K_S^0K^+$ invariant mass spectrum is shown in figure 2. The distribution was fitted with a Gaussian (a width of 5.2 MeV/c^2 was determined from Monte Carlo) and a third-order polynomial to describe the background, yielding 39.2 ± 8.8 events in the signal region.

To normalize the $D^+ \to K_S^0K_S^0K^+$ channel we use $D^+ \to K^-\pi^+\pi^+$ mode analyzed in detail in [3] and obtain $BR(D^+ \to K_S^0K_S^0K^+) = (0.28 \pm 0.08 \pm 0.05)\%$, which corresponds to $BR(D^+ \to \overline{K^0}\,\overline{K^0}\,K^+) = (1.1 \pm 0.3 \pm 0.2)\%$.

References

[1] H.Albrecht *et al.* (ARGUS Collaboration), preprint DESY 94-052 (1994)

[2] H.Albrecht *et al.* (ARGUS Collaboration), Nucl. Instr. and Methods **A275** (1989) 1

[3] H.Albrecht *et al.* (ARGUS Collaboration), Z. Phys. **C52** (1991) 353

Paper presented at XXVII Int. Conf. on High Energy Physics: Session Pa-2
Glasgow, UK, 20–27 July 1994

Hadronic B Decays to Charm Mesons (Review)

Hitoshi Yamamoto[†]

Harvard University
42 Oxford St, Cambridge, MA 02138, USA

Abstract

We review the phenomenology of hadronic B meson decays to final states containing charm and charmonium mesons. After discussing a test of factorization, we extract the coefficients $a_{1,2}$ of the factorized effective Hamiltonian for each of the decay groups $D\pi$, ψK and DD_s separately. We also comment on the possible charm deficit in B meson decays.

1. Introduction

Non-leptonic decays are notoriously resistant to rigorous understanding since hadrons are surrounded by a cloud of light quark and gluon which can have infinite degrees of freedom (like the chaotic motions of fluid) and the products of the decaying quark can interact strongly with this cloud. In recent years, however, we have seen many new results coming out of CLEO, ARGUS, CDF, and LEP experiments, and also new theoretical fronts have been pushed forward based on Heavy Quark Effective Theory (HQET) and QCD sum rules. In between, models based on factorization have provided convenient framework to guide the analyses[1, 2]. Here we will focus on reviewing the phenomenological aspects while the theoretical part is left to another talk[3].

2. Test of Factorization

The idea of factorization in non-leptonic decays goes back to early 60's when Schwinger estimated the $\Delta I = 3/2$ part of Kaon decay from the semileptonic rate[4], and was thought to be good only for order of magnitude estimations. For certain heavy hadron decays, however, there are reasons to believe that the factorization can work well. We take $\bar{B}^0 \to D^{*+}\pi^-$ as an example which is caused by the 4-fermion operator

$$(\bar{d}u)_\mu(\bar{c}b)^\mu$$

where $(\bar{q}_1 q_2)_\mu \equiv \bar{q}_1^a \gamma_\mu (1 - \gamma_5) q_2^a$ is color singlet $V - A$ current ($a = 1, 2, 3$: color index). The factorization hypothesis consists in assuming that the current $(\bar{d}u)$ creates π^-, the current $(\bar{c}b)$ generates the transition

† E-mail: yamamoto@huhepl.harvard.edu

$B \to D^*$, and that they occur independently; or, that the amplitude can be 'factorized':

$$\langle D^{*+}\pi^- | (\bar{d}u)_\mu(\bar{c}b)^\mu | \bar{B}^0 \rangle = \langle \pi^- | (\bar{d}u)_\mu | 0 \rangle \langle D^{*+} | (\bar{c}b)^\mu | \bar{B}^0 \rangle$$

where (with f_π being the pion decay constant)

$$\langle \pi^- | (\bar{u}d)_\mu | 0 \rangle = -if_\pi q_\mu \quad (q : \pi \text{ 4-momentum}).$$

If the $d\bar{u}$ pair interacts with the color field of B meson as it passes through it, or if the π and D^* re-scatter by final-state interaction, then the two processes are not independent, and factorization would not work. However, the $d\bar{u}$ pair is colorless as it is generated by W and moving fast through the color field tightly together; thus, we expect that it will escape the color field without much interaction. Also, by the time the π is formed ($\sim$1fm/c in its rest frame, $\sim$10fm in the B rest frame), it is many times the meson radius away from D^*; thus, there will be little final-state interaction. We can hope that factorization works in this case[6].

The matrix element $\langle D^{*+} | (\bar{c}b)^\mu | \bar{B}^0 \rangle$ is the same as that appearing in the corresponding semileptonic decay $\bar{B}^0 \to D^{*+}l^-\nu$ (at the same $q^2 = m_\pi^2$), and thus one expects that there is a simple relation between the two decay rates. In fact, we have[5, 7]

$$\frac{\mathcal{B}(\bar{B}^0 \to D^{*+}X^-)}{\left.\frac{d\mathcal{B}}{dq^2}(\bar{B}^0 \to D^{*+}l^-\nu)\right|_{q^2 = m_X^2}} = 6\pi^2 f_X^2 |V_{ud}|^2 \quad (1)$$

which holds for $X^- = \pi^-, \rho^-, a_1^- \ldots$ as long as factorization works and $q^2 = m_X^2$ is small. The LHS of (1) - denoted as R(measured) - can be measured and then compared to the RHS which is the expectation from factorization - denoted as R(fact.).

The result is shown in Table 1. The branching ratios of the hadronic decays are measurements by CLEO[8]

X	$\mathcal{B}(D^{*+}X^-)$ (%)[a]	$dB/dq^{2[b]}$ (%/GeV^2)	R(measured) (GeV^2)	f_X (GeV)	R(fact.) (GeV^2)
π	$0.26\pm0.03\pm0.04\pm0.01$	0.22 ± 0.2	$1.1\pm0.1\pm0.2$	0.132	1.0
ρ	$0.74\pm0.10\pm0.14\pm0.03$	0.25 ± 0.2	$3.0\pm0.4\pm0.6$	0.215	2.7
a_1	$1.26\pm0.20\pm0.22\pm0.04^{[c]}$	0.32 ± 0.2	$4.0\pm0.6\pm0.5$	0.205	2.5

(a) CLEO measurements. The first error is statistical, second systematic, and the third is due to uncertainties in D^0 branching fractions.
(b) From CLEO and ARGUS measurements of $B \to D^*l^-\nu$ fitted to various models.
(c) It is assumed that $D^{*+}a_1^-$ dominates $D^{*+}\pi^+\pi^-\pi^-$ in the region $1.0 < M_{3\pi} < 1.6$ GeV.

Table 1. Test of factorization. Branching fraction of $B \to D^*X$ is compared to the corresponding semileptonic decay evaluated at $q^2 = m_X^2$.

where D^{*+} is detected by the decay chain $D^{*+} \to D^0\pi^+, D^0 \to K^-\pi^+, K^-\pi^+\pi^0, K^-\pi^+\pi^-\pi^+$, and a_1^- is detected in the mode $a_1^- \to \rho^0\pi^-$. The differential semileptonic rate is obtained by fitting q^2 dependence of various models[9] to the combination of CLEO and ARGUS measurements[10]. By comparing R(measured) and R(fact.), one can see that factorization seems to be working for $D^{*+}\pi^-$ and $D^{*+}\rho^-$, within the error of about 25%, but not so well for $D^{*+}a_1^-$. It could be that a_1 (1230 MeV) is already too heavy and moving too slowly for factorization to hold, but the discrepancy is only 2σ which could well be due to fluctuation.

3. Effective Factorized Hamiltonian

By scaling down the operator $(\bar{d}u)_\mu(\bar{c}b)^\mu$ (or similarly for $(\bar{s}c)_\mu(\bar{c}b)^\mu$) from the W mass scale to b mass scale one obtains the QCD corrected effective Hamiltonian

$$\mathbf{H}_{\text{eff}} = c_1\mathbf{O}_1 + c_2\mathbf{O}_2$$
$$\mathbf{O}_1 \equiv (\bar{d}u)_\mu(\bar{c}b)^\mu, \quad \mathbf{O}_2 \equiv (\bar{c}u)_\mu(\bar{d}b)^\mu$$

and $c_{1,2}$ are the Wilson coefficients given by

$$c_+ = c_1 + c_2, \quad c_- = c_1 - c_2$$
$$c_- = c_+^{-2} = [\alpha_s(\mu)/\alpha_s(M_W)]^{12/(33-2n_f)} \quad (2)$$
$$\to c_1(m_b) = 1.12, \quad c_2(m_b) = -0.26.$$

Without the QCD correction ($\mu = M_W$) we have $c_+ = c_- = 1$ or $c_1 = 1, c_2 = 0$; it does not, however, mean that $\mathbf{O}_2$ isn't there without the QCD correction since $\mathbf{O}_{1,2}$ are not orthogonal. In fact, Fierz identities give

$$\mathbf{O}_1 = \frac{1}{3}\mathbf{O}_2 + \frac{1}{2}[\bar{c}u]_\mu^i[\bar{d}b]_i^\mu, \quad \mathbf{O}_2 = \frac{1}{3}\mathbf{O}_1 + \frac{1}{2}[\bar{d}u]_\mu^i[\bar{c}b]_i^\mu$$

where $[\bar{q}_1q_2]_\mu^i \equiv (\bar{q}_1^a\lambda_{ab}^i\gamma_\mu(1-\gamma_5)q_2^b)$ is color-octet V-A current (λ^i: Gell-Mann matrices), and $\mathbf{H}_{\text{eff}}$ can be written in two ways in terms of *orthogonal basis*:

$$\mathbf{H}_{\text{eff}} = \frac{c_1}{2}[\bar{c}u]_\mu^i[\bar{d}b]_i^\mu + (\frac{c_1}{3} + c_2)\mathbf{O}_2$$
$$= (c_1 + \frac{c_2}{3})\mathbf{O}_1 + \frac{c_2}{2}[\bar{d}u]_\mu^i[\bar{c}b]_i^\mu. \quad (3)$$

Note that $c_1 + c_2/3 = 1$ to the first order due to the relation $c_+^2c_1 = 1$ (eq. 2); thus, one can say that the QCD correction keeps the coefficient of $\mathbf{O}_1$ intact and simply adds the octet-octet operator.

Now assume that
1) there is no contribution from the terms that put a color-octet pair into a meson, and that
2) matrix elements of $\mathbf{O}_{1,2}$ are dominated by the factorizable part $\mathbf{O}_{1,2}^{\text{fac}}$ which are defined by

$$\langle D^+\pi^-|\mathbf{O}_1^{\text{fac}}|\bar{B}^0\rangle \overset{\text{def}}{\equiv} \langle\pi^-|(\bar{d}u)_\mu|0\rangle\langle D^+|(\bar{c}b)^\mu|\bar{B}^0\rangle$$
$$\langle D^0\pi^0|\mathbf{O}_2^{\text{fac}}|\bar{B}^0\rangle \overset{\text{def}}{\equiv} \langle D^0|(\bar{c}u)_\mu|0\rangle\langle\pi^0|(\bar{d}b)^\mu|\bar{B}^0\rangle \quad (4)$$

etc. Then, one can introduce a 'factorized effective Hamiltonian' $\mathbf{H}_{\text{fac}}$, which is one-level higher than $\mathbf{H}_{\text{eff}}$, by inserting the $\mathbf{H}_{\text{eff}}$ in two ways corresponding to the two ways of writing $\mathbf{H}_{\text{eff}}$ (eq.3):

$$\mathbf{H}_{\text{fac}} \equiv a_1\mathbf{O}_1^{\text{fac}} + a_2\mathbf{O}_2^{\text{fac}}$$
$$\text{with} \quad \begin{cases} a_1 = c_1 + c_2/3 + \text{nf}_1 \\ a_2 = c_1/3 + c_1 + \text{nf}_2 \end{cases}$$

where $\text{nf}_{1,2}$ (try to) account for the non-factorizable effects: namely, the matrix elements of the octet-octet operators where a octet $\bar{q}q$ pair is put into a meson, and the non-factorizable parts of $\mathbf{O}_{1,2}$. The definition of $\mathbf{O}_{1,2}^{\text{fac}}$ (eq. 4) itself depends on the types of final state mesons, and so does the octet-octet contribution. Some effects cannot even be absorbed into $a_{1,2}$. For example, CLEO measures $\mathcal{B}(B \to \chi_{c2}X) = 0.25 \pm 0.10 \pm 0.03\%$ which is not expected in naive factorization picture[13]. It seems reasonable, however, to use a same set of $a_{1,2}$ for a group of related decay modes; namely, one set for $D\pi$, $D^*\pi$, $D\rho$, and $D^*\rho$ modes, another for DD_s, D^*D_s, DD_s^*, and $D^*D_s^*$ modes etc.

4. Extraction of $a_{1,2}$ for Each Decay Group

One can distinguish 3 classes of decay modes:
Class 1: Only $\mathbf{O}_1^{\text{fac}}$ contributes and the amplitude is proportional to a_1; e.g. $\bar{B}^0 \to D^+\pi^-$ where the hadron

current $B \to D$ emits π and thus the amplitude contains the pion decay constant f_π.

Class 2: Only $\mathbf{O}_2^{\text{fac}}$ contributes and the amplitude is proportional to a_2, sometimes called 'color-suppressed' decays.; e.g. $\bar{B}^0 \to D^0\pi^0$ where the hadron current $B \to \pi$ emits D thus the amplitude contains f_D.

Class 3: Both $\mathbf{O}_1^{\text{fac}}$ and $\mathbf{O}_2^{\text{fac}}$ contribute and the amplitude contains a_1 and a_2; e.g. $B^- \to D^0\pi^-$ whose amplitudes contains both f_π and f_D. This interference occurs since there are two identical quarks ($\bar{d}$) in the final state.

If both daughters are charged then it is class 1, if both are neutral then it is class 2, and if one is charged and the other is neutral then it depends on the quark contents of final state. Note that when D is emitted, it is not moving fast, thus it may interact with the color field of B meson before escaping; thus, factorization may not work well for class 2 and 3 decays of $D\pi$ decay mode group. Similarly, factorization may not hold for $D^{(*)}D_s^{(*)}$ or $\Psi^{(')}K^{(*)}$ decays where the emitted meson is $D_s^{(*)}$ or $\Psi^{(')}$, respectively.

In order to extract $a_{1,2}$ we need to express each decay rate in terms of these parameters as done in Ref.[1]. Here we will use a updated version given in Ref.[2]. For example, we have

$$A\big(\bar{B}^0 \to D^+\pi^-\big) = -i\frac{G_F}{\sqrt{2}}V_{ud}^*V_{cb}a_1f_\pi q_\mu \langle D^+|(\bar{c}b)^\mu|\bar{B}^0\rangle$$

where the form factor in the $B \to D$ transition is obtained from semileptonic decays by fitting to HQET-inspired forms. Together with the phase space factor $p/8\pi M^2$, $\tau_B = 1.63$ ps[12], and $|V_{cb}| = 0.039$[14], we obtain $\mathcal{B}(D^+\pi^-) = 0.264a_1^2$. For class-2,3 decays, one needs $B \to \text{light}(\pi, \rho, K)$ form factors which are calculated by a relativistic harmonic oscillator model since experimental data are not available.

In Table 2, we list measurements by CLEO and the model expectations. B mass distribution for the sum of the 8 $D^{(*)}D_s^{(*)}$ modes is shown in Fig. 1. Separate fits to the decay groups $D^{(*)}\pi^{(*)}(\pi^* \equiv \rho)$, $D^{(*)}D_s^{(*)}$, and $\Psi K^{(*)}$ gives

$$a_1 = 1.15 \pm.04 \pm.05 \pm.09 \quad (D^{(*)}\pi^{(*)} \text{ class 1}) \quad (a)$$
$$a_2/a_1 = 0.23 \pm.04 \pm.04 \pm.10 \quad (D^{(*)}\pi^{(*)} \text{ class 1,3}) \quad (b)$$
$$a_1 = 1.05 \pm.05 \pm.06 \pm.09 \quad (D^{(*)}D_s^{(*)} \text{ class 1}) \quad (c)$$
$$|a_2| = 0.26 \pm.01 \pm.01 \pm.02 \quad (\Psi K^{(*)} \text{ class 2}) \quad (d)$$

where the first error is statistical, second systematic, and the third is due to the uncertainties in the yield and lifetime ratios of charged vs neutral B mesons. The fits (a) and (b) are for $b \to c\bar{u}d$ transition and there exist class-3 decays; thus, it is possible to measure the relative sign of a_1 and a_2 through interference. The fits (c) and (d) are for $b \to c\bar{c}s$, and there is no corresponding class-3 decays preventing us from

$D^{(*)}\pi^{(*)}$ Class 1 Branching Fractions(%)			
mode	CLEO	Model	$a_1 = 1.15$
$D^+\pi^-$	$0.29\pm.04\pm.03\pm.05$	$0.264a_1^2$	0.35
$D^+\rho^-$	$0.81\pm.11\pm.12\pm.13$	$0.621a_1^2$	0.82
$D^{*+}\pi^-$	$0.26\pm.03\pm.04\pm.01$	$0.254a_1^2$	0.34
$D^{*+}\rho^-$	$0.74\pm.10\pm.14\pm.03$	$0.702a_1^2$	0.93

$D^{(*)}\pi^{(*)}$ Class 2 Branching Fractions(%)			
mode	CLEO 90% U.L.	Model	$a_2 = 0.26$
$D^0\pi^0$	<0.048	$0.201a_2^2$	0.014
$D^0\rho^0$	<0.055	$0.136a_2^2$	0.009
$D^{*0}\pi^0$	<0.097	$0.213a_2^2$	0.014
$D^{*0}\rho^0$	<0.117	$0.223a_2^2$	0.015

$D^{(*)}\pi^{(*)}$ group $R = \Gamma(\text{Class3})/\Gamma(\text{Class1})$			
mode	CLEO	Model	$a_2/a_1 = 0.23$
$D\pi$	$1.89\pm.26\pm.32$	$(1 + 1.23a_2/a_1)^2$	1.65
$D\rho$	$1.67\pm.27\pm.30$	$(1 + 0.66a_2/a_1)^2$	1.33
$D^*\pi$	$2.00\pm.37\pm.28$	$(1 + 1.29a_2/a_1)^2$	1.68
$D^*\rho$	$2.27\pm.41\pm.41$	$(1 + 0.75a_2/a_1)^2$	1.37

$D^{(*)}D_s^{(*)}$ (Class 1) Branching Fractions(%)			
mode	CLEO	Model	$a_1 = 1.05$
$D^+D_s^-$	$0.75\pm.25\pm.20\pm.18$	$1.213a_1^2$	1.33
$D^+D_s^{*-}$	$0.90\pm.34\pm.20\pm.22$	$0.859a_1^2$	0.94
$D^{*+}D_s^-$	$0.99\pm.28\pm.20\pm.24$	$0.824a_1^2$	0.90
$D^{*+}D_s^{*-}$	$1.69\pm.50\pm.36\pm.41$	$2.203a_1^2$	2.42
$D^0D_s^-$	$1.55\pm.28\pm.30\pm.38$	$1.215a_1^2$	1.33
$D^0D_s^{*-}$	$0.83\pm.27\pm.20\pm.20$	$0.862a_1^2$	0.95
$D^{*0}D_s^-$	$1.00\pm.47\pm.22\pm.24$	$0.828a_1^2$	0.91
$D^{*0}D_s^{*-}$	$2.12\pm.75\pm.52\pm.52$	$2.206a_1^2$	2.42

$\Psi K^{(*)}$ (Class 2) Branching Fractions(%)			
mode	CLEO	Model	$a_2 = 0.26$
ΨK^-	$0.110\pm.015\pm.009$	$1.819a_2^2$	0.123
ΨK^{*-}	$0.178\pm.051\pm.023$	$2.932a_2^2$	0.198
$\Psi \bar{K}^0$	$0.075\pm.024\pm.008$	$1.817a_2^2$	0.123
$\Psi \bar{K}^{*0}$	$0.169\pm.031\pm.018$	$2.927a_2^2$	0.198

Table 2. Values of a_1 and a_2 are fitted separately for $D^{(*)}\pi^{(*)}$, $D^{(*)}D_s^{(*)}$, and $\Psi K^{(*)}$ decay mode groups. Class 3 $D^{(*)}\pi^{(*)}$ decays are not used in the fit. The data is from Ref.[8, 11] where the first error is statistical and third systematic. When there is a third error, it reflects uncertainties in the branching ratios of charmed mesons (in particular, $\mathcal{B}(D_s^+ \to \phi\pi^+) = 3.7 \pm 0.9\%$). The model is an 'improved' BSW model of Ref.[2] where $f_D = f_{D^*} = 220$ MeV, $f_{D_s} = f_{D_s^*} = 280$ MeV, $f_\rho = 205$ MeV, $f_\Psi = 384$ MeV, and $(\tau_B/1.63\text{ps})^{1/2}|V_{cb}| = 0.039$ were used.

determining the sign of a_2/a_1. The interference effect is conveniently measured by taking the ratio of a class-3 decay rate to the corresponding class-1 decay rate, e.g. $R = \Gamma(B^- \to D^0\pi^-)/\Gamma(\bar{B}^0 \to D^+\pi^-)$, which becomes a function of a_1/a_2 as seen in Table 2. Note that $R > 1$ corresponds to $a_2/a_1 > 0$. The sign of a_2/a_1 is in a stark contrast to the case of $D \to K\pi$ decays where we had (updated with new measurements)

$$c_1(m_c) = 1.26 \qquad c_2(m_c) = -0.51$$
$$a_1 = 1.15 \pm 0.03 \quad a_2 = -0.51 \pm 0.03$$

which indicated that $c_i = a_i$ and prompted the so-called 'rule of discarding $1/N_c(N_c = 3)$ terms' in $1/N_c$ expansions[15]. For class-1 decays, it was shown by

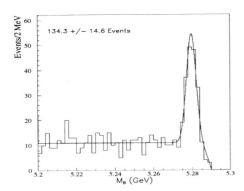

Figure 1. The beam-constrained mass for the sum of 8 $D^{(*)0,+}D_s^{(*)+}$ modes based on 1.56fb^{-1} of data collected by CLEO.

mode	CLEO Branching Ratio(%)	charm weight
D^+X	24.3±3.2±1.9±2.6[23]	1.0
D^0X	59.6±3.1±3.6±2.9[23]	1.0
D_sX	11.81±0.43±0.94±2.87*	1.0
Λ_c	6.4±0.8±0.8[24]	1.0
ΨX	1.13±0.04±0.06*	4.0
total # charm (n_c) = 1.07±0.08		

Table 3. Inclusive branching ratio measurements. New results for this conference are marked by '*'. A ΨX mode counts as 4 charms since a Ψ has two charms and we assume that there are as many charmonium states that do not decay through Ψ.

QCD sum rules that the contribution from the octet-octet term may cancel the 1/3 term in (2)[16]. For class 2 and 3 decays, however, nothing firm can be said at this point. The value of $c_{1,2}$ themselves may have significantly different values for $b \to c\bar{c}s$ vs $b \to c\bar{u}d$[17]. The positive sign of a_2/a_1, however, may have an implication on the phenomenological explanation[18] of B_{sl} (B semileptonic branching ratio)[14] which seems to be smaller than inclusive calculations[19].

If we assume a_1 is the same for the $D^{(*)}D_s^{(*)}$ and $D^{(*)}\pi^{(*)}$ groups, one can obtain the D_s decay constant.

$$f_{D_s} \overset{\text{assume}}{=} f_{D_s^*} = 285 \pm 11 \pm 29 \pm 25 \text{MeV}$$

where the last error reflects the model dependence of form factors, and the rate for the sum of $D^{(*)}D_s^{(*)}$ modes was extracted from the inclusive D_s spectrum.

5.   Charm Deficit

Table 3 shows the B meson inclusive branching ratios as measured by CLEO. The total number of charm per B decay n_c is then 1.07 ± 0.08. For a 'reasonable set of values' $m_b = \mu$(renormalization scale) = 4.8 GeV, $m_c = 1.5$ GeV, and $\Lambda_{\overline{MS}} = 180$ MeV, the expected

n_c is 1.15[20]. This is higher than the measurement, but only by 1σ. However, one possible explanation of the small B_{sl} is that $b \to c\bar{c}s$ mode is enhanced, either by a smaller effective m_c, or by non-perturbative effects[21, 19, 20]. Such scenario is becoming more and more unnatural, because 1) the good agreement between theory and experiment for the $D^{(*)}D_s^{(*)}$ decays as shown above, and 2) in baryonic decays data indicate $(b \to c\bar{c}s)/(b \to c\bar{u}d) = 0.20 \pm 0.13 \pm 0.04$[22]. Nonetheless, if the $b \to c\bar{c}s$ enhancement is the cause of the small B_{sl}, then one would expect n_c in the rage 1.2 to 1.3 which makes the charm deficit significant again.

References

[1] M.Bauer, B. Stech, and M. Wirbel, Z. Phys. **C34** (1987) 103;

[2] M. Neubert, V. Rieckert, B. Stech, and Q. P. Xu, *Heavy Flavors*, p286, Eds. A. Buras and M. Lindner (World Scientific, 1992), and references therein.

[3] M. Shifman, a talk in this conference; also see, for example, I. Bigi, B. Blok, M. Shifman, N. Uraltsev, and A. Vainstein, *B Decays, 2nd ed.*, Ed. S. Stone (World Scientific, 1994), and references therein.

[4] J. Schwinger, Phys. Rev. Lett. **12** (1964) 630; also see, R. P. Feynman, *Symmetries in Elementary Particle Physics*, p111, Ed. Zichichi (Academic Press, 1965).

[5] J. Bjorken, Nucl. Phys. **B** (Proc. Suppl.) **11** (1989) 325.

[6] D. Fakirov and B. Stech, Nucl. Phys. **B133** (1978) 313; M. Dugan and B. Grinstein, Phys. Lett. **B255** (1991) 583; S. Brodsky and A. Mueller, Phys. Lett. **B206** (1988) 685.

[7] No QCD correction is included in this expression since the coefficient of the operator $\mathbf{O}_1$ does not receive first-order QCD correction (see Section 3).

[8] M. S. Alam *et al.* (CLEO Collaboration), Phys. Rev. **D50** (1994) 43.

[9] The models for the semileptonic decays used are: M. Wirbel, B. Stech, and M. Bauer, Z. Phys. **C29** (1985) 637; N. Isgur, D. Scora, B. Grinstein, and B. Wise, Phys. Rev. **D39** (1989) 799; J.G. Korner and G.A. Schuler, Z. Phys. **C38** (1988) 511.

[10] D. Bortoletto and S. Stone, Phys. Rev. Lett. **65** (1990) 2951.

[11] T. Bergfeld *et al.* (CLEO Collaboration), CLEO CONF94-9, a contributed paper to this conference.

[12] P. Roudeau, a plenary talk in this conference.

[13] J. H. Kürn and R. Rückl, Phys. Lett. **135B** (1984) 477; G. T. Bodwin, E. Braaten, and G. P. Lepage, Phys. Rev. **D46** R1914.

[14] R. Patterson, a plenary talk in this conference.

[15] A. J. Buras, J.-M. Gérard, and R. Rückl, Nucl. Phys. **B268** (1986) 16.

[16] B. Blok and M. Shifman, Nucl. Phys. **B399** (1993) 441; *ibid.* **B399** (1993) 459, and references therein.

[17] B. Grinstein, W. Kilian, T. Mannel, and B. Wise, Nucl. Phys. **B363** (1991) 19.

[18] K. Honscheid, a talk in this conference;

[19] P. Ball, a talk in this conference.

[20] A. Falk, M. Wise, and I. Dunietz, CALT-68-1933.

[21] I. Bigi, B. Blok, M. Shifman, and A. Vainstein, Phys. Lett. **B323** (1994) 408.

[22] R. Davis, a talk in this conference.

[23] D. Bortoletto *et al.* (CLEO COllaboration), Phys. Rev. **D45** 21, with $\mathcal{B}(K^-\pi^+) = 3.91 \pm 0.19\%$ and $\mathcal{B}(K^-\pi^+\pi^+) = 9.3 \pm 1.0\%$.

[24] G. Crawford *et al.* (CLEO Collaboration), Phys. Rev. **D45** (1992) 752.

Semileptonic B Meson Decays and Interfering Amplitudes

Klaus Honscheid[†‡]

Department of Physics, The Ohio State University, Columbus Ohio 43210, USA

Abstract

Consequences of the interference between external and internal spectator amplitudes for the lifetimes and semileptonic decay fractions of B^0 and B^+ mesons are discussed. Extrapolating from the constructive interference observed in 11 exclusive hadronic B decays we find an inclusive semileptonic decay fraction of $(11.2 \pm 0.5 \pm 1.7)\%$, significantly closer to the experimental results than previous predictions.

1. Introduction

Although there has been significant progress in the calculation of QCD corrections in the decays of heavy flavour mesons, there are still some unsolved puzzles. One of the most intriguing is the low semileptonic decay fraction of B mesons [1]. Ignoring the small $b \rightarrow u$ fraction, the b quark in the B meson decays to a charm quark and emits a virtual W boson. This can transform itself into a lepton neutrino or a quark anti-quark pair. Taking into account the color factors and making some crude assumption about the quark masses, we can determine the relative rate of these processes and find an semileptonic decay fraction of approximately 15%. To obtain a more precise number we have to correct for hadronic effects due to the exchange of gluons between the quark lines. This enhances the hadronic rate with respect to the semileptonic rates resulting in $\mathcal{B}_{s.l.} \approx 13 - 14\%$. Bigi *et al* have recently performed an evaluation of $\mathcal{B}(B \rightarrow Xe\nu)$ based on the $1/m_Q$ expansion method in QCD [3] and found that the theory cannot accomodate a semileptonic branching fraction of B mesons of less than 12.5 %.

Experimentally, the semileptonic decay fraction of B mesons has been determined by the ARGUS and CLEO collaborations and by the four LEP experiments.

$\mathcal{B}_{s.l.}$ is determined by integrating over the measured lepton momentum spectrum. However, models have to be used to remove the background from $b \rightarrow c \rightarrow s$ cascade decays. The model dependence can be significantly reduced by selecting $\Upsilon(4S)$ decays with two final state leptons. A high momentum lepton tags this reaction as a $B\bar{B}$ event while the other lepton is used to measure the lepton momentum spectrum in semileptonic B decay. Following this procedure, CLEO has contributed a paper to this conference quoting a value of $(10.36 \pm 0.17 \pm 0.40)\%$ for the semileptonic B decay rate [2]. This is significantly below the lower bound allowed by theory and hence we have a problem.

2. Interfering Amplitudes in Hadronic B Decays

A solution to this problem would be a further enhancement of the hadronic decay rate with respect to the semileptonic rate. Hadronic B decays proceed via external or internal spectator diagrams. While the two diagrams lead to different final states in B^0 decays, both processes produce the same final state in charged B decays and hence the corresponding amplitudes will interfere. These two amplitudes combined with the factorization hypothesis form the framework of spectator models such as the model by Bauer, Stech, and Wirbel [6]. These models have been surprisingly successful in describing many features of heavy meson

† E-mail: kh@mps.ohio-state.edu
‡ The work reported here was done in collaboration with K. R. Schubert and R. Waldi, Technische Universität Dresden.

decay. Destructive interference between the internal and external spectator amplitude for hadronic D^+ decays reproduces the observed $D^0 - D^+$ lifetime difference. Bauer, Stech, and Wirbel describe the two amplitudes by phenomenological parameters a_1 and a_2. The values of these parameters have to be determined by experiments. Destructive interference as observed in D^+ decays is described by a relative minus sign between a_1 and a_2. The theoretical interpretation of these parameters is controversial [3] but it was generally expected that a similar but less pronounced interference pattern would be found in B decay. It came as surprise when the CLEO collaboration reported constructive interference in all exclusive hadronic B^+ decays observed so far [4]. Combining the experimental

$B^+(\bar{b}u)$ $\rightarrow$	QCD	$B^0(\bar{b}d)$ $\rightarrow$	QCD	CKM	PS
$\bar{c}u\,e\nu$	0.86	$\bar{c}d\,e\nu$	0.86		1.00
$\bar{c}u\,\mu\nu$	0.86	$\bar{c}d\,\mu\nu$	0.86		0.99
$\bar{c}u\,\tau\nu$	0.86	$\bar{c}d\,\tau\nu$	0.86		0.23
$\bar{c}u\,\bar{d}u$	$3(a_1+a_2)^2$	$\bar{c}d\,\bar{d}u$	$3a_1^2$	$|V_{ud}|^2$	1.00
		$\bar{c}u\,\bar{d}d$	$3a_2^2$	$|V_{ud}|^2$	1.00
$\bar{c}u\,\bar{s}u$	$3(a_1+a_2)^2$	$\bar{c}d\,\bar{s}u$	$3a_1^2$	$|V_{us}|^2$	0.98
		$\bar{c}u\,\bar{s}d$	$3a_2^2$	$|V_{us}|^2$	0.98
$\bar{c}u\,\bar{s}c$	$3a_2^2$	$\bar{c}d\,\bar{s}c$	$3a_2^2$	$|V_{cs}|^2$	0.48
$\bar{c}c\,\bar{s}u$	$3a_1^2$	$\bar{c}c\,\bar{s}d$	$3a_1^2$	$|V_{cs}|^2$	0.48
$\bar{c}u\,\bar{d}c$	$3a_2^2$	$\bar{c}d\,\bar{d}c$	$3a_2^2$	$|V_{cd}|^2$	0.49
$\bar{c}c\,\bar{d}u$	$3a_1^2$	$\bar{c}c\,\bar{d}d$	$3a_1^2$	$|V_{cd}|^2$	0.49

Table 3. Contributions from all $b \rightarrow c$ spectator diagrams. Partial widths are obtained as
$\Gamma = \Gamma_0(b \rightarrow ce^-\bar{\nu}) \times CKM \times QCD \times PS$.

decay	exp. average [%]	Neubert et al. [7]
$B^+ \rightarrow \bar{D}^0\pi^+$	0.45 ± 0.04	$0.265(a_1 + 1.230a_2)^2$
$B^+ \rightarrow \bar{D}^0\rho^+$	1.10 ± 0.18	$0.622(a_1 + 0.662a_2)^2$
$B^+ \rightarrow \bar{D}^{*0}\pi^+$	0.51 ± 0.08	$0.255(a_1 + 1.292a_2)^2$
$B^+ \rightarrow \bar{D}^{*0}\rho^+$	1.32 ± 0.31	$.70(a_1^2 + 1.49a_1a_2 + .64a_2^2)$
$B^+ \rightarrow \psi K^+$	0.106 ± 0.015	$1.819\,a_2^2$
$B^+ \rightarrow \psi K^{*+}$	0.17 ± 0.05	$2.932\,a_2^2$
$B^0 \rightarrow D^-\pi^+$	0.26 ± 0.04	$0.264\,a_1^2$
$B^0 \rightarrow D^-\rho^+$	0.69 ± 0.14	$0.621\,a_1^2$
$B^0 \rightarrow D^{*-}\pi^+$	0.29 ± 0.04	$0.254\,a_1^2$
$B^0 \rightarrow D^{*-}\rho^+$	0.74 ± 0.16	$0.702\,a_1^2$
$B^0 \rightarrow \psi K^0$	0.069 ± 0.022	$1.817\,a_2^2$
$B^0 \rightarrow \psi K^{*0}$	0.146 ± 0.029	$2.927\,a_2^2$

Table 1. Experimental averages and theoretically predicted decay fractions for hadronic B decays, assuming $|V_{cb}|^2 \cdot \tau_B = 2.35\,10^{-15}$s, and $f_D = f_{D^*} = 220$ MeV

decay fractions measured by ARGUS and CLEO [5] results in the averages listed in Table 2. The partial rates are determined under the assumption of equal decay fractions of the $\Upsilon(4S)$ to B^+B^- and $B^0\bar{B}^0$ pairs, i.e. $f^{+-}/f^{00} = 1$. This quantity is not well measured experimentally; we assume in the following $f^{+-}/f^{00} = 1.0 \pm 0.1$. The relative sign between a_1 and a_2 can be

The experimental results and a model prediction for the decay ratios in the modes $D\pi^-$, $D\rho^-$, and $D^*\pi^-$ are given in Table 2. They show a clear preference for the positive sign. The theoretical prediction for the decay $B^+ \rightarrow D^{*0}\rho^+$ is too uncertain [9] to include this mode in the determination of a_1 and a_2. Taking ratios of B^+ and B^0 decays eliminates the uncertainties due to $|V_{cb}|$ but leaves those originating from $\tau(B^+)/\tau(B^0)$ and f^{+-}/f^{00}. The main difference between different models are details of the $B \rightarrow \pi$ and $B \rightarrow \rho$ form factors. The predictions also depend on the D and D^* decay constants f_D and f_{D^*}. Following Neubert et al. [7] we assume $f_D = f_{D^*} = 220$ MeV. On the experimental side, the error due to the D^0 decay fractions cancels in the ratios involving $B \rightarrow D^*$ decays. A least square fit with seven $B \rightarrow D^{(*)}$ modes from Table 2, excluding only $B^+ \rightarrow D^{*0}\rho^+$, gives $a_1 = 1.04 \pm 0.05$ and $a_2 = 0.24 \pm 0.06$.

3. Assumptions

The distinction between interfering amplitudes for the B^+ and non-interfering for the B^0 may only be valid for two-body decays. On the other hand, many-body final states will most likely start as two colour singlet quark antiquark pairs, including intermediate massive resonances. Interference between final states via different resonant channels involves strong phases which modify the rate for each individual final state in a random way and disappear in the sum of all states. It seems therefore reasonable to extend the model for exclusive two body decays to the majority of hadronic final states in an inclusive picture at the quark level. We assume that the formation of two colour singlets is the essential step of hadron production, which is taken into account quantitatively by a_1 and a_2. We neglect modifications by decays into baryon anti-baryon pairs, where our assumption is not valid. Under the

	exp. average	Neubert et al. [7]
$R_1 = \dfrac{\Gamma(B^+\rightarrow \bar{D}^0\pi^+)}{\Gamma(B^0\rightarrow D^+\pi^-)}$	1.71 ± 0.38	$(1 + 1.23a_2/a_1)^2$
$R_2 = \dfrac{\Gamma(B^+\rightarrow \bar{D}^0\rho^+)}{\Gamma(B^0\rightarrow D^+\rho^-)}$	1.60 ± 0.46	$(1 + 0.66a_2/a_1)^2$
$R_3 = \dfrac{\Gamma(B^+\rightarrow \bar{D}^{*0}\pi^+)}{\Gamma(B^0\rightarrow D^{*+}\pi^-)}$	1.79 ± 0.39	$(1 + 1.29a_2/a_1)^2$

Table 2. Experimental results and theoretical predictions for ratios of B^+ and B^0 decay rates, scaled to $f_{D(D^*)} = 220$ MeV

obtained from $B^+ \rightarrow \bar{D}^0$ and $B^+ \rightarrow \bar{D}^{*0}$ decays, which have contributions from both amplitudes. A relative plus sign between the a_1 and the a_2 amplitudes would give $\Gamma(B^+ \rightarrow \bar{D}^{(*)0}\pi(\rho)^+)/\Gamma(B^0 \rightarrow D^{(*)-}\pi(\rho)^+) > 1$, while a minus sign would correspond to ratios below 1.

assumption of duality, the coefficients a_1 and a_2 can be used to predict the hadronic and semileptonic widths of the B^+ and B^0 mesons. The individual contributions are listed in Table 3. PS denotes the relative phase space factor and the perturbative QCD correction for the semileptonic width is given by [10]

$$\Gamma(b \to ce^-\bar{\nu}) = \Gamma_0(1 - \frac{2\pi}{3}\alpha_s + \frac{25}{6\pi}\alpha_s) \approx 0.86\Gamma_0$$

From the factors in Table 3 we obtain the following total widths, normalized to the lowest order semileptonic width $\Gamma_0(b \to ce^-\nu)$

$$\Gamma(B^+)/\Gamma_0 = 1.91 + 4.44(a_1^2 + a_2^2) + 5.99a_1a_2 \,,$$
$$\Gamma(B^0)/\Gamma_0 = 1.91 + 4.44(a_1^2 + a_2^2) \,.$$

Using these widths, we can calculate two important quantities.

- The average semileptonic decay fraction of B^0 and B^+,

$$\mathcal{B}(B \to e\nu X) = \frac{1}{2.22 + 5.16(a_1^2 + a_2^2) + 3.49a_1a_2} \,,$$

  decreases if a_2 changes sign from negative to positive.
- The lifetime ratio

$$\tau(B^+)/\tau(B^0) = 1 - \frac{a_1a_2}{0.32 + a_1a_2 + 0.74(a_1^2 + a_2^2)} \tag{1}$$

  is larger than 1 for negative and smaller than 1 for positive values of a_2.

To give consistent results, we determine a_1 and a_2 in a fit to the hadronic decay fractions used above, replacing the assumption of equal B^+ and B^0 lifetimes with the inclusive prediction in eq. 1 to rescale the theoretical expectations for B^+ and B^0 decays individually. This fit gives $\chi^2 = 11.6$ for 8 degrees of freedom, and

$$a_1 = 1.05 \pm 0.03 \pm 0.10$$
$$a_2 = 0.227 \pm 0.012 \pm 0.022$$

which implies

$$\mathcal{B}(B \to e\nu X) = (11.2 \pm 0.5 \pm 1.7)\%$$
$$\tau(B^+)/\tau(B^0) = 0.83 \pm 0.01 \pm 0.01 \,,$$

where the first error is statistical including uncertainties in the D^0 and D^+ decay fractions, and the second is from the error on $V_{cb}\sqrt{\tau(B)}$. The uncertainty on f^{+-}/f^{00} yields a negligible error. The predicted lifetime ratio is low but not inconsistent with the current experimental average of 1.00 ± 0.07 [11]. The semileptonic decay fraction is further reduced if we assume a small contribution of penguin decays. Assuming this fraction to be 2.5% leads to $\chi^2 = 11.3$ and $\mathcal{B}(B \to e\nu X) = 10.9\%$, while all errors and the values of a_1, a_2 and $\tau(B^+)/\tau(B^0)$ remain essentially unchanged.

4. Discussion

The discrepancy between the theoretical and the experimental semileptonic decay fraction of B mesons can be considerably reduced by the interpretation of recent results on hadronic B decays in the framework of a spectator model with interfering amplitudes. Our basic assumption is that the constructive interference observed in a few exclusive hadronic B decays is a general feature of B mesons that can be described by two coefficients a_1 and a_2. There is some experimental evidence that this assumption is correct

- The coefficient a_2 extracted from the interference observed in $B^+ \to D^{(*)}$ decays agrees well with the a_2 value obtained from B to charmonium transitions that can only proceed through the internal spectator diagram.
- A QCD based calculation [12] of inclusive ψ production in B decay falls short of a recent CLEO measurement [13]. However, if the coefficients in the calculation are replaced by the measured values of a_1 and a_2 we find good agreement.
- The measured $B \to \chi_{c1}$ decay fraction has been used to predict the $B \to \chi_{c2}$ rate [12, 13]. Again the agreement with recent experimental results can be improved by using a_1 and a_2 instead of the QCD coefficients in the calculation.

A careful study of inclusive decays as well as a search for color suppressed decays like $B^0 \to D^0\pi^0$ will allow us in the not too distant future to determine, if a_1 and a_2 are really universal coefficients in B decays.

References

[1] G. Altarelli and S. Petrarca, PL B261, 303 (1991); I. I. Bigi et al., PL B293, 430 (1992) and erratum ibid. B297, 477 (1993); W. Palmer, B. Stech, PR D48, 4174 (1993).
[2] CLEO Collaboration, International Conference on HEP, Glasgow, CLEO-CONF-94-6 (GLS 0243).
[3] I. I. Bigi, B. Blok, M. A. Shifman, N. G. Uraltsev, A. I. Vainshtein, "B Decays", ed. S. Stone, World Scientific (1994).
[4] M. S. Alam et al., Phys. Rev. D50, 43 (1994).
[5] T. E. Browder, K. Honscheid, S. Playfer, "B Decays", ed. S. Stone, World Scientific (1994).
[6] M. Bauer, B. Stech, M. Wirbel, ZP C34,103(1987).
[7] M. Neubert, V. Rieckert, B. Stech in 'Heavy Flavors', ed. by A. J. Buras and M. Lindner, World Scientific 1992.
[8] A. Deandrea et al., Preprint UGVA-DPT 1993/07-824.
[9] V. Rieckert, priv. communication.
[10] N. Cabibbo, L. Maiani, *Phys. Lett.* B79,109 (1978).
[11] V. Sharma, DPF 94, Albuquerque (1994).
[12] G.T. Bodwin, E. Bratten, T.C. Yuan, G.P. Lepage, Phys. Rev. D46, 3703 (1992). Glasgow, CLEO-CONF-94-11.
[13] CLEO Collaboration, International Conference on HEP, Glasgow, CLEO-CONF-94-11 (GLS 0248).

Paper presented at XXVII Int. Conf. on High Energy Physics: Session Pa-2
Glasgow, UK, 20–27 July 1994

B Decays to States with Baryon Pairs

Robin E. P. Davis

Department of Physics and Astronomy, University of Kansas
Lawrence, Kansas, 66045 U.S.A.

(Representing the CLEO Collaboration)

Abstract

The production mechanisms for the processes, $B \rightarrow$ baryon pairs $+ X$ have been studied. There is evidence that the dominant mechanism may be internal W emission and that the process, $b \rightarrow c\bar{u}d$, occurs more frequently than the process, $b \rightarrow c\bar{c}s$. The first observation of B decays to an exclusive Λ_c^+ channel is also presented.

1. Introduction

The decays of B mesons to inclusive Λ_c^+ channels have previously been observed by ARGUS[1] and by CLEO 1.5 [2], the latter measuring $BR(B \rightarrow \Lambda_c^+ X)$ to be $(6.4 \pm 0.8 \pm 0.8)\%$. Both groups observed the recoil spectrum of the Λ_c to be soft, implying that the X system was heavy.

The mechanism for B decays to Λ_c^+ final states is not understood. These decays could proceed through an external W process, as shown in Fig. 1(a) for b quark decay. This would require two quark pairs to be popped between the original quarks. The presence of such a process would also imply a corresponding semileptonic decay of the order of 10%, as observed in B decays to final states with charmed mesons.

These decays may also proceed through an internal W process, shown in Fig. 1(b) for b quark decay. Such processes are not expected to be colour suppressed to the same extent as B decays to meson final states via an internal W process. Only one quark pair is popped between the original quarks, the most likely possibilities being $u\bar{u}$, $d\bar{d}$ or $s\bar{s}$, (the latter occurs at a rate $\approx 1/3$ of either of the first two). With the coupling, $W^- \rightarrow \bar{u}d$, the only c quark will be on the top line, as seen in Fig. 1(b), which may produce a Λ_c^+ . (The contribution from Cabibbo suppressed processes such as, $W^- \rightarrow \bar{u}s$ is not

considered here). In contrast the coupling, $W^- \rightarrow \bar{c}s$, yields an s quark at the top and a $\bar{c}$ quark at the bottom. This may produce a Ξ_c^+ or Ξ_c^0 at the top, possibly with a $\overline{\Lambda_c^-}$ at the bottom of the diagram. Were this the case, the relatively larger masses of the Ξ_c states provide a natural explanation for the softness of the Λ_c recoil spectrum, as has recently been proposed[3].

The flavour of the parent B meson may be tagged by observing the sign of the high momentum lepton when the opposite B meson, B^+ or B^0, decays semileptonically, i.e. $\bar{b} \rightarrow \bar{c}W^+$, $W^+ \rightarrow l^+\nu_l$. Thus like sign $\Lambda_c l$ correlations, indicate the presence of the $b \rightarrow c\bar{u}d$ process, while the opposite sign correlations indicate the presence of the $b \rightarrow c\bar{c}s$ process.

2. Experimental Details

These preliminary results are based on data collected with the CLEO II detector[4] and have been reported more fully elsewhere[5]. The data sample consists of 2.036 fb^{-1}, taken on the $\Upsilon(4S)$ resonance, and 0.967 fb^{-1} on the continuum just below the $\Upsilon(4S)$ resonance, corresponding to $(2.19 \pm 0.04) \times 10^6$ B pairs.

The $\Lambda_c^{+\dagger}$ is reconstructed in the following decay

---

† References to data for a particular channel or final state always imply the inclusion of data for the charge conjugate system.

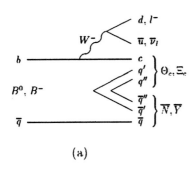

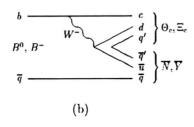

(a)

(b)

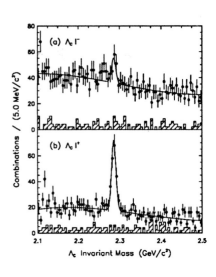

Figure 1. Quark diagrams for $B \to$ baryon pairs $+ X$ via (a) external and (b) internal W emission. Θ_c and and Ξ_c are charmed non-strange and strange baryons respectively.

Figure 2. (a). The Λ_c invariant mass in GeV/c^2 for (a) opposite sign ($\Lambda_c^+ \, l^-$) correlations and (b) like sign ($\Lambda_c^+ \, l^+$) correlations. The shaded histograms are for continuum data.

channels: $pK^-\pi^+$, $p\overline{K^0}$, $\Lambda\pi^+$ and $\Sigma^0\pi^+$. The number of Λ_c^+ events was obtained by fitting the mass spectra for each channel for the on resonance data and subtracting the corresponding spectra for the scaled continuum data. This yielded a sample of 3154 ± 160 Λ_c candidates from B decays.

The momenta of the tagging leptons were required to satisfy, $1.4 < p_l < 2.4$ GeV/c, thus ensuring a pure sample of primary leptons from B decays. Details of the lepton selection criteria are given elsewhere[5].

3. $\Lambda_c \, l$ Sign Correlations

The data for the like and opposite sign $\Lambda_c \, l$ correlations are shown in Fig. 2, with the unshaded (shaded) histogram being the $\Upsilon(4S)$ (continuum) data. The fits yielded 141 ± 16 like sign and 43 ± 16 opposite sign correlations. These numbers were corrected for contamination by secondary leptons (from $c \to sl\nu$ decays), hadron fakes, and finally for $B^0\overline{B}^0$ mixing. The corrected values were 148 ± 16 like sign events and 29 ± 19 opposite sign events. It was checked that these numbers are consistent with those expected from the initial sample of 3154 Λ_c events. In addition the lepton momentum spectra for these events were found to be consistent with those expected of primary leptons from B decays. Likewise the angular distribution between the lepton and Λ_c directions was flat, as expected.

These results, then, indicate that, for internal W

processes,

$$\frac{b \to c\overline{c}s}{b \to c\overline{u}d} \; = \; \frac{N(\Lambda_c^+ \, l^-)}{N(\Lambda_c^+ \, l^+)} \; = \; (20 \pm 13 \pm 4)\%.$$

Thus, in B decays to Λ_c final states, the process $b \to c\overline{u}d$ dominates, but the process $b \to c\overline{c}s$ is significant.

4. Search for External W Processes in $B \to \Lambda_c + X$

The contribution of external W production for B decays to Λ_c states was investigated in two ways. Both methods exploited the fact that semileptonic B decays to Λ_c final states are a signature of an external W process. In addition these decays are characterized by a relatively soft signal lepton, which has opposite sign to that of the lepton used to tag the flavour of the other B meson. For this purpose, the signal lepton was required to satisfy, $p_{l_{sig}} < 1.4$ GeV/c; only a small fraction of the signal leptons would fail to pass this cut.

In the first method, a search was made for $\Lambda_c^+ l^-_{sig}$ correlations. The wrong sign $\Lambda_c^+ l^+_{sig}$ signal contained 74 ± 16 events, which was consistent with zero after making background corrections, as expected. The right sign combinations contained 95 ± 20 events, which yielded a signal of 35 ± 26 events after background corrections were applied. This produced an upper limit[‡]

‡ All limits presented here are for a 90% confidence level.

of, $\frac{BR(\overline{B}\to\Lambda_c^+\overline{N}l^-\overline{\nu}_l)}{BR(\overline{B}\to\Lambda_c^+X)} < 6\%$.

Secondly, employing a missing mass technique to discrminate in favour of the undetected neutrino, a search was made for the decay, $\overline{B} \to \Lambda_c^+\overline{p}l^-\overline{\nu}_l$. This yielded an upper limit, $\frac{BR(\overline{B}\to\Lambda_c^+\overline{p}l^-\overline{\nu}_l)}{BR(\overline{B}\to\Lambda_c^+X)} < 6\%$.

Both searches gave upper limits of about 6% for semileptonic decays of B mesons to Λ_c^+ states, relative to decays to all Λ_c^+ states. The corresponding value for B decays to D final states is about 12%. This suggests that external W processes are more significant, for B decays, to meson final states than to baryon final states.

5. Search for Ξ_c Final States in B Decays

A search was made for B decays to Ξ_c^+ and Ξ_c^0 final states, where $\Xi_c^+ \to \Xi^-\pi^+\pi^+$ and $\Xi_c^0 \to \Xi^-\pi^+$. Signals were seen in both continuum events and in $\Upsilon(4S)$ events. After continuum subtraction, signals of 71.2 ± 21.1 Ξ_c^+ and 51.8 ± 18.7 Ξ_c^0 events were obtained for the $\Upsilon(4S)$ data. With reasonable assumptions for the Ξ_c branching ratios, these data yield the values: $BR(\overline{B} \to \Xi_c^+X) = (1.5 \pm 0.7)\%$ and $BR(\overline{B} \to \Xi_c^0X) = (2.4 \pm 1.3)\%$. The sum of these Ξ_c yields is roughly half that of the yield for Λ_c^+ noted above.

The observation of B decays to Ξ_c final states indicates the presence of internal $b \to c\overline{c}s$ processes accompanied by $u\overline{u}$ or $d\overline{d}$ popping. The kinematic limit for the Ξ_c momentum is then ≈ 1.2 GeV/c. There are a few events above this limit, suggesting the presence of a small component of the $b \to c\overline{u}d$ process, accompanied by $s\overline{s}$ popping.

6. Search for Exclusive B Decays to Λ_c^+

Attempts were made to reconstruct fully the decays $\overline{B} \to \Lambda_c^+\overline{p}\,(n)\pi$, where $n = 0, .., 4$ charged pions or where $n = 0, .., 3$ charged pions accompanied by one π^0. Since genuine B mesons will have an energy equal to the beam energy, the beam constrained mass of the B candidates, $M_B = \sqrt{E_{beam}^2 - (\Sigma\vec{p})^2}$, was used. Monte Carlo sudies indicated that the one sigma resolution of the energy difference, $\Delta E = |\Sigma E - E_{beam}|$, varied between 10 and 12 MeV, depending on the final state being considered. These candidates were therefore required to satisfy, $|\Sigma E - E_{beam}| < 25$ MeV. A signal of 15.0 ± 4.7 events was seen in the $\overline{B}^0 \to \Lambda_c^+\overline{p}\pi^-\pi^+$ decay channel. No signal was seen in either the energy sidebands, the Λ_c sidebands or the continuum events. The data are shown in Fig. 3. This yields a branching ratio, $BR(\overline{B} \to \Lambda_c^+\overline{p}\pi^-\pi^+) = (0.187 \pm 0.059 \pm 0.056 \pm 0.045)\%$, the third error resulting from the uncertainty in the Λ_c braching fraction.

In all other individual channels investigated, no significant signal was seen.

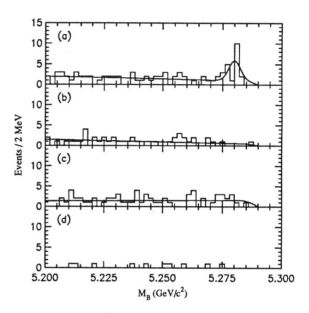

Figure 3. (a). The $\Lambda_c^+\overline{p}\pi^+\pi^-$ invariant mass in GeV/c² for $\Upsilon(4S)$ events. The same distribution for (b) the ΔE sidebands, (c) the Λ_c^+ sidebands and (d) the continuum.

7. Conclusions

The decay of B mesons to Λ_c final states was studied using Λ_c lepton sign correlations. Limits of about 6% were set on the contribution of external W processes. The internal processes proceeded mainly through the $b \to c\overline{u}d$ process, with the $b \to c\overline{c}s$ process contributing $(20 \pm 13 \pm 4)\%$. Decays of B mesons to Ξ_c final states proceeded mainly through a $b \to c\overline{c}s$ process, with some evidence for a contribution from the $b \to c\overline{u}d$ process. Finally a signal was observed for fully reconstructed events in the decay, $\overline{B} \to \Lambda_c^+\overline{p}\pi^-\pi^+$, with a measured braching ratio of $(0.187 \pm 0.059 \pm 0.056 \pm 0.045)\%$.

References

[1] ARGUS Collab., H. Albrecht et al., Phys. Lett. **B210** (1988) 263.
[2] CLEO Collab., G. Crawford et al., Phys. Rev. **D45** (1992) 752.
[3] I. Dunietz, P. S. Cooper, A. F. Falk and M. B. Wise, FERMILAB-PUB-94-132-T, 1994.
[4] CLEO Collab., Y. Kubota et al., Nucl. Instr. Meth. **A320** (1992) 66.
[5] CLEO Collab., D. Cinabro et al., CLEO CONF 94-8, 1994, submitted to ICHEP94, Glasgow; Y. Kubota et al., CLEO CONF 94-13, 1994, submitted to ICHEP94, Glasgow.

B_s^0 Production and Mass Measurements at LEP and CDF

M. Bonesini

Sezione INFN Milano, Italy

Abstract

Recent LEP and CDF data on B_s^0 mass measurements and production are described. The world average for m_{B_s} is 5368.1 ± 3.8 MeV, to be compared with theoretical predictions in the range $5345 - 5388$ MeV.

1. Introduction

About 12% of the b hadrons produced at LEP are B_s^0 mesons. The presence of the B_s^0 meson was inferred from the comparison of the rates of same sign dileptons at the $\Upsilon(4S)$ and at $p\bar{p}$ colliders [1] and from data at the $\Upsilon(5S)$ obtained from CUSB [2]. Preliminary evidence was then obtained at LEP from the partial reconstruction of its semileptonic decays via a study of opposite sign $D_s^- l^+$ combinations [3]. Firm evidence and a precise measurement of mass has been obtained later, both at LEP and Tevatron, from fully reconstructed charged mode decays [4]. The useful B_s^0 decay modes, for exclusive reconstruction, include $B_s^0 \to J/\psi(\psi')\phi$ (1), $B_s^0 \to D_s^{*-}(D_s^-)\pi^+(a_1^+; \rho^+)$ (2) and $B_s^0 \to K^-\overline{D^0}\pi^+(a_1^+; \rho^+)$ (3), ... where the J/ψ or ψ' are tagged via leptonic decay modes and the "D's" through decays with an intermediate ϕ, K or K*.

The main experimental problem is the search for a few B_s^0 candidates, distributed over many different decay modes, in the presence of potentially high sources of background. Backgrounds are due to track combinatorics (*combinatorial*, negligible in channels with a ϕ due to its narrowness) or π/K misidentification (*reflections*). For example, $\overline{B_d^0} \to D^+\pi^-$ could fake a $\overline{B_s^0} \to D_s^+\pi^-$, when the π^+ from D^+ decay is misinterpreted as a kaon.

All LEP experiments have searched for fully reconstructed B_s^0 in the channels (1) to (3), while CDF, having no particle identification (PID) capabilities to discriminate between π and K has searched for B_s^0

candidates only in channel (1). The experimental requirements, mainly due to the need to have a tight control over backgrounds, are:

- a good tracking resolution ($\delta p/p \sim 0.001 \times p$) to have precise mass reconstruction
- good vertex reconstruction capabilities, to exploit the multivertex topologies of the B_s^0 decay chains
- good PID, to discriminate effectively between energetic π and K.

On the top of this there is obviously the requirement to choose physical channels with small background (e.g. involving a ϕ), when possible.

2. The search at LEP: OPAL, ALEPH and DELPHI

All LEP experiments, measuring the B_s^0 mass, fulfill the previous requirements, in particular on particle identification through the energy loss of charged particles (dE/dx) and in DELPHI also using the barrel RICH detector [5]. As an example, in DELPHI the PID is obtained from dE/dx in the TPC (192 samplings) with a π/K separation at 1.5 σ's for $4 \leq p \leq 25$ GeV/c (average rejection factor 5) and from the barrel RICH (average rejection factor 12-15).

OPAL and ALEPH have analyzed samples from the 90+91+92 data taking (about 1.2×10^6 Z), while DELPHI has analyzed the 92 data sample only (about $.8 \times 10^6$ Z).

OPAL searched for B_s^0 candidates in the channels:

(1) $D_s^-(\to \phi\pi^-; \to K^{*0}K^-)\pi^+$ and (2) $J/\psi\phi$. Six candidates were found in the mass window 5.1-5.5 GeV in channel (1), with a combinatorial background of 0.7 ± 0.5 events, giving a mass of 5370 ± 40 MeV. From the single candidate in the channel (2): one $J/\psi \to e^+e^-$, the B_s^0 mass was determined as $m_{B_s} = 5359 \pm 19 \pm 7$ MeV. Systematic errors take into account track parameters and their covariance (1.9 MeV), mass scale errors (5 MeV) and additional systematics on momentum measurement (4 MeV).

ALEPH searched for B_s^0 candidates in the channels: (1) $D_s^- n\pi$, (2) $J/\psi(\psi')\phi$ and (3) $K^-\overline{D^0}\pi^+$. The analysis is characterized by a very good resolution in the mass constrained fit (about 8.5 MeV for $B_s \to \psi'\phi$) and about nine candidates were reconstructed. The B_s mass is measured using only two unambiguos candidates: (a) $B_s^0 \to \psi'\phi$ (which due to its very small error presently dominates the LEP average) and (b) $\overline{B_s^0} \to D_s^+(\to \phi\pi^+)\pi^-$, giving a weighted average $m_{B_s} = 5368.6 \pm 5.6 \pm 1.5$ MeV. The main sources of systematic errors are the mass scale (1.1 MeV) and the alignment of the tracking system (0.9 MeV).

The DELPHI analysis provided three B_s^0 candidates: one $D_s(\to \phi\pi)a_1$, one $D_s(\to \phi\pi)\pi$ and one $J/\psi\phi$. To take properly into account the sources of biases due to reflections (0.20 equivalent events), the combinatorial background (0.30 equivalent events) and the $D_s^* \to D_s\gamma$ decay, where the photon is not detected, a global likelihood fit was performed. The fit result $m_{B_s} = 5374 \pm 16$MeV takes into account statistical errors and the previous systematics. An additional systematic coming from the absolute mass scale calibration is estimated around 2 MeV.

3.   The search at Tevatron: CDF

In the 1988-89 Tevatron run, CDF showed the capability to trigger and reconstruct $B \to J/\psi(\to \mu^+\mu^-)X$ decays in $p\bar{p}$ collisions at $\sqrt{s} = 1.8$ TeV. B_s^0 candidates are searched for in the channel $J/\psi(\to \mu^+\mu^-)\phi$, where having no PID each track is considered as a π; as a K if instead $p_T \geq 2$ GeV. ϕ candidates are formed from pairs of tracks assigned to kaon mass, with combined mass consistent with the nominal ϕ mass value. In the full 1992-1993 data sample (run 1A: 19.3 pb^{-1}) 33 ± 7 B_s^0 candidates were reconstructed, from a binned likelihood fit to the mass spectra over a background of about 14 events, giving a preliminary mass value of $5367.7 \pm 2.4 \pm 4.8$ MeV. Systematic errors includes the p_T scale (1.1 MeV), uncertainties in tracking errors (1.0 MeV), stability of selection criteria (2.8 MeV), fitting procedure (1.2 MeV) and variation in the reconstructed J/ψ mass (3.2 MeV).

4.   World average and conclusions

The data on B_s^0 mass reconstruction, coming from LEP exclusive, fully reconstructed events and from CDF fit to the $(J/\psi)\phi$ mass plot, are shown in figure 1. The world average for B_s^0 mass is : 5368.1 ± 3.8 MeV, being dominated by the CDF measure and the LEP $\psi'\phi$ ALEPH candidate. This must be compared with theoretical predictions [6] in the range 5345-5388 MeV. Clearly more candidates of the type $\psi\phi$, $\psi'\phi$ at LEP are needed to reduce the errors on the world average.

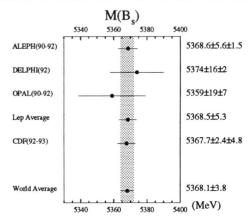

Figure 1. Summary of B_s^0 mass measurement from LEP and CDF, with averages computed assuming no correlation between experiments

Acknowledgments

I would like to thanks the many people of the LEP and CDF collaborations that have helped me in the preparation of this report, in particular V. Sharma (ALEPH), J. Hagemann (OPAL), Y. Arnoud, A. De Angelis, P. Kluit, W. Venus (DELPHI) and J. Incandela (CDF).

References

[1] C. Albajar *et al.*, Phys. Lett. **B186** (1987) 247;Phys. Lett. **B262** (1991) 171
    H. Albrecht *et al.*, Phys. Lett. **B192** (1987) 247
    M. Artuso *et al.*, Phys. Rev. Lett. **62** (1989) 2223
[2] J. Lee-Franzini *et al.*, Phys. Rev. Lett. **65** (1990) 2947
[3] P. Abreu *et al.*, Phys. Lett. **B289** (1992) 199
    D. Buskulic *et al.*, Phys. Lett. **B294** (1992) 145
    P.D. Acton *et al.*, Phys. Lett. **B295** (1992) 357
[4] P. Abreu *et al.*, Phys. Lett. **B324** (1994) 500
    R. Akers *et al.*, CERN-PPE/94-91
    D. Buskulic *et al.*, Phys. Lett. **B311** (1993) 425
    F. Abe *et al.*, Phys. Rev. Lett. **71** (1993) 1685
    J. D. Lewis, FERMILAB-CONF-94/128-E
[5] E. G. Anassontzis *et al.*, Nucl. Instr. Meth. **A323** (1992) 351
[6] W. Kwong and J. Rosner, Phys. Rev. **D44** (1991) 212

Beauty-Baryon Production and Mass Measurements at LEP

S. E. Tzamarias

Oliver Lodge Laboratory, Oxford Street, University of Liverpool, P.O.Box 147, Liverpool, U.K.

Abstract

With the large number of accumulated Z° hadronic decays and the ability of the LEP experiments to accurately track and identify charged particles it has been possible to measure the production and the decay properties of the B-baryons. At this Conference, measurements of the production and decay rate of the Λ_b and, for the first time, Ξ_b and measurements of the Λ_b polarization and its mass have been reported.

1. Introduction

In the last three years, each LEP experiment has accumulated about 1.7 million Z° hadronic decays corresponding to 0.75 million beauty flavored hadrons in total. The available energy at LEP and the size of the above samples enables studies of the production and decay properties of the beauty baryons (referred to in the following text as B-baryons). The selection of events where the b-quark is hadronized to a baryon is based either on inclusive kinematical properties of the B-baryon decay products or on the complete reconstruction of exclusive B-baryon decays. The inclusive approach has been successfully used to select B-baryon semileptonic decays and decays where a final state Λ° is produced with specific kinematical characteristics. In parallel, studies of exclusive decay channels have resulted in the determination of masses and have set limits on decay rates.

2. B-Baryon Semileptonic Decays

In the semileptonic decays, the spectator system contained in the initial state is transmitted to the final state. This property has been previously used to isolate different species of beauty-hadrons [1], [2]. In the same way the excess of events containing an energetic baryon (antibaryon) accompanied by a

negative (positive) lepton† produced in the same jet at large transverse momentum, as compared to those accompanied by a positive (negative) lepton‡, is a signature of a B-baryon decay. Accidental correlations of baryons and leptons, produced through a variety of processes, contribute with different weights to the right and wrong sign combinations. Such effects have to be estimated by dedicated Monte Carlo studies.

The observed baryon-lepton correlations at LEP involving protons, Λ° and Λ_c are attributed mainly to the Λ_b semileptonic decays, due to the fact that the heavier B-baryons either decay to a Λ_b or their production rate is small compared with the Λ_b. However, because of its strange content, the correlated production of the Ξ^- and a lepton can be a way to access the decays of the Ξ_b baryon.

2.1. Correlated Λ^0-lepton Production

A comparison of the right sign Λ°-lepton combinations with the wrong sign background resulted in the measurements§ of the B-baryon production rates reported by DELPHI[3] and OPAL[4]. In particular DELPHI obtains for the product branching ratios the

---

† "right sign combinations" in the following text
‡ "wrong sign combinations " in the following text
§ In presenting the experimental results, the terminology used in the original contributed paper is followed.

values:

$$\mathrm{BR}(b \to B - baryon)\mathrm{BR}(B - baryon \to \Lambda\mu X) = \\ 0.38 \pm 0.08 \pm 0.05\%$$

$$\mathrm{BR}(b \to B - baryon)\mathrm{BR}(B - baryon \to \Lambda e X) = \\ 0.19 \pm 0.13 \pm 0.03\%$$

and assuming lepton universality:

$$\mathrm{BR}(b \to B - baryon)\mathrm{BR}(B - baryon \to \Lambda l X) = \\ 0.32 \pm 0.07 \pm 0.04\%$$

Similarly, OPAL finds the branching ratios to be :

$$\mathrm{BR}(b \to \Lambda_b)\mathrm{BR}(\Lambda_b \to \Lambda\mu X) = \\ 0.339 \pm 0.049 \pm 0.038\%$$

$$\mathrm{BR}(b \to \Lambda_b)\mathrm{BR}(\Lambda_b \to \Lambda e X) = \\ 0.269 \pm 0.061 \pm 0.032\%$$

and assuming lepton universality:

$$\mathrm{BR}(b \to \Lambda_b)\mathrm{BR}(\Lambda_b \to \Lambda l X) = \\ 0.313 \pm 0.038 \pm 0.035\%$$

2.2.   Correlated Λ_c-lepton Production

DELPHI [3] probes the B-baryon production by studying the correlations of kinematically selected Λ_cs and leptons in the same jet. In the this analysis, the Λ_c is identified by its decay to K$p\pi$. This channel, although impaired by low statistics, provides a very pure B-baryon sample since the contribution from accidental Λ_c lepton combinations and from b meson semileptonic decays in the right sign combination sample, is negligible.

This study concludes the following product branching ratios:

$$\mathrm{BR}(b \to B - baryon)\mathrm{BR}(B - baryon \to \Lambda_c\mu X) = \\ 1.33 \pm 0.41^{+0.42}_{-0.35}\%$$

$$\mathrm{BR}(b \to B - baryon)\mathrm{BR}(B - baryon \to \Lambda_c e X) = \\ 1.26 \pm 0.52^{+0.42}_{-0.35}\%$$

and assuming lepton universality:

$$\mathrm{BR}(b \to B - baryon)\mathrm{BR}(B - baryon \to \Lambda_c l X) = \\ 1.30 \pm 0.32^{+0.42}_{-0.35}\%$$

2.3.   Correlated proton-muon Production

The correlated production of protons and muons was used by DELPHI[3] to study the B-baryon production. Such a pμ signature is interpreted as resulting from the direct semileptonic decay of a B-baryon to a proton or through its semileptonic decays to a charm baryon, which consequently decays to a proton. After the proper kinematical selection has been made,

the background involving genuine protons is almost completely eliminated. The remaining background consists mainly of misidentified charged kaons coming from b hadron decays.

In this analysis a global Likelihood fit was performed using combined particle identification information from dE/dx and Cherenkov Ring Imaging, the transverse momentum of the lepton, and the proper time estimation from the formation of a decay vertex. After correcting for inefficiencies and background contamination, the extracted product branching ratio was found to be :

$$\mathrm{BR}(b \to B - baryon)\mathrm{BR}(B - baryon \to p\mu X) = \\ 0.36 \pm 0.08 \pm 0.05^{+0.14}_{-0.04}\%$$

where the second and third error terms correspond respectively to the systematic errors due to the experimental technique and to the assumed kinematical properties of the B-baryons in the Monte Carlo.

2.4.   Correlated Ξ^--lepton Production

ALEPH[5] and DELPHI[6] have performed the first measurement of the Ξ^--lepton correlated production, where the Ξ^- hyperon is identified in its decay to a $\Lambda^\circ\pi^-$. An extra rejection of the combinatorial background is achieved in [6] by requiring the candidate Ξ^- trajectory to be recorded in the Micro Vertex Detector of the spectrometer in question.

After a kinematical selection was applied, an excess of right sign ($\Xi^\mp l^\mp$) combinations was observed in [5] and [6]. This was interpreted as being signature of Ξ_b production and decay. One source contributing to the excess was identified as semileptonic decays of other heavy flavored hadrons [5],[6]. This source contributes mainly to the right sign combinations and its quantitative estimation depends on very poorly known branching ratios. Another was identified as accidental Ξ^--lepton correlations (where the Ξ^- hyperon is produced during the hadronization process). This is expected to contribute almost equally to the right and wrong sign combinations and is found in [6] to be modelled well by the JETSET-7.3 Monte Carlo.

In the ALEPH analysis [5] the right and wrong sign combinations are compared. After correcting for inefficiencies and contributions to the signal of non Ξ_b hadron decays the following product branching ratio is obtained:

$$\mathrm{BR}(b \to \Xi_b)\mathrm{BR}(\Xi_b \to \Xi_c l\nu)\mathrm{BR}(\Xi_c \to \Xi^- X) = \\ 0.034 \pm 0.020\%$$

In the DELPHI analysis [6] the observed right and wrong sign combinations are compared directly to the Monte Carlo expectation. From this comparison, the probability that the observed signal was a fluctuation of non B-baryon semileptonic decays is estimated to be 10^{-4} and the product branching ratio was measured to be:

$$BR(b \rightarrow B - baryon)BR(B - baryon \rightarrow \Xi lX) = 0.059 \pm 0.021 \pm 0.01\%$$

Furthermore, assuming that the $BR(\Lambda_c \rightarrow \Xi X)$ is 0.3% and $BR(b \rightarrow$ B-baryon) is 10.$\pm$5%, the probability that a b-quark from the decay of a Z° will be hadronized to a Ξ_b is estimated to be :

$$BR(b \rightarrow \Xi_b) = 3.3 \pm 1.2 \pm 0.6\%$$

3. Kinematical Selection of Λ° from B-baryon Decays

In the hadronic decays of Z° to $b\bar{b}$ the production of Λ° hyperons is attributed both to the decays of b flavored hadrons and to the hadronization process. It is expected that Λ^0s from the former mechanism are produced with, high rapidity values with respect to the direction of the thrust axis, whilst the latter mechanism contributes mainly in the low rapidity region.

DELPHI measured the production rate of Λ° hyperons produced in b hadronic decays [7] of the Z° by comparing the measured rapidity distribution with the expectations from phenomenological hadronization models. This measurement, in connection with the measured branching ratio of the nonstrange b-mesons into Λ^0 at the $\Upsilon(4s)$, and under the assumption that :
a) the branching ratio of strange and nonstrange mesons into Λ° is the same, and b) the probability the b quark to be hadronized into a baryon is 8.0$\pm$2.0%, leads to the following branching ratio of the B-baryon into Λ° :

$$BR(B - baryon \rightarrow \Lambda^\circ X) = 0.15^{+0.21}_{-0.07}\%$$

4. Measurement of the Λ_b Polarization

The Λ_b baryon is expected to retain the initial b-quark spin [8] [10] if it is produced directly. As a result of the strong decays of the higher mass B-baryons to Λ_b, there will be a dilution of the polarization of the Λ_b sample produced at the Z°. However, a significant net polarization of the Λ_b can be expected [9] at LEP.

A Λ_b polarization measurement was performed by ALEPH [10] by measuring the ratio of the average mean lepton energy to the average neutrino energy (missing energy) in the semileptonic decays of Λ_b into Λ°. It has been shown in [9] that this ratio has a strong dependence on the polarization of the Λ_b and can be analytically expressed in terms of the polarization. Thus

the measured ratio of the average energies corresponds to the following Λ_b polarization :

$$P_{\Lambda_b} = -0.3^{+0.32}_{-0.27} \pm 0.04$$

The same procedure applied to a sample of selected semileptonic decays of B-mesons into D^{*+} (which should not retain any polarization information) resulted in the following value of the B-meson polarization :

$$P_{B-meson} = -0.05^{+0.20}_{-0.22}$$

5. Exclusive Decays and Mass Measurements

In searching for exclusive decays of Λ_b , DELPHI found [11] two candidates in the $\Lambda_c\pi$ and $D^\circ p\pi$ channels. From these events the mass of the Λ_b was estimated to be :

$$m_{\Lambda_b} = 5635^{+38}_{-29} MeV/c^2$$

but at the 2σ level mass values up to 6 MeV/c^2 are allowed because of the possibility that both the events were partially reconstructed.
OPAL reported [12] seven Λ_b candidate decays to $\Lambda_c\pi$ with an estimated background of 1$\pm$ 0.5 event. The fitted mass was:

$$m_{\Lambda_b} = 5620 \pm 30(stat.only)$$

In the same analysis the limits on the following branching ratios at the 90% confidence level are estimated to be:

$$BR(b \rightarrow \Lambda_b)BR(\Lambda_b \rightarrow \Lambda_c\pi) < 0.005 \qquad (1)$$
$$BR(b \rightarrow \Lambda_b)BR(\Lambda_b \rightarrow J/Psi\Lambda) < 0.0011$$

References

[1] ALEPH Collaboration: Phys. Lett. B278 (1992) 209.
DELPHI Collaboration: Phys. Lett. B311 (1993) 379.
OPAL Collaboration: Phys. Lett. B281 (1992) 394.
[2] DELPHI Collaboration: Phys. Lett. B28 (1992) 199.
[3] Lifetime and Production Rate of Beauty Baryons from Z° Decays , (DELPHI contributed paper to ICHEP-94).
[4] Measurement of the Product Branching Ratio f(b$\rightarrow \Lambda_b$)BR($\Lambda_b \rightarrow \Lambda^\circ l^- \bar{\nu} X$), (OPAL contributed paper to ICHEP-94).
[5] Search for strange b baryons through Ξ^- lepton correlations, (ALEPH contributed paper to ICHEP-94).
[6] Measurement of the production of Ξ^-l pairs in jets at LEP and interpretation of their origin in terms of strange-beauty baryon decays (DELPHI contributed paper to ICHEP-94).
[7] Measurement of Charged Particles, K_s°, $K^\pm$, p and Λ in $Z^\circ \rightarrow b\bar{b}$ Events and in the Decay of B Hadrons (DELPHI contributed paper to ICHEP-94).
[8] F. E. Close et al. , J. Phys. G18 (1992) 1726.
[9] G. Bonvicini and L. Randal, CERN preprint: CERN-PPE-94-07.
[10] Measurement of the Λ_b polarization at LEP (ALEPH contributed paper to ICHEP-94).
[11] Search for exclusive decay channels of the Λ_b baryon with DELPHI (DELPHI contributed paper to ICHEP-94).
[12] Search for exclusive Λ_b decays with OPAL detector at LEP (OPAL contributed paper to ICHEP-94).

Paper presented at XXVII Int. Conf. on High Energy Physics: Session Pa-2
Glasgow, UK, 20–27 July 1994

Charm and Beauty Hadron Production
at $\sqrt{s} \sim M_{Z^0}$

V. Gibson

University of Cambridge, Cavendish Laboratory,
Madingley Road, Cambridge, UK, CB3 0HE.

Abstract

New results are presented here from LEP on heavy quark fragmentation, the production of
L=1 charmed meson states and the production of excited beauty mesons.

1. Introduction

The production characteristics of heavy flavoured
hadrons are currently being studied extensively at
LEP. The combination of the large statistics now
available, ~ 1.7 million hadronic Z^0 decays, collected
by ALEPH, DELPHI, L3 and OPAL during 1990–
1993, the excellent impact parameter resolution due
to the silicon microvertex detectors and the improved
particle identification have enabled detailed studies
of exclusive final states to be performed. New results
are presented here on heavy quark fragmentation,
the production of L=1 charmed meson states and
the production of excited beauty mesons.

2. Heavy Quark Fragmentation

The study of heavy quark fragmentation provides an
important test of QCD since the mass of the heavy
quark sets the scale for perturbative calculations.
However, non-perturbative hadronization effects can
only be parameterized in the framework of a
fragmentation model, and it is the form of this
model that is currently one of the limiting factors
in measurements of heavy quark properties.

Indirect information about heavy quark fragmentation has been obtained using leptons from semileptonic decays as a signature for heavy quark production [1, 2, 3, 4], from J/ψ production [5] and
from charged particle multiplicities in b quark tagged
events [6, 7]. In each case, only the average of the
primordial hadron energy compared to the beam en-
ergy, $x_E = E_{\text{hadron}}/E_{\text{beam}}$, has been extracted.

A more direct measurement of b quark frag-

mentation has been obtained using the correlation
between the D meson and lepton produced in the
semi-leptonic decay, B $\rightarrow$ D$\ell\nu X$ [8, 9]. The D
mesons are reconstructed in the decay modes $D^{(*)0} \rightarrow$
$K^-\pi^+, K^-\pi^+\pi^-\pi^+$, $D^+ \rightarrow K^-\pi^+\pi^+$ and $D^{*+} \rightarrow$
$D^0\pi^+$. The energy of the B hadron is calculated
using the energy of the Dℓ pair and an estimate of
the neutrino energy from the visible energy in the Dℓ
hemisphere and either the beam energy (DELPHI)
or the conservation of energy between the two hemispheres (ALEPH). The latter method results in a
neutrino energy resolution of ~ 1.5 GeV for $x_E > 0.8$.

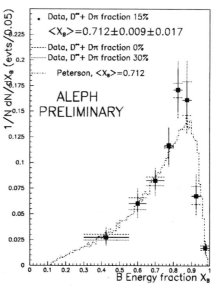

Figure 1. The ALEPH B meson energy fraction compared
to the Peterson expectation [10].

The resulting x_E distribution measured by ALEPH is shown in Figure 1.

Information about c quark fragmentation has been obtained from measurements of the D* energy spectrum [11, 12, 13]. D*'s are produced from the hadronization of charm quarks with $\langle x_E \rangle \sim 0.5$, from the decay of B hadrons with $\langle x_E \rangle \sim 0.3$ and from gluon splitting with $\langle x_E \rangle \sim 0.2$. The D* is reconstructed in the decay mode $D^{*+} \to D^0 \pi^+$, where the D^0 is produced together with a slow pion and reconstructed in the decay mode $D^0 \to K^- \pi^+$. The contributions to the D* data samples from c quark hadronization and B hadron decay are separated using leptons [13], jet shape variables in artificial neural networks [11, 13], forward multiplicity [13] and the D^0 lifetime [12, 13]. OPAL has measured the full range of x_E as shown in Figure 2 and finds an indication of $c\bar{c}$ production from gluon splitting with a mean multiplicity of $(4.4 \pm 1.6(stat) \pm 1.7(sys))\%$ assuming the Standard Model prediction for $\Gamma_{c\bar{c}}/\Gamma_{had}$ [13].

Table 1 is a summary of the measurements of $\langle x_E \rangle$. A comparison of the values obtained for charm fragmentation with those at lower energies provides clear evidence for scaling violations as predicted by QCD [13].

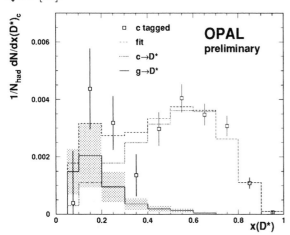

Figure 2. The OPAL D* energy spectrum for c quark tagged events. The error on the gluon splitting component is indicated by the shaded area.

3.   L=1 Charmed Mesons

A knowledge of the relative abundance of vector and pseudoscalar L=0 mesons and the amount of higher mass (L=1 or radial excitation) meson states is required for measurements such as the charged and neutral B meson lifetimes or for the interpretation of inclusive lepton spectra. Four L=1 charmed meson spin states are expected to exist and should decay via the strong interaction by emitting a pion.

DELPHI and ALEPH have searched for the $D_1(2420)^0$ meson state, which is a mixture of

			$\langle x_E \rangle_b$
L3	[1]	Leptons	$0.686 \pm 0.006 \pm 0.016$
OPAL	[2]	Global leptons	$0.697 \pm 0.006 \pm 0.011$
ALEPH	[3]	Global leptons	$0.714 \pm 0.004 \pm 0.012$
DELPHI	[4]	Global leptons	$0.702 \pm 0.004 \pm 0.011$
L3	[5]	J/ψ	$0.70 \pm 0.03^{+0.02}_{-0.01}$
OPAL	[6]	B multiplicity	$0.693 \pm 0.003 \pm 0.029$
DELPHI	[7]	B multiplicity	$0.688 \pm 0.004 \pm 0.028$
DELPHI	[8]	$D\ell$	$0.695 \pm 0.015 \pm 0.029$
ALEPH	[9]	$D\ell$	$0.712 \pm 0.009 \pm 0.017$
LEP Average			$0.702 \pm 0.002 \pm 0.008$
			$\langle x_E \rangle_c$
ALEPH	[3]	Global leptons	$0.487 \pm 0.008 \pm 0.009$
ALEPH	[11]	D*	$0.501^{+0.010}_{-0.011} \pm 0.007$
DELPHI	[12]	D*	$0.500^{+0.011}_{-0.012} \pm 0.005$
OPAL	[13]	D*	$0.515^{+0.008}_{-0.005} \pm 0.008$
LEP Average			$0.504 \pm 0.004 \pm 0.008$

Table 1. A summary of measurements of $\langle x_E \rangle$ for b and c quarks. For the LEP averages, common systematic errors have been averaged.

the $^1P_1$ and $^3P_1$ spin states, and the $D_2^*(2460)^0$, which is a $^3P_2$ meson state, in the decay channel $D_1^0, D_2^{*0} \to D^{*+} \pi^-$, followed by $D^{*+} \to D^0 \pi^+$ and $D^0 \to K^- \pi^+, K^- \pi^+ \pi^- \pi^+$ [12, 14]. The contributions from c quark hadronization and B hadron decay are separated using the energy of the D* and the decay length of the secondary vertex. The charm enriched $D^*\pi$–D* mass difference is shown in Figure 3 and the partial production rates, $\Gamma\left(c, b \to D_1^0, D_2^{*0} \to D^{*+} \pi^-\right)/\Gamma\left(c, b \to D^{*+}\right)$, are summarised in Table 2. ALEPH has also searched for the $D_2^*(2460)^+$ meson state through its decay $D_2^{*+} \to D^0 \pi^+$ and observe that D_2^{*+} production is suppressed in B hadron decays.

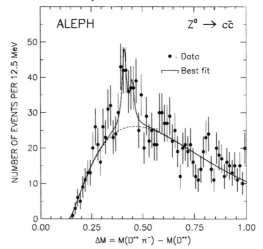

Figure 3. The ALEPH charm enriched $D^*\pi$–D* mass difference.

	$c \to D_1^0, D_2^{*0}$	$b \to D_1^0, D_2^{*0}$
DELPHI	$0.11 \pm 0.03 \pm 0.02$	$0.17 \pm 0.06 \pm 0.03$
ALEPH	$0.084 \pm 0.024 \pm 0.023$	$0.159 \pm 0.048 \pm 0.031$

Table 2. Summary of the D_1^0, D_2^{*0} partial production rates.

4. Excited Beauty Production

ALEPH, DELPHI and L3 have performed searches for the vector partner, B*, of the pseudoscalar B meson [15, 16, 17]. Since the mass difference between the B and the B* is $\sim$ 46 MeV, the B* meson decays via an electromagnetic transition, $B^* \to B\gamma$. At LEP energies these decays result in a photon spectrum that extends only up to 800 MeV. The B*–B mass difference is calculated from a measurement of the photon energy, using either converted photons (ALEPH and DELPHI) or calorimeter photons (L3), and the momentum vector of the B meson from its decay products. Shown in Figure 4 is the B*–B mass difference obtained by DELPHI and summarised in Table 3 are the measured B* production rates and mass differences. DELPHI has also obtained limits on the amount of isospin and strangeness splitting of $<$ 7.5 MeV and $<$ 8.5 MeV at the 95% confidence level respectively. In addition, ALEPH and DELPHI have also measured the angular distribution of photons and conclude that the longitudinal and transverse B* polarization states are equally populated.

5. Vector and Pseudoscalar Production

The probability of directly producing a charm or beauty vector meson, V, rather than a pseudoscalar, P, has been extracted from the D, D* [11, 12]

and B* [15, 16, 17] measured production rates. The results are summarised in Table 4. From simple counting arguments one would expect the ratio $V/(V + P) = 0.75$ and, in the B system, the measured value is consistent with that expected. However, in the D system the results indicate that the contribution due to the production of L=1 charmed mesons cannot be neglected. Figure 5 is a plot of $V/(V+P)$ versus the probability of producing an L=1 meson state, H, and shows that $V/(V+P) = 0.75$ would require both a large probability H and a small branching ratio, $Br\left(D_1^0, D_2^{*0} \to D^{*+}\pi^-\right)$.

$V/(V + P)$:	D system	B System
ALEPH	0.53 ± 0.16	$0.80 \pm 0.04 \pm 0.057 \pm 0.024$
DELPHI	0.45 ± 0.06	$0.73 \pm 0.04 \pm 0.06$
L3		$0.77 \pm 0.07 \pm 0.10$

Table 4. The $V/(V+P)$ ratio measured in the D, B systems.

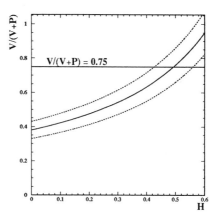

Figure 5. $V/(V + P)$ versus the production rate of L=1 charmed mesons. The dotted lines are the 1σ errors.

Acknowledgments

I am grateful to the many colleagues who provided me with detailed information about their results. In particular, I wish to thank T.Behnke, D.Bloch, B.Clare, P.Colas, J.P.Lees, A.Nippe, S.Schael and W.Venus for their generous help.

References

[1] L3 Collaboration, Phys. Lett. **B261** (1991) 177.
[2] OPAL Collaboration, Zeit. f. Physik **C60** (1993) 199.
[3] ALEPH Collaboration, CERN-PPE/94-017.
[4] DELPHI Collaboration, this conference.
[5] L3 Collaboration, Phys. Lett. **B288** (1992) 412.
[6] OPAL Collaboration, Zeit. f. Physik **C61** (1994) 209.
[7] DELPHI Collaboration, this conference.
[8] DELPHI Collaboration, Zeit. f. Physik **C57** (1993) 181.
[9] ALEPH Collaboration, this conference.
[10] C.Peterson *et al.*, Phys. Rev. **D 27** (1983) 105.
[11] ALEPH Collaboration, CERN-PPE/93-208.
[12] DELPHI Collaboration, this conference.
[13] OPAL Collaboration, this conference.
[14] ALEPH Collaboration, this conference.
[15] ALEPH Collaboration, this conference.
[16] DELPHI Collaboration, this conference.
[17] L3 Collaboration, this conference.

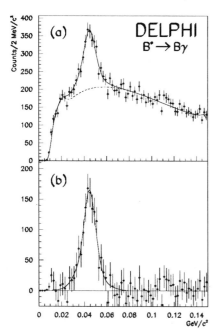

Figure 4. The DELPHI B*–B mass difference.

	$\dfrac{\Gamma(b \to B^*)}{\Gamma(Z^0 \to b\bar{b})}$ (%)	$M(B^*) - M(B)$ (MeV)
ALEPH	$32.2 \pm 1.2 \pm 1.9$	$45.1 \pm 0.6 \pm 0.9$
DELPHI	$28.7 \pm 1.5 \pm 2.3$	$45.3 \pm 0.4 \pm 0.6$

Table 3. A summary of B* rates and mass differences.

Parallel Session Pa-3

Heavy Ion Collisions

Conveners: C. W. Fabjan (CERN)
W. A. Zajc (Columbia University)

Scientific secretaries: S. Gowdy
S. Dorris (reserve)

m_t-dependence of Boson Interferometry in SPb Reactions at CERN SPS

B Lörstad[§]

Department of Particle Physics, Lund University
S-22362 Lund, Sweden

On behalf of the NA44 Collaboration

Abstract

Using the focusing spectrometer at CERN SPS we have measured the correlation function of $\pi\pi$ and KK pairs produced in SPb reactions. When analysed in the longitudinal center of mass system the correlation function can be adequately parametrized with Gaussian functions in all three dimensions. The extracted radii parameters are all similar and show a common $1/\sqrt{m_t}$ dependence. This result excludes the validity of the commonly used and discussed parametrizations of the correlation function in Q^2, where Q is the four-momentum difference within the pair. The results emphasize the presence of strong momentum-spacetime correlations and hydrodynamical flows both in longitudinal and transversal directions. It also implies that we are not measuring the total source sizes by the Bose-Einstein effect in these complex reactions.

1. Introduction

New results has been achieved by the NA44 collaboration on three dimensional analysis of the correlation function of $\pi^+\pi^+$ pairs and K^+K^+ pairs produced in SPb reactions at the CERN SPS[1, 2, 3]. The analysis is made in the longitudinal center of mass system of the pair (LCMS), i.e. the system where the sum of the two particle momenta is transverse to the beam direction. The momentum difference of the particle pair is resolved into Q_{long}, parallel to the beam direction, and Q_t perpendicular to the beam direction. Q_t is further resolved into a component $Q_{t,out}$ parallel to the pair momentum sum and $Q_{t,side}$, perpendicular to the pair momentum sum and the beam. By fitting the correlation function to the Eq. (1) we can extract the corresponding radius parameters, R_{long}, $R_{t,out}$ and $R_{t,side}$.

$$C(Q) = N[1 + \lambda \exp(-Q_{t,out}^2 R_{t,out}^2 - Q_{t,side}^2 R_{t,side}^2 - Q_{long}^2 R_{long}^2)] \qquad (1)$$

The new results, displayed in table 1, show mainly

§ E-mail: bengt@quark.lu.se

that $R_{t,out} \approx R_{t,side} \approx R_{long}$ and $\lambda_{KK} > \lambda_{\pi\pi}$. What is the significance of these new results?

2. Experimental setup and data analysis

The focusing spectrometer of the NA44 experiment has been described in detail elsewhere[4].

A multiplicity trigger is used to select central collisions, typically at the level of 10% of the total inelastic cross-section. The resulting particle density is roughly the same in the three different samples we present here.

We present results on several data sets, as seen in table 1. Systematic errors are estimated by varying the analysis conditions and refitting the data. The systematic errors are found to be at worst equal to the statistical errors.

Figure 1 shows the projections on to the three axes. Eq. (1) gives a fair description of the data.

System	λ	$R_{t,out}$ [fm]	$R_{t,side}$ [fm]	R_{long} [fm]	mean $p_t[MeV]$
$\pi^+\pi^+$	0.56 ± 0.02	4.02 ± 0.14	4.15 ± 0.27	4.73 ± 0.26	150
$\pi^+\pi^+$	0.55 ± 0.02	2.97 ± 0.16	2.95 ± 0.24	3.09 ± 0.19	450
K^+K^+	0.82 ± 0.04	2.77 ± 0.12	2.55 ± 0.20	3.02 ± 0.20	225

Table 1. SPb reactions, preliminary NA44 results

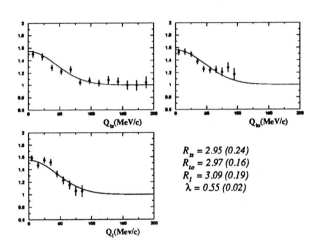

$R_{si} = 2.95\ (0.24)$
$R_{lo} = 2.97\ (0.16)$
$R_{l} = 3.09\ (0.19)$
$\lambda = 0.55\ (0.02)$

Figure 1. The $Q_{t,out}, Q_{t,side}$ and Q_{long} projections. The line represents a Gaussian fit to the data points. Data corresponds to the pion sample at high transverse momentum[2].

3. Possible parametrizations

The longitudinal, side and out-components are defined in the longitudinal centre of mass system of the pair, LCMS, where the sum of the two particle momenta, $\vec{K} = \vec{p_1} + \vec{p_2}$, is transverse to the beam direction. With cylindrical symmetry the pair is characterized by the mean rapidity of the pair, $Y = (y_1 + y_2)/2$, the magnitude of the sum of the transverse momenta of the pair and the relative momenta of the pair, $Q = p_1 - p_2$. This system, LCMS, is connected to the CMS of the pair by a boost along $\vec{K}$, with a boost velocity given by

$$\beta_t = \frac{K_t}{E_1 + E_2} = \frac{|\vec{p_{1,t}} + \vec{p_{2,t}}|}{E_1 + E_2} \qquad (2)$$

In the CMS the energy difference beween the two particles vanishes which yields a relation between the energy difference, the out-component and the transverse velocity of the pair

$$\gamma_t \Delta E - \gamma_t \beta_t Q_{t,out} = 0 \qquad (3)$$

or

$$\Delta E = \beta_t Q_{t,out} \qquad (4)$$

i.e. we have

$$Q_{inv}^2 = Q_{long}^2 + Q_{t,side}^2 + (1 - \beta_t^2)Q_{t,out}^2 \qquad (5)$$

The Q-components are here defined in the LCMS of the pair.

We can now test the hypothesis that the two-particle correlation is described by a spherical system in CMS, the old so-called Goldhaber approach still very common nowadays

$$C(Q) = C(Q_{long}, Q_{t,out}, Q_{t,side}) = 1 + \lambda \exp(-R^2 Q^2) \qquad (6)$$

by fitting to Eq.(1).

In the hypothesis of a spherical system in CMS we should find in LCMS that $R_{t,side} = R_{long} = R$ and $R_{t,out} = R/\gamma_t$, i.e. only the out-component is Lorentz contracted. The $R_{t,out}$ contraction from the low p_t $\pi\pi$ sample to the high p_t $\pi\pi$ sample can be approximated by the ratio of the mean m_t values resulting in a $R_{t,out}$ prediction for the high p_t sample of $R_{t,out} \approx 1.7$ fm, whereas the other two R components stay constant. This is in contradiction with the results of table 1.

By the correlation measurement at two different p_t-settings we thus have shown that a simple parametrization using Q_{inv} is inadequate in describing the SPb data. This means that the question if the correlation function in Q is Gaussian or exponential or something else is not very relevant. It also implies that a parametrization in a power law of Q^2 can not describe our data. Arguments have been given that such a power law would imply strong fluctuations of the size of the interaction region, or that the interaction region is itself a fractal[5]. In simple hadron systems such a power law in Q^2 is compatible with data permitting a natural explanation of intermittency in these reactions[6].

4. Hydrodynamical models

Earlier data on interferometry from high-energy heavy-ion collisions seem to be consistent with hydrodynamical models with one-dimensional expansion of matter along the beam-axis[7, 8]. The effective hydrodynamical length in this longitudinal direction has a specific dependence on the transverse mass of the produced particles, m_t. In a Bjorken scaling model we get[9, 10]

$$R_{long} = \sqrt{\frac{T_f}{m_t}} \frac{\tau_0}{\cosh y} \qquad (7)$$

where τ_0 is the inverse gradient of the four-velocity at the center, being close to the mean proper time at freeze-

Pair type	R_{long} [fm]	$\overline{m_t}$	$R_{long} * \sqrt{m_t}$
$\pi\pi$	4.73 ± 0.26	0.20	2.1 ± 0.1
$\pi\pi$	3.09 ± 0.19	0.47	2.1 ± 0.1
KK	3.02 ± 0.20	0.53	2.2 ± 0.2

Table 2. SPb reactions, preliminary NA44 results

out, T_f the temperature at freeze-out and y the rapidity of the produced system of particles in the system of the observer, $y = (y_1 + y_2)/2$ and m_t the average transverse mass, $m_t = (m_{t_1} + m_{t_2})/2$. The mean freeze-out time, τ_0, is a constant in a Bjorken scaling model, in a Landau model τ_0 is a slowly decreasing function of rapidity. The parameter R_{long} is not the total length of the system, it is a length of homogeneity, inversely proportional to the gradient of longitudinal velocity within the system. This formula was derived for one-dimensional expansion, but describes also the three-dimensional case[11]. In LCMS the rapidity of the system of the two particles is always zero, $y_1 + y_2 = 0$, why here the Eq. 7 takes the simplified form

$$R_{long} = \sqrt{\frac{T_f}{m_t}}\tau_0 \qquad (8)$$

We see in Table 2 that our data follow Eq. (8) with an accuracy corresponding to the R_{long} measurement accuracy.

The NA35 Collaboration has studied the R_{long}-dependence on rapidity and p_t in the nucleon-nucleon center of mass system. Their data follow nicely the $1/\cosh y$ formulation, Eq. (7), and support the $1/\sqrt{m_t}$ dependence [7].

All radii parameters given in table 1 can to a first approximation be summarized by a simple relation:

$$R_{t,out} = R_{t,side} = R_{long} = const./\sqrt{m_t} \qquad (9)$$

The validity of Eq. (9) can be tested by a simple χ^2-test which is accepted with an acceptable goodness of the fit, $\chi^2/ndf = 10/8$.

Our data can apparently be described by a spherical source in LCMS with radius parameters showing a $1/\sqrt{m_t}$ dependence.

The empirically found relation (9) can be shown to be a special case for a cylindrically symmetric, finite, three-dimensionally expanding boson source[12]. The velocity gradient together with the freeze-out temperature generate a thermal length-scale in all three dimensions. If the geometrical length-scales are much larger than the thermal length-scale the Bose-Einstein correlation function becomes symmetric in the longitudinally comoving system and the side, out and longitudinal radius parameters measure the same (thermal) length which exhibit a $1/\sqrt{m_t}$ dependence.

The influence of resonances seems to be of secondary importance. We can see this also on that the fitted λ value, see table 1, show no p_t dependence.

The measured correlation functions are approximately reproduced by the RQMD generator which has significant rescattering before freezeout[13].

In the future PbPb reactions we expect still larger geometrical sizes but roughly the same thermal sizes, i.e. a still cleaner situation for the simple $1/\sqrt{m_t}$ rule to be valid. The model foresees only a minor change of the measured radius parameters, as compared to SPb.

The analysis presented implies that the technique of studying the space-time development of the reactions via the Bose-Einstein effect is not as general as often supposed. In the heavy-ion reactions the correlation function seems to mainly be sensitive to local or thermal sizes not the physical size.

Acknowledgements

I want to thank Tamás Csörgő, Budapest, for very fruitful discussions and common work on the understanding of the Bose-Einstein correlation function.

The NA44 Collaboration wishes to thank the staff of the CERN PS-SPS accelerator complex for their excellent work. We thank the technical staff at CERN and the collaborating institutes for their valuable contributions. We are grateful for the support given by the Austrian Science Foundation; the Science Research Council of Denmark; the Japanese Society for the Promotion of Science and the Ministry of Education, Science and Culture, Japan; the Research Council of Sweden; the US Department of Energy; and the National Science Foundation (Nuclear Physics) through grants PHY8906284 and PHY8958491.

References

[1] NA44 Collaboration: Directional Dependence of $\pi^+\pi^+$ Correlations, to be published
[2] m_T Dependence of Boson Interferometry in Heavy Ion Collisions at the CERN SPS, NA44 Collaboration: H. Beker et al., CERN preprint: CERN-PPE/94-119
[3] Kaon Interferometry in Heavy-ion Collisions at the CERN SPS, NA44 Collaboration: H. Beker et al., CERN preprint: CERN-PPE/94-75
[4] H. Bøggild et al., Phys. Lett. **B302** (1993) 510
[5] A. Bialas, Nucl. Phys. **A545** (1992) 285c
[6] UA1-Collaboration: N. Neumeister et al., Z. Phys. **C60** (1993) 633
[7] G. Roland for the NA35 collaboration, Nucl. Phys. **A566** (1994) 527c
[8] B. Lörstad and Yu.M. Sinyukov, Phys. Lett. **265B** (1991) 159
[9] A.N. Makhlin and Yu.M. Sinyukov, Z. Phys. **C39** (1988) 39
[10] Yu.M. Sinyukov, Nucl. Phys. **A498** (1989) 151c
[11] B.R. Schlei et al., Phys. Lett. **B293** (1992) 275
[12] T. Csörgő and B. Lörstad, Lund University preprint LUNFD6/(NFFL-7082) 1994, submitted to Phys. Rev. Lett.
[13] H. Sorge, H. Stöcker, and W. Greiner, Nucl. Phys **A498** (1989) 567

Strangeness enhancement and space-time characteristics of pion production in ultrarelativistic nucleus-nucleus collisions from the NA35 experiment

K. Kadija[†]

Max-Planck-Institut für Physik, München, Germany

NA35 Collaboration

Abstract

Average multiplicities and spectra of strange particles produced in central S+S, S+Ag and S+Au collisions at 200 GeV per nucleon are studied and compared with the data on strange particle production in proton-nucleus and nucleon-nucleon interactions. S+S and S+Ag data extrapolated to the full phase space show that strangeness production relative to the negative hadron production is similarly enhanced in both reactions. It is also shown that the ratio of $\bar{\Lambda}$ to Λ rapidity distributions for p+S, S+S, S+Ag and S+Au collisions is consistent with the corresponding ratio obtained from pp data. Using boson interferometry as a method for measuring the space-time evolution of the pion source in heavy ion collisions, the dependence of the two-pion correlation functions (in terms of the three components of the pair momentum difference: Q_{Tside}, Q_{Tout} and Q_{Long}) on rapidity and transverse momentum is studied.

1. Introduction

This paper presents the recent results on the production of strange particles (Λ, $\bar{\Lambda}$, K^0_s, K^+, and K^-) in pS, and central SS, SAg, and SAu collisions at 200 GeV per nucleon, obtained from an analysis of NA35 Streamer Chamber data. Additionally the results of a study of two-pion Bose-Einstein correlations measured in the sulphur induced reactions on S, Cu, Ag and Au, have been obtained from an analysis of Streamer Chamber data, and from an analysis of the data from the second large-volume tracking chamber, the Time Projection Chamber (TPC).

2. Strange particle production

For all data samples we looked at the rapidity dependence of the p_T distributions. Since no

significant variations were observed, we parametrized the transverse momentum (or transverse mass) spectra with the function :

$$\rho(p_T|T) = C(T) \cdot p_T \cdot e^{-m_T/T} \qquad (1)$$

The transverse mass is defined as $m_T = \sqrt{m_0^2 + p_T^2}$, where m_0 is the particle rest mass and $C(T)$ is the normalization factor. The fitted shape parameter T using (1) for different reactions is given in table 1. The T parameter for Λ increases with increasing size of the colliding system. A similar tendency is observed for $\bar{\Lambda}$ particles. However the T parameters for K^0_s seem to be independent of the reaction type, and the K^+ shape parameter for SAg collisions is higher than the corresponding K^- parameter.

The characteristics of the observed rapidity distributions can be summarized as follows (for more details see [1]). The projectile and target mass asymmetry is reflected in the Λ rapidity distributions which for pS

† On leave from Rudjer-Boskovic-Institute, Zagreb, Croatia

	Λ	$\bar{\Lambda}$	K_s^0	K^+	K^-
p+S	182 ± 17	132 ± 18	205 ± 16	-	-
S+S	204 ± 17	180 ± 24	210 ± 16	-	-
S+Ag	234 ± 17	221 ± 24	231 ± 17	254 ± 31	181 ± 28
S+Au	240 ± 18	223 ± 22	227 ± 18	-	-

Table 1. Fitted shape parameter T of the transverse momentum distributions. The values correspond to the result obtained using parametrization given by Eq. 1. All values are given in MeV.

and SAg reach a maximum at a rapidity of about 1 to 1.5. The rapidity distribution of Λ hyperons produced in central SS collisions is flat between 1 and 3. The $\bar{\Lambda}$ and K_s^0 rapidity distributions are less sensitive to the initial asymmetry of the system. The yield of K^+ mesons produced in SAg collisions (in the target rapidity region $y \leq 3$)is approximately a factor of two higher than the corresponding yield of K^- mesons.

For pS and SAu collisions the shapes of the rapidity distributions of K_s^0 and $\bar{\Lambda}$ particles in the forward (projectile) region ($y \geq 3$), are similar. In the Λ rapidity distributions we do not observe any projectile nucleus related peak. There is a significant difference in shape (but not in the yield) in the region $y \geq 3$, between the rapidity distribution of Λ hyperons produced in SAu collisions and the "reflected" rapidity distribution for SS collisions.

The ratio of the $\bar{\Lambda}$ to Λ yields is suggested (e.g. by thermodynamic models) to reflect the net baryon density of the particle source. In figure 1 the ratio of $\bar{\Lambda}$ to Λ rapidity distributions for pS(a), SS(b), SAg(c) and SAu(d) is presented. For comparison we show also the corresponding ratio calculated using a parametrization of the $\bar{\Lambda}$ and Λ rapidity distributions for pp collisions at 200 GeV [2]. The results for pS and SS collisions are consistent with the parametrization of pp data. The ratios at mid-rapidity for central SAg and SAu collisions are lower than the parametrization of the pp results. However, due to the large errors of the original pp data this difference is at the limit of significance.

Finally, we estimate the average multiplicity (in full phase space) of strange particles produced in pS, SS and SAg collisions. The mean Λ, $\bar{\Lambda}$ and K_s^0 multiplicities, and the ratio of the mean strange particle multiplicity to the the mean multiplicity of negative hadrons, are presented in table 2, together with corresponding data for pp and nucleon-nucleon collisions at 200 GeV per nucleon [2]. The pS multiplicities presented in table 2 were evaluated for events with charged particle multiplicity greater than 5. Note that our previously published multiplicities for pS interactions [3] referred to the minimum bias sample. The ratios of the strange particle multiplicity to the corresponding negative hadron multiplicity are similar for central SS and SAg collisions. They are significantly higher than

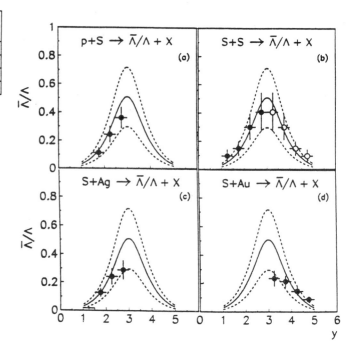

Figure 1. The ratio of $\bar{\Lambda}$ to Λ rapidity distributions for pS(a), SS(b), SAg(c) and SAu(d) collisions at 200 GeV/n (full circles). For SS collisions the ratio reflected at $y_{cm} = 3$ is shown by open circles. The corresponding ratio calculated using parametrizations of the Λ and $\bar{\Lambda}$ rapidity distributions for pp collisions at 200 GeV is shown by solid lines. The dashed lines indicate a 'one standard deviation' corridor.

	$< \Lambda >$	$< \bar{\Lambda} >$	$< K_s^0 >$
p+p	0.096 ± 0.015 (0.034 ± 0.005)	0.013 ± 0.005 (0.0046 ± 0.0018)	0.17 ± 0.01 (0.060 ± 0.004)
N+N	0.096 ± 0.015 (0.030 ± 0.005)	0.013 ± 0.005 (0.0040 ± 0.0016)	0.20 ± 0.03 (0.062 ± 0.009)
p+S	0.28 ± 0.03 (0.049 ± 0.006)	0.049 ± 0.006 (0.0086 ± 0.0011)	0.38 ± 0.05 (0.067 ± 0.001)
S+S	9.40 ± 1.0 (0.096 ± 0.009)	2.2 ± 0.4 (0.022 ± 0.004)	10.5 ± 1.7 (0.11 ± 0.019)
S+Ag	15.2 ± 1.2 (0.089 ± 0.009)	2.6 ± 0.3 (0.015 ± 0.002)	15.5 ± 1.5 (0.091 ± 0.011)

Table 2. Mean total multiplicities of Λ, $\bar{\Lambda}$ and K_S^0 produced in pS, central SS and central SAg collisions at 200 GeV/n. The corresponding multiplicities for pp and nucleon-nucleon interactions at 200 GeV are included for comparison. The numbers in brackets give the ratio of the mean strange particle multiplicity to the mean multiplicity of negative hadrons.

the corresponding ratios measured for nucleon-nucleon and pS reactions.

3.   Two-pion Bose-Einstein Correlations

A pion pair has six degrees of freedom in momentum space. In the most general case, for expanding particle sources without any spatial symmetry the two-pion correlation function depends on all six components.

The two-single particle momentum vectors may be decomposed into the average **k** and relative **Q** momentum vectors of the pair, each carrying three degrees of freedom. The relative momentum vector may be decomposed into transverse sideward, Q_S, transverse outward, Q_O, and longitudinal, Q_L, components [4]. The longitudinal component is parallel to the collision axis, while the transverse sideward and outward components are perpendicular and parallel to the average transverse momentum vector k_T, respectively. Since Q_O and Q_L components are not invariant to boost along the direction of the average transverse momentum vector and along the collision axis, respectively, their magnitude depends on the reference frame chosen for the analysis. The reference frame used in our analysis is fixed at y=3, the nucleon-nucleon center of mass in the laboratory frame.

The experimental correlation function C was studied as a function of three relative momentum components in different windows in average transverse momentum, and in single-particle rapidity. It was fitted with a gaussian function in all three relative-momentum components :

$$C(Q_S, Q_O, Q_L) = 1 + \lambda e^{((-Q_S^2 R_S^2 - Q_O^2 R_O^2 - Q_L^2 R_L^2)/2)} \quad (2)$$

where λ is the correlation intensity, and R_S, R_O and R_L are the parameters which characterise the pion source, or the effective interferometric source sizes. The corresponding distributions in configuration space are also gaussians.

Now we will show the general features of the measured correlation functions for different reactions (for more details see [5]). First we estimated the intercepts of the correlation functions. Defined as the value of the correlation function for a vanishing relative vector **Q**, the intercept may be estimated by studying the behaviour of the correlation function as a function of the invariant four-momentum difference Q_i of the pair, when Q_i approaches zero. In spite of low statistics near $Q_i = 0$ and numerous systematical problems in that region, we estimated that the true intercept is between 1.6 and 2.1. Our estimation is compatible with the expectation that for incoherent pion emission in the presence of long-lived resonances the intercept should be around 1.7 [6].

The results on the rapidity dependence of the fitted parameters indicate that for all studied systems there is no prominent feature in the rapidity dependence of the R_S and R_O parameters. The longitudinal parameter R_L, however varies strongly with rapidity in accordance with expectations for a boost invariant longitudinal expansion. The measured parameters R_S, R_O and the peak value of R_L range between 4 fm and 6 fm. The highest values are found for SAu, the heaviest projectile-target combination.

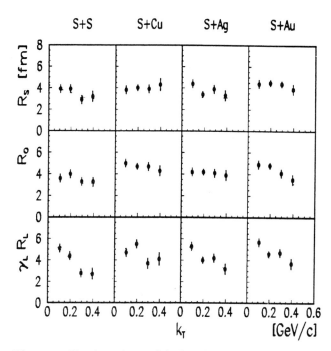

Figure 2. The dependence of the interferometric parameters on the average pion-pair momentum k_T is shown for the SS, SCu, SAg and SAu data from the TPC in the rapidity interval $3.5 < y < 4.5$. The R_L measurements are boosted to the reference frame corresponding to the middle of the corresponding rapidity interval, using the boost factor $\gamma_L = \cosh(y_{mid} - 3)$.

The dependence of the fitted parameters on the average pion-pair momentum k_T is shown in figure 2 for SS, SCu, SAg and SAu data from the TPC in the rapidity interval $3.5 < y < 4.5$. The correlation functions have been evaluated in independent intervals of k_T. The result indicate that R_L decreases with increasing k_T in a similar way for all studied systems. The longitudinal interferometric parameter depends both on transverse momentum and rapidity, in accordance with expectations for a boost invariant longitudinal expansion. This enables one to estimate the decoupling proper time for all studied systems to be around 4 fm/c. The two transvere components R_S and R_O are similar in magnitude and only weakly decrease in the k_T range studied suggesting a short duration of pion emission ($< 2fm/c$), and a fast pair decoupling at proper time ($\sim 4fm/c$).

References

[1] NA35 Collaboration: T. Alber *et al.*, IKF-HENPG/1-94.
[2] M. Gazdzicki and O. Hansen, Nucl. Phys. **A528** (1991) 754.
[3] NA35 Collaboration: J. Bartke *et al.*,Zeit. Phys. **C48** (1990) 191.
[4] G. Bertsch, M. Gong and T. Tohyama, Phys. Rev. **C37** (1988) 1896.
[5] NA35 Collaboration: T. Alber *et al.*, IKF-HENPG/9-94.
[6] S. Pratt, T. Csorgo and J. Zimanyi, Phys. Rev. **C42** (1992) 2646.

Paper presented at XXVII Int. Conf. on High Energy Physics: Session Pa-3
Glasgow, UK, 20–27 July 1994

Results on K_S^0, Λ, Ξ^- and Ω^- production in SW collisions at $200 \cdot A$ GeV/c

The WA85 Collaboration

S Abatzis[†], A Andrighetto[‡§], F Antinori[‡], R P Barnes[‖], A C Bayes[‖], M Benayoun[¶], W Beusch[‡], J N Carney[‖], B de la Cruz[+], D Di Bari[*], J P Dufey[‡], J P Davies[‖], D Elia[*], D Evans[‖], R Fini[*], B R French[‡], M Girone[*], B Ghidini[*], H Helstrup[‡], A K Holme[‖], A Jacholkowski[‡], J Kahane[¶], J B Kinson[‖], A Kirk[‡], K Knudson[‡], J C Lassalle[‡], V Lenti[*], Ph Leruste[¶], V Manzari[*], F Navach[‡], J L Narjoux[¶], E Quercigh[‡], L Rossi[‡], K Šafařík[‡], M Sené[¶], R Sené[¶], G Vassiliadis[†], O Villalobos Baillie[‖], A Volte[¶] and M F Votruba[‖]

[†] Athens University, Nuclear Physics Department, GR-15771 Athens, Greece
[‡] CERN, European Organization for Nuclear Research, CH-1211 Geneva 23, Switzerland
[‖] University of Birmingham, Birmingham B15 2TT, UK
[¶] Collège de France, IN2P3, F-75231 Paris, France
[+] CIEMAT, E-28040 Madrid, Spain
[*] Dipartimento di Fisica dell'Università and Sezione INFN, I-70126 Bari, Italy
[♯] Universitetet i Bergen, N-5007 Bergen, Norway

Presented by Karel Šafařík[††]

Abstract

We report the results from the WA85 experiment at CERN SPS. This experiment was designed to study the production of strange particles in central SW collisions at $200 \cdot A$ GeV/c. We have measured the inverse slope of the K_S^0 m_T distribution in central rapidity and $p_T > 1.2$ GeV/c to be (219 ± 4) MeV with an additional systematic uncertainty of about ± 10 MeV. This value is slightly lower but still comparable with the values already presented for Λ, $\overline{\Lambda}$, Ξ^- and $\overline{\Xi}^+$ which are all between 230 and 240 MeV. Along with published production ratios for $\overline{\Lambda}/\Lambda$, $\overline{\Xi}^+/\Xi^-$, Ξ^-/Λ and $\overline{\Xi}^+/\overline{\Lambda}$ we present here the ratios for K_S^0/Λ and $K_S^0/\overline{\Lambda}$ in central rapidity and medium p_T (> 1 GeV/c).

Finally, we recall the first observation of Ω^- and $\overline{\Omega}^+$ signal in relativistic ion collisions and estimate the production ratio of $(\Omega^- + \overline{\Omega}^+)/(\Xi^- + \overline{\Xi}^+) = 0.8 \pm 0.4$ (or > 0.39 at 95% confidence level, assuming Poisson distribution) for $p_T > 1.6$ GeV/c. We compare the production of multistrange baryons and antibaryons in central SW collisions with the values for pp interactions. The enhancement observed in relativistic ion collisions is not easy to explain using standard production mechanisms for strange particles in hadronic interactions.

§ Permanent address: Dipartimento di Fisica dell'Università, I-35131 Padua, Italy
††E-mail: karel@cernvm.cern.ch

1. Introduction

The WA85 experiment was designed to detect strange particles produced in heavy relativistic ion collisions in the central rapidity region with medium to high p_T. The production of strangeness has been suggested as an useful probe for the dynamics of hadron matter in relativistic heavy ion collisions [1, 2]. The enhancement of strange particle production and in particular of multistrange antibaryons relative to their yields in hadronic interactions is expected if during the collision a Quark–Gluon Plasma has been formed [2]. Strangeness could also be enhanced in a dense hadronic gas if it were to exist for a sufficiently long time to reach chemical equilibrium [3].   However, multistrange antibaryons have very low production cross–sections in hadronic interactions and are unlikely to equilibrate during the lifetime of a dense hadronic gas [2, 4]. Therefore, their enhancement can point towards the QGP formation in ion collisions.

The WA85 experiment was performed at the CERN Omega Spectrometer. The incoming $200 \cdot A$ GeV/c sulphur beam from SPS was identified by a quartz Čerenkov counter. It was incident on a thin tungsten target placed inside the Omega magnet with a field of 1.8 T. Charged tracks produced in the interaction were detected by seven multiwire proportional chambers. Each of them consists of three detecting planes. They had been modified so that they were sensitive only in a "butterfly" shape [5]. Their sensitive area can be hit only by central rapidity tracks with $p_T > 0.6$ GeV/c which ensures a moderate detected multiplicity and hence high reconstruction efficiency.   Two silicon microstrips detectors with $50 \mu m$ pitch and 512 channels each were mounted 15 cm downstream from the target, above and below the beam line, in order to sample the charged multiplicity in the pseudorapidity range $2.1 < \eta < 3.4$. Another quartz Čerenkov counter was placed behind the Omega magnet in order to veto the non–interacting sulpher ions. A forward hadron calorimeter was assembled 20 m downstream of the magnet. To trigger on central SW events we required low energy deposited in the calorimeter and at least 6 hits in each of the two silicon microstrip detectors. The selected centrality corresponds to about 30% of the inelastic cross–section.

Strange particles have been detected observing their V^0 decays like $K_S^0 \rightarrow \pi^+\pi^-$ and $\Lambda \rightarrow p\pi^-$ and cascade decays like $\Xi^- \rightarrow \Lambda\pi^-$ and $\Omega^- \rightarrow \Lambda K^-$ (and their antiparticles, when applicable). The WA85 collaboration has already published results on Λ, $\overline{\Lambda}$, Ξ^- and $\overline{\Xi}^+$ production [6, 7] and also the first observation of Ω^- and $\overline{\Omega}^+$ signal in relativistic ion collisions [8]. The main results will be reviewed here together with preliminary results on K_S^0 production and the Ω/Ξ

Particle	Statistics
K_S^0	10,400
Λ	21,400
$\overline{\Lambda}$	5,300
Ξ^-	500
$\overline{\Xi}^+$	200
$\Omega^- + \overline{\Omega}^+$	11

Table 1. Statistics of V^0 particles and cascades.

Particle	T, MeV
K_S^0	219 ± 5
Λ	232 ± 3
$\overline{\Lambda}$	230 ± 6
Ξ^-	239 ± 11
$\overline{\Xi}^+$	234 ± 15

Table 2. Inverse slopes of V^0 particles and cascades.

production ratio anounced recently at the Divonne–les–Bains symposium [9].

2. Results

The selection used to identify V^0 particles and cascades have been described elsewhere [6, 7, 8]. As several particle decays can share a common decay topology, it is necessary to do further selections based on the decay kinematics (e.g. using the decay angle or the Podolanski–Armenteros variable α [10]) to obtain unambiguous samples. The yields of unambiguous V^0 and cascade candidates are given in table 1.

All results presented here have been corrected for acceptance, detection and reconstruction efficiencies. The Λ ($\overline{\Lambda}$) yields have also been corrected for feed–down from Ξ's ($\overline{\Xi}$'s) decays.

In figure 1 the m_T distribution for K_S^0 in the rapidity region $2.5 < y_{lab} < 3.0$ is shown. It is compared with previously published data for Λ and $\overline{\Lambda}$ [6] measured in the slightly shifted rapidity region $2.3 < y_{lab} < 2.8$. We fit the K_S^0 spectra by $dN/dm_T \propto m_T^{3/2} \exp(-m_T/T)$ and obtain for inverse slope parameter $T = (219 \pm 5)$ MeV. The inverse slopes obtained for other hyperons [7] are given in table 2. The errors shown are statistical only. The systematic error has been estimated by simulation to be about ± 10 MeV. The inverse slope for K_S^0 is slightly lower but still comparable with the values for Λ, $\overline{\Lambda}$, Ξ^- and $\overline{\Xi}^+$ which all are between 230 and 240 MeV

The relative production rates of K_S^0 and Λ ($\overline{\Lambda}$) has been measured in the $y - p_T$ region $2.5 < y_{lab} < 3.0$ and $1.0 < p_T < 2.5$ GeV/c where the acceptance windows overlap. The production ratios are given in table 3. There are also reviewed other already published

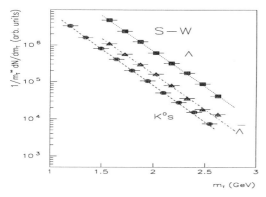

Figure 1. Transverse mass distribution for K_S^0, Λ and $\overline{\Lambda}$.

Ratio	Value
K_S^0/Λ	1.4 $\pm$ 0.1
$K_S^0/\overline{\Lambda}$	6.4 $\pm$ 0.4
$\overline{\Lambda}/\Lambda$	0.20 $\pm$ 0.01
$\Xi^-/\overline{\Xi}^+$	0.45 $\pm$ 0.05
Ξ^-/Λ	0.095 $\pm$ 0.006
$\overline{\Xi}^+/\overline{\Lambda}$	0.21 $\pm$ 0.02
$(\Omega^- + \overline{\Omega}^+)/(\Xi^- + \overline{\Xi}^+)$	0.8 $\pm$ 0.4

Table 3. Reletive particle production rates.

ratios which were obtained in $2.3 < y_{lab} < 3.0$ and $1.2 < p_T < 3.0\,\text{GeV}/c$.

We have also detected clear Ω^- and $\overline{\Omega}^+$ signal [8]. After corrections we have estimated the production ratio $(\Omega^- + \overline{\Omega}^+)/(\Xi^- + \overline{\Xi}^+) = 0.8 \pm 0.4$ in the overlaping region $2.5 < y_{lab} < 3.0$ and $p_T > 1.6\,\text{GeV}/c$. Assuming Poisson distrubution for produced Ω^- ($\overline{\Omega}^+$) we can set the 95% confidence level lower limit for this ratio as $(\Omega^- + \overline{\Omega}^+)/(\Xi^- + \overline{\Xi}^+) > 0.39$. If we restrict the window to the same $m_T > 2.3\,\text{GeV}$ region we obtain $(\Omega^- + \overline{\Omega}^+)/(\Xi^- + \overline{\Xi}^+) = 1.7 \pm 0.9$ (or > 0.79 at 95% confidence level).

The $\overline{\Xi}^+/\overline{\Lambda}$ ratio was measured in central rapidity and p_T between 1 and 2 GeV/c in pp interactions at the CERN ISR by the AFS collaboration [11]. Their measured the value $\overline{\Xi}^+/\overline{\Lambda} = 0.06 \pm 0.02$ which is more then three times lower than our result for central SW collisions. The same collaboration get the 90% upper limit for $\overline{\Omega}^+/\overline{\Xi}^+ < 0.15$ in central rapidity and $p_T > 1.4\,\text{GeV}/c$ which is much lower than our lower limit for $(\Omega^- + \overline{\Omega}^+)/(\Xi^- + \overline{\Xi}^+)$ in central SW collisions. These comparisons are displayed in figure 2.

3. Conclusions

We have reported the results on strange particle production in central SW collisions at $200 \cdot A$ GeV/c.

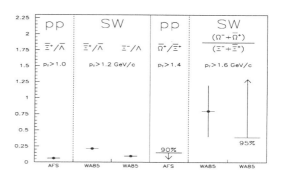

Figure 2. Comparison of Ξ/Λ and Ω/Ξ ratios in pp and central SW collisions.

The inverse m_T slope for K_S^0 has been measured to be slightly lower but still comparable with the values for Λ, $\overline{\Lambda}$, Ξ^- and $\overline{\Xi}^+$. The preliminary values for the K_S^0/Λ and $K_S^0/\overline{\Lambda}$ ratios have been given. The relative production rates of $\overline{\Xi}^+/\overline{\Lambda}$ and $(\Omega^- + \overline{\Omega}^+)/(\Xi^- + \overline{\Xi}^+)$ in central SW collisions are significantly higher than similar ratios measured in pp interactions. This enhancement is not easy to explain using standard production mechanisms for strange particle production in hadronic interactions [2, 4].

References

[1] J. Rafelski and B. Müller, Phys. Rev. Lett. **48** (1982) 1066; and *ibid.* **56** (1986) 2334(E).

[2] P. Koch, B. Müller and J. Rafelski, Phys. Rep. **142** (1986) 167; J. Ellis and U. Heinz, CERN preprint: CERN-TH5548/89.

[3] T. Matsui, B. Svettiski and L.D. McLerran, Phys. Rev. **D34** (1986) 2047; K.S. Lee, M. Rhoades-Browne and U. Heinz, Phys. Rev. **C37** (1988) 1452.

[4] H.C. Eggers and J. Rafelski, Int. J. Mod. Phys. **A6** (1991) 1067.

[5] W. Beusch *et al.*, Nucl. Instr. Meth. **A249** (1986) 391.

[6] WA85 Collaboration: S. Abatzis *et al.*, Phys. Lett. **B244** (1990) 130; and *ibid.* **B259** (1991) 508; WA85 Collaboration: J.L. Narjoux *et al.*, Nucl. Phys. **A525** (1991) 445c.

[7] WA85 Collaboration: S. Abatzis *et al.*, Phys. Lett. **B270** (1991) 123; WA85 Collaboration: J. Kinson *et al.*, Nucl. Phys. **A544** (1992) 321c; WA85 Collaboration: D. Evans *et al.*, Nucl. Phys. **A566** (1994) 233c.

[8] WA85 Collaboration: S. Abatzis *et al.*, Phys. Lett. **B316** (1993) 613; WA85 Collaboration: F. Antinori *et al.*, Nucl. Phys. **A566** (1994) 491c.

[9] WA85 Collaboration: F. Antinori *et al.*, Proc. of the NATO Advanced Reasearch Workshop on Hot Hadronic Matter, Divonne-les-Bains, June 1994, *to be published*.

[10] J. Podolanski and R. Armenteros, Phil. Mag. **45** (1954) 13.

[11] AFS Collaboration: T. Åkesson *et al.*, Nucl. Phys. **B246** (1984) 1.

Strange Particle Production in Sulphur-Sulphur Interactions at 200 GeV/c per nucleon.

S Abatzis[1], A Andrighetto[10], F Antinori[5], R P Barnes[4], A C Bayes[4], M Benayoun[6],
W Beusch[5], R Blaes[12], I J Bloodworth[4], J Bohm[7], A Bravar[13], J N Carney[4],
B de la Cruz[9], S Clewer[4], J P Davies[4], D Di Bari[2], C J Dodenhoff[4], J P Dufey[5], D Elia[2],
D Evans[4], R Fini[2], B R French[5], B Ghidini[2], H Helstrup[3], A K Holme[3],
A Jacholkowski[2], T Kachelhoffer[12], J Kahane[6], V A Katchanov[11], J B Kinson[4],
A Kirk[5], K Knudson[5], P Ladrón de Guevara[9], J C Lassalle[5], V Lenti[2], Ph Leruste[6],
R Lietava[4], R A Loconsole[2], G Løvhøiden[3], V Manzari[2], A Michalon[12], M Morando[10],
F Navach[2], J L Narjoux[6], M Passaseo[5], F Pellegrini[10], A Penzo[13], E Quercigh[5], R Ricci[8],
L Sandor[7], K Šafařík[5], A V Singovsky[11], M Sené[6], R Sené[6],
T F Thorsteinsen[3], G Undheim[3], J Urban[7], G Vassiliadis[1], O Villalobos Baillie[4],
A Volte[6], C Voltolini[12], M F Votruba[4], and P Zavada[7].

1. Athens University, Athens, Greece
2. Dipartimento di Fisica dell'Università and Sezione INFN, Bari, Italy
3. Universitetet i Bergen, Bergen, Norway
4. University of Birmingham, Birmingham, UK
5. CERN, Geneva, Switzerland
6. Collège de France, IN2P3, Paris, France.
7. Institute of Experimental Physics, Košice, Slovakia.
8. Laboratorio Nazionale di Legnaro, Legnaro, Italy.
9. CIEMAT, Madrid, Spain.
10. Dipartimento di Fisica dell'Università and Sezione INFN, Padua, Italy
11. IHEP, Protvino, Russia
12. CRN, Strasbourg, France.
13. Dipartimento di Fisica dell'Università and Sezione INFN, Trieste, Italy.

Presented by O. Villalobos Baillie[††]

Abstract

New results on the production of strange particles in Sulphur Sulphur interactions have been obtained by the WA94 collaboration. We present m_T spectra for Λ, $\overline{\Lambda}$, Ξ^- and $\overline{\Xi^-}$ particles. Particle production ratios have been obtained in the kinematic region $1.2 \leq p_T \leq 3.0$ GeV/c and $2.5 \leq y_{lab} \leq 3.0$.

1. Introduction

An enhancement of strange particle production relative to non-strange particle production in heavy ion

††E-mail: ovb@i.ph.bham.ac.uk

collisions has been proposed as an indicator for a phase transition to a Quark-Gluon Plasma (QGP) [1]. Gluons are produced abundantly in a QGP, with a rapid subsequent production of $q\bar{q}$ pairs, among them $s\bar{s}$ pairs, through gluon fusion. At the temperatures expected for a transition to a QGP the larger mass of the s quark does not greatly suppress $s\bar{s}$ production with respect to $u\bar{u}$ and $d\bar{d}$ production. In addition, in an environment in which the baryon density is already high, as is the case at the CERN SPS [2], production of $u\bar{u}$ and $d\bar{d}$ pairs is initially suppressed relative to $s\bar{s}$ because of Pauli blocking [3]. In consequence, the strangeness content would increase rapidly in a QGP. It has been pointed out that the strangeness content would increase in the case of a dense, long-lived hadronic system, a Hadron Gas, through the processes of pair production and associated production [4]. However, in this case the timescale for achieving the full strangeness increase is considerably longer owing to the small cross sections for the strangeness production reactions, and it is thought to be long in comparison with the lifetime of the colliding system. For this reason the strange antibaryons and multistrange objects, which are produced only *via* a chain of strangeness production and redistribution reactions, are indicators of special interest; the timespan available makes these the species least likely to have achieved an appreciable enhancement in a Hadron Gas. In contrast, if a QGP is formed, the strangeness enhancement is achieved prior to hadronization, and therefore affects all particle species.

2. Data Sample

The WA94 experiment [5] is the second heavy ion experiment to be performed at the CERN Omega Spectrometer. The aim of the experiment is to measure strange and multistrange particle production in sulphur sulphur interactions, and to measure proton and antiproton spectra under the same trigger conditions. The use of a sulphur sulphur system means that the rapidity distributions are symmetric about the centre-of-mass rapidity, y_{CM}. The initial state system is isoscalar, so the constraints of isospin symmetry can be applied in the analysis of particle spectra. Finally, the use of a symmetric system simplifies comparisons with the Pb Pb system planned for the WA97 experiment [6].

Two different experimental configurations have been used for the WA94 experiment. Hyperon spectra were measured using the Omega MWPC in "butterfly" mode, as in WA85 [7]. 100 million triggers were taken in this configuration in 1991, and 60 million pS triggers in 1993. A silicon telescope was used in conjunction with the Omega Ring Imaging CHerenkov (RICH) in order to record charged particle spectra. 20 million SS

Particle	WA94 $2.5 \leq y_{lab} \leq 3.0$ Inverse slope (MeV)	WA85 $2.3 \leq y_{lab} \leq 2.8$ Inverse slope (MeV)
Λ	214 ± 3	232 ± 3
$\overline{\Lambda}$	206 ± 5	230 ± 6
Ξ^-	227 ± 10	239 ± 11
$\overline{\Xi^-}$	209 ± 13	234 ± 15

Table 1. Inverse slopes for specified central rapidity interval.

triggers were taken in this configuration. In this report, we present results on Λ, $\overline{\Lambda}$, Ξ^- and $\overline{\Xi^-}$ production, using the 100 million SS triggers obtained in 1991. The apparatus and trigger have been described elsewhere [8].

The selection procedures for V^0s and cascades are summarized below. Track pairs which have a sufficient number of space points, trace through all the chambers and which are of opposite charge are considered as V^0 candidates if (i) the tracks form a vertex (distance of closest approach $d < 1$ cm), (ii) the V^0 momentum vector for this vertex points back to the target (angle to line of flight $\theta \leq 0.75°$), and (iii) the decay tracks should not trace back to the target (bend plane impact parameter $y_\pi > 4$ cm for the pion and $y_b > 2$ cm for the baryon).

For cascades the requirement that the V^0 should point back to the target is relaxed, and the V^0 decay tracks are only required to trace through 4 chambers. In addition, (i') a third track intersects the V^0 line of flight (distance of closest approach $d < 1.6$ cm), (ii') the reconstructed cascade should trace back to the target ($y_\Xi < 2$ cm), and (iii') the decay track should miss the target (bend plane impact parameter $y_d > 4$ cm).

3. Transverse Mass Distributions and Ratios

These selections yield 56 000 Λs, 18 000 $\overline{\Lambda}$s, 602 Ξ^-s and 313 $\overline{\Xi^-}$s. The transverse mass distributions of these particles are shown in figure 1, calculated in the rapidity interval $2.5 < y_{lab} < 3.0$. The Λ and $\overline{\Lambda}$ distributions have been corrected for feed-down from Ξ and $\overline{\Xi}$ decays. The distributions have been fitted using the expression

$$\frac{1}{m_T^{\frac{3}{2}}} \frac{dN}{dm_T} = A \exp\left(-m_T/\tau\right). \tag{1}$$

The inverse slopes τ obtained are given in table 1. For comparison the inverse slopes obtained by the WA85 collaboration in an equivalent centre-of-mass rapidity interval for SW interactions are also given [9]. The SS values are in general some 15 MeV lower.

Table 2 gives a list of hyperon production ratios for Ξs, Λs and their antiparticles in SS interactions obtained in the kinematic range $1.2 \leq p_T \leq 3.0$ GeV/c and $2.5 \leq y_{lab} \leq 3.0$. The values obtained by WA85 in

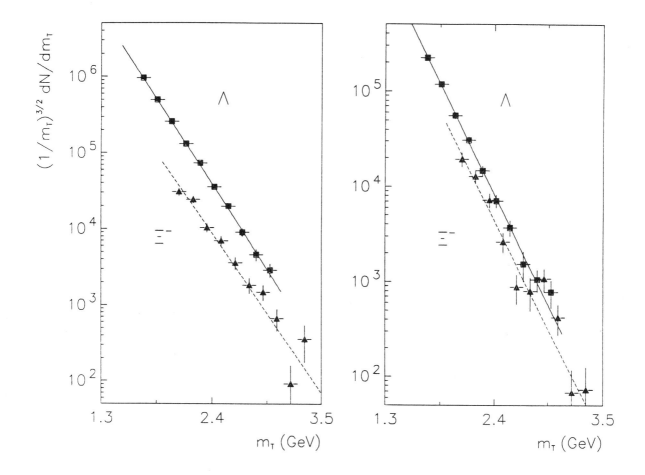

Figure 1. Transverse mass distributions for Λ, $\overline{\Lambda}$, Ξ^- and $\overline{\Xi^-}$. WA94 SS data.

Ratio	WA94 $2.5 \leq y_{lab} \leq 3.0$ $1.2 \leq p_T \leq 3.0$ GeV/c	WA85 $2.3 \leq y_{lab} \leq 3.0$ $1.2 \leq p_T \leq 3.0$ GeV/c
$\overline{\Lambda}/\Lambda$	0.23 ± 0.01	0.20 ± 0.01
$\overline{\Xi^-}/\Xi^-$	0.51 ± 0.06	0.45 ± 0.05
Ξ^-/Λ	0.094 ± 0.007	0.095 ± 0.006
$\overline{\Xi^-}/\overline{\Lambda}$	0.22 ± 0.02	0.21 ± 0.02

Table 2. Relative hyperon yields at central rapidity.

SW interactions in a similar kinematic region are also given. We see that under the central trigger selections used by WA85 and WA94 the hyperon production ratios obtained in SS and SW interactions are very similar, and are all compatible within 1 s.d.

4. Summary

In conclusion, the WA94 collaboration has studied hyperon production in SS interactions. The inverse slopes of the m_T distributions for Λ, $\overline{\Lambda}$, Ξ^- and $\overline{\Xi^-}$

particles have slightly lower values than in central SW interactions, and the relative production yields in central SS and SW are very similar to one another. In particular the $\overline{\Xi^-}/\overline{\Lambda}$ ratio (0.22 ± 0.02) is about 5 s.d. larger than the value (0.06 ± 0.02) obtained by the AFS collaboration [10] in pp interactions.

References

[1] J. Rafelski and B. Müller, Phys. Rev. Lett. **48** (1982) 1066.
[2] H.R. Schmidt and J. Schukraft, J. Phys. G. **19** (1993) 1705.
[3] P. Koch, B. Müller and J. Rafelski, Phys. Rep. **142** (1986) 167.
[4] T. Matsui, B. Svettisky and L.D. McLerran, Phys. Rev. **D34** (1986) 2047.
    K.S. Lee, M. Rhoades-Browne and U. Heinz, Phys. Rev. **C37** (1988) 1452.
[5] WA94 Proposal. CERN/SPSLC/ 91-5 P 257 (1991).
[6] WA97 Proposal. CERN/SPSLC/91-29 P 263 (1991).
[7] W. Beusch et al. Nucl. Instr. Meth. **A249** (1986) 391.
[8] S. Abatzis et al. Nucl. Phys. **A566** (1994) 499c.
[9] S. Abatzis et al. Nucl. Phys. **A566** (1994) 225c.
[10] T. Åkesson et al. Nucl. Phys. **B246** (1984) 1.

Low-Mass Electron-Pair Production in p-Be, p-Au and S-Au Collisions at CERN SPS Energies

Th. Ullrich for the CERES collaboration

Physikalisches Institut der Universität Heidelberg, Philosophenweg 12, 69120 Heidelberg, Germany

G. Agakichiev[a,1], R. Baur[b], A. Breskin[c], R. Chechik[c], A. Drees[b], C. Jacob[a], U. Faschingbauer[a],
P. Fischer[b], Z. Fraenkel[c], Ch. Fuchs[a], E. Gatti[d], P. Glässel[b], Th. Günzel[b], M. Hemberger[a],
C.P. de los Heros[c], F. Hess[a], D. Irmscher[b], H. Kraner[e], K. Lee[b], B. Lenkeit[b], L.H. Olsen[b],
Y. Panebrattsev[a,1], A. Pfeiffer[b], I. Ravinovich[c], P. Rehak[e], A. Schön[b], J. Schukraft[f],
M. Sampietro[d], S. Shimansky[f,1], A. Shor[c], H.J. Specht[b], V. Steiner[c], S. Tapprogge[b],
G. Tel-Zur[c], I. Tserruya[c], Th. Ullrich[b], J.P. Wurm[a], V. Yurevich[f,1]

Abstract

We report on the production of low-mass electron pairs in p-Be, p-Au collisions at 450 GeV and 200 GeV/u S-Au collisions for central rapidities at the CERN SPS. For both p-Be and p-Au collisions the low-mass spectra can within the systematical errors satisfactorily be explained by electron pairs from hadronic decays, whereas in the heavier S-Au system for invariant masses $0.2 < m < 1.5$ GeV/c^2 an enhancement over the hadronic contribution by a factor of $4.96 \pm 0.73^{+1.95}_{-2.1}$ is observed.

1. Introduction

The production of lepton pairs is considered a useful probe to study the dynamical evolution of nuclear collision processes. Leptons interact only electromagnetically, and their mean free paths are much larger than the transverse size of the collision volume. They are produced during the whole space-time evolution of the system, beginning at the early hot stage up to the point where the hadrons cease to interact. Later a large amount of additional lepton pairs is produced by the electromagnetic decays of hadronic particles. Since all stages of the collision have somewhat different contributions to the lepton spectrum, a careful analysis should,

in principle, be able to unfold the whole space-time history of the hadronic collision.

The study of dilepton production in ultrarelativistic nuclear collisions was initiated by the suggestion that it might serve as a probe for a quark-gluon plasma possibly formed at ultrarelativistic energies [1]. If at CERN-SPS energies the achieved energy densities and temperatures are not sufficiently high to form a quark-gluon plasma, there still may be a significant production of lepton pairs in the low invariant mass region $2m_\pi \leq m \leq 600$ MeV/c^2 from the annihilation of pions in the hot and dense hadron gas [2, 3].

Up to now, two experiments have succeeded to measure dimuons in heavy-ion collisions at the CERN SPS, one at high masses [4], the other also in the low-mass range [5, 6]. We present here the preliminary results of the first measurement of low-mass electron pairs in S-Au collisions taken with the CERES/NA45 spectrometer and compare them with those from p-Be and p-Au collisions obtained in the same experiment.

[a] MPI für Kernphysik, Heidelberg, Germany
[b] Universität Heidelberg, Heidelberg, Germany
[c] Weizmann Institute, Rehovot, Israel
[d] Politecnico di Milano, Italy
[e] Brookhaven National Laboratory, Upton, USA
[f] CERN, Geneva, Switzerland
[1] visiting from JINR, Dubna, Russia

2. Experimental Setup and Data-Taking

The CERES experiment is an electron pair spectrometer, consisting mainly of two azimuthally symmetric RICH detectors with high thresholds to significantly reduce the sensitivity to hadrons. A double superconducting solenoid between the two detectors provides an azimuthal deflection allowing the momentum determination. The photon detectors are located in the focal planes of the mirrors upstream of the target to reduce the charged particle flux. A radial-drift silicon detector situated closely behind the target is used for tracking and for the rejection of photon conversion pairs produced downstream of the target. An additional silicon pad detector measures charged particle multiplicity both for first-level triggering and off-line analysis. The second-level trigger is formed by a systolic processor array which searches for distant pairs of Cherenkov rings while suppressing the background of close pairs from π^0-Dalitz decays and conversions. A more detailed description of the CERES/NA45 spectrometer can be found in refs. [7, 8].

The S-Au results described in this report were obtained from the analysis of data taken during the SPS fixed-target running period in spring 1992. A total of $3.6 \cdot 10^6$ multiplicity triggers and $2.7 \cdot 10^6$ second-level triggers were recorded. The p-Be and p-Au data were taken in summer 1993 in a combined run of CERES with the BaF$_2$ calorimeter of the TAPS-collaboration [9]. The data samples correspond to $2.1 \cdot 10^9$ minimum bias events in p-Be and $2.7 \cdot 10^8$ in p-Au collisions.

3. Event Reconstruction

The off-line electron reconstruction is very similar in almost all aspects for p-Be, p-Au and S-Au events. A pattern recognition algorithm reconstructs ring images without the prior knowledge of the Cherenkov ring centers. In the first step, electronic noise and large hits from highly ionizing particles traversing the photon detectors, which would otherwise confuse the ring reconstruction, are eliminated. Ring candidates are then identified using a Hough transformation on the remaining picture. In the vicinity of these candidates, single-photon hits are reconstructed and used to determine the position of the rings by a fitting procedure. Various ring quality criteria are applied to distinguish genuine Cherenkov rings from fake rings originating from random combinations of hits. For the S-Au data sample, these cuts are performed by artificial neural networks in order to optimize the efficiency of the decision. The accepted rings in both RICH detectors are then combined to tracks, identified by their common angle θ with respect to the beam axis. Tracks with an unresolved double ring in the first RICH originating

from photon conversions are rejected. The remaining tracks surviving all the cuts are combined into pairs.

4. Analysis and Normalization

The combinatorial background originating from unrecognized partners of low-mass Dalitz and conversion pairs is *the* central problem of the experiment, and is the only significant source of physics background. Due to the fact that the inclusive electron spectrum from π^0-Dalitz decays and conversions is considerably softer than that of pairs with $m > 0.2$ GeV/c^2, the signal-to-background ratio (S/B) can be significantly improved by a $p_\perp$-cut on the single electrons. The results discussed here are presented with a $p_\perp$-cut of 200 MeV/c for the S-Au and 50 MeV/c for the p-Be and p-Au data. Further rejection cuts, most of them exploiting the small opening angle of the low-mass pairs, were applied to improve the S/B ratio. The combined effect of all these cuts results in an improvement of the S/B ratio by one order of magnitude.

The combinatorial background left in the e$^+$e$^-$-sample is determined by the number of like-sign pairs. The pair signal is then extracted by subtracting the like-sign contribution from the e$^+$e$^-$-sample.

The final S-Au sample for $m > 0.2$ GeV/c^2 consists of 4249 pairs, of which 2346 are e$^+$e$^-$, 905 are e$^+$e$^+$ and 998 are e$^-$e$^-$, resulting in a signal of 445 ± 65 with a S/B ratio of 1/4.3, while in the high-statistics p-Be (p-Au) sample a signal of 5760 ± 184 (1126 ± 100) pairs is obtained at a S/B ratio of 1/2.2 (1/4.5).

In the absence of *new* physics, the main sources of electron pairs are expected to be hadronic decays. For pair masses below 140 MeV/c^2, the π^0-Dalitz decay dominates the spectrum, whereas at higher masses the decays $\eta \rightarrow$ e$^+$e$^-\gamma$, $\omega \rightarrow$ e$^+$e$^-\pi^0$ and $\rho/\omega \rightarrow$ e$^+$e$^-$ should be significant. We have calculated the invariant mass spectrum with a generator containing all the hadronic sources, i.e. the π^0, η, η', ρ, ω and ϕ. Their $p_\perp$-distributions were generated assuming $m_\perp$-scaling, and the rapidity distribution was a fit to dn/dη as measured by WA80 [10] for S-Au, modified to reflect the ratio of $\sigma_{central}$ to σ_{tot} as measured by NA27 [11]. The Dalitz decays were treated according to the Kroll-Wada expression with the experimental transition form factors taken from ref. [12]. The laboratory momenta of the electrons were convoluted with the experimental resolution.

The preliminary results for the p-Be, p-Au and S-Au data samples are shown in Figure 1 [13, 14]. All three spectra are normalized to represent *pair density per charged particle density* within the CERES rapidity acceptance $2.1 < y < 2.65$; the average charged particle densities used in the normalization are quoted in the figure. The systematic errors due

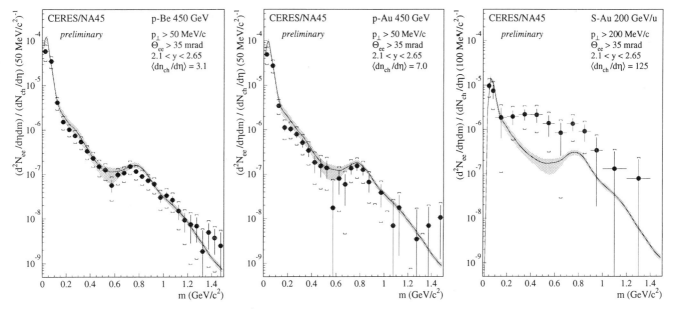

Figure 1. Inclusive mass spectra of e^+e^--pairs in p-Be, p-Au and S-Au collisions. The data are normalized to represent pair density per charged particle density within the CERES rapidity acceptance. No pair-acceptance corrections are applied.

to reconstruction efficiency, acceptance and trigger enrichment are marked by brackets, whereas the bars reflect the statistical errors only. The shaded region indicates the systematical error on the total contribution from hadronic decays. The data and the predictions are *not* corrected for pair acceptance. This correction would require deeper knowledge of all sources of pairs, which does obviously not exist yet for the S-Au case.

As a quantitative measure of an observed excess we define an enhancement as the integral of the data over the integral sum of the predicted sources in the mass range $0.2 < m < 1.5$ GeV/c^2. For both the p-Be and the p-Au sample, the measured inclusive e^+e^--pair spectra can well be explained, within the present systematical errors, by electron pairs from hadronic decays, whereas in the S-Au sample a statistically significant enhancement of $4.96 \pm 0.73(\text{stat})^{+1.95}_{-2.1}(\text{syst})$ is observed.

5. Conclusions

Inclusive e^+e^--pair spectra have been measured in the CERES/NA45 experiment in the rapidity range $2.1 < y < 2.65$ in 450 GeV/c p-Be, p-Au and 200 GeV/u S-Au collisions. The shape and the yield of the invariant mass spectra observed in p-Be and p-Au collisions are well described by known hadronic sources, and there is no need to invoke any unconventional source. In the S-Au data sample, however, a significant enhancement is found which starts to rise at pair masses above $m \sim 250$ MeV/c^2. This structure could be interpreted as the opening of the two-pion annihilation channel $(\pi\pi \to e^+e^-)$ at $m = 2m_\pi$. The spectral shape of this

particular source would also explain the enhancement in the ρ-region due to the pion form factor.

Our measurements are in qualitative agreement with recent results from the HELIOS-3 collaboration reporting an excess of muon pairs in S-W collisions in the same mass region, but obtained at more forward rapidities [5, 6].

The analysis of open pairs in our S-Au sample suffers from low statistics, not allowing deeper investigations of the shape and kinematics of the observed excess. We are presently improving our setup to make use of the Pb beam provided by the CERN-SPS starting in 1994, and we will continue this program [15].

References

[1] E. V. Shuryak, Phys. Lett. **78B** (1978) 150.
[2] J. Cleymans, V. V. Goloviznin and K. Redlich, Zeit. Phys. **C59** (1993) 495.
[3] P. Koch, Zeit. Phys. **C57** (1993) 283.
[4] C. Lourenço, Proc. of the Quark Matter Conference in Borlänge (1993), Nucl. Phys. **A566** (1994) 77c.
[5] M. Masera, contribution to this conference.
[6] G. London, Proc. of the Workshop on Dilepton Prod. in Rel. Heavy Ion Coll., GSI Darmstadt (1994).
[7] CERES/NA45 Collaboration, Status Report to the CERN-SPSLC 94-2, SPSLC/M529 (1994).
[8] R. Baur *et al.*, Nucl. Instr. Meth. **A343** (1994) 231.
[9] CERES/NA45 Collaboration, Addendum CERN/SPSLC 92-48, SPSLC/P237 Add 2 (1992).
[10] R. Albrecht *et al.*, Zeit. Phys. **C55** (1992) 539.
[11] M. Aguilar-Benitez *et al.*, Zeit. Phys. **C50** (1991) 405.
[12] L. G. Landsberg, Phys. Rev. **128** (1985) 301.
[13] R. Baur, Doctoral thesis, Universität Heidelberg (1994).
[14] Th. Ullrich, Doctoral thesis, Universität Heidelberg (1994).
[15] CERES/NA45 Collaboration, Proposal to the CERN-SPSLC 94-1, SPSLC/P280 (1994).

Dimuon production below Mass 2.5 GeV/c² in p–W and S–W Interactions at 200 GeV/c/A

Massimo Masera

Dipartimento di Fisica Sperimentale dell'Università di Torino and INFN

On behalf of the ***HELIOS-3*** Collaboration

Abstract

Final results are presented on dimuon production per charged particle in the invariant mass range below 2.5 GeV/c² in p–W and S–W interactions at 200 GeV/c/A, obtained using the HELIOS-3 dimuon spectrometer at the CERN SPS in a large kinematic region. There is a large difference in the shape and absolute value of p-W and S-W dimuon spectra. The spectrum observed in p-W interactions can be interpreted as a sum of known dimuon sources, while, in S-W interactions, an excess with respect to these contributions is observed.

1. Introduction

According to lattice QCD calculations, at high energy densities a phase transition to a state in which partons are deconfined (the Quark Gluon Plasma) should occur. The only direct probes from the plasma phase are both direct and virtual photons, since they decouple at early times and are not sensitive to hadronization processes.

The HELIOS-3 experiment was designed to study virtual photons, detected as muon pairs, at low transverse mass: in this way, the dimuon production was studied from threshold up to the J/ψ mass at all p_t. Data from interactions of p and ^{32}S at 200 GeV/c per nucleon on a tungsten target were collected in 1990 at the CERN SPS. A comparison of the dimuon mass spectra between p–W and ^{32}S–W is therefore possible.

At low mass (i.e. from threshold up to 1.35 GeV/c²), the dimuon yield is dominated by Dalitz and two body decays of mesons. The dilepton production in this mass range was extensively investigated in the past in proton nucleus collisions and an anomalously high production of low mass pairs related to the prediction of final state annihilations of quark-antiquark pairs into dileptons [1] was claimed [2]. More recent measurements by the HELIOS-1 collaboration [3] concerning the dilepton production in p–Be collisions at 450 GeV/c show no evidence for anomalous pair production, since data can be well understood in terms of *standard* sources. At high mass (i.e. above the Φ) dimuons come mostly from the Drell-Yan process, while in the intermediate region (1.35 – 2.5 GeV/c²), the physical processes leading to dimuon production are not well under control since the perturbative QCD approach is not justified here. According to the theoretical calculations [4], a clear thermal signal in the dilepton spectrum is expected in the mass region below 2 GeV/c² in central S-W interactions at 200 GeV/c, in addition to pairs from the Drell-Yan process and from charm decay.

In this paper we shall concentrate on the global feature of the mass spectra in p–W and S–W collisions and on the *continuum*, leaving aside the two-body decays.

2. Set–up, data reduction and analysis

The HELIOS-3 (NA34) experiment [5] consists of a muon spectrometer based on a large superconducting dipole magnet, scintillator hodoscopes and MWPCs, a hadron absorber made of Al_2O_3 (6 λ_i) followed by iron (more than 5 λ_i). An 8 mrad conic hole and a tungsten rod starting at 146 cm from the target insured that ion fragments interacted far from the target. The absorber was located 25 cm downstream of the 12% λ_i tungsten target. Between the target and the absorber, two silicon ring detectors of suitable granularity measured the event multiplicity in the dimuon acceptance.

With the 200 GeV/c sulphur beam, we collected 9×10^6 dimuon triggers which was reduced by beam and target cuts to 2.3×10^5 dimuons. Similar selection resulted in 45000 dimuons for the proton beam run.

Two uncorrelated muons from π or K decay can be measured in the same event and taken as a dimuon. To reduce the statistical errors for the shape of this combinatorial background, we mixed μ pairs from different like-sign events. The overall normalization was estimated from the like-sign $\mu\mu$ as $N_{comb}^{+-} = 2R\sqrt{N^{++}N^{--}}$. The values of 1.09 ± 0.02 for the sulphur runs and 1.57 ± 0.10 for the proton runs were obtained for the coefficient R by a Monte Carlo method.

A second background from dimuons produced by secondary hadrons interacting in the absorber was largely rejected by an appropriately chosen target cut. We have estimated the spectral shape and absolute rate of the remaining background with a Monte Carlo tuned to fit the results of special runs with π beams impinging on the dump face and protons on the W rod.

The acceptance and resolution of the apparatus were extensively studied by Monte Carlo methods and checked at the Φ and at J/ψ mass. We restricted ourselves to the kinematic region

$$
\begin{aligned}
M_T &\geq (4(7-2y) \\
M_T &\geq \sqrt{(2M_\mu)^2 + \left(\frac{17.5}{cosh(Y)}\right)^2}
\end{aligned}
\quad (1)
$$

The multiplicity of charged particle measured in the pseudorapidity region $3.5 < \eta < 5.2$ was used to group our data according to their centrality.

We grouped our data into 6 multiplicity classes, with enough statistics for the subsequent analysis. For each class we estimated the impact parameter and the average number of projectile participants (VENUS 3.11, FRITIOF). The data acquisition system handled two kinds of triggers: the *dimuon* triggers on one hand and the *no muon* triggers on the other, the former being generated after a fast track recognition in the spectrometer. In order to collect a significative number of central events, a minimum charged particle multiplicity production was required at trigger level by means of the Silicon Ring counters. The multiplicity threshold was the same for both dimuon and no muon triggers. Three different thresholds were used in the whole experiment. The no muon triggers were

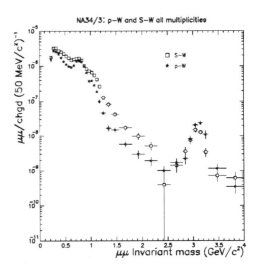

Figure 1. Superimposed $p - W$ and $s - W$ $\mu\mu$ mass spectra.

downscaled with respect to the dimuon triggers and the low multiplicity triggers were downscaled with respect to the high multiplicity ones. The no muon events were used to normalize the dimuon yield to the number of charged particles in each multiplicity class. The $(\mu\mu/ch.)$ ratios were calculated at the trigger level, so that the multiplicity trigger acceptances cancelled:

$$
\left(\frac{\mu\mu}{ch.}\right)_{\alpha\beta} = \frac{1}{\langle m_{\alpha\beta}\rangle} \left(\frac{S_\alpha}{B_\alpha}\frac{\sum_{j=1}^{N_{\alpha\beta}}\frac{1}{a_j}}{N_\alpha}\right)\left(\frac{\mathcal{B}_\alpha}{\mathcal{S}_\alpha}\frac{\mathcal{N}_\alpha}{\mathcal{N}_{\alpha\beta}}\right) \quad (2)
$$

where
α = multiplicity component of the trigger, β = multiplicity class,
$S_\alpha, \mathcal{S}_\alpha$ = dimuon and nomuon triggers before downscaling,
$\langle m_{\alpha\beta}\rangle$ = average charged multiplicity,
$B_\alpha, \mathcal{B}_\alpha$ = dimuon and nomuon effective beams,
$N_\alpha, \mathcal{N}_\alpha$ = dimuon and nomuon triggers taken,
$N_{\alpha\beta}, \mathcal{N}_{\alpha\beta}$ = dimuon and nomuon triggers taken per multiplicity class.
The various triggers contributing to each multiplicity class were then combined.

3. Results

In figure 1 the invariant mass spectra for dimuons produced both in p–W and in S–W collisions (all multiplicities) are shown. The dimuon yield is normalized to the number of charged particles in the rapidity acceptance of the spectrometer. The shape of the two spectra look very different: in particular the level of the continuum is higher (roughly a factor of

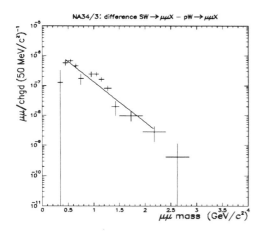

Figure 2. $[S\text{--}W \to \mu\mu X]_{central} - [p\text{--}W \to \mu\mu X]$

2) in S–W data than in p–W data and even the shape is different, the slope being lower for S–W data. The production of the ϕ meson is enhanced in S–W data, while the production of $\rho + \omega$ and J/ψ is suppressed [5]. To appreciate better the difference between p–W and S–W dimuon mass spectra, in figure 2 the dimuon yield in S–W reactions minus the same quantity in p–W reactions is plotted as a function of the invariant mass. Except for a peak denoting the enhancement of the ϕ vector meson and the suppression of the J/ψ meson, the *subtracted* spectrum does not show appreciable structures for any multiplicity class and can be fitted by means of a simple exponential function. Moreover, the slope of the function does not depend on centrality.

In order to see if our results can be understood in terms of standard sources, we extrapolated the HELIOS–1 generator [3] for the low mass dimuon production to our experimental conditions, adding an evaluation of the relative amount of dimuons in the intermediate mass region originating from Drell–Yan process and charmed mesons decays normalized to the ω meson, both for p–W and S–W collisions (See [5] for a detailed description of the method).

Even if the model to evaluate the sources at low mass needs some further tuning, we can preliminarily conclude that the features of the dimuon mass spectrum in p–W collisions can be described by the decays of mesons, while the model underestimates the dimuon yield for S-W collisions. A more quantitative evaluation of the difference between the contribution from known sources and data was done for the intermediate mass region [6]. To this purpose, we define the following ratio as a measure of the observed excess:

$$\frac{D}{S} = \frac{Integral\ contents\ of\ data\ histogram}{Integral\ sum\ of\ predicted\ sources} \quad (3)$$

In the p-W case the ratio is compatible within the errors with 1, while the S-W ratio is more than 3σ from unity for each of the three more central multiplicity classes (for the low multiplicity classes the amount of data was insufficient to make the comparison), as reported in Table 1. For these calculations, the charm production cross section was assumed to be $8 \pm 2\,nb$, as estimated by the NA38 collaboration in S–A collisions at 200 GeV/c/A [7]. We compare our results to the similar results found by the NA38 collaboration in S–U interactions. They find an excess of about 1.4 (with a small error due to their high statistics) in the mass region $1.5 < m_{\mu\mu} < 2.5\,GeV/c^2$ [7]. If we restrict ourselves to this mass interval, we find $D/S = 1.96 \pm 0.58$.

P.Part.	$1.35 < M < 1.6$	$1.35 < M < 2.5$
$1. \pm 0.$	0.97 ± 0.14	0.91 ± 0.10
26.6 ± 4.8	4.50 ± 0.85	3.46 ± 0.54
29.4 ± 2.6	3.23 ± 0.62	2.94 ± 0.42
30.6 ± 1.7	4.20 ± 0.83	3.27 ± 0.54

Table 1. D/S vs. number of proj. participants (P.Part.).

4. Conclusions

We conclude that the dimuon yield per charged particle in S–W collisions is higher than in p–W and that this excess extends over the whole kinematic region, continuously in invariant mass. This excess does not show a dependence on the centrality of the collision.

While the p–W dimuon mass spectra can be described in terms of the known dimuon sources, the S–W data cannot be accounted by these sources. The excess with respect to yield due to known processes is qualitatively and quantitatively in agreement with the resutlts of the NA38 collaboration in the intermediate mass range.

References

[1] J.D. Bjorken and H. Weisberg, Phys. Rev. **D13** (1976) 1405
[2] G.G. Henry Ph. D. Thesis, University of Chicago, 1978. K.J. Anderson et al., Phys. Rev. Lett. **37** (1976) 799.
[3] T. Åkesson et Al., *Lepton–pair production in p–Be collisions at 450 GeV/c*, to be submitted to Z. Phys. C.
[4] K.Kajantie et al., Phys. Rev. **D34**(1986)2746 and references therein.
[5] M.A. Mazzoni, Proc. of QM 93 Conf., Nucl. Phys. **A566**, 95c.
[6] J. Antos et al., *Proceedings of the XXVII Rencontre de Moriond, Perturbative QCD and Hadronic Interactions, Editions Frontières, (1992) 483*
[7] C. Lourenço Proc. of the 5th Conf. on the Intersections of Part. and Nucl. Phys., St. Petersburg, Florida, USA, 1994.

Paper presented at XXVII Int. Conf. on High Energy Physics: Session Pa-3
Glasgow, UK, 20–27 July 1994

Experimental Status of the AGS Relativistic Heavy Ion Program

T. Craig Sangster[‡]

Lawrence Livermore National Laboratory, Livermore, CA 94550

Abstract

The universal motivation for colliding large nuclei at relativistic energies is the expectation that a small volume of the primordial quark soup, generally referred to as the *Quark-Gluon Plasma* (QGP), can be created and studied. The QGP is formed via a phase transition caused by either the extreme baryon densities and/or the extreme temperatures achieved in the overlap zone of the two colliding nuclei. Experiments at the Brookhaven National Laboratory Alternating Gradient Synchrotron (AGS) using a beam of Si nuclei at 14.6 GeV per nucleon on various nuclear targets have been completed. These same experiments are now actively searching for signatures of QGP formation using a beam of Au nuclei at 11.7 GeV per nucleon. This paper briefly summarizes some of the key results from the Si beam program and the current status of the experimental Au beam program at the AGS.

1. Introduction

By colliding relativistic heavy ion beams with stationary nuclei, extremely dense baryonic matter is created in the laboratory. Estimates based on experimental observation and theoretical calculations indicate that densities between 4 and 9 times the groundstate matter density, ρ_0, should be achieved in small impact parameter collisions at energies of approximately 10 GeV per nucleon. Model predictions which explicitly include a nuclear matter equation-of-state (EOS) show considerable sensitivity to the EOS parameters at these densities. In addition, at these densities theorists predict that nuclear matter may undergo a transition from the normal bound states of quarks and gluons (hadronic matter) to a state in which the quarks and gluons are free to move within the high density volume. This primordial state is generally referred to as the *Quark-Gluon Plasma* (QGP) and has not existed since the Big Bang.

The experimental relativistic heavy ion program at the Brookhaven National Laboratory Alternating

Gradient Synchrotron (AGS) began in 1986, utilizing a 14.6 GeV per nucleon Si beam for a broad spectrum of measurements designed to study both detailed properties and gross features of Si+A collisions. The original large experiments included E802, E810, E814 and E858. E802 measured particle spectra and the transverse energy of produced particles at mid-rapidity with extensive event characterization including total charged particle multiplicity and zero degree energy. E810 offered a 4π examination of charge particle production using a series of time-projection chambers with limited single particle identification capabilities. E814 measured particle spectra forward of mid-rapidity and incorporated transverse energy measurements at both target and mid-rapidities. Finally, E858 consisted of a beam line spectrometer optimized to search at zero degrees for antinuclei as well as the standard suite of produced particles.

The current AGS experimental relativistic heavy ion program is based on measurements using an 11.7 GeV per nucleon Au beam. All of the major experiments have upgraded to accomodate the higher charged particle multiplicities and most have added additional inclusive or event characterization measurements to study either

‡ E-mail: sangster1@llnl.gov

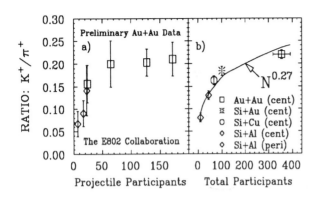

Figure 1. a) K/π ratio for the symetric systems Si+Al and Au+Au as a function of the number of projectile participants only. b) The K/π ratio for central collisions of several systems as a function of the total number of participants (both target and projectile). The data in both panels are measurments by the E802 Collaboration.

new phenomena or extend the original Si beam coverage. Optimism is high that the much larger Au+A systems will produce a considerable increase in both the spatial extent and the peak value of the maximum baryon densities achieved. Indeed, the experimental assault on the QGP phase boundary may be just beginning. The real challenge at the AGS is whether a subset of collisions in which some fraction of the system has crossed the deconfinement boundary can be identified using only hadronic probes (no AGS experiment utilizes leptonic probes). Since the phase boundary is reached via extreme densities at AGS energies, the key that unlocks the QGP may be a combination of both new and exotic probes and a systematic exploration of collective phenomena leading to an improved understanding of the nuclear EOS.

The remainder of the paper will give just a brief survey of some key Si beam results and, where available, mention the corresponding preliminary Au beam findings. The intent is to demonstrate both the scope of the anticipated Au beam measurements and the extent of our current understanding of relativistic heavy ion collisions.

2. Recent Results

At the AGS, the QGP would likely be created via high baryon densities rather than through extreme temperatures. Therefore, calorimeter based measurements of transverse energy, E_t, at mid-rapidity were among the first published Si beam results from experiments E802 and E814. These measurements [1, 2] showed a high degree of stopping in small impact parameter Si+A collisions. In the context of relativistic heavy ion colli-

sions, stopping means a lack of projectile energy in a forward cone, or effectively, the transfer of longitudinal beam momentum into transverse components. Stopping is generally equated with the creation of high baryon densities. Identical measurements with the Au+Au system [3] now show that the E_t scales essentially with the number of projectile participants.

Due to the unavoidable rehadronization process, hadronic probes of QGP formation are not only difficult to measure but also difficult to interpret. Perhaps the most widely accepted potential hadronic signature is strangeness enhancement. Excess strangeness (via an enhancement in the K/π ratio) was heralded early in the Si beam program but diligent efforts to understand the collision dynamics led to the realization that a number of non-QGP mechanisms (*eg.,* rescattering of mesons and resonances) lead to higher than expected strangeness production. Figure 1 shows the K to π ratios measured by the E802 series of experiments including preliminary data from the Au beam experiment, E866. Using the K/π ratio to observe strangeness enhancement necessarily assumes that the π yield represents a plasma-independent benchmark of the temperature or density of the emitting system. Figure 1a shows the measured K/π ratio for the two symetric systems Si+Al and Au+Au as a function of the number of projectile participants. Here the ratio rises quickly with the number of projectile participants and then appears to saturate in the preliminary Au+Au data indicating that the increased volume (and presumably, increased density) does not promote further strangeness production (as observed via the K/π ratio). However, in central collisions of several different systems (figure 1b), the measured K/π ratio continues to rise smoothly as a function of the total number of participating nucleons (both target and projectile). Clearly, the K/π ratio is only one of the missing pieces in the QGP puzzle.

In general, collision models such as ARC [4] and RQMD [5] produce the observed K/π ratios without invoking QGP formation, relying instead on rescattering mechanisms and the formation of resonance matter. Therefore, interest is high in measurments of multi-strange, multi-quark objects such as strangelets [6] and Ξ hyperons. Indeed experiment E810 has recently published results [7] on the production of the Ξ⁻ relative to the singly strange Λ. Here it was found that the measured ratio of N(Ξ⁻) to N(Λ) is three times greater than predicted by a cascade model (AGSHIJET+N^*) suggesting an enhancement in the production of the multiply strange hyperons. Future experiments, discussed in the next section will focus heavily on these more exotic hadronic probes.

Identical particle correlations (HBT) have been studied extensively in the E802 series of experiments. These correlations can be used to estimate the space-

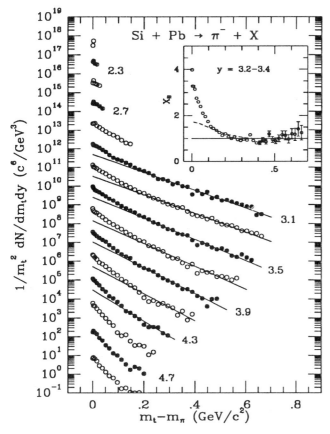

Figure 2. Experiment E814 π^- spectra for central ($\sigma/\sigma_{GEO} = 2\%$) Si + Pb collisions and a variety of rapidity intervals. Starting with y=4.7, the data in each successively lower rapidity bin has been multiplied by increasing powers of 10. The lines through the data points are simple Boltzman fits to the region $m_t > 300 MeV/c^2$.

time extent of the emitting source (the overlap region of the two colliding nuclei) which may be sensitive to the formation of the QGP. The Si beam results for both pions and kaons have been published [8]. The extracted RMS source radii are generally consistent with the nuclear radius of the Si projectile. Preliminary central Au+Au $\pi^-\pi^-$ correlations indicate that the source radius again simply scales with the number of projectile partipants, *ie*, there is no apparent extended source which might suggest the formation of the QGP.

One of the most intriguing results from the Si beam program has been the observation of an enhancement in the transverse mass spectrum of pions at low m_t. The enhancement has been seen in data from both E810 and E814. Figure 2 shows π^- spectra for central Si+Pb collisions from the E814 experiment [9] for a variety of rapidity intervals. As seen in the inset, the enhancement, relative to a Boltzman spectrum, reaches a factor of four in the lowest m_t bin. A similar enhancement has been observed in the π^+ spectra as well as with a much lighter Al target.

What makes this data so appealing is that the enhancement is likely caused by the decay of resonance matter. Both ARC and RQMD include contributions from Δ decays which preferentially produce pions with low transverse momenta in these rapidity intervals. Indeed, RQMD predicts that the density of purely resonance matter approaches that of normal nuclear matter at the peak of the total baryon density. The E814 collaboration has performed a straightforward calculation [10] which assumes that the pion enhancement is due entirely to the formation and decay of resonances. The results of this calculation indicate that approximately 30-40% of all nucleons in the participant zone are in the Δ resonance. In a purely thermal picture, this fraction can be explained by assuming a temperature of 140±20 MeV.

Figure 3 shows a composite of all particle species from central Si+Au collisions measured by the E802 collaboration (experiments E802 and E859). It is worth noting that a second level trigger implemented during E859 provided the necessary statistics to allow the ϕ and Λ measurements as well as the superb K^- and $\bar{p}$ spectra. The addition of a forward spectrometer to the E802 apparatus will significantly extend the single particle coverage shown in the figure. A projectile hodoscope has also been implemented which will provide an event-by-event reaction plane for impact parameters less than $\approx$ 9-fm. The E866 experiment will primarily focus on measurements of both the ϕ, Λ and resonance production as well as on single and multi-particle correlations with the event reaction plane (collective phenomena such as hydrodynamical flow and shadowing are likely measurements and should contribute significantly to our understanding of the nuclear EOS).

Finally, it is worth mentioning that excellent summaries of both the BNL and CERN relativistic heavy ion programs are available in the recent Quark Matter proceedings [11, 12] and the proceedings of the Heavy Ion Physics at the AGS (HIPAGS) workshops [13, 14].

3. Future Experiments

A number of new experiments are poised to begin making measurements at the AGS during the coming year. The first to take the floor will be experiment E864, a high sensitivity search for novel new forms of matter. E864 will focus primarily on the production of long-lived ($\tau \geq 50$ ns) multi-strange quark matter (strangelets and the H^0 dibaryon) and light anti-nuclei. The measurements will be made using an open geometry spectrometer with broad acceptance in both rapidity ($\Delta y = \pm 0.5$ around mid-rapidity) and transverse momentum ($P_t/Z \leq 2 GeV/c$).

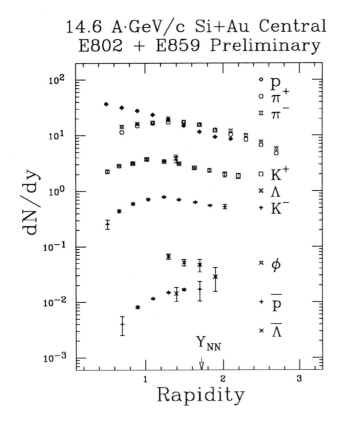

14.6 A·GeV/c Si+Au Central E802 + E859 Preliminary

Figure 3. Composite of all measured particle species from experiments E802 and E859.

4.   Summary

To date there have been few surprises in the preliminary Au beam measurements. Quantities such as the total transverse energy and the identical particle correlation (HBT) radii appear to scale with the number of projectile participants. However, most of the Au beam data acquired to date has yet to be analyzed and, in this paper, the emphasis has been on what measurements are possible rather than on specific Au beam findings. The Si beam results suggest that the current set of experiments have the sensitivity to see new phenomena and model calculations indicate that, relative to Si+A collisions, a significant increase in the Au+Au central density should be expected. Furthermore, several new experiments are poised to look at new, exotic probes (the H^0 dibaryon and strange quark matter) while current experiments are now beginning to probe new physics regimes (*eg.*, collective phenomena) which promise a more complete understanding of the nuclear equation of state and the dynamics of hot, dense matter. Therefore, the outlook for the AGS relativistic heavy ion program is filled with expectations of discovery.

References

[1] T. Abbott *et al.*, the E802 Collaboration, Phys. Lett **B197** (1987) 285; Phys. Rev. **C44** (1991), 1611; Phys. Rev **C45** (1992) 2933.

[2] J. Barrette *et al.*, the E814 Collaboration, Phys. Rev. Lett. **64** (1990) 1219.

[3] L. Ahle *el al.*, the E802 Collaboration, submitted to Phys. Rev. Lett. (1994).

[4] Y. Pang *et al.*, Phys. Rev. Lett. **68** (1992) 2743; T. J. Schlagel *et al.*, Phys. Rev. Lett. **69** (1992) 3290.

[5] H. Sorge *et al.*, Ann. Phys. (N.Y.) **192** (1989) 266; Nucl.Phys. **A498** (1989) 567c.

[6] C. Griener, P Kock and H. Stoecker, Phys. Rev. Lett **58** (1987) 1825; C. Greiner, D. H. Rischke, H. Stoecker and P. Koch, Phys. Rev. **D38** (1988) 2797; C. Greiner and H. Stoecker, Phys. Rev. **D44** (1992) 3517.

[7] S. E. Eiseman *et al.*, Phys. Lett. **B325** (1994) 322.

[8] Y. Akiba *et al.*, Phys. Rev. Lett. **70** (1993) 1057.

[9] T. K. Hemmick, Nucl. Phys. **A566** (1994) 435c.

[10] J. Stachel, Nucl. Phys. **A566** (1994) 185c.

[11] *Quark Matter '91*, Proceedings of the Ninth International Conference on Ultra-Relativistic Nucleus-Nucleus Collisions, edited by T. C. Awes, F. E. Obenshain, F. Plasil, M. R. Strayer and C. Y. Wong, Gatlinburg, Tennessee, November 11-15, 1991, North Holland (1992); Nucl. Phys. **A544** (1992).

[12] *Quark Matter '93*, Proceedings of the Tenth International Conference on Ultra-Relativistic Nucleus-Nucleus Collisions, edited by E. Stenlund, H.-A. Gustafsson, A. Oskarsson and I. Otterlund, Borlange, Sweden, June 20-24, 1993, North Holland (1994); Nucl. Phys. **A566** (1994).

[13] Proceedings of the Workshop on Heavy Ion Physics at the AGS, edited by O. Hansen, Brookhaven National Laboratory, Upton, New York, March 5-7, 1990, BNL-44911.

[14] *HIPAGS '93*, Proceedings of Heavy Ion Physics at the AGS, edited by G. S. F. Stephans, S. G. Steadman and W. L. Kehoe, MIT-LNS, Cambridge, Massachusetts, January 13-15, 1993, MITLNS-2158.

Experiment E896 will focus almost exclusively on a search for the H^0 dibaryon via the decay topologies $H^0 \rightarrow \Sigma^- p$ and $H^0 \rightarrow \Lambda\Lambda$. The experiment will be sensitive to shorter lifetimes than possible with the E864 apparatus and should be commissioned by 1995. The multi-strange quark matter searches of E896 and E864 add an exciting new dimension to the experimental relativistic heavy ion program at the AGS and may be the best opportunity for identifying QGP signatures before the startup of the Relativistic Heavy Ion Collider (RHIC) in 1999.

Finally, E895 will carry out a systematic measurement of the energy and mass dependence of particle production, collective phenomena and multi-particle correlations in Au+A reactions using the Lawrence Berkeley Laboratory EOS TPC, the MUSIC ion chamber and the EOS TOF wall. E895 will measure the four-momenta of light mass particles (including $\pi^\pm$, $K^\pm$, K^0_s, Λ, n, p, d, and the isotopes of He, Li and Be), projectile fragments from $6 \leq Z \leq 79$ and anti-protons. It is expected that E895 will begin taking data during a lower energy Au beam run in 1995.

Beyond the Standard Model

Conveners: T. Yanagida (Tohoku University)
G. G. Ross (Oxford University)

Scientific secretaries: P. McCallum
S. Ryan (reserve)

Technicolor and Precision Tests of the Electroweak Interactions[†]

Kenneth Lane[‡]

Department of Physics, Boston University,
590 Commonwealth Avenue, Boston, MA 02215, USA

Abstract

Precision electroweak measurements have been claimed to eliminate almost all models of technicolor. We show that the assumptions made to calculate the oblique parameters S,T,U apply to QCD–like technicolor models which were ruled out long ago on much firmer grounds. These assumptions are invalid in modern "walking" technicolor models.

1. Introduction

Technicolor—dynamical breaking of electroweak symmetry by an asymptotically free gauge interaction— was invented in 1979 [1],[2]. Extended technicolor— the gauge mechanism for introducing quark and lepton flavors and for breaking flavor symmetry—followed quickly [3],[4]. It was already pointed out in Ref. [4] that ETC theories generically have large flavor–changing neutral currents and that an ETC scale Λ_{ETC} of $O(1000 \, \text{TeV}/\text{times mixing angles})$ was needed to avoid conflict with experiment in the neutral kaon system (also see Ref. [5]). This large scale implied ridiculously small quark and lepton masses, as well as light pseudo–Goldstone bosons (technipions) that were soon ruled out by experiment. Technicolor was dead.

The most promising solution to the FCNC problem was not long in coming [6]. Holdom showed that, if the technifermion bilinear condensate, $\langle \bar{\psi}\psi \rangle$, has a large anomalous dimension, γ_m, it is possible to have a very large ETC scale without unduly small fermion and technipion masses. Unfortunately, Holdom did not provide a convincing field–theoretic explanation of how this large γ_m could occur. His idea lay dormant until 1986 when several groups pointed out that a technicolor gauge theory with a very slowly running coupling,

$\alpha_{TC}(\mu) \simeq$ constant for $\Lambda_{TC} \sim 1 \, \text{TeV} < \mu < \Lambda_{ETC}$, gives rise to $\gamma_m(\mu) \simeq 1$ over this large energy range [7]. This "walking technicolor" permitted the increase in Λ_{ETC} needed to eliminate FCNC. Thus, the resurrection of technicolor was brought about by abandoning the notion that its gauge dynamics were QCD–like, with *precocious* asymptotic freedom and all that implies. (For a recent review of technicolor, its problems and proposed solutions, see Ref. [8].)

In 1990, it was rediscovered that technicolor dynamics (TC, *not* ETC, in this case) could affect electroweak parameters that were just then beginning to be very precisely measured in LEP experiments [9]. Estimating the effects of technicolor on the "oblique" parameter S (or its equivalent), many authors showed that one–family TC models were inconsistent with its then–measured value. Once again, technicolor was dead.

This news received considerable attention in journals and on the conference circuit. Little attention was given to the protests of technicolor afficionados that the technicolor killed by the precision tests had been dead for a decade. Walking technicolor was *not* ruled out by these tests and it remains unclear how to confront it with the precision electroweak measurements. I am grateful to the organizers of the "Beyond the Standard Model" session at this conference for this opportunity to review the issues. I will do that as clearly as I can.

In the next section, I state the definition of the

† Invited talk given at the 27th International Conference on High Energy Physics, Glasgow, 20–27th July 1994.
‡ email: lane@buphyc.bu.edu

S,T,U parameters popularized by Peskin and Takeuchi, give their most recent values, and detail the assumptions that have been used to calculate these parameters in technicolor models. In Section 3, I show that all these assumptions are wrong or, at best, questionable in walking technicolor. This, of course, will not convince its detractors that technicolor is still viable; nor is it intended to. My intent is to persuade that the S,T,U–argument against technicolor is far from made. Finally, in Section 4, I discuss some other aspects of precision electroweak tests. These include the question of technicolor (here ETC is involved) and the rate for $Z^0 \rightarrow b\bar{b}$, as well as some other curiosities in the precision electroweak data.

2. Technicolor and Precision Electroweak Tests—The Problem

The standard $SU(2) \otimes U(1)$ model of electroweak interactions has passed all experimental tests faced so far. The parameters of this model—$\alpha(M_Z)$, M_Z, $\sin^2 \theta_W$—are so precisely known that they may be used to limit new physics at energy scales above 100 GeV. The quantities most sensitive to new physics are defined in terms of electroweak current correlation functions:

$$\int d^4x \, e^{-iq\cdot x} \langle \Omega|T(j_i^\mu(x) j_j^\nu(0))|\Omega\rangle = \tag{1}$$
$$ig^{\mu\nu}\Pi_{ij}(q^2) + q^\mu q^\nu \text{ terms}.$$

Assuming that the scale Λ_{new} of this physics is *well above* $M_{W,Z}$, one may define "oblique" correction factors S, T and U that measure its effects by

$$S = 16\pi\left[\Pi'_{33}(0) - \Pi'_{3Q}(0)\right],$$
$$T = \frac{4\pi}{M_Z^2 \cos^2\theta_W \sin^2\theta_W}\left[\Pi_{11}(0) - \Pi_{33}(0)\right], \tag{2}$$
$$U = 16\pi\left[\Pi'_{11}(0) - \Pi'_{33}(0)\right].$$

Here, the prime denotes differentiation at $q^2 = 0$, and these are the leading terms in an expansion in M_Z^2/Λ_{new}^2. The parameter S is a measure of the splitting between M_W and M_Z induced by weak–isospin conserving effects. The parameter T is defined in terms of $\rho \equiv M_W^2/M_Z^2 \cos\theta_W^2 = 1 + \alpha T$. The U–parameter measures weak–isospin breaking in the W and Z mass splitting.

Langacker recently made a global "best fit" to a set of precisely–measured electroweak quantities, using the CDF measurement of the top–quark mass, $m_t = 174 \pm 10 \,^{+13}_{-12}$ GeV[11]. He extracted the following values of S,T,U due to potential *new physics* [12]:

$$S = -0.15 \pm 0.25 \,^{-0.08}_{+0.17}$$
$$T = -0.08 \pm 0.32 \,^{+0.18}_{-0.11} \tag{3}$$
$$U = -0.56 \pm 0.61.$$

The first error is the net experimental error, assuming a standard Higgs boson mass of 300 GeV; the second error is the effect of varying M_H from 60 to 1000 GeV.

It is clear that S,T,U can be computed precisely only if the new physics is weakly coupled. It would have been impossible to calculate the QCD analogs of S,T,U without experimental information on the hadronic weak currents—the color and flavor of quarks, the spectrum of hadrons, and so on. New standard–model data is still leading to revisions. A year ago, the quoted value of S was rather different, -0.8 ± 0.5, from Eq. (3) (see [8]); the change is due to the fact that we now know the top–quark mass [11]. No data is available for technicolor—a strong gauge theory at a scale of several 100 GeV. Assumptions must be made to estimate its contributions to S,T,U.

The assumptions made to calculate S amount to assuming that technicolor is just QCD scaled up to a higher energy, with N_D elecroweak doublets of technifermions belonging to the fundamental representation of a strong $SU(N_{TC})$ technicolor gauge group:

1.) Techni-isospin is a good symmetry, i.e., custodial $SU(2)$ breaking by ETC interactions is negligible.
2.) Asymptotic freedom sets in quickly above the technicolor scale Λ_{TC}.
3.) Appropriate combinations of spectral functions of current correlators may be estimated using vector-meson dominance, i.e., saturating the spectral integrals with the lowest–lying spin–one resonances. Why this works in QCD is a mystery, but it is consistent with the precocious asymptotic freedom of QCD (see the discussion in Section 3).
4.) The spectrum of techni-hadrons may be scaled from QCD using, e.g., large–N_{TC} arguments.
5.) Chiral lagrangians may be used to describe the low–energy dynamics of technipions, with coefficients of terms scaled from the QCD values[10].

As an oft–cited example of how these assumptions are employed, I present a simplified version of Peskin and Takeuchi's calculation of S [9]. If techni-isospin is a good symmetry, then S may be written as the following spectral integral:

$$S = -4\pi\left[\Pi'_{VV}(0) - \Pi'_{AA}(0)\right]$$
$$= \frac{1}{3\pi}\int_0^\infty \frac{ds}{s}\left[R_V(s) - R_A(s)\right]. \tag{4}$$

Here, $\Pi_{VV(AA)}$ is the polarization function for the product of two vector (axial-vector) weak isospin currents (e.g., $j_\mu^3 j_\nu^3$); $R_{V(A)}$ is the analog for these current of $R(s) = \sigma(e^+e^- \rightarrow \text{hadrons})/\sigma(e^+e^- \rightarrow \mu^+\mu^-)$. They are the spin–one spectral functions to which Weinberg's two sum rules apply [13]:

$$\int_0^\infty ds \, [R_V(s) - R_A(s)] = F_\pi^2$$
$$\int_0^\infty ds \cdot s \, [R_V(s) - R_A(s)] = 0 \,. \tag{5}$$

These sum rules, written here for conserved currents, are implied by the strength of the singularity at $x \to 0$ in $\langle \Omega | T(j_{L\mu}(x) j_{R\nu}(0)) | \Omega \rangle$. The second sum rule, in particular, requires asymptotic freedom for its validity. In Eqs. (5), $F_\pi = 246 \, \text{GeV}$ is the decay constant of the technipions that become the longitudinal components of the W and Z.

In the evaluation of S, the spectral functions R_V and R_A are approximated by saturating them with the lowest-lying vector (ρ_T) and axial-vector (a_{1T}) meson poles, using Eqs. (5) to help fix their parameters. Their masses are scaled from QCD using large-N_{TC}. In the narrow width approximation,

$$S = 4\pi \left(1 + \frac{M_{\rho_T}^2}{M_{a_{1T}}^2} \right) \frac{F_\pi^2}{M_{\rho_T}^2} \simeq 0.25 \, N_D \, \frac{N_{TC}}{3} \,. \tag{6}$$

It appears from Eq. (6) that all technicolor models with $N_D > 1$ and $N_{TC} > 3$ are ruled out; this includes the popular one-family model ($N_D = 4$).

The other main method of calculating S uses chiral lagrangians. Technicolor models with N_D-doublets have $4(N_D^2 - 1)$ physical technipions. Golden and Randall, Holdom and Terning, and others [9] estimated their leading chiral-logarithmic contribution, S_{π_T}, to S[†]. This approach is valid, independent of the nature of technicolor dynamics, so long as ETC interactions are weak enough that a chiral perturbation expansion is accurate. Assuming all technipions are degenerate and that the cutoff scale for the chiral logs is M_{ρ_T}, these authors obtained

$$S > S_{\pi_T} \simeq \frac{1}{12\pi} (N_D^2 - 1) \log \left(\frac{M_{\rho_T}^2}{M_{\pi_T}^2} \right) \simeq 0.08 (N_D^2 - 1) \,. \tag{7}$$

Eqs. (6) and (7) agree for the popular choice of the one-family model, $N_D = N_{TC} = 4$, in which case $S \simeq 1$, almost 4σ away from the central value quoted above. This agreement is accidental; see Ref. [14]. Nevertheless, except for the simplest possible technicolor model, such estimates of S have led to the oft-repeated observation that, to paraphrase Ref. [15], "technicolor is not only really very dead, it's really most sincerely dead!"

---

† Holdom and Terning also estimated the non-chiral log part of the relevant coefficient in the chiral lagrangian by scaling from QCD. I will discuss below why such scaling is problematic.

3. Walking Technicolor and S,T,U

While chiral symmetry breaking and bound state formation in QCD are nonperturbative phenomena, requiring strong-coupling methods for their study, much interesting physics of quarks and gluons occurs above 1 GeV where it is possible to exploit asymptotic freedom. Walking technicolor, is essentially nonperturbative over the entire range, Λ_{TC} to Λ_{ETC}. Let us see how this affects the basic assumptions made in calculating S. For now, leave the question of techni–isospin aside. That has as much to do with ETC interactions as with walking TC.

The assumption that asymptotic freedom sets in quickly above Λ_{TC} is patently wrong. This assumption was used implicitly (and is essential) in approximating the spectral functions $R_V(s)$ and $R_A(s)$. It tells how these functions behave at large s and, in turn, how fast $\Pi_{VV}(q^2) - \Pi_{AA}(q^2)$ falls at large q^2. In an asymptotically free theory, $\Pi_{VV}(q^2) - \Pi_{AA}(q^2) \sim q^{-4}$ above Λ_{TC}. In a walking gauge theory, $\Pi_{VV}(q^2) - \Pi_{AA}(q^2) \sim q^{-2}$ until the coupling becomes small, at $q^2 \lesssim \Lambda_{ETC}^2$. Consequently, the convergence of the second spectral integral to zero (Eq. (5)) is much slower in a walking gauge theory, and $R_V - R_A$ cannot be approximated by a *single, close pair* of vector and axial-vector meson poles. It follows that the masses and widths of hadrons in a walking gauge theory cannot simply be scaled up from QCD; the spectrum of a walking gauge theory is a mystery. While the integral for S is dominated by low energies, the spectral sum rules connect the low and high energy behavior of $R_V - R_A$. In a walking theory, the spectral weight of $R_V - R_A$ is shifted to higher energies. Thus, it is possible that S is smaller in such a theory than in a QCD-like one.

Another reason to be skeptical of scaling from QCD is that some or all technifermions may belong to higher-dimensional representations of the TC gauge group. Then, large-N_{TC} arguments are inapplicable.

The assumption of a reliable chiral–perturbative expansion in a walking gauge theory is also unjustified. Like the technifermion bilinear, the operators $\overline{\psi}\psi\overline{\psi}\psi$ involved in ETC generation of technipion masses have large anomalous dimensions [7]. In the extreme walking case, these become relevant operators so that $M_{\pi_T} \sim \Lambda_{TC}$; i.e., the technipions are *not* approximate Goldstone bosons. In generic walking TC theories, then, the chiral Lagrangian estimate of a lower bound for S is also likely to be incorrect.

Now return to the question of techni–isospin conservation, and T and U as well. This assumption appeared plausible because, otherwise, T ought to be too large. However, ETC theories need to have rather large isospin breaking to account for the top-quark mass of $O(F_\pi)$! Can this be consistent with small S and T?

The T-parameter is notoriously difficult to calculate (which partly explains why so few attempt it). The main problem is that T is directly determined by physics at higher scales (Λ_{TC}) even in ordinary TC theories; there is no derivative in its definition (see, e.g., Ref. [16]). This may point the way out. It is possible that there are several scales of chiral symmetry breaking in TC theories (e.g., see Ref. [17])[†]. The highest scales, mainly responsible for generating $M_{W,Z}$, may respect weak isospin. The lower scales, which contribute to S, may not. It has long been known and was emphasized in Ref. [18] that this can lead to a small and even a negative value for S. Whether multiscale theories can generate a large m_t is a model–dependent question. See Ref. [19] for an example that may produce large m_t. There is practically nothing we can say about U. It is generally presumed to be of $O(S \cdot T)$. We are unaware of attempts to compute it in a walking technicolor theory.

4.   Other Electroweak Discrepancies

The deviation of the measured $Z^0 \rightarrow b\bar{b}$ rate from the standard–model expectation is [12]

$$\Delta_{b\bar{b}} \equiv \Gamma(Z \rightarrow b\bar{b})/\Gamma(Z \rightarrow b\bar{b})_{SM} - 1 = 0.031 \pm 0.014,$$
$$(8)$$

i.e., 2.2σ away from zero. This rate may turn out to be the most incisive test of TC/ETC theories. The reason for this is that the top–quark is so heavy that the ETC boson which generates m_t is probably very light, of order a few TeV (an exception to this will be mentioned below). Consequently, the Fierzed ETC interaction

$$\xi^2 \frac{1}{\Lambda_{ETC}^2(t)} \left(\overline{T}_L \gamma^\mu \frac{\vec{\tau}}{2} T_L \right) \cdot \left(\overline{\psi}_L \gamma_\mu \frac{\vec{\tau}}{2} \psi_L \right) \quad (9)$$

modifies the coupling of left–handed b-quarks to the Z^0[20]. Here, $\Lambda_{ETC}(t)$ is the ETC scale involved in generating m_t; T_L is a left–handed technifermion doublet and $\psi_L = (t, b)_L$; and ξ is a model–dependent factor expected to be $O(1)$.
In a QCD–like technicolor theory,

$$\Delta_{b\bar{b}} = -0.065 \xi^2 \left(\frac{m_t}{175 \, \text{GeV}} \right), \quad (10)$$

in clear conflict with the value quoted in Eq. (8). The situation is little improved if α_{TC} walks because a low $\Lambda_{ETC}(t)$ is still needed to produce such a large m_t [21].
Clearly this is a problem of the ETC, not just the TC, interaction. Two modifications to ETC can eliminate the conflict with $\Delta_{b\bar{b}}$. The first, which appears to be necessary anyway to explain the large m_t, is

known as strong extended technicolor (SETC). An ETC scale of $O(1 \, \text{TeV})$ makes no sense dynamically. There is not enough splitting between the scale at which ETC breaks to TC and the TC scale itself. To maintain a substantial hierarchy between $\Lambda_{ETC}(t)$ and Λ_{TC}, it seems necessary that some ETC interactions be strong enough to participate with TC in the breakdown of electroweak symmetry [22]. This requires some fine tuning of the ETC coupling and leads to a composite scalar state light compared to $\Lambda_{ETC}(t)$ [23]. The increased $\Lambda_{ETC}(t)$ leads to a $\Delta_{b\bar{b}}$ too small to detect [24].

The second modification of ETC which can eliminate conflict with $\Delta_{b\bar{b}}$ is to give up the time–honored, but apparently inessential, assumption that the ETC gauge group commutes with electroweak $SU(2)$[‡]. Chivukula, Simmons and Terning have recently considered the magnitude of $\Delta_{b\bar{b}}$ in such noncommuting ETC theories *without* the assumption of SETC [25]. They found that it is possible to obtain $\Delta_{b\bar{b}}$ of order the value in Eq. (10), but with *either* sign. This will be especially interesting if the deviation in Eq. (8) survives.

Finally, I draw attention to two other curiosities in the precision measurements. The first involves $\sin^2 \theta_W$. The SLD measurement reported at this conference is [26]

$$\sin^2 \theta_W (\text{SLD}) = 0.2292 \pm 0.0009 \pm 0.0004. \quad (11)$$

The LEP average value reported here is [27]

$$\sin^2 \theta_W (\text{LEP}) = 0.2321 \pm 0.0003 \pm 0.0004. \quad (12)$$

These differ by 2.9σ. An equivalent (and perhaps more direct) expression of this intercontinental disagreement is provided by the left–right asymmetry. The SLD measurement is (from Ref. [12], whose notation we follow)

$$A_e^0 (\text{SLD}) = 0.164 \pm 0.008 \quad (13)$$

The asymmetry inferred from LEP measurements of the forward–backward asymmetry in $e^+ e^- \rightarrow Z^0 \rightarrow e^+ e^-$ and the angular distribution of τ–polarization is

$$A_e^0 (\text{LEP}) = 0.129 \pm 0.010 \quad (14)$$

The disagreement here is 2.7σ.

The second discrepancy is smaller and wouldn't be worth mentioning if it weren't in a quantity of such great theoretical interest. It is the QCD coupling renormalized at M_Z, $\alpha_S(M_Z)$. The LEP average value, extracted from the Z^0 lineshape, is [12]

$$\alpha_S(M_Z|\text{LEP}) = 0.124 \pm 0.005 \pm 0.002. \quad (15)$$

Most low–energy measurements of $\alpha_S(M_Z)$ give a lower value. The one with the smallest quoted error is

---

† If the lower scales in these multiscale TC models are close to M_Z, the assumption that oblique corrections are characterized by just the lowest derivatives S,T,U is also incorrect.

‡ See [4] for a discussion of this assumption.

extracted from the charmonium spectrum using lattice–QCD methods to separate out the confining potential's contribution [28]:

$$\alpha_S(M_Z|\text{Lattice}) = 0.115 \pm 0.002. \qquad (16)$$

These values differ by 1.5σ. Langacker stresses that the value of $\alpha_S(M_Z)$ extracted from the Z^0 lineshape is sensitive to certain types of new physics. His global fit, allowing a nonzero $\Delta_{b\bar{b}}$, gave the result in Eq. (8) *and* $\alpha_S(M_Z) = 0.103 \pm 0.11$, 2σ away from the LEP measurement.

What are we to make of these discrepancies? The deviation $\Delta_{b\bar{b}}$ is 2σ from zero. Shall we say that the standard model is ruled out? Surely, almost everyone believes that will happen someday. The LEP and SLD measurements of $\sin^2\theta_W$ differ by almost 3σ. Is this just experimental error? If so, who's wrong? Low and high–energy determinations of the QCD coupling are on the verge of being inconsistent. Is this just (!) the effect of new physics at high energies? Given these discrepancies, might it not be premature to say that essentially nonperturbative theories such as walking technicolor are ruled out by the values of S and T? At the very least, we ought to bear in mind Vernon Hughes' admonition [29]:

Half of all three sigma measurements are wrong.

I am grateful to Sekhar Chivukula, Mitchell Golden, Elizabeth Simmons and John Terning for their careful reading of the manuscript and helpful comments. This research was supported in part by the Department of Energy under Contract No. DE–FG02–91ER40676.

References

[1] S. Weinberg, Phys. Rev. **D13** (1976) 974; *ibid.* **D19** (1979) 1277.

[2] L. Susskind, Phys. Rev. **D20** (1979) 2619.

[3] S. Dimopoulos and L. Susskind, Nucl. Phys. **B155** (1979) 237.

[4] E. Eichten and K. Lane, Phys. Lett. **90B** (1980) 125.

[5] J. Ellis, M. Gaillard, D. Nanopoulos and P. Sikivie, Nucl. Phys. **B182** (1981) 529.

[6] B. Holdom, Phys. Rev. **D24** (1981) 1441; Phys. Lett. **150B** (1985) 301.

[7] T. Appelquist, D. Karabali and L.C.R. Wijewardhana, Phys. Rev. Lett. **57** (1986) 957; K. Yamawaki, M. Bando and K. Matumoto, Phys. Rev. Lett. **56** (1986) 1335; T. Akiba and T. Yanagida, Phys. Lett. **169B** (1986) 432; T. Appelquist and L.C.R. Wijewardhana, Phys. Rev. **D36** (1987) 568.

[8] K. Lane, *An Introduction to Technicolor*, (Lectures given June 30–July 2, 1993 at the Theoretical Advanced Studies Institute, University of Colorado, Boulder.), Boston University Preprint BUHEP-94-2, to appear in the 1993 TASI Lectures, published by World Scientific.

[9] A. Longhitano, Phys. Rev. **D22** (1980) 1166; Nucl. Phys. **B188** (1981) 118; R. Renken and M. Peskin, Nucl. Phys. **B211** (1983) 93; B.W. Lynn, M.E. Peskin and R.G. Stuart, in Trieste Electroweak 1985, 213; M. Golden and L. Randall, Nucl. Phys.

B361 (1990) 3; B. Holdom and J. Terning, Phys. Lett. **247B** (1990) 88; M.E. Peskin and T. Takeuchi, Phys. Rev. Lett. **65** (1990) 964; A. Dobado, D. Espriu and M.J. Herrero, Phys. Lett. **255B** (1990) 405; H. Georgi, Nucl. Phys. **B363** (1991) 301.

[10] J. Gasser and H. Leutwyler, Nucl. Phys. **B250** (1985) 465.

[11] F. Abe, et al., The CDF Collaboration, *Evidence for Top-Quark Production in $\bar{p}p$ Collisions at $\sqrt{s} = 1.8$ TeV*, FERMILAB–PUB–94/097-E (1994), submitted to Physical Review D; Phys. Rev. Lett. **73** (1994) 225.

[12] P. Langacker, *Theoretical Study of the Electroweak Interaction — Present and Future*, to appear in the proceedings of the 22nd INS Symposium on Physics with High Energy Colliders, Tokyo, March 1994.

[13] S. Weinberg, Phys. Rev. Lett. **18** (1967) 507; K.G. Wilson, Phys. Rev. **179** (1969) 1499; C. Bernard, A. Duncan, J. Lo Secco and S. Weinberg, Phys. Rev. **D12** (1975) 792.

[14] R.S. Chivukula, M. Dugan and M. Golden, Phys. Lett. **292B** (1992) 435.

[15] Coroner, Munchkin City, Land of Oz, in *The Wizard of Oz*, Metro–Goldwyn–Mayer Studios, (1939).

[16] T. Appelquist, T. Takeuchi, M.B. Einhorn and L.C.R. Wijewardhana, Phys. Lett. **232B** (1989) 211; Phys. Rev. **D41** (1990) 3192.

[17] K. Lane and E. Eichten, Phys. Lett. **222B** (1989) 274; K. Lane and M.V. Ramana, Phys. Rev. **D44** (1991) 2678.

[18] B. Holdom, Phys. Lett. **259B** (1991) 329; E. Gates and J. Terning, Phys. Rev. Lett. **67** (1991) 1840; M. Luty and R. Sundrum, Phys. Rev. Lett. **70** (1993) 127; T. Appelquist and J. Terning, Phys. Lett. **315B** (1993) 139.

[19] T. Appelquist and J. Terning, Phys. Rev. **D50** (191) 994 2116.

[20] R.S. Chivukula, S.B. Selipsky, and E.H. Simmons, Phys. Rev. Lett. **69** (1992) 575; N. Kitazawa Phys. Lett. **313B** (1993) 395.

[21] R.S. Chivukula, E. Gates, E.H. Simmons and J. Terning, Phys. Lett. **311B** (1993) 157.

[22] T. Appelquist, M.B. Einhorn, T. Takeuchi and L.C.R. Wijewardhana, Phys. Lett. **220B** (1989) 223; V.A. Miransky and K. Yamawaki, Mod. Phys. Lett. **A4** (1989) 129; K. Matumoto, Prog. Th. Phys. **81** (1989) 277; V.A. Miransky, M. Tanabashi and K. Yamawaki, Phys. Lett. **221B** (1989) 177; V.A. Miransky, M. Tanabashi and K. Yamawaki, Mod. Phys. Lett. **A4** (1989) 1043.

[23] R.S. Chivukula, A.G. Cohen and K. Lane, Nucl. Phys. **B343** (1990) 54; T. Appelquist, J. Terning and L.C.R. Wijewardhana, Phys. Rev. **D44** (1991) 871.

[24] N. Evans, Phys. Lett. **331B** (1994) 378; C.D. Carone, E.H. Simmons and Y. Su, work in progress, private communication.

[25] R.S. Chivukula, E.H. Simmons and J. Terning, Phys. Lett. **331B** (1994) 383.

[26] M. Fero, "Precise Measurement of the Left–Right Cross Section Asymmetry in Z Boson Production by e^+e^- Collisions, invited talk in Session Pa-1 of the 27th International Conference on High Energy Physics, Glasgow, 20–27th July 1994.

[27] K. Moenig, "Determination of the Electroweak Mixing Angle from Forward–Backward Asymmetries with Quarks and leptons", invited talk in Session Pa-1 of the 27th International Conference on High Energy Physics, Glasgow, 20–27th July 1994.

[28] C.T.H. Davies, et al., "A Precise Determination of α_S from Lattice QCD", hep-ph 9408328.

[29] V. Hughes, cited in G. Taubes, *Bad Science, The Short Life and Weird Times of Cold Fusion*, Random House, New York (1993).

Paper presented at XXVII Int. Conf. on High Energy Physics: Session Pa-4
Glasgow, UK, 20–27 July 1994

Stability of chiral hierarchies

S.T. Love

Department of Physics
Purdue University
West Lafayette IN 47907-1396, USA

Abstract

The need for a fine tuned hierarchy between a strong coupling high energy compositeness scale and a much lower chiral symmetry breaking scale exists in many models of dynamical electroweak symmetry breaking. We explore the stability of such hierarchies against quantum fluctuations. A nonperturbative Wilson renormalization group equation approach is introduced.

A common feature of many of the currently studied models of dynamical electroweak symmetry breaking is the presence of some strong interactions acting at a high energy scale, $\Lambda > 10\ TeV$, which produces an essentially composite scalar bosonic degree of freedom. This dynamics also plays an important role in the electroweak symmetry breaking whose characteristic scale is much lower; $\Lambda_F \simeq 250\ GeV$. Thus these models require that a significant hierarchy can be established between these scales. The hierarchy is achieved by a fine tuning of parameters close to the critical value for the chiral symmetry breaking. A prototype of this behavior is exhibited by the Nambu Jona-Lasinio (NJL) model [1], where a fine tuning of the four-fermion coupling allows the emergence of a chiral symmetry breaking scale far below the compositeness scale. In more recent work, such fine tunings are necessary ingredients in strong extended technicolor models [2], models involving heavy quark condensation [3] and their generalizations. In order for this hierarchy to be maintained and not have the electroweak scale driven to be of order Λ, it is necessary that the chiral symmetry phase transition be of second order. That is, the order parameter characterizing the chiral transition must remain zero as the theory is scaled from Λ into the infrared until one reaches the electroweak scale. If, on the other hand, the transition turns first order at a scale $e^{-t_0}\Lambda >> \Lambda_F$, then the order parameter will jump discontinuously to

be of this value and it will be impossible to maintain the hierarchy all the way down to the electroweak scale. Instead the hierarchy will destabilize after t_0 e-foldings. It is important to recognize that this question is distinct from that of the naturalness of the fine tuning of additive quadratic divergences. Clearly, it becomes necessary to explore [4] when the hierarchy can be self consistently maintained and not destroyed by quantum fluctuations (Coleman- Weinberg phenomenon [5]).

Since models with a single scalar quartic self coupling or the minimal Nambu-Jona Lasinio model exhibit a Gaussian second order chiral transition, we are led to investigate generalizations containing multiple scalar quartic self couplings. In particular, we focus on a model possessing a global chiral $U(2)_L \times U(2)_R$ symmetry which has two independent scalar quartic self couplings. The model degrees of freedom include left and right handed chiral fermions ψ_{iL} and ψ_{iR}, $i = 1, 2$, transforming as the fundamental representation of the left and right handed $U(2)$ groups respectively which further carry the fundamental, N_C, representation of a gauged symmetry. It is assumed that this chiral symmetry is spontaneously broken as a consequence of some unspecified dynamics acting at scale Λ. This symmetry breaking is further assumed to produce a gauge singlet scalar composite Σ_{ij} which has the $U(2)_L \times U(2)_R$ quantum numbers of the fermion bilinear $\bar{\psi}_{jR}\psi_{iL}$ and whose vacuum expectation value, $v/\sqrt{2}$, acts an an order parameter for the chiral symmetry breaking. Since we are assuming the chiral symmetry phase transition is second order, we are led to study a Ginzburg-Landau effective Lagrangian at scale Λ which includes the Yukawa coupling $\frac{\pi}{\sqrt{2}}g(0)(\bar\psi_L\Sigma\psi_R + \bar\psi_R\Sigma^\dagger\psi_L)$ and the invariant potential function

$$V(x,y,0) = \frac{1}{2}m^2(0)x + \frac{\pi^2}{12}\lambda_1(0)x^2 + \frac{\pi^2}{6}\lambda_2(0)y. \quad (1)$$

Here $x = tr(\Sigma^\dagger\Sigma)$, $y = tr(\Sigma^\dagger\Sigma)^2$ are independent $U(2)_L \times U(2)_R$ invariants. The Coleman-Weinberg instability is signalled by the appearance of a non-trivial global minimum of the effective potential with vanishing renormalized mass appearing at the scale $v = e^{-t_0}\Lambda$. In such a case, the phase transition is driven first order by quantum fluctuations and one can technically achieve a hierarchy of only t_0 e-foldings.

Using the 1-loop perturbation theory improved effective potential while keeping the Yukawa coupling fixed, the renormalization group trajectories are found [4] to either run to the infrared quasi fixed point near the origin, lead to a first order transition or simply run away in which case the model is ill defined. In particular, for the region of coupling space corresponding to the initial couplings $\lambda_1(0) = 0$ and $\lambda_2(0)$ and $g^2(0)$ both large and positive, the transition goes first order for sufficiently large $\lambda_2(0)/g^2(0)$ ratio ($\gtrsim 7$). Moreover, this occurs, in general, near to the compositeness scale. For example, for $\lambda_2(0) = 10$ and $g^2(0) = 1$ (and $N_C = 3$), the hierarchy destabilizes after ~ 1.3 e-foldings (which corresponds to $v \sim 0.27\Lambda$). However, since the couplings are very large, the 1-loop perturbative approximation can certainly be called into question. For instance, using the 2-loop perturbative renormalization group functions for these large initial couplings, the renormalization group trajectories simply run away. Clearly, some nonperturbative approximation scheme is required to properly deal with the system in the vicinity of the strong coupling compositeness scale. The purely bosonic $U(2)_L \times U(2)_R$ model (no chiral fermions) has been simulated using lattice Monte Carlo techniques [6] and was seen to undergo a Coleman-Weinberg instability. Another approach [7] includes the chiral fermions and uses a large N_C approximation in the vicinity of the compositeness scale so that the Yukawa coupling dominates. Retaining only it and the fine tuned scalar mass term needed to cancel the additive quadratic divergence, the model at scale Λ reduces to the minimal NJL model which is exactly soluble in the large N_C limit and is known to exhibit a (trivial) second order chiral transition. Thus the large N_C approximation allows any sized hierarchy to be technically achieved. Running the couplings using this approximation (in which $\lambda_1(t) = 0$) until $\lambda_2(t) = 3g^2(t) = \frac{48}{N_Ct}$ has decreased sufficiently to

be smoothly joined onto a 2-loop perturbative (including Yukawa coupling) running, it is found that sizeable hierarchies can be established. To the extent that the large N_C approximation is nonperturbative, this procedure is a self consistent one. On the other hand, it can be reliably employed for only a very limited range of the initial parameter space.

An alternate nonperturbative method is provided by the continuous Wilson renormalization group equation (WRGE) [8] which has been extended to include chiral fermions [9]. This approach incorporates the contributions from a complete set of local operators (including irrelevant ones). Using a local action approximation [11] which ignores anomalous dimensions and derivative interactions and further neglecting operators higher than bilinear in the fermion fields, the WRGE for fixed Yukawa coupling reduces to an equation for the potential function, $V(x,y,t)$, at scale $e^{-t}\Lambda$ given by

$$\begin{aligned}
\frac{\partial V}{\partial t} &= 4V - 2xV_x - 4yV_y \\
&+ \frac{1}{8\pi^2}\ell n[(1 + V_x + 2xV_y)^2 - 2(x^2 - y)V_y^2] \\
&+ \frac{1}{16\pi^2}\ell n[(1 + V_x)^2 + 2x(1 + V_x)V_y \\
&+ 2(x^2 - y)V_y^2] + \frac{1}{16\pi^2}\ell n[(1 + V_x)(1 + V_x \\
&+ 6xV_y + 2xV_{xx} + 8yV_{xy} + 4x(3y - x^2)V_{yy}) \\
&+ 6(x^2 - y)V_y(3V_y + 2V_{xx} + 4xV_{xy} \\
&+ 4yV_{yy}) + 8(x^2 - y)(x^2 - 2y)(V_{xy}^2 - V_{xx}V_{yy})] \\
&- \frac{N_C}{4\pi^2}\ell n[1 + \frac{\pi^2}{2}xg^2(0) + \frac{\pi^4}{8}(x^2 - y)g^4(0)], \quad (2)
\end{aligned}$$

with $V_x = \frac{\partial V}{\partial x}$ etc, subject to the initial condition of Eq.(1). For $t \geq 0$, each action constructed using the $V(x,y,t)$ satisfying this equation lies on the same Wilson renormalization group trajectory and produces the same physics on all scales less than $e^{-t}\Lambda$. Unfortunately, the solution to Eq.(2) is currently beyond our numerical abilities. Thus we make the further truncation of retaining terms only up to linear in y with coeficients which are arbitrary functions of x. Eq.(2) then reduces to two coupled equations which are of a similiar (although considerably more complicated) form to what we previously solved in obtaining nonperturbative mass bounds [11]. While the truncations used are drastic and uncontrolled, they still include contributions from an infinite number of operators.

The resulting equations are then numerically solved for t values up to some t^*, where t^* lies in a region where $V(x,y,t)$ is found to be linear in $t - t^*$ with a slope of the same form as the linearized in $t - t^*$ 1-loop effective potential. The effective potential is then constructed as $V_{eff}(x,y) = V(x,y,t^*) + V_{1-loop}(x,y,t^*)$, where $V_{1-loop}(x,y,t^*)$ is the 1-loop effective potential which accounts for the effects of the degrees of freedom carrying momentum less than $e^{-t^*}\Lambda$. Note that the 1-loop effective potential also includes an infinite number of operators as is necessary to allow a smooth joining to the WRGE solution. In this 1-loop expression, we have also included the efeects of the anomalous dimensions. A Coleman-Weinberg instability is signalled by a non-trivial global minimum of $V_{eff}(v) = V_{eff}(x,y)|_{y=\frac{1}{2}x^2=\frac{1}{2}v^4}$ with vanishing renormalized mass. If such a minimum appears at $v = e^{-t_0}\Lambda$, then the system can sustain a hierarchy only over t_0 e-foldings. For the special case of $\lambda_1(0) = 0, \lambda_2(0) = 10, g^2(0) = 1$, we integrated the WRGE and found that for $t^* \sim 1$, $V(x,y,t)$ was linear in $t - t^*$ and smoothly joined onto the 1-loop effective potential. The transition was seen to go first order at $t_0 \sim 2.2$. Thus a hierarchy of only ~ 2.2 e-foldings can be established ($v \sim 0.11\Lambda$). This result is in qualitative agreement with that found using the 1-loop perturbative approximation. In a similar manner, one can nonperturbatively investigate [12] the initial parameter space and map out the model phase structure.

This work was performed in collaboration with T.E. Clark and was supported in part by the U.S. Department of Energy under grant DE-AC02-76ER01428 (Task B).

References

[1] Y. Nambu and G. Jona-Lasinio, Phys. Rev. **122** (1961) 345; see also W.A. Bardeen and S.T. Love, Phys. Rev. **D45** (1992) 4672.

[2] For a review, see T. Appelquist in the *Proceedings of the Fourth Mexican School of Particles and Fields*, Mexico City 1990, ed. by L.J. Lucio M and A. Zepeda, (World Scientific, 1991) 1 and references therein.

[3] For a review, see W.A. Bardeen in *Gauge Theories, Past and Future*, ed. by R. Akhoury et al., (World Scientific, 1992) 51 and references therein.

[4] R.S. Chivukula, M. Golden and E. Simmons, Phys. Rev. Lett. **70** (1993) 1587.

[5] S. Coleman and E. Weinberg, Phys. Rev. **D7** (1973) 1888.

[6] Y. Shen, Phys. Lett. **315B** (1993) 146.

[7] W.A. Bardeen, C.T. Hill and D. Jungnickel, Phys Rev. **D49** (1994) 1437.

[8] K. Wilson and J. Kogut, Phys. Rept. **12C** (1974) 75; K. Wilson, Rev. Mod Phys. **55** (1983) 583; F. Wegner and A. Houghton, Phys. Rev. **A8** (1973) 401; J. Polshinski, Nucl. Phys. **B231** (1984) 269; S. Weinberg in *Proceedings of the 1976 International School of Subnuclear Physics*, Erice, ed. by A. Zichichi (Plenum Press, 1978).

[9] T.E. Clark, B. Haeri and S.T. Love, Nucl. Phys **B402** (1993) 628.

[10] P. Hasenfratz and J. Nager, Z. Phys. **C37** (1988) 477.

[11] S.T. Love in *Proceedings of the International Europhysics Conference on High Energy Physics*, Marseilles 1993 ed. by J. Carr and M. Perrottet (Editions Frontieres, 1994) 208; T.E. Clark, B. Haeri, S.T. Love, M.A. Walker and W.T.A. ter Veldhuis, Phys. Rev. **D50** (1994) 606.

[12] T.E. Clark and S.T. Love, Purdue preprint PURD-TH-94-10.

Paper presented at XXVII Int. Conf. on High Energy Physics: Session Pa-4
Glasgow, UK, 20–27 July 1994

Beyond the Standard Model in the Lepton Sector

José W. F. Valle [†]

† Departament de Física Teórica, Universitat de València and
Instituto de Física Corpuscular - C.S.I.C., E-46100 Burjassot, València, SPAIN

Abstract

I review some of the physics motivations and potential of various extensions of the standard model that pertain to the lepton sector. These include extensions of the lepton multiplet content, closely related to the properties of neutrinos, extensions of the electroweak breaking sector, such as supersymmetry, as well as possible extensions of the gauge sector. They may all lead to new signatures at levels accessible to experiment.

1. Introduction.

Our present standard model leaves open many of the fundamental issues in particle physics, such as the mechanism of mass generation and the properties of neutrinos. Extensions of the basic picture that seek to address these issues, such as higher unification and supersymmetry, may lead to extensions of the lepton multiplet and/or Higgs boson content, and thereby affect the physics of the lepton sector in an important way that fortunately can be probed in a variety of present and future experiments.

2. Neutral Heavy Leptons.

There are many motivations to extend the lepton sector of the electroweak theory. Extra heavy leptons may arise in models with a higher unification, for example those with left-right symmetry [1] or superstrings [2]. These models may contain isosinglet neutral heavy leptons and typically, also neutrino masses [3].

They may induce lepton flavour violating (LFV) decays such as $\mu \to e\gamma$, which are exactly forbidden in the standard model. Although these are a generic feature of models with massive neutrinos, in some cases, they may proceed in models where neutrinos are strictly massless [3]-[5].

In the simplest models of seesaw type [6] the NHLS are superheavy so that the expected rate for LFV processes is expected to be low, due to limits on neutrino masses. However, in other variants [2] this is not the case [4, 5] and this suppression need not be present. Indeed, present constraints on weak universality violation allow for decay branching ratios larger than the present experimental limits [7] so that these already are probing the masses and admixtures of the NHLS with considerable sensitivity. Similar estimates can be done for the corresponding tau decays [7, 8]. The results are summarized in table 1. See also figures 5 and 6 given in ref. [8]. Clearly these branching ratios lie within the sensitivities of the planned tau and B factories, as shown in ref. [9].

The physics of rare Z decays nicely complements what can be learned from the study of rare LFV muon and tau decays. The stringent limits on $\mu \to e\gamma$ preclude any possible detectability at LEP of the corresponding $Z \to e\mu$ decay. While experimentally closer, under realistic luminosity and experimental resolution assumptions, it is still unlikely that one will be able to see even the $e\tau$ or $\mu\tau$ decays of the Z at LEP [10]. In any case, there have been dedicated searches

Table 1. Allowed τ decay branching ratios

channel	strength
$\tau \to e\gamma, \mu\gamma$	$\lesssim 10^{-6}$
$\tau \to e\pi^0, \mu\pi^0$	$\lesssim 10^{-6}$
$\tau \to e\eta^0, \mu\eta^0$	$\lesssim 10^{-6} - 10^{-7}$
$\tau \to 3e, 3\mu, \mu\mu e,$ *etc.*	$\lesssim 10^{-6} - 10^{-7}$

Table 2. Allowed branching ratios for rare Z decays.

channel	strength
$Z \to N_\tau \, \nu_\tau$	$\lesssim 10^{-3}$
$Z \to e\tau$	$\lesssim 10^{-6} - 10^{-7}$
$Z \to \mu\tau$	$\lesssim 10^{-7}$

which have set good limits [11].

If lighter than the Z, NHLS may also be produced in Z decays such as † [12],

$$Z \to N_\tau + \nu_\tau \qquad (1)$$

Note that the isosinglet neutral heavy lepton N_τ is singly produced, through the off-diagonal neutral currents characteristic of models containing doublet and singlet leptons [13]. Subsequent N_τ decays would then give rise to large missing energy events, called zen-events. As seen in table 2 this branching ratio can be as large as $\lesssim 10^{-3}$ a value that is already superseded by the good limits on such decays from the searches for acoplanar jets and lepton pairs from Z decays at LEP, although some inconclusive hints have been recently reported by ALEPH [11]

Finally we note that there can also be large rates for lepton flavour violating decays in models with radiative mass generation [14]. For example, this is the case in the models proposed to reconcile present hints for neutrino masses [15]. The expected decay rates may easily lie within the present experimental sensitivities and the situation should improve at PSI or at the proposed tau-charm factories.

3. Supersymmetry.

If supersymmetry exists at the TeV scale it helps to stabilize the gauge hierarchy problem, one of the

† There may also be CP violation in lepton sector, even when the known neutrinos are strictly massless and lead to Z decay asymmetries $\mathcal{O}\,(10^{-7})$ [5]

central issues in particle theory today. The most conventional realization of the idea of supersymmetry postulates the conservation of R parity. As a result of this *ad hoc* selection rule, in the so-called minimal supersymmetric standard model SUSY particles are only produced in pairs, with the lightest of them (LSP) being stable.

Nobody knows the origin of this R parity symmetry and why it is there. There are many ways to break it, either explicitly or spontaneously (RPSUSY models). If R parity is broken spontaneously it shows up primarily in the couplings of the W and the Z, leading to rare Z decays such as the single production of the charginos and neutralinos [16], for example,

$$Z \to \chi^\pm \tau^\mp \qquad (2)$$

where the lightest chargino mass is assumed to be smaller than the Z mass. In the simplest models, the magnitude of R parity violation is correlated with the nonzero value of the ν_τ mass and is restricted by a variety of experiments. Nevertheless the R parity violating Z decay branching ratios, as an example, can easily exceed 10^{-5}, well within present LEP sensitivities. Similarly, the lightest neutralino (LSP) could also be singly-produced as $Z \to \chi^0 \nu_\tau$ [16]. Being unstable due to R parity violation, χ^0 is not necessarily an origin of events with missing energy, since some of its decays are into charged particles. Thus the decay $Z \to \chi^0 \nu_\tau$ would give rise to zen events, similar to those of the MSSM but where the missing energy is carried by the ν_τ. Another possibility for zen events in RPSUSY is the usual pair neutralino production process, where one χ^0 decays visibly and the other invisibly. The corresponding zen-event rates can be larger than in the MSSM.

Although the ν_τ can be quite massive in these models, it is perfectly consistent with cosmology [17] including primordial nucleosynthesis [18], since it decays sufficiently fast by majoron emission [19]. On the other hand, the ν_e and ν_μ have a tiny mass difference in the model of ref. [20]. This mass difference can be chosen to lie in the range where resonant ν_e to ν_μ conversions provides an explanation of solar neutrino deficit [21]. Due to this peculiar hierarchical pattern, one can go even further, and regard the rare R parity violating processes as a tool to probe the physics underlying the solar neutrino conversions in this model [22]. Indeed, the rates for such rare decays can be used in order to discriminate between large and small mixing angle MSW solutions to the solar neutrino problem [21]. Typically, in the nonadiabatic region of small mixing one can have larger rare decay branching ratios, as seen in Fig. 5 of ref. [22].

Table 3. Allowed branching ratios for rare decays in the RPSUSY model. χ denotes the lightest electrically charged SUSY fermion (chargino) and χ^0 is the lightest neutralino.

channel	strength
$Z \to \chi\tau$	$\lesssim 6 \times 10^{-5}$
$Z \to \chi^0 \nu_\tau$	$\lesssim 10^{-4}$
$\tau \to \mu + J$	$\lesssim 10^{-3}$
$\tau \to e + J$	$\lesssim 10^{-4}$

It is also possible to find manifestations of R parity violation at the superhigh energies available at hadron supercolliders such as LHC. Either SUSY particles, such as gluinos, are pair produced and in their cascade decays the LSP decays or, alternatively, one violates R parity by singly producing the SUSY states. An example of this situation has been discussed in ref. [23]. In this reference one has studied the single production of weakly interacting supersymmetric fermions (charginos and neutralinos) via the Drell Yan mechanism, leading to possibly detectable signatures. More work on this will be desirable.

Another possible signal of the RPSUSY models based on the simplest $SU(2) \otimes U(1)$ gauge group is rare decays of muons and taus. In this model the spontaneous violation of R parity generates a physical Goldstone boson, called majoron. Its existence is quite consistent with the measurements of the invisible Z decay width at LEP, as it is a singlet under the $SU(2) \otimes U(1)$ gauge symmetry. In this model the lepton number is broken close to the weak scale and can produce a new class of lepton flavour violating decays, such as those with single majoron emission in μ and τ decays. These would be "seen" as bumps in the final lepton energy spectrum, at half of the parent lepton mass in its rest frame. The allowed rates for single majoron emitting μ and τ decays have been determined in ref. [24] and are also shown in table 3 to be compatible with present experimental sensitivities [25]. Moreover, they are ideally studied at a tau-charm factory [9]. This example also illustrates how the search for rare decays can be a more sensitive probe of neutrino properties than the more direct searches for neutrino masses, and therefore complementary.

4. Higgs Bosons.

Another possible, albeit quite indirect, manifestation of the properties of neutrinos and the lepton sec-

tor is in the electroweak breaking sector. Many extensions of the lepton sector seek to give masses to neutrinos through the spontaneous violation of an ungauged U(1) lepton number symmetry, thus implying the existence of a physical Goldstone boson, called majoron [26]. As already mentioned above this is consistent with the measurements of the invisible Z decay width at LEP if the majoron is (mostly) a singlet under the $SU(2) \otimes U(1)$ gauge symmetry.

Although the original majoron proposal was made in the framework of the minimal seesaw model, and required the introduction of a relatively high energy scale associated to the mass of the right-handed neutrinos [26], there are many attractive theoretical alternatives where lepton number is violated spontaneously at the weak scale or lower. In this case although the majoron has very tiny couplings to matter and the gauge bosons, it can have significant couplings to the Higgs bosons. As a result one has the possibility that the Higgs boson may decay with a substantial branching ratio into the invisible mode [27]

$$h \to J + J \tag{3}$$

where J denotes the majoron. The presence of this invisible decay channel can affect the corresponding Higgs mass bounds in an important way.

The production and subsequent decay of a Higgs boson which may decay visibly or invisibly involves three independent parameters: its mass M_H, its coupling strength to the Z, normalized by that of the standard model, ϵ^2, and its invisible decay branching ratio. The LEP searches for various exotic channels can be used in order to determine the regions in parameter space that are already ruled out, as described in ref. [28]. The exclusion contour in the plane ϵ^2 vs. M_H, was shown in Fig. 2 of ref. [29].

Another mode of production of invisibly decaying Higgs bosons is that in which a CP even Higgs boson is produced at LEP in association with a massive CP odd scalar [30]. This production mode is present in all but the simplest majoron model containing just one complex scalar singlet in addition to the standard model Higgs doublet. Present limits on the relevant parameters are given in ref. [30].

Finally, the invisible decay of the Higgs boson may also affect the strategies for searches at higher energies. For example, the ranges of parameters that can be covered by LEP2 searches for a total integrated luminosity of 500 pb^{-1} and various centre-of-mass energies have been given in Fig. 2 of the first paper in ref. [28]. Similar analysis were made for the case of a high energy linear e^+e^- collider (NLC) [31], as well as for the LHC [32].

5. New Gauge Bosons.

Superstring extensions of the standard model suggest the existence of additional gauge bosons at the TeV scale and this may affect the lepton sector and the interactions of neutrinos. For example, an additional Z' at low energies would modify the couplings of leptons to the Z and be thereby restricted by low energy neutral current data [33], as well as by the LEP precision data on Z decays [34]. In string models the Higgs sector is constrained in such a way that these limits are strongly correlated with the top quark mass [35]. The recent data from the CDF collaboration leads to contraints around a TeV on the Z' mass for various models of the string type that fit in the E_6 gauge group. The limits are much weaker in the case of unconstrained models.

Acknowledgements

This work has been supported by DGICYT under Grant number PB92-0084.

References

[1] R.N. Mohapatra and G. Senjanovic, *Phys. Rev.* **D23** (1981) 165 and references therein.

[2] R. Mohapatra, J. W. F. Valle, *Phys. Rev.* **D34** (1986) 1642; J. W. F. Valle, *Nucl. Phys. B (Proc. Suppl.)* **B11** (1989) 118

[3] For a recent review see J. W. F. Valle, *Gauge Theories and the Physics of Neutrino Mass*, *Prog. Part. Nucl. Phys.* **26** (1991) 91-171 and references therein.

[4] J. Bernabeu, A. Santamaria, J. Vidal, A. Mendez, J. W. F. Valle, *Phys. Lett.* **B187** (1987) 303; J. G. Korner, A. Pilaftsis, K. Schilcher, *Phys. Lett.* **B300** (1993) 381; A. Barroso, J. P. Silva, *Phys. Rev.* **D50** (1994) 4581

[5] G. C. Branco, M. N. Rebelo, J. W. F. Valle, *Phys. Lett.* **B225** (1989) 385; N. Rius, J. W. F. Valle, *Phys. Lett.* **B246** (1990) 249

[6] M Gell-Mann, P Ramond, R. Slansky, in *Supergravity*, ed. D. Freedman et al. (1979); T. Yanagida, in *KEK lectures*, ed. O. Sawada et al. (1979)

[7] M. C. Gonzalez-Garcia, J. W. F. Valle, *Mod. Phys. Lett.* **A7** (1992) 477

[8] A. Ilakovac, A. Pilaftsis, RAL preprint RAL/94-032

[9] R. Alemany *et al.*, in ECFA/93-151, ed. R. Aleksan, A. Ali, p. 191-211

[10] M. Dittmar, J. W. F. Valle, contribution to the High Luminosity at LEP working group, yellow report CERN-91/02, p. 98-103, Fig. 3.22 and 3.23

[11] See, *e.g.*, OPAL collaboration, *Phys. Lett.* **B247** (1990) 448, *ibid.* **B254** (1991) 293 L3 collaboration, *Phys. Rep.* **236** (1993) 1-146; *Phys. Lett.* **B316** (1993) 427, *ibid.* **B295** (1992) 371, ALEPH collaboration, CERN-PPE 94-93

[12] M. Dittmar, M. C. Gonzalez-Garcia, A. Santamaria, J. W. F. Valle, *Nucl. Phys.* **B332** (1990) 1; M. C. Gonzalez-Garcia, A. Santamaria, J. W. F. Valle, *ibid.* **B342** (1990) 108.

[13] J. Schechter and J. W. F. Valle, *Phys. Rev.* **D22** (1980) 2227

[14] A. Zee, *Phys. Lett.* **B93** (1980) 389; K. S. Babu, *Phys. Lett.* **B203** (1988) 132

[15] J. T. Peltoniemi, D. Tommasini, and J W F Valle, *Phys. Lett.* **B298** (1993) 383 J. T. Peltoniemi, and J W F Valle, *Nucl. Phys.* **B406** (1993) 409; for another scheme, see E. Akhmedov, Z. Berezhiani, G. Senjanovic and Z. Tao, *Phys. Rev.* **D47** (1993) 3245.

[16] P. Nogueira, J. C. Romão, J. W. F. Valle, *Phys. Lett.* **B251** (1990) 142; R. Barbieri, L. Hall, *Phys. Lett.* **B238** (1990) 86. M. C. Gonzalez-Garcia, J. W. F. Valle, *Nucl. Phys.* **B355** (1991) 330

[17] E. Kolb, M. Turner, *The Early Universe*, Addison-Wesley, 1990.

[18] For a review see G. Steigman; proceedings of the *International School on Cosmological Dark Matter*, (World Scientific, 1994), ed. J. W. F. Valle and A. Perez, p. 55

[19] J. W. F. Valle, *Phys. Lett.* **B131** (1983) 87; G. Gelmini, J. W. F. Valle, *Phys. Lett.* **B142** (1984) 181; M. C. Gonzalez-Garcia, J. W. F. Valle, *Phys. Lett.* **B216** (1989) 360. A. Joshipura, S. Rindani, PRL-TH/92-10; for an early discussion see J. Schechter and J. W. F. Valle, *Phys. Rev.* **D25** (1982) 774

[20] A Masiero, J. W. F. Valle, *Phys. Lett.* **B251** (1990) 273; J. C. Romao, C. A. Santos, and J. W. F. Valle, *Phys. Lett.* **B288** (1992) 311; G. Giudice, A. Masiero, M. Pietroni, A. Riotto, *Nucl. Phys.* **B396** (1993) 243; M. Shiraishi, I. Umemura, K. Yamamoto, *Phys. Lett.* **B313** (1993) 89

[21] M. Mikheyev, A. Smirnov, *Sov. J. Nucl. Phys.* **42** (1986) 913; L. Wolfenstein, *Phys. Rev.* **D17** (1978) 2369; *ibid.* **D20** (1979) 2634.

[22] J. C. Romão and J. W. F. Valle, *Phys. Lett.* **B272** (1991) 436; *Nucl. Phys.* **B381** (1992) 87.

[23] M. C. Gonzalez-Garcia, J. C. Romão, J. W. F. Valle, *Nucl. Phys.* **B391** (1993) 100

[24] J. C. Romão, N. Rius, J. W. F. Valle, *Nucl. Phys.* **B363** (1991) 369.

[25] Particle Data Group, *Phys. Rev.* **D50** (1994) 1173

[26] Y. Chikashige, R. Mohapatra, R. Peccei, *Phys. Rev. Lett.* **45** (1980) 1926

[27] A. Joshipura and J. W. F. Valle, *Nucl. Phys.* **B397** (1993) 105; J. C. Romao, F. de Campos, and J. W. F. Valle, *Phys. Lett.* **B292** (1992) 329. A. S. Joshipura, S. Rindani, *Phys. Rev. Lett.* **69** (1992) 3269; R. Barbieri, and L. Hall, Nucl. Phys. **B364**, 27 (1991). G. Jungman and M. Luty, Nucl. Phys. **B361**, 24 (1991). E. D. Carlson and L. B. Hall, Phys. Rev. **D40**, 3187 (1989)

[28] A. Lopez-Fernandez, J. Romao, F. de Campos and J. W. F. Valle, *Phys. Lett.* **B312** (1993) 240; B. Brahmachari, A. Joshipura, S. Rindani, D. P. Roy, K. Sridhar, *Phys. Rev.* **D48** (1993) 4224.

[29] F. de Campos et al., talk at Moriond94, FTUV/94-28, HEP-PH/9405382.

[30] F. de Campos et al., *Phys. Lett.* **B336** (1994) 446-456

[31] O. Eboli, et al. *Nucl. Phys.* **B421** (1994) 65

[32] J. W. F. Valle, *Nucl. Phys. B (Proc. Suppl.)* **31** (1993) 221-232; J. C. Romao, F. de Campos, L. Diaz-Cruz, and J. W. F. Valle, *Mod. Phys. Lett.* **A9** (1994) 817; J. Gunion, *Phys. Rev. Lett.* **72** (1994) 199; D. Choudhhury, D. P. Roy, *Phys. Lett.* **B322** (1994) 368.

[33] CHARM collaboration these proceedings

[34] D. Schaile, these proceedings and references therein.

[35] M. C. Gonzalez-Garcia, J. W. F. Valle, *Phys. Lett.* **B259** (1991) 365 and references therein.

Paper presented at XXVII Int. Conf. on High Energy Physics: Session Pa-4
Glasgow, UK, 20–27 July 1994

Multiple Point Criticality, Fine Structure Constants and Mass Hierarchies*

D.L. Bennett[†], C.D. Froggatt[‡] and H.B. Nielsen[§]

† Royal Danish College of Pharmacy, Copenhagen
‡ Department of Physics and Astronomy, University of Glasgow
§ Niels Bohr Institute, Copenhagen

Abstract

The so-called principle of multiple point criticality is presented as a general way of explaining the existence of fine-tuned quantities in Nature (e.g., the gauge coupling constants, the smallness of the expected Higgs mass and Θ_{QCD} and the the effectively vanishing cosmological constant). More specifically, the principle states that Nature seeks out a functional form for the action of a gauge field theory such that the vacuum is just barely in a Coulomblike phase but such that infinitesimal changes in the action can result in a confining or a Higgsed vacuum. The implications of having such a vacuum have been used to calculate the Planck scale values of the Standard Model gauge couplings and to explain the mass hierarchy of the three generations of fermions.

1. Introduction

Multiple Point Criticality (MPC) is put forward as a fundamental principle of Nature [1]. While this principle was discovered in connection with theoretical attempts to calculate the Standard Model (SM) gauge couplings [2], it now appears that this principle is, in a generalized form, a prototype mechanism that can explain the appearence of fine-tuned quantities in Nature. A recent development relates this mechanism to the mild form of non-locality that results from the assumption of universally fixed amounts of extensive quantities. Moreover, MPC can provide very (i.e., exponentially) small Higgs field expectation values and thereby approximately conserved gauge quantum numbers which in turn can provide the mass hierarchy of leptons and quarks.

2. MPC as a finetuning mechanism

The essence of the principle of MPC is that Nature seeks out values of action parameters (in, for example, a gauge field theory) corresponding to the point in the phase diagram spanned by these parameters at which a maximum number of different "phases" come together. Generally speaking, different "phases" correspond to distributions of field degrees of freedom that typically change discontinuously in going from one phase to another. The idea that MPC can play the role of a general finetuning mechanism relies on the existence of abstract extensive quantities that can have primordially fixed values such that the universe can only be realized as an inhomogeneous mixture of (more than one) "phase". The forced coexistence of more than one "phase" fine-tunes the variables conjugate to the extensive quantities to values at the "phase" transition in a manner analogous to the way in which, for a certain fixed amount of energy, it is possible to constrain a fixed amount of water (in a thermos flask for example) to coexist in all three phases. In this event, the values of temperature and pressure are "fine-tuned" to the water

* Delivered by H.B. Nielsen

triple point values.

Strictly speaking, the assumption of fixed four-dimensional extensive quantities is tantamount to having a mild form of non-locality. To illustrate this, one can think of a situation where the spacetime distribution of an extensive quantity, fixed say at some rather small value, is known for most of the fixed amount of this extensive quantity to be spatially concentrated in our laboratory at some initial spacetime event. Let us now assume that we observe a small amount of this extensive quantity at an event differing from this initial event. Even if this differing event is causally unrelated to the initial event, we can make the statistically correct claim that the amount of this fixed extensive quantity in the laboratory has decreased. Such a violation of locality is manifested in the same way for *any* event differing from the initial one (with spatial coordinates coinciding with our laboratory) and can therefore be accomodated by a diffeomorphism invariant action. In effect this mild form of nonlocality can be absorbed into a quantity β conjugate to the extensive quantity that is rendered dynamical by writing the δ-function expressing the constraint on the value of the extensive quantity as an integral over a sharply peaked distribution of values for the conjugate quantity. As a prototype for the jth extensive variable that has a fixed value, we can think of an integral of the form $\int d^4x \sqrt{g} \mathcal{L}_j(x)$. This procedure, which is familiar in statistical mechanics when approximating a microcanonical ensemble by a canonical ensemble, leads to the following approximate expression for the partition function:

$$Z = \int \mathcal{D}\phi \mathcal{D}A \mathcal{D}\psi \; e^{i[\phi,A,\psi]} \prod_j \delta \left(\int d^4x \sqrt{g} \; \mathcal{L}_j(x) - \text{fix. val.} \right) =$$
$$\prod_j \left(\frac{1}{2\pi} \int d\beta_j \int \mathcal{D}\phi \mathcal{D}A \mathcal{D}\psi \; e^{i[\phi,A,\psi]} e^{i\beta_j (\int d^4x \sqrt{g} \mathcal{L}_j(x) - \text{fix. val.})} \right).$$

According to the MPC model for finetuning, one should expect to find the fine-tuned parameters observed in Nature at parameter values that coincide with critical behavior. Since the cosmological constant value $\Lambda_{eff} = 0$ corresponds to the border between finite and infinite space spheres, it is not surprising that computer simulations [3, 4] of quantum gravity indicate singular behaviour for the value $\Lambda_{eff} = 0$ for the cosmological constant. According to our MPC model for finetuning, the value of the cosmological constant realized in Nature is expected to be at a phase border. We can therefore claim the phenomenologically indicated value $\Lambda_{eff} = 0$ as our theoretical prediction for the value of the cosmological constant. Likewise we can claim that our finetuning model explains the hierarchy problem in the sense that Planck scale MPC implies that multiple point parameters should also be at the border between Higgsed and unHiggsed phases. At such boundaries there is a change of sign in m^2_{Higgs}

which, for transitions that are weakly first order, would imply values of m^2_{Higgs} that, relative to the Planck scale, are strongly suppressed.

3. Standard Model Gauge Couplings from MPC

The principle of MPC was "discovered" in connection with theoretical attempts to calculate the SM gauge coupling constants in the context of a Yang-Mills Lattice Gauge Theory (LGT). We made the observation that the critical couplings from LGT for the non-Abelian subgroups of the SM were very close to being three times larger than the the values of experimental couplings extrapolated to the Planck scale using the assumption of a "desert" in doing the renormalization group extrapolation. This suggested what we here take as an assumption — namely that that the usual Standard Model Group (SMG) arises as the diagonal subgroup that survives the Planck scale breakdown of a more fundamental "antiunified" gauge group $SMG \times SMG \times SMG$ (i.e., the cartesian product of SMG factors with one SMG for each of the $N_{gen} = 3$ generations of quarks and leptons). Our prediction for Planck scale gauge couplings comes from applying the principle of MPC to the "antiunified" gauge group† SMG^3 and then claiming that it is the diagonal subgroup couplings corresponding to the multiple point of the phase diagram for SMG^3 that are realized in Nature. In the case of the two non-Abelian inverse squared couplings, it is not difficult to see that the $N_{gen} = 3$ (equal) MPC values are enhanced by a factor $N_{gen} = 3$ in going to the diagonal subgroup. However, for the $U(1)$ coupling, the situation is complicated by (gauge invariant) "interactions" between the $N_{gen} = 3$ SMG factors of SMG^3 that lead to an enhancement factor that differs from the naively expected factor $N_{gen} = 3$ when going to the diagonal subgroup. The enhancement factor ranges from 6 to 8 (depending on the approximation used) with the favoured value being 6.8.

The phases in which we are interested can be classified according to the gauge transformation properties of the vacuum [8]. It turns out that there is a possible phase (the boundary of which should, according to the principle of MPC, include the multiple point) for each *pair* (K, H) consisting of a subgroup K and invariant subgroup H such that $K \subseteq SMG^3$ and $H \triangleleft K$. It is important that also discrete subgroups are considered. For the gauge group SMG^3, (infinitely) many phases are possible. We have developed approximate techniques using generalized

---

† Actually we use an approximation where the subgroups of the SM are considered separately. Critical coupling values for $SU(3)$, $SU(2)$, and $U(1)$ are taken from the literature [5, 6, 7].

	$1/\alpha(M_Z) \xrightarrow{RG}$	$1/\alpha(\mu_{Pl})$	enhance. fac.	$1/\alpha_{multi.\ point}$	$1/\alpha_{pred}(\mu_{Pl})$	$1/\alpha_{Parisi\ imp\ pred}(\mu_{Pl})$
SU(3)	8.47 ± 0.5	53 ± 0.7	3	15	45	$56._7$
SU(2)	29.7 ± 0.2	$49._5$	3	$13._1$	39	$49._5$
U(1)		$55._5$	6.8	7.9	54	68

Table 1. Comparison of theoretically predicted and experimental values of the three Standard Model gauge coupling at the Planck scale.

plaquette actions that can bring a large number of phases together at an approximate multiple point. In Table 1 our predictions for the SMG inverse fine-structure constants at the Planck scale are denoted by $1/\alpha_{pred}(\mu_{Pl})$. These are obtained by multiplying $1/\alpha_{multi.\ point}$ by the factor by which the inverse fine-structure constant is enhanced (i.e., $N_{gen} = 3$ for the non-Abelian subgroups and 6.8 for the $U(1)$ subgroup) due to the Planck scale breakdown of the gauge group SMG^3 to the diagonal subgroup. These are to be compared to the Planck scale experimental values $1/\alpha(\mu_{Pl})$. As an indication of the calculational uncertainty, we give the predicted values using only "Parisi improved" values for the fine-structure constants in the last column of Table 1.

4. Mass Hierarchies of Quark-Lepton Generations

In related work [9], the mass hierarchy of fermions (leptons and quarks) is understood as a consequence of Higgsed gauge symmetries that are only weakly broken because MPC predicts that vacuum expectation values for the Higgs fields near the multiple point should be small. The mass spectrum of quarks and leptons — especially the large mass gaps between generations — would then suggest the assignment of different gauge quantum numbers to different generations. The feature that seems to be necessary is, for example, that the (gauge) quantum number difference between left and right μ is not the same as that between the left and right e. This suggests extensions of the SMG (at the fundamental scale) having many features in common with SMG^3 although the large top quark mass presents a problem for a SMG^3 model. A possible solution might be to enlarge SMG^3 with an additional Abelian gauged flavour symmetry group $U(1)_f$.

5. Conclusion

The MPC idea is a prototype for a mechanism that can explain the occurence of fine-tuned quantities in general. In this role, it may be able to provide an explanation for the gauge coupling constants, the smallness of the expected Higgs mass and Θ_{QCD} and the the effectively vanishing cosmological constant. The smallness of Higgs

vacuum expectation values is a consequence of MPC which predicts that also the boundary of a Higgsed phase (of a gauge field theory say) should include a point that coincides with the multiple point in the phase diagram spanned by a suitable choice of action parameters. Small Higgs expectation values would allow approximately conserved gauge quantum numbers. The mass hierarchy of the quarks and leptons could be explaind by having values of these quantum numbers for each of the three generations of quarks and leptons that differ by different amounts.

In the context of a lattice gauge theory in which it is assumed that the usual SMG is realized as the diagonal subgroup surviving the Planck scale breakdown of a more fundamental "antiunified" gauge group $SMG^{N_{gen}}$ ($N_{gen} = 3 = $ number of quark — lepton generations), MPC predicts that the values of gauge couplings realized at the Planck scale coincide with those of the diagonal subgroup of SMG^3 corresponding to the multiple point of SMG^3. This prediction agrees with extrapolated data for all three SMG gauge couplings to within the accuracy of our calculation.

The Planck scale coupling values predicted using MPC coincide with extrapolated experimental couplings where a "desert" is assumed in the RG extrapolation to the Planck scale. A "non-desert" RG development would lead to Planck scale values for gauge coupling that would not agree with our predictions. For this reason, MPC can be said to predict the absence of supersymmetric partners at observable energies. In practice our model also predicts no proton decay inasmuch as $SU(5)$ is not a feature of our model.

References

[1] D.L. Bennett & H.B. Nielsen, *Intl. J. Mod. Phys. A* **9** (1994) (to appear in September number) & references herein.
[2] D.L. Bennett. H.B. Nielsen, & I. Picek, *Phys. Lett.* **B208** (1988) 275
[3] H.W. Hamber, *Nucl. Phys.* **B 400** (1993) 347
[4] J. Ambjørn & S. Varsted, *Nucl.Phys.* **B 373** (1992) 557
[5] C.P. Bachas & R.F. Dashen, *Nucl.Phys.* **B 210** (1982) 583
[6] G. Bhanot, *Phys. Lett.* **B 108** (1982) 337
[7] J.-M. Drouffe & J.-B. Zuber, *Phys. Rep. 102* (1983) 1
[8] C.D. Froggatt & H.B. Nielsen, *Origin of Symmetries* (World Scientific, Singapore, 1991)
[9] C.D. Froggatt, G. Lowe, and H.B. Nielsen, *Nucl. Phys.* **B414** (1994) 579; ibid. **B420** (1994) 3

Paper presented at XXVII Int. Conf. on High Energy Physics: Session Pa-4
Glasgow, UK, 20–27 July 1994

Classical/Quantum Duality

M. J. Duff[†]

Isaac Newton Institute for Mathematical Sciences
University of Cambridge
20 Clarkson Road, Cambridge CB3 OEH, U.K.

Abstract

String theory requires two kinds of loop expansion: classical (α') worldsheet loops with expansion parameter $< T >$ where T is a modulus field, and quantum ($\hbar$) spacetime loops with expansion parameter $< S >$ where S is the dilaton field. Four-dimensional string/string duality (a corollary of ten-dimensional string/fivebrane duality) interchanges the roles of S and T and hence interchanges classical and quantum.

There is now a consensus that the really important questions of string theory will never be answered within the framework of a weak coupling perturbation expansion. Here I describe some recent work which begins to address this strong coupling problem. It is based on the idea that the same physics may equally well be described by the fundamental four-dimensional superstring or by a *dual* four-dimensional superstring [1] that corresponds to a soliton solution‡ of the fundamental string. In this respect, the idea provides a stringy generalization of the old Montonen-Olive conjecture [3] of a duality between the electrically charged particles of a fundamental supersymmetric theory and its magnetically charged solitons. Indeed, the latter duality is in fact subsumed by the former in that the solitonic magnetic *H-monopoles* [4, 5] of the fundamental string are the fundamental electric winding states of the dual string [6, 7].

This four-dimensional string/string duality is a corollary of the ten-dimensional string/fivebrane duality which states that the same physics may equally well be described by the fundamental ten-dimensional superstring (an extended object with one spatial dimension) or by a dual ten-dimensional superfivebrane [8] (an extended object with five spatial dimensions) that corresponds to a soliton solution of the fundamental string [9, 10]. The pay-off, if such a conjecture proves to be true, is that the strongly coupled string corresponds to the weakly coupled fivebrane. After compactification to four dimensions, the fivebrane will appear as an H-monopole or a dual string according as it wraps around 5 or 4 of the compactified dimensions [9] which, for concreteness and simplicity, we take to be a six-dimensional torus§. The inverse tension of the dual string, $2\pi\tilde{\alpha}'$, is related to that of the fundamental string, $2\pi\alpha'$, by the Dirac quantization rule [1]

$$8GR^2 = n\alpha'\tilde{\alpha}' \quad n = integer \qquad (1)$$

where G is Newton's constant and R is the compactification scale. One's first guess might therefore be to assume that the strongly coupled four-dimensional fundamental string corresponds to the weakly coupled dual string, but in fact something more subtle and interesting happens. The fundamental string exhibits a minimum/maximum length duality, $R \to \alpha'/R$,

---

† On leave of absence from the Center for Theoretical Physics, Texas A&M University, College Station, Texas 77843. Research supported in part by NSF Grant PHY-9411543.

‡ This *dual* string of [1] is not to be confused with the *stringy cosmic string* of [2]. The two solutions are different.

§ It could in principle also appear as a membrane by wrapping around 3 of the compactified dimensions, but the fundamental four-dimensional string obtained in this way does not admit the membrane soliton [1].

	Fundamental string	Dual string
Moduli	$T = b + ie^{-\sigma}$	$S = a + ie^{-\eta}$
Worldsheet coupling	$< e^{\sigma} > = \alpha'/R$	$< e^{\eta} > = g^2/2\pi$
Large/small radius	$R \to \alpha'/R$	$g \to 1/g$
T-duality	$O(6, 22; Z)$	$SL(2, Z)$
Axion/dilaton	$S = a + ie^{-\eta}$	$T = b + ie^{-\sigma}$
Spacetime coupling	$< e^{\eta} > = g^2/2\pi$	$< e^{\sigma} > = \alpha'/R$
Strong/weak coupling	$g \to 1/g$	$R \to \alpha'/R$
S-duality	$SL(2, Z)$	$O(6, 22; Z)$

Table 1. Duality of dualities

called T-duality, manifest order by order in perturbation theory. There is also evidence that it exhibits a minimum/maximum coupling constant duality [11, 12], $g \to 1/g$, called S-duality, which is intrinsically nonperturbative. In going from the string to the dual string, these two dualities trade places leading to a *duality of dualities* [13, 14, 1, 15] as illustrated in table 1.

String theory requires two kinds of loop expansion: classical (α') worldsheet loops with expansion parameter $< e^{\sigma} >$ where σ is a modulus field, and quantum ($\hbar$) spacetime loops with expansion parameter $< e^{\eta} >$ where η is the dilaton field. Introducing the axion field a and another pseudoscalar modulus field b, four-dimensional string/string duality interchanges the roles of $S = a + ie^{-\eta}$ and $T = b + ie^{-\sigma}$, and hence interchanges classical and quantum. Thus this duality of dualities exhibited by four-dimensional strings is entirely consistent with the earlier result that ten-dimensional string/fivebrane duality interchanges the spacetime and worldsheet loop expansions [16], and is entirely consistent with the Dirac quantization rule (1) that follows from a earlier string/fivebrane rule [10]. Thus, for $n = 1$, we have

$$< e^{\eta} > = g^2/2\pi = 8G/\alpha' = \tilde{\alpha}'/R^2$$

$$< e^{\sigma} > = \tilde{g}^2/2\pi = 8G/\tilde{\alpha}' = \alpha'/R^2 \qquad (2)$$

where $\tilde{g}$ is the dual string spacetime loop expansion parameter.

Group theoretically, these dualities are given by $O(6, 22)$ in the case of T-duality and $SL(2, Z)$ in the case of S-duality. It has been suggested [17, 7] that these two kinds of duality should be united into a bigger group $O(8, 24)$ which contains both as subgroups. This would have the bizarre effect of eliminating the distinction between classical and quantum.

References

[1] M. J. Duff and R. R. Khuri, Nucl. Phys. **B411** (1994) 473.
[2] B. R. Greene, A. Shapere, C. Vafa, and S. T. Yau, Nucl. Phys. **B340** (1990) 33.
[3] C. Montonen and D. Olive, Phys. Lett. **B72** (1977) 117.
[4] R. R. Khuri, Phys. Lett. **B259** (1991) 261; Nucl. Phys. **B387** (1992) 315.
[5] J. Gauntlett, J. H. Harvey and J. Liu, Nucl. Phys **B409** (1993) 363.
[6] M. J. Duff, R. R. Khuri, R. Minasian and J. Rahmfeld, Nucl. Phys. **B418** (1994) 195.
[7] M. J. Duff and J. Rahmfeld, CTP-TAMU-25/94, hep-th/9406105.
[8] M. J. Duff, Class. Quantum Grav. **5** (1988) 189.
[9] A. Strominger, Nucl. Phys. **B343** (1990) 167.
[10] M. J. Duff and J.X. Lu, Nucl. Phys. **B354** (1991) 141.
[11] A. Font, L. Ibanez, D. Lust and F. Quevedo, Phys. Lett. **B249** (1990) 35.
[12] C. Vafa and E. Witten, hep-th/9408074, HUTP-94/A017, IASSNS-HEP-94-54.
[13] J. H. Schwarz and A. Sen, Phys. Lett. **B312** (1993) 105.
[14] P. Binetruy, Phys. Lett. **B315** (1993) 80.
[15] A. Sen, TIFR/TH/94-03, hep-th/9402002.
[16] M. J. Duff and J.X. Lu, Nucl. Phys. **B357** (1991) 534.
[17] M. J. Duff and J.X. Lu, Nucl. Phys. **B347** (1990) 394.

Paper presented at XXVII Int. Conf. on High Energy Physics: Session Pa-4
Glasgow, UK, 20–27 July 1994

Supersymmetric Unification: a mini-review of recent developments*

V. Barger[†], M. S. Berger[§], and P. Ohmann[†]

† Physics Department, University of Wisconsin, Madison, Wisconsin 53706
§ Physics Department, Indiana University, Bloomington, Indiana 47405

Abstract

Some recent results in supersymmetric grand unified theories are reviewed.

1. Introduction

The Standard Model (SM) of particle interactions has proven very successful in describing collider physics. To go beyond, one is interested in discovering new states or eliminating free parameters of the SM. Usually each of these avenues involves new or larger symmetries. The idea of supersymmetric (SUSY) grand unified theories (GUTs) is no exception: the gauge group of the Standard Model is included in a larger grand unified group and a new symmetry relating particles of different spin is introduced. This approach then predicts the existence of many new states (the sparticles) and can eliminate free parameters (e.g. $\sin \theta_W$) that exist in the Standard Model.

Not long after the unification of the electroweak interactions the idea of a further unification of all the forces in the Standard Model into a single gauge group was born[1]. Shortly thereafter the implications for the value of the weak mixing angle was derived[2]. The low-energy theory was then made supersymmetric[3] yielding a slightly different value for $\sin \theta_W$. Before the precision data from LEP both these versions of a grand unified theory incorporating a desert between the electroweak and the GUT scale were experimentally viable. With the recent precise electroweak data, the supersymmetric version alone can describe the experimental results in the absence of an intermediate scale[4].

The other development that is central to the

success of SUSY unification is electroweak symmetry breaking. Supersymmetry protects the hierarchy of the electroweak scale and the GUT scale; in addition the breakdown of the electroweak symmetry can be understood when the supersymmetry is local[5]. The large value of the top quark Yukawa coupling enhances large logs that cause the spontaneous breakdown of the electroweak symmetry[6].

Following the revival of interest in SUSY GUTs caused by the unification of the gauge couplings, some of the more model-dependent earlier predictions were reinvestigated. In particular, the relation between the bottom quark and the tau lepton mass that occurs in some minimal versions of grand unified theories was updated. The equality of b and τ Yukawa couplings at the GUT scale was first proposed in Ref. [7]. The importance of a large top Yukawa coupling in suppressing the bottom quark mass was emphasized by Ibañez and Lopez[8]. More recently the correlation between the bottom quark mass and the tau lepton mass was explored, and an inconsistency in the nonsupersymmetric desert prediction was uncovered[9]. Moreover b-τ coupling unification is perfectly viable in the minimal supersymmetric extension to the Standard Model. While Yukawa coupling unification is not as general as that of gauge coupling unification (it involves specific assumptions about the GUT symmetry breakdown), the success of the simplest relation added extra impetus to the interest in supersymmetric GUTs. The m_b/m_τ relation implies that the top quark Yukawa coupling is probably at its infrared quasi-fixed point, which in turn limits the relation of the top quark and the

* Talk presented by V. Barger

ratio of the Higgs vevs in supersymmetry to a narrow corridor of values[10]–[13]. When the uncertainty on the top quark mass from CDF is reduced, then only small (≈ 1) and large ($\approx m_t/m_b$) values of $\tan\beta$ will be allowed, with the small $\tan\beta$ solution preferred. [The situation is complicated somewhat by the presence of threshold corrections at the electroweak and grand unified scales—if large enough and if $\alpha_3(M_Z)$ is at the lower end of its experimentally allowed range, then the fixed-point solution might not apply.] The relationship implied by the top quark Yukawa coupling fixed point on the value of $\tan\beta$ also occurs in a top quark condensate mode[14] when the scale Λ is near the GUT scale.

2. Evolution of Dimensionless Couplings

The gauge couplings evolve according to renormalization group equations (RGE) with the solution

$$\alpha_i^{-1}(Q) = \alpha_i^{-1}(M_G) - \frac{b_i}{2\pi}t \ . \tag{1}$$

at the one-loop level where $t = \ln(Q/M_G)$ defines the scale. The parameters b_i are determined by the particle content of the effective theory.

The evolution of the top quark Yukawa coupling is described by the RGE,

$$\frac{d\lambda_t}{dt} = \frac{\lambda_t}{16\pi^2}\left[-\frac{13}{15}g_1^2 - 3g_2^2 - \frac{16}{3}g_3^2 + 6\lambda_t^2 + \lambda_b^2\right] \ . \tag{2}$$

Figures 1 and 2 show the solution of these renormalization group equations for values of the bottom quark running mass. One sees that the top Yukawa coupling is driven to its infrared fixed point[10]–[21].

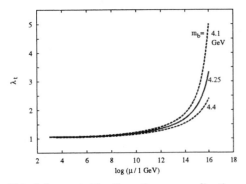

Fig. 1. If λ_t is large at M_G, then the renormalization group equation causes $\lambda_t(Q)$ to evolve rapidly towards an infrared fixed point as $Q \to m_t$ (from Ref. [10]).

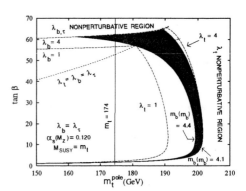

Fig. 2. Contours of constant $m_b(m_b)$ in the $m_t(m_t), \tan\beta$ plane with contours of constant GUT scale Yukawa couplings (adapted from Ref. [10]).

Converting this relation for the top quark pole mass yields[19]

$$m_t^{\text{pole}} \approx (200\,\text{GeV})\sin\beta \ . \tag{3}$$

The value of 200 GeV that appears in the above equation is subject to some uncertainty due to varying $\alpha_3(M_Z)$ and to threshold effects[13, 22].

Adding a singlet N to the minimal supersymmetric model provides an additional coupling $\lambda H_1 H_2 N$ in the superpotential, which could conceivably suppress the bottom quark mass sufficiently that the top quark Yukawa coupling could be reduced. However constraints on the perturbativity of the coupling λ preserves the fixed point condition[20, 21]. A four generation model is not easily compatible with Yukawa unification[23].

3. RGE Evolution of Sparticle Masses

An attractive property of models based on supergravity is that the symmetry breakdown in the electroweak sector can be attributed to large logs that contribute to the Higgs potential[24]–[34]. One must arrive at the correct scale for the electroweak interactions without breaking color or charge. This is accomplished by imposing two minimization conditions obtained from the Higgs potential.

The minimum of the Higgs potential must occur by the acquisition of vacuum expectation values. Minimizing the tree-level potential with respect to the two neutral CP-even Higgs degrees of freedom yields the two conditions

$$\frac{1}{2}M_Z^2 = \frac{m_{H_1}^2 - m_{H_2}^2\tan^2\beta}{\tan^2\beta - 1} - \mu^2 \ . \tag{4}$$

$$-B\mu = \frac{1}{2}(m_{H_1}^2 + m_{H_2}^2 + 2\mu^2)\sin 2\beta \ . \tag{5}$$

where m_{H_1} and m_{H_2} are soft-supersymmetry breaking parameters and μ is the Higgs mass in the superpotential. In order to avoid large cancellations between the terms on the right-hand side of Eq. (4), some naturalness criteria are inposed, which in turn typically imply that the sparticle masses are not too high ($\lesssim 1$ TeV).

For the low $\tan\beta$ fixed-point solution as few as two inputs for the soft-supersymmetry breaking parameters are needed—a universal scalar mass m_0 and a common gaugino mass $m_{1/2}$[30]. The low energy sparticle mass can be given in terms of these inputs.

The heaviest chargino and the two heaviest neutralino states are primarily Higgsino with masses approximately equal to $|\mu|$. Typical mass relationships are displayed in Figure 3.

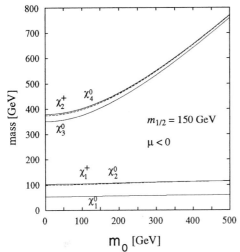

Fig. 3. The chargino and neutralino masses are plotted versus m_0 for $m_{1/2} = 150$ GeV for a low value of $\tan\beta$ and $\mu < 0$ (from Ref.[31]).

For the low-$\tan\beta$ solution, the mass of the lightest Higgs h comes mainly from radiative corrections[19, 21, 35, 36, 37, 38]. Experiments at LEP II will cover the region $m_h \lesssim \sqrt{s}/2$. Recent work[39] has shown that a $h \rightarrow b\bar{b}$ search at the Tevatron may be possible. The heavy Higgs states are (approximately) degenerate $\approx M_A$; see Figure 4. The Higgs discovery potential at e^+e^- colliders has recently been discussed[40].

The squark and slepton masses also display simple asymptotic behavior at large $|\mu|$; see Figure 5. The first and second squark generations are approximately degenerate. The splitting of the stop quark masses grows as $|\mu|$ increases and the lightest stop can be as light as 45 GeV (or even lighter with fine tuning). The masses could be much larger than is indicated in the figure since the value of m_0 could be large.

While the universality of the scalar masses has been assumed for the Figures presented above, recently there has been much interest in considering the implications of nonuniversality on the supersymmetric spectrum and on reconsidering the constraints from flavor changing neutral currents[41].

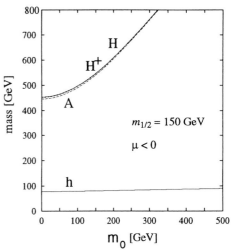

Fig. 4. The supersymmetric Higgs masses are plotted versus m_0 for $m_{1/2} = 150$ GeV for a low value of $\tan\beta$ and $\mu < 0$ (from Ref.[31]).

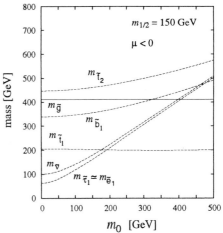

Fig. 5. The squark and slepton masses are plotted versus m_0 for $m_{1/2} = 150$ GeV for a low value of $\tan\beta$ and $\mu < 0$.

The MSSM has an R-parity symmetry so the lightest supersymmetric particle (LSP) is stable. Usually the LSP is the lightest neutralino, but for small values of m_0 the supersymmetric partner of the tau lepton can be lighter. For the lightest particle to be neutral, as required, there is an upper bound on the value of $m_{1/2}$ for small m_0. In particular such an upper bound exists for no-scale models ($m_0 = 0$), and is more stringent for $\mu > 0$ due to the mixing between the left- and right-handed $\tilde{\tau}$. The phenomenological issues of the Yukawa unified no-scale model have been examined in Ref. [42].

The LSP can naturally account for the dark matter of the Universe[43, 44]. Large values of μ result in the lightest neutralino being predominantly gaugino. This leads to a reduced rate of annihilation of neutralinos and can provide too much relic abundance and overclose the Universe. However the s-channel h pole can enhance the annihilation rate and rescue the dark matter explanation[45].

4. Proton Decay

One of the major additions to particle physics from the concept of grand unified theories is that the proton might be unstable. Stringent experimental limits on proton decay rule out many models, including the nonsupersymmetric version of SU(5). At first sight it might appear that the supersymmetric versions of SU(5) are safe, since the GUT scale is considerably higher and therefore proton decay occurring through the dimension six operators is much suppressed. However, dangerous dimension five operators are introduced in the supersymmetric versions of grand unified models. In the minimal supersymmetric SU(5) GUT, one must have very heavy sleptons to avoid the proton decay bound[46, 47]. However, other models can greatly suppress or eliminate entirely proton decay.

5. Possibilities for Experimental Searches

There are many interesting signals for supersymmetry at present and future colliders. The missing p_T signal at the Tevatron or at the LHC is a classic experimental signature of supersymmetry. If the charginos and the neutralinos are sufficiently light, then trilepton signals are possible[48]:

$$W^{\pm *} \to \chi_1^\pm \chi_2^0 \to \ell^\pm \ell^+ \ell^- \chi_1^0 \chi_1^0 \ . \qquad (6)$$

Gluinos will be produced abundantly at hadron colliders, and decays can produce like-sign dilepton signals[49]. On the other hand, for some regions of parameter space the gluino may decay predominantly into stop [50]:

$$\tilde{g} \to \tilde{t}t \ . \qquad (7)$$

If the stop is lighter than the top then stoponium bound states can be formed which subsequently decay into photon pairs or Higgs bosons[51]. A future high energy e^+e^- collider (NLC) would provide an opportunity to produce and study the properties of sleptons, charginos, and supersymmetric Higgs bosons[52].

6. Implications for $b \to s\gamma$ decay

The measured rate for the inclusive decay $b \to s\gamma$ [53]

$$\mathrm{BR}(B \to s\gamma) = (2.32 \pm 0.51 \pm 0.29 \pm 0.32) \times 10^{-4} \qquad (8)$$

is close to the SM prediction. The predicted rate in SUSY models for small $\tan\beta$ is somewhat larger than the SM for $\mu > 0$ and generally smaller than the SM rate for $\mu < 0$[54]. Figure 6 shows the general trend of contours for the inclusive rate for $\mu < 0$. Unfortunately the current theoretical uncertainty is at least $\pm 25\%$[56],

so until further theoretical progress is made, one cannot determine the sign of μ. SUSY contributions to $B^0 - \overline{B}^0$, $D^0 - \overline{D}^0$ and $K^0 - \overline{K}^0$ could also be relevant to placing restrictions on models[57]. The implications of the $Z \to b\bar{b}$ measurements at LEP on supersymmetric unification have recently been investigated[58].

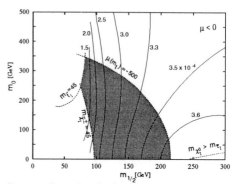

Fig. 6. Contour lines for the $b \to s\gamma$ inclusive rate for $\mu < 0$ (from Ref. [55]).

7. Conclusions

According to all RGE sparticle mass spectrum analyses, two broad conclusions about the implications of SUSY unification can be drawn:

- Interesting regions of the SUSY parameter space can be covered at the Tevatron with the main injector, and possibly further improvements in the luminosity or upgrades of the center-of-mass energy[59].
- The LHC and the NLC are guaranteed to be SUSY factories if supersymmetry exists; the task of determining how to pull the signals out of the backgrounds is continuing[60].

8. Acknowledgements

This research was supported in part by the University of Wisconsin Research Committee with funds granted by the Wisconsin Alumni Research Foundation, in part by the U.S. Department of Energy under contract nos. DE-AC02-76ER00881 and DE-FG02-91ER40661, and in part by the Texas National Laboratory Research Commission under grant nos. RGFY93-221.

References

[1] H. Georgi and S. Glashow, Phys. Rev. Lett. **32** (1974) 438.
[2] H. Georgi, H. Quinn, and S. Weinberg, Phys. Rev. Lett. **33** (1974) 451.
[3] S. Dimopoulos, S. Raby, and F. Wilczek, Phys. Rev. **D24** (1981) 1681; S. Dimopoulos and H. Georgi, Nucl. Phys. **B193** (1981) 150; N. Sakai, Z. Phys. **C11** (1981) 153.
[4] U. Amaldi, W. de Boer, and H. Furstenau, Phys. Lett. **B260** (1991) 447; J. Ellis, S. Kelley and D. V. Nanopoulos, Phys. Lett. **B260** (1991) 131; P. Langacker and M. Luo, Phys. Rev. **D44** (1991) 817.

[5] P. Nath, these proceedings.

[6] L. E. Ibañez and G. G. Ross, Phys. Lett. **B110** (1982) 215; H. P. Nilles, Phys. Lett. **B115** (1982) 193.

[7] M. Chanowitz, J. Ellis, and M. K. Gaillard, Nucl. Phys. **B128** (1977) 506.

[8] L. E. Ibañez and C. Lopez, Phys. Lett. **B126** (1983) 54; Nucl. Phys. **B233** (1984) 511.

[9] A. Giveon, L. J. Hall, and U. Sarid, Phys. Lett. **B271** (1991) 138; H. Arason, et al., Phys. Rev. **D47** (1991) 232.

[10] V. Barger, M.S. Berger, and P. Ohmann, Phys. Rev. **D47** (1993) 1093.

[11] G. Anderson, S. Dimopoulos, L. J. Hall, and S. Raby, Phys. Rev. **D47** (1993) 3072.

[12] M. Carena, S. Pokorski, and C. E. M. Wagner, Nucl. Phys. **B406** (1993) 59; W. Bardeen, M. Carena, S. Pokorski, and C. E. M. Wagner, Phys. Lett. **B320** (1994) 110.

[13] P. Langacker and N. Polonsky, Phys. Rev. **D49** (1994) 1454; N. Polonsky, Talk presented at the XVI Kazimierz Meeting on Elementary Particle Physics, Penn U. preprint UPR-0588-T, Kazimierz, Poland (1993), hep-ph 9310292.

[14] W. A. Bardeen, M. Carena, T. E. Clark, K. Sasaki, and C. E. M. Wagner, Nucl. Phys. **B369** (1992) 33.

[15] B. Pendleton and G. G. Ross, Phys. Lett. **98B** (1981) 291; C. T. Hill, Phys. Rev. **D24** (1981) 691; J. Bagger, S. Dimopoulos, and E. Masso, Phys. Rev. Lett. **55** (1985) 1450; W. Zimmermann, Commun. Math. Phys. **97** (1985) 211; J. Kubo, K. Sibold, and W. Zimmerman, Phys. Lett. **B200** (1989) 191.

[16] C. D. Froggatt, I. G. Knowles, and R. G. Moorhouse, Phys. Lett. **B249** (1990) 273; **B298** (1993) 356.

[17] S. Dimopoulos, L. Hall and S. Raby, Phys. Rev. Lett. **68** (1992) 1984; Phys. Rev. **D45** (1992) 4192.

[18] V. Barger, M. S. Berger, T. Han, and M. Zralek, Phys. Rev. Lett. **68** (1992) 3394.

[19] V. Barger, M. S. Berger, P. Ohmann, and R. J. N. Phillips, Phys. Lett. **B314** (1993) 351.

[20] B. C. Allanach and S. F. King, Phys. Lett. **B328** (1994) 360.

[21] P. Langacker and N. Polonsky, Univ. of Pennsylvania preprint UPR-0594T (1994), hep-ph 9403306.

[22] L. J. Hall, R. Rattazzi, and U. Sarid, Lawrence Berkeley preprint LBL-33997, hep-ph 9306309; R. Hempfling, Phys. Rev. **D49** (1994) 6168; M. Carena, M. Olechowski, S. Pokorski, and C. E. M. Wagner, Max Planck Institute preprint MPI-TH-93-103, hep-ph 9402253; B. D. Wright, University of Wisconsin preprint MAD/PH/812, hep-ph 9404217.

[23] J. F. Gunion, D. W. McKay, and H. Pois, University of California preprint UCD-94-25, hep-ph 9406249.

[24] G. Gamberini, G. Ridolfi, and F. Zwirner, Nucl. Phys. **B331** (1990) 331.

[25] G. G. Ross and R. G. Roberts, Nucl. Phys. **B377** (1992) 571.

[26] S. Kelley, J. L. Lopez, D. V. Nanopoulos, H. Pois, and K. Yuan, Nucl. Phys. **B398** (1993) 3.

[27] M. Olechowski and S. Pokorski, Nucl. Phys. **B404** (1993) 590.

[28] P. Ramond, Institute for Fundamental Theory Preprint UFIFT-HEP-93-13 (1993), hep-ph 9306311; D. J. Castaño, E. J. Piard, and P. Ramond, Phys. Rev. **D49** (1994) 4882.

[29] W. de Boer, R. Ehret, and D. I. Kazakov, Inst. für Experimentelle Kernphysik preprint IEKP-KA/93-13, Contribution to the International Symposium on Lepton Photon Interactions, Ithaca, NY (1993), hep-ph 9308238; W. de Boer, Karlsruhe preprint IEKP-KA-94-01, hep-ph 9402266; W. de Boer, R. Ehret, D. I. Kazakov, and W. Oberschulte, Karlsruhe preprint IEKP-KA-94-05, hep-ph 9405342.

[30] M. Carena, M. Olechowski, S. Pokorski, and C. E. M. Wagner, Nucl. Phys. **B419** (1994) 213.

[31] V. Barger, M. S. Berger, and P. Ohmann, Phys. Rev. **D49** (1994) 4908.

[32] G. Kane, C. Kolda, L. Roszkowski, and J. D. Wells, Phys. Rev. **D49** (1994) 6173.

[33] B. Ananthanarayan, K. S. Babu, and Q. Shafi, Bartol preprint BA-94-02; B. Ananthanarayan and Q. Shafi, UNIL-TP-3-94, Talk presented at Workshop on Yukawa Couplings and the Origin of Mass, Gainesville, FL, 1994.

[34] R. Arnowitt and P. Nath, Phys. Rev. Lett. **69** (1992) 725; Phys. Lett. **B289** (1992) 368.

[35] M. Diaz and H. Haber, Phys. Rev. **D46** (1992) 3086.

[36] R. Hempfling and A. H. Hoang, Phys. Lett. **B331** (1994) 99.

[37] J. A. Casas, J. R. Espinosa, M. Quiros, and A. Riotto, CERN preprint CERN-TH.7334/94.

[38] J. L. Lopez, D. V. Nanopoulous, H. Pois, X. Wang, and A. Zichichi, Phys. Lett. **B306** (1993) 73.

[39] J. F. Gunion and T. Han, Davis preprint UCD-94-10, April, 1994, hep-ph 9404244; W. Marciano, A. Stange, and S. Willenbrock, Illinois preprint ILL-TH-94-8, April, 1994, hep-ph 9404247.

[40] A. Sopczak, CERN-PPE-94-073, Talk given at 15th Autumn School: Particle Physics in the Nineties, Lisbon, Portugal, 11-16 Oct. 1993; CERN-PPE-93-197, Presented at Workshop on Physics and Experiments with Linear Colliders, Waikoloa, HI, 26-30 Apr. 1993.

[41] SUSY-94 Conference, Ann Arbor, MI, May 1994.

[42] J. F. Gunion and H. Pois, Phys. Lett. **B329** (1994) 136.

[43] L. Roszkowski, Phys. Lett. **B262** (1991) 59.

[44] R. G. Roberts and L. Roszkowski, Phys. Lett. **B309** (1993) 329.

[45] R. Arnowitt and P. Nath, Phys. Rev. Lett. **70** (1993) 3696; J. L. Lopez, D. V. Nanopoulos and K. Yuan, Phys. Rev. **D48** (1993) 2766.

[46] R. Arnowitt and P. Nath, Phys. Rev. **D38** (1988) 1479.

[47] J. Hisano, H. Murayama, and T. Yanagida, Nucl. Phys. **B402** (1993) 46.

[48] R. Arnowitt and P. Nath, Mod. Phys. Lett. **A2** (1987) 331; H. Baer and X. Tata, Phys. Rev. **D47** (1992) 2739; J. L. Lopez, D. V. Nanopoulos, X. Wang, and A. Zichichi, Phys. Rev. **D48** (1993) 2062.

[49] V. Barger, W.-Y. Keung, and R. J. N. Phillips, Phys. Rev. Lett. **55**, 166 (1985); R. M. Barnett, J. F. Gunion, and H. Haber, in *High Energy Physics in the 1990's*, ed. by S. Jensen (World Scientific, Singapore, 1989), p. 230.

[50] H. Baer, M. Drees, C. Kao, M. Nojiri, and X. Tata, University of Wisconsin preprint MAD/PH/825 (1994).

[51] M. Drees and M. Nojiri, Phys. Rev. **D49** (1994) 4595; V. Barger and W.-Y. Keung, Phys. Lett. **B211** (1988) 355.

[52] See e.g. Proc. of the 1993 Hawaii LCWS Conference.

[53] B. Barish, et al., CLEO collaboration, these proceedings and CLEO CONF 94-1.

[54] C. Kolda, L. Roszkowski, J. D. Wells, and G. L. Kane, Michigan preprint UM-TH-94-03, Feb. 1994; J.-W. Wu, R. Arnowitt, and P. Nath, Texas A and M preprint CTP-TAMU-03-94, hep-ph 9406346.

[55] V. Barger, M. S. Berger, P. Ohmann, and R. J. N. Phillips, University of Wisconsin preprint MAD-PH-842, July, 1994, hep-ph 9407273 (to appear in Phys. Rev. **D**).

[56] A. J. Buras, M. Misiak, M. Munz, and S. Pokorski, Max Planck Institute preprint MPI-PH-93-77.

[57] Y. Kizukuri, G. C. Branco, and G. C. Cho, CERN preprint CERN-TH-7345-94, hep-ph 9408229.

[58] J. E. Kim and G. T. Park, Seoul National University preprint SNUTP 94-66, hep-ph 9408218; J. D. Wells, C. Kolda, and G. L. Kane, University of Michigan preprint UM-TH-94-23, hep-ph 9408228; M. Carena and C. E. M. Wagner, CERN preprint CERN-TH.7393/94 hep-ph 9408253.

[59] See e.g. T. Kamon, J. L. Lopez, P. McIntyre, and J. T. White, Texas A&M preprint CTP-TAMU-19/94, June, 1994.

[60] See proceedings of recent LHC and e^+e^- workshops.

The Next-to-Minimal Supersymmetric Standard Model

T. Elliott, S. F. King[†] and P. L. White[‡]

Physics Department, University of Southampton
Southampton, SO9 5NH, U.K.

Abstract

We review the next-to-minimal supersymmetric standard model (NMSSM) from both the low-energy phenomenological point of view, and in the context of a supergravity-inspired grand unified framework. In the low-energy approach we discuss the upper bound on the lightest CP-even neutral Higgs scalar in the NMSSM and MSSM, including one-loop radiative corrections. Then we describe a recent renormalisation group analysis based on the constraints of coupling constant unification and correct electroweak symmetry breaking, assuming universal soft supersymmetry breaking parameters. The result of this analysis is that the top quark mass is always less than 170 GeV, and in general large top mass can only be achieved in two quite precise regions of parameter space, leading to specific predictions for Higgs and SUSY particle masses which are only sensitive to essentially one free parameter, namely $M_{1/2}$.

The most widely studied extension to the standard model is supersymmetry (SUSY) [1], in which the particles of the theory are supplemented by the inclusion of their superpartners. SUSY requires the introduction of a non-minimal Higgs sector with at least two doublets [2]. The most commonly considered supersymmetric model, the MSSM, has, in addition to the usual matter and gauge particle content, a Higgs sector containing two Higgs doublet superfields H_1 and H_2. However the MSSM is not the most general low energy manifestation of SUSY GUTs. It is possible that SUSY GUTs give rise to a low energy theory which contains an additional gauge singlet field, the so called next-to-minimal supersymmetric standard model (NMSSM) [3, 4]. In the NMSSM [3, 4] the particle content of the MSSM is supplemented by a gauge singlet superfield, N. The motivation for the NMSSM is that it has the potential (or rather the superpotential) to solve the μ problem which plagues the MSSM. The μ problem is simply the statement that the mass term $\mu H_1 H_2$ in the

† Talk presented by S. F. King.
‡ Address from 1st October 1994: Department of Physics, University of Oxford, 1 Keble Road, Oxford OX1 3NP.

superpotential of the MSSM is controlled by a mass μ which phenomenologically must take a value of order the weak scale, but theoretically is undetermined.

In our analysis we shall drop all quark and lepton Yukawa couplings apart from that of the top quark so that the superpotential of the NMSSM is just

$$W_{NMSSM} \approx h_t Q H_2 t^c + \lambda N H_1 H_2 - \frac{k}{3} N^3, \quad (1)$$

where the superfield $Q^T = (t_L, b_L)$ contains the left–handed top and bottom quarks, and t^c contains the charge conjugate of the right–handed top quark. The cubic term in N is necessary to avoid a Peccei-Quinn symmetry which would force the existence of a light pseudo-Goldstone mode once the symmetry is broken. However there still remains a Z_3 symmetry under which all the matter and Higgs superfields Φ transform as $\Phi \to \alpha \Phi$ where $\alpha^3 = 1$. Note that we have eliminated the μ term. The gauge singlet field acquires a vacuum expectation value (vev) x which plays the role of the mass parameter μ in the MSSM.

Adopting the usual convention of using the same symbols for both component Higgs fields and superfields, the fields H_1, H_2, and N develop vevs which may be assumed to be of the form

$$< H_1 >= \begin{pmatrix} \nu_1 \\ 0 \end{pmatrix}, \quad < H_2 >= \begin{pmatrix} 0 \\ \nu_2 \end{pmatrix}, \quad < N >= x = r\nu,$$
$$(2)$$

where ν_1, ν_2 and x are real, $\sqrt{\nu_1^2 + \nu_2^2} = \nu = 174$ GeV, and $\tan\beta = \nu_2/\nu_1$. The low energy physical spectrum of the Higgs scalars consists of three CP-even neutral states, two CP-odd neutral states, and two charged scalars. A third CP-odd state is a Goldstone mode which becomes the longitudinal component of the Z^0, while a further two charged degrees of freedom become those of the $W^\pm$s.

In the MSSM the effect of radiative corrections is known to be important in the calculation of the upper-bound on lightest CP-even Higgs boson mass m_h [5]. Several authors have performed similar calculations in the NMSSM involving loops of top quarks and stop squarks [6, 7, 8, 9, 10] as well as Higgs bosons and Higgsinos [11]. For reasonable values of the soft parameters, we find that the upper-bound on the lightest CP-even Higgs mass is about $m_h < 150$ GeV, with a very mild m_t dependence [11]. By contrast, in the MSSM the bound is $m_h < 90$ GeV for small m_t, and approaches the NMSSM bound as $m_t \to 200$ GeV. For example for a top quark mass of about $m_t = 175$ GeV, the bound in the NMSSM (MSSM) is $m_h < 130 - 145$ GeV ($m_h < 120 - 130$ GeV), for physical squark masses (and trilinear couplings) in the range 500 GeV - 1 TeV [11].

The phenomenological implications of the NMSSM are well known [4] but worth emphasising. In the NMSSM there is the possibility that h is very light and has not yet been discovered because it is only very weakly coupled to the Z. This would correspond to h containing a sizeable admixture of N. Another distinguishing signature of the NMSSM would be the discovery of light charged scalars at LEP II, since in the NMSSM the charged Higgs masses are allowed to be arbitrarily light, whereas in the MSSM they must exceed the W mass. Although neither of these interesting signatures is present in the GUT-scale analysis which we now discuss, they are both worth searching for experimentally.

So far we have discussed the NMSSM from the low-energy phenomenological point of view. We now present the first results of a GUT-scale RG analysis of the NMSSM, imposing simultaneously the constraints of correct electroweak symmetry breaking and coupling constant unification [12]. We shall assume a soft SUSY breaking potential which gives rise to three universal soft parameters at the M_X, namely m_0, $M_{1/2}$, A_0 †. We shall use the one-loop SUSY RG equations to

---

† Note that the B parameter does not occur in the NMSSM since

integrate from the GUT scale M_X to a low-energy scale Q. Below M_X, the three soft mass parameters evolve into 32 separate soft parameters, corresponding to 3 gaugino masses M_i, 11 trilinear couplings A_i (those of the MSSM plus A_λ and A_k) and 18 scalar masses m_i^2 (including the soft Higgs masses $m_{H_i}^2$, m_N^2). We assume no inter-generational mixing, and since we drop Yukawa couplings which are small compared to h_t, the first and second generation soft masses will run identically. The unification constraints are: $g_i^2(M_X) = g_X^2$, $\lambda(M_X) = \lambda_0$, $k(M_X) = k_0$, $h_t(M_X) = h_{t0}$, $M_i(M_X) = M_{1/2}$, $m_i^2(M_X) = m_0^2$, $A_i(M_X) = A_0$.

A somewhat similar analysis to that described above has recently been performed in the NMSSM [13]. However this did not consider the effect of low-energy Higgs and SUSY particle threshold effects on gauge coupling unification. In our analysis we input the gauge couplings $g_1(M_Z)$ and $g_2(M_Z)$ and run them up through the 24 SUSY and Higgs thresholds to find M_X and g_X, which must of course be consistent with our original input values. By iterating this procedure we obtain solutions which satisfy both the requirements of correct electroweak symmetry breaking and coupling constant unification *simultaneously*. In our approach, m_t, $r = x/\nu$ and $\tan\beta = \nu_2/\nu_1$ are all outputs ‡. Finally we find it convenient to scale dimensionful quantities by $M_{1/2}$, and denote the resulting scaled quantity by a tilde. Thus $\tilde{m}_0 = m_0/M_{1/2}$.

There are a number of phenomenological constraints which will cut down the allowed regions of parameter space. We shall require that all sleptons and stops are heavier that 43 GeV and all charginos are heavier than 47 GeV. Charged Higgs bosons are required to be heavier than 45 GeV. Gluinos and squarks other than stops are required to be heavier than 100 GeV. The lightest neutralino is required to be the lightest SUSY particle. The lightest CP-even neutral Higgs boson h is required to satisfy $m_h/R_{ZZh}^2 \geq 60$ GeV, where m_h is the mass and R_{ZZh} is the ZZh coupling scaled by the standard model coupling. Finally we require m_t to be large enough. In fact the requirement that $m_t > 150$ GeV puts a strong restriction on the parameter space of this model, and singles out two quite narrow regions of parameter space:

(a) $A_0/m_0 \sim 3$, $\tilde{m}_0 \sim 0.5$, and $h_{t0} \sim 2 - 3$. This region is associated with $\tan\beta \sim 1.7$ and $r \sim 10 - 100$ depending on $M_{1/2}$, which is controlled by fine-tuning λ_0 and k_0 (the required tuning is substantially worse than in the MSSM).

(b) $A_0/m_0 \sim 0.5$, $\tilde{m}_0 \sim 5$ and $h_{t0} \sim 0.4 - 0.5$ for $k_0 \sim 2 - 3$, and $\lambda_0 < 0.5$. This region is associated with $\tan\beta \sim 10 - 100$ and $r \sim 1 - 10$, depending on $M_{1/2}$,

---

we have set $\mu = 0$.

‡ Our values of m_t which we quote always refer to the one-loop physical pole mass $m_t = m_t^{pole} = m_t(m_t)[1 + \frac{4}{3\pi}\alpha_s(m_t)]$.

which is controlled by a mild tuning of h_{t0} (similar to the tuning in the MSSM).

In Table 1 we show the full Higgs and SUSY spectrum corresponding to an example of a point in regions (a) and (b), respectively. We have arranged to have $M_{1/2} \approx 500$ GeV in both cases, leading to a similar gluino mass which we take to be $(\alpha_s(Q)/\alpha_X)M_{1/2}$, but any value of $M_{1/2}$ in the range 100 GeV-5 TeV is possible. The heavier Higgs and SUSY particle masses scale approximately linearly with $M_{1/2}$, but the top quark mass is roughly insensitive to $M_{1/2}$. We find that taking $\tilde{m}_0 = 2$ in (a) and (b) would lead to a reduction in the top quark mass of about 15 GeV in both regions. Conversely we find that taking $\tilde{m}_0 < 0.5$ in region (a) and $\tilde{m}_0 > 5$ in region (b) can lead to larger top quark masses than those quoted in Table 1. However such extreme values of $\tilde{m}_0$ are dangerous, since $\tilde{m}_0 \ll 1$ may result in the LSP being a chargino, while $\tilde{m}_0 \gg 1$ may result in there being too much dark matter in the Universe.

In Table 1 region (a) the Higgs sector consists of a 72 GeV CP-even neutral scalar which is much lighter than all the other Higgs states, and has standard model-like couplings to the Z boson ($R_{ZZh} = 0.995$), which would make it accessible to LEP very soon in this example. The accompanying SUSY spectrum has the first neutralino as the LSP, although the lighter chargino, the second neutralino and all the sleptons are all less than a factor of two heavier. Since in this example $r = 21$ and at low-energies $\lambda = 0.25$, $k = 0.12$, the spectrum will be difficult to distinguish from that of the MSSM.

In Table 1 region (b) the lightest CP-even Higgs boson also has standard model-like couplings ($R_{ZZh} = 1.000$) but its mass is now well beyond the reach of LEP II in this case. The remaining Higgs spectrum follows the previous pattern. The lighter end of the SUSY spectrum is now dominated by the neutralinos and charginos, and most of the squarks and sleptons are now very heavy indeed. Since in this example $r = 3$ and at low-energies $\lambda = 0.26$, $k = 0.6$ it should be possible to distinguish the spectrum from that of the MSSM, for example by studying the spectrum of neutralinos.

We conclude that the NMSSM is well motivated as a solution to the μ problem. Without the imposition of unification constraints, the bound on the lightest CP-even Higgs boson h in the NMSSM is roughly $m_h < 150$ GeV, with only a mild dependence on m_t. A light h which is very weakly coupled to the Z is an interesting possibility. Another possibility is a charged Higgs boson light enough to be visible at LEP II. Both these possibilities are not allowed in the MSSM. Imposing the unification constraints discussed in the text implies that $m_t > 150$ GeV is very difficult to achieve in the NMSSM. In fact only two regions of parameter space

Parameter	Region (a)	Region (b)
$\tilde{A}_0/\tilde{m}_0$	3.4	0.5
$\tilde{m}_0$	0.5	5
$M_{1/2}$ (GeV)	507	513
λ_0, k_0, h_{t0}	0.60,0.144,3.0	0.44,3.0,0.45
$\tan\beta, r$	1.66,21.0	28.3,3.0
$\alpha_s(M_Z)$	0.111	0.113
M_X (GeV)	0.82×10^{16}	0.98×10^{16}
g_X	0.695	0.693
Particle	(a) Mass (GeV)	(b) Mass (GeV)
Top Quark	162.5	148.5
CP-even Higgs	72,611,1230	120,572,2492
CP-odd Higgs	1134,1229	464,2493
Charged Higgs	1229	2494
Neutralinos	224,429	125,147
Neutralinos	892,931,938	235,445,635
Charginos	419,935	137,438
Gluino	1209	1221
Sleptons	319-434	2572-2589
Stops	830,1017	1829,2378
Sbottoms	1005,1065	2370,2770
Other Squarks	1065-1116	2770-2791

Table 1. The Higgs and SUSY spectrum for typical points whose parameters correspond to the regions (a) and (b) with Q=150 GeV.

are then possible, leading to quite precise predictions for the Higgs and SUSY spectrum, which are only sensitive to essentially one free parameter, $M_{1/2}$. In region (a) we always find $\tan\beta \approx 1.7$, while region (b) is associated with much larger $\tan\beta$. The two spectra are shown in table 1 for the choice $M_{1/2} = 500$ GeV.

References

[1] H.P. Nilles, *Phys. Rep.* **110** (1984) 1; H.E. Haber and G.L. Kane, *Phys. Rep.* **117** (1985) 75.
[2] J.F. Gunion, H.E. Haber, G.L. Kane and S. Dawson, "The Higgs Hunter's Guide" (Addison-Wesley, Reading, MA, 1990).
[3] P. Fayet, *Nucl. Phys.* **B90** (1975) 104.
[4] J. Ellis, J.F. Gunion, H.E. Haber, L. Roszkowski and F. Zwirner, *Phys. Rev.* **D39** (1989) 844.
[5] H. Haber and R. Hempfling, *Phys. Rev. Lett.* **66** (1991) 1815; Y. Okada, M. Yamaguchi and T. Yanagida, *Prog. Theor. Phys.* **85** (1991) 1; J. Ellis, G. Ridolfi and F. Zwirner, *Phys. Lett.* **B257** (1991) 83.
[6] U. Ellwanger and M. Rausch de Traubenberg, *Z. Phys.* **C53** (1992) 521.
[7] U. Ellwanger and M. Lindner, *Phys. Lett.* **B301** (1993) 365.
[8] U. Ellwanger, *Phys. Lett.* **B303** (1993) 271.
[9] T. Elliott, S.F. King and P.L. White, *Phys. Lett.* **B305** (1993) 71.
[10] T. Elliott, S.F. King and P.L. White, *Phys. Lett.* **B314** (1993) 56.
[11] T. Elliott, S. F. King and P. L. White, *Phys. Rev.* **D49** (1994) 2435.
[12] T. Elliott, S. F. King and P. L. White, Southampton preprint SHEP 93/94-19, hep-ph/9406303; SHEP 93/94-20.
[13] U. Ellwanger, M. Rausch de Trauenberg and C. A. Savoy, *Phys. Lett.* **B315** (1993) 331.

Paper presented at XXVII Int. Conf. on High Energy Physics: Session Pa-4
Glasgow, UK, 20–27 July 1994

Supergravity Grand Unification

Pran Nath[†] and R. Arnowitt[‡]

[†] Theoretical Physics Division, CERN, CH-1211 Geneva 23, Switzerland*
[‡] Center for Theoretical Physics, Department of Physics, Texas A & M University, College Station, TX 77843, USA

Abstract

A brief review is given of supergravity grand unification. Constraints arising from radiative breaking of the electroweak symmetry, proton-stability and from the current limits on dark matter are discussed. Predictions of the model are testable in future accelerator and proton-stability experiments.

Supergravity grand unification was proposed in reference [1]. Currently it is the only model which contains in it spontaneous breaking of supersymmetry which is phenomenologically viable [2]. Recent analyses of the high precision LEP data [3] appear to provide credence to the ideas of supersymmetry and grand unification and have led to a renewed activity in further investigations of low energy consequence of supergravity unification [4-6]. In this paper we give a brief review of supergravity grand unification and of the recent developments. N=1 supergravity grand unified theories have the remarkable property that supersymmetry can be broken via a hidden sector generating a well defined set of soft SUSY breaking terms. The breaking of supersymmetry here does not suffer from any of the problems encountered in spontaneous breaking of global supersymmetry. The spectrum of the theory is chosen so that the light fields of the theory after spontaneous breaking of the grand unification group G to $SU(3)_C \times SU(2)_L \times U(1)_Y$ and after spontaneous breaking of supersymmetry, corresponds to the light fields of the minimal supersymmetric standard model (MSSM) with a pair of light Higgs doublets. The effective theory below the GUT scale is characterized by a soft SUSY breaking

potential of the form [1,7,8]:

$$V_{SB} = m_0 z_i z_i^\dagger + \left(A_0 W^{(3)} + B_0 W^{(2)} + h.c. \right)$$

where z_i are the light scalar fields, and $W^{(2)}, W^{(3)}$ are the quadratic and cubic parts of the effective superpotential W_{eff} below the unification scale, such that $W_{eff} = W^{(2)} + W^{(3)} + W^{(4)}/M_{H_3}$. Here the cubic part of the superpotential contains the interaction of the quarks and leptons with Higgs, the quadratic part is given by $W^{(2)} = \mu_0 H_2 H_1$ where H_1 (H_2) give masses to the down (up) quarks, and the part quartic in the fields contains baryon number violating interactions which lead to proton decay [9,10]. Additionally there is a universal gaugino mass term $m_{1/2}\lambda\lambda$. There are 7 parameters occurring in the theory at this stage. These are $m_0, m_{1/2}, A_0, B_0; \mu_0; \alpha_G, M_G$ and the sign of μ. In eq. 2, M_G is the GUT scale and α_G is the GUT coupling constant. Another aspect of supergravity grand unification is the remarkable phenomenon that electro-weak symmetry breaking can be induced by supersymmetry breaking [1]. The most attractive mechanism for accomplishing this is via renormalization group effects [11]. Here one uses the renormalization group equations to evolve the gauge and Yukawa couplings, and the soft SUSY breaking parameters down to the electro-weak scale. Under the assumption that the color and charge conservation hold, the low energy potential then involves only the VEVS of the two

* Permanent address: Department of Physics, Northeastern University, Boston, MA 02115, USA

Higgs fields. The effects of one loop corrections to the effective potential are important and should be taken into account [12]. After breaking of the electro-weak symmetry one can determine μ_0 by fixing the mass of the Z-boson to its experimental value, and one can also eliminate B_0 in terms of $\tan\beta$. Furthermore α_G and M_G can be determined using the high precision LEP data on α_1, α_2 and α_3. Using these determinations the parameters reduce to the following 4 parameters $m_0, m_{1/2}, A_t, \tan\beta$ and the sign of μ, where A_t is the value of A_0 at the electro-weak scale. There are 32 light supersymmetric states below the GUT scale. These consist of 12 squarks, 9 sleptons, 1 gluino, 2 charginos, 4 neutralinos, 2 CP even neutral Higgs one CP odd neutral Higgs and a charged Higgs. Masses of these 32 particles can be determined in terms of 4 parameters. Thus supergravity grand unification makes 28 predictions. The above situation is to contrasted for globally supersymmetric grand unification [13,14]. In these theories there is no phenomenologically viable way of breaking supersymmetry and one resorts to breaking supersymmetry by hand consistent with the condition that they maintain the ultraviolet properties of the theory [15]. However, for SU(5) theory one can add up to 57 arbitrary parameters to the theory.

In addition to the color and charge conservation the supergravity grand unification analysis imposes several other constraints. Thus the lower limits of the mass spectra are bounded by experiment at CDF, DØ and LEP, and the upper limits are bounded by naturalness which we assume to be $m_0, m_{\tilde{g}} \leq 1$ TeV. An important aspect of the analysis in the appearance of scaling among the mass spectra over a significant part of the parameter space [4]. Specifically one finds that the neutralino, chargino and gluino masses obey the following approximate scaling relations.

$$
\begin{aligned}
2m_{\widetilde{Z}_1} &\simeq m_{\widetilde{W}_1} \simeq m_{\widetilde{W}_2} \\
m_{\widetilde{Z}_3} &\simeq m_{\widetilde{Z}_4} \simeq m_{\widetilde{W}_2} \simeq |\mu|, \\
m_{\widetilde{W}_1} &\simeq \tfrac{1}{4}m_{\tilde{g}} \quad (\mu > 0), \\
m_{\widetilde{W}_1} &\simeq \tfrac{1}{3}m_{\tilde{g}} \quad (\mu < 0).
\end{aligned}
$$

Similarly the heavier three of the four Higgs obey the following relation: $m_{H^+} \simeq m_{H^0} \simeq m_A$ while the lightest Higgs obeys the relation $m_{h^0} \leq 130$ GeV. Proton stability also imposes strong constraints on supergravity GUT models. Specifically supergravity models which have an SU(5) GUT group, or the GUT group has an SU(5) embedding, generate dimension 5 operators via exchange of Higgs triplet fields, which contain baryon number violation. These dimension 5 operators when dressed by chargino, gluino and neutralino exchanges generate dimension 6 operators which lead to proton decay. A large number of decay modes result such as [9,10] $\bar{\nu}_i K^+, \bar{\nu}_i\pi^+, \mu^+ K^0$ etc. Of these $\bar{\nu}_i K^+$ are the

most dominant. The current experimental limit on this decay mode is $\tau(p \to \bar{\nu}K) > 10^{32}$ yr [16]. It is found that there is a significant region of the parameter space consistent with this experimental limit [4,10].

An interesting aspect of supergravity unified models is that the lightest neutralino is also the lightest supersymmetric particle over much of the parameter space. Recently an accurate method has been developed to compute the neutralino relic density [17,18], and it is found that supergravity grand unification is consistent with the COBE data, and makes interesting predictions for the detection of neutralinos in dark matter detectors [19]. Another important constraint on supergravity grand unification arises due to the inclusive decay $b \to s\gamma$. The first measurement of this decay has been reported at this conference. The experimental limits put stringent constraints on the parameter space, on dark matter analyses and on the event rate in dark matter analyses [20]. A promising consequence of the above analyses is that a part of the parameter space is sensitive to detectors with current sensitivities even when all the constraints are included [19,20].

In summary supergravity grand unification is currently the only superunified model which includes spontaneous breaking of supersymmetry, allows for unification of gauge couplings consistent with precision LEP data, and is consistent with proton stability and dark matter constraints. The model makes many predictions which would be accessible at future accelerator and proton stability experiments.

References

[1] A. H. Chamseddine, R. Arnowitt and P. Nath, Phys. Rev. Lett. 29 (1982) 970.

[2] For a review see P. Nath, R. Arnowitt and A. H. Chamseddine, "Applied N=1 Supergravity." World Scientific Singapore (1984); H. P. Nilles, Phys. Rep. 110 (1984) 1.

[3] P. Langacker, Proc. PASCOS90-Symposium, Eds. P. Nath and S. Reucroft (World Scientifc, Singapore 1990); J. Ellis, S. Kelley and D. V. Nanopoulos, Phys. Lett. 249B (1990) 441; B260 (1991) 131; U. Amaldi, W. de Boer and H. Furstenau, Phys. Lett. 260B (1991) 447.

[4] R. Arnowitt and P. Nath, Phys. Rev. Lett. 69 (1992) 725; P. Nath and R. Arnowitt, Phys. Lett. B289 (1992) 368.

[5] G. Ross and R. Roberts, N. P. B377 (1992)971; M. Drees and M. Nojiri, Nucl. Phys. B369, (1992) 54; S. Kelley et al, Phys. Lett. B272 (1991) 423; K. Inoue et al, Phys. Rev. D45 (1992) 387; M. Olechowski and S. Pokorski, Nucl. Phys. B404 (1993) 590; M. Carena, et al N. P. B406 (1993) 59; G. Kane et al, UM-TH-94-03 (94); W. deBoer et al, IEKP-KA/93/12(93); D. Castano et al, UFIFT-HEP-93-18 (93); V. Barger et al, Phys. Rev. D49 (1994) 4908.

[6] For an overview see P. Nath and R. Arnowitt, in "From Superstrings to the Real Superworld", World Scientific, Singapore (1992), edited by A. Zichichi; R. Arnowitt and P. Nath, Swieca Summer School Lectures, Campos do Jordao, Brazil (1993), World Scientific, Singapore; J. Lopez, D. Nanopoulos and A. Zichichi, hep-ph/9402299.

[7] L Hall, J. Lykken and S. Weinberg, Phys. Rev. D22 (1983) 2359.

[8] P. Nath, R. Arnowitt and A. H. Chamseddine, Nucl. Phys. B227 (1983) 121; S. Soni and A. Weldon, Phys. Lett. B216 (1983) 215.

[9] S. Weinberg, Phys. Rev. D26 (1982) 287; N. Sakai and T. Yanagida, Nucl. Phys. B197 (1982) 533; S. Dimopoulos, S. Raby and F. Wilczek, Phys. Lett. 112B (1982) 133; J. Ellis, D. V. Nanopoulos and S. Rudaz, Nucl. Phys. B202 (1982) 43.

[10] R. Arnowitt, A. H. Chamseddine, and P. Nath, Phys. Lett. 156B (1985) 215: P. Nath, R. Arnowitt and A. H. Chamseddine, Phys. Rev. 32D (1985) 2348; R. Arnowitt and P. Nath, Phys. Rev. 49D (1994) 1479: J. Hisano, H. Murayama and T. Yanagida, Nucl. Phys. B402 (1993) 46.

[11] K. Inoue et. al. , Prog. Theor. Phys. 68 (1982) 927; C. Ibanez and G. G. Ross Phys. Lett. B110 (1982) 227; J. Ellis et. a l. , Phys. Lett. 125B (1983) 275: L. Alvarez-Gaume et. al. , Nucl. Phys. B250 (1983) 495.

[12] G. Gamberini, G. Ridolfi and F. Zwirner, Nucl. Phys. B331 (1990) 331; R. Arnowitt and P. Nath, Phys. Rev. B46 (1992) 3981.

[13] E. Witten, Phys. Lett. 105B (1981) 267.

[14] S. Dimopoulos and H. Georgi, Phys. Lett. 117B (1982) 287; N. Sakai, Zeit. Phys. C11 (1981).

[15] L. Girardello and M. T. Grisaru, NP B194, (1982) 65.

[16] R. Becker-Szendy et. al. Phys. Rev. D47 (1993) 4028.

[17] R. Arnowitt and P. Nath, Phys. Lett. B299 (1993) 58; E. ibid B303 (1993) 403.

[18] P. Nath and R. Arnowitt, Phys. Rev. Lettl 70 (1993) 3696.

[19] See P. Nath and R. Arnowitt, Talk in Parallel Session 12-a at this Conf. ; R. Arnowitt and P. Nath, CERN TH. 7362/94; CTP-TAMU-37/94; NUB-TH7362/94.

[20] See P. Nath and R. Arnowitt, Talk in Parallel Session 21-a at this conf. ; P. Nath and R. Arnowitt, CERN TH. 7363/94; NUB-TH. 3099/94; CTP-TAMU-38/94.

Paper presented at XXVII Int. Conf. on High Energy Physics: Session Pa-4
Glasgow, UK, 20–27 July 1994

Supersymmetry at LEPII, the Tevatron, and Future Accelerators

J. F. Gunion[†‡]

† Davis Institute for High Energy Physics,
Department of Physics, University of California at Davis, Davis CA 95616, U.S.A.

Abstract

I present a brief review of prospects for discovering supersymmetry, focusing primarily on the Tevatron and LEPII, but commenting on the LHC and a next linear e^+e^- collider. Special emphasis is given to expectations in the context of models with GUT boundary conditions motivated by Supergravity and Superstrings. An overview of related conference contributions is given.

1. Introduction

The success of gauge coupling unification in the context of the Minimal Supersymmetric Model (MSSM) lends considerable credence not only to the possibility that this extension of the Standard Model is correct, but also to the idea that the boundary conditions for all the soft-supersymmetry-breaking parameters at the unification scale could be relatively simple and universal. Supergravity and superstring theory each provide particularly attractive and well-motivated examples of such boundary conditions. These, and their phenomenological implications, especially for the Tevatron and LEPII, are briefly reviewed, with emphasis on the very real possibility that supersymmetry could be discovered at these two (highly complementary) accelerators. My discussion will be based on the study of Ref. [1]. References to the many related studies are given therein; in particular, see Ref. [2].

The four basic parameters of supersymmetry breaking are: a) the gaugino masses M_a (where a labels the group); b) the scalar masses m_i (where i labels the various scalars, e.g. Higgs, sleptons, squarks); c) the soft Yukawa coefficients A_{ijk}; and d) the B parameter which specifies the soft mixing term between the two Higgs scalar fields. The supersymmetry-breaking schemes considered here will be: i) 'no-scale' or

‡ Work supported, in part, by U.S. DOE.

minimal supergravity (labelled by MS) and ii) dilaton-like superstring (labelled by D). Predictions in these models for the B parameter are rather uncertain, and so we shall leave it a free parameter. In the MS models the only other source of supersymmetry breaking is via the gaugino masses M_a, which are taken to have a universal value $M_a \equiv M^0$ at M_U; the m_i^0 and A_{ijk}^0 are taken to be zero. In the D models the M_a, m_i and A_{ijk} parameters all take on universal values at M_U related by:

$$M^0 = -A^0 = \sqrt{3}m^0. \qquad (1)$$

These latter dilaton-like boundary conditions are certainly those appropriate when supersymmetry breaking is dominated by the dilaton field in string theory, but also apply for a remarkably broad class of models (including Calabi-Yau compactifications, and orbifold models in which the MSSM fields all belong to the untwisted sector) so long as the moduli fields do not play a dominant role in supersymmetry breaking. For a brief review and detailed references, see Ref. [1].

Given either choice of boundary conditions, if the top quark mass is fixed (we shall quote results for $m_t(m_t) = 170\,\mathrm{GeV}$, corresponding to a pole mass of about 178 GeV) only two free parameters and a sign remain undetermined after minimizing the potential. The two parameters can be taken to be $\tan\beta$, the ratio of the neutral Higgs field vacuum expectation values, and $m_{\tilde{g}}$, the gluino mass. The parameter

B is determined in terms of these, as are all other superpotential parameters, including the magnitude of the Higgs superfield mixing parameter μ. However, the sign of μ is not determined. Four models result — MS^+, MS^-, D^+, D^-, the superscript indicating the sign of μ — the phenomenology of which can be explored in the two dimensional $m_{\tilde{g}}$–$\tan\beta$ parameter space.

The discussion so far has obscured one fundamental problem facing the gauge coupling unification success: namely, the scale M_U at which the couplings naturally unify is $\sim 2 \times 10^{16}\,\mathrm{GeV}$, i.e. much less than the natural scale for supergravity and string unification of $M_S \sim 10^{18}\,\mathrm{GeV}$. A variety of excuses for this have been discussed. In Ref. [1] two extreme approaches are adopted: i) ignore the difference — a fuller understanding of the feed-down of SUSY breaking from the full supergravity or superstring theory could resolve the discrepancy; ii) assume that the unification at M_U is only apparent (i.e. accidental) and introduce a minimal set of additional matter fields at high scale with masses chosen precisely so as to give coupling unification at M_S. I will not go into details regarding these extra fields; a discussion and references can be found in Ref. [1]. The models with such extra fields will be termed the 'string-scale-unified' versions of the previously listed models, and will be denoted by SMS^+, SMS^-, SD^+, and SD^-.

2. Phenomenology

To systematically investigate the resulting 8 models, we first establish the allowed region of $m_{\tilde{g}}$–$\tan\beta$ parameter space for each subject to: a) all predicted SUSY partner particles (including the light Higgs h^0) are unobservable; b) the lightest SUSY particle is either the lightest neutralino $\tilde{\chi}_1^0$ (as is always the case for the allowed parameter space of the models explored here) or the sneutrino $\tilde{\nu}$; c) the top quark Yukawa remains perturbative at all scales from m_W up to M_U or M_S; d) proper electroweak symmetry breaking and a global minimum are obtained. We do not impose $b \to s\gamma$, relic abundance, or proton decay constraints, as these all have considerable uncertainties and/or require additional model-dependent input. We also do not require exact $b - \tau$ Yukawa unification. Figure 1 shows the D and SD parameter space boundaries; SMS results are similar. The lower $m_{\tilde{g}}$ limit is set either by $m_{\tilde{l}_R} < m_Z/2$ or $m_{\tilde{\chi}_1^+} < m_Z/2$. The upper limit on $\tan\beta$ results from requiring that the lighter $\tilde{\tau}$ eigenstate not be the LSP. The lower limit on $\tan\beta$ results from the requirement that λ_t remain perturbative at all RGE scales. In the D, SD, and SMS models there is no upper limit on $m_{\tilde{g}}$ (but $m_{\tilde{g}} \lesssim 700\,\mathrm{GeV}$ for MS models), although standard considerations of naturalness and

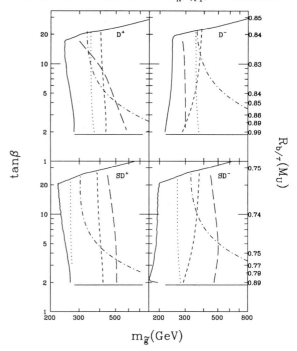

Figure 1. Parameter space boundaries and discovery contour limits for the D and SD models. LEPII discovery limits for $\tilde{l}_R\tilde{l}_R$, $\tilde{\chi}_1^+\tilde{\chi}_1^-$, Zh^0 are the dotted, short-dash, and dot-dash curves, respectively; Tevatron 'SS plus 3ℓ' discovery limits are the long-dash curves.

accurate gauge coupling unification both suggest that $m_{\tilde{g}} \lesssim 1\,\mathrm{TeV}$. Note that the deviations from exact $b - \tau$ unification, $R_{b/\tau} \equiv \lambda_b/\lambda_\tau = 1$ (see the right-hand axis of the figure), are at most 25%.

Within the allowed parameter spaces shown, the masses of the SUSY particles scale with $m_{\tilde{g}}$; variation of the masses with $\tan\beta$ at fixed $m_{\tilde{g}}$ is relatively limited for $m_{\tilde{g}}$ values above about 500 to 600 GeV, where one finds $m_{\tilde{\chi}_1^0} < m_{\tilde{l}_R}, m_{\tilde{\chi}_1^+}, m_{\tilde{\chi}_2^0} < m_{\tilde{\nu}} < m_{\tilde{l}_L}$, with $\tilde{l}_R, \tilde{\chi}_1^+, \tilde{\chi}_2^0, \tilde{\nu}, \tilde{l}_L$ clustering between 0.2 to 0.4 times $m_{\tilde{g}}$. First and second generation squark masses are of order $m_{\tilde{g}}$, while the lighter stop is substantially lighter, roughly $m_{\tilde{t}_1} \sim 0.7 m_{\tilde{g}}$. It is the restricted size of the soft scalar mass parameter, m^0, relative to M^0 that causes the sleptons to be rather light in both the minimal-supergravity and dilaton-like models. Indeed, slepton masses are largely generated by renormalization-group evolution from the M^0 gaugino seed value at M_U; only the squarks acquire masses comparable to $m_{\tilde{g}}$, as a result of the driving terms proportional to α_s in the RGE's.

Despite these broad similarities of all the models, there are important details that vary as a function of model, $\tan\beta$ and $m_{\tilde{g}}$. The most important issue for Tevatron phenomenology is whether $\widetilde{\chi}_2^0 \to \nu\widetilde{\nu}$ and $\widetilde{\chi}_1^+ \to \ell^+\widetilde{\nu}$ are kinematically allowed or not. When allowed, the $\widetilde{\nu}$ decays invisibly, $\widetilde{\chi}_2^0$ decays are dominated by the *invisible* $\nu\widetilde{\nu}$ channel (especially for $\mu < 0$), and the ℓ in $\widetilde{\chi}_1^+$ decays is relatively soft. When the $\widetilde{\chi}_2^0$ decays invisibly and the ℓ from $\widetilde{\chi}_1^+$ is soft, SUSY detection at the Tevatron becomes difficult. Note that it is the low scalar slepton and sneutrino masses predicted in the $m^0 < M^0$ models considered here that allow a delicate variation as to which channels are allowed.

LEPII is less sensitive to this kind of detail since it will generally discover anything for which adequate energy is available. The fairly similar mass scales for sleptons and charginos as a function of $m_{\widetilde{g}}$–$\tan\beta$ in the various models imply similar discovery limits for the models at LEPII. To specify the actual discovery boundaries in parameter space we assume $\sqrt{s} = 200\,\text{GeV}$, with integrated luminosity of $L = 500\,\text{pb}^{-1}$. In this case one can observe $\widetilde{l}_R\widetilde{l}_R$, $\widetilde{\chi}_1^+\widetilde{\chi}_1^-$ pair production for $m_{\widetilde{l}_R}, m_{\widetilde{\chi}_1^+} < 95\,\text{GeV}$. The resulting discovery limits are indicated by the dotted and short-dashed lines in Figure 1. Note the large equivalent $m_{\widetilde{g}}$ values probed, $\sim 300-400\,\text{GeV}$. Further, Zh^0 production can be observed for $m_{h^0} \lesssim 105\,\text{GeV}$, i.e. the portion of parameter space to the left of the dot-dashed line.

To explore the Tevatron discovery limit, we employed ISASUSY [3] to generate all types of SUSY production processes, including complete decay chains. Events were generated for a series of $m_{\widetilde{g}}$–$\tan\beta$ choices within the allowed parameter domain for each model. At Tevatron energies $\widetilde{\chi}\widetilde{\chi}$ production, including especially $\widetilde{\chi}_2^0\widetilde{\chi}_1^\pm$, has the largest rate. Next in importance are $\widetilde{l}\widetilde{l}, \widetilde{l}\widetilde{\nu}, \widetilde{\nu}\widetilde{\nu}, \widetilde{g}\widetilde{\chi}$ and $\widetilde{q}\widetilde{\chi}$, as well as $\widetilde{t}_1\widetilde{t}_1$, with $\widetilde{g}\widetilde{g}, \widetilde{g}\widetilde{q}, \widetilde{q}\widetilde{q}$ processes being relatively small (due to the large $\widetilde{g}$ and $\widetilde{q}$ masses compared to the Tevatron energy).

We then imposed cuts appropriate to looking for a variety of different types of signals. After examining backgrounds for these same cuts, we found that for $L = 1\,\text{fb}$ only three types of signal were useful: i) the missing energy ($\not{E}_T$) signal; ii) the same-sign (SS) dilepton signal; and iii) the tri-lepton (3ℓ) signal. More or less independent of model, the $\not{E}_T$ signal will allow SUSY detection out to about $m_{\widetilde{g}} = 300\,\text{GeV}$. The missing energy signal has significant contributions from many types of production processes, including, in particular, $\widetilde{\chi}_2^0\widetilde{\chi}_1^\pm$ (where one of the leptons is missed or soft) and $\widetilde{g}\widetilde{\chi}, \widetilde{q}\widetilde{\chi} - \widetilde{g}\widetilde{g}, \widetilde{q}\widetilde{g}, \widetilde{q}\widetilde{q}$ sources contribute at a lesser rate. The discovery boundaries arising from combining the SS and 3ℓ signals (both of which are essentially background-free for our cuts — we require 5 or more events in one or the other) are shown by the long-dash curves in Figure 1. Only in the D^- case is the coverage of parameter space as limited ($m_{\widetilde{g}} \lesssim 300\,\text{GeV}$) as for the $\not{E}_T$ signal; in the

D^+, SD^+ and SD^- cases the $SS + 3\ell$ signal probes out to $m_{\widetilde{g}} \lesssim 500\,\text{GeV}$. As discussed earlier, this difference is due to the dominance of the invisible $\nu\widetilde{\nu}$ decay mode of the the $\widetilde{\chi}_2^0$ for the D^- case. In the D^+, SD^+ and SD^- cases, the $\widetilde{\nu}$ is sufficiently heavy that $\widetilde{\chi}_2^0 \to \nu\widetilde{\nu}$ decays are kinematically forbidden, implying significant 3-body decays to leptons for the $\widetilde{\chi}_2^0$ and $\widetilde{\chi}_1^\pm$.

Experimentally, in models with light sleptons the signature for $\not{E}_T$, SS, or 3ℓ events from $\widetilde{\chi}_2^0\widetilde{\chi}_1^\pm$ production is a small number of associated jets. Indeed, events with few or no jets is the most characteristic feature of models in which the m^0 parameter is smaller than M^0. If sleptons and sneutrinos are heavy due to a large value for m^0, then the final states resulting from the crucial $\widetilde{\chi}_2^0\widetilde{\chi}_1^\pm$ process will contain three leptons only part of the time. The smaller number of purely leptonic final state events means that the SS and 3ℓ signals generally cannot probe much beyond $m_{\widetilde{g}} \sim 300\,\text{GeV}$. For a review of such scenarios see Ref. [4].

Finally, we note that Figure 1 delineates fairly clearly the role of the LHC and a next linear e^+e^- collider (NLC) for exploration of supersymmetry with minimal-supergravity or dilaton-like boundary conditions. For gluino masses below $m_{\widetilde{g}} \sim 500\,\text{GeV}$, discovery of supersymmetry at LEPII and/or the Tevatron would be quite likely, but event rates could be very low. The gluino and heavier squarks would be likely to escape detection unless $m_{\widetilde{g}}$ is substantially below 500 GeV. At the LHC the $\widetilde{g}$ and $\widetilde{q}$'s would be produced at high rates, allowing detailed studies of their properties, including cascade decays. An NLC with $\sqrt{s} \geq 500\,\text{GeV}$ would be an extremely valuable complement, allowing precise determination of the masses and decays of the inos appearing in the $\widetilde{g}, \widetilde{q}$ cascade decays. For $m_{\widetilde{g}}$ much beyond 500 GeV, discovery of supersymmetry at LEPII or the Tevatron will not be possible (except for the h^0 which might be light enough to be observed if $\tan\beta$ is small). However, observation of the gluino and squarks up to $m_{\widetilde{g}} \sim 1-1.5\,\text{TeV}$ should be straightforward at the LHC, and the $\widetilde{\chi}_2^0, \widetilde{\chi}_1^\pm, \widetilde{l}_R, \widetilde{l}_L$ (with masses of order 1/4 to 2/5 of $m_{\widetilde{g}}$) can be easily discovered and studied at an NLC with $\sqrt{s}$ in the 500 GeV to 1 TeV range. Overall, the minimal-supergravity and dilaton-like boundary conditions imply a very real possibility of discovering supersymmetry at LEPII and/or the Tevatron, and would certainly guarantee exciting prospects for the future at LHC and an NLC.

3. Other Recent Work

The above establishes a basic phenomenological framework for discussing SUSY detection. Of course, there were many contributions to the conference relevant to this topic. I give a brief overview; the reader should consult the papers for details.

First, of course, are the steadily improving limits on the production of SUSY particles at LEP. These eliminate portions of the supersymmetric parameter space, providing important constraints on model building. Especially important are constraints deriving from non-observation of $\widetilde{\chi}\widetilde{\chi}$ decays of the Z [5], which provide critical restrictions on the allowed domain in the μ–$m_{\widetilde{g}}$ parameter space in the context of the MSSM.

Additional constraints that could be included in restricting the allowed parameter space of a given model are those coming from $B - \overline{B}$ and $K - \overline{K}$ mixing. If $m_{H^{\pm}}$, $m_{\widetilde{t}_1}$, and/or $m_{\widetilde{\chi}_1^{\pm}}$ are small and $\tan\beta$ is small, then Ref. [6] shows that the associated new loop-diagram contributions are such that consistency with the well-established mixing results is not guaranteed, and such constraints should be included. Unfortunately, sensitivity to the additional loop diagrams diminishes rapidly for $\tan\beta$ values above 2.

The impact of an invisibly decaying $\widetilde{\nu}$ and (possibly) $\widetilde{\chi}_2^0$ upon SUSY detection (emphasized above), was also examined for LEP200 and the Tevatron in Ref. [7].

In models with $m^0 > M^0$, or if we ignore the unification context altogether, then one cannot entirely rule out the possibility that the gluino is very light [8]. As pointed out in Ref. [9] (see also references therein), a light gluino can reconcile the apparent difference between $\alpha_s(m_Z)$ as extrapolated from deep inelastic scattering data (which yields a value of about 0.108 in the absence of a light gluino), and the $\alpha_s(m_Z) = 0.122$ value extracted from LEP data.

Detection of the SUSY Higgs bosons is a critical issue. Currently, there are recent limits from LEP [10]. In the near future, we have seen that Higgs detection in the Zh^0 mode at LEPII can provide an important discovery channel for SUSY. SUSY Higgs detection at hadron colliders is substantially more difficult. New modes for Higgs discovery at the Tevatron and LHC have been explored during the course of the last year [11]. Techniques were developed for: a) detection of an invisibly decaying h^0 in Wh^0 and $t\bar{t}h^0$ associated production [12]; and b) using b-tagging to detect the h^0, H^0 and/or A^0 in their primary $b\bar{b}$ decay modes via $W\,Higgs$, $t\bar{t}\,Higgs$ and $b\bar{b}\,Higgs$ associated production [13]. The results of these studies are easily summarized. The most promising mode at the Tevatron is Wh^0 associated production with b-tagging. However, for integrated luminosity of 10 fb^{-1} or less, the Tevatron will at best probe m_{h^0} values up to the LEPII discovery limits. In contrast, at the LHC the b-tagging detection modes could ensure that at least one of the SUSY Higgs bosons will be found, in principle closing the famous hole [11] in parameter space where no SUSY Higgs would

be found at the LHC employing the standard $\gamma\gamma$ (or $\ell\gamma\gamma$) and 4ℓ final states. However, for these modes to be viable, it is necessary that b-tagging be about 40% efficient and 99% pure (*i.e.* no more than 1% mis-tagging probability for light quark and gluon jets). It is not yet clear that the required efficiency and (especially) purity can be achieved in the high luminosity, multiple-interaction LHC environment.

With regard to specific models, we note that the supergravity/superstring models discussed earlier [1] all predict relatively large masses (generally $\gtrsim 200$ GeV) for the H^0, A^0 and $H^{\pm}$. The lighter h^0 is predicted to have mass below about 115 GeV and relatively SM-like couplings. Figure 1 shows that for much of parameter space, the h^0 would be observable at LEPII with $\sqrt{s} = 200$ GeV; and it is *guaranteed* to be found at LEPII or an NLC with $\sqrt{s} \gtrsim 230 - 250$ GeV. Observation of the h^0 at the LHC would also be possible. In contrast, the heavier H^0, A^0 and $H^{\pm}$ might escape observation. At a hadron collider, their decays to ino-pair and slepton-pair final states are important and dilute normal detection modes, while the SUSY decay modes are not easily employed in their own right. The ability of a linear e^+e^- collider to observe A^0H^0 and H^+H^- pair production (the only viable discovery modes when the $H^0, A^0, H^{\pm}$ are heavy) is restricted by machine energy. For $\sqrt{s} = 500$ GeV, discovery would only be possible for masses below about 220-230 GeV. Thus, there is a significant chance that these heavier MSSM Higgs bosons would also not be seen in the first years of operation of the NLC (i.e. prior to upgrading the NLC energy to ~ 1 TeV).

Regarding the charged Higgs, the CDF group has searched for $t \rightarrow H^+b$ decays in $t\bar{t}$ events in dilepton final states. In the context of a two-Higgs-doublet model they exclude $m_{H^+} \lesssim m_t - m_b$ for $m_t \lesssim 105$ GeV and large $\tan\beta$ values [15]. Of course, if $m_t \sim 170$ GeV this analysis does not restrict m_{H^+}.

In considering H^+ detection at either hadron or e^+e^- colliders, one cannot ignore the possibility that $H^+ \rightarrow \widetilde{t}\,\widetilde{b}$ decays could dominate if allowed [14], yielding much more complicated final state signatures.

Extensions of the MSSM to include an additional singlet Higgs field continue to be of interest. In one contribution to this conference [16], it is demonstrated that the lightest Higgs (S_1) in this 'NMSSM' model must have $m_{S_1} \leq 156$ GeV. In related work, it was shown that the S_1 or the next lightest S_2 is guaranteed to be observable at an NLC (with $\sqrt{s} \geq 300$ GeV), via $ZS_{1,2}$ production, provided the theory remains perturbative at all scales during RGE evolution [17].

Of course, the supersymmetric extension of the SM may not turn out to be that of the minimal model. If there is unifying group larger than $SU(5)$, such as E_6 or a $L - R$ symmetric group, then one must reassess the impact of the additional SUSY particles on the RGE coupling unification and radiative electroweak symmetry breaking. Assuming that this program is successful, many new effects and signals for SUSY could arise in such models. For example, in one contribution [18] it is demonstrated that virtual effects from E_6 model interactions could give rise to $\tau \to eee$ and $Z \to e\tau$ decays at an observable level. In $L - R$ models [19], the doubly-charged Higgsino ($\widetilde{\Delta}^{++}$) not only enhances slepton pair production in e^+e^- collisions via virtual u-channel exchange diagrams, but also would provide a number of unusual and clean signals when produced directly in e^+e^-, e^-e^-, $e^-\gamma$, and $\gamma\gamma$ collisions.

If R-parity violation is present in the supersymmetric theory, then detection phenomenology undergoes considerable change. Early work [20] pointing out the importance of leptonic signatures (as opposed to missing energy signatures) has recently been extended in Ref. [21] to show that these leptonic signatures could be spectacular if the *only* source of R-parity violation is a superpotential term of the type $W \ni L_i L_j E_k$, where the L and E superfields are those for the lepton doublets and singlets, respectively. In this case, the LSP $\widetilde{\chi}_1^0$ decays entirely to visible leptons, and the importance of leptonic signatures is apparent.

Finally I mention the results of Ref. [22] in which the possibility of including a fourth generation in the standard MSSM context is considered. The result is that this remains a possibility without violating perturbative limits on *any* of the Yukawa couplings, including those associated with the fourth generation, but only if exact $b-\tau$ Yukawa unification is not required. The allowed t' and b' masses will be accessible with increased luminosity at the Tevatron. For $m_t \gtrsim 160\,\text{GeV}$, the ν' and τ' masses are such that these new leptons would certainly be observed at LEPII.

4. Conclusions

Overall, we see that the Tevatron with $L = 1\,\text{fb}^{-1}$ and LEPII with $\sqrt{s} = 200\,\text{GeV}$ and $L = 500\,\text{pb}^{-1}$ would be relatively complementary in searching for SUSY in the minimal-supergravity and dilaton-like superstring/supergravity-motivated MSSM models outlined earlier. Experimentalists should be encouraged by the relatively large values of the $m_{\widetilde{g}}$ parameter that can be explored by combining these two machines. If these kinds of models are correct, we may not have to wait until the LHC and/or an NLC to find the first signal for SUSY.

New modes for Higgs detection at hadron colliders have been developed, and, at the LHC, show considerable promise for providing a true guarantee that at least one of the MSSM Higgs bosons will be detectable. In this regard, b-tagging at the LHC could prove crucial, and deserves maximal effort on the part of the LHC detector collaborations.

Finally, supersymmetric models with extended gauge groups, R-parity violation, or a fourth generation all provide interesting new phenomena and experimental signatures, many of which could prove to be of particular interest at Tevatron energies.

References

[1] H. Baer, J.F. Gunion, C. Kao, H. Pois, preprint UCD-94-19.
[2] See, for example, J. Lopez, D. Nanopoulos and A. Zichichi, CTP-TAMU-80/93, and T. Kamon, J. Lopez, P. McIntyre, and J.T. White, CTP-TAMU-19/94, and references therein.
[3] F. Paige and S. Protopopescu, in *Supercollider Physics*, p. 41, ed. D. Soper (World Scientific, 1986); H. Baer, F. Paige, S. Protopopescu and X. Tata, in *Proceedings of the Workshop on Physics at Current Accelerators and Supercollliders*, eds. J. Hewett, A. White and D. Zeppenfeld, (Argonne National Laboratory, 1993).
[4] See, for example, H. Baer, M. Drees, C. Kao, M. Nojiri and X. Tata, FSU-HEP-940311, and references therein.
[5] For example, see the L3 contribution GLS-0625.
[6] G. Branco, G. Cho, Y. Kizukuri, N. Oshimo, contribution GLS-0914, CERN-TH.7345/94.
[7] A. Datta, M. Guchhait and S. Chakravarti, contribution GLS-0713; A. Datta, M. Guchhait and M. Drees, contribution GLS-0712.
[8] See G. Farrar, preprint RU-94-35, and references therein.
[9] J. Blumlein and J. Botts, contribution GLS-0896, and references therein.
[10] See the talk by A. Sopczak, and contribution GLS-0636 from the L3 collaboration.
[11] For a recent review and references, see J.F. Gunion, UCD-94-24, to appear in Proceedings of the Zeuthen Workshop on Elementary Particle Theory — *LEP200 and Beyond*, Teupitz, Germany, April (1994), eds. T. Riemann and J. Blumlein.
[12] J.F. Gunion, Phys. Rev. Lett. **72** (1994) 199; S. Frederiksen, N. Johnson, G. Kane and J. Reid, preprint SSCL-577; D. Choudhury and D.P. Roy, Phys. Lett. **B322** (1994) 368.
[13] J. Dai, J.F. Gunion and R. Vega, Phys. Rev. Lett. **71** (1993) 2699, Phys. Lett. **B315** (1993) 355, and preprint UCD-94-7; A. Stange, W. Marciano and S. Willenbrock, Phys. Rev. **D49** (1994) 1354, and preprint ILL-TH-94-8.
[14] A. Bartl, K. Hidaka, Y. Kizukuri, T. Kon, W. Majerotto, Phys. Lett. **B315** (1993) 360, contribution GLS-0779.
[15] CDF Collaboration, contributed paper GLS-0417, CDF/ANAL/EXOTIC/2571.
[16] B.R. Kim and S.K. Oh, contributed paper GLS-0365.
[17] B.R. Kim, S.K. Oh and A. Stephan, Proceedings of *Physics and Experiments with Linear e^+e^- Colliders*, eds. F. Harris, S. Olsen, S. Pakvasa and X. Tata, Hawaii, April (1993), p. 860; J. Kamoshita, Y. Okada and M. Tanaka, Phys. Lett. **B328** (1994) 67.
[18] A. Pilaftsis, contribution GLS-0766.
[19] K. Huitu, J. Maalampi, M. Raidal, contribution GLS-0752.
[20] P. Binetruy and J.F. Gunion, INFN Eloisatron Project Working Group Report, ed. A. Ali, Ettore Majorana, Erice-Trapani (1988) p. 64; H. Dreiner and G. Ross, Nucl. Phys. **B365** (1991) 597.
[21] V. Barger, M.S. Berger, P. Ohman, R.J.N. Phillips, contributed paper GLS-0400, MAD/PH/831.
[22] J.F. Gunion, D. McKay, and H. Pois, contribution GLS-0371, preprint UCD-94-25.

Paper presented at XXVII Int. Conf. on High Energy Physics: Session Pa-4
Glasgow, UK, 20–27 July 1994

Quark and Lepton Mass and Mixing Angle Predictions

C. D. Froggatt

Department of Physics and Astronomy, University of Glasgow, Glasgow G12 8QQ, U.K.

Abstract

We review the different approaches to the fermion mass problem. We discuss infrared fixed point predictions, Yukawa unification for large $\tan\beta$, texture zeros and chiral flavour symmetries.

1. Introduction

The quark-lepton mass spectrum is rather peculiar. Neutrino masses are consistent with zero † and the charged fermion masses range over five orders of magnitude; from less than 1 Mev for the electron to over 100 Gev for the top quark. Here we consider the spectroscopy of quarks and charged leptons. The major qualitative features of this spectrum are:

- The large mass ratios of order 60 between fermions of a given electric charge, i. e. of the same family; the quark-lepton mass hierarchy.
- The similarity between the quark and charged lepton mass spectra; the three generation structure.
- The smallness of the quark mixing angles in the weak coupling matrix V_{CKM}; the quark mixing hierarchy.

These properties of the fermion spectrum provide our main experimental clues to the underlying flavour dynamics contained in the physics beyond the Standard Model (SM).

There are three main approaches to the quark-lepton mass problem:

1 Attempts to derive a fermion mass or mass relation exactly from some dynamical or theoretical principle; e. g. fermion masses as infrared fixed points of the renormalisation group equations.

2 Searches for relationships between mass and mixing angle parameters using symmetries and/or ansätze

† It is possible to generate Majorana mass terms by the so-called see-saw mechanism [1, 2] in extensions of the Standard Model

to make detailed fits to the data; e. g. the phenomenologically successful relation for the Cabibbo angle $\theta_c \simeq \sqrt{\frac{m_d}{m_s}}$ derived from mass matrix ansätze with texture zeros.

3 Attempts to naturally explain all the qualitative features of the fermion spectrum, fitting all the data within factors of order unity; e. g. mass protection by chiral gauge quantum numbers beyond the SM.

We shall now consider examples of mass and mixing angle predictions from each of these approaches.

2. The Top Quark Mass as a Fixed Point

It was pointed out some time ago [3] that the three generation fermion mass hierarchy does not develop naturally out of the general structure of the renormalisation group equations (RGE) for the Yukawa coupling constants as an infrared fixed point. However it was soon realised [4] that the top quark mass might correspond to a fixed point value of the SM RGE, predicting approximately $m_t \simeq 100$ Gev [4, 5]. In practice one finds that such an infrared fixed point behaviour of the running top quark Yukawa coupling constant $g_t(\mu)$ does not generically set in until $\mu < 1$ Gev, where the QCD coupling constant $g_3(\mu)$ varies rapidly. The scale relevant for the physical top quark mass prediction is of course $\mu = m_t$; at this scale $g_3(\mu)$ is slowly varying and there is an effective infrared stable quasifixed point behaviour giving a running top quark mass prediction $m_t(\mu = m_t) \simeq 225$ Gev [6].

More precisely the SM quasifixed point prediction for the top quark mass requires the following assumptions:

1 The desert hypothesis of no new interactions beyond those of the SM up to some high energy scale $\mu = M_X \simeq 10^{15} - 10^{19}$ Gev, e. g. the grand unification scale or the Planck scale.

2 The SM coupling constants remain positive and finite in the desert, such that perturbation theory and the RGE can be applied up to $\mu = M_X$.

3 The top quark Yukawa coupling constant is large at $\mu = M_X$:

$$1 \leq g_t(M_X) \leq \sqrt{4\pi} \qquad (1)$$

so that it enters the domain of attraction of the infrared quasifixed point.

The nonlinearity of the RGE then strongly focuses $g_t(\mu)$ at the electroweak scale to its quasifixed point value. The RGE for the Higgs self-coupling $\lambda(\mu)$ similarly focuses $\lambda(\mu)$ towards a quasifixed point value, leading to the SM fixed point predictions for the running top quark and Higgs masses:

$$m_t \simeq 225 \text{ Gev} \quad m_H \simeq 250 \text{ Gev} \qquad (2)$$

Unfortunately the prediction for the top quark mass is inconsistent with the LEP results [7] and the CDF measurement [8].

There are two interesting modifications to the fixed point top mass prediction in the Minimal Supersymmetric Standard Model (MSSM) with supersymmetry breaking at the electroweak scale or Tev scale:

- The introduction of the supersymmetric partners of the SM particles in the RGE for the Yukawa and gauge coupling constants leads to a 15% reduction in the fixed point value of $g_t(m_t)$ [9, 10].
- There are two Higgs doublets in the MSSM and the ratio of Higgs vacuum values, $\tan\beta = v_2/v_1$, is a free parameter; the top quark couples to v_2 and so m_t is proportional to $v_2 = (174 \text{ Gev}) \sin\beta$.

The MSSM fixed point prediction for the running top quark mass is [11]:

$$m_t(m_t) \simeq (190 \text{ Gev}) \sin\beta \qquad (3)$$

For large $\tan\beta$ it is possible to have a bottom quark Yukawa coupling satisfying $g_b(M_X) \geq 1$ which then approaches an infrared quasifixed point. Indeed with

$$\tan\beta \simeq m_t/m_b \simeq 50 \qquad (4)$$

we can trade the mystery of the top to bottom quark mass ratio for that of a hierarchy of vacuum expectation values, $v_2/v_1 \simeq m_t/m_b$, and have all the third generation Yukawa coupling constants large:

$$g_t(M_X) \geq 1 \quad g_b(M_X) \geq 1 \quad g_\tau(M_X) \geq 1 \qquad (5)$$

Then m_t, m_b and $R = m_b/m_\tau$ all approach fixed point values in agreement with experiment [12]. This large $\tan\beta$ scenario is consistent with the idea of Yukawa unification [13]:

$$g_t(M_X) = g_b(M_X) = g_\tau(M_X) = g_G \geq 1 \qquad (6)$$

as occurs in the supersymmetric grand unified (SUSY-GUT) SO(10) model with the two MSSM Higgs doublets in a single **10** irreducible representation. However it should be noted that the equality in Eq. (6) is not necessary. For example in SU(5) finite unified theories [14] the Yukawa couplings are related to the SUSY-GUT coupling constant and satisfy $g_t^2(M_X) = 4g_b^2(M_X)/3 = \mathcal{O}(1)$, giving the same fixed point predictions. In fact one does not need a symmetry assumption at all, since the weaker assumption of large third generation Yukawa couplings, Eq. (5), is sufficient for the fixed point dynamics to predict the running masses $m_t \simeq 180$ Gev, $m_b \simeq 4.1$ Gev and $m_\tau \simeq 1.8$ Gev in the large $\tan\beta$ scenario.

The origin of the large value of $\tan\beta$ is of course a puzzle, which must be solved before the large $\tan\beta$ scenario can be said to explain the large m_t/m_b ratio. It is possible to introduce approximate symmetries [15, 16] of the Higgs potential which ensure a hierarchy of vacuum expectation values (a Peccei-Quinn symmetry and a continuous $\mathcal{R}$ symmetry have been used). However these symmetries then result in a light chargino [17], in conflict with the LEP lower bound of order 45 Gev, unless the SUSY breaking scale M_{SUSY} is fine-tuned to be much larger than the electroweak scale: $M_{SUSY}^2 \geq \tan\beta M_Z^2$.

Also, in the large $\tan\beta$ scenario, SUSY radiative corrections to m_b are generically large: the bottom quark mass gets a contribution proportional to v_2 from one-loop gluino or charged Higgsino exchange diagrams, whereas its tree level mass is proportional to v_1. These loop diagrams give a fractional correction $\delta m_b/m_b$ to the bottom quark mass proportional to $\tan\beta$ and generically of order unity [16, 18]. The presence of the above-mentioned Peccei-Quinn and $\mathcal{R}$ symmetries would ensure a hierarchical SUSY spectrum, with the squarks and sleptons much heavier than the gauginos and Higgsinos, which protects m_b from large radiative corrections by providing a suppression factor in the loop diagrams and giving $\delta m_b/m_b \ll 1$. However, in the absence of experimental information on the superpartner spectrum, the predictions of the third generation quark-lepton masses in the large $\tan\beta$ scenario must, unfortunately, be considered unreliable.

3. Mass Matrix Ansätze and Texture Zeros

The best known ansatz for the quark mass matrices is due to Fritzsch [19] and takes the following form:

$$M_U = \begin{pmatrix} 0 & C & 0 \\ C & 0 & B \\ 0 & B & A \end{pmatrix} \quad M_D = \begin{pmatrix} 0 & C' & 0 \\ C' & 0 & B' \\ 0 & B' & A' \end{pmatrix}$$

The ansatz contains 6 complex parameters A, B, C, A', B' and C'. Four of the phases can be rotated away by redefining the phases of the quark fields, leaving just 8 real parameters (the magnitudes of A, B, C, A', B' and C' and two phases ϕ_1 and ϕ_2) to reproduce 6 quark masses and 4 angles parameterising V_{CKM}. There are thus two relationships predicted by the Fritzsch ansatz. It is necessary to *assume*:

$$|A| \gg |B| \gg |C|, \qquad |A'| \gg |B'| \gg |C'| \tag{7}$$

in order to obtain a good fermion mass hierarchy.

The first prediction is a generalised version of the phenomenological result $\theta_c \simeq \sqrt{\frac{m_d}{m_s}}$ for the Cabbibo angle, which originally motivated the ansatz:

$$|V_{us}| \simeq \left| \sqrt{\frac{m_d}{m_s}} - e^{-i\phi_1} \sqrt{\frac{m_u}{m_c}} \right| \tag{8}$$

and is well satisfied experimentally. However the second relationship:

$$|V_{cb}| \simeq \left| \sqrt{\frac{m_s}{m_b}} - e^{-i\phi_2} \sqrt{\frac{m_c}{m_t}} \right| \tag{9}$$

cannot be satisfied with a heavy top quark. Using $\sqrt{\frac{m_s}{m_b}} \simeq 0.18$ and $|V_{cb}| \leq 0.055$, an upper limit of $m_t < 100$ Gev is obtained [20]. The limit is valid in the SM whether the ansatz is applied at the electroweak scale or at the GUT scale. This is also true in the MSSM for $\tan \beta \leq \frac{m_t}{m_b}$ †. So the Fritzsch ansatz is now excluded by the data.

The failure of the Fritzsch ansatz to accomodate a heavy top quark led Dimopoulos, Hall and Raby [10] to consider another ansatz, in the context of an SO(10) SUSY-GUT, combining the Fritzsch form for the up quark mass matrix, $M_U = Y_u v_2$, with the Georgi-Jarlskog form [22] ‡ for the down quark and charged lepton mass matrices $M_D = Y_d v_1$ and $M_E = Y_e v_1$:

$$Y_u = \begin{pmatrix} 0 & C & 0 \\ C & 0 & B \\ 0 & B & A \end{pmatrix} \quad Y_d = \begin{pmatrix} 0 & F e^{i\phi} & 0 \\ F e^{-i\phi} & E & 0 \\ 0 & 0 & D \end{pmatrix}$$

† There is a loophole in the unappealing limit $\tan \beta > \frac{m_t}{m_b}$. If the ansatz is applied at the SUSY-GUT scale in this case, the bound can be raised to $m_t < 145$ Gev [21].

‡ The Georgi-Jarlskog ansatz was constructed to give the GUT scale mass relations $m_b = m_\tau$, $m_s = m_\mu/3$ and $m_d = 3m_e$ which, in the presence of a heavy top quark, requires a supersymmetric grand unification to agree with experiment.

	U			D		
1	0	$\sqrt{2}\lambda^6$	0	0	$2\lambda^4$	0
	$\sqrt{2}\lambda^6$	λ^4	0	$2\lambda^4$	$2\lambda^3$	$4\lambda^3$
	0	0	1	0	$4\lambda^3$	1
2	0	λ^6	0	0	$2\lambda^4$	0
	λ^6	0	λ^2	$2\lambda^4$	$2\lambda^3$	$2\lambda^3$
	0	λ^2	1	0	$2\lambda^3$	1
3	0	0	$\sqrt{2}\lambda^4$	0	$2\lambda^4$	0
	0	λ^4	0	$2\lambda^4$	$2\lambda^3$	$4\lambda^3$
	$\sqrt{2}\lambda^4$	0	1	0	$4\lambda^3$	1
4	0	$\sqrt{2}\lambda^6$	0	0	$2\lambda^4$	0
	$\sqrt{2}\lambda^6$	$\sqrt{3}\lambda^4$	λ^2	$2\lambda^4$	$2\lambda^3$	0
	0	λ^2	1	0	0	1
5	0	0	λ^4	0	$2\lambda^4$	0
	0	$\sqrt{2}\lambda^4$	$\frac{\lambda^2}{\sqrt{2}}$	$2\lambda^4$	$2\lambda^3$	0
	λ^4	$\frac{\lambda^2}{\sqrt{2}}$	1	0	0	1

Table 1. Approximate forms for the symmetric textures. The parameter λ is the CKM matrix element V_{us} used in the Wolfenstein parameterisation of V_{CKM}.

$$Y_e = \begin{pmatrix} 0 & F & 0 \\ F & -3E & 0 \\ 0 & 0 & D \end{pmatrix}$$

where the phase freedom in the definition of the fermion fields has been used to make the parameters A, B, C, D, E and F real and we have again to assume:

$$|A| \gg |B| \gg |C|, \qquad |D| \gg |E| \gg |F| \tag{10}$$

Thus there are 7 free parameters in the Yukawa coupling ansatz and $\tan \beta$ available to fit 13 observables. This ansatz gives 5 predictions which are, within errors, in agreement with data for $1 < \tan \beta < 60$ [10, 23, 24]. Due to the SUSY-GUT scale prediction $V_{cb} \simeq \sqrt{\frac{m_c}{m_t}}$, fits tend to give m_t close to its fixed point and a large value for $|V_{cb}|$. A fit satisfying Yukawa unification is obtained by setting $A = D$ and $\tan \beta \simeq 60$ §.

The predictions arise due to the reduction in the number of free parameters, obtained by requiring the presence of zeros and symmetries between mass matrix elements. A recent systematic analysis [25] of *symmetric* quark mass matrices with 5 or 6 "texture" zeros at the SUSY-GUT scale yielded another 5 ansätze consistent with experiment. The hierarchical structure of the parameters in the ansätze (cf. Eq. 10) suggests a parameterisation of the form shown in Table 1 from [25], where it is natural to interpret λ as a symmetry breaking parameter for some approximate symmetry beyond those of the Standard Model Group (SMG). The nature of this symmetry is discussed in the next section.

§ A non-supersymmetric SO(10) model with an intermediate symmetry breaking scale and Yukawa unification is discussed in [24]

4.   Chiral Symmetries and Mass Protection

A Dirac mass term, $m\bar{\psi}_R\psi_L + h.c.$, connects a left-handed fermion component ψ_L to its right-handed partner ψ_R. If ψ_L and ψ_R have different quantum numbers, i. e.   belong to inequivalent irreducible representations (IRs) of a symmetry group G (G is then called a *chiral* symmetry), the mass term is forbidden in the limit of exact G symmetry and they represent two massless particles. G thus "protects" the fermion from gaining a mass. Such a fermion can gain a mass only when G is spontaneously broken.

Consider, for example, an $SMG \times U(1)_f$ model, whose fundamental mass scale is M, broken to the SMG by the VEV of a scalar field ϕ_S where $\langle\phi_S\rangle < M$ and ϕ_S carries $U(1)_f$ charge $Q_f(\phi_S) = 1$. Suppose further that $Q_f(\phi_{WS}) = 0$, $Q_f(b_L) = 0$ and $Q_f(b_R) = 2$. Then it is natural to expect the generation of a b mass of order:

$$\left(\frac{\langle\phi_S\rangle}{M}\right)^2 \langle\phi_{WS}\rangle \tag{11}$$

via (see Fig. 1) the exchange of two $\langle\phi_S\rangle$ tadpoles, in addition to the usual $\langle\phi_{WS}\rangle$ tadpole, through two appropriately charged vector-like superheavy (i.e.   of mass M) fermion intermediate states [3]. We identify

$$\epsilon_f = \frac{\langle\phi_S\rangle}{M} \tag{12}$$

as the $U(1)_f$ flavour symmetry breaking parameter. In general we expect mass matrix elements of order

$$M(i,j) \simeq \epsilon_f^{n_{ij}} \langle\phi_{WS}\rangle \tag{13}$$

where

$$n_{ij} =\mid Q_f(\psi_{L_i}) - Q_f(\psi_{R_j}) \mid \tag{14}$$

is the degree of forbiddenness due to the $U(1)_f$ quantum number difference between the left and right states. We now consider models based on this idea.

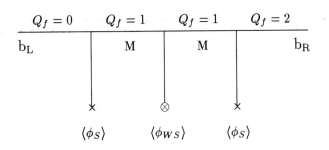

$Q_f = 0$	$Q_f = 1$	$Q_f = 1$	$Q_f = 2$
b_L	M	M	b_R
	$\langle\phi_S\rangle$	$\langle\phi_{WS}\rangle$	$\langle\phi_S\rangle$

Figure 1. Feynman diagram which generates the b quark mass.

The texture of the fermion mass matrices in a recent effective operator analysis [26]of SO(10) SUSY-GUT models, with Yukawa unification and having 8

predictions, has been interpreted as due to a global abelian chiral flavour symmetry. There is assumed to be a specified sparse spectrum of superheavy fermion states in **16** and $\overline{\bf 16}$ representations, generating Yukawa matrices for the quarks and leptons of the form:

$$Y_u = \begin{pmatrix} 0 & \frac{-1}{27}C & 0 \\ \frac{-1}{27}C & 0 & x'_u B \\ 0 & x_u B & A \end{pmatrix} \quad Y_d = \begin{pmatrix} 0 & C & 0 \\ C & Ee^{i\phi} & x'_d B \\ 0 & x_d B & A \end{pmatrix}$$

$$Y_l = \begin{pmatrix} 0 & C & 0 \\ C & 3Ee^{i\phi} & x'_l B \\ 0 & x_l B & A \end{pmatrix}$$

Here the x_i and x'_i are SO(10) Clebsch Gordon coefficients; these Clebschs can take on a (very large) number of discrete values which are scanned and found to lead to just 9 solutions consistent with experiment. For fixed values of the Clebschs, the Yukawa matrices depend on 6 free parameters: A, B, C, E, ϕ and $\tan\beta$. The texture zeros reflect the assumed absence of superheavy fermion states which could mediate the transition between the corresponding Weyl states.

We now turn to models in which the chiral flavour charges are part of the extended gauge group. The values of the chiral charges are then strongly constrained by the anomaly conditions for the gauge theory. It will also be assumed that any superheavy state needed to mediate a symmetry breaking transition exists, so that the results are insensitive to the details of the superheavy spectrum. Consequently there will be no exact texture zeros but just highly suppressed elements given by expressions like Eq. 13. The aim in these models is to reproduce all quark-lepton masses and mixing angles within a factor of 2 or 3.

In a recent paper [27], Ibanez and Ross consider the extension of the MSSM by an abelian flavour group $U(1)_f$. They then consider the construction of an anomaly free $MSSM \times U(1)_f$ model having quark mass matrices with a texture very close to that of solution 2 in Table 1. The quarks and leptons are assigned the following $U(1)_f$ charges:

$$\begin{pmatrix} d_L & u_R & d_R & e_L & e_R \\ s_L & c_R & s_R & \mu_L & \mu_R \\ b_L & t_R & b_R & \tau_L & \tau_R \end{pmatrix}$$

$$= \begin{pmatrix} -4 & 4 & 4 & -7/2 & 7/2 \\ 1 & -1 & -1 & 1/2 & -1/2 \\ 0 & 0 & 0 & 0 & 0 \end{pmatrix} \tag{15}$$

In addition to the two Higgs doublets of MSSM, which are taken to be neutral under $U(1)_f$, two Higgs singlets, θ and $\bar{\theta}$, are introduced with $U(1)_f$ charges +1 and -1 respectively and equal vacuum expectation values. Anomaly cancellation is only possible in the context of

Fit Results	$m_t^{phys} = 100\,GeV$	$m_t^{phys} = 200\,GeV$	
		unbiased	biased
χ^2	3.7	5.6	6.9
m_e (MeV)	1.0	1.0	1.0
m_μ (MeV)	120	160	110
m_τ (GeV)	1.4	1.5	1.5
m_d (MeV)	4.9	4.9	4.9
m_s (MeV)	600	790	530
m_b^{phys} (GeV)	5.4	5.5	5.3
m_u (MeV)	4.9	4.9	4.9
m_c (GeV)	0.73	0.53	0.84
V_{us}	0.19	0.22	0.22
V_{cb}	0.016	0.012	0.0048
V_{ub}	0.0030	0.0027	0.0027

Table 2. Results of an $SMG^3 \times U(1)_f$ model fit to fermion masses and mixing angles. All masses are running masses evaluated at 1 GeV unless otherwise stated. The third column shows a fit biased in favour of obtaining $m_c > m_s$.

superstring theories via the Green Schwarz mechanism [28]; consequently the $U(1)_f$ symmetry is broken slightly below the string scale. The $U(1)_f$ charge assignments of Eq. 15 generate Yukawa matrices, via Eq. 13, of the following form:

$$Y_u \simeq \begin{pmatrix} \epsilon^8 & \epsilon^3 & \epsilon^4 \\ \epsilon^3 & \epsilon^2 & \epsilon \\ \epsilon^4 & \epsilon & 1 \end{pmatrix} \quad Y_d \simeq \begin{pmatrix} \bar{\epsilon}^8 & \bar{\epsilon}^3 & \bar{\epsilon}^4 \\ \bar{\epsilon}^3 & \bar{\epsilon}^2 & \bar{\epsilon} \\ \bar{\epsilon}^4 & \bar{\epsilon} & 1 \end{pmatrix}$$

$$Y_e \simeq \begin{pmatrix} \bar{\epsilon}^5 & \bar{\epsilon}^3 & 0 \\ \bar{\epsilon}^3 & \bar{\epsilon} & 0 \\ 0 & 0 & 1 \end{pmatrix}$$

The correct order of magnitude for all the masses and mixing angles are obtained by fitting ϵ, $\bar{\epsilon}$ and $\tan\beta$.

In the antigrand unified model [29, 30], the fundamental non-simple gauge group SMG^3 breaks down near the Planck scale to the usual SMG. The extra chiral gauge quantum numbers of SMG^3 can readily explain the generation mass gaps but not the splitting within each generation. So we are led to extend the gauge group further and $SMG^3 \times U(1)_f$ is the only non-trivial anomaly-free extension with no new fermions and the $U(1)_f$ charges are essentially unique:

$$\begin{pmatrix} d_L & u_R & d_R & e_L & e_R \\ s_L & c_R & s_R & \mu_L & \mu_R \\ b_L & t_R & b_R & \tau_L & \tau_R \end{pmatrix}$$
$$= \begin{pmatrix} 0 & 0 & 0 & 0 & 0 \\ 0 & 1 & -1 & 0 & -1 \\ 0 & -1 & 1 & 0 & 1 \end{pmatrix} \quad (16)$$

A good order of magnitude fit to the data can now be obtained [31] and results are shown in Table 2. All the data are fitted within a factor of 2, except for m_s and V_{cb} which are fitted within a factor of 3.

References

[1] C. D. Froggatt and H. B. Nielsen, Nucl. Phys. **B164** (1979) 144.
[2] M. Gell-Mann, P. Ramond and R. Slansky in *Supergravity*, p315; Eds. P. van Nieuwenhuizen and D. Z. Freedman (North Holland, New York, 1980); T. Yanagida, Proc. of the Workshop on Unified Theory and Baryon Number in the Universe 1979, p.95; Eds. A. Sawada and H. Sugawara (KEK, Tsukuba-Gu, Ibaraki-ken, Japan, 1979).
[3] C. D. Froggatt and H. B. Nielsen, Nucl. Phys. **B147** (1979) 277.
[4] B. Pendleton and G. G. Ross, Phys. Lett. **B98** (1981) 291.
[5] W. M. Marciano, Phys. Rev. Lett. **62** (1989) 2793.
[6] C. T. Hill, Phys. Rev. **D24** (1981) 691; C. T. Hill, C. N. Leung and S. A. Rao, Nucl. Phys. **B262** (1985) 517; W. A. Bardeen, C. T. Hill and M. Lindner, Phys. Rev. **D41** (1990) 1647.
[7] D. Schaile, these Proceedings; M. Vysotsky, these Proceedings.
[8] H. Jensen, these Proceedings.
[9] J. Bagger, S. Dimopoulos and E. Masso, Phys. Rev. Lett. **55** (1985) 920; M. Olechowski and S. Pokorski, Phys. Lett. **B257** (1991) 388.
[10] S. Dimopoulos, L. J. Hall, and S. Raby, Phys. Rev. Lett. **68** (1992) 1984; Phys. Rev. **D45** (1992) 4192.
[11] V. Barger, these Proceedings.
[12] C. D. Froggatt, I. G. Knowles and R. G. Moorhouse, Phys. Lett. **B298** (1993) 356.
[13] B. Ananthanarayan, G. Lazarides and Q. Shafi, Phys. Rev. **D44** (1991) 1613.
[14] G. Zoupanos, these Proceedings.
[15] G. Anderson, S. Raby, S. Dimopoulos, L. J. Hall and G. D. Starkman, Phys. Rev. **D49** (1994) 3660.
[16] L. J. Hall, R. Rattazzi and U. Sarid, Lawrence Berkeley Lab preprint: LBL-33997; and Stanford University preprint: SU-ITP-94-15.
[17] A. Nelson and L. Randall, Phys. Lett. **B316** (1993) 516.
[18] M. Carena, M. Olechowski, S. Pokorski and C. E. M. Wagner, CERN Preprint: CERN-TH-7163-94.
[19] H. Fritzsch, Phys. Lett. **B70** (1977) 436; *ibid.* **B73** (1978) 317.
[20] F. Gilman and Y. Nir, Annu. Rev. Nucl. Part. Sci. **40** (1990) 213.
[21] K. S. Babu and Q. Shafi, **D47** (1993) 5004.
[22] H. Georgi and C. Jarlskog, Phys. Lett. **86B** (1979) 297; J. A. Harvey, P. Ramond and D. B. Reiss, Phys. Lett. **92B** (1980) 309; Nucl. Phys. **B199** (1982) 223.
[23] V. Barger, M. S. Berger, T. Han and M. Zralek, Phys. Rev. Lett. **68** (1992) 3394; G. W. Anderson, S. Raby, S. Dimopoulos and L. J. Hall, Phys. Rev. **D47** (1993) 3702.
[24] N. G. Deshpande and E. Keith, paper submitted to this conference: gls0262.
[25] P. Ramond, R. G. Roberts and G. G. Ross, Nucl. Phys. **B406** (1993) 19.
[26] G. W. Anderson, S. Raby, S. Dimopoulos, L. J. Hall and G. D. Starkman Phys. Rev. **D49** (1994) 3660.
[27] L. E. Ibanez and G. G. Ross, Phys. Lett. **B332** (1994) 100.
[28] M. Green, and J. Schwarz, Phys. Lett. **B149** (1984) 117; L. E. Ibanez, Phys. Lett. **B303** (1993) 55.
[29] H. B. Nielsen, these Proceedings.
[30] C.D. Froggatt and H.B. Nielsen, *Origin of Symmetries* (World Scientific, Singapore, 1991).
[31] C.D. Froggatt, G. Lowe and H.B. Nielsen, Nucl. Phys. **B414** (1994) 579.

Paper presented at XXVII Int. Conf. on High Energy Physics: Session Pa-4
Glasgow, UK, 20–27 July 1994

Finite Unification and Top Quark Mass*

Jisuke Kubo[†], Myriam Mondragón[‡] and George Zoupanos[§]

† Max-Planck-Institut für Physik, Werner-Heisenberg-Institut, D-80805 Munich, Germany
‡ Inst. für Theoretische Physik, Philosophenweg 16 D-69120 Heidelberg, Germany
§ Physics Dept., Nat. Tech. Univ., GR-157 80 Zografou, Athens, Greece

Abstract

In unified gauge theories there exist renormalization group invariant (RGI) relations among gauge and Yukawa couplings that are compatible with perturbative renormalizability, which could be considered as a Gauge-Yukawa Unification. Such relations are even necessary to ensure all-loop finiteness in Finite Unified Theories (FUTs), which have vanishing β-functions beyond the unification point. We elucidate this alternative way of unification, and then present its phenomenological consequences in $SU(5)$-based models.

1. Introduction

The original unification philosophy relates the gauge and separately the Yukawa couplings. A logical extension is to relate the couplings of the two sectors; Gauge-Yukawa Unification (GYU). Within the assumption that all the particles appearing in a theory are elementary, the theories based on extended supersymmetries as well as superstring theories are well-known possibilities for GYU.

There exists an alternative way to unify couplings which is based on the fact that within the framework of renormalizable field theory, one can find RGI relations among parameters and improve the calculability and predictive power of a given theory [1]-[3]. Any RGI relation among couplings (which does not depend on the renormalization scale μ explicitly) can be expressed, in the implicit form $\Phi(g_1, \cdots, g_A) = $ const., which has to satisfy the partial differential equation (PDE) $\mu\, d\Phi/d\mu = \sum_{a=1}^{A} \beta_a\, \partial\Phi/\partial g_a = 0$, where β_a is the β-function of g_a. This PDE is equivalent to the set to ordinary differential equations, the reduction equations

(REs)[1],

$$\beta_g \frac{dg_a}{dg} = \beta_a\ ,\ a = 1, \cdots, A\ , \qquad (1)$$

where g and β_g are the primary coupling and its β-function, and a does not include it. Since maximally $(A - 1)$ independent RGI "constraints" in the A-dimensional space of couplings can be imposed by Φ_a's, one could in principle express all the couplings in terms of a single coupling g. The strongest requirement is to demand power series solutions to the REs,

$$g_a = \sum_{n=0} \rho_a^{(n+1)}\, g^{2n+1}\ , \qquad (2)$$

which formally preserve perturbative renormalizability. Remarkably, the uniqueness of such power series solutions can be decided at the one-loop level [1]. To illustrate this, let us assume that the β-functions have the form

$$\beta_a = \frac{1}{16\pi^2}[\sum_{b,c,d\neq g} \beta_a^{(1)\,bcd} g_b g_c g_d + \sum_{b\neq g} \beta_a^{(1)\,b} g_b g^2] + \cdots\ ,$$

$$\beta_g = \frac{1}{16\pi^2} \beta_g^{(1)} g^3 + \cdots\ , \qquad (3)$$

where $\cdots$ stands for higher order terms, and $\beta_a^{(1)\,bcd}$'s are symmetric in b, c, d. We then assume that the $\rho_a^{(n)}$'s

* Presented by G. Z.
† On leave of absence from Kanazawa Univ., Japan
§ Partially supported by C.E.U. projects (SC1-CT91-0729; CHRX-CT93-0319).

with $n \leq r$ have been uniquely determined. To obtain $\rho_a^{(r+1)}$'s, we insert the power series (2) into (1) and collect terms of $O(g^{2r+3})$ and find $\sum_{d \neq g} M(r)_a^d \rho_d^{(r+1)} =$ lower order quantities, where the r.h.s. is known by assumption, and

$$
\begin{aligned}
M(r)_a^d &= 3 \sum_{b,c \neq g} \beta_a^{(1)\,bcd} \rho_b^{(1)} \rho_c^{(1)} + \beta_a^{(1)\,d} \\
&\quad - (2r+1)\beta_g^{(1)} \delta_a^d,
\end{aligned}
\tag{4}
$$

$$
\beta_g^{(1)} \rho_a^{(1)} = \sum_{b,c,d \neq g} \beta_a^{(1)\,bcd} \rho_b^{(1)} \rho_c^{(1)} \rho_d^{(1)} + \sum_{d \neq g} \beta_a^{(1)\,d} \rho_d^{(1)}.
\tag{5}
$$

Therefore, the $\rho_a^{(n)}$'s for all $n > 1$ for a given set of $\rho_a^{(1)}$'s can be uniquely determined if $\det M(n)_a^d \neq 0$ for all $n \geq 0$.

Among the existing possibilities in the framework of susy $SU(5)$ GUTs, there are two models that are singled out by being strongly motivated [2,3]. The first is the $SU(5)$-FUT [2]. In this theory, there exist RGI relations among gauge and Yukawa couplings that yield the vanishing of all β-functions to all orders [4]. (It has been recently found that the quantum corrections to the cosmological constant in a finite theory is weakened [5].) The second is the minimal $SU(5)$ susy model which can be successfully partially-reduced [3], and is attractive because of its simplicity. In the following, we will give more emphasis in discussing the $SU(5)$-FUT and then we compare the predictions of the two models.

2. $N = 1$ Finiteness

Let us consider a chiral, but anomaly free, globally supersymmetric gauge theory based on a simple group G with the gauge coupling g. The superpotential of the theory is given by

$$
W = \sum_{i,j} \frac{1}{2} m_{ij}\, \phi^i \phi^j + \frac{1}{6} \sum_{i,j,k} \lambda_{ijk}\, \phi^i \phi^j \phi^k \,,
\tag{6}
$$

where the matter chiral superfield ϕ^i belongs to an irreducible representation of G. The non-renormalization theorem ensures that there are no extra mass and cubic-interaction-term renormalizations, implying that the β-functions of λ_{ijk} can be expressed as linear combinations of the anomalous dimension matrix γ_{ij} of ϕ^i. Therefore, all the one-loop β-functions of the theory vanish if

$$
\beta_g^{(1)} = 0 \text{ and } \gamma_{ij}^{(1)} = 0
\tag{7}
$$

are satisfied, where $\beta_g^{(1)}$ and $\gamma_{ij}^{(1)}$ are the one-loop coefficients of β_g and γ_{ij}, respectively. A very interesting result is that these conditions are necessary and sufficient for finiteness at the two-loop level [6].

A natural question is what happens in higher loops. Since the finiteness conditions impose relations among couplings, they have to be consistent with the REs (1). Interestingly, there exists a powerful theorem [4] which provides the necessary and sufficient conditions for finiteness to all loops. The theorem makes heavy use of the non-renormalization property of the supercurrent anomaly [7]. In fact, the finiteness theorem can be formulated in terms of one-loop quantities, and it states that for susy gauge theories we are considering here, the necessary and sufficient conditions for β_g and β_{ijk} to vanish to all orders are [4]:
(a) The validity of the one-loop finiteness conditions, i.e., (7) is satisfied.
(b) The REs (1) admit a unique power series solution, i.e., the corresponding matrix M defined in (4) with $\beta_g^{(1)} = 0$ has to be non-singular.
The latter condition is equivalent to the requirement that the one-loop solutions $\rho_a^{(1)}$'s are isolated and nondegenerate. Then each of these solutions can be extended, by a recursion formula, to a formal power series in g giving a theory which depends on a single coupling g, and has β-functions vanishing to all orders.

3.   Finite Unified Models based on $SU(5)$

From the classification of theories with $\beta_g^{(1)} = 0$ [8], one can see that using $SU(5)$ as gauge group there exist only two candidate models which can accommodate three fermion generations. These models contain the chiral supermultiplets $\mathbf{5}$, $\overline{\mathbf{5}}$, $\mathbf{10}$, $\overline{\mathbf{5}}$, $\mathbf{24}$ with the multiplicities $(6,9,4,1,0)$ and $(4,7,3,0,1)$, respectively. Only the second one contains a $\mathbf{24}$-plet which can be used for spontaneous symmetry breaking (SSB) of $SU(5)$ down to $SU(3) \times SU(2) \times U(1)$. (For the first model one has to incorporate another way, such as the Wilson flux breaking to achieve the desired SSB of $SU(5)$.) Here we would like to concentrate only on the second model.

The most general $SU(5)$ invariant, cubic superpotential of the (second) model is:

$$
\begin{aligned}
W &= H_a \left[f_{ab}\, \overline{H}_b \mathbf{24} + h_{ia}\, \overline{\mathbf{5}}_i \mathbf{24} + \overline{g}_{ija}\, \mathbf{10}_i \overline{\mathbf{5}}_j \right] + p\, (\mathbf{24})^3 \\
&\quad + \frac{1}{2}\, \mathbf{10}_i \left[g_{ija}\, \mathbf{10}_j H_a + \hat{g}_{iab}\, \overline{H}_a \overline{H}_b + g'_{ijk}\, \overline{\mathbf{5}}_j \overline{\mathbf{5}}_k \right],
\end{aligned}
\tag{8}
$$

where $i,j,k = 1,2,3$ and $a,b = 1,\cdots,4$, and we sum over all indices in W (the $SU(5)$ indices are suppressed). The $\mathbf{10}_i$'s and $\overline{\mathbf{5}}_i$'s are the usual three generations, and the four $(\mathbf{5} + \overline{\mathbf{5}})$ Higgses are denoted by H_a, $\overline{H}_a$.

Given the superpotential, the $\gamma^{(1)}$'s can be easily computed ($\beta_g^{(1)}$ vanishes of course). To ensure finiteness of the model to all orders, we have to find $\rho^{(1)}$'s that are isolated and nondegenerate solutions of (5) and are consistent with the vanishing $\gamma^{(1)}$'s. In most of the previous studies of the present model [9], however, no attempt was made to find isolated and non-degenerate solutions, but rather they have used the freedom offered by the degeneracy in order to make specific ansätze that could lead to phenomenologically acceptable predictions (see also [10]). Here we concentrate on finding an isolated and non-degenerate solution that is phenomenologically interesting. As a first approximation to the Yukawa matrices, a diagonal solution, i.e., without intergenerational mixing, may be considered. It turned out that this can be achieved by imposing the $Z_7 \times Z_3$ discrete symmetry and a multiplicative Q-parity on W, and that, in order to respect these symmetries, only g_{iii}, $\overline{g}_{iii}$, f_{ii} and p are allowed to be non-vanishing. Moreover, we found that under this situation there exists a unique reduction solution that satisfies the finiteness conditions (a) and (b) [2]:

$$\rho_{g_{iii}} = \sqrt{8/5}, \rho_{\overline{g}_{iii}} = \sqrt{6/5}, \rho_p = \sqrt{15/7},$$

$$\rho_{f_{44}} = 1, \rho_{f_{ii}} = 0, \text{for } i = 1, 2, 3. \qquad (9)$$

4. Phenomenological Consequences

In the above model, we found a diagonal solution for the Yukawa couplings, with each family coupled to a different Higgs. However, we may use the fact that mass terms do not influence the β-functions in a certain class of renormalization schemes, and introduce appropriate mass terms that permit us to perform a rotation in the Higgs sector such that only one pair of Higgs doublets, coupled mostly to the third family, remains light and acquires a non-vanishing v.e.v. (Too rapid proton decay [11] can be avoided also in this way.) Thus, effectively, we have at low energies the minimal susy standard model with only one pair of Higgs doublets. Adding soft susy breaking terms we can obtain susy breaking. (See [12] for the conditions on the soft breaking terms that do not spoil two-loop finiteness.)

Since the $SU(5)$ symmetry is spontaneously broken below M_{GUT}, the finiteness conditions obviously do not restrict the renormalization property at low energies, and all it remains is a boundary condition on the gauge and Yukawa couplings; these couplings at low energies have to be so chosen that they satisfy (9) at M_{GUT}. So we examine the evolution of the gauge couplings according to their renormalization group equations at two-loops. Representative results are summarized in table 1, where we have used $m_\tau = 1.78$ GeV, $\alpha_{em}^{-1}(M_Z) = 127.9$ and $\sin \theta_W(M_Z) = 0.232$, and to simplify our numerical analysis, we have assumed a unique threshold M_S for all the superpartners.

M_S [TeV]	$\alpha_S(M_Z)$	$\tan \beta$	m_b [GeV]	m_t[GeV]
1.0	0.117	54.1	5.13	185
0.5	0.121	53.5	5.27	186
0.2	0.121	54.1	5.14	185

Table 1. The predictions for different M_S.

All the quantities except M_S in table 1 are predicted. The dimensionless parameters (except $\tan \beta$) are defined in the $\overline{\text{MS}}$ scheme, and the masses are pole masses. We see from table 1 that the low energy predictions are relatively stable against the change of M_S and m_t agrees with the CDF result [13].

To compare the predictions above with those of the partially-reduced, minimal $SU(5)$ GUT [3], we present its predictions in table 2.

M_S [TeV]	$\alpha_S(M_Z)$	$\tan \beta$	m_b [GeV]	$m_t[GeV]$
1.0	0.118	47.4	5.36	180
0.5	0.120	47.6	5.42	180
0.2	0.124	47.4	5.55	182

Table 2. The predictions of the partially-reduced, minimal $SU(5)$ GUT for the same low-energy inputs.

These predictions do not differ very much from these of the $SU(5)$-FUT model. We would like to stress that both models have the strongest predictive power as compared with any other known GUTs as it was promised.

References

[1] W. Zimmermann, Commun. Math. Phys. **97** (1985) 211; R. Oehme and W. Zimmermann, Commun. Math. Phys. **97** (1985) 569.

[2] D. Kapetanakis, M. Mondragón and G. Zoupanos, Z. Phys. **C60** (1993) 181; M. Mondragón and G. Zoupanos, CERN preprint, CERN-TH.7098/93.

[3] J. Kubo, M. Mondragón and G. Zoupanos, to appear in Nucl. Phys. **B**.

[4] C. Lucchesi, O. Piguet and K. Sibold, Helv. Phys. Acta. **61** (1988) 321.

[5] E.Elizalde and S. Odintsov, Phys. Lett. **B333** (1994) 331; I.L. Shapiro, Phys. Lett. **B329** (1994) 181.

[6] A.J. Parkes and P.C. West, Phys. Lett. **B138** (1984) 99; Nucl. Phys. **B256** (1985) 340; D.R.T. Jones and L. Mezinescu, Phys. Lett. **B136** (1984) 242; B138 (1984) 293.

[7] O. Piguet and K. Sibold, Int. Journ. Mod. Phys. **A1** (1986) 913.

[8] S. Hamidi, J. Patera and J.H. Schwarz, Phys. Lett. **B141** (1984) 349.

[9] S. Hamidi and J.H. Schwarz, Phys. Lett. **B147** (1984) 301; D.R.T. Jones and S. Raby, Phys. Lett. **B143** (1984) 137; J.E. Bjorkman, D.R.T. Jones and S. Raby, Nucl. Phys. **B259** (1985) 503, J. León et al, Phys. Lett. **B156** (1985) 66.

[10] A.V. Ermushev, D.I. Kazakov and O.V. Tarasov, Nucl. Phys. **B281** (1987) 72.

[11] N. Deshpande, Xiao-Gang, He and E. Keith, Phys. Lett. **B332** (1994) 88.

[12] I. Jack and D.R.T Jones, Phys. Lett. **B333** (1994) 372.

[13] CDF Collaboration: F. Abe et al., Fermilab preprint, FERMILAB-PUB-94-116-E.

Paper presented at XXVII Int. Conf. on High Energy Physics: Session Pa-4
Glasgow, UK, 20–27 July 1994

Nambu mass hierarchies in low energy string models

Emilian Dudas

Laboratoire de Physique Théorique et Hautes Energies
Université Paris-Sud, Bat. 211, F-91405 Orsay Cedex, France

Abstract

This paper explores a recent idea of Nambu to generate hierarchies among Yukawa couplings in the context of effective supergravity and superstrings models. The Yukawa couplings are homogeneous functions of the moduli and a geometrical constraint between them with a crucial role in the Nambu mechanism is found in a class of models of no-scale type. The Yukawas are dynamical variables at low energy to be determined by a minimization process.

1. Nambu mass hierarchies

A mystery of the Standard Model is the difference between the mass of the top quark and the mass of the other fermions. The top quark mass is roughly of the order the electroweak scale $v \simeq 250 GeV$, whereas in a first approximation all the other fermions are massless. No definite solution of this puzzle was found and so new ideas are necessary.

An interesting idea was recently proposd by Nambu [1]. The Yukawa couplings are regarded as dynamical variables to be determined by minimizing the vacuum energy density. All the other parameters are held fixed, including the vev's of the scalar fields. If Λ is the cut-off and μ is a typical mass of the theory, the vacuum energy density can be written as

$$< V >= V^{(0)} \, \Lambda^4 + V^{(2)} \, \Lambda^2 + V^{(4)} \, \ell n \frac{\Lambda}{\mu} \, . \quad (1)$$

Nambu imposes the vanishing of quartic $V^{(0)}$ and quadratic $V^{(2)}$ divergences. The first condition is automatic in supersymmetric theories and the second gives a constraint between the Yukawas known as the Veltman condition.

In the example chosen by Nambu, for two couplings λ_1 and λ_2, the vacuum energy reads

$$< V >= -A(\lambda_1{}^4 + \lambda_2{}^4) + B(\lambda_1{}^2 \ell n \lambda_1{}^2 + \lambda_2{}^2 \ell n \lambda_2{}^2) \quad (2)$$

and the Veltman condition is

$$\lambda_1{}^2 + \lambda_2{}^2 = a^2 \, . \quad (3)$$

A picture in the case $B = 0$ is shown in Fig.1. The shaded regions are excluded by the Veltman condition, eq.(3). For $B \neq 0$ new minima for $< V >$ appear close to the boundary. They correspond to the configurations $(\lambda_1, \lambda_2) = (a, a \, e^{\frac{-Aa^2}{B}})$ or $(a \, e^{\frac{-Aa^2}{B}}, a)$. The hierarchy is obtained if $\frac{Aa^2}{B} >> 1$. The mechanism is easily generalized to more couplings, in which case *one* coupling $\lambda_{i_0} \simeq a$ and all the others are exponentially suppressed $\frac{\lambda_i}{\lambda_{i_0}} << 1$, $i \neq i_0$. The applicability of this idea to the Standard Model is under study [2].

An analog of the Veltman condition can be obtained in superstring models, imposing the vanishing of the quadratic divergences coming from supergravity [3].

2. Yukawas as dynamical variables in low-energy supergravity and superstrings

The question of the dynamical nature of the Yukawa couplings find a natural answer in superstrings. In

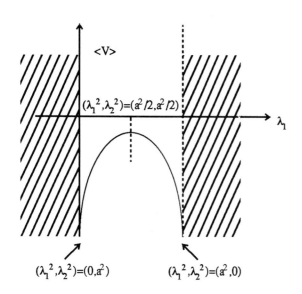

$(\lambda_1^2, \lambda_2^2) = (a^2/2, a^2/2)$

$\langle V \rangle$

λ_1

$(\lambda_1^2, \lambda_2^2) = (0, a^2)$ $(\lambda_1^2, \lambda_2^2) = (a^2, 0)$

Figure 1. The vaccum energy as a function of λ_1, neglecting the logarithmic corrections.

these models, the Yukawa couplings have a non-trivial dependence on the moduli fields which caracterize the complex structure of the compact manifold. In the effective supergravity theory, the existence of moduli manifests usually in flat directions in the scalar potential. They appear due to some approximate, non-compact duality symmetries acting on the moduli. As a consequence, the vev's of the moduli are not determined at the tree level of supergravity and the Yukawas can be considered as dynamical variables. The duality symmetries form an $SL(2, Z)$ group and are described by

$$T_\alpha \rightarrow \frac{a_\alpha T_\alpha - ib_\alpha}{ic_\alpha T_\alpha + d_\alpha} \; , \quad a_\alpha d_\alpha - b_\alpha c_\alpha = 1 \; , \quad (4)$$

where $a_\alpha \cdots d_\alpha$ are integer numbers and T_α are the moduli. There are two distinct possibilities :

i) The number n of undetermined T_α > The number M of Yukawas +1. In this case we can freely perform the minimization with respect to all the Yukawas.

ii) The number n of undetermined T_α < The number M of Yukawas +1. In this case, we will have generically geometrical constraints.

The most simple and interesting case is to have only one constraint, corresponding to the same number of Yukawas and moduli. This is the case which will be investigated in the next section.

Consider a model containing the dilaton-type field S and the moduli T_α, specific to the superstring effective supergravities. The Kähler potential and the

superpotential read

$$K = -\frac{3}{n} \sum_{\alpha=1}^{n} \ell n(T_\alpha + T_\alpha^+) - \ell n(S + S^+) +$$
$$+ K_i^j \phi^i \phi_j^+ + \cdots \qquad ,$$
$$W = \frac{1}{3} \lambda_{ijk} \phi^i \phi^j \phi^k \qquad , \qquad (5)$$

where the dots stand for the higher order terms in the fields ϕ^i. The Kähler metric depends on the moduli T_i and eventually on S. The low-energy spontaneously broken theory contains the normalized fields $\hat{\phi}^i$ defined by $\phi^i = (K^{-1/2})_l^i \hat{\phi}^l$ and the Yukawas $\hat{\lambda}_{ijk}$. In order to obtain the relation between λ_{ijk} and $\hat{\lambda}_{ijk}$, consider the scalar potential [4], which contains the piece

$$V \supset e^K (K^{-1})_j^i D_i W \bar{D}^j \bar{W} = \hat{W}_i \bar{\hat{W}}^i \; , \qquad (6)$$

where $D_i W = \partial W / \partial \phi^i + K_i W$ and $\hat{W} = \frac{1}{3} \hat{\lambda}_{ijk} \hat{\phi}^i \hat{\phi}^j \hat{\phi}^k$. From eq.(6) we get the required relation

$$\hat{\lambda}_{ijk} = e^{\frac{K}{2}} (K^{-1/2})_i^{i'} (K^{-1/2})_j^{j'} (K^{-1/2})_k^{k'} \lambda_{i'j'k'} \; , \quad (7)$$

which mathematically express the dependence of $\hat{\lambda}_{ijk}$ on the moduli through the Kähler potential K.

3.   Constraints between low energy Yukawas

The condition to have constraints between $\hat{\lambda}_{ijk}$ (combinations which do not depend on the moduli) is [5]

$$rang \left(\frac{\partial \hat{\lambda}_I}{\partial t_\alpha} \right) < min(M, n) \; , \qquad (8)$$

where $I = 1 \cdots M$ replaces the indices i, j, k and $t_\alpha = T_\alpha + T_\alpha^+$. The condition to have just one constraint is (in the case $M = n$)

$$det \left(\frac{\partial \hat{\lambda}_I}{\partial t_\alpha} \right) = 0 \; . \qquad (9)$$

A *natural* solution for eq.(9) is $\sum_\alpha t_\alpha \frac{\partial \hat{\lambda}_I}{\partial t_\alpha} = 0$, so the Yukawas $\hat{\lambda}_{ijk}$ to be *homogeneous functions* of the moduli. This homogeneity property translates into a scaling property for the Kähler metric

$$t_\alpha \frac{\partial}{\partial t_\alpha} K_j^i = -K_j^i \; . \qquad (10)$$

This suggest us to consider the no-scale models [6], which were introduced in order to get flat directions on the scalar potential, in connexion with the positivity of the energy in supergravity.

The class of the possible constraints is reduced if the Kähler space spanned by the scalar fields is a homogeneous space, such that the transformation of the Kähler potential K under (4) is a Kähler type transformation

$$K \to K + \frac{3}{n} \sum_{\alpha=1}^{n} \ell n |ic_\alpha T_\alpha + d_\alpha|^2 \ . \quad (11)$$

Defining $F_\alpha = \frac{3}{n} \ell n (ic_\alpha T_\alpha + d_\alpha)$ and using eq.(11), we obtain the transformation law of $\hat{\lambda}_{ijk}$ under (4)

$$\hat{\lambda}_{ijk} \to \Big(\prod_{\alpha=1}^{n} e^{\frac{F_\alpha + F_\alpha^+}{2}} \Big) e^{-\frac{n}{6}(F_i + F_j + F_k + h.c.)} \, \hat{\lambda}_{ijk} \ . \quad (12)$$

As a consequence, in this case the only possible constraints are multiplicative, in contrast with the Veltman-type constraint, eq.(3) which is additive.

A very simple example is provided by a model containing two moduli T_1, T_2, the dilaton S and two observable fields ϕ^i. The model is defined by

$$K = -\frac{3}{2} \ell n (t_1 - |\phi_1|^2) - \frac{3}{2} \ell n (t_2 - |\phi_2|^2) \ - $$
$$\ell n (S + S^+) \ ,$$
$$W = \frac{1}{3} \lambda_1 \phi_1^3 + \frac{1}{3} \lambda_2 \phi_2^3 + W(S) \ , \quad (13)$$

where $W(S)$ is a non-perturbative contribution to the superpotential which will fix the value of S and simultaneously break supersymmetry , as in the usual gaugino condensation scenario [7]. The Kähler potential parametrizes a $[SU(1,2)/U(1) \times SU(2)]^2 \times [SU(1,1)/U(1)]$ manifold and the symmetry of the model is $U(1)^2 \times$ *diagonal dilatation*. The low-energy Yukawas $\hat{\lambda}_i$ as functions of the high-energy λ_i read from eq.(7)

$$\hat{\lambda}_1^2 = \frac{8}{27} [1/(s + s^+)] (t_1/t_2)^{\frac{3}{2}} \lambda_1^2 \ ,$$
$$\hat{\lambda}_2^2 = \frac{8}{27} [1/(s + s^+)] (t_2/t_1)^{\frac{3}{2}} \lambda_2^2 \quad (14)$$

and the resulting constraint is obvious from eq.(14)

$$\hat{\lambda}_1 \hat{\lambda}_2 = \frac{8}{27} \frac{1}{(s + s^+)} \lambda_1 \lambda_2 = fixed \ . \quad (15)$$

The model is easily generalized to n couplings and n moduli. The constraint (15) is valid at the Planck scale and must be run to low-energy in order to be used in the dynamical determination of the couplings.

To compute the vacuum energy at a low-energy scale $\mu_0 \sim M_{susy}$ we proceed in the usual way. Using boundary values for the independent model parameters at the Planck scale M_P (identified here with the unification scale), we evolve the running parameters down to the scale μ_0 using the renormalization group (RG) equations and the effective potential approach. The one-loop effective potential has two pieces

$$V_1(\mu_0) = V_0(\mu_0) + \Delta V_1(\mu_0) \ , \quad (16)$$

where $V_0(\mu_0)$ is the RG improved tree level potential and $\Delta V_1(\mu_0)$ summarizes the quantum corrections given by the formula

$$\Delta V_1(\mu_0) = \frac{1}{64\pi^2} Str M^4 \left(\ell n \frac{M^2}{\mu_0^2} - \frac{3}{2} \right) \ . \quad (17)$$

In (17) M is the field-dependent mass matrix containing the Yukawa coupling dependence and all parameters are computed at the scale μ_0. The vacuum state is determined by the equation $\partial V_1 / \partial \phi_i = 0$. The vacuum energy is simply the value of the effective potential at the minimum.

A dynamical determination of the couplings and gravitino mass $m_{\frac{3}{2}}$ was also undertaken in [8]. The main difference with respect to our analysis is that in the approach proposed in that paper, the minimization is performed freely, with no constraint for the couplings.

Acknowledgments

I would like to thank P. Binétruy for his collaboration which led to the present work and C. Kounnas for interesting discussions.

This work was supported in part by the CEC Science project no. SC1-CT91-0729.

References

[1] Y. Nambu, Proceedings of the *International Conference on Fluid Mechanics and Theoretical Physics in honor of Proffesor Pei-Yuan Chou's 90th anniversary*, Beijing, 1992; preprint EFI 92-37.

[2] T. Gherghetta and Y. Nambu, as cited in T. Gherghetta, Proceedings of the Yukawa workshop, Gainesville, February 1994.

[3] P. Binétruy and E. Dudas, LPTHE 94/35, hep-ph/9405429.

[4] E. Cremmer, S. Ferrara, L. Girardello and A. Van Proeyen, Nucl. Phys. B212 (1983) 413; J. Bagger, Nucl. Phys. B211 (1983) 302.

[5] P. Binétruy and E. Dudas, LPTHE 94/73.

[6] E. Cremmer, S. Ferrara, C. Kounnas and D. Nanopoulos, Phys. Lett. B133 (1983) 61; N. Dragon, U. Ellwanger and M.G. Schmidt, Nucl. Phys. B255 (1985) 540.

[7] S. Ferrara, L. Girardello and H.P. Nilles, Phys. Lett. B125 (1983) 457.

[8] C. Kounnas, I. Pavel and F. Zwirner, preprint CERN-TH.7185/94, LPTENS-94/08, hep-ph/9406256 (june 1994).

Neutron Electric Dipole Moment in Two-Higgs-Doublet Model*

T. Hayashi[†] , Y. Koide[††] , M. Matsuda[♯‡] and M. Tanimoto[♭‖]

† Kogakkan University, Ise, Mie 516, JAPAN
†† Department of Physics, University of Shizuoka, 52-1 Yada, Shizuoka 422, JAPAN
‡ Department of Physics and Astronomy, Aichi University of Education, Kariya 448, JAPAN
♭ Institut für Theoretische Physik, Universität Wien, A-1090 Wien, AUSTRIA

Abstract

The effect of the "chromo-electric" dipole moment on the electric dipole moment(EDM) of the neutron is studied in the two-Higgs-doublet model. The Weinberg's operator $O_{3g} = GG\tilde{G}$ and the operator $O_{qg} = \bar{q}\sigma\tilde{G}q$ are both investigated in the cases of $\tan\beta \gg 1$, $\tan\beta \ll 1$ and $\tan\beta \simeq 1$. The neutron EDM is considerably reduced due to the destructive contribution with two light Higgs scalars exchanges.

1. Introduction

The electric dipole moment(EDM) of the neutron is of central importance to probe a new origin of CP violation, because it is very small in SM [1]($d_n^{SM} \simeq 10^{-30} - 10^{-31}$ e.cm). Beginning with the papers of Weinberg [2], there has been considerably renewed interest in the neutron EDM induced by CP violation of the neutral Higgs sector. Some studies [3, 4, 5] revealed the importance of the "chromo-electric" dipole moment, which arises from the three-gluon operator $GG\tilde{G}$ found by Weinberg [2] and the light quark operator $\bar{q}\sigma\tilde{G}q$ introduced by Gunion and Wyler [3], in the neutral Higgs sector. Thus, it is important to study the effect of these operators systematically in the model beyond SM. We study the contribution of above two operators to the neutron EDM in the two-Higgs-doublet model(THDM) [6]. The 3×3 mass matrix of the neutral Higgs scalars is carefully investigated in the typical three cases of $\tan\beta \gg 1$, $\tan\beta \simeq 1$ and $\tan\beta \ll 1$. In this model CP symmetry is violated through the mixing among $CP = +$ and $CP = -$ Higgs scalar states.

* Presented by Masahisa MATSUDA.
‡ E-mail: masa@auephyas.aichi-edu.ac.jp.
‖ Permanent address: Science Education Laboratory, Ehime University, Matsuyama 790, JAPAN

In order to give reliable predictions [7], one needs the improvement on the accuracy of the description of the strong-interaction hadronic effects. Chemtob [8] proposed a systematic approach which gives the hadronic matrix elements of the higher-dimension operators involving the gluon fields. We employ his model to estimate the hadronic matrix elements of the operators.

2. CP violation parameter in THDM

The simplest extension of SM is the one with the two Higgs doublets [6]. This model has the possibility of the soft CP violation in the neutral Higgs sector, which does not contribute to the flavor changing neutral current in the B, D and K meson decays. Weinberg [9] has given the unitarity bounds for the dimensionless parameters of the CP nonconservation in THDM. However, the numerically estimated values of these parameters are not always close to the Weinberg's bounds [9]. Although it is difficult to estimate the magnitudes of the CP violation parameters $\text{Im}Z_i(i = 1, 2)$ generally, we found that the neutral Higgs mass matrix is simplified in the extreme cases of $\tan\beta \ll 1$, $\tan\beta \simeq 1$ and $\tan\beta \gg 1$, in which the CP violation parameters are easily calculated. The

CP violation parameters $\mathrm{Im}Z_i^{(n)}$ are deduced to

$$
\begin{aligned}
\mathrm{Im}Z_1^{(k)} &= -\frac{\tan\beta}{\cos\beta}u_1^{(k)}u_3^{(k)}, \\
\mathrm{Im}Z_2^{(k)} &= \frac{\cot\beta}{\sin\beta}u_2^{(k)}u_3^{(k)}, \quad (1)
\end{aligned}
$$

where $u_i^{(k)}$ denotes the i-th component of the k-th eigenvector of the 3×3 Higgs mass matrix and $\tan\beta \equiv v_2/v_1(v_{1(2)}$ is the vacuum expectation value of $\Phi_{1(2)}^0$ giving the masses of $d(u)$-quark sector).

In this model, Higgs potential is generally given as

$$
\begin{aligned}
V_H(\Phi_1,\Phi_2) &= \frac{1}{2}g_1(\Phi_1^\dagger\Phi_1 - |v_1|^2)^2 \\
&+ \frac{1}{2}g_2(\Phi_2^\dagger\Phi_2 - |v_2|^2)^2 \\
&+ g(\Phi_1^\dagger\Phi_1 - |v_1|^2)(\Phi_2^\dagger\Phi_2 - |v_2|^2) \\
&+ g'|\Phi_1^\dagger\Phi_2 - v_1^*v_2|^2 \\
&+ Re\{h(\Phi_1^\dagger\Phi_2 - v_1^*v_2)^2\} \\
&+ \xi[\frac{\Phi_1}{v_1} - \frac{\Phi_2}{v_2}]^\dagger[\frac{\Phi_1}{v_1} - \frac{\Phi_2}{v_2}],
\end{aligned} \quad (2)
$$

where the parameters satisfy the conditions [10]

$$
\begin{aligned}
g_1 &\geq 0, \\
g_2 &\geq 0, \\
g &> -\sqrt{g_1 g_2}, \\
g + g' - |h| &\geq -\sqrt{g_1 g_2}, \\
\xi &\geq 0, \\
g' - |h| + \bar\xi &\geq 0, \\
\bar\xi - g &\geq -\sqrt{g_1 g_2} \quad (\text{where } \bar\xi \equiv \frac{\xi}{|v_1 v_2|^2}).
\end{aligned} \quad (3)
$$

It is noted that, in the case of MSSM, SUSY imposes the conditions on the parameters

$$
\begin{aligned}
g_1 &= g_2 = \frac{1}{4}(g_W^2 + g_W'^2), \\
g &= \frac{1}{4}(g_W^2 - g_W'^2), \\
g' &= -\frac{1}{2}g_W^2, \\
h &= 0.
\end{aligned} \quad (4)
$$

Here $h=0$ means that in MSSM CP violation is not caused throygh Higgs sector. The simplest SUSY extention from MSSM that can have CP violation in the Higgs sector is also discussed [11].

Let us estimate $u_i^{(k)}$ by studying the Higgs mass matrix $\mathbf{M}^2$ whose components are

$$
M_{11}^2 = 2g_1|v_1|^2 + g'|v_2|^2 + \frac{\xi + \mathrm{Re}(hv_1^{*2}v_2^2)}{|v_1|^2},
$$

$$
\begin{aligned}
M_{22}^2 &= 2g_2|v_2|^2 + g'|v_1|^2 + \frac{\xi + \mathrm{Re}(hv_1^{*2}v_2^2)}{|v_2|^2}, \\
M_{33}^2 &= (|v_1|^2 + |v_2|^2)\left[g' + \frac{\xi - \mathrm{Re}(hv_1^{*2}v_2^2)}{|v_1 v_2|^2}\right], \\
M_{12}^2 &= |v_1 v_2|(2g + g') + \frac{\mathrm{Re}(hv_1^{*2}v_2^2) - \xi}{|v_1 v_2|}, \\
M_{13}^2 &= -\frac{\sqrt{|v_1|^2 + |v_2|^2}}{|v_1^2 v_2|}\mathrm{Im}(hv_1^{*2}v_2^2), \quad (5) \\
M_{23}^2 &= -\frac{\sqrt{|v_1|^2 + |v_2|^2}}{|v_1 v_2^2|}\mathrm{Im}(hv_1^{*2}v_2^2).
\end{aligned}
$$

As a phase convension, we take h to be real and

$$
v_1^{*2}v_2^2 = |v_1|^2|v_2|^2\exp(2i\phi). \quad (6)
$$

At first, we consider the case of $\tan\beta \gg 1$ with retaining the order of $\cos\beta$ and setting $\cos^2\beta = 0$ and $\sin\beta = 1$. Then, the mass matrix becomes simple, so the eigenvectors of $\mathbf{M}^2$ in Eq.(5) are easily obtained as follows:

$$
\begin{aligned}
u^{(1)} &= \{\cos\beta - \epsilon\sin\beta, \quad -\sin\beta, \quad 0\}, \quad (7) \\
u^{(2)} &= \{\sin\beta c_\phi, \quad (\cos\beta - \epsilon\sin\beta)c_\phi, \quad -s_\phi\}, \\
u^{(3)} &= \{\sin\beta s_\phi, \quad (\cos\beta - \epsilon\sin\beta)s_\phi, \quad c_\phi\},
\end{aligned}
$$

where $c(s)_\phi \equiv \cos(\sin)\phi$ and

$$
\epsilon \simeq \frac{2(\bar\xi - g - g_2)}{\bar\xi + g' - 2g_2}\cos\beta. \quad (8)
$$

The diagonal masses are given as

$$
M_1^2 = 2g_2, \quad M_2^2 = g' + \bar\xi + h, \quad M_3^2 = g' + \bar\xi - h \quad (9)
$$

in the $v^2 \equiv v_1^2 + v_2^2$ unit. The lightest Higgs scalar to yield CP violation is the second Higgs scalar with the mass M_2 since $\bar\xi$ is positive from Eq.(3) and we take h to be negative as convention. The Higgs scalar with M_1 does not contribute to CP violation because of $u_3^{(1)} = 0$. The absolute values of g' is expected to be $O(1)$, but h seems to be small as estimated in some works [12, 13]. For example Froggatt et al. give the numerical values for the parameters in the case of $\tan\beta \gg 1$ by using infrared fixed point analysis through the renormalization group equations as

$$
\begin{aligned}
g_1 &\simeq 0.96, \quad g_2 \simeq 0.88, \quad g \simeq 0.82 \\
g' &\simeq -1.20, \quad h \simeq -0.09. \quad (10)
\end{aligned}
$$

Therefore, the masses M_2 and M_3 may be almost degenerated. Then, CP violation is reduced by the cancellation between the two different Higgs exchange contributions $\mathrm{Im}Z_i^{(2)}$ and $\mathrm{Im}Z_i^{(3)}$ since $u_i^{(2)}u_3^{(2)}$ and $u_i^{(3)}u_3^{(3)}(i=1,2)$ have same magnitudes with opposite signs. Thus, it is noted that the lightest single Higgs exchange approximation gives miss-leading of CP violation in the case of $\tan\beta \gg 1$.

For $\mathrm{Im}Z_1$, our result reaches the Weinberg bound, but for $\mathrm{Im}Z_2$ the our calculated value is suppressed compared with the Weinberg bound in the order of $1/\tan\beta$.

CP violation in the case of $\tan\beta \ll 1$ is similar to the one of $\tan\beta \gg 1$. For $\mathrm{Im}Z_2$, our numerical result reaches the Weinberg bound, while for $\mathrm{Im}Z_1$ the calculated value is suppressed from the Weinberg bound in the order of $\tan\beta$. The relative sign between $\mathrm{Im}Z_1$ and $\mathrm{Im}Z_2$ is just the same as in the case of $\tan\beta \gg 1$.

The last case to be considered is of $\tan\beta \simeq 1$. In this mass matrix, the off diagonal components are very small compared to the diagonal ones because $g_1 \simeq g_2$ is suggested by some analyses [12, 13] and h is also small as in the case of $\tan\beta \gg 1$. We can calculate $\mathrm{Im}Z_i$ by fixing both values of h and M_2/M_3. For both $\mathrm{Im}Z_2$ and $\mathrm{Im}Z_1$, the calculating values are roughly $1/3$ of the Weinberg bounds. The relative sign between $\mathrm{Im}Z_1$ and $\mathrm{Im}Z_2$ is opposite.

3. Formulation of the neutron EDM

The low energy CP-violating interaction is described by an effective Lagrangian,

$$L_{CP} = \sum_i C_i(M, \mu) O_i(\mu) , \qquad (11)$$

where O_i are the three gluon operator with the dimension six and the quark-gluon operator with the dimension five as follows:

$$
\begin{aligned}
O_{qg}(x) &= -\frac{g_s^3}{2}\overline{q}\sigma_{\mu\nu}\tilde{G}^{\mu\nu}q , \\
O_{3g}(x) &= -\frac{g_s^3}{3}f^{abc}\tilde{G}^a_{\mu\nu}G^b_{\mu\alpha}G^c_{\nu\alpha} , \qquad (12)
\end{aligned}
$$

where q denotes u, d or s quark. The QCD corrected coefficients C_i are given by the two-loop calculations in Refs. [2, 3]. The coefficients C_i are given as

$$C_{ug} = \frac{\sqrt{2}G_F m_u}{64\pi^4}\{f(\frac{m_t^2}{m_H^2}) + g(\frac{m_t^2}{m_H^2})\}\mathrm{Im}Z_2(\frac{g_s(\mu)}{g_s(M)})^{-\frac{74}{23}},$$

$$
\begin{aligned}
C_{dg} = &\frac{\sqrt{2}G_F m_d}{64\pi^4}\{f(\frac{m_t^2}{m_H^2})\tan^2\beta\mathrm{Im}Z_2 \\
&- g(\frac{m_t^2}{m_H^2})\cot^2\beta\mathrm{Im}Z_1\}(\frac{g_s(\mu)}{g_s(M)})^{-\frac{74}{23}},
\end{aligned}
$$

$$C_{3g} = \frac{\sqrt{2}G_F}{(4\pi)^4}\mathrm{Im}Z_2 h(\frac{m_t^2}{m_H^2})(\frac{g_s(\mu)}{g_s(M)})^{-\frac{108}{23}},$$

$$(13)$$

where the functions $f(x), g(x), h(x)$ are deduced from loop integral as given in Refs. [2, 3].

For the strong interaction hadronic effect, the systematic technique has been developed by Chemtob [8] in the operator with the higher-dimension involving the gluon fields. The hadronic matrix elements of the two operators are approximated by the intermediate states with the single nucleon pole and the nucleon plus one pion. Then, the nucleon matrix elements are defined as

$$
\begin{aligned}
\langle N(P)|O_i(0)|N(P)\rangle &= A_i\overline{U}(P)i\gamma_5 U(P), \\
\langle N(P')|O_i|N(P)\pi(k)\rangle &= B_i\overline{U}(P')\tau^a U(P) , \qquad (14)
\end{aligned}
$$

where $U(P)$ is the normalized nucleon Dirac spinors with the four momuntum P. Using A_i and $B_i(i = ug, dg, sg, 3g)$, the neutron EDM, d_n^γ, are written as

$$d_n^\gamma = \frac{e\mu_n}{2m_n^2}\sum_i C_i A_i + F(g_{\pi NN})\sum_i C_i B_i , \qquad (15)$$

where μ_n is the neutron anomalous magnetic moment. The $F(g_{\pi NN})$ was given by calculating the pion and nucleon loop corrections using the chiral Lagrangian for $N\pi\gamma$ [8]. The coefficients A_i and B_i were given by the large N_c current algebra and the η_0 meson dominance [8].

4. Numerical results of the neutron EDM

Let us begin with discussing the numerical results in the case of $\tan\beta \gg 1$. The contributions of O_{ug} and O_{3g} are are negligibly small because the CP violation parameters are roughly estimated as

$$\mathrm{Im}Z_2^{(2)} \simeq -\mathrm{Im}Z_2^{(3)} \simeq \frac{1}{\tan^2\beta} \ll \mathrm{Im}Z_1^{(2,3)},$$

$$\mathrm{Im}Z_1^{(3)} \simeq -\mathrm{Im}Z_1^{(3)} \simeq \frac{1}{2}\tan^2\beta. \qquad (16)$$

The main contribution follows from the one of $O_{dg}+O_{sg}$, in which the operator O_{sg} is dominant due to the s-quark mass. The coefficient C_{sg} is

$$
\begin{aligned}
C_{sg} = (const.) \times m_s\{&f(\frac{m_t^2}{m_{H_2}^2}) - f(\frac{m_t^2}{m_{H_3}^2}) \\
&- \frac{1}{2}g(\frac{m_t^2}{m_{H_2}^2}) + \frac{1}{2}g(\frac{m_t^2}{m_{H_3}^2})\}.
\end{aligned}
\qquad (17)
$$

As the mass difference of these two Higgs scalar masses becomes smaller, the neutron EDM is considerably reduced since the second Higgs scalar exchange contributes in the opposite sign to the lightest Higgs scalar one as shown in the above equation. Thus, it is found that the second lightest Higgs scalar also significantly contributes to CP violation.

In the case of $\tan\beta \ll 1$, the contributions of O_{ug} and O_{3g} become very large due to the large $\mathrm{Im}Z_2$. However, these contribute to the neutron EDM in opposite signs, so they almost cancel each other. The remaining contribution is the one of $O_{dg} + O_{sg}$.

In the case of $\tan\beta \simeq 1$, the dominant contribution is the one of $O_{dg} + O_{sg}$. In both regions of the large and small m_{H2}/m_{H3}, the predicted neutron EDM is reduced. At $m_{H2}/m_{H3} \simeq 1$, the cancellation mechanism by the second lightest Higgs scalar operates well, while around $m_{H2}/m_{H3} \simeq 0$, the large mass difference of the two Higgs scalars leads to the small mixing between the scalar and pseudscalar Higgs bosons.

5. Summary

We have studied the effects of the four operators O_{ug}, $O_{dg} + O_{sg}$ and O_{3g} on the neutron EDM. The contribution of O_{sg} dominates over that of other operators. Moreover, the contributions of O_{ug} and O_{3g} cancel out each other due to their opposite signs. This qualitative situation does not depend on the detail of the strong interaction hadronic model. Thus, the Weinberg's three gluon operator is not a main source of the neutron EDM in THDM. The CP violation mainly follows from the two light neutral Higgs scalar exchanges. Since these two exchange contributions are of opposite signs, the CP violation is considerably reduced if the mass difference of the two Higgs scalars is small. Since our predicted neutron EDM lies around the present experimental bound, experimental improvement can reveal the new physics beyond SM. The present upper limit for d_n^γ is $8 \times 10^{-26} e \cdot cm$ which was given at the 26th ICHEP. Historically to reduce the upper limit by one order of magnitude experimentally, it has taken almost 10 years. We hope that a rapid experimental reduction of the upper limit will be achieved, and that a finite value will be reported soon at an ICHEP.

References

[1] M. Kobayashi and T. Maskawa, Prog. Theor. Phys. **49**(1973) 652.
[2] S. Weinberg, Phys. Rev. Lett. **63** (1989) 2333.
[3] J.F. Gunion and D. Wyler, Phys.Letts.**248B** (1990)170.
[4] A. De Rújula, M.B. Gavela, O. Pène and F.J. Vegas, Phys.Lett.**245B** (1990) 640; N-P. Chang and D-X. Li, Phys. Rev. **D42** (1990) 871;D. Chang, T.W. Kephart, W-Y. Keung and T.C. Yuan, Phys. Rev. Lett. **68** (1992) 439.
[5] S.M.Barr, A.Zee, Phys. Rev. Lett. **65** (1990) 21;S.M. Barr, Phys. Rev. Lett. **68** (1992) 1822,Phys. Rev. **D47** (1993) 2025.
[6] J.F. Gunion, H.E. Haber, G.L. Kane and S. Dawson, *"Higgs Hunter's Guide"*, Addison-Wesley, Reading, MA(1989).
[7] A. Manohar and H. Georgi, Nucl.Phys.**B234** (1984)189.
[8] M. Chemtob, Phys. Rev. **D45** (1992) 1649.
[9] S. Weinberg, Phys. Rev. **D42** (1990) 860.
[10] B. Kasterning, Private communications and see the preprint hep-ph@9307225 .
[11] J. Ellis, J.F. Gunion, H.E. Haber, L. Roszkowski and F. Zwirner, Phys. Rev. **D39** (1989) 844;See also Refs.[5].
[12] M. Chemtob, Z.Phys. **C60**(1993)443.
[13] M.A. Luty, Phys. Rev. **D41** (1990) 2893;C.D. Froggatt, I.G. Knowles and R.G. Moorhouse, Phys. Lett. **249B** (1990)273.

Paper presented at XXVII Int. Conf. on High Energy Physics: Session Pa-4
Glasgow, UK, 20–27 July 1994

Grand Unified Theories:
SUSY or Naturally Split Heavy Fermions?

J.L. Chkareuli[†], I.G. Gogoladze and A.B. Kobakhidze

Institute of Physics, Georgian Academy of Sciences, 380077 Tbilisi, Georgia

Sussex-Tbilisi Collaboration

Abstract

We argue that besides the familiar SUSY $SU(5)$ case there could appear the unification of the standard coupling constants in the extended non-SUSY $SU(N)$ GUTs (N is non-prime number, $N \geq 6$) through the natural split-multiplet mechanism for the complementary heavy fermions. The special theorem regulating this process is established and the minimal $SU(6)$ model is considered in detail.

1. Introduction

It has been known for the last decade that with no new physics in "Grand Plateau" the unification of the standard coupling constants definitely fails. With the data obtained at LEP this failure was shown to be overwhelming [1].

On the contrary, the minimal SUSY extension of the Standard Model (SM) [2] gives the perfect unification - a result which many people are incline to consider almost the confirmation of SUSY in laboratory.

In spite of our own belief in the beauty and relevance of SUSY we present here the alternative possibility for the unification of the standard coupling constants naturally appearing in the extended $SU(N)$ GUTs beyond of the ordinary $SU(5)$ model [3]. These GUTs whereas they break down to the SM, are proved to have a radiative splitting mechanism for the complementary heavy fermions inducing a few special types of the split-multiplet models postulated the last decade [4,1].

2. The split-multiplet mechanism.

Let us consider a general $SU(N)$ GUT containing besides the "standard" anomaly free set of the fermion multiplets with the ordinary quarks and leptons n

† E-MAIL: jlc@physics.iberiapac.ge

complementary pairs of the $SU(N)$-conjugated chiral fermions (in the left-handed basis)

$$n \cdot [\psi_1(r) + \overline{\psi}_2(r)] \qquad (1)$$

where r stands for dimension of the particular antisymmetric representation used only following to the well-known simplicity criterion [5].

The $SU(N)$-invariant mass term of the complementary fermions $\psi_1(r)$ and $\overline{\psi}_2(r)$ is supposedly suppressed by some global (or discrete) symmetry D which could be assigned also to the adjoint scalar Φ_j^i ($i, j = 1, ..., N$) of $SU(N)$

$$\psi_1 \to \psi_1 e^{i\alpha_1}, \ \overline{\psi}_2 \to \overline{\psi}_2 e^{-i\alpha_2}, \ \Phi \to \Phi e^{i(\alpha_2 - \alpha_1)} \qquad (2)$$

So, only the fully invariant Yukawa coupling

$$\overline{\psi}_2 \Phi \psi_1 \qquad (3)$$

could induce masses of the complementary fermions during the starting symmetry breaking

$$SU(N) \otimes D \xrightarrow{\Phi} SU(m) \otimes SU(N-m) \otimes U(\mathrm{I}) \qquad (4)$$

when the scalar Φ_i^j develops its "standard" VEV:

$$< \Phi_j^i > = \Lambda \, diag[1...1, -\frac{m}{N-m}, ..., -\frac{m}{N-m}]_j^i \quad (5)$$

The following simple theorem [6] regulates this process.

Theorem. *The $SU(N)$ GUT symmetry breaking (4) induced by the adjoint scalar (5) having the invariant Yukawa coupling (3) with the complementary fermion multiplets (1) leaves to be massless all their $SU(m) \otimes SU(N-m) \otimes U(I)$ submultiplets whose the total $U(I)$ hypercharges are equal to zero.*

The proof of the theorem simply follow from the evident observation that the form of the VEV (5) completely repeats the form of the $U(I)$ generator in (4), wich does not coinside in general with the ordinary hypercharge $U(1)$ of the SM.

So, we are led to a natural split-multiplet mechanism for the complementary fermions. A part of them having zero hypercharges necessarily survive under the breaking (4) on the grand scale Λ and receive their masses only on the intermediate one when the subsymmetries $SU(N-m)$ and/or $SU(m)$ breaks.

To have $SU(N)$ GUT broken at once to the SM below the unification point introduce now besides the basic scalar Φ_j^i $N-5$ fundamental scalar fields $\phi_i^{(s)}$ ($s = 1, ..., N-5$) developing the orthogonal VEVs $\lambda^{(s)}$ which are all of order the grand scale $O(\Lambda)$,

$$SU(N) \otimes D \xrightarrow{\Phi, \phi^{(s)}} SU(3) \otimes SU(2) \otimes U(1) \quad (6)$$

One can be easily seen that the scalars $\phi_i^{(s)}$ do not influence as yet massless split ("neutral") complementary fermions directly but only through the "intersecting" terms in the general Higgs potential of scalars Φ and $\phi^{(s)}$

$$V(\Phi, \phi) = ... + \frac{H}{4}(\overline{\Phi}\Phi)^2 + \frac{h}{2}Tr(\overline{\Phi}\Phi\overline{\phi}\phi) + ... \quad (7)$$

(index s is omitted) inducing in the VEV matrix (5) the $SU(3) \otimes SU(2) \otimes U(1)$-invariant correction of order $\epsilon \sim \frac{h}{H}(\frac{\lambda}{\Lambda})^2$ and split fermion masses $M_{SF} \sim \epsilon\Lambda$ (all hypercharged complementary fermions have masses $M_{HF} \sim \Lambda$).

Now taking $\epsilon \ll 1 (h \ll H)$ we would have rather light "neutral" fermions which could contribute to the standard constant α_3, α_2 and α_1 in interval $M_{SF} \div M_G$ making them to unify if it is the case. *The natural order for ϵ seems to be originated from the radiative corrections, $\epsilon \sim \alpha_{GUT}^2$.* We consider it as our end point. On the other hand some unknown mechanism could keep ϵ very small giving extremely light "neutral" complementary fermions being in the TeV region.

3.   Group-theoretical constraints

Consider now the concrete representations for the complementary fermions (1). Let ψ_1 and $\bar{\psi}_2$ be p-index antisymmetric tensors with k $SU(m)$ indices and $p-k$ $SU(N-m)$ ones during the basic symmetry breaking (4) of $SU(N)$. According to our theorem the massless (or light, see above) submultiplets in them have the zero hypercharges, i.e.

$$k - (p-k)\frac{m}{N-m} = 0, \quad k = \frac{m}{N}p \quad (8)$$

So, the split submultiplets in the complementary pairs can appear if there is satisfied the division criterion (8). On can see that it fails for the prime rank-number N ($N = 5, 7, ...$) apart from the trivial cases of unbroken symmetry ($m = N$) or singlet complementary fermions ($p = N$).

4.   Minimal "standard" model: SU(6)

The division criterion (9) suggests the simplest "symmetrical" solution to this minimal case ($m = 3, p = 2$)

$$SU(6) \otimes D \xrightarrow{\Phi} SU(3) \otimes SU(3) \otimes U(I) \xrightarrow{\phi} \text{SM} \quad (9)$$

with fermion content

$$3 \cdot (2 \cdot \bar{6} + 15) + n \cdot (15 + \overline{15}) \quad (10)$$

where the first term includes three families of ordinary quarks and leptons [7] and the second one corresponds to the complementary fermions with the light split submultiplets

$$n \cdot (15 + \overline{15}) \xrightarrow{\Phi} n \cdot [(3, 3) + (\bar{3}, \bar{3})]$$
$$\xrightarrow{\phi} n \cdot [(3, 2) + (\bar{3}, 2) + (3, 1) + (\bar{3}, 1)] \quad (11)$$

Scalar sector besides two heavy scalars $\Phi(35)$ and $\phi(6)$ includes also two Salam-Weinberg doublets $H_1(6)$ and $H_2(15)$ as usually it is in $SU(6)$ to get masses to up and down quarks [7] (numbers in brackets stand for reps of scalars).

An inspection of fermion submultiplets (11) together with the extra scalar doublet in the model shows that we have directly received so called the ABC split-multiplet Ansatz (well consistent with unification) found recently by Amaldi et al.[1] after they have scanned over 1600 split combinations. The only difference is that our extra scalar doublet as Higgs one must be light (of order of Fermi scale) whereas the masses of the splitted fermions M_{SF} will depend on a number n of the starting complementary pairs to provide for the final unification.

Using as input parameters $\alpha_s = 0.118$ and $\sin^2 \theta_W = 0.2333$ [1] in the standard RG equations for the running constants α_3, α_2 and α_1

$$\mu \frac{d}{d\mu} \alpha_i^{-1} = -\frac{1}{2\pi} \left(b_i + \frac{b_{ij}}{4\pi} \alpha_j + O(\alpha_j^2) \right) \qquad (12)$$

with the one-loop and two-loop b-factors [1] we lead to evolution of standard couplings shown in Figs.1-3 for $n = 1$, $n = 2$ and $n = 3$ respectively.

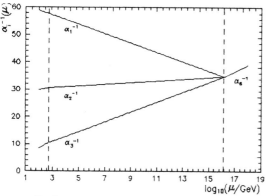

Figure 1. Evolution of the standard coupling constants in the $SU(6)$ model with one family of complementary fermions: $M_{SF} = 5.4 \cdot 10^2$ GeV, $M_G = 1.3 \cdot 10^{16}$ GeV, $\alpha_{GUT}^{-1} = 34.7$.

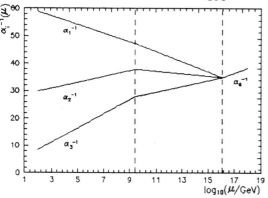

Figure 2. Evolution of the standard coupling constants in the $SU(6)$ model with two families of complementary fermions: $M_{SF} = 2.4 \cdot 10^9$ GeV, $M_G = 1.2 \cdot 10^{16}$ GeV, $\alpha_{GUT}^{-1} = 34.8$.

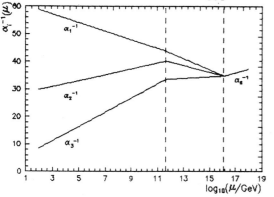

Figure 3. Evolution of the standard coupling constants in the $SU(6)$ model with three families of complementary fermions: $M_{SF} = 3.9 \cdot 10^{11}$ GeV, $M_G = 1.3 \cdot 10^{16}$ GeV, $\alpha_{GUT}^{-1} = 34.8$. One can see clearly the natural "radiative" distance between split-multiplet mass M_{SF} and the grand scale M_G.

All Figs.1-3 demonstrate the perfect unification practically at the same point $(1.2 - 1.3) \cdot 10^{16}$ GeV corresponding proton life-time $\tau_p \sim 10^{36}y$. The Fig.3 seems to be the most impressive. *One can see clearly the natural "radiative" distance between split-multiplet mass M_{SF} and the grand scale M_G in the "symmetrical" $SU(6)$ model with three family of the complementary fermions.*

Asymmetrical case $(m = 4, p = 3)$ in $SU(6)$-model $(SU(6) \rightarrow SU(4) \otimes SU(2) \otimes U(\text{I}))$ does not lead to unification.

5. Conclusion

We have discussed here a new possible round in the building of the non-SUSY $SU(N)$ GUTs.

The natural split-multiplet mechanism presented here whereas it provides for unification in general its $SU(6)$ version allows to predict the electroweak angle value as well if we take the mass scale M_{SF} of splitted fermions as of the pure radiative origin, $M_{SF} \sim \alpha_{GUT}^2 M_G$. So the "standard" $SU(6)$ model with three families of the complementary fermions seems to compare well with the SUSY SM as to the observable aspects of unification.

Also we found [8] a number of constructive split-multiplet models in a case of higher symmetries containing quark-lepton families, particularly in $SU(8)$ [7], $SU(9)$ [9] and $SU(11)$ [5] when it as a preliminary breaks to $SU(8)$.

Acknowledgements

One of us (J.C.) is grateful to A.Anselm, S.Dimopoulos and H.Nielsen for interesting discussions.

References

[1] U. Amaldi *et al.*, Phys. Lett. B260(1991)131; B281(1992)374.
[2] S. Dimopoulos and H. Georgi, Nucl. Phys. B193(1981)150.
[3] H. Georgi and S.L. Glashow, Phys. Rev. lett. 32(1974)438.
[4] P.H. Frampton and H. Georgi, Phys. lett. B135(1984)515.
[5] H. Georgi Nucl. phys. B156(1979)126.
[6] J.L. Chkareuli, *Talk at the inter-University Seminar*, Imperial College, London,1993 (unpublished).
[7] P. Langacker, Phys. Rep. C72(1981)185.
[8] J.L. Chkareuli, I.G. Gogoladze and A.B. Kobakhidze, Nucl. Phys. B(1994), in press.
[9] P.H. Frampton, Phys. Lett. B89(1979)352.

Parallel Session Pa-5

Low *x* Physics

Conveners: H. Abramowicz (Tel-Aviv University)
G. Levin (St Petersburg)

Scientific secretaries: M. Utley
A. Wilson (reserve)

Paper presented at XXVII Int. Conf. on High Energy Physics: Session Pa-5
Glasgow, UK, 20–27 July 1994

Theoretical advances in small x physics

R. K. Ellis

Fermilab
P O Box 500, Batavia, IL 60510, USA.

Abstract

Theoretical advances in small x physics are reviewed. Emphasis is placed on the purely theoretical results without comparison with data.

1. Introduction

My brief is to discuss the advances in the theoretical treatment of small x processes. For the most part I shall avoid the practical questions, such as whether the theoretical predictions are supported by the data and which features of the data are especially sensitive to the expected behaviour at small x. These are difficult questions which are addressed in the presentation of Martin[1]. Theoretical aspects of the small x problem are also treated in the talks of Lipatov and Stirling at this conference[2].

2. BFKL equation

The BFKL (Balitski-Fadin-Kuraev-Lipatov) equation predicts a steep small x growth for gluon distribution[3].

$$xg(x) \sim x^{-\omega_L} \qquad (1)$$

where the exponent ω_L is given by,

$$\omega_L = \frac{12\ln 2}{\pi}\alpha_S(Q_0^2) = 2.65\alpha_S(Q_0^2) \qquad (2)$$

What is the BFKL equation? Define an unintegrated gluon distribution $f(x, k_T^2)$ and it moments $f(\omega, k_T^2)$. In terms of the normal gluon distribution function $g(x, Q^2)$ these two functions are given by,

$$g(x, Q^2) = \int_0^{Q^2} dk_T^2 \; f(x, k_T^2) \qquad (3)$$

$$f(\omega, k_T^2) = \int_0^1 dx \; x^\omega f(x, k_T^2). \qquad (4)$$

The BFKL equation is a ladder equation for f which resums terms of order $(\alpha_S/\omega)^n$

$$f(\omega, k_T^2) = f^0(\omega, k_T^2) + \frac{3\alpha_S}{\pi\omega} \int \frac{dl_T^2}{l_T^2} K(k_T^2, l_T^2) f(\omega, l_T^2) \qquad (5)$$

The equation is scale free so we seek a solution of the form $(k_T^2)^\gamma$. The eigenvalue condition for a solution to homogeneous equation is

$$1 = p\chi(\gamma); \; p = \frac{3\alpha_S}{\pi\omega} \qquad (6)$$

where

$$\chi(\gamma) = 2\psi(1) - \psi(\gamma) - \psi(1-\gamma) \qquad (7)$$

The function $\chi(\gamma)$ is fixed by the moments of the kernel K and $\psi(z) = \Gamma'(z)/\Gamma(z)$ is the digamma function. The function χ has the following properties,

$$\chi(\gamma) \rightarrow 4\ln 2 + 14\zeta(3)\left(\gamma - \frac{1}{2}\right)^2 + \ldots \text{ when } \gamma \rightarrow \frac{1}{2};$$

$$\chi(\gamma) \rightarrow \frac{1}{\gamma} + 2\zeta(3)\gamma^2 + O(\gamma^4), \text{ when } \gamma \rightarrow 0, \qquad (8)$$

and is shown plotted in figure 1.

The function γ defined by Eq. (6) is the BFKL anomalous dimension. Expanding the BFKL anomalous dimension for small a,($a = \alpha_S/(2\pi)$).

$$\gamma(w) \rightarrow 6\frac{a}{\omega} + 288\zeta(3)\frac{a^4}{\omega^4} + \ldots \qquad (9)$$

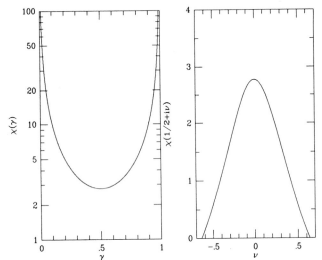

Figure 1. The BFKL kernel χ parallel and perpendicular to the real axis

Thus the BFKL equation gives a prediction for the small ω behaviour of the gluon anomalous dimension.

2.1. An alternative formulation of BFKL

The derivation of the BFKL equation is quite complicated[3, 4] and involves sums over classes of Feynman diagrams. An alternative formulation of the BFKL equation in terms of colour dipoles has been given by Mueller[5] and Nikolaev and Zakharov[6]. These authors write down the infinite momentum frame wave function for a colour singlet $q\bar{q}$ pair in a mixed representation of momenta and co-ordinates, namely the longitudinal momentum fraction z and the transverse separation b. During the emission of the soft radiation, the $q\bar{q}$ pair can be considered[5, 6] a dipole of fixed transverse separation b. The modification of the wave function due to the emission of soft radiation can be written as,

$$\Psi_{\alpha\beta}^{[1]}(\vec{b},\vec{b}_1;z,z_1) = \frac{-igt^A}{\pi}\Psi_{\alpha\beta}^{[0]}(\vec{b};z)\left[\frac{\vec{b}_1}{\vec{b}_1^{\,2}} - \frac{\vec{b}_2}{\vec{b}_2^{\,2}}\right]\cdot\epsilon \quad (10)$$

where b_1 and b_2 are the transverse separation of the emitted gluon from the quark and anti-quark. z_1 is the longitudinal momentum fraction of the emitted gluon and ϵ is its polarization. The light cone probability density is given by the square of the above wave function,

$$\frac{d\Phi^{[1]}(\vec{b},\vec{b}_1;z,z_1)}{dz_1 d^2\vec{b}_1} = \frac{\alpha_S C_F}{\pi}\frac{1}{2z_1}\left[\frac{\vec{b}^{\,2}}{\vec{b}_1^{\,2}\vec{b}_2^{\,2}}\right]\Phi^{[0]}(\vec{b};z) \quad (11)$$

In the large N_c approximation we treat the gluon as a $q\bar{q}$ pair. Emitting yet another gluon, we find that it can be emitted from the dipole of separation b_1 or from the dipole of separation b_2 or as a virtual correction to the

original dipole of separation b. The consequent growth in the interaction cross section (gluon distribution) is,

$$\frac{d\sigma}{d\ln(1/x)} \sim \int d^2 b_1 \left[\sigma(b_1) + \sigma(b_2) - \sigma(b)\right]\frac{\vec{b}^2}{[\vec{b}_1^2][\vec{b}_2^2]} \quad (12)$$

Eq. (12) leads to a simple definition of the function χ in terms of the eikonal factor in transverse co-ordinate space.

$$(\vec{b}^{\,2})^\gamma\chi(\gamma) = \frac{1}{\pi}\int d^2\vec{b}_1\left[(\vec{b}_1^{\,2})^\gamma + (\vec{b}_2^{\,2})^\gamma - (\vec{b}^{\,2})^\gamma\right]\frac{\vec{b}^2}{[\vec{b}_1^2][\vec{b}_2^2]} \quad (13)$$

Evaluating the integral we obtain the result of Eq. (7). The colour dipole approach to small x physics offers the prospect of more information than the traditional BFKL approach because the small momentum part of the IMF wave function is completely calculated[7].

2.2. High energy and mass singularity factorization

In a recent paper by Catani and Hautmann[8] the relationship between the normal factorization of collinear singularites and the BFKL equation has been clarified. In order to regulate the mass singularities, the BFKL equation is generalized to d dimensions,

$$f(w,k_T) = \delta^{d-2}(k_T) + \frac{3\bar{\alpha}}{\pi\omega}\int\frac{d^{d-2}l_T}{\pi l_T^2}K(k_T^2, l_T^2)f(\omega, l_T) \quad (14)$$

The important point is that the kernel K is unchanged, because in the soft limit only a single polarization dominates. This ladder equation generates a mass singularity in the integrated gluon distribution function for every rung. In the dimensional regularization scheme this appears as a pole in $d - 4 = -2\epsilon$. A formal power series solution allows one to factorize the mass singularity poles in the $\overline{MS}$ scheme to all orders. The gluon distribution g is derived from the solution to the BFKL equation.

$$g(\omega, \mu^2) = \int\frac{d^{d-2}k_T}{\pi}f(\omega, k_T^2)\Theta(\mu^2 - k_T^2) \quad (15)$$

This gluon distribution satisfies the property of factorization to all orders at small ω.

$$g^0(\omega, \epsilon) = g(\omega)\Gamma(\omega, 1/\epsilon) \quad (16)$$

From the function Γ one can derive the anomalous dimension, which is identical to the BFKL result, Eq. 6. The perturbative result for the anomalous dimension is $\gamma(p) = p + 2\zeta(3)p^4 + 2\zeta(5)p^6 + \dots$ in accord with Eq. (9).

Having a method of factorizing the small x terms one can calculate the subleading terms in small x anomalous dimension qg but not gg. This is because the leading singularities in qg diagrams are from diagrams of the type shown in figure 2a, involving an impact factor attached to a sum of Lipatov rungs. In the gg case non-ladder diagrams of the type shown in figure 2b also give a leading contribution.

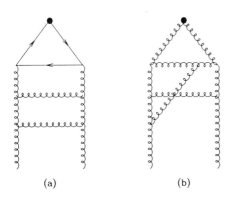

(a)   (b)

Figure 2. Diagram which (a) is and (b) is not calculable using the techniques of ref[8].

The authors of ref. [8] give an implicit expression for $\gamma_{qg}(p)$ in $\overline{MS}$ scheme to all orders. Expanding this expression we obtain for the first five terms,

$$\gamma_{qg}(p) = \frac{\alpha_S}{2\pi} T_R \frac{2}{3}$$
$$\left[1 + 1.67p + 1.56p^2 + 3.42p^3 + 5.51p^4 + \dots\right]$$

Results for the qg anomalous dimensions to all orders in DIS scheme and DIS coefficient functions in $\overline{MS}$ scheme are given in ref. [8]. The complete numerical analysis not yet done, but ref. [8] gives the first results on next-to-next-to-leading terms in γ at small x and elucidates the relationship between factorization of mass singularities at small x and BFKL.

3. GLAP based approach

The use of the BFKL equation to describe low x physics has a number of shortcomings. Firstly, the BFKL equation is formulated for a fixed coupling constant, and describes a diffusion in $\ln k^2$. It therefore contains sensitivity to low momentum scales where perturbation theory is not valid. Secondly, there is, at present, little understanding of the procedure for including subleading terms. Thirdly, the BFKL anomalous dimension is a poor representation of perturbative anomalous dimension away from $\omega = 0$. Figure 3 shows this where fixed order perturbation theory anomalous dimensions (L,NL,NNL,NNNL) are compared with the full BFKL result. Experience with perturbation theory shows us that the anomalous dimension is a rapidly changing

function between $\omega = 0$ and $\omega = 1$. The constraint of momentum conservation requires, in a theory without quarks, that $\gamma_{gg}(\omega = 1) = 0$. The BFKL anomalous dimension which resums terms singular at $\omega = 0$ does not satisfy this constraint.

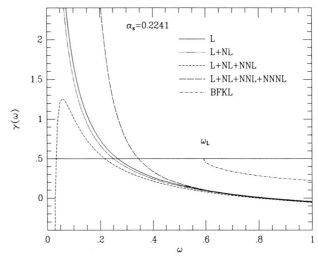

Figure 3. The BFKL anomalous dimension compared with perturbation theory.

We therefore turn to another approach. The Gribov-Lipatov-Altarelli-Parisi (GLAP) equation[9] is completely understood in principle to all orders and in practice to 2nd order, with limited information on small ω behaviour in yet higher order. The GLAP equation (ignoring quarks at small ω) is given by,

$$\frac{dg(\omega)}{d\ln Q^2} = \gamma(\omega)g(\omega) \tag{17}$$

where (dropping terms which are not singular at $\omega = 0$),

$$\gamma(\omega) \to c_1 \frac{a}{\omega} + c_2 \frac{a^2}{\omega} + c_3 \frac{a^3}{\omega^2} + c_4 \frac{a^4}{\omega^4} + \dots \tag{18}$$

The moments are defined by, $(y = \ln(1/x))$.

$$g(\omega) = \int_0^1 dx\, x^\omega g(x) \equiv \int_0^\infty dy \exp(-\omega y)\left[x g(x)\right] \tag{19}$$

The variable ω is conjugate to $\ln(1/x)$, so the small x region probes behavior at small ω.

We therefore have two small parameters in the problem, α_S and ω, and it is important to establish at the outset the relationship between them. If ω becomes too small perturbation theory will be violated. Consider a regime in which $\alpha_S \sim \epsilon^2$ and $\omega \sim \epsilon$ where ϵ is a small parameter,

$$
\begin{array}{cccc}
\epsilon & \epsilon^2 & \epsilon^3 & \epsilon^4 \\
\alpha_S/\omega, & \alpha_S, & \alpha_S\omega, & \alpha_S\omega^2 \quad : \gamma_0 \\
 & \alpha_S^2/\omega, & \alpha_S^2 & \quad : \gamma_1 \\
 & & \alpha_S^3/\omega^2 & \quad : \gamma_2 \\
 & & & \alpha_S^4/\omega^4 \quad : \gamma_3
\end{array} \tag{20}
$$

It is therefore possible to imagine a regime in which a finite number of orders in perturbation theory gives a consistent approximation. We will first perform two analytic exercises for the terms of order ϵ before proceeding to describe the results of a full numerical program. Assume $\gamma = 6a/\omega$, $t = 6/b_0 \ln(a(Q_0^2)/a(Q^2))$. The solution to GLAP equation is

$$f(\omega, t) = \exp\left(\frac{t}{\omega}\right) f(\omega, 0) \qquad (21)$$

and hence the inverse Mellin transform is given by,

$$xf(x, t) = \frac{1}{2\pi i} \int_C d\omega \, \exp\left(\frac{t}{\omega} + \omega y\right) f(\omega, 0) \qquad (22)$$

Let us assume a simple form for the distribution function at small x,

$$xf(x, 0) = \frac{A}{x^{\omega_0}}, \quad f(\omega, 0) = \frac{A}{\omega - \omega_0} \qquad (23)$$

The initial distribution contains a pole in the complex plane at a position determined by the slope of the distribution in x space. The behaviour after evolution depends on the position of this pole.

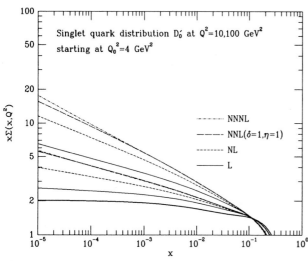

Figure 4. Evolution of the quarks starting with a flat distribution.

3.1.   Case I, $\omega_0 < \omega_s$

The saddle point evaluation of the integral gives the result

$$xf(x) = \frac{1}{2}\sqrt{\frac{\omega_s^3}{\pi t}} \exp\left(2\sqrt{yt}\right) f(\omega_s, 0). \qquad (24)$$

where the saddle point is $\omega_s = \left(\frac{t}{y}\right)^{\frac{1}{2}}$. At small x the saddle point approaches the origin and the anomalous dimension becomes large because of the a/ω terms.

3.2.   Case II, $\omega_0 > \omega_s$

In this case the singularity at ω_0 is the rightmost singularity. Shifting contour through this singularity we get,

$$xf(x, t) = A\exp\left(\frac{t}{\omega_0} + y\omega_0\right) + O\left(\frac{\omega_S}{\omega_0}\exp(-\omega_0 y)\right) \qquad (25)$$

The second term is suppressed at small x. We only need the anomalous dimension at the pole value $\omega = \omega_0$ fixed by the starting distribution. The evolution is controlled by the form of the starting distribution.

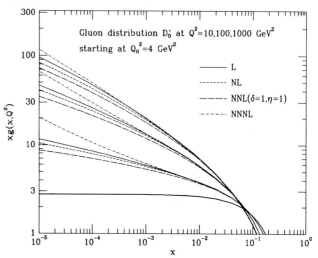

Figure 5. Evolution of the gluons starting with a flat distribution.

In summary, we find that for a flat initial distribution $\omega \sim \omega_s$ and finite order perturbation theory breaks down when γ becomes too big. On the other hand for a steep initial distribution $\omega \sim \omega_0$ and perturbation theory appears under control.

3.3.   Numerical program

The consequences of the GLAP equation at small x have been investigated in ref. [10] by performing the inverse Mellin transform numerically. The program of ref. [10] is a descendant of program due to DFLM[11]. The integration has been performed in the complex ω-plane with various approximations for the anomalous dimensions.

Fig. 4 shows the evolution of the quarks starting with a flat distribution. Figure 4 shows three sets of curves; the starting distribution which is the same in all approximations, four curves at $Q^2 = 10$ GeV^2 and four curves at $Q^2 = 100$ GeV^2. Figure 4 illustrates the importance of the NNL terms[8] for the quark distribution. The corresponding result for the gluons is shown in figure 5. Here the NNNL terms have a real impact at small x. The overall conclusion is that at small x and with a flat starting distribution,

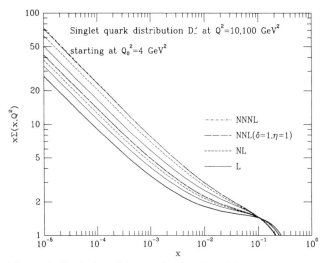

Figure 6. Evolution of the quarks starting with a steep distribution.

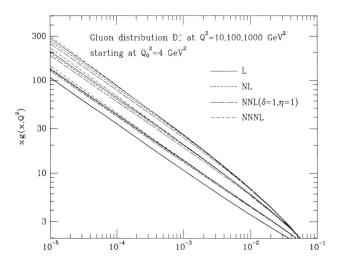

Figure 7. Evolution of the gluons starting with a steep distribution.

perturbation theory is not adequate at small x. Below $x = 10^{-3}$ the $D0'$ evolution cannot be trusted.

If we start with a steeper starting distribution, in this case the D'_- distribution of MRS, the resultant curves are shown in figures 6 and 7. As suggested by our analytic argument the effective value of ω is pinned down at $\omega \sim \frac{1}{2}$ which is the value of the exponent choosen in the starting distribution. The perturbative corrections are much more controlled. To show that these conclusions persist when we consider a physical quantity we show the results for F_2 at $Q^2 = 15$ GeV^2 in fig.8. The two sets of curves representing the results of evolving from a flat or a steep starting distribution. The data shown predates the Glasgow conference and are plotted to show the kinematic range covered by the data.

4. Conclusions

There have been considerable conceptual advances in description of small x with BFKL. The simplicity of the impact factor formulation of BFKL is a great step forward. However there are many phenomenological problems still outstanding. The GLAP approach to the description of small x data allows interpolation throughout the HERA region, if the starting distribution is already steep at low Q^2. However the evolution from distributions which are flat at low Q^2 will require going beyond the first two orders of perturbation theory.

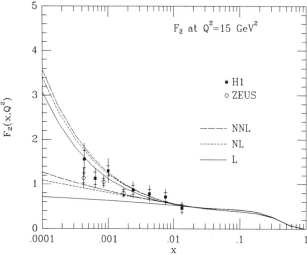

Figure 8. Comparison of the HERA points with the theory.

References

[1] A. Martin, these proceedings.
[2] L. Lipatov, these proceedings;
    W. J. Stirling, these proceedings.
[3] L. N. Lipatov, Sov. J. Nucl. Phys. **23** (1976) 338;
    E.Kuraev, L. N. Lipatov and V. Fadin, Sov. Phys. JETP **45** (1977) 199;
    Ya.Balitski and L. N. Lipatov, Sov. J. Nucl. Phys. **28** (1978) 822.
[4] L.V. Gribov, E.M Levin and M.G. Ryskin, Phys. Rep. **100** (1982) 1.
[5] A. H. Mueller, Nucl. Phys. **B415** (1994) 373.
[6] N. Nikolaev and Zakharov, Phys. Lett. **B327** (1994) 157.
[7] A. H. Mueller, Columbia preprint, CU-TP-640, (1994);
    A. H. Mueller and B. Patel, Columbia preprint, CU-TP-625, (1994).
[8] S. Catani and F. Hautmann, Cavendish preprint, HEP-94/01 (1994);
    S. Catani and F. Hautmann, Phys. Lett. **B315** (1993) 157.
[9] G. Altarelli and G. Parisi, Nucl. Phys. **B126** (1977) 298;
    Yu. L. Dokshitzer Sov. Phys. JETP **46** (1977) 641;
    cf. L. N. Lipatov, Sov. J. Nucl. Phys. **20** (1975) 95;
    V.N. Gribov and L.N. Lipatov, Sov. J. Nucl. Phys. **15** (1972) 438.
[10] R.K. Ellis, Z. Kunszt and E. Levin, Nucl. Phys. **B420** (1994) 517.
[11] M. Diemoz et al, Zeit. Phys. **C39** (1988) 21.

Paper presented at XXVII Int. Conf. on High Energy Physics: Session Pa-5
Glasgow, UK, 20–27 July 1994

Low x phenomena

A.D. Martin

Department of Physics, University of Durham, Durham DH1 3LE, England.

Abstract

We review recent developments in the application of perturbative QCD to phenomena at small x.

Both H1 [1] and ZEUS [2] presented measurements of $F_2(x, Q^2)$ obtained from the 1993 HERA run. A sample of these data is shown in figure 1. The dramatic rise of $F_2(x, Q^2)$ with decreasing x, discovered in the 1992 data, is now firmly established. The data are compatible with Altarelli-Parisi (or GLAP) evolution from "starting" parton distributions in which the sea quarks have the small x behaviour

$$x\mathcal{S} \sim x^{-\lambda} \text{ with } \lambda \sim 0.3, \tag{1}$$

see, for example, the MRS(A) curve [3] in figure 1.

Also OPAL [7] presented a measurement of the photon structure function F_2 at $x = $ few $\times 10^{-2}$. No rise with decreasing x is seen at this value of x. However both HERA and LEP2 have the potential to measure the photon structure function at much smaller x. Here we concentrate on the structure of the proton since many results have already been obtained in the HERA small x regime ($x \lesssim 10^{-3}$).

1. Deep-inelastic map

To orient ourselves we show in figure 2 a map of the kinematic regime for deep inelastic electron-proton scattering.

1.1. GLAP evolution (large Q^2)

Starting from a known structure of the proton at $Q^2 = Q_0^2$ we may evolve up to large $\log Q^2$ using the Altarelli-Parisi (or GLAP) equations which are typically of the form

$$\partial g / \partial \log Q^2 = P_{gg} \otimes g + \dots \tag{2}$$

where the convolution is over the longitudinal momentum fraction. For simplicity, we concentrate on the gluon, the dominant parton at small x. Effectively the GLAP equations resum the leading $(\alpha_s \log Q^2)^n$ contributions, which correspond (in a physical gauge) to the n-rung gluon ladder of fig. 3. In fact the leading log arises from the strongly-ordered region of transverse momenta

$$Q^2 \gg k_{Tn}^2 \gg k_{Tn-1}^2 \gg \dots \tag{3}$$

When we evolve to high Q^2 we probe the proton

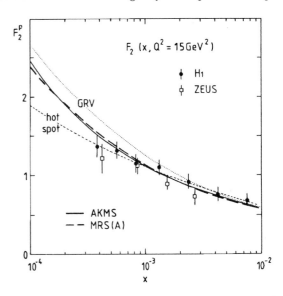

Figure 1. A sample of the latest HERA data for F_2 [1,2]. The GLAP-based MRS(A) analysis [3] and the BFKL-based AKMS "prediction" [4] give almost indistinguishable descriptions of the HERA data. Also shown are the GRV parton [5] and "hot-spot" shadowing [6] predictions.

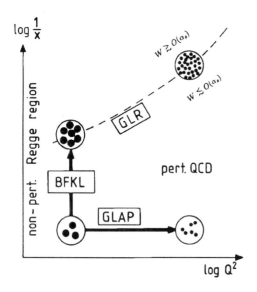

Figure 2. The gluonic content of the proton as "seen" in different deep-inelastic (x, Q^2) regions. W is the ratio of the quadratic to the linear term on the right hand side of (10).

structure ever more finely, to transverse sizes $\sim 1/\sqrt{Q^2}$, see figure 2.

The parton distributions are essential to calculate the cross sections, σ, for "hard" hadronic processes. First the QCD subprocess, $\hat{\sigma}$, are calculated in the strongly-ordered $k_T^2 = 0$ approximation and then the factorization theorem gives $\sigma = xg(x, \mu^2) \otimes \hat{\sigma}(\mu^2) + \dots$ where the scale $\mu^2 \sim$ hard scattering p_T^2.

1.2. BFKL equation (small x)

On the other hand, when we evolve up to large $1/x$ (i.e. small x) we encounter $(\alpha_s \log(1/x))^n$ terms which have to be resummed. Indeed the dramatic rise observed in F_2 with decreasing x may be associated with the growth of the gluon density which arises from the resummation of these terms; a growth which, via $g \to q\bar{q}$, is transmitted to the sea quarks probed by the photon. To leading order the summation is accomplished by the BFKL (or Lipatov) equation [8], which may be written in the differential form

$$-x\partial f(x, k_T^2)/\partial x =$$

$$\frac{3\alpha_s}{\pi} k_T^2 \int_0^\infty \frac{dk_T'^2}{k_T'^2} \left[\frac{f(x, k_T'^2) - f(x, k_T^2)}{|k_T'^2 - k_T^2|} + \frac{f(x, k_T^2)}{(4k_T'^4 - k_T^4)^{\frac{1}{2}}} \right]$$

$$\equiv K \otimes f. \qquad (4)$$

There is now no strong-ordering in k_{nT} of the emitted gluons and we have to work in terms of the unintegrated gluon distribution $f(x, k_T^2)$ in which the "last" k_T^2 integration along the gluon ladder (of figure 3a) is unfolded, that is

$$xg(x, \mu^2) = \int^{\mu^2} \frac{dk_T^2}{k_T^2} f(x, k_T^2). \qquad (5)$$

At small x the gluon distribution $f(x, k_T^2, \mu^2)$ becomes independent of the scale μ^2.

From (4) we see that the small x behaviour of f is controlled by the largest eigenvalue λ_L of the eigenfunction equation $K \otimes f_n = \lambda_n f_n$, since as $x \to 0$

$$f \sim \exp(\lambda_L \log(1/x)) \sim x^{-\lambda_L}.$$

Indeed for fixed α_s there is an analytic solution for the leading small x behaviour

$$f \sim x^{-\lambda_L}(k_T^2)^{\frac{1}{2}} \exp\left(-c \frac{\log^2(k_T^2/\bar{k}_T^2)}{\log(1/x)}\right) \qquad (6)$$

where

$$\lambda_L = (3\alpha_s/\pi)4\log 2. \qquad (7)$$

This singular $x^{-\lambda_L}$ Lipatov behaviour is in contrast to the naive Regge-type expectations that

$$f \sim x^{1-\alpha_P(0)} \sim x^{-0.08} \qquad (8)$$

where $\alpha_P(0)$ is the intercept of the Pomeron.

A second feature of the solution (6) of the BFKL equation is the diffusion in k_T with decreasing x, as manifested by the Gaussian form in $\log k_T^2$ with a width which grows as $(\log(1/x))^{\frac{1}{2}}$ as x decreases. The physical origin of the diffusion is clear. Since there is no strong-ordering in k_T, there is a "random walk" in k_T as we proceed along the gluon chain and hence evolution to smaller x is accompanied by diffusion in k_T. We foresee that the diffusion will be a problem in the applicability of the BFKL equation since, with decreasing x, it leads to an increasingly important contribution from the infrared and ultraviolet regions of k_T^2 where the equation is not expected to be valid.

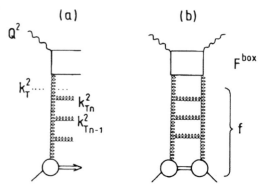

Figure 3. (a) Gluon ladder, (b) diagrammatic representation of the BFKL contribution to F_2, see (13).

For running α_s the singular behaviour and diffusion in k_T are confirmed. In addition it is found that [4]

$$f \sim C(k_T^2)x^{-\lambda} \qquad (9)$$

where the value $\lambda \approx 0.5$ is much less sensitive to the treatment of the infrared region in (4) than is the normalization C.

1.3. Shadowing region

The $x^{-\lambda}$ growth of the gluon cannot go on indefinitely with decreasing x. It would violate unitarity. The growth must eventually be suppressed by gluon recombination, which is represented by an additional quadratic term so that (4) has the symbolic form

$$-x\partial f/\partial x = K \otimes f - V \otimes f^2. \qquad (10)$$

The additional term contains a factor $\alpha_s^2/k_T^2 R^2$ since the gluon-gluon interaction behaves $\sim \alpha_s^2/k_T^2$, whereas $1/R^2$ arises because the smaller the transverse area (πR^2), in which the gluons are concentrated within the proton, the stronger the effect of recombination. The precise form of this equation, originally proposed by GLR [9], is still a matter of debate [10]. The region where shadowing should be calculable perturbatively is just below the dashed line in figure 2.

2. Small x behaviour of F_2

The small x behaviour of xg (and $x\bar{q}$) arising from GLAP evolution depends on the form of the starting distributions. For singular starting distributions, $xg \sim x^{-\lambda}$ with $\lambda > 0$, the small x behaviour is stable to evolution in Q^2. The larger the value of λ the sooner the stability sets in with decreasing x. MRS(A) partons [3], with $xg \sim x^{-0.3}$, are an example of this behaviour. On the other hand, for non-singular starting distributions, $xg \sim x^{-\lambda}$ with $\lambda \leq 0$, we find the double leading logarithm (DLL) form

$$xg \sim \exp(2[\xi(Q_0^2, Q^2)\log(1/x)]^{\frac{1}{2}}). \qquad (11)$$

That is xg grows as $x \to 0$ faster than any power of $\log(1/x)$ but slower than any power of x. The larger the "evolution length",

$$\xi = \int_{Q_0^2}^{Q^2} \frac{dq^2}{q^2} \frac{3\alpha_s(q^2)}{\pi}, \qquad (12)$$

the faster the growth. An example is the "dynamical" GRV partons [5] which evolve from valence-like forms at a low scale $Q_0^2 = 0.3$ GeV^2, and for which (11) mimics a behaviour $xg \sim x^{-0.4}$ in the HERA regime.

Given the solution $f(x, k_T^2)$ of the BFKL equation we can use the k_T-factorization theorem to predict F_2, see figure 3b:

$$F_2 = f \otimes F^{\text{box}} + F_2^{\text{bg}} \simeq C'(k_T^2)x^{-\lambda} + F_2^{\text{bg}} \qquad (13)$$

where $\lambda \simeq 0.5$, and $F_2^{\text{bg}} \simeq 0.4$ is determined from the large x behaviour of F_2. Once the overall normalisation of the BFKL term is adjusted by a suitable choice of the infrared parameters in (4), then an excellent description of all the $F_2(x, Q^2)$ HERA data is obtained. Indeed the BFKL-based "prediction" [4] gives an equally good, and almost indistinguishable, description as the GLAP-based order fit [3], see fig 1. With GLAP, the steepness is either incorporated (as a factor $x^{-\lambda}$) in the starting distributions or generated by evolution from a low scale Q_0^2. The steepness can be adjusted to agree with the data by varying λ or Q_0^2. On the other hand the leading $\log(1/x)$ BFKL prediction for the shape $F_2 - F_2^{\text{bg}} \sim x^{-\lambda}$, with $\lambda \simeq 0.5$, is prescribed. It remains to see how well it survives a full treatment of sub-leading effects.

Conventional shadowing with gluons spread uniformly across the proton ($R = 5$ GeV^{-1}) leads to only a small suppression in F_2 in the HERA regime. If the gluons were concentrated in "hot spots" of area πR^2 with, say, $R = 2$ GeV^{-1} the effect would be much stronger, see fig. 1. But could shadowing be identified since we do not know the partons at small x? Simulated F_2 data (of accuracy and x range which may eventually be accessible at HERA) have been used [11] to see how well R could be determined. The conclusion is that the interplay between the linear and non-linear terms in (10) leads to a considerable ambiguity between the size of the parton distributions and the amount of shadowing.

Is GLAP evolution adequate in the HERA regime? For sufficiently small x the $(\alpha_s\log 1/x)^n$ terms must be resummed with the full Q^2 dependence (and not just the leading and next-to-leading $\log Q^2$ terms). Ellis et al. [12] have made a theoretical study of the applicability of GLAP evolution and find that it is adequate in the HERA small x regime, *provided* that the evolution occurs from a sufficiently singular starting distribution, $xg \sim x^{-\lambda}$ with $\lambda \gtrsim 0.35$.

3. Identification of BFKL behaviour

The *inclusive* nature of F_2, and the necessity to provide "non-perturbative" input distributions of parton densities for its description, prevents its observed small x behaviour being a sensitive discriminator between BFKL and conventional dynamics. For this purpose it is necessary to look into the properties of the final state.

The two characteristic features of BFKL dynamics are the absence of strong-ordering of the gluon k_T's along the chain (the diffusion in k_T) and the consequent $(x/x')^{-\lambda}$ or $\exp(\lambda \Delta y)$ growth of the cross section, where x and x' are the longitudinal momentum fractions of the gluons at the ends of the chain, which spans the rapidity interval $\Delta y = \log(x'/x)$. Recall $\lambda \simeq 0.5$. Some processes which exploit these characteristic features are shown in figure 4.

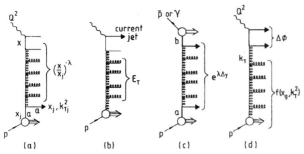

Figure 4. Processes that may be used to identify BFKL dynamics.

The idea [13] in figure 4a is to detect deep-inelastic (x, Q^2) events which contain a measured jet (x_j, k^2_{Tj}) in the kinematic regime where (i) the jet longitudinal momentum, x_j, is as large as is experimentally feasible $(x_j \sim 0.1)$, (ii) $z \equiv x/x_j$ is small, and (iii) $k^2_{Tj} \approx Q^2$ is sufficient to suppress diffusion into the infrared region. The beauty of this measurement is that attention is focussed directly on the BFKL $z^{-\lambda}$ behaviour at small z. The difficulty is to cleanly separate the forward going jet from the proton remnants. The preliminary results from the H1 collaboration [14] are encouraging and favour the BFKL over the conventional description.

Inspection of figure 4b suggests, that due to the relaxation of strong-ordering of the gluon k_T's at small x, more transverse energy E_T should be emitted in the central region (between the current jet and the proton remnants) than would result from conventional evolution. Indeed Monte Carlo predictions based on QCD cascade models† fall well below the observed central plateau of height $E_T \approx 2.1$ GeV per unit of rapidity [15]. A BFKL-based calculation [16], at the parton level, yields about 1.7 GeV per unit of rapidity, but much less if conventional dynamics is used. No hadronization effects have been allowed for.

Recently there has been renewed interest in the original proposal of Mueller and Navelet [17] that the cross section for the production of a pair of minijets should, according to BFKL dynamics, rise as $\exp(\lambda \Delta y)$ as the rapidity interval Δy becomes large. The studies [18] show that the effect is masked by the fall-off of the parton densities at large x, but that instead the rate of weakening of the azimuthal (back-to-back) correlation between the jets, could possibly be an indicator of BFKL effects.

BFKL dynamics may be also identified via the weakening of the azimuthal correlation between a pair of jets produced in deep-inelastic scattering at HERA, see figure 4d. At sufficiently large values of $\Delta\phi \equiv \phi - \pi$, BFKL dynamics dominates over the fixed-

order QCD contribution from 3+1 jet production, leading to a distinctive tail in the azimuthal distribution which directly probes the k_T dependence of the gluon distribution [19].

4.   Conclusions

In the HERA small x regime GLAP evolution (from appropriately parametrized starting distributions) is able to mimic BFKL dynamics as far as the description of $F_2(x, Q^2)$ is concerned. Moreover it will be difficult to isolate shadowing contributions even with improved measurements of F_2. Measurements which are less inclusive than F_2, offer more chance to identify the characteristic BFKL $x^{-\lambda}$ behaviour and diffusion in k_T. However opening up the final state brings the problems of hadronization and jet identification, and loses some of the small x "reach" (e.g. $x \rightarrow x/x_j$ where $x_j \sim 0.1$). On the theoretical side, the sub-leading corrections to the BFKL leading $\log(1/x)$ formalism are urgently needed for future quantitative studies of small x phenomena.

References

[1] H1 collaboration: V. Brisson, these proceedings.
[2] ZEUS collaboration: M. Lancaster, these proceedings.
[3] A.D. Martin, R.G. Roberts and W.J. Stirling, Phys. Rev.**D50**; these proceedings.
[4] A.J. Askew, J. Kwiecinski, A.D. Martin and P.J. Sutton, Phys. Rev. **D49** (1994) 4402.
[5] M. Glück, E. Reya and A. Vogt, Z. Phys. **C53** (1992) 127; Phys. Lett. **B306** (1993) 391.
[6] A.J. Askew *et al.*, Phys. Lett. **B325** (1994) 212.
[7] OPAL collaboration: J. Ward *et al.*, paper gls 0497.
[8] E.A. Kuraev, L.N. Lipatov and V.S. Fadin, Sov. Phys. JETP **45** (1977) 199; Ya.Ya. Balitsky and L.N. Lipatov, Sov. J. Nucl. Phys. **28** (1978) 822.
[9] L.V. Gribov, E.M. Levin and M.G. Ryskin, Phys. Rep. **100** (1983) 1.
[10] J. Bartels, Phys. Lett. **B298** (1993) 204; E.M. Levin, M.G. Ryskin and A.G. Shuvaev, Nucl. Phys. **B378** (1992) 589; J. Bartels and M.G. Ryskin, DESY preprint 93-081.
[11] K. Golec-Biernat, M.W. Krasny and S. Riess, paper gls 0369.
[12] R.K. Ellis, Z. Kunszt and E.M. Levin, Fermilab-PUB-93/350-T; R.K. Ellis, these proceedings.
[13] A.H. Mueller, J. Phys. **G17** (1991) 1443; W.-K. Tang, Phys. Letts. **B278** (1992) 363; J. Bartels, A. De Roeck and M. Loewe, Z. Phys. **C54** (1992) 635; J. Kwiecinski, A.D. Martin and P.J. Sutton, Phys. Rev. **D46** (1992) 921, Phys. Lett. **B278** (1992) 254.
[14] H1 collaboration: A. De Roeck, Int. Workshop on DIS, Eilat, Israel, Feb. 1994; G. Raedel, these proceedings.
[15] H1 collaboration: DESY preprint 94-033, Z. Phys. **C**.
[16] K. Golec-Biernat, J. Kwiecinski, A.D. Martin and P. Sutton, Phys. Lett. **B335** (1994) 220; Phys. Rev. **D50** (1994) 217.
[17] A.H. Mueller and H. Navelet, Nucl. Phys. **B282** (1987) 727.
[18] V. Del Duca and C.R. Schmidt, Phys. Rev. **D49** (1994) 4510; DESY preprint 94-114; W.J. Stirling, Durham preprint DTP/94/04; Phys. Lett. **B329** (1994) 386.
[19] A.J. Askew, D. Graudenz, J. Kwiecinski and A.D. Martin, CERN-TH.7357/94, Phys. Lett. (in press).

---

† A good description has been obtained by a Monte Carlo based on the colour dipole model. This model contains the essence of BFKL dynamics provided the full integration over the emitted gluon k_T is performed.

New Results on Deep Inelastic Scattering at low x from H1

Gaby Rädel[‡]

Deutsches Elektronensynchroton DESY, Hamburg, Germany

On behalf of the H1 Collaboration

Abstract

We present new results on the proton structure function F_2 for values of x_{Bj} down to 10^{-4}. The results are based on data taken in 1993 by the H1 experiment at HERA. From a leading order QCD analysis of the structure function information on the gluon content in the proton is obtained. Studies on exclusive final states at low x_{Bj} have been performed. The results demonstrate that in future these studies can help to decide whether DGLAP- or BFKL-dynamics are to be used in the present small x_{Bj} regime.

1. Introduction

In 1992, at DESY in Hamburg a new collider, HERA, started operation by colliding electrons of 27 GeV with protons of 820 GeV. During the second running period in 1993 H1 recorded data corresponding to an integrated luminosity of about $0.5\,\mathrm{pb}^{-1}$ of which $271\,\mathrm{nb}^{-1}$ was used for the following analysis. With a squared centre of mass energy of $s = 87600\,\mathrm{GeV}^2$ HERA opens a completely new kinematical domain to study deep inelastic scattering. Compared to earlier fixed target experiments higher Q^2 and lower x_{Bj} values, down to $\approx 10^{-4}$, can be reached. In addition, HERA detectors are designed to determine the kinematicle variables by measuring the scattered electron as well as by reconstructing the hadronic final state. A detailed description of the H1 detector can be found in [1].

2. The Structure Function $F_2(x, Q^2)$

Already the analysis of the 1992 data revealed the interesting and widely unexpected result of a proton structure function F_2 that rises strongly towards low x_{Bj} [2]. However, the significance was limited due to statistics. The high statistics of 1993 data enables us

to make a more precise measurement and extend the analysis to higher values of $Q^2 (\leq 1600\,\mathrm{GeV}^2)$. Also very low values of $Q^2 (4$–$8\,\mathrm{GeV}^2)$ could be studied, thanks to a few hours of datataking when the interaction point was shifted by 80 cm towards the proton direction in order to increase the detector acceptance for electrons scattered under very small angles. Fig. 1 shows the result for F_2, obtained by H1 from the 93 data, for the lower Q^2 values of 4.5–$65\,\mathrm{GeV}^2$. The strong rise observed in the '92 data is confirmed with higher statistical significance. A description of the F_2 analysis is given in [3], where also the result for the full (x, Q^2)-range is shown. On top of the data some parametrizations are displayed. Two predictions are based on Altarelli-Parisi evolution in Q^2 [4], but assuming a different behaviour for the input gluon distribution at $Q^2 = 5\,\mathrm{GeV}^2$. MRSD0' assumes a flat gluon distribution, based on Regge arguments, and is ruled out by the data. MRSH is based on a singular gluon distribution $xg \sim x^{-\lambda}$, with $\lambda \simeq 0.3$, which gives a starting distribution for the evolution that is similar to the gluon distribution predicted by Lipatov equations [5]. MRSH was fitted to data including the '92 data of HERA. This parametrization describes the data rather well, however it tends to be above the data at very low values of x. For comparison two parametrizations based on Lipatov evolution [5], called here AKMS1 and

‡ E-mail: raedel@dice2.desy.de

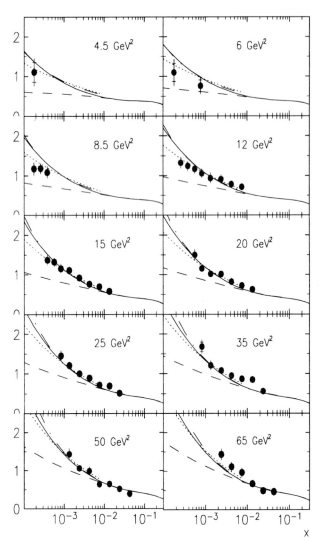

Figure 1. The proton structure function F_2 as determined by H1 from 1993 data (points) as a function of x, preliminary. The inner error bars show the statistical error, the full error bars represent systematical ans statistical errors added in quadrature. An overall error on the normalization of $\pm 5\%$ is not shown. Overlayed are the following parametrizations: full line: MRSH; dashed line: MRSD0'; dash-dotted line: AKMS1; dotted line: AKMS2. For explanation see text.

AKMS2 [6], are shown. The difference between the two is gluon shadowing at very small x. AKMS1 does not include shadowing, while AKMS2 represents the scenario of 'hot spots', i.e. there are small regions in the proton where shadowing has set in. Whether shadowing of gluons is existing at low x, and at which value of x it sets in is another interesting question of low x physics, which can be investigated at HERA. However, from fig. 1 it is obvious that with the present precision of the data it is not possible to determine which of the scenarios: DGLAP or BFKL evolution, shadowing or no shadowing, is valid in the HERA kinematic region. H1 performed a leading order QCD fit to F_2 using a

program which is based on DGLAP equations [7]. Only H1 data was used in the fit. Parameters relevant to the high x region have been fixed to values known from fixed target experiments. Λ_{QCD} was set to 240 MeV and the momentum sum rule was imposed. Free parameters

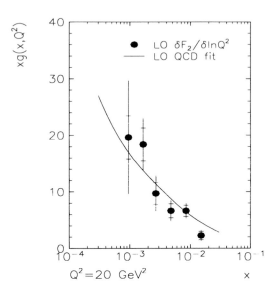

Figure 2. The preliminary gluon distribution as a function of x at $Q^2 = 20$ GeV^2 as obtained from a LO QCD fit (full line), and from an analysis of the scaling violations (LO) (points). The inner error bars show the statistical error, the full error bars represent systematical ans statistical errors added in quadrature.

are the exponent λ in the gluon distribution $xg \sim x^{-\lambda}$ and the exponent and normalization of the quark-singlet distribution. The χ^2 of the fit is 65 for 86 degrees of freedom, which shows that the data with the current precision can be described by LO QCD and Altarelli-Parisi evolution. We obtain $\lambda = 0.38 \pm 0.08$. The fit is shown in fig. 2 for a Q^2 of 20 GeV as a function of x. The same plot also shows the result of another leading order analysis where xg was derived from scaling violation following a suggestion of Prytz [8] in the approximation that in LO at small x the contribution of the quarks can be neglected compared to the gluons.

3.   Hadronic Final States in DIS

The inclusive F_2 measurement has turned out not to be conclusive (yet) on the question whether HERA data at low x are in a new region where conventional DGLAP fails and BFKL evolution has to be used instead. Therefore, it was suggested to study exclusive final states, which are expected to be more sensitive to the type of evolution. Two of such analyses are presented here.

3.1. The Transverse Energy Flow

In the naive quark-parton model the transverse momentum of the scattered electron is balanced by a single jet associated with the struck quark, usually called the current jet. Higher order QCD processes modify this picture. The low x domain, the region away from the expected current jet towards the proton remnant is of particular interest, as it may be the region most sensitive to new effects based on BFKL dynamics. Expectations for the properties of hadronic final states are available in the form of Monte Carlo models, which are based on standard QCD evolution but differ widely in their predictions. For instance the MEPS model is an option of the LEPTO generator [9] based on DGLAP dynamics, while the CDM model [10] provides an implementation of the colour dipole model of a chain of independent radiating dipoles connected via the emitting gluons. Recently also analytical calculations predicting the transverse energy flow at HERA have been performed [11] both for DGLAP and BFKL dynamics.

The transverse energy flow has been studied by H1 and a detailed description of the analysis can be found in [12]. The data analysed corresponds to a luminosity of 22.5 nb^{-1}. Fig. 3 shows the transverse energy flow in

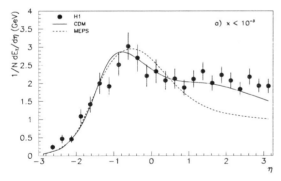

Figure 3. Transverse energy flow E_T in the laboratory system as a function of the pseudorapidity η with $x < 10^{-3}$. The proton direction is to the right. The error bars contain the statistical and systematic errors added in quadrature, except for an overall 6% energy scale uncertainty.

the laboratory system for values of $x < 10^{-3}$ corrected for detector effects as a function of the pseudorapidity η. The data show a plateau of $E_T \approx 2$ GeV per unit of rapidity away from the current quark. Different models are compared to the data. While the CDM model describes the data reasonably well, the DGLAP based MEPS model fails to describe the plateau away from the current quark and clearly undershoots the data in this region. Comparing to analytical calculations at parton level [11] one notices that BFKL dynamics predicts a fairly flat plateau at low x with $E_T \approx 2$ GeV per unit

x range	data	MEPS MRSD$^{0(-)'}$	CDM
$2 \cdot 10^{-4} - 2 \cdot 10^{-3}$	$128 \pm 12 \pm 26$	69 (53)	32
$2 \cdot 10^{-4} - 1 \cdot 10^{-3}$	$85 \pm 9 \pm 17$	37 (27)	21
$1 \cdot 10^{-3} - 1 \cdot 10^{-3}$	$43 \pm 7 \pm 9$	32 (26)	11

Table 1. Number of DIS events with a selected forward jet compared to Monte Carlo predictions. (Preliminary.)

of rapidity but much less E_T if DGLAP dynamics are assumed.

3.2. Associated jets with a high x_{jet}

Another possible footprint of the BFKL dynamics is the rate of jets produced in a DIS event with the following characteristics. The transverse size $1/k_{jt}^2$ of the selected jet should be close to $1/Q^2$ and the momentum fraction x_j of the jet should be as large as possible whereas the momentum fraction x_{Bj} of the quark struck by the virtual photon should be as small as possible. The rate of those jets is sensitive to the type of evolution dynamics. For the DGLAP case, due to the strong ordering of k_t there is little room for the evolution in Q^2 if $1/k_{jt}^2 \approx 1/Q^2$ such that the expected jet rate is higher for BFKL then for DGLAP dynamics. In a sample of DIS events with $Q^2 \approx 20$ GeV^2 and $2 \cdot 10^{-4} < x < 2 \cdot 10^{-3}$ we have counted the jets with $x_j > 0.05$ and $0.5 < k_{jt}^2/Q^2 < 6$. The resulting number of events, corrected for background contribution, is given in table 1 and compared to expectations of the MEPS and CDM models simulated in our detector. We see that the predictions tend to be below the observations and do not depend significantly on the parametrization of the structure function. The size of the errors do not allow yet a firm conclusion. We can however notice that the rate of jets rises with decreasing x as expected from BFKL dynamics.

References

[1] H1 collab., I.Abt et al., DESY-93-103 (1993).
[2] H1 collab., I. Abt et al., Nucl. Phys. **B407** (1993) 515
[3] V.Brisson, *Structure Functions from the H1 Experiment at HERA*, these proceedings.
[4] A. D. Martin, W. J. Stirling, R. G. Roberts, Phys. Lett. **306B** (1993) 145, Erratum **309B** (1993) 492.
[5] E. A. Kuraev, L. N. Lipatov, V. Fadin, Phys. Lett. **60B** (1975) 50;Ya. Ya. Balitskij, L. N. Lipatov, Sov. J. Nucl. Phys. **28** (1978) 822.
[6] A. J. Askew et al., Phys. Lett. **325B** (1994) 212
[7] L. F. Abbott et al., Phys. Rev. **D22** (1980) 582.
[8] K. Prytz, Phys. Lett. **311B** (1993) 286.
[9] M. Bengtsson, G. Ingelman, T. Sjöstrand, Nucl. Phys. **B301** (1988) 554.
[10] L. Lönnblad, Computer Phys. Comm. **71** (1992) 15.
[11] K. Golec-Biernat et al., *Transverse energy flow at HERA*, Durham preprint DTP/94/30.
[12] H1 collab., I. Abt et al., DESY-94-033.

New results on DIS at low x from ZEUS

Fernando Barreiro

Universidad Autónoma de Madrid, Spain

On behalf of the ZEUS Collaboration

Abstract

I summarize the most important results obtained to date by the ZEUS Collaboration on Deep Inelastic Scattering (DIS) at low x. The main emphasis is on a discussion of events with a Large Rapidity Gap (LRG), their main characteristics, jet structure, energy flow and exclusive vector meson production. Particular attention is paid to the interpretation of these events as due to the scattering on pointlike constituents of a colourless object in the proton: the pomeron.

1. Introduction

In the Quark Parton Model (QPM), DIS is understood to proceed via the exchange of a current which is subsequently absorbed by a quark in the proton, giving rise to final states consisting of the scattered lepton, the struck quark and the diquark remnant. Multihadronic final states are the result of the fragmentation of the colour string joining the current quark with the proton remnant. QCD corrections to the next order in perturbation theory are given by QCD Compton and Boson Gluon Fusion (BGF) processes. Since the probability to find valence quarks in the proton tends to zero as the Bjorken variable x goes to the kinematic limits i.e. 0 and 1, BGF processes are expected to be dominant at low x values. In Fig. 1 we show a textbook example of an event as expected in the QPM. In addition to the scattered electron and the current jet a continuous energy flow stretching from the jet axis to the proton direction is observed. In contrast, no energy flow is observed between the current jet to the scattered electron.

One of the most important results obtained at HERA so far, has to do with the strong rise of the cross section or F_2 at low x. There are two sources of this strong rise. On the one hand, quark pair production via the

‡ E-mail: F35FER@DHHDESY3

so-called BGF discussed previously.

Because of the configuration in colour space, hadrons

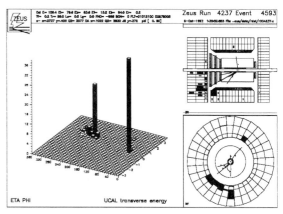

Figure 1. A DIS event as expected in the QPM

are produced along the two strings joining the quark (antiquark) with the diquark (resp. quark which emitted the gluon) in the proton. Hadrons thus fill the complete phase space in pseudorapidity. In contrast, we have found at low x a new class of events which are characterized by a large rapidity gap (LRG).

They are interpreted to proceed via the exchange of a colourless object in the proton: the pomeron (P). In the process $\gamma^* P \to q\bar{q}$, hadrons will be the result of the fragmentation of only one string i.e. that connecting the quark and the antiquark, thus giving rise to a void between the proton and one of the final state partons. Since the calorimeter in the proton direction covers up to pseudorapidity values of 4.3 units, selecting events with $\eta_{max} \leq 1.5$, where η_{max} is defined as the pseudorapidity of the calorimeter cell with energy deposit in excess of $400 \; MeV$ closest to the proton beam direction, is tantamount to requiring events with a rapidity gap larger than 2.8 units.

Although diffractive processes have been studied for 30 years now, their true nature is far from being understood. In particular the connection with the usual calculational techniques in strong interaction physics, namely QCD, is still missing, both in the perturbative as well as in the non-perturbative regimes. We have used two models to make comparisons with our data and thus get into a deeper understanding of these processes. One model follows the original idea of Ingelman and Schlein [1], acording to which one introduces parton densities in the pomeron in the same way as one introduces parton densities in a hadron. Thus the cross sections for diffractive *ep* collisions will be the result of convoluting a pomeron flux in the proton vertex, given by Regge phenomenology, with the cross section for $\gamma - parton$ two body scattering. This model has been coded in a Monte Carlo program, POMPYT, by P. Bruni and G. Ingelman [2]. The parton densities in the pomeron can be chosen and varied at will. We have used two parameterizations, which are proportional to $(1 - z)^5$, soft, and $z(1 - z)$, hard. The latter is in accord with the original proposal by Donnachie and Landshoff [3]. As an alternative we have used a Monte Carlo, written by A. Solano [4], of the Nikolaev-Zakharov model [5]. In this model one considers quantum fluctuations of the virtual photon into $q\bar{q}$ and $q\bar{q}g$ final states which subsequently interact with the pomeron perturbatively. In lowest order the pomeron is considered to be a two-gluon system. In this model one arrives at an effective quark density in the pomeron which lies somewhere in between the two previously discussed.

2. Experimental setup and data selection

The data presented here have been taken with the ZEUS detector [7] operating at HERA, the $e - p$ collider at DESY (Hamburg, Germany). I will restrict myself to the 1993 data taking period, where the integrated luminosity collected by the experiment amounted to $550 \; nb^{-1}$. We select DIS events by looking for scattered electron candidates using the pattern of energy deposition in the calorimeter. The electron energy was required to be larger than $5 \; GeV$. The efficiency for finding isolated electrons in this energy range was greater than 97%. Restricting ourselves to $Q^2 \geq$

$10 \; GeV^2$ and $y \geq 0.04$ we select a sample of 38192 events which is found to be free from beam-gas and photoproduction background [8]. Our data populates a region in the Q^2, x plane which extends two orders of magnitude above (below) that covered by previous fixed target experiments [6].

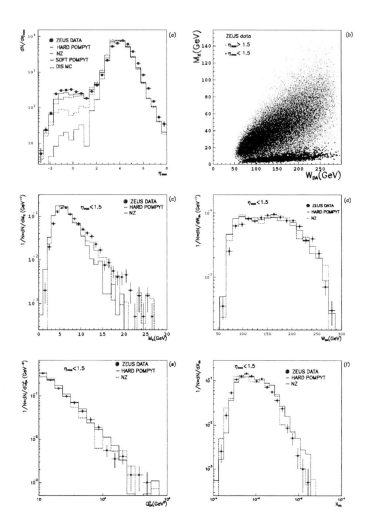

Figure 2. General characteristics of DIS LRG events

3. Events with a LRG, general characteristics

The distribution in η_{max} for the DIS sample is shown in Fig. 2a. Notice that the data exhibit a tail which is an order of magnitude above the expectations in the standard model Monte Carlo LEPTO. The shape of this tail is properly described by the Nikolaev Zakharov model as well as by POMPYT with a hard parton density. In fact, one can fit the η_{max} distribution to the linear sum of the expectations in DIS and diffractive scattering. Depending on the model used for the latter we obtain for the relative diffractive contribution $12.0 \pm 1.8\%$ and $9.2 \pm 1.5\%$

for Nikolaev-Zakharov and hard POMPYT respectively. Incidentally, soft POMPYT cannot describe the shape of the η_{max} distribution.

Figs. 2b-f show relevant distributions in the mass of the hadronic system, W, Q^2 and Bjorken x. Again Monte Carlo models of the type described above give a rough description of the main characteristics exhibited by these large rapidity gap events.

If we interpret these LRG events as due to pomeron exchange one can calculate the fraction of the proton momentum carried by the pomeron, ξ, using the simple relation $\xi = \frac{M_X^2 + Q^2}{M_X^2 + W^2}$. In Fig. 3 one can see how events with a LRG defined as $\eta_{max} \leq 1.5$ saturate the tail in ξ. The average value for these events being 3.2×10^{-3} corresponding to an average pomeron momentum of $2.6\,GeV$.

Since we cannot yet tag on forward going protons

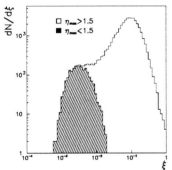

Figure 3. The pomeron fractional momentum

and thus cannot determine the t distribution associated with the proton vertex for which there exist clear predictions in Regge theory, we try to find indirect evidence that LRG events are due to pomeron exchange. It is instructive to look at the ratio r of large rapidity gap events to all DIS events as a function of W, Fig. 4a. This ratio is found to be constant for W values in excess of $140\,GeV$ where our acceptance is large and W independent. We consider this as further evidence that LRG events are due to pomeron exchange. It is equally interesting to look at the ratio of LRG events to all DIS events as a function of Q^2 for various x bins, Fig.4b-d. We find this ratio to be Q^2 independent. Thus, LRG events exhibit the same scaling violation effects as normal DIS events. If LRG events are interpreted as due to pomeron exchange our data suggest that we are scattering on a pomeron pointlike constituent.

4. Jet structure in events with a LRG

If the interpretation discussed so far were correct then we should be able to observe jet production in events with a LRG. We look for jets in pseudorapidity-azimuth space using the cone algorithm. We perform the search

both in the laboratory as well as in the $\gamma^* - p$ c.m. system. In the latter, a cluster is called a jet when the transverse energy collected in a cone of radius unity (with the metric $R = \sqrt{(\Delta\eta^2 + \Delta\phi^2)}$), is larger than $2\,GeV$.

We find the fractions of 1-, 2- and 3-jet events to be

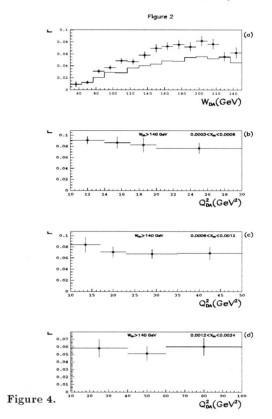

Figure 4.

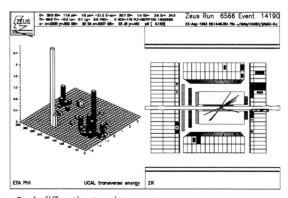

Figure 5. A diffractive two-jet event

$5.9 \pm 0.5\%$, $3.5 \pm 0.4\%$ and $0.4 \pm 0.1\%$. Most important we find that the tail of the hadronic transverse energy distribution is saturated by events with multijet structure, Fig. 6a. Thus, as in in any other collider process, there is an underlying $2 \rightarrow 2$ scattering responsible for diffraction. As also shown in Fig. 6 the two jets are produced back-to-back in the transverse plane and the jet transverse energies reach values up to approximately

10 *GeV*. In Fig. 5 we show one such event where one

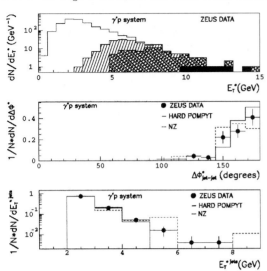

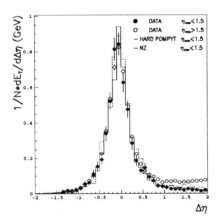

Figure 6. Characteristics of diffractive two-jet events

can clearly see the scattered electron, two jets and no trace of the proton remnant.

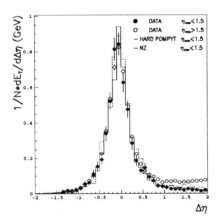

Figure 7. Jet profiles for DIS events with and without LRG

It is illustrative to look at the energy flow around the jet axis for jet events in the LRG sample. One can clearly see, Fig. 7, that in addition to the central jet core, both tails tend to zero no matter whether you move from the jet axis towards the electron or proton directions., in agreement with the hard POMPYT or NZ Monte Carlo programs.

Fig. 7 also illustrates that the absence of colour flow between the jet axis and the proton direction is not a consequence of the selection criteria, as exemplified by the jet profiles in the normal DIS sample where we demanded that the jets be produced at negative pseudo-rapidities. Furthermore the jet core is very similar for DIS events with and without a LRG.

5.   Energy flow in events with a LRG

The same conclusions reached in the preceeding section can be obtained from a comparative study of the energy flow in DIS events with and without a LRG, i.e. without restriction to those events with jet structure [9].

The main results are summarized in Fig. 8 where

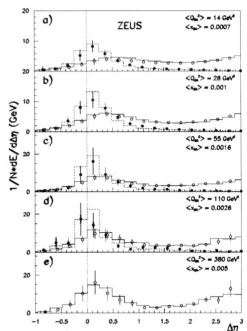

Figure 8. Energy flow around the direction of the hadronic system

we show the corrected energy flows for the two classes of events discussed above. The correction procedure based on standard Monte Carlo techniques is done in such a way that the origin is made to coincide with the direction of the struck parton. Events with and without LRG exhibit marked differences. For the former the position of the peak is shifted towards positive values, with the shift becoming less pronounced as Q^2 increases. Substantial energy flow is observed for large $\Delta\eta$ values. For the latter, however, the position of the peak is independent of Q^2 and well centered at zero, with furthermore negligible energy flow at large $\Delta\eta$ values.

6.   Exclusive vector meson production

Just as in e^+e^- annihilation one distinguishes between omnia and production in the continuum, it is also appropiate when discussing diffraction not only to concentrate on hadron production in the continuum, see preceeding sections, but also to consider exclusive vector meson production. The relative rates for ρ, ϕ, J/Ψ, Υ as well as their production characteristics will in the future be a fertile testing ground for PQCD calculations. Again present available statistics allow us to present only the results of our investigation on the lowest lying vector meson state, i.e. the ρ. They are summarized in Fig. 9. For $7 \leq Q^2 \leq 10\ GeV^2$, we obtain a cross-section for $\gamma^* p \rightarrow \rho^0 p$ of $123 \pm 15(stat) \pm 39(syst)\ nb$ to be compared with the Brodsky et al. calculation of $165\ nb$ [10].

ZEUS PRELIMINARY

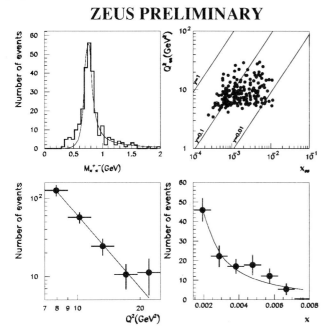

Figure 9. The Q^2 and x dependence of ρ production

7. Strange particle production

One of the main differences between the two models for diffraction that we have been discussing so far has to do with the heavy quark content of diffractive events. In the Nikolaev Zakharov model, heavy quark production is strongly suppressed as a consequence of the uncertainty principle. Fluctuations of the virtual photon into heavy quark pairs are characterized by much smaller transverse sizes. Present statistics preclude an analysis of the charm content of events with a LRG. We have to restrict ourselves, for the time being, with an investigation of the strangeness content of DIS events with and without a LRG. The results are summarized in Fig. 10 where we show the transverse momenta and pseudorapidities of the neutral kaons in both samples along with comparisons with Monte Carlo expectations. Clearly more statistics is needed to be able to discriminate between different models.

8. Conclusions

Approximately 10% of the DIS events with $Q^2 \geq 10\ GeV^2$ are of a diffractive nature. If interpreted

as due to pomeron exchange we find that the average pomeron momentum is 2.6 GeV. Diffractive events exhibit the same scaling violations as normal DIS events. The natural interpretation is that we are scattering on pointlike constituents in the pomeron, as corroborated by our observation of multijet structures in DIS LRG events. From the point of view of low x physics, HERA experiments can be considered as fixed target experiments, our stationary target being a colorless object in the proton, the pomeron. More statistics is needed to unravel its true nature.

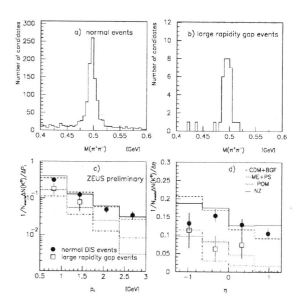

Figure 10. Neutral kaon transverse momentum and pseudorapidity in DIS with and without LRG

Acknowledgement

This report was written while visiting Oxford University under the exchange program between the Ministry of Education, Spain, and the Royal Society, London. Their support is gratefully acknowledged. I would like to thank Drs. L. Labarga and J. Terron as well as Mr. J.M. Hernandez and J. Puga for their help in the preparation of the manuscript.

References

[1] G. Ingelman and P. Schlein, Phys. Lett. **B152** (1985) 256.
[2] P. Bruni and G. Ingelman, *DESY 93-187*.
[3] A. Donnachie and P.V. Landshoff, Phys. Lett. **B191** (1987) 309.
[4] A. Solano, *Ph. D. Thesis, University of Torino, unpublished.*
[5] N.N. Nikolaev and B.G. Zakharov, Zeit. Phys. **C53** (1992) 331.
[6] M. Lancaster, *these proceedings.*
[7] ZEUS Coll., M. Derrick *et al.*, Phys. Lett. **B315** (1993) 481
[8] ZEUS Coll., M. Derrick *et al.*, Phys. Lett. **B332** (1994) 228
[9] ZEUS Coll., M. Derrick *et al.*, DESY 94-117.
[10] S.J. Brodsky *et al.*, SLAC-PUB-6412.

Paper presented at XXVII Int. Conf. on High Energy Physics: Session Pa-5
Glasgow, UK, 20–27 July 1994

Exclusive ρ^0 and ϕ Muoproduction at Large Q^2

A. Sandacz[||]

Soltan Institute for Nuclear Studies, Warsaw, Poland

On behalf of the New Muon Collaboration

Abstract

In this contribution we present results on exclusive ρ^0 and ϕ production in Deep Inelastic Scattering of muons on deuterium, carbon and calcium. The experiment was carried out at CERN by the New Muon Collaboration (NMC) using a 200 GeV muon beam. The data cover the kinematic range $2 < Q^2 < 25$ GeV^2, $40 < \nu < 180$ GeV and the average value of the Bjorken scaling variable is about 0.03. We discuss virtual photoproduction cross sections as a function of Q^2 and ν, and the vector meson decay angular distributions.

The exclusive ρ^0 (or ϕ) reaction is

$$\mu + N \rightarrow \mu + N + \rho^0 (\text{or } \phi)$$

in which the only particle produced is the ρ^0 (or ϕ) meson. The selection of the event samples and the corrections applied to the data for the present results are similar to those used in reference [1].

1. Virtual photoproduction cross sections

The cross sections for exclusive ρ^0 (ϕ) virtual photoproduction are calculated for intervals (Q^2, ν) using the muon cross sections and virtual photon flux. They include contributions from transverse and longitudinal virtual photons.

To investigate the Q^2 dependence of the cross sections we averaged them over ν in each Q^2 bin. We observe no significant dependence on ν.

In figure 1 the Q^2 dependence of the cross section for exclusive ρ^0 virtual photoproduction is shown. The cross sections are given per nucleon and they include contributions from coherent and incoherent processes. Also shown are the EMC data on protons [2]. The errors shown are statistical; the systematic errors are about

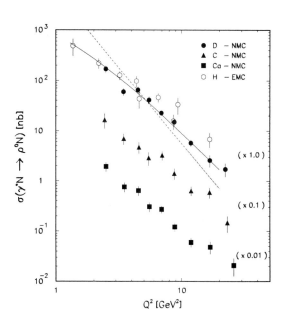

Figure 1. Exclusive ρ^0 virtual photoproduction cross section per nucleon as a function of Q^2.

20%. The main contribution to the systematic error comes from uncertainties in the background estimates. This error is largely independent of Q^2 and ν.

|| E-mail: sandacz@fuw.edu.pl

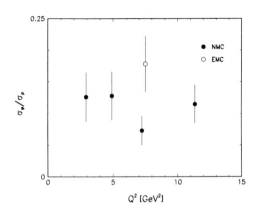

Figure 2. The ratio $\sigma_\phi/\sigma_{\rho^0}$ as a function of Q^2.

The measured total cross sections for carbon and calcium (in the figure scaled by factor 0.1 and 0.01 correspondingly) are close to those for deuterium. Fig. 1 indicates fair agreement between the proton and deuteron data. However, the cross sections depend on the polarisation of the virtual photons which is different in the two experiments, complicating their comparison. The mean polarisation $< \epsilon >$ in the present experiment was somewhat lower than that in reference [2].

The solid curve represents the prediction of a model by Donnachie and Landshoff [3], in which an exchange of two nonperturbative gluons is assumed. It was calculated for the reaction $\gamma^*p \to \rho^0 p$ assuming the values of the virtual photon polarisation as in ref. [2]. The dashed curve, normalised arbitrarily, represents a dependence $\propto 1/Q^6$ predicted by models [4] for large Q^2.

To compare the Q^2 dependence for the different nuclei, we have parametrised the data according to

$$\sigma(Q^2) \propto (\frac{1}{Q^2})^\beta, \qquad (1)$$

where β is fitted parameter. The fits for different nuclei yield values for β which are compatible and a combined fit to all data yields $\beta = 2.02 \pm 0.07$.

We do not observe any significant nuclear dependence of the magnitude of the total (coherent + incoherent) cross sections per nucleon. However, the incoherent cross sections for carbon and calcium are significantly smaller than that for deuterium.

The cross section for ϕ production is about one order of magnitude smaller than that for ρ^0 production, but it has a similar Q^2 dependence with $\beta = 2.27 \pm 0.39$.

The ratio $\sigma_\phi/\sigma_{\rho^0}$ for the meson production cross sections is shown as a function of Q^2 in fig. 2 together with the result of a previous experiment [5]. The errors shown are statistical. The systematic errors on this ratio are about 10%. One may expect the ratio $\sigma_\psi/\sigma_{\rho^0}$ to

be related to the ratio of the squares of the charges of the valence quarks [4-6], which in this case is 2/9. The present results give a ratio which is about a factor two smaller than this.

2. Decay angular distributions

From the analysis of the decay angular distributions we determined the values of the density matrix elements r_{00}^{04}, r_{1-1}^{04}, $\mathrm{Im}r_{1-1}^3$ and r_{1-1}^1. The relevant formalism has been developed in reference [7].

We do not observe any significant A or Q^2 dependences of these matrix elements. For the ρ^0 data combined over all Q^2 range and averaged over the three nuclei we obtained from the fits to the angular distributions the following values

$$r_{00}^{04} = 0.58 \pm 0.04,$$
$$r_{1-1}^{04} = -0.03 \pm 0.04,$$
$$\mathrm{Im}r_{1-1}^3 = 0.02 \pm 0.07,$$
$$r_{1-1}^1 = 0.16 \pm 0.06.$$

The matrix element r_{00}^{04} represents the probability to produce a longitudinally polarised meson (helicity = 0). The values of r_{1-1}^{04} and r_{1-1}^3 are consistent with zero, which is predicted for these matrix elements by the hypothesis of s-channel helicity conservation (SCHC). If, in addition to SCHC, there is natural parity exchange in the t channel, the fourth matrix element r_{1-1}^1 can be related to r_{00}^{04} [7]. Using the measured value of r_{00}^{04} we obtain $r_{1-1}^1(\mathrm{pred.}) = 0.21 \pm 0.02$, in agreement with the fitted value. Our results thus support the hypothesis of SCHC.

Assuming SCHC and using the measured r_{00}^{04} one can evaluate the ratio $R (= \sigma_L/\sigma_T$ for exclusive ρ^0 virtual photoproduction) from the expression

$$R = \frac{1}{\epsilon} \frac{r_{00}^{04}}{1 - r_{00}^{04}}. \qquad (2)$$

From the present data we obtain $R = 2.0 \pm 0.3$ at $< Q^2 >= 6$ GeV^2.

References

[1] NMC, P. Amaudruz *et al.*, Z. Phys. **C54** (1992) 239.
[2] EMC, J.J. Aubert *et al.*, Phys. Lett. **B161** (1985) 203.
[3] P.V. Landshoff, Proc. of Joint Lepton-Photon Symposium and Europhysics Conf. on HEP, Geneva 1991, vol.2, p. 363; Eds. S. Hegarty, K. Potter and E. Quercigh (World Scientific 1992).
[4] S.J. Brodsky *et al.*, preprint: SLAC-PUB-6412 (1994), submitted to Phys. Rev. **D** and references cited therein.
[5] EMC, J. Ashman *et al.*, Z. Phys. **C39** (1988) 169.
[6] T.H. Bauer *et al.*, Rev. Mod. Phys. **50** (1978) 261.
[7] K. Schilling and G. Wolf, Nucl. Phys. **B61** (1973) 381.

Jets With Large Rapidity Separation

Andrew Brandt

Fermi National Accelerator Laboratory, P.O. Box 500
Batavia, IL 60510

On behalf of the DØ Collaboration

Abstract

Preliminary experimental results are presented from a study of events with jets that have a large rapidity separation. The DØ detector was used to examine these events produced by the Fermilab Tevatron p$\bar{\text{p}}$ collider at $\sqrt{s} = 1.8$ TeV. An analysis of the calorimeter tower multiplicity between the two highest transverse energy jets shows a significant excess of events with low multiplicity, which is qualitatively consistent with the exchange of a strongly interacting color singlet. Another analysis investigates the decorrelation in azimuthal angle of jets as a function of their rapidity separation compared to BFKL and Monte Carlo predictions.

1. Introduction

The DØ detector [1] is well-suited to jet studies due to its excellent calorimetry and coverage out to large pseudorapidity ($|\eta| \approx 4$). In this paper, two new analyses are presented which take advantage of this excellent forward coverage: a study of rapidity gap events and a study of phi decorrelation for jets with large η separation.

2. Rapidity Gaps

Rapidity gaps, which are regions of rapidity containing no particles, are typically associated with color singlet exchange. The DØ collaboration has published a study of rapidity gaps between jets [2], where the two highest transverse energy (E_T) jets have $E_T > 30$ GeV, $|\eta| > 2$, and a separation of $\Delta\eta_c > 3$, where $\Delta\eta_c = |\eta_1 - \eta_2| - 1.4$ is the distance in η between the edges of the jet cones of radius 0.7. Although rapidity gaps were observed with an experimental definition (no electromagnetic towers of $\Delta\eta \times \Delta\phi = 0.1 \times 0.1$ with more than 200 MeV), this did not directly imply color singlet exchange since inefficiencies can create false gaps and there is a

background from multiplicity fluctuations in color octet (gluon exchange) events. It was possible, however, to place an upper limit on the fraction of events with a rapidity gap between the jets of 0.011 (95% CL) [2]. This upper limit provides a significant constraint on the rapidity gap cross section and the survival probability, which is the fraction of events produced with a gap that are not contaminated by particles from spectator interactions [3].

A new analysis of the same data makes use of the expected differences in the particle multiplicity distributions of color singlet and color octet events. Color singlet exchange is expected to give zero multiplicity for events that survive underlying event contamination [3], and a minimum bias-like multiplicity for events that do not survive [4]. Color octet exchange, however, is expected to give a negative binomial (or similar) multiplicity distribution, which peaks at a larger value [5]. Thus an excess of low multiplicity events would indicate the presence of color singlet exchange.

Although the color octet multiplicity between jets is expected to have a negative binomial distribution (NBD), it is crucial to show that an excess at low multiplicity is not created by detector effects. A Monte Carlo study of color octet events using similar jet requirements as the DØ analysis and including estimated DØ acceptance and efficiencies yields a multiplicity distribution that is well-described by a NBD [6]. Further support for the NBD is shown in a sample of color-octet data events that are obtained by demanding the presence of a third jet between the leading two jets, a topology which is highly suppressed for color singlet exchange. Figure 1 shows the multiplicity of electromagnetic towers with $E_T > 200$ MeV, denoted by NEM, for such events with a region of radius 1.0 around the third jet excluded to avoid biases from the jet multiplicity. The resulting NBD fit shows no excess at low multiplicity and gives a $\chi^2/df = 1.1$. Figure 2 shows the tower multiplicity for the sample

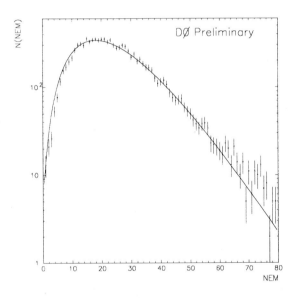

Figure 1. NEM distribution from color-octet tagged data (3-jet sample) with $\Delta\eta_c > 3$. The solid line is the NBD fit.

with at least two jets, and has a significant (41σ) excess at low particle multiplicity compared to a NBD fit starting from NEM=4. The χ^2/df is 0.9 compared to 2.1 if the fit is started from NEM=0. The fractional excess above the fit, $(NEM_{data} - NEM_{fit})/N$, is $\left(1.4 \pm 0.2^{(stat)} \pm 0.2^{(sys)}\right) \times 10^{-2}$, where only systematic errors from the fit have been considered at this point. The excess is insensitive to tower clustering, which attempts to account for the difference between using tower multiplicity and particle multiplicity. The excess also shows the qualitative behavior expected of color singlet exchange—it has little dependence on $\Delta\eta_c$ or tower threshold. If the excess were to be interpreted as color singlet exchange, it would have a magnitude well above the 10^{-3} level expected from electroweak

exchange [7]. The measured excess is not inconsistent with the 10^{-1} estimate of a strongly interacting color singlet [3], considering that the portion of color singlet events with a high multiplicity spectator interaction would escape detection by this method. Due to this fact, this measurement could in principal be used to set a lower limit on color singlet exchange, independent of the survival probability.

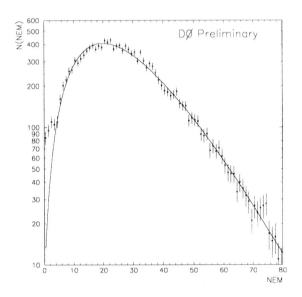

Figure 2. NEM distribution from the complete data sample with $\Delta\eta_c > 3$. A clear excess above the NBD (solid line) fit is observed at low multiplicities.

3. Phi Decorrelation

Quantum Chromodynamics (QCD) calculations of jet final states have typically been limited to leading order (LO), or next-to-leading order (NLO) in powers of the strong coupling constant (α_s) due to the complexity of the calculations. While LO and NLO provide a reasonable description of jet data in most kinematical regions, it has been noted that higher order terms may be important for the study of jets with large rapidity separations which would become decorrelated in E_T and ϕ due to soft gluons emitted between the jets [8, 9]. Techniques have been developed [8, 9] applying BFKL (Balitsky–Fadin–Lipatov–Kuraev) theory [10] to resum soft gluon emissions to all orders in order to investigate this decorrelation. A useful variable to quantify the decorrelation is $\cos(\pi - \Delta\phi)$, where $\Delta\phi$ is the difference in azimuth between the jets with the largest rapidity interval $\Delta\eta = \eta_1 - \eta_2$. Back-to-back jets (as expected at leading order) would have $\cos(\pi - \Delta\phi) = 1$, while this quantity decreases as the jets become more decorrelated. Figure 3 shows that the BFKL prediction of [9] has much more decorrelation than predicted by the NLO calculation of JETRAD [11] or the parton shower Monte Carlo HERWIG [12].

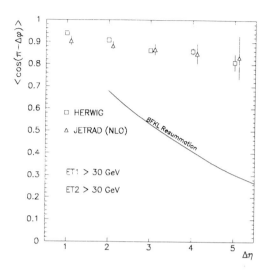

Figure 3. $< \cos(\pi - \Delta\phi) >$ versus $\Delta\eta$ with jet $E_T > 30$ GeV.

We are currently unable to plot the data with these cuts (jet $E_T > 30$ GeV) since the leading jet in the primary trigger for this analysis does not become fully efficient until $E_T > 50$ GeV. Figure 4 shows the same quantity, but all jets are required to have $E_T > 20$ GeV, and one of the two jets comprising the largest $\Delta\eta$ pair must have $E_T > 50$ GeV. The decorrelation in the data increases with $\Delta\eta$ and is well-described by the HERWIG Monte Carlo, but the NLO Monte Carlo does not provide enough decorrelation. The BFKL calculation is not yet available for these cuts.

4. Conclusion

We have used the DØ detector to study jets with large rapidity separation. The search for rapidity gap events between jets has resulted in a significant excess of events with low multiplicity between the jets. This excess cannot be explained by detector effects and is qualitatively consistent with the exchange of a strongly interacting color singlet. After the completion of studies of systematic effects, these data can be used to set a lower limit on the cross section for color singlet exchange.

We have also made a first measurement of the phi decorrelation of jets as a function of their rapidity interval. The jets clearly become more decorrelated with increasing $\Delta\eta$, in a manner that is well-described by HERWIG, but not by JETRAD. Predictions based on BFKL theory are not directly comparable with the data at this time, but show significantly more decorrelation

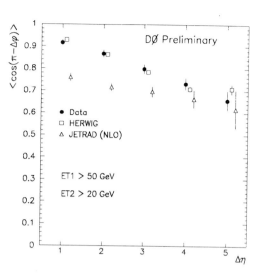

Figure 4. $< \cos(\pi - \Delta\phi) >$ versus $\Delta\eta$ with jet $E_T > 50$ and 20 GeV.

than HERWIG or JETRAD when similar cuts are applied to these Monte Carlos.

References

[1] S. Abachi *et al.* (DØ Collaboration), Nucl. Instrum. and Meth. A**338**, 185 (1994).

[2] S. Abachi *et al.*(DØ Collaboration),Phys. Rev. Lett. 72, 2332 (1994).

[3] J. D. Bjorken, Phys. Rev. D**47**, 101 (1992).

[4] R. S. Fletcher and T. Stelzer, Phys. Rev. D**48**, 5162 (1993).

[5] I. Dremin, submitted to Physics Uspekhi, FIAN TD-6, (1994) and references therein.

[6] R. Fletcher, private communication.

[7] H. Chehime *et al.*, Phys. Lett. B **286**, 397 (1992).

[8] V. Del Duca and C.R. Schmidt, Phys. Rev. D **49**, 4510 (1994); preprint DESY 94-114 (1994).

[9] W.J. Stirling, preprint DTP/94/04 (1994).

[10] L.N. Lipatov, Yad. Fiz. **23**, 642 (1976) [Sov. J. Nucl. Phys. **23**, 338 (1976)]; E.A. Kuraev, L.N. Lipatov and V.S. Fadin, Zh. Eksp. Teor. Fiz. **71**, 840 (1976) [Sov. Phys. JETP **44**, 443 (1976)]; **72**, 377 (1977) [**45**, 199 (1977)]; Ya.Ya. Balitsky and L.N. Lipatov, Yad. Fiz. **28** 1597 (1978) [Sov. J. Nucl. Phys. **28**, 822 (1978)].

[11] W.T. Giele, E.W.N. Glover and D.A. Kosower, Nucl. Phys. **B403**, 633 (1993).

[12] G.Marchesini and B.R.Webber, Nucl. Phys. **B310**, 461 (1988).

Parallel Session Pa-6

DIS and Structure Functions

Conveners: W. J. Stirling (University of Durham)
E. Hughes (SLAC)

Scientific secretaries: V. A. Jamieson
I. Fleck (reserve)

Proton structure function $F_2(x, Q^2)$ at HERA
H1 Collaboration

Violette Brisson

Laboratoire de l'Accélérateur Linéaire IN2P3 - CNRS
et Université de Paris-Sud, 91405 Orsay Cedex, France

Abstract

The proton structure function has been measured in the H1 experiment at HERA. About 20000 events, corresponding to an integrated luminosity of 270 nb^{-1} have allowed to determine F_2 for x as low as 2.10^{-4} and Q^2 up to ~ 2000 GeV^2. A strong rise of F_2 at small x is observed.

1. Introduction

The new kinematical domain opened by HERA for the study of deep inelastic scattering extends to Q^2 as high as 10^5 GeV^2, and x Bjorken as low as 2.10^{-5} for small Q^2; it allows to investigate the so far unknown evolution of the F_2 structure function when the momentum of the struck quark is very low, and to measure the gluon contribution in this region; at very high Q^2, it could allow to detect deviations from Altarelli Parisi evolution equations due to the presence of new physics.

The HERA integrated luminosity available in 1993 (530 nb^{-1}, 270 nb^{-1} being used in this analysis) presently limits this domain to $4.5 < Q^2 < 2000$ GeV^2 and $2.10^{-4} < x < 0.15$, in which about 20000 events have been produced. This represents about 12 times the statistics which was taken in 1992 and used in our first deep inelastic papers[1]. Results of F_2 measurements are given for nearly a hundred (x, Q^2) values in the mentioned domain, together with the contribution to F_2 of "large rapidity gap" events coming probably from diffractive interactions.

2. Experimental determination of F_2

The deep inelastic cross section can be written as

$$\frac{d^2\sigma(x, Q^2)}{dx dQ^2} = \frac{4\pi\alpha^2}{xQ^4} \left[(1 - y + \frac{y^2}{2}) F_2(x, Q^2) \right.$$

$$\left. -\frac{y^2}{2} F_L(x, Q^2) \pm (y - \frac{y^2}{2}) x F_3(x, Q^2) \right]$$

and, with F_L ($= 2$ x F_1 .R) small and computable in QCD (until it can be measured) and xF_3 small for $Q^2 << M_z^2$, reduces to:

$$\frac{d^2\sigma(x, Q^2)}{dx dQ^2} = \frac{2\pi\alpha^2}{xQ^4} \left[2(1 - y) + \frac{y^2}{1 + R} \right] F_2(x, Q^2)$$

$$= \frac{N \text{events}(x, Q^2)}{\text{Luminosity}} \times \text{corrections}$$

Corrections have to be made for efficiencies (computed from the events), and for acceptance, smearing and radiative corrections (by Monte Carlo, with the choice of parameterizations for the quark distributions).

2.1. Detector

The masterpiece of the H1 detector[2] is the large Liquid Argon calorimeter for both electromagnetic and hadronic calorimetry, inserted in a cryogenic coil (1.2 Tesla) with a big iron yoke, and surrounding a tracker made of jet chambers in the central part and of sandwiches of different chambers in the forward part. The L.A. calorimeter is closed by a backward electromagnetic calorimeter made of lead/scintillator sandwiches.

The direction of emission of the scattered electron is closely related to Q^2; at low Q^2, electrons reach essentially the backward calorimeter, and for $Q^2 \geq 200$ GeV^2 they reach the L.A. calorimeter; this leads to different experimental problems and biases over the whole range: a good knowledge of the detector is required for reaching coherent results.

2.2. *Kinematical reconstruction*

The measurement of the differential cross sections $d^2\sigma/dx dQ^2$ requires the best possible estimation of the two scaling variables x, Q^2 (or y). The two physics independent relations, $\Sigma p_T = 0$ and $\Sigma(E - P_z) = 2E_{ebeam} = 53.2$GeV, help to reduce background and to check calibrations. The determination of x, y, Q^2 is presently made using different methods:

A - <u>Electron only</u> - The kinematics is obtained from the scattered electron, the hadrons being used for determining the vertex and $\Sigma(E - p_z)$. This method is quite precise, except at low y (high x) where the electron angle is completely insensitive to x (see fig.2). Q^2 is always well determined.

B - <u>Mixed variables</u> - Q^2 is determined from the electron, and y from the hadrons with $y_{hadrons} = y_{Jacquet\ Blondel} = \Sigma(E_H - Pz_H)/2E_{ebeam}$. This is good at high x (low y) and poor at low x. It requires a good knowledge of the hadronic energy scale.

C - <u>Double angle (D.A.)</u> - Only the electron direction and hadronic system angle are used. The advantage is the independence w.r.t. any energy scale. The performances are comparable to the mixed variable method.

D - <u>"Σ" method</u> - The difference with the mixed variable method is in the y calculation, taken equal to $\frac{\Sigma(E_H - Pz_H)}{\Sigma(E_{TOT} - Pz_{TOT})}$; the denominator being measured and not taken as $2\ E_{ebeam}$, large incident radiative corrections are then removed, and hadronic scale uncertainties cancel at high y. This method is a good check of the evaluation of the radiative corrections in the electron method, which is nevertheless more precise. At low y it is equivalent to the mixed or D.A. method. We have used all these methods and checked the good agreement (see later), which is the best way of being confident in the results.

The resolutions in x and Q^2 are shown in fig.1, which illustrates the advantages and drawbacks of the different methods.

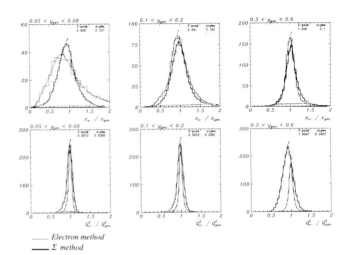

——— *Electron method*
——— *Σ method*

Figure 1. Resolutions in x, Q^2 for three domains of y.

The binning in x an Q^2 chosen for the results is shown in fig.2, where the events are also represented as points in the x, Q^2 plane. The bins are always much larger than the Q^2 resolution $(\Delta Q^2/Q^2) \sim (4\ to\ 6)\%$ and at least about twice bigger than the x resolution $(\Delta x/x \sim 10\ to\ 20\%)$.

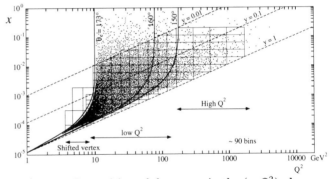

Figure 2. Repartition of the events in the (x, Q^2) plane (each point is 1 event), the grid corresponds to the chosen binning, and the lines are constant θ_e or y lines.

2.3. *Selection of events*

Starting from events with one identified electron in the L.A. or backward calorimeter and a reconstructed vertex, several analyses with different methods and cuts have been performed. In a dedicated data taking the interaction point has been shifted in order to increase the acceptance for electron angles close to the beampipe so decreasing the lower limit available in Q^2.

The most relevant cuts and the corresponding efficiencies measured with data are given in table 1. Kinematic cuts are part of the acceptance and are corrected for via a Monte Carlo.

SELECTION (evt kept if:)	REASON	EFFICIENCY
- e ⌈BEMC=shower< 4cm		100% ⇓
⎨ BEMC ↔ BPC	Good e i.D.	98%
⌊ L.A.=compact cluster		99% Overall
- Vertex position=IP± 30 cm	Remove b.g	95% (94±3)%
- No T.O.F.veto	"	99%
⌐		Trigger=99%
- $\theta_e < 173°(175°)$	Beam Pipe	part of
- Ee>8 GeV(10.3)	Trigger eff.	Acceptance
	Remove γ p	⇓
- E - p_z > 30 GeV	"	Monte Carlo
- P_{Tmiss} <15 GeV	Remove b.g	
- y_e <.8(.6)	Remove γ p	

Table 1. Most relevant cuts - Efficiencies computed with data

2.4. Background

The usual backgrounds of events not linked to e.p. collisions have been estimated to 1.1% for cosmic muons, 0.2% for halo muons and 0.2% for beam gas or beam wall events.

The most important background comes from the tail of photoproduction events where the electron goes into the beampipe and a hadron or photon fakes an electron in the backward or L.A. calorimeter. The cuts $E-p_z > 30$ GeV and $E_e > 8$ GeV help to suppress these events. The remaining events are estimated by a Monte Carlo (Pythia and VDM) verified on photoproduction events where the electrons are identified in the electron tagger (10%). Globally, the remaining background is $(1\pm1)\%$, subtracted statistically bin by bin.

2.5. Corrections, uncertainties

A - Acceptance corrections - Several Monte Carlo's with different parameterisations (MRSD′_, MRSH[3], and MRSD′_0 which does not fit at all the results and has finally been left out) have been used, and iterations have been made, each time reinjecting the F_2 values extracted in the preceding step. The product of acceptance by smearing due to resolution varies from 0.7 to 1.2 in the different bins.

B - Radiative corrections - Two methods have been used: a Monte Carlo (HERAKLES - ([4]) and an analytical calculation (TERAD ([4]). Both agree within ~ 2%. In our acceptance region, the corrections are always smaller than 10%.

C - Systematic uncertainties - The most important systematics come from an unperfect knowledge of energies, that we hope to improve in the future with a more detailed study of all our calibrations. These systematic errors on reconstructed electron energies have been evaluated as 1.7% in the backward calorimeter,

3% in the liquid argon (5% in the most backward part), 10% in the part with L.A. /backward calorimeters recovering, and 5% for the hadronic energies in L.A. All this gives an overall uncertainty of ~ 10% on F_2.

3.   Results on F_2 measurements

Results from the three kinematical methods are presented in fig.3 where F_2 is seen as a function of x for 16 values of Q^2. The good agreement between the three methods used in different analyses with different event selections is a good check of the reliability of the results. For getting final values on F_2, we have chosen the electron method for small x values ($\sim < 2.10^{-2}$) and the Σ method for larger x values. These final values are shown in fig.5, and will be further commented (see part 5). A present uncertainty of 10% on the normalisation of the luminosity reflects directly on the F_2 scale. This is not shown on the figure.

4.   Large rapidity gap events

A subsample of D.I.S events ($\sim 6\%$) does not show any energy flow in the forward part of the calorimeter. For these events the pseudorapidity of the most forward cluster η_{max} is less than 1.8, whilst for normal D.I.S events $\eta_{max} > 3$. A possible interpretation is an interaction with the exchange of a colourless object, the Pomeron. Two mechanisms are possible: one being based on vector meson dominance of the photon (VMD); the other corresponding to hard scattering with a parton (quark or gluon) inside the Pomeron (RAPGAP). The first mechanism (VMD) and the second, represented by the RAPGAP Monte Carlo, fit the η_{max} distribution of the events as well. The properties of these events are discussed in[5].

The contribution of these events to F_2 has been measured, with $F_2 = \frac{d\sigma}{dx\,dQ^2 dx_P dt} = \frac{4\pi\alpha^2}{xQ^4}(1-y+y^2/2)\times F_2^D(x,Q^2;x_P,t^2)$. The acceptance is the same as normal D.I.S events, and integrating over x_P ($x_{Pomeron}$) for $x_P < 10^{-2}$ (due to the η_{max} cut), one gets the results which appear in fig.4, together with the predictions of a phenomenological model by A. Capella et al[6]. The contribution to F_2^p is of the order of 8-10%, showing the same tendency of rising at low x, but cannot by itself explain the steep rise in $F_2^p(x,Q^2)$ at low x.

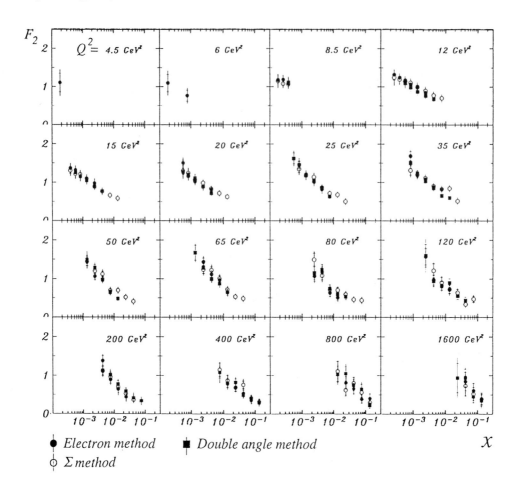

Figure 3. F_2 as a function of x for several Q^2 for the three kinematical methods.

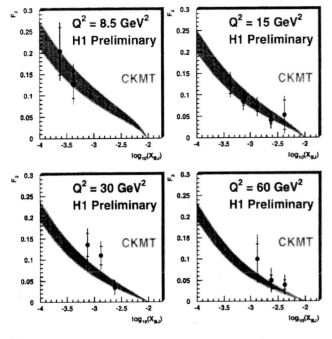

Figure 4. F_2 contribution from diffractive events.

5.   Interpretation and comparison with predictions

Keeping the diffractive event sample in our results and coming back to fig. 5, the first striking characteristic is the steep rise of F_2 when x decreases. A simple QCD fit à la Abbott/Barnett [7], using the Altarelli–Parisi equations at leading order, describes the data quite well, and gives a gluon density diverging as x^β with $\beta = -0.38 \pm 0.10$ at 5 GeV^2 (see G. Raedel's report in the "low x session"). The comparison with the three parameterizations shown in fig. 5 does not allow any firm conclusion, the errors in F_2 being still too large.

Finally, fig. 6 shows the F_2 results as a function of Q^2, for different values of x. For the largest x values, the continuity between these results and previous results of NMC, SLAC and BCDMS seems satisfying in spite of the statistics. The results are well described by the GRV prediction.

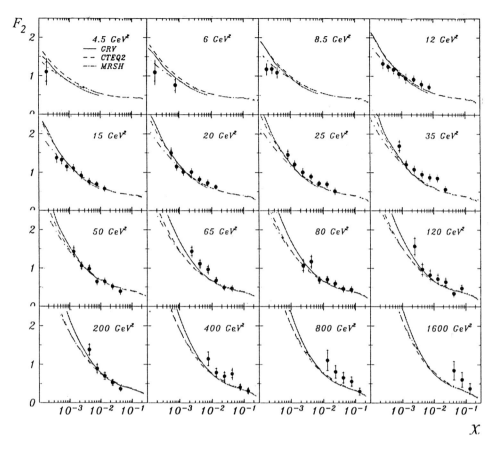

Figure 5. F_2 results, with different predictions.

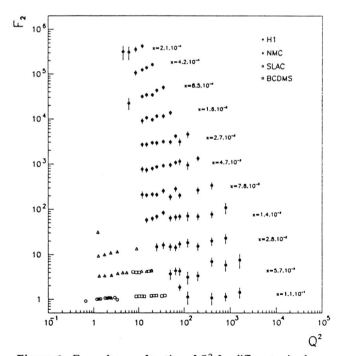

Figure 6. F_2 results as a function of Q^2 for different x in the range 2.1×10^{-4} to 1.1×10^{-1}. The data at each x value are scaled by a common factor which is different for the different x values.

References

[1] H1 Coll: I. Abt *et al.* , Nucl. Phys. **B 407** (1993) 515

[2] H1 Coll: I. Abt *et al.* , N.I.M. to be published

[3] A.D. Martin *et al.* , Phys. Lett. **B306** (1993) 145, *ibid.* B309 (1993) 492

[4] H. Spiesberger *et al.* , (HERAKLES); A. Akhundov, D. Bardin *et al.* , (TERAD)

[5] H1 Coll: I. Abt *et al.* , H1 report 94-133, to be published in Nucl. Phys. **B**

[6] A. Capella *et al.* , preprint LPTHE/94-42

[7] Atwood *et al.* , PR.D22 (1982) 584

Paper presented at XXVII Int. Conf. on High Energy Physics: Session Pa-6
Glasgow, UK, 20–27 July 1994

A measurement of the proton structure function $F_2(x, Q^2)$ at low-x and a determination of the low-x gluon distribution

Mark Lancaster[†]

Department of Nuclear & Particle Physics,
University of Oxford
Keble Road, Oxford, OX1 3RH, UK

On behalf of the ZEUS Collaboration

Abstract

A measurement of the proton structure function $F_2(x, Q^2)$ by the ZEUS detector at HERA from data taken during the 1993 running period is described. Results are presented for $7 < Q^2 < 10^4$ GeV^2 and x values as low as 3×10^{-4}. The F_2 values are used to extract the gluon distribution at $Q^2 = 20$ GeV^2 for x down to 8×10^{-4} using both published approximate methods and a global NLO fit to the ZEUS data at low-x combined with NMC data at larger x. A substantial rise in the gluon density and F_2 is found at small x in comparison with previous results obtained at larger values of x.

1. Introduction

The large centre of mass energy available at HERA allows measurements of the proton structure function to be made for x values as small as 10^{-4} for $Q^2 \gtrsim 7$ GeV^2. The data sample used corresponds to an integrated luminosity of 0.54 pb^{-1} and represents a twenty fold increase over that used in the first ZEUS measurement of F_2 [1]. Two independent analyses have been performed, one using our standard double angle approach and the other based on the energy and angle of the scattered electron. The size of the systematic errors in the double angle method has been reduced in comparison to our previous measurement through the increased statistics and improved understanding of the performance of the detector. The improved precision of the F_2 data has allowed the gluon distribution to be determined from a full NLO QCD fit.

2. ZEUS detector

ZEUS is a multipurpose detector that has been described elsewhere [2]. The principal detector components for the F_2 analysis are the inner tracking detectors and the high resolution uranium-scintillator calorimeter (CAL) [4]. The inner tracking detectors [3] operating in a magnetic field of 1.43T provide a vertex resolution of 4 mm in z, which compares to the width of the vertex distribution (determined by the proton bunch length) of 11 cm. The CAL is divided into three parts, forward, barrel and rear (FCAL,BCAL and RCAL) with each part subdivided into towers which in turn are subdivided longitudinally into electromagnetic (EMC) and hadronic (HAC) sections. The sections are subdivided into cells, each of which is viewed by two photomultiplier tubes. Under test beam conditions the CAL has an energy resolution, in units of GeV, of $\sigma_E = 0.35\sqrt{E}$(GeV) for hadrons and $\sigma_E = 0.18\sqrt{E}$(GeV) for electrons. The CAL also provides a time resolution of better than 1 ns for energy deposits greater than 4.5 GeV, which is used

† E-mail: lancaster@vxdesy.desy.de

for background rejection. Luminosity information is obtained through the detection of quasi-elastic $ep \to ep\gamma$ events in two lead scintillator calorimeters placed 35 and 107 m downstream of the main detector [5]. Non-ep backgrounds are rejected by veto detectors downstream of the interaction point (IP).

3.   Deep inelastic kinematics

Structure functions are expressed as functions of the variables Bjorken x and Q^2. Because the ZEUS detector is almost hermetic the kinematic variables x and Q^2 can be constructed in a variety of ways using combinations of electron and hadronic system energies and angles [6]. The ability to measure x and Q^2 in different ways offers a powerful systematic check on the resulting F_2 values. In this F_2 analysis two methods have been used to measure x and Q^2 : firstly the electron method where the kinematics are reconstructed from the energy (E'_e) and angle (θ'_e) of the scattered electron and secondly the double angle (DA) method in which only the angles of the scattered electron (θ'_e) and the hadronic system (γ_H) are used, which reduces the sensitivity to energy scale uncertainties. In the naïve quark-parton model γ_H is the scattering angle of the struck quark. In the double angle method in order that the hadronic system is well measured it is necessary to ensure a minimum of hadronic activity in the CAL away from the beam pipe. A suitable quantity for this purpose is the hadronic estimator of the variable y [7], defined by, $y_{JB} = \Sigma_h \frac{(E-P_z)}{2E_e}$ where E_e is the electron beam energy and the z axis points in the direction of the proton beam.

4.   Event selection and backgrounds

Data were collected with a trigger comprising of three levels. Deep inelastic scattering (DIS) events are selected at the first level using a logical OR of three conditions on sums of energy in the EMC calorimeter cells. At the second level using cuts based on the event times measured in the FCAL and RCAL and at the third level using cuts on the quantity δ, where $\delta \equiv \Sigma_i E_i(1 - \cos\theta_i) > 20$ GeV $- 2E_\gamma$ and E_i, θ_i are the energy and polar angle (with respect to the nominal IP) of calorimeter cells and E_γ is the energy measured in the photon calorimeter of the luminosity monitor. For fully contained events $\delta \sim 2E_e = 53.4$ GeV. For events from photoproduction processes δ peaks at low values; this is because the scattered electrons remain within the rear beam pipe and the bremsstrahlung spectrum is soft. Additionally at the third level tighter event time cuts and cuts to remove halo-muons and cosmics are applied.

The overall trigger acceptance after all three levels is above 95% independent of x and Q^2 in the ranges of interest for this analysis. The 2×10^6 events recorded by

the trigger are subject to final selection cuts. For the DA method the following cuts are employed : $E'_e > 5$ GeV, $y_e < 0.95$, $y_{JB} > 0.04$, $35 < \delta < 60$ and the impact point of the electron on the face of the RCAL be outside a square of 32 cm centred on the beam axis. For the electron analysis the E'_e cut is raised to 8 GeV and the y_{JB} cut removed since the need to reconstruct γ_H accurately is removed. The distribution of the events after the DA selection cuts is shown in figure 1 along with the bins used for the analysis. The bin sizes at low Q^2 ($Q^2 \lesssim 100$ GeV^2) are determined by resolution whilst for high Q^2 they are determined by statistics. Non-ep backgrounds are statistically subtracted and total < 1%. The predominant ep background arises from photoproduction events where a photon in the final state fakes an electron in the detector. The low δ values of photoproduction events in comparison to DIS events allow the background to be estimated from a fit to the δ spectrum. The results of the fit were cross checked with a photoproduction Monte-Carlo. The total photoproduction background was 2.5% and was predominantly concentrated at high-y where the largest background in any one bin was 12%.

5. F_2 extraction

For the bins used in this analysis the Z_0, F_L and radiative corrections are small such that the Born cross section can be expressed as :

$$\frac{d^2\sigma}{dxdQ^2} = \frac{2\pi}{xQ^4}F_2(1 + (1-y)^2)(1 + \Delta_{Z_0} + \Delta_{F_L} + \Delta_r).$$

The F_2 extracted is a pure photon exchange F_2. The effects of the Δ_i corrections, acceptance and event migration are corrected for using an event sample generated using the HERACLES [8] Monte-Carlo. The hadronic final state was simulated using the colour-dipole model [9] incorporating boson-gluon fusion as implemented in ARIADNE [10] for the QCD cascade, and JETSET [11] for the hadronisation. The detector simulation is based on the GEANT [12] program. The systematic errors were calculated by varying selection cuts and the analysis methods (see [13] for further details). The systematics are typically large at small-y ($\sim$ 20%) where uncertainties in the determination of γ_H dominate and at large-y ($\sim$ 10%) due to background and electron identification uncertainties. The F_2 values as a function of x for Q^2 values ranging from 8.5 to 2000 are shown in figure 2 along with the F_2 values calculated using some current parton distribution parameterisations. A clear rise in F_2 is seen which persists to large values of Q^2 in contrast to the predictions of parton distributions which embody a flat gluon distribution as a function of x for example the MRSD$'_0$ [14] parameterisation. The ZEUS F_2 values are found to satisfy a compact parameterisation of the form :

$$F_2 = [(1-x)(1+x)]^4(0.35 + Bx^{(C+D\log_{10}Q^2)}),$$

where $B = 0.0170 \pm 0.0041$; $C = -0.352 \pm 0.023$ and $D = -0.155 \pm 0.015$.

6. Determination of the gluon density

The gluon momentum density $xg(x, Q^2)$ is related only indirectly to F_2 through the QCD scaling violations expressed in terms of the Altarelli-Parisi equation [15] :

$$\frac{dF_2(x,Q^2)}{d\ln Q^2} = \frac{\alpha_s(Q^2)}{2\pi} \left[\int_x^1 \frac{dz}{z} \left(\frac{x}{z}\right) P_{qq}\left(\frac{x}{z}\right) F_2(z, Q^2) \right.$$
$$\left. + 2\sum_q e_q^2 \int_x^1 \frac{dz}{z} \left(\frac{x}{z}\right) P_{qg}\left(\frac{x}{z}\right) zg(z, Q^2) \right],$$

where the sum runs over all active quark flavours and e_q is the charge of quark q, $\alpha_s(Q^2)$ is the strong coupling constant and P_{qq}, P_{qg} are the quark and gluon splitting functions. The gluon term in the above equation dominates the scaling violations at low-x. Two approaches have been used to extract the gluon density at $Q^2 = 20$ GeV^2 from the ZEUS F_2 data. Firstly two approximate methods, Prytz [16] and EKL [17], have been used in which the gluon distribution is expressed directly in terms of the measured quantities : F_2 and $dF_2/d\ln Q^2$ and secondly from a full NLO QCD fit to the ZEUS F_2 data along with larger-x F_2 data from NMC [18]. The F_2 scaling violations are shown in figure 3 along with the straight line fits used to determine the F_2 and $dF_2/d\ln Q^2$ values necessary as input to the approximate methods. The full NLO QCD fit is also shown in the figure. The NLO fit takes the functional form for the singlet, valence, non-singlet and gluon distributions from the MRS parameterisations [14]. In particular a gluon distribution of the form : $xg(x, Q_0^2) = A_g x^{\delta_g}(1-x)^{\eta_g}$ is used. The parameters for the valence distributions are taken directly from MRSD$'_-$. From the fit a value of $\delta_g = 0.35$ at $Q^2 = 7$ GeV^2 is found. The results of the fit and the two approximate methods are shown in figure 4. The systematic errors shown in the figure were evaluated by repeating the analysis but using F_2 values offset by each of the systematic errors which in combination form the total F_2 systematic error. Included in the systematic error of the fit is the uncertainty due to the relative normalisation of the ZEUS ($\pm 3.5\%$) and NMC ($\pm 1.6\%$: 90 GeV data, $\pm 2.6\%$: 280 GeV data) data sets. In addition to the statistical and systematic errors shown in the figure there are additional theoretical errors. An error of $\sim 6\%$ due to the uncertainty in α_s is present in both approaches. Moreover the assumptions of the Prytz and EKL methods lead to further systematic uncertainties.

The Prytz method overestimates the gluon distribution since it neglects the quark contribution to the scaling violations, however it is relatively insensitive to the assumed shape of the gluon distribution. In contrast the EKL method is found to be very sensitive to the assumed x distribution of F_2 and the gluon. An x variation for F_2 and the gluon distribution of the form : $x^{-\omega_0}$ is assumed. Reasonable variations in the value of ω_0 i.e. $0.3 < \omega_0 < 0.5$ cause a 40% change in the extracted gluon distribution. For the NLO fit the effects of : valence quark parameterisation, strange quark content, quark mass, higher twist contributions were all investigated and found to be negligible. The treatment of the charm threshold was found to have a small ($\lesssim 5\%$) effect. The gluon shows a steep increase at low x in comparison to previous results obtained at larger values of x.

References

[1] ZEUS Collab., M. Derrick et al., Phys. Lett. B316 (1993) 412.

[2] ZEUS Collab., M. Derrick et al., Phys. Lett. B293 (1992) 465.

[3] C.B. Brooks et al., Nucl. Instr. Meth. A283 (1989) 477; B. Foster et al., Nucl. Instr. Meth. A338 (1994) 254; C. Alvisi et al., Nucl. Instr. and Meth. A305 (1991) 30.

[4] A. Andresen et al., Nucl. Inst. and Meth. A309 (1991) 101; A. Bernstein et al., Nucl. Inst. and Meth. A336 (1993) 23; A. Caldwell et al., Nucl. Inst. and Meth. A321 (1992) 356.

[5] K. Piotrzkowski, PhD Thesis University of Cracow 1993, DESY F35D-93-06 (1993).

[6] S. Bentvelsen, J. Engelen and P. Kooijman, Proceedings of the Workshop 'Physics at HERA' vol. 1, DESY 1992, 23; S. Bentvelsen, PhD Thesis University of Amsterdam 1994.

[7] F. Jacquet and A. Blondel, Proceedings of the study of an *ep* facility for Europe, DESY 79/48 (1979) 391, U. Amaldi ed.

[8] HERACLES 4.1: A. Kwiatkowski, H. Spiesberger and H.-J. Möhring, Proceedings of the Workshop 'Physics at HERA' vol. 3, DESY 1992, 1294; A.Kwiatkowski, H.Spiesberger and H.-J.Möhring, Z. Phys. C50 (1991) 165.

[9] B. Andersson et al., Z. Phys. C43 (1989) 625.

[10] ARIADNE 3.1: L. Lönnblad, Comput. Phys. Commun. 71 (1992) 15.

[11] JETSET 6.3: T. Sjöstrand, Comput. Phys. Commun. 39 (1986) 347; T. Sjöstrand and M. Bengtsson, Comput. Phys. Commun. 43 (1987) 367.

[12] GEANT 3.13: R. Brun et al., CERN DD/EE/84-1 (1987).

[13] ZEUS Collab., M. Derrick et al., DESY 94-143 (1994), submitted to Z. Phys. C.

[14] A.D. Martin, R.G. Roberts and W.J. Stirling, Phys. Lett. B306 (1993) 145; Phys. Lett. B309 (1993) 492 (erratum).

[15] V.N. Gribov and L.N. Lipatov, Sov. J. Nucl. Phys. 15 (1972) 438, 675; L.N. Lipatov, Sov. J. Nucl. Phys. 20 (1974) 181; G. Altarelli and G. Parisi, Nucl. Phys. 126 (1977) 297.

[16] K. Prytz, Phys. Lett. B311 (1993) 286; K. Prytz, RAL-94-036 (1994).

[17] R.K. Ellis, Z. Kunszt and E.M. Levin, Fermilab-PUB-93/350-T, ETH-TH/93/41.

[18] NMC Collab., P. Amaudruz et al., Phys. Lett. B295 (1992) 159.

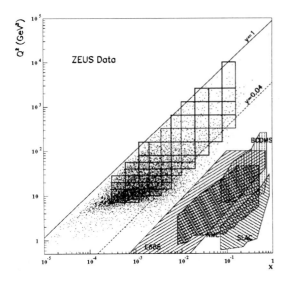

Figure 1. The x-Q^2 distribution of the ZEUS F_2 event sample and the bins used in the analysis. The x-Q^2 regions where fixed target F_2 measurements have been made are also shown.

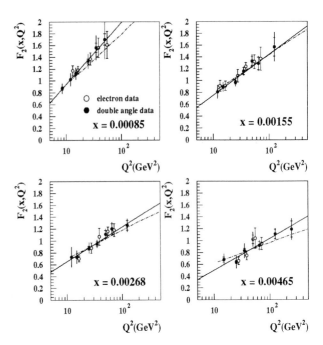

Figure 3. The F_2 structure function measurements of ZEUS together with the linear fits (solid lines), and the result from the global NLO fit, (dashed-dotted lines). The error bars show the statistical (inner error) and systematic error added together in quadrature.

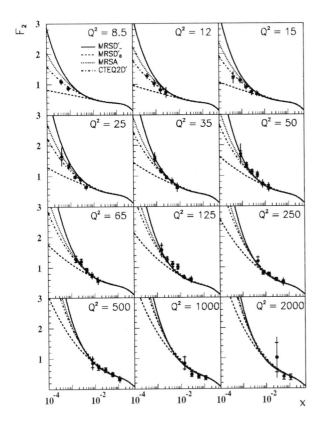

Figure 2. ZEUS 1993 final F_2 values (solid circles) plotted as functions of x at fixed Q^2 and compared to the following recent PDF calculations: MRSD′_ (full curve), MRSD′₀ (dashed curve), CTEQ2D′ (dash-dotted curve) and MRSA (dotted). The inner error bar shows the statistical error and the full bar the statistical and systematic errors added in quadrature. Q^2 is measured in GeV². The overall normalisation uncertainty of 3.5% is not included.

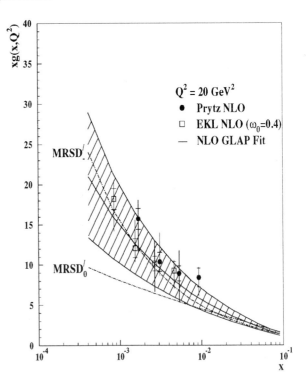

Figure 4. The gluon momentum density as a function of x at $Q^2 = 20 \; GeV^2$ as determined from the ZEUS data with Prytz and EKL in NLO. The error bars show the experimental statistical (inner error) and systematic error added to together in quadrature. The solid line shows the result of the NLO GLAP global fit with the associated error indicated by the hatched region. The gluon parameterisations of MRSD′_ and MRSD′₀ are shown as dash-dotted lines.

Paper presented at XXVII Int. Conf. on High Energy Physics: Session Pa-6
Glasgow, UK, 20–27 July 1994

New results on F_2^n/F_2^p, the Gottfried sum and $R^d - R^p$

E.-M. Kabuß*

Institut für Kernphysik, Universität Mainz, Becherweg 45, D 55099 Mainz, Germany

On behalf of the New Muon Collaboration (NMC)

Abstract

The New Muon Collaboration has re-evaluated the ratio F_2^n/F_2^p and the Gottfried sum $S_g = \int_0^1 (F_2^p - F_2^n)\frac{dx}{x}$. The value of $S_G = 0.235 \pm 0.026$ at $Q^2 = 4$ GeV^2 remains below the parton model prediction of $\frac{1}{3}$. In addition results are presented from measurements at 120, 200 and 280 GeV done in 1989, when a new low x trigger was added allowing to extend the x range down to $8 \cdot 10^{-4}$. With the data sets at several energies available, the assumption that R^d is equal to R^p can be tested, where R is the ratio of longitudinally to transversely polarised virtual photon absorption cross sections.

1. Introduction

The New Muon Collaboration (NMC) has measured the x and Q^2 dependence of deep inelastic muon scattering on hydrogen and deuterium at incident energies of 90, 120, 200 and 280 GeV to study structure functions and structure function ratios in a large kinematic range. Due to a complementary target setup, apparatus acceptance and flux normalisation cancel in the extraction of cross section ratios and thus small systematic erros were achieved.

2. Re-evaluation of F_2^n/F_2^p and the Gottfried sum

The structure function ratio F_2^n/F_2^p is derived from the cross section ratio (per nucleon) assuming $R^d = R^p$, where R is the ratio of longitudinally to transversely polarised virtual photon absorption cross sections, thus: $\sigma_{1\gamma}^d/\sigma_{1\gamma}^p = F_2^d/F_2^p$. Neglecting any possible nuclear effects in the deuteron one has $F_2^d = \frac{1}{2}(F_2^p + F_2^n)$ and $F_2^n/F_2^p = 2\sigma_{1\gamma}^d/\sigma_{1\gamma}^p - 1$. The ratio F_2^n/F_2^p from 90 and 280 GeV data has been published previously and

* supported by the BMFT

details of the method can be found in [1].

Meanwhile new precise results on the proton and deuteron structure functions were published by the NMC [2] extending the measurement down to $x = 0.008$. Parametrisations including the new NMC data differ at low x from extrapolations of previous parametrisations by up to 20%.

Thus a re-evaluation of the structure function ratio was made using the new results on F_2^d in the radiative corrections leading to changes mainly at low x. For the calculation of the radiative corrections the method of Akhundov et al. [3] was used. In addition an improved momentum calibration was available for the 90 GeV data changing the ratio slightly at high x.

The ratio F_2^n/F_2^p is used to determine the Gottfried sum [4]

$$S_G = \int_0^1 (F_2^p - F_2^n)\frac{dx}{x}.$$

In the quark parton model F_2 can be expressed in terms of the quark momentum distribution functions $F_2 = F_2(x) = \sum_i x e_i^2(q_i(x) + \bar{q}_i(x))$, e_i denoting the charge of quarks of flavour i. Thus the Gottfried sum represents the difference between the summed squared quark charges in the proton and the neutron. Inserting valence and seaquark distributions and assuming isospin symmetry between the proton and the neutron the Gottfried sum can be expressed as

$$S_G = \frac{1}{3} + \frac{2}{3}\int_0^1 (\overline{u}(x) - \overline{d}(x))\mathrm{d}x.$$

The first term arises from integration over the valence quarks. QCD corrections to the Gottfried sum are calculated to be negligible [6].

From the measured structure function ratio the Gottfried sum can be determined via

$$F_2^p - F_2^n = 2F_2^d \cdot \frac{1 - F_2^n/F_2^p}{1 + F_2^n/F_2^p}.$$

Due to the change in F_2^d at low x a significant change in the Gottfried sum due to the $1/x$-factor might be expected compared to the result of $S_G(Q^2 = 4\ \mathrm{GeV}^2) = 0.240 \pm 0.016$ published previously by the NMC [7]. Thus the Gottfried sum was re-evaluated using the new ratio F_2^n/F_2^p and F_2^d given by a fit to the NMC, SLAC and BCDMS data [2]. The contribution to the unmeasured region at $x < 0.004$ was estimated assuming a Regge-like behaviour ax^b of $F_2^p - F_2^n$.

Fig.1 shows the re-evaluated structure function difference and the Gottfried sum together with the previously published result. A value of $S_G = 0.235 \pm 0.026$ is obtained at $Q^2 = 4\ \mathrm{GeV}^2$, significantly below the naive parton model exspectation of $1/3$. The previous conclusions thus remain unchanged. Also the complete error analysis was redone taking all correlations between systematic errors properly into account resulting in a somewhat larger total error than previously published. Interpreted in the quark parton model, this result indicates a flavour symmetry breaking in the light quark sea of the nucleon. This interpretation is supported by recent results on Drell-Yan asymmetries from the NA51 experiment [5] yielding $\overline{u}/\overline{d}(x = 0.18) = 0.56 \pm 0.04(\mathrm{stat.}) \pm 0.05(\mathrm{syst})$.

Possible corrections to the Gottfried sum may stem from target mass effects, higher twist effects and from shadowing in the deuteron. Target mass effects were found to be negligible. The influence from higher twists was estimated from measured effects [1],[13] leading to a 5% increase of the Gottfried sum. The influence of shadowing is discussed below.

3. Measurement of F_2^n/F_2^p in an extended kinematic range

For the determination of the Gottfried sum only part of the NMC data were used. During the 1989 data taking a new small angle trigger was implemented allowing to extend the accessible kinematic range in x below 10^{-3}.

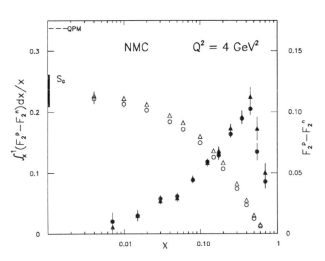

Figure 1. Results on $F_2^p - F_2^n$ (full symbols, right-hand scale) and the cumulative integral $\int_x^1 (F_2^p - F_2^n)\mathrm{d}x/x$ (open symbols, left-hand scale), given at $Q^2 = 4\ \mathrm{GeV}^2$ as functions of x. Triangles represent results published in 1991 [7] and circles show the re-evaluated results [8].

Data were taken at 120, 200 and 280 GeV. The complete data set now covers a range of $0.0008 < x < 0.8$ and $0.1 < Q^2 < 190\ \mathrm{GeV}^2$. The preliminary result for the x dependence of the measured ratio is shown in fig.2 compared to the published structure function ratio. The systematic error reaches 5% at the smallest x and is dominated by the uncertainty of the extrapolation of F_2 towards low x and Q^2.

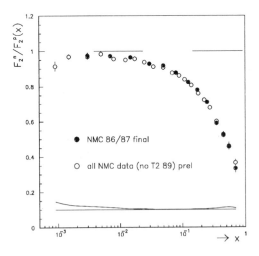

Figure 2. Published results on F_2^n/F_2^p versus x at average Q^2 (solid symbols) together with the total data set of NMC including the preliminary data from 1989 (open symbols). The band at the bottom indicates the preliminary systematic error on the measurement.

The naive parton model predicts that the ratio should approach unity for very small values of x. The measured ratio on the other hand seems no longer to increase below $x \approx 0.01$ reaching a value of about 0.97. This result is supported by recent results from the E665 collaboration [9].

There are various theoretical models available predicting shadowing at low x in the deuteron [10], where shadowing means that the cross section for a bound nucleon is smaller than for a free nucleon. The models predict effects of the order of 0.5%-2.5% for F_2^d leading to changes of 1%-5% for the ratio F_2^n/F_2^p, quite consistent with the data.

In this case the structure function ratio should be corrected for shadowing before calculating the Gottfried sum. The estimated decrease for S_G in the measured range varies from 2% to 20% depending on the model.

4. Determination of $\Delta R = R^d - R^p$

With the new data sets at four energies E_i the assumption $R^d = R^p$ (see sec.2) can be tested in a large x range.

The cross section ratio at fixed x and Q^2 can be written as a function of the three quantities F_2^d/F_2^p, ΔR and $\bar{R} = \frac{1}{2}(R^d + R^p)$. It is equal to the structure function ratio plus a correction term proportional to ΔR times the F_2 ratio with a coefficient depending on $\bar{R}$ and E_i. However, the dependence on $\bar{R}$ is weak and therefore the cross section ratio is almost insensitive to $\bar{R}$. Thus $F_2^d/F_2^p(Q^2)$ and ΔR are determined in a fit to the cross section ratio in each x interval. A weak constraint on $\bar{R}$ from previous measurements has been added to the fit to compensate for the lack of sensitivity. Details of the method are given in [11].

The results for ΔR are shown in fig.3 as a function of x. They cover the x range between 0.002 and 0.4, extending a previous determination [11] by an order of magnitude towards low x. The mean Q^2 of the measurement is 5 GeV^2. No significant x dependence of ΔR is observed. Averaging over x one obtains the preliminary result $\Delta R = 0.021 \pm 0.014(\text{stat.}) \pm 0.011(\text{syst.})$, compatible with zero. The main contribution to the systematic error stems from radiative corrections at low x and the correction for vertex smearing.

ΔR can be calculated from F_2 and the gluon distribution within perturbative QCD using the Altarelli-Martinelli relation [12]. The result is shown in fig.3 using the F_2 measurements from NMC and the gluon distribution from a QCD analysis of the same data [13]. In the calculation the same gluon distribution was used for the proton and the deuteron; it is in good agreement with our data. Assuming a 10% different gluon distribution in the proton and the deuteron, compatible with the uncertainty of the gluon distribution, leads to a larger prediction for ΔR in the x range between 0.01 and 0.1. Such large values are not favoured by the data [11].

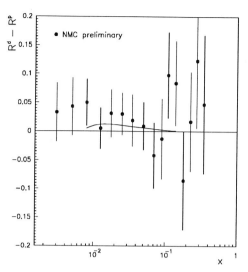

Figure 3. ΔR vs. x, compared to a perturbative QCD prediction (see text).

5. Summary

The re-evaluated value of the Gottfried sum is considerably below the value of 1/3. Interpreting this result in terms of the quark parton model and assuming isospin symmetry between the proton and the neutron this indicates a flavour symmetry breaking of the light quark sea of the nucleon. Preliminary results on F_2^n/F_2^p show an indication of shadowing in the deuteron below $x = 0.01$ of the order of 2-3% consistent with existing model predictions. Using results for cross section ratios at several energies a determination of $\Delta R = R^d - R^p$ was performed yielding values compatible with zero and with QCD predictions.

References

[1] NMC, P. Amaudruz *et al.*, Nucl. Phys. **B371** (1992) 3
[2] NMC, P.Amaudruz *et al.*, Phys. Lett. **B295** (1992) 159 and preprint CERN-PPE/92-124 (July 1992); Errata Oct. 26 (1992) and April 19 (1993)
[3] A.A. Akhundov *et al.*, Sov. J. Nucl. Phys. **26** (1977) 660, **44** (1986) 988,
D. Bardin and N Shumeiko, Sov. J. Nucl. Phys. **29** (1079) 499
[4] K. Gottfried, Phys. Rev. Lett. **18** (1967) 1174
[5] NA51, C.Racca, XXIX Recontres de Moriond, March 19-26th, 1994
[6] D.A. Ross and C.T. Sachrajda, Nucl. Phys. **B149** (1979) 497
[7] NMC, P. Amaudruz *et al.*, Phys. Rev. Lett. **66** (1991) 2712
[8] NMC, M. Arneodo *et al.*, Phys. Rev. **D50** (1994) R1
[9] E665, H. Melanson, this proceedings
[10] V.R. Zoller, Phys.Lett. **B279** (1992) 145;
B. Badelek and J. Kwiecinski, Nucl. Phys. **B370** (1992) 278;
W. Melnitchouk and A. Thomas, Phys. Rev. **D47** (1993) 3783
[11] NMC, P. Amaudruz *et al.*, Phys. Lett. **B294** (1992) 120
[12] G. Altarelli and G. Martinelli, Phys. Lett. **B76** (1978) 89
[13] NMC, M. Arneodo *et al.*, Phys. Lett. **B309** (1993) 222

Paper presented at XXVII Int. Conf. on High Energy Physics: Session Pa-6
Glasgow, UK, 20–27 July 1994

Structure Functions and Structure Function Ratio F_2^n/F_2^p at Low X_{Bj} and Q^2 in Inelastic Muon Scattering

Harry Melanson

Fermi National Accelerator Laboratory,
MS220, Batavia, IL, 60510, U.S.A.

E665 Collaboration

Abstract

Preliminary measurements of the structure functions F_2^p and F_2^d, and the structure function ratio F_2^n/F_2^p, in inelastic μN scattering are presented. The data were obtained by the Fermilab E665 experiment using a 465 GeV muon beam and liquid hydrogen and deuterium targets. The structure functions are presented in the range $x_{Bj} > 8 \times 10^{-4}$ and $Q^2 > 0.2 \, GeV^2/c^2$. The structure function ratio is presented as a function of x_{Bj} for $x_{Bj} > 10^{-6}$.

1. Introduction

In the single photon exchange approximation the double differential cross-section for lepton-nucleon scattering can be written as

$$\frac{d^2\sigma_{1\gamma}}{d(Q^{-2})d(lnx)} = 4\pi\alpha_{em}^2 F_2(x, Q^2) \times$$
$$[1 - y - \frac{Mxy}{2E} + \frac{y^2(1 + 4M^2x^2/Q^2)}{2(1 + R(x, Q^2))}] \qquad (1)$$

where E is the incoming lepton energy, M is the target mass, and $-Q^2$ is the square of the 4-momentum transferred from the lepton. In the lab frame ν is the lepton energy loss, $x = Q^2/2M\nu$ is the Bjorken scaling variable, and $y = \nu/E$.

In order to extract the structure function F_2 from the measured total cross-section, radiative corrections are calculated by the computer program FERRAD35[1] according to the formulation of Mo and Tsai[2]. The input F_2 is constructed from published fits to data and the low Q^2 interpolation at high W^2 of Donnachie and Landshoff [3]. R is taken as R_{slac}[4].

The data presented here were collected during the 1991 run of Fermilab experiment E665. The experimental apparatus is described in ([5]) . A muon

beam with average energy of 465 GeV impinged on cryogenic liquid H_2 and D_2 targets and on an evacuated vessel. The targets were cycled $\sim$ once/minute to reduce systematic uncertainty in the ratio measurement.

2. F_2^p and F_2^d

The behavior of the structure function F_2 is expected to be different in the small and large Q^2 limits. For $Q^2 \to \infty$ (Deep Inelastic Scattering - DIS), one expects scattering off point-like partons to dominate the total cross-section. Hence F_2 almost scales with x_{Bj} having only a logarithmic Q^2 dependence due to QCD radiative effects. For $Q^2 \to 0$ one expects the virtual photon cross-section to tend to the real photoproduction cross-section $\sigma_{\gamma N}$. Due to gauge invariance, $\lim_{Q^2 \to 0} F_2 = \frac{\sigma_{\gamma N} Q^2}{4\pi^2 \alpha}$. For point-like scattering one would expect $\sigma_{\gamma N}$ to vary as inverse square of energy. However $\sigma_{\gamma N}$ is measured to have a weak increase with energy at high energy, indicating a different scattering mechanism. The measurement of F_2 at low and high Q^2 helps to understand the transition between the dynamics of DIS and the real photoproduction limit.

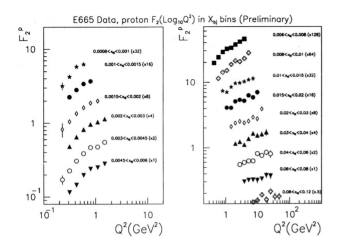

Fig. 1. F_2^p as a function of Q^2 in x_{Bj} bins. The errors shown are statistical only.

The muon small angle trigger (SAT) events were used for the F_2 measurement and the following kinematic cuts were made: $350 < E_{beam} < 600$ GeV, $\nu > 25$ GeV and $E_{scat\mu} > 80$ GeV. The sample consists of 664 nb^{-1} of μp and 749 nb^{-1} of μd data. The F_2 results for the proton are shown in Fig. 1 . The systematic uncertainty is of the order of 10-20% and is dominated by the level of knowledge of the reconstruction efficiency of the scattered muon. The results for the deuteron F_2 are similar. The results are preliminary and the systematic uncertainty is expected to reduce as the analysis progresses.

The measurement covers the range $8 \times 10^{-4} < x_{Bj} < 0.12$ and $Q^2 > 0.2$ GeV^2. The x_{Bj} values are comparable to those obtained at HERA and extend to lower values than those achieved at previous fixed target experiments. The Q^2 range extends from the regime of perturbative QCD at high Q^2 down to low Q^2 values where F_2 has a strong Q^2 dependence approaching the photoproduction limit.

3. F_2^n / F_2^p

For the extraction of the ratio the following cuts are made on the H_2 and D_2 data samples: $0.1 < y_{Bj} < 0.8$, $\nu > 40$ GeV, $\delta\nu/\nu < 0.3$, $Q^2 > 0.1$ GeV^2 (SAT) or $Q^2 > 0.001$ GeV^2 (Calorimeter trigger), and 350 GeV $< E_{beam} < 600$ GeV. The neutron cross-section is assumed to be the difference of the deuteron and the proton cross-sections. Three different methods are used to extract the structure function ratio, each method giving the best result in a different range of x_{Bj}. The ratio σ_n/σ_p (which is equal to F_2^n/F_2^p if $R^n = R^p$ ([4])) is shown in Fig. 2 for the three techniques, each

being shown where it has the smallest systematic error. The total systematic uncertainty is less than 3.5%, including uncertainties in the relative normalization, trigger acceptance and the effect of analysis cuts.

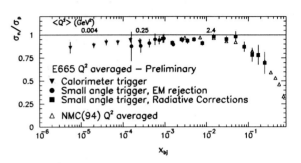

Fig. 2. σ_n/σ_p as a function of x_{Bj} . The errors shown are statistical only. Also shown are results from the CERN NMC experiment (CERN-PPE/94-32).

The cross-section ratio is presented at the average Q^2 of each x_{Bj} bin. There is good agreement with NMC in the region of overlap, while the E665 measurement extends three decades lower in x_{Bj}.

The average value of the ratio is $\sim$ 0.94 $\pm$ 0.01(stat)$\pm$0.035(syst) for $x_{Bj} < 0.05$. This may be due to shadowing in the deuteron. Using model calculations of shadowing [6] to correct the deuteron data can reduce the Gottfried sum by 10-15%. The measurement may also be interpreted as a difference in the proton and neutron structure functions. If this is the case then, using the measured Q^2 dependence to extrapolate the ratio to $Q^2 = 4$ GeV^2, the Gottfried sum will increase by ~ 0.05 per decade in x_{Bj}.

References

[1] P. Amaudruz, et.al., *Nucl. Phys.* **B273** (1992) 3.

[2] L.W. Mo and Y.S. Tsai, *Rev. Mod. Phys.* **41** (1969) 205.

[3] A. Donnachie and P.V. Landshoff, *Z. Phys.* **C61** (1994) 139.

[4] L.W. Whitlow, et.al, *Phys. Lett.* **B250** (1990) 193.

[5] M.R. Adams, et.al., *Nucl. Inst. Methods* **A291** (1990) 533.

[6] B. Badełek, J. Kwieciński, Preprint TSL/ISV-93-0090

W Charge Asymmetry at CDF:
Tests of Structure Functions

Howard S. Budd

Department of Physics and Astronomy
University of Rochester, Rochester, NY 14627

Representing the CDF Collaboration

Abstract

The charge asymmetry of W-bosons produced in $p\bar{p}$ collisions has been measured using 19,039 $W \to e\nu$ and $W \to \mu\nu$ decays recorded by the CDF detector during the 1992-93 Tevatron collider run. The asymmetry is sensitive to the slope of the proton's d/u quark distribution ratio down to $x < 0.01$ at $Q^2 \approx M_W^2$, where nonperturbative QCD effects are minimal. Of recent parton distribution functions, those of Martin, Roberts and Stirling are favored over those of the CTEQ collaboration. This difference is seen even though both sets agree, at the level of the nuclear shadowing corrections, with the recent NMC measurements of $F_2^{\mu n}/F_2^{\mu p}$.

1. Introduction

W^+ (W^-) bosons are produced in $p\bar{p}$ collisions primarily by the annihilation of u (d) quarks from the p with $\bar{d}$ $(\bar{u})$ quarks from the $\bar{p}$. Since the u quark tends to carry a larger fraction of the proton's momentum than the d quark, the W^+ (W^-) tends to be boosted in the p $(\bar{p})$ direction. The resulting charge asymmetry in the production of W's as a function of rapidity is related to the slope of the $d(x)/u(x)$ quark distribution ratio at low x $(0.007 < x < 0.24)$ and $Q^2 \approx M_W^2$ [1]. This measurement complements the F_2^n/F_2^p measured via deep inelastic scattering (DIS).

In this communication, the W charge asymmetry analysis from the 1992-93 data is presented. Relative to the 1988-89 data analysis [2], there is a seven fold increase in statistics from detector improvements and a luminosity of $\sim 20pb^{-1}$.

2. Charged lepton asymmetry in W Decays

The W-bosons are identified by their $W \to e\nu$ and $W \to \mu\nu$ decays. At the Tevatron ($\sqrt{s} = 1.8$ TeV),

the longitudinal momentum of the neutrino cannot be reconstructed. Since the $W^\pm$ rapidity is indeterminate, the charge asymmetry of the decay leptons is measured:

$$A(\eta) = \frac{d\sigma(l^+)/d\eta - d\sigma(l^-)/d\eta}{d\sigma(l^+)/d\eta + d\sigma(l^-)/d\eta} \quad (1)$$

where $d\sigma(l^\pm)/d\eta$ is the cross section for $W^\pm$ decay leptons as a function of lepton pseudorapidity, η [3]. (Positive η is along the proton beam direction.) Since $A(\eta)$ is a ratio, normalization uncertainties in both the theory and the data tend to cancel, and the analysis becomes simpler.

The asymmetry analysis [4] of the 1992-93 data has 19,039 $W \to e, \mu\nu$ events. These are obtained by selecting isolated, identified, and well-tracked e's and μ's with transverse energy $E_T > 25$ GeV . The missing transverse energy of the event in the calorimeter and muon system must be $\not{E}_T > 25$ GeV. To suppress QCD background, events with a jet whose $E_T > 20$ GeV are rejected. As the acceptance and efficiencies for detecting l^+ and l^- are found to be equal, $A(\eta)$ reduces to the difference in the number of l^+ and l^- over the sum. Since CP invariance gives $A(+\eta) = -A(-\eta)$, data at $-\eta$

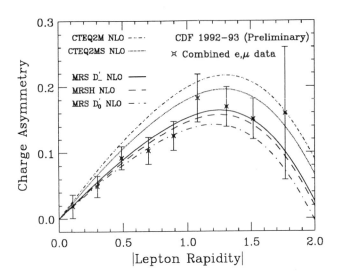

Figure 1. The measured charge asymmetry and predictions from recent PDF's. The data are fully corrected for trigger efficiencies and backgrounds. Systematic errors are included.

PDF Set	$0.2 < \lvert\eta\rvert < 1.7$		$\overline{A}$	
	χ^2 (7 dof)	Prob.	$\Delta\overline{A}$	Prob.
CTEQ 2M	24.	< 0.01	4.6	< 0.01
CTEQ 2MS	11.	0.15	2.9	< 0.01
MRS H	1.8	0.97	-0.1	0.96
MRS D$'_-$	1.9	0.97	0.5	0.61
MRS D$'_0$	3.6	0.83	-0.9	0.35

Table 1. χ^2 comparisons of the predicted NLO asymmetries for the most recent MRS and CTEQ distributions. The comparison of the weighted means ($\overline{A}$) is sensitive to systematic shifts, and indicates the MRS H distributions fit the asymmetry data best.

is combined with that at $+\eta$ to increase the statistics in η bins and to further reduce the effect of small undetected differences in the efficiencies for l^+ and l^-. Systematic errors are negligible relative to statistical errors and corrections to the raw measurement are small (5% or less). Hence, the asymmetry measurement is robust. Figure 1 shows the asymmetry measurement.

3.   Comparisons with Predictions

Predictions of $A(\eta)$ are from calculations of $d\sigma(l^\pm)/d\eta$ which use next to leading order (NLO) QCD partonic cross sections [5], NLO parton distribution functions (PDF), and the well-known, purely leptonic V-A decay of the W. Experimental cuts and detector effects [4] are also included in the calculations. Figure 1 also shows the asymmetries predicted by the most recent PDF's from Martin, Roberts and Stirling (MRS) [6] and the CTEQ [7] collaboration. Both groups have access to recent DIS results from the CCFR [8] neutrino data,

NMC [9] muon data, and HERA [10, 11] ep collider data. CTEQ2M and MRSH are post HERA PDF's. To quantify the data's discriminating power to the various predictions, Table 1 shows the goodness of fit χ^2 over seven η bins ($0.2 < \lvert\eta\rvert < 1.7$) and the χ^2 test of the error weighted mean difference ($\Delta\overline{A}$) of the seven data points against calculations.

The DIS $F_2^{\mu n}/F_2^{\mu p}$ and $p\overline{p}$ W charge asymmetry ($A(\eta)$) measurements provide complementary information on the proton structure. $A(\eta)$ is sensitive to the slope of the $d(x)/u(x)$ ratio [1, 12] in the x range $0.007 - 0.27$, whereas the $F_2^{\mu n}/F_2^{\mu p}$ is sensitive to the magnitude of this ratio. $F_2^{\mu n}/F_2^{\mu p}$ is more sensitive to the $\overline{u}$ and $\overline{d}$ sea distributions than $A(\eta)$. Both the MRS and CTEQ NLO predictions on $F_2^{\mu n}/F_2^{\mu p}$ agree (at the level of the 100% uncertainty in the deuteron shadowing corrections [13, 14]), with the recent NMC [9] measurement. What is different is that PDF's which predict the largest difference between the d/u ratio at small x relative to moderate x, also predict the largest W charge asymmetries. Thus, the fact that the charge asymmetry discriminates between PDF's which fit the NMC $F_2^{\mu n}/F_2^{\mu p}$ measurements demonstrates that its sensitivity to the d/u ratio (and not to $\overline{u}$ or $\overline{d}$) at very low x is better than that of the muon scattering experiments. In addition to having very low systematics, the asymmetry data does not have the deuteron shadowing uncertainties, nor is it sensitive to any low Q^2 higher twist corrections.

References

[1] E.L. Berger, F. Halzen, C.S. Kim and S. Willenbrock, Phys. Rev. **D40** (1989) 83.

[2] F. Abe *et al.*, Phys. Rev. Lett. **68** (1992) 1458.

[3] The pseudorapidity, $\eta = -\ln\tan(\theta/2)$, is the rapidity for a massless particle.

[4] M. Dickson, Ph. D. Thesis, "Charge Asymmetry in W-boson decays from $p\overline{p}$ collisions", University of Rochester preprint UR-1349, May 1994 (unpublished).

[5] W. Giele, E. Glover, D.A. Kosower, Nucl. Phys. **B403** (1993) 633.

[6] A.D. Martin, R.G. Roberts and W.J. Stirling, RAL-93-077 (1993).

[7] J. Botts *et al.*, Phys. Lett. **B304** (1993) 159

[8] CCFR Collaboration, P.Z. Quintas *et al.*,Phys. Rev. Lett. **71** (1993) 1307; CCFR Collaboration, W.C. Leung *et al.*, Phys. Lett. **B317** (1993) 655.

[9] NMC Collaboration, P. Amaudruz *et al.*, Phys. Lett. **B295** (1992) 159;Nucl. Phys. **B371** (1992) 3.

[10] H1 Collaboration: I. Abt *et al.*, preprint DESY-93-117 (August 1993).

[11] ZEUS Collaboration: M. Derrick *et al.*, preprint DESY-93-110 (August 1993).

[12] A.D. Martin, R.G. Roberts and W.J. Stirling, Mod. Phys. Lett. **A4** (1989) 1135.

[13] A.D. Martin, R.G. Roberts and W.J. Stirling, Phys. Lett. **B306** (1993) 145.

[14] B. Badelek, J. Kwiecinski, Nucl. Phys. **B370** (1992) 278

MRS(1994): parton distributions of the proton

A.D. Martin[†], R.G. Roberts[§] and W.J. Stirling[†]

†Department of Physics, University of Durham, Durham DH1 3LE, England.
§Rutherford Appleton Laboratory, Chilton OX11 0QX, England.

Abstract

To obtain improved parton densities of the proton, we present a new global analysis of deep-inelastic and related hard scattering data including, in particular, the recent measurements of F_2 at HERA, of the asymmetry of the rapidity distributions of $W^\pm$ production at the FNAL $p\bar{p}$ collider and of the asymmetry in Drell-Yan production in pp and pn collisions. We discuss the evolution of the new partons to low values of Q^2.

The increase in the precision of deep-inelastic and related data over the last few years has led to a considerable improvement in our knowledge of the parton distributions of the proton, at least for $x \gtrsim 10^{-2}$. Here we present an updated analysis [1] which incorporates new recent data. The new data are (i) the H1 [2] and ZEUS [3] measurements of F_2, which mainly constrain the sea quarks in the previously unexplored small x domain ($x \lesssim 10^{-3}$), (ii) the measurement of the asymmetry of Drell-Yan production in pp and pn collisions by NA51 [4]

$$A_{DY} = \frac{\sigma_{pp} - \sigma_{pn}}{\sigma_{pp} + \sigma_{pn}} = -0.09 \pm 0.02 \pm 0.025 \quad (1)$$

at $x = \sqrt{\tau} = 0.18$ and, (iii) the asymmetry of the rapidity distributions of the charged leptons from $W^\pm \to \ell^\pm \nu$ decays by CDF [5]

$$A(y_\ell) = \frac{\sigma(\ell^+) - \sigma(\ell^-)}{\sigma(\ell^+) + \sigma(\ell^-)}. \quad (2)$$

These asymmetry data are shown in Figs. 1 and 2 respectively, together with the predictions of our previous global analysis [6] and the equivalent set of CTEQ partons [7]. Neither set gives a satisfactory description of both asymmetries. The deficiency is not surprising. The high precision muon and neutrino deep-inelastic structure function data (of BCDMS, NMC and

CCFR), which provide the core constraints of the global analyses, determine essentially the parton combinations $u + d$, $\bar{u} + \bar{d}$ and $u + \bar{u}$, but do not pin down the remaining combination $\bar{d} - \bar{u}$. Indeed the Drell-Yan asymmetry experiment was proposed [8] just because it was uniquely equipped to determine this combination. The $W^\pm$ rapidity asymmetry is proportional to the slope of u/d at $x = M_W/\sqrt{s} \simeq 0.05$ at Fermilab. The asymmetry data therefore offer a fine-tuning of the $u, d, \bar{u}$ and $\bar{d}$ parton densities in the region $x \sim 0.1$.

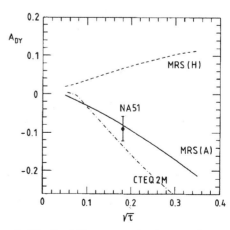

Figure 1. The Drell-Yan asymmetry in pp and pn collisions. The MRS(H) and CTEQ2M curves pre-date the NA51 measurement, (1), whereas it is included in the MRS(A) global fit.

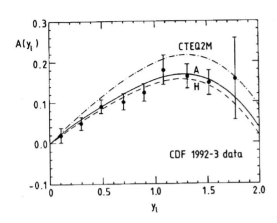

Figure 2. The $W^\pm \to \ell^\pm \nu$ rapidity asymmetry, (2), measured by [5], together with the next-to-leading order descriptions obtained using MRS(H), CTEQ2M and MRS(A) partons. These data are included in the MRS(A) fit.

Our basic procedure is to parametrize the parton distributions f_i at a sufficiently large Q_0^2 ($Q_0^2 = 4$ GeV^2) so that $f_i(x, Q^2)$ can be calculated at higher Q^2 using next-to-leading order Altarelli-Parisi evolution equations. An excellent overall description of the data is obtained with the following simple parametrization

$$xu_v = A_u x^{\eta_1}(1-x)^{\eta_2}(1 + \epsilon_u\sqrt{x} + \gamma_u x)$$
$$xd_v = A_d x^{\eta_3}(1-x)^{\eta_4}(1 + \epsilon_d\sqrt{x} + \gamma_d x)$$
$$xS = A_S x^{-\lambda}(1-x)^{\eta_S}(1 + \epsilon_S\sqrt{x} + \gamma_S x)$$
$$xg = A_g x^{-\lambda}(1-x)^{\eta_g}(1 + \gamma_g x), \tag{3}$$

where the valence distributions $u_v \equiv u - \bar{u}$ and $d_v \equiv d - \bar{d}$, and where the total sea distribution $S \equiv 2(\bar{u} + \bar{d} + \bar{s} + \bar{c})$. We assume that $s = \bar{s}$. At present there are not enough experimental constraints on the gluon to justify the introduction of an extra parameter ϵ_g in xg, or to determine the exponent λ independent of that of the sea-quark distribution S. Three of the four A_i coefficients are determined by the momentum and flavour sum rules. The distributions are defined in the $\overline{\text{MS}}$ renormalisation and factorization scheme and the QCD scale parameter $\Lambda_{\overline{\text{MS}}}(n_f = 4)$ is taken as a free parameter.

The flavour structure of the quark sea is taken to be

$$2\bar{u} = 0.4(1-\delta)S - \Delta$$
$$2\bar{d} = 0.4(1-\delta)S + \Delta$$
$$2\bar{s} = 0.2(1-\delta)S$$
$$2\bar{c} = \delta S \tag{4}$$

at $Q^2 = Q_0^2 = 4$ GeV^2, with

$$x\Delta \equiv x(\bar{d} - \bar{u}) = A_\Delta x^{0.4}(1-x)^{\eta_S}(1 + \gamma_\Delta x). \tag{5}$$

The first hint that the u, d flavour symmetry of the sea is broken (with $\bar{d} > \bar{u}$ on average) came from the

evaluation of the Gottfried sum by NMC [9]. Now the NA51 Drell-Yan asymmetry measurement, (1), provides further evidence that $\bar{d} > \bar{u}$, which we allow through the parametrization of Δ. The 50% suppression assumed for the strange sea in (4) is in excellent agreement with the CCFR next-to-leading order analysis [10] of their $\nu N \to \mu^-\mu^+ X$ data. The parameter δ in the charm sea in (4) is adjusted to reproduce the EMC deep-inelastic F_2^c data [11], as explained in [1].

Apart from the CCFR neutrino structure function measurements at $x = 0.015$ and 0.045, the new MRS(A) analysis gives a good description of all deep-inelastic and related data. In particular it leads to a much improved description of the Drell-Yan asymmetry (Fig. 1) with relatively modest changes in the partons (see Fig. 3). The values of the parameters are listed in Table 2 of [1]. From the highly constrained overall fit we conclude that the valence and sea quarks are well determined for $0.02 \lesssim x \lesssim 0.6$.

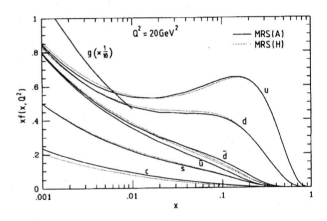

Figure 3. A comparison at $Q^2 = 20$ GeV^2 of the new MRS(A) partons [1] and the earlier MRS(H) partons [6].

The HERA measurements of F_2 [2, 3] are the only constraint on the parameter λ in (3) which controls the small x behaviour of the sea $xS \sim x^{-\lambda}$. In both the MRS(A) and MRS(H) analyses an excellent description of the HERA data is obtained with $\lambda = 0.3$, see, for example, Fig. 4. However the parameters λ and ϵ_S in (3) are highly correlated and it is possible to obtain acceptable fits for $0.2 \lesssim \lambda \lesssim 0.4$.

Since the sea quarks are driven by the gluon, via $g \to q\bar{q}$, we have assumed a common $x^{-\lambda}$ behaviour at small x. There is, as yet, no experimental confirmation of this assumption, and indeed the ambiguity in the gluon distribution is by far the largest uncertainty in the parton densities. The only information on the gluon is (i) that it carries about 43% of the proton's momentum at $Q^2 = 4$ GeV^2, (ii) that its value at $x \sim 0.3 - 0.4$ is constrained by the WA70 [12] and UA6 [13] measurements of large p_T prompt photon

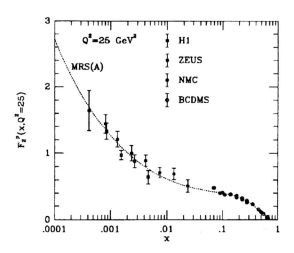

Figure 4. The description of the F_2 structure function measurements at $Q^2 = 25$ GeV^2 by MRS(A) partons. The updated HERA data [2,3] are shown.

production, $pp \to \gamma X$, and (iii) through its influence on the observed scaling violations in the structure function data, although here there is a correlation with the value found for the QCD coupling. We stress that all the recent parton analyses are global "best fits" to the data and so the spread of the gluons obtained underestimates the true uncertainty in its distribution.

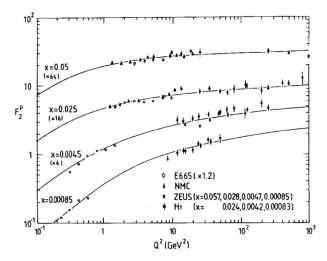

Figure 5. The description of sample E665 [16], NMC [17] and updated H1 [2] and ZEUS [3] F_2 data by MRS(A) partons modified as in (6). The E665 data are preliminary and in the global low Q^2 fit [14] they have been renormalized upwards by 20% to obtain consistency with the NMC measurements of F_2.

Finally, we extrapolate the MRS(A) partons to low Q^2 and attempt to describe E665, NMC and SLAC data for F_2 down to $Q^2 = 0.5$ GeV^2 [14]. As expected it is necessary to suppress the distributions by incorporating the theoretical requirement that they vanish as Q^2 as

$Q^2 \to 0$. We find a satisfactory description of the F_2 data can be obtained if the parton distributions are modified as follows

$$f_i(x, Q^2) \longrightarrow \frac{Q^2}{Q^2 + M(x)^2} f_i(x, Q^2) \qquad (6)$$

where

$$M^2 = 0.015 \exp[1.54\sqrt{\ell n(1/x)}] \qquad (7)$$

or, equally acceptable,

$$M^2 = 0.07 \, x^{-0.37} \qquad (8)$$

in GeV^2. That is M^2 increases from about 0.15 GeV^2 at $x = 0.1$ to about 0.9 GeV^2 at $x = 0.001$. In other words, the suppression sets in at higher values of Q^2, $Q^2 \sim M^2$, as x decreases. This trend is expected on theoretical grounds since, with decreasing x, the onset of shadowing corrections is predicted to occur at higher values of Q^2 [15]. Fig. 5 shows the description of a sample of the low Q^2 data, together with the latest H1 and ZEUS measurements of F_2.

References

[1] A.D. Martin, R.G. Roberts and W.J. Stirling, RAL preprint 94-055, Phys. Rev. **D50** (in press).
[2] H1 collaboration: K. Müller, Proc. of 29th Rencontre de Moriond, March 1994 (update: V. Brisson, these proceedings).
[3] ZEUS collaboration: G. Wolf, Proc. of International Workshop on DIS, Eilat, Israel, Feb. 1994; M. Roco, Proc. of 29th Rencontre de Moriond, March 1994 (update: M. Lancaster, these proceedings).
[4] NA51 collaboration: A. Baldit et al., Phys. Lett. **B322** (1994) 244.
[5] CDF collaboration: A. Bodek, Proc. of International Workshop on DIS, Eilat, Israel, Feb. 1994.
[6] A.D. Martin, R.G. Roberts and W.J. Stirling, Proc. Workshop on QFT aspects of HE Physics, Kyffhässer, Germany, eds. B. Geyer and E.-M. Ilgenfritz, Leipzig (1993) p. 11.
[7] CTEQ collaboration, J. Botts et al., unpublished.
[8] S.D. Ellis and W.J. Stirling, Phys. Lett. **B256** (1991) 258.
[9] NMC: P. Amaudruz et al., Phys. Rev. Lett. **66** (1991) 2712.
[10] CCFR collaboration: A. Bazarko et al., Columbia preprint, NEVIS-1492 (1993).
[11] EMC: J.J. Aubert et al., Nucl. Phys. **B213** (1983) 31.
[12] WA70 collaboration: M. Bonesini et al., Z. Phys. **C38** (1988) 371.
[13] UA6 collaboration: G. Sozzi et al., Phys. Lett. **B317** (1993) 243.
[14] A.D. Martin, R.G. Roberts and W.J. Stirling, in preparation.
[15] L.V. Gribov, E.M. Levin and M.G. Ryskin, Phys. Rep. **100C** (1983) 1.
[16] E665 collaboration: A. Kotwal, Proc. VI Rencontres de Blois, "The Heart of the Matter", June 1994.
[17] NMC: P. Amaudruz et al., Phys. Lett. **B295** (1992) 159.

Results on the spin-dependent structure function $g_1(x)$ of the proton

Arnold Staude

Sektion Physik der Ludwig-Maximilians-Universität München,
Schellingstr. 4, D-80799 München, Germany

Representing the Spin Muon Collaboration (SMC)

Abstract

We have measured the spin-dependent structure function g_1 of the proton in deep inelastic scattering of polarized muons off polarized protons, in the kinematic range $0.003 < x < 0.7$ and $1\,\mathrm{GeV}^2 < Q^2 < 60\,\mathrm{GeV}^2$. Its first moment, $\int_0^1 g_1^p(x)dx$, is found to be 0.136 ± 0.011 (stat.) ± 0.011 (syst.) at $Q^2 = 10\,\mathrm{GeV}^2$. This value is smaller than the prediction of the Ellis–Jaffe sum rule by two standard deviations, and is consistent with previous measurements. A combined analysis of all available proton, deuteron and neutron data confirms the Bjorken sum rule to within 10% of the theoretical value.

1. Introduction

Measurements of the spin-dependent structure functions g_1 for protons [1, 2], neutrons [3] and deuterons [4] have given in the past interesting and sometimes surprising results. Presented here is a new measurement by the SMC at CERN [5]. In our experiment, g_1^p is measured by deep inelastic scattering (DIS) of muons with energy $E = 190\,\mathrm{GeV}$ and longitudinal polarization P_μ off a butanol ($C_4H_{10}O$) target, in which the free protons have a longitudinal polarization P_p. The observed cross-section asymmetry is:[†]

$$\left(\frac{d^2\sigma^{\uparrow\downarrow}}{dQ^2dx} - \frac{d^2\sigma^{\uparrow\uparrow}}{dQ^2dx}\right) \bigg/ \left(\frac{d^2\sigma^{\uparrow\downarrow}}{dQ^2dx} + \frac{d^2\sigma^{\uparrow\uparrow}}{dQ^2dx}\right)$$
$$= |P_\mu P_p| fD \left[A_1^p + \frac{2(1-y)}{2-y}\gamma A_2^p\right] \quad (1)$$

where the symbols $\uparrow\downarrow$ and $\uparrow\uparrow$ describe parallel and antiparallel orientation of the muon and the target spin, respectively. Q^2, x and y are the well known scaling

[†] The quantities $A_1^p, A_2^p, D, f, F_2, R, g_1^p$ are functions of x and Q^2. For simplicity this has not been written explicitly.

variables used in DIS. The kinematic factor $\gamma = \sqrt{\frac{2Mx}{Ey}}$ is small in our kinematic region ($\gamma^2 \leq 10^{-2}$), due to the high beam energy. The depolarization factor D ($D = 0.2 - 0.9$ in our measurement) for the exchanged virtual photon contains the spin-independent structure function R: $D = y(2-y)/[y^2 + 2(1-y)(1+R)]$. The dilution factor f is the fraction of events which originate from scattering off free protons ($f \approx 0.12$ for butanol). A_1^p is an asymmetry and A_2^p a ratio of virtual photon absorption cross sections. They are constrained by positivity relations to $|A_1^p| \leq 1$ and $|A_2^p| \leq \sqrt{R}$. A_1^p and A_2^p, together with R and the spin-independent structure function F_2, determine g_1^p:

$$g_1^p = \frac{F_2}{2x(1+R)(1+\gamma^2)}\left(A_1^p + \gamma A_2^p\right) \quad (2)$$

A_2^p has been recently measured by the SMC at $E = 100\,\mathrm{GeV}$ with the target polarized transversely, studying the dependence of the cross section on the angle between scattering plane and polarization plane [6]. The result is shown in Fig. 1. A_2^p is small, < 0.2, and compatible with 0. Since A_2^p enters in Eq.(1) and (2) with the small factor

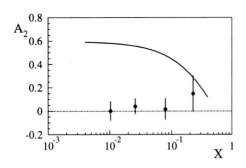

Figure 1. The A_2^p asymmetry at the average Q^2 of each x bin. Only statistical errors are shown with the data points. The solid line represents the positivity limit for R taken from the SLAC parametrization.

γ, it has been neglected. The uncertainty caused by this approximation is included in the systematic error.

The structure function g_1^p has in the quark picture a simple physical interpretation:

$$g_1^p(x) = \frac{1}{2}\left[\frac{4}{9}\delta u(x) + \frac{1}{9}\delta d(x) + \frac{1}{9}\delta s(x)\right] \qquad (3)$$

where $\delta u(x) = u^+(x) + \overline{u}^+(x) - u^-(x) - \overline{u}^-(x)$. The distribution functions $u^+(\overline{u}^+)$ are for up quarks (antiquarks) with spin parallel to the proton spin and $u^-(\overline{u}^-)$ are for up quarks (antiquarks) with spin antiparallel. In a corresponding way, $\delta d(x)$ and $\delta s(x)$ are combinations of distribution functions for down and strange quarks.

2. Beam and experimental setup

The positive muons of the beam originate mainly from pion decays where a neutrino is emitted opposite to the beam direction. Hence the muons have a negative polarization $P_\mu = -0.803 \pm 0.035$. The polarization is measured with a polarimeter [7], analysing the energy spectrum of positrons from decaying beam muons.

The target consists of an upstream and downstream cell, each 60 cm long, separated by 30 cm and polarized in opposite directions. The free protons of the target material are polarized by dynamic nuclear polarization (DNP) at low temperature in a longitudinal magnetic field of 2.5 T. The average polarization during data taking was 0.86. It was continuously measured by nuclear magnetic resonance with 3% accuracy. The spin directions of both cells were reversed, every 5 hours by field rotation and once per week via DNP.

The scattered muons traverse a large apperture dipole magnet and are identified by their penetration of a 2 m thick Fe absorber. The muon tracks are measured with 150 detector planes. The large redundancy ensures a very stable reconstruction efficiency, mandatory for

a stable acceptance. Due to a good vertex resolution, events can be uniquely attributed to one of the target cells. Transverse vertex cuts ensure that the accepted beam phase space is identical for both target cells.

3. Determination of A_1^p and g_1^p

The asymmetry A_1^p is extracted from the data using a strategy originally developed by EMC [2]. The four event samples, two for each target cell, collected before and after a spin reversal, are combined such as to obtain A_1^p without the need to know the beam flux before and after the spin reversal, the target thicknesses and the acceptances for the two target cells, provided their ratio is constant during the 10 hours of a measurement cycle. The result for A_1^p, obtained with $4.4 \; 10^6$ events with $Q^2 > 1\,\mathrm{GeV}^2$ and $y < 0.9$, is shown in Fig. 2. It extends the kinematic region explored until now to much lower values of x. Our measurement confirms the old results from EMC and SLAC, also shown in Fig. 2. The agreement with the latest SLAC results [8] is also good. The average Q^2 of our data increases from $1.2\,\mathrm{GeV}^2$ for the lowest x bin to $58\,\mathrm{GeV}^2$ for the highest. Systematic errors arise from the uncertainties in P_μ, P_p, R and f, the radiative corrections, the momentum resolution, the kinematic smearing corrections, the time stability of the acceptance ratio and the neglect of A_2^p. They are added in quadrature to the total systematic error shown as a shaded band in Fig. 2. The total systematic error has a strong point to point correlation.

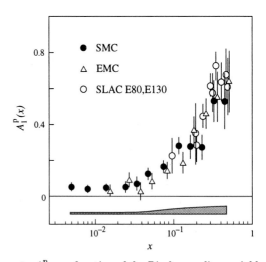

Figure 2. A_1^p as a function of the Bjorken scaling variable x. Only statistical errors are shown with the data points. The systematic errors for the SMC points is indicated by the shaded area.

To evaluate g_1^p Eq. (2) is used. For F_2, the NMC parametrisation [9] is taken with a slight extrapolation for the lowest x point. For R the SLAC parametrization [10] is used. R is not known experimentally for $x < 0.1$.

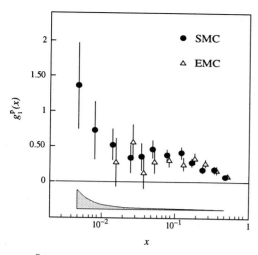

Figure 3. $g_1^p(x)$ at the average Q^2 of each x bin. Only statistical errors are shown with the data points. The EMC points are reevaluated using the NMC F_2 parametrization.

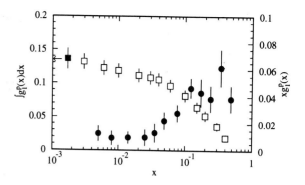

Figure 4. The solid circles (right-hand axis) show the structure function xg_1^p as a function of the Bjorken scaling variable x, at $Q^2 = 10\,\text{GeV}^2$. The open boxes (left-hand axis) show $\int_{x_m}^1 g_1^p(x)dx$, where x_m is the value of x at the lower edge of each bin. Only statistical errors are shown. The solid square shows our result $\int_0^1 g_1^p(x)dx$, with statistical and systematic errors combined in quadrature.

However, the corresponding uncertainty on g_1^p is weak since the explicit dependence of g_1^p on R in Eq.(2) is largely canceled by the R dependence of D, and because F_2 and R have correlated errors. The result for g_1^p is shown in Fig. 3. Again, the average Q^2 for the points increases with x.

4. Determination of Γ_1^p

Theoretical predictions exist for the first moment of g_1^p:

$$\Gamma_1^p = \int_0^1 g_1^p(x)dx \qquad (4)$$

where $g_1^p(x)$ is taken at a fixed common Q^2. We evaluated Γ_1^p from our data by evolving g_1^p in each x bin to $Q^2 = 10\,\text{GeV}^2$, under the assumption that A_1^p is independent of Q^2. This is consistent with the data and with theoretical calculations [11] which predict a negligible Q^2 dependence. Fig. 4 shows the values of xg_1^p, evolved to $Q^2 = 10\,\text{GeV}^2$ for each x bin. Over the measured x range, the value of the integral is:

$$\int_{0.003}^{0.7} g_1^p(x, Q^2 = 10\,\text{GeV}^2)dx = 0.131 \pm 0.015 \qquad (5)$$

where the statistical and systematic errors, which have about equal size, are combined in quadrature. The contribution to Γ_1^p from the unmeasured regions are calculated with further assumptions. For $x > 0.7$ we take $A_1^p = 0.7 \pm 0.3$, consistent with the positivity limit $|A_1^p| \leq 1$ and the QCD expectation [12] that A_1^p approaches 1 at $x = 1$. For the region $x < 0.003$ we assume a Regge-type dependence $g_1^p = const$ [13], that we fit to our two lowest data points. We obtain $\int_0^{0.003} g_1^p(x)dx = 0.004$, to which we assign an error as

big as the contribution itself.

Adding the contributions from the unmeasured x regions to (5) yields:

$$\Gamma_1^p(10\,\text{GeV}^2) = 0.136 \pm 0.016. \qquad (6)$$

Fig. 4 shows how the integral depends on the lower integration limit.

Recently, a steep rise of g_1^p at low x has been considered theoretically [14]. Although our data are consistent with a rise (Fig. 3), we consider that the errors are too large to rule out a flat Regge extrapolation. If such a rise was real, the value of Γ_1^p could increase significantly.

5. Test of the Ellis-Jaffe sum rule

In the quark picture, using Eq.(3), Γ_1^p can be written as:

$$\Gamma_1^p = \frac{1}{12} \int_0^1 (\delta u(x) - \delta d(x))dx +$$

$$\frac{1}{36} \int_0^1 (\delta u(x) + \delta d(x) - 2\delta s(x))dx +$$

$$\frac{1}{9} \int_0^1 (\delta u(x) + \delta d(x) + \delta s(x))dx. \qquad (7)$$

In the framework of QCD, assuming flavour $SU(3)$ symmetry, the first two integrals can be shown to be $F + D$ and $3F - D$, respectively. F and D are the coupling constants for axial currents between states of the baryon octet. The last integral in Eq. (7) is $\Delta\Sigma$, the fraction of the proton spin carried by quarks. The additional assumption $\Delta s = \int_0^1 \delta s dx = 0$ entails $\Delta\Sigma = 3F - D$ and leads to the Ellis-Jaffe sum rule [15] $\Gamma_1^p = \frac{1}{18}(9F - D)$. At finite Q^2, QCD corrections have to be applied. Using the experimental values for F and

D [16] and applying LO QCD corrections [17], the Ellis-Jaffe sum rule predicts:

$$\Gamma_1^p(10\,\mathrm{GeV}^2) = 0.176 \pm 0.006. \qquad (8)$$

This prediction is 2.4 standard deviations above the measured value (5). The probable reason for this violation of the Elli-Jaffe sum rule is a polarization of the strange sea. Under the assumption that this is the only reason one can derive:

$$\Delta s(10\,\mathrm{GeV}^2) = -0.12 \pm 0.06 \qquad (9)$$

and consequently

$$\Delta\Sigma(10\,\mathrm{GeV}^2) = 0.22 \pm 0.14. \qquad (10)$$

The conclusion that the strange sea has a negative net polarization and that quarks carry only a small fraction of the proton spin was already drawn by EMC. It is also reached in a recent comprehensive analysis by Ellis and Karliner [18] who apply higher order QCD corrections and use all available spin-dependent structure function data, including the preliminary E143 results [8].

6. Test of the Bjorken sum rule

The Bjorken sum rule [19] was derived from current algebra and it assumes flavour SU(2) symmetry. It is today considered to be a rigorous prediction of QCD [17]. The sum rule is:

$$\Gamma_1^p - \Gamma_1^n = \frac{1}{6}\left|\frac{g_A}{g_V}\right| \qquad (11)$$

where Γ_1^n is the first moment of g_1 for the neutron and g_A and g_V are the axial vector and the vector coupling constant measured in the β-decay of the neutron. At finite Q^2, QCD corrections have to be applied. For the test of the sum rule we have combined our results with all other published results [1, 2, 3] and evolved all data to $Q^2 = 5\,\mathrm{GeV}^2$. We do not choose $Q^2 = 10\,\mathrm{GeV}^2$ as before because the SLAC data are centered at much smaller Q^2. The regions in the Γ_1^p-Γ_1^n allowed by the Bjorken sum rule and by the experiments are shown in Fig. 5. One can observe a reasonable overlap of all allowed regions. The borders of the bands are the one standard deviation contours. For the prediction of the Bjorken sum rule QCD corrections up to α_s^3 have been applied [20]. It is:

$$\Gamma_1^p(5\,\mathrm{GeV}^2) - \Gamma_1^n(5\,\mathrm{GeV}^2) = 0.185 \pm 0.004. \qquad (12)$$

A fit to the data gives:

$$\Gamma_1^p(5\,\mathrm{GeV}^2) - \Gamma_1^n(5\,\mathrm{GeV}^2) = 0.163 \pm 0.017. \qquad (13)$$

The prediction and the measured value differ by only 1.2 standard deviations. Hence one can conclude that the Bjorken sum rule is experimentally verified on the 10% level.

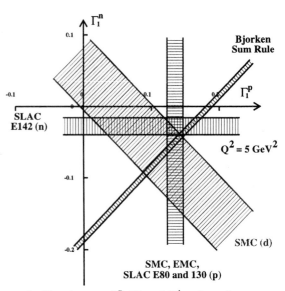

Figure 5. The moments Γ_1^p, Γ_1^n and Γ_1^d evaluated at $Q^2 = 5\,\mathrm{GeV}^2$ and the prediction of the Bjorken sum rule. The shaded areas represent the allowed regions.

References

[1] SLAC E-80: M.J. Alguard *et al.*, Phys. Rev. Lett. **37** (1976) 1261;ibid. 41 (1978) 70; SLAC E-130 G. Baum *et al.*, Phys. Rev. Lett. **51** (1983) 1135.
[2] EMC: J. Ashman *et al.*, Phys. Lett. **B206** (1988) 364;Nucl. Phys. B328 (1989) 1.
[3] SLAC E142: D.L. Anthony *et al.*, Phys. Rev. Lett. **71** (191993) 959.
[4] SMC: B. Adeva *et al.*, Phys. Lett. **B302** (1993) 533.
[5] SMC: D. Adams *et al.*, Phys. Lett. **B329** (1994) 399.
[6] SMC: D. Adams *et al.*, Phys. Rev. Lett. **B336** (1994) 125.
[7] SMC: B. Adeva *et al.*, Nucl. Instrum. Methods A343 (1994) 363.
[8] SLAC E143: J. McCarthy, Glasgow 94 proceedings
[9] NMC: P. Amaudruz *et al.*, Phys. Rev. Lett. **B295** (1992) 159.
[10] L.W. Whitlow *et al.*, Phys. Rev. Lett. **B250** (1990) 193.
[11] G. Altarelli, P. Nason and G. Ridolfi, Phys. Lett. **B320** (191994) 152.
[12] S.J. Brodsky, M. Burkardt, and I. Schmidt, SLAC PUB 6087 (1994).
[13] R. L. Heimann, Nucl. Phys. B64 (1973) 429; J. Ellis and M. Karliner, Phys. Lett. **B213** (1988) 73.
[14] S.D.Bass and P.V.Landshoff, Cavendish preprint HEP 94/4 F.E.Close and R.G.Roberts, Preprint, RAL-94-071
[15] J. Ellis and R.L. Jaffe, Phys. Rev. D9 (1974) 1444; D10 (1974) 1669.
[16] Z.Dziembowski and J.Franklin, Nucl. Part. Phys. 17 (1991) 213
[17] J. Kodaira *et al.*, Phys. Rev. D20 (1979) 627; J. Kodaira et al., Nucl. Phys. B159 (1979) 99; J. Kodaira, Nucl. Phys. B165 (1980) 129.
[18] J. Ellis and M. Karliner, CERN-TH-7324/94.
[19] J.D. Bjorken, Phys. Rev. 148 (1966) 1467; Phys. Rev. D1 (1970) 1376.
[20] S.A. Larin and J.A.M. Vermaseren, Phys. Lett. **B259** (1991) 345.

Results on the spin distribution of valence and sea quarks in the nucleon

J P Nassalski[‡]

CERN, Division PPE, 1217 Geneva 23, CH and SINS, ul.Hoza 69, 00-681 Warszawa, PL

On behalf of the Spin Muon Collaboration

Abstract

From the combined analysis of the SMC data on inclusive and semi-inclusive cross section asymmetries in polarised deep inelastic muon scattering on hydrogen and deuterium targets, the x-dependences of the spin carried by the valence *up*, *down* and the non-strange *sea* quarks were determined.

1. Introduction

Recent results on the spin structure function of the proton $g_1^p(x)$ [1] are found to be consistent with the earlier determinations ([2], [3]) and confirm [3] that all quarks carry only a fraction of the nucleon spin and that the fraction carried by s quarks is negative: $\Sigma = 0.27 \pm 0.13$ and $\Delta\bar{s} = -0.05 \pm 0.02$. Similar conclusions were obtained from $g_1^d(x)$ [4] and also from $g_1^n(x)$ ([5],[6]).

The x-dependence of polarisations of the non-strange sea ($\bar{q} \equiv \bar{u} = \bar{d}$) and of the valence quarks can be determined from the combined analysis of the SMC data on semi-inclusive (of charged hadrons) and inclusive (of muons) cross section asymmetries [7].

2. Measurements of asymmetries

The data on polarised muon deep inelastic scattering from polarised hydrogen [1] and deuterium [4] targets were collected at CERN using beams of energy 190 GeV and 100 GeV respectively. Spectrometer had good acceptance for hadrons carying a fraction $z > 0.2$ of the virtual photon energies bigger than 20(10) GeV while hadrons from the target fragmentation were largely

suppressed. High energy electrons from the radiative photons were removed using calorimeter. Hadrons were not identified. With the cut $Q^2 > 1$ GeV^2 the common kinematic region of x was $0.006 < x < 0.6$.

The target was made of two cells filled with butanol or deuterated butanol polarised in opposite directions and polarisations in both cells were periodically reversed.

Typical polarisations were $\pm 80\%$ for protons $\pm 40\%$ for deuterons and -81% for muons.

The measured asymmetry of semi-inclusive lepton-nucleon cross sections is defined, e.g. for positive hadrons from the hydrogen target, as:
$A_{mp}^+ = (\sigma_{p\uparrow\downarrow}^+ - \sigma_{p\uparrow\uparrow}^+)/\sigma_{p\uparrow\downarrow}^+ + \sigma_{p\uparrow\uparrow}^+)$, where arrows indicate the relative beam-target spin configurations. Due to simultaneous exposure of oppositely polarised target cells and frequent polarisations reversals this assymetry can be determined from the observed hadron yields only.

The asymmetry of semi-inclusive virtual photon-nucleon cross sections is determined from A_{mp}^+ using beam (P_B) and target (P_T) polarisation values, the target dilution factor (f), virtual photon depolarisation factor (D) and correcting for radiative effects. In case of deuterium target additional correction accounted for the D-state. This asymmetry can be expressed in terms of the polarised (Δq) and unpolarised (q) quark distribution functions and of the quark fragmentation

‡ E-mail: jan@cernvm.cern.ch.

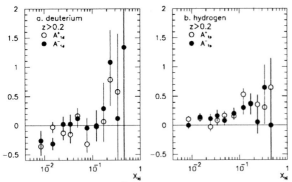

Figure 1. Asymmetries $A_1^{\pm}$ from (a)deuterium and (b)hydrogen calculated from hadron cross sections integrated over $z > 0.2$.

functions (D_q^+):

$$A_{1p}^+ = \frac{A_{mp}^+}{P_B P_T f D} = \frac{\sum_i e_i^2 \Delta q_i D_{q_i}^+}{\sum_i e_i^2 q_i D_{q_i}^+}. \tag{1}$$

Four semi-inclusive asymmetries determined for positive and negative hadrons from deuterium and hydrogen target separately are shown in Fig.1.

3. Determination of quark polarisations

The asymmetries $A_{1p(d)}^{\pm}$ provide a set of four equations with the four unknowns, $\Delta u_v, \Delta d_v, \Delta \bar{q}$ and $\Delta \bar{s}$:

$$A_{1p(d)}^{\pm} = C_{1p(d)}^{\pm} \Delta u_v + C_{2p(d)}^{\pm} \Delta d_v + C_{3p(d)}^{\pm} \Delta \bar{q} + C_{4p(d)}^{\pm} \Delta \bar{s}. \tag{2}$$

The coefficients $C_{ip(d)}^{\pm}$ depend on the unpolarised quarks distributions and on the quark fragmentation functions for which parametrisations [10] and the EMC data [8] were used respectively. In this expression the charge and isospin invariance of the fragmentation functions were used. The contribution from the last term was found to be negligible. The asymmetries were assumed to be independent on Q^2. The quark distributions and the fragmentation functions were taken at $Q^2 = 10 \text{GeV}^2$.

4. Results

The eqs.(2) were solved to obtain the distribution of valence quarks. The equality $x(\Delta u_v(x) - \Delta d_v(x)) =$

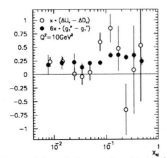

Figure 2. Comparision of the results obtained from hadron and from muon asymmetries. The structure functions were obtained from the fit to the world data.

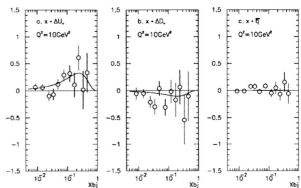

Figure 3. Polarisation of (a)u_v, (b)d_v and (c)non-strange sea quarks as a function of x_{Bj}.

$6x(g_1^p(x) - g_1^n(x))$ was used to check the consistency of semi-inclusive and inclusive results, seen in Fig.2. For further analysis, in addition to four eqs.(2), two equations involving inclusive asymmetries from hydrogen and deuterium were added and the quark distributions were determined from the fit which accounted for the correlations between semi-inclusive and inclusive asymmetry data. The results are shown in Fig.3. The u_v quarks are seen to be polarised in the proton direction for all values of x while the polarisation of the d_v quarks is opposite. In the region dominated by the sea the $\Delta \bar{q}$ is consistent with zero within small statistical errors. The lines in the figure show the predictions from ref.[9] which agree with the results on Δu_v and $\Delta \bar{q}$ but do not fully account for the negative values of Δd_v.

The polarised quark distributions $\Delta u_v(x), \Delta d_v(x)$ and $\Delta \bar{q}(x)$ were integrated over the full range of x assuming, in the unmeasured regions, the same behaviour as used in the analysis of $g_1^{d(p)}$. The integrated values of $\Delta u_v, \Delta d_v$ and $\Delta \bar{q}$ are $0.83 \pm 0.26, -0.67 \pm 0.33$ and 0.068 ± 0.068 respectively, where the errors are statistical only. Within the errors they agree with the results obtained from the first moment of g_1^p.

References

[1] SMC: D. Adams *et al.*, Phys. Lett. **B329** (1994) 399.
[2] M.L. Alguard *et al.*, Phys. Rev. Lett. **37** (1976) 1261; *ibid.* **41** (1978) 70;G. Baum*et al.*, Phys. Rev. Lett. **51** (1983) 1135; and G. Baum*et al.*,Phys. Rev. Lett. **45** (1980) 2000.
[3] EMC: J.Ashman *et al.*, Phys. Lett. **B206** (1988) 364;and Nucl. Phys. **B328** (1989) 1.
[4] SMC: B. Adeva *et al.*, Phys. Lett. **B302** (1993) 533.
[5] P.L. Anthony *et al.*, Phys. Rev. Lett. **71** (1993) 959.
[6] J. Ellis and M. Karliner, CERN preprint: CERN-TH-7324/94.
[7] W. Wislicki, 29th Rencontres de Moriond, *QCD and High Energy Interactions*, Meribel, France, March 1994.
[8] EMC: M. Arneodo *et al.*, Nucl. Phys. **B321** (1989) 541.
[9] T. Gehrmann and W.J. Stirling, University of Durham report: DTP/94/38.
[10] A. Donnachie and P.V. Landshoff, Zeit. Phys. **C61** (1994) 139; M. Glueck*et al.*, Phys. Lett. **B306** (1993) 391.

Spin Structure Measurements at SLAC

J.S. McCarthy

University of Virginia

on behalf of the SLAC E143 Collaboration

Abstract

Experiment E143 at SLAC finished data taking early in 1994. Electron beams with current of 50 to 200 nA and a beam polarization of 85% were scattered from polarized solid ammonia targets, $^{15}NH_3$ and $^{15}ND_3$. The electrons were detected in two spectrometers for three incident beam energies; 29.1, 16.2 and 9.7 Gev. The helicity of the electron was randomly reversed at the source during the measurements. The first analysis of the data have used the measured asymmetries $A_\perp$ and $A_\parallel$ to extract g_1^p/F_1^p and g_1^d/F_1^d at 29 GeV, over a range of $0.029 < x < 0.8$ and $1.3 < Q^2 < 10$ $(\text{GeV/c})^2$. The spin structure functions g_1^p and g_1^d have been obtained for a fixed momentum transfer and then used to test QCD sum rules.

1. Introduction

In 1993, the program to study the spin structure of the nucleons with the polarized electron beam at SLAC and the Virginia - Basel polarized target that was initiated in 1991 with the formation of the E143 Collaboration completed the first stage, namely the experimental data acquisition run at energies below 30 GeV and preliminary analysis of the measured data. The experiment counted the number of electrons scattered into two spectrometers for the configurations of parallel and antiparallel beam and target spins at three beam energies (29.1, 16.2 and 9.7 GeV), and for opposite orientations of the target spin transversal to the beam helicity, at one energy (29.1 GeV). In the initial phase of the analysis we have extracted from these numbers the ratios g_1^p/F_1^p and g_1^d/F_1^d for the 29 GeV data, over the range $0.029 < x < 0.8$ and $1.3 < Q^2 < 10$ $(\text{GeV/c})^2$. These quantities have been used to obtain values for the spin structure functions g_1^p and g_1^d, at a fixed value of the momentum transfer, by taking the appropriate values of the unpolarized structure function F_1.

In what follows, we will discuss the SLAC program

on the spin structure of the nucleons, the details of the experiment and the current status of the data analysis.

1.1. Experimental method

In the recent past the E142 collaboration at SLAC has measured the neutron spin structure function using a ^{3}He target [1] and the Spin Muon collaboration (SMC)[2] at CERN has measured g_1^p and g_1^d using butanol targets. Our experiment uses solid ordinary and deuterated ammonia $^{15}NH_3$ and $^{15}ND_3$ targets. The present experiment, E143, used the SLAC polarized electron beam with energies E of 9.7, 16.2, and 29.1 GeV scattering from polarized proton and deuteron targets in End Station A (ESA) to measure g_1^p, g_2^p, g_1^d, and g_2^d.

The longitudinally polarized electron beam was produced by photoemission from a strained-lattice GaAs crystal illuminated by a flash-lamp-pumped Ti-sapphire laser operated at 850 nm [4]. Beam pulses were typically 2 μsec long, contained 2–4×10^9 electrons, and were delivered at a rate of 120 Hz. The helicity was selected randomly on a pulse-to-pulse basis to minimize instrumental asymmetries. The longitudinal beam polarization P_b was measured in ESA using Møller scattering from thin ferromagnetic foils (49% Fe, 49% Co, 2% Va) magnetized by a Helmholtz coil. The average beam polarization was 0.85 ± 0.03, where the error is dominated by the overall systematic uncertainty in measuring the foil polarization using an induction coil technique.

The polarized target assembly contained two 3–cm–long target cells that could be selected individually by remote control. The permeable target cells were immersed in a vessel filled with liquid He and maintained at 1 K by use of a high power evaporation refrigerator. The first (top) cell was filled with granules of $^{15}ND_3$ (98% isotopic purity), and the second cell contained $^{15}NH_3$ (99.7% isotopic purity). A superconducting Helmholtz coil provided a uniform field of 4.8 T in the active target volume.

The ammonia granules were pre-irradiated [5] with 30 to 350 MeV electron beams to create a dilute assembly of paramagnetic atoms. During the experiment, they were exposed to 138 GHz microwaves to drive the hyperfine transition which aligns the nucleon spins. This technique of dynamic nuclear polarization produced proton polarizations of 65 to 80% in the NH_3 target in 10 to 20 minutes, and deuteron polarizations of 30% in about 60 minutes. The heating of the target by the beam current of 4×10^9 electrons per linac pulse caused a fast drop of a few percent in the polarization in a period of minutes. The polarization then slowly decreased due to radiation damage: after eight to twelve hours of exposure to the incident electron beam the hydrogen polarization had dropped to 50 to 55%. The deuterium polarization decayed more slowly, in a pattern consistent with its slower build up than hydrogen's: it dropped to $\sim 22\%$ in about 16 hours. Most of the radiation damage was repaired by annealing the target at about 80 K. The electron beam was rastered over the 4.9 cm^2 front surface of the target to spread the beam heating and radiation damage as uniformly as possible.

The target polarization P_t was measured using a series LCR resonant circuit and Q-meter detector [6]. The inductance was supplied by an NMR coil embedded in the ammonia granules. The NMR was calibrated by measuring the thermal-equilibrium (TE) signal near 1.6 K with beam and microwaves off.

1.2. Data analysis and preliminary results

A very large amount of data was accumulated during the long (November 1993 to February 6, 1994) data run. From this sample, we plan to extract the longitudinal spin structure functions for the proton, neutron and deuteron, in six different kinematic regions: 3 energies, two angles at each energy. The range of Q^2 covered in the experiment – for values of the invariant mass

well above the nucleon resonances region – will allow studying the momentum transfer dependence of the structure functions over a decade of Q^2 change: 0.5 to 5 GeV^2, in the central region $0.07 \le x \le 0.2$. The 9.7 GeV data will allow the extraction of the structure function in the resonances region, at higher x. The transversal structure function will be extracted at one energy (29.1 GeV) for both nucleons.

At the time of writing this report, the proton longitudinal structure function at 29 GeV has been submitted for publication. Deuteron results are also available but still in a provisional form. Both sets will be presented here. It must be mentioned that to obtain preliminary physics results in the shortest possible time, the analysis of the data has been carried out so far based only on the quick computation of cross section asymmetries instead of using the more reliable but lengthier cross section differences method.

The experimental asymmetries $A_\parallel$ and $A_\perp$ are determined from

$$A_\parallel(\text{or} A_\perp) = \left(\frac{N_- - N_+}{N_- + N_+} \right) \frac{C_N}{f P_b P_t} + A_{RC}, \quad (1)$$

where the target polarization is parallel (transverse) to the beam direction for $A_\parallel$ ($A_\perp$); N_- and N_+ are the number of scattered electrons per incident charge for negative and positive beam helicity, respectively; C_N is a correction factor for the polarized nitrogen nuclei; f is the dilution factor representing the fraction of measured events originating from polarizable nucleons within the target; and A_{RC} is the radiative correction. The expression for the neutron asymmetry is

$$A_n = \left(1 + \frac{\sigma_p}{\sigma_n} \right) \frac{A_d}{\gamma} - \left(\frac{\sigma_p}{\sigma_n} \right) A_p \quad (2)$$

where σ_p/σ_n is extracted from deep inelastic scattering data. $\gamma \simeq 0.92$ is the effective polarization of the nucleons in the deuteron, correcting for those in the D-state.

The dilution factor f for NH_3 varied with x between 0.13 and 0.17; it was determined from the number of measured counts expected from each component of the $^{15}NH_3$ target, which contained about 13% free protons, 65% ^{15}N, 10% ^4He, 6% Al, 5% Cu, and 1% Ti by weight. The relative systematic error in f ranged from 2.2 to 2.6%, as determined from uncertainties in the target composition and uncertainties in the expected ratios of cross sections from different nuclei. Similarly, a dilution factor for ND_3 can be computed, using the appropriate substitutions. Its values range from 0.22 to 0.25.

The internal radiative corrections for both $A_\parallel$ and $A_\perp$ were evaluated using the formulae of Kukhto and Shumeiko [8]. The cross section components of the asymmetry were "externally radiated" according to Tsai

[9] to form the "fully radiated" asymmetry corrections A_{RC}. The corrections varied slowly with x and changed $A_\parallel$ by typically $< 2\%$. Systematic errors were estimated based on uncertainties in the $A_\parallel$ and $A_\perp$ models developed to fit all existing data (including the 9.7 and 16.2 GeV data of this experiment) and correspond to relative errors on $A_\parallel$ of typically 2% for $x > 0.1$, increasing to 11% at $x = 0.03$. The statistical errors at low x take into account the removal of the elastic tail contributions which make up 25% of the counts in this kinematic region.

The values of g_1^p/F_1^p from this experiment [11] at $E = 29.1$ GeV are displayed in Fig. 1 along with results of previous experiments. Data from the two spectrometers are consistent in the overlap region $0.07 < x < 0.55$, and therefore have been averaged together. Since the two data sets differ by about a factor of 2 in average Q^2, the comparison indicates no strong Q^2-dependence for g_1^p/F_1^p. The systematic errors include contributions from P_b, P_t, f, and A_{RC} discussed above, as well as 3 to 5% in d arising from the uncertainty in R.

It can be seen in Fig. 1 that both the previous SLAC data [20] and the higher Q^2 SMC data [2] ($< Q^2 > = 10$ (GeV/c)^2) are in agreement with this experiment, indicating that to a good approximation, g_1/F_1 is independent of Q^2 over the (x, Q^2) range where this ratio has been measured. The SLAC E130 data are plotted assuming $A_\perp = 0$ (that experiment measured $A_\parallel$ only), and the SMC data are plotted assuming $g_1/F_1 \approx A_1$, which is a good approximation at their beam energy of 190 GeV.

Values of xg_1^p at the average $Q^2 = 3$ (GeV/c)^2 of this experiment are shown in Fig. 2. The evaluation at constant Q^2 is model-dependent, and we made the assumption that g_1^p/F_1^p depends only on x [12]. The integral of g_1^p over the measured range $0.029 < x < 0.8$ is proportional to the area under the data points in Fig. 2, yielding $\int_{0.029}^{0.8} g_1^p(x)dx = 0.120 \pm 0.004 \pm 0.009$, where the first error is statistical, and the second is systematic.

The extrapolation from $x = 0.8$ to $x = 1$ was done assuming g_1 is proportional to $(1-x)^3$ at high x[19]; this yields $\int_{0.8}^{1} g_1^p(x)dx = 0.001 \pm 0.0005$. The extrapolation to $x = 0$ is more model dependent, and could be large if g_1^p were to increase strongly at low x. We use this value to estimate $\int_{0}^{0.029} g_1^p(x)dx = 0.008 \pm 0.001 \pm 0.005$. The systematic error was estimated by varying x_{max} for the fit from 0.03 (for which only SMC and EMC data contribute) to 0.12 (for which the present data dominate). Given the two assumptions that g_1/F_1 depends only on x and that g_1^p is constant at low x, we obtain the total integral $\Gamma_1^p = 0.129 \pm 0.004 \pm 0.010$. This is in good agreement with the value from SMC [2], $\Gamma_1^p = 0.122 \pm 0.011 \pm 0.011$, obtained at $Q^2 = 3$

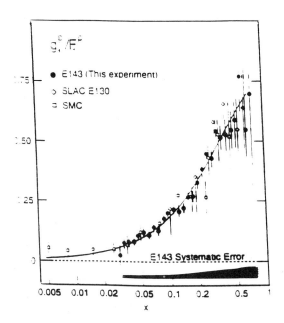

Figure 1. Ratios g_1^p/F_1^p from this experiment (E143) as a function of x. The errors are statistical only. Systematic errors are indicated by the lower band. The average Q^2 varies from 1.3 (GeV/c)^2 at low x to 10 (GeV/c)^2 at high x. Also shown are data from SLAC E130 [3] and SMC [5].

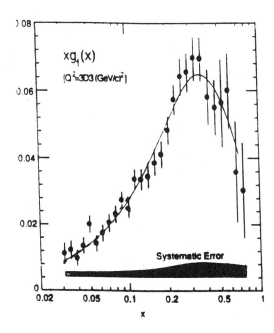

Figure 2. The structure function g_1^p (scaled by x) from this experiment evaluated at fixed $Q^2 = 3$ (GeV/c)^2. The systematic errors are indicated by the lower band. The curve is given by $g_1 = 0.29$, the value used for the low–x extrapolation.

(GeV/c)^2 assuming $g_1/F_1 \approx A_1$ is independent of Q^2. Our result is more than two standard deviations below the Ellis-Jaffe sum rule prediction of 0.160 ± 0.006, evaluated using the QCD corrections of Ref. [16] with

$\alpha_s = 0.35 \pm 0.05$ at $Q^2 = 3$ (GeV/c)^2 [17].

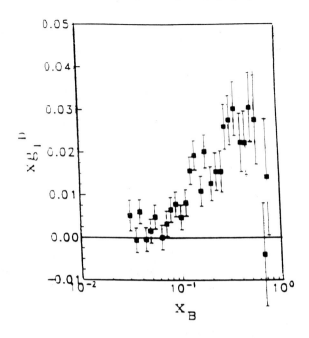

Figure 3. The structure function g_1^d (scaled by x) from this experiment evaluated at fixed $Q^2 = 3$ (GeV/c)^2. No systematic errors are given.

A more accurate determination of $\Delta\Sigma$ can be obtained from the deuteron integral $\Gamma_1^d = \int_0^1 g_1^d(x)dx$ since only the combination $3F - D$ is needed as external input. The input to the deuteron integral is the spin structure function g_1^d, which has been extracted in a very similar fashion as the proton's. The current preliminary values of the x weighted g_1^d are shown in Fig. 3. The integral in the measured range is $\int_{0.029}^{0.8} g_1^d(x)dx = 0.042 \pm 0.003 \pm 0.004$. The extrapolations to $x = 1$ and to $x = 0$ have been estimated in the same way as for the proton. Their contributions are small, 0.001 ± 0.001 each, yielding $\Gamma_1^d = 0.044 \pm 0.003 \pm 0.004$ The resulting QCD corrected total quark helicity, including the uncertainties in α_s and F and D, is $\Delta\Sigma = 0.331 \pm 0.052$, which is the most precise value for this quantity.

For $Q^2 = 3$ (GeV/c)^2 and for three flavors, the Bjorken sum rule prediction with third order QCD corrections [15] is $\Gamma_1^{p-n} = \Gamma_1^p - \Gamma_1^n = \frac{1}{6}(g_A/g_V)(1 - \alpha_s(Q^2)/\pi - 3.58(\alpha_s(Q^2)/\pi)^2 - 20.22(\alpha_s(Q^2)/\pi)^3) = 0.171\pm0.008$, Using our deuteron data we obtain $\Gamma_1^{p-n} = 0.162 \pm 0.019$, which is consistent with the prediction within errors.

References

[1] SLAC E142, P. L. Anthony *et al.*, Phys. Rev. Lett. **71**, 959 (1993).

[2] SMC, D. Adams *et al.,*, Phys. Lett. **B329**, 399 (1994).

[3] SMC, B. Adeva *et al.* Phys. Lett. **B302**, 533 (1993).

[4] T. Maruyama, E. L. Garwin, R. Prepost, G. H. Zapalac, Phys. Rev. B **46**, 4261 (1992); R. Alley *et al.*, Report No. SLAC–PUB–6489 (1994).

[5] D. G. Crabb *et al.*, Phys. Rev. Lett. **64**, 2627 (1990); W. Meyer *et al.*, Nucl. Instrum. Meth. **215**, 65 (1983).

[6] G. R. Court *et al.*, Nucl. Instrum. Meth. **A324**, 433 (1993).

[7] G. G. Petratos *et al.*, Report No. SLAC–PUB–5678 (1991).

[8] T. V. Kukhto and N. M. Shumeiko, Nucl. Phys. **B219**, 412 (1983); I. V. Akusevich and N. M. Shumeiko, J. Phys. G **20**, 513 (1994).

[9] Y. S. Tsai, Report No. SLAC–PUB–848, 1971; Y. S. Tsai, Rev. Mod. Phys. **46**, 815 (1974).

[10] L.W. Whitlow *et al.* Phys. Lett. **B250**,193 (1990).

[11] Tables corresponding to Fig. 1 and Fig. 2 are available in SLAC E143, K. Abe *et al.*, Report No. SLAC–PUB–6508 (1994).

[12] G. Altarelli, P. Nason, and G. Ridolfi, Phys. Lett. **B320**, 152 (1994).

[13] NMC, P. Amaudruz *et al.*, Phys. Lett. **B295**, 159 (1992).

[14] L. W. Whitlow *et al.*, Phys. Lett. **B282**, 475 (1992).

[15] S. A. Larin and J. A. M. Vermaseren, Phys. Lett. **B259**, 345 (1991) and references therein.

[16] S. A. Larin, Report No. CERN–TH.7208/94.

[17] M. Schmelling and R. D. St.Denis, Report No. CERN/PPE93–193; S. Nerison, Report No. CERN–TH.7188/94.

[18] for example F. E. Close and R. G. Roberts, Phys. Lett. **B316**, 165 (1993); J. Ellis and M. Karliner, Phys. Lett. **B313**, 131 (1993).

[19] S.J. Brodsky, M. Burkardt and I. Schmidt, report No. SLAC–PUB-6087 (1994)

[20] SLAC-E130, G. Baum *et al.*, Phys. Rev. Lett. **51**, 1135 (1983).

Spin-dependent Parton Distributions

T. Gehrmann[†] and W.J. Stirling[†§]

[†]Department of Physics, University of Durham, Durham DH1 3LE, England.
[§]Department of Mathematical Sciences, University of Durham, Durham DH1 3LE, England.

Abstract

We perform a global leading-order QCD fit to recent polarized structure function data in order to extract a consistent set of spin-dependent parton distributions. Assuming that there is no significant intrinsic polarization of the quark sea, the data are consistent with a modest amount of the proton's spin carried by the gluon, although the shape of the gluon distribution is not well constrained. We show how inelastic J/ψ production in polarized photon-hadron scattering can, in principle, provide definitive information on the shape of the gluon distribution.

Several experiments [1, 2, 3] have recently presented new measurements of the polarized deep-inelastic structure function g_1. Combined with earlier measurements [4, 5], the data cover a broad range in x and Q^2 and provide, for the first time, detailed information on the spin-dependent parton distributions. We present here a summary of a recent analysis [6] in which we perform a leading-order QCD fit to the high-Q^2 data and extract a consistent set of parton distributions.

The fact that the measured value [3] of the integral of g_1, $\Gamma_1^p = 0.142 \pm 0.008 \pm 0.011$, is less than the Ellis-Jaffe prediction (0.18) [7] suggests that the gluon makes a significant contribution. At leading order, we can write [8] (for 3 quark flavours)

$$g_1(x, Q^2) = \frac{1}{2} \sum_{q, \bar{q}} e_q^2 \Delta q(x Q^2) - \frac{\alpha_s(Q^2)}{6\pi} \Delta G(x, Q^2).$$

In our model, we assume that there is no polarized sea-quark distribution at $Q^2 = 4$ GeV^2. The only *a priori* constraints on the distributions are (i) the specification of the first moments by the sum-rule and hyperon decay data, and (ii) the requirement of positivity of the individual helicity distributions, $|\Delta f| \leq f$, $(f = q, G)$. In addition, Regge and coherence arguments can be used to fix the $x \to 0$ behaviour. Unfortunately neither the neutron [1] nor deuteron [2] g_1 data are precise enough

to constrain the Δd distribution: the fit is dominated by g_1^p which depends mainly on Δu. For consistency, we choose the same $\Lambda_{\text{LO}}^{(4)} = 177$ MeV and $Q_0 = 2$ GeV values as [9], and similar starting parametrizations at $Q^2 = Q_0^2$:

$$
\begin{aligned}
x\Delta u_v &= \eta_u A_u x^{a_u} (1-x)^{b_u} (1+\gamma_u x) \\
x\Delta d_v &= \eta_d A_d x^{a_d} (1-x)^{b_d} (1+\gamma_d x) \\
x\Delta \bar{q} &= 0 \quad (q = u, d, s, c) \\
x\Delta G &= \eta_G A_G x^{a_G} (1-x)^{b_G} (1+\gamma_G x)
\end{aligned}
$$

with normalization factors A_f $(f = q, G)$ to ensure that $\int_0^1 dx\, \Delta f(x, Q_0^2) = \eta_f$: We impose a cut $Q^2 > 4$ GeV^2 on the data to suppress higher-twist contributions. The fit to the g_1^p structure function data from SLAC [4], EMC [5] and SMC [3] is shown in Fig. 1 and the resulting parameters are listed in Table 1. The shape of the gluon distribution is not well constrained. In the fit shown in Fig. 1, $\gamma_G = 0$ (the set A gluon) has been chosen. Equally good fits can be obtained with other values. To span the range allowed by positivity, we define two other sets which have $\gamma_G = 18.0$ (set B) and $\gamma_G = -3.5$ (set C), with the other parameters fitted to the data. Fig. 2 shows the set A gluon, quark-singlet, u-valence and d-valence distributions at Q_0^2 obtained from the fit. For comparison, the unpolarized distributions of Ref. [9] are

Parameter	Value	Comments
η_u	0.848	$\eta_u = 2F$
b_u	3.64	$=$ unpolarized b_u
a_u	0.46	fitted
γ_u	18.36	fitted
η_d	-0.294	$\eta_d = F - D$
b_d	4.64	$=$ unpolarized b_d
a_d	0.46	$= a_u$ (Regge)
γ_d	18.36	$= \gamma_u$ (constrained)
η_G	1.971	from Γ_1^p
b_G	7.44	fitted
a_G	1.0	coherence arguments
γ_G	0.0	constrained

Table 1. Parameters for the set A partons

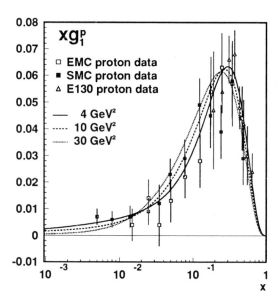

Figure 1. Fit to the g_1^p structure function with set A gluon

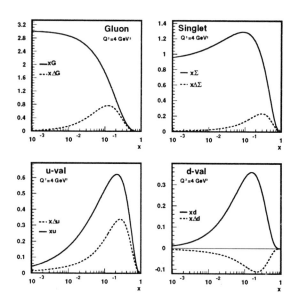

Figure 2. The polarized gluon (set A), quark singlet, u_v and d_v distributions at $Q_0^2 = 4$ GeV^2 obtained from the fit to the deep inelastic scattering data.

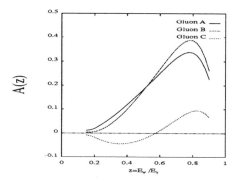

Figure 3. The asymmetry $\mathcal{A}(z)$ predicted by the different gluon distributions, for a photon beam of energy $E_\gamma = 45$ GeV on a stationary proton target [12].

also shown. Note that perturbative evolution generates a polarized sea distribution for $Q^2 > Q_0^2$. However in the range of Q^2 relevant to the structure function measurements the polarized sea is small in comparison to Δu and Δd. This appears to be consistent with the preliminary measurements of $\Delta \bar{q}$ from inclusive hadron production, reported by SMC at this conference [10].

Inelastic J/ψ production in polarized photon-nucleon scattering provides a possible method of measuring ΔG [11]. The cross section $d\Delta\sigma^{\gamma N}/dp_T^2 dz$ (where $z = E_{J/\psi}/E_\gamma$) is proportional to ΔG in leading order. The asymmetry $\mathcal{A}(z)$, defined by integrating over $p_T^2 > 0.25$ GeV^2, is shown in Fig. 3 for the three gluons.

References

[1] SLAC-E142 collaboration: D.L. Anthony *et al.*, Phys. Rev. Lett. **71** (1993) 959.

[2] SMC: B. Adeva *et al.*, Phys. Lett. **B302** (1993) 553.

[3] SMC: D. Adams *et al.*, Phys. Lett. **B329** (1994) 399.

[4] SLAC-Yale collaboration: M.J. Alguard *et al.*, Phys. Rev. Lett. **37** (1976) 1261; G. Baum *et al.*, Phys. Rev. Lett. **45** (1980) 2000; **51** (1983) 1135.

[5] EMC: J. Ashman *et al.*, Nucl. Phys. **B328** (1989) 1.

[6] T. Gehrmann and W.J. Stirling, Durham preprint DTP/94/38 (1994), to be published in Zeit. Phys. **C**.

[7] J. Ellis and R.L. Jaffe, Phys. Rev. **D9** (1974) 1444, erratum **D10** (1974) 1669.

[8] G. Altarelli and G.G. Ross, Phys. Lett. **B212** (1988) 391.

[9] J.F. Owens, Phys. Lett. **B266** (1991) 126.

[10] SMC: J. Nassalski, these proceedings.

[11] J.Ph. Guillet, Z. Phys. **C39** (1988) 75.

[12] V. Breton, *Measurement of ΔG by J/ψ Photoproduction at SLAC*, SLAC proposal, 1994.

Paper presented at XXVII Int. Conf. on High Energy Physics: Session Pa-6
Glasgow, UK, 20–27 July 1994

Spin Dependence of Diffractive Processes and Polarisation at small x

F. E. Close

Rutherford Appleton Laboratory,
Chilton Didcot, Oxon OX11 0QX, Great Britain

Abstract

The value implied for the net quark spin content of the nucleon depends sensitively on the $x \to 0$ unknown region. We assess possibilities for this domain and their implications

The accumulation of data [1,2,3] on the spin dependent inelastic structure functions $g_1(x, Q^2)$ with p, d, n over a wide range of Q^2 and x have at last begun to lead to a consistent picture. The independent analyses of refs. [4, 5] agree that Bjorken's sum rule is confirmed to high accuracy, that for $x \gtrsim 0.2$ the polarisation of the **valence** quarks is canonical [6] and that all experiments agree on the inferred spin content of the nucleon **if** they make the common assumption

$$g_1 \simeq x^{\alpha_{A_1}}, x \to 0 \qquad (1)$$

where α_{A_1} is the intercept of the a_1 Regge trajectory (assumed to lie in the range - $0.5 < \alpha_{A_1} < 0$). Typically this results in

$$\Delta q = 0.30 \pm 0.07(stat) \pm 0.10(syst) \qquad (2)$$

More detailed analyses, as in refs. [4, 5] essentially agree on such a magnitude. This is about 50% of the naive expectation based on $\Delta q \equiv 3F - D$ and is consistent with the historically measured values though the central value has increased significantly from the original [7] estimate of a value consistent with zero.

A superficial glance at the SMC [2] data hints that $g_1^p(x)$ may be rising for $x < 0.01$ (which is a result of $A(x)$ being roughly constant while the unpolarised structure function is growing). If this trend is confirmed, and if it continues to smaller values of x, then the naive Regge pole extrapolation will be inadequate.

This leads us to the main point of this paper: *what empirical knowledge or theoretical constraints are there on the high energy behaviour (or small x behaviour) of spin dependent total cross sections (polarised structure functions)?* The literature allows the possibility of considerable polarisation dependence in the diffractive region out to large energies and small values of x.

In the DLA of QCD, the leading log $\frac{1}{x}$ behaviour of $F_2(x)$ is driven by the leading behaviour of the gluon-gluon splitting function at small z, $P_{gg}(z) = 2/z$ and leads to the well-known result $F_2(x \to 0) \sim \exp(k\sqrt{\ln \frac{1}{x}})$.

The helicity structure of the three-gluon vertex leads to a similar behaviour for Δg, Δq driven by $\Delta P_{gg} = 4$ and hence g_1 (if we neglect complications from the anomaly term). This yields $g_1 \sim \exp(\sqrt{2}k\sqrt{\ln \frac{1}{x}})$ and hence the relation

$$g_1 \sim [F_2]^{\sqrt{2}} \qquad (3)$$

The precise behaviour will depend on the input polarised gluon distribution $\Delta G(x)$ which, in general, is expected to be non-zero [8]. This provides an example of a naturally generated growth for g_1 at small x in QCD.

An explicit calculation of the spin dependent diffractive scattering in the Landshoff-Donnachie model [9, 10] implies a logarithmic growth

$$g_1(x) \sim (1 + 2 \log x) \qquad (4)$$

which would also modify analyses if realised though the inferred Δ_q remains consistent with that in eq (2).

Finally we consider an extreme point of view where a rapid rise at small x is expected. General theorems on the high energy behaviour of the spin dependent total cross sections show that *if* negative signature cuts reach $J = 1$ at $t = 0$ there can be a leading contribution to $xg_1(x) \sim 1/\log^2 x$ [11, 12, 13]. Such a behaviour was discussed in an analysis of the first EMC results [14]. Allowing such a rapid rise has been criticised [15] but there seems to be no compelling argument for the decoupling of such non-factorisable contributions to the amplitude. Isoscalar t−channel exchanges with axial-vector quantum numbers, as listed in eqs(4.1,4.2) of ref [16], do include the possible contributions from the negative signature cuts of refs. [11, 12, 13]. We are unaware of any general theorems based on symmetry principles, angular momentum etc. that forbid the above behaviour although it may be that the magnitude of such contributions is indeed small or even vanishing in specific dynamic models.

The combined SMC and EMC data prefer a parametrisation $xg_1^p(x) = (0.17 \pm 0.03)/\ln^2 x, (x < 0.135)$ which leads to $I_p(0,1) = 0.165 \pm 0.010$ ($\Delta q = 50 \pm 16\%$).

In any event this range of possibilities serves

(i) to illustrate that our limited understanding of the small x region does allow for an estimate of the integral of $g_1^p(x)$ which is entirely consistent with the original Ellis-Jaffe sum rule [17] whose value, including $O(\alpha_s^2)$ corrections, is 0.172 ± 0.009 at $Q^2 = 10 \text{ GeV}^2$.

(ii) as a challenge for future experiments to eliminate.

The resulting values inferred for Δq vary considerably and so highlight the importance of being able to discriminate between, at least, a roughly constant or falling a_1 pole (non-diffractive or Lorentz scalar diffraction) on the one hand and a (logarithmic) growth on the other.

Possible routes for resolving these questions include reduction of the systematic and statistical uncertainties in the SMC data for $x \lesssim 0.05$ to confirm the apparent rise; measurement of the sea polarisation directly via semi-inclusive production of fast K^- and π [19, 20] or precise data for the deuteron at small x where, if diffraction dominates, $g_1^d(x)$ would be positive. Present data are not accurate enough to rule out this possibility.

If any of these imply that there is significant non-trivial spin dependence and growth in the diffractive region at small x, then this may stimulate investigation of the possibility of creating longitudinally polarised proton beams at HERA. Polarised electron - proton interactions at HERA could turn out to have significant physics interest.

References

[1] EM Collaboration, J. Ashman et al., Nucl. Phys. **B328** (1990) 1.

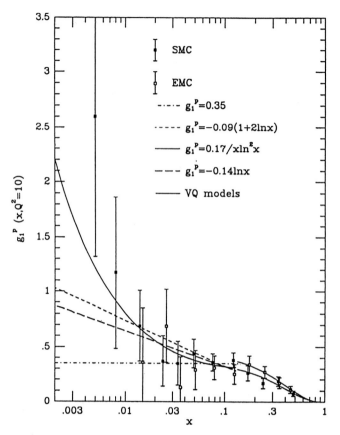

Figure 1. $g_1^p(x)$ at $Q^2 = 10 \text{ GeV}^2$. Data are from refs.

[2] SM Collaboration, D. Adams et al., Phys. Lett. **B329** (1994) 399.
[3] SLAC-E142 Collaboration, D.L. Anthony et al., Phys. Rev. Lett.**71** (1993) 959.
[4] F.E. Close and R.G. Roberts, RAL-94-071, Phys. Lett. (in press).
[5] J. Ellis and M. Karliner, hep-ph-9407287.
[6] F.E. Close and R.G. Roberts, Phys. Lett. **B316** (1993) 165.
[7] EM Collaboration, J. Ashman et al., Phys. Lett. **B206** (1988) 364.
[8] F.E. Close and D. Sivers, Phys. Rev. Lett. **39** (1977) 1116.
[9] A. Donnachie and P.V. Landshoff, Zeit. Phys. **C61** (1994) 139.
[10] S. Bass and P.V. Landshoff Cavendish Laboratory Report HEP 94/4, submitted to Phys. Lett.
[11] A.H. Mueller and T.L. Trueman, Phys. Rev. **160** (1967) 1306.
[12] L. Galfi, J. Kuti and A. Patkos, Phys. Lett. **B31** (1970) 465.
[13] J.Kuti, in 2nd International Conf on Polarised Targets, Berkeley (1971).
[14] F.E. Close and R.G. Roberts, Phys. Rev. Lett. **60** (1988) 1471.
[15] E. Leader, 24 International Conf. on High Energy Physics, Munich (1988).
    M. Anselmino, B. Ioffe and E. Leader, Sov. J. Nucl. Phys. **49** (1989) 136.
[16] R. Heimann, Nucl. Phys. **B64** (1973) 429.
[17] J. Ellis and R.L. Jaffe, Phys. Rev. **D9** (1974) 1444.
[18] HERMES proposal, K.Coulter et al., DESY/PRC 90-1(1990),
    SLAC Proposals E143, E154 and E-155 (1991,1993)
[19] F.E. Close and R.G. Milner, Phys. Rev. **D44** (1991) 3691.
[20] L.L. Frankfurt et al., Phys. Lett. **B230** (1989) 141.

Paper presented at XXVII Int. Conf. on High Energy Physics: Session Pa-6
Glasgow, UK, 20–27 July 1994

Higher-order QCD Corrections to Deep-inelastic Sum Rules

Andrei L. Kataev[†]

Theoretical Physics Division, CERN, CH-1211 Geneva 23, Switzerland;
Institute for Nuclear Research of the Russian Academy of Sciences,
117312 Moscow, Russia.

Abstract

A brief review of the current status of the studies of the effects of the higher-order perturbative QCD corrections to the deep-inelastic sum rules is presented.

1. Introduction

Up to recently the consideration of the QCD predictions for the structure functions (SFs) of deep-inelastic scattering (DIS) was the basic sourse of information about the structure of a nucleon. However, the recent measurements of the SFs of both polarized and non-polarized DIS [1],[2] in the wide interval of the $x = Q^2/2pq$ variable open the possibility of a more precise determination of the number of the DIS sum rules (SRs), namely of the polarized Bjorken SR $BjpSR = \int_0^1 g_1^{ep-en}(x, Q^2)dx$, the polarized Ellis-Jaffe SR $EJSR = \int_0^1 g_1^{p(n)}(x, Q^2)dx$ and of the non-polarized Gross-Llewellyn Smith SR $GLSSR = (1/2)\int_0^1 F_3^{\nu p+\bar{\nu}p}(x, Q^2)dx$. In view of this experimental progress the detailed studies of the theoretical predictions for the DIS SRs started to attract special attention. In this talk we concentrate on the discussions of the effects of the perturbative QCD corrections to these quantities.

2. The polarized Bjorken SR

The theoretical expression for the $BjpSR$ has the following form

$$BjpSR = \frac{1}{3} \mid \frac{g_A}{g_V} \mid \left[1 - a(1 + \sum_{i \geq 1} d_i a^i) + O(\frac{1}{Q^2})\right], \quad (1)$$

† E-mail: Kataev@cernvm.cern.ch

where $a = \alpha_s/\pi$ and the exact expressions for the coefficients d_1 and d_2, namely $d_1^{ex} = 4.583 - 0.333f$ and $d_2^{ex} = 41.440 - 7.607f + 0.177f^2$, were calculated in the $\overline{MS}$ scheme in Refs. [3] and [4] respectively. However, this scheme is not the unique prescription for fixing the renormalization scheme ambiguities. For example, one can use the principle of minimal sensitivity (PMS) [5] or the effective charges (ECH) approach [6]. These methods assume the role of "optimal" prescriptions, in the sense that they might provide better convergence of the corresponding approximations for physical quantities in the non-asymptotic regime. Therefore, applying these methods, one can try to estimate the effects of the $O(a^{N+1})$ corrections starting from the N-th order approximation $D_N^{opt}(a_{opt})$. As was originally explained in Ref. [5], rewriting the N-th order optimized expression $D_N^{opt}(a_{opt})$ of the physical quantity in terms of the coupling constant a of the initial scheme one can get the following relation $D_N^{opt}(a_{opt}) = D_N(a) + \delta D_N^{opt} a^{N+1}$. It is now possible to consider the term δD_N^{opt} as the one, that simulates the coefficient of the $O(a^{N+1})$ correction to the physical quantity $D(a)$ calculated in the certain initial scheme. Its concrete form $\delta D_N^{opt} = \Omega_N(d_i, c_i) - \Omega_N^{opt}(d_i^{opt}, c_i^{opt})$ ($1 \leq i \leq N - 1$) depends on the coefficients d_i of the physical quantity and c_i of the QCD β-function defined as $\beta(a) = -\beta_0 a^2(1 + \sum_{i \geq 1} c_i a^i)$. The correction terms Ω_N^{opt} reflect the dependence on the way of realization of the "optimal" prescription and are rather small. Within the ECH approach one has $\Omega_N^{opt} = 0$. Moreover, in the case of the PMS approach, $\Omega_3^{PMS} = 0$ [7] and therefore $\delta D_3^{ECH} = \delta D_3^{PMS}$.

The above-mentioned procedure was recently used to estimate the $O(a^4)$ correction to the $BjpSR$ [8, 9] and to roughly fix the uncertainty in the value of the $O(a^5)$ term [9]. The table, taken from Ref. [9], summarizes the results of estimates of the coefficients d_i^{est}, obtained by re-expansion of the ECH for the $BjpSR$ into the initial $\overline{MS}$ scheme, and demonstrates their dependence on the number of flavours f. We consider the satisfactory agreement of the obtained estimates d_2^{est} with the results d_2^{ex} of Ref. [4] as an argument in favour of the applicability of this procedure.

f	d_2^{ex}	d_2^{est}	d_3^{est}	$d_4^{est} - c_3 d_1$
1	34.01	27.25	290	2557
2	26.93	23.11	203	1572
3	20.21	19.22	130	854
4	13.84	15.57	68	342
5	7.83	12.19	18	27
6	2.17	9.08	-22	-135

The results of estimates of the $NNLO$, N^3LO and N^4LO corrections in the series for $BjpSR$.

The existing ambiguities in d_4^{est} are related to the assumption used that the real value of d_3 does not differ from d_3^{est} and to the lack of knowledge of the 4-loop coefficient of the QCD β-function. However, even without application of any additional assumption about its value (e.g. for $f = 3, 4, 5$ one can use the "geometric progression" guess $c_3 = c_2^2/c_1$), it is possible to conclude that in the currently available region of energies $Q^2 = 2$–$10\ GeV^2$ the higher-order QCD corrections to the $BjpSR$ are not negligibly small. The results discussed were used in the process of the determination of the value of $\alpha_s(M_Z) = 0.122^{+0.005}_{-0.009}$ [10] using the $BjpSR$ measurements [1]. This result should be compared with the result $\alpha_s(M_Z) = 0.115 \pm 0.005(exp) \pm 0.003(th)$ extracted in Ref. [11] from the $GLSSR$ data [2]. Its theoretical uncertainty comes from the uncertainty of the estimates [12] of the higher-twist terms.

3.   The Ellis-Jaffe SR

The theoretical expression for the $EJSR$ consists of two parts: $EJSR(Q^2) = EJ_{NS}(Q^2) + EJ_{SI}(Q^2)$. The first non-singlet part is a renormalization-group-invariant quantity and, apart from the overall factor, coincides with $BjpSR$. For the case of $f = 3$ active flavours, one has [8, 9]:

$$EJ_{NS}^{p(n)} = \left[1 - a - 3.583a^2 - 20.215a^3 - 130a^4 - O(a^5)\right]$$
$$\times (\pm a_3/12 + a_8/36) + O\left(\frac{1}{Q^2}\right),$$
(2)

where $a_3 = \Delta u - \Delta d$, $a_8 = \Delta u + \Delta d - 2\Delta s$ and Δu, Δd, Δs can be interpreted as the measure of the polarization of the quarks in a nucleon. The $O(a^2)$ correction to EJ_{SI}, which contains the anomalous-dimension term, was calculated recently [13]. In order to estimate the value of the $O(a^3)$ correction the methods of Ref. [5] were supplemented by the considerations of the quantities with anomalous dimensions [14]. For $f = 3$ numbers of flavours, the estimates were obtained [15] for the renormalization-invariant definition of the singlet contribution and in the case when the Q^2-dependence of $\Delta\Sigma = \Delta u + \Delta d + \Delta s$ is specified. The more definite renormalization-invariant estimates have the following form [15]:

$$EJ_{SI} = \left[1 - 0.333a - 0.549a^2 - 2a^3\right]\frac{1}{9}\Delta\Sigma_{inv} + O\left(\frac{1}{Q^2}\right).$$
(3)

In order to obtain the $O(\alpha_s^3)$ estimates in the case when the Q^2-dependence of $\Delta\Sigma = \Delta u + \Delta d + \Delta s$ is specified, it is necessary to fix the value of the 4-loop coefficient of the corresponding anomalous dimension function, which starts its expansion from the $O(a^2)$ level, namely $\gamma(a) = \sum_{i \geq 1} \gamma_i a^{i+1}$ [15]. For the case of $f = 3$ the final result [15] reads:

$$EJ_{SI} = \left[1 - a - 1.096a^2 - 3.7a^3\right]\frac{1}{9}\Delta\Sigma(Q^2) + O(\frac{1}{Q^2}).$$
(4)

Note that we used an additional assumption about the value of the non-calculated term γ_3 [15]: $\gamma_3 \approx \gamma_2^2/\gamma_1$, whereas the expression for the γ_2-term is known [16].

It can be seen that the perturbative contributions to eqs. (3), (4) are significantly smaller than the coefficients of eq. (2). This fact has an important phenomenological consequence, namely the possibility of describing available data of Ref.[1] by allowing Δs to be non-zero [10]. The outcomes of the fits [10] are: $\Delta s = -0.10 \pm 0.03$, $\Delta\Sigma = 0.31 \pm 0.07$ at $Q^2 = 10\ GeV^2$. Note, however, that in view of the controversial claims about the possible contributions of the higher-twist terms in eqs. (2)-(4) [17], the analysis of the polarized DIS data [1] deserves further experimental and theoretical studies. One of the possible clarifying advancements could be the determination, from the experimental data, of the Q^2-dependence of the $BjpSR$ and of the $EJSR$. In the case of the $GLSSR$ this work was already started [18]. Another important theoretical problem is related to the study of the consequences of the manifestation of the axial anomaly in the theoretical expression for the *EJSR* [19].

4. DIS vs. e^+e^- annihilation

The new non-trivial connection between the characteristics of the e^+e^- annihilation and DIS was discovered recently [20]:

$$D^{e^+e^-}(Q^2) \times GLSSR(Q^2) \sim 1 + \frac{\beta(a)}{a}\left[C_1 a + C_2 a^2\right] + O(a^4) \tag{5}$$

These characteristics are the analytical $O(a^3)$ approximations of the function $D^{e^+e^-}(Q^2)$ [21, 22] and of the *GLSSR* [4]. In eq. (5) C_1 and C_2 are the analytical numbers, which depend on the structure of the non-Abelian gauge group. It should be stressed that the corresponding perturbative expression for the *GLSSR* equals the one of the *BjpSR* plus the $O(a^3)$ contribution of the light-by-light-type graphs [4]. Equation (5) demonstrates the appearance of the radiative corrections in quark-parton formula of ref. [23] starting from the $O(a^2)$ level. This formula connects the amltitude, related to the axial anomaly, for the $\pi^0 \longrightarrow \gamma\gamma$ decay with the quark-parton expressions for the $D^{e^+e^-}$ function and the *BjpSR*. The most interesting, yet non-explained, feature of eq. (5) is the factorization of the factor $\beta(a)/a$ at the $O(a^3)$-level. We believe that the detailed study of this relation could have important theoretical and phenomenological consequences.

Acknowledgements
We are grateful to E. Hughes and W. J. Stirling for their invitation to present the talk at this Conference.

References

[1] SMC Collab., B. Adeva et al., *Phys. Lett.* **B302** (1993) 533; E142 Collab., P.L. Anthony et al., *Phys.Rev.Lett.* **71** (1993) 959; SMC Collab., D. Adams et al., *Phys. Lett.* **B329**(1994) 399; E143 Collab., results presented at ICHEP-94.

[2] CCFR Collab., W.C. Leung et al., *Phys. Lett.* **B317** (1993) 385.

[3] S.G. Gorishny and S.A. Larin, *Phys. Lett.* **B172** (1986) 109; E.B. Zijlstra and W. van Neerven, *Phys. Lett.* **B297** (1992) 377.

[4] S.A. Larin and J. Vermaseren, *Phys. Lett.* **B259** (1991) 345.

[5] P.M. Stevenson, *Phys.Rev.* **D23** (1981) 2916.

[6] G. Grunberg, *Phys.Rev.* **D29** (1984) 2315.

[7] J. Kubo and S. Sakakibara, *Z. Phys.* **C14** (1982) 345.

[8] A.L. Kataev and V.V. Starshenko, preprint CERN-TH.7198/94 (hep-ph/9405394) to appear in Proc. of the Workshop "QCD at LEP: Determination of α_s from Inclusive Observables" Aachen, Germany, 11 April 1994, eds. W. Bernreuther and S. Bethke, Aachen Reprt PITHA 94/33 (1994); A.L. Kataev, V.V. Starshenko, submitted for publication.

[9] A.L. Kataev and V.V. Starshenko, preprint CERN-TH.7400/94 (hep-ph/9408395); to appear in Proc. QCD-94 Workshop, Monpellier, France, July 1994; *Nucl. Phys. Proc. Suppl. B*, ed. S. Narison.

[10] J. Ellis and M. Karliner, preprint CERN-TH.7324/94; TAUP-2178-94 (hep-ph/9407287).

[11] J. Chýla and A.L. Kataev, *Phys. Lett.* **B297** (1992) 385.

[12] V.M. Braun and A.V. Kolesnichenko, *Nucl.Phys.* **B283** (1987) 723.

[13] S.A. Larin, *Phys. Lett.* **B334** (1994) 192.

[14] A.L. Kataev, Proc. QCD-90 Workshop, Montpellier, France, July 1990; *Nucl. Phys. Proc. Suppl.* **B23** (1991) 72; ed. S. Narison.

[15] A.L. Kataev, preprint CERN-TH.7333/94 (hep-ph/9408248), submitted for publication.

[16] S.A. Larin, *Phys. Lett.* **B303** (1993) 113; K.G. Chetyrkin and J.H. Kuhn, *Z. Phys.* **C60** (193) 334.

[17] I.I. Balitsky, V.M. Braun and A.V. Kolesnichenko, *Phys. Lett.* **B242**(1990) 245; **B318** (1993) 648 (Err.); G.G. Ross, and R.G. Roberts, *Phys. Lett.* **B322** (1994) 425; V.D. Burkert and B.L. Ioffe, JETP **78** (1994) 619; X.Ji and P. Unrau, *Phys. Lett.* **B333** (1994) 228; E. Stein, P. Gornicki, L. Mankiewicz, A. Schafer and W. Greiner, preprint UFTP 366/1994 (hep-ph/9409212).

[18] A.L. Kataev and V.A. Sidorov, *Phys. Lett.* **B331** (1994) 179; A. L. Kataev and V. A. Sidorov, preprint CERN-TH.7235/94 (hep-ph/9405254); preprint JINR E2-94-344 (1994) to appear in Proc. Quarks-94 Int. Seminar, Vladimir, Russia, May 1994; World Scientific, eds. D.Yu. Grigoriev, V.A. Matveev, V.A. Rubakov, D.T. Son and A.N. Tavkhelidze.

[19] A.V. Efremov and O.V.Teryaev, preprint JINR E2-88-287; Proc. of the Int. Hadron Symposium, Bechine, Czechoslovakia, June 1988; eds. J. Fischer et al., Czech Academy of Sciences Press., Prague 1989, p. 302; G. Altarelli and G. Ross, *Phys. Lett.* **B212** (1988) 391; G. Altarelli and W.J. Stirling, *Part. World* **1** (1989) 40.

[20] D. Broadhurst and A.L. Kataev, *Phys. Lett.* **B315** (1993) 179.

[21] S.G. Gorishny, A.L. Kataev and S.A. Larin, *Phys. Lett.* **B259** (1991) 144.

[22] L.R. Surguladze and M.A. Samuel, *Phys.Rev.Lett.* **66** (1991) 560; *ibid.* 2416(Err.).

[23] R.J. Crewther, *Phys.Rev.Lett.* **28** (1972) 1421.

Longitudinal electron polarization at HERA and the status of HERMES

Michael Düren

Phys. Inst. der Univ. Erlangen-Nürnberg, D-91058 Erlangen, Germany
E-mail: dueren@desy.de

On behalf of the HERA Polarization Group and of the HERMES Collaboration

Abstract

In May 1994 spin rotators have been brought into operation at HERA and for the first time longitudinal electron polarization has been produced in a high energy storage ring. About 65% polarization has been achieved. Longitudinal polarization at HERA will be used by the HERMES experiment starting in 1995 and later also by the collider experiments H1 and ZEUS.

HERMES has installed and tested the novel technique of a storage cell target in the HERA electron beam. It has been shown experimentally that the shielding of the storage cell from the beam halo, from RF bunch fields and from synchrotron radiation works without problems.

1. Electron polarization at HERA

Longitudinally polarized electron beams are perfect probes in two basic fields of high energy physics: the investigation of the spin structure of the nucleon as it will be done by the HERMES experiment and the investigation of the weak interaction with a polarized beam as planned by the collider experiments H1 and ZEUS.

Electrons in a storage ring become naturally transversely polarized due to the Sokolov-Ternov effect [1]. Spin diffusion and depolarizing resonances counteract the polarization build-up. Empirical correction schemes have been invented which allow to optimize the degree of polarization, making use of the fast and reliable HERA Compton polarimeter [2].

As the experiments require longitudinal polarization, a spin-rotator is needed in front and behind each interaction region in order to rotate the spin direction from the vertical to the longitudinal direction and vice versa.

From the Thomas-BMT equation [3] follows that the precession angle of the spin in a dipole at the HERA energy of 27.52 GeV is 62.5 times larger than the orbit deflection angle by the same magnet. A combination of horizontal and vertical dipole magnets allows to rotate the polarization axis from the vertical to the longitudinal direction (see figure 1). The 'mini'-rotator scheme from Buon and Steffen [4] achieves this with a closed vertical bump of only 22 cm height.

As spin rotators are strong sources for depolarization, several measures were taken to minimize the effect of the rotators: there are no quadrupoles between the dipoles of each rotator, the beam optics between the rotators is horizontally spin-matched (i.e. the effect of the quadrupole fields on the spin for electrons with horizontal betatron motions is compensated) and the beam optics in the ring is vertically spin-matched from rotator to rotator.

After activating the spin rotators in May 94 for the first time, polarization went up to $P = 55\%$ (figure 2). With additional fine tuning it was possible to obtain longitudinal polarization of about $P \approx 65\%$. The polarization was reproducible and stable.

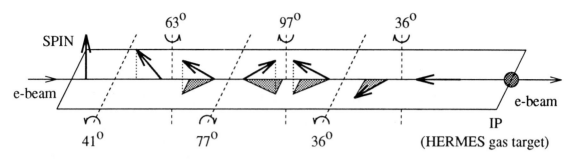

Figure 1. Alternating vertical and horizontal dipole magnets rotate the spin from the vertical to the longitudinal direction and vice versa.

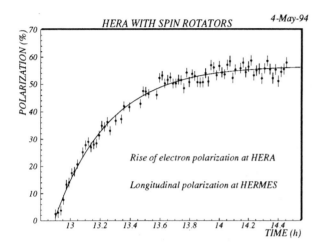

Figure 2. Polarization rise with activated spin rotators. Transverse polarisation above 55% is measured with the HERA polarimeter. Spin rotators turn the polarization vector into longitudinal direction at the HERMES experimental area.

2. Status of HERMES

The HERMES experiment will start data taking in spring 1995 and is currently assembling the detector. To study the spin structure of the nucleon, a polarized internal gas target will be used [5]. In order to gain experience with the novel technique of a storage cell target an unpolarized version of the target has already been installed this year [6].

The elliptical storage cell is constructed from 125 μm thin ultra-pure (99.995%) aluminum with a size of $29.0 \times 9.8 \times 400$ mm^3. The cells for the final experiment will have the same elliptical opening but a reduced wall thickness. In order to prevent wake field excitation in the storage cell and resonant RF losses in the target chamber, a metallic mesh has been installed making a smooth, electrically connected transition between the elliptical storage cell and the thin walled beam pipe.

In order to prevent synchrotron radiation from hitting the cell walls and thereby heating up the cell or producing background in the detector, a two-stage collimator system has been installed. It has elliptical openings of 13.0×5.2 mm^2 resp. 17.2×6.0 mm^2. Its

geometry is selected such that only double scattered synchrotron radiation may enter the detector. The HERMES collimators are the smallest apertures in HERA. The collimators are made out of 12 cm thick tungsten and can absorb the showers that are produced by halo electrons.

Test measurements during electron beam operation at HERA have given the following results:

- The small apertures of the collimators do not reduce the lifetime of the stored beam.
- There is no heating of the storage cell due to synchrotron radiation or RF bunch fields.
- The background from synchrotron radiation and from electromagnetic showers is tolerable. More detailed results will come from measurements which are currently running.
- A reduction of the lifetime of the stored beam is observed when gas is injected into the storage cell. The reduction agrees with the calculations. In the final experiment the life time limitation due to the HERMES target will be better than 20h for the anticipated densities of the polarized targets.

As there is no major interference between the collider experiments and the internal target experiment, HERMES can take data during the whole running period of HERA in 1995. It is planned to collect high statistics on inclusive and semi-inclusive deep inelastic scattering from several polarized target configurations (H, D, ^{3}He) during 1995.

References

[1] A.A. Sokolov and I.M. Ternov, Sov. Phys. Doklady **8**, 1203 (1964).
[2] D. Barber et al., Nucl. Instr. Meth. **A329** (1993) 79; M. Düren, *The HERA Polarimeter*, Proc. of 10th Int. Symp. of High Energy Spin Physics, Nov. 1992, Nagoya; D. Barber et al., Nucl. Instr. Meth. **A338** (1994) 166.
[3] V.Bargman, L. Michel, V. Telegdi, Phys. Rev. Lett. **2** (1959) 435.
[4] J. Buon and K. Steffen, Nucl. Instr. Meth. **A245** (1986) 248.
[5] HERMES Collaboration, *Technical Design Report*, DESY-PRC 93/06 (1993)
[6] K. Zapfe, *The HERMES Experiment at HERA*; Proc. of the conf. 'The heart of the Matter', June 1994, Chateau de Blois.

Parallel Session Pa-7

Neutrino Masses, Mixing and Oscillations

Conveners: K. Winter (CERN)
A. Smirnov (ICTP)

Scientific secretaries: N. Brook
F. Thomson (reserve)

Paper presented at XXVII Int. Conf. on High Energy Physics: Session Pa-7
Glasgow, UK, 20–27 July 1994

Early Results from the LSND Neutrino Experiment

Richard L. Imlay

Physics Department, Louisiana State University, Baton Rouge, LA 70803, U.S.A.

Representing the LSND Collaboration[‡]

Abstract

The Liquid Scintillator Neutrino Detector (LSND) at the Los Alamos Meson Physics Facility (LAMPF) took its first data in 1993. Below 60 MeV clear signals are seen for neutrino-electron elastic scattering, for ν_eC scattering and for 15.1 MeV gammas from the neutral current excitation of ^{12}C. We have analyzed a sample of $\nu_\mu + C \longrightarrow \mu^- + X$ events near threshold and observe a rate less than half of that given by a Fermi gas calculation. LSND's primary goals are to search for $\bar{\nu}_\mu \longrightarrow \bar{\nu}_e$ and $\nu_\mu \longrightarrow \nu_e$ oscillations with high sensitivity. For the $\bar{\nu}_\mu \longrightarrow \bar{\nu}_e$ oscillation channel we look for the reaction $\bar{\nu}_e + p \longrightarrow e^+ + n$. We see an excess of events above the estimated background.

The Liquid Scintillator Neutrino Detector (LSND) experiment consists of a cylindrical tank approximately 8.5 m long by 5.5 m in diameter. On the inside surface of the tank are mounted 1220 8 inch Hammamatsu phototubes, and the tank is filled with 180 tons of liquid scintillator consisting of mineral oil and 0.031 g/l of b-PBD. The low scintillator concentration allows the detection of both Cerenkov light and scintillation light. Surrounding the detector tank is a liquid-scintillator veto shield which tags cosmic ray muons.

[‡]*K.McIlhany*,[a] I. Stancu,[a] W. Strossman,[a] G. J. VanDalen,[a] W. Vernon,[b] D. Bauer,[c] D. Caldwell,[c] A. Lu,[c] S. Yellin,[c] D. Smith,[d] A. Eisner,[e] Y. Wang,[e] I. Cohen,[f] R. D. Bolton,[g] R. Burman,[g] J. Donahue,[g] F. Federspiel,[g] G. T. Garvey,[g] W. C. Louis,[g] V. Sandberg,[g] M. Schillaci,[g] D. H. White,[g] D. Whitehouse,[g] R. Imlay,[h] W. Metcalf,[h] R. M. Gunasingha,[h] B. Boyd,[i] K. Johnston,[i] B. B. Dieterle,[j] R. Reeder,[j] M. Albert,[g] J. Hill,[g] A. Fazely,[l] C. Athanassopoulos,[m] L. B. Auerbach,[m] V. Highland,[m] J. Margulies,[m] D. Works,[m] Y. Xiao[m]

[a] University of California, Riverside
[b] University of California, San Diego and IIRPA
[c] University of California, Santa Barbara
[d] Embry-Riddle Aeronautical University
[e] University of California IIRPA [f] Linfield College
[g] Los Alamos National Laboratory
[h] Louisiana State University [i] Louisiana Tech University
[j] University of New Mexico [l] Southern University
[m] Temple University

A typical 45 MeV electron can be reconstructed with a position resolution of $\sim$ 25 cm, an angular resolution of $\sim$ 15 degrees, and an energy resolution of $\sim$ 6%. Excellent particle identification for particles above and below Cerenkov threshold is obtained through the fit to the Cerenkov cone and from the time distribution of the scintillation light, which is relatively slower for particles below Cerenkov threshold [1]. The energy distribution. for a sample of electrons from cosmic muon decays in the tank is used to obtain the energy resolution (6% at 50MeV) and calibration.

A particle identification parameter, PID, is employed which is defined as the product of three quantities: the chisquare of the fit to the Cerenkov cone, the chisquare of the position fit (which minimizes the time to each hit phototube), and the fraction of hit phototubes with time more than 12 ns after the fitted time corrected for time-of-flight to the phototube. The PID distributions for electrons from cosmic-ray muon decay and for cosmic-ray neutrons with electron equivalent energies in the range $38 < E_e < 56$ MeV shows excellent electron/neutron particle separation of about 10^{-3}.

The detector is located at a mean distance of 29 m from the A6 LAMPF beam stop and at an average angle of 12 degrees relative to the incident proton direction. The beam stop consists of a 20 cm water target positioned 1 m upstream of a Cu beam dump. The neutrinos arise from pion and muon decay and

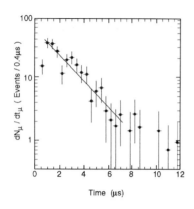

Figure 1. Muon decay time

can be separated into two types - those from decay in flight and those from decay at rest. The decay-at-rest neutrino energy spectrum has a maximum energy of 52.8 MeV, while the pion decay-in-flight spectrum has an average energy of 100 MeV with an energy tail extending beyond 250 MeV. As π^- produced in the beam stop are strongly absorbed, the decay-at-rest neutrino flux is almost entirely due to ν_μ from π^+ decay and $\bar{\nu}_\mu$ and ν_e from μ^+ decay. The neutrino flux is calculated from measured pion cross sections [2] and the uncertainty in the decay-at-rest and decay-in-flight neutrino fluxes are estimated to be 7% and 15%, respectively.

The data sample corresponds to an exposure of 1625 Coulombs of protons on the A6 beam-stop during a 1.5 month run in the autumn of 1993. The average beam duty factor was 7%.

We have measured the quasielastic reaction $C(\nu_\mu, \mu^-)X$ near threshold using the decay-in-flight ν_μ beam. The experimental signature of a quasielastic event consists of a muon and electron occurring within $17\mu s$ of each other, figure 1, and reconstrucing within a distance of 200 cm of each other, and at least 30 cm from the locus of the PMT faces. Almost all of the background is suppressed by the anticounter. In addition, the energy of the muon is required to be less than 120 MeV, limited by the upper energy of the neutrino flux, and the energy of the corresponding electron to be less than 60 MeV and above the approximately 13 MeV. The selection criteria yield a relatively pure event sample of 270 events of which 40 ± 2 are cosmic ray background, as estimated from the event sample obtained with the LAMPF beam off. The most important beam-related background comes from $\bar{\nu}_\mu + p \rightarrow \mu^+ + n$, which is estimated by calculation to give 14 ± 5 events. The sum of all other neutrino related background is at

the 5% level.

The light observed from quasielastic events comes from both the produced proton and the μ^-. Further, the light output as a function of particle energy differs for the muons and protons. Because it is not possible to recover the energy of either the muon or the incident neutrino given only the total light deposited, we show in figure 2 the visible energy spectrum of the quasielastic events, measured in number of photoelectrons. The

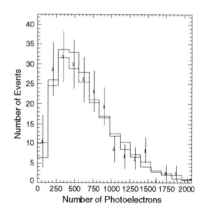

Figure 2. Visible energy spectrum

visible energy spectrum predicted by a Coloumb-corrected Fermi gas model[3] normalized to the number of observed events, indicates that the shape of the spectrum is not particularly sensitive to the nuclear dynamics involved in the interaction.

The observed number of events corresponds to a flux-averaged cross section of $(8.4 \pm 0.7 \pm 1.6) \times 10^{-39} \text{cm}^2$ in the energy region $120 < E_\nu < 240 \text{MeV}$. The flux weighted average neutrino energy is 180MeV. The Coulomb corrected Fermi gas model gives a beam-averaged cross section of $2.4 \times 10^{-39} \text{cm}^2$. An *ab initio* calculation based on a continuum random phase approximation[4] adjusted to agree with the μ^- capture rate on ^{12}C yields the value $2.0 \times 10^{-39} \text{cm}^2$. An earlier calculation[5] gives $1.1 \times 10^{-39} \text{cm}^2$.

In summary, the visible energy distribution of the final μ^-p state from $^{12}C(\nu_\mu, \mu^-)X$ has been measured and seen not to be especially sensitive to details of the structure of ^{12}C. The cross section near threshold for the reaction, on the other hand, suggests the presence of nuclear effects not accounted for in the Fermi gas model, or in a recent *ab initio* independent particle model calculation.

Low energy ν_e, ν_μ and $\bar{\nu}_\mu$ arise from stopping π^+ and μ^+ in the beam dump. Figure 3 shows a preliminary distribution of electrons with less than 50 MeV in the detector. The cosmic ray background has been removed by subtracting a properly normalized distribution of events obtained with the beam off. The largest contribution of events in figure 3 comes from the charged

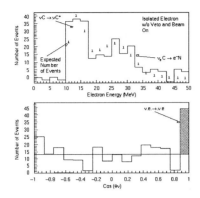

Figure 3. The electron (a)energy and (b)Cosθ

current reaction $\nu_e + {}^{12}\mathrm{C} \Longrightarrow e^- + {}^{12}\mathrm{N}$ (below 35 MeV) and from the 15.1 MeV gamma from the neutral current reaction $\nu + {}^{12}\mathrm{C} \Longrightarrow \nu + {}^{12}\mathrm{C}^*$. The angular distribution of the events shows the contribution from neutrino-electron elastic scattering in the forward direction. A small contribution also arises from ν_e scattering on ${}^{13}\mathrm{C}$.

A primary goal of LSND is to search for $\bar{\nu}_\mu$ to $\bar{\nu}_e$ oscillations with high sensitivity. We look for the reaction $\bar{\nu}_e + p \Longrightarrow e^+ + n$. We require a positron between 38 MeV and 56 Mev in coincidence with a 2.2 MeV gamma ray from neutron absorption on a free proton within 0.5 ms. We search above 38 MeV because

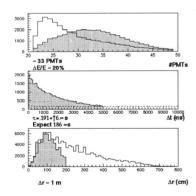

Figure 4. The response of the detector to 2.2MeV gammas from cosmic ray neutrons

the background is expected to be small in this region (see figure 4) and because the $\bar{\nu}_\mu$ spectrum peaks in this region.

A sample of 2.2 MeV gammas associated with cosmic ray neutrons was analysed to determine the detector response to these gammas. Many of these events

have several gammas. Figure 4 shows that the energy resolution is about 20%. The distribution of the time of the gamma spatially closest to the neutron shows the expected shape. Also shown is the distance of the earliest gamma from the neutron position. For the oscillation search we require a gamma within 2m and 0.5ms. The accidental rate of such gamma is 10% and thus background processes without a neutron are reduced by a factor of ten by requiring a gamma.

Figure 5 shows 8 electrons with an associated gamma in the energy region 38 MeV to 56 MeV . Present estimates of backgrounds yield about one event. We are

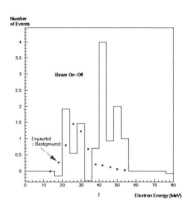

Figure 5. Elctron energy for events with associated gammas within 2.0m and 0.5ms

studying possible backgrounds while looking forward to additional data.

LSND is scheduled to start data taking again in August and anticipates obtaining three times as much integrated beam as was obtained in our first run. Many minor improvements or upgrades have been made that should improve the quality of the data. For measurements using decay in flight neutrinos, such as the $\nu_\mu \Longrightarrow \nu_e$ oscillation search, we anticipate reducing the cosmic ray background by a factor of 2 or more by measuring the event time relative to the 5 ns time structure of the LAMPF beam.

This work is supported by U.S. Department of enengy and National science foundation.

References

[1] R.A. Reeder *et al.*, Nucl. Instr. Meth. **A334** (1993) 353.
[2] R.L. Burman, M.E. Potter and E.S. Smith, Nucl. Instr. Meth. **A291** (1990) 621.
[3] T.K. Gaisser and J.S. O'Connell, Phys. Rev. **D34** (1986) 822; ${}^1 2C$ nucleus is modeled with binding energy 25 MeV, Fermi momentum 220 MeV/c and 6 neutrons.
[4] E. Kolbe, K. Langanke and S. Krewald, Phys. Rev. **C49** (1994) 1122.
[5] C.W. Kim and S.L., Mintz, Phys. Rev. **C31** (1985) 274.

Search for neutrino oscillations at KARMEN

B. Seligmann

Queen Mary and Westfield College, Mile End Road, London E1 4NS

On behalf of the KARMEN Collaboration[‡]

Abstract

The KARMEN experiment is using a high-resolution 56 ton liquid scintillation calorimeter to study neutrino-nucleus interactions (ν_μ, ν_e, $\bar{\nu}_\mu$) and to search for appearance oscillations ($\nu_\mu \to \nu_e$, $\bar{\nu}_\mu \to \bar{\nu}_e$) at the ISIS spallation neutron facility. Being an almost wholly active target of ^{12}C and ^{1}H nuclei, the calorimeter introduces a unique, spectroscopic quality to neutrino detection at energies from 2 MeV to 53 MeV. Duty factors below 2.5×10^{-4} enable the effective identification of cosmogenic background events. Hence, after four years of data taking and analysis (4×10^{13} neutrinos per cm^2) all oscillation candidates can be convincingly attributed to various background processes. Exclusion contours are presented eliminating, at 90% CL, $\sin^2 2\theta > 0.048$ (for $\nu_\mu \to \nu_e$) and $\sin^2 2\theta > 0.0062$ (for $\bar{\nu}_\mu \to \bar{\nu}_e$) for $\Delta m^2 > 1 eV^2$.

1. Introduction

Searches for neutrino-flavour oscillations have so far been abortive and are usually summarized as exclusion contours in the ($\sin^2 2\Theta$, Δm^2) parameter space, where $\sin^2 2\Theta$ represents the strength of neutrino mixing and Δm^2 is the mass difference between neutrino eigenstates [1]. For large Δm^2 the boundary line of an excluded sector runs towards

$$\sin^2 2\Theta = 2 P_{excl}. \qquad (1)$$

The minimum oscillation probability to be excluded, P_{excl}, depends on the characteristics of the particular experiment and on statistics,

$$P_{excl} = N_{excl} (90\% CL) / N_f. \qquad (2)$$

‡ *Kernforschungszentrum Karlsruhe and Universität Karlsruhe*: B. Armbruster, G. Drexlin, V. Eberhard, K. Eitel, H. Gemmeke, W. Grandegger (now at INFN, Frascati, Italy), M. Kleifges, J. Kleinfeller, R. Maschuw (now at ISKP, Universität Bonn, Germany), P. Plischke, J. Rapp, J. Wochele, J. Wolf, S. Wölfle (now at INFN), B. Zeitnitz; *Universität Erlangen-Nürnberg*: B.E. Bodmann, E. Finckh, J. Hößl, W. Kretschmer, O. Stumm; *Queen Mary and Westfield College, London*: J.A. Edgington; *Oxford University*: N.E. Booth.

The number, N_f, of expected events for full oscillation ($P = 1$) is determined by the flux of primary neutrinos into the detection volume and by the neutrino detection efficiency. The number of oscillation events to be excluded, N_{excl}, derives from the total number of measured oscillation candidates and the number of background events contained therein [2]. In this context, the KARMEN [3] oscillation results presented in this paper profit considerably from the efforts towards detector calibration, flux normalisation and background control which were neccessary to obtain precision results on neutrino-nucleus interactions [4] from the same data set.

2. ISIS neutrinos and the KARMEN detector

The KARMEN experiment uses the ISIS facility at the Rutherford Appleton Laboratory (Oxfordshire, UK) — a spallation target driven by a pulsed, 800 MeV/200 μA proton beam extracted at 50 Hz — as its neutrino source. The beam stop delivers equal fluxes of ν_μ, ν_e and $\bar{\nu}_\mu$ from π^+ and μ^+ decay at rest, with the unambiguous energy spectra and time distributions shown in figure 1.

π^- and μ^- are captured by the heavy target nuclei (U or Ta), so that source contamination with $\bar{\nu}_e$ from the $\pi^- \rightarrow \mu^-$ decay chain is limited to 8×10^{-4}.

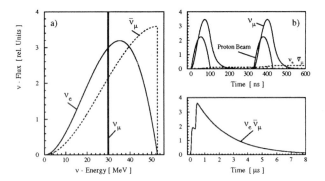

Figure 1. Energy and time structure of ISIS neutrinos.

The KARMEN detector[5], located at a mean distance of 17.5 m from the beam dump, is a segmented liquid-scintillator calorimeter with a resolution of

$$\sigma(E)/E = 11.5\%/\sqrt{E(MeV)}, \qquad (3)$$

for energy and $\sigma(t) = 0.7$ ns for relative timing and position measurements. Of the 56 tonne total mass of the calorimeter, 96% is hydrocarbon scintillator while 0.1% is gadolinium (as Gd_2O_3-coated paper within the lucite segmentation walls) which ensures neutron detection efficiencies in the region of 20% (depending on cuts) with a detector threshold as high as 2 MeV. Layers of steel shielding (6 000 tons) and veto counters together with the extremely low ISIS duty factors (1.5×10^{-5} for ν_μ , 2.5×10^{-4} for ν_e and $\bar{\nu}_\mu$) allow the effective suppression of cosmogenic background.

3.   Neutrino oscillation results

3.1.   Search for $\nu_\mu \rightarrow \nu_e$ - appearance

The detection process for electron neutrinos is based on the exclusive charged current reaction $^{12}C(\nu_e, e^-)^{12}N_{g.s.}$ [4]. The oscillation of a monoenergetic ν_μ ($E_\nu = 29.8$ MeV) to ν_e would induce a spatially correlated, delayed coincidence between a monoenergetic electron of 12.5 MeV kinetic energy during the prompt ν_μ-time window and a positron with an energy of up to 16.3 MeV from ^{12}N decay during the subsequent beam pause. Detailed Monte Carlo simulations and measurements of cosmic muon induced reactions show that even with a narrow cut on the visible electron energy (10 - 14 MeV) a detection efficiency of 82% is maintained. Electrons are looked for in two time windows (0 - 110 ns, 330 ns - 440 ns) limiting the relative contamination with primary ν_e to 3.22×10^{-3}.

The sequential positron is expected not further than 0.5 m away from the initial event, in the time

interval from 0.5 - 36.0 ms, with a visible energy between 3.5 MeV and 15.0 MeV. The sequence is vetoed by cosmic ray activity in the $20\,\mu s$ preceding the prompt part and in the $10\,\mu s$ before the delayed part of the coincidence. **Flux independence** for the oscillation probabilty P ($\nu_\mu \rightarrow \nu_e$) is obtained by applying the same conditions to the simultaneously present ν_e from μ^+-decay in the ISIS target.

The analysis of a data set accumulated between June 1990 and May 1994 (6 021 Coulomb of protons on target) gives a combined efficiency of 31.7% and produces a total of **3 candidate events** with the required signature, to be compared to 158.4 events expected for full oscillation. Cosmogenic background measured with high statistics between beam pulses contributes only 0.10 ± 0.02 events, whereas ν_e - **contamination** from μ^+-decay amounts to 4.5 ± 0.2 events.

3.2.   Search for $\bar{\nu}_\mu \rightarrow \bar{\nu}_e$ - appearance

The signature for $\bar{\nu}_\mu \rightarrow \bar{\nu}_e$ oscillations at KARMEN is, again, a spatially correlated delayed coincidence :

$$\bar{\nu}_\mu \xrightarrow{osc} \bar{\nu}_e + p \rightarrow n + e^+$$
$$\downarrow$$
$$Gd(n, \gamma)$$

The flux-averaged cross section for the initial inverse β-decay has been calculated to be as high as 1.084×10^{-40} cm^2 [6] and implies 20 580 events expected for P=1 and 100% detection efficiency, compared to 500 in the $\nu_\mu \rightarrow \nu_e$ case. Changes in the energy spectrum of the positrons due to the dependence of the oscillation probability on the mass term Δm^2 are detectable and included in our analysis. Energy and time windows on the positrons (20 MeV - 50 MeV / $0.5\,\mu s$ - 6.5 μs) result in an efficiency of 58% for full oscillation.

For the secondary neutron detection the capture reaction $Gd(n, \gamma)$ is preferable over $H(n, \gamma)$, since it releases on average three gamma quanta with a total energy of about 8 MeV, well above low-energy background.   Due to its unrivalled capture cross section for thermal neutrons, $\sigma_{therm} = 49\,000$ b, the small amount of gadolinium in the KARMEN detector is sufficient to maintain a capture rate competitive with n-p capture.   The neutron detection efficiency was studied in detail, including an analysis of the reaction $^{12}C(\mu^-, \nu_\mu n)^{11}B$ as a cosmic-ray induced process which causes a delayed coincidence similar to our oscillation signature. Neutrons are captured by Gd in the KARMEN detector after an average 107 μs. Hence, the time interval, 20 μs to 250 μs, which we allow for neutron detection, leads to a time-cut efficiency of 69% With a coincidence volume for positron and neutron detection of $45 \times 45 \times 60$ cm^3 we obtain a total efficiency of 17.6%.

Applying all cuts and the same deadtimes after cosmics activity as in the $\nu_\mu \rightarrow \nu_e$ analysis (20 μs, 10μs) we find **25 candidate events** for $\bar{\nu}_\mu \rightarrow \bar{\nu}_e$ oscillation The cosmogenic background (mainly neutrons from the detector walls) is measured off-beam and corresponds to 25.3 events in the oscillation window. There is also a small background due to charged current ($^{12}C(\nu_e, e^-)^{12}N_{g.s.}$) interactions which is measured to be 2.3 events, giving a total of **27.6 background events** to be expected. Hence, all of the surviving 25 events can be attributed to cosmogenic and neutrino-induced background.

3.3. *Probability limits and exclusion plots*

From the three $\nu_\mu \rightarrow \nu_e$ candidates with a background of 4.5 ± 0.2 we calculate that any more than 3.7 non-background events are excluded. This corresponds to an upper limit for the oscillation probability,

$$P_{excl}(\nu_\mu \rightarrow \nu_e) = 2.4 \times 10^{-2} \, (90\% \, \text{CL}) \qquad (4)$$

and to the exclusion contour plotted as one of the solid lines in figure 2.

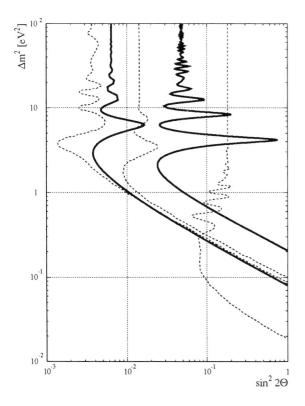

Figure 2. Present KARMEN oscillation limits (solid lines, r.h.: $\nu_\mu \rightarrow \nu_e$, l.h.: $\bar{\nu}_\mu \rightarrow \bar{\nu}_e$); broken lines (from left to right): BNL776, E645, GOESGEN (for references, see [1]).

In the $\bar{\nu}_\mu \rightarrow \bar{\nu}_e$ case, there is sufficient statistics to perform a maximum likelihood analysis based on the 2.2 μs decay time for the prompt oscillation signal over a level, cosmic-ray induced background. Initially we restrict the likelihood fit to positron energies between 30 MeV and 50 MeV, where the ratio of detection efficiency to background rate is best. There remain 0.1 ± 2.9 non-background events, excluding any more than 5.0 events attributable to $\bar{\nu}_\mu \rightarrow \bar{\nu}_e$ transitions at a 90 % confidence level, whereas for full oscillation we would expect 1629 coincidences. In a second fit we also use the additional information contained in the positron energy spectrum between 20 MeV and 50 MeV. Both methods lead to the same upper limit for the oscillation probability,

$$P_{excl}(\bar{\nu}_\mu \rightarrow \bar{\nu}_e) = 3.1 \times 10^{-3} \, (90\% \, \text{CL}) \qquad (5)$$

clearly excluding a mixing strength of 1% for most of the parameter space shown in figure 2.

4. Conclusion

In both oscillation channels investigated at KARMEN the measured background exceeds the total number of candidate events. The $\nu_\mu \rightarrow \nu_e$ result is fully independent of the primary neutrino flux, but limited by statistics. The sensitivity to $\bar{\nu}_\mu \rightarrow \bar{\nu}_e$ oscillations is intrinsically higher due to the larger cross section for the $\bar{\nu}_e$- detection process. Here, our negative statement concerning the appearance of oscillation events is reconfirmed in two stages of a maximum-likelihood analysis. After two more years of data taking we expect to exceed the presently best limit for neutrino mixing (BNL776, see figure 2).

Acknowledgements

We acknowledge the financial support from the Bundesministerium für Forschung und Technologie and from the Science and Engineering Research Council. We thank the Rutherford Appleton Laboratory, in particular the staff of the ISIS Division, for their hospitality and assistance.

References

[1] L. Oberauer and F. von Feilitzsch, Rep. Prog. Phys. **55** (1992) 1093 (and references therein).
[2] Particle Data Group, Review of Particle Properties, Phys. Rev. **D 45** (1992) III.40.
[3] B. Zeitnitz (KARMEN collab.), Prog. in Part. and Nucl. Phys. **32** (1994) 351.
[4] B.E. Bodmann *et al.*(KARMEN collab.), Phys. Lett. **B 332** (1994) 251.
[5] G. Drexlin *et al.*, Nucl. Instr. and Meth. **A 289** (1990) 490.
[6] G. Drexlin (KARMEN collab.), Prog. in Part. and Nucl. Phys. **32** (1994) 375.

Search for Neutrino Oscillations at 15, 40 and 95 meters from a nuclear power reactor at Bugey

Elemér NAGY[‡]

Centre de Physique des Particules de Marseille,
Faculté des Sciences de Luminy

On behalf of the BUGEY-3 Collaboration

Abstract

High statistics measurements of $\bar{\nu}_e$ energy spectra are presented, carried out at 15, 40 and 95 meters from a 2800 MW reactor, using detection modules filled with ^6Li -loaded liquid scintillator. No oscillations have been observed. Exclusion zones for oscillation parameters are deduced from the observed consistency of the spectra at the 3 distances. The minimum excluded values of the δm^2 and $sin^2 2\theta$ parameters are $1 \cdot 10^{-2}$ eV^2 and $2 \cdot 10^{-2}$ (at 90% CL), respectively.

1. Introduction

The Bugey nuclear power plant runs four Pressurized Water Reactors (PWR) of 2800 thermal MW, each producing $5 \cdot 10^{20}$ $\bar{\nu}_e$ per second. We present here a measurement of the neutrino spectra performed at 15, 40 and 95 meters using a novel neutron detection technique. Three identical detection modules have been used: one (module 1) located under the reactor building, at 15 meters from the core, and two (module 2 and module 3) outside the reactor building, inside a concrete bunker 40 meters away from the core. The data taken with module 1 were also used to extract the neutrino signal from another reactor located at 95 meters when the nearest one was stopped. We have recorded about 150 000 events, the highest number of electron-anti-neutrinos ever detected. In addition, in about 40% of the whole data taking period we have carried out the measurements *simultaneously* at the two locations. This has the advantage, when comparing data at two distances, of being less sensitive to the modification of the source spectrum due to the evolution with time of the fuel composition.

‡ E-mail: nagy@frcpn11.in2p3.fr

2. Detection, Calibration and Monitoring

The detection principle is shown in Figure 1. The signature of a neutrino event is:

• a prompt light pulse from the positron which can be related to the positron kinetic energy, E_{e+}, and thus to the neutrino energy, $E_{\bar{\nu}} \simeq E_{e+} + 1.8$ MeV

• a delayed (by 30 μs on the average) and mono-energetic light pulse due to the produced neutron which is thermalized and captured with high probability by the ^6Li nuclei in the liquid. It then gives rise to an alpha and a tricium of well defined kinetic energy in the final state.

• An additional signature is obtained by the good pulse shape discrimination (PSD) property of the scintillator. As shown in Figure 2, the quantity

$$R_{PSD} = \frac{delayed\ charge}{total\ charge} \qquad (1)$$

can be used with good efficiency to distinguish heavy particles (alphas, tritium or slow protons) from electrons for the same total number of photoelectrons.

Each detection cell was calibrated every month using an $Am\text{-}Be$ source emitting neutrons and $4.4 MeV$ gammas. A dedicated anti-multi-Compton trigger

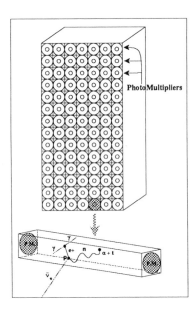

Figure 1. The schematic view of one detector module

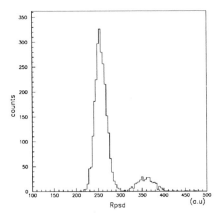

Figure 2. Distribution of the R_{PSD} ratio obtained using an *Am-Be* source: the peak at low R_{PSD} value is due to Compton electrons, the one at high R_{PSD} value is due to recoil protons at the e^- equivalent energy of 4.3 MeV. The delayed charge in Equ.(1) was obtained by integrating the pulse with a gate delayed by 25 ns.

helped to enhance the Compton edge at $4.2 MeV$ from which we deduced our energy scale and the electron (positron) R_{PSD} value at this energy. We calculated the overall uncertainty on the energy scale to be $0.034 MeV$ at 4.2 MeV. Our energy resolution at 4.2 MeV is 6% which was obtained from the upper half width of the observed Compton peak. A separate measurement with different gamma sources allowed us to verify the linearity of the whole opto-electronic chain.

By triggering on recoil protons we tagged neutrons emitted by the *Am-Be* source to determine all

15 m		40 m		95 m	
ON	OFF	ON	OFF	ON	OFF
92519	3746	47054	11625	1932	259

Table 1. Event statistics

parameters of the neutron capture by ^6Li nuclei: the position and width of the peak of the capture energy, E_c, their variation along the longitudinal cell axis, as well as the PSD peak position and its width.

The overall gains of the opto-electronic chains were measured every day with the help of a monitored nitrogen spark-gap light pulser. The light pulses were brought simultaneously through optical fibers to the 98 cells and to several reference PMT's and photodiodes. This procedure permits interpolation of the monthly calibrations and thereby follow up and correct for any variation in the transparency of the liquid or in the PMT gains.

3.   Data Reduction, Background Subtraction

The trigger rate was typically 3 Hz in each of the detector modules. Triggers were rejected if a cosmic ray counter gave a signal in the preceding $100 \mu s$. Using results of neutron calibrations, an elliptical cut at 2.2 sigmas in the E_c–$R_{PSD}^{neutron}$ plane was applied to neutron candidates. The positron energy was required to be between 1 and 6 MeV with no simultaneous energy deposit bigger than 1.5 MeV outside the positron cell. A 3 σ cut was performed on the $R_{PSD}^{e^+}$ of the positron candidate. Finally, it was required that the positron candidate should precede the neutron candidate by at most 60 μs and the two candidates should be either in the same cell or in adjacent cells having a common face. Typically, in module 1 we have observed $\sim$ 60 candidate events per hour. The total number of events used in the final analysis is shown in Table 1 for reactor on and off and for the three distances, respectively.

There are two main types of background. The *accidental* background rate at the first order is equal to the rate of events where the neutron preceeds the light particle (electron). Data taken during reactor-off periods gave us the rate of the *correlated* component of the background once the accidental background is subtracted.

The observed event rates were corrected for the deadtime of the detector modules, for losses due to electronics or HV power failures in some detection channels. The signal event rate was obtained by subtracting first the accidental background from the data separately in the reactor-on and off periods. Next, the remaining events from the reactor-off period were subtracted from the remaining reactor-on events. The

	15 m	40 m	95 m
Signal/h	62.62 ± 0.23	15.39 ± 0.17	1.33 ± 0.19
Backg/h	2.50 ± 0.07	6.94 ± 0.09	1.94 ± 0.18
S/B	25.0	2.2	0.7

Table 2. Signal and background rates

actual signal event rates, the total background rates and the signal-to-background ratios above $1 MeV$ are summarized in Table 2 for 15, 40 and 95 meters, respectively.

4. Results

In order to compare the data with the oscillation hypothesis we have carried out a detailed Monte Carlo simulation of the signal events including:

• simulation of the neutrino flux and spectrum for each day of the data taking,

• simulation of the neutrino interaction in hydrogen together with the capture of the produced neutron and the detection of the products of the capture,

• simulation of the detection of the positron and the measurement of its energy.

Using this simulation we have calculated the normalisation error of the obtained neutrino spectra to be 5 % at each detection position. The normalisation error on the *ratio* of spectra measured at two different positions is only 2 % since here the uncertainties of the initial neutrino flux do not enter.

Figure 3 shows the *ratios* of the positron spectra at $40/15m$ and at $95/15m$. As can be seen, the ratios exhibit no variation with the positron energy, moreover their fitted values of 0.140 ± 0.001 and 0.025 ± 0.001 agree within the quoted normalisation error with $(15/40)^2$ and $(15/95)^2$, the ratios of the solid angles upon which the detectors are seen from the center of the reactor cores. They are therefore perfectly compatible with *no oscillation* of the produced anti-neutrinos.

Our conclusion on non-oscillation is further supported by the observed *normalised* spectra which agree within the statistical and systematical errors with the Monte Carlo calculation at all the three distances when assuming no oscillations. Figure 4 shows the obtained exclusion contour using measurements at *all the three distances and informations on the initial neutrino flux*. Also shown are the hitherto excluded area in earlier reactor experiments [*GOESGEN:* G.Zacek *et al.*, Physical Review D34 (1986) 2621; *KRASNOYARSK:* G.S.Vidyakin *et al.*, J. Moscow Phys. Soc. 1 (1991) 85] and the region for a possible $\nu_e - \nu_\mu$ oscillation put forward by the *KAMIOKANDE* collaboration [K.S.Hirata *et al.* Physics Letters B280 (1992) 146].

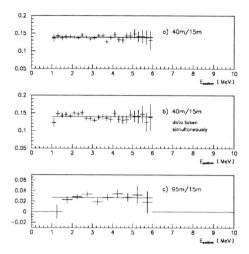

Figure 3. The ratio of the positron energy spectra at $40/15m$ and $95/15m$. Also shown for $40/15m$ the part of the data taken simultaneously which is independent of the fuel evolution of the reactor. The solid lines indicate the result of the fit to a constant line.

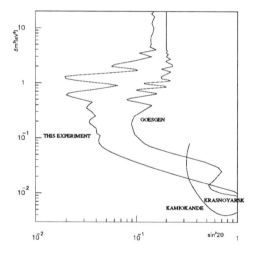

Figure 4. The 90% exclusion contour obtained from the positron energy spectra measured at 40, 15 and 95 metres and using information on the initial neutrino flux. For the other curves see the text.

In conclusion, we have studied neutrino oscillations using a novel neutron detection technique and increased significantly the statistics compared to all previous measurements on reactors. Comparing both the shapes and the integrated values of the positron spectra at 15 m, 40 m and 95 m distances we have increased the exclusion region in the plane of the oscillation parameters with respect to previous experiments. A detailed description is given in the conference paper *Ref. gls0923* with references therein.

Testrun results and present status of the CHORUS experiment

M. de Jong*

NIKHEF-K, Amsterdam NL

CHORUS collaboration, CERN

Abstract

The present status and testrun results of the CHORUS experiment are decribed. The CHORUS experiment is devoted to the measurement of mixing between neutrino flavours. It is being performed at the wide band neutrino beam of the CERN-SPS. A search is made for $\nu_\mu \rightarrow \nu_\tau$ oscillations through the detection of τ's in the final state. With an exposure of 2.4×10^{19} protons, the limits on the mixing angle $sin^2(2\theta) \sim 3 \times 10^{-4}$ for $m_{\nu_\tau}^2 - m_{\nu_\mu}^2 > 50 eV^2$ can be reached.

1. Introduction

Mixing between neutrino flavours has been proposed as a solution to the so-called solar ν puzzle [1]. It has also been pointed out that a non-zero mass of ν's could explain the dark matter in the universe [2]. One may observe neutrino oscillations experimentally through the disappearence of neutrinos with a certain flavour or the appearence of neutrino's with another flavour. The oscillation probabilty is usually written as:

$$P(\nu_a \rightarrow \nu_b) = sin^2(2\theta)sin^2(1.27L/E\Delta m_{ab}^2), \quad (1)$$

where θ is the mixing angle, E the energy of the neutrino (GeV), L the distance between the source and the detector (km) and Δm_{ab}^2 is the difference in mass squared of the neutrinos (eV^2). The neutrino flavours a and b stand for e, μ or τ. In case of negative results, the results are usually presented as exclusion plots. In this, neutrino oscillations are excluded as a function of Δm_{ab}^2 and $sin^2(2\theta)$ (eq. 1), where the boundary varies with the oscillation frequency. The quality of the experiment is given by the minimal probability, P_{min}, at which oscillations might occur. For slow oscillations $(E/L \ll \Delta m_{ab}^2)$, the smallest mass diference is reached when mixing is at its maximum,

i.e. $sin^2(2\theta) = 1$: $\Delta m_{ab}^2 \geq \frac{E}{1.27L}\sqrt{P_{min}}$. For fast oscillations $(E/L \gg \Delta m_{ab}^2)$, effectively half of the original neutrino's have oscillated. The limit on the mixing angle is then $sin^2(2\theta) \geq 2P_{min}$. The CHORUS experiment [3] is designed for the detection of a minimal oscillation probablity of $P_{min}(\nu_\mu \rightarrow \nu_\tau) = 1 \times 10^{-4}$, which is more than an order of magnitude better than at present [4], [5]. If neutrino oscillations occur at the present limit, CHORUS will observe ~ 60 events.

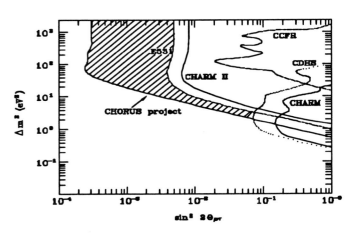

Figure 1. Domains of $\Delta m_{\mu\tau}^2$ and $sin^2(2\theta_{\mu\tau})$ covered by previous experiments and to be explored by CHORUS

* E-mail: MJG@VXCERN.CERN.CH

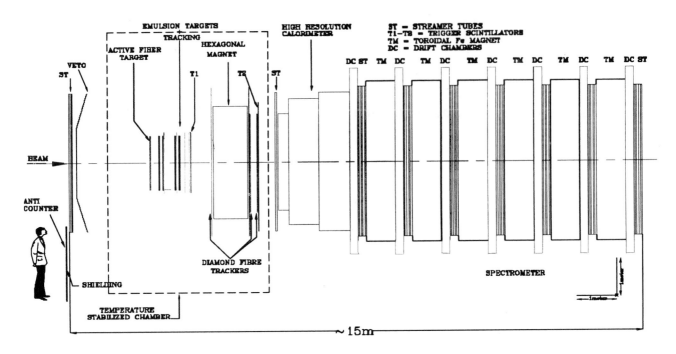

Figure 2. The CHORUS detector

2.   The experiment

The search for $\nu_\mu - \nu_\tau$ oscillations is being performed by detecting the inclusive reaction $\nu_\tau N \rightarrow \tau^- X$ in the ν_μ beam of the CERN-SPS. The detector is shown in figure 2. Here follows a brief description of the detector; a more detailed description is given in [3], [6]. The target region consists of an array of emulsion sheets and scintillating fibers. The particle trajectories reconstructed in the scintillating fibers are projected onto the emulsion sheets which are then scanned in order to find the interaction vertex. The sanning is being performed (semi-)automatically using computer controlled microscopes which are equipped with a high resolution camera. The obtained resolution is such that the decay of a τ particle, typically $500\mu m$ away from the vertex, can be detected. This provides a unique tool to differentiate between ν_μ and ν_τ interactions. In order to reduce the number of events to be scanned in the emulsion, reconstruction of the kinematics of the final state and subsequent event selection is performed a priori. This selection is based on the kinematics of the τ decay. The momentum of muons is measured in the spectrometer, whereas showers from pions and electrons are detected in the calorimeter. Low energy particles ($\leq 3GeV$) are momentum analysed in an aircore magnet upstream of the calorimeter. The readout of the detector is triggered by a combination of hits in the two trigger hodoscopes (T1 and T2) and the absence of a hit in veto plane (V) (see figure 2).

The time correlation between T1 and V is used to distinguish between charged particles accompanying the ν beam and back scattered particles from the neutrino interactions inside the target. The corresponding time distribution $\Delta(T1 - V)$ is shown in figure 3. From this it can be seen that indeed the neutrino triggers are not vetoed by back scattered particles. The fraction of those events is found to be $\sim 15\%$.

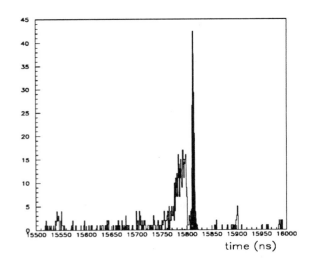

Figure 3. Number of events for incident μ's (black) and ν_μ's (white) as a function of the time difference between hits recorded in the trigger plane (T1) and the veto plane (V).

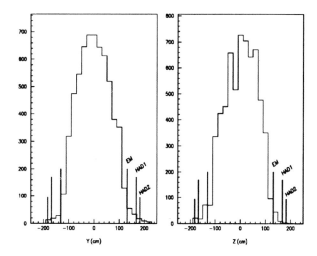

Figure 4. Number of events with an interaction vertex in the calorimeter as a function of Y (left) and Z (right).

Interactions inside the calorimeter [7] are also used to monitor the beam position at the detector. The recontructed vertex positions perpendicular to the incident neutrino beam is shown in figure 4. The beam is found to be well centered. As a consequence, the usefull incident flux is maximised.

3. Prospects

The CHORUS experiment has been taking data since may 1994. During a total of two times 150 days an estimated 500.000 events with charge current interactions will be collected. A sample of $\sim$ 40.000 candidates will then be selected by applying kinematical cuts. For these candidates, the nuclear emulsion target will be scanned (semi-)automatically, yielding results in about 1-2 years.

References

[1] B. Pontecorvo, Zh. Eksp. Teor. Fiz. **34** (1958) 247.
[2] S.S. Gershtein and Ya.B. Zeldovich, Sov. Phys. JETP Lett. **4** (1966) 174.
[3] M. de Jong *et al.*, CERN-PPE/93-131, (CERN preprint).
[4] N. Ushida *et al.*, Phys. Rev. Lett. **57** (1986) 2897.
[5] M. Gruwé *et al.*, Phys. Lett. **B309** (1993) 463.
[6] T. Patzak *et al.*, Proceedings of this conference.
[7] S. Buontempo *et al.*, CERN-PPE/94-19, (CERN preprint).

Paper presented at XXVII Int. Conf. on High Energy Physics: Session Pa-7
Glasgow, UK, 20–27 July 1994

Results of Neutrino Experiments and the Possible Pattern of Neutrino Masses and Mixing*

David O. Caldwell

Physics Department, University of California, Santa Barbara, CA 93106, USA

Abstract

There is increasing evidence for the three indications for neutrino mass: (1) the deficit of solar ν's, (2) the reduction in atmospheric ν_μ's relative to ν_e's, and (3) the need for a hot component of the dark matter of the universe. If these indeed result from neutrino mass, there are only two viable patterns of neutrino masses and mixing which could occur. Either (A) the ν_e, ν_μ, and ν_τ are almost degenerate in mass, being ~ 2 eV each, or (B) the ν_e and a sterile neutrino, ν_s, can be light, while the ν_μ and ν_τ are ~ 3 eV. Case (A) will be established or rejected soon for the much more likely case of Majorana neutrino mass by neutrinoless double beta decay experiments, while case (B) will be tested shortly by the LSND $\nu_\mu \to \nu_e$ oscillation experiment. Preliminary indications from that experiment, if borne out, will have wide-ranging consequences for particle physics and cosmology. Not only would this be the first laboratory demonstration of particle physics beyond the Standard Model, but also it would prove the existence of some hot dark matter and make very likely the mixed dark matter scenario in which the Hubble constant is about 50 km·s^{-1}·Mpc^{-1}, and the universe has critical density.

1. Status of Experiments Indicating Neutrino Mass

Although there is new information from the four experiments which measure fewer electron neutrinos from the sun than solar models predict, there have been no qualitative changes recently. There is good agreement between the SAGE and GALLEX experiments, which show weak (or zero) suppression for low energy ν_e's from the solar p-p process. The Homestake Cl-Ar experiment displays strong suppression at the moderate energy of the ^{7}Be ν_e's, while the Kamiokande experiment measures a moderate suppression of the high energy ^{8}B ν_e's. It is very difficult to produce an astrophysical explanation of these observations because lowering the central temperature of the sun to reduce ν_e production has much more effect on the ^{8}B ν_e's (flux proportional to temperature T^{18}) than on the ^{7}Be ν_e's (flux $\sim$ T^8). Since the Cl-Ar signal since 1986 is appreciably larger than the average over the whole experiment, if only those recent data are used and some nuclear physics inputs are taken to be in error, an astrophysical solution becomes possible. However, as experimental errors get smaller, the solution in terms of neutrino oscillations becomes ever more likely, with favored parameters of $\Delta m_{ei}^2 \sim 6 \times 10^{-6}$ eV^2 and $\sin^2 2\theta_{ei} \sim 7 \times 10^{-3}$. Note that these mass difference and mixing angle parameters are about the same whether the oscillation is $\nu_e \to \nu_\mu$ or $\nu_e \to \nu_s$, a sterile neutrino not having the usual weak interaction.

There is considerable new information on the deficit of ν_μ's relative to ν_e's produced in the atmosphere. For example, the IMB and Kamiokande observations are in excellent agreement, if the same flux calculations are used to interpret both sets of data. On the other hand, the Baksan result does not agree, even if the same fluxes are used. Also, the new Fréjus analysis, in which a larger

* Supported in part by the U.S. Department of Energy.

fiducial volume is used, is in stronger disagreement with Kamiokande, IMB, Soudan II, and now even a low-statistics result from MACRO. Most important are two new pieces of information from Kamiokande, reported at this Conference. First the response of the water Cherenkov detector to electrons and muons has now been checked using a detector mock-up at the Tristan accelerator, validating the ability to separate ν_μ and ν_e events. Second, while previous Kamiokande data were for events < 1.3 GeV and which showed no zenith-angle dependence, a new analysis of multi-GeV events displays a pronounced zenith-angle dependence, corresponding to a distance dependence. Comparing the two sets of data gives information not only over a wide energy range but also over a range of distances from the neutrino source of 20 to 12,000 km. Remarkably, these can be fit by oscillation parameters of $\Delta m_{\mu i}^2 \sim 10^{-2}$ eV^2 and $\sin^2 2\theta_{\mu i} > 0.6$.

If the observations are due to neutrino mass, they result from $\nu_\mu \to \nu_\tau$ and not $\nu_\mu \to \nu_e$. There are now three reasons for this conclusion. First, the recent ν_e disappearance limits from Bugey and Krasnoyarsk (reported at this Conference) taken with the recent Kamiokande results, exclude almost all the $\nu_\mu \to \nu_e$ parameter space. Second, the new Fréjus analysis [1] more than excludes all of the Δm^2-$\sin^2 2\theta$ space for $\nu_\mu \to \nu_e$, while it is marginal for $\nu_\mu \to \nu_\tau$. Third, recent measurements of atmospheric muons over a wide range of momenta and heights in the atmosphere vindicate the higher flux calculations which agree with the number of ν_e's observed but show a deficit of ν_μ's [2].

A third indication of neutrino mass is the apparent need [3] for a hot component of the non-baryonic dark matter which constitutes probably more than 90% of the mass of the universe. The model for matter which best fits the structure of the universe on all distance scales is one having about 20% in the hot component, $\sim 75\%$ in the cold component, and $\sim 5\%$ as baryons. As various measures of this structure are analyzed in more detail, this model has been faring better than others, except for the criticism that it forms structure too late. Very recently this criticism has been refuted by a detailed simulation [4] in which the principle apparently negative information from damped Lyman α systems in quasar absorption spectra (indicating collapsed protogalaxies at redshifts $Z \gtrsim 3$) could be fitted for a hot component no more than 20%. This would imply a total neutrino mass in all species of $m_\nu = 91h^2(0.25\Omega) = 5$ eV if the universe has critical density ($\Omega = 1$) and the Hubble constant, $h = 0.5$ (in units of 100 km$\cdot$s$^{-1}\cdot$Mpc^{-1}).

2. Patterns of Neutrino Masses and Mixing

The conventional assumption is that $\nu_e \to \nu_\mu$ explains the solar neutrino deficit and that ν_τ supplies the hot dark matter. This will be tested by the CHORUS and NOMAD experiments at CERN and E803 at Fermilab. However, if the atmospheric ν_μ deficit is due to neutrino mass via $\nu_\mu \to \nu_\tau$, this cannot be a correct mass scheme, and these experiments will give a null result. If all of the above three phenomena result from neutrino mass, there are only two viable patterns of those masses [5]. If there are no sterile neutrinos, the only possibility allowed by the small Δm^2 values required by $\nu_e \to \nu_\mu$ for the solar deficit and $\nu_\mu \to \nu_\tau$ for the atmospheric one is $m_{\nu_e} \approx m_{\nu_\mu} \approx m_{\nu_\tau} \approx 1.7$ eV to give the needed ~ 5 eV for hot dark matter. If neutrinos are Majorana particles, for which there is strong theoretical prejudice, then neutrinoless double beta decay should soon eliminate this possibility or confirm its existence, since this is in the range of current experimental limits, given the uncertainty in nuclear matrix elements.

A sterile neutrino may be introduced, provided it does not exceed the limit of 3.5 neutrino species at the time of nucleosynthesis. This limitation can be avoided only for the small mixing angle solution for solar $\nu_e \to \nu_s$, since any other use of a light ν_s would bring it into equilibrium in the early universe [6]. The ν_μ and ν_τ then provide the atmospheric ν_μ deficit and share the dark matter, making $m_{\nu_\mu} \approx m_{\nu_\tau} \approx 2.5$ eV. While a combination of the SNO and SuperKamiokande experiments will be able to demonstrate $\nu_e \to \nu_s$ to check this mass pattern, the LSND oscillation experiment at Los Alamos will have results sooner which will check for a mass difference between the light ν_e-ν_s sector and the heavier ν_μ-ν_τ pair via $\nu_\mu \to \nu_e$ for which $\Delta m_{e\mu}^2 \approx 6$ eV^2 (where LSND is most sensitive), for m_{ν_e} small, as indicated by neutrinoless double beta decay.

3. Implications of Possible $\nu_\mu \to \nu_e$ Oscillations

It is intriguing that there is a hint of oscillations from a short LSND run, as reported at this Conference. There is an excess of 8 events of the type $\bar{\nu}_e + p \to e^+ + n$, where about one event (of which 0.3 is due to the well-measured beam-off background) is expected. For $\Delta m_{e\mu}^2 \approx 6$ eV^2 this result, interpreted as $\bar{\nu}_\mu \to \bar{\nu}_e$ oscillations in the $\bar{\nu}_\mu$ beam, does not conflict with the KARMEN or BNL E776 experiments, which are least sensitive for this Δm^2 because of differences in source-detector distances. Furthermore, the energy dependence of the LSND events is consistent with this Δm^2. Nevertheless, the LSND collaboration is not claiming a positive effect, but rather awaits results of a more extensive run which started in August 1994, but if the excess observed were due to oscillations, this would have far reaching consequences.

Of course, the evidence for neutrino mass would be proof of physics beyond the Standard Model, and the implied pattern of neutrino masses and mixings would provide important guidance to a more comprehensive theory. The cosmological implications would be even more profound. First, the mixed dark matter scenario for structure formation would be validated, although it would be desirable to check that the ν_τ contributes equally with the ν_μ, which could be done by a long-baseline oscillation experiment. Second, as indicated above, a value of $m_\nu = m_{\nu_\mu} + m_{\nu_\tau} = 5$ eV would imply that $h = 0.5$ and $\Omega = 1$. Observational values of h group around 0.5 or 0.8, with small stated errors in each case, and this result would support the former, as well as indicating that our universe has critical density. Because the number of neutrinos (about $100/cm^3$ of each species) is fixed, having two 2.5 eV masses already brings Ω to 0.2, whereas the most successful low-Ω models have $\Omega = 0.2$–0.3. Thus there would be so much hot dark matter in a low-Ω universe that structure would form much too late. There is also an independent constraint on h due to the age of globular cluster stars.

It is indeed remarkable that a neutrino experiment could have such wide-spread implications, but this is indicative of the exciting state of this field.

References

[1] H. Meyer, *Particle and Nuclear Astrophysics and Cosmology in the Next Millenium*, Snowmass 1994 (to be published).

[2] G. Barr, T.K. Gaisser and T. Stanev, Phys. Rev. **D39** (1989) 3532;
W. Frati *et al.*, Phys. Rev. **D48** (1993) 1140;
D.H. Perkins, Astropart. Phys. **2** (1994) 249.

[3] E.L. Wright *et al.*, Astrophys. J. **396** (1992) L13;
M. Davis, F.J. Summers and D. Schlegel, Nature (london) **359** (1992)393;
A.N. Taylor and M. Rowan-Robinson, Nature (London) **359** (1992) 396;
R.K. Schaefer and Q. Schafi, BA-93-53 (submitted to Phys. Rev. **D**) and Nature (London) **359** (1992) 199;
J.A. Holtzman and J.R. Primack, Astrophys. J. **405** (1993) 428.

[4] A. Klypin *et al.*, Astrophys. J. **416** (1993) 1;
R. Noltenius, A. Klypin and J.R. Primack, Astrophys. J. **422** (1994) L45;
A. Klypin *et al.*, UCSC preprint: SCIPP-94-09 (submitted to Ap. J.).

[5] These mass patterns were first discussed at the January 1993 Moriond Workshop [D.O. Caldwell, in *Perspectives in Neutrinos, Atomic Physics and Gravitation*, p187; Ed. J. Trân Thanh van *et al.* (Editions Frontiers 1993)] and a theoretical structure for them was provided in D.O. Caldwell and R.N. Mohapatra, Phys. Rev. **D48** (1993) 3259.
See also J.T. Peltoniemi and J.W.F. Valle, Nucl. Phys. **B406** (1993) 409;
X. Shi, D.N. Schramm and B.D. Fields, Phys. Rev. **D48** (1993) 2563.

[6] The ν_s could be utilized for the vacuum oscillation solution to the solar ν_e deficit, since the Δm^2 is so small, but this explanation is disfavoured by information from supernova 1987a. Specifically, it does not work for an explanation of the atmospheric effect as $\nu_\mu \to \nu_s$ and ν_s cannot be the hot dark matter, as explained uin the first reference given in [5].

Schemes for Neutrino Mass and Mixing

José W.F. Valle

Departament de Física Teórica, Universitat de València and
Instituto de Física Corpuscular - C.S.I.C., E-46100 Burjassot, València, SPAIN

Abstract

I briefly review various schemes of neutrino mass generation which are motivated by present experimental hints from solar and atmospheric neutrinos as well as cosmological data on the amplitude of primordial density fluctuations.

1. Preliminaries

Neutrinos are the only apparently massless electrically neutral fermions in the standard model and the only ones without right-handed partners. It is rather mysterious that they seem to be so special when compared with the other fundamental fermions. Indeed, having no electric charge, a majorana mass term for neutrinos may arise even in the absence of right-handed components. On the other hand, many unified extensions of the standard model such as SO(10), do require the presence of right-handed neutrinos in order to realize the extra symmetry. Either way one expects neutrinos to be massive. Moreover, there is, in these theories, a natural mechanism, called seesaw, to understand the relative smallness of neutrino masses [1, 2]. In general the seesaw mechanism provides just a general scheme, rather than detailed predictions. These will depend, among other factors, upon the structure not only of the Dirac type entries, but also on the possible texture of the large Majorana mass term [3].

Although attractive, the seesaw mechanism is by no means the only way to generate neutrino masses. There are many other attractive possibilities, some of which do not require any new large mass scale. The extra particles required to generate the neutrino masses have masses at scales accessible to present experiments [4].

It is also quite plausible that B-L or lepton number, instead of being part of the gauge symmetry [5] may be a spontaneously broken global symmetry. The scale at which such a symmetry gets broken does not need to high, as in the original proposal [6], but can be rather low, close to the weak scale [7]. Such a low scale for lepton number breaking could have important implications not only in astrophysics and cosmology but also in particle physics.

Unfortunately, present theory is not capable of predicting the scale of neutrino masses any better than it can fix the masses of the other fermions, say the muon. One should at this point turn to experiment.

There are several limits on neutrino masses that follow from observation. The laboratory bounds may be summarized as [8]

$$m_{\nu_e} \lesssim 5\,eV, \quad m_{\nu_\mu} \lesssim 250\,keV, \quad m_{\nu_\tau} \lesssim 31\,MeV \quad (1)$$

and follow purely from kinematics. These are the most model-independent of the neutrino mass limits. The improved limit on the ν_e mass was given by Lobashev at this conference [9], while that on the ν_τ mass may be substantially improved at a future tau factory [10].

In addition, there are limits on neutrino masses that follow from the nonobservation of neutrino oscillations [11], which involve neutrino mass differences versus mixing, and disappear in the limit of unmixed neutrinos.

Another important limit arises from the nonobservation of $\beta\beta_{0\nu}$ decay, i.e. the process by which nucleus $(A, Z - 2)$ decays to $(A, Z) + 2\,e^-$. This lepton number violating process would arise from majorana neutrino exchange. In fact, as shown in ref. [12], a nonvanishing $\beta\beta_{0\nu}$ decay rate requires neutrinos to be majorana particles, irrespective of which mechanism induces it. This establishes a very deep connection which, in some special models, may be translated into a lower limit on the neutrino masses. The negative searches for $\beta\beta_{0\nu}$ in ^{76}Ge and other nuclei leads to a limit of about one or two eV on a weighted average neutrino mass parameter characterizing this process. Better sensitivity is expected from the upcoming enriched germanium experiments. Although rather stringent, this limit may allow relatively large neutrino masses, as there may be strong cancellations between the contributions of different neutrino types. This happens automatically in the case of a Dirac neutrino due to the lepton number symmetry [13].

In addition to laboratory limits, there is a cosmological bound that follows from avoiding the overabundance of relic neutrinos [14]

$$\sum_i m_{\nu_i} \lesssim 50\,eV \tag{2}$$

This limit only holds if neutrinos are stable on cosmological time scales. There are many models where neutrinos decay into a lighter neutrino plus a majoron [2],

$$\nu_\tau \to \nu_\mu + J \ . \tag{3}$$

Lifetime estimates in various majoron models have been discussed in ref. [15]. These decays can be fast enough to obey the cosmological limits coming from the critical density requirement, as well as those that come from primordial big-bang nucleosynthesis [16]. Note also that, since these decays are *invisible*, they are consistent with all astrophysical observations. In view of the above it is worthwhile to continue in the efforts to improve present laboratory neutrino mass limits, including searches for distortions in the energy distribution of the electrons and muons coming from weak decays such as $\pi, K \to e\nu$, $\pi, K \to \mu\nu$, as well as kinks in nuclear β decays [17].

2. Hints for Neutrino Mass

In addition to the above limits there are some positive *hints* for neutrino masses that follow from the following cosmological, astrophysical and laboratory observations.

2.1. Dark Matter

Recent observations of cosmic background temperature anisotropies on large scales by the COBE satellite [18], when combined with cluster-cluster correlation data e.g. from IRAS [19], indicate the need for the existence of a hot *dark matter* component, contributing about 30% to the total mass density [20]. A good fit is provided by a massive neutrino, such as a ν_τ of a few eV mass.

This suggests the possibility of having observable ν_e to ν_τ or ν_μ to ν_τ oscillations that may be accessible to the CHORUS and NOMAD experiments at CERN, as well as at the proposed P803 experiment at Fermilab [21]. This mass scale is also consistent with the recent hints reported here by Caldwell [22].

2.2. Solar Neutrinos

The data collected up to now by the two high-energy experiments Homestake and Kamiokande, as well as by the low-energy data on pp neutrinos from the GALLEX and SAGE experiments still pose a persisting puzzle [23, 24].

Comparing the data of GALLEX with the Kamiokande data indicates the need for a reduction of the ^{7}Be flux relative to the standard solar model expectation. Inclusion of the Homestake data only aggravates the discrepancy,

The simplest astrophysical solutions to the solar neutrino data are highly disfavored [25]. The most attractive way to account for the data is to assume the existence of neutrino conversions involving very small neutrino masses $\sim 10^{-3}$ eV [26]. The region of parameters allowed by present experiments is given in ref. [27]. Note that the fits favour the non-adiabatic over the large mixing solution, due mostly to the larger reduction of the ^{7}Be flux found in the former.

2.3. Atmospheric Neutrinos

An apparent decrease in the expected flux of atmospheric ν_μ's relative to ν_e's arising from the decays of π's, K's and secondary muon decays produced in the atmosphere, has been observed in two underground experiments, Kamiokande and IMB, and possibly also at Soudan2 [28]. This atmospheric neutrino deficit can be ascribed to neutrino oscillations. Although the predicted absolute fluxes of neutrinos produced by cosmic-ray interactions in the atmosphere are uncertain at the 20 % level, their ratios are expected to be accurate to within 5 %.

Combining these experimental results with observations of upward going muons made by Kamiokande, IMB and Baksan, and with the negative Frejus and NUSEX results [30] leads to the following range of neutrino oscillation parameters [29]

$$\Delta m^2_{\mu\tau} \approx 0.005 - 0.5\,eV^2, \ \sin^2 2\theta_{\mu\tau} \approx 0.5 \tag{4}$$

Recent results from Kamiokande on higher energy neutrinos strengthen the case for an atmospheric neutrino problem [31].

3. Models Reconciling Present Hints

Can we reconcile the present hints from astrophysics and cosmology in the framework of a consistent elementary particle physics theory? The above observations suggest an interesting theoretical puzzle whose possible resolutions I now discuss.

3.1. Three Almost Degenerate Neutrinos

It is difficult to reconcile these three observations simultaneously in the framework of the simplest seesaw model with just the three known neutrinos. The only possibility is if all three neutrinos are closely degenerate [32].

It is known that the general seesaw models have two independent terms giving rise to the light neutrino masses. The first is an effective triplet vacuum expectation value [33] which is expected to be small in left-right symmetric models [5]. Based on this fact one can in fact construct extended seesaw models where the main contribution to the light neutrino masses (~ 2 eV) is universal, due to a suitable horizontal symmetry, while the splittings between ν_e and ν_μ explain the solar neutrino deficit and that between ν_μ and $\nu_t au$ explain the atmospheric neutrino anomaly [34].

3.2. Three Active plus One Sterile Neutrino

The alternative way to fit all the data is to add a fourth neutrino species which, from the LEP data on the invisible Z width, we know must be of the sterile type, call it $\nu_{sterile}$. The first scheme of this type gives mass to only one of the three neutrinos at the tree level, keeping the other two massless [35]. In a seesaw scheme with broken lepton number, radiative corrections involving gauge boson exchanges will give small masses to the other two neutrinos ν_e and ν_μ [36]. However, since the singlet neutrino is superheavy in this case, there is no room to account for the three hints discussed above.

Two basic schemes have been suggested to reconcile all three hints. In addition to a light sterile neutrino $\nu_{sterile}$, they invoke additional Higgs bosons beyond that of the standard model. In these models the $\nu_{sterile}$ either lies at the dark matter scale [37] or, alternatively, at the solar neutrino scale [38]. In the first case the atmospheric neutrino puzzle is explained by ν_μ to $\nu_{sterile}$ oscillations, while in the second it is explained by ν_μ to ν_τ oscillations. Correspondingly, the deficit of solar neutrinos is explained in the first case by ν_e to ν_τ oscillations, while in the second it is explained by ν_e to $\nu_{sterile}$ oscillations. In both cases it is possible to fit all observations together. However, in the first case there is a clash with the bounds from big-bang nucleosynthesis. In the latter case the $\nu_{sterile}$ is at the MSW scale so that nucleosynthesis limits are satisfied. They single

out the nonadiabatic solution uniquely. Note however that, since the mixing angle characterizing the ν_μ to ν_τ oscillations is nearly maximal, the second solution is in apparent conflict with eq.(4) but agrees with figure 5 of reference [31]. Another theoretical possibility is that all active neutrinos are very light, while the sterile neutrino $\nu_{sterile}$ is the single neutrino responsible for the dark matter [39].

4. Outlook

Besides being suggested by theory, neutrino masses seem to be required to fit present astrophysical and cosmological observations, in addition to the recent LSND hints discussed here [22].

Neutrinos could be responsible for a wide variety of measurable implications at the laboratory. These new phenomena would cover an impressive range of energies, starting with β and nuclear $\beta\beta_{0\nu}$ decays. Searches for the latter with enriched germanium could test the quasidegenerate neutrino scenario for the joint explanation of hot dark matter and solar and atmospheric neutrino anomalies. Moving to neutrino oscillations, here one expects much larger regions of oscillation parameters in the ν_e to ν_τ and ν_μ to ν_τ channels will be be probed by the accelerator experiments at CERN than now possible with present accelerators and reactors. On the other hand more data from low energy pp neutrinos as well as from Superkamiokande, Borexino, and Sudbury will shed light on the solar neutrino issue.

For the far future we look forward to the possibility of probing those regions of ν_μ to ν_e or $\nu_{sterile}$ oscillation parameters suggested by present atmospheric neutrino data. This will be possible at the next generation of long baseline experiments. Similarly, a new generation of experiments capable of more accurately measuring the cosmological temperature anisotropies at smaller angular scales than COBE, would test different models of structure formation, and presumably shed further light on the need for hot neutrino dark matter.

Neutrinos may also imply rare processes with lepton flavour violation, as well as new signatures at LEP energies and even higher. Such experiments may be complementary to those at low energies and can also indirectly test neutrino properties in an important way.

Acknowledgements

This paper has been supported by DGICYT under Grant number PB92-0084.

References

[1] M. Gell-Mann, P. Ramond and R. Slansky, in *Supergravity*; Eds. D. Freedman *et al.* (1979); T. Yanagida, in *KEK lectures*; Eds. O. Sawada *et al.* (1979)

[2] For a recent review see: J.W.F. Valle, Prog. Part. Nucl. Phys. **26** (1991) 91.

[3] A.Yu. Smirnov, Phys. Rev. **D48** (1994) 3264; E. Papageorgiou, contributied paper GLS0807.

[4] A. Zee, Phys. Lett. **B93** (1980) 389; K.S. Babu, Phys. Lett. **B203** (1988) 132.

[5] R.N. Mohapatra and G. Senjanovic, Phys. Rev. **D23** (1981) 165 and references therein.

[6] Y. Chikashige, R. Mohapatra and R. Peccei, Phys. Rev. Lett. **45** (1980) 1926.

[7] J.W.F. Valle, these proceedings.

[8] Particle Data Group: L. Montanet *et al.*, Phys. Rev. **D50** (1994) 1173.

[9] V. Lobashev, these proceedings.

[10] J. Gomez-Cadenas and M.C. Gonzalez-Garcia, Phys. Rev. **D39** (1989) 1370; J. Gomez-Cadenas, *et al.*, Phys. Rev. **D41** (1990) 2179.

[11] J. Schneps, Nucl. Phys. B (Proc. Suppl.) **31** (1993) 307.

[12] J. Schechter and J.W.F. Valle, Phys. Rev. **D25** (1982) 2951.

[13] J.W.F. Valle, Phys. Rev. **D27** (1983) 1672 and references therein; L. Wolfenstein, Nucl. Phys. **B186** (1981) 147.

[14] E. Kolb and M. Turner, *The Early Universe*, (Addison-Wesley 1990).

[15] J.W.F. Valle, Phys. Lett. **B131** (1983) 87; G. Gelmini and J.W.F. Valle, Phys. Lett. **B142** (1984) 181; M.C. Gonzalez-Garcia and J.W.F. Valle, Phys. Lett. **B216** (1989) 360; A. Joshipura and S. Rindani, PRL-TH/92-10; for an early discussion see J. Schechter and J.W.F. Valle, Phys. Rev. **D25** (1982) 774.

[16] G. Steigman, Proc. of the Int. Sch. on Cosmological Dark Matter, p.55; Eds. J.W.F. Valle and A. Perez (World Scientific 1994).

[17] See, e.g. J. Deutsch *et al.*, Nucl. Phys. **A518** (1990) 149 and Phys.World **2** (1991) 81; A. Hime, Nucl. phys. B (Proc. Suppl.) **31** (1993) 50.

[18] G.F. Smoot *et al.*, Astrophys. J. **396** (1992) L1; E.L. Wright *et al.*, Astrophys. J. **396** (1992) L13.

[19] R. Rowan-Robinson, Proc. of the Int. Sch. on Cosmological Dark Matter, p.7 *op. cit.*

[20] E.L. Wright *et al.*, Astrophys. J. **396** (1992) L13; M. Davis, F.J. Summers, and D. Schagel, Nature (London) **359** (1992) 393; A.N. Taylor and M. Rowan-Robinson, *ibid.* **359** (1992) 396; R.K. Schaefer and Q. Shafi, *ibid.* **359** (1992) 199; J.A. Holtzman and J.R. Primack, Astrophys. J. **405** (1993) 428; A. Klypin *et al.*, Astrophys. J. **416** (1993) 1.

[21] CHORUS and NOMAD proposals CERN-SPSLC/91-21 (1992) and CERN-SPSC/90-42 (1992); K. Kodama *et al.*, FNAL proposal P803 (1991).

[22] D. Caldwell, these proceedings.

[23] J.R. Davis, in Proc. of the 21th Int. Cosmic Ray Conf., vol. 12, p. 143; Ed. R.J. Protheroe (University of Adelaide Press 1990).

[24] GALLEX collaboration, Phys. Lett. **B285** (1992) 376; *ibid.***B285** (1992) 390; *ibid.* **B314** (1993) 445; and *ibid.* **B327** (1994) 377.

[25] J. Bahcall and H. Bethe, Phys. Rev. **D47** (1993) 1298 and Phys. Rev. Lett. **65** (1990) 2233; V. Berezinsky, LNGS-93/86; S. Bludman, N. Hata and P. Langacker, Phys. Rev. **D45** (1992) 1820;

X. Shi and D. Schramm, FERMILAB-PUB-92-322-A.

[26] M. Mikheyev and A. Smirnov, Sov. J. Nucl. Phys. **42** (1986) 913; L. Wolfenstein, Phys. Rev. **D17** (1978) 2369; and *ibid.***D20** (1979) 2634.

[27] N. Hata and P. Langacker, Phys. Rev. **D50** (1994) 632 and Pennsylvania preprints: UPR-0592-T and UPR-0625-T and references therein.

[28] Kamiokande collaboration, Phys. Lett. **B205** (1988) 416; *ibid.* **B280** (1992) 146; and *ibid.* **B283** (1992) 446; IMBcollaboration, Phys. Rev. **D46** (1992) 3720.

[29] Proc. of Int. Workshop on the ν_μ/ν_e Problem in Atmospheric Neutrinos; Eds. V. Berezinsky and G. Fiorentini (Gran Sasso 1993).

[30] M.M. Boliev *et al.*, in Proceedings of the 3rd Int. Workshop on Neutrino Telescopes, p.235; Ch. Berger *et al.*, Phys. Lett. **B245** (1990) 305; and *ibid.* **227** (1989) 489; M. Aglietta *et al.*, J. Europhys. Lett. **15** (1991) 559.

[31] Kamiokande collaboration, preprint: ISSN 1340-3745.

[32] D.O. Caldwell and R.N. Mohapatra, Phys. Rev. **D48** (1993) 3259; A.S. Joshipura, preprint: PRL-TH/93/20 (to appear in Zeit. Phys.); S.T. Petcov and A. Smirnov, Phys. Lett. **B322** (1994) 109.

[33] J. Schechter and J.W.F. Valle, Phys. Rev. **D22** (1980) 2227.

[34] A. Ioannissyan and J.W.F. Valle, Phys. Lett. **B332** (1994) 93; D.O. Caldwell and R.N. Mohapatra, preprint: UCSB-HEP-94-03; B. Bamert and C.P. Burgess, preprint: McGill-94/07; D. Caldwell and R.N. Mohapatra, Maryland report: UMD-PP-94-90; D.G. Lee and R.N. Mohapatra, Maryland Report: UMD-PP-94-95; A.S. Joshipura, preprint: PRL-TH/94/08.

[35] J. Schechter and J.W.F. Valle, Phys. Rev. **D21** (1980) 309.

[36] D. Choudhury *et al.*, Phys. Rev. **D50** (1994) 3486; a similar model was considered by G. Hou and Wong, contributed paper GLS0703.

[37] J.T. Peltoniemi, D. Tommasini and J.W.F. Valle, Phys. Lett. **B298** (1993) 383.

[38] J.T. Peltoniemi and J.W.F. Valle, Nucl. Phys. **B406** (1993) 409; E. Akhmedov, Z. Berezhiani, G. Senjanovic and Z. Tao, Phys. Rev. **D47** (1993) 3245.

[39] J.T. Peltoniemi, Mod. Phys. Lett. **A38** (1993) 3593.

Parallel Session Pa-8

Lattice Gauge Theory

Convener: C. T. H. Davies (Glasgow University)

Scientific secretaries: H. Shanahan
A. Alikhan (reserve)

Paper presented at XXVII Int. Conf. on High Energy Physics: Session Pa-8
Glasgow, UK, 20–27 July 1994

Lattice QCD with dynamical quarks:
New results and future prospects*

Norman H. Christ

Department of Physics
Columbia University
New York, NY 10027

Abstract

Two topics are discussed. First, the dependence of the chiral condensate $\langle \bar{\psi}\psi \rangle$ is studied numerically in the region of the QCD phase transition for a $16^3 \times 4$ lattice with two flavors of dynamical quarks of mass $ma = 0.01$. In addition to varying the temperature, we also study a large range of "valence" quark masses $10^{-10} \leq m_{\mathrm{val}}a \leq 10$, where the valence mass m_{val} is the mass that appears explicitly in the propagator connected the two ψ fields in the chiral condensate. We see a non-linear dependence on m_{val} suggestive of second order behavior. As a second topic, we describe the design of a new, dedicated machine for lattice QCD with a peak speed of 0.8Tflops.

1. Introduction

For the past few years, it has been possible to carry out lattice QCD calculations which include all the relevant quark and gluon degrees of freedom. Such full QCD calculations have been done for the QCD phase transition, the hadron spectrum and for certain hadronic matrix elements. However, more than a hundred-fold increase in computation speed can be achieved by omitting the effects of quark loops, working in the so-called "quenched" approximation. In the case of the QCD phase transition, the effects of the quark loops are quite dramatic, changing the order of the transition and significantly increasing the differences between the normal vacuum and the plasma phase. The first-order, "deconfining" transition of pure $SU(3)$ gauge theory changes to an apparently second-order, "chiral symmetry restoration" transition when two flavors of quarks are included.

The effects of quark loops on the hadron spectrum and matrix elements are less visible. So far,

comparison of full and quenched calculations have not shown differences greater that the systematic and statistical errors inherent in these calculations, errors probably not smaller than $\approx 10\%$. Either the "quenched" approximation is better for these quantities or the dynamical quarks used in those calculation are sufficiently heavy ($m_\pi \geq 400\mathrm{MeV}$) that the effects of the quark loops are suppressed, just as the effects of the heavier strange quark loops are suppressed according to Zwieg's rule.

In what follows we describe two topics. In the first we examine the QCD phase transition for two light quark flavors with relatively small mass. Previous studies[1] of this system have seen no evidence for the two-state behavior, characteristic of a first-order transition. Rather they find large, slow fluctuations in the Monte Carlo evolutions suggestive of a nearby second-order critical point, presumably at vanishing quark mass. This corresponds nicely with theoretical expectations[2]. Preliminary to searching for actual critical behavior as $m \to 0$ and $\beta \to \beta_c$, we study what appears to be critical behavior in the order parameter $\langle \bar{\psi}\psi \rangle$ for fixed quark mass $ma = 0.01$ but varying

---

* This research was supported in part by the U. S. Department of Energy.

valence mass, m_{val}, the mass which appears explicitly in the propagator defining $\bar{\psi}\psi$. Second, we outline the characteristics of a new 0.8Tflops machine. Such a machine should be able to do extensive full QCD calculations on a lattice as large as $32^3 \times 64$ with quark masses as small as 0.005 in lattice units.

2. The valence mass dependence of $\langle\bar{\psi}\psi\rangle$[‡]

At present, the bulk of the evidence that the two-flavor, QCD phase transition is second order is indirect: the failure to see a first-order signal suggests that the transition is most likely second order. Seeing the predicted, universal critical behavior as $m \to 0$ for temperatures in the critical region would provide a convincing demonstration that the transition is, in fact, second order[3]. Here we discuss a related phenomena which is somewhat easier to study.

First we dissect the chiral order parameter,

$$\langle\bar{\psi}\psi\rangle = \frac{1}{3\Omega}\langle\text{tr}\frac{1}{D+im_{\text{val}}}\rangle_{\beta,m_{\text{sea}}}, \qquad (1)$$

distinguishing its dependence on the gauge coupling constant g through the quantity $\beta = 6/g^2$, the quark mass appearing in the normal quark loops, m_{sea}, (here referred to as the mass of the "sea" quarks), and the "valence" quark mass entering the explicit quark propagator that defines $\bar{\psi}\psi$. Here $\langle\ \rangle$ represents the usual, finite temperature quantum expectation value, D the Dirac operator, Ω the space-time volume and the trace is taken over color, spin and space-time coordinates of the Dirac propagator. As is standard in finite temperature lattice QCD calculations, we work on a Euclidean lattice with a fixed extent in the time direction, here $N_t = 4$. This describes a quantum statistical ensemble at a temperature $T = \frac{1}{N_t a}$ which can be varied by changing the coupling g and thereby changing the lattice spacing a.

Next we argue that the non-local quantity $\bar{\psi}\psi_{m_{\text{val}}}$ should show non-analytic behavior as a function of β in the limit $m_{\text{val}} \to 0$. This should be true even for $m_{\text{sea}} \neq 0$, so the underlying theory will show only "cross-over", *not* critical, behavior in β. Recall that $\bar{\psi}\psi$ can be written

$$\langle\bar{\psi}\psi\rangle = 2m_{\text{val}}\int_0^\infty d\lambda \frac{\rho(\lambda,\beta,m_{\text{sea}})}{\lambda^2+m_{\text{val}}^2} \qquad (2)$$

where $\rho(\lambda)$ is the density of Dirac eigenvalues per unit space-time volume, per color. As is clear from this equation, $\langle\bar{\psi}\psi\rangle$ will vanish in the limit $m_{\text{val}} \to 0$ provided $\rho(0) = 0$. At zero temperature $\rho(0)$ is non-vanishing, giving rise to the spontaneous breaking of

[‡] The work reported in this section was done in collaboration with S. Chandrasekharan, D. Chen, W. Lee, R. D. Mawhinney and D. Zhu.

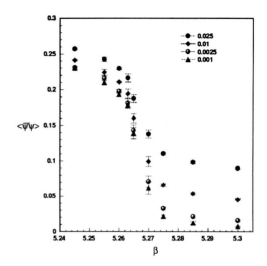

Figure 1. $\bar{\psi}\psi$ is shown as a function of $\beta = 6/g^2$ for a variety of values of the valence mass, m_{val}. The β-dependence becomes increasing singular as $m_{\text{val}} \to 0$.

chiral symmetry seen even in quenched calculations. At high temperature one expects no long-range order so that $\rho(0) = 0$. Thus $\langle\bar{\psi}\psi\rangle$ should be non-analytic as β varies between 0 and ∞. If m_{sea} is above a critical value m_c, the underlying theory will undergo the first-order transition of pure QCD and $\bar{\psi}\psi$ will show a corresponding discontinuity. For $m_{\text{sea}} < m_c$, $\bar{\psi}\psi$ presumably cannot be a discontinuous function of β but will instead show continuous, but non-analytic behavior as β passes through the cross-over region of the underlying theory.

Next we compute $\langle\bar{\psi}\psi\rangle$ according to Equation (1) for a $16^3 \times 4$ lattice with $m_{\text{sea}}a = 0.01$ for nine values of β, 5.245, 5.255, 5.26, 5.2625, 5.265, 5.27, 5.275, 5.285 and 5.3, surrounding the critical value ≈ 5.265. The resulting values of $\bar{\psi}\psi$ are shown in Figure 1. This figure is suggestive of the behavior just described with the β-dependence becoming increasingly steep as m_{val} decreases. Likewise, if we plot $\langle\bar{\psi}\psi\rangle$ as a function of m_{val} for a range of values of β we see striking non-linear dependence on m_{val} as shown in Figure 2.

For $5.26 \leq \beta \leq 5.275$, the curves in Figure 2 are well fit by a powerlaw, $\langle\bar{\psi}\psi\rangle \sim m_{\text{val}}^{1/\delta}$, in the mass interval [0.00025,0.005] with δ varying between 10 and 1.4. For $m_{\text{val}} > 0.005$ a cut-off-dependent, linear term is important, while for $m_{\text{val}} \leq 0.00025$, we see the effects of finite volume which cuts off the spectrum and causes $\langle\bar{\psi}\psi\rangle$ to approach zero linearly in m_{val}. The critical exponent δ that might be deduced from Figure 1 with a more thorough analysis and perhaps better statistics probably should not agree with that of the complete theory with $m_{\text{val}} = m_{\text{sea}} \to 0$. However, the region in which clear critical behavior is seen may correspond to the range $0.00025 \leq m \leq 0.005$ suggested here.

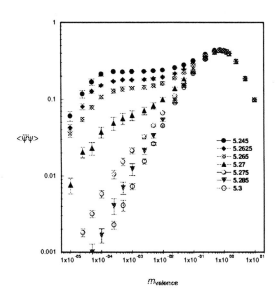

Figure 2. $\bar{\psi}\psi$ is plotted as a function of m_{val} for a series of values of β. For $0.00025 \leq m_{\text{val}} \leq 0.01$ the curves are well described by a powerlaw $\bar{\psi}\psi \sim m_{\text{val}}^{1/\delta}$.

Thus, this fairly extensive study of the dependence of the m_{val}-dependence of $\langle\bar{\psi}\psi\rangle$ has found interesting non-linear behavior suggesting critical dependence and indicating a possible mass range in which actual critical behavior will be seen in the complete theory. Certainly, no first-order discontinuities have been seen in the possibly sensitive probe $\langle\bar{\psi}\psi_{m_{\text{val}}\to 0}\rangle$.

3. Design of a 0.8 Gflops QCD Machine[†]

The continuing, enormous advances in computer technology offer important opportunities for the construction of dedicated machines that can very efficiently support large-scale lattice QCD calculations. One such project, centered at Columbia, has been underway for the past year and is described here. This machine is based on cost-effective, digital signal processors (DSPs). These are simple 32-bit microcomputers, available with a price/performance of $\approx \$1/\text{Mflop}$. The final machine is planned to consist of 16,384 of these DSPs, interconnected as a $16^3 \times 4$ mesh. With 2 Mbytes of memory on each node, the complete machine will have 32Gbytes of memory and a peak speed of 0.8Tflops.

The fundamental node of this parallel machine is shown in Figure 3. The critical ingredient in that figure is the custom gate array. This device provides i) refresh and error checking and correcting for the memory made of standard 60ns DRAM, ii) an automatic buffer that fetches ahead from memory and retains recently read data for the DSP, iii) bi-

[†] The project described in this section is the joint work of I. Arsenin, D. Chen, N. Christ, R. Edwards, A. Gara, S. Hansen, A. Kennedy, R. D. Mawhinney, J. Parsons, and J. Sexton

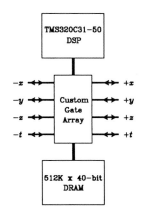

Figure 3. A block diagram of a single node.

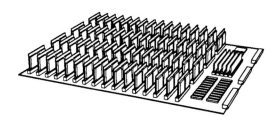

Figure 4. A possible arrangement of 64 daughter boards connected to a mother board using standard SIMM sockets.

directional, 50MHz serial communication for each of the eight directions in our 4-D mesh, iv) direct memory access for these serial transfers with sufficient addressing arithmetic that a series of equally spaced blocks of data can be automatically transmitted to/from any number of nearest neighbor nodes.

Sixty four of these nodes, configured as a $4 \times 4 \times 2 \times 2$ mesh will be mounted on a single mother board as is suggested in Figure 4. In addition to the off-node connections required by our mesh architecture, each mother board will be fitted with two standard SCSI interfaces. These will support connections to the host workstation and allow convenient connection of standard tape and disk devices.

The design of this machine is more than one-half complete with the first prototype hardware expected at the end of this year and the full machine planned for the end of 1995. The complete machine should cost \$3M and, based on actually code running on a gate level simulator, we expect a sustained performance of ≈ 0.4 Gflops for staggered fermion conjugate gradient code.

References

[1] F. R. Brown, *et al.*, Phys. Rev. Lett. **65** (1990) 2491; M. Fukugita *et al.*, Phys Rev. Lett. **65** (1990) 816; Phys. Rev. **D42** (1990) 2936.

[2] R. Pisarski and F. Wilczek, Phys. Rev. **D29** (1984) 338.

[3] F. Karsch, Phys. Rev. **D49** (1994) 3791.

Paper presented at XXVII Int. Conf. on High Energy Physics: Session Pa-8
Glasgow, UK, 20–27 July 1994

Lattice Results for Heavy Light Matrix Elements

A. Soni

Brookhaven National Laboratory
Physics Department
Upton, NY 11973

Abstract

Lattice results for heavy light matrix elements are reviewed and some of their implications are very briefly discussed. Despite the fact that in most cases the lattice results for weak matrix elements at the moment have only a modest accuracy of about 20–30% they already have important phenomenological repercussions; e.g. for V_{td}/V_{ts}, x_s/x_d and $B \to K^* \gamma$.

I. As samples of "new" projects, I briefly discuss four projects

a. The NRQCD group [1] reports a preliminary result on the mass splitting $m_{B_S^*} - m_{B_S}$. They use 100 configurations on a $16^3 \times 32$ lattice of the HEMCGC group (dynamical, staggered $n_f = 2$, $am = .01$ and $\beta = 5.6$). Their very preliminary result is

$$
\begin{aligned}
m_{B_S^*} - m_{B_S} = \ & [50 \pm 5(\text{statistical}) \pm 10(am) \\
& \pm 15(\text{scale})] MeV \quad (1)
\end{aligned}
$$

Since rough phenomenological estimates for the splitting invariable yield about 50 MeV, such a lattice calculation will be very interesting if the errors can be brought down to 0 (5 MeV).

b. The LANL collaboration [2] is acquiring many interesting results via their large scale simulations on the CM-5. So far they have analyzed 58 configurations of size $32^3 \times 64$ at $\beta = 6.0$. This lattice has the distinction of having the largest physical volume used so far for weak matrix element calculations. Comparison with results previously obtained on smaller lattices will therefore be very valuable. Here are some of their preliminary findings:

$$(1) \qquad f_K/f\pi \qquad = 1.163 \pm .023;$$

$$(2) \qquad \frac{f_+^{D \to \pi e \nu}(q^2 = 0)}{f_+^{D \to K e \nu}(q^2 = 0)} = 0.86 \pm .08; \qquad (2)$$

$$(3) \qquad \frac{A_2^{D \to K^* e \nu}(0)}{A_1^{D \to K^* e \nu}(0)} = .77 \pm .22.$$

c. The Fermilab Static Group (FSG) [3] is now finishing a comprehensive study with the use of their static method. They reported interesting results on f_B, f_{B_S}/f_{B_u} and $m_{B_S} - m_{B_u}$. With their method they find a significant lattice spacing (a) dependence for f_B whereas the other two quantities appear insensitive to a. Their key results are:

$$f_B = 188 \pm 23(\text{stat}) \pm 15(\text{sys})^{+27}_{-0}(\text{extr}) \pm 14(a) \quad (3)$$

$$f_{B_S}/f_{B_u} = 1.216 \pm .041 \pm .016 \quad (4)$$

$$m_{B_S} - m_{B_u} = 86 \pm 12 \pm 7 (\text{MeV}) \quad (5)$$

d. MILC collaboration [4] is undertaking a dedicated study of f_B using primarily the Intel Paragon machine. They have analyzed so far 40 configurations ($24^2 \times 80$, $\beta = 6.3$). Their preliminary results for the decay constants are given below:

$$
\begin{aligned}
f_B &= 174 \pm 7 \text{ MeV} \\
f_{B_S} &= 198 \pm 7 \text{ MeV} \\
f_D &= 205 \pm 5 \text{ MeV} \qquad (6) \\
f_{D_S} &= 228 \pm 5 \text{ MeV}
\end{aligned}
$$

II. A illustrative sample of weak matrix elements results are compiled in Table I. The ones mentioned above that are now reporting final results are included where relevant.

III. Phenomenological implications. While in many cases the accuracy of the existing lattice results is not that great, being typically about 20%, (an exception is B_K [5]) yet they have important implications already. This is in great part due to the fact in many cases little reliable information exists about several of these matrix elements. Thus an answer with even a modest accuracy of 20% can have crucial impact. Of course lattice methods will continue to provide refined results in many cases.

I discuss some of the key implications that emerge. The lattice results for f_B and the B parameter along with the experimental result on B-$\bar{B}$ mixing leads to:

$$\left|\frac{V_{td}}{V_{ts}}\right| = .22 \pm .08 \qquad (7)$$

Using the above along with the lattice results for (see Table 1):

$$f_{B_S}/f_B = 1.16 \pm .10 \qquad (8)$$

leads to an indication for the expectation for B_S-$\bar{B}_S$ mixing:

$$\frac{x_s}{x_d} = 18 \pm 14. \qquad (9)$$

Finally, the lattice result for $B \to K^* + \gamma$:

$$H_{K^*}^{\text{lattice}} \equiv \frac{BR(B \to K^*\gamma)^{\text{lattice}}}{BR(b \to s\gamma)} = 6.0 \pm 1.2 \pm 3.4\% \quad (10)$$

has important repercussions. Recall two recent experimental results [6,7]:

$$BR(B \to K^*\gamma) = (4.5 \pm 1.5 \pm .9) \times 10^{-5} \qquad (11)$$

$$BR(b \to s\gamma) = (2.32 \pm .51 \pm .29 \pm .32) \times 10^{-4} \quad (12)$$

Together they imply:

$$H_{K^*}^{\text{expt}} \simeq (19.4 \pm 7.8)\% \qquad (13)$$

While the errors in the experiment as well as in the lattice calculations [8–10] are too large at present to allow one to draw strong conclusions, the difference between the two is a quantitative measure of the long-distance contributions. The point is that while the lattice calculation is by construction of a short-distance piece only, experiments may also be seeing some long-distance contamination coming, for example, from $B \to \psi_{\text{virtual}} + K^*$, $\psi_{\text{virtual}} \to \gamma$. Improved lattice calculations as well as experiments are therefore highly desirable to quantify the extent of the long-distance contributions to such important radiative decays.

Acknowledgements

I am thankful to Christine Davies for inviting me to give this mini-review. I have also benefitted from discussions with her and with Claude Bernard, Sara Collins, Estia Eichten, Rajan Gupta, Paul MacKenzie, Junko Shigemitsu, Jim Simone, and John Sloan for numerous discussions. This research was supported in part under the DOE grant number DE-AC0276CH00016.

References

[1] NRQCD group: S. Collins, C. Davis, U. Heller, A. Khan, J. Shigemitsu, and J. Sloan (private communication).
[2] The LANL Collaboration: T. Bhattacharya, J. Grandy, R. Gupta, G. Kilcup, J. Labrenz, S. Sharpe, and P. Tamayo (private communication).
[3] The Fermi-lab Static Group (FSG): T. Duncan, E. Eicheten, J. Flynn, B. Mill, and H. Thacker, hep-lat 9407025.
[4] The MILC Collaboration: C. Bernard *et al* (private communication).
[5] S. Sharpe in *Lattice '93*, p. 403.
[6] R. Ammar *et al.* (CLEO), Phys. Rev. Lett. **71** (1993) 674.
[7] B. Barish *et al.* (CLEO), preprint CLEO-CONF-94-1.
[8] C. Bernard *et al.*, Phys. Rev. Lett. **72** (1994) 1402.
[9] K.D. Bowler *et al.* (UKQCD), Phys. Rev. Lett. **72** (1994) 1397;HEP-LAT 9407013.
[10] See, A. Abada talk [for the APE group]; See also M. Ciuchini *et al.*, Univ. of Rome preprint 94/1020.
[11] M.B. Gavela *et al.*, Nucl. Phys. B**306** (1988) 677.
[12] C. Bernard and A. Soni, Lattice '89, p. 495.
[13] The 90% CL errors on the summary of the lattice results are subjective.
[14] C. Bernard *et al.*, Phys. Rev. D**38** (1988) 3540.
[15] M.B. Gavela *et al.*, Phys. Lett. **206B** (1988) 113.
[16] C. Bernard *et al.*, Phys. Rev. D**49** (1994) 2536.
[17] T. Degrand and R. Loft, Phys. Rev. D**38** (1988) 954.
[18] R.M. Baxter *et al.* (URQCD), Phys. Rev. D**49** (1994) 1594.
[19] A. Abada *et al.*, Nucl. Phys. B**376** (1992) 172.

SAMPLE OF RESULTS FOR HADRON MATRIX
ELEMENTS FROM QUENCHED LATTICE QCD

QUANTITY	VALUE	AUTHORS (REMARKS)
The "B" Parameters		
$\hat{B}_K$	$.825 \pm .027 \pm .023$	Gupta, Kilcup, Sharpe (Staggered) [5]
	$.85 \pm .20$	ELC (Wilson) [11]
	$.86 \pm .11 \pm .05$	Bernard, Soni (Wilson) [12]
$\hat{B}_K$	$.82 \pm .10$	Most likely $\equiv$ 90% CL [13]
		(inc. statistical and systematic errors)
$\hat{B}_B$	$1.3 \pm .2$	Bernard, *et al.* [14]
	$1.16 \pm .07$	ELC [15]
$\hat{B}_B \simeq \hat{B}_{B_S}$	$1.2 \pm .2$	Most Likely (90% CL) [13]
The Decay Constants		
f_K/f_π	$1.08 \pm .03 \pm .08$	Bernard, Labrenz, Soni [16]
f_D (MeV)	$174 \pm 26 \pm 46$	Bernard, *et al.* [14]
	190 ± 33	Degrand, Loft [17]
	210 ± 40	ELC [15]
	185^{+4+42}_{-3-7}	UKQCD [18]
	$208 \pm 9 \pm 32$	Bernard, Labrenz, Soni [16]
f_D (MeV)	197 ± 25	Most Likely (90% CL) [13]
f_{D_S} (MeV)	222 ± 16	Degrand, Loft [17]
	$234 \pm 46 \pm 55$	Bernard, *et al.* [14]
	230 ± 50	ELC [15]
	$212 \pm 4^{+46}_{-7}$	UKQCD [18]
	$230 \pm 7 \pm 35$	Bernard, Labrenz, Soni [16]
f_{D_S} (MeV)	221 ± 30	Most Likely (90% CL) [13]
f_B (MeV)	205 ± 40	ELC [19]
	$160 \pm 6^{+53}_{-19}$	UKQCD [18]
	$187 \pm 10 \pm 37$	Bernard, Labrenz, Soni [16]
	$188 \pm 23 \pm 15^{+27}_{-0} \pm 14$	FSG [3]
f_B (MeV)	173 ± 40	Most Likely (90% CL) [13]
f_{B_S} (MeV)	194^{+6+62}_{-5-9}	UKQCD [18]
	$207 \pm 9 \pm 40$	Bernard, Labrenz, Soni [16]
f_{B_S} (MeV)	201 ± 40	Most Likely (90% CL) [13]
f_{B_S}/f_B	$1.22^{+.04}_{-.03}$	UKQCD [18]
	$1.11 \pm .02 \pm .05$	Bernard, Labrenz, Soni [16]
	$1.22 \pm .04 \pm .02$	FSG [3]
f_{B_S}/f_B	$1.16 \pm .10$	Most Likely (90% CL) [13]
Radiative B Decays		
$R_{K^\bullet} \equiv \frac{\Gamma(B \to \gamma K^\bullet)}{\Gamma(b \to \gamma_s)} = 6.0 \pm 1.2 \pm 3.4\%$		Bernard, Hsieh, Soni [8]
$8.8^{+28}_{-25} \pm 3.0 \pm 1.0$		UKQCD [9]

Table 1.

Lattice results for Heavy-Light matrix elements (From APE, ELC and UKQCD Collaborations)

As. Abada[†]

† Laboratoire de Physique Théorique et Hautes Energies Université de Paris XI 91405 Orsay FRANCE

Abstract

We review recent lattice computations relevant for D and B decays. Decay constants f_{D,D_s}, f_{B,B_s}, $D \to K(K^*)$, $B \to \pi, \rho$ semi-leptonic form factors together with the slope of the Isgur-Wise function calculations are presented. Some recent results of $B \to K^* \gamma$ form factors will be given. $1/M$ corrections to the asymptotic scaling laws are discussed.

B physics is now an active field (where several thousand of physicists are engaged) in which lattice QCD takes advantage from recent improvements increasing the statistics and improving the control of the systematics through theoretical progress (improved actions···). In addition to phenomenological predictions, lattice QCD can test the scaling laws predicted by HQET (Heavy Quark Effective Theory). Up to now, precise predictions can be made only in the quenched approximation for which the systematic errors cannot be evaluated; however, results obtained in the unquenched theory[1] suggest that the quenching effect is small when one deals with heavy quarks. In general, comparison with experiment shows an agreement with lattice data inside error bars which are still sizable although decreasing. This is a review of recent calculations done in the quenched approximation using the Wilson and S.W-clover (continuum limit improved) actions on heavy-light meson decays.

1. Strategy to study B meson on the lattice

Since the inverse lattice spacing a^{-1} ranges from 2 to 4 GeV, one cannot study B directly meson on the lattice. Indirect informations can be obtained through the following:

-One uses a set of relatively heavy mesons with masses up to $0.7a^{-1}$, i.e. heavier than the D but lighter than the B (" fictitious D mesons"). We call this mass region the "moving quark" one.

-On the other hand, a method proposed by Eichten[3] allows one to put infinite mass on the lattice and the latter is considered in this approach as a static source of color. We call this mass region the "static quark" one (where heavy flavours are studied at lowest order in $\frac{1}{M}$ expansion, M being the heavy meson mass).

A physical quantity computed in these two mass regions is interpolated to the B with the help of the scaling laws of the HQET. The value in the static limit reduces the uncertainties due to the extrapolation. This method has shown to be very effective (Fig.1) in the estimation of the decay constants (DC). In semi-leptonic (SL) decays, the calculation in the static limit is not yet available, but one can study the scaling behaviour and try an extrapolation to the B. The predictions concerning the B SL decays remain at a semi-quantitative level but it shows that the extrapolation may be done and improvements in the near future are expected. The next section is an illustration of the method explained above.

2. Leptonic decays $D(B) \to \ell\nu$

A hadron mass can be obtained from the study of an appropriate Euclidean correlation function as the coefficient of its exponential time dependence: $G(t) = \int d^3\mathbf{x}\langle \bar{u}\gamma_0\gamma_5 c(\mathbf{x},t)\bar{c}\gamma_0\gamma_5 u(\mathbf{0},0)\rangle \underset{t\to\infty}{\simeq} \frac{f_D^2 m_D}{2}e^{-m_D t}$. The determination of the expectation value in this equation is a non perturbative problem which can be solved numerically. The second approach (static) is based

Ref.	β	f_D(MeV)	f_{D_s}(MeV)
ELC(W)[4]	6.4	210 ± 15	227 ± 15
APE (C)[6]	6.0	218 ± 9	240 ± 9
BLS(W)[7]	6.3	$208(9) \pm 35 \pm 12$	$230(7) \pm 30 \pm 18$
UKQCD (C)[8]	6.2	$185^{+4\ +42}_{-3\ -7}$	$212^{+4\ +46}_{-4\ -7}$
WA75[9]		-	$232 \pm 45 \pm 20 \pm 48$
CLEO2[10]		-	$344 \pm 37 \pm 52 \pm 42$
ARGUS[11]			267 ± 28

Table 1. W (C) refer to Wilson (S. W-clover) action. (ARGUS's result relies on the factorization assumption.)

on the expansion of the heavy quark (H) propagator in inverse powers of the quark mass as proposed by Eichten[3]; the H is static and does not live effectively on the lattice but the quantity $f_H \sqrt{M_H}$ can be measured and is predicted to be independent of the heavy mass. The confrontation between the two methods is presented in Fig.1. The HQET tells us that when $M_H \to \infty$, the vector (V) and pseudoscalar (P) DC scale with the mass of the heavy quark, M_H, [3]-[5]($M = M_P = M_V = M_H$, $\beta_0 = 11 - \frac{2}{3}N_f$) as: $\frac{M}{f_V} = f_P = \frac{C}{\sqrt{M}}\alpha_s(M)^{-2/\beta_0}$.

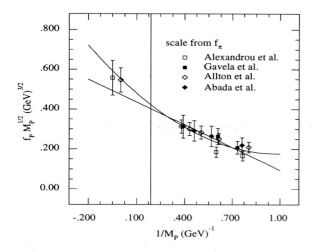

Figure 1. Linear and quadratic fits in $1/M$ are shown; the vertical line shows the physical B.

In Fig.1 we notice the consistency between the moving quark results and the static ones (several similar results have been obtained since). It appears that there are large corrections to the asymptotic scaling behaviour. The lattice results compared to the experimental ones are reported in Table 1(2) concerning the $D(B)$ meson. From Table 1, one can see that the different lattices agree more or less. Up to $5\% - 10\%$ we find: $f_D \sim 210$MeV and $f_{D_s} \sim 230$MeV. f_{D_s} which has been predicted by lattice since several years, will provide an important check since the large experimental errors may be substantially reduced in the future. In Table 2, the general tendency is $f_B \sim 200$MeV (up to 20%), in agreement with QCD Sum Rules calculations.

The B−parameter: the predictions for the $B - \bar{B}$ mix-

Ref.	β	f_B(MeV)	$\frac{f_{B_s}}{f_{B_d}}$
ELC(W)[4]	6.4	205 ± 40	1.08 ± 0.06
UKQCD (C)[8]	6.2	$160^{+6\ +53}_{-6\ -19}$	1.22 ± 0.04
HEMCGC[1]	5.6	200 ± 48	-

Ref.	β	f_B^{stat}(MeV)	$\frac{f_{B_s}}{f_{B_d}}^{stat}$
APE (C)[12]	6.2	$290 \pm 15 \pm 45$	$1.11(3)$
APE [14]	6.0	$350 \pm 40 \pm 30$	$1.14(4)$
APE (C)[14]	6.0	328 ± 36	$1.19(5)$
UKQCD (C)[8]	6.2	$253^{+16\ +105}_{-15\ -14}$	1.14^{+4}_{-3}
BLS [7]	6.3	$235(20) \pm 21$	1.11 ± 0.05
Allton(W)[13]	6.0	$310 \pm 25 \pm 50$	1.09 ± 0.04

Table 2. The HEMCGC unquenched result agrees with those obtained in the quenched approximation. f_B^{stat} values are obtained at lowest order in $1/M$.

ing depend on the $B-$parameter of the heavy light $\Delta B = 2$ four quark operator. ELC gives[4]: $B_{D^0} = 1.05 \pm 0.08$, $B_{B^0} = 1.16 \pm 0.07$ and $\frac{B_{D_s}}{B_{D_d}} \simeq \frac{B_{B_s}}{B_{B_d}} = 1.02 \pm 0.02$; the prediction for the physically relevant combination in $B - \bar{B}$ mixing and CP violation is: $f_{B_d}\sqrt{B_{B_d}} = 220 \pm 40$MeV.

3. Semi-leptonic decays $D(B) \to K, K^*(\pi, \rho)\ell\nu$

In this study, we first calculate $D \to K, K^*$ then extrapolate to $B \to \pi, \rho$. The amplitudes are expressed in terms of 4 form factors (FF) f^+, V and $A_{1,2}$ and we need to know them at momentum transfer $q^2 = 0$ (where we have the maximum of phase space). The present lattices run in the close vicinity of $q^2 = 0$ for the D meson, far from so for the B one. In the latter case we proceed in 2 steps:

-The first is to extrapolate to the B mass at fixed momentum near the no recoil point (q^2_{max}) and this is doable with the help of HQET: when $M \to \infty$ at fixed $\vec{q}$ and $||\vec{q}|| \ll M$, the FF scale as[16]: $f^+, V, A_2 \sim M^{1/2}$, and $A_1 \sim M^{-1/2}$).

- The 2nd and difficult step is to extrapolate to $q^2 = 0$; people often use the Nearest Pole Dominance approximation VMD ($F(q^2) = \frac{F(0)}{1-q^2/M_t^2}$, M_t is the exchanged meson mass in the t-channel) which has no firm theoretical grounding.

D meson study: lattice results compared to model predictions and experimental data are reported in Table 3; the 2 first lines have been recently obtained using the S.W-clover action. There is agreement between lattices, models and experiments for f^+ and A_1. For V the central value is below within errors. Concerning A_2, there used to be a problem but now the central value agrees with the experimental average although with large errors.

B meson study: from the first studies by ELC[17] and APE[18], it appears that the HQET scaling laws near q^2_{max} for V and $A_{1,2}$ are affected by large corrections. The B FF predictions at $q^2 = 0$, which rely on the VMD

Ref.	$f^+(0)$	$V(0)$	$A_1(0)$
EXP[24]	.77(4)	1.16±.16	.61(5)
APE[18]	.72(9)	1.00±.20	.64±.11
UKQCD[19]	$.67^{+7}_{-8}$	$.98^{+10}_{-13}$	$.70^{+5}_{-10}$
ELC[17]	.60 ± .15 ± .07	.86±.24	.64±.16
APE[15]	.63±.08	.86±.10	.53±.03
BLS[20]	.90 ± .08 ± .21	1.43 ± .45 ± .49	.83 ± .14 ± .28
SR[23]	$.60^{+.15}_{-.10}$	1.10±.25	.50±.15
QM.1[21]	.76	1.23	.88
QM.2[21]	.8	1.1	.8

Ref.	$A_2(0)$	$V(0)/A_1(0)$	$A_2(0)/A_1(0)$
EXP[24]	.45(9)	1.90±.25	.74±.15
APE[18]	.46±.34	1.59±.29	.73±.45
UKQCD[19]	$.68^{+11}_{-17}$		
ELC[17]	.40 ± .28 ± .04	1.3±.2	.6±.3
APE[15]	.19±.21	1.6±.2	.4±.4
BLS[20]	.59 ± .14 ± .24	1.99 ± .22 ± .33	.7 ± .16 ± .17
SR[23]	.60±.15	2.2±.2	1.2±.2
QM.1[21]	1.15	1.4	1.3
QM.2[21]	.8	1.4	1.0

Table 3. $D \to K, K^*$ semileptonic form factors: EXP, LAT, QM and SR refer to experimental average, lattice, quark model and QCD sum rules calculations respectively.

assumption[17],[18], are still plagued by large errors but one expects important improvement in the near future.

The Isgur-Wise function $\xi(x)$: when the final meson is heavy, SL FF are expressed in terms of one universal function, unknown apart from the no recoil point $\xi(1) = 1$. In practice we try to measure its slope around this point $\rho^2 = -\xi'(1)$. In the D mass region, UKQCD found $\rho^2 = 1.2^{+7}_{-3}$[25] while CLEO2 gives $\rho^2 = 1.01 \pm 0.15 \pm 0.09$[26]. There is now an other alternative[27] for the determination of ρ^2(UKQCD) [27] for masses $m \geq m_{D_s}$.

4. Radiative Decay $B \to K^* \gamma$

The decay rate is expressed in terms of $T_{1,2}(q^2)$ where for a real photon ($q^2 = 0$), we have the exact condition $T_1(0) = T_2(0)$; the method to extract $T_{1,2}$ is the same as the SL one:

-Use the HQET scaling rules near q^2_{max} (at leading order, $T_1 \sim \sqrt{M}$, $T_2 \sim \frac{1}{\sqrt{M}}$) to extrapolate to M_B. With the S.W-clover action, APE($\beta = 6.0$)[28] and UKQCD($\beta = 6.2$)[29] find for $T_2(q^2_{max})$: 0.21(2) and 0.269^{+17}_{-9} respectively.

-The problem is: how to extrapolate to $q^2 = 0$? If we apply VMD on the 2 factors simultaneously, we find that they scale differently at $q^2 = 0$ ($T_1(0) \sim M^{-1/2}$ and $T_2(0) \sim M^{-3/2}$) in contradiction with the fact that they must be equal at $q^2 = 0$. So for which one is VMD better?

* Applying VMD on T_2, APE[28], UKQCD[29] and Bernard et al.,[30] find for $T_2(0)$: $0.084(7)$, 0.112^{+7+16}_{-7-16} and $0.10 \pm 0.01 \pm 0.03$ respectively.

* Applying VMD on T_1, APE[28] finds a larger value $T_1(0) = 0.20(7)$.

There is thus a contradiction between the 2 approaches; it seems to us that the higher value is favoured because indications from lattices (APE and UKQCD) show that the q^2 dependence of T_2 is much weaker than would be predicted by VMD. Using the 1st approach, UKQCD finds BR(B $\to$ K$^*\gamma$) = $(1.7 \pm 0.6(\text{stat})^{+11}_{-9}(\text{sys}) \times 10^{-5}$ while APE, when applying VMD on T_1, finds a value closer (preliminary) to CLEO[31] result: BR = $(4.5 \pm 1.5 \pm 0.9) \times 10^{-5}$.

5. Conclusion

There have been good quantitative studies for f_{D_s} ($\sim$ 230MeV), f_D ($\sim$ 210MeV), f_B ($\sim$ 200MeV (20%)) and for $D \to K^{(*)}\ell\nu$ (agreement up to 10%). The study of $\frac{1}{M}$ corrections (which are found to be large) to HQET are now under control. Concerning the $B \to \pi(\rho)\ell\nu$ and $B \to K^*\gamma$, since the q^2 behaviour is still largely unknown, the predictions at $q^2 = 0$ are only qualitative.

This work was supported in part by the CEC Science Project SC1-CT91-0729 and Human Capital and Mobility Programme, Contract CHRX-CT93-0132.

References

[1] HEMCGC: Bitar *et al.*, Phys. Rev. **D48** (1993) 370.
[2] B.Sheikholeslami and R. Wohlert, Nucl.Phys. B259(1985) 572.
[3] E. Eichten, Nucl.Phys.B(proc.Suppl.)4(1988) 170.
[4] ELC: As. Abada *et al.*, Nucl.Phys.B376(1992) 172.
[5] M.B.Voloshin M.A.Shifman, Sov.J.Nuc.Phys.47(1988)511.
[6] APE: C.R. Allton *et al.*, Nucl.Phys.B(Proc.Suppl.)34(1993) 456.
[7] C.W. Bernard *et al.*, Phys.Rev.D49, 2536 (1994).
[8] UKQCD: Hartmut Wittig *et al.*, Nucl.Phys.B(Proc.Suppl.) 34(1993) 462.
[9] WA75: S.Aoki *et al.*, Prog.Theor.Phys.89,131(1993).
[10] CLEO2: D. Acosta *et al.*, CLNS 93/1238 CLEO-93-14.
[11] ARGUS: H. Albrecht *et al.*, Z.Phys.C54,1(1992).
[12] APE: C.R. Allton *et al.*, Phys.Lett.B326(1994) 295.
[13] C.R. Allton *et al.*, Nucl.Phys. B349(1991) 598.
[14] APE: C.R. Allton *et al.*, LPTENS 93/12-Rome 93/928.
[15] V. Lubicz *et al.*, Phys.Lett.274B(1992)415-420.
[16] N. Isgur and M.B. Wise, Phys. Rev. **D42** (1990) 2388.
[17] ELC: As. Abada *et al.*, Nuc.Phys.B416 (1994) 675.
[18] APE: C.R. Allton *et al.*, ROME prep. 94/981.
[19] UKQCD: D. Richards, these proceedings, Pa-2b.
[20] C. Bernard *et al.*, Phys. Rev. **D43** (1992) 2140, Phys. Rev. **D45** (1992) 869.
[21] M. Bauer, B. Stech and M. Wirbel, Z.Phys.C29(1985) 637; C34 (1987) 103.
[22] N. Isgur, D. Scora, B. Grinstein and M.B. Wise, Phys. Rev. **D39** (1989) 799.
[23] P. Ball, V.M. Braun, H.G. Dosch, Phys. Rev. **D44** (1991) 3567.
[24] M.S. Witherell, USCB-HEP-93-06.
[25] UKQCD: S.P. Booth, Phys. Rev. Lett. **72** (1994) 462.
[26] CLEO: R. Kutschke, these proceedings, Pa-16c.
[27] UKQCD: L. Lelouche *et al.*, to be published.
[28] APE: As. Abada *et al.*, to be published.
[29] UKQCD: K.C. Bowler *et al.*, SHEP 93/94-29.
[30] C. Bernard *et al.*, Phys. Rev. Lett. **72** (1994) 1402.
[31] CLEO: R. Ammar *et al.*, Phys. Rev. Lett. **72** (1993) 674.

Paper presented at XXVII Int. Conf. on High Energy Physics: Session Pa-8
Glasgow, UK, 20–27 July 1994

Quark Model from Lattice QCD

Keh-Fei Liu[†] and Shao-Jing Dong[‡]

Department of Physics, University of Kentucky, Lexington, KY 40506, USA

Abstract

We study the valence approximation in lattice QCD of hadrons where the cloud quarks and antiquarks are deleted by truncating the backward time propagation (Z graphs) in the connected insertions. Whereas the sea quarks are eliminated via the quenched approximation and in the disconnected insertions, it is shown that the ratios of isovector to isoscalar matrix elements in the nucleon reproduce the SU(6) quark model predictions in a lattice QCD calculation. We also discuss how the hadron masses are affected.

1. Introduction

In addition to its classification scheme, the quark model is, by and large, quite successful in delineating the spectrum and structure of mesons and baryons. One often wonders what the nature of the approximation is, especially in view of the advent of quantum chromodynamics (QCD). In order to answer this question, we need to understand first where the quark model is successful and where it fails.

To begin with, we need to define what we mean by the quark model. We consider the simplest approach which includes the following ingredients:

- The Fock space is restricted to the valence quarks only.

- These valence quarks, be them the dressed constituent quarks or the bare quarks, are confined in a potential or a bag. To this zeroth order, the hadron wavefunctions involving u,d, and s quarks are classified by the totally symmetric wavefunctions in the flavor-spin and orbital space according to the $SU(6) \times O(3)$ and totally antisymmetric/symmetric in the color space for the baryons/mesons.

- The degeneracy within the the multiplets is lifted by the different quark masses and the residual interaction between the quarks which is weak

† E-mail: liu@ukcc.uky.edu
‡ E-mail: super124@ukcc.uky.edu

compared to the confining potential. The one-gluon exchange potential is usually taken as this residual interaction to describe the hyper-fine and fine splittings of the hadron masses.

Given what we mean by the quark model, it is easier to understand where the quark model succeeds and fails. It is successful in describing hadron masses, relations of coupling and decay constants, magnetic moments, Okubo-Zweig rule, etc. It is worthwhile noting that all these are based on the valence picture aided with $SU(6) \times O(3)$ group for its color-spin and space group. On the other hand, it fails to account for the U(1) anomaly (the η' mass) , the proton spin crisis and the $\pi N \sigma$ term. All these problems involve large contribution from disconnected insertions involving sea-quarks [1]. It is natural not to expect the valence quark model to work. There are other places where the valence quark model does not work well. These include $\pi\pi$, πN scatterings, current algebra relations, and the form factors of the nucleon which are better described by meson effective theories with chiral symmetry taken into account. For example, the $\pi\pi$ scattering is well described in the chiral perturbation theory, the πN scattering and the nucleon electromagnetic ,axial, and pseudoscalar form factors (especially the neutron charge radius), Goldberg-Treiman relation are all quite well given in the skyrmion approach [2]. One common theme of these models is the chiral symmetry which involves meson cloud and hence the higher Fock space beyond the valence.

2. Valence Approximation

It is then clear that there are three ingredients in the classification of quarks, i.e. the valence, the cloud, and the sea quarks. The question is how one defines them unambiguously and in a model independent way in QCD. It has been shown recently [3] that in evaluating the hadronic tensor in the deep inelastic scattering, the three topological distinct contractions of quark fields lead to the three quark-line skeleton diagrams. The self-contraction of the current leading to a quark loop is separated from the quark lines joining the nucleon interpolating fields. This disconnected insertion (D.I.) refers to the quark lines which are of courses connected by the gloun lines. This D.I. defines the sea-parton. One class of the connected insertion (C.I.) involves an anti-quark propagating backwards in time between the currents and is defined as the cloud anti-quark. Another class of the C.I. involves a quark propagating forward in time between the currents and is defined to be the sum of the valence and cloud quarks. Thus, in the parton model, the antiquark distribution should be written as

$$\bar{q}^i(x) = \bar{q}^i_c(x) + \bar{q}^i_s(x). \qquad (1)$$

to denote their respective origins for each flavor i. Similarly, the quark distribution is written as

$$q^i(x) = q^i_V(x) + q^i_c(x) + q^i_s(x) \qquad (2)$$

Since $q^i_s(x) = \bar{q}^i_s(x)$, we define $q^i_c(x) = \bar{q}^i_c(x)$ so that $q^i_V(x)$ will be responsible for the baryon number, i.e. $\int u_V(x)dx = \int [u(x) - \bar{u}(x)]dx = 2$ and $\int d_V(x)dx = \int [d(x) - \bar{d}(x)] = 1$ for the proton.

We can reveal the role of these quarks in the nucleon matrix elements which involve the three-point function with one current. The D.I. in the three-point function involves the sea-quark contribution to the m.e. It has been shown that the this diagram has indeed large contributions for the flavor-singlet scalar and axial charges [4] so that the discrepancy between the valence quark model and the experiment in the $\pi N \sigma$ term and the flavor-singlet g_A can be understood. Thus we conclude that in order to simulate the valence quark model, the first step is to eliminate the quark loops. This can be done in the well-known quenched approximation by setting the fermion determinant to a constant.

In order to reveal the effect of the cloud degree of freedom, we have calculated the ratios of the isoscalar to isovector axial and scalar charges in a quenched lattice calculation. The ratio of the isoscalar (the C.I. part) to isovector axial charge can be written as

$$
\begin{aligned}
R_A &= \left.\frac{\langle p|\bar{u}\gamma_3\gamma_5 u + \bar{d}\gamma_3\gamma_5 d|p\rangle}{\langle p|\bar{u}\gamma_3\gamma_5 u - \bar{d}\gamma_3\gamma_5 d|p\rangle}\right|_{\text{C.I.}} \\
&= \left.\frac{g^1_A}{g^3_A}\right|_{\text{C.I.}} = \left.\frac{\int dx[\Delta u(x) + \Delta d(x)]}{\int dx[\Delta u(x) - \Delta d(x)]}\right|_{\text{C.I.}} \qquad (3)
\end{aligned}
$$

where $\Delta u(\Delta d)$ is the polarized parton distribution of the u(d) quark and antiquark in the C.I. For the non-relativistic case, g^3_A is 5/3 and g^1_A for the C.I. is 1 Thus, the ratio R_A should be 3/5. Our lattice results based on quenched $16^3 \times 24$ lattices with $\beta = 6$ for the Wilson κ ranging between 0.154 to 0.105 which correspond to strange and twice the charm masses are plotted in Fig. 1 as a function of the quark mass $ma = ln(4\kappa_c/\kappa - 3)$. We indeed find this ratio for the heavy quarks (i.e. $\kappa \geq 0.133$ or $ma \geq 0.4$ in Fig.1). This is to be expected because the cloud antiquarks which involves Z-graphs are suppressed for non-relativistic quarks by $O(p/m_q)$. Interestingly, the ratio dips under 3/5 for light quarks. We interpret this as due to the cloud quark and antiquark, since in the relativistic valence quark models (i.e. no cloud nor sea quarks) the ratio remains to be 3/5. To verify that this is indeed caused by the cloud antiquarks from the backward time propagation, we perform the following approximation. In the Wilson lattice action, the backward time hopping is prescribed by the term $-\kappa(1 - \gamma_4)U_4(x)\delta_{x,y-a_4}$. We shall amputate this term from the quark matrix in our calculation of the quark propagators. As a result, the quarks are limited to propagating forward in time and there will be no Z-graph and hence no cloud quarks and antiquarks. The Fock space is limited to 3 valence quarks. Thus we shall refer to this as the *valence approximation* and we believe it simulates what the naive quark model is supposed to describe by design. After making this valence approximation for the light quarks with $\kappa = 0.148, 0.152$, and 0.154 (The quark mass turns out to differ from before only at the perturbative one-loop order,i.e. $O(\alpha_s)$, which is very small. we find that the ratio R_A becomes 3/5 with errors less than the size of the circles in Fig. 1. Since the valence quark model prediction of R_A is well reproduced by the valence approximation, we believe this proves our point that the deviation of R_A from 3/5 in Fig. 1 is caused by the backward time propagation, i.e. the cloud quarks and antiquarks.

Similar situation happens in the scalar matrix elements. In the parton model description of the forward m.e., the ratio of the isovector to isoscalar scalar charge of the proton for the C.I. is then approximated according to eqs. (1) and (2) as

$$R_S = \left.\frac{\langle p|\bar{u}u - \bar{d}d|p\rangle}{\langle p|\bar{u}u + \bar{d}d|p\rangle}\right|_{\text{C.I.}} = \frac{1 + 2\int dx[\bar{u}_c(x) - \bar{d}_c(x)]}{3 + 2\int dx[\bar{u}_c(x) + \bar{d}_c(x)]} \qquad (4)$$

Since the quark/antiquark number is positive definite, we expect this ratio to be $\leq 1/3$. For heavy quarks where the cloud antiquarks are suppressed, the ratio is indeed $1/3$ (see Fig. 2). For quarks lighter than $\kappa = 0.140$, we find that the ratio is in fact less than $1/3$. The lattice results of the valence approximation for the light quarks, shown as the dots in Fig. 2, turn out to be $1/3$. This shows that the deviation of R_S from $1/3$ is caused by the cloud quarks and antiquarks. With these findings, we obtain an upper-bound for the violation of GSR [3], i.e. $n_{\bar{u}} - n_{\bar{d}} \leq -0.12 \pm 0.05$. This clearly shows that $n_{\bar{u}} - n_{\bar{d}}$ is negative and is quite consistent with the experimental result $\int dx[\bar{u}^p(x) - \bar{d}^p(x)] = -0.14 \pm 0.024$.

3. Hadron Spectroscopy

To further explore the consequences of the valence approximation, we calculate the baryon masses. Plotted in fig. 3 are masses of Δ, N, ρ, and π as a function of the quark mass ma on our lattice with quenched approximation. We see that the hyper-fine splittings between the Δ and N, and the ρ and π grow when the quark mass approaches the chiral limit as expected. However, it is surprising to learn that in the valence approximation, the Δ and N become degenerate within errors, so do the ρ and π as shown in Fig. 4. Since the one-gluon exchange is not switched off in the valence approximation, the hyper-fine splitting is probably not due to the one-gluon exchange potential as commonly believed. Since this is a direct consequence of eliminating the cloud quark/antiquark degree of freedom, one can speculate that it has something to do with the cloud. It seems that a chiral soliton like the skyrmion might delineate a more accurate dynamical picture than the one-gluon exchange spin-spin interaction.

To conclude, we find that the valence approximation in QCD reproduces the SU(6) results of the valence quark model better than we anticipated. Especially in hadron masses, we find that there are no hyper-fine splittings.

References

[1] K.F. Liu, Phys. Lett. **281B**, 141 (1992).
[2] For example, *Chiral Solitons*, ed. K.F. Liu (World Scientific, 1987).
[3] K.F. Liu and S.J. Dong, Phys. Rev. Lett., **72**, 1790 (1994).
[4] S.J. Dong and K.F. Liu, Nucl. Phys. B (Proc. Suppl.) **30**, 487 (1993).

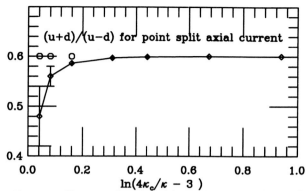

Figure 1. The ratio R_A of eq. (3) as a function of the quark mass $ma = ln(4\kappa_c/\kappa - 3)$.

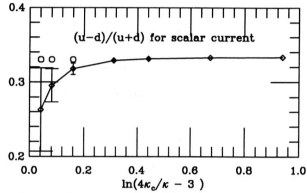

Figure 2. The ratio R_S of eq. (4) as a function of the quark mass ma.

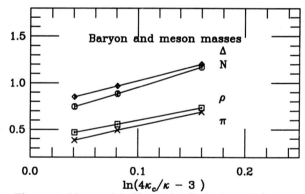

Figure 3. Masses of Δ, N, ρ, and π (in lattice units) as a function of the quark mass ma in the quenched approximation.

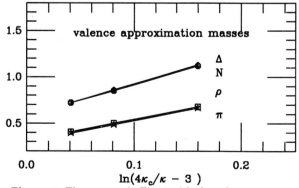

Figure 4. The same as in Fig. 3 with the valence approximation.

Paper presented at XXVII Int. Conf. on High Energy Physics: Session Pa-8
Glasgow, UK, 20–27 July 1994

A Solution to the Strong CP Problem

G. Schierholz

Deutsches Elektronen-Synchrotron DESY, D–22603 Hamburg, Germany
and
Gruppe Theorie der Elementarteilchen, Höchstleistungsrechenzentrum HLRZ,
c/o Forschungszentrum Jülich, D–52425 Jülich, Germany

Abstract

One may argue that QCD solves the strong CP problem by itself, without having to introduce new symmetries and particles. To test this idea, a lattice simulation is performed. The problem is investigated in the CP^3 model first. It is found that the model has a first order phase transition in θ from a confining phase at small θ to a deconfining phase at large θ, and that the critical value of θ decreases towards zero as β is taken to infinity. This suggests that θ is tuned to zero in the continuum limit. Preliminary studies of the SU(2) Yang-Mills theory in four dimensions show a phase transition in θ as well, so that it is quite likely that the strong CP problem in QCD is solved along the same line.

In QCD, as well as in other theories that possess instantons, the proper vacuum states are superpositions of vacua of different winding numbers n:

$$|\theta\rangle = \sum_n \exp(\mathrm{i}\theta n)|n\rangle, \theta \in [0, 2\pi]. \qquad (1)$$

These so-called θ vacua are realized by adding a CP violating term to the action,

$$S_\theta = S - \mathrm{i}\theta Q, \qquad (2)$$

where S is the standard action and Q is the topological charge. A priori θ is a free parameter. Since no CP violation has been observed in the strong interactions, θ must however be very close to zero. † This constitutes the strong CP problem. The present upper bound is $\theta \le 10^{-9}$ [1].

A popular picture of the QCD vacuum is that of a dual superconductor [2] in which color magnetic monopoles condense and color electric charges, i.e.

quarks and gluons, are confined by a dual Meissner effect. This picture has been successfully tested in lattice simulations [3]. In the θ vacuum these monopoles acquire a color electric charge of the magnitude $\theta/2\pi$ [4]. For $\theta \ne 0$ one would expect that the long-range color electric forces are screened by monopoles and that confinement is lost. So QCD would only be a viable (continuum) theory for $\theta = 0$.

What makes a lattice simulation at non-vanishing values of θ very difficult is the fact that the action is complex. As a result, standard lattice techniques are not immediately applicable. This has led us to investigate the problem in a simpler model first.

A model, which in many respects is similar to QCD, is the CP^{N-1} model in two space-time dimensions. The CP^{N-1} model deals with N-component, complex scalar fields $z_a(x)$ of unit length: $\bar{z}_a(x)z_a(x) = 1$, $a = 1, \cdots, N$. Out of these fields one constructs composite vector fields

† In the presence of quarks the θ angle can be rotated into a phase of the quark mass matrix M and vice versa, due to the $U_A(1)$ anomaly. The effective angle is in this case $\bar{\theta} = \theta + \arg \det M$.

$$A_\mu(x) = \frac{\mathrm{i}}{2}\bar{z}_a(x) \overset{\leftrightarrow}{\partial}_\mu z_a(x). \qquad (3)$$

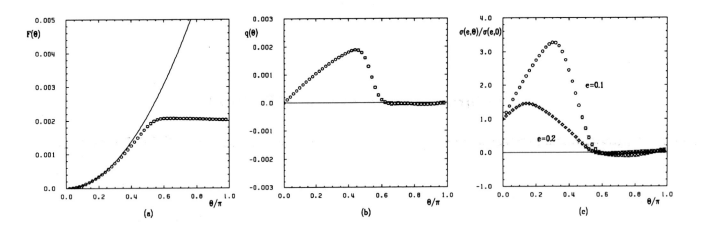

Figure 1. The free energy $F(\theta)$ (a), the charge density $q(\theta)$ (b) and the string tension $\sigma(e, \theta)$ (c) as a function of θ on the $V = 64^2$ lattice at $\beta = 2.7$. The solid curve in (a) is the prediction of the large-N expansion to leading order. Only the first half of the θ interval is displayed. In the second half of the interval $F(\theta) = F(2\pi - \theta)$.

Then the action [5] can be written [6]

$$S = \beta \int d^2x \overline{D_\mu z}_a(x) D_\mu z_a(x), \qquad (4)$$

where $D_\mu = \partial_\mu + iA_\mu$. Thus the model describes a set of charged scalar fields interacting minimally with a composite gauge field. The topological charge is given by

$$Q = \frac{1}{2\pi} \int d^2x \epsilon_{\mu\nu} \partial_\mu A_\nu(x) \equiv \frac{1}{2\pi} \int d^2x F_{01}. \quad (5)$$

The θ dependence of the theory is governed by the partition function

$$Z(\theta) = \sum_Q \exp(i\theta Q)\, p(Q) \equiv \exp(-V F(\theta)), \quad (6)$$

where $p(Q)$ is the probability of finding a field configuration with charge Q, and $F(\theta)$ is the free energy per space-time volume V. In terms of $F(\theta)$ the average topological charge density is given by

$$\frac{1}{V}\langle\theta|Q|\theta\rangle \equiv -iq(\theta) = -i\frac{dF(\theta)}{d\theta}, \qquad (7)$$

and the string tension of two external particles of charge e and $-e$ (in units of the intrinsic charge) turns out to be

$$\sigma(e,\theta) = F(\theta + 2\pi e) - F(\theta). \qquad (8)$$

We have chosen to investigate the CP^3 model. For details of the calculation see ref. [7, 8].

If our idea is correct, we should find a first order phase transition in θ from a confining phase to a Higgs or Coulomb phase. On a finite lattice and at a finite value of β the phase transition is expected to occur at a value $\theta = \theta_c(\beta, V) > 0$, where V now is the lattice volume. Only on an infinite lattice and at $\beta = \infty$, i.e. in the continuum limit, would we expect that $\theta_c = 0$.

A first order phase transition manifests itself in a kink in the free energy, as well as in a discontinuity in the first derivative of the free energy, i.e. the topological charge density. In Fig. 1 I show $F(\theta)$ on the $V = 64^2$ lattice at $\beta = 2.7$. For comparison I also show the prediction of the large-N expansion to leading order [6], $F(\theta) = \text{const.} \cdot \theta^2$. We see a distinctly marked kink at $\theta = \theta_c \approx 0.5\,\pi$: while $F(\theta)$ increases roughly proportional to θ^2 up to $\theta = \theta_c$, $F(\theta)$ turns out to be constant (within the error bars) for $\theta \geq \theta_c$. In Fig. 1 I also show the topological charge density on the same lattice. According to (6) this can be interpreted as a background electric field. We see that $q(\theta)$ increases almost linearly with θ up to $\theta = \theta_c$, where it jumps to zero and then stays zero over the rest of the interval (again within the error bars). Thus the phase transition is marked by a collapse of the background electric field, presumably due to pair production.

To show that the phase transition is a deconfining phase transition, I have plotted the string tension in Fig. 1, again on the 64^2 lattice at $\beta = 2.7$, for two different charges. To keep the discussion simple, I have restricted myself to the case of small fractional charges. This matters because the vacuum will change its properties

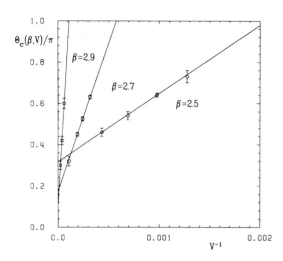

Figure 2. The critical value $\theta_c(\beta, V)$ as a function of V^{-1} for three values of β. The lines are a linear fit to the data points.

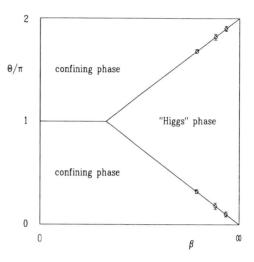

Figure 3. The phase diagram. The horizontal line at $\theta = \pi$ is the strong coupling prediction, and the symbols are the lattice data extrapolated to infinite volume.

if it is exposed to a strong external electric field. We see that the string tension is zero (within the error bars) for $\theta \geq \theta_c$. This result is a consequence of the property that $F(\theta)$ is constant for $\theta \geq \theta_c$. The string tension reaches its peak at $\theta = \theta_c - 2\pi e$.

In Fig. 2 I show all our results for $\theta_c(\beta, V)$ for a variety of lattice volumes ranging from $V = 28^2$ to $V = 200^2$ and for three values of β: $\beta = 2.5$, $\beta = 2.7$ and $\beta = 2.9$. The lattice data display strong finite size effects. For a first order phase transition we expect

$$\theta_c(\beta, V) - \theta_c(\beta, \infty) \propto V^{-1} \qquad (9)$$

for fixed β. When $\theta_c(\beta, V)$ is plotted against V^{-1}, we find that for all three values of β our data fall on a straight line, in accordance with the predictions of a first order phase transition. This allows us to extrapolate the lattice results to the infinite volume.

We find that the extrapolated values of θ_c fall rapidly to zero as β is taken to infinity. Our results are consistent with a decay like $\theta_c \propto 1/\xi$, where ξ is the correlation length. (For our values of β the correlation length is 4.5, 8.8 and 18.5, respectively.) In the strong coupling limit the model is known to have a first order phase transition at $\theta = \theta_c = \pi$ [9]. This suggests a phase diagram of the form shown in Fig. 3.

Thus $\theta = 0$ is the only value at which one can take the continuum limit, at least within the confining phase. This resolves the strong CP problem.

As a next step towards solving QCD, we are currently investigating the problem in the SU(2) Yang-Mills theory in four dimensions [10]. Preliminary results indicate a first order phase transition in θ, just as in

the case of the CP^3 model. Because of lack of space I cannot show a figure here. To establish the phase diagram firmly, we will have to repeat the calculation on lattices of various sizes and for several values of β still, as we did for the CP^3 model.

[1] V. Baluni, Phys. Rev. **D19** (1979) 2227;
R. Crewther, P. Di Vecchia, G. Veneziano and E. Witten, Phys. Lett. **B88** (1979) 123; Erratum, *ibid.* **B91** (1980) 487.
[2] G. 't Hooft, in *High Energy Physics*, Proceedings of the EPS International Conference on High Energy Physics, Palermo, 1975, ed. A. Zichichi (Editrice Compositori, Bologna, 1976); G. 't Hooft, Phys. Scripta **25** (1982) 133; S. Mandelstam, Phys. Rep. **C23** (1976) 245.
[3] A. S. Kronfeld, G. Schierholz and U.-J. Wiese, Nucl. Phys. **B293** (1987) 461; A. S. Kronfeld, M. L. Laursen, G. Schierholz and U.-J. Wiese, Phys. Lett. **B198** (1987) 516; F. Brandstaeter, G. Schierholz and U.-J. Wiese, Phys. Lett. **B272** (1991) 319; V. Singh, D. A. Browne and R. W. Haymaker, Phys. Lett. **B306** (1993) 115; for a recent review see: T. Suzuki, Nucl. Phys. **B** (Proc. Suppl.) **30** (1993) 176, and references therein.
[4] E. Witten, Phys. Lett. **B86** (1979) 283.
[5] H. Eichenherr, Nucl. Phys **B146** (1978) 215; E. Cremmer and Scherk, Phys. Lett. **B74** (1978) 341.
[6] A. D'Adda, P. Di Vecchia and M. Lüscher, Nucl. Phys. **B146** (1978) 63; E. Witten, Nucl. Phys. **B149** (1979) 285.
[7] Š. Olejník and G. Schierholz, Nucl. Phys. **B** (Proc. Suppl.) **34** (1994) 709.
[8] G. Schierholz, Nucl. Phys. **B** (Proc. Suppl.) **37A** (1994) 203.
[9] N. Seiberg, Phys. Rev. Lett. **53** (1984) 637.
[10] F. Brandstaeter and G. Schierholz, in progress.

The electroweak phase transition on the lattice

Zoltán Fodor*

Deutsches Elektronen-Synchrotron, DESY, 22603 Hamburg, Germany

Abstract

The finite temperature electroweak phase transition is studied on the lattice. The results of the simulations obtained by the 3-dimensional effective theories and the 4-dimensional SU(2)-Higgs model are reviewed.

1. Introduction

The perturbative sector of the electroweak (EW) theory is extremely successful and we have even reached a point at which the Higgs mass (m_H) starts to appear in the EW precision data. However, there are basic questions in the theory, which can not be answered within the perturbative framework. One of them is the finite temperature electroweak phase transition.

At high temperatures (T) the spontaneously broken EW symmetry is restored. Since the baryon-number violating processes are unsuppressed at high T, the cosmological EW phase transition plays a crucial role in the understanding of the observed baryon asymmetry [1]. The idea of the EW baryogenesis needs a departure from thermal equilibrium, thus a sufficiently strong first order phase transition via bubble nucleation. A strong first order phase transition could explain the observed asymmetry, a weak one could have washed out any B+L asymmetry.

Unfortunately, the perturbative treatment of the phase transition suffers from infrared problems. In the realistic Higgs mass range $(m_H > 63\ GeV)$ the perturbative approach predicts $\mathcal{O}(100\%)$ corrections [2, 3, 4] for the relevant quantities (e.g. interface tension or latent heat). Some of the nonperturbative estimates (e.g. magnetic mass [2]) suggest a weaker, others (e.g. vacuum-condensate [5]) a stronger first order phase transition than the perturbative approach. The only

way to solve the problem seems to be the use of Monte-Carlo simulations on the lattice.

Since fermions always have nonzero Matsubara frequencies, the perturbative treatment of these, at high temperatures very massive, modes could be satisfactory. Therefore, the starting point of the lattice analyses is the $SU(2)$-Higgs model, which contains all the essential features of the standard model of electroweak interactions.

In Sect. 2 the basic idea of the dimensional reduction and the different reduced 3-dimensional models are presented. Sect. 3 deals with the results of the simulations (3-dimensional ferromagnet model [6], 3-dimensional gauge-Higgs model [7], 4-dimensional, finite temperature $SU(2)$-Higgs model [8, 9]).

2. 4-dimensional $SU(2)$-Higgs model and effective 3-dimensional models

The 4-dimensional $SU(2)$-Higgs model at finite T is defined by the following action

$$S = \int_0^\beta d\tau \int d^3x \left[\frac{1}{4} F_{\mu\nu}^a F_{\mu\nu}^a + (D_\mu \phi)^\dagger (D_\mu \phi) - \frac{1}{2} m^2 \phi^\dagger \phi + \lambda (\phi^\dagger \phi)^2 \right], \tag{1}$$

where D_μ and $F_{\mu\nu}^a$ are the usual covariant derivative and the Yang-Mills field strength, respectively. $\beta = 1/T$, and the τ integration is over periodic bosonic fields. This model has been studied on the lattice by ref [8, 9].

The origin of the perturbative infrared problems

* On leave from Institute for Theoretical Physics, Eötvös University, Budapest, Hungary

is the appearance of zero Matsubara modes in the bosonic sector. Therefore, similarly to the case of the fermion fields with nonzero Matsubara frequencies one can integrate out all the massive, non-static bosonic modes of (1) at the one-loop level. Since these modes are heavy in the high temperature limit, the perturbative treatment of them could be well-founded. This dimensional reduction gives an effective 3-dimensional gauge-Higgs model, where in addition, also an isovector field (A_0^a), the fourth component of the gauge fields, is present

$$
S = \int d^3 x \left[\frac{1}{4} F_{ij}^a F_{ij}^a + \frac{1}{2} (D_i A_0)^a (D_i A_0)^a \right.
$$
$$
+ (D_i \phi)^\dagger (D_i \phi) + \frac{1}{2} m_D^2 A_0^a A_0^a + \frac{1}{4} \lambda_A (A_0^a A_0^a)^2 + m_3^2 \phi^\dagger \phi
$$
$$
\left. + \lambda_3 (\phi^\dagger \phi)^2 + \frac{1}{2} h_3 A_0^a A_0^a \phi^\dagger \phi \right]. \tag{2}
$$

Here all the 3-dimensional couplings g_3^2, λ_3, λ_A and h_3 have dimension $[GeV]$. These parameters and the masses m_D and m_3 can be expressed in terms of the 4-dimensional couplings and the temperature [10, 11]. This model has been studied on the lattice by ref [7].

The next step is the elimination of the gauge degrees of freedom. One obtains a a 3-dimensional $\mathcal{O}(4)$ ferromagnet model with cubic and quartic terms in the action.

$$
S = \int d^3 x \left[(D_i \phi)^\dagger (D_i \phi) + \bar{m}_3^2 \phi^\dagger \phi + \bar{\lambda}_3 (\phi^\dagger \phi)^2 \right.
$$
$$
\left. - 2 \bar{g}_3^2 (\bar{m}_T^2 + \phi^\dagger \phi)^{3/2} - \bar{g}_3^2 (\bar{m}_E^2 + \phi^\dagger \phi)^{3/2} \right]. \tag{3}
$$

The parameters of this action can be similarly expressed in terms of the 4-dimensional couplings and the temperature as in the previous case [6]. The infrared stability is ensured by including magnetic $(\bar{m}_T)$ and electric $(\bar{m}_E)$ screening mass terms. Since the first of them has a nonperturbative origin, the approximation contains an uncertainty connected with the magnetic mass. This model has been studied on the lattice by Ref. [6]. Their choice of $\bar{m}_T$ has been suggested by the solution of the one-loop gap-equations of the $SU(2)$-Higgs theory at finite temperature [2].

3. Lattice simulations

The results obtained by the different groups are summarized. First the results of the 3-dimensional $\mathcal{O}(4)$ ferromagnet model, then those of the 3-dimensional gauge-Higgs model are presented. Finally the analyses based on the 4-dimensional $SU(2)$-Higgs model are considered.

3.1. The 3-dimensional $\mathcal{O}(4)$ ferromagnet model

After discretizing the action (3) and performing the mean field analysis of this effective scalar model Ref. [6]

presented the results of their Monte-Carlo simulations. The typical lattice sizes and statistics for a given lattice size were $8^3 - 18^3$ and 10^6 sweeps, respectively. The parameters used in this work correspond to the physical values of the W mass and vacuum expectation value of the Higgs field ($m_W = 80 \; GeV$ and $v = 246 \; GeV$), however, the Higgs mass ($m_H \approx 35 \; GeV$) was considerably smaller than the experimental bound. This value has been selected: i) to have a strong signal of a first order transition; ii) to be free of the uncertainties due to renormalisation prescriptions; iii) to be able to compare the results with other 3-dimensional analyses, e.g. [7].

The simulations have shown a considerably weaker first order phase transition than the mean-field analysis. For the critical temperature (T_c), jump in the order parameter at the critical temperature (φ_c), latent heat $(\Delta\epsilon)$ and interface tension (σ) the simulations have given $T_c = 114.6(36)$, $\varphi_c/T_c = 0.68(4)$, $\Delta\epsilon/T_c^4 = 0.122(8)$ and $\sigma/T_c^3 \approx 6.4 \cdot 10^{-4}$, respectively. The corresponding mean field results are $T_c = 99.6$, $\varphi_c/T_c = 1.3$, $\Delta\epsilon/T_c^4 = 0.262$ and $\sigma/T_c^3 = 0.024$, respectively.

Since the non-perturbative dynamics of the scalar fields seems to weaken the phase transition, any observation of hard first order phase transition could result only from the non-perturbative effects related to the gauge degrees of freedom.

3.2. The 3-dimensional gauge-Higgs model

In [11] the one- and two-loop effective potential is constructed using the dimensional reduction idea (cf. eq. 2). With the help of the renormalisation group leading logarithms have been summed.

The lattice results have been presented in [7]. The used W mass and gauge coupling were $m_W = 80.6 \; GeV$ and $g = 2/3$, respectively. The runs have been done on lattices of sizes $8^3 - 32^3$.

In the broken phase the perturbative and lattice results are in very good agreement, e.g. the predictions for the expectation value of the Higgs field agree within 1%. However, for other quantities, which are crucial for the cosmological phase transition, the lattice simulations suggest a stronger first order phase transition than the perturbative approach. For $m_H = 35 \; GeV$ the critical temperatures obtained on the lattice and in the perturbative approach are $T_c = 85 \; GeV$ and $T_c = 95 \; GeV$, respectively; for $m_H = 80 \; GeV$ the values are $T_c = 162.1(26) \; GeV$ and $T_c = 173.3 \; GeV$, respectively. The jump in the order parameter is $\varphi_c/T_c = 0.73(4)$ obtained by the lattice simulation and $\varphi_c/T_c = 0.47$ in perturbation theory.

The informations obtained from the above lattice studies are in qualitative agreement with the vacuum-condensate picture [5]. Using the vacuum energy-shift suggested by the above data and following [5], the electroweak baryogenesis could be possible up to Higgs mass of about 80 GeV. The exact determination of this bound, however, needs further study.

3.3. 4-dimensional SU(2)-Higgs model at finite temperature I.

The most straightforward way to study the problem on the lattice is discretizing the action of (1) and performing the simulations on asymmetric thermal lattices, $L_t \ll L_x, L_y, L_z$ (L_t is the extension of the lattice in the temperature direction).

In [8] the typical lattice sizes were $2 \cdot 16^3 - 2 \cdot 36^3$ and approximately 7000 measurements have been done for each set. The simulations have been performed for $m_W = 80\ GeV$, $m_H \approx m_W$ and $g^2 = 0.5$. The lattice results (two-state signal, multihistogram and finite size analysis) show a clear first order phase transition. The phase transition is stronger than the one obtained in the one-loop perturbative approach. The jump in the order parameter is $\varphi_c/T_c = 0.68$ given by the lattice simulation and $\varphi_c/T_c = 0.3$ in perturbation theory. The latent heat and the metastability temperature range $(\delta T/T_c)$ exceeds perturbative estimates by an order of magnitude, thus e.g. $\delta T/T_c = 0.076$ on the lattice and $\delta T/T_c = 0.008$ in the perturbative approach.

3.4. 4-dimensional SU(2)-Higgs model at finite temperature II.

A 4-dimensional, finite T analysis has ben done by [9] too. The largest lattice used was $2 \cdot 32^2 \cdot 256$ with $\mathcal{O}(10^5)$ updating. The simulations have been performed for two set of parameters: $m_W = 80\ GeV$, $m_H = 18\ GeV$, $g_{bare}^2 = 0.5$ (low) point; $m_W = 80\ GeV$, $m_H = 49\ GeV$, $g_{bare}^2 = 0.5$ (high) point. A moderate renormalisation of the gauge-coupling, $g_R^{2,low} = 0.5476(90)$ and $g_R^{2,low} = 0.5781(95)$, has been found.

The latent heat has been calculated from the discontinuity of the energy density ($\Delta\epsilon$). The necessary partial derivatives along the *lines of constant physics* have been determined by use of the one-loop renormalisation group equations, whereas the critical points have been given by the inspection of the gauge-invariant effective potential [12, 13, 4]. The obtained values are: $(\Delta\epsilon/T_c^4)^{low} = 1.68(17)$ and $(\Delta\epsilon/T_c^4)^{high} = 0.125(19)$.

The interface tension has been determined using the two-coupling method of Potvin and Rebbi [14]. The obtained results are: $(\sigma/T_c^3)^{low} = 0.84(16)$ and $(\sigma/T_c^3)^{high} = 0.008(2)$.

The lattice results for $\Delta\epsilon$ and σ are in qualitative good agreement with the two-loop resummed perturba-

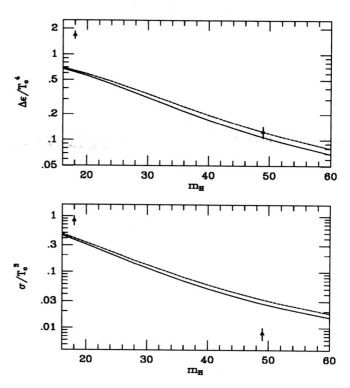

Figure 1. The perturbative and the lattice results for $\Delta\epsilon$ and σ for different Higgs masses. The solid line corresponds to g_R^{low} the dashed one to g_R^{high}.

tive results [3] (see Fig. 1). Note, that the $L_t = 3$ simulations [15] confirm the above conclusions.

References

[1] V. A. Kuzmin, V. A. Rubakov and M. E. Shaposhnikov, Phys. Lett. **B155** (1985) 36.
[2] W. Buchmüller, Z. Fodor, T. Helbig and D. Walliser, Ann. Phys. (NY) **234** (1994) 260.
[3] Z. Fodor, A. Hebecker, DESY-94-025 (1994), Nucl. Phys. B, in press.
[4] Z. Fodor, these proceedings.
[5] M. Shaposhnikov, Phys. Lett. **B316** (1993) 112.
[6] F. Karsch, T. Neuhaus, A. Patkós BI-TP 94/27.
[7] K. Kajantie, K. Rummukainen, M.E. Shaposhnikov, Nucl. Phys. **B407** (1993) 356; K. Farakos, K. Kajantie, K. Rummukainen, M.E. Shaposhnikov, CERN-TH.7244/94 (1994).
[8] B. Bunk, E. M. Ilgenfritz, J. Kripfganz, A. Schiller, Nucl. Phys. **B403** (1993) 453.
[9] F. Csikor, Z. Fodor, J. Hein, K. Jansen, A. Jaster, I. Montvay, Phys. Lett. **B334** (1994) 405.
[10] A. Jakovác, K. Kajantie, A. Patkós, Phys. Rev. **D49** (1994) 6810;.
[11] K. Farakos, K. Kajantie, K. Rummukainen, M.E. Shaposhnikov, CERN-TH.6973/94 (1994).
[12] M. Lüscher, unpublished notes (1988).
[13] W. Buchmüller, Z. Fodor and A. Hebecker, Phys. Lett. **B331** 131 (1994).
[14] J. Potvin, C. Rebbi, Phys. Rev. Lett. **62** (1989) 3062.
[15] Z.Fodor, J. Hein, K. Jansen, A. Jaster, I. Montvay, DESY-94-159.

Parallel Session Pa-9

CP Violation and $B\bar{B}$ Mixing

Conveners: D. Wegener (Universitat Dortmund)
F. DeJongh (FERMILAB)

Scientific secretaries: A. Pilaftsis
M. Peardon (reserve)

Paper presented at XXVII Int. Conf. on High Energy Physics: Session Pa-9
Glasgow, UK, 20–27 July 1994

Search for CP-Violating Rare K_L Decays at FNAL

Katsushi Arisaka

Department of Physics, University of California Los Angeles
Los Angeles, CA USA

On behalf of the FNAL E799 Collaboration

Abstract

The FNAL E799 collaboration has carried out a high sensitivity search for several rare K_L decays. The largest contribution to the decay mode $K_L \rightarrow \pi^0 l\bar{l}$ is considered to be CP-violating, and the branching ratio is expected at the 10^{-11} level in the Standard Model. We have set the following upper limits for this type of decay mode:

$\text{Br}(K_L \rightarrow \pi^0 e^+ e^-) < 4.2 \times 10^{-9}$,
$\text{Br}(K_L \rightarrow \pi^0 \mu^+ \mu^-) < 5.1 \times 10^{-9}$, and
$\text{Br}(K_L \rightarrow \pi^0 \nu \bar{\nu}) < 5.7 \times 10^{-5}$.

In addition, the study is under way on various decays such as $K_L \rightarrow \pi^0 \pi^0 \gamma$, $K_L \rightarrow e^+ e^- e^+ e^-$, and $K_L \rightarrow e^+ e^- \gamma \gamma$. The latest results of our analysis will be presented.

1. Introduction

The search for the origin of CP violation has been a major effort at FNAL in Kaon physics over the last decade. A precision measurement of the direct CP violation parameter ϵ'/ϵ was carried out by the experiment E731, which has set the final result of $Re(\epsilon'/\epsilon) = (7.4 \pm 2.9(sys) \pm 5.2(stat)) \times 10^{-4}$. This collaboration was expanded to E799 and with substantial detector upgrade, several rare K_L decay modes have been studied. Taking advantage of high precision measurement of photon and electron energies at higher beam energy at FNAL, our effort was mainly concentrated on the decay modes whose final states include photons and/or electrons. This paper will report the progress on these rare K_L decay studies.

2. Search for Direct CP Violation

The decay $K_L \rightarrow \pi^0 l\bar{l}$ is known to be dominated by direct CP violation. In the case of $K_L \rightarrow \pi^0 e^+ e^-$ or $K_L \rightarrow \pi^0 \mu^+ \mu^-$, however, the situation becomes complicated due to the contributions from indirect CP violation from K_1 decay and from the CP-conserving part via $K_2 \rightarrow \pi^0 \gamma^* \gamma^*$ process. Recent study shows that indirect CP violation has a similar contribution as the direct CP violating part, while the CP conserving part is expected to be negligible by Chiral Perturbation Theory[1].

In the case of $K_L \rightarrow \pi^0 \nu \bar{\nu}$, only the direct CP violation part becomes a major contribution to the decay process since both the indirect CP violating and CP conserving part are negligible due to the absence of electromagnetic processes[5]. The expected branching ratio is also a factor of six larger than in the case of $K_L \rightarrow \pi^0 e^+ e^-$. However, experimentally, a lack of kinematical constraints on the final state makes this mode extremely challenging.

3. Study of Other Rare Processes

Along with the studies of the above CP violating decay modes which are very rare ($\sim 10^{-11}$), several interesting, but less-rare decay modes can be studied

Decay Mode	Previous		E799	
$K_L \to \pi^0 e^+ e^-$	$< 5.5 \times 10^{-9}$	[3]	$< 4.2 \times 10^{-9}$	[6]
$K_L \to \pi^0 \mu^+ \mu^-$	$< 1.2 \times 10^{-6}$	[4]	$< 5.2 \times 10^{-9}$	[7]
$K_L \to \pi^0 \nu \bar{\nu}$	$< 2.4 \times 10^{-4}$	[8]	$< 5.8 \times 10^{-5}$	[9]
$K_L \to e^+ e^- \gamma \gamma$	$(6.6 \pm 3.2) \times 10^{-7}$	[10]	$(6.5 \pm 1.2(stat) \pm 0.6(sys)) \times 10^{-7}$	[11]
$K_L \to e^+ e^- e^+ e^-$	$(3.07 \pm 1.25) \times 10^{-8}$	[12]	$(3.96 \pm 0.79(stat) \pm 0.32(sys)) \times 10^{-8}$	[13]
$K_L \to \pi^0 \pi^0 \gamma$	-		$< 2.3 \times 10^{-4}$	[15]
$\pi^0 \to e^+ e^-$	$(2 \pm 1) \times 10^{-8}$	[16]	$(8.0^{+4.1}_{-2.9}(stat) \pm 0.5(sys)) \times 10^{-8}$	[17]
$\pi^0 \to \mu^\pm e^\mp$	$< 1.6 \times 10^{-8}$	[18]	$< 8.6 \times 10^{-9}$	[19]

Table 1. Recent Results from E799.

in detail. Such decay modes include: $K_L \to e^+ e^- \gamma \gamma$, $K_L \to e^+ e^- e^+ e^-$, and $K_L \to \pi^0 \pi^0 \gamma$. The process $K_L \to e^+ e^- \gamma \gamma$ is important to study since this is a major background source in the $K_L \to \pi^0 e^+ e^-$ search. Understanding of two photon mediated processes such as $K_L \to e^+ e^- e^+ e^-$ and $K_L \to \mu^+ \mu^- \gamma$ will give us information on long distance contributions in the $K_L \to \mu^+ \mu^-$ decay mode: by extracting the short distance contribution in $K_L \to \mu^+ \mu^-$, one can obtain a constraint on V_{td} and the top quark mass. Other processes such as $K_L \to \pi^0 \pi^0 \gamma$ provide an excellent testing ground for Chiral Perturbation Theory. Using decays in flight of $K_L \to \pi^0 \pi^0 \pi^0$, some rare π^0 decays can be studied as well, such as $\pi^0 \to \mu^\pm e^\mp$ and $\pi^0 \to e^+ e^-$. Our latest study on the above decay modes are summarized in this paper.

4. E799 Detector

The E799 detector, consists of four major components.

- Vacuum decay tanks with several photon veto counters.
- A charged particle spectrometer consisting of four drift chamber modules and $200MeV/c$ Pt kick analyzing magnet.
- An EM calorimeter made of 804 lead-glass blocks of 18.7 radiation lengths depth.
- A muon identification system.

A neutral K_L beam is produced by 800 GeV protons from the FNAL Tevatron at a target located about 150 m upstream of the detector. The typical beam has an intensity of 1.4×10^{12} protons per spill, resulting in 5.3×10^7 K_L's per spill. K_L's, produced on a beryllium target with 4.8 mrad targetting angle have a broad energy spectrum from 10 to 200 GeV which peaks around 50 GeV. Only 2.7% of the K_L's decay in flight in the 40 m long decay tank, and 0.8 - 30% of decays are accepted by the detector, depending on the decay mode.

5. Data Collection

The data were collected during the 1991 Fermilab Fixed target run, which started on October 13 and ended on January 9, 1992. During the period from October 19 to November 19, a pre-shower detector was installed to collect special data samples for the study of the $K_L \to \pi^0 \gamma \gamma$ and $K_L \to \pi^0 \pi^0 \gamma$ decay modes. Overall, there are 405 million physics triggers written on tape, resulting in 1 Tbytes of data on 1330 tapes.

6. Analysis

The analysis of the data consisted of particle identification and event reconstruction. Charged particle trajectories were retraced from the drift chamber information, and their momenta were calculated from the bend angle through the analysing magnetic field. The K_L decay position was determined from the intersection of tracks in the decay volume. Electron identification was achieved by comparing the track momentum with the associated cluster energy in the electromagnetic calorimeter. Photons were identified by a significant energy deposit ($> 1GeV$) in the calorimeter which could not be associated with a track incident upon the calorimeter. Muons were identified by the association of a charged particle track with a minimal energy deposit in the calorimeter and a recorded hit in the scintillator banks behind the 3 meter thick steel filter.

7. Results

The latest results from E799 are summarized in table 1 together with the previous measurements. Final plots for the three $K_L \to \pi^0 l\bar{l}$ searches are shown in figures 1, 2, and 3. For the $K_L \to \pi^0 e^+ e^-$ search, the final data sample in figure 1 shows no signal candidates with a background environment dominated by $K_L \to \pi^\pm e^\mp \nu$ decays. Figure 2 shows the very clean final data sample for the $K_L \to \pi^0 \mu^+ \mu^-$ search. Lastly, the final data sample for the $K_L \to \pi^0 \nu \bar{\nu}$ search is shown in figure 3 with the dominant sources of background coming from $K_L \to \pi^\pm e^\mp \nu$ and $\Lambda \to n\pi^0$ decays.

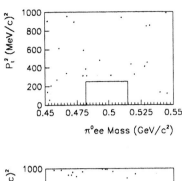

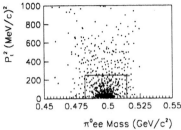

Figure 1. Plot of P_T^2 versus $M_{\pi^0 ee}$ for data (top) and $K_L \to \pi^0 e^+ e^-$ Monte Carlo (bottom).

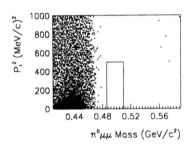

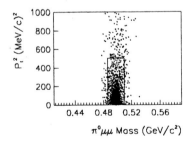

Figure 2. Plot of P_T^2 versus $M_{\pi^0 \mu\mu}$ for data (top) and $K_L \to \pi^0 \mu^+ \mu^-$ Monte Carlo (bottom).

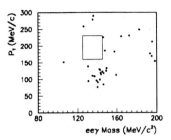

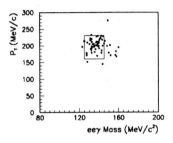

Figure 3. Plot of P_T versus $M_{ee\gamma}$ for data (top) and $K_L \to \pi^0 \nu\bar{\nu}$ Monte Carlo (bottom).

E799

University of California Los Angeles, University of Chicago, University of Colarado, Elmhurst College, Fermilab, University of Illinois, Osaka University and Rutgers University.

References

[1] C. O. Dib, I. Dunietz, and F. J. Gilman,Phys. Rev. **D39** (1989) 2639.P. Heiliger and L. M. Sehgal,Phys. Rev. **D47** (1993) 4920.G. Ecker, A. Pich, and E. de Rafael, Nucl. Phys. B 291, 692 (1987).

[2] P. Heiliger and L. M. Sehgal,Phys. Rev. **D47** (1993) 4920.

[3] K. E. Ohl *et al.*,Phys. Rev. Lett. **64** (1990) 2755.

[4] A. S. Carroll *et al.*,Phys. Rev. Lett. **44** (1980) 525.

[5] L. Littenberg,Phys. Rev. **D39** (1989) 3322.

[6] D.A. Harris *et al.*,Phys. Rev. Lett. **71** (1993) 3918.

[7] D.A. Harris *et al.*,Phys. Rev. Lett. **71** (1993) 3914.

[8] G. E. Graham *et al.*, Phys. Letters B295, 169 (1992).

[9] M. Weaver *et al.*,Phys. Rev. Lett. **72** (1994) 3758.

[10] W. M. Morse *et al.*,Phys. Rev. **D45** (1992) 36.

[11] T. Nakaya *et al.*, (submitted to Phys. Rev. Letters).

[12] T. Akaga *et al.*,Phys. Rev. **D47** (1993) R2644.

[13] P. Gu *et al.*,Phys. Rev. Lett. **72** (1994) 3000.

[14] A. S. Carroll *et al.*,Phys. Rev. Lett. **44** (1980) 525.

[15] D. Roberts *et al.*,Phys. Rev. **D50** (1994) 1874.

[16] J. Fischer *et al.*, Phys. Letters B73, 364 (1978). J. S. Frank *et al.*,Phys. Rev. **D28** (1983) 423.C. Niebuhr *et al.*,Phys. Rev. **D40** (1989) 2797.

[17] K. S. McFarland *et al.*,Phys. Rev. Lett. **71** (1994) 31.

[18] A. M. Lee *et al.*,Phys. Rev. Lett. **64** (1990) 165.

[19] P. Krolak *et al.*, Phys. Letters B320, 407 (1993).

New Measurements of CP Violation Parameters as Tests of CPT in K Meson Decay*

G.D. Gollin[†‡] and W.P. Hogan[§]

† Dept. of Physics, University of Illinois at Urbana-Champaign, Urbana, Illinois 61801-3080, USA
§ Department of Physics, Rutgers University, Piscataway, New Jersey 08855, USA

(FNAL E773 collaboration)

Abstract

We report new results for the phase of η_{+-}, the $K_L - K_S$ mass difference, the K_S lifetime, and the phase difference $Arg(\eta_{00}) - Arg(\eta_{+-})$ in $K \to \pi\pi$ decay. In addition, we report a measurement of the magnitude and phase of $\eta_{+-\gamma}$ in $K \to \pi^+\pi^-\gamma$ decay.

Planck-scale dynamics could lead to CPT-violating effects[1, 2, 3, 4] such as the existence of small differences in particle-antiparticle masses and lifetimes. Defining the amplitude ratios η_{+-}, η_{00} and their phases ϕ_{+-}, ϕ_{00} in the usual way, it can be shown[5] that

$$\frac{m_{K^0} - m_{\overline{K^0}}}{m_K} \approx \left(\frac{\Delta m}{m_K}\right) \sqrt{2}|\eta_{+-}| \, tan(\phi_{+-} - \phi_\epsilon + \frac{\Delta\phi}{3}) \, . \tag{1}$$

Here, Δm is the $K_L - K_S$ mass difference, ϵ is the CP-impurity in K_L, K_S, and $\Delta\phi$ is $\phi_{00} - \phi_{+-}$. The small value for Δm provides considerable "leverage" in testing CPT; published values[6] yield $|m_{K^0} - m_{\overline{K^0}}|/m_K \leq 2.5 \times 10^{-18}$, less than two orders of magnitude away from the domain in which Planck-scale physics might play a role. A CP-violating, T-conserving mixing of K^0 and $\overline{K^0}$ would shift η_{00} and η_{+-} in the same direction in the complex plane, while a CPT violating relationship among the various $K \to \pi\pi$ decay amplitudes would split them apart [7].

In Fermilab Experiment 773 we measured ϕ_{+-}, ϕ_ϵ, and $\Delta\phi$ by studying the proper time dependence of neutral K meson decays into $\pi^0\pi^0$ and $\pi^+\pi^-$ final states downstream of regenerators in a pair of K_L beams[8]. In addition to our CPT-related $\pi\pi$ preliminary results, we also report an improved measurement of $\eta_{+-\gamma}$, a CP-

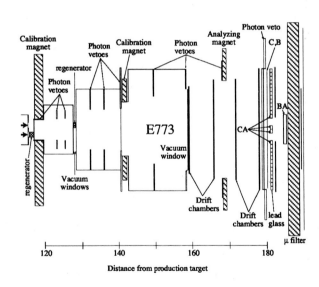

Figure 1. Elevation view of the E773 detector. Kaons in the beams travel to the right in the figure.

violation parameter in $K_L \to \pi^+\pi^-\gamma$ decays.

The detector (figure 1) was a reconfigured version of the E731 spectrometer ([6]) which had been used to measure $Re(\epsilon'/\epsilon)$. Two K_L beams passed through regenerators; data were recorded simultaneously for $\pi^0\pi^0$ and $\pi^+\pi^-$ decays in both beams. A drift chamber spectrometer and lead glass electromagnetic calorimeter provided kinematic information about charged particles

---

* These results comprise the thesis work of R.A. Briere, J.N. Matthews, and B. Schwingenheuer. See paper ICHEP94 Ref. gls0167 for a more detailed description of the experiment.
‡ E-mail address: gollin@uihepa.hep.uiuc.edu.

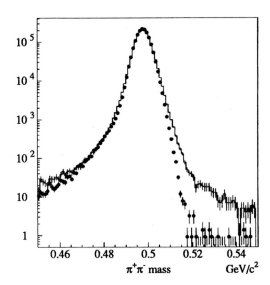

Figure 2. $\pi^+\pi^-$ invariant mass distributions for events satisfying all other analysis cuts. Data (histogram) and Monte Carlo (points) are shown. The data's high-side tail contains contributions from δ-rays which are not simulated by the Monte Carlo.

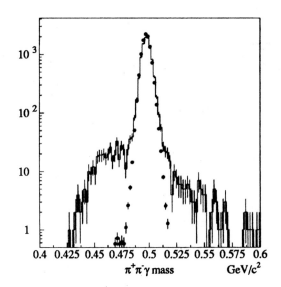

Figure 3. $\pi^+\pi^-\gamma$ invariant mass distributions. Data (histograms) and Monte Carlo (points) are shown; the simulation did not include background modeling.

and photons in the final state. Muons and electrons were used to calibrate the detector. Veto counters allowed us to discard events in which photons might have missed the lead glass array.

Events which came from $\pi\pi$ and $\pi^+\pi^-\gamma$ decays reconstructed with invariant mass close to the known kaon mass. Backgrounds from K_{e3}, 3π, and Λ decays were suppressed through kinematic and calorimetric requirements. Cuts on activity in the veto system and on event topology served to reduce backgrounds from decays with undetected photons. Reconstructed K mass distributions are shown in figures 2–4. In all, 1,824k $\pi^+\pi^-$, 10.8k $\pi^+\pi^-\gamma$, and 375k $\pi^0\pi^0$ events contributed to the results presented.

We used a detailed Monte Carlo simulation to calculate detection efficiency, to study backgrounds, and to determine the effects of various sources of systematic uncertainty. The simulation was verified with the large samples of K_{e3}, $\pi^+\pi^-\pi^0$, and $3\pi^0$ decays which satisfied the experiment triggers. The effects of spurious detector activity were studied by combining data from "accidental" triggers with simulated event data. Shown in figure 5 are comparisons of the $\pi\pi$ vertex distributions for data and Monte Carlo.

Our fits to background-subtracted data included free parameters describing the regenerator, beam intensities and K energy spectra. In the $Arg(\eta_{+-})$ fit we constrained $\Delta m = 0.5286 \times 10^{10}\hbar s^{-1}c^{-2}$ ([6]), and $\tau_S = 0.8922 \times 10^{-10}s$ ([9]). (These values correspond to $\phi_\epsilon = 43.33°$.) Sources of systematic errors included uncertainties in our determination of

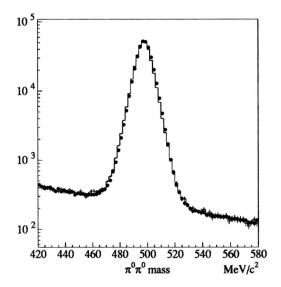

Figure 4. $\pi^0\pi^0$ invariant mass distributions for events satisfying all other cuts. Data (histogram) and Monte Carlo (points) are shown.

acceptance, backgrounds, and regeneration parameters; these will decrease with additional analysis work. We found that $\phi_{+-} = (43.35 \pm 0.70 \pm 0.79)°$. The systematic error was obtained by adding (uncorrelated) contributions in quadrature. Increasing the values of Δm and τ_S by one (Particle Data Group) standard deviation ([9]) would change ϕ_{+-} by $+0.38°$ and $-0.62°$ respectively.

In a separate fit we determined Δm and τ_S by constraining $\phi_{+-} \equiv \phi_\epsilon = \tan^{-1}\left(2\Delta mc^2\tau_S/\hbar\right)$. We found that $\Delta m = (0.5286 \pm 0.0029 \pm 0.0022) \times$

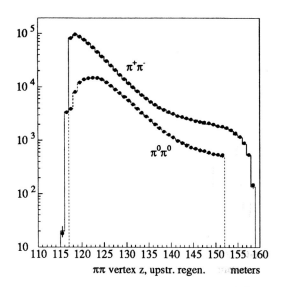

Figure 5. Decay vertex z distributions for $K \to \pi^+\pi^-$ and $K \to \pi^0\pi^0$ decays in the upstream regenerator beam. Shown are data (histogram) and Monte Carlo (points) for approximately 70% of the data sample.

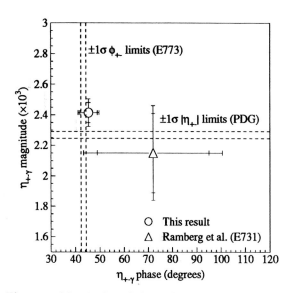

Figure 6. Magnitude and phase of $\eta_{+-\gamma}$ from this experiment and from E731. The smaller error bars indicate statistical uncertainties. The larger errors correspond to a sum, in quadrature, of the quoted statistical and systematic errors. For comparison, the vertical dashed lines indicate the $\pm 1\sigma$ bounds on our ϕ_{+-} measurement while the horizontal dashed lines indicate the $\pm 1\sigma$ bounds on the Particle Data Group's world-average value for $|\eta_{+-}|$.

$10^{10}\hbar s^{-1}c^{-2}$ and $\tau_S = (0.8929 \pm 0.0014 \pm 0.0014) \times 10^{-10}s$, corresponding to $\phi_\epsilon = 43.35°$. When ϕ_{+-} was unconstrained, we found that $\phi_{+-} - \phi_\epsilon = (-0.84 \pm 1.42 \pm 1.22)°$, $\Delta m = (0.5268 \pm 0.0041 \pm 0.0029) \times 10^{10}\hbar s^{-1}c^{-2}$, and $\tau_S = (0.8942 \pm 0.0026 \pm 0.0018) \times 10^{-10}s$.

Our preliminary result for $\phi_{00} - \phi_{+-}$ is based on approximately 70% of the full data set. We found that $\Delta\phi$ returned by the fit varied somewhat with the value of the minimum photon energy cut, and report the average of two fits which used 2.2 GeV and 4.0 GeV thresholds. Systematic uncertainties included this effect, acceptance calculation, background subtractions, and lead glass performance. We find $\Delta\phi = (0.67 \pm 0.85 \pm 1.1)°$. The statistical and systematic errors will decrease as the analysis continues.

We extracted information about $\eta_{+-\gamma}$ from the interference between the inner bremsstrahlung $K_{L,S}$ $\pi\pi\gamma$ decay amplitudes. Sources of systematic error included uncertainties associated with the regeneration amplitude, backgrounds, beam parameters, and the (previously measured[10]) $K_S \to \pi\pi\gamma$ branching ratio. Our preliminary result is $|\eta_{+-\gamma}| = (2.414 \pm 0.065 \pm 0.062) \times 10^{-3}$ and $\phi_{+-\gamma} = (45.47 \pm 3.61 \pm 2.40)°$. These errors are significantly smaller than those of the best previous measurement ([11]), as shown in figure 6.

In conclusion, our two-pion results are consistent with CPT conservation in $K \to \pi\pi$ decays. Our $\eta_{+-\gamma}$ result is consistent with the absence of an unusual source of CP violation in $K \to \pi\pi\gamma$ decays.

This work was supported in part by the Department of Energy and the National Science Foundation.

References

[1] J. Ellis and J.S. Hagelin, Nucl. Phys. **B241** (1984) 381.

[2] P. Huet and M.E. Peskin, SLAC preprint: SLAC-PUB-6454, submitted to Nucl. Phys. **B** (1994).

[3] J. Ellis, N.E. Mavromatos, and D.V. Nanopoulos, Phys. Lett. **B293** (1992) 37.

[4] J. Ellis, N.E. Mavromatos, and D.V. Nanopoulos, CERN preprint: CERN-TH.6755/92 (1992).

[5] R. Carosi *et al.*, Phys. Lett. **B237** (1990) 303.

[6] E731 collaboration: L.K. Gibbons *et al.*, Phys. Rev. Lett. **70** (1993) 1199.

[7] See for example V.V. Barmin *et al.*, Nucl. Phys. **B247** (1984) 293   or J.W. Cronin, Acta Phys. Pol. **B15** (1984) 419.

[8] The E773 collaboration consists of A.R. Barker, R.A. Briere, E. Cheu, L.K. Gibbons, D.A. Harris, G. Makoff, K.S. McFarland, A. Roodman, B. Schwingenheuer, Y.W. Wah, B. Winstein, and R. Winston (The University of Chicago); E.C. Swallow (Elmhurst College and The University of Chicago); G.J. Bock, R. Coleman, M. Crisler, J. Enagonio, R. Ford, Y.B. Hsiung, D. A. Jensen, E.J. Ramberg, R. Tschirhart, and T. Yamanaka (Fermilab); E.M. Collins and G.D. Gollin (University of Illinois); P. Gu, P. Haas, W.P. Hogan, S. Kim, J.N. Matthews, S.S. Myung, S. Schnetzer, S.V. Somalwar, G. Thomson, and Y. Zou (Rutgers University).

[9] Particle Data Group, Phys. Rev. **D45**, *Review of Particle Properties* (1992).

[10] E731 collaboration: E.J. Ramberg *et al.*, Phys. Rev. Lett. **70** (1993) 2525.

[11] E731 collaboration: E.J. Ramberg *et al.*, Phys. Rev. Lett. **70** (1993) 2529.

Paper presented at XXVII Int. Conf. on High Energy Physics: Session Pa-9
Glasgow, UK, 20–27 July 1994

Next-to-leading prediction of ϵ'/ϵ: an upgraded analysis

Marco Ciuchini[†]

INFN, Sezione Sanità,
V.le Regina Elena 299, 00161 Roma, Italy

Abstract

We present an updated theoretical prediction of ϵ'/ϵ, using the next-to-leading $\Delta S = 1$ effective hamiltonian and lattice QCD matrix elements. The CP violating phase is costrained by using both the experimental values of ϵ and x_d, assuming the theoretical determination of f_B. Predictions of $\cos \delta$ and $\sin 2\beta$ are also obtained in this way. For ϵ'/ϵ, our estimate is $\epsilon'/\epsilon = (2.8 \pm 2.4) \times 10^{-4}$.

We repeat the combined analysis of the CP violation parameter ϵ and the B-mixing parameter x_d in order to estimate ϵ'/ϵ, along the lines followed in refs. [1, 2]. The main steps of this analysis are the following:

1 The CP violating phase δ of the CKM matrix is constrained by comparing the theoretical prediction for ϵ with its experimental value. To this purpose, the relevant formula is

$$|\epsilon|_{\xi=0} = C_\epsilon B_K A^2 \lambda^6 \sigma \sin \delta \{F(x_c, x_t)+ \tag{1}$$
$$F(x_t)[A^2 \lambda^4 (1 - \sigma \cos \delta)] - F(x_c)\},$$

where $x_q = m_q^2/M_W^2$ and the functions $F(x_i)$ and $F(x_i, x_j)$ are the so-called *Inami-Lim* functions [3], obtained from the calculation of the basic box-diagram and including QCD corrections. $F(x_t)$ is known at the next-to-leading order, which has been included in our calculation [4]. In eq. (1),

$$C_\epsilon = \frac{G_F^2 f_K^2 m_K M_W^2}{6\sqrt{2}\pi^2 \Delta M_K}, \tag{2}$$

where ΔM_K is the mass difference between the two neutral kaon mass eigenstates. Moreover, $\rho = \sigma \cos \delta$ and $\eta = \sigma \sin \delta$, where λ, A, ρ and η are the parameters of the CKM matrix in the Wolfenstein parametrization [5]. Finally, B_K is the renormalization group invariant B-factor [6].

† E-mail: ciuchini@vaxsan.iss.infn.it.

2 The theoretical estimate of the B-meson coupling constant f_B is used to further constrain δ, by comparing the theoretical prediction of the B mixing parameter x_d with its experimental value. From the $\Delta B = 2$ effective hamiltonian, one can derive

$$x_d = \frac{\Delta M}{\Gamma} = C_B \frac{\tau_B f_B^2}{M_B} B_B A^2 \lambda^6 \Big(1 +$$
$$\sigma^2 - 2\sigma \cos \delta \Big) F(x_t), \tag{3}$$
$$C_B = \frac{G_F^2 M_W^2 M_B^2}{6\pi^2},$$

where B_B is the B-parameter relevant for $B - \bar{B}$ matrix element

$$\langle \bar{B}_d | (\bar{d}\gamma_L^\mu b)^2 | B_d \rangle = 8/3 f_B^2 M_B^2 B_B. \tag{4}$$

Notice that $f_B B_B^{1/2}$ must be known, for the experimental value of x_d to give a constraint on δ.

3 From the $\Delta S = 1$ effective hamiltonian, one can calculate the expression of ϵ' in terms of CKM matrix elements, Wilson coefficients and local operator matrix elements. One has

$$\epsilon' = \frac{e^{i\pi/4}}{\sqrt{2}} \frac{\omega}{\text{Re}A_0} \left[\omega^{-1}(\text{Im}A_2)' - (1 - \Omega_{IB})\,\text{Im}A_0 \right],$$
$$\tag{5}$$

where $(\text{Im}A_2)'$ and $\text{Im}A_0$ are given by

$$
\begin{aligned}
\text{Im}A_0 = & -G_F \text{Im}\left(V_{ts}^* V_{td}\right) \Big\{ -\left(C_6 B_6 + \right. \\
& \frac{1}{3}C_5 B_5\Big) Z + \left(C_4 B_4 + \frac{1}{3}C_3 B_3\right) X + \\
& C_7 B_7^{1/2}\left(\frac{2Y}{3} + \frac{Z}{6} + \frac{X}{2}\right) + \\
& C_8 B_8^{1/2}\left(2Y + \frac{Z}{2} + \frac{X}{6}\right) - \\
& C_9 B_9^{1/2}\frac{X}{3} + \left(\frac{C_1 B_1^c}{3} + C_2 B_2^c\right) X \Big\},
\end{aligned}
\tag{6}
$$

and

$$
\begin{aligned}
(\text{Im}A_2)' = & -G_F \text{Im}\left(V_{ts}^* V_{td}\right)\Big\{ C_7 B_7^{3/2}\left(\frac{Y}{3} - \right. \\
& \frac{X}{2}\Big) + C_8 B_8^{3/2}\left(Y - \frac{X}{6}\right) + \\
& C_9 B_9^{3/2}\frac{2X}{3} \Big\}.
\end{aligned}
\tag{7}
$$

Here $\omega = \text{Re}A_2/\text{Re}A_0$ and we have introduced $(\text{Im}A_2)'$ defined as

$$
\text{Im}A_2 = (\text{Im}A_2)' + \Omega_{IB}(\omega \text{Im}A_0).
\tag{8}
$$

Ω_{IB} accounts for the isospin breaking contribution, see for example ref. [7]. The Wilson coefficients C_i have been evaluated at the next-to-leading order for $\mu = 2$ GeV, using the anomalous dimension matrices given in refs. [8, 9] and the initial conditions computed in refs. [10, 11] (given for HV in ref. [12]). Concerning the local operator matrix elements, their values are given by a set $\{B_i\}$ of B-parameters multiplied by the vacuum insertion approximation results. In turn, these can be written in terms of the three quantities (see eq. (6) and eq. (7))

$$
\begin{aligned}
X &= f_\pi\left(M_K^2 - M_\pi^2\right), \\
Y &= f_\pi\left(\frac{M_K^2}{m_s(\mu) + m_d(\mu)}\right)^2 \\
&\sim 12 X\left(\frac{0.15\,\text{GeV}}{m_s(\mu)}\right)^2, \\
Z &= 4\left(\frac{f_K}{f_\pi} - 1\right) Y.
\end{aligned}
\tag{9}
$$

The numerical values of the B-parameters have been taken from lattice calculations [15] For those B-factors which have not yet been computed on the lattice, we have used educated guesses, see ref. [13].

More details on this analysis can be found in ref. [13, 14]. Compared to our previous work [2], the main improvements are the following:

Parameters	
$(f_B B_B^{1/2})_{th} = (200 \pm 40)$ MeV	$V_{cb} = A\lambda^2 = 0.040 \pm 0.006$
$m_s(2\text{GeV}) = (128 \pm 18)$ MeV	$x_d = 0.685 \pm 0.076$
$\Lambda_{QCD}^{n_f=4} = (330 \pm 100)$ MeV	$\Omega_{IB} = 0.25 \pm 0.10$
$\tau_B = (1.49 \pm 0.12) \times 10^{-12}$ s	$m_t = (174 \pm 17)$ GeV
$|V_{ub}/V_{cb}| = \lambda\sigma = 0.080 \pm 0.015$	

Table 1. Values of the fluctuating parameters used in the numerical analysis.

1 The constraint on δ coming from x_d is used in the analysis, taking f_B from the theory. Since there is increasing theoretical evidence that the value of f_B is large (~ 200 MeV) and that the relevant B-parameter B_B is close to one, this constraint is quite effective.

2 Updated values of the experimental parameters entering in the phenomenological analysis, such as the B meson lifetime τ_B, the $B_d^0 - \bar{B}_d^0$ mixing parameter x_d, the CKM matrix elements, ($|V_{cb}|$, $|V_{ub}|/|V_{cb}|$), etc., have been used.

3 The value of the strange quark mass m_s has been taken from lattice calculations [16], thus making a more consistent use of lattice results for the B-parameters of the relevant penguin operators.

4 All the results are presented with an estimate of the corresponding errors. These errors come from the limited precision of measured quantities, e.g. τ_B, and from theoretical uncertainties, e.g. the values of hadronic matrix elements.

The results of our analysis have been obtained by varying the experimental quantities, e.g. the value of the top mass m_t, τ_B, etc. and the theoretical parameters, e.g. the B-parameters, the strange quark mass $m_s(\mu)$, etc., according to their errors. Values and errors of the input quantities used in the following are reported in tables 1-3. We assume a gaussian distribution for the experimental quantities and a flat distribution (with a width of 2σ) for the theoretical ones. The only exception is $m_s(\mu)$, taken from quenched lattice QCD calculations, for which we have assumed a gaussian distribution, according to the results of ref. [16].

The theoretical predictions ($\cos\delta$, $\sin 2\beta$, ϵ'/ϵ, etc.) depend on several fluctuating parameters. We have obtained numerically their distributions, from which we have calculated the central values and the errors reported below.

Using the values given in the tables and the formulae given previously, we have obtained the following results:

1 The distribution for $\cos\delta$, obtained by comparing the experimental value of ϵ to its theoretical

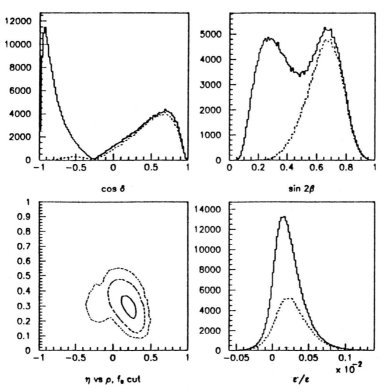

Figure 1. Distributions of values for $\cos\delta$, $\sin 2\beta$ and ϵ'/ϵ, using the values of the parameters given in the tables. The solid istograms are obtained without using the x_d constraint. The dashed ones use this constraint, assuming that $f_B B_B^{1/2} = 200 \pm 40$ MeV. The contour-plot of the event distribution in the $\rho - \eta$ plane is also shown.

Constants	
$G_F = 1.16634 \times 10^{-5} \mathrm{GeV}^{-2}$	$f_\pi = 132$ MeV
$m_c = 1.5$ GeV	$f_K = 160$ MeV
$m_b = 4.5$ GeV	$\lambda = \sin\theta_c = 0.221$
$M_W = 80.6$ GeV	$\epsilon_{exp} = 2.268 \times 10^{-3}$
$M_\pi = 140$ MeV	$\mathrm{Re}A_0 = 2.7 \times 10^{-7}$ GeV
$M_K = 490$ MeV	$\omega = 0.045$
$M_B = 5.278$ GeV	$\mu = 2$ GeV
$\Delta M_K = 3.521 \times 10^{-12}$ MeV	

Table 2. Values of the constants used in the numerical analysis.

prediction, is given in figure 1. As already noticed in refs. [1, 2] and [17, 18], large values of f_B and m_t favour $\cos\delta > 0$, given the current measurement of x_d. When the condition 160 MeV $\leq f_B B_B^{1/2} \leq 240$ MeV is imposed (f_B-cut), most of the negative solutions disappear, giving the dashed istogram of figure 1, from which we estimate

$$\cos\delta = 0.47 \pm 0.32 . \qquad (10)$$

2   The value of $\sin 2\beta$ depends on $\cos\delta$. The distribution of $\sin 2\beta$ is shown in figure 1, without (solid) and with (dashed) the f_B-cut. When the f_B-cut is imposed, one gets larger values of $\sin 2\beta$ [1].

From the dashed distribution, we obtain

$$\sin 2\beta = 0.65 \pm 0.12 . \qquad (11)$$

Figure 1 also contains the contour-plot of the event distribution in the $\rho - \eta$ plane, showing the effect of the ϵ and x_d constraints, when the f_B-cut is imposed.

3   In figure 2, several informations on ϵ'/ϵ are provided. Contour-plots of the distribution of the generated events in the ϵ'/ϵ–$\cos\delta$ plane are shown, without and with the f_B-cut. One notices a very mild dependence of ϵ'/ϵ on $\cos\delta$. As a consequence one obtains approximatively the same prediction in the two cases (see also figure 1)

$$\epsilon'/\epsilon = (2.3 \pm 2.1) \times 10^{-4} \quad no-cut, \qquad (12)$$

and

$$\epsilon'/\epsilon = (2.8 \pm 2.4) \times 10^{-4} \quad f_B-cut. \qquad (13)$$

In figure 2, we also give ϵ'/ϵ as a function of m_t. The band corresponds to the 2σ prediction.

In spite of several differences, the bulk of our results overlap with those of ref. [19]. It is reassuring that theoretical predictions, obtained by using different approaches to evaluate the operator matrix elements, are in good agreement.

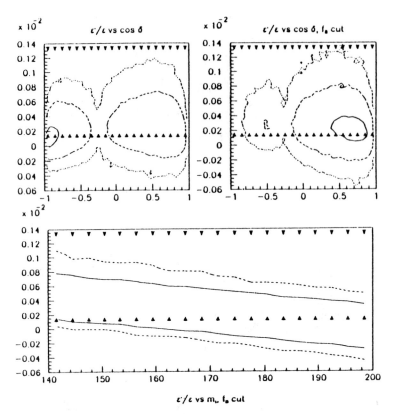

Figure 2. Above, contour-plots of the event distributions in the plane ϵ'/ϵ–$\cos\delta$ without and with the f_B-cut. Below, ϵ'/ϵ as a function of m_t.

B-parameters	
$B_K = 0.75 \pm 0.15$	$B_9^{(3/2)} = 0.62 \pm 0.10$
$B_{1-2}^c = 0 - 0.15^{(*)}$	$B_{3,4} = 1 - 6^{(*)}$
$B_{5,6} = B_{7-8}^{(3/2)} = 1.0 \pm 0.2$	$B_{7-8-9}^{(1/2)} = 1^{(*)}$

Table 3. Values of the B-parameters, for operators renormalized at the scale $\mu = 2$ GeV. The only exception is B_K, which is the RG invariant B-parameter. $B_9^{(3/2)}$ has been taken equal to B_K, at any scale. The value reported in the table is $B_9^{3/2}(\mu = 2\text{GeV})$. Entries with a $^{(*)}$ are educated guesses, the others are taken from lattice QCD calculations.

On the basis of the latest analyses, it seems very difficult for ϵ'/ϵ to be larger than 10×10^{-4}. This may happen by taking the matrix elements of the dominant operators, Q_6 and Q_8, much different than usually assumed. One possibility, discussed in ref. [19], is to take $B_6 \sim 2$ and $B_8 \sim 1$, instead of the usual values $B_6 \sim B_8 \sim 1$. To our knowledge, no coherent theoretical approach can accomodate so large value of B_6.

Acknowledgments

The precious collaboration of E. Franco, G. Martinelli and L. Reina is acknowledged.

References

[1] M. Lusignoli et al., Nucl. Phys. **B369** (1992) 139.

[2] M. Ciuchini et al., Phys. Lett. **B301** (1993) 263.

[3] T. Inami, C.S. Lim, Prog. Th. Phys. **65** (1981) 297; *Erratum* **65** (1981) 1772.

[4] A.J. Buras, M. Jamin and P.H. Weisz, Nucl. Phys. **B347** (1990) 491.

[5] L. Wolfenstein, Phys. Rev. Lett. **51** (1983) 1945.

[6] A.J. Buras, W. Slominski and H. Steger, Nucl. Phys. **B238** (1984) 529; *ibid.* **B245** (1984) 369.

[7] A.J. Buras and J.-M. Gerard, Phys. Lett. **B192** (1987) 156.

[8] A.J. Buras et al., Nucl. Phys. **B400** (1993) 37; *ibid.* **B400** (1993) 75.

[9] M. Ciuchini et al., Nucl. Phys. **B415** (1994) 403.

[10] J.M. Flynn, L. Randall, Phys. Lett. **B224** (1989) 221; *Erratum* **B235** (1990) 412.

[11] G. Buchalla, A.J. Buras, M.K. Harlander, Nucl. Phys. **B337** (1990) 313.

[12] A.J. Buras et al., Nucl. Phys. **B370** (1992) 69; Addendum,*ibid.* **B375** (1992) 501.

[13] M. Ciuchini et al., ROME prep. 94/1024.

[14] M. Ciuchini at al., to appear in the proceedings of the *"PARTICLE PHYSICS AND ASTRONOMY"* conference, Hanoi (December 1993).

[15] see, e.g., ref. [13] and references therein.

[16] C.R. Allton et al., ROME prep. 94/1018, CERN-TH.7256/94 (June 1994).

[17] M. Schmidtler, K.R. Schubert, Zeit. Phys. **C53** (1992) 25.

[18] A. Ali and D. London, CERN-TH.7248/94; CERN-TH.7398/94.

[19] A. Buras, M. Jamin, M.E. Lautenbacher, Nucl. Phys. **B408** (1993) 209.

Measurements of CP and T Violation Parameters in the Neutral Kaon System at CPLEAR

T. Ruf

PPE Division, CERN, CH-1211 Geneva 23, Switzerland

On behalf of the CPLEAR Collaboration

University of Athens, University of Basle, Boston University, CERN, LIP and University of Coimbra, Delft University of Technology, University of Fribourg, University of Ioannina, University of Liverpool, J. Stefan Inst. and Phys. Dep. University of Ljubljana, CCPM, IN2P3-CNRS et Université d'Aix-Marseille II, CSNSM, IN2P3-CNRS, Paul-Scherrer-Institut (PSI), Saclay CE-DAPNIA/SPP, KTH Stockholm, University of Thessaloniki, ETH-ITP Zurich

Abstract

The CPLEAR experiment is designed to determine CP and T violation parameters in the neutral kaon system by measuring time-dependent decay rate asymmetries of CP and T conjugate processes. New results from the high statistics runs in 1992 and 1993 are reported on η_{+-}, η_{+-o}, x and the $K_L - K_S$ mass difference. A first direct measurement of T violation and the observation of CP-allowed $K_S \rightarrow \pi^+\pi^-\pi^o$ decays are also reported. All our preliminary results are consistent with CPT conservation, leading to an improved limit on CPT violation in the neutral kaon system.

1. Introduction

CP violation may be established either by observing processes that are forbidden by CP conservation (e.g. $K_L \rightarrow \pi^+\pi^-$) or by observing a difference in probabilities for a given process and its CP-conjugated process. The CPLEAR collaboration is using the second approach which gives a possibility to explore a wide range of the CP violation phenomena in the neutral kaon system.

K^o and $\overline{K}^o$ mesons are produced in equal amounts in $p\bar{p}$ annihilations at rest through the channels $K^+\pi^-\overline{K}^o$ and $K^-\pi^+K^o$. The strangeness of the neutral kaon at the time of its production is tagged by the charge of the accompanied charged kaon. Semileptonic decays of the neutral kaon offer the possibility to tag the strangeness of the neutral kaon also at the time of its decay (if the $\Delta S = \Delta Q$ rule holds) thus allowing a direct measurement of T violation and a test of CPT conservation.

A detailed description of the experiment can be found elsewhere [1] and only a few important items are mentioned here. The high rate of 200 MeV/c antiprotons ($10^6\,\bar{p}$/s) is delivered by the LEAR machine at CERN. The antiprotons are stopped inside a gaseous hydrogen target of 16 bar pressure. A cylindrical detector is placed inside a solenoid of 1 m radius, 3.6 m length, providing a magnetic field of 0.44 T. The charged tracking system consists of two proportional chambers, six drift chambers and two layers of streamer tubes. Fast kaon identification is provided by a threshold Čerenkov counter sandwiched between two scintillators. An electromagnetic calorimeter made of 18 layers of Pb converters and streamer tubes is used for photon detection and electron identification. An efficient and fast on-line data reduction is achieved with a multi-level trigger system based on custom-made hardwired processors.

Kinematical constraints (energy-momentum conservation, K^o mass) and geometrical constraints (K^o flight direction and vertex separation) are used in the analysis to suppress the background from unwanted K^o decay channels and the background from $p\bar{p}$ annihilation events. In addition they improve the lifetime resolution.

Knowing the initial strangeness of the neutral kaon, we are able to calculate time-dependent CP violating

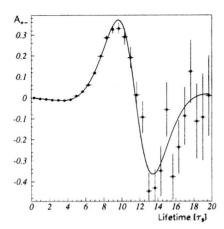

Figure 1. Time dependent decay rate asymmetry for $\pi^+\pi^-$ final states.

decay rate asymmetries:

$$A(t) = \frac{R(\overline{K}^o_{t=0} \to \overline{f})(t) - R(K^o_{t=0} \to f)(t)}{R(\overline{K}^o_{t=0} \to \overline{f})(t) + R(K^o_{t=0} \to f)(t)} \quad (1)$$

which have the advantage that detector acceptances cancel for a CP symmetric detector. The P-asymmetry of the detector can be controlled by changing the magnetic field regularly and the C-asymmetry has to be determined with data in the lifetime region where the CP violation effect on the ratio $\overline{K}^o/K^o$ is expected to be small.

2. CPLEAR Results 1994

The results presented here are preliminary, and mainly based on the high-statistics runs in 1992 and 1993 with altogether 10^9 events on tape.

2.1. CP violation in 2π decays

A value of the CP violation parameter η_{+-} is obtained by fitting the expected time-dependent decay rate asymmetry of the $\pi^+\pi^-$ decay mode:

$$A_{+-}(t) = \quad (2)$$
$$2\Re(\varepsilon_L) \; - \; \frac{2|\eta_{+-}|e^{\frac{1}{2}(\Gamma_S - \Gamma_L)t}}{1 + |\eta_{+-}|^2 \, e^{(\Gamma_S - \Gamma_L)t}} \cos(\Delta mt - \varphi_{+-})$$

to the data (see fig.1). Γ_S and Γ_L are the decay widths of K_S and K_L respectively, Δm denotes the $K_L - K_S$ mass difference and ε_L represents the CP violation parameter of K_L in the $K^o - \overline{K}^o$ oscillations. The fit takes into account the residual background contribution, mainly from semileptonic decays, and regeneration corrections. We obtain:

$$\varphi_{+-} = 44.7^\circ \pm 0.9^\circ_{stat.} \pm 1.1^\circ_{syst.} \pm 0.7^\circ_{\Delta m} \quad (3)$$

$$|\eta_{+-}| = [2.163 \pm 0.045_{stat.} \pm 0.064_{syst.} \pm 0.010_{\Delta m}] \cdot 10^{-3}$$

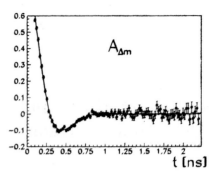

Figure 2. Asymmetry $A_{\Delta m}$ showing the $K^o \overline{K}^o$ oscillation

Systematic effects arising from the CP-asymmetry of the detector are studied in detail and the systematic error should be reduced to $\pm 0.4^\circ$ for φ_{+-} and $\pm 0.02 \cdot 10^{-3}$ for $|\eta_{+-}|$. The error introduced by the uncertainty of the world average value of Δm will be reduced in the future by our own measurement.

2.2. $K_S - K_L$ mass difference

By tagging the strangeness of the neutral kaon at the time of its decay with semileptonic decays (assume $\Delta S = \Delta Q$ rule valid) we measure a time-dependent rate asymmetry (see fig. 2) between $\Delta S = 0$ and $\Delta S = \pm 2$ transitions, which can be parametrized as:

$$A_{\Delta m}(t) = \frac{e^{-\frac{1}{2}(\Gamma_S + \Gamma_L) \cdot t}}{e^{-\Gamma_S t} + e^{-\Gamma_L t}} \cdot \cos(\Delta mt) . \quad (4)$$

The result for the oscillation frequency is:

$$\Delta m = (534.7 \pm 3.2_{stat.} \pm 0.9_{syst.} \pm 3.0_{MC}) \cdot 10^7 \hbar s^{-1}$$

where the last error should become much smaller as more simulated data are available to study the CP-asymmetry of the detector.

2.3. Direct measurement of T violation and a test of CPT conservation

T violation can be observed by measuring the oscillation rate difference of $K^o \to \overline{K}^o$ and its T-conjugated process $\overline{K}^o \to K^o$. The T-violating asymmetry is given (assuming the $\Delta S = \Delta Q$ rule) by:

$$A_T = \frac{R(\overline{K}^o_{t=0} \to e^+\pi^-\nu) - R(K^o_{t=0} \to e^-\pi^+\overline{\nu})}{R(\overline{K}^o_{t=0} \to e^+\pi^-\nu) + R(K^o_{t=0} \to e^-\pi^+\overline{\nu})} , \quad (5)$$

which is a constant as a function of the decay time. Our result is:

$$A_T = (4.5 \pm 2.1_{stat.} \pm 2.0_{syst.} \pm 1.5_{MC}) \cdot 10^{-3} . \quad (6)$$

Similarly we can measure the rate difference between $K^o \to K^o$ and $\overline{K}^o \to \overline{K}^o$, which is sensitive to CPT violation for $t > 4\tau_S$:

$$A_{CPT} = \frac{R(\overline{K}^o_{t=0} \to e^-\pi^+\bar{\nu}) - R(K^o_{t=0} \to e^+\pi^-\nu)}{R(\overline{K}^o_{t=0} \to e^-\pi^+\bar{\nu}) + R(K^o_{t=0} \to e^+\pi^-\nu)}$$

$$= (-0.4 \pm 2.0_{stat.} \pm 2.0_{syst.} \pm 1.6_{MC}) \cdot 10^{-3} \quad (7)$$

The main systematic error results from the different reconstruction efficiencies for π^+e^- and π^-e^+ final states and should be further reduced as more simulation and calibration data become available.

2.4. Test of the $\Delta S = \Delta Q$ rule

For all previous measurements using semileptonic decays, we assumed the validity of the $\Delta S = \Delta Q$ rule. This rule can also be studied using semileptonic decays. The parameter x, which is the ratio of the $\Delta S = \Delta Q$ forbidden decay amplitude and the allowed amplitude, is measured to be:

$$\Im m\,(x) = (10.1 \pm 4.1_{stat.} \pm 1.3_{syst.} \pm 5.0_{MC}) \cdot 10^{-3}$$

$$\Re e\,(x) = (4.3 \pm 7.6_{stat.} \pm 4.0_{syst.} \pm 8.0_{MC}) \cdot 10^{-3} \quad (8)$$

2.5. CP violation and CP conservation in 3π decays

Mainly two amplitudes contribute to the $\pi^+\pi^-\pi^o$ decay mode of the K_S: the CP-allowed ($l = 1$) but angular-momentum-suppressed amplitude, and the CP-forbidden ($l = 0$) amplitude. The $l = 1$ amplitude has opposite signs for $X > 0$ and $X < 0$ where $X \propto (E_{\pi^+} - E_{\pi^-})$. The charged pion energies E_{π^+} and E_{π^-} are measured in the kaon rest frame. The decay rate asymmetry for $X > 0$ and $X < 0$ is shown in fig. 3 (left) and can be parametrized as:

$$A^{><}_{+-o} = 2\Re e\,(\varepsilon_S) - 2[(\Re e\,(\eta_{+-o}) \pm \lambda)\cos(\Delta mt) -$$
$$\Im m\,(\eta_{+-o})\sin(\Delta mt)]e^{-\frac{1}{2}(\Gamma_S - \Gamma_L)\cdot t} \quad (9)$$

where λ describes the CP-allowed contribution and ε_S represents the CP violation parameter of K_S in the $K^o - \overline{K}^o$ oscillations. From the fit result of $\lambda = 0.051 \pm 0.016_{stat.} \pm 0.020_{syst.}$ we obtain a branching ratio of the CP-allowed decay $K_S \to \pi^+\pi^-\pi^o$:

$$BR(K_S \to \pi^+\pi^-\pi^o) = \left(8.2\,^{+6.0}_{-4.4}\,^{+7.3}_{-4.9}\right) \cdot 10^{-7}\ . \quad (10)$$

The CP-allowed part vanishes in the decay rate asymmetry when all data are added [see eq.(9)], and we remain sensitive only to the CP violation parameter η_{+-o}. From a fit to the total asymmetry shown in fig. 3 (right) we obtain the results:

$$\Im m\,(\eta_{+-o}) = (16 \pm 24_{stat.} \pm 18_{syst.}) \cdot 10^{-3} \quad (11)$$

$$\Re e\,(\eta_{+-o}) = (5 \pm 22_{stat.} \pm 7_{syst.}) \cdot 10^{-3}\ . \quad (12)$$

The systematic error is dominated by the uncertainty in the background estimate and should become smaller with the growing understanding of the different background sources.

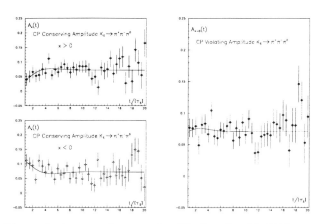

Figure 3. Asymmetries measuring CP allowed and forbidden amplitudes in $K_S \to \pi^+\pi^-\pi^o$.

3. Consequences for CPT conservation

The best limit on CPT violation can be obtained by comparing the phase of η_{+-} with the superweak angle $\varphi_{SW} \equiv \tan^{-1}\left(\frac{2\Delta m}{\Gamma_S - \Gamma_L}\right)$. Note that the phase difference between φ_{+-} and φ_{SW} can be as large as $3°$ [2, 3] even in the absence of CPT violation, with currently available data on $\Im m\,(\eta_{+-o})$ and $\Im m\,(x)$[4] (by not assuming the Standard Model). Using our improved limits for $\Im m\,(\eta_{+-o})$ and $\Im m\,(x)$, our measurements of φ_{+-} and Δm, $\Delta\Gamma$ from [4], a possible CPT violation contribution to η_{+-} can be shown to be less than 6.5% with 90% CL. If CPT violation arises only from the $K^o - \overline{K}^o$ mass difference, our limit on the mass difference is given by:

$$\left|\frac{M_{\overline{K}^o} - M_{K^o}}{M_K}\right| < 2.3 \cdot 10^{-18}, \quad (13)$$

which is several orders of magnitude better than existing limits for other particles [4].

4. Summary

The analysis of the last two high-statistics runs shows that the CPLEAR approach to explore CP violation in the neutral kaon system is successful and already gives results that are comparable to the world average values for φ_{+-} and Δm. The limits on CP violation in 3π decays and on the violation of the $\Delta S = \Delta Q$ rule are improved. A first direct measurement of T violation is reported. The statistical significance of all our results will be increased by approximately a factor of 2 by the end of 1995.

References

[1] R. Adler et al., *Phys. Lett.* **B286** (1992) 180.
[2] L. Lavoura, *Modern Phys. Lett.* **A7** (1992) 1367.
[3] T. Nakada, Proc. of Lepton-Photon Symp., Ithaca, 1993.
[4] Review of Particle Properties, *Phys. Rev.* **D45** (1992).

Some Prospects for the Determination of the Unitarity Triangle before the LHC Era

Markus E. Lautenbacher[†]

Physik Department, Technische Universität München,
D–85748 Garching, Germany.

Abstract

Anticipating improved determinations of m_t, $|V_{cb}|$, $|V_{ub}/V_{cb}|$, B_K and $F_B\sqrt{B_B}$ in the next five years we make an excursion into the future in order to find a possible picture of the unitarity triangle, of quark mixing and of CP violation around the year 2000. We then analyse what impact on this picture will result from the measurements of the four possibly cleanest quantities: $BR(K^+ \to \pi^+\nu\bar{\nu})$, x_d/x_s, $\sin(2\alpha)$ and $\sin(2\beta)$. In the course of our investigations we extend the analysis of the unitarity triangle beyond the leading order in the Wolfenstein parameter λ. We will also shortly present the status of direct CP violation in $K \to \pi\pi$ and $K_L \to \pi^0 e^+ e^-$.

1. CKM Matrix and Unitarity Triangle

1.1. Wolfenstein Parametrization Beyond Leading Order

In the Standard Model (SM) with three fermion generations, CP violation arises from a single phase in the unitary 3×3 Cabibbo-Kobayashi-Maskawa (CKM) matrix. For phenomenological applications it is useful to expand each element of the CKM matrix as a power series in the small parameter $\lambda = |V_{us}| = 0.22$. For the leading order in λ the result is [1]

$$V_{CKM} = \begin{pmatrix} 1 - \frac{\lambda^2}{2} & \lambda & A\lambda^3(\varrho - i\eta) \\ -\lambda & 1 - \frac{\lambda^2}{2} & A\lambda^2 \\ A\lambda^3(1 - \varrho - i\eta) & -A\lambda^2 & 1 \end{pmatrix}$$
$$+ \mathcal{O}(\lambda^4) \tag{1}$$

This parametrization being an expansion in λ respects unitarity of the CKM matrix only approximately up to terms of order $\mathcal{O}(\lambda^5)$. With e.g. LHC expected to test unitarity to a very high precision one has to extend the expansion (1) to higher order terms in λ. As always with next-to-leading order expansions the definition of

† E-mail: `lauten@feynman.t30.physik.tu-muenchen.de`

higher terms is not unique. A particularly nice form is to relate the parameters $(\lambda, A, \varrho, \eta)$ of the approximate Wolfenstein parametrization to the parameters s_{ij} and δ of the fully unitary standard parametrization [2] of the CKM matrix through [3]

$$s_{12} \equiv \lambda \quad s_{23} \equiv A\lambda^2 \quad s_{13}\,e^{-i\delta} \equiv A\lambda^3(\varrho - i\eta)\;. \tag{2}$$

1.2. Unitarity Triangle Beyond Leading Order

The unitarity of the CKM-matrix provides us with several relations of which

$$V_{ud}V_{ub}^* + V_{cd}V_{cb}^* + V_{td}V_{tb}^* = 0 \tag{3}$$

is the most useful one. In the complex plane the relation (3) can be represented as a triangle, the so-called "unitarity–triangle" (UT). Phenomenologically this triangle is very interesting as it involves simultaneously the CKM elements V_{ub}, V_{cb} and V_{td} which are under extensive discussion at present.

In the usual analyses of the unitarity triangle only terms $\mathcal{O}(\lambda^3)$ are kept in (3). Including the next-to-leading terms by keeping $\mathcal{O}(\lambda^5)$ corrections and rescaling all terms in (3) by $|V_{cd}V_{cb}^*| = A\lambda^3 + \mathcal{O}(\lambda^7)$ we find

$$\frac{1}{A\lambda^3}V_{ud}V_{ub}^* = \bar{\varrho} + i\bar{\eta} \qquad \frac{1}{A\lambda^3}V_{td}V_{tb}^* = 1 - (\bar{\varrho} + i\bar{\eta}) \quad (4)$$

with $\bar{\varrho}$ and $\bar{\eta}$ defined by [3]

$$\bar{\varrho} = \varrho\left(1 - \frac{\lambda^2}{2}\right) \qquad \bar{\eta} = \eta\left(1 - \frac{\lambda^2}{2}\right). \quad (5)$$

Thus we can represent (3) as a triangle, the UT, in the complex $(\bar{\varrho}, \bar{\eta})$ plane. This is shown in figure 1.

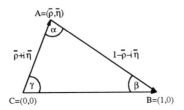

Figure 1. Unitarity triangle in the complex $(\bar{\varrho}, \bar{\eta})$ plane.

We observe that beyond the leading order in λ the point 'A' *does not* correspond to (ϱ, η) but to $(\bar{\varrho}, \bar{\eta})$. Clearly within 3% accuracy $\bar{\varrho} = \varrho$ and $\bar{\eta} = \eta$. Yet in the distant future the accuracy of experimental results and theoretical calculations may improve considerably so that the more accurate formulation given here will be appropriate. For instance the experiments at LHC should measure $\sin(2\beta)$ to an accuracy of $(2-3)\%$ [4].

With figure 1 it is then a matter of simple trigonometry to calculate $\sin(2\phi_i)$ in terms of $(\bar{\varrho}, \bar{\eta})$ and vice versa.

In sects. 2–4 we will now summarize the phenomenological analysis of the UT presented in [3].

2.   The UT from Present Day Experiments

2.1.   *Tree Level B-Decays*

Measurements of tree level B-decays can be used to derive the CKM elements $|V_{cb}|$, $|V_{ub}/V_{cb}|$. This then allows to determine

$$R_b \equiv \frac{|V_{ud}V_{ub}^*|}{|V_{cd}V_{cb}^*|} = \sqrt{\bar{\varrho}^2 + \bar{\eta}^2} = \left(1 - \frac{\lambda^2}{2}\right)\frac{1}{\lambda}\left|\frac{V_{ub}}{V_{cb}}\right| \quad (6)$$

which represents a circle centered around $(0,0)$ in the complex $(\bar{\varrho}, \bar{\eta})$ plane. Thus R_b is simply the length $\overline{AC}$ in the rescaled UT of figure 1.

2.2.   *Indirect CP Violation*

The usual box diagram calculation together with the experimental value for ε_K from K^0-$\bar{K}^0$ mixing specifies a hyperbola in the $(\bar{\varrho}, \bar{\eta})$ plane with $\bar{\eta} > 0$ [5, 6]:

$$\bar{\eta}\left[(1-\bar{\varrho})A^2\eta_2 S(x_t) + [\eta_3 S(x_c, x_t) - \eta_1 x_c]\frac{1}{\lambda^4}\right] = \frac{0.223}{A^2 B_K} \quad (7)$$

Here $S(x_i)$, $S(x_i, x_j)$, $x_i = m_i^2/M_W^2$ are the Inami-Lim functions, B_K is the renormalization group invariant non-perturbative parameter describing the size of $< \bar{K}^0|(\bar{s}d)_{V-A}(\bar{s}d)_{V-A}|K^0 >$ and $\eta_1 = 1.1$ [7], $\eta_2 = 0.57$ [8], $\eta_3 = 0.36$ [9]–[12] represent QCD corrections to the box diagrams.

2.3.   *B^0-$\bar{B}^0$ Mixing*

The experimental knowledge of the $B_d^0 - \bar{B}_d^0$ mixing described by the parameter $x_d = \Delta M/\Gamma_B$ determines $|V_{td}|$. This then specifies via

$$R_t \equiv \frac{|V_{td}V_{tb}^*|}{|V_{cd}V_{cb}^*|} = \sqrt{(1-\bar{\varrho})^2 + \bar{\eta}^2} = \frac{1}{\lambda}\left|\frac{V_{td}}{V_{cb}}\right| \quad (8)$$

a circle centered around $(1,0)$ in the complex $(\bar{\varrho}, \bar{\eta})$ plane. Here R_t is simply the length $\overline{AB}$ in the rescaled UT of figure 1.

All the QCD corrections to ε_K, $B^0 - \bar{B}^0$ mixing and $BR(K^+ \to \pi^+\nu\bar{\nu})$ used here include except for η_3 the next-to-leading order. Hence, in all formulae of this paper m_t corresponds to the running top quark mass in the $\overline{MS}$ scheme evaluated at m_t i.e. $m_t = \overline{m}_t(m_t)$. The physical top quark mass as the pole of the renormalized propagator is for the range of m_t considered here by $(7 \pm 1)\,GeV$ higher than m_t.

Using eqs. (6)–(8) together with present day and envisioned future ranges of input parameters as of table 1 and $\Lambda_{\overline{MS}} = 300\,MeV$, $m_c = 1.3\,GeV$, one can determine the allowed ranges for the upper corner 'A' of the UT and make predictions for various quantities. The result is shown in figure 2 and table 2, respectively.

Looking at table 2 one sees that by the year 2000 one can expect predictions for $\sin(2\beta)$, $|V_{td}|$, $BR(K^+ \to \pi^+\nu\bar{\nu})$ good to $\pm(10-15)\%$ and for x_s up to $\pm20\%$. Thus a measurement of $BR(K^+ \to \pi^+\nu\bar{\nu})$ or x_s at the level of $\pm10\%$ could serve as a possible test of the corresponding SM predictions. Huge uncertainties for predicting $\sin(2\alpha)$ and $\sin(2\gamma)$ remain however, even with improved input in the future. Turning the argument around, this signals that a measurement of one of these angles would

Parameter Range	(I) (1994)	(II) ($\sim$ 1997)	(III) ($\sim$ 2000)
$|V_{cb}|$	0.038 ± 0.004	0.040 ± 0.002	0.040 ± 0.001
$|V_{ub}/V_{cb}|$	0.08 ± 0.02	0.08 ± 0.01	0.08 ± 0.005
B_K	0.7 ± 0.2	0.75 ± 0.07	0.75 ± 0.05
$F_{B_d}\sqrt{B_{B_d}}$ [MeV]	200 ± 30	185 ± 15	185 ± 10
x_d	0.72 ± 0.08	0.72 ± 0.04	0.72 ± 0.04
m_t [GeV]	165 ± 15	170 ± 7	170 ± 5

Table 1. Present day and envisioned ranges of input parameters for the determination of the UT from tree level B-decays, indirect CP violation and B^0-$\bar{B}^0$ mixing.

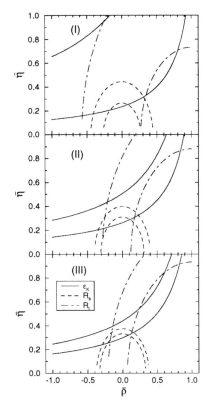

Figure 2. Unitarity triangle in the $(\bar{\varrho}, \bar{\eta})$ plane determined by ε_K, $|V_{cb}|$, $|V_{ub}/V_{cb}|$ and x_d using ranges (I)–(III) as of table 1.

Parameter Range	(I)	(II)	(III)
$\sin(2\alpha)$	0.17 ± 0.84	0.35 ± 0.65	0.50 ± 0.49
$\sin(2\beta)$	0.59 ± 0.21	0.60 ± 0.14	0.61 ± 0.09
$\sin(2\gamma)$	0 ± 1	0 ± 0.88	0 ± 0.68
$|V_{td}| \times 10^3$	9.4 ± 2.5	9.5 ± 1.4	9.4 ± 1.0
x_s	16.0 ± 8.3	13.4 ± 4.3	12.9 ± 2.8
$BR(K^+ \to \pi^+ \nu \bar{\nu})$ $\times 10^3$	1.04 ± 0.42	1.07 ± 0.24	1.03 ± 0.15

Table 2. Predictions for various quantities using input parameters as of table 1

allow to put stringent constraints on some of the input parameters of table 1, e.g. the non-perturbative ones B_K and $F_{B_d}\sqrt{B_{B_d}}$.

3. The UT from CP Violating B-Asymmetries

Measuring the CP-asymmetries in neutral B-decays will give the definitive answer whether the CKM description of CP violation is correct. Assuming that this is in fact the case, we want to investigate the impact of the measurements of $\sin(2\phi_i)$ on the determination of the unitarity triangle. Since in the rescaled triangle of figure 1 one side is known, it suffices to measure two angles to determine the triangle completely.

With the CP-asymmetries simply given by

$$A_{CP}(B^0 \to \psi K_S) = -\sin(2\beta)\frac{x_d}{1 + x_d^2} \quad (9)$$

$$A_{CP}(B^0 \to \pi^+ \pi^-) = -\sin(2\alpha)\frac{x_d}{1 + x_d^2} \quad (10)$$

one can determine $\sin(2\beta)$ without any theoretical uncertainties from measuring the CP-asymmetry in $B^0 \to \psi K_S$, while for $\sin(2\alpha)$ the measurement of several other channels is required in order to remove the penguin contributions.

Assuming a measurement of $\sin(2\beta)$ and $\sin(2\alpha)$ to give

$$\sin(2\beta) = \begin{cases} 0.60 \pm 0.18 & \text{(a) HERA-B [13]} \\ 0.60 \pm 0.06 & \text{(b) SLAC [14]} \end{cases} \quad (11)$$

$$\sin(2\alpha) = \begin{cases} -0.20 \pm 0.10 & \text{(I)} \\ 0.10 \pm 0.10 & \text{(II) SLAC [14]} \\ 0.70 \pm 0.10 & \text{(III)} \end{cases} \quad (12)$$

with the errors expected from different experiments indicated, one can again determine the UT in $(\bar{\varrho}, \bar{\eta})$ space. The result is shown in figure 3. Here the solid line labeled 'superweak' reflects the implicit relation holding between $\bar{\varrho}$ and $\bar{\eta}$ in the superweak scenario where $\sin(2\beta) = -\sin(2\alpha)$.

Comparing figs. 2 and 3 it is obvious that a combined measurement of $\sin(2\beta)$ and $\sin(2\alpha)$ at the expected precision will have a large impact on the determination of the UT and CKM parameters (For a discussion of $\sin(2\beta)$ and $\sin(2\gamma)$ see [3].). E.g. using $\sin(2\beta) = 0.6 \pm 0.06$, $\sin(2\alpha) = 0.1 \pm 0.1$ and range (II) of table 1 for $|V_{cb}|$, x_d and m_t one obtains $\sin(2\gamma) = 0.54 \pm 0.12$, $|V_{td}| = (8.8 \pm 0.4) \times 10^{-3}$, $x_s = 16.3 \pm 1.3$ and $BR(K^+ \to \pi^+ \nu \bar{\nu}) = (1.01 \pm 0.11) \times 10^{-10}$.

The ability to make predictions for $|V_{td}|$, x_s and $BR(K^+ \to \pi^+ \nu \bar{\nu})$ to an accuracy of $\pm(5-10)\%$ stems from the absent or small theoretical uncertainties in eqs. (9) and (10), as well as from the expected high precision for the measurement of CP violating B-asymmetries. However, this predictive power can only be achieved through a measurement of both $\sin(2\beta)$ and $\sin(2\alpha)$. Finally, we note that the predictions resulting from a measurement of CP violating B-asymmetries are generally more precise than those using ε_K, x_d, $|V_{cb}|$ and $|V_{ub}/V_{cb}|$ as input data.

4. $\sin(2\beta)$, $\sin(2\alpha)$ from Indirect CP Violation and B^0-$\bar{B}^0$ Mixing versus a Direct Measurement

It is useful to combine the results of sects. 2 and 3 by making the customary $\sin(2\beta)$ versus $\sin(2\alpha)$ plot [15]. This plot demonstrates very clearly the correlation between $\sin(2\alpha)$ and $\sin(2\beta)$. The allowed ranges for

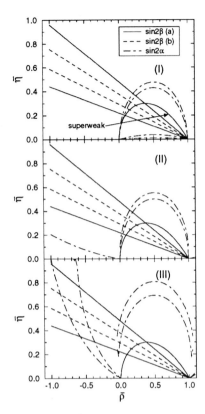

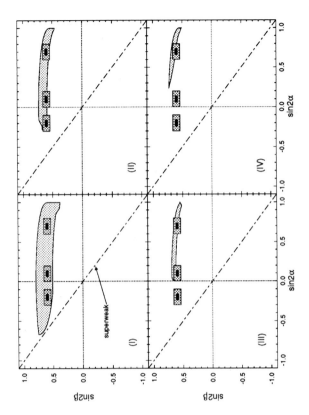

Figure 3. Determination of the unitarity triangle in the $(\bar{\varrho}, \bar{\eta})$ plane by measuring $\sin(2\beta)$ and $\sin(2\alpha)$ as of eqs. (11) and (12), respectively. For $\sin(2\alpha)$ we always find two solutions in $(\bar{\varrho}, \bar{\eta})$ and for $\sin(2\beta)$ we only use the solution consistent with $|V_{ub}/V_{cb}| \leq 0.1$.

Figure 4. $\sin(2\alpha)$ versus $\sin(2\beta)$ plot corresponding to the parameter ranges (I)–(IV) as of table 1 and eq. (13). The dark shaded rectangles are given by eqs. (12) and (11) (b). The black rectangles illustrate the accuracy of future LHC measurements.

$\sin(2\alpha)$ and $\sin(2\beta)$ corresponding to the choices of parameters in table 1 are shown in figure 4 together with the results of the independent measurements of $\sin(2\beta) = 0.60 \pm 0.06$ and $\sin(2\alpha)$ given by (12). The latter are represented by dark shaded rectangles. The black rectangles illustrate the accuracy of future LHC measurements ($\Delta \sin(2\alpha) = \pm 0.04$, $\Delta \sin(2\beta) = \pm 0.02$) [4]. We also show the results of an analysis in which the accuracy of various parameters is as in range (II) of table 1 but with the central values modified. Parameter range (IV) is given by

$$
\begin{aligned}
|V_{cb}| &= 0.038 \pm 0.002 & |V_{ub}/V_{cb}| &= 0.08 \pm 0.01 \\
B_K &= 0.70 \pm 0.07 & \sqrt{B_{B_d}} F_{B_d} &= (185 \pm 15)\, MeV \\
x_d &= 0.72 \pm 0.04 & m_t &= (165 \pm 7)\, GeV
\end{aligned}
$$
$$(13)$$

In addition we show the prediction of superweak theories which in this plot is represented by a straight line.

There are several interesting features visible on this plot: First, the impact of the direct measurements of $\sin(2\beta)$ and $\sin(2\alpha)$ is clearly visible in figure 4.

Next, in cases (III) and (IV) we have examples where the measurements of $\sin(2\alpha)$ are incompatible with the predictions coming from ε_K and $B^0 - \bar{B}^0$ mixing. This

would be a signal for physics beyond the standard model. The measurement of $\sin(2\alpha)$ is essential for this. Furthermore, case (IV) shows that for a special choice of parameters the predictions for the asymmetries coming from ε_K, $B^0 - \bar{B}^0$ mixing, $|V_{cb}|$ and $|V_{ub}/V_{cb}|$ can be quite accurate when these four constraints can only be satisfied simultaneously in a small area of the $(\bar{\varrho}, \bar{\eta})$ space. Decreasing $|V_{cb}|$, $|V_{ub}/V_{cb}|$ and m_t and increasing F_B would make the allowed region in the case (IV) even smaller.

Finally, we also observe that the future measurements of B-asymmetries and the improved ranges for the parameters relevant for ε_K and $B^0 - \bar{B}^0$ mixing will probably allow to rule out the superweak models. This was also already indicated by figure 3 (III).

5. Direct CP Violation in $K \rightarrow \pi\pi$ and $K_L \rightarrow \pi^0 e^+ e^-$

$Re(\varepsilon'/\varepsilon)$ measures the ratio of direct to indirect CP violation in $K \rightarrow \pi\pi$ decays. The short distance QCD corrections to ε'/ε have been calculated at the next-to-leading order level [16, 17]. The result of these analyses can be summarized in an analytic formula for $Re(\varepsilon'/\varepsilon)$ as a function of m_t, $\Lambda_{\overline{MS}}$, m_s, hadronic matrix element parameters B_6, B_8 and CKM elements [18]. A simplified version of this formula is given by

$$Re(\varepsilon'/\varepsilon) = 12 \cdot 10^{-4} \left[\frac{\eta \lambda^5 A^2}{1.7 \cdot 10^{-4}}\right] \left[\frac{150 \, MeV}{m_s(m_c)}\right]^2$$
$$\times \left[B_6 - Z(x_t)B_8\right], \qquad (14)$$

where $Z(x_t) = 0.175 \cdot x_t^{0.93}$. Eq. (14) clearly shows that in the SM ε'/ε is governed by QCD (B_6) and electroweak (B_8) penguin contributions. For $m_t = (170 \pm 10) \, GeV$ and using ε_K-analysis to determine η one finds [16] $Re(\varepsilon'/\varepsilon) = (6 \pm 4) \times 10^{-4}$ for $B_6 = B_8 \approx 1$ (lattice, $1/N$ expansion). For $B_6 \approx 2$, $B_8 \approx 1$ (QCD penguin domination) values as high as $Re(\varepsilon'/\varepsilon) = (15 \pm 5) \times 10^{-4}$ are possible. Thus the remaining theoretical uncertainty stemming from hadronic parameters somehow resembles the still existing experimental discrepancy between E731 $Re(\varepsilon'/\varepsilon) = (7.4 \pm 5.9) \times 10^{-4}$ [19] and NA31 $Re(\varepsilon'/\varepsilon) = (23 \pm 7) \times 10^{-4}$ [20].

For the decay $K_L \rightarrow \pi^0 e^+ e^-$ a recent next-to-leading order analysis [21] of the directly CP violating contribution indicates this part of the amplitude to be the dominant one. One obtains $BR(K_L \rightarrow \pi^0 e^+ e^-)_{dir} = (6 \pm 3) \times 10^{-12}$ [21] and $BR(K_L \rightarrow \pi^0 e^+ e^-)_{indir} \leq 1.6 \times 10^{-12}$, $BR(K_L \rightarrow \pi^0 e^+ e^-)_{cons} = (1.0 \pm 0.8) \times 10^{-12}$ for the indirectly CP violating and CP conserving contributions, respectively [22, 23]. The present experimental bound is $BR(K_L \rightarrow \pi^0 e^+ e^-) \leq 4.3 \times 10^{-9}$ [24].

6. Summary and Conclusions

We have shown that in order to compete with the accuracy expected from LHC for the determination of the UT one needs to extend the usual Wolfenstein parametrization of the CKM matrix to the next-to-leading order in the expansion in terms of λ. To this end we have proposed a form of the next-to-leading order expansion for which the UT at next-to-leading order in λ nicely resembles the UT in leading order when coordinates are expressed in $(\bar{\varrho}, \bar{\eta})$ instead of the usual ones (ϱ, η).

Our analysis investigated how well the UT can possibly be determined around the year 2000 from data on ε_K, B^0–$\bar{B}^0$ mixing, $|V_{cb}|$ and $|V_{ub}/V_{cb}|$. We have found that along this line it will be possible to make predictions for $|V_{td}|$, $\sin(2\beta)$ and $BR(K^+ \rightarrow \pi^+ \nu \bar{\nu})$ up to an error of $\pm(10\text{–}15)\%$. However, for x_s and $\sin(2\alpha)$, $\sin(2\gamma)$ there will remain sizeable/huge uncertainties, respectively. This results from theoretical uncertainties being present already in the determination of some of the input parameters of this approach.

On the other hand, the future determination of $\sin(2\alpha)$ and $\sin(2\beta)$ from CP violating B-asymmetries at HERA-B, SLAC, KEK being (almost) free of theoretical uncertainties turns out to have an impressive impact

on our knowledge of the UT. Along this line it will e.g. be possible to predict $|V_{td}|$, x_s and $BR(K^+ \rightarrow \pi^+ \nu \bar{\nu})$ up to an error of $\pm(5\text{–}10)\%$. Future LHC B-physics experiments around the year 2005 will refine these studies as evident from figure 4 and [4]

Any discrepancy found between the indirect determination of $\sin(2\alpha)$, $\sin(2\beta)$ from $\{\varepsilon_K, x_d, |V_{cb}|, |V_{ub}/V_{cb}|\}$ and a direct measurement in CP violating B-asymmetries would signal new physics beyond the SM.

Finally, we shortly summarized the status of direct CP violation in $K \rightarrow \pi\pi$ where for ε'/ε both experiment and the non-perturbative part of theory need some improvements. While direct CP violation is known to give only a small contribution to the whole amplitude in $K \rightarrow \pi\pi$, our recent analysis of the direct CP violating part in the decay $K_L \rightarrow \pi^0 e^+ e^-$ indicates that there this contribution seems to be the dominant one.

Acknowledgments

The author would like to thank A. J. Buras and G. Ostermaier for the most pleasant collaboration on the work presented here.

References

[1] L. Wolfenstein, Phys. Rev. Lett. **51** (1983) 1945.
[2] Particle Data Group, Phys. Rev. **D 45** (1992) No.11 part II.
[3] A. J. Buras, M. E. Lautenbacher, and G. Ostermaier, Phys. Rev. **D 50** (1994) 3433.
[4] L. Camilleri, CERN preprint CERN-PPE/93-159.
[5] G. R. Harris and J. L. Rosner, Phys. Rev. **D 45** (1992) 946.
[6] C. O. Dib, I. Dunietz, F. J. Gilman, and Y. Nir, Phys. Rev. **D 41** (1990) 1522.
[7] S. Herrlich and U. Nierste, Nucl. Phys. **B419** (1994) 292.
[8] A. J. Buras, M. Jamin, and P. H. Weisz, Nucl. Phys. **B347** (1990) 491.
[9] W. A. Kaufman, H. Steger, and Y. P. Yao, Mod. Phys. Lett. **A3** (1988) 1479.
[10] G. Buchalla, A. J. Buras, and M. K. Harlander, Nucl. Phys. **B337** (1990) 313.
[11] A. Datta, J. Fröhlich, and E. A. Paschos, Zeitschr. f. Physik **C46** (1990) 63.
[12] J. M. Flynn, Mod. Phys. Lett. **A5** (1990) 877.
[13] H. Albrecht *et al.* (HERA-B), DESY preprint DESY-PRC 92/04 (1992).
[14] BaBar collaboration - Status Report, SLAC preprint SLAC-419 (June 1993).
[15] Y. Nir, CP-Violation, SLAC-PUB-5874.
[16] A. J. Buras, M. Jamin, and M. E. Lautenbacher, Nucl. Phys. **B408** (1993) 209.
[17] M. Ciuchini, E. Franco, G. Martinelli, and L. Reina, Phys. Lett. **301B** (1993) 263.
[18] A. J. Buras and M. E. Lautenbacher, Phys. Lett. **318B** (1993) 212.
[19] L. K. Gibbons *et al.*, Phys. Rev. Lett. **70** (1993) 1203.
[20] G. D. Barr *et al.*, Phys. Lett. **B317** (1993) 233.
[21] A. J. Buras, M. E. Lautenbacher, M. Misiak, and M. Münz, Nucl. Phys. **B423** (1994) 349.
[22] A. G. Cohen, G. Ecker, and A. Pich, Phys. Lett. **304B** (1993) 347.
[23] A. Pich, CERN-Th-7114-93 and refs. therein.
[24] D. A. Harris *et al.*, Phys. Rev. Lett. **71** (1993) 3918.

Paper presented at XXVII Int. Conf. on High Energy Physics: Session Pa-9
Glasgow, UK, 20–27 July 1994

Results on Time-Depedent $B^0 - \bar{B}^0$ Mixing at ALEPH

Yi-Bin Pan[†]

University of Wisconsin - Madison[*]

ALEPH collaboration

Abstract

Results on time dependent B_d° and B_s° oscillations at ALEPH are presented. An analysis of D^* - lepton and D^* - jet charge correlation yields a measurement of the B_d° mixing parameter: $\Delta m_d = (0.497 \pm 0.070 \pm 0.036)ps^{-1}$, where the first error is statistical and the second is systematic. Another analysis of events with high transverse momentum leptons in opposite hemispheres yields a measurement of $\Delta m_d = (0.44 \pm 0.05^{+0.09}_{-0.08})ps^{-1}$, and a 95% confidence limit of $\Delta m_s > 3.9\,ps^{-1}$. Finally, an analysis using events with a single lepton, where the jet charge on both sides is used intead of the lepton in the opposite hemisphere, yields a 95% confidence limit of $\Delta m_s > 6.0\,ps^{-1}$.

1. Introduction

Let B° stand for either B_d° or B_s°, and $\overline{B}^\circ$ for either $\overline{B}_d^\circ$ or $\overline{B}_s^\circ$. Due to the weak interaction, these flavor eigenstates are linear combinations of states with well defined masses which differ by Δm. The probabilities that a meson created as a B° (or $\overline{B}^\circ$) will decay in the same state (unmixed), or opposite state (mixed), are given by:

$$P_u(t) = \frac{1}{2\tau}e^{-t/\tau}(1 + \cos \Delta mt), \qquad (1)$$

and

$$P_m(t) = \frac{1}{2\tau}e^{-t/\tau}(1 - \cos \Delta mt), \qquad (2)$$

where the subscripts u denotes "unmixed", m denotes "mixed", t is the proper time, and τ is the lifetime of the B_s or B_d. The key points are to determine the particle/antiparticle state of the mesons when they are produced and when they decay, and to reconstruct the proper time between. The proper time is calculated using the reconstructed production and

† E-mail: PAN@VXALUW.CERN.CH
* Supported by the US Department of Energy, grant DE-AC02-76ER0081.

decay vertices, and an estimated meson momentum. The first analysis discussed here enhances the B_d° signal by reconstructing specific decays of the B_d°, while the other two analyses look for B_d° and B_s° oscillations on top of a non-oscillating background, with no attempt made to separate the different b hadrons.

2. Δm_d measurement from $D^\star$ - lepton and $D^\star$ - jet charge correlations

First we report an update of an analysis already published[1] which measures the B_d° oscillation parameter (Δm_d). B_d° mesons are reconstructed in the decay $B_d^\circ \to D^{*-}X$, where the $D^{*-}X$ decays to $D^\circ \pi^-$, and the D° is reconstructed in either the $K^-\pi^+$ or $K^-\pi^+\pi^\circ$ mode. (The charge conjugate of this decay chain is also implied.) The initial state is determined by either jet charge or a lepton in the opposite hemisphere, while the final state is given by the charge of the D^*. The D° decay vertex is used to estimate the decay point of the B_d°. The momentum weighted jet-charge is defined as

$$Q_J^{\kappa=0.5} = \frac{\sum_{i=1}^n P_{\|i}^k q_i}{\sum_{i=1}^n P_{\|i}^k}, \qquad (3)$$

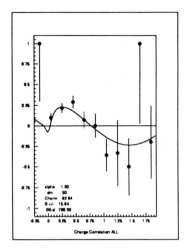

Figure 1. Charge correlation function vs decay length, for all samples combined.

Sub-sample	Events	Background
$K\pi$ jet charge	432±73	52±7
$K\pi$ lepton	147±8	19±4
$K\pi\pi^0$ jet charge	174±17	130±11
$K\pi\pi^0$ lepton	69±4	46±7

Table 1. Event statistics.

where $k = 0.5$ and $P_{\|i}$ is the momentum parallel to the thrust axis of track i in the opposite hemisphere. A jet charge (Q_{D^*}) for the D^* side of the event is the average of the track charges in the hemisphere. Removing events where $|Q_J^{\kappa=0.5} - Q_{D^*}| < 0.05$ produces a mistag for jet charge of 27.3%. A 25% mistag for leptons in the opposite hemisphere is attained by requiring that the leptons have momentum and transverse momentum greater than 3.0 and 0.75 GeV/c, respectively. The event statistics are listed in table 1. The final value is $\Delta m_d = (0.497\pm0.070\pm0.036)ps^{-1}$, where the first error is statistical and the second is systematic. A charge correlation function is defined for presentation of the result:

$$QQ = \frac{N^{ss} - N^{os}}{N^{ss} + N^{os}}, \qquad (4)$$

where N^{ss} (N^{os}) is the number of where either the jet charge value or lepton charge has the same (opposite) sign as the charge of the reconstructed D^*. The charge correlation function is plotted as a function of decay length in figure 1, with the result of the fit superimposed.

3. Dilepton analysis

The next analysis is also an update of a previous result[2]. Every event is used that has two high transverse momentum leptons ($p_T > 1.25$ GeV/c) which are in opposite hemispheres. Most of these leptons

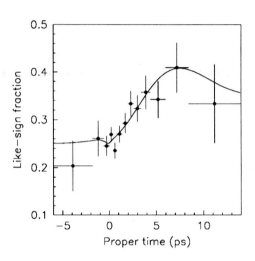

Figure 2. The fraction of like-signed dileptons as a function of reconstructed proper time. The superimposed fit assumes maximal B_s^o mixing.

are produced in semileptonic b decays. The sign of the lepton indicates the charge of the b quark when the b hadron decays. As no attempt is made to determine which of the hadrons may have oscillated, both sides of the event are fit simultaneously for the probability that either side has mixed. The decay point of the b hadron is reconstructed by first removing the leptons, and then assigning the remaining tracks to either the primary vertex or a single secondary vertex in each hemisphere. A grid point search is performed to find the optimal secondary vertex point and track assignment combination that minimizes the combined χ^2 of the vertices. The tracks assigned to the secondary vertices form charm tracks which are intersected with the lepton in the same hemisphere to give the b hadron decay points. The momentum of the hadrons is reconstructed as the sum of the momentum of the charged tracks assigned to the decay vertex plus the neutrino momentum estimated from the missing energy in the hemisphere, plus a fraction of neutral momentum in the hemisphere. A fit to the entire event sample gives $\Delta m_d = (0.44 \pm 0.05^{+0.09}_{-0.08})ps^{-1}$. In figures 2 is plotted the like-signed fraction of dileptons as a function of reconstructed proper time. Superimposed is the fit (which assumes maximal B_s^o mixing). The dilepton sample can also be used to set a limit on B_s^o oscillations. Fig. 3 shows the data log-likelihood curve. A naive limit curve is drawn at 1.92 log-likelihood units. A Monte Carlo simulation is used to determine the superimposed 95% confidence limit curve. This curve includes the

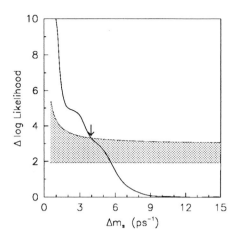

Figure 3. The data log likelihood curve is superimposed on the 95% confidence limit curve. Also drawn is the naive limit line at 1.92. The arrow indicates the limit at $\Delta m_s = 3.9\ ps^{-1}$.

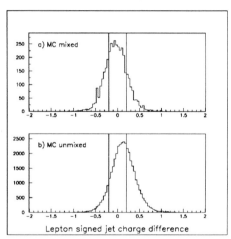

Figure 4. Plotted are the Monte Carlo lepton signed jet charge difference distributions for a) mixed, and b) unmixed events.

effects of systematic uncertainties on quantities such as the fractions of the various b hadrons in the sample, and fractions of leptons which come from subsequent charm decays. The data curve intersects this curve at $\Delta m_s = 3.9\ ps^{-1}$. This is taken as the lower limit.

4. limit on B_s^0 oscillation using leptons and rapidity weighted jet charge

The main difference between this analysis and the previous one is that a rapidity weighted jet charge using both sides of the event is used instead of a lepton in the opposite hemisphere to determine the initial state of the B_s^0 meson at production time ($t = 0$). The jet charge is defined as

$$Q_{jet} = \frac{\sum_{i=1}^{n} y_i q_i}{\sum_{i=1}^{n} y_i}, \tag{5}$$

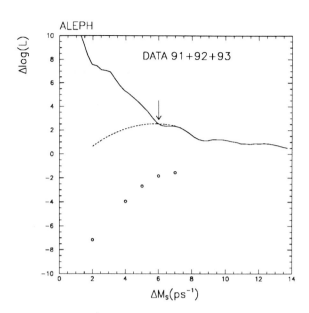

Figure 5. The data $\Delta \log L$ curve is superimposed over the Monte Carlo 95% confidence curve. The open circles are the average $\Delta \log L$ values measured at the input Δm_s for many independent Monte Carlo samples. The 95% confidence limit of $\Delta m_s > 6\ ps^{-1}$ is taken from where the 95% limit curve and the data curve cross.

where y_i is the rapidity defined as:

$$y_i = \ell n \frac{E_i + P_{i\|}}{E_i - P_{i\|}}, \tag{6}$$

and where q_i is the charge of track i and E_i and $P_{i\|}$ are the energy and momentum component along the jet axis of track i. The jet charges of both sides of the event are used. We require $|Q_{jet}^{same} - Q_{jet}^{opp}| > 0.2$. Figure 4 shows the lepton signed jet charge difference distributions for a) mixed, and b) unmixed events. The data likelihood curve is shown in figure 5. The superimposed limit curve is calculated similarly to that of the dilepton analysis, except that the likelihood differences used in the limit curve are defined with respect to the likelihood at maximal mixing ($\Delta m_s = 30\ ps^{-1}$), rather than the likelihood at its minimum value. The data curve crosses the 95% confidence limit curve at the lower limit point of $\Delta m_s = 6\ ps^{-1}$. Assuming a B_s^0 lifetime of 1.5 ps implies $x_s > 9.0$.

References

[1] Aleph Collaboration: D. Buskulic *et al.*, Phys. Lett. **B313** (1993) 498.
[2] Aleph Collaboration: D. Buskulic *et al.*, Phys. Lett. **B322** (1994) 441.

Paper presented at XXVII Int. Conf. on High Energy Physics: Session Pa-9
Glasgow, UK, 20–27 July 1994

Measurements of neutral B-Meson oscillations using the OPAL detector

Sachio Komamiya[‡]

ICEPP, University of Tokyo,
7-3-1 Hongo, Bunkyo-ku, Tokyo 113 Japan

On behalf of the OPAL Collaboration

Abstract

The oscillation frequency of the B_d^0 meson, Δm_d, is measured using the OPAL detector at the LEP e^+e^- collider. Independent analyses of three different channels, $D^{*+} + \ell$, $D^{*+}\ell +$ jet charge and $\ell + \ell$, have been performed and the combined result of $\Delta m_d = 0.520 \pm 0.054$ ps^{-1} is obtained. Using double lepton events, a lower limit of 1.3 ps^{-1} (95% C.L.) is obtained for the B_s^0 oscillation frequency Δm_s.

1. Introduction

Neutral B-meson oscillation takes place via second order electroweak transitions in the Standard Model. Similar to the K^0-meson oscillation, the probabilities of having a B_d^0 or a $\bar{B}_d^0$ at proper time t, when B_d^0 is produced at $t = 0$, are given by

$$
\begin{aligned}
P_{B_d^0}(t) &= \frac{e^{-t/\tau}}{\tau} \cos^2(\frac{\Delta m_d}{2}t) \\
P_{\bar{B}_d^0}(t) &= \frac{e^{-t/\tau}}{\tau} \sin^2(\frac{\Delta m_d}{2}t),
\end{aligned}
$$

where τ is the average lifetimes of the two B_d^0 mass eigenstates. In the case of B_d^0 oscillations these two lifetimes are expected to be very close to each other. In K^0-meson oscillations, on the other hand, the difference of the lifetimes of the two mass eigenstates (K_S and K_L) is very large. Hence phenomenology of B_d^0 oscillations is somewhat different from that of K^0 oscillations.

Independent analyses to measure the B_d^0-$\bar{B}_d^0$ oscillation frequency Δm_d for three different channels are performed by the OPAL collaboration. A brief explanation of the experimental method is described below, together with descriptions of the advantages and disadvantages, for each analysis. Throughout this report charge conjugate processes are also implied.

(A) $D^{*+} + \ell$ [1]

In this analysis, the decay $D^{*+} \to D^0 \pi^+$ is reconstructed and a high p_t lepton is tagged in the opposite hemisphere. The charge of the lepton tags the b-flavour at the B_d^0 production time ($t = 0$), and the b-flavour at the decay of B_d^0 is determined by the $D^{*\pm}$ charge. The distance between the primary vertex and the D^0 decay vertex is measured as an estimator of the B_d^0 decay length. This analysis is straight forward and well understood. All the known effects are incorporated in the likelihood function for the fit. The B_d^0-$\bar{B}_d^0$ oscillation is measured without B_s^0 contamination in the data sample. The size of systematic errors is relatively small. The disadvantages of this analysis are the presence of background of D^{*+}'s coming from $c\bar{c}$ events, the low statistics, and the indirect measurement of the B_d^0 decay length.

(B) $D^{*+}\ell +$ jet charge [2]

In this analysis the D^{*+} and ℓ^- are required to be in the same hemisphere; hence, the sample is very clean $b\bar{b}$ events. As for the first analysis, Δm_d is

‡ Mailing address: CERN, PPE Division,
CH 1211, Genève 23
E-mail address: SACHIO at CERNVM.CERN.CH

measured without B_s^0 contamination in the data sample. The b-flavour of the B_d^0 meson at $t = 0$ is determined by the jet charges of both of the hemispheres. This novel technique improves the determination of the b-flavour at $t = 0$. The B_d^0 decay length is directly measured as the length from the primary vertex to the lepton-D^0 vertex. This analysis also suffers from low statistics.

(C) $\ell + \ell$ [3]

High p_t leptons are required in both thrust hemispheres in this analysis. The purity of $b\bar{b}$ events in the dilepton sample is high (97%). A reconstructed B-hadron vertex is required to be present in one or both thrust hemispheres. The b-flavour of the B_d^0 at the decay time is determined from the charge of the lepton in the hemisphere where the vertex is reconstructed. The b-flavour at $t = 0$ is tagged by the charge of the lepton in the other hemisphere. Among the three analyses, this one yields the greatest statistics. Since high p_t leptons come not only from B_d^0 decays but also from B^+, B_s^0, Λ_b and their cascade decays ($b \rightarrow c \rightarrow \ell$), the Δm_d measurement is sensitive to the uncertainties of the lepton fractions from B_s^0 and cascade decays ($b \rightarrow c \rightarrow \ell$) in the sample. Despite these disadvantages, this analysis is also sensitive to the B_s^0 oscillation parameter Δm_s.

2. $D^{*+} + \ell$ Analysis

D^{*+} candidates are reconstructed in the decay chain of $D^{*+} \rightarrow D^0 \pi^+ \rightarrow K^- \pi^+ \pi^+$. Kaons and pions are identified using dE/dx information obtained from the OPAL jet chamber. The invariant mass range of the selected D^0 candidates is

$$1.79 \text{ GeV} < M_{K^- \pi^+} < 1.94 \text{ GeV},$$

The mass difference of the reconstructed D^{*+} and D^0 is required to be in the range of

$$0.142 \text{ GeV} < \Delta M \equiv M_{K^- \pi^+ \pi^+} - M_{K^- \pi^+} < 0.149 \text{ GeV}.$$

To reduce combinatorial background, $|\cos \theta^*|$ is required to be less than 0.8, where θ^* is the angle between the D^0 flight direction and the direction of the kaon in the D^0 rest frame. The momentum of the $K^- \pi^+ \pi^+$ combination should lie between 7 GeV and 30 GeV. The upper boundary is used to reduce $c\bar{c} \rightarrow D^{*+} X$ background, and the lower boundary removes combinatorial background.

The flavour of the B_d^0 meson at $t = 0$ is tagged by a lepton in the opposite hemisphere of the D^{*+}. To reduce leptons from cascade decays ($b \rightarrow c \rightarrow \ell$) and those from $c\bar{c}$, the lepton momentum is required to be greater than 3 GeV and p_t with respect to jet axis is required to be greater than 0.75 GeV.

The decay length of the B_d^0 is not directly measured; instead, the distance between the primary vertex and the $D^0 \rightarrow K^- \pi^+$ vertex is measured in the x-y plane. Using the D^0 momentum direction, the three-dimensional decay length, L, is obtained. Since the flight direction of the D^0 is approximately the same as the B_d^0 flight direction, L is approximately equal to the sum of the B_d^0 and D^0 decay lengths ($L \approx L_{B_d^0} + L_{D^0}$). The boost factor of B_d^0 is not measured event by event but the fragmentation function proposed by Peterson *et al.* is convoluted in the likelihood function.

The distribution function of L used in the likelihood function is given by

$$f_{B_d^0}(L) = R(L - L') \otimes P_{\text{fragm}}((\beta\gamma)_{B_d^0}) \otimes$$
$$P_{D^0}((\beta\gamma)_{D^0}, L'_{D^0}) \otimes P_{B_d^0}((\beta\gamma)_{B_d^0}, L'_{B_d^0}),$$

where $\otimes$ denotes convolution integration, $L'_{B_d^0}$ and L'_{D^0} are the true decay lengths, and $(\beta\gamma)_{D^0} (= p_{K\pi}/m_{D^0})$ is the measured boost factor of the D^0. The convolution is performed with a condition of $L' = L'_{B_d^0} + L'_{D^0}$. In the above formula $P_{\text{fragm}}((\beta\gamma)_{B_d^0})$ is the fragmentation function, $R(L - L')$ is the resolution function of the L measurement, and $P_{D^0}((\beta\gamma)_{D^0}, L'_{D^0})$ is the D^0 decay length distribution. The B_d^0 decay distribution function $P_{B_d^0}((\beta\gamma)_{B_d^0}, L'_{B_d^0})$ for mixed and unmixed cases is given by

$$P_{B_d^0}^{mixed}((\beta\gamma)_{B_d^0}, L'_{B_d^0}) = \frac{\exp(-L'_{B_d^0}/\tau\beta\gamma)}{\tau\beta\gamma}$$
$$\cos^2(\frac{\Delta m_d}{2} \frac{L'_{B_d^0}}{\beta\gamma}),$$

$$P_{B_d^0}^{unmixed}((\beta\gamma)_{B_d^0}, L'_{B_d^0}) = \frac{\exp(-L'_{B_d^0}/\tau\beta\gamma)}{\tau\beta\gamma}$$
$$\sin^2(\frac{\Delta m_d}{2} \frac{L'_{B_d^0}}{\beta\gamma}).$$

Fitting simultaneously the like-sign ($D^{*+}\ell^+$) and the unlike-sign ($D^{*+}\ell^-$) decay length distributions with the expected distribution functions using the unbinned likelihood method, Δm_d is measured to be 0.57 ± 0.11 ps^{-1}. The major source of the systematic error is the uncertainty in the fragmentation function ($\delta\Delta m_d = \pm 0.012$ ps^{-1}). Summing up all the systematic errors, the total systematic error is estimated to be ± 0.018 ps^{-1}. In Fig.1, the plot of the asymmetry

$$\frac{N(D^{*+}\ell^+) - N(D^{*+}\ell^-)}{N(D^{*+}\ell^+) + N(D^{*+}\ell^-)}$$

as a function of measured decay length is shown together with the predictions for $\Delta m_d = 0.57$ ps^{-1} and 0 ps^{-1}.

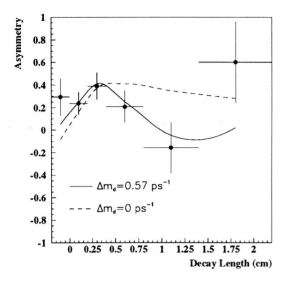

Figure 1. The plot of the asymmetry $(N(\mathrm{D}^{*+}\ell^+) - N(\mathrm{D}^{*+}\ell^-))/(N(\mathrm{D}^{*+}\ell^+) + N(\mathrm{D}^{*+}\ell^-))$ for data and the best fit curve for the $\mathrm{D}^{*+} + \ell$ analysis.

3. Analysis of $D^{*+} + \ell^- + \text{jet charge}$

This method requires a D^{*+} and ℓ^- in the same hemisphere, hence the background contribution from $e^+e^- \to c\bar{c}$ events is very small. The charge of the B_d^0 meson at production ($t = 0$) is determined by the jet charge of both hemispheres. This novel technique is developed by the OPAL collaboration[4] as described later. Since the background level is low, weaker cuts are applied to select D^{*+} candidates than for the $\mathrm{D}^{*+} + \ell$ analysis. The invariant mass range of the selected D^0 candidates is

$$1.79 \text{ GeV} < M_{\mathrm{K}^-\pi^+} < 1.94 \text{ GeV}.$$

For D^{*+} selection, the following conditions are required:

$$\Delta M \equiv M_{\mathrm{D}^0\pi^+} - M_{\mathrm{D}^0} < 0.15 \text{ GeV} \quad \text{and,}$$
$$x_{\mathrm{K}^-\pi^+\pi^+} \equiv E_{\mathrm{K}^-\pi^+\pi^+}/E_{\mathrm{beam}} > 0.15.$$

In this analysis, the D^0 satellite peak (a broad mass peak in the $\mathrm{K}^-\pi^+$ invariant mass distribution due to $\mathrm{D}^0 \to \mathrm{K}^-\pi^+\pi^0$, where the π^0 is missing) is also included to enlarge the statistics. For the satellite peak

$$1.41 \text{ GeV} \quad < \quad M_{\mathrm{K}^-\pi^+} < 1.77 \text{ GeV},$$
$$\Delta M \quad < \quad 0.16 \text{ GeV},$$
$$x_{\mathrm{K}^-\pi^+\pi^+} \quad > \quad 0.20,$$

are required. The invariant mass of the $\mathrm{D}^{*+} + \ell^-$ system is required to satisfy $2.8 \text{ GeV} < M_{\mathrm{D}^{*+}\ell^-} < 5.3 \text{ GeV}$.

After applying the above cuts, 187 events are selected with a background of 34 ± 6 events for

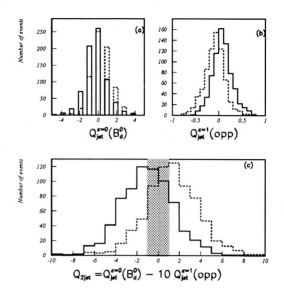

Figure 2. The jet charge distributions for the B_d^0 hemisphere $Q_{jet}(\mathrm{B}_\mathrm{d}^0)$, for opposite hemisphere $Q_{jet}(opp)$ and for the combined one Q_{2jet} are plotted for the simulated events with B_d^0 and $\bar{\mathrm{B}}_\mathrm{d}^0$.

the D^{*+} peak, and 369 events are selected with an estimated background of 96 ± 14 events for the satellite peak. The combinatorial background in the signal region of the ΔM peak is estimated using the shape of the distribution of the wrong sign $(\mathrm{D}^{*+}\ell^+)$ events.

The flavour of the B_d^0 meson at $t = 0$ is tagged using the jet charges of the same and the opposite hemispheres of the $\mathrm{D}^{*+}\ell^-$. In the $\mathrm{D}^{*+}\ell^-$ hemisphere the jet charge is determined by the sum of particles charges $(Q_{\mathrm{jet}}(\mathrm{B}_\mathrm{d}^0) = \Sigma Q_i)$. Since B_d^0 is a neutral particle, the sum of the charge is not affected by mixing. Since the particle charge is not weighted by kinematical variables, there is no kinematical bias in $Q_{\mathrm{jet}}(\mathrm{B}_\mathrm{d}^0)$ after the mixing. In the opposite hemisphere of $\mathrm{D}^{*+}\ell^-$, the jet charge is determined by the sum of particle charges weighted by the longitudinal momentum $(Q_{\mathrm{jet}}(opp) = \Sigma Q_i p_{iL}/E_{\mathrm{beam}})$. A linear combination of the two jet charges,

$$Q_{2\mathrm{jet}} = Q_{\mathrm{jet}}(\mathrm{B}_\mathrm{d}^0) - 10 \, Q_{\mathrm{jet}}(opp),$$

is defined and it is used to determine the charge of the B_d^0 at $t = 0$. In Fig.2, $Q_{\mathrm{jet}}(\mathrm{B}_\mathrm{d}^0)$, $Q_{\mathrm{jet}}(opp)$ and the combined jet charge $Q_{2\mathrm{jet}}$ are plotted for the case of B_d^0 (broken lines) and $\bar{\mathrm{B}}_\mathrm{d}^0$ (solid lines). When $|Q_{2\mathrm{jet}}| > 1$ is required, an efficiency of 70% and a correct tag fraction of 72% are obtained. The variable $Q_{2\mathrm{jet}}$ is significantly more powerful in identifying the b-flavour than using $Q_{\mathrm{jet}}(opp)$ alone. If only $Q_{\mathrm{jet}}(opp)$ is used to obtain a correct tag fraction of 72%, the efficiency decreases to 26%. To obtain 70% efficiency with $Q_{\mathrm{jet}}(opp)$ alone, the

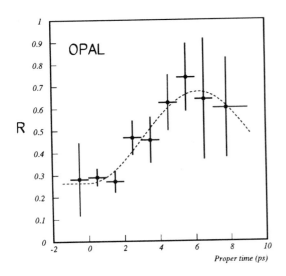

Figure 3. The distribution of asymmetry of mixed $(Q_{2jet}Q_\ell < 0)$ and unmixed $(Q_{2jet}Q_\ell > 0)$ events as a function of decay proper time.

correct tag fraction $1 - f$ drops to 65% and the delusion factor $1 - 2f$ largely increases.

The fraction of mixed B_d^0 mesons is experimentally given by

$$R(t) = \frac{N_{\mathrm{mix}}(t) - N_{\mathrm{mix}}^{\mathrm{bkg}}(t)}{N_{\mathrm{tot}}(t) - N_{\mathrm{tot}}^{\mathrm{bkg}}(t)},$$

which is fitted by a predicted function of

$$R(t) = f + \frac{1 - 2f}{1 + N_{\mathrm{B+}}(t)/N_{B_d^0}(t)} \sin^2 \frac{\Delta m_{\mathrm{d}}}{2} t,$$

where f is the mistag fraction, and $N_{B_d^0}(t)/N_{\mathrm{B+}}(t)$ is the ratio of B_d^0 and B^+ at time t, which can be written as

$$N_{\mathrm{B+}}(t)/N_{B_d^0}(t) = N_{\mathrm{B+}}(0)/N_{B_d^0}(0)\ \exp(t(\frac{1}{\tau_{B_d^0}} - \frac{1}{\tau_{\mathrm{B+}}})).$$

Both f and Δm_{d} are taken as free parameters in the fit. The experimental plot of $R(t)$ is shown in Fig.3 together with the best fit result of $\Delta m_{\mathrm{d}} = 0.508 \pm 0.075$ ps^{-1} and $f = 0.26 \pm 0.03$. The Monte Carlo prediction of $f = 0.28$ is consistent with the fit result. In this analysis, the largest systematic error in Δm_{d} comes from the uncertainty in the B^+ fraction ($\delta\Delta m_{\mathrm{d}} = \pm 0.019$ ps^{-1}). Uncertainties in the decay time resolution and the difference of the B_d^0 and B^+ lifetimes are the next largest systematic errors. Combining all the systematic errors, Δm_{d} is measured to be $0.508 \pm 0.075 \pm 0.025$ ps^{-1}.

4. $\ell + \ell$ Analysis

In this analysis, we do not try to isolate particular B-hadron species, so it is sensitive to both Δm_{d} and Δm_{s}. On the other hand, the Δm_{d} measurement suffers from the uncertainty in the B_s^0 fraction and the lepton fraction from cascade decays.

After selecting lepton candidates, a neural network with input parameters of three kinematical variables (p^ℓ, p_t^ℓ and ω) is used to enrich leptons from B-hadron direct decay (b$\rightarrow\ell$) and to reduce cascade decay leptons (b$\rightarrow$c$\rightarrow\ell$). Here, p^ℓ is the lepton momentum, p_t^ℓ is the lepton transverse momentum calculated with respect to the jet axis, and ω is the sum of the charged particle and electromagnetic cluster energies recorded close to the lepton candidate. Since direct decay leptons are more isolated than the cascade leptons, ω tends to be smaller for b$\rightarrow\ell$ than for b$\rightarrow$c$\rightarrow\ell$. Cutting on the network output increases the efficiency for b$\rightarrow\ell$ by 40% at fixed cascade fraction relative to making cuts only on combinations of p^ℓ and p_t^ℓ.

The B-hadron decay vertex is reconstructed using the lepton candidate track and the two tracks in the same jet which have the most significant separation from the primary vertex. Additional tracks which match to the reconstructed seed vertex are added to form the secondary vertex.

The energy of the jet which contains the lepton candidate and the reconstructed vertex is calculated based on the overall energy-momentum conservation of the event. This jet contains particles from the long lived B-hadron as well as fragmentation particles which come mainly from the primary vertex. To calculate the B-hadron energy E_{B}, the energy sum of the fragmentation particles is estimated event by event and is subtracted from the jet energy.

	e-e	e-μ	μ-μ	total
unlike	633	1378	853	2864
like	296	638	452	1386

Table 1. A summary of the number of dilepton events.

The decay proper time t is calculated using the formula

$$t = \frac{L_{xy}}{\sin\theta} \frac{m_{\mathrm{B}}}{\sqrt{E_{\mathrm{B}}^2 - m_{\mathrm{B}}^2}},$$

where L_{xy} is the distance from the primary vertex to the reconstructed secondary vertex in the x-y plane, θ is the polar angle of the jet axis, and a m_{B} is set to B_d^0 mass of 5.28 GeV. The resolution of the boost factor $(\beta\gamma)_{\mathrm{B}} = \frac{\sqrt{E_{\mathrm{B}}^2 - m_{\mathrm{B}}^2}}{m_{\mathrm{B}}}$ is 7% (σ) for the central Gaussian and 12% in rms, for vertices with L_{xy} larger than 0.2 cm.

The number of dilepton events (lepton candidates in both thrust hemispheres) with at least one secondary vertex reconstructed in the event are listed in Table 1. A large fraction of dilepton events have two reconstructed vertices one in each thrust hemisphere (1662 events for unlike-sign and 821 events for like-sign). According to the Monte Carlo, the fractions of $e^+e^- \rightarrow c\bar{c}$ events and light quark pair events in the dilepton event sample are 3.0% and 0.7%, respectively. The number of cascade decay leptons over the number of all the leptons from B-hadron decay in the dilepton sample is about 10%.

In order to determine Δm_d, proper time distributions for like-sign and unlike-sign leptons are simultaneously fitted using the maximum likelihood technique. Events with two reconstructed vertices and those with one vertex are treated properly. The likelihood function is constructed as a weighted sum of expected proper time distributions for all the lepton sources. The distribution for each lepton source is parametrised using a Monte Carlo dilepton sample in which the origin of the lepton candidate is known.

In Fig.4, the fraction of like-sign leptons is plotted as a function of the measured proper time. The predicted curves for the best fit value of $\Delta m_d = 0.5$ ps^{-1} and that for no B$_d^0$-mixing ($\Delta m_d = 0$) are shown in the figure, where Δm_s is fixed to 10 ps^{-1} for both curves.

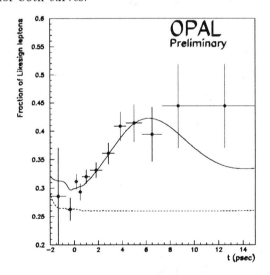

Figure 4. The distribution of the same charge fraction as a function of measured decay proper time. The predicted curves for $\Delta m_d = 0.5$ ps^{-1} and $\Delta m_s = 10$ ps^{-1} (solid curve) and that for $\Delta m_d = 0$ and $\Delta m_s = 10$ ps^{-1} (broken curve) are shown.

The main sources of the systematic error in Δm_d are the uncertainty in the cascade decay fraction ($\delta \Delta m_d = \pm 0.05$ ps^{-1}) and in the B$_s^0$ fraction ($\delta \Delta m_d = \pm 0.06$ ps^{-1}). The overall systematic error is ± 0.09 ps^{-1}. Treating Δm_d, the cascade decay fraction and the B$_s^0$ fraction as free parameters,

a three parameter fit is performed with Gaussian constraints for the two additional free parameters. The fitted values of the B$_s^0$ and cascade fractions are consistent with the values used in the single parameter fit.

This analysis is also sensitive to Δm_s. The equal log-likelihood contours in the plane of Δm_d-Δm_s are shown in Fig.5. The expected sensitivity of Δm_s is estimated with two methods. In the first method, a sample of about one million $Z^0 \rightarrow q\bar{q}$ events are analysed to verify the fitting procedure. To include the B$_d^0$ and B$_s^0$ oscillation effects, the charges of the leptons coming from B$_d^0$ and B$_s^0$ are artificially altered as a function of true decay proper time for given Δm_s and Δm_d values. The same fit procedure as used for the data is performed with $\Delta m_s = 1,2,4$ and 8 ps^{-1} and with fixed $\Delta m_d = 0.5$ ps^{-1}. In each case the fitted value of Δm_s is consistent with the generated value. Note that the trials with different generated values of Δm_s are not statistically independent in this test. In the second method, 140 independent sets of samples with the same size as the data are generated for four sets of parameters ($\Delta m_d = 0.5$ ps^{-1} $\Delta m_s = 1,2,4$ and 8 ps^{-1}), and the statistical behaviour of the fit is studied. The data is generated with a fast simulation using the same proper time distributions as used in the likelihood fit. In Fig.6, the results of the fit are shown for the four input values of Δm_s, which are denoted by Δm_s^*. For small values of Δm_s^*, the maximum likelihood value is found at Δm_s^* (the second column) and the expected lower limit of Δm_s is found just above Δm_s^*. For $\Delta m_s^* = 8$ ps^{-1}, however, the optimal Δm_s can be found anywhere and the expected lower limit is usually small than 8 ps^{-1}. We conclude that our fit is sensitive to Δm_s of $\lesssim 4$ ps^{-1}.

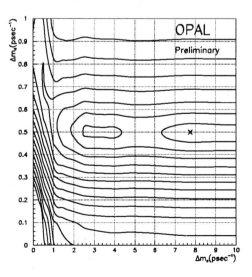

Figure 5. The equal log-likelihood contour in the plane of Δm_d vs. Δm_s. The contours are drawn for $1\sigma, 2\sigma, 3\sigma$ ..., which correspond to $\Delta \ln L = 0.5, 2.0, 4.5, 8.0, ...$

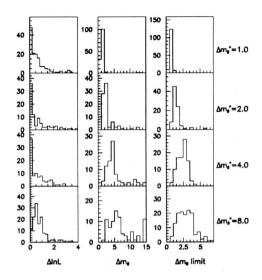

Figure 6. The distributions of $\ln L_{\max} - \ln L(\Delta m_s{}^*)$ (first column), Δm_s value at the maximum L (second column), and the 95% C.L. lower limit of Δm_s (third column), for four input $\Delta m_s{}^*$ values. The plots are obtained using 140 independent data sets with the similar sample size as for the data.

The lower limit of Δm_s is obtained by fixing Δm_d to the LEP average value of 0.523 ± 0.052[4]. In the averaging, we exclude Δm_d values from double lepton analyses, since these Δm_d measurements are correlated with Δm_s. In the absence of systematic errors, a 95% C.L. lower limit of $\Delta m_s = 1.9$ ps^{-1} is obtained corresponding to $\Delta \ln L \equiv \ln L_{\max} - \ln L = 1.92$. This method is valid as long as the distribution of $\Delta \ln L$ is consistent with the χ^2 distribution with degree of freedom one. As demonstrated in the first column of the Fig.6, this assumption is valid at least for $\Delta m_s{}^* \lesssim 4$ ps^{-1}. In the presence of the systematic errors, parameters in the likelihood fit (cascade decay fraction, B_s^0 fraction, B-hadron lifetimes, Δm_d etc.) are optimised for each Δm_s with Gaussian constraints using the external knowledge of uncertainties of these parameters. A lower limit of 1.3 ps^{-1} (95 % C.L.) is obtained from the $\ln L$ distribution. As can be seen in the third column of Fig.6, a weak limit of $\Delta m_s \lesssim 2$ ps^{-1} may accidentally happen in some cases for large $\Delta m_s{}^*$.

Analysis	Reference	Δm_d (ps^{-1})
D$^{*+} + \ell$	[1]	$0.57 \pm 0.11 \pm 0.02$
D$^{*+}\ell$ + jet charge	[2]	$0.508 \pm 0.075 \pm 0.025$
$\ell + \ell$	[3]	$0.50 \pm 0.04 \pm 0.09$

Table 2. The measured values of Δm_d with statistical and systematic errors for the three analyses.

5. Summary

We have measured Δm_d using three independent methods. The results are listed in Table 2. Combining these three results, taking into account small correlations in the systematic errors, the OPAL Δm_d value for this conference is 0.520 ± 0.054 ps^{-1}.

The 95% C.L. lower limit of Δm_s is obtained to be 1.3 ps^{-1} from the dilepton analysis. The potential sensitivity of Δm_s is estimated to be $\gtrsim 4$ ps^{-1} with the dilepton analysis.

Acknowledgement

I would like to thank all the members of the OPAL B-oscillation working group, C. Dallapiccola, H. Fukui, H. Jawahery, M. Jimack, R. Kowalewski, G.D. Long, X.C. Lou, E. de Silva and S. Tarem.

References

[1] OPAL Collaboration: R. Akers *et al.*, CERN preprint: CERN-PPE/94-90 (to be published in Phys. Lett.).
[2] OPAL Collaboration: R. Akers *et al.*, Phys. Lett. **B327** (1994) 411.
[3] OPAL Collaboration: R. Akers *et al.*, OPAL physics note: 152 (1994).
[4] S. Tarem, to be published in The Proceedings of the Recontre de Moriond (March 1994).

Measurement of the B_d^0 oscillation frequency using D^*, kaons, leptons and jet or hemisphere charges

P. Billoir

L.P.N.H.E., Universités Paris VI and Paris VII
BP 200, 4 place Jussieu, F75232 PARIS CEDEX 05, France

representing the DELPHI Collaboration

Abstract

The time-dependent oscillation of B_d^0 is studied by two methods in $Z \to b\bar{b}$ events (DELPHI experiment at LEP) using a correlation between the quark signs at B decay and at production point (given by the sign in the opposite hemisphere). In the first method, the decay sign is given by a D^*, the production sign is estimated by momentum weighted hemisphere charges; in the second one, leptons, kaons (identified with the RICH) and jet charges are used in a cumulative way. The results are in agreement with the expected shape of oscillation, and the value of Δm is fitted to $0.521 \pm 0.040 \, (stat) \pm 0.038 \, (syst) \, \hbar/c^2 \, ps^{-1} = 3.43 \pm 0.26 \, (stat) \pm 0.25 \, (syst) \, 10^{-4} \, eV/c^2$.

1. Introduction

The Standard Model predicts a mixing of the $B^0 - \bar{B}^0$ system in both d and s flavours, as in the neutral kaon system [1], depending on the CKM matrix elements V_{td} and V_{ts}; the probability of decay with oscillation can be expressed as a function of the proper time t:

$$Prob(B^0 \to \bar{B}^0 decay) = 1/\tau \; e^{-t/\tau} \sin^2(\omega t/2)$$

where τ is the mean lifetime and $\omega = \Delta m c^2/\hbar$. LEP provides many $Z \to b\bar{b}$ interactions, where the quarks are fragmented into two opposite, well distinguished jets, with a relatively long flight of the B hadron; this gives good conditions to determine, on the one side, the nature $(b/\bar{b})$ of the produced quark, and on the other side the nature $(B^0/\bar{B}^0)$ of the decaying meson.

The aim of this paper is to show an evidence for $B^0 - \bar{B}^0$ time dependent oscillation and to fit the value of its frequency, by combining different sign indicators, in order to improve the statistical precision: charged D^*, large p_t leptons, secondary kaons, jet charge. The flight distance is estimated either with the decay point of the

D^0 from the D^*, or, when using leptons or kaons, with a rough vertex estimator, practically independent of the sign indicator; its precision (less or about $500 \, \mu m$) is well suited to see the oscillations of B_d^0, which are expected to be slow from the low measured probability of the time-integrated mixing [2]. On the contrary the oscillation of the B_s^0 is expected to be much faster, so that its effect is smoothed, especially at long distances; moreover the B_s^0 is disfavoured by the D^* selection, and in inclusive channels short flight distances are contaminated by non-b background: as a consequence, this paper does not study the B_s^0 oscillation.

The principle of the method is to divide the event in two hemispheres: in the first one a "production sign" is defined, correlated to the $b/\bar{b}$ sign at the production point; in the second one, the flight distance of the B hadron is evaluated and a "decay sign" is defined, correlated to the $b/\bar{b}$ sign in the decaying hadron. Then the sign correlation is studied as a function of the flight distance δ, closely related to the flight time t ($\delta = p_B/m_B \; t$) because the momentum p_B of the B hadron has a narrow distribution.

The DELPHI detector is described in [3]. The muon identification is more detailed in [4]; the silicon microvertex detector is described in [5], and the RICH detector, used here mainly to distinguish the kaons, in [6]. In this study the data taken in 1992 and 1993 are used, representing 1.7 million hadronic Z events.

Throughout the paper the charge conjugate of the quoted channels and states will be implicitly referred to whenever it makes sense.

2. First method: D^*-hemisphere charge correlation

2.1. D^* selection and D^0 decay distance

The decay $D^{*+} \rightarrow D^0 \pi^+$ followed by $D^0 \rightarrow K^- \pi^+$ is selected mainly thanks to the small mass difference between D^* and D with the following conditions: momentum of K and π from D^0 greater than 1 GeV/c, momentum of π from D^* between 0.45 and 4.5 GeV/c, $X_E = E_{D^*}/E_{beam}$ between 0.15 and 0.5 (in order to suppress direct charm production),

$$1.79 < M(K\pi) < 1.94 \; GeV/c^2 \quad \text{if} \quad X_E > 0.25$$
$$1.82 < M(K\pi) < 1.90 \; GeV/c^2 \quad \text{if} \quad X_E < 0.25$$

then, θ^* being the angle the D^0 flight and the K direction in the D^0 rest frame:

$$\cos(\theta^*) > -0.6 \quad \text{if} \quad X_E < 0.25$$
$$\cos(\theta^*) > -0.8 \quad \text{if} \quad X_E > 0.25$$

Defining $\Delta M = M(K\pi\pi) - M(K\pi)$, the events are selected by $0.1435 < \Delta M < 0.1475 GeV/c^2$.

Another sample of D^* with $D^0 \rightarrow K^- \pi^+ \pi^0$ (π^0 not seen) is selected in the band $1.55 < M(K\pi) < 1.70$ with $0.140 < \Delta M < 0.152$ and $0.25 < X_E < 0.25$; the kaons are identified by the RICH or the ionization in the TPC when possible. The distribution of ΔM in both samples is shown on figure 1.

The position of the primary vertex is found by an iterative rejection of the track contributing most to the χ^2, accounting for the beam spot position [7] . The D^0 decay point (which actually dominates the error on the distance) is determined with the $K\pi\pi$ combination.

2.2. Combination of hemisphere charges

The weighted charge Q_H, reflecting the charge of the quark emitted in each hemisphere, is computed as:

$$Q_H = \frac{\sum_i (\vec{p_i}.\vec{e_s})^\kappa q_i}{\sum_i (\vec{p_i}.\vec{e_s})^\kappa}$$

where $\vec{e_s}$ is the unit vector of the sphericity axis, $\vec{p_i}$ the momentum and q_i the charge of track i; the exponent κ is 0.6 (actually the result does not depend

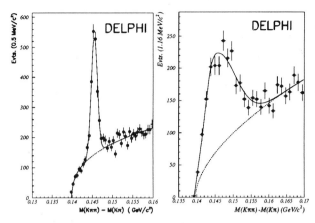

Figure 1. Distribution of $\Delta M = M(K^-\pi^+\pi^+) - M(K^-\pi^+)$ with $D^0 \rightarrow K^-\pi^+$ (left) and $D^0 \rightarrow K^-\pi^+\pi^0$ (right)

strongly on this choice). After correcting for a small positive bias due to nuclear interactions in the detector, the sign of Q_H is the sign of $b/\bar{b}$ quark with a probability $\epsilon = 0.628 \pm 0.008$ from the simulation. If the B^0 has (not) mixed, the charges of the D^* and the opposite hemisphere are of unlike (like) sign, and the charge correlation is oscillating with the decay time according to:

$$C(t) = \frac{N_{like} - N_{unlike}}{N_{like} + N_{unlike}} = (2\epsilon - 1)\cos(\omega t)$$

In order to improve the charge tagging, the difference $\Delta Q_H = Q_H(D^* \, hem.) - Q_H(opposite \, hem.)$ is used, and ϵ^{unlike} is defined as the probability that the D^* and ΔQ_H have unlike signs. Then, for a D^* originating from a B^0, this probability depends of course on whether the B^0 has mixed or not. A detailed simulation gives:

$$\epsilon^{unlike}_{mix} = 0.532 \pm 0.024 \quad ; \quad \epsilon^{unlike}_{unmix} = 0.275 \pm 0.010$$

Other contributions (charged B, $c\bar{c}$ events, Cabibbo-suppressed decays) are reviewed in table 1.

2.3. Probability distribution and fitting procedure

For each event a new variable $t = t_B + t_D$ is defined:

$$\frac{m_B}{p_B}d_B + \frac{m_D}{p_D}d_D = \frac{m_B}{p_B}d + \left(\frac{m_D}{p_D} - \frac{m_B}{p_B}\right)d_D \simeq \frac{m_B}{p_B}d$$

with a resolution $\sigma_t = t\sqrt{(\sigma_d/d)^2 + (\sigma_{p_{B^0}}/p_{B^0})^2}$. The mean B momentum is taken, and a gaussian dispersion is assumed (a parametrization as a function of the reconstructed D^* momentum has a negligible effect on ω measurement). The expected time distributions $P^{mix(unmix)}_{channel}(t,\omega)$ for the channels of table 1 are obtained by convoluting the theoretical ones $P^{mix(unmix)}_{unsmeared}(t,\omega)$ with the resolution functions. For

like sign	unlike sign	relat. fract.	ϵ^{unlike}
$B_d^0 \to D^{*-}X$		1.	0.275 ± 0.010
	$B_d^0 \to \bar{B}_d^0 \to D^{*+}X$	0.22	0.532 ± 0.024
$B^+ \to D^{*-}X$		0.28	0.239 ± 0.018
	$c\bar{c} : \bar{c} \to D^{*-}X$	0.93	0.601 ± 0.010
	$B_d^0 \to D^{*+}X$	0.03	0.500 ± 0.071
	$B^+ \to D^{*+}X$	0.04	0.657 ± 0.057
$B_s^0 \to D^{*-}X$		0.04	0.284 ± 0.052
	$B_s^0 \to \bar{B}_s^0 \to D^{*+}X$	0.04	0.605 ± 0.054

Table 1. Estimates from simulation of different contributions to the D^* sample with their relative fractions. These contributions are classified as like or unlike sign events assuming an exact tag of the original B meson. The ϵ^{unlike} probability is also given and the quoted uncertainty comes from the limited statistics of the simulation. The quoted values were obtained after applying the event selection described in Section 3.

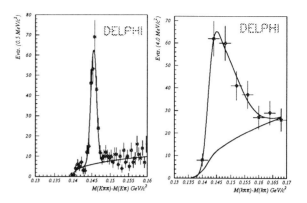

Figure 2. Distribution of $\Delta M = M(K^-\pi^+\pi^+) - M(K^-\pi^+)$ with $D^0 \to K^-\pi^+$ (left) and $D^0 \to K^-\pi^+\pi^0$ (right) in the D^*-lepton sample

charm events the time distribution $P_{c\bar{c}}(t)$ is determined from simulation and for the combinatorial background $P_{bgd}(t)$ is obtained from the upper side band in the ΔM distribution (no difference is observed between like and unlike sign events). The contribution of B_s^0 is found to be negligible.

An unbinned maximum likelihood fit is applied, with the following function $\mathcal{L}^{unlike}$ for unlike sign events:

$$f_{B^0}\left[\epsilon_{mix}^{unlike}P_{B^0}^{mix}(t, \Delta m) + \epsilon_{unmix}^{unlike}P_{B^0}^{unmix}(t, \Delta m)\right] +$$

$$f_{B\pm}\epsilon_{B\pm}^{unlike}P_{B\pm}(t) + f_{c\bar{c}}\epsilon_{c\bar{c}}^{unlike}P_{c\bar{c}}(t) + f_{bgd}\epsilon_{bgd}^{unlike}P_{bgd}(t)$$

where the f's are the fractions of the different channels in the selected sample, and the ϵ's are the probabilities defined above. The same expression holds for $\mathcal{L}^{like}$ events, replacing ϵ by $1 - \epsilon$.

2.4. D^*-lepton combination

In this analysis, the purity is improved by requesting, in the decay hemisphere, a lepton with $p > 3 \; GeV/c$ and a sign opposite to the D^*; figure 2 gives the distribution of Δm. The "production" sign is given by the charge of the opposite hemisphere only, with the condition $|Q| > 0.15$ (the probability of right sign is then 0.714). The fraction of misidentified leptons is evaluated from like sign D^*-lepton combinations.

2.5. Results, consistency checks and systematic uncertainties

The values of $\epsilon_{mix}, \epsilon_{B\pm}, \epsilon_{c\bar{c}}, f_{B\pm}$ and the effective time distribution of charm events are taken from the simulation, while $\epsilon_{bgd}, f_{bgd}, f_{c\bar{c}}, \tau_B$ are obtained from the data, and the energy fraction of the B is the value measured by DELPHI, $X_B = 0.695 \pm 0.03 \pm 0.01$ [8] (increased by 10 % for the $K\pi\pi^0$ events to account for a

bias due to the selection criteria). The free parameters are ω and ϵ_{unmix}. The result with the D^* sample is:

$$\omega = 0.50 \pm 0.12 \; ps^{-1} \quad ; \quad \epsilon_{unmix}^{unlike} = 0.271 \pm 0.036$$

and with the D^*-lepton sample:

$$\omega = 0.44 \pm 0.10 \; ps^{-1} \quad ; \quad \epsilon_{unmix}^{like} = 0.761 \pm 0.066$$

The fitted values of ϵ are in good agreement with the simulated ones. It was checked that the result is not significantly changed by other choices of free parameters, or by a parametrization of B energy from the D^* momentum. The value of $\epsilon_{c\bar{c}}$ was cross-checked with an estimation from a sample enriched in $c\bar{c}$ by the cut $X_E > 0.5$.

The same fitting procedure, applied to a sample generated with $\omega = 0.475 \; ps^{-1}$, gives 0.48 ± 0.06 and reproduces well the charge tagging probabilities.

Figure 3 shows the fit of $C(t)$ to the data, with the different contributions: the oscillation is damped by the inclusion of charged B, and almost suppressed by the charm and combinatorial background at small values of t.

The various contributions to systematic errors are given in table 2. The global uncertainty amounts to 0.061 for the D^* analysis, and 0.031 with D^*-lepton correlation. Accounting for sample overlap and common systematic contributions, the two analyses can be combined to give:

$$\omega = 0.456 \pm 0.068 \; (stat) \pm 0.043 \; (syst) \; ps^{-1}$$

3. Second method: lepton, kaon and jet charge sign correlation

3.1. Sign indicators

The "production sign" in the opposite hemisphere is defined by one of three indicators:

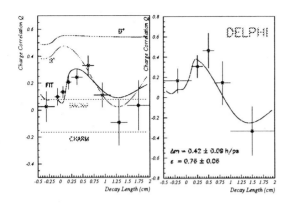

Figure 3. Fit of charge correlation $C(t)$ on D^* selected events, with contributions of different channels (left), and on D^*-lepton events (right)

parameter	range	D^*	D^*-lepton
parametrization and time resol.		± 0.030	
B moment. param.		± 0.030	± 0.020
B lifetime	one σ of the	± 0.010	± 0.010
charm fract.	measured	± 0.024	
backgd fract.	values	∓ 0.005	∓ 0.005
fake leptons			∓ 0.010
fract. of $B^{\pm}$	$17 \pm 10\ \%$	∓ 0.021	∓ 0.020
ϵ_{mix}	$\pm 15\ \%$	∓ 0.019	
$\epsilon_{B\pm}$	wght exponent	∓ 0.005	
$\epsilon_{c\bar{c}}$	from 0.2 to 1	± 0.019	
total		0.061	0.030

Table 2. Different contributions (in ps^{-1}) to the systematic uncertainty on Δm in the D^* and D^*-lepton analyses

- A **lepton** with a momentum $p > 3\ GeV/c$ and a large transverse momentum w.r.t. the axis of the jet without it $p_t^{out} > 1\ GeV/c$ gives a good purity in b and avoids most of the cascades $b \to c \to l$. Accounting for cuts, efficiencies and misidentifications, and also for time-integrated mixing, this indicator is defined in 8 % of the b hemispheres, (where it gives a ratio *right sign/wrong sign* of 5), 2 % of the c and 1 % of the u, d, s hemispheres.

- A secondary **kaon** from the dominant decay chain $b \to c \to s$ is selected by the conditions: standard level of identification in the RICH detector (see [6]), $3 < p < 15\ GeV/c$, $i.p./\sigma(i.p.) > 1.5$ (where $i.p.$ is the impact parameter w.r.t. the main vertex). The proportions of decays with a right/wrong sign kaon (excluding ambiguous cases with both K^+ and K^-, which are rejected in this study), are roughly 50/10 %. Accounting for efficiency and contamination, and including the mixing effect, this indicator is defined in 18 % of the b hemispheres, with a *right/wrong* ratio around 2; the probabilities are respectively 4,

5.5 and 9 % for u/d, s, c flavours, which then give an important background.

- The weighted **charge** of the most energetic **jet** in the hemisphere (defined as in previous section) is used also (no combination is done here with the charge in the decay hemisphere). In order to improve the b purity, a b-tagging condition is defined as: $\Sigma[i.p./\sigma(i.p.)]^2/(ntr - 1) > 2$, where the sum is over the ntr "measurable" charged tracks in the jet (i.e. with at least two hits in the Vertex Detector), excepted the most contributing one (to get rid of contamination by bad measurements). This sign is then defined in 32% of b hemispheres, with a *right/wrong* ratio of 1.7.

In order to optimize the discrimination power and to avoid double counting, mutually exclusive indicators are defined:

- $j + l$: jet sign (without b-tag) and lepton sign in agreement in this hemisphere; the subset of hemispheres where both signs are defined and disagree is smaller and poorly discriminating: then it was ignored.

- $j + K$: jet sign and kaon sign in agreement (same remarks)

- j only: jet sign (with b-tag), when the other ones are not defined, provided $|Q_{jet} - 0.015| > 0.1$ (this condition gives in average 67 % of right sign assignments).

The "decay sign" is given either by a lepton selected as previously, or by a kaon, without the condition on impact parameter, in order to not bias the decay distance distribution.

3.2. Flight distance estimation

The estimator is designed to be inclusive, to be used with any sign indicator. The interaction point is determined as in previous section; the decay point is estimated through a "pseudo-secondary vertex" (without any cut on the χ^2), including all "measurable" tracks (see above) with a direction within a cone around the thrust axis of the main jet (half-opening angle 25 degrees), where the B decay products are concentrated: this subset is actually a mixture of primary particles and products of B and subsequent D decay products, in proportions which are variable, but do not depend on the B flight. As a result, the distance from the main vertex to this one depends linearly on the actual flight distance. The resolution is improved by requesting the "pseudo-longitudinal" error of the vertex fit to be less than 600 μm: this is the longitudinal precision that would be obtained if all tracks used in the fit would actually come from the same point, and it is depends only on the directions, not on the offsets of the tracks. It was checked that the distribution of this estimator δ is not strongly affected by the selection of a lepton or a kaon in the hemisphere. Figure 4 illustrates the precision of this estimator (the negative side represents the dispersion) and shows that the simulation reproduces well the observed distribution.

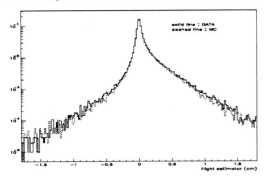

Figure 4. Distribution of the flight estimator δ for all events: real data (solid line) and simulation (dashed line)

The time dependence is transformed into a dependence on δ, with a good significance for oscillation (figure 5 shows the probability of mixing as a function of δ for different values of ω).

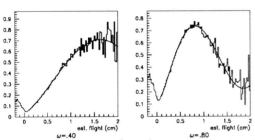

Figure 5. Probability of B_d^0 oscillation as a function of the flight distance estimator δ

3.3. Parametrisation of the sign correlation distribution

For a given flavour, the probabilities of tagging the sign and measuring the flight are assumed to be independent in opposite hemispheres (this is a good approximation, at least for heavy flavours), and the flight estimator is built independently of the sign indicators, so the probabilities can be factorized and summed up over all possible event configurations. In practice, 7 *categories* of hemispheres are defined: $u/d, s, c, B^{\pm}, B_d^0, B_s^0, b$-baryons.

For each category and each sign indicator the probabilities $P_{cat,prod}^{right}$ and $P_{cat,prod}^{wrong}$ of a *right* or *wrong* "production" sign are computed from simulation. For the B_d^0 this probability is linearly parametrized as a function of ω to account for time-integrated mixing; the B_s^0 is assumed to give smoothed constant values.

Let δ be the flight distance estimator. The distribution $g_{cat}(\delta)$ for b categories is the convolution of the exponential b-decay time distribution with the

fragmentation function (which is assymmetric) and with the resolution function of δ itself (which is not a simple gaussian); for other categories again there is no obvious theoretical parametrization: the simplest solution is to perform the convolutions through the simulation itself. Moreover small values of δ are largely contaminated by u, d, s, c background and contain very little information on the oscillation frequency, because they correspond to times where the $\sin^2(\omega t/2)$ factor is small. In practice the functions $g_{cat}(\delta)$ were parametrized for $\delta > 2\ mm$.

The "decay" sign probabilities $P_{cat,dec}^{right}$, $P_{cat,dec}^{wrong}$ to find a right/wrong sign with $\delta > 2\ mm$ are evaluated from simulation; for non-B_d^0 categories, the distance-dependent probability is simply:

$$\mathcal{P}_{cat,dec}^{right/wrong}(\delta) = P_{cat,dec}^{right/wrong}\, g_{cat}(\delta)$$

For the B_d^0, $P_{dec,norev}^{right/wrong}$ (without oscillation) and $P_{mdec,rev}^{right/wrong}$ (with full reversal at any time) are computed separately (actually the right/wrong probabilities are not far from being simply exchanged when the B^0 is reversed). Then the distance-dependent probability may be written:

$$\mathcal{P}_{dec}^{right/wrong}(\delta) =$$

$$[\, P_{dec,norev}^{right/wrong}\,(1-P_{osc}(\delta)) + P_{dec,rev}^{right/wrong}\,P_{osc}(\delta)\,]\, g_{B_d^0}(\delta)$$

where $P_{osc}(\delta)$ is the probability for a B_d^0 decaying at δ to be reversed. Again this probability is a complex convolution, and it was parametrized by a polynomial of degree 4 or 5 in δ for 16 different values of ω between 0.2 and 0.95 (see figure 5); a linear extrapolation gives then its value at any ω.

Finally one can define, for a given couple $(prod, dec)$, the probability to find a like/unlike sign correlation between the hemispheres as a function of δ:

$$Prb_{prod,dec}^{like\ sign}(\delta) = \sum_{flavours}$$

$$R_{flav}\,[\, P_{flav,prod}^{right}\,\mathcal{P}_{flav,dec}^{wrong}(\delta) + P_{flav,prod}^{wrong}\,\mathcal{P}_{flav,dec}^{right}(\delta)\,]$$

where R_{flav} is the fraction of this flavour in hadronic events, and the same expression for $Prob_{prod,dec}^{unlike\ sign}(\delta)$ (inverting *right* and *wrong*)

The ud, s, c flavours correspond to categories defined above. The b flavour probabilities are the sum of contributions of the different B hadron categories, weighted by their fractions f_{bcat}:

$$P_{b,prod}^{right/wrong} = \sum_{bcat} f_{bcat} P_{bcat,prod}^{right/wrong}(\omega)$$

$$\mathcal{P}_{b,dec}^{right/wrong}(\delta) = \sum_{bcat} f_{bcat} \mathcal{P}_{bcat,dec}^{right/wrong}(\delta,\omega)$$

where the dependence on ω holds for B_d^0 only.

decay sign ↓ prod. sign →	$j+l$	$j+K$	j only
l	1383	1347	7350
K	2264	4494	12575

Table 3. Number of entries for each sign combination with $\delta > 2\ mm$

3.4. Fitting procedure and results

An unbinned maximum likelihood method is applied to the global set of *like sign* and *unlike sign* events, by minimizing:

$$\mathcal{L} = -\sum_{like} \ln(Prb^{l.s.}_{p,d}(\delta,\omega)) - \sum_{unlike} \ln(Prb^{u.s}_{p,d}(\delta,\omega))$$

In order to reduce the contamination by light flavours, only events with $\delta \geq 2\ mm$ are used in the fit. Then the probability that an event enters twice in the fit (both hemispheres are selected for "decay" and "production") is about 7 % for $b\bar{b}$ events; moreover the two entries correspond to independent values of δ. Then the statistical effect of this kind of double counting can be neglected. Table 3 gives the number of events selected with $\delta > 2\ mm$ for each combination of sign indicators.

The result of the fit cumulating all sign indicators is illustrated by the dependence of the charge correlation C (with the same definition as before, but exchanging *like* and *unlike*) on figure 6: the data deviate largely from a non-mixing situation, and also from a time-independent mixing hypothesis.

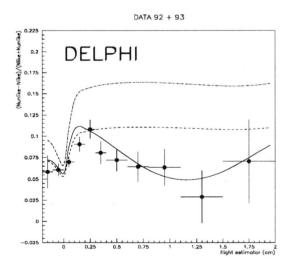

DATA 92 + 93

DELPHI

Figure 6. ratio $C = (N_{u.s.} - N_{l.s.})/(N_{u.s.} + N_{l.s.})$ as a function of δ with cumulated sign correlations; solid line: expected shape with the fitted value of ω, dash-dotted line: without mixing dotted line: with a time-independent mixing with $\chi=0.17$

Various sources of systematic errors have been examined; they are summarized in table 4.

The result is:

$$\Delta m = 0.586 \pm 0.049\ (stat) \pm 0.062\ (syst)$$

B^0_d fraction	0.020
B^0_s fraction	0.012
global B lifetime	0.004
B^0_d lifetime	0.030
b fragmentation	0.003
K^+/K^- multiplicities in B decays	0.022
electron efficiency and contamination	0.008
muon efficiency and contamination	0.008
kaon efficiency and contamination	0.032
geometrical acceptance	< 0.020
parametrization	0.020
choice of δ_{min}	< 0.020
total	0.062

Table 4. Systematic errors on $\omega = \Delta mc^2/\hbar$ with the inclusive method

4.   Conclusion

The time-dependent $B^0_d - \bar{B}^0_d$ oscillation was observed unambiguously with the expected shape, using a sign correlation between the production and the decay of the mesons, and an evaluation of the decay time through their flight distance; its frequency (or equivalently the difference between the mass eigenstates) was measured by a maximum of likelihood fit.

A first method, using charged D^* (possibly accompanied by a lepton of opposite charge) and a combination of hemisphere charges, gives:

$$\Delta mc^2/\hbar = 0.456 \pm 0.068\ (stat) \pm 0.043\ (syst)\ ps^{-1}$$

A second one, cumulating sign indicators from high p_t leptons, secondary kaons and jet charges, gives:

$$\Delta mc^2/\hbar = 0.586 \pm 0.049\ (stat) \pm 0.062\ (syst)\ ps^{-1}$$

They may be combined, neglecting statistical overlaps and accounting for common systematic errors:

$$\Delta mc^2/\hbar = 0.521 \pm 0.040\ (stat) \pm 0.038\ (syst)\ ps^{-1}$$

$$\Delta m = 3.43 \pm 0.26\ (stat) \pm 0.25\ (syst)\ 10^{-4}\ eV/c^2$$

This result is in good agreement with time-integrated evaluations and previous time-dependent measurements.

References

[1] M. Gell-Mann and A. Pais, Phys. Rev. **97** (1955) 1387
[2] J. Bartel et al. (CLEO Coll.) CLNS/93-1207 (1993)
    H. Albrecht et al. (ARGUS Coll.) Z. Phys. **C55** (1992)
[3] DELPHI Collaboration, N.I.M. **A303** (1991) 233
[4] MUCFIX, G.Wilkinson and P. Collins, DELPHI 93-13
    MUFLAG, H. de Boeck and G. Wilkinson, DELPHI 93-14
[5] N. Bingefors et al. (DELPHI Coll.), N.I.M. **A328** (1993) 447
[6] E.G. Anassontzis et al., N.I.M. **A323** (1992) 351
[7] P. Billoir and S. Qian, N.I.M. **A311** (1992) 139
[8] DELPHI Collaboration, contributed paper to the Marseille Conference

Parallel Session Pa-10

Searches for New Particles

Conveners: Y. Sirois (IN2P3)
　　　　　　N. Hadley (University of Maryland)

Scientific secretaries:　P. Reeves
　　　　　　　　　　　　R. Bates (reserve)

Paper presented at XXVII Int. Conf. on High Energy Physics: Session Pa-10
Glasgow, UK, 20–27 July 1994

Rare and unexpected decays of the Z^0

Andrea Venturi[†]

European Laboratory for Particle Physics (CERN),
CH-1211 Geneva 23, Switzerland

On behalf of the LEP Experiments

Abstract

Recent results from the LEP experiments on searches for monojet events, radiative decays of the Z^0 into new scalar particles and on deviations from the QED are presented here. Furthermore updates of the $f\bar{f}\gamma\gamma$ and $\ell^+\ell^- V$ analysis are reported.

1. Introduction

Despite the good agreement between the present LEP results and the predictions of the Standard Model in the sector of the electroweak precision measurements, continuous efforts have been done by the four Collaborations to search for rare or "forbidden" Z^0 decays and deviations from the standard predictions. In this paper two distinct parts can be identified: the results of the searches for rare events and the investigations of deviations from the Standard Model predictions. With the number of events collected by the four experiments and their good performances, the present sensitivity to branching ratio is 10^{-5}, 10^{-6}.

2. Search for rare events

2.1. Monjet events

The monojet topology is commonly considered as being background free for new particle searches in e^+e^- collisions; it provides, for example, a clear signature for the production of a light Higgs boson ($e^+e^- \to H\nu\bar{\nu}$) or of the light neutralinos ($e^+e^- \to \chi\chi'$ with $\chi' \to \chi Z^*$). ALEPH searched for monojet events using all the data collected until 1993[1] (about 1.94M Z^0's hadronic decays), by taking advantage of the hermeticity, the

† E-mail: venturi@cernvm.cern.ch.

M_{jet} (GeV/c^2)	P_t (GeV/c)	M_{recoil} (GeV/c^2)	particle composition
3.3	20.3	61	e^+e^-
3.2	6.6	80	*hadronic*
5.3	18.5	69	*hadronic*

Table 1. Kinematical properties of the three ALEPH monojet events.

redoundancy and the low detection thresholds of the apparatus. The monojet topology was required both in the space and in the transverse plane and after the explicit rejection of 3-prongs and candidate γ conversions monojets, three monojet events survived the selection. The contribution of the standard processes $e^+e^- \to f\bar{f}$ and $\gamma\gamma \to f\bar{f}$ has been estimated to be less than 1/100 of events. Taking into account all the four-fermion final state processes involving a Z^0 and part of those involving a W the expected number of events is 2.75 but the probability to obtain a set of events at least as unlikely as the selected one, with respect to the jet mass and transverse momentum, is only 4.8% (see table 1 and fig. 1).

A preliminary result of the searches for the same kind of events has been presented by DELPHI using the data collected in 1992 and 1993[2] (about 1.5M Z^0's hadronic decays). No monojet event candidate that cannot be

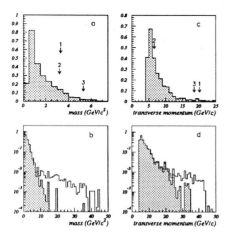

Figure 1. Expected jet mass and transverse momentum distributions for the considered "standard" processes ($Z^0 \to \gamma^* \nu \bar{\nu}$ contribution is shaded) and indication of the three events selected by ALEPH.

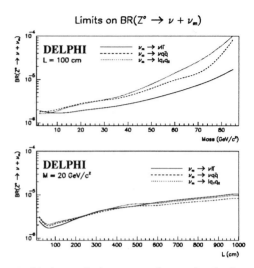

Figure 2. Limits on the heavy neutrino production branching ratio as a function of the mass or of the decay length, for different ν_m decay modes.

explained as a "standard" Z^0 decay (for example $f\bar{f}\gamma$ with missing γ or $\tau^+\tau^-$ with one "invisible" τ) has been selected, while the expected number of events from standard four fermion final state process $f\bar{f}\nu\bar{\nu}$ is ~ 0.4.

2.2.   Long lived neutral heavy particles

Long lived neutral heavy particles were searched for in DELPHI[3], more precisely an isosinglet neutral heavy lepton ν_m, by looking for the process $Z^0 \to \nu_m\bar{\nu}$. Its branching ratio can be expressed as[4]:

$$BR(Z^0 \to \nu_m\nu) =$$
$$BR(Z^0 \to \nu\bar{\nu})|U|^2 \left(1 - \frac{M_{\nu_m}^2}{M_Z^2}\right)^2 \left(1 + \frac{1}{2}\frac{M_{\nu_m}^2}{M_Z^2}\right) \quad (1)$$

where M_{ν_m} is the heavy neutrino mass and $|U|^2$ can be interpreted as the coupling strength of the ν_m to the Z^0 or the mixing parameter between the heavy neutrino and its standard partner. The heavy neutrino can decay via neutral and charged weak currents and the mean decay length, function of M_{ν_m} and of $|U|^2$, is $\sim 1\ m$ for masses in the range $3 - 5\ GeV/c^2$ and production branching ratios $\sim 10^{-6}$.

This kind of process has been investigated by looking for events with monojet topology and with: a) a displaced vertex in the tracking chambers (the effective accepted transverse decay length R is between 12 and 110 cm) or b) a cluster of hits in the outer detectors spatially (and temporally) confined ($R < 300\ cm$). In the sample of events considered (equivalent to the production of about 2M Z^0's) no event has been selected and preliminary limits on the branching ratio of the order of 3×10^{-6} ($|U|^2 < 8 \times 10^{-5}$) have been established at 95% C.L. (see fig. 2).

3.   Search for deviation from the standard predictions

3.1.   Search for $Z \to S\gamma$

The decay $Z^0 \to S\gamma$, where S is a scalar particle, can have a "visible" branching ratio ($10^{-4 \div 5}$) both in models where Z^0 is composite and S is its scalar partner, and in extensions of the Standard Model where S is the Higgs boson and the decay $Z^0 \to H^0\gamma$ via loop is enhanced with respect to the standard prediction.

Using the data collected between 1990 and 1992 (about 1.1M Z^0's hadronic decays), ALEPH investigated this decay mode by looking for $\ell^+\ell^-\gamma$, $q\bar{q}\gamma$ and $gg\gamma$ final state events and by comparing the observed distribution of the mass recoiling against the photon with the standard Monte Carlo predictions[5]. The resolution on the recoiling mass, by rescaling the energies of the particles with the constraints of the center of mass energy and of the measured directions is (FWHM) about 0.5 GeV/c^2 for $e^+e^-\gamma$ and $\mu^+\mu^-\gamma$ events and 5.0 GeV/c^2 for $\tau^+\tau^-\gamma$ and hadronic events. Asssuming the width of S smaller than the experimental resolution the preliminary resulting limits (95% C.L.) for $BR(Z^0 \to S\gamma) \times BR(S \to f\bar{f})$ are less than 10^{-5} in the leptonic channels and 10^{-4} in the hadronic channels for S masses up to 88 GeV/c^2.

The hadronic channel has been investigated also by OPAL using the data collected between 1991 and 1993 (about 1.8M Z^0's hadronic decays)[6]. The mass of the hadronic system is calculated as the mass recoiling against the photon with the constraint of the center of mass energy. They obtain a resolution which decreases from 5.8 GeV/c^2 at $M_S = 20\ GeV/c^2$ to 0.6 GeV/c^2 at $M_S = 80\ GeV/c^2$. Assuming that S is scalar a further cut is applied on the decay angle of the hadronic system and a tipical (preliminary) limit for the product $BR(Z^0 \to S\gamma) \times BR(S \to q\bar{q}) < 2.5 \times 10^{-5}$ (95% C.L.) has been extracted from the resulting recoiling mass spectrum. Thinking at the Higgs boson, they searched for the decays $S \to b\bar{b}$, by tagging b quark events with their secondary vertices. The resulting tipical limit is $BR(Z^0 \to S\gamma) \times BR(S \to b\bar{b}) < 1.5 \times 10^{-5}$ (95% C.L.). OPAL has also investigated, with no assumption on the spin of S, the case in which S decays with an invisible signature[7]. Using single photon selected events, the limit for the product $BR(Z^0 \to S\gamma) \times BR(S \to inv.)$ was evaluated by comparing the resulting recoiling mass spectrum with the one expected from Standard Model. For $M_S < 64 \; GeV/c^2$ the 95% C.L. limit is 4.3×10^{-6} while for $M_S < 84 \; GeV/c^2$ is 1.4×10^{-5}.

3.2. Measurement of $e^+e^- \to \gamma\gamma(\gamma)$

In the framework of the Standard Model the reaction $e^+e^- \to \gamma\gamma(\gamma)$ is purely electromagnetic and has been proposed as a suitable process to search for deviation from QED due to new phenomena at LEP[8]. The effects of of such a breakdown of QED on the differential cross section at Born level can be parametrized as:

$$\frac{d\sigma}{d\Omega} = \frac{\alpha^2}{s} \frac{1 + \cos^2\theta}{1 - \cos^2\theta}(1 + \delta) \tag{2}$$

where δ contains the information about the new phenomena. It can be expressed by introducing phenomenolgical parameters as in the QED cutoff model [9], where $\delta = \pm s^2/2(1/\Lambda_\pm^4)(1 - \cos^2\theta)$ and $\Lambda_\pm$ are the cutoff parameters, or by assuming the exchange in the t channel of an exited electron e^* of mass M_{e^*} and coupling λ_γ[10]; in this case $\delta = s^2\lambda_\gamma^2/(2M_{e^*}^4)(1 - \cos^2\theta)H(\cos^2\theta)$ where $H(\cos^2\theta) = a[a + (1 - \cos^2\theta)/(1 + \cos^2\theta)]/[(1 + a)^2 - \cos^2\theta]$ and $a = 2M_{e^*}^2/s$.
DELPHI presented the results of the measurement of the total and differential cross sections for the reaction $e^+e^- \to \gamma\gamma(\gamma)$ using the data collected between 1990 and 1992 ($\mathcal{L} = 36.9 \; pb^{-1}$)[11]. The results agreed with the QED predictions and the following lower limits were obtained at 95% C.L. on the parameters introduced above: $\Lambda_+ > 143 \; GeV$, $\Lambda_- > 120 \; GeV$ and $M_{e^*} > 132 \; GeV/c^2$ ($\lambda_\gamma = 1$).

3.3. Limits on the τ's anomalous magnetic and electric dipole moments

The anomalous electromagnetic couplings of the τ lepton are much less known than those of the electron and the muon, due to its short lifetime that prevents the measurement of its precession in a magnetic field.
A non-null anomalous magnetic (electric) dipole moment would lead to an additional term $F_2(q^2)/(2m_\tau)\sigma^{\mu\nu}q_\nu$

($F_{EDM}(q^2)\sigma^{\mu\nu}\gamma_5 q_\nu$) in the τ's electromagnetic current. As a consequence the partial width of the process $Z^0 \to \tau\tau\gamma$ would become:

$$\Gamma(Z \to \tau\tau\gamma) = \Gamma_0 + \frac{\alpha^2 F_2(0)^2 m_Z^3}{64\pi \sin^2\theta_W(1 - \sin^2\theta_W)m_\tau^2}$$
$$\times [(c_V^2 + c_A^2) - \frac{1}{9}(c_V^2 - c_A^2)] \tag{3}$$

where $c_V = 1/4 - \sin^2\theta_W$, $c_A = 1/4$ and Γ_0 is the standard width[12] (the contribution of the electric dipole moment is identical with $F_2(0)/2m_\tau$ replaced with $F_{EDM}(0)$). An important feature of this anomalous contribution is that the spectrum of the emitted photon is indipendent of the energy while in conventional bremsstrahlung the soft photon emission is strongly favoured.
DELPHI presented a study of $Z^0 \to \tau\tau\gamma$ events using the data collected between 1992 and 1993 (about 1.3M Z^0's hadronic decays)[13]. After the selection of $\tau^+\tau^-$ pairs with an isolated and energetic photon ($E_\gamma > 3 \; GeV$), the resulting spectrum of the photon energy was compared with the one obtained with the standard Monte Carlo simulation. The agreement is

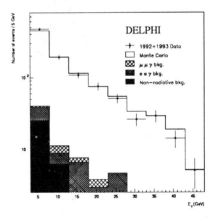

Figure 3. Distribution of the photon energy in $\tau^+\tau^-\gamma$ candidates.

good (see fig. 3) and the following preliminary limits were extracted for the anomalous dipole moments (95% C.L.):

$$F_2(q^2 = 0) < 0.072$$
$$F_{EDM}(q^2 = 0) < 4 \times 10^{-16} \; e \; cm \tag{4}$$

It is worth noting that other limits exist for these anomalous dipole moments but they are either in different kinematical domains ($q^2 = (35 \; GeV)^2$)[14], extracted from the angular distribution of the τ's pairs production at PETRA, or derived indirectly from $\Gamma(Z^0 \to \tau^+\tau^-)$, assuming the standard gauge symmetry $SU(3) \otimes SU(2) \otimes U(1)$ for the anomalous dipole couplings[15].

3.4. Search for high mass resonances in photon pairs

The interest in the search for events with photon pairs of large invariant mass was motivated by the L3 observation of four events of the type $\ell^+\ell^-\gamma\gamma$ with $m_{\gamma\gamma}$ clustered around 60 GeV/c^2[16]. DELPHI presented the results of this analysis using the data collected between 1990 and 1992[17]. The resulting limits (95% C.L.) are ($M_X = 60\ GeV/c^2$):

$$
\begin{aligned}
BR(Z^0 \to \ell^+\ell^- X)BR(X \to \gamma\gamma) &< 1.1 \times 10^{-5} \\
BR(Z^0 \to q\bar{q}X)BR(X \to \gamma\gamma) &< 1 \times 10^{-5} \\
BR(Z^0 \to \nu\bar{\nu}X)BR(X \to \gamma\gamma) &< 7.5 \times 10^{-6} \quad (5) \\
\Gamma_X BR^2(X \to \gamma\gamma) &< 7\ MeV \\
BR(Z^0 \to \gamma X)BR(X \to \gamma\gamma) &< 6.8 \times 10^{-6}
\end{aligned}
$$

These results confirm the preliminary results presented in the HEP93 conference in Marseille where a complete review of the LEP results was presented by G.W. Wilson[18].

Preliminary results, using the 1993 data, were presented by DELPHI and OPAL. DELPHI searched for high mass photon pairs in the final state $\ell^+\ell^-\gamma\gamma$, $\nu\bar{\nu}\gamma\gamma$ and $q\bar{q}\gamma\gamma$[19]. Only one candidate, identified as $e^+e^-\gamma\gamma$, was found with $m_{\gamma\gamma}$ near 60 GeV/c^2.

OPAL updated the hadronic channel and no new event was found (three events with $m_{\gamma\gamma} > 40\ GeV/c^2$), setting the following upper limit on the production branching ratio: $BR(Z^0 \to q\bar{q}X)BR(X \to \gamma\gamma) < 4 \times 10^{-6}$ for $M_X > 40\ GeV/c^2$ (95% C.L.)[6].

3.5. Study of $\ell^+\ell^-V$ events

DELPHI presented new preliminary results, using the data collected between 1992 and 1993 (about 1.5M Z^0 hadronic decays), of the study of events with two leptons and an accompanying pair of charged particles ($\ell^+\ell^-V$)[20]. They observed in each lepton channel (e, μ, τ) (40,41,18) events with an expectation of (39.0, 35.2, 10.7) signal events and (1.7, 0, 1.5) background events, demonstrating a good agreement of the $\ell^+\ell^-V$ production rate with the SM expectation. In addition 7 events have a V mass in the region including the J/ψ ($3.1 \pm 0.5\ GeV/c^2$) and 2 events in the region of the V masses around the Υ ($9.5 \pm 1.0\ GeV/c^2$) while the expectations are 3.1 and 0.5 events respectively.

4. Conclusions

Searches for Z^0 rare decays and deviations from the Standard Model gave negative results with the present sensitivity and even the ALEPH monojet event analysis require more statistics to understand the nature of the selected events. Furthermore the $f\bar{f}\gamma\gamma$ and $\ell^+\ell^-V$ anomalies reported in the past[16, 21] disappeared, revealing themselves as likely statistical fluctuations.

Acknowledgments

I would like to thank the colleagues of the LEP experiments for their help during the preparation of the talk and of this report. In particular I would like to thank J.A. Barrio, J. Fuster, J.F. Grivaz, P. Mättig and G.W. Wilson.

References

[1] The ALEPH Collaboration: D. Buskulic *et al.*, CERN preprint: CERN-PPE/94-93 (submitted to Phys. Lett. B).

[2] DELPHI Collaboration: J. Chrin *et al.* "Search for monojet events using the DELPHI detector at LEP", DELPHI note: DELPHI 94-115.

[3] DELPHI Collaboration, "Searching for long lived neutral heavy particles using the DELPHI detector at LEP", contributed paper: gls0276.

[4] M. Gronau, C. Leung and J. Rosner, Phys. Rev. **D29** (1984) 2539;
M. Dittmar, M.C. Gonzalez-Garcia, A. Santamaría, J.W.F. Valle, Nucl. Phys. **B332** (1990) 1.

[5] ALEPH Collaboration, "Search for the decay $Z \to S\gamma$, where S is a scalar", contributed paper: gls0567.

[6] The OPAL Collaboration, "Search for a narrow resonance in Z^0 decays into hadrons and isolated photons", OPAL Physics-Note: OPAL-PN140.

[7] The OPAL Collaboration: R. Akers *et al.*, CERN preprint: CERN-PPE/94-105 (submitted to Z. Phys C).

[8] D. Treille *et al.*, ECFA preprint ECFA 87-108 in: ECFA Workshop on LEP 200, CERN report 87-08 Vol. 2, A Böhm and W. Hoogland eds., (1987), 414;
F. Boudjema *et al.*, in: Z Physics at LEP 1, CERN report 89-08 Vol. 2, G. Altarelli and C. Verzegnassi eds., (1989) 185.

[9] S. Drell, Ann. Phys **4** (1958) 75;
F.E. Low, Phys Rev. Lett. **14** (1965) 238.

[10] A Litke, Harvard Univ., Ph. D. Thesis (1970), unpublished.

[11] DELPHI Collaboration: P Abreu *et al.*, Phys. Lett **B327** (1994) 386.

[12] J.A. Grifols and A. Méndez, Phys. Lett. **B255** (1991) 611.

[13] DELPHI Collaboration: J.A. Barrio *et al.*, "A study of $\tau\tau\gamma$ events using the DELPHI detector at LEP", contributed paper: gls0239.

[14] D.J. Silverman and G.L. Shaw, Phys. Rev. **D27** (1983) 1196;
F. del Aguila and M. Sher, Phys. Lett. **B252** (1990) 116.

[15] R. Escribano and E. Massó, Phys. Lett. **B301** (1993) 419.

[16] L3 Collaboration: O. Adriani *et al.*, Phys. Lett. **B295** (1992) 337.

[17] DELPHI Collaboration, "A search for a high mass resonance in photonic final states", contributed paper: gls0273.

[18] G.W. Wilson, Proc. of the International Europhysics Conference on High Energy Physics, Marseille 1993, p.285; Eds. J. Carr and M. Perrottet (Ed. Frontieres 1994).

[19] DELPHI Collaboration: F. Barão *et al.*, "Preliminary results on the search for $\ell^+\ell^-\gamma\gamma$, $\nu\bar{\nu}\gamma\gamma$ and $q\bar{q}\gamma\gamma$ events in 1993", contributed paper: gls0238.

[20] DELPHI Collaboration: P. Abreu *et al.*, "Z^0 decays to two leptons and a charged particle-antiparticle pair", contributed paper: gls0237.

[21] The ALEPH Collaboration: D. Decamp *et al.*, Phys. Lett. **B263** (1991) 112.

SUSY Searches at LEP

Tetsuro Mashimo[†‡]

† International Centre for Elementary Particle Physics, University of Tokyo,
7-3-1 Hongo, Bunkyo-ku, Tokyo 113, Japan

Abstract

Results are presented of a few recent searches at LEP for the particles predicted by theories of supersymmetry. Searches for the Higgs particles predicted by the supersymmetry models are not covered here.

1. Introduction

Supersymmetry (SUSY) is a symmetry between bosons and fermions. There are several good reasons for considering supersymmetry relevant in particle physics. Notably it solves the so-called naturalness or hierarchy problem of the Standard Model.

The supersymmetry requires every fundamental particle to have a partner with spin differing by half a unit. For example, the leptons and quarks have spin 0 partners called sleptons and squarks. Within each "supermultiplets" the number of fermionic and bosonic degrees of freedom are equal, e.g. an ordinary lepton or quark ' f ' is associated with two SUSY scalar partners, ' $\tilde{f}_L$' and ' $\tilde{f}_R$', corresponding to the two helicity states of the ' f '. Supersymmetry must be broken so that ordinary particles and its superpartners are not degenerate in mass. The mass splittings cannot be very large in order for supersymmetry to be effective in solving the hierarchy problem.

Usually it is assumed that so-called R-parity is conserved. It takes the value $+1$ for ordinary particles and -1 for their superpartners. As a consequence supersymmetric particles are produced in pairs and they decay until the lightest supersymmetric particle (LSP) is reached. The LSP is stable and it is expected to be neutral and colourless from cosmological arguments. The LSP therefore behaves like a neutrino in ordinary matter and escapes detection; the event is characterized by missing energy and momentum. The most natural candidate for the LSP is the lightest of neutralinos, mass eigenstates formed by the mixing among the superpartners of photon, Z^0, and neutral Higgs bosons.

Within ≈ 1 year of the LEP startup in 1989, many searches were carried out for SUSY particles [1, 2, 3, 4]. The clean conditions of e^+e^- reactions allowed easy direct searches and the new energy region was quickly explored. With increased statistics Z^0 line shape measurements (Γ_Z, Γ_{inv} §) became precise enough to set indirect limits on the production of new particles independent of their decay modes. The limits are now quite stringent [6, 7]. The activities of direct SUSY searches at LEP, however, have not completely died down yet. I will present results of a few recent SUSY searches at LEP. My presentation does not cover the searches for Higgs particles predicted by SUSY theories. The topic is one of the subjects of the talk by Dr. M. Pieri.

2. Neutralino searches by L3 (preliminary)

The L3 Collaboration has submitted to this conference a contribution paper on preliminary results of their neutralino searches [8]. They searched for neutralino production in the reactions $e^+e^- \to \tilde{\chi}_1^0 \tilde{\chi}_2^0$ and $e^+e^- \to \tilde{\chi}_2^0 \tilde{\chi}_2^0$, where $\tilde{\chi}_1^0$ is the lightest neutralino and $\tilde{\chi}_2^0$ is the

‡ E-mail: mashimo@cernvm.cern.ch.

§ Though less precise, Γ_{inv} can be directly measured using single photon events and limits are obtained on new physics including SUSY particles. See [5] for example.

$$e^+e^- \rightarrow \chi^0_1\chi^0_2 \text{ and } e^+e^- \rightarrow \chi^0_2\chi^0_2$$ 94/07/14 09.09

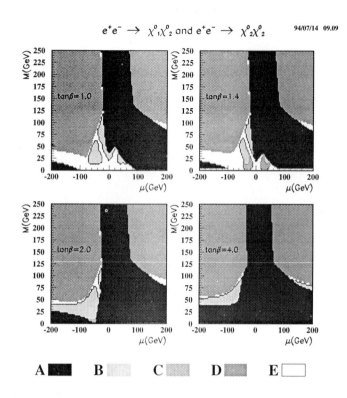

A ▮ B ▮ C ▮ D ▮ E ▯

Figure 1. Domains excluded by L3 at 95% C.L. in the (M,μ) plane for $\tan\beta = 1.0$, 1.4, 2.0, and 4.0 (upper left, upper right, lower left, and lower right, respectively). The dark band in the centre (A) is the region excluded by the constraints from the Z^0 width measurements. The regions (B) and (C) are excluded by the studies of $Z^0 \rightarrow \tilde{\chi}^0_1\tilde{\chi}^0_2$ and $Z^0 \rightarrow \tilde{\chi}^0_2\tilde{\chi}^0_2$ channels, respectively. The region (D) is not kinematically accessible in $Z^0 \rightarrow \tilde{\chi}^0_1\tilde{\chi}^0_2$. The rest (E) is the region not excluded by the present studies.

next to lightest one. As in the other previous studies at LEP [3, 4], the $\tilde{\chi}^0_2$ is assumed to decay into the $\tilde{\chi}^0_1$ and either a fermion pair or a photon: $\tilde{\chi}^0_2 \rightarrow \tilde{\chi}^0_1 f\bar{f}$ or $\tilde{\chi}^0_2 \rightarrow \tilde{\chi}^0_1\gamma$. The $\tilde{\chi}^0_1$ is considered to be stable by R-parity conservation and is not observed in the detector. Using 65 pb^{-1} data collected during 1991–1993 they searched for monojets, single photon events, acoplanar jets, and acoplanar lepton and photon pairs. No evidence for neutralino production was found and they set model independent upper limits on the square of the couplings $Z^0\tilde{\chi}^0_1\tilde{\chi}^0_2$ and $Z^0\tilde{\chi}^0_2\tilde{\chi}^0_2$ at the order of $10^{-5} \sim 10^{-4}$ for most of the neutralino masses from 0 to 45 GeV. In the Minimal Supersymmetric extension of the Standard Model (MSSM) all the masses and couplings of neutralinos and charginos (mixtures of winos and charged higgsinos) can be computed with three input parameters: gaugino mass parameter M, Higgs/higgsino mass parameter μ, and the ratio of vacuum expectation values of the two Higgs doublets $\tan\beta$. Interpreting the above negative results in the framework of the MSSM they have excluded the regions

in the (M,μ) plane shown in figure 1. The figure also includes the regions excluded by the constraints from the measurements of the total and invisible widths of the Z^0. Shown in figure 2 are 95% C.L. lower limits on the masses of $\tilde{\chi}^0_1$ and $\tilde{\chi}^0_2$ as a function of $\tan\beta$.

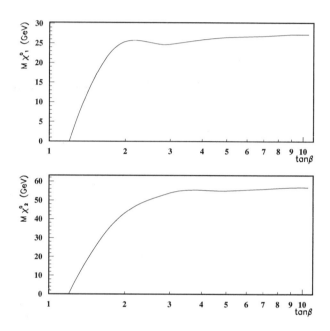

Figure 2. 95% C.L. lower limits on the masses of $\tilde{\chi}^0_1$ (upper figure) and of $\tilde{\chi}^0_2$ (lower one) as a function of $\tan\beta$.

3.   Search for Scalar Top

Among the supersymmetric partners of quarks, scalar top is special since the radiative corrections to the mass $m_{\tilde{t}}$ is large due to the large mass of the top quark [9, 10]. Mixing between supersymmetric partners of the right-handed and left-handed top quarks, $\tilde{t}_L$ and $\tilde{t}_R$, results in a large mass splitting between two mass eigenstates, $\tilde{t}_1$ and $\tilde{t}_2$. The lower mass state $\tilde{t}_1$ can be lighter than the top quark itself and can be the lightest charged SUSY particle [9, 10]. Its mass could be even quite close to the mass of the LSP.

The $\tilde{t}_1$ is a left-right mixed state, $\tilde{t}_1 = \tilde{t}_L \cos\theta_{\text{mix}} + \tilde{t}_R \sin\theta_{\text{mix}}$, where the θ_{mix} is determined by the top quark mass and the soft SUSY breaking parameters. The coupling of $\tilde{t}_1$ to Z^0 therefore depends strongly on the mixing angle θ_{mix}. Figure 3 shows the total cross section at the Z^0 peak as a function of the scalar top mass $m_{\tilde{t}_1}$ and the mixing angle θ_{mix}. The cross section is generally large. However, the $\tilde{t}_1$ decouples from Z^0 at θ_{mix} close to 0.98 ($\cos^2\theta_{\text{mix}} = \frac{4}{3}\sin^2\theta_{\text{W}}$). In this case

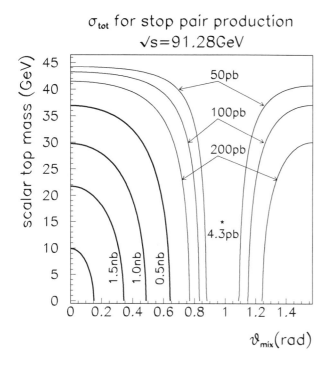

σ_{tot} for stop pair production
$\sqrt{s}=91.28\text{GeV}$

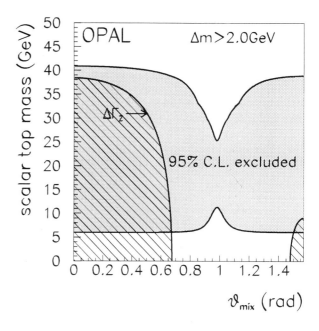

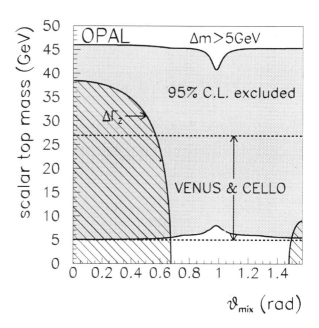

Figure 3. Equal value contours for the total cross section of $\tilde{t}_1\bar{\tilde{t}}_1$ production in the $(m_{\tilde{t}_1},\theta_{mix})$ plane ($\sqrt{s} = 91.28\text{GeV}$). The first order QCD and QED corrections [9] are included.

Figure 4. The excluded region in the $(\theta_{mix},m_{\tilde{t}_1})$ plane at 95% C.L., where the mass difference is assumed to be:
$m_{\tilde{t}_1} - m_{\tilde{\chi}_1^0} \geq 2\text{GeV}$ (upper figure),
$m_{\tilde{t}_1} - m_{\tilde{\chi}_1^0} \geq 5\text{GeV}$ (lower figure).
The region excluded from the limit on the Z^0 total decay width ($\Delta\Gamma_Z \leq 26$ MeV at 95% C.L.[6]) and the limits from previous publications [12, 15] are also shown.

the $\tilde{t}_1$ pairs are produced only via virtual γ exchange; its cross section becomes an order of 1 pb. At LEP energies the dominant decay mode of $\tilde{t}_1$ is the flavour changing two body decay $\tilde{t}_1 \rightarrow c\tilde{\chi}_1^0$ which occurs at the one-loop order [9]. Four-body decays $\tilde{t}_1 \rightarrow b\tilde{\chi}_1^0 f_1\bar{f}_2$ are negligible. Three-body decays, $\tilde{t}_1 \rightarrow \tilde{\nu}\ell b$ and $\tilde{t}_1 \rightarrow \tilde{\ell}\nu b$ are kinematically forbidden, since the scalar leptons have been already excluded at LEP energies [1]. The lifetime of the $\tilde{t}_1$ is much longer than the time scale of hadronisation. A $\tilde{t}_1$-hadron will be formed before the decay of the $\tilde{t}_1$. The signature of the $\tilde{t}_1$ events is two acoplanar jets with missing energies.

Lower limits on scalar quark masses from p$\bar{\text{p}}$ colliders [11] were obtained with the assumptions that all the five or six squark flavours are degenerate in mass and that masses of the left- and right-handed partners are equal. The assumptions are not valid for the $\tilde{t}_1$ search. Also it is difficult at hadron colliders to search for scalar quark in case the mass difference between the scalar quark and the neutralino is small. Searches at the e^+e^- colliders [2, 12, 13, 14] are sensitive even in this case. The VENUS Collaboration at TRISTAN published the results of their search dedicated to $\tilde{t}_1$ [15]. They ignored the small contribution from Z^0-exchange process so that their limits are independent of the θ_{mix}.

The OPAL Collaboration recently searched for the $\tilde{t}_1$

productions at the Z^0 resonance [16]. In their analysis, the masses of $\tilde{t}_1$ and $\tilde{\chi}^0$, and the mixing angle θ_{mix} were treated as free parameters. To maintain high efficiency over a wide range of $m_{\tilde{t}_1}$ and $m_{\tilde{\chi}_1^0}$ the cuts on the visible energy, the polar angle of the jets, and the acoplanarity angle were optimized separately for two $\tilde{t}_1$ mass regions, $m_{\tilde{t}_1} \lesssim 35\,\mathrm{GeV}$ and $m_{\tilde{t}} \gtrsim 25\,\mathrm{GeV}$. No events remained after selection cuts in the both search regions. The limits obtained by this analysis are shown in figure 4 in the $(\theta_{\mathrm{mix}}, m_{\tilde{t}_1})$ plane. Figure 5 shows the excluded region in the $(m_{\tilde{t}_1}, m_{\tilde{\chi}_1^0})$ plane for two choices of θ_{mix} ranges. As seen in the figure, the excluded region by

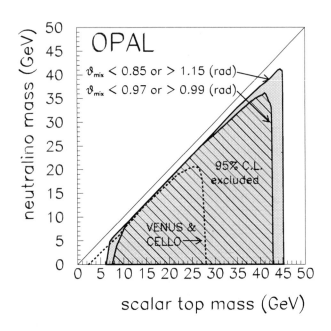

Figure 5. The excluded region in the $(m_{\tilde{t}_1}, m_{\tilde{\chi}_1^0})$ plane at 95% C.L., where the mixing angle is assumed to be $\theta_{\mathrm{mix}} \leq 0.85$ or ≥ 1.15 rad (shaded area), and $\theta_{\mathrm{mix}} \leq 0.97$ or ≥ 0.99 rad (hatched area). The dashed curve shows the contour of the excluded regions from previous publications [12, 15].

the OPAL analysis contains all of the regions excluded by lower energy experiments except for a small region at low $m_{\tilde{t}_1}$, where the acoplanarity angle of the two jets becomes too small at LEP energies.

References

[1] ALEPH Collaboration: D. Decamp *et al.*, Phys. Lett. **B236** (1990) 86;
L3 Collaboration: B. Adeva *et al.*, Phys. Lett. **B233** (1989) 530;
OPAL Collaboration: M.Z. Akrawy *et al.*, Phys. Lett. **B240** (1990) 261;
OPAL Collaboration: M.Z. Akrawy *et al.*, Phys. Lett. **B313** (1993) 333.

[2] DELPHI Collaboration: P. Abreu *et al.*, Phys. Lett. **B247** (1990) 148.

[3] ALEPH Collaboration: D. Decamp *et al.*, Phys. Lett. **B244** (1990) 541;

DELPHI Collaboration: P. Abreu *et al.*, Phys. Lett. **B247** (1990) 157;
OPAL Collaboration: M.Z. Akrawy *et al.*, Phys. Lett. **B248** (1990) 211.

[4] ALEPH Collaboration: D. Decamp *et al.*, Phys. Rep. **216** (1992) 253.

[5] OPAL Collaboration: R. Akers *et al.*, CERN-PPE/94-105, to appear in Zeit. Phys. **C** (Contribution paper submitted to the 27th International Conference on High Energy Physics, Glasgow, July 1994, Ref. No. GLS0499).

[6] The LEP Collaborations: ALEPH, DELPHI, L3 and OPAL, CERN-PPE/93-157 (1993).

[7] D. Schaile, CERN-PPE/93-213, to appear in Fortschritte der Physik.

[8] L3 Collaboration: M. Acciarri *et al.*, Contribution paper submitted to the 27th International Conference on High Energy Physics, Glasgow, July 1994, Ref. No. GLS0625.

[9] K. Hikasa and M. Kobayashi, Phys. Rev. **D36** (1987) 724;
M. Drees and K. Hikasa, Phys. Lett. **B252** (1990) 127.

[10] J. Ellis and S. Rudaz, Phys. Lett. **B128** (1983) 248;
G. Altarelli and R. Rückl, Phys. Lett. **B144** (1984) 126;
S. Dawson, E. Eichten and C. Quigg, Phys. Rev. **D31** (1985) 1581;
J. Ellis and G.L. Fogli and E. Lisi, Nucl. Phys. **B393** (1993) 3.

[11] UA1 Collaboration: C. Albajar *et al.*, Phys. Lett. **B198** (1987) 261;
CDF Collaboration: F. Abe *et al.*, Phys. Rev. Lett. **62** (1989) 1825;
UA2 Collaboration: J. Alitti *et al.*, Phys. Lett. **B235** (1990) 363;
H. Baer, X. Tata and J. Woodside, Phys. Rev. **D44** (1991) 207;
CDF Collaboration: F. Abe *et al.*, Phys. Rev. Lett. **69** (1992) 3439.

[12] CELLO Collaboration: H.J. Behrend *et al.*, Zeit. Phys. **C35** (1987) 181.

[13] TOPAZ Collaboration: I. Adachi *et al.*, Phys. Lett. **B218** (1989) 105;
AMY Collaboration: Y. Sakai *et al.*, Phys. Lett. **B234** (1990) 534.

[14] MARK II Collaboration: T. Barklow *et al.*, Phys. Rev. Lett. **64** (1990) 2984.

[15] VENUS Collaboration: J. Shirai *et al.*, Phys. Rev. Lett. **72** (1994) 3313.

[16] OPAL Collaboration: R. Akers *et al.*, CERN-PPE/94-103, to appear in Phys. Lett. **B** (Contribution paper submitted to the 27th International Conference on High Energy Physics, Glasgow, July 1994, Ref. No. GLS0486).

Search for heavy neutral Higgs bosons

F. Richard

Laboratoire de l'Accélérateur Linéaire, IN2P3-CNRS
et Université de Paris-Sud, F-91405 Orsay Cedex, France

Abstract

Recent LEP data are presented which allow to extend the search for heavy neutral Higgs boson in the standard model. A combined limit reaching 64.5 GeV at the 95 % C.L. is obtained. Delphi results on 4b final states are combined with these data to cover the search for heavy Higgs bosons in the case of the minimal supersymmetric extension of the standard model. The full kinematical range reachable at LEP1 is excluded. The search for the radiative process Hγ performed by Delphi is interpreted in terms of anomalous couplings in the bosonic sector.

1. Introduction

The aim of the present paper is to update the searches for heavy neutral bosons performed by the four LEP experiments. In the Standard Model (SM) Higgs search (section 2), based on the process $e^+e^- \rightarrow HZ^*$, the LEP experiments have analyzed about 7M hadronic events collected up to the end of 1993. This allows a significant exploration of the mass domain predicted by MSSM, the Minimal Supersymmetric[1] extension of the SM : $m_H \sim 50$-120 GeV.

In MSSM, one predicts two CP=1 neutral bosons, called h and H, and one CP=-1 state called A. At LEP1, the process $e^+e^- \rightarrow hA$ contributes when h and A have similar masses. A heavy Higgs boson decays primarily (90 %) into $b\bar{b}$ and the resulting final state containing four beautiful hadrons has recently been explored by the DELPHI collaboration (section 3).

In SM and MSSM, the radiative process Z$\rightarrow$Hγ proceeds primarily through W$^+$W$^-$ and $t\bar{t}$ loops. The predicted branching ratio is depressingly low, of order 10^{-6}, and is not substantially modified in the supersymmetric scenario. As recently emphasized in [2], anomalous couplings in the bosonic sector could dramatically enhance this cross-section, by several orders of magnitude. This prediction takes into account our present knowledge of boson couplings which is poorly constrained by the LEP1 and FNAL precision measurements. I will present the results of a search for Hγ based on DELPHI data where the standard background is reduced by selecting $b\bar{b}$ final states (section 4).

2. SM Higgs search

2.1. General features

The HZ* channel has been searched using the decay of Z* into $\nu\bar{\nu}$ or $\ell^+\ell^-$ (primarily $\mu^+\mu^-$ and e^+e^-). Including all LEP data analyzed so far ($\sim$ 7M hadronic events), one expects $\sim$ 5 events produced at m_H=70 GeV.

Selection against backgrounds are studied on simulated data to avoid biasing the cuts against the candidates found in real data. There are potential problems in this procedure due to discrepancies between data and simulation and also to the practical limitations in generating large background samples. For the H$\nu\bar{\nu}$ channel, cuts are tuned to reach an almost background free selection which can only be guaranteed if the simulation sample is several times larger than the data sample which, given the large amount of data collected at LEP, cannot be easily achieved.

Due to lack of space, I will not attempt to

Experiment	DATA	ϵ (%) (60GeV)	Signal (60GeV)	Background
ALEPH[3]	1.94M	42.0	2.32	0.26+0.15-0.10
DELPHI[4] (prelim.)	1.62M	34.9	1.58	1.12±0.28
L3[5] (prelim.)	1.60M	31.6	1.42	0.5±0.5
OPAL[6]	1.90M	32.4	1.75	0.22+0.08-0.05
SUM	7.06M		7.07	2±0.6

compare the various methods developed by the four LEP experiments. The results depend primarily on detector properties. For the $H\nu\bar{\nu}$ channel, the relevant features are the hermeticity of the detector (e.g. there are dead regions not covered by the calorimeters) and the energy resolution of the hadronic final states.

2.2. Results on $H\nu\bar{\nu}$

The table summarizes the main parameters relevant for this analysis. One can note a few features. Seven Higgs events are expected for a mass of 60 GeV while no candidate remains in the data. The predicted background of 2 ± 0.6 is not sufficiently precise to cause any worry.

2.3. Results on $H\ell^{+}\ell^{-}$

This channel is unavoidably contaminated by the final state virtual radiation. It is therefore suitable to use b-tagging which should reduce this background by about an order of magnitude. In addition it is possible to reconstruct very precisely the Higgs mass ($\sigma_M \sim 0.5$-1 GeV) using the leptons. The various candidates are displayed in figure 1 which shows no significant mass accumulation. Two of the candidates labelled (b) have been tagged as $b\bar{b}$ using the microvertex information, one, labelled (μ), shows a large pt muon in one of the hadronic jets. I have also included a DELPHI candidate, not published, which was found in 1989.

2.4. Results

The following limits, including the 93 data, have been obtained at the 95 % confidence level :

$$ALEPH[3] \qquad 60.3 \; GeV$$
$$DELPHI[4](prel.) \qquad 58.3 \; GeV$$
$$L3[5](prel.) \qquad 58.0 \; GeV$$
$$OPAL[6] \qquad 56.9 \; GeV$$

Note that the OPAL result is significantly affected by a $H\ell^{+}\ell^{-}$ candidate at 61 GeV.

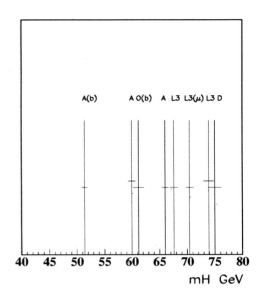

Figure 1. Leptonic candidates

There is not yet(?) a standard procedure agreed by the four experiments to combine these limits. A simple addition is certainly incorrect since it does not account for a well known effect observed for a given experiment : when the amount of data increases, the cuts have to be tightened to reduce the background at the zero event level (for $H\nu\bar{\nu}$) and therefore the efficiency should decrease at a given mass. As an example, ALEPH[7] estimates that the efficiency should be decreased by 15 % to reduce the background by 3. The reduction on efficiency has to be estimated by each experiment. As a first guess, I have assumed a reduction of 20 %.

Figure 2 summarizes the results obtained by the 4 experiments. The combined limit is 64.5 GeV taking into account the reduction in efficiency.

The 95 % C.L. limit line is modulated by the presence of $H\ell^{+}\ell^{-}$ candidates. All selected candidates show an indication of b-tagging except the L3 candidate at 67.6 GeV (events without b-tagging are removed in the ALEPH analysis). The recipe to draw this line follows [8]. It should be noted however that a gaussian mass resolution is assumed while one expects an additional low mass tail due to initial state radiation. This tail has to be computed but one can safely estimate that the corresponding effect is negligible compared to the uncertainty on the combined efficiency.

3. Z→4b

The QCD allowed process gives $BR(Z\rightarrow 4b) \sim 3 \times 10^{-4}$ with an uncertainty of about $\pm$ 40 %. In the DELPHI[9] analysis, at least four jets were selected requesting that

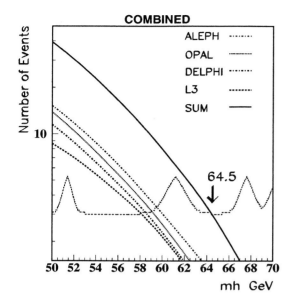

Figure 2. SM Higgs limits

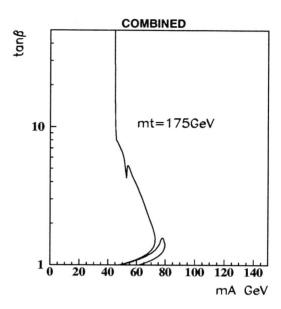

Figure 4. MSSM limits

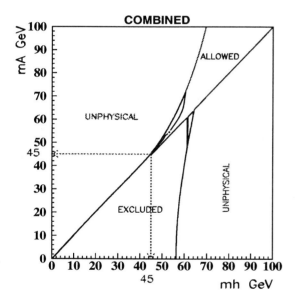

Figure 3. MSSM limits

more than 2 jets had at least 2 particles with significative offsets. The results are based on 1991 and 1992 data and correspond to about 10^6 hadronic events. 105 events were selected while $97 \pm 9 \pm 10$ events were expected.

From this result a 95 % C.L. limit on BR(Z→hA→4b) can be derived and, depending on the masses of h and A, varies between 3 and 5×10^{-4}.

This result complements the Z→hZ* search (from the 4 LEP experiments) and allows to exclude a large region of parameters in the MSSM scheme. First order

radiative corrections[10] are computed assuming a top mass at 175 GeV and the top-squark masses degenerate at 1 TeV. One obtains the exclusions contours of figure 3 and 4. The main conclusion is that, in MSSM, searches have reached the kinematical limit at LEP1.

Recent two-loop calculations[11] of radiative corrections reduce significantly their effect and therefore give an even firmer basis for this result.

In a contribution to this conference[12], it has been emphasized that if the top-squark mass becomes lighter than the top mass, the simple minded scheme for radiative correction breaks down. Using a more sophisticated scheme, they get, at intermediate Higgs mass, very strong suppression for the Z→hZ* process which could no more be excluded by a single LEP experiment. One should wait for a transparent interpretation of the mechanism responsible for this behaviour, but I would like to stress that this conclusion is based on the L3 data alone. I have checked that the LEP combined data are largely sufficient to exclude the numerical example given in[12].

4. Z→Hγ

This process suffers from the large radiative background which can be somewhat reduced by demanding an energetic photon well isolated from the hadronic jets. In the DELPHI[13] analysis, based on 1.7 M hadronic events, the isolation angle varies between 20° and 120° depending on the mass of the hadronic system. The photon sample has a purity of 75 %. The mass

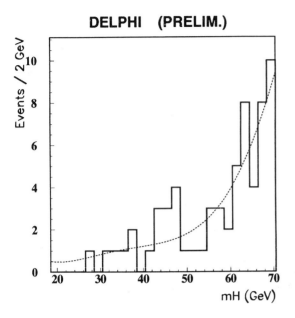

Figure 5. Mass distribution of radiative candidates

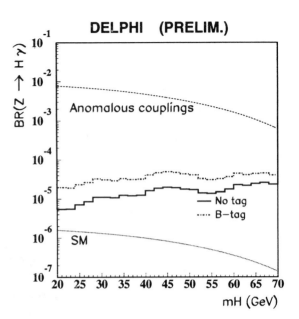

Figure 6. Limits on radiative branching ratio

resolution, essential for this analysis, is almost constant ~ 2 GeV, using kinematical constraints in conjunction with the photon energy measurement.

The mass spectrum given in figure 5 is obtained using b-tagging (at least 3 significant offsets). The dashed line indicates the estimated background. In figure 6, the resulting limits on BR(Z→Hγ) are given with and without b-tagging. These limits can exclude the presence of strong anomalous couplings[2] but are far above the SM predictions.

It may happen that H→ γγ becomes dominant[2] in the presence of strong anomalous couplings. In this case one can use the limit on BR(Z→ 3γ) given in [14]: 1.7×10^{-5}.

5. Summary

The SM Higgs 95 % C.L. mass limits are :

$$m_H \geq 60.3 \, GeV \quad ALEPH$$
$$m_H \geq 64.5 \, GeV \quad LEP$$

The MSSM Higgs 95 % C.L. mass limits are :

$$m_h \geq 45 \, GeV \quad DELPHI$$
$$m_A \geq 45 \, GeV \quad +LEP$$

One has :

$$BR(Z \to H \gamma) \leq \text{few } 10^{-5} \, DELPHI$$

If $m_H \leq 80$ GeV, this result sets useful limits on anomalous couplings in the bosonic sector.

References

[1] For a review on the Higgs sector in SUSY, see J. Gunion, H. Haber, G. Kane and S. Dawson, The Higgs Hunter's Guide, Addison-Wesley, Reading 1990.

[2] K. Hagiwara et al. Phys. Lett. B318 (1993) 155.

[3] ALEPH Coll., Contribution gls0568, ICHEP94 and ALEPH 94-034.

[4] DELPHI Coll., Contribution gls0304, ICHEP94 and DELPHI 94-85 PHYS 402.

[5] L3 Coll., Contribution gls0642, ICHEP94 and M. Pieri private communication.

[6] R. Akers et al.(OPAL Coll.), Phys. Lett. 327B (1994), 397.

[7] P. Janot, talk given at Int. Conf. on Neutrino Physics and Astrophysics, Eilat(May 1994).

[8] J.-F. Grivaz and F. Le Diberder, Nucl. Instr. & Meth. A 333 (1993) 320.

[9] DELPHI Coll., DELPHI 93-59 PHYS 287.

[10] Y. Okada, M. Yamaguchi and T. Yanagida, Prog. Theor. Phys. Lett. 85 (1991) 1; J. Ellis, G. Ridolfi and F. Zwirner, Phys. Lett. B257 (1991) 83; H.E. Haber and R. Hempfling, Phys. Rev. Lett. 66 (1991) 1815.

[11] R. Hempfling and A.H. Hoang, Phys. Lett. B 331 (1994) 99. J. Kodaira et al., HUPD-9316 (Nov 1993).

[12] J. Rosiek and A. Sopczak,Contribution gls0837, ICHEP94.

[13] DELPHI Coll., Contribution gls0186, ICHEP94 and DELPHI 94-119 PHYS 436.

[14] DELPHI Coll., Contribution gls0175, ICHEP94 and Phys. Lett. B327 (1994) 386.

Paper presented at XXVII Int. Conf. on High Energy Physics: Session Pa-10
Glasgow, UK, 20–27 July 1994

Search for Non-Minimal Higgs bosons at LEP

Marco Pieri

I.N.F.N. Firenze
Largo Fermi, 2
50125 Firenze, ITALY

Abstract

I will report on the searches made by the four LEP experiments for the Higgs bosons in the framework of the two doublet Higgs Model. These searches are based on the data sample accumulated until now by the LEP experiments at centre of mass energies around the Z peak. No signal has been observed and limits have been derived under the different assumptions considered.

1. Introduction

Higgs bosons [1] are predicted by gauge theories of electroweak interactions with spontaneous symmetry breaking. The Minimal Standard Model [2] (SM) contains one complex Higgs doublet which gives rise to one neutral Higgs boson. Its search is covered elsewhere in these proceedings [3]. The simplest extension of the standard model introduces two Higgs doublets: one couples to up-type quarks and leptons, the other to down-type quarks and leptons. This gives, after the generation of the $W^\pm$ an Z masses, 5 physical particles: two scalar neutral bosons: h^0 and H^0 with $M_{h^0} < M_{H^0}$, a pseudoscalar neutral boson: A^0 and two charged scalar bosons: $H^\pm$. The free parameters of the Higgs sector of the general two doublet model are: the masses of the Higgs bosons, $\tan\beta$ which is the ratio of the vacuum expectation values of the two Higgs fields and α which is the mixing angle in the neutral scalar sector.

The Minimal Supersymmetric extension of the Standard Model (MSSM) has the same physical states but it is characterized by additional constraints on the parameters, such that, at the tree level, the MSSM Higgs sector has only two free parameters out of M_{h^0}, M_{A^0} and $\tan\beta$. At the tree level, in the MSSM, the following relations should be satisfied:

$$M_{h^0} < M_{A^0} \tag{1}$$

$$M_{h^0} < M_Z \tag{2}$$

$$M_{H^0} > M_Z \tag{3}$$

$$M_{H^\pm} > M_W \tag{4}$$

This implies that h^0 and A^0 could be in the reach of LEP while H^0 and $H^\pm$ are not. Due to one loop corrections [4], which depend on the top and scalar quarks masses, the relationships between the Higgs bosons masses, the production widths and the decay modes are modified. In particular relations (1) and (2) are not necessarily satisfied and if the A^0 is lighter then one half the h^0 mass the decay $h^0 \to A^0 A^0$ is allowed.

The results I will report here are based on the data collected by the 4 LEP experiments from 1989 to 1993 at centre of mass energies around the Z resonance. These data correspond to approximately 75 pb^{-1} of integrated luminosity per experiment and 1.8 million $Z \to q\bar{q}$ produced in each experiment.

2. Search for h^0 and A^0

To search for h^0 and A^0 two different processes can be exploited at LEP:

$$Z \rightarrow h^0 f\bar{f} \tag{5}$$

$$Z \rightarrow h^0 A^0. \tag{6}$$

These two processes are complementary, in fact:

$$\frac{\Gamma\left(Z \to h^0 f\bar{f}\right)}{\Gamma\left(Z \to h^0_{SM} f\bar{f}\right)} = \sin^2(\beta - \alpha) \qquad (7)$$

$$\Gamma\left(Z \to h^0 A^0\right) \propto \cos^2(\beta - \alpha). \qquad (8)$$

Process (5) is essentially the same as the Minimal Standard Model Higgs production, while process (6) needs a separate analysis which takes into account the combination of the different h^0 and A^0 decay modes. The h^0, A^0 decays are similar to the SM if $\tan\beta > 1$, this is theoretically favoured by the top–bottom mass difference. The main decay modes of the neutral Higgs bosons are shown in Table 1.

Mass range (GeV/c^2)	h^0	A^0
0–0.21	$\gamma\gamma$, e^+e^-, A^0A^0	$\gamma\gamma$, e^+e^-
0.21–3	2–4 prongs, A^0A^0	2–4 prongs
3–10	$\tau^+\tau^-$, $c\bar{c}$, A^0A^0	$\tau^+\tau^-$, $c\bar{c}$
> 10	$b\bar{b}$, $\tau^+\tau^-$, $c\bar{c}$, A^0A^0	b, $\tau^+\tau^-$, $c\bar{c}$

Table 1. h^0 and A^0 decay modes in the different mass ranges.

Three different methods are used to search for h^0 and A^0:

- taking into account the suppression of the cross section with respect to the SM Higgs boson production, limits on $\sin^2(\beta - \alpha)$ are derived from the SM Higgs search negative results;

- requiring that the partial width of the process $Z \to h^0 A^0$ be less than the maximum allowed value for non SM contribution to Γ_Z (13.9 MeV at 95% C.L. [6]), a limit on $\cos^2(\beta - \alpha)$ is derived, this limit is independent of the decay branching ratios of h^0 and A^0;

- a direct search for the process $e^+e^- \to h^0 A^0$ is performed in many different channels; negative results of these searches also give limits on $\cos^2(\beta - \alpha)$.

Figure 1 shows the limit on $\sin^2(\beta - \alpha)$ which has been obtained by ALEPH using 1.23 million Z hadronic decays. The limit shown assumes that the h^0 does

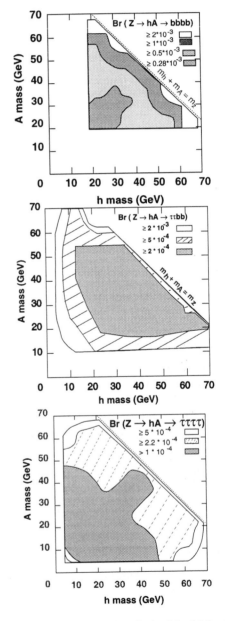

Figure 2. *Branching ratio limits obtained by L3 for the processes: $Z \to b\bar{b}b\bar{b}$, $Z \to b\bar{b}\tau^+\tau^-$ and $Z \to \tau^+\tau^-\tau^+\tau^-$.*

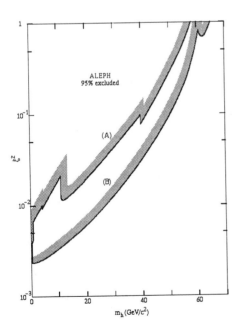

Figure 1. *Curve (A) shows the 95% C.L. upper limit obtained by ALEPH for ξ^2, the ratio of the production cross section of a non-minimal CP-even Higgs boson h^0 to the SM Higgs boson, as function of m_{h^0}.*

not decay into A^0A^0 in which case the limit would be degraded by no more than 10% in the whole mass range and would be the same as long as $M_{H^0} \gtrsim 2m_b$.

The direct search for the pair production of h^0A^0 has been carried out by the 4 LEP experiments in many different channels given by the various combinations of the decay modes of the h^0 and A^0. No indication of a signal has been found and limits on the branching ratios have been derived. Figure 2 shows the limits obtained by L3 in the channels: $Z\rightarrow b\bar{b}b\bar{b}$, $Z\rightarrow b\bar{b}\tau^+\tau^-$ and $Z\rightarrow \tau^+\tau^-\tau^+\tau^-$ using a data sample corresponding to 1.3 million Z hadronic decays.

The branching ratio limits can be converted into limits on $\cos^2(\beta - \alpha)$ according to the hypotheses made on the value of $\tan\beta$, typically $\tan\beta > 1$.

Making use of the upper limits on $\sin^2(\beta - \alpha)$ and $\cos^2(\beta - \alpha)$ a given mass point in the M_{A^0}, M_{h^0} plane is excluded in the general two doublet model whenever the following relation is satisfied:

$$\sin^2(\beta - \alpha)_{max} + \cos^2(\beta - \alpha)_{max} < 1. \qquad (9)$$

Figure 3 shows the corresponding exclusion plot obtained by OPAL with a data sample corresponding to approximately 1.9 million Z hadronic decays [7].

In the MSSM, given M_{A^0}, $\tan\beta$ and the top and scalar quarks masses, all the cross sections and branching ratios are predicted [4]. Limits have been obtained by all LEP experiments both in the M_{A^0}, M_{h^0} plane and in the M_{A^0}, $\tan\beta$ plane [7, 8, 9]; Figure

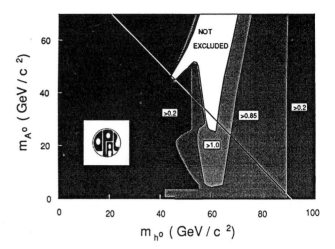

Figure 4. *OPAL 95% C.L. excluded domain in the M_{A^0}, M_{h^0} plane in the framework of the MSSM for various ranges of tanβ.*

4 shows the OPAL 95% excluded area in the M_{A^0}, M_{h^0} plane for $m_t < 200$ GeV/c^2 and $m_S < 1$ TeV/c^2, where m_S is the common mass scale for the squarks; the influence of different assumptions on $\tan\beta$ is also indicated. The corresponding 95% C.L. lower limit on the masses of the h^0 and A^0 are respectively 44.5 and 24.3 GeV/c^2 for $\tan\beta \geq 1$.

3. Search for charged Higgs bosons

Charged Higgs are required in models with at least two doublets. In the MSSM the mass of these particles is predicted to be higher than M_W; therefore evidence of charged Higgs bosons in the mass range accessible at LEP would be contrary to the MSSM.

The partial width of the Z into a pair of charged Higgs bosons is only a function of the charged Higgs boson mass:

$$\Gamma(Z \rightarrow H^+H^-) = \frac{G_F M_Z^3}{6\sqrt{2}\pi}\left(\frac{1}{2} - \sin^2\theta_W\right)^2 \beta_{H^\pm}^3, \qquad (10)$$

where $\beta_{H^\pm} = (1 - 4M_{H^\pm}^2/M_Z^2)^{1/2}$; the decay branching ratios also depend on $\tan\beta$:

$$\Gamma(H^+ \rightarrow \ell^+\nu_\ell) = \frac{\sqrt{2}G_F}{8\pi}M_{H^\pm}m_\ell^2\tan^2\beta, \qquad (11)$$

$$\Gamma(H^+ \rightarrow u_i\bar{d}_j) = 3|V_{ij}|^2\frac{\sqrt{2}G_F}{8\pi}M_{H^\pm} \times$$
$$\times \left(m_i^2\cot^2\beta + m_j^2\tan^2\beta\right). \qquad (12)$$

Given that a lower limit on $M_{H^\pm}$ of 19 GeV/c^2 has been set by experiments at PETRA [10] LEP experiments concentrated on charged Higgs bosons in a mass range above about 20 GeV for which the main decay mode

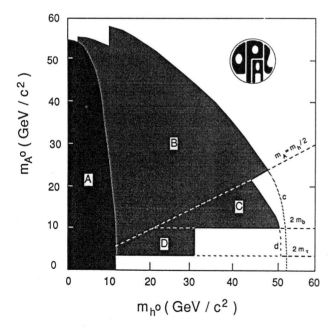

Figure 3. *OPAL exclusion plot in the M_{A^0}, M_{h^0} plane of the general two doublet model, valid for any tanβ. The shaded area indicates the excluded domain.*

would be $H^+ \rightarrow \tau^+\nu_\tau$ and $H^+ \rightarrow c\bar{s}$. The three channels: $Z \rightarrow c\bar{s}\bar{c}s$, $Z \rightarrow c\bar{s}\tau^-\bar{\nu}_\tau$ ($\bar{c}s\tau^+\nu_\tau$) and $Z \rightarrow \tau^+\nu_\tau\tau^-\bar{\nu}_\tau$ have been used.

In the following I will give a brief description of the analysis in the channel $c\bar{s}\bar{c}s$ which is the most delicate due to the large QCD background.

The strategy of the search is the following:

- select hadronic events;
- select 4–jet events;
- perform a kinematical fit and compute the mass of the dijet systems;
- search for an excess of events in the mass spectrum.

The crucial point of the analysis is the reconstruction of the 4 jets which should correspond to the 4 partons in the final state. The mass resolution which is obtained by DELPHI [11] after the kinematical fit which takes into account the four-momentum conservation and the fact that the two dijet masses must be equal, is 1.1 GeV/c^2 (FWHM) for $M_{H^\pm} = 43$ GeV/c^2.

DELPHI find no excess in the data in the hadronic channel as well as in the leptonic channel $Z \rightarrow \tau^+\nu_\tau\tau^-\bar{\nu}_\tau$.

Combining the limits obtained in the two channels DELPHI exclude at 95% C.L the existence of charged Higgs bosons with a mass less than 43.5 GeV/c^2 independently of the decay branching ratios (Figure 5). Similar limits have been obtained by the other LEP experiments [8, 12]

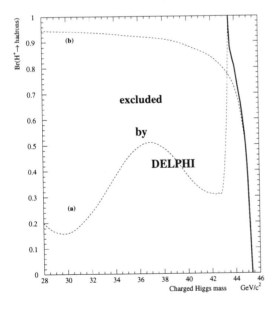

Figure 5. *DELPHI 95% C.L. $H^\pm$ mass exclusion plot as function of the $H^\pm$ branching ratio into hadrons. The region above curve (a) is excluded by the hadronic analysis, while the region below curve (b) is excluded by the leptonic analysis.*

4. Conclusions

The four LEP experiments have searched for the neutral Higgs bosons of the two doublet model in many different channels and they have found no indication of a signal. Limits have been derived in the general two doublet model and in the supersymmetric model.

The existence of the charged Higgs has been excluded at the 95% C.L. up to a mass of 43.5 GeV. These searches at the Z have almost approached the kinematical limit, however major improvements are expected with LEP200.

Acknowledgments

I would like to thank P. Janot, F. Richard, P. Sherwood and A. Sopczak for providing me with the latest results of the LEP experiments.

References

[1] P.W. Higgs, Phys. Lett. **12** (1964) 132;
F. Englert and R. Brout, Phys. Rev. Lett. **13** (1964) 321;
G.S. Guralnik, C.R. Hagen and T.W.B. Kibble, Phys. Rev. Lett. **13** (1964) 585.
[2] S.L. Glashow, Nucl. Phys. **22** (1961) 579;
S. Weinberg, Phys. Rev. Lett. **19** (1967) 1264;
A. Salam, Elementary Particle Theory, Ed. N. Svartholm, Stockholm, "Almquist and Wiksell" (1968), 367.
[3] See F. Richard talk, these proceedings.
[4] A. Brignole and F. Zwirner, Phys. Lett. **B299** (1993) 72 andreferences therein.
[5] ALEPH Collaboration: D. Buskulic *et al.*, Phys. Lett. **B313** (1993) 312.
[6] D. Schaile, Fortschr. Phys. **42** (1994) 429.
[7] OPAL Collaboration: R. Akers *et al.*, "Search for Neutral Higgs Bosons in the Minimal Supersymmetric Extension of the Standard Model", CERN-PPE/94-104, to be published in Zeitschrift für Physik C.
[8] L3 Collaboration: O. Adriani *et al.*, Zeit. Phys. **C57** (1993) 355.
[9] ALEPH Collaboration: D. Buskulic *et al.*, Phys. Lett. **B313** (1993) 312;
DELPHI Collaboration: P. Abreu *et al.*, Nucl. Phys. **B373** (1992) 3.
[10] JADE Collaboration: W. Bartel *et al.*, Phys. Lett. **B114** (1982) 211;
TASSO Collaboration: M. Althoff *et al.*, Phys. Lett. **B122** (1983) 95;
CELLO Collaboration: H.J. Behrend *et al.*, Phys. Lett. **B193** (1987) 376.
[11] DELPHI Collaboration: P. Abreu *et al.*, "Search for Pair Produced Heavy Scalars in Z^0 Decays", CERN-PPE/94-83, to be published in Zeitschrift für Physik C.
[12] ALEPH Collaboration: D. Decamp *et al.*, Phys. Rep. **216** (1992) 253;
OPAL Collaboration: M.Z. Akrawy *et al.*, Phys. Lett. **B242** (1990) 299.

Paper presented at XXVII Int. Conf. on High Energy Physics: Session Pa-10
Glasgow, UK, 20–27 July 1994

Limits on additional Z bosons from high precision measurements of purely leptonic neutrino scattering

Antonio Capone[§||]

§ Università "La Sapienza" and I.N.F.N. Sezione di Roma, Rome, Italy

On behalf of the CHARM II Collaboration

Abstract

High precision measurements of purely leptonic neutrino interactions have allowed the CHARM II collaboration to put new constraints on the existence of additional contributions to the neutral currents amplitude. The analysis of data collected from 1987 to 1991 has given the possibility to put limits on the masses of additional Z bosons in the framework of E_6 superstring-inspired theories, Left-Right symmetric models and on the so-called Z^1.

1. Introduction

The Standard Model of electroweak interactions has been by now well investigated by many experiments, and has been spectacularly successful. Nevertheless extensions of S.M. have been proposed to answer open questions such as: why do the S.M. needs so many (21) parameters, why the fermion masses assume their observed values; why do there exist three different leptonic families, etc. . . Many of these extensions foresee the existence of additional Z bosons and of other contributions to neutral current interaction amplitudes. Up to now, limits to the existence of these new bosons have been estabilished by LEP and CDF experiments.

The CHARM II experiment has studied low energy neutral current purely leptonic neutrino interactions; the high precision reached in this study is such that the results obtained can constrain the existence of an extra Z boson.

2. CHARM II experiment

The CHARM II detector [1] was designed and operated to obtain a precise determination of the electroweak

|| E-mail: capone@cernvm.cern.ch

parameters $(\sin^2 \theta_w,\ g_V,\ g_A)$ from the study of the purely leptonic neutral current processes

$$\nu_\mu + e \to \nu_\mu + e \qquad \overline{\nu}_\mu + e \to \overline{\nu}_\mu + e \quad . \quad (1)$$

It consisted of a massive target calorimeter followed by a muon spectrometer. The detector was exposed to the horn focused Wide Band neutrino Beam (WBB) at the 450 GeV Super Proton Syncrotron (SPS). The signature for neutrino-electrons is a single, forward scattered electron producing an electromagnetic shower in the calorimeter. The separation of neutrino-electron scattering events from background, which consists of semileptonic neutrino reactions producing predominantly electromagnetic final states, can be achieved observing that the variable $E_e \theta_e^2$, the product of electron energy and the square of the scattering angle, is kinematically constrained to values smaller than $1\ MeV$. The main contributions to the background come from coherent and diffractive neutrino production of single π^0 in neutral current interactions

$$\nu + A \to \nu + A + \pi^0 \qquad \nu + N \to \nu + N + \pi^0 \quad , \quad (2)$$

and quasi-elastic electron-neutrino interactions on nucleons

$$\nu_e + N \to e^- + N \quad . \quad (3)$$

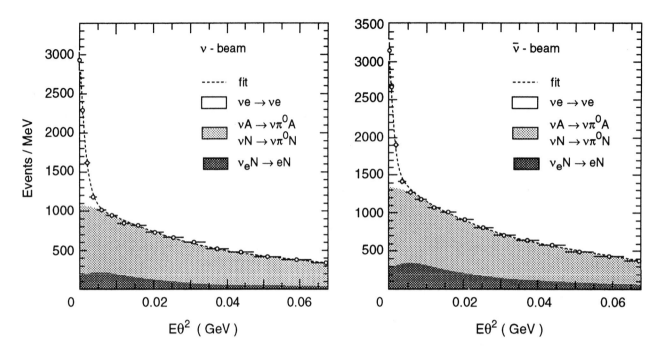

Figure 1. CHARM II 1987-1991 data and results of the best fit. Only the projection in $E_e\theta_e^2$ of the 2-dim. distributions are shown. The different background components are cumulative

A small fraction of background is due to inclusive neutrino interactions with a large electromagnetic component in the final state. Previous results, based on part of the final statistics have been already published [2],[3],[4]. From the measurement of ratio

$$R = \frac{\sigma(\nu_\mu e)}{\sigma(\overline{\nu}_\mu e)} = 3\frac{(1 - 4\sin^2\theta_w + 16/3\sin^4\theta_w)}{(1 - 4\sin^2\theta_w + 16\sin^4\theta_w)} \quad (4)$$

CHARM II obtained in 1991 $\sin^2\theta_w^{\nu e} = 0.237 \pm 0.009_{stat} \pm 0.007_{syst}$ [2]. The measurement of the shape of differential cross sections $d\sigma_{\nu_\mu e}/dy$ and $d\sigma_{\overline{\nu}_\mu e}/dy$, allowed not only another determination of the mixing angle $\sin^2\theta_w^{\nu e} = 0.212 \pm 0.027_{stat} \pm 0.006_{syst}$, well in agreement with the result mentioned before, but also the study of the helicity structure of the neutral current weak interactions. In the framework of the electroweak theory, 't Hooft [5] has derived the expression

$$\frac{d\sigma_{\overline{\nu}}^\nu}{dy} = \frac{G_F^2 s}{4\pi}[(g_V \pm g_A)^2 + (g_V \mp g_A)^2(1 - y)^2]. \quad (5)$$

This expression can be written also in terms of the righthanded and lefthanded electroweak coupling constants of the electron to the Z^0 using the relations:

$$4g_R^2 = (g_V - g_A)^2 \quad \text{and} \quad 4g_L^2 = (g_V + g_A)^2 \quad (6)$$

As result of the fit to the observed differential cross sections $d\sigma_{\nu_\mu e}/dy$ and $d\sigma_{\overline{\nu}_\mu e}/dy$, CHARM II has obtained [4]

$$\frac{g_R^2}{g_L^2} = 0.60 \pm 0.19_{stat} \pm 0.09_{syst} \quad (7)$$

which confirms the existence of the right-handed coupling of the electron to the Z^0 by three standard deviations. Recently CHARM II has published results obtained with the full sample data collected between 1987 and 1991 [6]. The $E_e\theta_e^2$ distributions of the selected events in the energy range 3-24 GeV are shown in figure 1, together with the results of the best fit to two-dimensional ($E_e, E_e\theta_e^2$) distributions. The pronounced peaks at low $E_e\theta_e^2$ contain 2677 ± 82 $\nu_\mu e$ and 2752 ± 8 $\overline{\nu}_\mu e$ events. The absolute normalizations of the neutrin and antineutrino fluxes have been obtained from inclusive neutrino-nucleon scattering, with known cross section, used as monitor. From the ratio of $\nu_\mu e$ and $\overline{\nu}_\mu e$ differential cross sections, with the inclusion in the analysis of the knowledge of relative neutrino to antineutrino flux (and of the experimental selection efficiencies), we have obtained the precise determination of the mixing angle:

$$\sin^2\theta_w^{\nu e} = 0.2324 \pm 0.0058_{stat} \pm 0.0059_{syst}, \quad (8)$$

well in agreement with results obtained at LEP [7]. From the combined fit of the $\nu_\mu e$ and $\overline{\nu}_\mu e$ differ cross sections, CHARM II has also determined simultaneously the two electroweak parameters g_V and g_A:

$$g_A^{\nu e} = -0.503 \pm 0.006_{stat} \pm 0.016_{syst}$$

$$g_V^{\nu e} = -0.035 \pm 0.012_{stat} \pm 0.012_{syst}.$$

These values also agree, within the errors as shown in figure 2, with values obtained at LEP [7] from

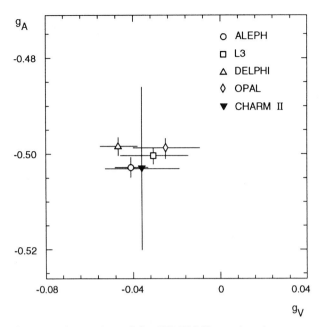

Figure 2. Comparison of the CHARM II neutrino-electron scattering results with measurements of the forward-backward asymmetry and γ_e for $e^+e^- \rightarrow e^+e^-$ annihilations at the Z^0 pole in the $g_V - g_A$ plane.

$e^+e^- \rightarrow l^+l^-$, despite the large difference of energy scales, $Q^2 \sim 0.01\ GeV^2$ for νe and $Q2 \sim 10^4 GeV^2$ for e^+e^-. These neutral current couplings, in particular $g_V^{\nu e}$, are sensitive to the presence of an additional Z boson: this fact, and the high precision reached by the CHARM II experiment, enables us to set limits on the existence of extra neutral gauge bosons.

3. Limits on the existence of extra Z bosons

The contribution of this extra boson to the neutral current interaction is model dependent so limits have to be given accordingly.

3.1. *Theoretical framework*

We have examined the effect of additional Z^0 bosons as foreseen by GUT theories (E_6)[8], and by Left-Right symmetric extensions of the Standard Model, and of a Z boson, heavier than the usual Z^0, but coupling to the known fermions with the same strengh as the ordinary one. We have assumed GUT based on the E_6 group. Assuming the following sheme for the symmetry breaking of E_6 [9]: $E_6 \rightarrow SO(10) \otimes U(1)_\psi$, $SO(10) \rightarrow SU(5) \otimes U(1)_\chi$ and $SU(5) \rightarrow SU(3)_C \otimes SU(2)_L \otimes U(1)_Y$ two additional neutral gauge bosons can be introduced. Let be Z'_ψ and Z'_χ the eigenstates associated with the symmetry breakings of the model. Several models, assuming the minimal Higgs sector, predict an extra neutral gauge boson $Z^{0\prime}$, a linear combination of Z'_χ

and Z'_ψ,

$$Z^{0\prime} = Z'_\chi \cos\theta_6 + Z'_\psi \sin\theta_6 \qquad (9)$$

could be the symmetry eigenstate of the additional $U(1)$. The mixing angle θ_6 determines the coupling of the heavy boson to the fermions. Special cases of E_6 model are obtained with $\theta_6 = 0^o$ (χ model), $\theta_6 = 90^o$ (χ model) and $\theta_6 = -52.24^o$ (η model). One other model that suggests the existence of an additional neutral boson is the Left-Right symmetric extension of the S.M. [10]. Also for this model there exists a parameter, here denoted as $\alpha_{L,R}$, that effectively fixes the coupling of $Z^{0\prime}_{L,R}$ to standard fermions. These $Z^{0\prime}$ could then mix with the usual symmetry breaking eigenstate of $SU(2) \otimes U(1)$, Z^0, giving the mass eigenstates Z and Z':

$$\begin{pmatrix} Z \\ Z' \end{pmatrix} = \begin{pmatrix} \cos\theta & \sin\theta \\ -\sin\theta & \cos\theta \end{pmatrix} \begin{pmatrix} Z^0 \\ Z^{0\prime} \end{pmatrix}$$

where

$$\tan^2\theta = \frac{M_0^2 - M_Z^2}{M_{Z'}^2 - M_0^2} \quad \text{and} \quad M_0 = \frac{M_W}{\rho \cos\theta_W}$$

assuming $\rho = 1$. The weak neutral current effective Lagrangian is then

$$L_{NC} = \frac{g}{\cos\theta_W} Z_\mu^0 (J_3^\mu - \sin^2\theta_w J_{em}^\mu) + g' Z_{i\mu}^{0\prime} J_i^\mu$$

where i can indicate χ, ψ, η or alternatively LR extra neutral gauge bosons. Clearly the extra term implies a value of the effective coupling constants of neutral currents to fermions that is a function of $M_{Z'}$ and θ.

$$g_{V,A}^{eff} = f_{V,A}^i(M_0, M_{Z'}, \theta, \sin^2\theta_w, m_t)$$

3.2. *CHARM II results*

CHARM II has compared g_V^{eff}, g_A^{eff} with g_V^{meas}, g_A^{meas} (assuming $M_Z = 91.187 \pm 0.007\ GeV$). Leaving as free parameters $M_{Z'}$ and θ (it has been assumed $m_t = 150\ GeV$) CHARM II has evaluated the χ^2 variable

$$\chi^2 = \left(\frac{g_V^{meas} - g_V^{eff}}{\Delta g_V^{meas}}\right)^2 + \left(\frac{g_A^{meas} - g_A^{eff}}{\Delta g_A^{meas}}\right)^2$$

and then the values of $M_{Z'}$ and θ limits that correspond to 95% confidence level [11]. In figure 3 are shown 95% C.L. limits for θ and $M_{Z'}$ obtained by this analysis compared with similar limits obtained by L3 at LEP [12]. At LEP, limits for θ and $M_{Z'}$ can be derived from analyses based on the energy dependence of cross sections and asymmetries of Z final states [13]. The CHARM II limits are comparable and even more stringent than the L3 limits on $M_{Z'}$, due to the fact that low-Q^2 current amplitudes are in principle more sensitive to the $Z - Z'$ interference and the Z' exchange

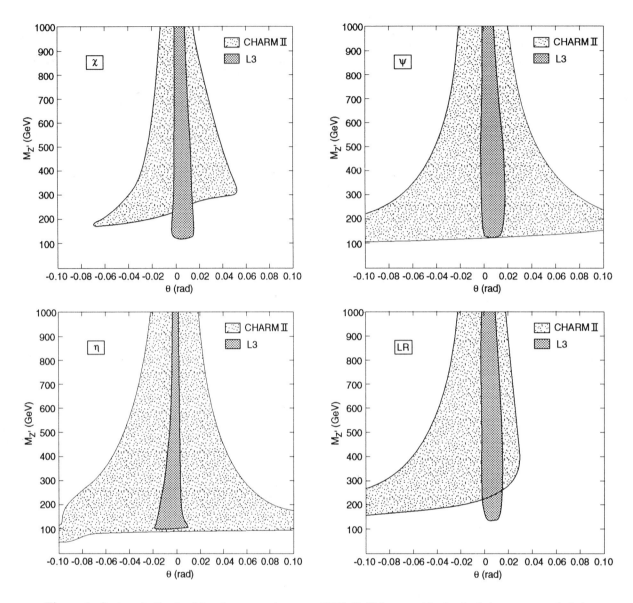

Figure 3. Contour in the $\theta - M_{Z'}$ plane assuming $m_t = 150 GeV$. Values outside the shaded areas are excluded at the 95% *C.L.*. L3 contours were derived assuming $m_H = 300 GeV$ and $\alpha_s = 0.12$.

Model	CHARMII	L3	CDF
χ	262	117	280-340
ψ	135	118	180-320
η	100	100	230-340
LR	253	130	230-310

Table 1. 95% lower limits for $M_{Z'}$ in GeV assuming $m_t = 150 GeV$ and $\theta = 0$. L3 bounds were derived by fixing $m_H = 300 GeV$ and $\alpha_s = 0.12$. CDF limits are from a direct search assuming Z' decay into known fermions (highest values) and all known and supersymmetric fermions (lowest values).

term contribution. In table 1 are also listed the limits on $M_{Z'}$ obtained by the CDF collaboration [14] from direct search of search of Z' decays into fermions. In the past, bounds to the existence of a second neutral gauge boson Z^1, clone to the usual Z^0, i.e. such that it has the same coupling of the Z^0 to fermions, have been put by neutrino-electron scattering experiments [15] and neutral current data analysis [16]. The neutral current coupling constants, in the presence of a Z^1, can be expressed [17] in terms of the S.M. predictions in the following way:

$$g_V^{eff} = g_V^{SM} + \frac{3}{5}\left(\frac{g'M_Z}{gM_{Z^1}}\right)^2 , \; g_A^{eff} = g_A^{SM} + \frac{3}{10}\left(\frac{g'M_Z}{gM_{Z^1}}\right)^2$$

Assuming $g/g' = 1$ the CHARM II data bound such a Z^1 to have a mass $M_{Z^1} > 398 GeV$ at 95% C.L.. In table 2 is shown a comparison of 90% C.L. limits obtained by CHARM II and similar limits in the Particle

	χ	ψ	η	LR	Z'
CHARM II	287	150	108	278	433
PDG	320	154	125	325	426

Table 2. Indirect search limits on $M_{Z'}$ at 90%.

Data Group [18] compilation.

4. Conclusions

The high precision reached by CHARM II collaboration in testing the electroweak sector of the S.M. is such that, even studying low Q^2 neutral current interactions, limits on the existence of extra neutral gauge bosons can be obtained. These limits are competitive and in some cases more stringent than similar limits obtained at LEP and by CDF.

References

[1] CHARM II Collab., K. de Winter et al., Nucl. Inst. and Meth. A 278 (1989) 670, CHARM II Collab., D. Geiregat et al., Nucl. Inst. and Meth. A 325 (1992) 92

[2] CHARM II Collab., D. Geiregat et al., Phys. Lett. B 259 (1991) 499.

[3] CHARM II Collab., P. Vilain et al., Phys. Lett. B 281 (1992) 159.

[4] CHARM II Collab., P. Vilain et al., Phys. Lett. B 302 (1993) 351.

[5] G. 't Hooft, Phys. Lett. B 37 (1971) 195.

[6] CHARM II Collab., P. Vilain et al., Phys. Lett. B 335 (1994) 246.

[7] The LEP Collabs.: ALEPH, DELPHI, L3 and OPAL, Phys. Lett. B 276 (1992) 247, and CERN-PPE/93-157, ALEPH CERN-PPE/94-30 (subm. Z. Phys. C), DELPHI CERN-PPE/94-31 (subm. Nucl. Phys. B) and L3 CERN-PPE/94-45 (subm. Z. Phys. C)

[8] V. A. Benyakov and S. G. Kovalenko, JINR/E2-88-395 (1988); J.L. Hewett, T.G. Rizzo Phys. Reports C 183 (1989) 193; P. Langacker, M. Luo, A.K. Mann, Phys. Rev. D 44 (1991) 817; P. Langacker, M. Luo, A.K. Mann, Phys. Rev. D 45 (1992) 278, and reference therein.

[9] D.London and J.L. Rosner, Phys. Rev. D 34 (1986) 1530, and reference therein.

[10] R.W. Robinett and J.L. Rosner, Phys. Rev. D 25 (1982) 3036; C.N. Leung and J.L. Rosner, Phys. Rev. D 29 (1982) 2132, and reference therein

[11] CHARM II Collab., P. Vilain et al., Phys. Lett. B 332 (1994) 465.

[12] L3 Collab. O. Adriani et al., Phys. Lett. B 306 (1993) 187; For an analysis of all LEP data in terms of a different parametrization see also: G. Altarelli at al., Phis. Lett. B 318 (1993) 139.

[13] A. Leike, S. Riemann, T Riemann, Phys. Lett. B 291 (1992) 187.

[14] CDF Collab. F. Abe et al. Phys. Rev. Lett. 68 (1992) 1463.

[15] CHARM Collab., J. Dorenbosch et al., Z. Phys. C 41 (1989) 567; E734 Collab., L.A. Ahrens et al., Phys. Rev. D 41 (1990) 3297; E225 Collab., R.C. Allen et al., Phys. Rev. D 47 (1993) 11.

[16] U. Amaldi et al., Phys Rev. D 36 (187) 1385.

[17] J.A. Grifols and S. Peris, Phys. Lett. B 168 (1986) 264; J.L. Rosner, Commun. Nucl. Part. Phys. 14 (1985) 229.

[18] Particle Data Group, Phys. Rev. D 45-II (1992)

Search for a new light gauge boson with the Crystal Barrel Detector

F Ould-Saada[†]

Physik-Institut, Universität Zürich, Winterthurerstra190, CH-8057 Zürich

Crystal Barrel Collaboration[1]

Abstract

We have searched for new light gauge bosons produced in π^0, η and η' decays by studying the kinematically well-constrained reactions $\bar{p}p \to \pi^0\pi^0 P$, where $P \equiv \pi^0, \eta, \eta'$ decays through the emission of a single photon recoiling against a missing state X (where X is a long-lived weakly interacting particle or $X \to \nu\bar{\nu}$). No signal has been observed and branching ratio upper limits (90 % C.L.) of 6×10^{-5} have been obtained for masses of the gauge boson lying between ~ 65 MeV and 125 MeV (π^0 decay), 6×10^{-5}, for X masses between ~ 200 MeV and 525 MeV (η decay), and 4×10^{-5}, for X masses between ~ 50 MeV and 925 MeV (η' decay). The π^0-decay limit represents a factor of 4 to 8 improvement when compared to the existing limit, whereas the η and η' decay limits have been measured for the first time, thereby extending the m_X range from 130 MeV up to 925 MeV.

1. Introduction

There exist various extensions of the Standard Model ($SU(3) \times SU(2) \times U(1)$) of strong and electroweak interactions. Some of them require an extra gauge group $U'(1)$ and, hence, a new gauge boson X. This possibility is realised in grand unified theories [2], in supersymmetric theories [3], in superstring-inspired models [4] and in models including a new long-range interaction, the fifth force [5]. Some X bosons could be light enough to be detected in rare or (Standard Model) forbidden decays of light mesons (π, K, η, ...) [6, 7]. To look for such new light particles, with masses of the order of the pion mass and with small couplings, high rates and precision are needed. Constraints on branching ratios for the decay of a pseudoscalar $P \to \gamma X$, P being a π^0, an η or an η' are summarised in ref. [7]. Two possibilities are considered depending on the interaction of the X boson: (I) X interacts weakly with both leptons and quarks, in which case it decays in our detector ($P \to \gamma e^+ e^-$ or $P \to \gamma \nu\bar{\nu}$). The decay $X \to \nu\bar{\nu}$ is experimentally more favourable to study since $X \to e^+ e^-$ is overwhelmed by the Dalitz decay $\pi^0 \to \gamma e^+ e^-$; (II) X interacts weakly with quarks only and hence has a long lifetime and does not decay in our detector. In both cases the analysis consists of looking for a photon and a missing mass. The decay $X \to e^+ e^-$ is not considered in this work.

Consider the decay $P \to \gamma\gamma$. In the rest frame of the decaying pseudoscalar P, the photon energy is given by $E_\gamma^* = m_P/2$, where m_P is the mass of the pseudoscalar P. Because of detector inefficiencies, one of the two photons can be lost. This leads to a peak in the energy distribution with a width determined by the experimental resolution. If one replaces the missing photon by a missing massive gauge boson X, the photon energy distribution peaks at $E_\gamma^* = \frac{m_P}{2}\left(1 - \frac{m_X^2}{m_P^2}\right)$, where m_X is the mass of the gauge boson X.

To look for a hypothetical gauge boson X in the decays $P \to \gamma X$, we exploit the fact that the annihilation of antiprotons with protons is a rich source of mesons (e.g., $\pi^0, \eta, \eta', \omega$) and that the Crystal Barrel detector is ideally designed for measurements of final

† E-mail: ouldsada@cernvm.cern.ch.

states with many photons. We use the well-constrained reactions $\bar{p}p \to \pi^0\pi^0 P$ because of the relatively high branching ratios $BR(\bar{p}p \to \pi^0\pi^0\pi^0) = (0.63 \pm 0.10)\%$ [8], $BR(\bar{p}p \to \pi^0\pi^0\eta) = (0.65 \pm 0.07)\%$ [9] and $BR(\bar{p}p \to \pi^0\pi^0\eta') = (0.40 \pm 0.08)\%$ [10] at rest in liquid hydrogen.

2. The data

The data have been collected using the Crystal Barrel detector at the Low Energy Antiproton Ring (LEAR) at CERN. Antiprotons with a momentum of 200 MeV/c are stopped in a 4-cm-long liquid hydrogen target. A matrix of silicon counters in front of the target defines and monitors the incident $\bar{p}$ beam (typically 10^4 $\bar{p}/s$). The target is surrounded by two cylindrical proportional wire chambers (PWCs), a jet drift chamber (JDC) to track charged particles, and a barrel-shaped calorimeter consisting of 1380 CsI(Tl) crystals, 16 radiation lengths deep, with photodiode readout. A detailed description of the detector, the trigger conditions and the reconstruction procedure is given in Ref. [11].

The analysis is based on 15×10^6 (18×10^6 for η') triggered all-neutral events. The triggering was performed using the PWCs and the inner layers of the JDC to veto charged tracks. One Million events containing exactly 5 electromagnetic showers (PEDs) with energy deposits exceeding the threshold energy $E_{cut} = 20$ MeV are selected. Events with a PED induced in the last crystal rows around the beam entrance and exit pipes are removed to suppress energy leakage. The next step is to reconstruct two π^0's out of the 5γ sample (818,655 events). The invariant masses of all combinations of two photons are calculated and events containing two π^0's and a single γ are kept. The surviving data sample consists of 187,145 events. Once the $\pi^0\pi^0\gamma$ events are selected, a kinematic fit with 3 constraints (3-C fit) ($\pi^0\pi^0 P_{miss}$, where P_{miss} is a missing π^0, η or η') is performed, ignoring the remaining single photon. A confidence level greater than 15% is required. We are left with 95,392 $\pi^0\pi^0\pi^0_{miss}$, 17,943 $\pi^0\pi^0\eta_{miss}$ and 4,165 $\pi^0\pi^0\eta'_{miss}$ fit events.

The method used to search for an X signal now consists of plotting the energy E^*_γ of the single γ in the rest frame of P_{miss}. The measured energy and momentum of the fifth photon and the fit values of P_{miss} are used to calculate E^*_γ.

3. The background

The background contribution can be split into two categories: 5γ final states without and with missing energy and momentum. The first source of background comes from real $\pi^0\pi^0\gamma$ events, due to the finite resolution of the detector. Here it is mainly the

channel $\bar{p}p \to \omega\pi^0$ ($\omega \to \pi^0\gamma$) which feeds into the fit $\pi^0\pi^0\pi^0_{miss}$, and to a lesser extent into $\pi^0\pi^0\eta_{miss}$. To reduce this background the selected 5γ data events are kinematically fit to the following final states: $\bar{p}p \to \pi^0\omega$ (7-C fit), $\bar{p}p \to \eta\omega$ (7-C fit), $\bar{p}p \to \pi^0\gamma\gamma$ (6-C fit) and $\bar{p}p \to \eta\gamma\gamma$ (6-C fit). If one of the 5γ combinations fits one of the above final states with a $C.L. > 1\%$, the event is rejected. About 25% of events are rejected for $\pi^0\pi^0\pi^0_{miss}$, while the proportion of rejected events is negligible in the case of $\pi^0\pi^0\eta_{miss}$ and $\pi^0\pi^0\eta'_{miss}$. The second source of background consists of the following final states: $\bar{p}p \to \pi^0\pi^0 P$, where one photon from a P is undetected. In order to reduce the missing photon contribution, an event is discarded if $|\cos(\theta_{\gamma miss})| \geq 0.95$ or $|\cos(\theta_{\gamma miss})| \leq 0.02$. We are left with 48,158 $\pi^0\pi^0\pi^0_{miss}$, 10,827 $\pi^0\pi^0\eta_{miss}$ and 2,848 $\pi^0\pi^0\eta'_{miss}$ events.

For the η decay we also take into account the channel $\bar{p}p \to K_S K_L$, where $K_S \to \pi^0\pi^0$ and K_L interacts in the barrel and produces one PED. The K_L and K_S emerge back to back and therefore events are rejected for which the invariant mass of the two π^0's is in the region $455 \leq M_{\pi^0\pi^0} \leq 506$ MeV/c^2 and the angle between the K_S direction and the fifth photon is greater than 167°. About 50% of the events far from the $\eta \to \gamma\gamma$ peak are rejected. This reduces the $\pi^0\pi^0\eta_{miss}$ sample to 8,961 events.

The remaining background events tend to accumulate along the line of maximum possible γ energy in the laboratory, E^{lab}_γ, in a two dimensional plot E^{lab}_γ vs. E^*_γ. This happens for events where the fifth photon has the same direction as P_{miss}. This is the case for the small fraction of $\pi^0\pi^0\gamma$ events ($K_L K_S$, $\omega\pi^0$, ...) that have not been removed by the above cuts. The following cuts are therefore applied: $E^{lab}_\gamma/E^*_\gamma \leq 2.6$ for η decay, $E^{lab}_\gamma/E^*_\gamma \leq 1.7$ for η' decay and $E^{lab}_\gamma/E^*_\gamma \leq 10.0$ for π^0 decay. About 30% of the remaining background events are rejected by these cuts, without affecting the signal. The final sample consists of 24,503 $\pi^0\pi^0\pi^0_{miss}$, 5,121 $\pi^0\pi^0\eta_{miss}$ and 2,198 $\pi^0\pi^0\eta'_{miss}$ events.

The acceptance and energy resolution are obtained using Monte Carlo simulation [12]. The photon energy resolution is $\sigma \sim 5$ MeV. The following efficiencies are obtained: $\epsilon_{\pi^0} = (11 \pm 1)\%$ for the π^0 decay, $\epsilon_\eta = (16 \pm 1)\%$ for the η decay, and $\epsilon_{\eta'} = (22 \pm 2)\%$ for the η' decay. The uncertainties include the dependence of the efficiency on m_X. The number of expected events for a given branching ratio $BR(X) = BR(P \to \gamma X)$ is $N_X = N_{\bar{p}} \times BR(\bar{p}p \to \pi^0\pi^0 P) \times BR(X) \times \epsilon$. For the $3\pi^0$ final state, a multiplicative factor 3 is included, to allow for the possible decay of any of the three π^0's. The 15×10^6 analysed 0-prong events correspond to $N_{\bar{p}} = (360 \pm 20) \times 10^6$ annihilations at rest. We then expect $N^{\pi^0}_X = 76 \pm 11$, $N^\eta_X = 35 \pm 7$, and $N^{\eta'}_X = 38 \pm 7$

signal events assuming a branching ratio $BR(X)$ of 10^{-4}.

4. Results

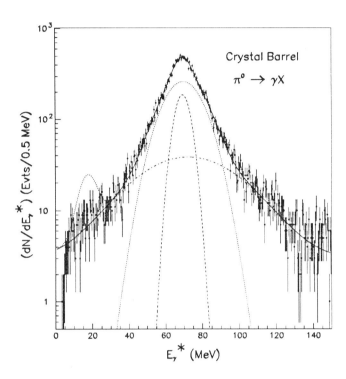

Figure 1. Energy of the single γ in the P_{miss} rest frame for the $\pi^0\pi^0 P_{miss}$ kinematically fit sample after background suppression, . The different contributions to the ten-parameter fit (full line) described in the text are shown separately: a narrow gaussian corresponding to $\pi^0\omega$ (dashed line), a broader gaussian corresponding to $\pi^0\pi^0\pi^0$ (finely dotted line), a much broader gaussian corresponding to other final states (like $\pi^0\pi^0\omega$), where two photons are lost (dashed-dotted line) on top of a constant background. A signal corresponding to a branching ratio for $\pi^0 \to \gamma X$ with $m_X = 120$ MeV/c^2 of 5×10^{-4} is also drawn (dotted line).

The energy of the single γ in the π^0 rest frame is shown in fig.1. A ten-parameter fit to the data includes the sum of three gaussians and a constant background term. The three gaussians have maxima around $m_{\pi^0}c^2/2$ (at 69.2, 69.7 and 72.0 MeV). These peak positions and the resolutions (4.2, 10.3 and 26.0 MeV) are in agreement with what we expect for $\pi^0\omega$ events (no missing photon), $\pi^0\pi^0\pi^0$ events (where one photon is missing), and other smaller background sources like $\omega\pi^0\pi^0$ (where 2 photons are missing). The third gaussian is, as expected, wider than the first two and its amplitude much smaller (32 events/0.5 MeV compared to 187 for the first and 263 for the second gaussian). The background term is due to events

where the fifth photon found does not belong to the missing π^0. The global fit shows that the spectrum is well understood. The amplitudes are consistent with Monte Carlo predictions using the experimental branching ratios. To look for a signal, various fits have been performed, with similar results[12]. An upper limit of $BR(\pi^0 \to \gamma X) < 6 \times 10^{-5}$ is obtained at 90% $C.L.$ for m_X lying between 65 MeV/c^2 and 125 MeV/c^2. Near $m_X = 0$ we obtain $BR(\pi^0 \to \gamma X) < 2.8 \times 10^{-4}$. A signal corresponding to $BR(\pi^0 \to \gamma X) = 5 \times 10^{-4}$, the existing direct measurement [16] is also indicated in fig.1.

In the case of η and η' the photon energy distribution shows a flatter and lower background than in the π^0 case (fig.2 and 3, respectively). The main reason is the

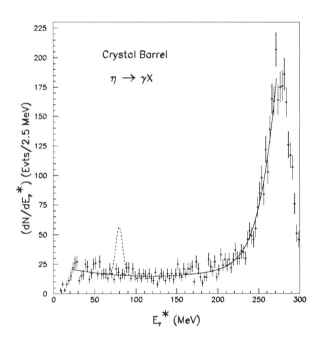

Figure 2. Energy of the single γ in the η_{miss} rest frame for the $\pi^0\pi^0\eta_{miss}$ kinematically fit sample after background suppression. The full curve corresponds to a six-parameter fit to the data (gaussian + 2nd order polynomial). A signal corresponding to a branching ratio for $\eta \to \gamma X$ with $m_X = 460$ MeV/c^2 of 5×10^{-4} is also indicated (dashed line).

reduced contribution from 6γ events ($\pi^0\pi^0 P$, where one photon from the P is lost). This is due to the smaller BR for $\eta, \eta' \to \gamma\gamma$ ($\sim 2\%$ for $\eta' \to \gamma\gamma$ and $\sim 39\%$ for $\eta \to \gamma\gamma$ compared to $\sim 99\%$ for $\pi^0 \to \gamma\gamma$), the higher γ efficiency for the η and η' decays and the lower combinatorial background (one for $\pi^0\pi^0\eta$ and $\pi^0\pi^0\eta'$ vs. three for $\pi^0\pi^0\pi^0$). In fig.2 a six-parameter fit to the data is performed which includes one gaussian and a background term (second-order polynomial). No significant signal is found on top of the background curve. An upper limit of $BR(\eta \to \gamma X) < 6 \times 10^{-5}$ is obtained at 90% *C.L.* for masses of the X boson between 200 MeV/c^2 and 525 MeV/c^2. A weaker upper limit of $BR(\eta \to \gamma X) < 3 \times 10^{-4}$ is obtained down to $m_X \sim 50$ MeV. From fig.3 an upper limit of $BR(\eta' \to \gamma X) <$

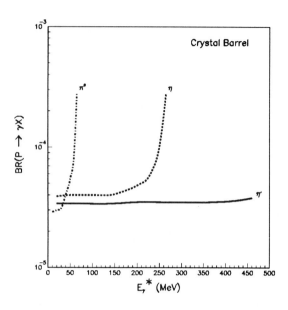

Figure 4. Branching ratio upper limit for the decays $\pi^0 \to \gamma X$ (dashed-dotted line), $\eta \to \gamma X$ (dotted line) and $\eta' \to \gamma X$ (full line) as function of E_γ^* (lower x-axis).

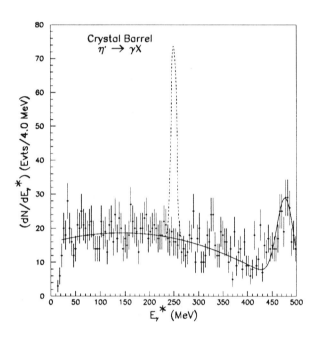

Figure 3. Energy of the single γ in the η'_{miss} rest frame for the $\pi^0\pi^0\eta'_{miss}$ kinematically fit sample after background suppression. The full curve corresponds to a six-parameter fit to the data (gaussian + 2nd order polynomial). A signal corresponding to a branching ratio for $\eta' \to \gamma X$ with $m_X = 662$ MeV/c^2 of 5×10^{-4} is also indicated (dashed line).

4×10^{-5} is obtained at 90% *C.L.* for masses of the X boson between 50 MeV/c^2 and 925 MeV/c^2. A signal corresponding to $BR(P \to \gamma X) = 5 \times 10^{-4}$ is indicated in fig.2 and 3 (dashed curves). The upper limit for the decay $P \to \gamma X$ as a function of mass is given in fig. 4 for the three pseudoscalars.

5. Summary

To summarise, we have searched for new light gauge bosons produced in π^0 η, and η' decays. No signal has been observed and branching ratio upper limits (90 % *C.L.*) of 6×10^{-5} have been obtained for m_X in the range between 65 MeV and 125 MeV (π^0 decay), of 6×10^{-5}, for X masses lying between 200 MeV and 525 MeV (η decay), and of 4×10^{-5}, for X masses lying between 50 MeV and 925 MeV (η' decay). The π^0-decay limit improves the existing limit [16, 17] by a factor of

4 to 8, whereas the η and η' upper limits have been measured for the first time, thereby extending the m_X range from 130 MeV up to 925 MeV.

References

[1] University of California (Berkeley), Universität Bochum, Universität Bonn, Academy of Science (Budapest), R.A.L (Chilton), CERN, Universität Hamburg, Universität Karlsruhe, Queen Mary and Westfield College (London), University of California (Los Angeles), Universität Mainz, Universität München, Carnegie Mellon University (Pittsburgh), CRN Strasbourg, Universität Zürich.

[2] P. Langacker, Phys. Rep. **72C**(1981)185.

[3] P. Fayet, Phys. Lett. **69B**(1977)489; Nucl. Phys. **B187**(1981)184; S. Weinberg, Phys. Rev. **D26**(1982)287.

[4] J. Ellis et al., Nucl. Phys. **B276**(1986)14; J. Schwarz, Superstrings: the First 15 Years, World Sc. Pub., Singapore (1985).

[5] S. Glashow, Proc. Conf. Rencontres de Moriond, (1986).

[6] M.I. Dobroliubov and A.Yu. Ignatiev, Nucl. Phys. **B309**(1988)655.

[7] M.I. Dobroliubov, Yad. Fiz. **52**(1990)551.[Sov. J. Nucl. Phys. **52**(1990)352].

[8] C. Amsler et al., to be published in Phys. Lett.

[9] C. Amsler et al., Phys. Lett. **B322**(1994)431.

[10] C. Amsler et al., to be published.

[11] E. Aker et al., Nucl. Instrum. Methods **A321**(1992)69.

[12] C. Amsler et al., Phys. Lett.**B333**(1994)271.

[13] R. Brun et al., CERN DD/EE/84-1, CERN (1987).

[14] C. Amsler et al., Z. Phys. **C58**(1993)175.

[15] Review of Particle Properties, Phys. Rev. **D45**(1992).

[16] M. S. Atiya et al., Phys. Rev. Lett. **69**(1992)733.

[17] R. Meijer Drees et al., Phys. Rev. **D49**(1994)4937.

Paper presented at XXVII Int. Conf. on High Energy Physics: Session Pa-10
Glasgow, UK, 20–27 July 1994

Search for Leptoquarks in ep collisions at $\sqrt{s} = 296$ GeV

Bruce Straub

Columbia University
New York, NY 10027

ZEUS Collaboration

Abstract

Using the ZEUS detector at HERA, we have searched for leptoquarks decaying into eq, νq, μq, or τq in a data sample of 0.55 pb^{-1}. No leptoquark signal was observed. Limits on coupling *vs.* mass were determined for the various leptoquark types. For electroweak coupling strength, scalar leptoquarks which decay to eq with masses below 242 GeV were excluded at 95% confidence.

1. Introduction

Leptoquarks (LQs) are color-triplet bosons with both lepton and baryon number. In ep collisions, a LQ would be produced as an s-channel resonance via electron-quark fusion. Using the ZEUS detector[1] at HERA, in a data sample of 0.55 pb^{-1}, we have searched for LQs which decay to eq, νq, μq, and τq in collisions of 26.7 GeV electrons with 820 GeV protons.

LQs decaying into eq or νq, called first-generation LQs, would have an event topology identical to neutral or charged current deep-inelastic scattering (DIS) events respectively. The signal for a LQ would be a peak at M_{LQ}^2/s in the DIS x-distribution (M_{LQ} is the leptoquark mass). LQs decaying into eq can also be distinguished from neutral-current DIS by their distribution in $y = Q^2/xs$. At fixed x, the neutral-current DIS cross section behaves roughly as y^{-2}, so this background can be supressed by a cut of the form $y > y_{min}$. In $LQ \to eq$, y is related to θ^*, the LQ-rest-frame angle between the incident and final-state electrons, by $y = (1 - \cos\theta^*)/2$. Scalar LQs would have a flat y distribution, while vector LQs would have a $(1 - y)^2$ distribution.

We have set coupling *vs.* mass limits for all $SU(3) \times SU(2) \times U(1)$ invariant first-generation LQs which conserve baryon and lepton number[2]. In the narrow-width approximation, the production cross section is:

$$\sigma_{ep \to LQ} = \frac{\pi}{4s}\left(g_R^2 + g_L^2\right) q\left(M_{LQ}^2/s\right) \begin{cases} \times 1 & \text{scalar} \\ \times 2 & \text{vector} \end{cases}$$

where g_L and g_R are the left and right-handed couplings and $q(x)$ is the quark density to which the LQ couples.

There exist limits on LQ couplings from low-energy experiments[3, 4, 5]. An important one is derived from the agreement between standard-model calculations and measurements of the $\pi \to e\nu_e$ decay rate. Because of the resulting severe limit, $g_L g_R < (M_{LQ}/8.8 \text{ Tev})^4$, we consider only first-generation LQs for which either g_L or g_R vanish.

A LQ formed in eq could also couple to μ or τ leptons[6]. Stringent limits[3, 4] on $\mu A \to e + X$ effectively rule out LQs coupling to both eq and $\mu q'$, if q and q' are both light quarks. If, however, q' is a heavy quark, then such LQs could exist with relatively large couplings ($g \sim 0.1$), as could LQs coupling to eq and $\tau q'$ (even if q' is light).

2. Simulation of signals and backgrounds

The backgrounds considered were: neutral and charged-current DIS, simulated using `Lepto`[7], `Heracles`[8] and `Ariadne`[9], and direct and resolved photoproduction (γp) processes, generated using `Herwig`[10]. γp events

from DIS and γp was 0.46 events. The overall efficiency of the μq cuts for scalar and vector LQs decaying into μc is above 60% over the M_{LQ} range.

Significant $\not{P}_t$ is also expected in τq LQ decays. We based the τq search on the νq sample before the isolated-electron rejection was applied (48 events). Separate selections were made for each τ decay mode. For $\tau \rightarrow e\nu_\tau \bar{\nu}_e$, we required $\not{P}_t > 15$ GeV and an isolated electron with energy above 10 GeV. For $\tau \rightarrow \mu\nu_\tau \bar{\nu}_\mu$, all events in the μq sample were accepted. Finally, for $\tau \rightarrow \nu_\tau +$ hadrons, we required $E_t > 40$ GeV (to reduce γp) and $\not{P}_t/E_t < 0.7$ (to reject charged-current DIS). Also, an isolated, compact ($R_{\eta\phi} < 0.3$) calorimeter cluster with energy above 10 GeV had to be found with $\theta > 10.4°$, $P_t > 5$ GeV, and 1, 2, or 3 matching CTD tracks. Here also, we accepted any νq event with $\not{P}_t > 80$ GeV. No events passed the τq cuts for any of the three modes. The estimated background from DIS and γp was 0.68 events. The efficiency of the cuts exceeded 40% for scalar (vector) LQs with $M_{LQ} > 110$ GeV ($M_{LQ} > 160$ GeV).

4.   Procedure for calculating limits

To determine coupling limits *vs.* M_{LQ} for first-generation LQs, we applied M_{LQ} dependent cuts to the eq and νq samples. For the eq events, the cut $x_{min}(M_{LQ}) < x_{DA} < x_{max}(M_{LQ})$ selected events within the x peak region. The additional cut $y_{DA} > y_{min}(M_{LQ})$ was applied to suppress neutral-current DIS. For the νq sample, only an x cut was applied: $x_{min}(M_{LQ}) < x_{JB} < x_{max}(M_{LQ})$.

Using the Monte Carlo samples, we determined the values of x_{min}, x_{max} (and y_{min} for eq decays), for which, in the absence of a signal, the *average cross-section limit* would be minimized. These cut parameters were fit to a polynomial in M_{LQ}, as were the resulting signal efficiencies and expected background.

We took uncertainties in the luminosity (3.3%), the background estimation (10%), and the signal efficiency (2%) into account by treating these quantities as Gaussian random variables and setting the LQ cross-section limits to the value for which, in repeated experiments, we would have observed more events than we did with 95% probability. The effect of these uncertainties is to increase the cross-section limits by at most 4%.

5.   Coupling Limits

The coupling limit *vs.* M_{LQ} curves for scalar LQs are shown in figure 3 and for vector LQs in figure 4 (all limits are at 95% confidence level). The coupling and state names follow the conventions of reference [2]. For fermion number (F) equal to -2, scalar and vector LQs

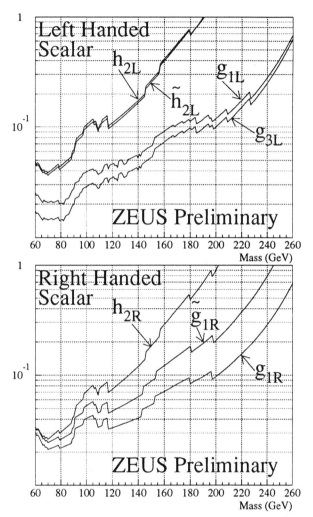

Figure 3. The 95% confidence level limits on couplings for first-generation scalar leptoquarks.

and the couplings are labeled S, V, and g respectively (for $F = 0$, R, U, and h are used). The subscripts give the dimension of the $SU(2)$ representation. Since the $e^- q$ initial state has $F = -2$, much stronger limits are set on those couplings. Table 1 summarizes the mass limits for coupling strengths of $g = 0.1$ and $g = (4\pi\alpha_{EW})^{1/2} = 0.31$.

For flavor-violating LQs we set limits on $g\mathcal{B}$ where g is the coupling to eq at the production vertex and $\mathcal{B}$ is the branching fraction into the final state. For $LQ \rightarrow \mu c$ we set limits on $g_{eu}\mathcal{B}_{\mu c}$ as shown in figure 5. For g_{eu} with electroweak strength and a branching fraction $\mathcal{B}_{\mu c}$ of 50%, we have excluded S_1 LQs with $M_{LQ} < 238$ GeV and $\tilde{V}_2$ LQs with $M_{LQ} < 246$ GeV. Also shown in figure 5 are limits on $g_{ed}\mathcal{B}_{\tau b}$. Again assuming electroweak coupling for g_{ed} and $\mathcal{B}_{\tau b} = 50\%$, we have excluded $\tilde{S}_1$ LQs with $M_{LQ} < 207$ GeV, and V_2 LQs with $M_{LQ} < 216$ GeV.

can be backgrounds for $LQ \rightarrow eq$ if a fake electron is found. The structure function parameterizations used were MRSD0[11] for the proton, and GRVG0[12] for the photon. `Pythia`[13] was used to simulate scalar LQs decaying to eq, νq, μc, and τb. We searched for LQs with masses between 60 GeV and 260 GeV and generated Monte Carlo samples at 20 GeV intervals in this region. To simulate vector LQs, the samples were reweighted according to the generated y.

3. Data selection and reconstruction

We use a coordinate system in which beam protons travel in the $+z$ direction for which the polar angle, θ, is zero. This analysis relied mainly on the uranium-scintillator calorimeter[14], the central tracking detector (CTD)[15], and the vertex detector (VXD)[16]. The calorimeter has three parts: Forward ($1.6° < \theta < 36.8°$), Barrel ($36.8° < \theta < 129.4°$), and Rear ($129.4° < \theta < 177.4°$). The acceptance of the CTD covers $13° < \theta < 167°$, and the VXD covers $9° < \theta < 165°$.

Separate event selections were made for eq and νq final states. The μq and τq searches were performed by making additional cuts on the νq sample. Cuts common to both samples were: the requirement that an acceptable vertex was reconstructed in the CTD and the VXD, the rejection of events with more than 5 GeV in the electron calorimeter of the luminosity monitor (to reduce γp background), calorimeter timing cuts (to reject beam-gas and cosmic rays), and rejection of beam-halo muons and cosmic rays using pattern recognition.

Events in the $LQ \rightarrow eq$ sample were required to have an isolated electron with energy above 10 GeV and a matching CTD track. $E - P_z$ was required to be between 35 GeV and 65 GeV (E is the total energy measured in the calorimeter, P_z the total z-momentum). To reduce low-Q^2 backgrounds, the transverse energy (E_t) had to exceed 20 GeV and the energy with $\theta > 150°$ had to be less than 5 GeV. A total of 1330 events passed these cuts. The (M_{LQ} dependent) efficiency of the trigger and offline cuts for $LQ \rightarrow eq$ was between 74% and 82% for scalar LQs. Using triggers in unpaired e^- and p bunches, we estimate the non-ep contamination of this sample to be well below 1%. We used the double-angle (DA) method to reconstruct x and y for the eq sample. Figure 1 shows the distribution of x_{DA} for the entire eq sample and for $Q^2_{DA} > 500$ GeV^2. No LQ signal is seen.

The $LQ \rightarrow \nu q$ selection required that the net transverse momentum measured in the calorimeter ($\not{P}_t$) exceed 10 GeV and that $E - P_z < 55$ GeV. Of the 48 events passing these cuts, 15 were rejected because an isolated electron of than 10 GeV was found. Three more non-ep triggers were rejected by scanning. A final cut (to reject γp events with mismeasured $\not{P}_t$) required

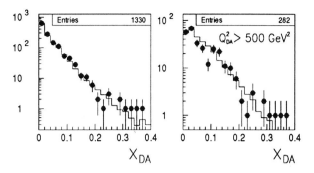

Figure 1. The dots are the number of events *vs.* x_{DA} for the entire eq sample, and for those events with $Q^2_{DA} > 500$GeV^2. The histograms are neutral current DIS Monte Carlo.

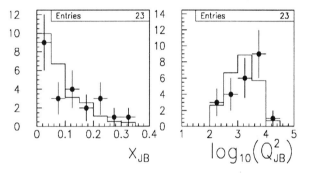

Figure 2. Distributions of x_{JB} and Q^2_{JB} (GeV^2) for the νq sample (dots) and charged-current DIS Monte Carlo (histograms).

that $\not{P}_t/E_t > 0.4$, leaving 23 events, consistent with the charged-current DIS Monte Carlo estimation of 24.6 events. The M_{LQ} dependent efficiency of the trigger and offline cuts for scalar LQs decaying into νq was above 76%. We used the Jacquet-Blondell (JB) method to reconstruct x and y for the νq events. Figure 2 shows x_{JB} and Q^2_{JB} distributions for the selected events and for charged-current DIS Monte Carlo. The measured distributions agree well with the Monte Carlo expectation.

The μq candidates were selected using only the calorimeter and the CTD. Because high-energy muons typically deposit only a few GeV in the calorimeter, we could base our search for $LQ \rightarrow \mu q$ on the νq sample (for which $\not{P}_t > 10$ GeV). We required an isolated calorimeter cluster which was compatible with being a minimum ionizing particle, had a matching CTD track, and was within $15°$ in azimuth of the $\not{P}_t$ vector. To preserve efficiency for high-mass LQs, where the muon polar is often too small to be in the CTD acceptance, we also accepted any νq candidate with $\not{P}_t > 80$ GeV. No events passed the μq cuts. The estimated background

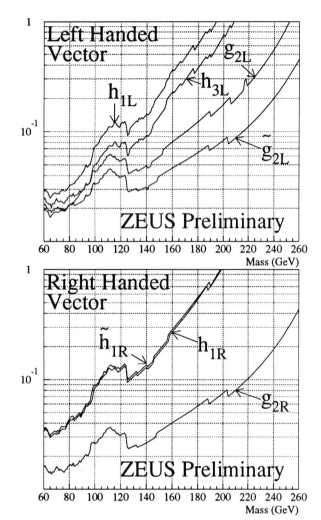

Figure 4. The 95% confidence level limits on couplings for first-generation vector leptoquarks.

coupling/ state		Q	$\mathcal{B}_{\nu q}$	M_{LQ} limit $g = 0.1$	M_{LQ} limit $g^2 = 4\pi\alpha_{EW}$
g_{1L}	S_1	$-1/3$	$1/2$	164 GeV	242 GeV
g_{3L}	S_3	$-4/3, -1/3$	$0, 1/2$	183 GeV	245 GeV
h_{2L}	R_2	$-5/3$	0	98 GeV	155 GeV
$\tilde{h}_{2L}$	$\tilde{R}_2$	$-2/3$	0	100 GeV	156 GeV
g_{1R}	S_1	$-1/3$	0	191 GeV	242 GeV
$\tilde{g}_{1R}$	$\tilde{S}_1$	$-4/3$	0	153 GeV	214 GeV
h_{2R}	R_2	$-5/3, -2/3$	$0, 0$	132 GeV	162 GeV
g_{2L}	V_2	$-4/3$	0	170 GeV	224 GeV
$\tilde{g}_{2L}$	$\tilde{V}_2$	$-1/3$	0	215 GeV	251 GeV
h_{1L}	U_1	$-2/3$	$1/2$	108 GeV	157 GeV
h_{3L}	U_3	$-5/3, -2/3$	$0, 1/2$	143 GeV	171 GeV
g_{2R}	V_2	$-4/3, -1/3$	$0, 0$	219 GeV	252 GeV
h_{1R}	U_1	$-2/3$	0	104 GeV	164 GeV
$\tilde{h}_{1R}$	$\tilde{U}_1$	$-5/3$	0	103 GeV	162 GeV

Table 1. First-generation LQ mass limits for couplings $g = 0.1$ and $g^2 = 4\pi\alpha_{EW}$. The columns labeled Q and $\mathcal{B}_{\nu q}$ give the charge and the branching ratio into νq for those members of $SU(2)$ multiplet which can be produced in $e^- p$ collisions. The nomenclature is taken from reference [2]

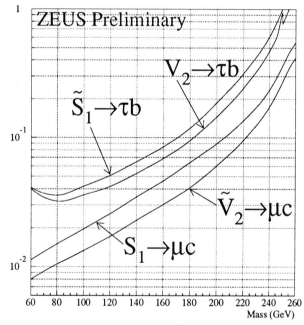

Figure 5. The two lower curves are the 95% confidence level limits on $g_{eu}\mathcal{B}_{\mu c}^{1/2}$ for S_1 and $\tilde{V}_2$ LQs. The two upper curves give the limits on $g_{ed}\mathcal{B}_{\tau b}^{1/2}$ for $\tilde{S}_1$ and V_2 LQs.

References

[1] The ZEUS Detector, Status Report 1993, DESY 1993.
[2] W. Buchmüller *et. al.*, Phys. Lett. **B191** (1987) 442.
[3] W. Buchmüller, Phys. Lett. **B177** (1986) 377.
[4] S. Davidson *et. al.*, Z. Phys. **C61** (1994) 613.
[5] M. Leurer, Phys. Rev. Lett. **71** (1993) 1324, Phys. Rev. **D49** (1994) 333, Phys. Rev. **D50** (1994) 536.
[6] I.I. Bigi *et. al.*, Phys. Lett. **B166** (1986) 238.
[7] G. Ingelman, T. Sjöstrand, Lund Preprint LU TP 80-12. G. Ingelman, LEPTO version 6.1, Proc. of the HERA Workshop **V3** (1991) 1366.
[8] A. Kwiatkowski *et al.*, Proc. of the HERA Workshop **V3** (1991) 1294.
[9] L. Lönnblad, Proc. of the HERA Workshop **V3** (1991) 1440.
[10] B.R. Webber *et al.*, Computer Phys. Comm. **67** (1992) 465.
[11] A.D. Martin *et al.*, Phys. Rev. **D47** (1993) 867.
[12] M. Glück, E. Reya, A. Vogt, Phys. Rev. **D46** (1992) 1973.
[13] H.U. Bengtsson, T. Sjöstrand, Computer Phys. Comm. **46** (1987) 43. **Pythia** was modified to produce νq, μc, and τb final states in addition to eq.
[14] A. Andresen *et al.*, Nucl. Inst. Meth. **A309** (1991) 101, A. Bernstein *et al.*, Nucl. Inst. Meth. **A336** (1993) 23, A. Caldwell *et al.*, Nucl. Inst. Meth. **A321** (1992) 356.
[15] C.B. Brooks *et al.*, Nucl. Instr. Meth. **A283** (1989) 477, B. Foster *et al.*, Nucl. Instr. Meth. **A338** (1994) 254.
[16] C. Alvisi *et al.*, Nucl. Instr. Meth. **A305** (1991) 30.

Search for Squarks and Excited Leptons at HERA

Torsten Köhler

RWTH-Aachen
52074 Aachen, Germany

On behalf of the H1 and ZEUS collaboration

Abstract

A direct search for excited leptons (e^* and ν^*) and for R-parity violating SUSY particles ($\tilde{q}$) is presented, using the H1 and the ZEUS detector at the ep collider HERA. No evidence is found for any new resonant state with masses up to ≈ 275 GeV in data samples corresponding to an integrated luminosity of ≈ 0.5 pb^{-1} for each experiment. Rejection limits are derived.

1. Introduction

The Standard Model (SM) has been very successful in describing all experimental observations in particle physics. But there remain open questions, e.g. about the masses and charges of the particles or about the symmetry between the lepton and quark families. New theories try to answer these questions and most of them predict new heavy particles. For example, Compositeness models manage with new layers of substructure. A consequence of substructure in the fermion sector would be the existence of excited states of the known fermions. Supersymmetric (SUSY) models predict partners for all particles of the SM, with a spin-1/2 difference.

At the ep collider HERA, with a centre of mass energy, $\sqrt{s}$, of 296 GeV, a completely new mass domain for the search of new heavy particle states is accessible. Since the discovery of new particles would have large implications for any new theory beyond the SM, such searches have high priority at any new collider.

Here we report about the search for excited leptons and squarks at the ep collider HERA with the two experiments H1 and ZEUS. The data were taken 1993 and correspond to an integrated luminosity of ≈ 0.5 pb^{-1} for each experiment. First results with 1992 data can be found elsewhere [1, 2].

The new heavy particles could be produced as single intermediate states formed between the incoming electron and a gauge boson radiated off the proton or a constituent of the proton. In the narrow-width approximation the ep cross section is given by

$$\sigma_{ep} = \frac{4\pi^2}{s}(2J+1)\frac{\Gamma}{M}\mathcal{B}\,f_{i/p}(M^2/s), \qquad (1)$$

where J, M, and $\mathcal{B}$ are the angular momentum, the mass, and the branching ratio of the heavy state, respectively. $f_{i/p}(x)$ denote the quark density functions in case of squark production, or the probability to find a gauge boson with momentum fraction x inside the proton for excited leptons. The decay width, Γ, contains the coupling of the new particles.

2. Experimental Set-up

A description of the H1 and the ZEUS detector can be found elsewhere [3, 4]. Here we briefly concentrate on the components relevant for the analyses.

In both experiments tracks of charged particles are measured in a combination of drift and proportional chambers surrounding the interaction point. For H1, outside the tracking detectors there is a finely segmented liquid argon (LAr) calorimeter with energy resolutions of $\sigma_E/E \approx 12\%/\sqrt{E}$ for electrons and $\sigma_E/E \approx 50\%/\sqrt{E}$

for hadrons (E in GeV). In the backward part there is a lead-scintillator calorimeter with $\sigma_E/E \approx 10\%/\sqrt{E}$. The tracking system and calorimeters are placed in a uniform field of 1.2 T parallel to the beam axis. For ZEUS, the tracking system is surrounded by a solenoid, producing a field of 1.4 T. A uranium-scintillator calorimeter (CAL) encloses the solenoid. The energy resolutions are $\sigma_E/E \approx 18\%/\sqrt{E}$ for electrons and $\sigma_E/E \approx 35\%/\sqrt{E}$ for hadrons. The time resolution of the CAL is < 1 ns. In both experiments the return iron yoke is fully instrumented to measure the energy tails of hadronic showers and to detect muons. The luminosity monitors are placed in the electron beam direction (polar angle $\theta \approx 180°$) and consist of an electron tagger and a photon tagger.

3. Excited Leptons

Excited states of known leptons are natural ingredients of Composite models [5]. In ep collisions excited electrons (e^*) could be generated dominantly via the exchange of low-Q^2 photons whereas excited neutrinos (ν^*) could be formed at a wider Q^2 range through W exchange. The partial decay widths are approximately given by $\Gamma = \alpha M^3 c_{vl^*l}^2 / \Lambda^2$, where M is the excited lepton mass and α the fine structure constant. Λ can be interpreted as the substructure scale. The used phenomenological ansatz is described explicitly in ref. [6], where also the coupling constants c_{vl^*l} are introduced. In this model the excited electron and neutrino form a doublet which couples via a magnetic transition to only left-handed electrons or neutrinos.

At HERA a mass range is to be explored where the decay of the e^* and ν^* into heavy gauge bosons (W or Z) and a light fermion may become dominant. For more details see also ref. [7].

Searches for excited leptons have been performed at H1 and ZEUS. A detailed description of the analyses can be found in refs. [8, 9]. Here we only describe briefly the basic strategy. Looking for isolated leptons or photons with high (transverse) energy, for large missing transverse momentum, p_T^{miss}, in case of neutrinos in the final state, and for jets or hadronic activity with large transverse energy, E_T^{had}, in decay channels, where jets are expected, is the most general search strategy for excited leptons.

The decay channels of excited electrons under study are $e^* \rightarrow e\gamma$, $e^* \rightarrow eZ$, and $e^* \rightarrow \nu W$, with the subsequent decays $Z \rightarrow ee$, $Z \rightarrow \nu\bar{\nu}$, $Z \rightarrow q\bar{q}$, and $W \rightarrow e\nu$, $W \rightarrow q\bar{q}'$. For excited neutrinos equivalent decay channels are analysed, except $Z \rightarrow \nu\bar{\nu}$. These decay channels have clean signatures and high detection efficiencies.

As an example the ZEUS analysis for some special decay channels of the e^* and ν^* are explained more explicitly.

The preselection cuts to obtain the fiducial data sample are: $p_T^{miss} > 8$ GeV, or at least one electromagnetic (e.m.) cluster (localized energy deposit) with $\theta < 150°$, or total transverse energy, E_T, greater than 30 GeV and $\Sigma(E - p_z) > 20$ GeV. In addition events with more than 5 GeV energy in a backward cone ($\theta > 150°$) are rejected.

The decay channel $e^* \rightarrow e\gamma$ has a very spectacular and clean signature, especially when the e^* is produced elastically, which is expected in this model to account for about 50%. The further analysis to find events in this channel requires at least two isolated e.m. clusters with $E_{em1} > 10$ GeV, $\theta_{em1} < 150°$, $E_{em2} > 2$ GeV, and 30 GeV $< \Sigma(E - p_z) < 60$ GeV. The average detection efficiency, ϵ, is 80%. 25 events are found, where 26.1 are expected from the NC deep inelastic scattering (DIS) process and one from the elastic Compton process $ep \rightarrow e\gamma p$. The highest invariant mass is at ≈ 50 GeV. The mass spectrum of the $e\gamma$ pairs is well described by the Monte Carlo simulation.

In case of an excited lepton decay into the gauge bosons W or Z the most promising search strategy is to look for the subsequent decays $W \rightarrow q\bar{q}'$ or $Z \rightarrow q\bar{q}$ because of the high branching ratios. One may directly search for jets in the final state or just for hadronic activity with large transverse energy, E_T^{had}. For the decay channels $e^* \rightarrow eq\bar{q}$ and $\nu^* \rightarrow eq\bar{q}'$ the analysis requires at least one e.m. cluster with $E_{em1} > 10$ GeV and $\theta_{em1} < 125°$, 30 GeV $< \Sigma(E - p_z) < 60$ GeV, and $E_T^{had} > 60$ GeV. With detection efficiencies of 49% (for e^*) and 43% (for ν^*) two data events are found, whilst the expectation from the NC DIS process is 4.7.

If there is an additional neutrino in the final state ($e^* \rightarrow \nu q\bar{q}'$, $\nu^* \rightarrow \nu q\bar{q}$), the selection cuts are $p_T^{miss} > 15$ GeV, an invariant mass of the hadronic system, M_{had}, greater than 50 GeV, $\Sigma(E - p_z) < 50$ GeV, and a cut against beam-gas background events. For the ν^* search and $M_{had} > 125$ GeV the p_T^{miss}-cut is relaxed to 5 GeV. Three candidates are found, compatible with the background expectation from NC DIS, CC DIS, and photoproduction processes of 1.6 events (for e^*, $\epsilon = 53\%$) and 3.4 events (for ν^*, $\epsilon = 65\%$).

Similar analyses are performed by H1.

In both experiments no evidence is found for the production and decay of any new heavy lepton. Therefore rejection limits are derived for e^* and ν^* as a function of their masses, which are shown in Figures 1 and 2, respectively†. Comparable results are obtained by both experiments. The decay channels for the massive gauge bosons W and Z are combined taking

---

† ZEUS results are given on $\frac{\sqrt{c^2+d^2}}{\Lambda}\sqrt{\mathcal{B}}$, H1 shows $\frac{|c|}{\Lambda}\sqrt{\mathcal{B}}$, assuming $c = d$. So there is a factor of $\sqrt{2}$ difference in comparing H1 and ZEUS results

into account different efficiencies and expectations. The uncertainties on these limits are of $\mathcal{O}(10\%)$. For excited electrons and a special choice of the coupling $c^2_{\gamma e^* e} = 1/16$ the total decay width is 28(210) GeV at $M = 225(250)$ GeV, taking into account the limits for Λ obtained from the H1 analysis. If $c^2_{\gamma \nu^* \nu} = 1/4$ is chosen, the width of the excited neutrino is 52(132) GeV for $M = 165(180)$ GeV. Current rejection limits for the direct single production of new heavy leptons obtained by the LEP experiments exclude masses $\lesssim 90$ GeV [10]. Obviously, limits are derived in a new mass region directly accessible for the first time at HERA.

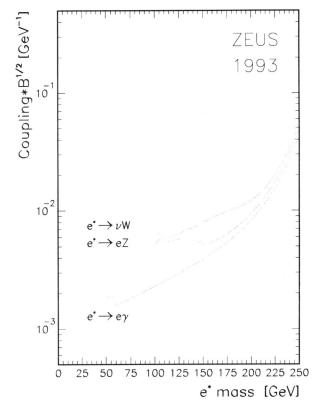

Figure 1. Rejection limits at the 95% CL for the e^* for different decay modes. Regions above the curves are excluded. Decay modes of the W and Z bosons are combined. Here, 'Coupling' stands for $\sqrt{c^2 + d^2}/\Lambda$.

4. Squarks

Scalar partners of the known quarks, squarks, with otherwise identical quantum numbers and couplings to the SM gauge bosons, are predicted by the Minimal Supersymmetric Model (MSSM) [11]. In an extension of the MSSM single squark production is possible at HERA, if the R-parity is not conserved, which is defined by $R_p = (-1)^{3B+L+2S}$. Here, B denotes the baryon number, L the lepton number, and S the spin of the particles. For all SM particles $R_p = 1$ whilst for all

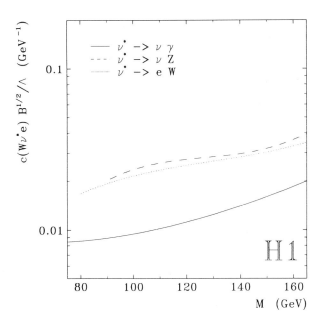

Figure 2. Rejection limits at the 95% CL for the ν^* for different decay modes. Regions above the curves are excluded. Decay modes of the W and Z bosons are combined.

SUSY particles $R_p = -1$. At HERA, specifically the R_p-violating couplings λ' between a lepton, a quark, and a squark are of interest [12]. Only squarks of the first generation, degenerated in mass, are considered. Squarks may either decay via their Yukawa coupling into fermions, or via their gauge coupling into a quark and the lightest supersymmetric particle (LSP) (see Fig. 3). The LSP is assumed to be the photino, $\tilde{\gamma}$, which may, in this extension of the MSSM, decay into two quarks and a lepton of the first generation. The production cross sections for up(down)-type squarks are the same as for $\tilde{S}_{1/2}(S_0)$ leptoquarks, also the partial decay widths into fermions are the same.

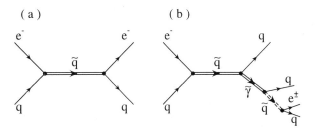

Figure 3. Squark production at HERA. In (a) the R_p-violating squark decay and in (b) the decay via gauge coupling is shown.

A search for the R_p-violating single production of up- and down-type squarks ($\tilde{u}, \tilde{d}$) has been performed by the H1 collaboration [13].

The branching ratio of the squarks to the R_p-violating decay channel giving finally an electron or neutrino and a jet, or for the gauge decay with a first generation lepton and three jets in the final state, depends on the coupling strength λ'_{111} and on the ratio $M_{\tilde{\gamma}}/M_{\tilde{q}}$.

The first decay channel dominates for large coupling values λ'_{111} or large photino masses $M_{\tilde{\gamma}}$. There the analysis procedure for the squark search follows precisely the search method for leptoquarks. The expected background is due to the NC or CC DIS process, which is undistinguishable on the event-by-event basis from the squark signal. Therefore the event selection is essentially a selection for high-Q^2 DIS events. The squark signal would then show up as an excess of events in a small window in the mass-Bjorken-y-plane.

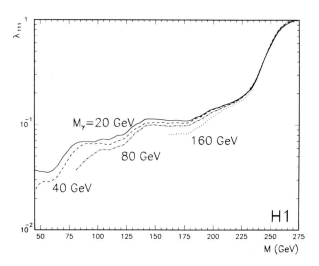

Figure 4. Rejection limits at the 95% CL for the coupling λ'_{111} as a function of the squark mass for various fixed photino masses. Regions above the curves are excluded. The limits combine all charged and neutral decays of the $\tilde{d}$ and $\tilde{u}$.

The basic selection criteria to select NC DIS events are: requirement of an electron in the LAr calorimeter, total missing transverse momentum, p_T^{miss}, less than 15 GeV, a reconstructed z-vertex, $|\Sigma(E - p_z) - 2E_e| \leq$ 10 GeV, where E_e is the incident electron beam energy, and little energy in the backward calorimeter and in the electron tagger. A mass dependant Bjorken-y-cut is applied in order to optimize the signal-to-background ratio. 34 events are selected with masses above 45 GeV, with an expectation of 24.2 ± 2 events from a DIS Monte Carlo event simulation [14].

CC DIS events are selected by the requirements of finding no electron, $p_T^{miss} \geq 15$ GeV, a reconstructed z-vertex, and matching of total transverse energy with p_T^{miss} within 50%. In addition cosmic and beam halo muons are rejected. The squark mass is reconstructed using only the final state hadrons. We find 13 events with $M \geq 45$ GeV, where 15.3 ± 0.3 are expected from CC DIS Monte Carlo simulations.

To select candidates for the squark gauge decays, additional cuts to the NC DIS selection are applied: a certain amount of hadronic energy in the hemisphere

of the outgoing electron or positron is required and the Bjorken-y-cut is fixed at 0.4. The number of data events with masses greater than 45 GeV is 66, where 53 ± 3 events are expected from a NC DIS event simulation. No positron has been found whilst for a signal one would expect as much e^+ as e^- in this decay channel.

In each selection the number of data events as well as the invariant mass spectra agree well with the expectation from standard physics. There is no evidence for any squark production in the mass range 45 GeV $\leq M \leq 275$ GeV. Therefore rejection limits are derived, combining all charged and neutral decay modes of the $\tilde{d}$ and $\tilde{u}$. The rejection limits on the coupling λ'_{111} are shown in Figure 4 as a function of the squark mass for various photino mass hypotheses starting always at $M_{\tilde{\gamma}} = M_{\tilde{q}}$. The uncertainties on these limits are of $\mathcal{O}(10\%)$. The CDF limit [15] at 95% CL is at 100 GeV, rather independent of the coupling.

5. Acknowledgements

I wish to thank all my colleagues for their support and for fruitfull discussions.

References

[1] H1 Collaboration: I. Abt *et al.*, Nucl. Phys. **B396** (1993) 3.

[2] ZEUS Collaboration: M. Derrick *et al.*, Phys. Lett. **B316** (1993) 207.

[3] H1 Collaboration: I. Abt *et al.*, DESY preprint: DESY 93-103, Hamburg (July 1993).

[4] ZEUS Collaboration: M. Derrick *et al.*, Phys. Lett. **B303** (1993) 183; *ibid.* **B293** (1992) 465; *ibid.* **B297** (1992) 404.

[5] See e.g. M.E. Peskin, Proc. of the Xth Symposium on Lepton-Photon Interactions 1981, p. 880; Ed. W. Pfeil (Bonn 1981).

[6] K. Hagiwara, S. Komamiya and D. Zeppenfeld, Z. Phys. **C29** (1985) 115.

[7] F. Boudjema, A. Djouadi and J.L. Kneur, Z. Phys. **C57** (1993) 425.

[8] H1 Collaboration: T. Ahmed *et al.*, DESY preprint: DESY 94-138, Hamburg (August 1994).

[9] ZEUS Collaboration: M. Derrick *et al.*, ICHEP94 Ref. 0667, contribution to the 27th International Conference on High Energy Physics, Glasgow (July 1994).

[10] ALEPH Collaboration: D. Decamp *et al.*, Phys. Rep. **216** (1992) 253; L3 Collaboration: O. Adriani *et al.*, Phys. Lett. **B288** (1992) 404; L3 Collaboration: B. Adeva *et al.*, Phys. Lett. **B252** (1990) 525; OPAL Collaboration: M.Z. Akrawy *et al.*, Phys. Lett. **B257** (1991) 531; *idem*, Phys. Lett. **B244** (1990) 135.

[11] For reviews see H.P. Nilles, Phys. Rep. **110** (1984) 1; H.E. Haber and G.L. Kane, Phys. Rep. **117** (1985) 75.

[12] J. Butterworth and H. Dreiner, Nucl. Phys. **B397** (1993) 3, and references therein.

[13] H1 Collaboration: T. Ahmed *et al.*, DESY preprint: DESY 94-154, Hamburg (August 1994).

[14] G. Ingelman, (LEPTO version 5.2), program manual unpublished; H. Bengtsson, G. Ingelman and T. Sjöstrand, Nucl. Phys. **B301** (1988) 554.

[15] CDF Collaboration: S.M. Moulding *et al.*, Fermilab preprint: FERMILAB-CONF-92-341-E (November 1992).

Paper presented at XXVII Int. Conf. on High Energy Physics: Session Pa-10
Glasgow, UK, 20–27 July 1994

Searches for New Gauge Bosons and Excited Quarks at FNAL

J P Wolinski[†]

Texas A&M University, College Station, TX

On behalf of the CDF and D0 Collaborations

Abstract

Various recent results of new particle searches at the Fermilab Tevatron are presented. No evidence is found for W′, Z′, H⁺, excited quark, or gaugino production in p$\bar{\text{p}}$ collisions at $\sqrt{s} = 1.8$ TeV. Excluded mass regions for each particle are determined.

1. Introduction

The history of particle physics indicates that as the physical universe is probed on smaller length scales, via higher energy processes, new phenomena continually appear which challenge our current understanding of nature. Thus, it is imperative that the Fermilab Tevatron, the worlds highest energy particle collider, be used for searches of new phenomena. The CDF and D0 experiments have been actively studying their data for evidence of previously unobserved particles. Presented below are the latest results of searches at the Tevatron for W′, Z′, H⁺, excited quarks and gauginos. The bulk of this article was derived from papers contributed to the ICHEP '94 conference([1],[2],[3],[4],[5]).

2. Search for W′ → eν at CDF and D0

Various extensions to the standard model predict an additional W boson. In left-handed models, such a W′ is essentially a heavy version of the standard W boson[6]. If it is heavy enough, it would decay predominantly to WZ pairs. In left-right symmetric models, the W′ would decay to $e_R\nu_R$[7]. Detection of such a decay mode is complicated by the unknown properties of the ν_R. We will assume that the ν_R is massless and stable. The coupling strength of the W′ to fermions is proportional to $(a+b\gamma_5)$, yielding $\Gamma(W′ \to f_i f_j) \propto \frac{a^2+b^2}{2} \equiv \lambda^2$. In

† E-mail : wolinski@fnald.fnal.gov

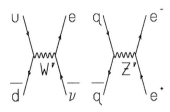

Figure 1. Typical Feynman diagrams for W′ and Z′ production in $p\bar{p}$ collisions.

the standard model, a $= 1$, b $= -1$, and $\lambda^2 = 1$; this is termed the "standard strength" condition and will be assumed in the W′ analysis. A typical p$\bar{\text{p}}$→W′X production diagram is depicted in figure 1.

Assuming a light, stable ν_R, the CDF[1] and D0[8] experiments have searched for p$\bar{\text{p}}$→W′→eν. The signature of this process is a hard electron accompanied by large $\not{E}_T$. A W′ signal would be indicated by a peak in the $M_T(e,\not{E}_T)$ distribution. CDF requires $|\eta(e)| < 1.05$, $E_T(e) > 30$ GeV, and $\not{E}_T > 30$ GeV. The D0 cuts are similar: $|\eta_e| < 1.1$ or $1.5 < |\eta_e| < 2.5$, $E_T(e) > 25$ GeV, and $\not{E}_T > 25$ GeV. Additional tracking, isolation and electron identification criteria are also imposed.

Various background sources must be considered in this analysis. W′ production can be mimicked by Z^0→e⁺e⁻ if one electron is undetected. This background is reduced by vetoing events with additional tracks (p$_T$ > 10 GeV/c) consistent with being an electron (ie., a track with EM shower). QCD dijet production can simulate W′ events if one jet is misidentified as an electron and the other jet is undetected. Thus, events are rejected if they contain a track cluster pointing at a calorimeter crack or collinear with the $\not{E}_T$ direction. Background from $W \to \tau\nu \to e\nu\nu\nu$ is subtracted later.

The data used for this analysis was collected during the 1989 Tevatron collider run. CDF (D0) accumulated a total integrated luminosity of 19.7 (13.4) pb^{-1} (the difference is due to accelerator and experimental details). Applying the previously stated analysis cuts, CDF and D0 obtain W′ candidate samples of 10526 and 12798 events, respectively.

There are three principal sources of background in these W′ samples, which are estimated as follows. For the $Z^0 \to e^+e^-$ and $W \to \tau\nu$ modes, expected yields were determined using the ISAJET Monte Carlo program (with detector simulation) and previously measured cross sections. Contamination from QCD dijet events was estimated using non-isolated "electron" (ie., jet) data. This allows calculation of the likelihood to produce events with a fake electron and fake $\not{E}_T$. CDF estimates these background sources to total 440 events.

For the CDF data, a binned ln(L) fit is performed. Contributions from W and W′ events are added in the form $\alpha \cdot W′ + (1 - \alpha) \cdot W$. Leading order Monte Carlo is used, assuming $\Gamma(W′) = \Gamma(W)M(W′)/M(W)$ and using the previously measured W p_T spectrum. A 3% systematic error is folded in, arising primarily from uncertainties in structure functions, $\not{E}_T$ resolution, higher order corrections, W p_T, and the energy scale. The D0 data is analysed by counting the number of W′ candidates above 350 GeV/c^2.

CDF observes no evidence for W′ production and obtains M(W′)>652 GeV/c^2 (95% confidence level). The corresponding D0 result is M(W′)>620 GeV/c^2. The previous W′ mass limit[1] was 512 GeV/c^2.

3. Search for Z′ → e⁺e⁻ at CDF and D0

Most standard model extensions predict a Z′. Typically these models predict the Z′ couplings but not M(Z′). Figure 1 depicts a typical p$\bar{p} \to$ Z′ production diagram.

The CDF[2] and D0[8] experiments have searched for Z′ decaying to two hard electrons. The CDF criteria are: $|\eta(e)_{1(2)}| < 1.1$ (2.4), E$_T$(e) >25 GeV, and p$_T$(e)$_1$ >13 GeV/c. The D0 requirements are similar: $|\eta(e)_{1(2)}| <1.1$ (2.5), E$_T$(e) >30 GeV, and the harder electron must have a track match. Additional tracking, electron identification, and isolation cuts are imposed.

The only appreciable background in this analysis is from Drell-Yan γ,Z→e$^+$e$^-$ (at high mass, even this is negligible, with $\leq$1 event for M>250 GeV/c^2). CDF (D0) used 19.7 (14.4) pb^{-1} data for this analysis. Applying the analysis cuts above, CDF (D0) obtains

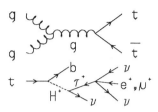

Figure 2. Typical $t\bar{t} \to H^+bH^-\bar{b}$ production diagram.

1371 (886) events. CDF then performs a binned ln(L) fit to the data. Similar to the W′analysis, the Drell-Yan and Z′ distributions are modeled by leading order Monte Carlo. The Z′ width and p$_T$ spectrum are also modeled in analogy with the W′ analysis. A 6% systematic error, arising primarily from luminosity, efficiency and acceptance uncertainties, is included in the fit. Since there are no events with M(e$^+$e$^-$) > 350 GeV/c^2, the Poisson statistic is actually used to calculate a limit. CDF obtains M(Z′)>505 GeV/c^2, while D0 finds M(Z′)>480 GeV/c^2. The old limit was 412 GeV/c^2[2]. Note that this limit is for the simplest type of Z′, the so-called "sequential" Z′. Mass limits for Z′'s from various other specific models have been calculated by CDF[2].

4. Search for t→H⁺b at CDF

Charged Higgs particles are expected in models which contain two Higgs doublets. They are likely to be produced in top quark decays, where t→H$^+$b competes with t→W$^+$b. These branching ratios are determined by M$_t$, M$_H$, and tan(β). H$^+$ then decays primarily to cs and $\tau\nu$. Since, BR($\tau\to$e or μ) $\simeq$ 36%, $\ell^+\ell^-$+$\not{E}_T$ can be used as a signature of $t\bar{t} \to H^+bH^-\bar{b}$ production (see figure 2). Note that $t\bar{t} \to W^+bW^-\bar{b}$ and $t\bar{t} \to W^+bH^-\bar{b}$ also yield dileptons + jets + $\not{E}_T$. However, the leptons and jets produced in t→H$^+$b decays are too soft to have been observed in the previous CDF top analysis (which searched only for t→W$^+$b decays). Furthermore, leptons from semileptonic b decays are non-isolated, unlike the leptons from H$^+ \to \tau\nu \to \ell\nu$.

Thus, this analysis[3] searches for isolated, low p$_T$ lepton pairs with large $\not{E}_T$. The primary analysis cuts used were $|\eta_{e(\mu)}| < 1.2(1.0)$, p$_T(\ell)_{1(2)} > 9(6)$ GeV/c, and $\not{E}_T$> 20 GeV. Back-to-back $\mu\mu$ pairs were rejected since they are likely to come from cosmic rays. In addition, an event is rejected as background if it passes any of the cuts listed below (also listed is the background source each cut is intended to reduce):

- 70<M($\ell\bar{\ell}$)<110, M($\ell\bar{\ell}$)<12 GeV/c^2: Z^0, J/ψ, $\Upsilon \to \ell\bar{\ell}$
- M(eμ) < 10 GeV/c^2: b→c$\ell\nu$, c→s$\ell\nu$.
- $\Delta\phi(\not{E}_T, \ell) > 165°$ if p$_T(\ell) > 25$ GeV/c: W→$\ell\nu$ + jets (jet misidentified as e).
- $\Delta\phi(\not{E}_T,$jet$) < 30°$: Drell-Yan γ,Z→$\ell\bar{\ell}$ + mismea-

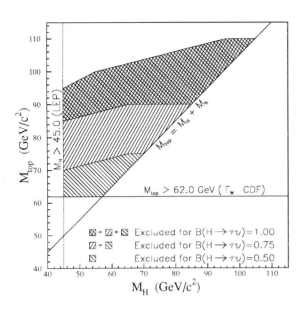

Figure 3. 95% confidence level excluded regions in the M(t) vs. M(H+) plane.

sured jets (giving large $\not{E}_T$).

- $\Delta\phi(\not{E}_T, \ell) < 30°$: $Z \to \tau^+\tau^- \to \ell\bar{\ell}$.

Various other matching, lepton identification, and isolation cuts were also used.

After applying all cuts, CDF observes 2 H+ event candidates in 19.3 pb^{-1} data. ISAJET Monte Carlo (with detector simulation) is used to determine signal acceptance and efficiencies, while lepton identification efficiencies are calculated from data. The background contributions are estimated to be:

- WW: 0.9 events.
- $Z \to \tau\tau$: 0.4 events.
- Drell-Yan $\gamma \to \ell\bar{\ell}$: 0.4 events.
- heavy flavors: 0.5 events
- QCD multi-jets, W + jets: 0.8 events.

The total background is 3.0 ± 1.0 events. Thus, the CDF observation is consistent with background. Figure 3 shows the 95% confidence level excluded regions in the M(t) vs. M(H+) plane, assuming BR(t→H+b) = 1.0 and using a calculated $\sigma(t\bar{t})$[11]. Excluded regions have also been determined assuming calculated t and H+ branching ratios[12] and various $\tan(\beta)$ values[3].

5. Search for excited quarks at CDF

Composite quarks are a feature of many standard model extensions. If these composite quarks, q*, are

produced in an excited state (via, for instance, quark-gluon fusion), they may then decay to qγ or qW. The Lagrangian that governs these decays depends on three unknown constants, f_s, f and f'. In this analysis, it will be assumed that $f_s = f = f' = 1$.

Thus, the q* signature used in this analysis is a resonance formed by a jet + (γ or W). The analysis cuts used to select γ's, W's and jets are listed below:

- γ: neutral Em cluster with $p_T > 30$ GeV, cone isolation < 4 GeV, consistent with γ shower shape (rejects π^0, η), require $\not{E}_T < 0.8 \times E_T(\gamma)$ (to reject cosmic ray bremsstrahlung).
- W→(e or μ)ν: e or μ with $p_T > 20$ GeV, $\not{E}_T > 20$ GeV, e(μ) $|\eta| < 0.95$ (0.6), require radial $\eta - \phi$ separation between closest jet and e(μ) = 0.9 (0.25).
- leading jet: $E_T > 15$ GeV, $\Delta\phi$(jet-$\not{E}_T$)> 0.4 (to reject mismeasured jets).

Events with > 1 lepton are vetoed to reduce background from Z^0+ jets→$\ell\ell$ X. QCD background is diminished by requiring $\cos(\theta^*) > 2/3$, where θ^* is the C.M. angle between the jet and the proton beam.

The CDF data sample used in this analysis consists of ~4 pb^{-1} from the 1989 run and ~20 pb^{-1} from the 1992 run. The details of the W and γ analyses are slightly different, although $ln(\mathcal{L})$ fits are performed in both cases. For the W mode, $P_z(\nu)$ is constrained by requiring $M(\ell,\not{E}_T) = M(W)$, and selecting the solution yielding the smaller M(jet,W). The M(jet,W) spectrum is then fit with a QCD background Monte Carlo distribution plus a q* signal.

In the q*→qγ mode, improved mass resolution is obtained by assuming that the γ and jet are back-to-back, and setting E_T(jet) = $E_T(\gamma)$. The M(jet,γ) spectrum is then fit with a QCD background distribution, including fake γ's.

In both cases the $ln(\mathcal{L})$ distributions are smeared with ~20% systematic error (due primarily to uncertainties in detector response, acceptance, and total integrated luminosity). The resulting excluded mass regions obtained are 80 < M(jet,γ) < 460 GeV/c^2 and 150 < M(jet, W) < 530 GeV/c^2. Combining these two results, 80 < M(jet, γ or W) < 540 GeV/c^2 (see figure 4).

6. Search for SUSY trilepton events at CDF

The minimal supersymmetry model (MSSM) contains 2 Higgs doublets, 4 $\tilde{\chi}^0$'s, and 2 $\tilde{\chi}^{\pm}$'s. Theoretical calculations suggest that the production cross section for $p\bar{p} \to \tilde{\chi}_1^{\pm}\tilde{\chi}_2^0$ may be appreciable[13], and that the $\tilde{\chi}_1^{\pm}$ and $\tilde{\chi}_2^0$ leptonic branching ratios may also be large. CDF has searched for three-lepton final states, arising from the decays $\tilde{\chi}_1^{\pm} \to \tilde{\chi}_1^0 \ell^{\pm}\nu$ and $\tilde{\chi}_2^0 \to \tilde{\chi}_1^0 \ell^+\ell^-$. The $\tilde{\chi}_1^0$ is stable and undetected, due

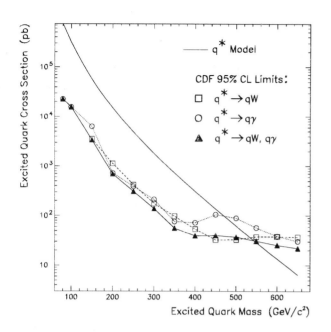

Figure 4. q* cross section upper limit vs. M(q*).

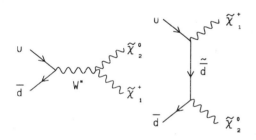

Figure 5. Typical $\tilde{\chi}_1^{\pm}\tilde{\chi}_2^0$ production diagrams.

to R-parity conservation. Theoretical calculations used in this analysis derive from a model in which the MSSM is combined with grand unification[14], allowing most sparticle masses and branching ratios to be determined from the following SUSY parameters: M($\tilde{g}$), M($\tilde{q}$), tan(β), M(H$_A$), μ, M$_t$, A$_t$. Figure 5 depicts the $\tilde{\chi}_1^{\pm}\tilde{\chi}_2^0$ production diagrams.

The trilepton modes searched for by CDF are eee, eeμ, e$\mu\mu$, and $\mu\mu\mu$. An electron is defined as a shower in the EM calorimeter accompanied by a charged track, while a muon is a muon chamber hit associated with a minimum ionizing energy cluster. At least one of the leptons must be high quality (p$_T$>11 GeV/c, $|\eta_{e(\mu)}|$ <1.0 (0.6)) while the 2 additional leptons may be lower quality (p$_T$> 5 (e), 4(μ) GeV/c, $|\eta_{e(\mu)}|$ <2.4 (1.2)).

All leptons must be well isolated from each other and other tracks, and the event must contain a l^+l^- pair.

The primary trilepton background is Drell-Yan γ, Z$\rightarrow\ell^+\ell^-$ (with additional fake lepton). Requiring $\Delta\phi(\ell\ell) < 170°$ vetoes Drell-Yan events. Z, J/ψ, and Υ background is vetoed by rejecting $\ell^+\ell^-$ pairs in the mass regions 75–105, 2.9–3.3, and 9–11 GeV/c^2.

In 19.1 pb^{-1} data, CDF observes no signal events. The total estimated background (from Drell-Yan γ, Z, WW, WZ, and b$\bar{b}$) is 0.75 events, consistent with no events. It is observed that signal acceptance depends only on M($\tilde{\chi}_1^{\pm}$). Folding in this information with the ~ 20% systematic error (due to lepton identification, Monte Carlo, and luminosity uncertainties), the 95% confidence level upper limit on $\sigma\cdot$BR, plotted vs. M($\tilde{\chi}_1^{\pm}$), can be directly compared to theoretical calculations, for various SUSY parameter values. ISAJET 7.06 provided the theoretical predictions for the following SUSY parameter value ranges: 2.0 < tan(β) < 15, −500 < μ < −400, M($\tilde{q}$) = 1.2 × M($\tilde{g}$), M$_t$ = 170 GeV/c^2, M(H$_A$) = 500 GeV/c^2, various M($\tilde{g}$) values. CDF excludes M($\tilde{\chi}_1^{\pm}$) < 46 GeV/c^2 for the SUSY parameter values listed above.

7. Conclusion

The Tevatron collider experiments have searched for various exotic physics processes. In these studies, they find no evidence for physics beyond the standard model. Further data collection is now in progress, with the hope that a larger event sample will allow discovery of interesting new phenomena that expand our understanding of the physical universe.

References

[1] CDF Collaboration: S. Kopp *et al.*, Fermilab preprint: FERMILAB-CONF-94/155-E.
[2] CDF Collaboration: K. Maeshima *et al.*, Fermilab preprint: FERMILAB-PUB-94/198-E. Submitted to Phys. Rev. Lett.
[3] CDF Collaboration: J. Wang *et al.*, Fermilab preprint: FERMILAB-PUB-94/195-E. Submitted to Phys. Rev. Lett.
[4] CDF Collaboration: R. Harris *et al.*, Phys. Rev. Lett. **72** (1994) 3004.
[5] CDF Collaboration: J. Wolinski *et al.*, Fermilab preprint: FERMILAB-CONF-94/149-E.
[6] G. Altarelli *et al.*, CERN preprint: CERN-TH.5323/89.
[7] ex., J. Pati *et al.*, Phys. Rev. **D11** (1975) 2558.
[8] G. Eppley, D0 Collaboration, private communication.
[9] ex., P. Chiapetta *et al.*, Phys. Lett. **B264** (1991) 85.
[10] ex., F. del Aguila *et al.*, , Phys. Rev. **D41** (1990) 134.
[11] Laenen *et al.*, Fermilab preprint: FERMILAB-PUB-93/270-T.
[12] Barger *et al.*, Phys. Rev. **D41** (1990) 3421; Drees & Roy, Phys. Lett. **B269** (1991) 155.
[13] Baer and Tata, Florida State Univ. preprint: FSU-HEP-921222.
[14] Drees and Nojiri, Nuc. Phys. **B369** (1992) 54.

Paper presented at XXVII Int. Conf. on High Energy Physics: Session Pa-10
Glasgow, UK, 20–27 July 1994

Search for Supersymmetry and Leptoquark States at FNAL

Sharon Hagopian

The Florida State University
Department of Physics
Tallahassee, Florida U.S.A

Abstract

Searches have been made for first generation scalar and vector leptoquarks by the DØ collaboration and for second generation scalar leptoquarks by the CDF collaboration. The data sample is from the 1992-93 $p\bar{p}$ run at $\sqrt{s} = 1.8$ TeV at the Fermilab Tevatron Collider. Assuming that leptoquarks are pair produced and decay into charged leptons and quarks with branching fraction β, mass limits at the 95% Confidence Level (CL) have been obtained. For first generation scalar leptoquarks the lower mass limit is 130 GeV/c^2 for $\beta = 1.0$ and 116 GeV/c^2 for $\beta = 0.5$. For first generation vector leptoquarks with κ, the anomalous coupling, of 1.0 and $\beta = 1.0$, the lower mass limit is 240 GeV/c^2 and for $\kappa = 1.0, \beta = 0.5$, the lower mass limit is 240 GeV/c^2. For $\kappa = 0$ and $\beta = 1.0$, the lower mass limits is 190 GeV/c^2 and for $\kappa = 0$, $\beta = 0.5$, the lower mass limit is 185 GeV/c^2. For second generation scalar leptoquarks, the mass limits are 133 GeV/c^2 for $\beta = 1.0$ and 98 GeV/c^2 for $\beta = 0.5$. A search for squarks and gluinos, predicted by Supersymmetric models, was made by DØ in the three or more jets plus $\not{E}_t$ channel. The number of events observed was consistent with background. For heavy squarks, a lower gluino mass limit of 146 GeV/c^2 was obtained, and for equal squark and gluino masses a mass limit of 205 GeV/c^2 was obtained at the 95% CL.

1. Introduction

The discovery of new particles not contained in the Standard Model (SM) would help in choosing among the many extensions to the Standard Model have been proposed. This report will discuss searches for two types of new particles: leptoquarks and supersymmetric particles using data from the 1992-1993 Fermilab $p\bar{p}$ collider run at $\sqrt{s} = 1.8$ TeV.

2. Leptoquarks

Leptoquarks (LQ) are exotic particles which have both lepton and baryon quantum numbers [1]. They appear in extended gauge theories and composite models, and can be scalar or vector particles depending on the model [2]. Leptoquarks link quark and lepton multiplets of the same generation. They would be easily pair-produced at $p\bar{p}$ colliders, with a production cross section that depends only slightly on the unknown coupling λ of the leptoquark to ordinary leptons and quarks [3]. Leptoquarks decay into a charged lepton and a quark, with branching fraction β, or into a neutrino and a quark, with branching fraction $(1 - \beta)$.

3. The DØ Detector

The DØ detector is described in detail elsewhere [4]. It has uranium-liquid argon calorimeters which provide very nearly hermetic coverage for good $\not{E}_t$ measurement and good hadronic and electromagnetic resolution for good electron and jet energy measurement. It also has a central tracking system and a muon spectrometer with coverage at large and small angles.

4.   First Generation Leptoquark Search in DØ

First generation leptoquarks would decay into an electron and a quark or into an electron neutrino and a quark. Two possible experimental signatures for their pair production would be:

1) two electrons + two jets
2) one electron + E_t + two jets

The DØ sample for the first channel consisted of 14,780 events with two electromagnetic clusters with $E_t > 15$ GeV, from an integrated luminosity of 13.4 ± 1.6 pb^{-1}.

The offline requirements were:

1) two electrons with $E_t > 25$ GeV passing good electron quality cuts
2) two jets with $E_t > 25$ GeV passing jet quality cuts

All nine events passing these requirements have $M(ee)$ near the Z mass. No events remain after making a 10 GeV/c^2 cut around the Z mass. The main background for this channel is Drell-Yan production of two electrons, mainly at the Z resonance, with two jets. The estimated background of Drell-Yan + two jet events with $M(ee)$ outside this mass region is 0.3 events.

The sample for the second channel consisted of 11,480 events. The offline requirements were:

1) one electron with $E_t > 20$ GeV passing jet quality cuts
2) two jets with $E_t > 20$ GeV passing good electron quality cuts
3) $E_t > 40$ GeV
4) transverse mass $(e, E_t) > 105$ GeV/c^2
5) no jet-E_t correlations

No events remained after these cuts. The estimated background from W+ two jet and QCD events was 0.9 events.

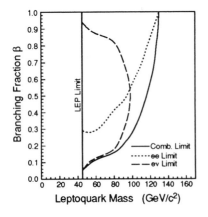

Figure 1. DØ 95% confidence level lower limit on the first generation scalar leptoquark mass as a function of β.

5.   First Generation Scalar Leptoquark Mass Limits

A limit on the leptoquark mass as a function of the branching fraction β can be calculated by comparing the experimental cross section limit with the theoretical prediction. The 95% CL upper limit of the experimental cross section can be obtained from the observation of zero events in each channel, the luminosity, and the DØ detection efficiency for these two channels, which is a function of leptoquark mass. For a mass of 130 GeV/c^2, the efficiency for the 2 electron channel was 12% and for the 1 electron + E_t channel it was 9%. The 95% CL upper limit experimental cross section was compared with the theoretically predicted cross section obtained using ISAJET [5] with the MT-LO parton distribution functions [6] to determine the lower mass limit as a function of β. Figure 1 shows the DØ 95% confidence limit on the mass of the first generation scalar leptoquark. The LQ lower mass limit for $\beta = 1$ is 130 GeV/c^2 and for $\beta = 0.5$ is 116 GeV/c^2. These limits differ from those previously published by DØ [7] due to a revision of the luminosity calculation.

6.   First Generation Vector Leptoquark Mass Limits

Recently, a cross section calculation for the pair production of vector leptoquarks has become available [8]. Since vector leptoquarks are composite particles in some models, their production cross section depends on κ, the anomalous coupling parameter, where $\kappa = 1$ for gauge coupling and $\kappa = 0$ for maximum anomalous coupling. Assuming the same detection efficiency for vector leptoquarks as for scalar leptoquarks, and using the calculated vector LQ cross section, one can translate the results of the scalar LQ search into mass limits for vector LQ. The 95% CL mass limits for vector leptoquarks for $\kappa = 1.0$ (gauge coupling) derived under this assumption are $M_{LQ} > 240$ GeV/c^2 for $\beta = 1.0$; $M_{LQ} > 240$ GeV/c^2 for $\beta = 0.5$ (see Figure 2a). The 95% CL mass limits for vector leptoquarks for $\kappa = 0$ (maximum anomalous coupling) are $M_{LQ} > 190$ GeV/c^2 for $\beta = 1.0$; $M_{LQ} > 185$ GeV/c^2 for $\beta = 0.5$ (see Figure 2b).

7.   The CDF Detector

The CDF detector is described elsewhere [9]. The momenta of charged particles are measured in the central tracking chamber, which is surrounded by a 1.4 T superconducting solenoidal magnet. This is surrounded by electromagnetic and hadronic calorimeters, which are used to identify jets. Outside the calorimeters, drift

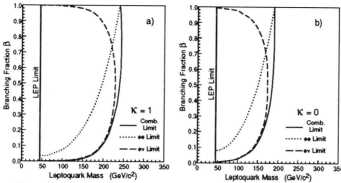

Figure 2. DØ 95% confidence level lower limit on the first generation vector leptoquark mass as a function of β, for (a)$\kappa = 1$ and (b)$\kappa = 0$ (see text). These limits assume the *same* detection efficiency for the decay products of scalar and vector leptoquarks.

chambers in the region $|\eta| < 1.0$ provide muon identification.

8. Search for Second Generation Leptoquarks in CDF

A second generation leptoquark (S_2) would decay into a muon and a quark with branching fraction β, or into an muon neutrino and a quark, with branching fraction $(1 - \beta)$. CDF has made a search for $S_2\bar{S}_2$ pairs in the decay channel where both leptoquarks decay into muon+quark. The experimental signature is 2 muons + 2 jets. The CDF trigger sample, based on 19.3±0.7 pb^{-1} of data from the 1992-93 Tevatron run, was 7,958 events. The offline requirements were:

1) two good, isolated central muons with $p_t > 20$ GeV/c

2) two jets with $E_t > 20$ GeV

After these cuts, 7 events remained. To remove background from Z production, events with $75 < M(\mu\mu) < 105$ GeV/c^2 were rejected. Two events remained after this cut, with dimuon invariant masses of 18.9 GeV/c^2 and 57.9 GeV/c^2. Background processes include Drell-Yan production of two muons with two jets, $t\bar{t}$ production in the dimuon channel, $Z \to \tau\bar{\tau}$, and fake muons. The total expected background is 1.35 ± 0.50 events.

9. Second Generation Scalar Leptoquark Mass Limits

Two candidate events are observed, consistent with the total background of 1.35±0.50 events. The signal detection efficiencies were determined using the ISAJET Monte Carlo program [5] with CTEQ2L structure functions [10] followed by a CDF detector simulation. The total efficiency ranges from 1.2% for 40 GeV/c^2 leptoquarks to 16.8% for 100 GeV/c^2, and is 12.5% for 120 GeV/c^2. Using these efficiencies and the observed

number of events, 95% CL limits on the cross-section times branching ratio were obtained. By comparing these with the theoretical prediction for the cross-section which is based on ISAJET with CTEQ2L structure functions, lower limits on the leptoquark mass as a function of β were obtained. These are shown in Figure 3. The 95% CL lower limit on the mass of a second generation scalar leptoquark for $\beta = 1.0$ is 133 GeV/c^2, and the lower limit for $\beta = 0.5$ is 98 GeV/c^2.

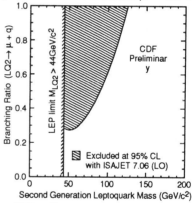

Figure 3. CDF 95% confidence level lower limit on the second generation scalar leptoquark mass as a function of β.

10. Minimal Supersymmetric Standard Model

One of the simplest supersymmetric extensions of the standard model (SM) is the Minimal Supersymmetric Standard Model (MSSM) [11]. Supersymmetry is a spacetime symmetry which relates bosons to fermions and introduces supersymmetric partners (sparticles) for all the SM particles. R-parity, the SUSY multiplicative quantum number, is defined as $R = +1$ for standard model particles and $R = -1$ for sparticles. We assume that R-parity is conserved, which implies that sparticles are produced in pairs and decay to the stable Lightest Supersymmetric Particle (LSP), which is usually assumed to be the lightest Neutralino ($\tilde{Z}_1$).

11. Search for Squarks and Gluinos

The experimental signature for squarks and gluinos is jets and/or leptons and $\not{E}_t$, since the LSP does not interact in the detector. In the DØ search, 3 or more jets were required. Events with leptons were rejected to reduce the background from W and Z leptonic decays. The sample was 9,625 events from an integrated luminosity of 13.4 ± 1.6 pb^{-1}. Offline requirements were:

1) a single interaction
2) $\not{E}_t > 75$ GeV
3) three or more jets with $E_t > 25$ GeV passing jet quality cuts
4) reject electrons and muons
5) no jet-$\not{E}_t$ correlations

Of the 17 events surviving these cuts, one event was rejected because it contained a muon consistent with a cosmic ray, and two other events were rejected because their large $\not{E}_t$ was caused by vertex reconstruction errors. The final candidate data sample contained 14 events, consistent with the $18.5 \pm 1.9^{+7.6}_{-7.1}$ background events expected from $W + 2, 3$ jets and QCD.

12. MSSM Signal Simulation

The MSSM model was used for the signal calculation, assuming SUGRA-inspired degeneracy of squark masses [12]. Only squark and gluino production were considered, no slepton or stop production. The mass of the top quark was set to 140 GeV/c^2. To further specify the parameters, the following values of MSSM parameters were used:

1) $\tan\beta = 2.0$ (ratio of the Higgs vacuum expectation values)
2) $M(H^+) = 500$ GeV/c^2 (mass of the charged Higgs)
3) $\mu = -250$ GeV (Higgsino mass mixing parameter)

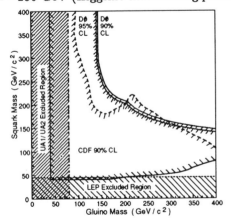

Figure 4. DØ, CDF, LEP and UA1/UA2 squark and gluino mass limits as a function of squark and gluino mass.

Squark and gluino events were simulated using the ISASUSY event generator [13] and processed through the DØ triggering, detector simulation, and reconstruction programs. The detection efficiency, ϵ, was determined for 28 squark and gluino mass combinations using masses between 100 and 400 GeV/c^2. As an example, for 200 GeV/c^2 equal mass squarks and gluinos, $\epsilon = 18.6\%$. For $m_{\tilde{g}} = 150$ GeV/c^2 and $m_{\tilde{q}} = 400$, $\epsilon = 6.3\%$. And for $m_{\tilde{g}} = 400$ GeV/c^2 and $m_{\tilde{q}} = 150$, $\epsilon = 8.3\%$. A combination of linear fitting and linear interpolation was used to find efficiencies between grid points.

13. Calculation of Mass Limits from Cross Sections

Using these signal detection efficiencies, the luminosity and the number of visible events above SM background, a 95% CL upper limit cross section was determined. This was compared with a leading order theoretical cross section [13] to determine the lower mass limit for each squark and gluino mass combination. For heavy squarks, a lower gluino mass limit of 146 GeV/c^2 was obtained, and for equal squark and gluino masses, a mass limit of 205 GeV/c^2 was obtained at the 95% CL.

14. Acknowledgements

I am grateful to the members of the CDF and DØ collaborations for their hard work. Special thanks are due to D. Norman, DØ, for the leptoquark analysis, M. Paterno, DØ, for the squark and gluino analysis, and to S. Park, CDF, for the second generation leptoquark analysis.

References

[1] J.C. Pati and A. Salam, Phys. Rev. **D10** (1974) 275; H. Georgi and S. Glashow, Phys. Rev. Lett. **32** (1974) 438; E. Eichten *et al.*, Phys. Rev. Lett. **50** (1983) 811.
[2] V. D. Angelopoulou *et al.*, Nucl. Phys. **B292** (1987) 59; E. Eichten, Phys. Rev. **D34** (1986) 1547.
[3] J.L. Hewett and S. Pakvasa, Phys. Rev. **D37** (1988) 3165.
[4] S. Abachi *et al.*, Nucl. Instr. Meth. **A338** (1994) 185.
[5] F. Paige and S. Protopopescu, BNL Report 38304 (1986).
[6] J. B. Morfin and W. F. Tung, Zeit. Phys. **C52** (1991) 13.
[7] S. Abachi *et al.*, Phys. Rev. Lett. **72** (1994) 965.
[8] J. L. Hewett *et al.*, Proc. of the Workshop on Phys. at Current Accel. and Supercolliders 1993, p.342, Eds. J. Hewett, A. White and D. Zeppenfeld (Argonne Nat. Lab, 1993).
[9] F. Abe *et al.*, Nucl. Instr. Meth. **A771** (1988) 387.
[10] CTEQ Collaboration, Fermilab preprint: FNAL-PUB-93-094.
[11] H. Nilles, Phys. Rep. **110** (1984) 1; P. Nath *et al.*, Applied N-1 Supergravity, (World Scientific 1984); H. Haber and G. Kane, Phys. Rep. **117** (1985) 117.
[12] G. Ross and R. G. Roberts, Nucl. Phys. **B377** (1992) 571.
[13] H. Baer *et al.*, Proc. of the Workshop on Phys. at Current Accel. and Supercolliders 1993, p.703; Eds. J. Hewett, A. White and D. Zeppenfeld (Argonne Nat. Lab, 1993).

Parallel Session Pa-11

QCD and Jet Physics

Conveners: T. Hebbeker (CERN/Humboldt)
R. K. Ellis (Fermilab)

Scientific secretaries: H. Newton
H. Shanahan (reserve)

Multi-Jet Production and a Determination of α_s

S Söldner–Rembold

Albert-Ludwigs-Universität Freiburg, Fakultät für Physik, 79104 Freiburg im Breisgau, Germany

On behalf of the ZEUS and H1 Collaborations

Abstract

Multi-jet production in deep-inelastic electron-proton scattering (DIS) has been studied at HERA using the JADE algorithm. The ZEUS collaboration has compared the partonic scaling variables and the rate of two jet production to perturbative $\mathcal{O}(\alpha_s^2)$ QCD calculations. The H1 collaboration has observed the running of α_s as a function of Q^2. A preliminary measurement yields $\alpha_s(M_Z) = 0.121 \pm 0.009(\text{stat.}) \pm 0.012(\text{syst.})$.

1. Introduction

Deep-inelastic neutral current ep scattering without QCD corrections leads to a 1+1 parton configuration in the final state, where "+1" denotes the proton remnant. At leading order, $\mathcal{O}(\alpha_s)$, QCD processes contribute significantly to the ep cross section at HERA energies: Boson-Gluon-Fusion, where the virtual boson interacts with a $q\bar{q}$ pair originating from a gluon in the proton, and QCD-Compton scattering, where a gluon is radiated by the scattered quark. Both processes lead to a two ($\hat{=}$2+1) jet topology.

On the partonic level, the kinematics and the rate R_{2+1} of two jet production can be described by perturbative QCD calculations with only one free parameter, the strong coupling constant α_s. HERA has the unique opportunity to study the running of α_s over a wide range in Q^2 ($10 < Q^2 < 10^4$ GeV^2) from the Q^2 dependence of the 2+1 jet production rate.

A determination of $\alpha_s(Q^2)$ requires detailed understanding of the jet kinematics. The ZEUS collaboration has therefore compared the measurement of the underlying parton dynamics and the jet rates to next-to-leading order (NLO or $\mathcal{O}(\alpha_s^2)$) calculations. The H1 collaboration has determined the value of $\alpha_s(M_Z)$. In addition, first evidence is presented for the running of α_s from DIS at HERA.

2. Monte Carlo simulations

The LEPTO 6.1 Monte Carlo event generator contains the exact $\mathcal{O}(\alpha_s)$ matrix element (ME) and the parton shower (PS) in the leading log approximation [1]. In order to simulate at the same time the hard emission of partons and the higher order parton shower, a combined option (MEPS) exists which is used to describe the HERA data for the correction of experimental inefficiencies.

3. Theoretical calculations

The Monte Carlo program does not include the exact NLO matrix element calculation. However, the NLO corrections to the 2+1 jet cross section due to irresolvable 3+1 jet events and due to virtual corrections are significant [2]. They are taken into account in the program DISJET of T. Brodkorb and E. Mirkes [3]. A similiar program by D. Graudenz called PROJET [4] is available, but it does not include the NLO corrections to the longitudinal part of the cross section.

4. Jet finding

Both HERA experiments have used the JADE algorithm [5] to relate partons to observable jets. The scaled invariant mass of two massless objects (partons or calorimeter cells) i and j is given by

$$y_{ij} = \frac{2E_i E_j (1 - \cos\theta_{ij})}{W^2}. \qquad (1)$$

The minimum y_{ij} of all possible combinations is found. If the value of this minimum y_{ij} is less than the cut-off parameter y_{cut}, the two objects i and j are merged by adding their four-momenta and the process is repeated until all $y_{ij} > y_{cut}$.

In the data, a fictitious cluster (called pseudo-particle) in the forward (z) direction is added to which the missing longitudinal momentum for each event is assigned. The pseudo-particle is treated like any other particle in the JADE scheme. The pseudo-particle procedure together with the choice of the visible hadronic invariant mass W_{vis} as jet scale minimizes detector corrections. W_{vis} is calculated from just those calorimeter cells associated with the hadrons.

The JADE algorithm has been used here since it is currently the only algorithm which allows comparison to $\mathcal{O}(\alpha_s^2)$ calculations. However, it has been shown previously that the performance of the JADE algorithm in reconstructing jets is worse than for other algorithms [6].

the backward calorimeter, <u>or</u> with $y_{e'} < 0.7$, $\theta_{e'} < 148°$ and $Q_{e'}^2 > 100$ GeV^2 in the central calorimeter.

ZEUS has limited the kinematic range for the jet analysis to $160 < Q^2 < 1280$ GeV, $0.01 < x < 0.1$ and $0.04 < y < 0.95$. At high Q^2, jet structures should be more pronounced and hadronization uncertainties are minimized. At high x, the phase space for jet production increases and the systematic error from the structure function dependence of the jet rate is reduced.

The data corresponds to a luminosity of 0.24 pb^{-1} (H1) and 0.55 pb^{-1} (ZEUS).

6.   Two jet properties

In Fig. 1, the jets are ordered in pseudorapidity $\eta_j = -\ln\tan(\theta_j/2)$. The higher η jet is usually found very close to the forward beam pipe. Fig. 1a shows that the prediction of the η_j distribution by the ME and the MEPS Monte Carlo models describe the data fairly well apart from the very forward region $\eta_j > 3.6$, where the predictions are significantly below the data. In this region the results depend on the description of the initial state parton shower and the target fragmentation in the Monte Carlo generator as well as on the simulation of the response of the calorimeter around the forward beam pipe.

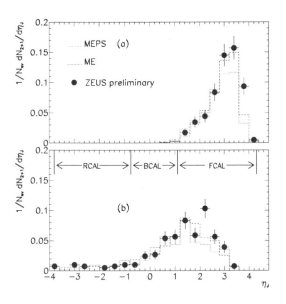

Figure 1. Pseudorapidity η_j of the two jets: (a) higher η jet; (b) lower η jet. Uncorrected data are compared to the MEPS and the ME simulations. The acceptance ranges of the different sections of the ZEUS calorimeter are indicated.

5.   Data sets

The H1 event sample is defined by $W^2 > 5000$ GeV^2, an identified scattered electron with $E_{e'} > 14$ GeV, $160° < \theta_{e'} < 172.5°$ and $10 < Q_{e'}^2 < 100$ GeV^2 in

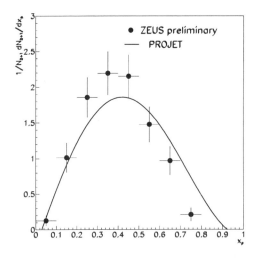

Figure 2. Uncorrected x_p distribution compared to a $\mathcal{O}(\alpha_s^2)$ QCD calculation (PROJET).

The cross section for 2+1 jet production is obtained by integrating over the partonic scaling variables $x_p = Q^2/(2q \cdot p_p) = x/\xi$ and $z_p = (P \cdot p_p)/(P \cdot q)$ [7]. The momentum p_p of the incoming parton is given by the fraction ξ of the proton momentum P, $p_p = \xi P$. Experimentally, x_p is calculated from the invariant mass $M_{JJ}^2 = y_{cut} W^2$ of the two jet system using

$$x_p = \frac{Q^2}{Q^2 + M_{JJ}^2}.$$

z_p is measured from the relative contribution to $(E - p_z)$ of the partons or cells assigned to the jet in the lab,

$$z_p = \frac{\sum_{jet}(E - p_z)}{\sum_{hadrons}(E - p_z)}.$$

The uncorrected x_p distribution is compared to the PROJET calculation in Fig. 2. The mean of the distribution lies at $\langle x_p \rangle \approx 0.5$ $(Q^2 \approx M_{JJ}^2)$, i. e. the two jet system has a large invariant mass $(\langle M_{JJ} \rangle \approx 23$ GeV). The singularity in the 2+1 cross section at $x_p \to 1$ is cut off by the y_{cut} parameter.

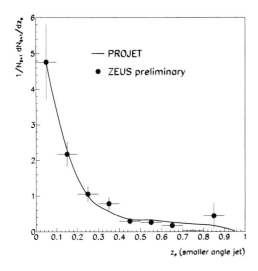

Figure 3. z_p distribution compared to a $\mathcal{O}(\alpha_s^2)$ QCD calculation (PROJET). The correction to the parton level is done using the ME model.

Only the z_p distribution for the smaller angle jet is shown in Fig. 3, since $z_p^{(1)} + z_p^{(2)} \approx 1$ and $z_p^{remnant} \approx 0$. The z_p distribution is well described by the PROJET calculation. The cross section rises strongly at $z_p \to 0$, because of the small influence of y_{cut} on the cut-off of the z_p singularity in the JADE algorithm. This leads to the forward peak in the jet angular distribution in the lab.

The transverse momentum P_T of the jets in the γ^*-parton CMS is given in LO by $P_T^2 = Q^2 z_p (1 - x_p)(1 - z_p)/x_p$. The average transverse momentum $\langle P_T \rangle$ of the jets in the γ^*-parton CMS is about 10 GeV (Fig. 4) and the minimum P_T is about 3 GeV. This is sufficiently large to ensure the validity of a perturbative QCD calculation. The distribution is well described by the two Monte Carlo models.

7. Jet rates and the determination of α_s

ZEUS has defined the 2+1 jet rate R_{2+1} by the ratio of the number of events

$$R_{2+1} = \frac{N_{2+1}}{N_{2+1} + N_{1+1}}.$$

This definition reduces the dependence on the 3+1 jet rate, which is only calculated at the tree level in PROJET and DISJET. Experimentally, the acceptance correction factors for the 3+1 jet rate are large.

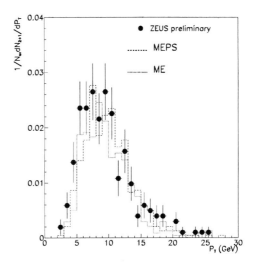

Figure 4. The transverse momentum P_T of one of the two jets in the γ^*-parton center of mass system. The uncorrected data are compared to the MEPS and the ME simulations.

In Fig. 5, the corrected jet production rates are shown as a function of the jet resolution parameter y_{cut}. The correction to the parton level is done using the MEPS model. The 2+1 jet rate increases with finer jet resolution (smaller y_{cut}).

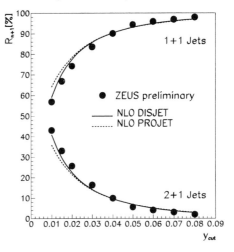

Figure 5. The corrected jet production rate R_{n+1} in % as a function of y_{cut} is compared to the NLO calculation of the programs PROJET [4] and DISJET [3] at the parton level. Only statistical errors are shown.

For comparison the NLO calculations of the programs DISJET [3] and PROJET [4] are also shown. The difference between them is due to the missing NLO corrections to the longitudinal cross section.

The errors shown are the statistical binomial errors which are highly correlated, because all 2+1 jet events at a given y_{cut} are included in the points at smaller y_{cut}. These correlations are avoided by redefining the data in terms of the differential jet rate

$$D_{1+1}(y_{cut}) = \frac{R_{1+1}(y_{cut}) - R_{1+1}(y_{cut} - \Delta y_{cut})}{\Delta y_{cut}},$$

where every event enters only once. In Fig. 6 the differential jet rate D_{1+1} is shown together with the statistical errors and the DISJET calculation.

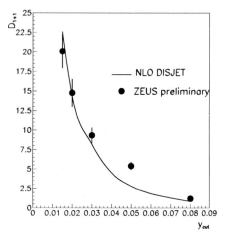

Figure 6. The differential jet rate D_{1+1} calculated from the corrected jet rate R_{1+1} (Fig. 5) as a function of y_{cut}. D_{1+1} is compared to the NLO calculation of the program DISJET [3].

Comparing Fig. 6 with the jet production rates R_{n+1} shows that the apparent systematic deviations from the QCD models above and below $y_{cut} = 0.04$ in Fig. 5 are caused by the correlation between the points. The differential jet rate D_{1+1} is well described by the NLO QCD calculations, apart from a deviation at $y_{cut} = 0.05$.

The QCD calculations contain α_s as the only free parameter. For the comparisons in Figs. 5 and 6, a value of $\Lambda_{\overline{MS}}^{(5)} = 312$ MeV was chosen which corresponds to $\alpha_s(M_Z^2) = 0.124$. This is a value measured from jet rates in e^+e^- annihilations [8].

H1 has extracted α_s from the $R_{2+1} = \sigma_{2+1}/\sigma_{tot}$ measurement in different Q^2 ranges by fitting it to the jet rate at $y_{cut} = 0.02$ using the PROJET calculation (Fig. 7a).

The jet angles θ_j have to be inside the range $10° < \theta_j < 160°$ which reduces the dependence on the description of the very forward region. In order to minimize the systematic error due to the parametrization of the parton densities, an additional cut $\xi > 0.01$ was introduced. The parton densities affect R_{2+1} mainly through the 1+1 jet cross section at low x [2]. For 1+1 jet events, $\xi = x > 0.01$, and for 2+1 jet events the cut is trivially fullfilled because $\xi > y_{cut} = 0.02$.

The running of $\alpha_s(Q^2)$ is preferred by the data in Fig. 7b, where the curves represent $\alpha_s(Q^2) = $ const.

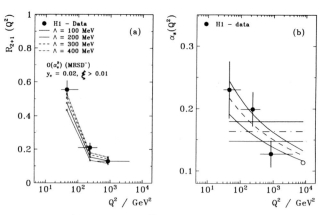

Figure 7. a) R_{2+1} versus Q^2 at $y_{cut} = 0.02$ and $\xi > 0.01$. PROJET calculations with different values of $\Lambda_{\overline{MS}}^{(4)}$ and the MRSD$^-$ structure function are superimposed. b) α_s versus Q^2. The curves represent $\alpha_s(Q^2) = $ const. and a running $\alpha_s(Q^2)$ with $\alpha_s(M_Z) = 0.121$. The open circle is the world average $\alpha_s(M_Z) = 0.118$.

and an $\mathcal{O}(\alpha_s^2)$ calculation of the Q^2 dependence. An extrapolation yields $\alpha_s(M_Z) = 0.121 \pm 0.009(\text{stat.}) \pm 0.012(\text{syst.})$, where the preliminary systematic error includes the y_{cut} dependence (± 0.003), the uncertainties due to the hadronic energy scale of the calorimeter ($\pm^{0.006}_{0.007}$), the parton densities (± 0.005) and the renormalization scale (± 0.006). At low Q^2 the model dependence of the hadronization correction is another important source of systematic errors.

8.   Conclusions

Jet production in DIS at high Q^2 is well described by perturbative $\mathcal{O}(\alpha_s^2)$ QCD calculations. First evidence from HERA for the running of α_s has been presented and a preliminary H1 measurement yields $\alpha_s(M_Z) = 0.121 \pm 0.009(\text{stat.}) \pm 0.012(\text{syst.})$.

References

[1] G. Ingelman, Proc. of the Workshop on Physics at HERA 1991, Vol 3 p. 1366; Eds. W. Buchmüller and G. Ingelman (DESY, Hamburg, 1992); M. Bengtsson, G. Ingelman and T. Sjöstrand, Nucl. Phys. **B301** (1988) 554.

[2] D. Graudenz, Phys. Lett. **B256** (1991) 518.

[3] T. Brodkorb, E. Mirkes, University of Wisconsin Preprint: MAD-PH-821 (April 1994).

[4] D. Graudenz, PROJET 3.6, to be published.

[5] JADE Collaboration: W. Bartel *et al.*, Z. Phys. **C33** (1986) 23; JADE Collaboration: S. Bethke *et al.*, Phys. Lett. **B213** (1988) 235.

[6] V. Hedberg *et al.*, DESY preprint: DESY 93-190 (1993).

[7] K. H. Streng, T. F. Walsh, P. M. Zerwas, Z. Phys. **C2** (1979) 237.

[8] S. Bethke, Lectures given at the Scottish Universities Summer School, St. Andrews, Scotland, August 1–21, 1993, Heidelberg preprint: HD-PY 93/7.

Paper presented at XXVII Int. Conf. on High Energy Physics: Session Pa-11
Glasgow, UK, 20–27 July 1994

Jets in Photoproduction at HERA

Helmut Hufnagel

Physikalisches Institut, Universität Heidelberg, Heidelberg, Germany
On behalf of the ZEUS and H1 collaborations

Abstract

The interactions of quasi-real photons with protons have been studied with the H1 and the ZEUS detectors at the HERA collider. The data allow qualitative and quantitative QCD tests to be made. The presence of hard scattering at a CMS-energy of 200 GeV is confirmed by the observation of jets in the final state. Jet kinematics are used to reconstruct the momentum fraction of the parton in the photon involved in the hard scattering process. The presence of a direct contribution in addition to the dominating resolved part is clearly observed. The observation of a photon remnant in resolved photoproduction events is reported and the properties of this remnant are studied. Inclusive jet cross-sections have been measured and are compared with leading order QCD predictions. Two-jet events are used to study the parton distributions in the photon in a leading-order QCD analysis. The two-jet cross cross section at HERA is dominated by gluon-gluon scattering, and therefore provides a sensitive means of determining the gluon density in the photon. Using the quark densities measured in $\gamma\gamma$-collisions, a first measurement of the gluon density function in the photon is obtained.

1. Introduction

The electron-proton collider HERA gives access to the study of photon-proton interactions at high CMS energies of $\sqrt{s_{\gamma p}} \approx 200 GeV$, about one order of magnitude higher than what has been reached so far in fixed target experiments. The quasi-real photons with energy E_γ are emitted by electrons which are scattered through small angles.

The observation of hard photon-proton interactions reveals the structure of the photon. In addition to the electromagnetic coupling to a charged object the photon can also interact as an object containing quarks and gluons. An example for the pointlike coupling to a charged constituent of the proton is shown in fig. 1a. These processes are usually referred to as "direct" photoproduction. Fig. 1b and c show examples of "resolved" photoproduction events in which the hadronic component of the photon is revealed.

The resolved component of the photon is usually taken to consist of two contributions: the "hadronic" part which can be described by the vector dominance

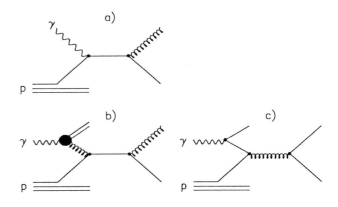

Figure 1. Examples for interactions of a quasi-real photon and a proton: a) direct γp-interaction, b) and c) resolved γp-interactions.

model (VDM) as a fluctuation of the photon into a vector meson state with the same quantum numbers (fig. 1b) and the "anomalous" part which is due to the splitting of a photon into a $q\bar{q}$-pair (fig. 1c).

An important feature of the event topology in resolved photoproduction is the presence of a photon remnant in contrast to direct processes where the full photon momentum enters the hard subprocess.

For a leading order QCD $2 \to 2$ scattering process as shown in fig. 1 the momentum fraction x_γ of the photon which enters the hard subprocess can be approximately reconstructed as:

$$x_\gamma \approx \frac{E_{t,1}e^{-\eta_1} + E_{t,2}e^{-\eta_2}}{2E_\gamma} \qquad (1)$$

where $E_{t,i}$ denotes the transverse energies and $\eta_i = -\ln tan(\Theta/2)$ the pseudorapidities of the two outgoing partons (Θ = polar angle w.r.t. the proton direction).

2. Experimental Setup

A detailed description of the H1 and the ZEUS detectors can be found elsewhere [1],[2].

Both detectors consist of a tracking system surrounded by calorimeters and instrumented iron structures for backing calorimetry and muon detection. The tracking detectors are placed in a uniform solenoidal magnetic field. The jet-identification for the following studies is based on a calorimetric measurement.

The luminosity measurement is provided by electron and photon calorimeters inside the HERA tunnel for the detection of the elastic Bremsstrahlung process $e + p \to e + p + \gamma$. The electron calorimeter ("electron-tagger") can also be used to tag the outgoing electron in photoproduction events in the acceptance region $10^{-8} GeV^2 < Q^2 < 10^{-2} GeV^2$ and $7 GeV < E_\gamma < 20 GeV$.

In 1993 HERA was operated with 84 colliding bunches with a typical luminosity of $10^{30} cm^{-2} sec^{-1}$. The following studies are based on an integrated luminosity of about $0.3 pb^{-1}$ for the H1 and $0.55 pb^{-1}$ for the ZEUS experiment.

3. Hard Scattering in Photoproduction

The reconstruction of the momentum fraction x_γ according to equation (1) allows one to demonstrate the presence of direct and resolved processes in a hard photoproduction sample. In an analysis performed by the ZEUS collaboration events with at least two jets have been selected using a cone algorithm on a grid in pseudorapidity η and azimuthal angle Φ with cone radius $R = 1$. The jet energies and directions are treated according to the Snowmass accord [3], requiring a transverse energy of $E_t > 6 GeV$. Jets are considered in the pseudorapidity interval $-1.125 < \eta_{jet} < 1.875$ and some further cuts have to be applied to suppress background events and to improve the

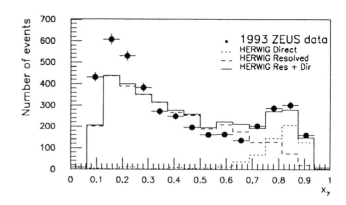

Figure 2. x_γ^{rec}-distribution (full circles). The histograms represent the prediction of the LO-QCD generator HERWIG for the direct component (dotted line), the resolved component (dashed line) and the sum of these two contributions (full curve).

correlation between the reconstructed and the true value of x_γ.

The photon energy E_γ is given by $E_\gamma = yE_e$ and the "Bjorken-y" can be reconstructed with the method of Jacquet-Blondel [4] using the hadronic energy-flow as measured with the calorimeter.

The reconstructed x_γ^{rec}-spectrum is shown in fig. 2. The curves in fig. 2 represent the prediction obtained with the leading order QCD generator HERWIG [5] and a full detector simulation. The LAC1 parameterization [6] was assumed for the parton distributions of the photon. The Monte-Carlo predictions are shown separately for the direct and the resolved component. In the high x_γ region ($x_\gamma^{rec} > 0.6$) the data are well described by the sum of the two contributions whereas the resolved component alone is not able to reproduce the "peak" at $x_\gamma \approx 0.8$. In the region of $x_\gamma^{rec} < 0.5$ the direct contribution is negligible and the events observed in the data sample can only be explained by resolved photon processes. The agreement between data and Monte-Carlo in this region is poor as the event rate in this region depends strongly on the unknown gluon density in the photon.

4. Properties of the Photon Remnant

As demonstrated in fig. 2 the bulk of hard photoproduction events at HERA is due to resolved photoproduction. In a resolved process only a part of the photon momentum enters the hard subprocess and the rest is carried by other partons. These spectator partons fragment into a photon remnant which is expected to appear close to the photon direction. A study of the photon remnant was performed by the ZEUS collaboration. A sample of events has been selected using the k_t jet clustering algorithm [7] to group all calorimeter cells into three

1993 Data ZEUS Preliminary

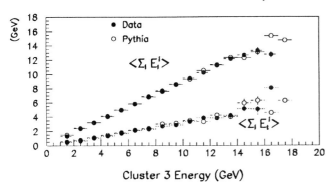

Figure 3. Average $\sum_i E_t^i$ and $\sum_i E_l^i$ as a function of the third cluster energy. The data (full circles) are compared to the Monte-Carlo prediction (empty circles).

clusters (excluding the proton remnant). The clusters are ordered according to their p_t and the following cuts are applied: $p_t^{cluster 1,2} > 5 GeV$, $\eta^{cluster 1,2} < 1.6$ and $\eta^{cluster3} < -1$. The selected sample is dominated by resolved photoproduction and the third cluster can be associated with the photon remnant. Fig. 3 shows the average total transverse and longitudinal energy of the third cluster, with respect to the cluster axis, as a function of the cluster energy. The data are compared to a Monte-Carlo model (based on the PYTHIA [8] generator and a full detector simulation) in which the fragmentation of the remnant is treated as for the hard jets. The good agreement of data and Monte-Carlo demonstrates the jet-like properties of the photon remnant.

5.   Inclusive Jet Cross Sections

A sample of photoproduction events for which the outgoing electron has been detected by the electron tagger has been used by the H1-collaboration to measure the inclusive jet spectra as functions of E_t and η. Jets have been selected with a cone algorithm in the pseudorapidity region $-1 < \eta < 1.5$ requiring a minimum transverse energy $E_t > 7GeV$. Fig. 4 shows the differential cross sections $d\sigma/dE_t$ (fig. 4a) and $d\sigma/d\eta$ (fig. 4b) corrected to the hadron level. The data are compared to a leading order QCD calculation using PYTHIA with two different parameterizations (GRV-LO [9], LAC2 [6]) of the parton distributions in the photon which are indistinguishable in the given kinematic range, both giving a good agreement with the data.

6.   Gluon Content of the Photon

The quark content of the photon has been measured in $\gamma\gamma$ experiments down to $x_\gamma \geq 0.006$ [10]. For these measurements a highly virtual photon is used to probe

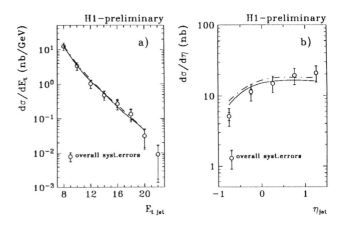

Figure 4. a) Inclusive jet E_t spectrum integrated of the pseudorapidity interval $-1.0 < \eta < 1.5$; b) Inclusive η spectrum for jets with $E_t > 7GeV$. The inner error bars represent statistical errors, the outer error bars the statistical and systematic errors added in quadrature. The overall systematic uncertainty is shown separately. The measurement is compared to the PYTHIA prediction using the photon parton distributions GRV-LO (full line) and LAC2 (dashed-dotted line).

a quasi-real photon. The gluon content is not directly accessible in these measurements and at present the scattering of two quasi-real photons gives only poor constraints of the gluon density in the photon [11]. HERA gives for the first time direct access to the gluons in the photon using a parton from the proton to probe the photon-structure. The parton distributions of the proton are well constrained by lepton-nucleon scattering experiments.

In order to measure parton densities down to small values of x_γ it is necessary to include forward going jets. H1 uses jets with a minimum transverse energy $E_t > 7GeV$ in the pseudorapidity interval $-0.2 < \eta_{jet} < 2.5$ which gives access to the partons in the range $0.03 < x_\gamma < 1$. The outgoing electron is tagged with the electron calorimeter so that the photon energy E_γ is given by the difference between the beam and the tagged electron energies.

This analysis faces the additional problem, that the standard hard scattering MC's like PYTHIA do not describe the energy flow at large pseudorapidities. The data show a much higher pedestal energy between the jets compared to the predictions of the Monte-Carlo generators. The inclusion of the multiple scattering option within PYTHIA however gives a very substantial improvement in the description of the energy flow and the jet-jet correlations. Remaining differences between data and the Monte-Carlo simulation with multiple interactions are then corrected using multiple interactions as the model for the additional energy flow.

Control distributions have been studied in detail and are very well described by the LO-Monte-Carlo. This justifies a simple LO analysis of the data for which a NLO calculation was not available.

Using an unfolding procedure [12] and the correlation between x_γ^{rec} according to equation (1) and x_γ^{true} as given by the Monte-Carlo the reconstructed x_γ^{rec}-distribution for the data sample was converted to the x_γ^{true}-distribution which is shown in fig. 5. The data are compared to the PYTHIA prediction for the direct component and the quark part of the resolved photon contribution based on the GRV-LO parameterization [9] of the photon parton densities. The Monte-Carlo distributions are normalized to the integrated luminosity. The sum of the two components gives a good description of the data for $x_\gamma > 0.2$. The excess of events over the quark part of the resolved contribution in the region $x_\gamma < 0.2$ can be attributed to the gluon content of the photon.

After a subtraction of the direct contribution and the quark part of the resolved component which is constrained by $\gamma\gamma$-experiments the gluon density in the photon can be extracted. The result is shown in fig. 6 which gives x times the gluon density $g(x)$ at an effective scale $\hat{p}_t^2 \approx 60 GeV^2$. It is important to note that this result was achieved in the framework of a leading order interpretation. The inner error bars in fig. 6 represent the statistical and the outer error bars the statistical and systematic errors added in quadrature. Several sources of systematic uncertainties have been taken into account. The dominating sources are the uncertainty of the hadronic energy scale and the correction for the imperfect description of the energy flow by the Monte-Carlo generator. The gluon content in the photon is restricted to small x_γ values $x_\gamma < 0.2$ as expected. Despite the large error bars the data already constrain the parton distributions in the photon and discriminate between different parameterizations. The measurement presented in fig. 6 is compared to the LAC1, LAC3 and GRV-LO parameterizations of the photon parton distributions.

7. Conclusions

It has been demonstrated that HERA gives access to hard scattering in photoproduction at high center of mass energies. The observation of a direct and a resolved photon component has been reported. The properties of the photon remnant have been studied. For the first time a direct measurement of the gluon density in the photon has been performed in leading order. Much more precise data can be expected in the coming years. Apart from a better understanding of the energy flow in the events NLO calculations will be essential to make progress.

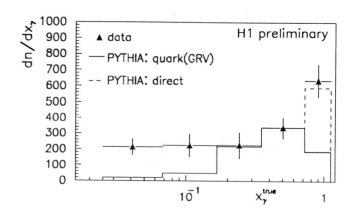

Figure 5. x_γ^{true}-distribution as obtained after the unfolding procedure. The data (full triangles) are compared to the PYTHIA prediction of the direct component (dashed line) and the quark part of the resolved contribution (full line) using the GRV-LO parameterization. Only statistical errors are shown.

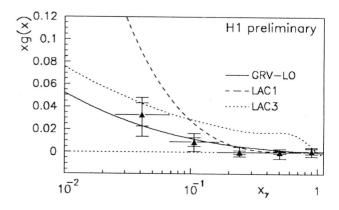

Figure 6. 'Measured gluon density in the photon (triangles), compared with the GRV-LO (full) and the LAC1 (dotted) distributions.

References

[1] ZEUS Collaboration, *The ZEUS detector*, Status Report (1993)

[2] H1 Collaboration, *The H1 Detector at HERA*, DESY 93-103 (1993)

[3] J. E. Huth et al., Fermilab-Conf-90/249-E (1990).

[4] F. Jacquet and A. Blondel, *Proc. of the Study for an ep Facility for Europe*, ed. U.Amaldi, DESY 79/48 (1979) 391.

[5] G. Marchesini et al., Comp. Phys. Comm. **67** (1992) 465.

[6] H. Abramowicz, K. Charchula and A. Levy, Phys. Lett. **B269** (1991) 458.

[7] S. Catani, Yu.L. Dokshitzer and B.R. Webber, Phys. Lett. **B285** (1992) 291.

[8] T. Sjöstrand, CERN-TH-6488 (1992).

[9] M. Glück, E. Reya and A. Vogt, Z. Phys. **C53** (1992) 651.

[10] Opal Collab., R. Akers et al., Z. Phys. **C61** (1994) 199.

[11] AMY Collab., R.Tanaka et al., Phys. Lett. **B277** (1992) 215.

[12] V. Blobel, DESY 84-118, and Proceedings of the 1984 CERN School of Computing, Aiguablava (Spain), CERN 1985.

Paper presented at XXVII Int. Conf. on High Energy Physics: Session Pa-11
Glasgow, UK, 20–27 July 1994

Jet Physics at DØ and CDF

James T. Linnemann[†]

Michigan State University, Department of Physics and Astronomy,
East Lansing, MI 48824, USA

for the DØ Collaboration

Abstract

This paper describes recent experimental results in QCD jet production from the DØ and CDF groups at the Fermilab Tevatron Collider using $\bar{p}p$ collisions at $\sqrt{s} = 1.8$ TeV. Included are calorimetric measurements of transverse energy flow in forward and central jets, inclusive single jet cross sections, and dijet production as a function of the rapidity of the two jets.

1. Introduction

I will present some selected results of analyses of data from the 1992-1993 run of the Fermilab Tevatron. As the graphs indicate, all results are preliminary from both experiments. For most analyses, final systematic error studies are in progress; in some instances final corrections are also lacking. For sake of brevity, references are not provided for structure functions nor well-known Monte Carlo generators.

2. Transverse Energy Flow

A recent DØ measurement [1] has taken up the study of the pattern of deposition of E_T around a jet axis. The technique is to form jets as seen by the calorimeter and measure the fraction of E_T captured in a cone of a given radius:

$$\psi(\Delta R) = \int_0^{\Delta R} p(E_T, r)dr \bigg/ \int_0^{1.0} p(E_T, r)dr \quad (1)$$

where $\Delta R = \sqrt{(\Delta \eta)^2 + (\Delta \phi)^2}$; $\Delta \eta$ and $\Delta \phi$ are the difference of the pseudorapidity and phi of a calorimeter cell from the center of a jet under study; $p(E_T, r)$ is the density of E_T as a function of r; and r is the ΔR

† E-mail: linnemann@msupa.pa.msu.edu

from the jet center to a cone smaller than the reference cone. In practice, the jet center is found and E_T in cells whose center is within ΔR of the center are summed. The reference cone size of $\Delta R = 1.0$ contains most of the E_T of a jet. Note that higher values of $\psi(\Delta R)$ at a given ΔR indicate narrower jets.

Figure 1 shows profiles for jets with $45 GeV < E_T < 70 GeV$ and contrasts central ($|\eta| < 0.2$) jets with forward ($2.5 < |\eta| < 3.0$) jets. The forward jets are seen to be narrower. Forward jets of a given E_T have higher E than central jets, and are more likely to have high x. Since quarks are more common at high x than gluons, this is qualitatively consistent with LEP [2] results which imply that quark jets are narrower than gluon jets; more quantitative studies are under way.

The argument that higher E means quarks and thus narrower jets also implies that jets should become narrower as E_T increases. This is borne out by the data shown in figure 2, which gives the jet profiles for 4 bins of E_T for central jets. The same trend is seen in the published CDF data [3].

These profiles can be compared with QCD expectations in several ways. Figure 3 shows the level of agreement between forward jets and a next-to-leading order (NLO) [4] parton calculation implemented in JETRAD [5].

Studies of similar plots show reasonable agreement

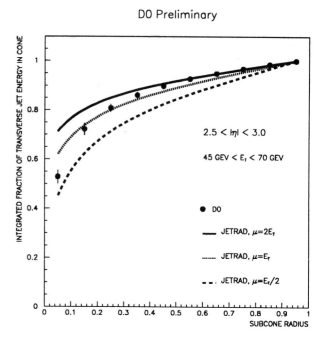

Figure 1. DØ Forward and Central Jet Shapes.

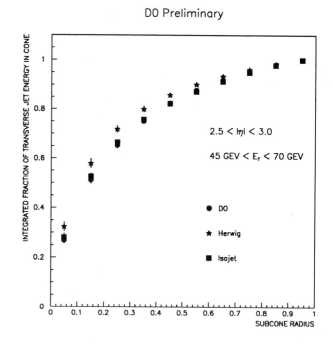

Figure 3. DØ Jet Shape Compared with JETRAD.

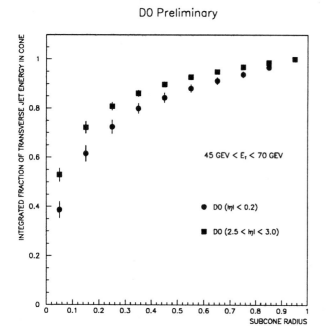

Figure 2. DØ Jet Shape vs E_T.

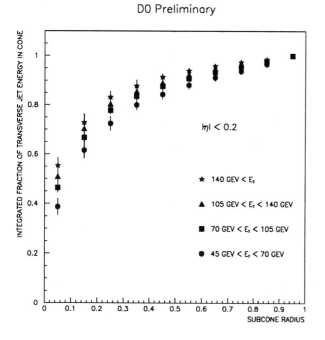

Figure 4. DØ Forward Jet vs Monte Carlo.

between the calculations and the data; JETRAD gives correct general trends in predicting narrowing of jets at high E_T and forward η. However, the NLO calculation, which is actually first order in transverse energy flow, retains substantial dependence on the renormalization scale μ, and there is no single choice of μ/E_T which describes all the data, implying a need for corrections to NLO, such as higher order perturbative terms or

nonperturbative fragmentation.

The profiles shown so far have all been corrected for effects of the underlying event and detector noise, as well as the broadening of the energy deposition due to particles showering in the calorimeter. Error bars include the systematic errors of these corrections. The profiles of central jets, when these corrections have been applied, are compatible with previously published CDF

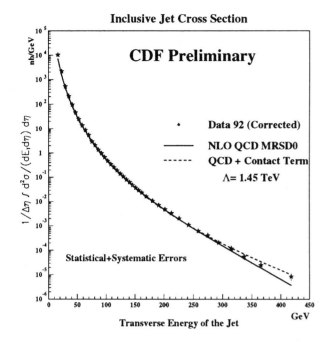

Figure 5. CDF Inclusive Jet Cross Section.

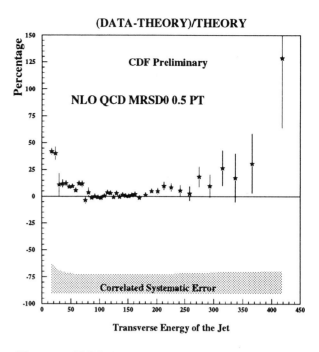

Figure 6. CDF Inclusive Jet Cross Section compared with a NLO calculation.

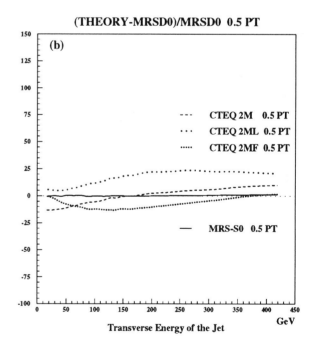

Figure 7. NLO Inclusive Jet Cross Section for various structure functions.

[3] data obtained by E_T flow from track momentum.

Fragmentation can be simulated with any of a range of QCD-inspired Monte Carlo models such as Isajet, Herwig, and Pythia. Figure 4 shows the comparison of forward jets with two of these generators. This comparison is done by running QCD events from the generators through the full DØ detector simulation. The comparison is after corrections for effects of the underlying event and detector noise, but the effects of showering in the calorimeter have not been removed, so as to make the confrontation of data and simulation more direct. For forward jets, Herwig tends to be too narrow. However, it is only fair to note that for central jets, the agreement is generally excellent for Herwig or Pythia, and instead Isajet jets are somewhat too wide. The Monte Carlo models give correct general trends, as did the parton-level model JETRAD. None of the Monte Carlo models quantitatively describe all the data, though Herwig probably comes closest.

The corrections for broadening of the apparent jet profile due to showering in the calorimeter are based on these simulations; these are the corrections used in the other plots in this analysis. The systematic errors used in the plots include the differences in the corrections deduced from the different generators. The differences in the corrections are smaller than the differences in the raw profiles.

3. Jet Inclusive Cross Sections

Single jet inclusive cross sections have been measured by CDF and by DØ. Figure 5 shows the present status of the CDF [6] measurement. The systematic errors in the absolute cross section range from $13 - 32\%$, while the statistical errors are mostly 2%, except the lowest and highest E_T where they increase to $5 - 25\%$. Essentially

Ratio of Spectra to Central Spectrum

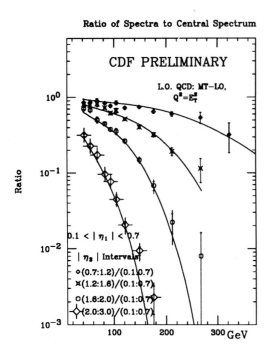

Figure 9. The CDF 2 Jet Cross Section/ Central η Bin.

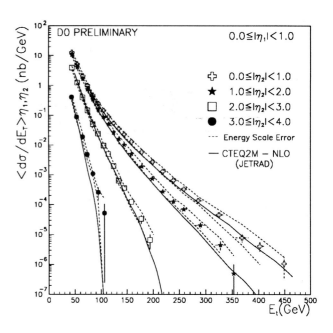

Figure 10. The DØ 2 Jet Cross Section.

all corrections have been performed on these data. Figure 6 shows a detailed comparison of the inclusive cross section measurement with an NLO calculation [4] with a particular choice of structure function. The agreement is excellent when the MRSD0 parton distribution function is used with a renormalization scale of $\mu = E_T/2$. The agreement is good enough to set a limit for a contact term [7] scale $\Lambda > 1.45 TeV$ at a 95% confidence level.

Figure 7 demonstrates that varying the structure function moves the predictions by perhaps ±20%; varying the choice of μ scale up or down by a factor of two typically moves the prediction by ±10%. The fact that the sensitivity to structure function choice is greater than the NLO sensitivity to renormalization scale indicates good prospects that these data will be able to contribute to global structure function fits.

The DØ jet inclusive results [8], shown in figure 8 (please page ahead) lie somewhat above the NLO prediction but agree in general shape. Analysis under way will present the cross sections for various central and forward η bins. Final corrections to the data are in progress.

4. Dijet Differential Cross Sections

The jet inclusive cross sections are certainly not the whole story; even the barest parton model tells us to expect a second jet balancing the E_T of the highest E_T jet seen in an event. Both CDF [6] and DØ [9] have also analyzed their jet data in terms of dijet cross sections

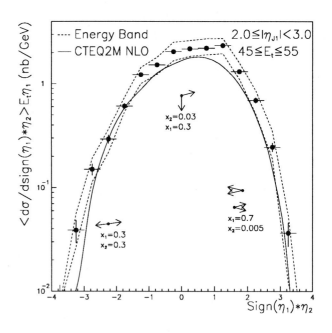

Figure 11. The DØ 2 Jet Cross Section vs signed η.

in the variables $d^3\sigma/dE_T d\eta_1 d\eta_2$. Here, E_T is the E_T of a jet in a particular range of E_T and η_1 and η_2 are the pseudorapidity of the highest and 2nd highest E_T jets found in the event. If both of the two highest E_T jets fall within the selected E_T band, the event is entered in the calculation again with the roles of the two jets

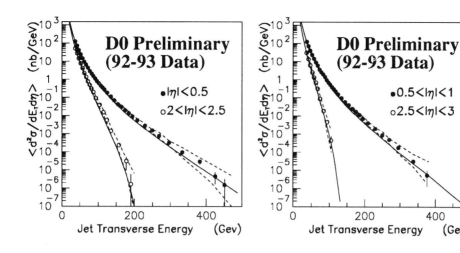

Figure 8. The DØ Jet Inclusive Cross Section.

reversed.

In the case of CDF, the E_T is that of a jet in $.01 < |\eta_1| < 0.7$. One useful way of looking at the data is to consider the ratio of the cross section for various bands of η_2 to the cross section for both jets central ($.01 < |\eta_2| < 0.7$). The ratio analysis has the advantage experimentally that many systematic errors cancel or are reduced in the ratios. The ratio view of the dijet cross section is shown in figure 9. The theoretical curves are for a leading-order calculation; the data differ from the LO predictions at high E_T and large $|\eta_2|$, indicating the need for a NLO calculation. The data are near final form; most corrections have been applied except for the effects of resolution in η; the resolution is small compared with the bin width so little effect is expected.

The DØ data cover a broader range of η, as seen in Figure 10. The theory curves in this case are JETRAD (NLO) calculations. At this stage in the analysis, final jet resolution correction of the data has not been done. Instead, the approximate jet resolution has been applied to the JETRAD spectra. Final results will instead remove jet resolution effects from the data so they can be compared directly with theory. The preliminary results again suggest some difficulties in matching the region at high E_T and large $|\eta_2|$.

Figure 10 only contains a subset of DØ data with $|\eta_1| < 1.0$. DØ analysis is under way on jets in the entire kinematic region $|\eta_1|, |\eta_2| < 4.0$. The full spectrum in η_1 and η_2 also is sensitive to the parton distribution functions. One way of plotting the data to emphasize these dependences is to plot the cross section in a bin of E_T as a function of $z = sgn(\eta_1)\eta_2$. As indicated in figure 11, positive values of z pick out configurations where the jets are both at the same end of the apparatus. In this "same-side" configuration, one jet comes from x

large and one comes from x small, so one is sensitive to the parton distribution function at small x which is not very highly constrained from hadron collider data. Negative z emphasizes "opposite-side" configurations where both jets are at intermediate x. This analysis can be repeated for various bands of $|\eta_1|$ and E_T. As the data analysis matures, this holds promise of providing useful constraints. At the present stage, one can only say that the general shape is reasonable.

References

[1] B. Abbott and K. Streets, DØ note 2176, and B. Abbott, Proceedings of APS Division of Particles and Fields, Albuquerque, N.M. 1994.

[2] G. Wilson, these proceedings; see also B. Webber, these proceedings; OPAL Collaboration, CERN-PPE/93-02,(1993).

[3] F. Abe et. al., Phys. Rev. Lett. **70** (1993) 713.

[4] S. Ellis, Z. Kunszt, D. Soper, Phys. Rev. Lett. **64** (1989) 2188;F. Aversa, P. Chiappetta, M. Greco, P. Guillet, Phys. Lett. **B210** (1988) 225,Nucl. Phys. **B327** (1989) 105.

[5] W.T.Giele, E.W.N. Glover, D.A. Kosower

[6] A. Bhatti for CDF collaboration, ICHEP paper GLS 0368.

[7] E. Eichten, K. Lane, M. Peskin, Phys. Rev. Lett. **50** (1983) 811.

[8] D. Elvira, DØ note 1689 and D. Elvira, Proceedings of APS Division of Particles and Fields, Albuquerque, N.M. 1994.

[9] F. Nang DØ note 2255 and F. Nang, Proceedings of APS Division of Particles and Fields, Albuquerque, N.M. 1994.

Paper presented at XXVII Int. Conf. on High Energy Physics: Session Pa-11
Glasgow, UK, 20–27 July 1994

Studies of Prompt Photon production
and
Multijet production at the Tevatron Collider

Elizabeth Buckley-Geer

Fermi National Accelerator Laboratory
Batavia, Illinois 60510

Presented on behalf of the CDF and D0 Collaborations

Abstract

We present measurements of inclusive isolated prompt photon production in $p\overline{p}$ collisions at a center-of-mass energy of 1.8 TeV from the Fermilab experiments CDF and D0. Precision measurements of prompt photon production from CDF constrain the gluon distribution, and recent results from D0 agree with CDF and QCD predictions. We also present studies of events with up to six jets in the final state from the CDF experiment. The mass distributions and mass ratio for these events is well described by the HERWIG parton shower Monte Carlo and by leading order QCD. Finally we present studies by both CDF and D0 of events with three jets in the final state.

1. Inclusive Isolated Prompt Photon Production

Prompt photon production at the Tevatron Collider is a precision test of Quantum Chromodynamics (QCD). At lowest order the dominant production mechanism is via Compton scattering off a gluon in the initial state. This implies that prompt photons provide a way to study the gluon distribution of the proton. Typical x_T values for the photons are in the range $0.01 - 0.1$.

1.1. Data Sample and Event Selection

In order to measure prompt photons both CDF and D0 use electromagnetic (EM) calorimeters segmented into towers in $\eta - \phi$ space. The main background is from neutral mesons, π^0, η and K_S^0 in jets which are suppressed by requiring that the photon candidate be isolated. CDF requires that there be less that 2 GeV of energy in a cone of $\Delta R = 0.7$ ($\Delta R = \sqrt{\Delta\eta^2 + \Delta\phi^2}$) around the photon while D0 requires that there be less than 2 GeV of transverse energy in an annulus between

$R = 0.2$ and $R = 0.4$. Additional cuts are applied to obtain the final sample, these are summarized in Table 1.

CDF had an isolation cut in the hardware trigger that allowed it to acquire more photon data at low p_T. The CDF sample for this analysis was 0.06 pb^{-1} above 6 GeV, 18 pb^{-1} above 16 GeV and 21 pb^{-1} above 50 GeV while the D0 sample was 0.005 pb^{-1} above 6 GeV, 0.022 pb^{-1} above 14 GeV and 3.86 pb^{-1} above 30 GeV.

1.2. Background subtraction methods

After all cuts the remaining background is predominantly from isolated π^0 and η mesons. The background subtraction methods for the two experiments are described separately.

1.2.1. CDF methods
The CDF experiment uses two methods to subtract the neutral meson backgrounds. The *profile method* uses the transverse profile at shower maximum in the central strip chambers. The transverse

Analysis Cut	CDF	D0
EM Energy/Total Energy	> 0.89	> 0.96
Neutral Cluster	No track	dE/dx separation
Shower profile	Good strip χ^2	Depth/transverse χ^2
Suppress η mesons	Extra strips < 1 GeV	
Reject cosmic rays	$\rlap{/}{E}_T/E_T^\gamma < 0.8$	$\rlap{/}{E}_T/E_T^\gamma < 0.5$
Good z-vertex	$|Z_v| < 50$ cm	
Central photon	$|\eta| < 0.9$	$|\eta| < 0.9$

Table 1. Isolated photon event selection cuts.

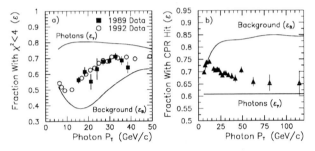

Figure 1. CDF background subtraction efficiency ϵ for photon candidates compared with simulated photons and background for a) the profile method and b) the conversion method.

profile of the shower is compared to the profile for a testbeam shower and a χ^2 is extracted. This χ^2 is larger for π^0 and η mesons than for single photons. The *conversion method* uses photon conversions occurring in the magnet coil which are then detected in the preshower detector. The probability of a π^0 and η meson converting is higher than a single photon. The efficiencies of the two methods are illustrated in figure 1 for photon candidates, simulated photons and background. The fraction of photons in the data is $f = (\epsilon - \epsilon_B)/(\epsilon_\gamma - \epsilon_B)$ where ϵ, ϵ_γ and ϵ_B are the efficiencies from the two methods for photon candidates, pure photons and pure background.

1.2.2. D0 Methods D0 uses three methods for background subtraction. Two of the methods rely on the probability that the background is more likely to convert than the signal. One expects that the calorimeter shower for a background event will start earlier that for a single photon so the ratio of energy in the first depth segment of the calorimeter is compared to the total shower energy. Conversions can also be tagged as track with twice the minimum ionizing energy using a dE/dx measurement in the Central Drift Chambers. The third method uses the asymmetry in the calorimeter showers caused by the opening angle between the two photons from a background event. This only works for low p_T photons. A functional form for the photon fraction f is extracted by fitting the three subtraction methods using the relationship above (figure 2).

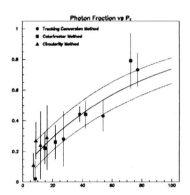

Figure 2. D0 photon fraction f for the three methods of background subtraction. The solid line is a fit and the dotted lines are the errors of the fit.

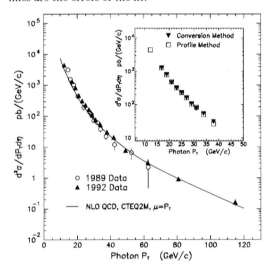

Figure 3. The isolated photon cross-section measured by CDF.

1.3. Inclusive Photon Results

The differential cross-section measured by CDF is shown in figure 3 for the two methods described; in the overlap region they agree to within 5%. Although there is qualatative agreement between the data and the QCD prediction[1], in figure 4 we show that the data has a steeper slope at low p_T regardless of the choice of parton distribution or renormalization scale. The overall systematic uncertainty is 10% at $p_T = 16$ GeV.

The differential cross-section measured by D0 is

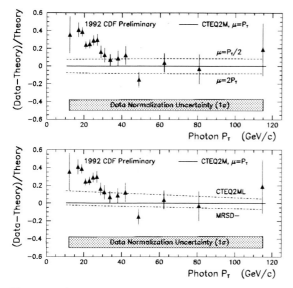

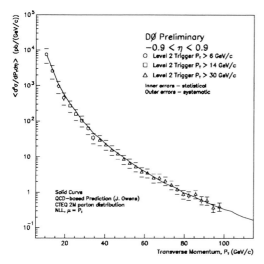

Figure 4. Comparison between data and QCD for different choices of renormalization scale and parton distributions.

Figure 5. The isolated photon cross-section measured by D0.

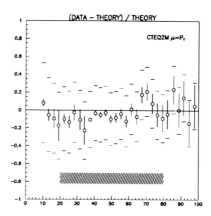

Figure 6. Comparison between data and QCD using CTEQ2M parton distributions.

2.1. Data Sample and Event Selection

The events were collected using a trigger that required $\sum E_T > 175$ GeV where the sum was over all Level 2 calorimeter clusters. A software Level 3 trigger further required that $\sum E_T > 300$ GeV where the sum was over offline calorimeter clusters with $E_T > 10$ GeV.

In additions events were required to pass the following selection criteria

1 $\sum E_T > 420$ GeV where the sum is over offline calorimeter clusters with corrected $E_T > 20$ GeV (jet cone $\Delta R = 0.7$).

2 $E_{Tot} < 2000$ GeV.

3 At least one reconstructed vertex with $|z| < 60$ cm.

4 Missing E_T significance $S < 6$ ($S \equiv \not{E}_T/(\sum E_T)^{1/2}$).

5 No significant energy in the calorimeters that is out-of-time with the proton-antiproton collision.

This resulted in a sample of 4632 events.

2.2. QCD Predictions

The leading order QCD predictions were obtained using the NJETS[3] program which is a parton level calculation using $2 \to N$ matrix elements. The following parameters were used in the calculation

1 $\sum E_T$ (parton) > 420 GeV, $E_T > 20$ GeV, $|\eta| < 3.0$, $\Delta R(j,j) > 1.0$.

2 MRSD0[4] parton distributions and $Q^2 = \langle E_T(jet) \rangle$

3 The parton transverse energies were smeared using a gaussian resolution function, $\sigma_{E_T} = 0.1 E_T$ (approximately the CDF resolution function).

Predictions have been generated for $2 \to N$ where $N = 2, 3, 4, 5$. We have also used the parton shower

---

shown in figure 5 and uses the same parameters for the QCD comparison. The linear comparison is shown in figure 6. Within the systematic errors there is good agreement between the data and the prediction. The shaded band in figure 6 corresponds to a $\pm 12\%$ normalization uncertainty on the luminosity.

2. Multijet Production at CDF

CDF has performed a study of multijet final states (up to 10 jets were observed) using a sample of events with large total transverse energy ($\sum E_T$). The aim of the study is to compare the data to leading order QCD predictions where available, and with parton shower Monte Carlo predictions. This is the continuation of a previous study done by CDF on event with large total transverse energy[2].

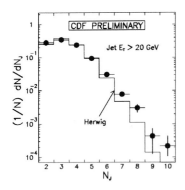

Figure 7. The jet multiplicity distribution. The jets were reconstructed with a cone size of $\Delta R = 0.7$ and the energies have been corrected.

Monte Carlo HERWIG[5] plus a full simulation of the CDF detector. We used the CTEQ1M[6] parton distributions and $Q^2 = stu/2(s^2 + t^2 + u^2)$.

The jet multiplicity distribution for the events is shown in figure 7 compared to the prediction from the HERWIG Monte Carlo. HERWIG underestimates the observed fraction of events with jet multiplicities larger that five and the discrepancy increases with increasing jet multiplicity. We suspect that this reflects a limitation of the HERWIG predictions. This effect has been observed previously in W + N-jet production[7].

2.3. Multijet mass distributions

In order to study the mass dependence of the events we require all events to have the center-of-mass scattering angle of the leading jet in the N-body rest-frame, $\cos \theta^\star < 0.67$. This ensures that the data are fully efficient for the chosen $\sum E_T$ threshold. The mass distributions for events with jet multiplicities up to six jets are shown in figure 8. They are compared to HERWIG and to NJETS, both can be seen to give a good description of the data in the fully efficient region which is $M_{Nj} > 600$ GeV. We have studied the variation of the NJETS prediction by changing the parton distributions and the Q^2 scale. There is no change in shape although the normalization varies.

We have also studied the $N - jet/2 - jet$ ratio as a function of M_{Nj}. This is shown in figure 9. The data are in reasonable agreement with the HERWIG predictions. There is some tendency for the HERWIG prediction to be high for low jet multiplicities and vice versa. The data are also well described by the range of NJETS predictions. The uncertainty due to the Q^2 scale dominates.

3. Three-jet Production

Studies of three-jet production have been performed by both CDF and D0. These studies use the same

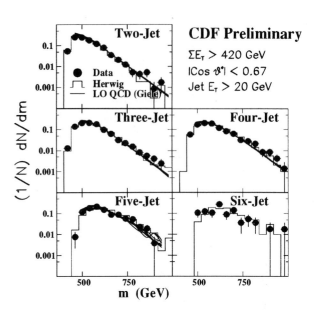

Figure 8. The multijet mass distribution. The jets were reconstructed with a cone size of $\Delta R = 0.7$ and the energies have been corrected.

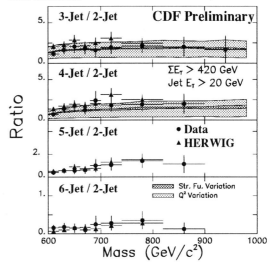

Figure 9. The $N - jet/2 - jet$ ratio as a function of M_{Nj}.

kinematic variables as previous UA1 and CDF studies [8]. These are

1   m_{3j}, the three-jet mass.

2   x_3, x_4 which are the energy fractions of two leading jet(jets are ordered so that $E_3 > E_4 > E_5$) $x_i = 2E_i/\sum E_j$.

3   $\cos \theta_3^\star$, the cosine of the leading-jet scattering angle.

4   $\psi^\star$, the angle between the production plan and the three-jet plane.

The event selection cuts for both CDF and D0 are summarized in Table 2. The CDF study starts from the

Analysis Cut	CDF	D0
Jet E_T	$E_T > 20$ GeV	$E_T > 20$ GeV
$\|\eta\|$		< 3.0
ΔR		> 1.4
Highest E_T jet		> 60 GeV
m_{3j}	> 500 GeV	$> 250 GeV$
x_3	< 0.9	< 0.9
$\| \cos\theta_3^{\star}\|$	< 0.6	< 0.95
$\psi^{\star}$		$20° < \psi^{\star} < 160°$

Table 2. Three-jet event selection cuts.

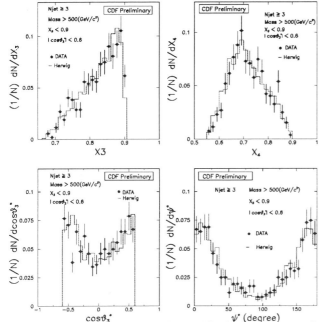

Figure 10. The three-jet kinematic variables for CDF measured at high m_{3j}.

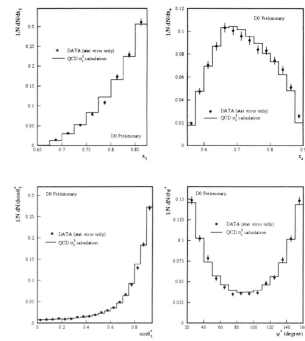

Figure 11. The three-jet kinematic variables for D0 measured at lower m_{3j}.

$\sum E_T$ sample descibed in section 2 while D0 uses an inclusive jet sample.

These cuts yield 522 events for the CDF sample and 7179 for the D0 sample which has larger angular acceptance and a lower mass cut.

In figure 10 we show the four kinematic variables described above for the CDF experiment compared to the predictions from the HERWIG Monte Carlo. The agreement is good. In figure 11 are shown the corresponding plots for D0. Here the Monte Carlo used is NJETS with no detector simulation. Again the agreement with theory is good.

4. Conclusions

The prompt photon cross-section from CDF is in qualatative agreement with next-to-leading order QCD but has a steeper slope at low p_T. Work is currently in progress to try and include the CDF data into the CTEQ global fits. The photon cross-section from D0 is in good agreement both with next-to-leading order QCD and CDF. The multijet mass distributions are well described by HERWIG and leading order QCD in the fully efficient region, as is the $N - jet/2 - jet$ mass ratio. The high-mass three-jet events from CDF are well described by the HERWIG Monte Carlo. The D0 events cover a larger mass and angular range and are well described by leading order QCD.

5. Acknowledgements

Thanks to John Womersley for providing me with the D0 photon plots and to Jerry Blazey for the D0 three-jet plots.

References

[1] H. Baer, J. Ohnemus and J.F. Owens, Phys. Lett. **B234** (1990) 127.
[2] CDF Collaboration: F. Abe *et al.*, Phys. Rev. **D45** (1992) 2249.
[3] W. Giele, private communication.
[4] A. Martin, R. Roberts and W. Stirling, Phys. Lett. **B309** (1993) 492.
[5] G. Marchesini and B. Webber, Nucl. Phys. **B310** (1988) 461.
[6] CTEQ Collaboration: J. Botts *et al.*, Phys. Lett. **B304** (1993) 159.
[7] W. Giele *et al.*, Snowmass Summer Study 1990, p.137.
[8] UA1 Collaboration: G. Arnison *et al.*, Phys. Lett. **B158** (1985) 494;
CDF Collaboration: F. Abe *et al.*, Phys. Rev. **D45** (1992) 1448

Soft Jets and Top Mass Measurement at the Tevatron

Lynne H Orr[†‡] and W J Stirling[§‖]

† Department of Physics and Astronomy, University of Rochester,
Rochester, NY 14627, USA
§ Departments of Physics and Mathematical Sciences, University of Durham,
Durham DH1 3LE, UK

Abstract

Extra soft jets in top events in $p\bar{p}$ collisions may arise not only from gluons radiated off initial state partons or final state b quarks, but may also be radiated from the t quarks themselves. We discuss predictions for distributions of soft gluons in $t\bar{t}$ production at the Tevatron and the implications for attempts to measure the top mass by reconstructing the invariant mass of its decay products.

1. Introduction

In $t\bar{t}$ production at the Tevatron, the final state particles may be accompanied by additional soft jets due to gluon radiation. These soft jets must be accounted for somehow in attempts to measure the top mass m_t by momentum reconstruction. In particular, one would like to know whether soft jets should be combined with the top's daughter W's and b's in such reconstructions. It is obvious that if the gluon has been radiated off the final b or $\bar{b}$, the gluon should be included, but if it was radiated off an intitial state quark, then it should not. Our intuition tells us that final-state radiation, as in the former case, corresponds to jets near the b or $\bar{b}$ direction, and that initial-state radiation, as in the latter case, corresponds to jets near the beam axis.

This intuitive picture is incomplete, however, because we must also consider radiation off the top quarks themselves. Do such gluons belong to the inital state or the final state? That this question cannot be answered indicates that the the initial/final state picture of gluon radiation is too naïve in the case of the top quark. Top production and decay must be considered simultaneously in a treatment of gluon radiation.

* Presented by L H Orr.
‡ E-mail: orr@urhep.pas.rochester.edu.
‖ E-mail: wjs@hep.durham.ac.uk.

In this talk we report results of a study [1] of soft gluon radiation in top production and decay in which all diagrams are correctly taken into account. Our aims are (i) to determine where the gluons come from and where they go, in a way that is relevant to m_t measurement, and (ii) to compare the correct results which those of simple, intuitive models that are in the spirit of what might be easily implemented in Mote Carlo Simulations.

2. Soft gluons: formalism and features

We work in the soft approximation (i.e., we assume that the gluons are less energetic than other particle in the event); for a discussion of the soft gluon formalism in top physics see [2]. We consider the process $q\bar{q} \rightarrow t\bar{t} \rightarrow bW^+\bar{b}W^-$ with emission of a soft gluon. The matrix element and phase space factorize so that we can write the gluon distribution as

$$\frac{1}{d\sigma_0}\frac{d\sigma}{dE_g d\cos\theta_g d\phi_g} = \frac{\alpha_s}{4\pi^2} E_g \left(\mathcal{F}_{\text{PROD}} + \mathcal{F}_{\text{DEC}} + \mathcal{F}_{\text{INT}}\right),$$

(1)

where $d\sigma_0$ is the differential cross section for the lowest-order process (with no gluon). $\mathcal{F}_{\text{PROD}}$ corresponds to gluons radiated in association with $t\bar{t}$ production, i.e., radiated before the t or $\bar{t}$ quark goes on shell. Similarly, $\mathcal{F}_{\text{DEC}}$ corresponds to gluons radiated in the decay of the

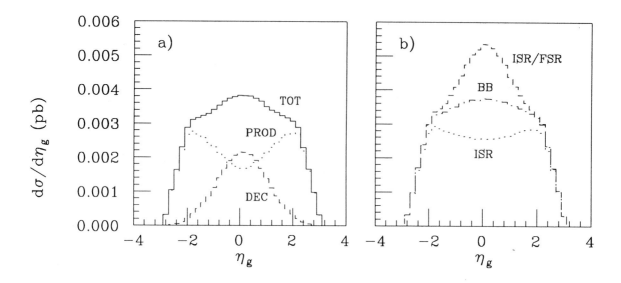

Figure 1. Gluon pseudorapidity distributions in $t\bar{t}$ production via $q\bar{q} \to t\bar{t} \to b\bar{b}W^{+}W^{-}$, in p$\bar{p}$ collisions at $\sqrt{s} = 1.8$ TeV. (a) Net distribution and contributions from production and decay. (b) Distributions arising from ISR, ISR/FSR, and BB models described in the text.

t or $\bar{t}$. $\mathcal{F}_{\mathrm{INT}}$ represents the interferences between the two and depends on the top width Γ_t. Expressions for $\mathcal{F}_{\mathrm{PROD}}$, $\mathcal{F}_{\mathrm{DEC}}$, and $\mathcal{F}_{\mathrm{INT}}$ can be found in [3].

The important point is that this production–decay-interference decomposition provides a gauge–invariant substitute for the initial/final state picture discussed above. It determines for us whether the gluon's momentum should be combined with those of the t decay products in reconstructing the top quark's four-momentum. Gluons associated with top production do not contribute to the on-shell top quark's momentum and should not be included. Gluons associated with the decay *do* contribute to the top momentum. For the interference term there is no such clear interpretation, but in the case of interest here it is negligible anyway.

Detailed discussions of the properties of this distribution (Eq. 1) can be found in [1] and [3]. Here we merely wish to point out some physical features of $\mathcal{F}_{\mathrm{PROD}}$ and $\mathcal{F}_{\mathrm{DEC}}$ which have consequences for the full distributions we see below, and which distinguish the correct distribution from those in simpler models. Being associated with $t\bar{t}$ production only, $\mathcal{F}_{\mathrm{PROD}}$ knows nothing about the decay of the top quark, and depends only on the momenta of the initial q and $\bar{q}$ and the t and $\bar{t}$, as well as that of the gluon itself. Similarly, $\mathcal{F}_{\mathrm{DEC}}$ knows nothing about the initial state and depends only on the momenta of the t, $\bar{t}$, b, $\bar{b}$, and gluon. Both $\mathcal{F}_{\mathrm{PROD}}$ and $\mathcal{F}_{\mathrm{DEC}}$ can be written as sums of "color antennae" which can be interpreted in terms of a pair of quarks connected by a color string. These antennae exhibit color coherence, or the string effect: more radiation appears between such paired quarks than outside of them.

3.   Gluon distributions at the Tevatron

Let us examine soft gluon distributions for $t\bar{t}$ production in p$\bar{p}$ collisions at 1.8 TeV center-of-mass energy at the Tevatron. The results shown are from [1], where a more complete discussion can be found. We take $m_t = 174$ GeV and work at the parton level, considering only the $q\bar{q}$ initial state (which dominates) and using minimal kinematic cuts, which are:

$$
\begin{aligned}
|\eta_b|, |\eta_{\bar{b}}| &\leq 1.5 \,, \\
|\eta_g| &\leq 3.5 \,, \\
10 \text{ GeV}/c \leq \; p_T^g &\leq 25 \text{ GeV}/c \,, \\
E_g &\leq 100 \text{ GeV} \,, \\
\Delta R_{bg}, \Delta R_{\bar{b}g} &\geq 0.5 \,.
\end{aligned}
\tag{2}
$$

3.1.   Angular distributions and top momentum reconstruction

We focus on angular distributions since we are interested in where soft jets will appear in detectors. Figure 1(a) shows the gluon pseudorapidity distribution. The total (solid line) is shown along with its decomposition according to Eq. 1 into production (dotted line) and decay (dashed line) contributions. The production piece is peaked in the forward direction and centrally suppressed. This reflects the color antennae connecting the initial-state quarks with the top quarks. The decay contribution is peaked in the central region, which is where the radiating top and bottom quarks tend to be produced. The net distribution is only slightly peaked in the center. Note that, while gluons at larger rapidities are almost exclusively associated with production (and hence should be ignored in top

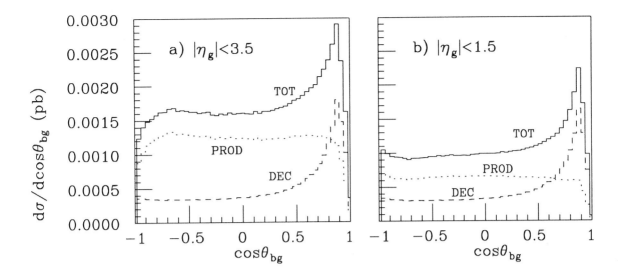

Figure 2. Distribution in the cosine of the angle between the gluon and the b-quark, (a) with cuts described in the text and (b) with the additional cut $|\eta_g| \leq 1.5$.

momentum reconstruction), central gluons are nearly as likely to have come from production as from decay.

In Figure 2 we test the second part of our guess (see introduction) by examining to what extent proximity of gluons to the b quark correlates with having come from the decay contribution. Fig. 2(a) shows the distribution in cosine of the angle between the b quark and the gluon with the same cuts and decomposition as in Fig. 1(a). The contribution from production is flat, as expected since it contains no explicit dependence on the b quark's momentum. The decay contribution does increase as the gluon approaches the b, leading to an excess above the production contribution close to the b. The excess is only a slight one, though, and the result is very sensitive to the cut on ΔR. Furthermore, no hadronization effects have been taken into account. We can improve the situation by recalling that forward gluons tend to come from production. If we tighten the gluon pseudorapidity cut to $|\eta_g| < 1.5$, we see more of an excess in decay gluons near the b, as shown in Fig. 2(b). Sensitivity to the ΔR cut and fragmentation effects remain a problem, however.

We now return to the pseudorapidity distribution to compare the correct distribution in Fig. 1(a) to those in Fig. 1(b), obtained from some simpler models that are intuitively appealing and easily implemented in Monte Carlo simulations. The ISR model (dotted line) includes radiation off the initial $q\bar{q}$ state only, as if the q and $\bar{q}$ formed a color singlet. We might expect this to correspond to the contribution associated with production, but we see by comparing to the dotted line in Fig. 1(a) that the ISR model overestimates radiation in the central region. In the ISR/FSR model (dashed line) we add to the ISR model radiation from the final $b\bar{b}$ pair as if they too formed a color singlet. This model

corresponds roughly to the naïve expectation mentioned in the introductory paragraph. Figure 1(b) shows that this model overestimates the total radiation and gets the shape wrong. In the BB model (dot-dashed line) we use the correct color structure but ignore radiation off the top quark. This model approximately reproduces the correct pseudorapidity distribution. However, it does not give the correct azimuthal distribution,[1] and, more important for m_t reconstruction, does not permit a production–decay decomposition.

3.2. Color structure and forward-backward asymmetry

Finally, we discuss briefly a forward-backward asymmetry in the radiation pattern (for appropriately chosen final states) that arises from the color structure of gluon emission in hadronic $t\bar{t}$ production. While not directly relevant to measurement of the top mass, the asymmetry is interesting because it is a result of the fact that the top quarks themselves can radiate before decaying. It also reveals major differences between the correct distribution and the simpler models.

This asymmetry arises from the string effect mentioned above. For example, in $q\bar{q} \rightarrow t\bar{t}$ the q–t antenna produces more radiation in the region between the t and q than, say, between the t and $\bar{q}$, resulting in a forward-backward asymmetry in the gluon radiation. To avoid cancellation of the effect by an equal and opposite asymmetry due to the $\bar{q}$ and $\bar{t}$, we try to preferentially select gluons that are more likely to be in the t than the $\bar{t}$ hemisphere, with the additional cuts $\Delta\phi_{b\bar{b}} > 135°$ and $\Delta\phi_{bg} < 90°$.

The resulting distribution is shown in Figure 3(a). A forward-backward asymmetry is evident, and we see from the decomposition that it comes entirely from the

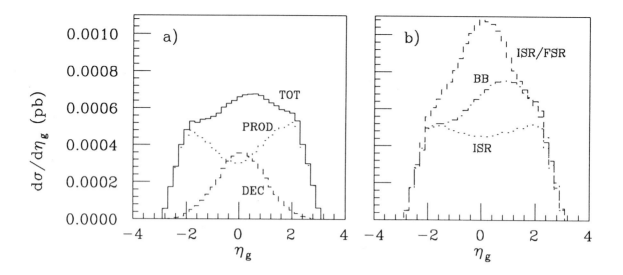

Figure 3. Forward–backward asymmetry in gluon pseudorapidity distributions in $t\bar{t}$ production. The cuts are as in Fig. 1 with the additional requirements $\Delta\phi_{b\bar{b}} > 135°$ and $\Delta\phi_{bg} < 90°$. The curves correspond to the (a) total (solid), production (dots) and decay (dashes) distributions, and to the distributions for the (b) ISR (dots), ISR/FSR (dashes) and BB (dash-dots) models.

production piece; the decay knows nothing about the initial quarks' direction. In Fig. 3(b) we show the same distribution for the three simpler models. There is no asymmetry for the ISR and ISR/FSR models because there is no connection between radiation in the initial and final states. In contrast, the BB model shows a more marked asymmetry than the correct distribution because without radiation from the intermediate top quarks there is a more direct color connection between the initial and final states.

4.   Summary

We have shown that the subject of gluon radiation in $t\bar{t}$ production and decay is a complicated one due to the rich color structure of the process. For purposes of top mass reconstruction, we saw that there is no simple prescription for dealing with additional soft jets in $t\bar{t}$ events, but that the production–decay decomposition provides some guidance. A comparison to simpler, intuitively appealing models such as one might easily implement in Monte Carlo simulations showed that they do not reproduce the correct distributions and/or do not allow for the production–decay decomposition. Finally, we discussed a forward–backward asymmetry in soft gluon radiation that illustrates the color structure, including in particular radiation off the top quarks themselves.

References

[1] L.H. Orr and W.J. Stirling, DTP/94/60, UR-1365, July 1994.
[2] V.A. Khoze, L.H. Orr and W.J. Stirling, Nucl. Phys. **B378** (1992) 413.
[3] V.A. Khoze, J. Ohnemus and W.J. Stirling, Phys. Rev. **D49** (1994) 1237.

*Paper presented at XXVII Int. Conf. on High Energy Physics: Session Pa-11
Glasgow, UK, 20–27 July 1994*

QCD Corrections to Higgs Boson Production

S. Dawson[*] and R. Kauffman[†]

[*] Physics Department, Brookhaven National Laboratory, Upton, N.Y. 11793
[†]Physics Department, Franklin and Marshall College, Lancaster, PA. 17604

Abstract

We compute analytic results for the QCD corrections to Higgs boson production in hadronic collisions in the limit in which the top quark is much heavier than the Higgs boson. The first non-leading corrections of $\mathcal{O}(\alpha_s^3 M_H^2/m_t^2)$ are given and numerical results presented for the LHC.

1. Introduction

One of the prime motivations for the construction of high energy hadron colliders is to unravel the mechanism of electroweak symmetry breaking. In the standard model of electroweak interactions there exists a physical scalar boson, called the Higgs boson, whose interactions generate the non-zero masses of the W and Z gauge bosons. The couplings of the Higgs boson are completely specified in the standard model; the only unknown parameter is the mass. For a given mass, therefore, it is possible to predict the properties and production mechanisms of the standard model Higgs boson unambiguously. In this note, we discuss the two-loop QCD radiative corrections of $\mathcal{O}(\alpha_s^3)$ to the production of the Higgs boson in hadronic interactions.

A particularly interesting mass region in which to search for the Higgs boson is the intermediate mass region, $80 < M_H < 150 \, \text{GeV}$. Since the number of events in observable channels is small, it is vital to understand the effects of radiative corrections in this region in order to determine the viability of the signal.

In the intermediate mass region, the primary production mechanism is gluon fusion through a top quark loop. For a heavy top quark, $m_t > 150 \, \text{GeV}$, it makes sense to expand the results in powers of $r \equiv M_H^2/m_t^2$. In such a limit, the computation of the two loop QCD radiative corrections becomes greatly simplified and it is possible to obtain analytic results. The leading corrections for $m_t \to \infty$ have been

computed previously and found to significantly increase the cross section.[1, 2]

Here we present analytic results for the first non-leading corrections of $\mathcal{O}(\alpha_s^3 r)$ to Higgs boson production in hadronic collisions and confirm the numerical results of reference 2, valid for arbitrary M_H/m_t.

2. Previous Results

The lowest order amplitude for the gluon fusion of a Higgs boson is sensitive to all of the quarks which can couple to the gluon and to the Higgs boson, but has the property that it primarily depends on the heaviest quark mass (in practice, on the top quark mass). The contribution to the spin and color averaged cross section from a single heavy quark with mass m_t is,

$$\sigma_0(gg \to H) \to \frac{\alpha_s^2}{\pi} \frac{M_H^2}{576 v^2} \left[1 + \frac{7}{60} r \right] \delta(s - M_H^2), \quad (1)$$

when $r \equiv M_H^2/m_t^2 << 1$.

In this note we will consider only the top quark, although we have in mind either the top quark or any new heavy fourth generation quark. For $r < 1$, the heavy quark limit of Eq. (1) is an extremely good approximation to the exact one-loop result.

3. Calculational Techniques

The evaluation of the two-loop diagrams arising in the virtual corrections to $gg \to H$ is an extension of the techniques used in the case of $\gamma\gamma \rightarrow H$.[3] The basic strategy is to expand the loop integrals in powers of the external momenta over m_t at every stage. This technique has been successfully used to compute the 2–loop contribution to the ρ parameter from a heavy top quark.[4] Each two loop graph gives a result of the form

$$\mathcal{A}_i^{\mu\nu} = -\delta_{AB}\frac{\alpha_s^2}{2\pi^2 v}\left(a_i g^{\mu\nu}k_1 \cdot k_2 + b_i k_1^\nu k_2^\mu + c_i k_1^\mu k_2^\nu\right) \quad , \tag{2}$$

where the incoming gluons have momenta k_1 and k_2, polarization indices μ and ν, and colors A and B. Gauge invariance requires that

$$\sum_i a_i = -\sum_i b_i, \tag{3}$$

where the sum runs over all the diagrams (the c_i terms do not contribute for on-shell gluons). In order to reduce the number of tensor structures and deal with scalar quantities only, we compute three contractions of each diagram : $\mathcal{A}_i^{\mu\nu}g_{\mu\nu}$, $\mathcal{A}_i^{\mu\nu}k_{1\mu}k_{2\nu}$ and $\mathcal{A}_i^{\mu\nu}k_{1\nu}k_{2\mu}$. From the contracted amplitudes the values of a_i and b_i can easily be found.

The various two-loop diagrams have either one, two or three gluon propagators. Diagrams with one gluon propagator can be written such that the gluon propagator contains no external momenta. For those diagrams with more than one gluon propagator we employ Feynman parametrization to combine the massless gluon propagators (top quark propagators are left alone); the loop momenta are then shifted to move the external momenta into the top-quark propagators.

The denominators arising from the heavy-quark propagators can be expanded in powers of the external momentum, e.g.,

$$\frac{1}{(q-k_1)^2 - m_t^2} = \frac{1}{q - m_t^2}\left(1 + \frac{2q \cdot k_1}{q - m_t^2} + ...\right) \quad . \tag{4}$$

To obtain the terms of $\mathcal{O}(M_H^2/m_t^2)$ each denominator must be expanded up to terms containing two powers of k_1 and two powers of k_2. The Feynman integrals are easily performed after the momentum integrations.

After contracting the two-loop amplitudes as in Eq. (5) and expanding the denominators all the contributions have the form

$$\int \frac{d^n p}{(2\pi)^n}\int\frac{d^n q}{(2\pi)^n}\frac{(p \cdot k_i)^\alpha (q \cdot k_i)^\beta (p^2)^\gamma (q^2)^\delta (p \cdot q)^\tau}{(q^2 - m_t^2)^k (p^2 - m_t^2)^l [(p-q)^2 - m^2]^j} \quad , \tag{5}$$

where m^2 can be zero or a product of Feynman paramaters times M_H^2. Using the symmetries of the numerators the powers of $p \cdot k_i$ and $q \cdot k_i$ can be written in terms of powers p^2, q^2, and $p \cdot q$ times powers of $k_1 \cdot k_2 = M_H^2/2$. The integrals can then be reduced to

the symmetric form

$$\int \frac{d^n p}{(2\pi)^n}\int\frac{d^n q}{(2\pi)^n}\frac{1}{[(p-q)^2 - m^2]^j (p^2 - m_t^2)^k (q^2 - m_t^2)^l} . \tag{6}$$

These integrals are well known in the literature.

4.   Analytic Results

To compute the radiative corrections for the inclusive production of the Higgs boson from gluon fusion, we need both the real contribution from $gg \rightarrow gH$ and the virtual corrections from $gg \rightarrow H$.

The final result for $gg \rightarrow gH$ can be written in the compact form:[2,5]

$$\sigma_{\text{TOT}}(gg \rightarrow HX) = \sigma_0\left\{\delta(1-z) + \frac{\alpha_s(\mu)}{\pi}\left[h(z)\right.\right.$$
$$+ \bar{h}(z)\log\left(\frac{M_H^2}{\mu^2}\right) + \frac{34r}{135}\delta(1-z)$$
$$\left.\left.- \frac{3r}{20}z(1-z)\right]\right\} + \mathcal{O}(r^2) \tag{7}$$

where σ_0 (with α_s evaluated at μ) is given in Eq. (1) and the functions $h(z)$ and $\bar{h}(z)$ are the same as those of reference 5 :

$$h(z) = \delta(1-z)\left(\pi^2 + \frac{11}{2}\right) - \frac{11}{2}(1-z)^3$$
$$+ C_A z \tilde{P}_{gg}(z)\log\left(\frac{(1-z)^2}{z}\right)$$
$$\bar{h}(z) = C_A z \tilde{P}_{gg}(z) \tag{8}$$
$$\tilde{P}_{gg}(z) = 2\left\{\left(\frac{z}{1-z}\right)_+ + \frac{1-z}{z} + z(1-z)\right\}.$$

The form of Eq. (7) makes it clear that the dominant contributions to the result are just a rescaling of the $r = 0$ result by the ubiquitous factor $1+7r/60$. Note the cancellation of the $\log(m_t/M_H)$ terms. There are also no terms proportional to s/m_t^2 which would invalidate the expansion.

The results for $q\bar{q} \rightarrow gH$ and $qg \rightarrow qH$ are given in references 2 and 5. At LHC energies, these subprocesses give a negligible contribution to the final result.

5.   Numerical Results

In this section we present numerical results for Higgs production in pp collisions at $\sqrt{s} = 15$ TeV. For our non-leading order parton distribution functions, we use the S1 fit of Morfin and Tung[6] translated into the $\overline{MS}$ prescription. For our leading order parton distribution functions, we also use a set provided by Morfin and Tung which is suitable for using with lowest order

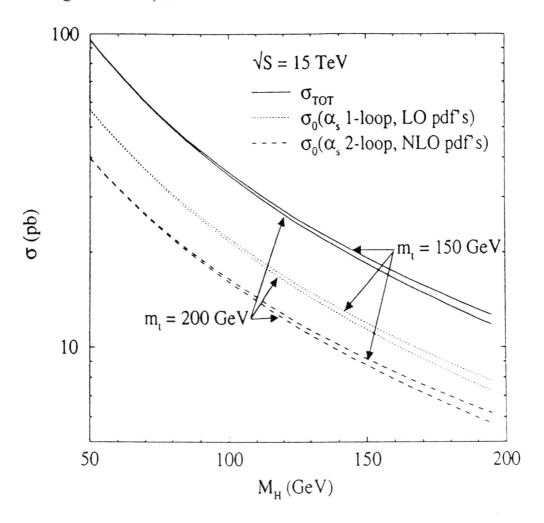

Figure 1. Lowest order (dotted and dashed) and radiatively corrected (solid) cross sections at the LHC. The curves labelled LO pdf and NLO pdf use the lowest order and next to leading order parton distribution functions of Morfin and Tung, respectively.

predictions for hard scattering processes. We take the renormalization scale $\mu = M_H$.

In figure 1 we show the lowest order and the radiatively corrected cross sections for $m_t = 150$ GeV and $m_t = 200$ GeV at the LHC. In all cases, the radiative corrections increase the cross section by a factor between 1.5 and 2. In this figure we have shown the contribution of changes in the structure functions and α_s by defining the lowest order cross section in two ways. In the first definition, we use the 1-loop value for α_s and the lowest order parton distribution functions, while the second definition uses the 2-loop value for α_s and the non-leading order parton distribution functions. Both definitions of the lowest order cross section are completely consistent to $\mathcal{O}(\alpha_s^2)$, but we see a significant numerical difference between the two in figure 1.

To emphasize this we have plotted the ratio of the radiatively corrected cross section for gluon fusion of Eq. (7) to the Born cross section of Eq. (1) in figure 2. This ratio is often called "the" K factor. The results of

reference 2 correspond to the dotted curves in figure 2 and our results agree completely with theirs. It should be stressed, again, that both definitions of a K factor as shown in figure 2 are completely consistent to $\mathcal{O}(\alpha_s^3)$, but differ by 50% numerically. From this figure we see that many of the $\mathcal{O}(\alpha_s^3)$ corrections can be absorbed into a redefinition of the parton distribution functions and the running of α_s.

It is also interesting to consider the μ dependence of our results. Contrary to naive expectations, the radiative corrections do not generally reduce the dependence of the cross section on μ. Indeed for a light Higgs boson ($M_H/m_t <$) the dependence on μ of the NLO result is more severe than the leading order result.

6. Conclusions

We have computed the $\mathcal{O}(\alpha_s^3 r)$ contributions to $pp \rightarrow gH$. They are dominated by the gluon fusion contribution and typically increase the lowest order

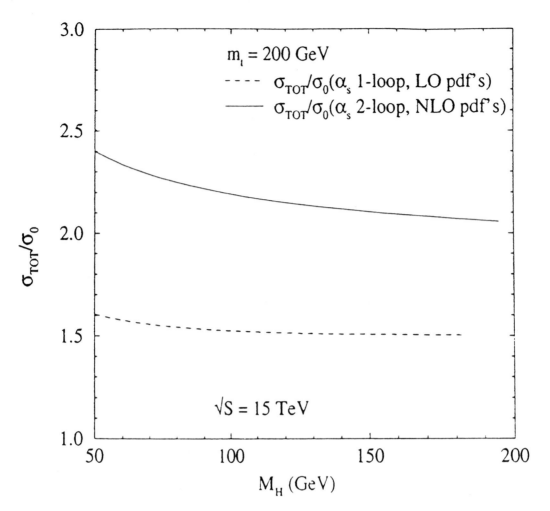

Figure 2. Ratio of the radiatively corrected cross section to the Born cross section at the LHC, $E = 15\ TeV$ with $m_t = 200\ GeV$.

cross section by a factor of between 1.5 and 2. The lowest order cross section is sensitive to whether the 1-loop or 2-loop α_s is used and which distribution functions are used.

The dominant numerical corrections to the gluon fusion contribution can be found from the $m_t \rightarrow \infty$ $\mathcal{O}(\alpha_s^3)$ results of references 1 and 2 by rescaling the cross section by the factor $(1 + 7r/60)$. The smallness of the $\mathcal{O}(\alpha_s^3 r)$ terms demonstrates the valididty of the $m_t \rightarrow \infty$ limit for the gluon fusion subprocess. Indeed, reference 2 found that the $m_t \rightarrow \infty$ results were good to within 15% even for $M_H > m_t$.

[4] J. van der Bij and M. Veltman, Nucl. Phys. **B231** (1984) 205; F. Hoogeveen, Nucl. Phys. **B259** (1985) 19.
[5] S. Dawson and R. Kauffman, Phys. Rev. **D49** (1993) 2298.
[6] J. Morfin and W. Tung, Zeit. Phys. **C52** (1991) 13.

References

[1] S. Dawson, Nucl. Phys. **B359** (1991) 283; A. Djouadi, M. Spira and P. Zerwas, Phys. Lett. **B264** (1991) 441.
[2] D. Graudenz, M. Spira and P. Zerwas, Phys. Rev. Lett. **70** (1993) 1372; M. Spira, Ph.D. thesis, Aachen 1993.
[3] S. Dawson and R. Kauffman, Phys. Rev. **D47** (1993) 1264.

High-p_T photon production at $p\bar{p}$ colliders

Werner Vogelsang

Institut für Physik, Universität Dortmund,
D-44221 Dortmund, Germany

Abstract

It is demonstrated by consistent NLO calculations for isolated hadronic prompt photon production that previous discrepancies between NLO expectations for the direct-γ production rates at small p_T^γ ($\gtrsim 11$ GeV) and isolated prompt photon data are removed. This is not only due to the use of experimentally confirmed steep small-x parton distributions, but also due to a consistent inclusion of isolated photonic fragmentation contributions in NLO.

Prompt photon production rates at high energy $p\bar{p}$ colliders are studied, among other reasons, in order to gain information on the gluon distribution $g(x, Q^2)$ of the proton. The high-p_T prompt photons are mainly due to the dominant Compton-like subprocess $gq \to \gamma q$ and, for small values of $x_T = 2p_T^\gamma/\sqrt{s}$, provide invaluable information on the small-x behavior of $g(x, Q^2)$. In practice, when measuring the prompt photon cross section at colliders [1-3], one introduces suitable isolation cuts designed to reduce the non-prompt photon background resulting, e.g., from the not yet satisfactorily measured photonic fragmentation functions $D_{q,g}^\gamma(z, \mu_F^2)$. This cut is charactarized by the opening angle 2δ of the photon isolation cone and an energy resolution parameter ϵ: If the total hadronic energy in the photon's isolation cone is less than ϵE_γ, with E_γ being the photon's energy, the photon is called isolated. A detailed description and discussion of the leading order (LO) calculations as well as of some estimates on the effects of the next-to-leading order (NLO) corrections, which are crucial for a meaningful theoretical analysis of recent data [1-3], can be found for example in [4].

The fully inclusive, i.e. non-isolated, total production cross section of one prompt photon, $ab \to \gamma X$, is generically of the form

$$
d\sigma_{ab}^\gamma \;=\; d\sigma_{dir} + d\sigma_{frag} = \sum_{f_a, f_b = q, \bar{q}, g} \int dx_a dx_b f_a(x_a, \mu^2) f_b(x_b, \mu^2)
$$

$$
\times \left[d\hat{\sigma}_{f_a f_b}^\gamma(p_\gamma, x_a, x_b, \mu^2, \mu_F^2) + \sum_{f=q,\bar{q},g} \int_{z_{min}}^1 \frac{dz}{z^2} d\hat{\sigma}_{f_a f_b}^f(p_\gamma, x_a, x_b, z, \mu^2, \mu_F^2) D_f^\gamma(z, \mu_F^2) \right] , \qquad (1)
$$

where $z_{min} = x_T(e^\eta + e^{-\eta})/2$. The fragmentation scale is denoted by μ_F and the factorization scale μ, entering the parton distributions $f(x, \mu^2)$, has as usual been assumed to coincide with the renormalization scale entering $\alpha_s(\mu^2)$. The direct (dir) term in eq.(1) receives contributions from the one-photon inclusive subprocesses $f_a f_b \to \gamma X$ ($d\hat{\sigma}_{f_a f_b}^\gamma$) which in LO ($\alpha\alpha_s$) are derived from $gq \to \gamma q$ and $q\bar{q} \to \gamma g$, and in NLO ($\alpha\alpha_s^2$) from $gq \to \gamma qg$, $q\bar{q} \to \gamma gg$, $gg \to \gamma q\bar{q}$, etc. [5, 6]. The non-direct fragmentation ($frag$) dependent term in eq.(1), sometimes referred to as bremsstrahlung contribution [2, 4], receives contributions from the one-parton inclusive subprocesses $f_a f_b \to fX$ ($d\hat{\sigma}_{f_a f_b}^f$) which are derived from the LO (α_s^2) $2 \to 2$ and NLO (α_s^3) $2 \to 3$ parton-parton subprocess cross sections as given in [7] and [8], respectively. The produced parton $f = q, \bar{q}, g$ then fragments into a photon as described by the relevant photonic fragmentation function $D_f^\gamma(z, \mu_F^2)$ in LO (α/α_s) [9, 10] and HO ($\alpha/\alpha_s + \alpha$) [9] as we shall discuss in more detail below. It should be mentioned that the purely perturbative NLO (hard) direct contribution in eq.(1) depends, via the necessity of separating collinear singularities [4, 6, 11] on the fragmentation scale μ_F entering the non-direct fragmentation contribution in eq.(1) also via the fragmentation functions $D_f^\gamma(z, \mu_F^2)$.

A realistic calculation of the contributions in eq.(1) to prompt photon production affords, however, an evaluation of the effects due to the isolation cut. In a theoretical study in LO this experimental criterion can be easily implemented into the calculation. Here the dominant contributions arise from hard $2 \to 2$ subprocesses for which the photon and the other final state particle, which will give rise to hadrons, are more or less back-to-back and thus separated from each other. The implementation of the isolation cut on the LO fragmentation contribution in eq.(1) is reflected merely in changing [4] the lower limit z_{min} of the z-integration in eq.(1) to $\max(z_{min}, 1/(1+\epsilon))$ and $\mu_F \to \mu_F(\delta, \epsilon)$.

In NLO, as mentioned above, important contributions to prompt photon production arise from the various possible 'direct' $2 \to 3$ processes $ab \to \gamma cd$. In contrast to the LO processes it is now possible kinematically that one of the final state partons carrying more energy than ϵE_γ happens to be inside the cone around the photon. Such contributions have to be excluded for the isolated cross section. Apart from a Monte Carlo program of Baer et al. [12] there exist two *analytical* calculations of the complete NLO corrections for the 'direct' (hard) part of *inclusive* prompt photon production, i.e. of the processes $ab \to \gamma cd$ [5, 6]. These calculations have been performed integrating over the *full* phase space of the outgoing unobserved particles c and d, and thus no longer allow for isolation cuts directly. Nevertheless they present the most convenient starting point for the treatment of the isolated 'direct' cross section since the latter can be written as the inclusive cross section minus a subtraction piece [4]:

$$d\sigma_{dir}^{isol} = d\sigma_{dir} - d\sigma_{dir}^{sub}(\delta, \epsilon) \ , \qquad (2)$$

$d\sigma_{dir}^{sub}$ being the cross section for producing a prompt photon which is accompanied by hadronic energy *more* than ϵE_γ inside the cone. The decomposition of $d\sigma_{dir}^{isol}$ in eq. (2) has several advantages: The inclusive cross section $d\sigma_{dir}$ is perturbatively well defined in itself in the sense that a complete cancellation of all poles has already taken place, i.e. infrared poles have cancelled between the virtual $(2 \to 2)$ and the $2 \to 3$ NLO contributions and mass singularities have been factored into the initial state parton distributions and the photon fragmentation functions [5, 6].

In order to find a semi-analytical expression for $d\sigma_{dir}^{sub}$, one may assume that δ is small, i.e. that the cone around the photon, needed for isolating it, is rather narrow [11]. It turns out that the leading behavior of $d\sigma_{dir}^{sub}$ for small δ is logarithmic in δ which is a remnant of the final state collinear singularities arising in the calculation of $d\sigma_{dir}^{sub}$. One should also consistently keep terms constant with respect to δ, since these turn out to be of numerical relevance. They are furthermore needed since they contain the dependence on the factorization

scheme which must be the same in the calculation of $d\sigma_{dir}^{sub}$ and $d\sigma_{dir}$. All remaining pieces in the subtraction cross section are suppressed by powers of δ^2 and are negligible. The only exception from this occurs when ϵ becomes very small. In this case the subtraction cross section is dominated by soft gluons being radiated into the cone which give rise to a logarithmic dependence on ϵ and eventually lead to an infrared divergence at $\epsilon = 0$ [4]. The reason for this is simple: A *completely* isolated cross section, with no hadronic energy at all in the isolation cone, is not a perturbatively well-defined quantity for a massless particle [4]. Although in reality ϵ is fixed by the experimental resolution, it is necessary to keep the contributions which are logarithmically dependent on ϵ in order to improve the accuracy of the approximation for the subtraction piece. Thus schematically we have the following structure of our approximated subtraction cross section:

$$d\sigma_{dir}^{sub} = A \ln \delta + B + C\delta^2 \ln \epsilon \ , \qquad (3)$$

where the coefficients A, B and C are functions of the kinematical variables. Note that A and B also depend on ϵ due to the isolation cuts. The contributing subprocesses to $d\sigma_{dir}^{sub}$ are the same as in the completely inclusive calculation $(d\sigma_{dir})$ [5, 6], namely $q\bar{q} \to \gamma gg$, $qg \to \gamma qg$, $gg \to \gamma q\bar{q}$, etc. Only the processes with (anti)quarks in the final state can lead to contributions to A and B whereas, as discussed above, only the first two subprocesses which involve gluon radiation can give $\ln \epsilon$ terms and contribute to C. The explicit result for $d\sigma_{dir}^{sub}$ can be found in ref. [11], where also the good accuracy of the small-cone approximation was proven over a wide range of the isolation parameters by comparing to a Monte-Carlo calculation.

In order to isolate the NLO fragmentation contribution, a procedure similar to that outlined above for the direct case can be followed [11]. For the NLO (α_s^3) partonic $2 \to 3$ subprocesses, the LO z-cut $\max(z_{min}, 1/(1+\epsilon))$ introduced above is in general no longer sufficient since a non-fragmenting parton from the $2 \to 3$ subprocess can also radiate into the cone around the photon, giving rise to additional hadronic energy accompanying the photon. If this happens we have to make sure that the sum of the energies of the fragmentation remnants, E_{frag}^{rem}, plus the energy of the additional non-fragmenting parton, E', be smaller than ϵE_γ. The required isolated NLO fragmentation contribution in eq.(1) can then be written as

$$d\sigma_{frag}^{isol} = d\sigma_{frag}^{z \geq 1/(1+\epsilon)} - d\sigma_{frag}^{sub}(\delta, \epsilon) \qquad (4)$$

where $d\sigma_{frag}^{z \geq 1/(1+\epsilon)}$ is the NLO fragmentation cross section with the insufficient LO z-cut implemented which can be calculated using the program of [8], and $d\sigma_{frag}^{sub}$ is the fragmentation subtraction cross section satisfying the conditions $E_{frag}^{rem} \leq \epsilon E_\gamma$ but $E_{frag}^{rem} + E' \geq \epsilon E_\gamma$ [11]. This latter subtraction term has been calculated in the small-cone approximation in [11] with its dominant and relevant contributions given by

$$d\sigma_{frag}^{sub}(\delta, \epsilon) = \epsilon \left[(A + A' \ln \epsilon) \ln \delta + B \right] \qquad (5)$$

with new coefficients A, A' and B as compared to eq.(3). Note that each cross section in eq.(4) vanishes for $\epsilon \to 0$, due to the constraint $z \geq 1/(1+\epsilon)$, and thus the fragmentation contribution is suppressed proportional to ϵ which explains the different structure of eq.(5) as compared to (3). The question about the appropriate isolation-parameter dependent fragmentation scale $\mu_F(\delta, \epsilon)$ can obviously not be answered unambiguously. One knows, however, that μ_F roughly controls the transverse size of the jet and thus merely kinematical considerations [4] point towards $\mu_F = \delta E_\gamma$. It has, however, been shown in [11] that the total isolated NLO cross section in eq.(1) is very insensitive to the specific choice of $\mu_F(\delta, \epsilon)$ since the μ_F-dependencies almost cancel in the differences in eqs.(2) and (4) for realistically small values of ϵ.

For our actual LO and NLO calculations [13] we use for the parton distributions $f(x, \mu^2)$ in eq.(1) the LO and HO GRV distributions [14], since the predictions for the steep small-x behavior of the structure functions as well as their predicted Q^2 dependence has, so far, been fully confirmed by recent HERA measurements [15]. The appropriate LO and HO fragmentation functions $D_{q,g}^\gamma(z, \mu_F^2)$ are taken, from [9], i.e., the ones relevant for inclusive prompt photon production. We furthermore use for our calculations of the isolated photon cross sections [2] $\delta = 0.7$ and $\epsilon = 2$ GeV$/p_T^\gamma$, although a commonly used fixed value of [4] $\epsilon = 0.15$ leaves our results essentially unchanged. In Fig.1 we present our LO and NLO results [13] for the isolated total prompt photon production cross section. To illustrate the importance of the fragmentation contribution $d\sigma_{frag} \sim D_f^\gamma$ in eq.(1) at small p_T^γ ($\lesssim 20$ GeV), the 'direct' contribution in eq.(1) is shown separately in the insert. (The vertical bars indicate the scale ambiguity due to $p_T^\gamma/3 \leq \mu \leq p_T^\gamma$). It should be noted that this latter 'direct' NLO result (dash-dotted curve) is already in better agreement with the Tevatron data [2], in particular at small p_T^γ ($\lesssim 20$ GeV) [16], than the result obtained with the older (flat) experimentally already disproved [15, 18] KMRS(B$_0$) parton distributions which is about 25% smaller [19]. It should be nevertheless emphasized that the separation into a direct and fragmentation contribution depends strongly on the factorization scale (μ_F) chosen, and their absolute values are factorization scheme dependent. Only the sum of both in eq. (1) is manifestly scheme invariant at a given perturbative order ($\mathcal{O}(\alpha \alpha_s^2)$).

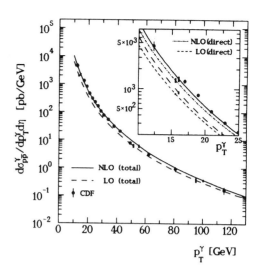

Figure 1. LO and NLO predictions [13] for isolated prompt photon production in $p\bar{p}$ collisions at $\sqrt{s} = 1.8$ TeV for $\eta = 0$, using the LO and HO GRV parton distributions [14] and fragmentation functions [9] in eq.(1) with $\mu = p_T^\gamma/2$ and $\mu_F = \delta p_T^\gamma$. These results are very similar (within 1%) to the ones obtained from averaging over the experimental rapidity range $|\eta| \leq 0.9$. The vertical bars illustrate the dependence of our results on the choice of scale: Upper edge ($\mu = p_T^\gamma/3$), lower edge ($\mu = p_T^\gamma$). The CDF data are taken from [2] and have an additional $\simeq 10\%$ normalization uncertainty.

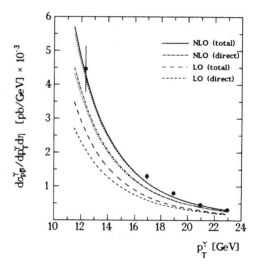

Figure 2. The LO and NLO GRV predictions of Fig.1 [13] shown on a linear scale in the small-p_T^γ region where the isolated fragmentation contributions are most important. The dotted curves result from using the NLO MRS(D$'_-$) parton distributions [20].

In order to demonstrate more clearly the important change in shape caused by the isolated NLO fragmentation contribution in the small-p_T^γ region, we show the various LO and NLO contributions [13] on a linear scale in Fig. 2. As expected [19], the NLO results are insensitive to the specific choice of parton distributions.

The agreement between data and our *total* isolated

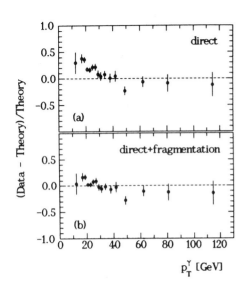

Figure 3. The isolated photon cross section data [2] compared to the NLO QCD predictions of Fig.1 [13]. The 'direct' contribution in eq.(1) is shown in (a), whereas the total (= direct + fragmentation) one is shown in (b).

predictions in Fig.1 [13] is seen better on a linear scale, as in Fig.3, where we show the default quantity (data − theory)/theory. It becomes clear from Fig.3(a) that the (factorization scheme dependent) isolated 'direct' contribution alone does *not* suffice to describe the data at $p_T^\gamma \lesssim 20$ GeV where the data appear to be significantly higher than theoretical expectations. However, the inclusion of the fragmentation contribution, Fig.3(b), appears to remove this discrepancy, taking into account the theoretically intrinsic ambiguities due to different choices of the scale μ in eq. (1) as shown in Figs. 1 and 2. Here, in Fig. 3, we have chosen $\mu = p_T^\gamma/2$ which is the favored choice obtained from the hadronic jet analysis of the CDF data [21].

Let us note that we find a similarly good agreement [22] between our total NLO results for the isolated prompt photon cross section and the D0 data [3]. It should be mentioned that the theoretical predictions as well as the data differ slightly from the ones for the CDF case since the D0 collaboration uses a different isolation criterion in restricting the hadronic energy inside a cone *annulus* of opening angles $\delta = 0.2$ and $\delta = 0.4$ [3].

We finally note that all our results are hardly changed if we use the simple asymptotic LO solutions for $D_f^\gamma(z, \mu_F^2)$, as parametrized by Owens [10]. The differences are immaterial due to the very similar shapes of $D_{q,g}^\gamma$ in the large-z region [9].

Acknowledgements

It is a pleasure to thank M. Glück, L.E. Gordon and E. Reya for a fruitful collaboration. We are also indebted to J. Huston and S.E. Kuhlmann from CDF and J. Womersley from D0 for correspondences on their recent data and for very helpful information. This work has been supported in part by the 'Bundesministerium für Forschung und Technologie', Bonn.

References

[1] J. Alitti *et al.,* (UA2 Collab.), Phys. Lett. **B263** (1991) 544.

[2] F. Abe *et al.,* (CDF Collab.), Phys. Rev. Lett. **68** (1992) 2734; Phys. Rev. **D48** (1993) 2998; FERMILAB Pub-94/208-E.

[3] D0 Collaboration, J. Kotcher, talk presented at the *9th Workshop on Proton-Antiproton Collider Physics,* Tsukuba, Japan, 1993, FERMILAB-Conf-93/387-E; J. Womersley, *private communication.*

[4] E. L. Berger and J. Qiu, Phys. Lett. **B248** (1990) 371; Phys. Rev. **D44** (1991) 2002.

[5] P. Aurenche, R. Baier, A. Douiri, M. Fontannaz and D. Schiff, Phys. Lett. **140B** (1984) 87; P. Aurenche, R. Baier, M. Fontannaz and D. Schiff, Nucl. Phys. **B297** (1988) 661.

[6] L. E. Gordon and W. Vogelsang, Phys. Rev. **D48** (1993) 3136.

[7] B. L. Combridge, J. Kripfganz and J. Ranft, Phys. Lett. **70B** (1977) 234; J.F. Owens, E. Reya and M. Glück, Phys. Rev. **D18** (1978) 1501.

[8] F. Aversa, P. Chiappetta, M. Greco and J. Ph. Guillet, Phys. Lett. **B211** (1988) 465; Nucl. Phys. **B327** (1989) 105.

[9] M. Glück, E. Reya and A. Vogt, Phys. Rev. **D48** (1993) 116.

[10] J. F. Owens, Rev. Mod. Phys. **59** (1987) 465.

[11] L. E. Gordon and W. Vogelsang, Phys. Rev. **D50** (1994) 1901.

[12] H. Baer, J. Ohnemus and J. F. Owens, Phys. Rev. **D42** (1990) 61. It should be mentioned that this Monte Carlo approach does *not* include the full fragmentation contribution in NLO ($\alpha\alpha_s^2$). Therefore these results are not strictly independent of the chosen fragmentation scheme to order $\alpha\alpha_s^2$.

[13] M. Glück, E. Reya, L.E. Gordon and W. Vogelsang, Phys. Rev. Lett. **73** (1994) 388.

[14] M. Glück, E. Reya and A. Vogt, Z. Phys. **C53** (1992) 127.

[15] I. Abt *et al.,* (H1 Collab.), Nucl. Phys. **B407** (1993) 515; M. Derrick *et al.,* (ZEUS Collab.), Phys. Lett. **B316** (1993) 412.

[16] Such an enhancement effect in the small p_T^γ region, due to the steeper CTEQ1M parton distributions [17], has been recently observed in ref. [2]. It also applies to the UA2 data at $\sqrt{s} = 630$ GeV [1] although there the discrepancy between the older (flat KMRS(B₀) distributions) 'direct' NLO expectations [2] and the small-p_T^γ ($\gtrsim 18$ GeV) data is less pronounced.

[17] J. Botts *et al.,* (CTEQ Collab.), Phys. Lett. **B304** (1993) 159.

[18] P. Amaudruz *et al.,* (NMC), Phys. Lett. **B295** (1992) 159.

[19] Our NLO results in Fig.1 remain practically unchanged if the MRS(D₋′) [20] parton distributions are used, since our results are at most 5 % larger.

[20] A. D. Martin, W. J. Stirling and R. G. Roberts, Phys. Lett. **B306** (1993) 145.

[21] S.D. Ellis, Z. Kunszt and D.E. Soper, Phys. Rev. Lett. **64** (1990) 2121.

[22] W. Vogelsang, work in preparation.

Recent Progress in the Theory of
Heavy Quark and Quarkonium Production
in Hadronic Collisions

Michelangelo L Mangano ‖

Istituto Nazionale di Fisica Nucleare, Pisa ITALY

Abstract

We review heavy quark and quarkonium production in high energy hadronic collisions. We discuss the status of the theoretical calculations and their uncertainties. We then compare the current theoretical results with the most recent measurements from the Tevatron Collider experiments

Heavy quark production in high energy hadronic collisions consitutes a benchmark process for the study of perturbative QCD. The comparison of experimental data with the predictions of QCD provides a necessary check that the ingredients entering the evaluation of hadronic processes (partonic distribution functions and higher order corrections) are under control and can be used to evaluate the rates for more exotic phenomena or to extrapolate the calculations to even higher energies. Likewise, production of quarkonium states, in addition to provide yet another interesting framework for the study of the boundary between perturbative and non-perturbative QCD, is important in view of the possible use of exclusive charmonium decays of b hadrons for the detection of CP violation phenomena.

In this presentation we review the current status of theoretical calculations, and discuss the implications of the most recent experimental measurements of b quarks and charmonium states performed at the Tevatron $p\bar{p}$ Collider. For more complete reviews, including a discussion of heavy quark production at fixed target energies, see Refs. [1, 2].

1. Open Flavour Production: Theory Overview

To start with, we briefly report on the current status of the theoretical calculations. One has to distinguish between calculations performed at a complete but fixed order in perturbation theory (PT), and those performed resumming classes of potentially large logarithmic contributions which arise at any order in PT. The exact matrix elements squared for heavy quark production in hadronic collisions are fully known up to the $\mathcal{O}(\alpha_s^3)$, both for real and virtual processes. These matrix elements have been used to evaluate at NLO the total production cross section [3], single particle inclusive distributions [4] and two particle inclusive distributions (a.k.a. correlations) [5].

Three classes of large logarithms can appear in the perturbative expansion for heavy quark production:

1 $[\alpha_s \log(S/m_Q^2)]^n \sim [\alpha_s \log(1/x_{Bj})]^n$ terms, where S is the hadronic CM energy squared. These small x effects are possibly relevant for the production of charm or bottom quarks at the current energies, while should have no effect on the determination of the *top* cross section, given the large t mass. Several theoretical studies have been performed [6], and the indications are that b production cross sections should not increase by more than 30-50% at Tevatron energies due to these effects.

‖ Address after Febr. 1, 1995: CERN, TH Division, Geneva, Switzerland.

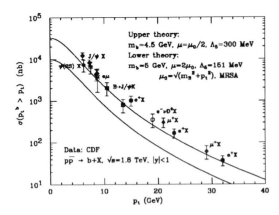

Figure 1. Bottom cross sections at CDF.

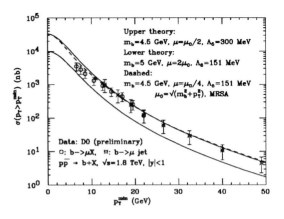

Figure 2. Bottom cross sections at D0.

2 $[\alpha_s \log(m_Q/p_{QQ}^T)]^n$ terms, where p_{QQ}^T is the transverse momentum of the heavy quark pair. These contributions come from the multiple emission of initial state soft gluons, similarly to standard Drell Yan corrections. These corrections have been studied in detail in the case of top production, where the effect is potentially large due to the heavy top mass [7]. They are not relevant for the redefinition of the total cross section of b quarks, but affect the kinematical distributions of pairs produced just above threshold [8], or in regions at the edge of phase space, such as $\Delta\phi = \pi$.

3 $[\alpha_s \log(p_T/m_Q)]^n$ terms, where p_T is the transverse momentum of the heavy quark. These terms arise from multiple collinear gluons emitted by a heavy quark produced at large transverse momentum, or from almost collinear branching of gluons into heavy quark pairs. Again these corrections are not expected to affect the total production rates, but will contribute to the large p_T distributions of c and b quarks. No effect is expected for the top at current energies. These logarithms can be resummed using a fragmentation function formalism. A first step in this direction was taken by Cacciari and Greco [9], who convoluted the NLO fragmentation functions for heavy quarks [10] with the NLO parton level cross section for production of massless partons[11]. A significant improvement in the stability w.r.t. scale changes has been observed for $p_T > 50$ GeV.

2. Single Inclusive Bottom Production

The status of b production at hadron colliders has been quite puzzling for some time. Data collected by UA1[12] at the CERN Collider ($\sqrt{S}$=630 GeV) were in good agreement with theoretical expectations based on the NLO QCD calculations[4]. On the contrary, the first measurements performed at 1.8 TeV by the CDF[13] experiment at the Fermilab Collider showed a significant discrepancy with the same calculation.

Owing to recent progress, the situation has considerably clarified. The latest results from the Fermilab 1.8 TeV $p\bar{p}$ Collider have been presented at this Conference by CDF[14] and by the new experiment, D0[15]. The current situation is summarized in Figs. 1 and 2, showing a comparison of the theoretical expectations with the results from CDF and D0 for integrated p_T distributions of b quarks.

The theoretical curves require some explanation. First of all, they do not differ much from the original prediction[4] using the DFLM structure functions. New structure function fits, including the first results from HERA, have recently become available. We use in our prediction one of these sets, namely MRSA[16]. Since the values of x probed by b production at the Tevatron in the currently measured p_T range only cover the region $x > 5 \times 10^{-3}$, we observe no significant change relative to the results obtained using older fits.

The second important point is the choice of a range for Λ_5. Deep inelastic scattering results tend to favour small values of Λ. For example, the set MRSA uses $\Lambda_5 = 151$ MeV. On the other hand, LEP data favour a higher value: the central value of Λ_5 at LEP is around 300 MeV. This value is also supported by other lower-energy results, such as the τ hadronic width (for a review of Λ_5 determinations, see the work by Catani[17]). It is therefore sensible to use the range from 151 to 300 MeV for Λ_5.

The upper curves in Fig.1 and Fig.2 correspond to the PDF set MRSA[16], $\Lambda_5 = 300$ MeV, $m_b = 4.5$ GeV and $\mu_R = \mu_F = \sqrt{p_T{}^2 + m_b^2}/2$. The lower curves correspond to $\Lambda_5 = 151$ MeV, $m_b = 5$ GeV and $\mu_R = \mu_F = 2\sqrt{p_T{}^2 + m_b^2}$. In the absence of fits with Λ_5 frozen to the desired values we chose to simply change the value of Λ_5 in the partonic cross section. A discussion of this

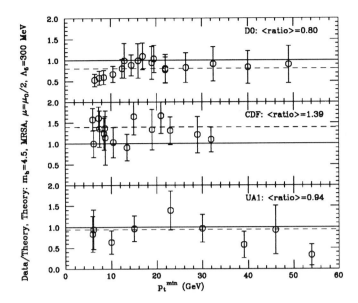

Figure 3. Ratio of data and theory for the integrated b p_T distribution at UA1, CDF and D0.

choice can be found in [1].

Studies shown in Ref. [1] also indicate that pre-HERA and post-HERA PDF sets predict b cross sections which do not differ by more than 5% within a large range of p_T. While such a stability is partly artificial, being related to the large overlap of correlated measurements entering the determination of the parton distribution fits, it however suggests that by now the uncertainty in the structure functions does not leave much room by itself for significant changes in the expected b cross section at Tevatron energies.

Coming back to the comparison of theory and data, from Fig.1 we see that the CDF data points are now consistent with the fixed-order theoretical prediction, although on the high side. The D0 points, instead, comfortably sit within the theoretical range. In order to better compare data among themselves and with theory, we plot the ratio between data points and the upper theoretical predition on a linear scale (Fig.3). From this figure we see that the UA1 and D0 data are well consistent with the upper theoretical curve, while CDF points are slightly above. Until the apparent difference between D0 and CDF will be understood, it is therefore appropriate to conclude that at present no significant discrepancy between theory and data or between data at different energies is being observed. Once the experimental statistics and systematics will be further reduced, it will be reasonable to assume that residual discrepancies of the same order as those currently observed may be explained in terms of small-x effects. Additional theoretical studies of these effects, such as a better understanding of the matching with the fixed-order next-to-leading-order calculations, should therefore be pursued.

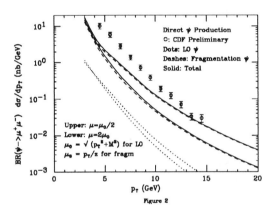

Figure 4. Preliminary CDF data for prompt ψ production (O) compared with theoretical predictions of the total fragmentation contribution (solid curves) and the total leading-order contribution (dashed curves).

3. Charmonium Production

The J/ψ and ψ' states are of particular interest since they are produced in abundance and are relatively easy to detect at a collider such as the Tevatron. In earlier calculations of direct charmonium production at large transverse momentum (p_T) in $p\bar{p}$ collisions [19] , it was assumed that the leading-order diagrams give the dominant contributions to the cross section. These calculations did not reproduce all aspects of the available data [20, 13], suggesting that there are other important production mechanisms. It was pointed out by Braaten and Yuan [21] in 1993 that fragmentation processes, while formally of higher order in the strong coupling constant α_s, will dominate at sufficiently

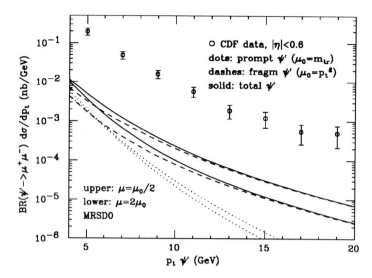

Figure 5. Preliminary CDF data for prompt ψ' production (O) compared with theoretical predictions of the total fragmentation contribution (solid curves) and the total leading-order contribution (dashed curves).

large p_T. The relevant fragmentation functions for the production of the S-wave and P-wave states have all been calculated to leading order in α_s ([21]-[27]). Explicit calculations of the contribution to ψ production at the Tevatron from the fragmentation of gluons and charm quarks have recently been completed by several groups [2, 28, 29]

In Fig.4, the sum of the fragmentation and of the leading-order contributions are compared with preliminary CDF data for prompt ψ production [30, 14]. ψ's from χ production and decay are included, both in the theory curves and in the data. The contribution to ψ production from b-hadron decays has instead been removed from the data via detection of the secondary vertex from which the ψ's originate [30, 14]. While the shapes of the leading-order curve and the fragmentation curve are both consistent with the data over the range of p_T that is available, the normalization of the leading-order contribution is too small by more than an order of magnitude. The fragmentation contribution has the correct normalization to within a factor of 2 or 3, which can be easily accounted for by the uncertainties of such a LO calculation (for a discussion of these uncertainties, see [2]). We conclude that the fragmentation calculation is not inconsistent with the CDF data on prompt ψ production. A similar conclusion can be reached [2], after inclusion of the $b \rightarrow \psi$ contributions, from a comparison with the D0 data [15].

We next consider the production of ψ', which should not receive any contributions from known higher charmonium states. The ψ' fragmentation contribution can be obtained from the $g \rightarrow \psi$, $c \rightarrow \psi$, and $\gamma \rightarrow \psi$ fragmentation contribution simply by multiplying

by the ratio of the electronic widths of the ψ' and ψ. The results are shown in Fig.5, along with the preliminary CDF data [30]. Again the contribution from b-hadron decays has been subtracted using the secondary vertex information. In striking contrast to the case of ψ production, the normalization of the fragmentation contribution to ψ' production is too small by more than an order of magnitude. That there is such a large discrepancy between theory and experiment in the case of ψ', but not for ψ, is extremely interesting. It suggests that there are other important mechanisms for production of S-wave states at large p_T beyond those that have presently been calculated. While such processes would certainly affect ψ production as well, their effect may not be as dramatic because of the large contribution from χ_c-production in the case of the ψ.

One possible such mechanism is the process $gg \rightarrow \psi gg$, with a gluon exchanged in the t-channel, which we expect to be at least as large as the direct and fragmentation processes calculated so far in the relevant region of p_T. However, this would not be enough to explain the factor of 30 or so observed discrepancy. A more likely possibility is that as yet undetected higher charmonium states, with significant BR's into ψ', can be produced with large rates in $p\bar{p}$ collisions. At this meeting, an interesting possibility was raised by F. Close [31]: possible hybrid charmonium states ($c\bar{c}g$ hadrons) are expected to have masses around 4.2 GeV, below the threshold for their only open charm decay to $\bar{D}D^{**}$. If such states existed, they would have large BR's into $\psi'\gamma$ or $\psi'\eta$. Other suggestions have also been made, including the possibility of 2^3P (χ-like) states [31, 32, 33]. Since the production rate for these states would be very big, even relatively small BR's could easily accomodate the current puzzling rate [33]. Searches for resonances in such channels are therefore encouraged.

4. Conclusions

Significant progress has taken place in this field over the past few years, both in theory and experiments. The latest measurements at 1.8 TeV indicate an acceptable agreement between the data and NLO QCD predictions for the b inclusive p_T spectrum, and the presence now of two experiments will hopefully reduce experimental uncertainties. Previously detected discrepancies, observed in the inclusive ψ final states, are now attributed to large sources of ψ direct production. New theoretical work has explained the abundance of 1^3S production (mostly understood as coming from gluon fragmentation into χ states), but cannot as yet account for the observed 2^3S rate. The possibility that new and possibly exotic charmonium states are being produced and observed at the highest energies available today opens perhaps new interesting frontiers for the already rich field of hadronic collider physics.

Acknowledgements

The work presented in this talk was carried out in collaboration with E. Braaten, M. Doncheski, S. Fleming, S. Frixione, P. Nason and G. Ridolfi. This work is supported in part by the EEC Programme "Human Capital and Mobility", Network "Physics at High Energy Colliders", contract CHRX-CT93-0357 (DG 12 COMA).

References

[1] S. Frixione, M. Mangano, P. Nason and G. Ridolfi, CERN-TH.7292/94 (1994), to appear in Nucl. Phys. B.

[2] E. Braaten, M. Doncheski, S. Fleming and M.L. Mangano, *Phys. Lett.* **333B** (1994), 548.

[3] P. Nason, S. Dawson and R. K. Ellis, *Nucl. Phys.* **B303** (1988), 607; W. Beenakker, H. Kuijf, W.L. van Neerven and J. Smith, *Phys. Rev.* **D40** (1989), 54.

[4] P. Nason, S. Dawson and R. K. Ellis, *Nucl. Phys.* **B327** (1988), 49 ; W. Beenakker et al., *Nucl. Phys.* **B351** (1991), 507.

[5] M. Mangano, P. Nason and G. Ridolfi, *Nucl. Phys.* **B373** (1992), 295.

[6] J.C. Collins and R.K. Ellis, *Nucl. Phys.* **B360** (1991), 3; S. Catani, M. Ciafaloni and F. Hautmann, *Nucl. Phys.* **B366** (1991), 135; E.M. Levin, M.G. Ryskin and Yu.M. Shabelsky, *Phys. Lett.* **260B** (1991), 429.

[7] E. Laenen, J. Smith and W.L. van Neerven, *Nucl. Phys.* **B369** (1992), 543.

[8] E. Berger and R. Meng, *Phys. Rev.* **D49** (1994), 3248.

[9] M. Cacciari and M. Greco, Univ. of Pavia FNT/T-93/43, hep-ph/9311260.

[10] B. Mele and P. Nason, *Nucl. Phys.* **B361** (1991), 626

[11] F. Aversa et al., *Phys. Lett.* **210B** (1988), 225; *Z. Phys.* **C49** (459), 1991; S. Ellis, Z. Kunszt, D. Soper, *Phys. Rev. Lett.* **62** (1989), 2188; **64** (1990), 2121.

[12] C. Albajar et al., UA1 Coll., *Phys. Lett.* **256B** (1991), 121.

[13] F. Abe et al., CDF Coll., *Phys. Rev. Lett.* **68** (1992), 3403; **69**(1992)3704; **71**(1993)500, 2396 and 2537.

[14] K. Byrum, CDF Coll., presented at this Conference.

[15] D. Hedin and L. Markosky, D0 Coll., presented at this Conference.

[16] A.D. Martin, W.J. Stirling and R.G. Roberts, Rutherford Lab preprint RAL-94-055, DTP/94/34 (1994).

[17] S. Catani, preprint DFF 194/11/93, to appear in the *Proceedings of the EPS conference*, Marseille, 1993.

[18] E.L. Berger and D. Jones, *Phys. Rev.* **D23** (1981), 1521; R. Baier and R. Rückl, *Z. Phys.* **C19** (1983), 251; B. Humpert, *Phys. Lett.* **184B** (1987), 105; R. Gastmans, W. Troost and T.T. Wu, *Nucl. Phys.* **B291** (1987), 731; E.W.N. Glover, A.D. Martin and W.J. Stirling, *Z. Phys.* **C38** (1988), 473; E.W.N. Glover, F. Halzen and A.D. Martin, *Phys. Lett.* **185B** (1987), 441.

[19] C. Albajar et al., UA1 Coll., *Phys. Lett.* **256B** (1991), 112.

[20] E. Braaten and T.C. Yuan, *Phys. Rev. Lett.* **71** (1993) 1673.

[21] C.-H. Chang and Y.-Q. Chen, *Phys. Lett.* **B284** (1991) 127; *Phys. Rev.* **D46** (1992) 3845.

[22] A.F. Falk, M. Luke, M.J. Savage, and M.B. Wise, *Phys. Lett.* **B312** (1993) 486.

[23] E. Braaten, K. Cheung, T.C. Yuan, *Phys. Rev.* **D48** (1993) 4230.

[24] E. Braaten and T.C. Yuan, Fermilab preprint FERMILAB-PUB-94/040-T (1994).

[25] T.C. Yuan, U.C. Davis preprint UCD-94-2 (1994);

[26] S. Fleming, Fermilab preprint FERMILAB-PUB-94/074-T (1994).

[27] M. Cacciari and M. Greco, INFN preprint, FNT/T-94/13, hep-ph/9405241.

[28] D.P. Roy and K. Sridhar, CERN-TH.7329/94, hep-ph/9406386.

[29] CDF Coll., Fermilab-Conf-94/136-E.

[30] F. Close, Rutherford Preprint, RAL 94-093 (1994).

[31] P. Cho, M.B. Wise and S.P. Trivedi, FNAL-PUB 94/256-T.

[32] D.P. Roy and K. Sridhar, CERN-TH.7434/94.

Paper presented at XXVII Int. Conf. on High Energy Physics: Session Pa-11
Glasgow, UK, 20–27 July 1994

QCD Corrections to the Z Boson Width*

J.H.Kühn

Institut für Theoretische Teilchenphysik
Universität Karlsruhe
D-76128 Karlsruhe, Germany

Abstract

Radiative QCD corrections significantly influence the theoretical predictions for the decay rates of the Z. The status of QCD calculations to the hadronic Z width is reviewed. The role of mass corrections from bottom quark final states is emphasized. An estimate of the theoretical uncertainties is given. New results for quartic mass terms of order $\mathcal{O}(\alpha_s)$ are presented. The impact of secondary radiation of bottom quarks on the determination of $\Gamma(Z \rightarrow b\bar{b})$ is discussed. The importance of precision measurements of α_s just below the bottom meson threshold is emphasized.

1. Introduction

Since experiments at the e^+e^- storage ring LEP started data taking a few years ago, more than 7 million events have been collected at the Z resonance. Besides the electroweak sector of the Standard Model, LEP provides an ideal laboratory for the investigation of strong interactions. Due to their purely leptonic initial state events are very clean from both theoretical and experimental point of view and represent the "golden" place for testing QCD. From cross section measurements (as well as from the analysis of event topologies) the strong coupling constant can be extracted with a present value [1] of $\alpha_s = 0.126 \pm 0.005 \pm 0.002$. Other observables which are measurable with very high precision are the (partial) Z decay rates into hadrons and bottom quarks. In the future the relative uncertainty of the partial decay rate into b quarks $\Delta\Gamma_b/\Gamma_b$ may become even smaller than one percent and an experimental error for α_s of 0.002 may be achieved.

The energy region of around 10 GeV just below the $B\bar{B}$ threshold will be covered with high statistics at future B meson factories. The cross section between the charm and bottom thresholds can be measured at the BEPC storage ring. These measurements could provide a precise value for α_s and — even more important — a beautiful proof of the running of the strong coupling constant.

In view of this experimental situation theoretical predictions with comparable or even higher accuracy become mandatory and higher order radiative corrections are required. Significant improvements in these calculations have been achieved in the last years and will be reviewed.

2. The Z Boson Width

2.1. Results for Massless Quarks

Higher order QCD corrections to e^+e^- annihilation into hadrons were first calculated for the electromagnetic case in the the approximation of massless quarks. Considering the annihilation process through the Z boson, numerous new features and subtleties become relevant at the present level of precision. An important distinction, namely "nonsinglet" versus "singlet" diagrams, originates from two classes of diagrams with intrinsically different topology and resulting charge structure. The first class of diagrams consists of nonsinglet contributions with one fermion

* Work supported by BMFT contract 056KA93P.

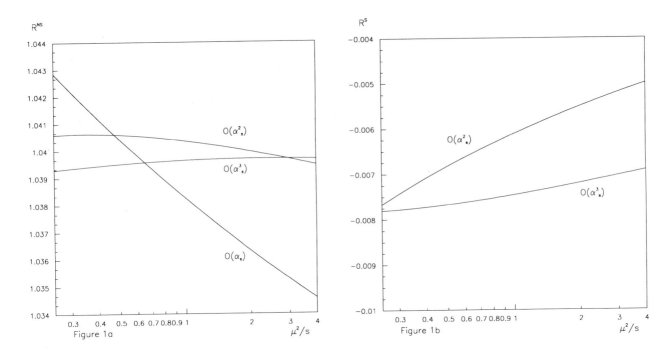

Figure 1. Renormalization scale dependence of the nonsinglet (a) and the axial singlet (b) massless QCD corrections ($\alpha_s(M_Z^2) = 0.12$).

loop coupled to the external currents. All these amplitudes are proportional to the square of the quark charge. QCD corrections corresponding to these diagrams contribute a correction factor which is independent from the current under consideration. Singlet contributions arise from a second class of diagrams where two currents are coupled to two different fermion loops and hence can be cut into two parts by cutting gluon lines only. They cannot be assigned to the contribution from one individual quark species. In the axial vector and the vector case the first contribution of this type arises in order $\mathcal{O}(\alpha_s^2)$ and $\mathcal{O}(\alpha_s^3)$ respectively. Each of them gives rise to a charge structure different from the nonsinglet terms.

The nonsinglet terms have been calculated in [3] and [4] to second and third order in α_s respectively. As shown in Figure 1a the scale dependence of the result (evaluated in the $\overline{\text{MS}}$-scheme and for a renormalization scale μ^2 between $s/4$ and $4s$) is reduced considerably through the inclusion of higher order terms. The dependence of the result due to the renormalization scale is an indicator for the influence of yet uncalculated higher order QCD corrections. The remaining variation of R_{NS} of about $+0.4/-3.5 \cdot 10^{-4}$ for $\alpha_s(M_Z^2) = 0.12$ translates into an uncertainty in α_s of $+0.11/-1.05 \cdot 10^{-3}$. The error estimate is in itself strongly dependent on the actual value of α_s. These numbers are quite comparable to the effect of an $(\alpha_s/\pi)^4$ term with a coefficient around 100 as advocated in [5].

Similar observations apply for the singlet contributions to the axial current correlator (see Figure 1b). The order $\mathcal{O}(\alpha_s^2)$ term [6] still exhibits a sizable scale dependence. Inclusion of the $\mathcal{O}(\alpha_s^3)$ term [7], however, leads to a fairly stable answer. It should be emphasized that the contribution of this singlet term, which is effectively present in the axial $b\bar{b}$ rate only, is larger than the total contribution of the α_s^3 term.

3. Mass Corrections

3.1. Quadratic Mass Corrections

The calculation of higher order QCD corrections with massive quarks may be simplified for small masses by expanding in $m^2/s \ll 1$. The operator product expansion of current correlators, including subleading terms, provides the theoretical framework. It has been developed in [16] and applied to the present problem in [12, 13]. The expansion is simultaneously performed in α_s and the quark mass:

$$R^{V/A} = R^{(0)} + R_{V/A}^{(1)} + R_{V/A}^{(2)} \tag{1}$$

The calculation is conveniently performed in the $\overline{\text{MS}}$-scheme with the running mass as expansion parameter. It has the remarkable property that no logarithms of the large ratio s/m^2 appear in the coefficients of the quadratic (but not of the quartic) mass terms. For the vector induced rate the first coefficient vanishes and the

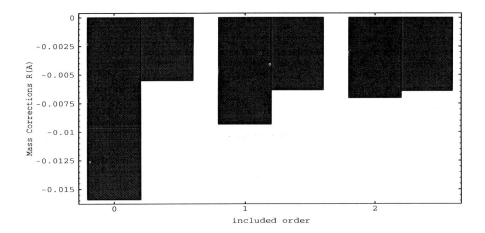

Figure 2. Mass Corrections to $R_A^{(1)}$. The left bar represents the result in the on-shell-scheme, the right one is obtained in the $\overline{\text{MS}}$-scheme.

corrections have been calculated in [8, 6, 9], [10]† and [12] respectively. For $n_f = 5$ one obtains

$$R_V^{(1)} = 12\frac{\bar{m}_b^2}{s}\frac{\alpha_s}{\pi}\left\{1 + 8.74\frac{\alpha_s}{\pi} + 45.15\left(\frac{\alpha_s}{\pi}\right)^2\right\}. \quad (2)$$

Similar considerations apply for the axial current induced two point function. In particular one can again demonstrate the absence of large logarithms. The expansion starts in this case with the Born term already. Nonsinglet terms have been evaluated in [13] to order $\mathcal{O}(\alpha_s^2)$, the leading singlet terms of order $\mathcal{O}(\alpha_s^2)$ were calculated in [14, 15]:

$$R_A^{(1)} = -6\frac{\bar{m}_b^2}{s}\left\{1 + \frac{11}{3}\frac{\alpha_s}{\pi} + \left(\frac{\alpha_s}{\pi}\right)^2\left(11.296 + \ln\frac{s}{m_t^2}\right)\right\} \quad (3)$$

As shown in Figure 2 the calculation in the on-shell scheme exhibits significant changes with the inclusion of coefficients with large logarithms. In the $\overline{\text{MS}}$-scheme the expansion is remarkably stable. The size of the corrections is comparable to the anticipated experimental precision.

3.2. Quartic Mass Corrections

The second order calculation of quartic mass corrections presented below is based on [2]. The operator product expansion included power law suppressed terms up to operators of dimension four induced by nonvanishing quark masses. Renormalisation group arguments similar to those employed already in [12, 13] allowed to deduce the $\alpha_s^2 m^4$ terms. The calculation was performed for vector and axial vector current nonsinglet correlators.

† Note that an erratum for the $\zeta(3)$ term turned out to be wrong and the originally published result proved to be correct (see [11]).

The first one is of course relevant for electron positron annihilation into heavy quarks at arbitrary energies, the second one for Z decays into b quarks and for top production at a future linear collider. Below only the results for R_V will be presented.

QCD corrections to the vector current correlator in order α_s and for arbitrary m^2/s were derived in [8]. These are conventionally expressed in terms of the pole mass denoted by m in the following. It is straightforward to expand these results in m^2/s.

$$
\begin{aligned}
R_V &= 1 - 6\frac{m^4}{s^2} - 8\frac{m^6}{s^3} \quad (4)\\
&\quad + \frac{\alpha_s}{\pi}\left[1 + 12\frac{m^2}{s} + \left(10 - 24\ln\left(\frac{m^2}{s}\right)\right)\frac{m^4}{s^2}\right.\\
&\quad \left. - \frac{16}{27}\left(47 + 87\ln\left(\frac{m^2}{s}\right)\right)\frac{m^6}{s^3}\right]
\end{aligned}
$$

The approximations to the correction function for the vector current correlator (including successively higher orders and without the factor α_s/π) are compared to the full result in Fig.3. For high energies, say for $2m_b/\sqrt{s}$ below 0.3, an excellent approximation is provided by the constant plus the m^2 term. In the region of $2m/\sqrt{s}$ above 0.3 the m^4 term becomes increasingly important. The inclusion of this term improves the agreement significantly and leads to an excellent approximation even up to $2m/\sqrt{s} \approx 0.7$ or 0.8. In order α_s the logarithms accompanying the m^4 terms can also be absorbed through a redefinition of m in terms of the $\overline{MS}$ mass [17, 18] at scale s.

$$
R_V = 1 - 6\frac{\bar{m}^4}{s^2} - 8\frac{\bar{m}^6}{s^3} \quad (5)
$$

$$
+ \frac{\alpha_s}{\pi}\left[1 + 12\frac{\bar{m}^2}{s} - 22\frac{\bar{m}^4}{s^2}\right. \quad (6)
$$

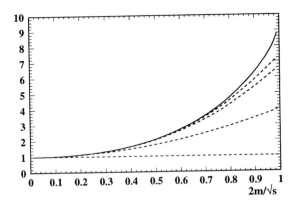

Figure 3. Comparison between the complete $\mathcal{O}(\alpha_s)$ correction function (solid line) and approximations of increasing order (dashed lines) in m^2 for vector induced rates.

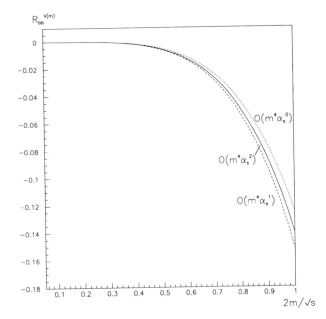

Figure 4. Contributions to R^V from m^4 terms including successively higher orders in α_s (order $\alpha_s^0/\ \alpha_s^1/\ \alpha_s^2$ corresponding to dotted/ dashed/ solid lines) as functions of $2m_{\text{pole}}/\sqrt{s}$.

$$-\frac{16}{27}\left(6\ln(\frac{\bar{m}^2}{s})+155\right)\frac{\bar{m}^6}{s^3}\Bigg]$$

This resummation is possible for the second and fourth powers of m in first order α_s and in fact for m^2 corrections to R_V and R_A in all orders of α_s. However, logarithmic terms persist in the m^4 corrections, starting from $\mathcal{O}(\alpha_s^2)$.

Motivated by the fact that the first few terms in the m^2/s expansion provide already an excellent approximation to the complete answer in order α_s, the three loop corrections have been calculated. Internal quark loops contribute in this order, giving rise to the

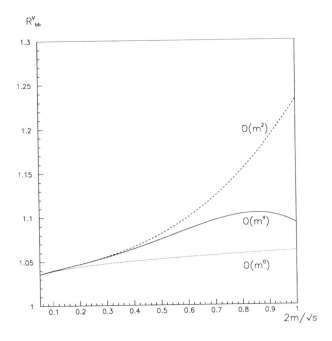

Figure 5. Predictions for R^V including successively higher orders in m^2.

terms proportional to $\sum m_i^2$ and $\sum m_i^4$ below.

$$
\begin{aligned}
R_V =\ & 1 + O(\bar{m}^2/s) - 6\frac{\bar{m}^4}{s^2}\left(1+\frac{11}{3}\frac{\alpha_s}{\pi}\right)\\
& + \left(\frac{\alpha_s}{\pi}\right)^2\frac{\bar{m}^4}{s^2}\left[f\left(\frac{1}{3}\ln\left(\frac{\bar{m}^2}{s}\right)-1.841\right)\right.\\
& \left. -\frac{11}{2}\ln\left(\frac{\bar{m}^2}{s}\right)+136.693+12\sum_i\frac{\bar{m}_i^2}{\bar{m}^2}\right.\\
& \left. -0.475\sum_i\frac{\bar{m}_i^4}{\bar{m}^4}-\sum_i\frac{\bar{m}_i^4}{\bar{m}^4}\ln\left(\frac{\bar{m}_i^2}{s}\right)\right]
\end{aligned}
\tag{7}
$$

Note that the sum over i includes also the quark coupled to the external current and with mass denoted by m. Hence in the case with one heavy quark of mass m one should set $\sum_i\frac{\bar{m}_i^4}{\bar{m}^4}=1$ and $\sum_i\frac{\bar{m}_i^2}{\bar{m}^2}=1$. In the opposite case when one considers the correlator of light (massless) quarks the heavy quark appears only through its coupling to gluons. There one finds:

$$R_V = 1 + \left(\frac{\alpha_s}{\pi}\right)^2\frac{\bar{m}^4}{s^2}\left[\frac{13}{3}-\ln\left(\frac{\bar{m}^2}{s}\right)-4\zeta(3)\right]\tag{8}$$

The Z decay rate is hardly affected by the m^4 contributions. The lowest order term evaluated with $\bar{m} = 2.6$ GeV leads to a relative suppression (enhancement) of about 5×10^{-6} for the vector (axial vector) current induced $Z\to b\bar{b}$ rate.

The situation is different in the low energy region, say several GeV above the charm or the bottom threshold. For definiteness the second case will be

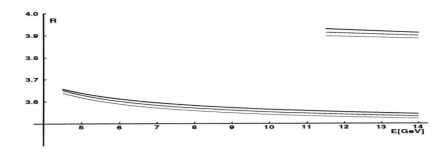

Figure 6. The ratio $R(s)$ below and above the b quark production threshold for $\alpha_s(M_Z) = 0.120, 0.125$ and 0.130. (From [19].)

considered and for simplicity all other masses will be put to zero. The contributions to R^V from m^4 terms are presented in Fig.4 as functions of $2m/\sqrt{s}$ in the range from 0.05 to 1. As input parameters $m_{\text{pole}} = 4.7\text{GeV}$ and $\alpha_s(m_Z^2) = 0.12$ have been chosen. Corrections of higher orders are added successively. The prediction is fairly stable with increasing order in α_s as a consequence of the fact that most large logarithms were absorbed in the running mass. The relative magnitude of the sequence of terms from the m^2 expansion is displayed in Fig.5. The curves for m^0 and m^2 are based on corrections up to third order in α_s with the m^2 term starting at first order. The m^4 curve receives corrections from order zero to two.

Of course, very close to threshold, say above 0.75 (corresponding to $\sqrt{s}$ below 13 GeV) the approximation is expected to break down, as indicated already in Fig.3. Below the $b\bar{b}$ threshold, however, one may decouple the bottom quark and consider mass corrections from the charmed quark within the same formalism.

Predictions for R around the $b\bar{b}$ threshold are displayed in Fig.3.2, with the $b\bar{b}$ contribution displayed seperately. A precise measurement would provide an independent determination of α_s and a beautiful proof of the running of α_s.

4. Secondary $b\bar{b}$ Production

The formulae for the QCD corrections to the total rate Γ_{had} have a simple, unambiguous meaning.

The theoretical predictions for individual $q\bar{q}$ channels, however, require additional interpretation. In fact, starting from order $\mathcal{O}(\alpha_s^2)$ it is no longer possible to assign all hadronic final states to well specified $q\bar{q}$ channels in a unique manner. For definiteness we shall try to isolate and define $\Gamma(Z \rightarrow b\bar{b})$. The thorough understanding of QCD and mass corrections is mandatory to disentangle weak corrections with a variation of about 1% for m_t between 150 and 200 GeV from QCD effects.

4.1. Non Singlet Contribution

The vector and axial vector induced rates receive (non singlet) contributions from the diagrams, where the heavy quark pair is radiated off a light $q\bar{q}$ system. The rate for this specific contribution to the $q\bar{q}b\bar{b}$ final state is given by [20]

$$
\begin{aligned}
R_{q\bar{q}b\bar{b}}^{NS} &= \frac{\Gamma_{q\bar{q}b\bar{b}}^{NS}}{\Gamma_{q\bar{q}}^{\text{Born}}} = \left(\frac{\alpha_s}{\pi}\right)^2 \frac{1}{27} \left[\ln^3 \frac{s}{m_b^2} - \frac{19}{2} \ln^2 \frac{s}{m_b^2} \right. \\
&\quad + \left(\frac{146}{3} - 12\zeta(2) \right) \ln \frac{s}{m_b^2} \\
&\quad \left. - \frac{2123}{18} + 38\zeta(2) + 30\zeta(3) \right] \\
&= \left(\frac{\alpha_s}{\pi}\right)^2 \cdot (0.922/0.987/1.059) \\
&\quad \text{for } m_b = (4.9/4.7/4.5)\,\text{GeV}.
\end{aligned}
$$

(9)

Including terms of order m_b^2/s this result is lowered by about 10%. The analytic formula for arbitrary m^2/s has been derived in [21].

Despite the fact that b quarks are present in the four fermion final state, the natural prescription is to assign these contributions to the rate into the $q\bar{q}$ channel. Therefore those events with primary light quarks and secondary bottom quarks must be subtracted experimentally from the partial rate $\Gamma_{b\bar{b}}$. This should be possible, since their signature is characterized by a large invariant mass of the light quark pair and a small invariant mass of the bottom system, which is emitted collinear to the light quark momentum. If this subtraction is not performed, the $b\bar{b}$ rate is overestimated by (for $m_b = 4.7$ GeV and $\alpha_s = 0.115\ldots0.18$)

$$\Delta \equiv \frac{\sum\limits_{q=u,d,s,c} \Gamma^{NS}_{q\bar{q}b\bar{b}}}{\Gamma_{b\bar{b}}} \approx 0.007\ldots0.016 \qquad (10)$$

A sizeable uncertainty remains in the prediction as a consequence of the large uncertainty in the effective values of α_s and m_b relevant for this lowest order calculation and the strong sensitivity of the result on these input parameters.

4.2. Singlet Contribution

The situation is more complicated for the four fermion final state from the singlet contribution which originates from the interference term $R^S_{q\bar{q}b\bar{b}}$ between the $q\bar{q}$ and $b\bar{b}$ induced amplitudes. It cannot be assigned in an unambiguous way to an individual $q\bar{q}$ partial rate.

For the vector current induced rate and after phase space integration this term vanishes as a consequence of charge conjugation (Furry's theorem).

For the axial current induced rate, however, this interference term gives a nonvanishing contribution which remains finite even in the limit $m_q \to 0$. Neglecting all masses one obtains

$$\begin{aligned} R^S_{b\bar{b}b\bar{b}} &= -\tfrac{1}{2}R^S_{b\bar{b}u\bar{u}} = +\tfrac{1}{2}R^S_{b\bar{b}d\bar{d}} \\ &= -\tfrac{1}{2}R^S_{b\bar{b}c\bar{c}} = +\tfrac{1}{2}R^S_{b\bar{b}s\bar{s}} = -0.153\left(\tfrac{\alpha_s}{\pi}\right)^2. \end{aligned} \qquad (11)$$

Among the final states from these singlet diagrams with at least one $b\bar{b}$ pair, only the $b\bar{b}b\bar{b}$ term remains after all compensations have been taken into account. Numerically it is tiny. Let us compare it with the other singlet contributions consisting of $b\bar{b}(g)$ jets. They can be assigned to $\Gamma_{b\bar{b}}$ in a unique way, although they are induced by the $b\bar{b}$ and the $t\bar{t}$ currents. These two cuts, in particular the leading term with two $b\bar{b}$ jets, dominate the four fermion final state by a factor of 20. Therefore it is suggestive to assign the total singlet contribution to $\Gamma_{b\bar{b}}$.

Acknowledgement

I would like to thank K.G. Chetyrkin and A. Kwiatkowski for an enjoyable collaboration on the topics covered in this review.

References

[1] D. Schaile, Precision Test of Electroweak Interactions, to be published in the Proc. of the 27th Int. Conf. on HEP, Glasgow, 1994.

[2] K. Chetyrkin, J.H. Kühn, Preprint TTP94–08, Karlsruhe University, June 1994.

[3] K.G. Chetyrkin, A.L. Kataev, F.V. Tkachov, Phys. Lett. B 85 (1979) 277; M. Dine, J. Sapirstein, Phys. Rev. Lett. 43 (1979) 668; W. Celmaster, R.J. Gonsalves, Phys. Rev. Lett. 44 (1980) 560.

[4] S.G. Gorishny, A.L. Kataev, S.A. Larin, Phys. Lett. 259 (1991) 144; L.R. Surguladze, M.A. Samuel, Phys. Rev. Lett. 66 (1991) 560; erratum ibid, 2416;

[5] A.L. Kataev, V.V. Starshenko, Preprint CERN-TH.7198/94.

[6] B.A. Kniehl, J.H. Kühn, Phys. Lett. B 224 (1990) 229; Nucl. Phys. B 329 (1990) 547.

[7] K. Chetyrkin, J.H. Kühn, Z.Phys.C 60 (1993) 497; Phys. Lett. 308 B (1993) 127; K.G. Chetyrkin and O.V. Tarasov, Phys. Lett. B 327 (1994) 114; S.A. Larin, T. van Ritbergen and J.A.M. Vermaseren, Phys. Lett. B 320 (1994) 159.

[8] J. Schwinger: Particles, Sources and Fields, Vol.2, Addison-Wesley 1973; J. Jersak, E. Laermann, P.M. Zerwas, Phys. Rev. D 25 (1982) 1218; T.H. Chang, K.J.F. Gaemers, W.L. van Neerven, Nucl. Phys. B202 (1980) 407. L.J. Reinders, H.Rubinstein, S. Yazaki, Phys. Rep. 127 (1985) 1.

[9] A. Djouadi, J.H. Kühn, P.M. Zerwas, Z.Phys. C46 (1990) 412.

[10] S.G. Gorishny, A.L. Kataev, S.A. Larin, Nuovo Cimento 92 (1986) 117.

[11] K.G. Chetyrkin and A. Kwiatkowski, Z. Phys. C59 (1993) 525.

[12] K.G. Chetyrkin, J.H. Kühn, Phys. Lett. B 248 (1990) 359.

[13] K.G. Chetyrkin, J.H. Kühn, A. Kwiatkowski, Phys. Lett. B 282 (1992) 221.

[14] K.G. Chetyrkin, A. Kwiatkowski, Phys. Lett. B 305 (1993) 285.

[15] K.G. Chetyrkin, A. Kwiatkowski, Phys. Lett. B 319 (1993) 307.

[16] K.G. Chetyrkin, V.P. Spiridonov, S.G. Gorishny, Phys. Lett. 160 B (1985) 149. K.G. Chetyrkin, V.P. Spiridonov, Sov. Journ. Nucl. Phys. 47 (1988) 522.

[17] R. Tarrach, Nucl. Phys. B183 (1981) 384.

[18] S. Narison, Phys. Lett. 197B (1987) 405.

[19] K. Chetyrkin, J.H. Kühn, Preprint TTP94–12, Karlsruhe University, September 1994.

[20] A.H. Hoang, M. Jeżabek, J.H. Kühn, T. Teubner, Phys. Lett. 325B (1994) 495; Erratum Phys. Lett. 327B (1994) 439.

[21] A.H. Hoang, M. Jeżabek, J.H. Kühn, T. Teubner, TTP94-11, Phys. Lett. B in print.

Measurement of hadronic spectral moments in τ decays and a determination of α_s

R. Stroynowski

Southern Methodist University, Dallas, TX 75275.

Representing the CLEO Collaboration

Abstract

This contribution describes new measurements of hadronic spectral moments made by the CLEO Collaboration and a comparison with updated results obtained by the ALEPH Collaboration.

1. Introduction

The τ is the only known lepton heavy enough to decay into hadrons. It provides a clean environment to study the hadronic weak currents and and allows for a wide range of studies of QCD effects. Within the framework of the Standard Model, which postulates lepton universality and no exotic decays, the total hadronic width of the τ is given by the difference of the total width and the partial widths for the electronic and muonic decays:

$$\Gamma(\tau \to hadrons) = \Gamma_{tot} - \Gamma_{\tau \to e} - \Gamma_{\tau \to \mu}. \quad (1)$$

In an analogy to the e^+e^- phenomenology, one can define a ratio R_τ

$$R_\tau = \frac{\Gamma(\tau^- \to \nu_\tau hadrons)}{\Gamma(\tau^- \to \nu_\tau e^- \bar{\nu}_e)} = \frac{1 - B_e - B_\mu}{B_e}, \quad (2)$$

where B_e and B_μ are the electronic and muonic branching fractions. This quantity has been calculated within the existing framework of QCD using analycity and Operator Product Expansion approaches. It has been shown that R_τ can be expressed as

$$R_\tau = N_c(V_{ud}^2 + V_{us}^2)\delta_{EW}[1 + \delta_{pert}(\alpha_s) + \delta_{non-pert} + \delta'_{EW}]. \quad (3)$$

Here, N_c describes the number of flavors, V denote K-M matrix elements, δ_{pert} is a polynomial expansion in powers of the strong coupling constant α_s, δ_{EW} and δ'_{EW} are the electroweak and mass corrections and the non-perturbative contribution $\delta_{non-pert}$ is estimated to be small. Additional information is contained, in principle, in the shape of the hadronic spectrum. Both ALEPH and CLEO Collaborations [1,2] use a procedure developed by Le Diberder and Pich [3] of extracting the value of α_s from the normalised spectral moments i.e., from the moments of the inclusive hadronic mass spectrum in tau decays. These moments are defined by the relation

$$R_\tau^{kl} = \frac{1}{\Gamma_l} \int\limits_0^{m_\tau^2} ds (1 - \frac{s}{m_\tau^2})^k (\frac{s}{m_\tau^2})^l \frac{dR_\tau}{ds}, \quad (4)$$

where s is the square of the invariant mass of the hadronic system and the moments can be normalised to R_τ

$$D^{kl} = \frac{R_\tau^{kl}}{R_\tau}. \quad (5)$$

2. Experimental procedure.

The CLEO Collaboration measured the mass spectra of the following exclusive channels in the 1-prong and 3-prong tau decays:

$$\tau^- \to \nu_\tau \pi^-$$
$$\tau^- \to \nu_\tau \pi^- \pi^0$$

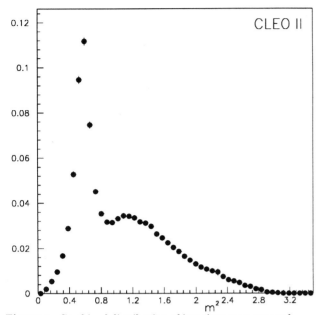

Figure 1. Combined distribution of invariant mass squared.

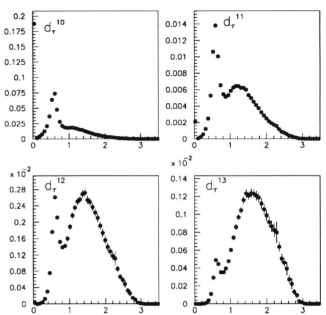

Figure 2. Differential distribution of the spectral moments for k=1 and l=0,1,2 and 3.

$$\tau^- \to \nu_\tau \pi^- \pi^0 \pi^0$$

$$\tau^- \to \nu_\tau \pi^- \pi^0 \pi^0 \pi^0$$

$$\tau^- \to \nu_\tau \pi^- \pi^0 \pi^0 \pi^0 \pi^0$$

$$\tau^- \to \nu_\tau \pi^- \pi^+ \pi^-$$

$$\tau^- \to \nu_\tau \pi^- \pi^+ \pi^- \pi^0$$

$$\tau^- \to \nu_\tau \pi^- \pi^+ \pi^- \pi^0 \pi^0$$

The single pion mass spectrum is represented by a delta function. The 5-prong decays have a very small branching fraction and have been neglected. In each decay channel the backgrounds from hadronic events, from 2 photon interactions, from pion misidentification and from migration from other tau decay channels have been removed. The mass distribution was then corrected for the detector mass resolution using a bin-by-bin correction matrix determined by Monte Carlo. Finally, each mass distribution was also corrected for the mass dependent efficiency effects.

3.   Results.

The resulting spectra have been added up using as weights the tau decay branching fractions as given by the Particle Data Group tables [4]. The resulting inclusive invariant mass squared distribution is shown in Fig.1.

The differential distributions of the spectral moments are illustrated in Fig.2. As can be expected from the functional form the l=0 and l=1 moments emphasise the single pion and the rho final state in the tau decays, while higher moments show sensitivity to higher mass resonances e.g., a_1.

Moment	Experiment	Value	Error
$D_\tau^{1,0}$	CLEO II	0.7287	0.0056
	ALEPH	0.7217	0.0065
$D_\tau^{1,1}$	CLEO II	0.1553	0.0012
	ALEPH	0.1556	0.0020
$D_\tau^{1,2}$	CLEO II	0.0559	0.0008
	ALEPH	0.0570	0.0013
$D_\tau^{1,3}$	CLEO II	0.0250	0.0005
	ALEPH	0.0259	0.0008

Table 1. Comparison of spectral moments measured by the CLEO II and ALEPH Collaborations.

The integrals of the differential distributions shown in Fig.2 provide the values of the spectral moments. They are summarised in Table 1 for the CLEO II data together with the updated results provided by the ALEPH Collaboration. All values of the spectral moments are in excellent agreements for the two sets of the measurements.

The measured values of the spectral moments were used in a global fit to extract the value of the strong coupling constant and the three non-perturbative expansion coefficients. The fit yields

$$\alpha_s(m_\tau) = 0.309 \pm 0.018 \pm 0.016, \qquad (6)$$

where the first error is experimental and the second is theoretical. A similar fit performed by the ALEPH group yielded

$$\alpha_s(m_\tau) = 0.387 \pm 0.025, \qquad (7)$$

where the error describes a sum of all experimental

and theoretical uncertainties. Since the differential spectral moments and their integrals are in excellent agreement for the two sets of measurements, the difference between the extracted values of α_s by CLEO and ALEPH is entirely due to the difference in their relative normalisation. The CLEO group used the Particle Data Group value for the electronic branching fraction B_e, while the ALEPH group used the recent ALEPH result.

It is interesting to compare this result with other determinations of the strong coupling constant. In another analysis submitted to this conference CLEO group extracted a value of α_s from the studies of jet production in e^+e^- annihilations at a cm energy just below the $\Upsilon(4S)$. The value extracted in that study

$$\alpha_s(10.53) = 0.164 \pm 0.015$$

is in good agreement with an extrapolation of the above result to the same energy

$$\alpha_s = 0.167 \pm 0.005 \pm 0.004.$$

Further extrapolation to the mass of the intermediate vector boson Z yields

$$\alpha(m_Z) = 0.114 \pm 0.003$$

which is somewhat lower then the average value from a compilation of many measurements presented by M. Shapiro at the Cornell Lepton-Photon conference last year [5]

$$\alpha_s(m_Z) = 0.123 \pm 0.006.$$

It is worth emphasising that although the absolute value of the α_s awaits the resolution of differences in the normalisation used by CLEO and ALEPH, the experimental precision of the determination appears to be more accurate than that obtained from higher energy experiments.

References

[1] J.P. Alexander *et al.*, CLEO preprint CLEO CONF 94-26, submitted to this conference.
[2] L. Duflot *et al.*, ALEPH preprint ALEPH 94-108.
[3] F. LeDiberder and A. Pich, Phys. Lett. **286B** (1992) 147.
[4] L. Montanet *et al.*, Phys. Rev. **D50** (1994) 1173.
[5] M. Shapiro, Proc. of the XVI International Symposium on Lepton and Photon Interactions, Ithaca, NY 1993, p.545; Eds. P. Drell and D. Rubin (AIP Press 1994).

Paper presented at XXVII Int. Conf. on High Energy Physics: Session Pa-11
Glasgow, UK, 20–27 July 1994

A Search for Jet Handedness in Hadronic Z^0 Decays

Hiroaki Masuda[†]

Stanford Linear Accelerator Center
Stanford University, Stanford, CA 94309, USA

Representing the SLD Collaboration

Abstract

We have searched for signatures of polarization in hadronic jets from $Z^0 \to q\bar{q}$ decays using the 'jet handedness' method. The charge asymmetry induced by the high SLC electron beam polarization was used to select quark or antiquark jets, expected to be left- and right-polarized, respectively. From our preliminary study, we find no evidence for jet handedness in our global sample nor in a sample of light quark jets. Assuming Standard Model values of quark polarizations, we set upper limits of 5.1% and 9.1% (preliminary), respectively, on the magnitude of the analyzing power of this technique at the 95% C.L. We have studied several alternative definitions of jet handedness and find no signal by any method.

1. Introduction

The transport of parton polarization through the hadronization process is of fundamental interest in QCD. It is presently an open question whether the polarization of a parton produced in a hard collision is observable via the final state fragmentation products in its resulting jet. The Z^0 resonance is an ideal place to study this issue because quarks produced in Z^0 decays are predicted by the Standard Model (SM) [1] to be highly longitudinally polarized. If a method of observing such polarization were developed, it could be applied to jets produced in a variety of hard processes, elucidating the spin dynamics of the underlying interaction.

Nachtmann [2] and Efremov *et al.* [3] have speculated that the underlying parton polarization may be observable semi-inclusively via a triple product of track momenta in a jet. They note that the simplest parity-conserving and spin-dependent amplitude has the form

$$M \propto \vec{\sigma} \cdot (\vec{k}_1 \times \vec{k}_2), \qquad (1)$$

where $\vec{\sigma}$ is the spin of the decaying particle, and the $\vec{k}_i$ are 3-momenta of two decay products. The simplest example of such a process is the strong decay of the a_1 meson [4]. For a jet an analogous triple vector product Ω may be defined which might contain information on the longitudinal parton polarization:

$$\Omega = \vec{t} \cdot (\vec{k}_1 \times \vec{k}_2), \qquad (2)$$

where $\vec{t}$ is a unit vector defining the jet axis, and $\vec{k}_1$ and $\vec{k}_2$ are the momenta of two particles in the jet chosen by some prescription, *e.g.*, the two fastest particles. The jet is defined as left- (right-) handed if Ω is negative (positive). For an ensemble of jets the handedness is defined as the asymmetry in the number of left- and right-handed jets:

$$H = \frac{N_{\Omega<0} - N_{\Omega>0}}{N_{\Omega<0} - N_{\Omega>0}}. \qquad (3)$$

It can then be asserted that

$$H = \alpha P, \qquad (4)$$

† E-mail: masuda@slacvm.bitnet

where P is the average polarization of the underlying partons in the ensemble of jets, and α is the analyzing power of the handedness method.

A method which observes such a polarization in an e^+e^- annihilation experiment could be applicable to jets resulting from lepton-hadron or hadron-hadron collisions, where the underlying parton polarization is unknown, to determine the parton polarization.

2.   Polarization

In the process $e^+e^- \to Z^0 \to q\bar{q}$ the cross sections for production of left- and right-handed quarks of flavor f are given at tree level by [1]

$$\sigma_L^f = (1 + A_f)(1 + \cos^2\theta + 2A_Z\cos\theta) \quad (5)$$
$$\sigma_R^f = (1 - A_f)(1 + \cos^2\theta - 2A_Z\cos\theta),$$

where $A_Z = (A_e - P_{e^-})/(1 - A_e P_{e^-})$; $A_f = 2v_f a_f/(v_f^2 + a_f^2)$; P_{e^-} is the longitudinal polarization of the electron beam; v_f and a_f are the vector and axial-vector couplings of fermion f to the Z^0; and θ is the polar angle of the outgoing quark with respect to the electron beam direction. The quark and antiquark in an event have opposite helicities, so we get

$$\sigma_{L(R)}^{\bar{f}}(\cos\theta) = \sigma_{R(L)}^f(-\cos\theta). \quad (6)$$

The SM predicts $A_{e,\mu,\tau} \approx 0.16$, $A_{u,c} \approx 0.67$, and $A_{d,s,b} \approx 0.94$, so the quarks are predominantly left-handed and the antiquarks are predominantly right-handed. In order to observe a net polarization in an ensemble of jets from Z^0 decay it is therefore necessary to distinguish quark jets from antiquark jets.

This can be achieved at the SLAC Linear Collider (SLC) where Z^0 bosons are produced in collisions of highly longitudinally polarized electrons with unpolarized positrons. In 1993 the average electron beam polarization was 0.630 ± 0.011 [6]. In this case the SM predicts a large difference in polar angle distributions between quarks and antiquarks, providing an unbiased separation of quark and antiquark jets. We define the 'helicity-based' polarization of jets at a given $\cos\theta$:

$$P_{hel}(\cos\theta) \equiv \frac{\sigma_R^f + \sigma_R^{\bar{f}} - \sigma_L^f - \sigma_L^{\bar{f}}}{\sigma_R^f + \sigma_R^{\bar{f}} + \sigma_L^f + \sigma_L^{\bar{f}}} = -2\frac{A_Z\cos\theta}{1 + \cos^2\theta}. \quad (7)$$

This jet polarization is independent of flavor, and reaches 0.72 and 0.52 in magnitude at large $|\cos\theta|$ for beam polarizations of -0.63 and $+0.63$, respectively. An alternative variable is the 'chirality-based' polarization of jets:

$$P_{chi}^f \equiv \frac{\sigma_R^f - \sigma_R^{\bar{f}} - \sigma_L^f + \sigma_L^{\bar{f}}}{\sigma_R^f + \sigma_R^{\bar{f}} + \sigma_L^f + \sigma_L^{\bar{f}}} = -A_f. \quad (8)$$

This jet polarization is independent of $\cos\theta$ and electron beam polarization but depends on quark flavor. It is accessible by charge ordering of the tracks used in the analysis as described below. The experimental challenge is to find observables sensitive to one or both of these expected jet polarizations.

3.   Handedness Measurement

In this paper we present the preliminary results of a search for jet handedness using a sample of approximately 50,000 hadronic Z^0 decays collected by the SLD experiment [5] in 1993. Electrons of mean longitudinal polarization $\pm 63\%$ were used to produce Z^0 bosons at the SLC. We have applied the methods suggested in [3, 4] and [10], which we also extended to be more inclusive. In each case we used both the helicity- and chirality-based methods of defining Ω and hence H. A handedness signal may be diluted in heavy quark events, $Z^0 \to c\bar{c}$ or $b\bar{b}$, since a large fraction of tracks in each jet are from the decays of a spinless heavy meson, and Dalitz *et al.* have concluded [7] that any effect resulting from D^* or B^* decays should be very small. We therefore divided our data cleanly into samples of light, $Z^0 \to u\bar{u}$, $d\bar{d}$ or $s\bar{s}$, and heavy flavor events using hadron lifetime information and sought evidence for jet handedness in each.

The trigger and initial selection of hadronic events is described in [6]. The analysis presented here is based on charged tracks measured in the Central Drift Chamber, and in the vertex detector. A set of cuts was applied to the data to select well-measured tracks and quark and antiquark jets in $Z^0 \to q\bar{q}$ events well contained within the detector acceptance. Tracks were required to have (i) a closest approach to the beam axis within 5 cm, and within 10 cm along the beam axis from the measured interaction point, (ii) a polar angle θ with respect to the beam axis with $|cos\theta| < 0.8$, and (iii) a minimum momentum transverse to this axis of $p_\perp > 150 \text{MeV/c}$. Events were required to contain a minimum of five such tracks, a thrust axis direction with respect to the beam axis, θ_T, within $|\cos\theta_T| < 0.71$, and a minimum charged visible energy greater than 20 GeV, where all tracks were assigned the charged pion mass. Two-jet events were selected using the JADE clustering algorithm [8] at $y_{cut} = 0.03$, with the requirement that the jet acollinearity angle be less than $20°$. From our 1993 data samples, a total of 17,853 events survived these cuts. The contamination from background sources was estimated to be $0.3 \pm 0.1\%$, dominated by $\tau^+\tau^-$ events.

In addition to considering this global sample, events were classified as being of light (u, d, or s) or heavy (c or b) quark origin based on impact parameters of charged tracks. The 9,977 events containing no track with impact parameter transverse to the beam axis more than 3σ from the collision point were assigned to the light quark sample, and all other events were assigned to the heavy quark sample. The purities of these two samples were estimated from simulations to be 84% and 70% respectively [9].

3.1. Method A

Following [4] we first considered the three highest momentum tracks in each jet in their rest frame if they had total charge ± 1. The invariant mass of both oppositely charged pairs was required to be in the range $0.6 < m < 1.6$ GeV/c^2. The tracks forming the higher mass pair were used to calculate $\Omega_{hel} = \vec{t} \cdot (\vec{k}_> \times \vec{k}_<)$ and $\Omega_{chi} = \vec{t} \cdot (\vec{k}_+ \times \vec{k}_-)$, where $|k_>| > |k_<|$, and $\vec{t}$ is the thrust axis signed so as to point along the jet direction. The distribution of Ω_{hel} for left- and right-handed electron beams and for forward ($\vec{t}_Z > 0$) and backward ($\vec{t}_Z < 0$) jets, and Ω_{chi} are shown in Fig. 1 for the light flavor sample.

A signal would be visible as a shift in this distribution, which in the case of the helicity-based analysis is of opposite sign for events produced with left- and right-handed electron beam polarization and for forward and backward jets. All the distributions appear to be symmetric about $\Omega = 0$, implying that any jet handedness is small.

The jet handedness was calculated according to Eq. (3) separately for each case. Results are summarized in Table 1. In all cases, the measured handedness is consistent with zero. Analyzing powers were calculated from Eq. (4). For the helicity-based analysis, the analyzing powers of the four helicity samples were then combined. The results are shown in Table 2. Since all analyzing powers are consistent with zero, we set upper limits at the 95% confidence level on the magnitudes of the analyzing power, also shown in Table 2.

We extended this method to use the N_{lead} highest momentum particles in each jet, with $3 \leq N_{lead} \leq 12$. We considered all zero charge pairs i,j among these N_{lead} particles, without imposing mass cuts, and calculated Ω_{hel}^{ij} and Ω_{chi}^{ij} for each pair in the N_{lead}-particle rest frame. Jets with fewer than N_{lead} tracks were excluded. The Ω^{ij} were then averaged to give Ω_{chi}^{jet} and Ω_{hel}^{jet}. The calculated jet handedness for this method is consistent with zero for all N_{lead}, both helicity- and chirality-based Ω definitions, and the global, light, and heavy flavor samples. For $N_{lead} \leq 10$, upper limits on the magnitudes of the analyzing powers in the range 5-9% can be derived, after which the sample size limits our accuracy.

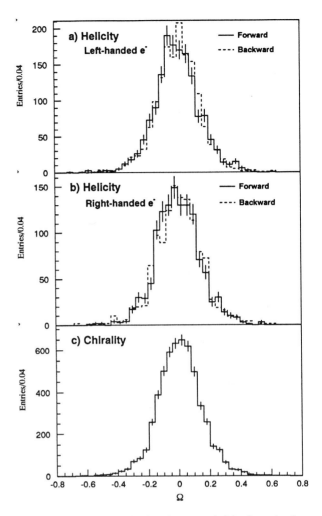

Figure 1. Measured distribution of (a) Ω_{hel} in forward hemisphere (solid histogram) and backward hemisphere (dashed histogram) with left-handed electron beam, (b) with right-handed electron beam, and (c) Ω_{chi} for the light flavor sample. Errors are statistical only. Errors on Ω_{chi} in the forward and backward hemispheres are added in quadrature and plotted only with Ω_{chi} in the forward hemisphere for clarity.

3.2. Method B

Following [10] we then attempted to select pairs of tracks likely to contain quarks from the same string breakup. In studies using the JETSET [11] Monte Carlo we found the relative rapidity with respect to the jet axis of tracks in a pair to be useful for this. Requiring opposite charge does not improve this selection, but was used in the chirality-based analysis.

In each jet the tracks were ordered in rapidity and assigned a number n_i, such that $1 \leq n_i \leq n_{tracks}$, where $n_i = 1$ for the track with highest rapidity. We then required pairs of tracks i,j to have $|n_i - n_j| < \Delta n$ and $\max(n_i, n_j) \leq n_{max}$. Since the signal is expected to increase with momentum transverse to the thrust axis, we also required $|p_{ti}| + |p_{tj}| > p_{min}$. We calculated Ω_{chi}^{ij}

Analysis	Maximum Expected Handedness (%)	Measured Jet Handedness (%)		
		All jets	Light Jets	Heavy Jets
Helicity:				
Left e^-, *forward*	-44	0.6 ± 1.9	2.1 ± 2.5	-1.2 ± 2.8
Left e^-, *backward*	$+44$	-2.5 ± 1.9	-5.1 ± 2.5	0.8 ± 2.8
Right e^-, *forward*	$+32$	1.8 ± 2.1	3.2 ± 2.8	0.1 ± 3.1
Right e^-, *backward*	-32	-2.4 ± 2.1	-1.5 ± 2.8	-3.4 ± 3.1
Chirality:	$+39$	-0.9 ± 1.0	-0.8 ± 1.3	-1.1 ± 1.5

Table 1. Expected maximum jet handedness (assuming $\alpha = +1$) and measured jet handedness in % using the first analysis.

	Analyzing Power (%)					
Analysis	All jets		Light Jets		Heavy Jets	
Helicity	-0.4 ± 2.6	(5.1)	-3.4 ± 3.4	(9.1)	3.4 ± 3.9	(9.7)
Chirality	-2.4 ± 2.6	(6.6)	-2.0 ± 3.4	(7.8)	-2.9 ± 3.8	(9.2)

Table 2. Analyzing powers of the helicity- and chirality-based analysis of jet handedness using Method A. Upper limits at the 95% C.L. on the magnitudes are shown in parentheses.

and Ω_{hel}^{ij} in the laboratory frame for each pair satisfying these criteria and took the average over all pairs for each case. Then Δn, n_{max}, and p_{min} were varied in an attempt to maximize the handedness signal. Figures 2 and 3 show the distributions of H for the light flavor sample in the helicity-based analysis for (a) left- and (b) right-handed electron beams for forward and backward jets as a function of p_{min} and Δn at fixed $n_{max} = 6$, respectively. Figure 4 shows the distribution of H for the light flavor sample in the chirality-based analysis as a function of (a) p_{min} and (b) Δn at fixed $n_{max} = 6$.

In no case did we find evidence for non-zero jet handedness. For all samples and both analyses we obtained upper limits in the range 5–9% for $n_{max} \leq 6$, $\Delta n \leq 6$, and $p_{min} < 2$ GeV/c. Statistics become poor in the potentially interesting, high-p_{min} region.

3.3. *Systematic Checks*

A number of systematic checks was performed for each method. All analysis methods were found to be insensitive to the track and event selection cuts, and to the jet-finding algorithm (we tried the E, E0, and P versions of the JADE algorithm, as well as the Geneva and Durham algorithms [12]) and y_{cut} values used to select 2-jet events. Each analysis was found to be insensitive to the values of the selection criteria for tracks used to define Ω. Each analysis was performed on samples of Monte Carlo events in which spin transport was not simulated, yielding H consistent with zero within $\pm 0.4\%$. We found no correlation between the values of Ω in the two jets in an event for any analysis method.

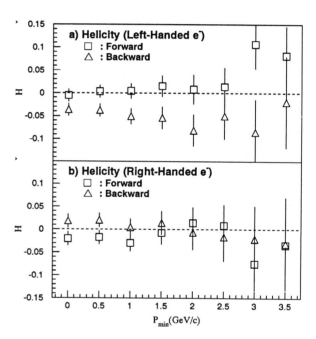

Figure 2. Measured distribution of H for (a) left- and (b) right-handed electron beams for forward (squares) and backward (triangles) as a function of p_{min} at fixed $n_{max} = 6$ for the light flavor sample in the helicity-based analysis. Errors are statistical only.

4. Conclusion

We have searched for evidence of parton polarization in hadronic Z^0 decays using two jet handedness methods suggested in [3, 4] and [10]. In an attempt to optimize a signal, we studied a wide range of parameters for each

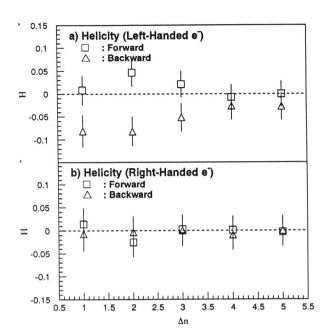

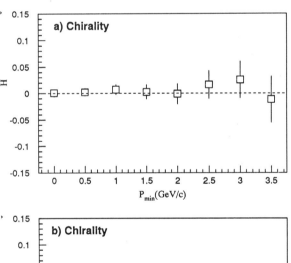

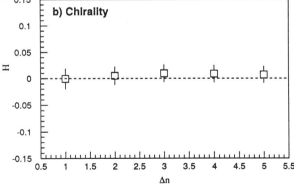

Figure 3. Same as Fig. 2 but as a function of Δn.

Figure 4. Same as Fig. 2 but in the chirality-based analysis as a function of (a) p_{min} and (b) Δn.

method. In each case we employed both helicity- and chirality-based analyses, and sought signals separately in samples of light and heavy quark jets as well as in the global sample. We found no evidence for a non-zero jet handedness, implying that the transport of quark polarization through the jet fragmentation process is small. For the method suggested in [4] we derive an upper limit of 9.1% on the magnitude of the analyzing power of a helicity-based analysis applied to a sample of light flavor jets. Averaged over all jets from $Z^0 \to q\bar{q}$ decays, a limit of 5.1% is derived. Similar limits are derived for a chirality-based analysis, as well as for all other methods we applied.

We thank the personnel of the SLAC accelerator department and the technical staffs of our collaborating institutions for their outstanding efforts on our behalf. We thank R. Dalitz, A. Efremov, R. Jaffe, and M. Ryskin for helpful comments relating to this analysis.

References

[1] See *e.g.*, B. Mele and G. Altarelli, Phys. Lett. **B299** (1993) 345.
[2] O. Nachtmann, Nucl. Phys. **B217** (1977) 314.
[3] A.V. Efremov, Phys. Lett. **B284** (1992) 394.
[4] N.A. Törnqvist, HU–TFT–92–50 (1992).
[5] SLD Design Report, SLAC–273 (1984).
[6] SLD Collab., K. Abe, *et al.*, Phys. Rev. Lett. **73** (1994) 25.
[7] R.H. Dalitz *et al.*, Zeit. Phys. **C42** (1989) 441.
[8] JADE Collab., W. Bartel *et al.*, Zeit. Phys. **C33** (1986) 23.
[9] A full discussion of flavor tagging can be found in SLD Collab., K. Abe, *et al.*, SLAC–PUB–6569, to be submitted to Phys. Rev. D.
[10] M.G. Ryskin, Phys. Lett. **B319** (1993) 346.
[11] T. Sjöstrand and M. Bengtsson, Computer Phys. Comm. **43** (1987) 367.
[12] SLD Collab., K. Abe *et al.*, Phys. Rev. Lett. **71** (1993) 2528.

Multi-color QCD at high energies and one-dimensional Heisenberg magnet

L. D. Faddeev[†‡] , G. P. Korchemsky[§¶] and L. N. Lipatov[‖]

† St.Petersburg Branch of Steklov Mathematical Institute, Fontanka 27, St.Petersburg 191011, Russia
‡ Research Institute for Theoretical Physics, University of Helsinki, SF 00014 Helsinki, Finland
§ Institute for Theoretical Physics, State University of New York at Stony Brook, New York 11794 – 3840, U.S.A.
¶ Laboratory of Theoretical Physics, JINR, Dubna 141980, Russia
‖ St. Petersburg Nuclear Physics Institute, Gatchina, 188350, Russia

Abstract

The equivalence between the multi-color QCD at high energies in a generalized leading logarithmic approximation and the one-dimensional Heisenberg magnet of spin $s = 0$ is demonstrated. It is shown, that the Schrodinger equation for the compound states of reggeized gluons has a sufficient number of conservation laws to be completely integrable. Using the holomorphic factorization of the wave functions we reduce the original quantum mechanical problem to the solution of the one-dimensional Heisenberg model with the spin operators being the generators of the $SL(2, \mathbb{C})$ group of conformal transformations.

1. Introduction

Despite of tremendous success of QCD in understanding of physics of strong interactions there exist well known phenomena like growth of the total PP and $P\bar{P}$ cross section with energy and small$-x$ behavior of the structure function of deep inelastic scattering, whose interpretation still represents a challenge. Although we have phenomenological models for description of these phenomena the understanding out of QCD is lacking. Both processes are intimately related to the Regge behavior of hadron-hadron scattering amplitudes which was a subject of intensive investigations since 60's. The problem became very actual recently after new experimental data came from Tevatron and HERA.

Considering the deep inelastic eP scattering, one uses the GLAP and BFKL evolution equations for calculation of the partonic distributions at small value of the Bjorken variable $x = Q^2/(2ME)$ where $-Q^2$ is the virtuality of the intermediate photon, E is photon energy in laboratory system and M is a mass of

proton. Namely, the GLAP equation [1] describes the Q^2-dependence of the structure functions and the BFKL equation [2] governs their $x-$dependence. In both cases the structure functions at small x and large Q^2 grow rapidly as $\exp\left(c\sqrt{\log(1/x)\log\log(Q^2)}\right)$ violating the Froissart bound $\log^2(Q^2/x)$ which follows from unitarity of the scattering amplitudes in direct channels. The reason of the Froissart theorem violation is that the evolution equations were obtained in the leading logarithmic approximation (LLA), in which the $s-$channel unitarity of the $S-$matrix of QCD is explicitly broken [2]. However the unitarity bound for the scattering amplitudes in the Regge kinematics is restored after one takes into account nonleading logarithmic corrections [3]. Thus one needs to build a new approach beyond LLA which will be consistent with unitarity conditions for the $S-$matrix.

One of possible ways to proceed is based on the so called eikonalization procedure of Cheng and Wu [4]. In this approach, called generalized LLA, one starts with the expression for the amplitude in the LLA and adds "minimal" number of nonleading logarithmic corrections which are needed to restore the s—channel unitarity of the LLA results.

It is well known that in the Regge kinematics the bare gluons propagating in the t—channel are dressed by virtual corrections to become reggeized [2]. As a result, the calculation of the scattering amplitudes can be performed in terms of propagation of reggeized gluons in the t—channel and their interaction with each other. Moreover, it is convenient to decompose the amplitude into t—channel partial waves f_ω describing the scattering of reggeized gluons with total angular momentum $j = 1 + \omega$. The asymptotic behavior of the scattering amplitude is determined by singularities of f_ω in the complex ω—plane, the so called Pomeranchuk singularities in the channel with the vacuum quantum numbers or pomerons. In the LLA [2] the pomeron singularity of partial waves f_ω appears at $\omega = \frac{\alpha_s N}{\pi} 4 \log 2$ due to the Feynman diagrams with two reggeized gluons propagating in the t—channel, the famous "ladder" diagrams. The corresponding f_ω obeys the Bethe-Salpeter equation whose solution describes a compound state of two reggeized gluons, the so called BFKL pomeron. However, two reggeon diagrams don't satisfy to the s—channel unitarity and in the generalized LLA one adds to them the diagrams with arbitrary *conserved* number n of reggeized gluons propagating in the t—channel. For fixed n the contribution of the corresponding diagrams satisfies the "generalized" Bethe-Salpeter equation describing the compound state of n reggeized gluons [5]

$$\omega \chi(\vec{b}_1, \ldots, \vec{b}_n; \vec{b}_0) \tag{1}$$
$$= \frac{\alpha_s}{2\pi} \sum_{i,j=1, i>j}^{n} (t_i^a t_j^a) \mathcal{K}(\vec{b}_i, \vec{b}_j) \, \chi(\vec{b}_1, \ldots, \vec{b}_n; \vec{b}_0)$$

Here, $\chi(\vec{b}_1, \ldots, \vec{b}_n; \vec{b}_0)$ is the wave function of n reggeized gluons with transverse two-dimensional coordinates $\vec{b}_i$, the vector $\vec{b}_0$ is the center of mass coordinate of the state, ω is the position of the pomeron singularities of the partial wave f_ω, t_i^a are generators of the adjoint representation of the $SU(N)$ gauge group acting only on the color indices of the i—th gluon. The integral operator $\mathcal{K}(\vec{b}_i, \vec{b}_j)$ is identical to analogous operator for the BFKL pomeron [2]. It describes pair wise interaction of the reggeized gluons in the t—channel and acts on the coordinates of i—th and j—th gluons.

2. Holomorphic factorization and conformal invariance

For arbitrary number of gluons n the equation (1) has the following interesting properties. It turns out [6] that

the kernel $\mathcal{K}$ is holomorphically separable

$$\mathcal{K}(\vec{b}_i, \vec{b}_k) = H(z_i, z_k) + H(\bar{z}_i, \bar{z}_k) \tag{2}$$

where the complex coordinates z and $\bar{z}$ are defined for all impact vectors $\vec{b}_i = (x_i, y_i)$, $i = 1, \ldots, n$ as follows

$$z_i = x_i + iy_i, \qquad \bar{z}_i = x_i - iy_i$$

and two operators in the r.h.s. of (2) act separately on holomorphic and antiholomorphic coordinates of the gluons. There are different equivalent expressions [6] for the operator H

$$H(z_i, z_k)$$
$$= P_i^{-1} \log z_{ik} P_i + P_k^{-1} \log z_{ik} P_k + \log(P_i P_k) + 2\gamma_E$$
$$= 2 \log z_{ik} + z_{ik} \log(P_i P_k) z_{ik}^{-1} + 2\gamma_E \tag{3}$$

where $z_{ik} = z_i - z_k$, $P_i = i\frac{\partial}{\partial z_i}$ and γ_E is the Euler constant. The same operator can be represented as [6]

$$H(z_i, z_k) = -\sum_{l=0}^{\infty} \frac{2l+1}{l(l+1) - \mathbf{M}_{ik}^2} + \frac{2}{l+1}, \tag{4}$$

$$\mathbf{M}_{ik}^2 = -(z_i - z_k)^2 \frac{\partial^2}{\partial z_i \partial z_k}$$

We may consider (1) as a Schrodinger equation for n pair-wise interacting particles with coordinates z_i, $\bar{z}_i$ and internal color degrees of freedom. The property of the kernel (2) implies that two particle holomorphic and antiholomorphic hamiltonians commute with each other. However, this does not mean that holomorphic and antiholomorphic degrees of freedom are completely independent because the color factors of the hamiltonians in (1) don't commute with each other. An essential simplification of (1) occurs in the limit of large number of colors, $N \to \infty$. It is well known that in this limit only planar diagrams survive. This leads to a simplification of the color structure of (1) and makes it possible to perform the replacement [6]

$$t_i^a t_k^a \to -\frac{N}{2} \delta_{i,k+1}$$

where the gluons with $i = 1$ and $i = n + 1$ are considering as coinciding. After this transformation, the equation (1) possesses the following properties [6]. First, the interaction between holomorphic and antiholomorphic degrees of freedom disappears. Second, inside each sector the interaction occurs in the b—space only between nearest neighbors. These properties lead to holomorphic factorization of the solutions of (1)

$$\chi(\vec{b}_i; \vec{b}_0) = \sum_a C_a \varphi_a(z_i; z_0) \bar{\varphi}_a(\bar{z}_i; \bar{z}_0)$$

where C_a are some constants and the sum is performed over all degenerate solutions of the Schrodinger equations for the holomorphic (φ) and antiholomorphic ($\bar{\varphi}$) wave functions:

$$
\begin{aligned}
H_n \varphi_a(z_1, \ldots, z_n; z_0) &= \varepsilon_n \varphi_a(z_1, \ldots, z_n; z_0), \\
\bar{H}_n \bar{\varphi}_a(z_1, \ldots, z_n; z_0) &= \bar{\varepsilon}_n \bar{\varphi}_a(z_1, \ldots, z_n; z_0) \quad (5)
\end{aligned}
$$

The positions ω of the pomeron singularities of the t−channel partial waves governing the high energy asymptotics of scattering amplitudes are expressed through the sum of energies ε_n and $\bar{\varepsilon}_n$ in the two sectors:

$$
\omega = \frac{\alpha_s}{4\pi} N (\varepsilon_n + \bar{\varepsilon}_n)
$$

The hamiltonians H_n and $\bar{H}_n$ describe nearest neighbour interaction of n particles

$$
H_n = \sum_{k=1}^{n} H_{k,k+1}, \qquad \bar{H}_n = \sum_{k=1}^{n} \bar{H}_{k,k+1} \qquad (6)
$$

with periodic boundary conditions $H_{n,n+1} = H_{n,1}$, $\bar{H}_{n,n+1} = \bar{H}_{n,1}$ and two-particle hamiltonians are given by one of the equivalent representations (3) and (4).

Thus, in the large N limit the original problem (1) is reduced to the diagonalization of two hamiltonians (5) corresponding to one-dimensional lattice models with nearest neighbour interaction. Notice that the number of lattice sites is equal to the number of reggeized gluons in the t−channel.

The hamiltonian H_n of the one-dimensional lattice model has the following remarkable properties. It acts on holomorphic coordinates of n gluons and is invariant under their conformal transformations

$$
z_i \to \frac{az_i + b}{cz_i + d}, \qquad (i = 1, \ldots, n)
$$

where $ad - bc = 1$. The infinitesimal generators of the conformal transformations are given by

$$
M^3 = \sum_{k=1}^{n} z_k \partial_k, \quad M^- = -\sum_{k=1}^{n} \partial_k, \quad M^+ = \sum_{k=1}^{n} z_k^2 \partial_k.
$$
$$(7)$$

and one easily checks that they commute with the operator $\mathbf{M}_{jk}^2$ defined in (4). As a consequence, all generators M^i commute with the hamiltonian H_n

$$
[\mathbf{M}^2, H_n] = [M^i, H_n] = 0
$$

where $\mathbf{M}^2 = (M^3)^2 + \frac{1}{2}(M^+ M^- + M^- M^+)$ is quadratic Casimir operator of the conformal group.

Using two equivalent forms (3) for two-particle hamiltonians we can write down two different representations for the operator H_n^T transposed to H_n:

$$
\begin{aligned}
H_n^T &= P_1 P_2 \ldots P_n \; H_n \; (P_1 P_2 \ldots P_n)^{-1} \\
&= (z_{12} z_{23} \ldots z_{n1})^{-1} \; H_n \; z_{12} z_{23} \ldots z_{n1}
\end{aligned}
$$

From this relation we conclude [6], that the following differential operator commutes with the hamiltonian

$$
A = i^n z_{12} z_{23} \ldots z_{n1} \partial_1 \partial_2 \ldots \partial_n, \qquad [A, H] = 0 \quad (8)
$$

and analogous operator for the antiholomorphic system. Thus, the model contains at least one nontrivial integral of motion which is a representative of a one-dimensional family of operators assumed to be also the integrals of motion [7]. As we will show in the next section this is indeed the case and the model (5) has sufficient number of conservation laws to be completely integrable [8, 9].

3. Multicolor QCD as XXX Heisenberg magnet

For fixed number n of reggeized gluons in the t−channel we have to analyze the one-dimensional models (5) defined on the lattice with n sites. The quantum inverse scattering method [10, 11, 12, 13] is a poweful tool for solution of such systems. The famous example of the lattice model which can be exactly solved by this method [12] is the XXX Heisenberg chain of interacting spins $s = 1/2$ with the hamiltonian

$$
H_{s=1/2} = \beta \sum_{k=1}^{n} \vec{\sigma}_k \vec{\sigma}_{k+1}
$$

where σ_k^a are Pauli matrices acting in the k−th site of the lattice. It is important for us that the quantum inverse scattering method allows one [15] to generalize this model to construct a family of *exactly solvable* XXX Heisenberg models for arbitrary *complex* values of the spin s. It turns out [8, 9] that the hamiltonians (6) describing multicolor QCD at high energies coincides with the hamiltonian of XXX Heisenberg magnet of spin $s = 0$!

The XXX Heisenberg magnet for spin $s = 0$ is defined as follows [8]. For $s = 0$ the spin operators S_k^a ($a = 1, 2, 3$) in all sites $k = 1, \ldots, n$ are realized as

$$
S_k^+ = z_k^2 \partial_k, \qquad S_k^- = -\partial_k, \qquad S_k^3 = z_k \partial_k \quad (9)
$$

where $S^\pm = S^1 \pm S^2$. We notice that the total spin of the lattice $\sum_{k=1}^{n} \vec{S}_k$ coincides with the generators of the conformal group (7). The exact integrability of the model is based on the existence of a fundamental matrix $R_{12}(\lambda)$ which acts in the space $V_1 \otimes V_2$ and obeys the Yang-Baxter equation

$$
\begin{aligned}
&R_{12}(\lambda - \mu) R_{31}(\rho - \lambda) R_{23}(\mu - \rho) \\
&= R_{23}(\mu - \rho) R_{31}(\rho - \lambda) R_{12}(\lambda - \mu)
\end{aligned}
$$

Here, V_k is the local quantum space in the k−th site and the spectral parameters λ, μ and ρ are arbitrary complex numbers. The solution of this equation is given by [16, 14]

$$R_{12}(\lambda) = \frac{\Gamma^2(i\lambda + 1)}{\Gamma(i\lambda - J_{12})\Gamma(i\lambda + J_{12} + 1)} \qquad (10)$$

where operator J_{12} is defined as a solution of the equation

$$J_{12}(J_{12} + 1) = 2\vec{S}_1 \vec{S}_2 = -(z_1 - z_2)^2 \partial_1 \partial_2 \qquad (11)$$

and we substituted the explicit form of the spin operators (9). Once we know the fundamental R−matrix, the hamiltonian of the XXX magnet of spin $s = 0$ is given by the general expression (6) with the two-particle hamiltonian defined as

$$
\begin{aligned}
H_{12} &= i\frac{d}{d\lambda} \log R_{f_1 f_2}(\lambda)\Big|_{\lambda=0} \\
&= \psi(-J_{12}) + \psi(J_{12} + 1) - 2\psi(1) \qquad (12)
\end{aligned}
$$

where $\psi(x) = \frac{d}{dx} \log \Gamma(x)$. One notices that the operators J_{12} and $\mathbf{M}_{12}$ defined in (11) and (4), respectively, are related as $\mathbf{M}_{12}^2 = J_{12}(J_{12} + 1)$. Substituting this expression into (4) one is able to perform the summation over l to get an expression for the hamiltonian which is identical to that in (12)! We conclude that the holomorphic and antiholomorphic QCD hamiltonians (6) coincide with the hamiltonian of a one-dimensional XXX Heisenberg model with spin $s = 0$.

This identification means that multicolor QCD at high energies is completely integrable model [8, 9]. To find the family of conservation laws one follows the standard procedure [11, 10]. In all sites of the lattice we define two operators $L_{k,a}(\lambda)$ and $\mathcal{L}_{k,f}(\lambda)$, the so called auxiliary and fundamental Lax operators [14]

$$
\begin{aligned}
L_{k,a}(\lambda) &= \lambda I + i\begin{pmatrix} 1 \\ z_k \end{pmatrix} \otimes (z_k, \; -1) \; \partial_k \,, \\
\mathcal{L}_{k,f}(\lambda) &= R_{k,f}(\lambda) \qquad (13)
\end{aligned}
$$

The operators $L_{k,a}(\lambda)$ and $\mathcal{L}_{k,f}(\lambda)$ depend on an arbitrary spectral parameter λ and act locally in the space $V_k \otimes \mathbb{C}^2$ and $V_k \otimes V_0$, respectively, where V_k is the quantum space in the k−th site and the dimensions of V_k and V_0 coincide. It can be checked that both Lax operators satisfy the Yang-Baxter equation. Taking the ordered product of Lax operators along the lattice we define the auxiliary monodromy matrix

$$T_a(\lambda) = L_{n,a}(\lambda)L_{n-1,a}(\lambda)\ldots L_{1,a}(\lambda)$$

and analogously the fundamental monodromy matrix

$$T_f(\lambda) = \mathcal{L}_{n,f}(\lambda)\mathcal{L}_{n-1,f}(\lambda)\ldots\mathcal{L}_{1,f}(\lambda)$$

Here the Lax operators are multiplied as matrices in auxiliary space. Taking trace of the monodromy matrices over the auxiliary space we get two operators [10], the auxiliary and fundamental transfer matrices,

$$\Lambda(\lambda) = \mathrm{tr}_a \, T_a(\lambda), \qquad \tau(\lambda) = \mathrm{tr}_f \, T_f(\lambda) \qquad (14)$$

which act in the total quantum space of the model. It turns out that monodromy matrices $T_a(\lambda)$ and $T_f(\lambda)$ satisfy the Yang-Baxter relations identical to that for the Lax operators and, as a consequence, operators τ and Λ commute with each other for different values of the spectral parameters [10, 11]

$$[\tau(\lambda), \Lambda(\mu)] = [\tau(\lambda), \tau(\mu)] = [\Lambda(\lambda), \Lambda(\mu)] = 0 \qquad (15)$$

Differentiating the both sides of this relation with respect to the spectral parameters λ and μ and putting $\lambda = \mu = 0$ we get a family of mutually commuting conservation laws of the model

$$I_k = \frac{1}{i}\frac{d^k}{d\lambda^k} \log \tau(\lambda)\Big|_{\lambda=0}, \qquad Q_{n-k} = \frac{1}{k!}\frac{d^k}{d\lambda^k}\Lambda(\lambda)\Big|_{\lambda=0}$$

where $k = 1, 2, \ldots$ and the k−th operator describes the interaction between $k + 1$ nearest neighbors on the lattice. In particular, the operator $I_1 = H_n = \sum_{k=1}^{n} H_{k,k+1}$ coincides with the hamiltonian of the model. Then, it follows immediately from (15) that the operators I_k and Q_j are mutually commuting conservation laws of the model

$$[I_k, H] = [Q_k, H] = [I_k, Q_j] = [Q_k, Q_j] = [I_k, I_j] = 0$$

One could find the explicit form of the operators Q_k by substituting the expression (13) for auxiliary Lax operators into the definition (14) of the auxiliary transfer matrix

$$\Lambda(\lambda) = 2\lambda^n + Q_2\lambda^{n-2} + Q_3\lambda^{n-3} + \ldots + Q_n$$

where the operators Q_k for $k = 2, 3, \ldots, n$ are given by

$$Q_k = \sum_{n \geq i_1 > i_2 > \cdots > i_k \geq 1} i^k z_{i_1 i_2} z_{i_2 i_3} \ldots z_{i_k i_1} \partial_{i_1} \partial_{i_2} \ldots \partial_{i_k}$$

We recognize that the operator Q_2 is the Casimir operator $\mathbf{M}^2$ of the conformal group (7) and the operator Q_n coincides with the definition (8) of the operator A.

Thus, we have a sufficient number of integrals of motion to solve exactly the Schrodinger equations (5) for the wave functions of compound states of n reggeized gluons in multicolor QCD which are equivalent to those for the XXX magnet of spin $s = 0$. It is well known [12] that the algebraic Bethe ansatz allows us to solve the one-dimensional XXX Heisenberg magnet of spin $s = \frac{1}{2}$. So, one may try to apply this method to the XXX magnet of spin $s = 0$. However, there are difficulties in applying the Algebraic Bethe Ansatz for spin $s = 0$. The spin operators $\vec{S}_k$ in the k-th site of the lattice form a representation of a Lie group and the important limitation of the algebraic Bethe ansatz is that this group must be compact. For XXX magnet of spin $s = \frac{1}{2}$ the spin operators form the fundamental representation of the compact $SU(2)$ group while for $s = 0$ the spin operators (9) belong to the principal series representation of the *noncompact* $SL(2, \mathbb{C})$ group [8]. Thus, to solve the model (5) one has to generalize the Bethe ansatz to the case of the noncompact $SL(2, \mathbb{C})$ group. This problem was considered in [8] where the spectrum of the QCD hamiltonians (5) was found in terms of generalized Bethe ansatz.

4. Conclusions

We have shown that the high energy behavior of hadron scattering amplitudes in multicolor QCD is described by completely integrable model. The compound states of reggeized gluons propagating in the t-channel satisfy the Bethe-Salpeter equation which is simplified significally in large N limit. Namely, in the impact parameter representation the effective QCD hamiltonian entering into this equation is invariant under $SL(2, \mathbb{C})$ conformal transformations and is holomorphically separable. As a consequence, to find the spectrum of the compound states of the reggeized gluons one has to diagonalize two one-dimensional hamiltonians in holomorphic and antiholomorphic sectors. It turns out that each of these hamiltonians coincide with the local hamiltonian of one-dimensional XXX Heisenberg magnet of spin $s = 0$ defined on the lattice with the number of sites equal to the number of reggeized gluons. The spin operators in all sites belong to an infinite dimensional principal series representation of the $SL(2, \mathbb{C})$ group. We found the family of mutually commuting conservation laws of the model by constructing the auxiliary and fundamental monodromy matrices which satisfy the Yang-Baxter equation. This makes it possible to apply the Bethe ansatz to find the solution of the model. The difficulty consists in the fact, that the $SL(2, \mathbb{C})$ group is noncompact and therefore the algebraic Bethe ansatz is not applicable here. Nevertheless, it is possible to modify it and to express the spectrum of the QCD Hamiltonian and its eigenfunctions in terms of the function of one variable satisfying the Baxter equation [8].

The work of G.P.K. was supported in part by the National Science Foundation under grant PHY9309888. The work of L.N.L. was supported by the Russian Fund of Fundamental Investigations under grant 93-02-16809. He thanks the Humboldt foundation for the award which gave him a possibility to work on this paper.

References

[1] V.N.Gribov and L.N.Lipatov, Sov. J. Nucl. Phys. 15 (1972) 438;
L.N.Lipatov, Sov. J. Nucl. Phys. 20 (1975) 94;
G.Altarelli and G.Parisi, Nucl. Phys. B26 (1977) 298

[2] V.S.Fadin, E.A.Kuraev and L.N.Lipatov, Phys. Lett. 60B (1975) 50;
I.I.Balitsky and L.N.Lipatov, Sov. J. Nucl. Phys. 28 (1978) 882

[3] G.P.Korchemsky, Phys. Lett. B325 (1994) 459

[4] H.Cheng and T.T.Wu, *"Expanding Protons: Scattering at High Energies"*, (MIT Press, Cambridge, Massachusetts, 1987)

[5] J.Bartels, Nucl. Phys. B175 (1980) 365;
J.Kwiecinski and M.Praszalowicz, Phys. Lett. B94 (1980) 413

[6] L.N.Lipatov, Phys. Lett. B309 (1993) 394; B251 (1990) 284

[7] L.N.Lipatov, Padova preprint, DFPD/93/TH/70, October 1993; hep-th/9311037

[8] L.D.Faddeev and G.P.Korchemsky, Stony Brook preprint, ITP-SB-94-14, April 1994; hep-th/9404173

[9] L.N.Lipatov, JETP Letters 59 (1994) 596.

[10] L.A.Takhtajan and L.D.Faddeev, Russ. Math. Survey 34 (1979) 11

[11] E.K.Sklyanin, L.A.Takhtajan and L.D.Faddeev, Theor. Math. Phys. 40 (1980) 688

[12] L.A.Takhtajan and L.D.Faddeev, Zapiski Nauchnih Seminarov LOMI, 109 (1981) 134

[13] V.E.Korepin, N.M.Bogoliubov and A.G.Izergin, *"Quantum inverse scattering method and correlation functions"*, Cambridge Univ. Press, 1993

[14] V.O.Tarasov, L.A.Takhtajan and L.D.Faddeev, Theor. Math. Phys. 57 (1983) 163

[15] V.E.Korepin and A.G.Izergin, Nucl. Phys. B205 (1982) 401;
Sov. Phys. Doklady, 26 (1981) 653

[16] P.P.Kulish, N.Yu.Reshetikhin and E.K.Sklyanin, Lett. Math. Phys. 5 (1981) 393

Comment on Jet Handedness and a Puzzling Handedness Correlation

A. Efremov*, I. Potashnikova and L. Tkatchev

JINR, Dubna, Russian Federation

Some more definite then in [1] indication to the jet handedness was obtained [2] using the DELPHI data collection. It was gained for fast pion triples $(+ + -)$ and $(- - +)$ with the total longitudinal momenta $k_L = k_1 + k_2 + k_3 \geq 5 \; GeV/c$ in neutral pairs invariant mass region $0.62 < m_{13} < m_{12} < 0.92 \; GeV/c^2$ (i.e. ρ-meson region). For charge (Q) criteria (i.e. particle "1" is positive) a very preliminary result was $H_Q \approx 1.2 \pm 0.5\%$, while charge independent (Z) criteria gives zero value $H_Z = -0.02 \pm 0.5\%$ as it should be due to cancellation of handedness of quark and antiquark jets.

As for the value of analyzing power α it should be find using a general expression $H_Q^{e^+e^-} = \sum_q w_q \alpha_Q^q P_q$, where the probabilities w's consist of a flavor rate production and of probability of the flavor to fragment into a triple obeying the applied cuts‡. E.g. in the most optimistic case when only light u and d quarks are dominated the average quark polarization $\overline{P} = (\sigma_d P_d - \sigma_u P_u)/(\sigma_d + \sigma_u) = -0.23$ and $\bar{\alpha} \approx -5 \pm 2\%$.

A puzzling phenomena was recently observed for opposite jet *handedness correlation* in $Z^0 \rightarrow$ 2-jet events [3].

The handedness of each jet was defined via sign of mixed product $X = \vec{t} \cdot (\vec{k}_1 \times \vec{k}_2)$ of unite thrust vector in direction of total jet momentum and momenta of $(+-)$-pair of pions of jet selected by cuts: *i*) The rapidities $|y_{1,2}| > y_{\min} > 1$, *ii*) The transversal to $\vec{t}$ momenta $k_{1,2}^T > k_{\min}^T > 0.5 \; GeV/c$, *iii*) The rapidity difference $|y_1 - y_2| < \Delta y \approx 1$, *iv*) The invariant mass $m_{12} < m_{\max}$.

Based on independent fragmentation of q and $\bar{q}$ (factorization) one can expect for the correlation

$$C = \frac{N_{RL} + N_{LR} - N_{RR} - N_{LL}}{N_{RL} + N_{LR} + N_{RR} + N_{LL}} = \sum_q \bar{w}_q \alpha^q \alpha^{\bar{q}} c_{q\bar{q}}. \quad (1)$$

where quark helicity correlation $c_{q\bar{q}} = 1$ for the SM of $Z^0 \rightarrow q \; \bar{q}$. Charge conjugation of the two jets gives $\alpha_Q^{\bar{q}} = -\alpha_Q^q$ for charge criteria and $\alpha_Z^{\bar{q}} = \alpha_Z^q$ for charge independent one (i.e. $|y_1| > |y_2|$). So the theory definitely predicts that $C_Q < 0$ and $C_Z > 0$ and both are rather small ($\approx \bar{\alpha}^2$).

The experiment [3] however (also very preliminary!)

definitely shows that both correlations are *positive* and rather *large*. They *grow* with increase of $y_{\min}$ and $k_{\min}^T$ and reach

$$C_Q = 24 \pm 5\% \quad \text{and} \quad C_Z = 10 \pm 4\% \quad (2)$$

at $y_{\min} = 1.8$, $k_{\min}^T = 0.65 \; GeV/c$ and $m_{\max} = 0.75 \; GeV/c^2$. No correlation were observed in JETSET and HERWIG MC-models. No correlation was also seen for two back-to-back jets from different events.

A physical reason for this phenomena is rather obscure yet. Which of the principle in base of (1) is broken? Break of factorization due to a high twist contribution is hardly probable since it should decrease with increase of rapidity interval between the two pairs (i.e. with increase of $y_{\min}$) in contradiction with the observation. Same sign helicity correlation ($c_{q\bar{q}} < 0$) seems also excluded since it should result in negative signs of C_Z.

Concerning the charge conjugation it is really hardly seen in selected events. E.g. charge correlation of leading particles in the pairs $C_{ch} = (N_{opp} - N_{same})/N \approx -9.7 \pm 6.0\%$ though similar picture is seen in the MC-generated events, $C_{ch}^{MC} = -3.1 \pm 4.4\%$, where with no doubt one have deal with $q \; \bar{q}$ jets.

In the spirit of model [4], where the handedness is a result of turn of q and $\bar{q}$ arising in string breaking in a longitudinal chromo-magnetic field from chromo-magnetic moments of initial q and $\bar{q}$, such correlation would corresponds to an *universal* (vacuum?) field as if quarks were monopoles rather then dipoles. Would in addition the direction of this field be occasional it explains rather small handedness value, $H_Q \approx 2.4 \pm 1.2\%$, seen with the same cuts.

A check of this phenomena in other e^+e^--experiments would be very desirable.

* Presented by A. Efremov. Partially supported by ISF (Grant RFE000) and RFFI (Grant 93-02-3811)
‡ It could be calculated using a Monte-Carlo generated events with the same cuts.

References

[1] See N. Masuda talk in this Proceedings.
[2] A.V. Efremov, I.K. Potashnikova, L.G. Tkatchev, L.S. Vertogradov. DELPHI collaboration. DELPHI 94-11 PHYS 355. 31 January 1994.
[3] A.V. Efremov, I.K. Potashnikova, L.G. Tkatchev, "Search for Jet Handedness Correlation in Hadronic Z-decays", Rancontre de Moriond, Meribel, 1994.
[4] M.G. Ryskin, Phys.Lett. **B319** (1993) 346.

Paper presented at XXVII Int. Conf. on High Energy Physics: Session Pa-11
Glasgow, UK, 20–27 July 1994

QCD Studies in e⁺e⁻ Collisions
with a Cone-based Jet Finder

Graham W. Wilson

Department of Physics, University of California, Riverside, CA 92521, USA

On behalf of the OPAL Collaboration

Abstract

A cone jet finding algorithm for e⁺e⁻ collisions is introduced. The jet rate dependence on cone size and minimum jet energy is used to make two competitive measurements of $\alpha_s(M_{Z^0})$ in $\mathcal{O}(\alpha_s^2)$. The energy flow within jets in e⁺e⁻ collisions is measured to be more concentrated near the jet core (narrower) than jets of similar energy in $\bar{p}p$ collisions. This effect appears to be mainly caused by differences between quark and gluon induced jets.

1. Introduction

Collimated sprays of hadrons, referred to as jets, were observed some time ago, firstly in e⁺e⁻ [1] and also in $\bar{p}p$ [2] collisions. The dynamics of strong interactions can be probed by studying such jets. At the present high energy accelerators, jets are formed in hadronic decays of the Z^0 and in hard scattering processes in $\bar{p}p$ collisions. In both the e⁺e⁻ and $\bar{p}p$ experiments, the jets are viewed as the experimental manifestation of the partons. The parton dynamics, expected to be described by perturbative QCD calculations, can be studied experimentally using jets provided the jets formed in the hadronisation process resemble the partons. The extent of this jet-parton equivalence depends on several factors amongst which the method used to group detected particles into a jet, known as the jet finder, is often especially important. The jet finder properties relating to jet counting, angular and energy resolution, experimental suitability and sensitivity to higher order effects also need to be considered when choosing a particular algorithm. With many jet finders available, different jet finders are often more suited to specific applications, and, in general, jet finders and their parameters are varied to study systematic effects.

The jet finders commonly used in e⁺e⁻ experiments are based on invariant mass algorithms such as the JADE algorithm [3] and differ markedly from the cone-based algorithms used in $\bar{p}p$ experiments (see [4, 5]). Comparisons of jets from e⁺e⁻ collisions with those from $\bar{p}p$ collisions are greatly hampered by this use of different jet finders in the two environments.

The OPAL collaboration has introduced a cone-based algorithm for e⁺e⁻ collisions [6, 7]. This jet finder has been used for two measurements : (i) $\alpha_s(M_{Z^0})$ from jet rates, (ii) energy flow within the jet in e⁺e⁻ and comparison with $\bar{p}p$ experiments. After first describing the jet finders, we shall present these two measurements.

2. Jet finders

Invariant mass jet finders are traditionally used in e⁺e⁻ experiments. Firstly, each particle is considered as an individual jet. Secondly, the two jets, i,j, with smallest scaled invariant mass squared, y_{ij}, are identified where $y_{ij} = M_{ij}^2/E_{\text{vis}}^2$, E_{vis} is the total energy of all detected particles and, in the JADE scheme, M_{ij}^2 is defined as $2E_i E_j(1 - \cos\theta_{ij})$. E_i is the energy of jet i and θ_{ij} is the angle between jets i and j. Jet i is combined with jet j into one jet using a particular "recombination scheme" if $y_{ij} < y_{\text{cut}}$, where y_{cut} is the one jet resolution parameter of this jet finder. The recombination procedure is continued until all jets are resolved i.e. $y_{ij} > y_{cut}$ for all i, j. Variants of this jet finder contain different prescriptions for the y_{ij} definition and the recombination scheme, but consist of the same steps. For all these jet finders, every particle is assigned to a jet.

Cone jet finders correspond more closely to one's intuitive idea of a jet and are used prevalently in $\bar{p}p$ experiments where the presence of beam remnants leads to jets being defined with a limited angular extent. There are two jet resolution parameters : the cone half-angle, R, and a minimum jet energy, ϵ.

In e^+e^- experiments, where the laboratory frame is the centre-of-mass frame, jets can naturally be measured in terms of angular extent and energy. Jet resolution parameters of $(R, \epsilon) = (0.7 \text{ rad}, 7 \text{ GeV})$ are chosen by OPAL to optimise jet finder performance. However in $\bar{p}p$ collisions, the laboratory frame is not in general the centre-of-mass frame of the hard scatter. Thus, one chooses to define $\bar{p}p$ jets using kinematic variables which are transformed simply by longitudinal boosts. The R parameter is defined as the cone half-angle in $\eta - \phi$ space, $R^2 = (\Delta\eta)^2 + (\Delta\phi)^2$, where η is the pseudo-rapidity (defined as $-\ln \tan \theta/2$)[†], and ϕ is the azimuth. Similarly, the transverse energy, E_T, is used for the energy measurement. We shall refer to these two choices of variables for cone jets as the $E - \chi$ metric and the $E_T - \eta - \phi$ metric.

3. OPAL analysis technique

The analysis was based on about 240,000 multihadronic events collected in 1991 at centre-of-mass energies within 0.5 GeV of the Z^0 mass. Charged tracks were required to have a transverse momentum with respect to the beam axis above 150 MeV and clusters detected in the electromagnetic calorimeter were required to have an energy greater than 250 MeV. Each event had to be well contained in the detector: the thrust axis satisfied $|\cos\theta_{thrust}| < 0.9$.

The cone jet finding algorithm used by OPAL follows closely that of CDF [5]. Each particle (charged track or electromagnetic cluster) was considered in turn as the "seed" axis of a cone of half-angle R. All particles lying within the cone were found, their momenta were summed, and if the cone axis did not coincide with the direction of the momentum sum then the cone axis was redefined as the momentum sum direction and the process was iterated until a stable solution was found. In addition, the direction bisecting the angle between each pair of candidate jets was also considered as a seed axis in order that configurations with two narrow

[†] θ being the polar angle with respect to the beam direction.

jets separated by an angle between R and $2R$ might be found as single jets. Candidate jets were required to have an energy exceeding ϵ. At this stage, if two candidate jets had some particles in common then the overlap fraction, f, was calculated as the fraction of the energy of the lower energy jet which overlapped with the other jet. If $f > 0.75$ then the lower energy jet was eliminated. On the other hand if $f < 0.75$, then the shared particles were assigned to the nearest jet. After this possible reassignment of particles to jets, jets with energy less than ϵ were again rejected. With jet resolution parameters of $(R, \epsilon) = (0.7 \text{ rad}, 7 \text{ GeV})$, an average of 2.3 jets per event were found.

This algorithm results in particles being assigned to the nearest jet. The overlap criteria ensure that each particle is assigned to at most one jet. The limited angular extent of the jets, R, and the minimum jet energy, ϵ, mean that soft particles far from the jet axes are often not assigned to any jet. These features lead to an improved angular resolution compared to "JADE"-type algorithms. For example, using the JADE E0 scheme with $y_{cut} = 0.06$, the angular resolution for three-jet events is 50 % larger.

4.   Measurement of $\alpha_s(M_{Z^0})$ from Jet Rates

The strong coupling constant, α_s, governs the rate of gluon radiation from quarks, and therefore one of the most direct methods of determining α_s is from the measurement of jet rates. The variation of the two-jet rate, R_2, with jet resolution parameter, y_{cut}, is usually used for such determinations. Analogously, with the cone jet finder, one can study the jet rate dependence on both ϵ and R. The jet rate dependence on R is sensitive to the angular distribution of gluon emission whilst the dependence on ϵ probes the energy distribution. The measured n-jet rate ($n = 2, 3, 4$), corrected for detector effects, is shown in Figure 1 as a function of ϵ for $R = 0.7$ rad and as a function of R for $\epsilon = 7$ GeV. These jet rates are compared with the predictions of the Jetset, Herwig and Ariadne parton shower models with parameters as described in [6]. In general, the agreement is good.

The jet rates, after correcting for hadronisation effects, can be compared with the predictions of the $\mathcal{O}(\alpha_s^2)$ QCD matrix element calculation of reference [8]. In practice it is useful to consider the differential two-jet rate dependence on jet resolution parameter y, $D_2(y)$, where y in this case represents either ϵ or R. These $D_2(\epsilon)$ and $D_2(R)$ distributions have been compared with the matrix element calculation by using the integration techniques described in [9] and applying them to these two event shape variables. The $\mathcal{O}(\alpha_s^2)$ QCD predictions

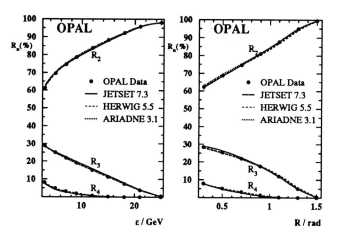

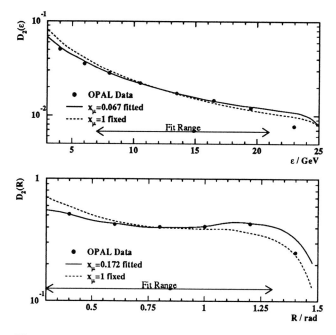

Figure 1. Measured jet rates as a function of ϵ for $R = 0.7$ rad, and as a function of R for $\epsilon = 7$ GeV. The data are presented at the hadron level (detector corrections only). The curves show the expectations of various parton shower models.

Figure 2. Measured differential two-jet rates, $D_2(\epsilon)$ for $R = 0.7$ rad and $D_2(R)$ for $\epsilon = 7$ GeV, corrected to the parton level. The results of fitting the $\mathcal{O}(\alpha_s^2)$ QCD calculations with $x_\mu = 1$ (dashed line) or treated as a free parameter (solid line) are superimposed.

for five quark flavours can be expressed in the form:

$$D_2(y) = \frac{1}{2\pi}\left\{ A(y)\alpha_s(\mu) + \frac{1}{2\pi}\left[B(y) + \frac{23}{3}\ln x_\mu A(y)\right]\alpha_s^2(\mu)\right\}$$

where the renormalisation scale μ is defined to be $\mu = x_\mu E_{\mathrm{CM}}$, with E_{CM} the centre-of-mass energy, and $A(y)$ and $B(y)$ are y-dependent coefficients computed with the techniques described above. The strong coupling constant, $\alpha_s(\mu)$, evaluated at a renormalisation scale of μ can itself be related to $\Lambda_{\overline{MS}}$, the QCD scale parameter [10]. For each $D_2(y)$ distribution (i.e. $y = \epsilon$ and R), two fits were undertaken. Firstly, a fit for $\Lambda_{\overline{MS}}$ in which x_μ was set to unity, and secondly a fit for $\Lambda_{\overline{MS}}$ in which x_μ was also treated as a fit parameter. The fits to the $D_2(\epsilon)$ and $D_2(R)$ distributions were performed for the range $7 < \epsilon < 21$ GeV and for the range $0.3 < R < 1.3$ rad, respectively. The fit results are shown in Figure 2. One observes that the fits with fixed scale are very poor. However, by permitting the renormalisation scale factor x_μ to vary, much better fits were obtained. The data exhibit a marked preference for small values of x_μ.

Systematic errors on the $\alpha_s(M_{Z^0})$ measurements have been estimated using the procedures of previous OPAL publications [11, 12] and are summarised in Table 1.

The experimental systematic error accounts for uncertainties on the detector corrections. This was evaluated as the maximum observed difference in the determined value of α_s resulting from changing the jet definition to charged tracks only or clusters only, restricting to the barrel region of the detector and finally using a different event generator. The fit range was also varied and an uncertainty assigned.

Hadronisation uncertainties were assessed by using different models and parameter choices to evaluate

	$D_2(\epsilon)$	$D_2(R)$
$\alpha_s(M_{Z^0})$	0.1188	0.1160
Statistical error	± 0.0004	± 0.0004
Experimental Syst.	± 0.0017	± 0.0026
Fit range variation	± 0.0011	$+0.0015$ -0.0020
Hadronization	± 0.0022	± 0.0067
x_μ variation	± 0.0075	± 0.0006
Overlap	$+0.0002$	$+0.0005$
Total Error	± 0.0081	± 0.0075

Table 1. The central values of $\alpha_s(M_{Z^0})$ derived from the two cone jet observables (representing averages of fits with $x_\mu = 1$ and x_μ fitted), together with the different error contributions.

the hadronisation corrections. This included adjusting the parameters of the Jetset model by ± 1 standard deviation about their optimised values determined from event shapes [13], and using a different model for heavy quark fragmentation. Quark mass effects were considered. Also, other parton shower models, Herwig and Ariadne, were used to evaluate the hadronisation correction. Finally, the minimum parton virtuality, Q_0, was varied from a default value of 1 GeV to 6 GeV in the Jetset model. The latter is the dominant systematic error (0.0060) for the $\alpha_s(M_{Z^0})$ determination from the $D_2(R)$ variable. The hadronisation corrections are significant, but apart from the Q_0 dependence (more a higher order effect), there is little model dependence.

Higher order effects were evaluated from the variation of $\alpha_s(M_{Z^0})$ with x_μ. The central value for $\alpha_s(M_{Z^0})$ is estimated from the average of the fixed ($x_\mu = 1$) and optimised scale fits and the systematic uncertainty is assigned as half the difference. This is the dominant systematic error (± 0.0075) for $\alpha_s(M_{Z^0})$ determined from the $D_2(\epsilon)$ distribution whilst the determination from the $D_2(R)$ distribution is rather insensitive to varying x_μ. The strong dependence of the fit quality on x_μ nevertheless suggests that higher order effects are important for the $D_2(R)$ distribution which is also indicated by the marked dependence of this $\alpha_s(M_{Z^0})$ determination on changing Q_0. Lastly, uncertainty arising from the overlap treatment was evaluated by changing f from 0.75 to 0.5.

The two measurements of $\alpha_s(M_{Z^0})$ obtained from the two cone jet rate variables are:

$$\alpha_s(M_{Z^0}) = 0.119 \pm 0.008 \ (D_2(\epsilon))$$
$$\alpha_s(M_{Z^0}) = 0.116 \pm 0.008 \ (D_2(R)) \ .$$

The two measurements are complementary. The results are consistent with the same value of $\alpha_s(M_{Z^0})$; they are also consistent with other measurements of $\alpha_s(M_{Z^0})$ and are among the most precise measurements of $\alpha_s(M_{Z^0})$ in $\mathcal{O}(\alpha_s^2)$ from event shape variables. For comparison, other measurements of $\alpha_s(M_{Z^0})$ in $\mathcal{O}(\alpha_s^2)$ from OPAL using event shape variables [12] and the same systematic error evaluation are illustrated in Figure 3. Averaging all the measurements we obtain

$$\alpha_s(M_{Z^0}) = 0.121 \pm 0.006 \ .$$

5. Measurement of Energy Flow Within the Jet and Comparison with $\overline{p}p$ Collisions

Results are presented on the angular distribution of energy flow with respect to the jet axis for jets in e^+e^- collisions. The cone jet finder was used with $\epsilon = 7$ GeV, $R = 0.7$ rad. Results are also presented with $R = 1.0$ rad for comparison with the $\overline{p}p$ measurements. Jets were required to have an energy exceeding 35 GeV. The selected jet sample had a mean energy of 44.5 GeV. This sample of almost beam energy jets from Z^0 decay is expected to consist predominantly ($\approx 97\%$) of quark jets. The fraction of jet energy in the sub-cone of half-angle r, $\psi(r)$, and also the differential distribution of energy flow denoted $\phi(r)$ were measured. These distributions have been corrected for detector effects and acceptance and are presented at the hadron level. These corrections are small. Experimental systematic errors were estimated in the same way as for the α_s measurements. In addition, the change induced by varying ϵ from 5 to 25 GeV was included in the systematic error assignment in order to assess the

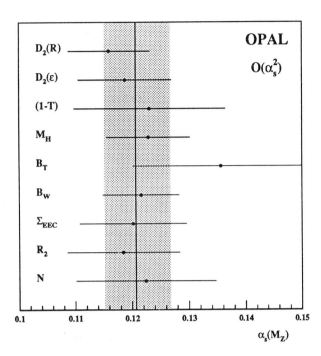

Figure 3. Compilation of $\alpha_s(M_{Z^0})$ measurements in $\mathcal{O}(\alpha_s^2)$ by OPAL from event shape variables. See [12] for the variable definitions.

possible influence of nearby jets. The total systematic error on $\phi(r)$ ranges from 1% to 8% (for $r \approx R$), while the systematic errors on the integral distribution, $\psi(r)$, are generally less than 1% but increasing to 3% near the jet core ($r \leq 0.2$).

Besides this intra-jet energy flow, the inter-jet energy flow was also measured [6]. This measurement is possible with e^+e^- collisions and is of particular interest because energy flow measurements far from the jet axes in $\overline{p}p$ collisions are complicated by the presence of the underlying event (beam particle remnants not involved in the hard scattering process).

The OPAL results on energy flow within the jet in e^+e^- collisions can be compared with similar studies of $\overline{p}p$ collsions at $\sqrt{s} = 1800$ GeV by CDF [14] and a preliminary study by D0 [15]. The CDF charged energy flow measurements are for jets ($R = 1.0$) with $40 < E_T < 60$ GeV and $0.1 < |\eta| < 0.7$ with a mean E_T of 45 GeV. This jet sample is of similar energy to OPAL, however it is expected to be mostly, ≈ 75 %, composed of gluon induced jets. The energy flow measurements for the OPAL and CDF jet samples are strikingly different despite the similar energy and the same cone jet finding algorithm. The jets from e^+e^- collisions are substantially narrower than their $\overline{p}p$ counterparts : $\psi(0.1) = 52 \pm 1$ % (OPAL) compared with $\psi(0.1) = 27 \pm 3$ % (CDF).

This comparison indicates a large difference between the two environments, but in order to be quantitative and to firmly establish this difference as genuine, we have controlled for two additional effects. Firstly, the energy flow for the OPAL data was also measured using E_T and the $E_T - \eta - \phi$ metric and restricting to $|\eta| < 0.7$. The results are essentially unchanged. Secondly, the energy flow measurements from CDF, which included higher E_T jets, were not corrected for the expected "pedestal" of energy from the underlying event. There are some ambiguities in evaluating this correction. The $\bar{p}p$ experiments have either estimated it with the energy flow at 90° to the jet axis in two-jet events or by using minimum bias events. Values of E_T density per unit area in $\eta - \phi$ space ranging from 0.5 to 1.6 GeV/R^2 are quoted in the literature. Even when the CDF data are corrected with an E_T density of 1.6 GeV/R^2, which is considered an overestimate as it includes jet energy which leaks out of the cone, a substantial difference persists.

The D0 collaboration has presented similar energy flow measurements for jets with $45 < E_T < 70$ GeV ($R = 1.0$) in $\bar{p}p$ collisions. Results were presented for both $|\eta| < 0.2$ and $2.5 < |\eta| < 3.0$. These calorimetric energy flow measurements complement the CDF central rapidity results based on charged track energy flow. The D0 data† in the central region are consistent with the CDF measurements. The jets in the forward region, $2.5 < |\eta| < 3.0$, are significantly narrower than those observed centrally.

The OPAL results using the $E_T - \eta - \phi$ metric for $R = 1.0$ are compared with the published CDF data in Figure 4. The expectation from the Herwig parton shower model for the e^+e^- data is indicated.

One observes a very large difference in the energy flow within the jet for jets produced in e^+e^- collisions compared with those from $\bar{p}p$ collisions. The e^+e^- jets are substantially narrower. This study has eliminated kinematic differences, namely jet energies, jet finders and the jet definition metric as the possible cause. The observed difference appears to be dynamical.

The physics processes involved in e^+e^- and $\bar{p}p$ collisions are very different. Hadron collisions contain underlying events (unable to explain the observed difference), and initial state strong interactions, both of which are completely absent in e^+e^- interactions. The colour flow in $\bar{p}p$ collisions, with coloured incoming partons and processes with exchanged coloured partons, is markedly different from the e^+e^- case where only the final state is coloured. Lastly, for the energy domains studied, the e^+e^- jet sample consists predominantly of quark jets and it is expected that the $\bar{p}p$ sample contains mostly gluon jets.

The OPAL collaboration has extensively studied [16, 17] the differences between quark and gluon jets produced in the same environment and with the

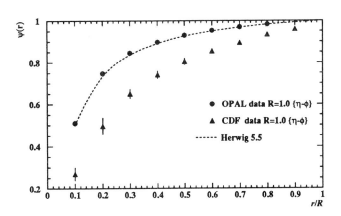

Figure 4. Fraction of jet energy within a sub-cone of radius r for jets defined with $R = 1.0$ using the $E_T - \eta - \phi$ metric. The CDF data are included for comparison. The dotted curve indicates the prediction of the Herwig model for the e^+e^- data.

same energy. These studies have firmly established experimentally that gluon jets are much broader than quark jets. The comparison of energy flow within the jet for quark jets compared to gluon jets (Figure 13(a) in [17]) is remarkably similar to the comparison of e^+e^- jets with $\bar{p}p$ jets shown in Figure 4. This strongly suggests that the narrower jet profile observed for e^+e^- collisions compared with $\bar{p}p$ collisions is mostly arising from differences between quark and gluon jet properties.

Acknowledgements

I thank D.R. Ward, J.W. Gary and especially L.A. del Pozo for their advice and explanations. I also thank J. Linnemann for his assistance with the D0 results.

References

[1] Mark II Collab.: G. Hanson *et al.*, Phys. Rev. Lett. **35** (1975) 1609.
[2] UA1 Collab.: G. Arnison *et al.*, Phys. Lett. **B123** (1983) 115.
[3] JADE Collab.: W. Bartel *et al.*, Zeit. Phys. **C33** (1986) 23.
[4] B. Flaugher and K. Meier, "Research Directions for the Decade", Snowmass (1990), pp128-133.
[5] CDF Collab.: F. Abe *et al.*, Phys. Rev. **D45** (1992) 1448.
[6] OPAL Collab.: R. Akers *et al.*, Zeit. Phys. **C63** (1994) 197.
[7] L.A. del Pozo, Ph.D. Thesis, Univ. of Cambridge (1993).
[8] R.K. Ellis, D.A. Ross and A.E. Terrano, Nucl. Phys. **B178** (1981) 421.
[9] Z. Kunszt and P. Nason, in "Z Physics at LEP 1", CERN 89-08 (1989).
[10] Particle Data Group, K. Hikasa *et al.*, Phys. Rev. **D45** (1992) III.54.
[11] OPAL Collab.: P. Acton *et al.*, Zeit. Phys. **C55** (1992) 1.
[12] OPAL Collab.: P. Acton *et al.*, Zeit. Phys. **C59** (1993) 1.
[13] OPAL Collab.: M. Akrawy *et al.*, Zeit. Phys. **C47** (1990) 505.
[14] CDF Collab.: F. Abe *et al.*, Phys. Rev. Lett. **70** (1993) 713.
[15] D0 Collaboration, D0 Note 2176 (1994). J. Linnemann, these proceedings.
[16] OPAL Collab.: G. Alexander *et al.*, Phys. Lett. **B265** (1991) 462.
[17] OPAL Collab.: P. Acton *et al.*, Zeit. Phys. **C58** (1993) 387.

---

† Corrected by D0 for an underlying event E_T density of 0.55 GeV/R^2 estimated from minimum bias events.

*Paper presented at XXVII Int. Conf. on High Energy Physics: Session Pa-11
Glasgow, UK, 20–27 July 1994*

Measurement of Scaling Violations in e^+e^- Annihilation

Glen D. Cowan

Universität GH Siegen, Adolf-Reichwein Str. 2, D-57068 Siegen, Germany

On behalf of the ALEPH Collaboration

Abstract

An analysis of scaling violations in fragmentation functions from e^+e^- annihilation is presented. Measurements of charged particle inclusive cross sections from the ALEPH experiment at LEP (E_{cm} = 91.2 GeV) are compared with corresponding measurements at lower center-of-mass energies. The observed energy dependence of the cross sections is compared to the predictions of perturbative QCD at next-to-leading order, and a value of the strong coupling constant $\alpha_s(M_Z^2) = 0.127 \pm 0.011$ is obtained.

1. Introduction

An analysis of the inclusive reaction $e^+e^- \rightarrow h + X$ is presented, where h represents a final state charged particle, for which one measures the scaled energy $x = E_h/E_{beam} \approx p_h/p_{beam}$, and X is the remainder of the event. In the quark-parton model, the inclusive cross section $(1/\sigma_{tot})(d\sigma_h/dx)$ is predicted to be independent of the center-of-mass energy E_{cm} (neglecting threshold and mass effects). In the framework of QCD, gluon radiation leads to an energy dependence of $(1/\sigma_{tot})(d\sigma_h/dx)$ (scaling violations), the magnitude of which depends on the strong coupling constant α_s. Qualitatively, as E_{cm} increases, the inclusive distribution is suppressed at high x and enhanced at low x. Such an energy dependence is observed in data from the ALEPH experiment (E_{cm} = 91.2 GeV) when compared to corresponding measurements at lower center-of-mass energies. The measurements are compared to the predictions of next-to-leading order (NLO) QCD, and α_s is determined. Another determination of α_s from scaling violations in e^+e^- annihilation has been carried out by the DELPHI experiment [1], where the analysis was based on the $O(\alpha_s^2)$ matrix elements as implemented in the JETSET model [2].

Sections 1 and 2 describe the theoretical and experimental ingredients used in the analysis. Section 3 describes the fit procedure used to obtain α_s, and in section 4 systematic uncertainties and consistency checks are discussed. A summary and the conclusions of the analysis are given in section 5.

2. Theoretical ingredients

The most general form for the inclusive distribution of x and polar angle $\cos\theta$ with respect to the beam axis of decay products from a spin-1 particle (such as a virtual photon or Z) is given by [3]

$$\frac{d^2\sigma}{dx\, d\cos\theta} = \frac{3}{8}\,(1+\cos^2\theta)\,\frac{d\sigma^T}{dx} + \frac{3}{4}\,\sin^2\theta\,\frac{d\sigma^L}{dx} + \frac{3}{4}\,\cos\theta\,\frac{d\sigma^A}{dx}\,, \tag{1}$$

where the T, L and A refer to the transverse, longitudinal and asymmetric cross sections. These in turn can be related to so-called *fragmentation functions* $D_i(x)$ by a convolution with the *coefficient functions* C_i,

$$\frac{d\sigma^{T,L}}{dx} = \sum_{i=q,\bar{q},g} \int_x^1 \frac{dz}{z} C_i^{T,L}(z, \alpha_s(\mu_F), \frac{\mu_F^2}{s}) D_i(\frac{x}{z}, \mu_F)\,, \tag{2}$$

where the sum is carried out over the kinematically accessible quark flavors (here $q = u, d, s, c, b$), μ_F is the factorization scale and $s = E_{cm}^2$. The coefficient functions are known to next-to-leading order $(O(\alpha_s))$ [4]. To leading order, equation (2) gives the familiar relation

$$\begin{aligned} \frac{1}{\sigma_{tot}}\frac{d\sigma}{dx} &= \frac{1}{\sigma_{tot}}\left(\frac{d\sigma^T}{dx} + \frac{d\sigma^L}{dx}\right) \\ &= \sum_{i=u,d,s,c,b} 2\,w_i(E_{cm})D_i(x)\,, \end{aligned} \tag{3}$$

where $w_i(E_{cm})$ is the event fraction for primary quark flavor i.

The fragmentation functions $D_i(x)$ contain information on the transformation of quarks and gluons (partons) into color-neutral hadrons, and cannot be calculated with perturbative QCD. Once determined at a given energy, however, their evolution in $s = E_{cm}^2$ is given by the DGLAP evolution equations [5]

$$\frac{dD_j(x,s)}{d\log s} = \sum_i \int_x^1 \frac{dz}{z} P_{ij}(z, \alpha_s(\mu_R), \frac{\mu_R^2}{s}) D_i(\frac{x}{z}, s) ,$$

(4)

where μ_R is the renormalization scale, $i, j = q, \bar{q}, g$, and the splitting functions P_{ij} are given by

$$P_{ij}(z, \alpha_s(\mu_R), \frac{\mu_R^2}{s}) = \frac{\alpha_s(\mu_R)}{2\pi} P_{ij}^{(0)}(z) + \left(\frac{\alpha_s(\mu_R)}{2\pi}\right)^2 P_{ij}^{(1)}(z, \frac{\mu_R^2}{s}) + O(\alpha_s^3) .$$

(5)

The functions $P_{ij}^{(0)}$ and $P_{ij}^{(1)}$ can be found in [6, 7].

The basic idea is then that measurable inclusive distributions are related to fragmentation functions by equation (2), and the energy dependence of the fragmentation functions is given by equations (4) and (5).

The first of several complications concerns the event-flavor composition as a function of E_{cm}. Events from different primary quark flavors (u,d,s,c,b) have different charged-particle inclusive spectra, since e.g. decays of heavy mesons (from b- and c-events) give rise to low momentum particles. The event fractions of various quark flavors, however, vary as a function of E_{cm}, since at low energies ($E_{cm} \ll M_Z$) the quarks couple to a virtual photon, whereas for $E_{cm} \approx M_Z$ the coupling is to a Z-boson. Figure 1 shows the fraction of hadronic events as a function of E_{cm}. This change in the event-flavor composition with E_{cm} gives rise to "scaling violations" of an artificial kind, in the sense that they have nothing to do with the gluon radiation one wishes to study. This effect must, therefore, be taken into account by measuring the inclusive distributions for all flavors, b- and light-quark events separately.

A second difficulty concerns the gluon fragmentation function $D_g(x)$. To lowest order, the inclusive distributions are only related to the quark fragmentation functions, as can be seen from equation (3). To $O(\alpha_s)$, however, the gluon fragmentation function is required in the convolution given by equation (2), and in any case (even at lowest order), $D_g(x)$ is needed for the energy evolution according to equation (4). It can be obtained from the inclusive particle spectra in identified gluon jets or from the transverse and longitudinal cross sections, by means of the relation

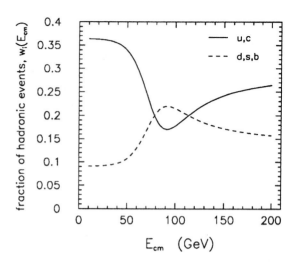

Figure 1. Flavor composition of hadronic events as a function of center-of-mass energy, as predicted by the Standard Model without radiative corrections.

$$\frac{1}{\sigma_{tot}} \frac{d\sigma^L}{dx} = \frac{\alpha_s}{2\pi} C_F \int_x^1 \frac{dz}{z} \left[\frac{1}{\sigma_{tot}} \frac{d\sigma^T}{dx} + 4\left(\frac{z}{x} - 1\right) D_g(x)\right]$$

(6)

as described in [3]. Since equation (6) is only given to $O(\alpha_s)$ the value of α_s here is not expected to be the same as that in next-to-leading order equations (2), (4). and (5). In the following it will therefore be referred to as β_s. The determination of $D_g(x)$ is further described in section 3.

A final problem concerns corrections to the energy evolution from non-perturbative or finite quark-mass effects. These can be effectively parameterized by means of a shift between the x value in the perturbative equations and the value x' for the measured distributions of the form

$$x' = x + h_0 \cdot \left[\frac{1}{(\sqrt{s})^\kappa} - \frac{1}{(\sqrt{s_0})^\kappa}\right] ,$$

(7)

where s_0 is the center-of-mass energy squared at which the fragmentation functions are parameterized and h_0 is a parameter governing the magnitude of the corrections, determined by comparison to data. Based on hadronization model studies and comparisons with data, the power κ was chosen to be one. This is in contrast to the situation in deep inelastic scattering where analogous corrections can be shown to decrease as $1/Q^2$.

3. Experimental ingredients

The inclusive charged particle spectra $(1/\sigma_{tot})(d\sigma/dx)$, where here $x = E_{hadron}/E_{beam} \approx p_{hadron}/p_{beam}$, were measured at $E_{cm} = 91.2$ GeV by the ALEPH experiment for events of all flavors, as well as for *uds*- and *b*-events. Details of the ALEPH detector can be found in [8, 9]. Of importance for this analysis is the large Time Projection Chamber (TPC) and the silicon microstrip vertex detector (VDET) which together provide a momentum resolution for charged tracks of typically $\Delta p/p = 0.0006(\text{GeV/c})^{-1} \cdot p$.

The ALEPH measurements are based on approximately 500000 hadronic events taken during 1992 at $E_{cm} = 91.2$ GeV. The track and event selection criteria are described in [12]. The measured distributions were corrected for effects of finite acceptance, resolution, secondary interactions, decays, etc. by means of bin-by-bin correction factors derived from a Monte Carlo event generator (JETSET [2]) and detector simulation program.

For determination of the inclusive spectra for *b*-events, the following procedure was used. First, the event is divided into hemispheres using the thrust axis and a hemisphere is chosen at random. Using information from the vertex detector, one then searches for tracks that do not originate from the primary vertex, indicating decay products of a *B*-hadron. If this is found, then the opposite hemisphere is used to determine the inclusive charged-particle spectrum. This technique minimizes the correlation between the identification probability for *b*-events (high for high multiplicity *B*-hadron decays) and the charged particle momentum spectrum. Background from *c*-, *uds*- and $\tau^+\tau^-$-events is subtracted using the Monte Carlo. Details on use of the tracking information to identify *b*-events can be found in [10].

It was assumed that the inclusive spectra for *u*-, *d*- and *s*-events are equal. The spectrum for the mixture *uds* was obtained in a way similar to that used for *b*-events, but in this case it was required that all of the tracks in one randomly chosen hemisphere were consistent with originating from the primary interaction point. Background from heavy quark and $\tau^+\tau^-$-events was subtracted using Monte Carlo models.

Systematic uncertainties in the measurements were estimated by varying the experimental cuts, in particular those related to vertex information. In addition, a possible dependence on the Monte Carlo generator used for the bin-by-bin correction factors was investigated by computing simplified correction factors based on several different event generators with a simplified detector simulation. Based on previous studies of the multiplicity distribution [13] an overall normalization error of 1% was assigned. The measured cross sections for all flavors, *b*- and *uds*-events are shown in figure 2 along with the corresponding predictions of the JETSET Monte Carlo. As can be seen, the *b*-events have a significantly softer spectrum than light quark (*uds*) events.

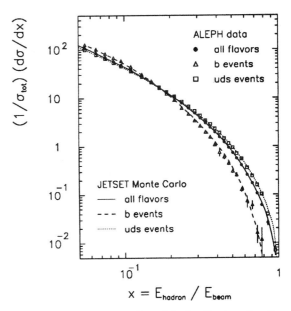

Figure 2. Inclusive charged-particle distributions for all primary quark flavors together, *b*- and *uds*-events with the predictions of the JETSET model.

As mentioned in section 2, two methods were employed to determine the gluon fragmentation function $D_g(x)$. In the first method, gluon jets are identified in three-jet events by requiring one high energy jet and another with evidence of a *B*-hadron by means of vertex information. The third jet is then with high probability a gluon jet. The inclusive distribution for $x = E_{hadron}/E_{jet}$ is then directly identified with the gluon fragmentation function. This method is especially useful for the high-*x* region. More details can be found in [11].

A second method, useful for the low-*x* region, employs the relation between D_g and $(1/\sigma)(d\sigma^{T,L}/dx)$ given by equation (6). The transverse and longitudinal cross sections are determined from the distribution in x and in polar angle $\cos\theta$ by

$$\frac{d\sigma^{T,L}}{dx} = \int_{-v}^{v} d\cos\theta\, W_{T,L}(\cos\theta, v)\, \frac{d^2\sigma}{dx\,d\cos\theta}\,, \quad (8)$$

where $v = 0.94$ delimits the angular range used and the weighting functions $W_{T,L}(\cos\theta, v)$ (given in [3]) extract the components with angular distributions proportional to $(1 + \cos^2\theta)$ and $\sin^2\theta$ respectively. The resulting distributions are shown in figure 3, which are in good agreement with the JETSET model. Similar measurements have been recently reported by the OPAL experiment [14].

In addition to the measurements by ALEPH described above, the inclusive charged-particle distributions from TASSO ($E_{cm} = 22, 35, 44$ GeV) [15], Mark

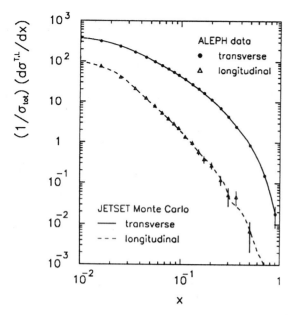

Figure 3. Measured transverse and longitudinal cross sections with the predictions of the JETSET model.

II (29 GeV) [16], TPC/Two-Gamma (29 GeV) [17], CELLO (35 GeV) [18], AMY (55 GeV) [19] and DEL-PHI (91.2 GeV) [1], were used.

4.   Determination of α_s

In order to compare the measured cross sections to the predictions of QCD, the fragmentation functions have been parameterized in the following way:

$$D_i(x, s_0) = N_i x^{b_i - 1} (1 - x)^{a_i} \exp(-c \log x^2) , \quad (9)$$

where $i = (uds), c, b, g$ and $s_0 = (22\,GeV)^2$ is the energy at which the parameterization is applied. Note that after the DGLAP energy evolution according to equation (4), the form of the fragmentation functions is different from that given at s_0. As motivated by perturbative QCD (see e.g. [20, 21]) the parameter c is taken to be flavor independent, and provides a gaussian shape in $\log x$ for the low momentum region.

All of the above mentioned data were used in a simultaneous fit with 16 free parameters: $N_i, a_i, b_i, (i = uds, c, b, g)$ and c for the fragmentation functions; h_0 for the non-perturbative corrections according to equation (7); β_s, the leading order coupling in equation (6); and the strong coupling constant $\alpha_s(M_Z^2)$. The fit is done in the range $0.1 < x < 0.8$, and results in a χ^2 of 198 for 190 degrees of freedom. The values of the parameters obtained are shown in Table 1.

Figure 4 shows the fit result compared only to the data from ALEPH (91.2 GeV) and TASSO (22 GeV). The suppression at high-x and enhancement at low-x

$\alpha_s(M_Z^2)$	0.1265 ± 0.0080
h_0	-0.13 ± 0.11 GeV
β_s	0.129 ± 0.004
c	0.309 ± 0.023

i	N_i	a_i	b_i
uds	0.376 ± 0.008	1.60 ± 0.06	-1.59 ± 0.09
c	0.350 ± 0.007	2.51 ± 0.21	-1.51 ± 0.14
b	0.298 ± 0.010	2.84 ± 0.17	-2.00 ± 0.12
g	0.427 ± 0.016	2.8 ± 0.8	-1.61 ± 0.27

Table 1. Values for the parameters obtained in the global fit. The statistical errors include the effects of correlations.

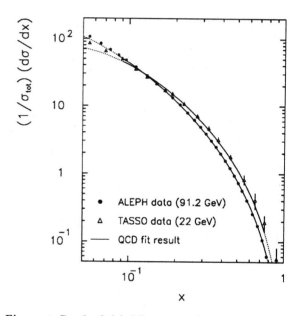

Figure 4. Result of global fit compared to the charged-particle inclusive distributions from ALEPH (91.2 GeV) and TASSO (22 GeV).

when going to higher E_{cm} are clearly visible, and are well described by the QCD fit.

5.   Systematic errors and consistency checks

A number of possible systematic uncertainties have been investigated. The renormalization scale μ_R appearing in the evolution equations was varied in the range $-1 < \log(\mu_R^2/s) < 1$, leading to a fairly small variation in the strong coupling of $\Delta\alpha_s = 0.0020$. Similarly, the factorization scale μ_F appearing in equation (2) was varied in the range $-1 < \log(\mu_F^2/s) < 1$, leading to larger change, $\Delta\alpha_s = 0.0063$.

An additional source of systematic error concerns the treatment of experiments in which only the quadratic sum of statistical and systematic uncertainties has been published. In such cases, the statistical part was estimated from the amount of data, and two approaches were used for treatment of bin-to-bin correlations of the systematic errors. In the default approach, the maximum possible normalization error was found, and the remaining parts of the systematic errors were treated as uncorrelated. In an alternative approach, the systematic errors were treated as entirely uncorrelated. The difference between the two methods leads to a maximum variation in α_s of 0.0048.

The final result for the strong coupling constant is then

$$\alpha_s(M_Z^2) = 0.1265 \pm 0.0080 \pm 0.0020 \pm 0.0063 \pm 0.0048 \tag{10}$$

or adding the errors in quadrature

$$\alpha_s(M_Z^2) = 0.127 \pm 0.011 . \tag{11}$$

Several additional consistency checks were carried out. It was determined that the value of α_s is relatively insensitive to the fit range used. Reducing the lower edge of the range to 0.05 leads, however, to a higher χ^2, which could be interpreted as a possible problem with the parameterization given by equation (9) and/or systematic errors in the measurements. The value of α_s was also found to be insensitive to the energy s_0 at which the fragmentation functions are parameterized.

Using the power $\kappa = 2$ for the non-perturbative corrections given by equation (7) yields $\alpha_s = 0.128 \pm 0.008 \, (stat.)$, consistent with the original result. The insensitivity to κ is expected, since the value of h_0 governing the magnitude of the correction is close to zero.

If instead of the shift in x, a rescaling is done of the form

$$x' = x \cdot \left[1 + h_1 \cdot \left(\frac{1}{(\sqrt{s})^\kappa} - \frac{1}{(\sqrt{s_0})^\kappa}\right)\right] , \tag{12}$$

with $\kappa = 1$, one obtains $\alpha_s = 0.139 \pm 0.018$ and $h_1 = 0.4 \pm 0.8$ GeV. Although the fit value of α_s is significantly larger, the χ^2 increases by 4 units and α_s and h_1 become highly correlated, corresponding to the much larger error. If the value of h_1 is fixed by comparison to Monte Carlo hadronization models, then one obtains α_s values close to the original one.

6. Summary and conclusions

The inclusive distribution $(1/\sigma_{tot})(d\sigma/dx)$ for charged particles has been measured by the ALEPH experiment for hadronic events of all flavors, light quark and b-events. In addition, the transverse and longitudinal distributions were measured and used to determined the gluon fragmentation function $D_g(x)$. Additional information on D_g was obtained from identified gluon jets.

A global analysis with these measurements and others at lower E_{cm} was carried out in the framework of next-to-leading order QCD. The fit resulted in $\chi^2 = 198$ for 190 degrees of freedom, indicating that QCD provides a good description of the observed scaling violations. The strong coupling constant was determined to be $\alpha_s(M_Z^2) = 0.127 \pm 0.011$. The analysis does not rely on information from Monte Carlo models for the form of the fragmentation functions or any non-perturbative corrections, with this information all coming from comparisons to data.

Acknowledgements

It is a pleasure to thank Bryan Webber and Paolo Nason for their help and guidance. On behalf of the ALEPH collaboration I thank our colleagues from the accelerator divisions for the successful operation of LEP. We are indebted to the engineers and technicians in all our institutions for their contribution to the good performance of ALEPH. Those of us from non-member countries thank CERN for its hospitality.

References

[1] P. Abreu at al., (DELPHI) Phys. Lett. B311 (1993) 408.
[2] M. Bengtsson and T. Sjöstrand, Phys. Lett. **185B** (1987) 435.
[3] P. Nason and B. Webber, CERN-TH.7018/93 (1993).
[4] G. Altarelli, R. K. Ellis, G. Martinelli and So-Young Pi, Nucl. Phys. B160 (1979) 301.
[5] V. N. Gribov and L. N. Lipatov, Sov. J. Nucl. Phys. 15 (1972) 78;
     G. Altarelli, G. Parisi, Nucl. Phys. B126 (1977) 298;
     Yu. .L. Dokshitzer, Sov. phys. JETP 46 (1977) 641.
[6] G. Gurci, W. Furmanski, R. Petronzio, Nucl. Phys. B175 (1980) 27.
[7] W. Furmanski and R. Petronzio, CERN-TH 2933 (1980);
     W. Furmanski and R. Petronzio, Phys. Lett. B97 (1980) 437.
[8] D. Decamp et al., (ALEPH) Nucl. Instr. Meth. A **294** (1990) 121.
[9] D. Decamp et al., (ALEPH) Phys. Rep. **216** (1992) 253;
     D. Buskulic et al., (ALEPH) *Performance of the ALEPH Detector at LEP*, submitted to Nucl. Instr. Meth. A.
[10] D. Buskulic et al., (ALEPH) Phys. Lett.B313 (1993) 535.
[11] D. Buskulic et al., (ALEPH) contributed paper GLS0539.
[12] D. Buskulic et al., (ALEPH) Z. Phys. C55 (1992) 209.
[13] D. Decamp et al., (ALEPH) Phys. Lett. B273 (1991) 181.
[14] OPAL Collaboration, submitted paper GLS0600.
[15] W. Braunschweig et al., TASSO Coll., Z. Phys. C47 (1990) 187.
[16] A. Petersen et al., MARK II Coll., Phys. Rev. D37 (1988) 1.
[17] H. Aihara et al., TPC/2γ Coll., LBL-23737 (1988).
[18] O. Podobrin, Ph. D. thesis, University of Hamburg;
     H. J. Behrend et al., CELLO Coll., in preparation. See also ref. [1].
[19] Y. K. Li et al., AMY Coll., Phys. Rev. D41 (1990) 2675.
[20] Yu. Dokshitzer, V.A. Khoze, A.H. Mueller and S.I. Troyan, *Basics of Perturbative QCD*, Editions Frontières, 1991.
[21] C. P. Fong and B. R. Webber, Nucl. Phys. B355 (1991) 54.

Paper presented at XXVII Int. Conf. on High Energy Physics: Session Pa-11
Glasgow, UK, 20–27 July 1994

A Test of Gluon Self Coupling

S. Banerjee[‡]

Tata Institute of Fundamental Research, Bombay 400005, India

L3 Collaboration

Abstract

The four LEP experiments, ALEPH, DELPHI, L3 and OPAL have studied the energy and angular correlation in four jet events from Z decays. The measurements lead to the determination of colour factor ratios $C_A/C_F = 2.18 \pm 0.26$ and $T_R/C_F = 1.52 \pm 0.74$. The non-zero value of C_A gives a clear evidence of gluon self coupling. The results are consistent with QCD.

1. Introduction

Self coupling of gluons is a fundamental property of QCD allowing it to describe strong interactions as asymtotically free nonabelian gauge theory [1]. The self coupling term contributes at tree level to the differential cross section for four parton final state in e^+e^- annihilation.

At Born level four parton final state could be due to double gluon bremsstrahlung, triple gluon coupling and gluon splitting into quark antiquark pair. The relative weights of the three processes are given by three constants C_F, C_A and T_R. These constants, known as colour factors, depend on the underlying gauge group. The determination of colour factors provides a crucial test of the theory of strong interactions.

Most of the results presented here come from studies of four jet final states in Z decays at LEP [2, 3, 4, 5]. The colour factors have also been determined from studies with three jet events at LEP [6] and from global event shape variables in hadronic decays of Z [7]. Measurements of jet and *beauty* cross sections in $\bar{p}p$ collider experiments [8] have also led to determination of colour factors.

The paper is organized is as follows. In section 2, the theoretical cross sections for four parton final state in e^+e^- annihilation are discussed. The L3 analysis of

four jet final states is presented in section 3. Section 4 describes results from other LEP experiments. The results are summarized in section 5.

2. Four Parton Cross Sections

The four parton cross section can be schematically written to $\mathcal{O}(\alpha_s^2)$ in terms of Lorentz invariant cross sections W_X and colour factors C_F, C_A and T_R

- $q\bar{q}gg$ final states

$$d^5\sigma \sim \alpha_s^2 C_F^2 \left[W_A + \left(1 - \frac{1}{2}\frac{C_A}{C_F} \right) W_B + \frac{C_A}{C_F} W_C \right]$$

- $q\bar{q}q\bar{q}$ final states

$$d^5\sigma \sim \alpha_s^2 C_F^2 \left[\frac{T_R}{C_F} W_D + \left(1 - \frac{1}{2}\frac{C_A}{C_F} \right) W_E \right]$$

There are contributions from (A) planar double gluon bremsstrahlung diagrams, (B) non-planar double gluon bremsstrahlung, (C) gluon self coupling, (D) planar diagrams relating to secondary fermion production from gluons g→ $q\bar{q}$, (E) brezel diagrams where primary and secondary quark lines cross for identical flavours.

The cross sections factorize into contributions from Lorentz space which depend on the kinematic configuration of the event $W_X(p_1, \cdots p_4)$ and contributions from colour space. Since colour cannot be directly observed, the cross sections are summed over the colour

‡ E-mail: banerjee@cernvm.cern.ch

degrees of freedom and one is left with three colour factors, C_F, C_A, $T_R (= N_F)$, where N_F is the number of active flavours.

At LEP, the number of active flavours is five. The colour factors for SU(N) symmetry are $C_A = N$, $C_F = \frac{N^2-1}{2N}$, $T_F = \frac{1}{2}$. For QCD at LEP energies, the colour factors are $C_F = 4/3$, $C_A = 3$, $T_R = 5/2$. The nonzero value of C_A is a consequence of the self coupling of gluons. For an Abelian toy model [9] on the other hand $C_A = 0$, $C_F = \frac{4}{3}$, $T_R = 15$.

3.　L3 Analysis of Four Jet Events

Data collected during the LEP running period 1991 to 1993 have been analysed. Hadronic decays of Z are selected using cuts on global quatities like visible energy $(0.6 < E_{vis}/\sqrt{s} < 1.4)$; energy imbalance transverse to $(E_\perp/E_{vis} < 0.4)$ and along $(|E_{\parallel}|/E_{vis} < 0.4)$ the beam direction; cluster multiplicities $(N > 12)$. This selection gives a data sample of 1.3 million events at $\sqrt{s} \approx 91.2$ GeV.

Energies of the smallest resolvable clusters are calculated using two different approaches. In the first approach, the energy deposits in the calorimeters and momenta of muons in the muon detector are considered and a linear energy calibration is made to optimise the energy resolution at $\sqrt{s} \approx m_Z$. In the alternate approach, the momenta of the charged particles measured in the inner tracker are also considered and the correlation among the various detectors are taken into account. These two approaches gave energy resolutions of 13% and 8% respectively at $\sqrt{s} \approx m_Z$ for hadronic events.

Jets are reconstructed using the JADE jet finding algoirthm [10]. This algorithm is used since it allows a direct comparison of the jet configuration to the theoretical calculations. Other jet algorithms like $k_\perp$ [11], LUCLUS [12], on the other hand, show better angular and energy resolutions. To benefit from both jet finding approaches, the smallest resolvable clusters are first preclustered using $k_\perp$ algorithm with $y_\perp = 0.001$, LUCLUS with $d_{join} = 2$ GeV or LUCLUS with $y_J = 0.005$. These preclusters are then made into jets using the JADE algorithm. An event is accepted as an n-jet event if it gets classified to be an n-jet type in both methods of energy calibration. This gives rise to 26K four jet events for jet resolution parameter $y_{cut} = 0.03$ with an estimated purity of 80-83%. The energy and angular resolutions for the four jets are summarized in table 1. Preclustering improves the resolution by $\sim 10\%$.

The scaled invariant mass between the jets $y_{ij} = \frac{2E_iE_j}{M_{tot}^2}(1 - \cos\theta_{ij})$ are shown in figure 1 and have been compared with JETSET [13] Monte Carlo simulation

	Resolution in x_i (E_i/E_{vis})	Resolution in angle
Jet 1	0.111	3.2°
Jet 2	0.107	4.0°
Jet 3	0.094	5.7°
Jet 4	0.088	8.6°

Table 1. Enegy and angular resolution of the four jets in the L3 four jet sample.

with ERT matrix element [14]. To extract the colour factors (C_k), a log likelihood fit is performed to the five dimensional differential four jet cross section

$$\ln \mathcal{L} = \sum_{events} \ln \frac{d^5(C_k, y_{ij})}{\sigma_{tot} C_k}$$

The differential four jet cross section is approximated by the parton cross section calculated using ERT matrix element with zero quark mass.

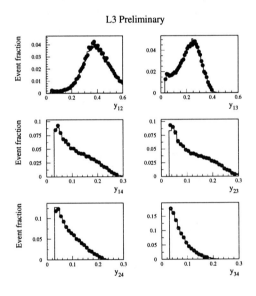

Figure 1. Measured invariant mass squared y_{ij} between two jets of the selected four jet sample. The circles represent L3 data and the solid line JETSET ME Monte Carlo prediction.

The detector effect has been studied using 250K four parton events from JETSET matrix element Monte Carlo processed through the L3 simulation and reconstruction programs. To study the effect of background from $n \neq 4$ parton events, 1.3 million Monte Carlo events from JETSET parton shower program are used. The colour factors are determined at detector and at generator levels and the correction factors are determined using

$$C_i^{DET} = f_i^{DET}(C_1^{GEN}, C_2^{GEN}).$$

Inverting the coupled equations and applying the corrections to the measured C_i's, one obtains colour

Source	$\Delta\left(\frac{C_A}{C_F}\right)$	$\Delta\left(\frac{T_R}{C_F}\right)$
Experimental	0.07	0.27
BG and unfolding	0.13	0.31
Hadronization	0.17	0.30
MC Statistics	0.20	0.35
Five parton BG	0.10	0.17

Table 2. Systematic errors in the colour factors as estimated in the L3 analysis.

factors corrected to hadron level. Similarly these factors are then corrected for hadronization effect using 6 million events from JETSET matrix element program.

Several sources of systematic errors have been studied and they are summarized in table 2. Experimental systematic uncertainties are computed by comparing the results from two different energy measurement methods as described earlier. Uncertainties due to background subtraction and detector unfolding are estimated by varying the three parton rate in the background and performing the unfolding in two different ways, detector → hadron → parton or detector → parton. Hadronization effect is looked into by changing various parameters in the Monte Carlo program. Effect of five parton background is estimated using JETSET parton shower events and alternately by a five parton event generator [15]. Quark mass effect has been studied in leading order using an event generator [16]. This effect is found to be negligibly small. The effect of jet resolution parameter in defining 4-jet category is still under study. All the systematic errors are combined in quadrature to give the final errors.

L3 measures the colour factors to be

$$\frac{C_A}{C_F} = 1.95 \pm 0.20 \text{ (stat)} \pm 0.31 \text{ (syst)}$$

$$\frac{T_R}{C_F} = 1.15 \pm 0.32 \text{ (stat)} \pm 0.62 \text{ (syst)}$$

with the correlation coefficient to be 0.01. These values are in good agreement with the QCD values. The nonzero value of C_A/C_F establishes triple gluon coupling at 5.5 σ level.

4. Results from Other LEP Experiments

The other three LEP experiments have also measured the colour factors using four jet events. The results from these studies are summarized in table 3 and in figure 2.

- ALEPH [3] have performed an unbinned log likelihood fit to the five dimensional differential distribution in invariant mass of the jets using a sample of 150K hadronic events collected during the 1989-90 LEP running period.

Source	C_A/C_F	T_R/C_F
ALEPH 4 Jet	2.24 ± 0.40	2.90 ± 1.45
ALEPH 3 Jet	4.49 ± 1.35	10.0 ± 4.95
ALEPH Combined	2.43 ± 0.31	2.75 ± 1.15
DELPHI 4 Jet	2.32 ± 0.25	1.33 ± 0.74
L3 4 Jet	1.95 ± 0.37	1.15 ± 0.70
OPAL 4 Jet	2.11 ± 0.32	2.01 ± 0.87
OPAL Event Shape	2.38 ± 0.60	1.60 ± 1.50
$\bar{p}p$ Collider [8]	$2.14^{+0.51}_{-0.74}$	$1.50^{+1.90}_{-1.20}$

Table 3. Colour factor ratios as determined in the LEP and $\bar{p}p$ experiments using different methods.

- DELPHI [4] have analysed the angular correlation in the four jet sample. They use the generalized Nachtmann Reiter angle $\cos\theta^\star_{NR}$ [17] and the angle between the two least energetic jets α_{34}. $\cos\theta^\star_{NR}$ distinguishes between $q\bar{q}gg$ final states and secondary $q\bar{q}$ production whereas α_{34} distinguishes between triple gluon vertex and double gluon bremsstrahlung. Using the data collected during the period 1990 to 1993, they have performed a binned likelihood fit to the double differential cross section.
- OPAL [5] have also done a binned likelihood fit to the data collected during the period 1991 and 1992. They used the two angles mentioned above and in addition the Bentsson Zerwas angle $\cos\chi_{BZ}$ [18] which also discriminates $q\bar{q}gg$ and $q\bar{q}q\bar{q}$ final states.

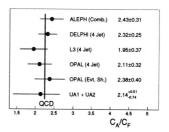

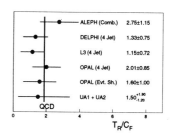

Figure 2. Colour factor ratios C_A/C_F and T_R/C_F as determined by the four LEP experiments and $\bar{p}p$ collider. The solid lines are expected value for QCD.

ALEPH [6] have used data collected in 1992 to study two jet rate and three jet topology. They use $k_\perp$ algorithm with jet resolution parameter $y_{cut} = 0.06$ to select three jet sample. The jets are energy ordered

$x_1 > x_2 > x_3$ and the Dalitz plot distribution along with two jet rate are fitted to $\mathcal{O}(\alpha_s^2)$ QCD. The fit yields the two colour factor ratios and also $C_F \cdot \alpha_s$. They have combined these results with their earlier measurements from four jet samples. These results are given in table 3 and figure 2.

OPAL [7] have studied the dependence of event shape cross sections on the colour factors using the data collected during 1990 and 1991. They have studied thrust, heavy jet mass and jet broadening variables to fit α_s together with colour factors in combined $\mathcal{O}(\alpha_s^2)$ + NLLA QCD calculations. In a given fit, only one colour factor and α_s are used as free parameters. However, the results for the pair of colour factor ratios are still correlated. The combined results from all the event shape variables are summarized in table 3.

5.   Summary and Conclusion

As can be seen from figure 2, all the measurements are consistent with one another. The results of the four LEP measurements have been combined by taking the average weighted by statistical errors including correlations. The dominant sources of systematic errors are due to hadronization and background due to 2 or 3 jet events which are highly correlated among the LEP experiments. Here, one has taken the average of the systematic errors as estimated by the four experiments. The results from the four LEP experiments and the combined result are shown in the T_R/C_F - C_A/C_F plane in figure 3.

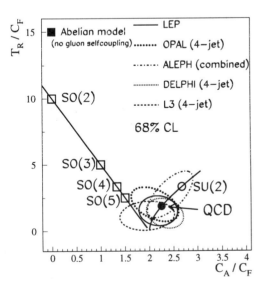

Figure 3. 68% CL contours for colour factor ratios T_R/C_F versus C_A/C_F as determined by the four LEP experiments and the average. The expectations from QCD and other symmetry groups are shown as points in the plane.

The combined result gives the values of colour factor ratios :

$$\frac{C_A}{C_F} = 2.18 \pm 0.26$$

$$\frac{T_R}{C_F} = 1.52 \pm 0.74$$

with the correlation coefficient $\rho = -0.055$.

The determination of the colour factors thus gives a clear evidence of gluon self coupling ($C_A \neq 0$). The evidence of gluon splitting ($T_R \neq 0$) is only at two standard deviation level with the current analyses.

Acknowledgement

We would like to thank our colleagues in the L3 collaboration and in particular J. Casaus and A. Ricker. We would also acknowledge helpful discussions with W. Gary, S. Kluth, A. Seitz and M. Schmelling.

References

[1] M. Gell-Mann, Acta Phys. Austriaca Suppl. **IX** (1972) 733;
H. Fritzsch and M. Gell-Mann, 16th International Conference on High Energy Physics, Batavia, 1972; editors J.D. Jackson and A. Roberts, National Accelerator Laboratory (1972);
H. Fritzsch, M. Gell-Mann and H. Leytwyler, Phys. Lett. **B47** (1973) 365;
D.J. Gross and F. Wilczek, Phys. Rev. Lett. **30** (1973) 1343;
D.J. Gross and F. Wilczek, Phys. Rev. **D8** (1973) 3633;
H.D. Politzer, Phys. Rev. Lett. **30** (1973) 1346;
G. 't Hooft, Nucl. Phys. **B33** (1971) 173.

[2] L3 Collaboration - B. Adeva et al., Phys. Lett. **B248** (1990) 227.

[3] ALEPH Collaboration - D. Decamp et al., Phys. Lett. **B284** (1992) 151.

[4] DELPHI Collaboration - P. Abreu et al., Phys. Lett. **B255** (1991) 466.

[5] OPAL Collaboration - M.Z. Akrawy et al., Z. Physik **C49** (1991) 49;
OPAL Collaboration - submitted to ICHEP94, OPAL Physics Note PN 133, May 1994.

[6] ALEPH Collaboration - submitted to ICHEP94, ref no. 0546, June 1994.

[7] OPAL Collaboration - submitted to ICHEP94, OPAL Physics Note PN 139, July 1994.

[8] A. Geiser, CERN-PPE/94-38, February 1994.

[9] S. Bethke, A. Ricker, P. Zerwas, Z. Phys. **C49** (1991) 59.

[10] JADE Collaboration, W.Bartel et al., Z. Phys. **C33** (1986) 23.

[11] Y.L. Dokshitzer, Contribution to the Workshop on Jets at LEP and HERA, Durham (1990).

[12] T. Sjöstrand, Comp. Phys. Comm. **28** (1983) 227.

[13] JETSET 7.3 Monte Carlo Program:
T. Sjöstrand, Comp. Phys. Comm. **39** (1986) 347;
T. Sjöstrand and M. Bengtsson, Comp. Phys. Comm. **43** (1987) 367.

[14] R.K. Ellis, D.A. Ross and A.E. Terrano, Nucl. Phys. **B178** (1981) 421.

[15] F. Wäckerle, Diploma Thesis, Karlsruhe Preprint, IKEP-KA/93-19

[16] A. Ballestrero, E. Maina, S. Moretti, Phys. Lett. **B294** (1992) 425.

[17] O. Nachtmann, A. Reiter, Z. Physik **C16** (1982) 45.

[18] M. Bengtsson, P. Zerwas, Phys. Lett. **B208** (1988) 306.

A Study of The Difference in Charged Multiplicity Between Bottom and Light Quark Initiated Events

Jan Chrin

IFIC, Centre mixte CSIC, Universitat de València,
Avda Dr. Moliner 50, E-46100 Burjassot (València), Spain

Abstract

The mean charged particle multiplicity in event samples of different flavour content has been measured at the Z^0 resonance using the DELPHI detector at LEP. The analysis made extensive use of a lifetime tag algorithm to select separate event samples of high b and uds purity, from which a difference in mean charged multiplicity between events initiated by b and uds quarks of $\delta_{bl} = 3.12 \pm 0.09 \pm 0.67$ was obtained. This result is combined with recent measurements from other LEP and SLC experiments to give an average of $\delta_{bl} = 3.16 \pm 0.47$ at $W = 91$ GeV. Data from various centre-of-mass energies are then examined in the context of theoretical expectations, allowing stringest tests of QCD models to be made. In particular, QCD calculations in modified leading logarithm approximation predict δ_{bl} to be independent of centre-of-mass energy; a recent numerical evaluation further claims that this value should lie within an upper bound of $\delta_{bl} < 4.1$.

1. Theoretical Motivation

The physics of b quarks has long been recognized as a particularly suitable arena for the study of Quantum Chromodynamics, QCD. The large mass of the b quark, $m_b \approx 4.8$ GeV/c^2, in comparison to the scale of the strong interaction, $\Lambda \approx 0.2$ GeV, results in a natural cut off for the emission of gluon bremsstrahlung, thereby avoiding the treatment of collinear divergences in perturbation theory. Furthermore, where the centre-of-mass energy, W, greatly exceeds the scale of the b quark mass, as is the case at the Z^0 resonance, the inclusive spectrum of heavy quark production is expected to be well described by perturbative QCD in modified leading logarithmic approximation (MLLA). One such consequence is that the effective angular cut off for the emission of gluons off quarks is directly proportional to the mass of the quark and takes the form $\Theta_0 = m_Q/E_Q$ [1, 2]. For the heavy b quarks, there is thus a resulting suppression of gluons in the forward direction around the b quark. Indeed, evidence for such gluon screening effects was first observed in the

depletion of multi-jets in b events [3]. When further invoking the hypothesis of local parton hadron duality (LPHD) [4], the predicted restriction of gluon emission in the forward direction is then expected to manifest itself in a suppression of the multiplicity of light hadrons accompanying the decay products of the B hadrons when compared with that arising from events initiated by the light uds quarks at the same centre-of-mass energy [2].

The extent of this corresponding loss in particle production has been the focus of recent theoretical investigation [5, 6, 7]. The most remarkable aspect to have arisen from these studies, however, is the realization that the expected loss in the 'companion' multiplicity is essentially *independent* of the centre-of-mass energy [5] - a striking prediction given the rapid rise of average multiplicity with centre-of-mass energy. Quantitatively, it was originally estimated that the particle loss due to these soft gluon screening effects was equivalent to the mean charged particle multiplicity of light quark events at the reduced centre-of-mass energy of $W = e^{0.5} m_Q$ GeV. The difference in the mean charged particle multiplicity between b events and uds events, after incorporating the contribution from the heavy hadron decay multiplicity, $\langle n \rangle_b^B$, is then predicted to depend on the mass of the heavy quark alone [5]:

$$\delta_{bl} = \langle n \rangle_b - \langle n \rangle_l = \langle n \rangle_b^B - N(q\bar{q}; e^{0.5} m_Q). \qquad (1)$$

Using experimental data as input to eq. (1) (see reference [5]) yields a value for δ_{bl} of 5.5 ± 0.8 for $m_b = 4.8$ GeV$/c^2$, with a further uncertainty due to higher order QCD corrections of the order of ± 1 tracks.

However, recent work by Petrov and Kisselev [6] have questioned the origin of the $e^{0.5}$ term in eq. (1). After quantifying the role of nonleading terms in the QCD calculation, they quote an upper bound value of:

$$\delta_{bl} < \langle n \rangle_b^B - N(q\bar{q}; e^{0.8} m_Q), \qquad (2)$$

which, depending on the heavy quark mass, leads to $\delta_{bl} < 3.7 - 4.1$. A less rigorous derivation of the absolute value gives $\delta_{bl} = 3.68$ for $m_b = 4.8$ GeV$/c^2$.

In another alternative approach, which employs the so called naive model [8, 9], the non-leading or 'companion' multiplicity in an event, $\Delta N(q\bar{q}; W)$, which refers to the *light* quark multiplicity which accompanies the decay products of the primary hadrons, is governed by the effective energy available to the fragmentation system following the production of the primary hadrons with energy fraction, $x_E = 2 \cdot E_{hadron}/W$. The multiplicity difference, δ_{bl}, can then be expressed by the following naive model formula [8, 9], presented here in a slightly modified form to better account for the mean multiplicity contribution from the decay products of the primary light hadrons, $\langle n \rangle_l^{dk}$, produced with average energy fraction, $\langle x_E \rangle_l$ [6]:

$$\delta_{bl} = \langle n \rangle_b^B - \langle n \rangle_l^{dk} + \Delta N(q\bar{q}; W) - N(q\bar{q}; W), \qquad (3)$$

where

$$\Delta N(q\bar{q}; W) = N\left(q\bar{q}; \frac{1 - \langle x_E \rangle_Q}{1 - \langle x_E \rangle_l} \cdot W \right). \qquad (4)$$

The inclusion of experimental values into the above equations (see reference [10]) results in an energy dependent variation of δ_{bl}, with values ranging from 4.2 ± 0.3 at 29 GeV to 1.9 ± 0.2 at 91 GeV, in direct contradiction with the MLLA+LPHD prediction.

2. Experimental Data

The DELPHI experiment at LEP, using data collected in 1992, has analyzed the charged particle multiplicity in event samples of different flavour content, from which measurements of the corrected mean charged multiplicity in $Z^0 \rightarrow b\bar{b}$ events, and the charged multiplicity difference between b and uds events, has been extracted [10]. The results obtained are then compared with the different models allowing a stringent test of the perturbative QCD prediction in MLLA to be made. An important feature of the analysis is the extensive use of a lifetime tag algorithm which enables event samples highly enriched in b and uds content to be selected. This lifetime tag algorithm exploits the good resolution offered by the three layered silicon microstrip vertex detector which enables the large values of the impact parameters of charged particles, d_i, originating from B decays to be measured with good accuracy ($\sigma_i = 24$ μm for $p_T > 10$ GeV$/c$). Tracks with positive impact parameter significance, $S = \pm d_i/\sigma_i$, within a given hemisphere, as determined by the plane perpendicular to the thrust axis, are then combined to give a hemisphere probability, P_h, which, by construction, gives the probability of the selected tracks to contain *no* decay products from long lived hadrons. Events initiated by b (uds) quarks therefore cluster around low (high) values of P_h. The capability of the hemisphere probability variable to extract highly enriched samples of b events (95% purity) has already been demonstrated by the ALEPH and DELPHI collaborations in their precise measurements of the Z partial width into $b\bar{b}$ pairs [11]. Here, the very same variable is being applied for the purpose of QCD studies in b jets.

The analysis proceeds by dividing each event in the data sample into two hemispheres with respect to the thrust axis and recording the charged particle multiplicity of the hemisphere *opposite* to that tagged by the lifetime tag variable in order to largely avoid, although not entirely eliminate, the bias introduced in the computation of P_h by the requirement of at least one track with positive S. Cuts on P_h were then applied in order to select samples of events enriched in b (95% purity) and uds (82% purity) contents. A third sample containing very approximately the nominal quark flavour ratios was also selected in order to allow some handle on the charm contribution to the hemisphere multiplicity measurements. A significant c enriched sample of events could not however be obtained owing to the lack of sensitivity of the lifetime tag algorithm to the charm contribution. The true mean hemisphere multiplicity, $\langle n_h \rangle$, of these three samples was then unfolded from that observed by maximum likelihood method using the function:

$$F_m^{MC} = \sum_n A_{mn} F_n, \qquad (5)$$

where F_n is a function that parametrises the shape of the original charged particle multiplicity distribution and where the elements of the acceptance matrix, A_{mn}, denote the probability of an event with original

Experiment	Reference	W	δ_{bl}
DELPHI (prelim.)	[10]	91	3.12 ± 0.68
OPAL	[12]	91	3.02 ± 0.80
SLD	[13]	91	3.31 ± 0.89
Mark II	[14]	91	3.3 ± 2.7
Average		91	3.16 ± 0.47
TOPAZ	[15]	58	3.2 ± 1.3
TASSO	[16]	42	3.3 ± 2.5
TASSO	[16]	35	3.6 ± 1.9
Mark II	[8]	29	5.0 ± 1.4
DELCO (corrected)	[17]	29	4.9 ± 1.5
TPC	[18]	29	5.7 ± 1.3
Average		29	5.2 ± 1.0

Table 1. Derived heavy and light quark multiplicity differences, δ_{bl}. The DELCO result appearing in the table has been corrected by +25% from that derived from published DELCO data, i.e. 3.9 ± 1.5, to account for the overestimated b purity in the inclusive lepton sample introduced by the use of an unrealistically high b quark semileptonic branching ratio [19]. In calculating the averages, a common systematic error of ± 0.2 (± 0.5) was assumed for the 91 (29) GeV data ([5]).

multiplicity n to be observed as an event registering m charged particles. The acceptance matrix, A_{mn}, is calculated using Monte Carlo techniques such that the elements of A_{mn} are *independent* of the shape of the multiplicity distribution of the generated Monte Carlo - an important ingredient in minimizing systematic errors. In the present analysis, F_n is represented by the negative binomial (NB) distribution whose free parameters give the true mean hemisphere multiplicity, $\langle n_h \rangle$, and the dispersion, D. The method was extensively tested on fully simulated Monte Carlo events and in all cases the NB distribution was able to reproduce the true mean to within 0.2%.

Having unfolded $\langle n_h \rangle$ in each of the three event samples of known flavour content, the three unknowns, $\langle n_h \rangle_b$, $\langle n_h \rangle_{uds}$ and $\langle n_h \rangle_c$, could then be extracted from simultaneous equations. Taking the event multiplicity as twice that of the hemisphere, led to the principal

measurements of:

$$\langle n \rangle_b = 23.32 \pm 0.08(stat) \pm 0.50(syst),$$
$$\delta_{bl} = 3.12 \pm 0.09(stat) \pm 0.67(syst).$$

The systematic errors are comprised of several contributions ranging from the uncertainty in the determination of the impact parameter resolution function from the data, used in constructing P_h, to the uncertainties in the physics processes that determine the flavour contents in the selected event samples. In addition, uncertainties in the modelling of detector effects contributed to the error on the absolute multiplicity values, but largely cancelled in the computation of the multiplicity difference, δ_{bl}. Nevertheless, a larger systematic error on δ_{bl}, in comparison to $\langle n \rangle_b$, is evident as a consequence of the large overlap in the P_h distribution between c and uds events, making the extraction of the light quark multiplicity less precise than that of the b.

The DELPHI measurement is in good agreement with recent results from the OPAL [12] and SLD [13] collaborations (see table 1). The smaller systematic error achieved by DELPHI is due to the purer sample of b events obtained and to the unfolding procedure applied which dispells with the need for different Monte Carlo generators to calculate the acceptance matrix.

3. Comparison with Theoretical Models

Table 1 summarizes the available results on δ_{bl} from different centre-of-mass energies. They are displayed in graphical form in figure 1, together with the theoretical predictions.

The data, although statistically rather limited at the lower centre-of-mass energies, remains compatible with the MLLA prediction of an energy independent multiplicity difference, δ_{bl}. This is exemplified by a straight line fit of the form $\delta_{bl} = gW + k$, which yields values of $g = -0.024 \pm 0.016$ and $k = 5.3 \pm 1.2$ with a χ^2/ν of $1.0/3$. Assuming zero gradient, $g=0$, gives a value for the constant, k, of 3.5 ± 0.4 with a χ^2/ν of $3.5/4$. It is also rather gratifying to see that the LEP/SLC average is within the QCD upper bound prediction of $\delta_{bl} < 4.1$ for $m_b = 4.7$ GeV/c^2.

The naive model, however, while appearing to give a good representation at the lower centre-of-mass energies, is evidently not so successful at $W = 91$ GeV, showing a discrepency at the level of 2.7 standard deviations, which suggests that the non-leading multiplicity is indeed *dependent* on the flavour of the event.

4. Summary and Outlook

The average charged particle multiplicity has been measured in event hemispheres of different flavour

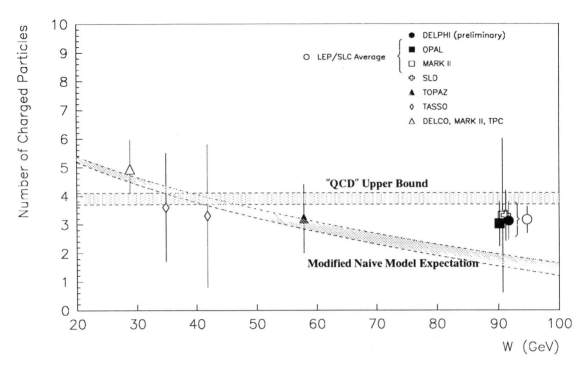

Figure 1. Experimental measurements of the charged particle multiplicity difference between b and uds events, δ_{bl}, as a function of centre-of-mass energy, W. Also shown is the QCD upper bound of $\delta_{bl} < 3.7 - 4.1$ and the expectation from the modified naive model using $\langle x_E \rangle_b = 0.69$ (upper bound) and $\langle x_E \rangle_b = 0.73$ (lower bound).

content, selected through the application of a lifetime tag algorithm, from which the difference in multiplicity between events initiated by b and uds quarks has been found to be:

$$\delta_{bl} = 3.12 \pm 0.09 \pm 0.67 \quad (DELPHI \ preliminary).$$

Combining this measurement with recent results from the OPAL [12] and SLD [13] collaborations yields:

$$\delta_{bl} = 3.16 \pm 0.47 \quad (LEP/SLC).$$

This average lies within the rigorous QCD upper bound prediction of $\delta_{bl} < 4.1$ and is in reasonable agreement with the less precise prediction for the absolute value of $\delta_{bl} = 3.68$ assuming $m_b = 4.8 \ \text{GeV}/c^2$ [6].

The modified naive model, on the other hand, is less successful at describing the higher energy data, suggesting that the non-leading event multiplicity is indeed dependent on the flavour of the event.

Further tests await data from higher energies (LEP 2) where it is interesting to note that the naive model predicts negative values for δ_{bl}, in sharp contrast to the MLLA prediction. In addition, precise measurements of δ_{cl} will further allow the QCD theory to be examined at the scale of the c quark mass.

References

[1] Yu.L. Dokshitzer, V.A. Khoze and S.I. Troyan *Perturbative Quantum Chromodynamics* (World Scientific 1989); Yu.L. Dokshitzer, V.A. Khoze, A.H. Mueller and S.I. Troyan *Basics of Perturbative QCD* (Editions Frontières 1991).

[2] Yu.L. Dokshitzer, V.A. Khoze and S.I. Troyan, J. Phys. G: Nucl. Part. Phys. **17** (1991) 1481; *ibid.* **17** (1991) 1602.

[3] DELPHI Coll.: P. Abreu *et al.*, Phys. Lett. **B307** (1993) 221; J. Chrin, Proc. XXVIII Rencontres de Moriond, Les Arcs, Savoie, France, March 1993, p. 313; Ed. J. Trân Thanh Vân (Editions Frontières 1994); J.A. Valls, Ph.D. Thesis, University of Valencia, April 1994.

[4] D. Amati and G. Veneziano, Phys. Lett. **B83** (1979) 87; Ya. I. Azimov, Yu.L. Dokshitzer, V.A. Khoze and S.I. Troyan, Z. Phys. **C27** (1985) 65.

[5] B.A. Schumm, Y.L. Dokshitzer, V.A. Khoze and D.S. Koetke, Phys. Rev. Lett. **69** (1992) 3025.

[6] V.A. Petrov and A.V. Kisselev, CERN preprint: CERN-TH 7318/94.

[7] J. Dias de Deus, CERN preprint: CERN-TH 7380/94.

[8] MARK II Coll.: P.C. Rowson *et al.*, Phys. Rev. Lett. **54** (1985) 2580.

[9] A.V. Kisselev, V.A. Petrov and O.P. Yushchenko, Z. Phys. **C41** (1988) 521.

[10] DELPHI Coll.: J. Chrin *et al.*, Paper Contrib. to the XXVII Int. Conf. on High Energy Physics, Glasgow, U.K., July 1994 (No. gls0184); DELPHI note: DELPHI 94-64 PHYS 385.

[11] ALEPH Coll.: D. Buskulic *et al.*, Phys. Lett. **B313** (1993) 535; DELPHI Coll.: P. Abreu *et al.*, CERN preprint: CERN-PPE/94-131, submitted to Z. Phys. **C**.

[12] OPAL Coll.: R. Akers *et al.*, Z. Phys. **C61** (1994) 209.

[13] SLD Coll.: K. Abe *et al.*, Phys. Rev. Lett. **72** (1994) 3145.

[14] MARK II Coll.: B.A. Schumm *et al.*, Phys. Rev. **D46** (1992) 453.

[15] TOPAZ Coll.: K. Nagai *et al.*, Phys. Lett. **B278** (1992) 506.

[16] TASSO Coll.: W. Braunschweig *et al.*, Z. Phys. **C42** (1989) 17.

[17] DELCO Coll.: M. Sakuda *et al.*, Phys. Lett. **B152** (1985) 399.

[18] TPC Coll.: H. Aihara *et al.*, Phys. Lett. **B184** (1987) 299.

[19] JADE Coll.: W. Bartel et al., Z. Phys. **C33** (1987) 339; J. Chrin, Z. Phys. **C36** (1987) 163.

Parallel Session Pa-12

Particle Astrophysics and Cosmology

Conveners: K. Olive (Minnesota)
M. Shaposhnikov (CERN)

Scientific secretaries: A. Alikhan
S. Morrison (reserve)

Paper presented at XXVII Int. Conf. on High Energy Physics: Session Pa-12
Glasgow, UK, 20–27 July 1994

Direct Search for Cold Dark Matter*

David O. Caldwell

Physics Department, University of California, Santa Barbara, CA 93106, USA

Abstract

It is increasingly likely that the universe has critical density, the only time-stable value, and that therefore at least 90% of its mass is in a nonbaryonic form outside the Standard Model of particle physics. Information on the dominant cold component of dark matter can be obtained from accelerator experiments, searches for dark matter annihilation products, and direct detection of the dark matter particles. This third approach has already eliminated a span of 12 orders of magnitude in mass for Dirac particles and 20 orders of magnitude in their interaction cross section. New direct detection experiments include numerous searches using a variety of scintillators and new types of cryogenic devices to detect nuclei struck by dark matter particles. These searches now especially seek the supersymmetric neutralino.

Observational evidence is increasing that the universe has critical density; i.e., the ratio of density to critical density $\Omega = 1$. The flat universe of $\Omega = 1$ is very likely because it is the only time-stable value for a zero cosmological constant. Inflation theory, which provides an explanation of several otherwise inexplicable puzzles, also gives a justification for a universe at critical density. On the other hand, very successful nucleosynthesis theory requires the density in baryons to be certainly less than 10%, necessitating $> 90\%$ of the mass of the universe to be in a nonbaryonic form which is outside the Standard Model of particle physics.

While it is likely that $\sim 5\%$ of the mass of the universe is in the form of familiar baryons, and $\sim 20\%$ in neutrinos (massless in the Standard Model) with small mass, that leaves $\sim 75\%$ to be a particle unknown in that Standard Model. This dominant particle can be searched for with accelerators, by looking for annihilation products, or by direct detection. We concentrate here on the last approach for Weakly Interacting Massive Particles (WIMPs) striking the nucleus of a detector. An example would be a heavy fourth-generation neutrino. The SLC/LEP limitation to

three generations of weak isodoublet neutrinos of mass $\lesssim 48$ GeV eliminated a fourth Majorana neutrino, since to be dark matter its mass would have to be ~ 6–8 GeV, which is determined by its annihilation rate when such neutrinos could have been in thermal equilibrium in the early universe. In contrast to the Majorana case, a Dirac neutrino could have had a wide mass range, since an initial particle-antiparticle asymmetry would allow the annihilation rate to be adjusted suitably.

The expected flux of cold dark matter particles is large. The density of dark matter particles required in our galaxy has a local conservative value of 0.3 GeV/cm^3 = 5×10^{-25} g/cm^3. Since the Maxwellian dark matter velocity distribution has $v_{\rm rms} \approx 300$ km/s, the flux of particles of mass M GeV is $\sim 10^7$ cm$^{-2} \cdot$ s^{-1}/M. Thus nuclear recoil event rates could be the order of 0.1–1/keV·kg·day at the level of the weak interaction. This rate is very small compared to typical radioactivity and cosmic ray backgrounds, however. Underground double beta decay experiments had achieved unprecedentedly low background rates in the MeV region, but when they were converted to search for dark matter, new problems arose in the 10–100 keV region of the nuclear recoils. The worst backgrounds were those induced by cosmic rays when the material

* Supported in part by the U.S. Department of Energy.

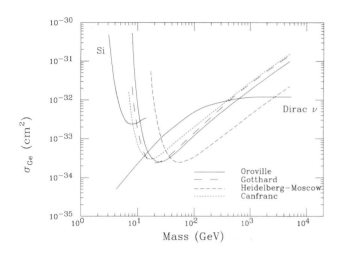

Figure 1. Exclusion plot for the mass and elastic cross section on Ge for dark matter particles. The weak interaction cross section is indicated by "ν_D". The solid-line result is from Ref. 2, the one with long dashes from Ref. 3, the one with short dashes from Ref. 4, and the very short dashes is the one from Ref. 5.

associated with the detector had been above ground.

Five such experiments [1-5] have searched for dark matter, and a compilation of the results which contribute to the boundaries are shown in the exclusion plot of Fig. 1. The plot is made for each particle mass in turn to be the source of all galactic dark matter, and the results are for the case of spin-independent interactions, for which there is nuclear coherence (cross sections proportional to the square of the number of neutrons). Particles having the normal weak interaction would lie along the line in Fig. 1 labelled "ν_D" and are excluded between 10 GeV and $\sim$ 4 TeV. Since $\sim$ 30 eV–4 GeV would give $\Omega > 1$, and LEP results close the 4–10 GeV range, all isodoublet Dirac neutrinos $\gtrsim$ 30 eV are eliminated as dark matter, if the upper mass limit is really [6] $\sim$ 1 TeV.

The results shown in Fig. 1 are not the published results for the data of Refs. 2–5, but rather they have been analyzed by a common procedure, one which we do not recommend, but which is especially easy to implement. This involves adding a calculated signal for that particular mass of particle until it can no longer be consistent with the data at some confidence level. The signal must exceed the limit at three adjacent data points by 1.2 standard deviations each to correspond to a 90% confidence level. Limits can change substantially when different analysis methods are used.

The experiment of Ref. 2 has extended the mass range at higher cross sections to cover 12 orders of magnitude, and the cross section range excluded is 20 orders of magnitude, but the Ge semiconductor detectors used essentially have reached their limits. Enriched

^{76}Ge recently reduced backgrounds [4], and application of diurnal effects through suitable geographic location [7] promises to make some further improvement. The background reductions and sensitivity increases needed now to go to cross sections well below the weak level for Dirac particles and especially to search for Majorana particles, particularly the neutralino, call for totally new approaches.

Because masses $\gtrsim$ 20 GeV are likely for both Dirac and Majorana particles, the emphasis now is not so much on low energy detection thresholds, where the most sensitivity for small masses is found, but rather on further reduction of backgrounds, and the heavier WIMP masses favor heavier detector nuclei. Since Majorana particles have axial, spin-dependent scattering, there is need for detector nuclei with spin. Initial limits on the neutralino, however, will come from the spin-independent interactions, as these provide nuclear coherence and hence dominate for the most accessible part of the supersymmetric parameter space.

Interest in spin has increased the use of scintillators, such as NaI and CaF$_2$. The NaI is ^{23}Na and ^{127}I, both 100% isotopes and both with spin. The ^{127}I would be the more effective component on two grounds: its matrix element is more favorable for scattering, and its greater mass would be kinematically preferred for the heavy WIMP mass. Unfortunately, that mass also means that at these very small recoil energies the ^{127}I is very ineffective at producing ionization and hence light. At a typical recoil energy the scintillation efficiency relative to that for electrons is 0.25 for Na and 0.07 for I. For coherent, rather than spin-dependent, scattering, the mass of the I is a detriment for very heavy nuclei because that coherence is lost more quickly as the mass of the WIMP increases.

So far backgrounds and thresholds are not quite as good as those with Ge detectors, but these are being improved, and large quantities (easily 10 kg and eventually $\sim 10^2$ kg) of NaI are feasible, so that better statistics aid the search for dark matter above the fluctuation in background. Results have already been reported [8] with NaI which are better than the limits for Majorana particles on the basis of scaling the Ge data by 7.8%, the abundance of ^{73}Ge, which is the only isotope in normal Ge having spin.

Three other groups [9] use NaI, and attempts are being made to obtain discrimination against radioactivity background electrons. The United Kingdom dark matter group is using NaI with low doping levels operated at 100° K, because uv and visible light are emitted in proportions which differ for nuclear and electron recoils. Both the BPRS (with Lyon) [10] and Osaka groups have also been working with CaF$_2$ (Eu), since ^{19}F has a particularly large matrix element for spin-dependent scattering, although a small scintillation efficiency relative to electrons (7% for F and 5% for Ca).

Liquid Xe as a scintillator has 48% isotopic content with nuclear spin, has high light output, can be scaled up to large mass, and particularly has possibilities for nuclear/electron recoil discrimination. A Rome group [11] has already operated a 1.5-liter prototype at Gran Sasso. The United Kingdom group [12] has been investigating pulse shape differences resulting from the two mechanisms for light production, which are stimulated to different extents by nuclear and electron recoils. The approach of a UCLA/CERN/ Aquila/Padova/Paris/Torino collaboration uses an electric field applied to prevent recombination, and then two signals are measured: (1) the primary scintillation, and (2) the ionization component, which is drifted and produces a secondary scintillation. Calculations indicate discrimination against electrons approaching 10^3.

Most of the recoil energy produced by a WIMP becomes heat, which can be detected at sufficiently low temperatures. For example, a Tokyo group [13] has obtained 3.8 keV resolution at 60 keV in a 2.8 g LiF crystal, which is an ideal material for spin-dependent interactions. Sapphire (Al_2O_3) also has been used, since the Al is a 100% isotope with spin. A French group [14] has operated a 24 g sapphire crystal at 0.055° K underground, achieving a good background, a threshold of 3 keV, and an energy resolution of 2 keV for 6 keV X-rays. The Munich group [15] has employed on a 31-g sapphire crystal a superconducting phase transition thermometer at 0.044° K with a SQUID readout to obtain a 210 eV resolution for 6 keV xrays. This is the best reported resolution per unit detector mass.

Another 100% isotope with spin is Nb, which becomes a superconductor at low temperatures. The Oxford group [16] has utilized differences in the phonon/quasi-particle ratio in Nb to provide some nuclear/electron discrimination. Most promising for providing this important reduction in background is the technique pioneered by the Berkeley group [17] in Ge, and recently also achieved by the Stanford group [18] in Si, in which both phonons and ionization are measured. Since electrons ionize efficiently and nuclear recoils produce mainly phonons, a background rejection $> 10^2$ has been demonstrated using a 60 g Ge crystal and neutron transmutation doped thermistors.

This technique will be applied in an experiment at a shallow (17 m.w.e.) site on the Stanford campus by the UCSB/LBL/UCB/Stanford/INR Baksan group. Since the technique is new and dilution refrigerators require attention, a location was chosen on the basis of ready access. The Oroville site [2] at 600 m.w.e. was by far the shallowest heretofore used for a dark matter search. Cosmic ray muons are a problem in that they produce neutrons which can give nuclear recoils.

A highly efficient muon veto counter is needed and will provide a deadtime after the passage of the muon until the neutron is at least of too low an energy to give a measurable recoil. The few unvetoed neutrons, produced mainly in the Pb shield needed to reduce external radioactivity, are moderated by polyethylene. According to calculations, the principal remaining source of neutrons are the Cu fixtures necessary to contain the detectors at low temperature. The shielding can be quite complete because the dilution refrigerator has been constructed with an unusual side exit so that cooling can be achieved in a separate cold box. We plan to take data with about one kg of normal Ge, 0.5 kg of enriched ^{73}Ge (spin 9/2), and 0.5 kg of enriched ^{76}Ge (spin 0) to provide appropriate cross checks and allow the simultaneous search for Dirac and Majorana dark matter. Some Stanford Si detectors will also be installed. If we can achieve electron background levels comparable to those we have had in the semiconductor experiment at Oroville, this should begin the exploration of the neutralino parameter space.

With so many promising new techniques, this era of discovery may be starting.

References

[1] S.P. Ahlen et al., Phys. Lett. **B195** (1987) 603.
[2] D.O. Caldwell et al., Phys. Rev. Lett. **61** (1988) 510.
[3] D. Reusser et al., Phys. Lett. **B255** (1991) 143.
[4] M. Beck et al., Heidelberg preprint (submitted to Phys. Lett., 1993).
[5] M. Sarsa et al., Nucl. Phys. (Proc. Supp.) **35** (1994) 154.
[6] K. Griest and M. Kamionkowski, Phys. Rev. Lett. **64** (1990) 615.
[7] J.I. Collar and F.T. Avignone III, Phys. Rev. **D47** (1993) 5238.
[8] C. Bacci et al., Phys. Lett. **B293** (1992) 460; A. Bottino et al., Phys. Lett. **B295** (1992) 330; C. Bacci et al., Astroparticle Phys. **3** (1994) 13.
[9] United Kingdom Collaboration; Pacific Northwest Laboratory, South Carolina, Zaragoza Collaboration; Osaka group.
[10] C. Bacci et al., Astroparticle Phys. **2** (1994) 117.
[11] P. Belli et al., Nucl. Instr. Meth. **A299** (1990) 191; **A310** (1991) 150; **A316** (1992) 55; **A327** (1992) 207; **A336** (1993) 336.
[12] G.J. Davies et al., Imperial College preprint IC-HEP-94-3 (1994, unpublished).
[13] M. Minowa et al., Nucl. Instr. Meth. **A327** (1993) 612.
[14] N. Coron et al., Astron. Astrophys. **278** (1993) L31.
[15] P. Ferger et al., Max-Planck-Institut preprint MPI-PhE/93-34 (1993, unpublished).
[16] R.J. Gaitskell, N.E. Booth, and G.L. Salmon, Workshop on Low Temperature Detectors, eds. N.E. Booth, G.L. Salmon (Oxford 1991, Editions Frontières 1992) p. 435; N.E. Booth et al., Nucl. Instr. Meth. **A315** (1992) 2011; R.J. Gaitskell, Oxford Univ. preprint OUNP-93-22 (1993, unpublished).
[17] T. Shutt et al., Phys. Rev. Lett. **69** (1992) 3425, 3531.
[18] B.A. Young et al., Nucl. Instr. Meth. **A311** (1992) 195.

Paper presented at XXVII Int. Conf. on High Energy Physics: Session Pa-12
Glasgow, UK, 20–27 July 1994

The EROS search for galactic dark matter

B Laurent[†], A Milsztajn[‡] and M Spiro[*]

CEA, DSM-DAPNIA, Service de Physique des Particules,
Centre de Saclay, F-91191 Gif-sur-Yvette Cedex

For the EROS collaboration

Abstract

We present preliminary results from a search for gravitational microlensing of stars in the Large Magellanic Cloud. The search consists of two complementary programs, one looking for short timescale microlensings in 8000 CCD images, and the other for longer timescale phenomena in 300 Schmidt photographic plates.

The first program did not yield any light curve consistent with a microlensing event, and allows us to set limits on the presence of dark objects with mass smaller than $10^{-4} M_\odot$ in the Galactic Halo. The second program has detected two light curves compatible with the microlensing hypothesis.

1. Introduction

The presence of large quantities of "dark matter" in the outer regions of spiral galaxies like our own has been inferred from the flat rotation curves obtained from 21 cm line observations [1]. Ordinary primordial hydrogen and helium is a viable candidate for dark matter if it is in a form that is not easily detected via emission or absorption of photons [2]. Possible forms include compact objects too light to burn hydrogen to ^{4}He ($M < 0.08 M_\odot$) [2] and cold fractal clouds of helium and molecular hydrogen [3].

We give here a status report on the search for unseen objects in the Galactic Halo being performed by our collaboration "EROS" (Expérience de Recherche d'Objets Sombres) at the European Southern Observatory at La Silla, Chile [4]. We use the gravitational microlensing effect [5] which would lead to an apparent temporary brightening of stars outside our Galaxy as the unseen object passes near the line of sight. The amplification A is given by $A = (u^2 + 2)/[u(u^2 + 4)^{1/2}]$ where u is the undeflected "impact parameter" of the light ray with respect to the unseen object, in units of the "Einstein radius". For the "standard" isothermal halo model, the probability that a given star in the Large Magellanic Cloud (LMC) is amplified by more than 0.3 magnitudes at any given time is calculated to be about 0.5×10^{-6} [5, 6]. For a deflector of mass M the typical time scale for the amplification is $\tau = 75$ days$\sqrt{M/M_\odot}$. The light curve of such an event should be symmetric in time, achromatic, and the event should not be repeated.

2. The CCD program

EROS consists of two complementary programs. The first one uses a CCD camera to monitor over 100,000 stars in one field of the LMC bar. The sampling time is 10 minutes making the program sensitive to deflector masses in the range $10^{-7} M_\odot < M < 10^{-3} M_\odot$, corresponding to event durations in the range 0.5 hour $< \tau <$ 5 days. We present here preliminary results from this program.

The CCD camera consists of sixteen buttable 576×405 pixels Thomson CCDs covering about $1°$ by $0.4°$. It is mounted on a 40 cm reflector (f/10). The telescope

† E-mail: blauren@hep.saclay.cea.fr
‡ E-mail: mimile@hep.saclay.cea.fr
* E-mail: spiro@hep.saclay.cea.fr

and camera are described in detail in [7]. We have used this setup to observe one field in the LMC bar from Dec 1991 to Mar 1992, from Aug 1992 to Mar 1993, and from Aug 1993 to Mar 1994. The 8100 exposures taken until March 1993 with red and blue filters have been analysed. (Over 6000 additional exposures from the 1993-94 season are still under analysis.) About 80,000 stars are seen in both colors on the images with a mean photometric precision of about 6%.

The data reduction, photometry and analysis are described in detail in [8]. We only give here a short summary of the analysis method and cuts designed to isolate microlensing-like events.

2.1. *Search for microlensing light curves*

In this analysis, the 1991-92 and 1992-93 data samples were considered separately. The efficiency of the cuts to accept real microlensing events is estimated with Monte-Carlo generated lensing events, superimposed on a random sample of the experimental light curves from both samples.

We start by searching for sequences of 4 points on the red and blue curves that exhibit significant fluctuations from the reference magnitudes. For the first and second most significant variation in each color, we calculate the mean amplitude, time and χ^2. We first reject stars for which the time of the first blue and red variation differ by more than 15 days (this loose cut does not affect our detection efficiency).

We then proceed to select curves with one and only one significant variation. We reject stars which show either a second significant variation or activity outside the largest luminosity variation. To that end, the most efficient cut requires that the two ratios of the χ^2's of the second and first most significant variations for the red and the blue be both small. At this stage, a total rejection factor of about 1000 has been achieved and only 88 stars are retained.

Most of these stars actually show "unphysical" flux variations, due to inaccurate photometry (local defects in the images, telescope guiding problems ...). These are eliminated by requiring an agreement between the time of maximum variation in the red and blue (better than four times the mean uncertainty on these times), leaving a sample of 11 stars.

In these 11 stars, six show long time scale variations (larger than 7 days) and are located in regions of the color-magnitude diagram known to contain many such long period variable stars. Rejecting such long time scales only affects our detection efficiency for lensing objects of mass larger than $10^{-3} M_\odot$.

The other five stars all show maximum variations smaller than 16 % (*i.e.* $u > 1.4$), whereas our Monte-Carlo simulations indicate that 90 % of selected

microlensing events at this stage should have $u < 1.2$. We finally impose a cut $u > 1.3$ leaving us with no candidate microlensing curve.

2.2. *Limits on the Halo composition*

From the absence of microlensing candidates in our sample, we are able to put limits on the presence of low-mass objects in the Galactic Halo. From our Monte-Carlo model of the Halo, we expect up to 10 microlensing events if the Halo is fully comprised of such low-mass objects. (This takes into account the effect of "blended" stars and the effect of LMC star size on the microlensing light curves; the latter is important for the lowest masses, $10^{-7} M_\odot$, and negligible above $10^{-5} M_\odot$.) Considering various possible mass distributions of low-mass objects, we are able to exclude at 90 % confidence level any distribution that relies only or mostly on dark objects with masses between 10^{-7} and $10^{-4} M_\odot$ in the Galactic Halo.

3.   The Schmidt plate program

The second program uses $5° \times 5°$ Schmidt plates of the LMC that allow us to monitor about eight million stars with a sampling rate of no more than two measurements per night. About four million stars brighter than 21-st magnitude are measured with sufficient accuracy in both colors (blue and red) to be used in the analysis. This makes this program primarily sensitive to deflector masses in the range $10^{-4} M_\odot < M < 1\ M_\odot$, corresponding to mean lensing durations in the range 1 day $< \tau < 100$ days. We have now analysed the full area of 300 photographic plates exposed during three observing seasons from october 1990 to march 1993. (The fourth season is presently under analysis.)

After an analysis of 40 % of the area, we reported two light curves [9] consistent with the microlensing hypothesis. The remaining 60 % have not brought any new candidate. Another event has been reported by the MACHO collaboration [10]. The OGLE [11] and MACHO collaborations [12] have reported the observation of the microlensing of stars in the galactic bulge.

For details on our data reduction and photometry, the reader is referred to [9, 4].

3.1. *Search for microlensing light curves*

Because of its "needle in the haystack" nature, the search for microlensing light curves has been performed from the same light curves with two independent algorithms, that use different error estimates, simulation programs and selection criteria. The two algorithms yielded the same two candidates reported in [9]. One algorithm is described in detail in [13]. Here we summarise the strategy used in the other algorithm. As in the previous section, the efficiency of the cuts to accept real microlensing events is estimated with Monte-Carlo generated lensing events, superimposed on a random sample of the experimental light curves.

The star sample is first cleaned. Any star situated in a zone where photometry is unreliable, such as close to the edge of the plates, or close to a bright gaseous nebula, or in the vicinity of a bright star, is rejected. Next, we retain stars with luminosities close enough to the linear response zone of the plates in both colors (in practice, we select stars between visible magnitudes of 17 and 21). These preliminary cuts reduce the star sample to about four million stars.

Then, we look for stars with significant luminosity variations in both colours at the same time. This is quantified by the χ^2 probability of a group of neighboring luminosity measurements with respect to the mean star luminosity. About 20,000 apparently variable stars are left at this stage. In order to reject periodic or erratic variable stars, we ask that the second such luminosity variation be much smaller than the first in both colors (*i.e.* it has a clearly larger probability of being a random fluctuation), and that outside these two largest variations there is no evidence of a correlated variation in the blue and red light curves. This leaves us with only 60 stars.

This last star sample is mostly comprised of stars selected because their luminosity measurements from one six-month observing season are higher in mean than those of the other two seasons. The light curves exhibit no significant variation however inside any single season. These are possibly due to an imperfect relative photometric alignment. We reject such stars by asking that the season showing maximum mean luminosity also show a larger spread in the luminosity measurements, as expected from Monte-Carlo simulations of microlensing events with time scales larger than a month. Only four stars survive this cut. Two are the candidates presented in [9], compatible with the expected characteristics of microlensing. The other two are very significantly chromatic (at least seven standard deviations between the amplitudes in the red and blue). We remark that *nowhere* in this analysis have the expected shape and achromaticity criteria been used except in the final sample of four.

3.2. *Interpretation*

The two candidates have been fitted for the theoretical microlensing light curve and agree well with this hypothesis. Their maximum amplifications are near the median expected from our Monte-Carlo simulations. Their time scales of 25 and 30 days correspond to a most probable value for the mass of the dark lenses slightly larger than 0.1 $M_\odot$. (This assumes that the lenses are situated in a spherical Halo of our Galaxy.) Because the time scale also depends on the distance and transverse velocity of the lens, the probability distribution for the lenses mass is rather wide however (a 95 % C.L. interval ranges from 0.02 to 0.9 $M_\odot$).

From our Monte-Carlo model of the Halo, we expect about 8 events for a Halo fully comprised of lenses of about 0.1 $M_\odot$ (resp. 3 events for 1 $M_\odot$). For lower masses, a slightly larger number of microlensing events is expected. From the fact that we do not detect microlensing phenomena with time scales shorter than 15 days, we will soon be in a position to give limits on the presence of objects less massive than 0.01 $M_\odot$ in the Galactic Halo.

The scarce statistics of candidates makes it hard at present to draw an interpretation on the possible mass and location of the lensing objects. Actually, we still cannot exclude that one or the other is a new kind of rare variable star. The variety of the lensed stars however – the MACHO collaboration star [10] is a red giant whereas our stars are main sequence or close to main sequence – favors a microlensing interpretation. In the coming year, we shall improve on our CCD camera and telescope, in order to increase our detection capability for long time scale microlensing.

Acknowledgments

This work is based on observations performed at the European Southern Observatory (La Silla, Chile), and is funded by CEA-DSM, CNRS-IN2P3 and CNRS-INSU.

References

[1] Reviews of dark matter : V. Trimble, Ann. Rev. Astron. Astrophys, 1987; and J.R. Primack *et al.*, Ann. Rev. Nucl. Sci., 1988. A review of the mass estimates of our Galaxy : M. Fich and S. Tremaine, Ann. Rev. Astron. Astrophys. 1991.

[2] B. J. Carr, *Comm. Astrophys.* **14** (1990) 257.

[3] D. Pfenniger, F. Combes and L. Martinet, Astron. Astroph. **285** (1994) 79.

[4] E. Aubourg *et al.*, The Messenger **72** (June, 1993) 20; E. Aubourg, Ph.D. Thesis, Saclay preprint Dapnia/SPP 92-22.

[5] B. Paczyński, Ap. J. **304** (1986) 1.

[6] K. Griest *et al.*, Ap. J. **372** (1991) L79.

[7] M. Arnaud *et al.*, Exper. Astron. **4** (1994) 265 and 279.

[8] E. Aubourg *et al.*, submitted to Astron. Astrophys. Lett. (1994);
F. Queinnec, Ph.D. thesis, Saclay report Dapnia/SPP 94-21.

[9] E. Aubourg *et al.*, Nature **365** (1993) 623.

[10] C. Alcock *et al.*, Nature **365** (1993) 621.

[11] A. Udalski *et al.*, Acta Astron. **43** (1993) 283; Ap. J. Lett. **426** (1994) L69; and Acta Astron. **44** (1994) 165.

[12] W. Sutherland *et al.*, talk at the Neutrino-94 conference (Eilat), to appear in *Nucl. Phys. B Conf. Suppl.*

[13] F. Cavalier, Ph.D. thesis, Orsay report LAL 94-18.

SUSY dark matter detection rates in Supergravity Grand Unification

Pran Nath[†] and R. Arnowitt[‡]

[†] Theoretical Physics Division, CERN, CH-1211 Geneva 23, Switzerland*

[‡] Center for Theoretical Physics, Department of Physics, Texas A & M University, College Station, TX 77843, USA

Abstract

An analysis of event rates in neutralino-nucleus scattering is given for dark matter detectors within the framework of N=1 supergravity grand unification.

1. Introduction

In this paper we give a brief discussion of detection rates for neutralino dark matter within the framework of N=1 supergravity grand unification [1]. We use radiative effects to break the electro-weak symmetry and the parameter space of the theory is then 4-dimensional and the parameters can be chosen as: m_0, $m_{1/2}$, A_t, $\tan\beta$ and the sign of μ, where m_0 is the universal scalar mass, $m_{1/2}$ is the universal gaugino mass, A_t is the trilinear coupling in the soft SUSY breaking terms computed at the electro-weak scale, and $\tan\beta = \langle H_2 \rangle / \langle H_1 \rangle$ where H_2 gives mass to the up quark and H_1 gives mass to the down quark, and μ is the Higgs mixing parameter. A remarkable aspect of supergravity grand unification is that the lightest neutralino ($\tilde{Z}_1$) is the lightest supersymmetric particle over most of the parameter space of the model consistent with the constraints of radiative breaking and the constraint of naturalness which are assumed to be : $m_0, m_{\tilde{g}} \leq 1$ TeV. For models with R parity conservation, $\tilde{Z}_1$ would then be absolutely stable and contribute to the cold dark matter in the universe. Thus one requires at least that $\Omega_{\tilde{Z}_1} h^2 < 1$, where $\Omega_{\tilde{Z}_1} = \rho_{\tilde{Z}_1}/\rho_c$; ρ_c is the critical matter density and h is the Hubble constant in units of 100 km/s(Mpc). One may also impose the more stringent constraint indicated by the COBE data which is that the ratio

of cold dark matter (CDM) to hot dark mater (HDM) is about 2. The assumption that the non-baryonic dark matter gives $\Omega_{NB} \simeq 0.9$ then leads to the constraint $0.1 < \Omega_{\tilde{Z}_1} h^2 < 0.35$ if one uses the current range of h, i.e. $0.5 < h < 0.75$. We use this constraint in our analysis. The analysis of relic density itself is carried out using the accurate method of [2]. It is found that experimental constraints from CLEO [3] on $b \to s\gamma$ decay significantly affect the relic density analyses [4] for $\mu > 0$.

2. The analysis

The current estimates give the density of dark matter in the solar neighborhood at $\rho = 0.3$ GeV cm^{-3}, and an average velocity of $\langle v \rangle = 320$ kms^{-1}. In elastic neutralino-nucleus scattering these correspond to recoil energies in the range (1-100) KeV for neutralino mass <150 GeV and nucleus mass <300 GeV. Currently there are several possibilities for the detection of recoil energies in this range. We have carried out an analysis of event rates in neutralino-nucleus scattering with several improvements over previous analyses [5]. Our analysis includes the heavy Higgs exchange in neutralino-nucleus scattering, includes loop corrections to the Higgs mixing angle and is carried out within the framework of the radiative breaking of the electro-weak symmetry. In addition as already pointed out we use the accurate method for computation of the relic density in imposing

* Permanent address: Department of Physics, Northeastern University, Boston, MA 02115, USA

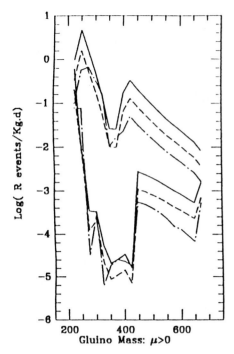

Figure 1. Maximum and minimum event rate curves for CaF$_2$ (dashed), Ge (dash-dot) and Pb (solid) vs gluino mass, when $m_t = 168$ GeV, $\mu > 0$.

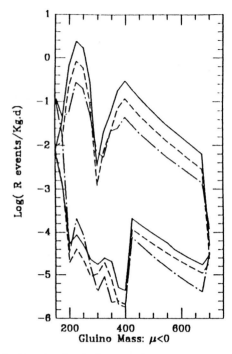

Figure 2. Same as fig. 1 when $\mu < 0$.

the COBE constraint. The analysis was carried out for several target nuclei [6,7]. In figs. 1 and 2 we exhibit the event rates for three target materials: CaF$_2$, Ge and Pb. The analysis shows that there is a region of the parameter space where the rate $R > 0.1$. This is the region which is currently accessible to experiment. However, one needs detectors of order $10^2 - 10^3$ more sensitive to probe a majority of the parameter space of supergravity grand unification. It is also found that the recent experimental results from CLEO [3] on the measurement of $b \rightarrow s\gamma$ can affect the event rates significantly [7]. For $\mu > 0$, there is generally a significant reduction both in the allowed parameter space consistent with the $b \rightarrow s\gamma$ constraint as well as in the maximum value of the event rates. The effects for $\mu < 0$ are significantly smaller. We note that even with inclusion of the $b \rightarrow s\gamma$ constraint, $R > 0.1$ over a reasonable part of the parameter space and hence is accessible to experiment with current technology.

References

[1] A.H. Chamseddine, R. Arnowitt and P. Nath, Phys. Rev. Lett. 29 (1982) 970; P. Nath, R. Arnowitt and A.H. Chamseddine, "Applied N=1 Supergravity." World Scientific Singapore (1984).

[2] R. Arnowitt and P. Nath, Phys. Lett. B299 (1993) 58; (E) B303 (1993) 403; P. Nath and R. Arnowtitt, Phys. Rev. Lett. 70 (1993) 3696; S. Kelley et. al. Phys. Rev. D47 (1993) 2461.

[3] E. H. Thorndike, Talk at this conf.: (ICHEP94 Ref. GLS0392).

[4] P. Nath and R. Arnowitt, to appear in Phys. Lett. B; F.Borzumati et al DESY 94-096.

[5] J. Ellis and R. Flores, Phys. Lett. B300 (1993) 175; M. Drees and M. Nojiri, Phys. Rev. D48, (1993) 3483 and the references quoted therein.

[6] R. Arnowitt and P. Nath, CERN-Th.7362/94; CTP-TAMU-37/94; NUB-TH.3098/94

[7] P. Nath and R. Arnowitt, CERN-TH.7363/94; NUB-TH.3099/94; CTP- TAMU-37/94

Gravitinos in the Early Universe

Willy Fischler

Theory Group, Department of Physics
University of Texas, Austin, TX 78712, USA

Abstract

This talk is based on the paper entitled "Gravitinos and a low ultimate temperature for the universe" [1]. The content of the talk is similar to the one given at the Nato workshop on "Electroweak physics and the early universe" [2]. It describes how the production of gravitinos in a thermal environment is larger than what would be naively expected if one uses the zero temperature cross sections. The implication of this result is that either supersymmetry is broken at energies lower than 10^5 GeV or the alternative, that the temperature of the early universe not exceed 10^5 GeV.

References

[1] W. Fischler, Gravitinos and a low ultimate temperature for the early universe, Physics Letters **B332** (1994) 277-282.
[2] W. Fischler, Gravitinos in the Early Universe, to be published in *Proceedings of the NATO ARW Electroweak Physics and the Early Universe*, Plenum Press, New York.

Paper presented at XXVII Int. Conf. on High Energy Physics: Session Pa-12
Glasgow, UK, 20–27 July 1994

Active Sterile Neutrino Conversions in a Supernova with Random Magnetic Fields

S. Pastor, V. Semikoz and José W. F. Valle [†]

† Departament de Física Teórica, Universitat de València and
Instituto de Física Corpuscular - C.S.I.C., E-46100 Burjassot, València, SPAIN

Abstract

Large enough random magnetic fields may affect in an important way neutrino conversion rates, even in the case where neutrinos have zero transition magnetic moments. We consider their effect in the case of active to sterile neutrino conversions in a supernova and show that for KeV neutrino masses these limits may overcome those derived for the case of zero magnetic field.

1. Introduction

There have been several hints for nonzero neutrino masses from astrophysical and comological observations which, taken altogether, point towards a class of extensions of the standard model that contain a light sterile neutrino [1].

So far the most stringent constraints for the neutrino mass matrix including a fourth neutrino species, ν_s, come from the nucleosynthesis bound on the maximum number of extra neutrino species that can reach thermal equilibrium before nucleosynthesis and change the primordially produced helium abundance [2]. This has been widely discussed in the case of the early Universe hot plasma without magnetic field, as well as recently for the case of a large random magnetic field (r.m.f.) [3].

Stringent constraints on the active to sterile neutrino oscillation parameters have been derived for the case of supernovae with zero magnetic field in ref. [4]. Here we summarize the results of ref. [5] on the effect that a large supernova r.m.f. has on the active sterile neutrino conversions. This was motivated by a recent paper [6] which showed that magnetic fields as strong as 10^{14} to 10^{16} Gauss might be generated during the first seconds of neutrino emission inside a supernova core. If such field is generated after collapse it could be viewed as the random superposition of many small dipoles with size $L_0 \sim 1$ Km [6]. Although the magnetic field in different domains is randomly aligned relative to the neutrino propagation direction, the neutrino conversion probabilities depend on the mean-squared random field via a squared magnetization value, leading therefore to nonvanishing averages over the magnetic field distribution.

The effect which we have found is of more general validity than that which could be ascribed to nonzero magnetic (transition) moments, as it would exist even these are negligible, as expected in the simplest extensions of the standard model.

2. Active-sterile neutrino conversions in the presence of a large r.m.f.

The equation of motion for a system of one active and one sterile neutrinos propagating in the presence of a large r.m.f. can be written in terms of weak eigenstates, as

$$i\frac{d}{dt}\begin{pmatrix} \nu_a \\ \nu_s \end{pmatrix} = \begin{pmatrix} H_{aa} & H_{as} \\ H_{as} & H_{ss} \end{pmatrix}\begin{pmatrix} \nu_a \\ \nu_s \end{pmatrix}, \qquad (2.1)$$

where the quantities in the evolution hamiltonian are given as

$$H_{aa} = (c^2 m_1^2 + s^2 m_2^2)/2q + V_{as} + A_{as} \quad (2.2)$$
$$H_{as} = cs\Delta$$
$$H_{ss} = (s^2 m_1^2 + c^2 m_2^2)/2q$$

and we have denoted by V_{as} and A_{as} the vector and axial parts of the neutrino potential that will describe the active to sterile conversions, given as

$$V_{as} \approx 4 \times 10^{-6} \rho_{14}(3Y_e + 4Y_{\nu_e} - 1)\text{MeV}, \quad (2.3)$$

$$A_{as}(q, B) = V_{axial}\frac{q_z}{q} \quad (2.4)$$

where the term V_{axial} is produced by the *mean axial current* and is proportional to the magnetization of the plasma in the external magnetic field, assumed to be pointed along the z-direction inside a given domain. In the above equations q is the neutrino momentum, m_1 and m_2 are the masses of the neutrinos, θ is their mixing angle and we use the standard definitions $\Delta = \Delta m^2/2q$; $\Delta m^2 = m_2^2 - m_1^2$; $c = \cos\theta$, and $s = \sin\theta$. The Y's denote particle abundances and ρ_{14} denotes the density in units of 10^{14} g/cc.

Notice that, although majorana neutrinos could have nonzero transition magnetic moments [7], we have neglected them in our present discussion. As we will see, even in this case, there may be a large effect of the magnetic field on the conversion rates.

From (2.1) one can easily obtain the probability $P_{\nu_a \to \nu_s}(t)$ for converting the active neutrinos ν_a emitted by the supernova into the sterile neutrinos, ν_s. In a strong random magnetic field one can write

$$P_{\nu_a \to \nu_s}(B, t) \approx \frac{\Delta^2 \sin^2 2\theta}{2\Delta_m^2}\left(1 - \exp(-\Delta_m^2 t/2\Gamma)\right), \quad (2.5)$$

which describes the aperiodic behaviour of the active to sterile neutrino conversion. The relaxation time defined as

$$t_{relax} = 2\Gamma/\Delta_m^2 = \langle\Delta_B^2\rangle L_0/\Delta_m^2 \quad (2.6)$$

depends on the mean squared magnetic field parameter

$$\langle\Delta_B^2\rangle^{1/2} = \frac{|\mu_{eff}|\langle\mathbf{B}^2\rangle^{1/2}}{\sqrt{3}}, \quad (2.7)$$

where μ_{eff} is defined in ref. [5] and L_0 is the domain size where the magnetic field is taken as uniform and constant. In (2.5) the quantity Δ_m

$$\Delta_m = [(V_{as} - \Delta\cos 2\theta)^2 + \Delta^2 \sin^2 2\theta]^{1/2} \quad (2.8)$$

is the standard oscillation frequency in the supernova medium [8].

Note that (2.5) is valid when $\Gamma \gg \Delta_m$ is fulfilled and this holds in the case of a very strong r.m.s. magnetic field $\mathcal{O}$ (10^{14} - 10^{16}) Gauss.

The relaxation time in (2.6) can be much larger than the mean active neutrino collision time $t_{coll} = \Gamma_a(B \neq 0)^{-1}$. In order to see this we have used the estimate [9],

$$\Gamma_a(B \neq 0) \lesssim 2B_{14}\Gamma_a(B = 0) \quad (2.9)$$

where B_{14} denotes the magnetic field strength in units of 10^{14} Gauss. As we can see this collision rate could be larger than $\Gamma_a(B = 0)$ by a factor $2B_{14}$. This allows us, following ref. [3], to average (2.5) over collisions so as to obtain

$$\langle P_{\nu_a \to \nu_s}(B)\rangle = \frac{\Delta^2 \sin^2 2\theta}{\langle\Delta_B^2\rangle 4\Gamma_a L_0} \equiv \frac{\sin^2 2\theta_B}{2}. \quad (2.10)$$

where we define the mixing angle in the presence of the magnetic field via

$$\sin^2 2\theta_B = \frac{\Delta^2 \sin^2 2\theta}{2\langle\Delta_B^2\rangle\Gamma_a L_0} = \frac{x}{2}\sin^2 2\theta_m, \quad (2.11)$$

in analogy with the case of zero magnetic field, where $P_{\nu_a \to \nu_s}(B \to 0) = \sin^2 2\theta_m/2$. The parameter x is defined as

$$x = \Delta_m^2/2\Gamma\Gamma_a(B \neq 0) \quad (2.12)$$

3. Supernova Constraints

There are two ways to place constraints on neutrino oscillation parameters using astrophysical criteria, depending on the relative value of the effective sterile neutrino effective mean free path $l_s \equiv \Gamma_s^{-1} \equiv [P(\nu_a \to \nu_s)\Gamma_a]^{-1}$ and the core radius R_{core}. If the trapping condition $l_s \leq R_{core}$ is fulfilled, the ν_S are in thermodynamical equilibrium with the medium and, due to the Stefan-Boltzman law, the ratio of the sterile neutrino luminosity to that of the ordinary neutrinos,

$$\frac{Q_s}{Q_a} \simeq \left(\frac{T(R_s)}{T(R_a)}\right)^4\left(\frac{R_s}{R_a}\right)^2 \simeq \left(\frac{\Gamma_a}{\Gamma_s}\right)^{\frac{1}{2}} = \left(\frac{\sin^2 2\theta_m}{2}\right)^{-\frac{1}{2}}, \quad (3.1)$$

does not depend on Γ_a. In this first regime one considers surface thermal neutrino emission and sets the conservative limit $(Q_s/Q_a)_{max} \gtrsim 10$ in order to obtain the excluded region of neutrino parameters, valid for $\Delta m^2 \gtrsim \text{KeV}^2$ [4] †

$$\sin^2 2\theta_m \lesssim 2 \times 10^{-2} \quad (3.2)$$

† The cosmological arguments that forbid neutrino masses in the KeV range or above are not applicable in models with unstable neutrinos that decay via majoron emission [1].

In the case nonzero r.m.f. we obtain this is replaced by

$$\sin^2 2\theta_m \lesssim \frac{4 \times 10^{-2}}{x} \qquad (3.3)$$

Another complementary constraint can be obtained from the requirement that in the non-trapping regime the sterile neutrino can be emitted from anywhere inside the star volume with a rate

$$\frac{dQ(B=0)}{dt} \simeq \frac{4}{3}\pi R_{core}^3 n_{\nu e}\Gamma_s \langle E_s \rangle$$
$$\simeq 1.4 \times 10^{55}\sin^2 2\theta_m \ \mathrm{J/s} \qquad (3.4)$$

which should not exceed the maximum observed integrated neutrino luminosity. For instance, for the case of SN1987A, this is $\sim 10^{46}$ J, so that one obtains the excluded region [4]

$$\sin^2 2\theta_m \gtrsim 7 \times 10^{-10} \qquad (3.5)$$

In the case of a strong magnetic field $B \neq 0$ we use the known estimate for the active neutrino collision rate (2.9) and the relationship between the corresponding conversion probabilities in order to obtain the ratio of sterile neutrino volume energy losses in the presence and absence of magnetic field

$$\frac{dQ(B=0)/dt}{dQ(B\neq 0)/dt} \sim \frac{1}{xB_{14}}\text{·,} \qquad (3.6)$$

where x is the small parameter in (2.12). From the last inequality we can find a region of abundances where our result for the conversion probability (2.10) is valid ($x \ll 1$) so that we obtain the excluded region

$$\sin^2 2\theta_m \gtrsim \frac{7 \times 10^{-10}}{xB_{14}} \ . \qquad (3.7)$$

Note that this constraint on the neutrino parameters can be more stringent than that of (3.4). In particular, for a supernova with strong magnetic field it is possible to exclude all region of large mixing angles, if the parameter x in (2.12) is $x \leq 0.04$, as we showed in Fig. 1 of ref. [5]. This will be realized for a r.m.s. field $B_{14} \sim 10^2$ [6] and 100 MeV mean sterile neutrino energy if the abundance parameter is less than

$$\mid 3Y_e + 4Y_{\nu e} - 1 \mid \leq 0.3 \times Y_e^{1/3}\rho_{14}^{-1/6} \ . \qquad (3.8)$$

This condition may indeed be realized for a stage of supernova after bounce [4,10]. Moreover, this assumption is not crucial for us, in contrast to the case of resonant neutrino spin-flip due to a neutrino magnetic moment.

4. Conclusions

The possible existence of huge random magnetic fields that might be generated during the first few seconds of neutrino emission in a supernova modifies the neutrino spectrum due to the magnetization of the medium, and thereby affect the active to sterile neutrino conversion rates. Their effect on the cooling rates may enable one to place more stringent limits than those that apply in the absence of a magnetic field. This happens despite the fact that in the presence of a large magnetic field the active to sterile neutrino conversion probability is suppressed relative to that in the zero field case due to the larger energy difference between the two diagonal entries in the neutrino evolution hamiltonian caused by the extra axial term. However, the sterile neutrino production rate could be larger in this case due to the effect of the large magnetic field. On the other hand the ratio of active and sterile neutrino thermal luminosities does not depend on the active neutrino production rate. However, the smaller the conversion probability the larger the sterile neutrino effective mean free path, and therefore they can leave the star more easily than in the case of zero magnetic field. This may lead to the exclusion of the complete large mixing angle region [5].

Acknowledgements

This paper has been supported by DGICYT under Grant number PB92-0084.

References

[1] J. W. F. Valle, these proceedings
[2] For a review see G. Steigman; proceedings of the *International School on Cosmological Dark Matter*, (World Scientific, 1994), ed. J. W. F. Valle and A. Perez, p. 55
[3] V. Semikoz and J.W.F.Valle, *Nucl. Phys.* **B425** (1994) 651-664.
[4] K. Kainulainen, J. Maalampi and J.T. Peltoniemi, *Nucl. Phys.* **B358** (1991) 435; G. Raffelt and G. Sigl, *Ann. Phys. (NY)* **1** (1993) 165.
[5] S. Pastor, V. Semikoz and J.W.F.Valle, FTUV/94-15, hep-ph 9404299, *Ann. Phys. (NY)* (1994) , in press
[6] C. Thomson and R.C. Dunkan, *Astrophys. J.* **408** (1993) 194.
[7] J. Schechter and J. W. F. Valle, *Phys. Rev.* **D24** (1981) 1883; *Phys. Rev.* **D25** (1982) 283
[8] M. Mikheyev, A. Smirnov, *Sov. J. Nucl. Phys.* **42** (1986) 913; L. Wolfenstein, *Phys. Rev.* **D17** (1978) 2369; *ibid.* **D20** (1979) 2634.
[9] B. Cheng, D.N. Schramm and J.W. Truran, *Phys. Lett.* **B316** (1993) 521.
[10] D. Notzold *Phys. Rev.* **D38** (1988) 1658

Ferromagnetic Vacuum and Galactic Magnetic Fields

Kari Enqvist*

Research Institute for Theoretical Physics, P.O. Box 9, FIN-00014 University of Helsinki, Finland[†]

Abstract

The primordial origin of galactic magnetic fields is discussed in the model where the Yang-Mills vacuum is non-trivial with $B \neq 0$. If the field is imprinted on the comoving plasma already at the GUT scale, the red-shifted field is large enough to act as a seed for the galactic dynamo today.

1. Introduction

The nearby galaxies have magnetic fields of the order of $B \simeq 10^{-6}$ G. This can be deduced from observations of the syncrotron radiation put out by electrons traversing the galactic fields. The best explanation for the origin of galactic magnetic fields is perhaps the galactic dynamo model, where differential rotation and turbulence of the ionized gas amplifies a weak seed field by several orders of magnitude [1]. At the scale of 100 kpc the dynamo mechanism requires a primordial field somewhere in the ballpark of of 10^{-18} G, with an uncertainty of a few orders of magnitude.

The origin of the seed itself is, however, a mystery. One interesting possibility is that the seed field is primordial, with an origin that predates nucleosynthesis. From a theoretical point of view the generation of a sufficiently large persistent magnetic field in the early universe is, however, rather difficult. Electromagnetism first occurs when the standard electroweak $SU(2) \otimes U(1)_Y$ theory is broken down to $U(1)_{\text{em}}$, and it has been suggested that a large field might actually be generated at the electroweak phase transition because of random fluctuations in the Higgs field [2]. The issue is then how to perform the statistical average over the fluctuations [3]. Other attempts, relying on the cosmic inflation or the QCD phase transition [4], yield a field that often comes out too small to be of cosmological interest.

* E-mail: enqvist@phcu.helsinki.fi
† On a leave of absence from Nordita, Blegdamsvej 17, DK-2100 Copenhagen Ø, Denmark.

In Yang-Mills theories there is also the possibility [5] that the vacuum is an analog of the ferromagnet with a non-zero background magnetic field. This is a non-perturbative effect, and the resulting field is typically very small. If one is willing, however, to go up all the way to the GUT scale one finds that a typical GUT phase transition could have given rise to a background field large enough to serve as the seed field [6].

2. Ferromagnetic universe

Because of quantum fluctuations, the Yang–Mills vacuum is unstable in a large enough background magnetic field [5]. There are indications from lattice calculations that this is a non-perturbative result [7]. Such magnetic field fluctuations in the early universe could be sufficient to trigger the phase transition to a new, ferromagnet–like ground state with a magnetic field made permanent by the charged plasma. In this scenario the primordial field is thus generated as a non-perturbative quantum effect.

The new vacuum results provided the β–function has a Landau singularity:

$$\left| \int_g^\infty \frac{dx}{\beta(x)} \right| < \infty. \tag{1}$$

Then the effective Lagrangian has a minimum away from the perturbative ground state Tr $F^2 = 0$, given by

$$\frac{1}{2} g^2 \text{Tr } F_{\mu\nu}^2 |_{\min} = \Lambda^4, \tag{2}$$

where Λ is the renormalization group invariant scale

$$\Lambda = \mu \exp\left(-\int_\infty^g \frac{dx}{\beta(x)}\right), \qquad (3)$$

where μ is a subtraction point associated with the definition of g.

The condition for the minimum can be realized in many ways. One of them is a constant non–abelian magnetic field $B_i^a = \epsilon_{ijk}F_{jk}^a$ with a non–zero component only in one direction in the group space, and with a length given by $g\sqrt{B^a B^a} = \Lambda^2$.

In pure SU(N) the one–loop, zero temperature effective energy for a constant background non–abelian magnetic field reads [5]

$$V(B) = \frac{1}{2}B^2 + \frac{11N}{96\pi^2}g^2 B^2 \left(\ln\frac{gB}{\mu^2} - \frac{1}{2}\right) \qquad (4)$$

with a minimum at $gB_{\min} = \mu^2 \exp\left(-\frac{48\pi^2}{11Ng^2}\right)$ and $V_{\min} \equiv V(B_{\min}) = -0.029(gB_{\min})^2$.

For a set of representative numbers, one might consider a (susy) SU(5) model with $\alpha_{\rm GUT} \simeq 1/25$ and $T_{\rm GUT} \simeq 10^{15}$ GeV, as in the supersymmetric Standard Model. This yields $B \simeq 5 \times 10^{-8}\mu^2$, which turns out to be a magnitude which is relevant for the dynamo mechanism.

In the early universe the effective energy picks up thermal corrections from fermionic, gauge boson, and Higgs boson loops. In SU(2) these are obtained by summing the Boltzmann factors $\exp(-\beta E_n)$ for the oscillator modes

$$E_n^2 = p^2 + 2gB(n + \frac{1}{2}) + 2gBS_3 + m^2(T), \qquad (5)$$

where $S_3 = \pm 1/2$ (± 1) for fermions (vectors bosons). In Eq. (5) I have included the thermally induced mass $m(T) \sim gT$, corresponding to a ring summation of the relevant diagrams. Numerically, the effect of the thermal mass turns out to be very important.

The detailed form of the thermal correction depends on the actual model, but we may take our cue from the SU(2) one–loop calculation, which for the fermionic and scalar cases can be extracted from the real–time QED calculation in [8]. The result is

$$\delta V_T^f = \frac{(gB)^2}{4\pi^2}\sum_{l=1}^\infty (-1)^{l+1} \int_0^\infty \frac{dx}{x^3} e^{-K_l^a(x)} \times$$
$$\times [\,x\coth(x) - 1\,],$$
$$\delta V_T^s = \frac{(gB)^2}{8\pi^2}\sum_{l=1}^\infty \int_0^\infty \frac{dx}{x^3} e^{-K_l^a(x)} \left[\frac{x}{\sinh(x)} - 1\right], \quad (6)$$

where the normalization is such that the correction vanishes for zero field, and

$$K_l^a(x) = \frac{gBl^2}{4xT^2} + \frac{m_a^2 x}{gB} \qquad (7)$$

where $a = f$, b stands for fermions or bosons.

For vector bosons there is the added complication that there exists a negative, unstable mode, which gives rise to an imaginary part. At high temperatures the instability is absent for fields such that $gB < m^2(T)$, which is the case we are interested in here, so that no regulation of the unstable $n = 0$, $S_3 = -1$ mode is needed. Thus one finds [6]

$$\delta V_T^v = \frac{(gB)^2}{8\pi^2}\sum_{l=1}^\infty \int_0^\infty \frac{dx}{x^3} e^{-K_l^b(x)} \left[x\frac{\cosh(2x)}{\sinh(x)} - 1\right]. \qquad (8)$$

At high temperature, the bosonic contributions are more important than the fermionic ones. When $B \ll T^2 \simeq m^2(T)$, we find numerically that $\delta V_T^v \simeq 0.02 \times (gB)^2$. This gives rise to a small correction to the magnitude of the field at the minimum. We may thus conclude that the Savvidy vacuum exists for all T.

The magnetic flux remains conserved because the primodial plasma is an extremely good conductor, and we may write

$$B(T) = \frac{\mu^2}{g}e^{-\frac{48\pi^2}{11Ng^2}}\left(\frac{T^2}{\mu^2}\right) \simeq 3 \times 10^{42}{\rm G}\left(\frac{a(t_{\rm GUT})}{a(t)}\right)^2, \qquad (9)$$

where $\mu \simeq T$, $g = g_{\rm GUT}$ and $a(t)$ is the scale factor of the universe, and the last figure is for susy SU(5). The Maxwell magnetic field B_{em} is a projection in the space of non–abelian magnetic fields, and we take it to be of the size comparable to B in Eq. (9).

One thus finds that the Maxwell magnetic field at $t_{now} \simeq 10^{10}$ yr is given by $B_{now} \simeq 3 \times 10^{42}{\rm G}(t_{\rm GUT}/t_*)(t_*/t_{now})^{4/3} \simeq 10^{-14}{\rm G}$. Such a magnetic field appears comparable to what is needed for the seed field in galactic dynamo models. Note also that at nucleosynthesis one obtains $B \sim 10^4$ G, which is well below the nucleosynthesis bound on magnetic fields [9].

3.   Absence of domains

In order to estimate the magnetic field today one needs to take into account the fact that in the universe there exists causal horizons. Naively one could argue that each horizon "bubble" (i.e. a bubble with a radius equal to the causal horizon at the GUT time $H^{-1} \simeq 10^{-28}$ cm) constitutes a magnetic domain. Thus one should average over all random domains, which now have a size of about 1 m, in order to obtain the average magnetic field today. If this were so, then the value of B and the magnetic energy $B^2/2$ at the time of protogalaxy collapse would very likely to be too small to be of interest for the observed galactic magnetic fields.

It turns out [10] that the proper physical situation is that when two bubbles meet, a new "joint" bubble is formed with the magnetic field lines frozen to the plasma particles. After a short time the joint plasma looses all memory of its origin, and so does the magnetic field, too. The situation is analogous to having two containers filled with identical gases which are separated by a wall. Once the wall is removed the joint system has no memory of the original two separate containers.

Let us adopt the conformal metric $d\tau^2 = a(\eta)^2(-d\eta^2 + dx^2 + dy^2 + dz^2)$, where η is the conformal time. The advantage of the conformal metric is that electric and magnetic fields are treated on an equal footing. The magnetohydrodynamics equation for infinite conductivity in an expanding universe reads then

$$\frac{\partial a^2 \mathbf{B}}{\partial \eta} = \nabla \times (\mathbf{v} \times a^2 \mathbf{B}) . \qquad (10)$$

We need also the general relativistic continuity equation

$$(nU^\mu)_{;\mu} = U^\mu \frac{\partial n}{\partial x^\mu} + \frac{n}{\sqrt{g}} \frac{\partial}{\partial x^\mu}(\sqrt{g}U^\mu) = 0, \qquad (11)$$

where n is the density of charged particles which is conserved, and U^μ is the four-velocity. Inserting this in Eq. (10) we obtain [10]

$$\frac{d}{d\eta}\left(\frac{a^2\mathbf{B}}{a^4 U^0 n}\right) \equiv \left(\frac{\partial}{\partial \eta} + \mathbf{v} \cdot \nabla\right)\frac{a^2\mathbf{B}}{a^4 U^0 n}$$
$$= \left(\frac{a^2\mathbf{B} \cdot \nabla}{a^4 U^0 n}\right)\mathbf{v} . \qquad (12)$$

In an adiabatically expanding universe $n \sim a^{-3}$. To find how U^0 scales, let us note that in the FRW metric $U_{\text{RW}}^0 = dt/d\tau = 1$, so that in the conformal metric $U^0 = d\eta/d\tau = 1/a(\eta)$. Of course, in our case this result is valid in the average only, and $\mathbf{v} = \mathbf{U}/U^0$ is locally non-vanishing (although $\langle\mathbf{v}\rangle = 0$). Thus we find that

$$a^4 n U^0 \simeq const. \qquad (13)$$

Eq. (12) can be solved. Let $\mathbf{X}(\eta_1)$ be the position of a plasma element at the time η_1 in comoving coordinates, and let $\mathbf{x} = \mathbf{x}(\mathbf{X}, \eta_2)$ be the position of the same plasma element at the time η_2 in comoving coordinates. Then Eq. (12) is solved by [1]

$$\frac{a(\eta_2)^2\mathbf{B}_i(\mathbf{x},\eta_2)}{a(\eta_2)^4 n(\eta_2) U^0(\eta_2)} = \frac{a(\eta_1)^2\mathbf{B}_j(\mathbf{X},\eta_1)}{a(\eta_1)^4 n(\eta_1) U^0(\eta_1)}\frac{\partial x_i}{\partial X_j} . \qquad (14)$$

Because of Eq. (13) we see that $a^2\mathbf{B}$ changes by the factor $\partial x_i/\partial X_j$.

The general solution (14) can be written by virtue of Eq. (13) as

$$a(\eta_2)^2\mathbf{B}_i(\mathbf{x}(\eta_2),\eta_2) = a(\eta_1)^2\mathbf{B}_j(\mathbf{X}(\eta_1),\eta_1)\frac{\partial x_i}{\partial X_j} . \qquad (15)$$

From a statistical point of view it is natural to assume isotropy so that

$$\langle\frac{\partial x_i}{\partial X_j}\rangle = \delta_{ij} . \qquad (16)$$

In other words, if we have an original displacement δX_j at $\eta = \eta_1$, then at a later time η_2 the corresponding displacement δx_i can in principle go in any direction. However, the original j-direction is the only preferred direction, so that if j turns into any $i \neq j$ then it is equally likely that the resulting displacement is positive or negative. Hence the statistical sum is zero. Eq. (16) is of course also valid when we consider the standard cosmology as a statistical model.

Thus Eqs. (15) and (16) lead us to the conclusion that $a^4\mathbf{B}^2$ is (statistically) constant. They also give rise to the strong result that

$$a(\eta_2)^2\langle\mathbf{B}_i(\mathbf{x}(\eta_2),\eta_2)\rangle = a(\eta_1)^2\langle\mathbf{B}_i(\mathbf{X}(\eta_1),\eta_1)\rangle , \qquad (17)$$

which demonstrates that, apart from a well understood redshift factor, the field $\mathbf{B}$ is statistically constant. Eq. (17) shows that the evolution of $a^2\mathbf{B}$ is *exactly* the same as the evolution of an invariant density such as $a^3 n$ having no domains. The same result holds for $a^4\langle\mathbf{B}^2\rangle$. It follows that the magnetic energy E_B scales like $1/a(\eta)$ and hence $E_B a$ remains a constant during the course of the evolution of the universe. Consequently the magnetic energy always corresponds to a magnetic field of $10^{-8}T^2$. Physically this is so because in the infinite conductivity limit there is no dissipation.

Acknowledgements

I wish to thank Poul Olesen for enjoyable collaboration.

References

[1] L. D. Landau and E.M. Lifshitz, *Electrodynamics of Continuous Media* (Pergamon, Oxford 1960); Ya.B. Zeldovich, A.A. Ruzmaikin and D.D. Sokoloff, *Magnetic Fields in Astrophysics* (McGraw-Hill, New York, 1980); E.N. Parker, *Cosmological Magnetic Fields* (Oxford Univ. Press, Oxford, 1979); A.A. Ruzmaikin, A.A. Shukurov and D.D. Sokoloff, *Magnetic Fields of Galaxies* (Kluwer, Dordrecht, 1988).

[2] T. Vachaspati, Phys. Lett. **B265** (1991) 258.

[3] K. Enqvist and P. Olesen, Phys. Lett. **B319** (1993) 178.

[4] C.J. Hogan, Phys. Rev. Lett. **51** (1983) 1488; M.S. Turner and L.W. Widrow, Phys. Rev. **D37** (1988) 2743; B. Ratra, Astrophys. J. Lett. **391** (1992) L1; W. Garretson, G.B. Field and S.M. Carroll, Phys. Rev. **D46** (1992) 5346;

[5] G.K. Savvidy, Phys. Lett. **B71** (1977) 133.

[6] K. Enqvist and P. Olesen, Phys. Lett. **B319** (1994) 195.

[7] H.D. Trottier and R.M. Woloshyn, Phys. Rev. Lett. **70** (1993) 2053; A.R. Levy and J. Polonyi, MIT-CTP-2161 (1993).

[8] W. Dittrich, Phys. Rev. **D19** (1979) 2385; P. Elmfors, D. Persson and B.-S. Skagerstam, Astropart. Phys. **2** (1994) 299.

[9] B. Cheng, D.N. Schramm and J.W. Truran, Phys. Rev. **D49** (1994) 5006.

[10] K. Enqvist and P. Olesen, preprint NORDITA-94/23 P.

Paper presented at XXVII Int. Conf. on High Energy Physics: Session Pa-12
Glasgow, UK, 20–27 July 1994

Standard Model CP-violation and Baryon asymmetry.

M.B. Gavela, P. Hernandez, J. Orloff, O.Pène, C. Quimbay.
presented by M.B. Gavela[†]

†, CERN, TH Division, CH-1211, Geneva 23, Switzerland

Abstract

Simply on CP arguments, we argue against a Standard Model explanation of baryogenesis via the charge transport mechanism, in the presence of a first order phase transition. A crucial role is played by the damping rate of quasi-quarks in a hot plasma, which induces loss of spatial coherence and suppresses reflection on the electroweak phase boundary even at tree-level. The resulting baryon asymmetry is many orders of magnitude below what observation requires. We comment as well on related works.

Sakharov's conditions [1] for baryogenesis imply that both baryon number-violating and C and CP-violating processes have to undergo an out-of-equilibrium period. The currently proposed scenario for Standard Model (SM) baryogenesis [2] is a charge transport mechanism [3], which occurs in the presence of a first order phase transition at a temperature $\sim 100\, GeV$. In this talk, we have summarised our study [4] [6] [7] of the SM C and CP effects in that framework. Even if one assumes an optimal sphaleron rate and a strong enough first order phase transition, we discard this scenario as an explanation of the observed baryon number to entropy ratio. As the details of our work have already appeared in the literature, we just sketch in what follows the backbone of the talk and go then into the subsequent discussion and comments at the conference. This discussion was interesting, contained some new elements, and should be clarified.

A first order phase transition can be described in terms of bubbles of "true" vacuum (with an inner vacuum expectation value of the Higgs field $v \neq 0$) appearing and expanding in the preexisting "false" vacuum (with $v = 0$ throughout). We can "zoom" into the vicinity of one of the bubbles. There the curvature of its wall can be neglected and the world is divided in two zones: $v = 0$ and $v \neq 0$. We work in the wall rest frame in which the plasma flows in the opposite direction. Consider thus a baryonic flux hitting the wall from the unbroken phase. The heart of the problem lies in the reflection and transmission properties of quarks bumpimg on the bubble wall. CP violation distinguishes particles from antiparticles and it is *a priori* possible to obtain a CP asymmetry on the reflected baryonic current, Δ_{CP}. The induced baryon asymmetry is at most $n_B/s \sim 10^{-2}\Delta_{CP}$, in a very optimistic estimation of the non-CP ingredients [2].

The three building blocks of the CP-asymmetry on the reflected baryonic current are: the CP-violating couplings of the CKM matrix, the presence of CP-even phases associated to complex reflection coefficients for certain values of the energy of the incoming quasi-particles [2], and the well-known fact that, at finite temperature, the fermionic on-shell self-energy cannot be completely renormalized away and induces physical transitions already at the one-loop level. The correct incoming asymptotic states are quasi-particles instead of particles, built up of a resummation of the thermal self-energies of the particles. Even starting from massless particles, the eigenstates of the effective thermal Dirac equation have an "effective mass", or plasma frequency, due to the QCD thermal self-energies. It gives the overall energy scale of the problem $\sim g_s T \sim 50$ GeV, for $T \sim 100$ GeV. This results in a shift in the position of the reflection coefficient threshold for a given quasi-particle. Nevertheless, the tree-level reflection region for a given flavour is still of the order of the corresponding current (non-thermal) mass m. In other words, the time required for complete reflection of a given quasi-particle is of the order of $1/m$.

On top of the above, the authors of ref.[2] have pointed out that electroweak thermal loops are present as well, and because the latter are flavour dependent, their resummation can lift the QCD degeneracy of the spectrum of quasi-quarks even far from the wall in the unbroken phase.

In our opinion, the important point to retain is that CP violation is a quantum phenomenon, and can only be observed when quantum coherence is preserved over time scales larger than or equal to the electroweak time scales needed for CP violation. This is however not the case in the plasma, where the incoherent scattering of quasi-quarks with thermal gluons induces a large damping rate, γ. We argue[4] [7] that the quantum phase of the quasi-quarks is in fact lost much before the time scales mentioned in the above paragraphs. Small momenta are relevant for the problem under study and it is known that, at zero momentum, the QCD contribution to the damping rate is $\gamma \sim 0.15\, g_s^2 T$, i.e. ~ 19 GeV [8]. The quasi-quark energy and momentum are not sharply defined, but spread like a resonance of width 2γ. It then has a finite life-time $\sim 1/2\gamma$, turning eventually into a new state, out of phase with the initial one. Although the life-time is larger than the overall QCD time scale mentioned above, $\sim 1/(50\text{GeV})$ [9]–[12], it is small in comparison with both the electroweak thermal self-energy time scales for any quasi-quark, and with the tree-level reflection times $\sim 1/m$ for all quasi-quarks but the top.

The problem can be rephrased in terms of spatial decoherence. Reflection is a spatial property. The quasi-quarks have a group velocity of $\sim 1/3$ and thus a mean free path, or coherence length, of $\sim 1/6\gamma$. Over larger scales, such as those needed for instance for total reflection, the quantum coherence of light quasi-quarks is damped and any pure quantum effect, such as CP violation, is suppressed.

We thus show that tree-level reflection is suppressed for any light flavour by a factor $\sim m/2\gamma$. The presently discussed CP-violation observable results from the convolution of this reflection effect with electroweak loops in which the three generations must interfere coherently in order to produce a CP-violation observable. It follows that further factors of this type appear in the final result, which is many orders of magnitude below what observation requires and has a standard type of GIM cancellations. We show as well that the effect is present at order α_W^2 in a perturbative expansion. The mechanism fails to explain the observed baryon asymmetry by more than 12 orders

of magnitude.

The analytical results correspond to the thin wall scenario. The latter provides an adequate physical description for typical momentum of the incoming particles $|\vec{p}|$ smaller than the inverse wall thickness l, i.e., $|\vec{p}| \ll 1/l$. For higher momenta, cutoff effects would show up, but it is reasonable to believe that the thin wall approximation produces an upper bound for the CP asymmetry. We work in a simplified scenario with just one spatial direction, perpendicular to the wall surface: phase space effects in the $3 + 1$ dimension case would further suppress the effect.

Using the following values for the masses in GeV, $M_W = 50$, $M_Z = 57$, $m_d = 0.006$, $m_s = 0.09$, $m_b = 3.1$, $m_u = 0.003$, $m_c = 1.0$, $m_t = 93.7$, and $\alpha_s = 0.1$, $\alpha_W = 0.035$ we obtain for the integrated asymmetry,

$$\Delta_{CP}^{uct} = 1.6\ 10^{-21}, \qquad \Delta_{CP}^{dbs} = -3\ 10^{-24}. \quad (1)$$

In both cases the asymmetry is dominated by the two heavier external quarks.

In ref. [2] Farrar and Shaposhnikov (FS) obtain $\Delta_{CP} \gtrsim 10^{-8}$, and conclude $n_B/s \sim 10^{-11}$ (see eq. (10.3) in [2]). Their result is many orders of magnitude above ours, eq. (1). The main origin of the discrepancy is that they have not considered the effect of the damping rate on the quasi-particle spectrum†.

For the sake of comparison, we considered first their approximation, i.e., with just the unbroken phase inside the thermal loops, and with zero damping rate $\gamma = 0$, for a thin wall. We confirm the validity of their numerical calculation. We then reconsidered the same case, although with $\gamma \neq 0$. In the energy region where the peak value for tha asymmetry, Δ_{CP}^{max}, was found for $\gamma = 0$ [2] and down quarks, the α_W expansion with non zero damping rate leads to:

$$\Delta_{CP}^{max} = \left[\sqrt{\frac{3\pi}{2}}\frac{\alpha_W T}{32\sqrt{\alpha_s}}\right]^3 J\frac{(m_t^2 - m_c^2)(m_t^2 - m_u^2)}{M_W^4}$$

$$\frac{(m_c^2 - m_u^2)}{M_W^2}\frac{(m_b^2 - m_s^2)(m_s^2 - m_d^2)(m_b^2 - m_d^2)}{(2\gamma)^9} \quad (2)$$

where $J = c_1 c_2 c_3 s_1^2 s_2 s_3 s_\delta$. This result shows the expected GIM cancellation and regular chiral behaviour. Its magnitude, $\sim 4\, 10^{-22}$, is lower than the dominant one at order α_W^2.

A final comment on the wall thickness l is pertinent. The mean free path for quasi-particles of lifetime $\sim 1/2\gamma$ and group velocity $1/3$ is $1/6\gamma \sim (120 GeV)^{-1}$. The thin wall approximation is valid only for $l \ll 1/6\gamma$,

† More precisely, they take into account the finite mean free path of the quasi-particles in the suppression factor, i.e. what fraction of the Δ_{CP} is transformed into a baryon asymmetry by the sphalerons, but not in the computation of Δ_{CP}.

while perturbative estimates[2] give $l \stackrel{>}{\sim} (10\,GeV)^{-1} \gg 1/6\gamma$. A realistic CP asymmetry generated in such scenario will be orders of magnitude below the thin wall estimate in eq. (1), reinforcing thus our conclusions, because a quasi-particle would then collide and loose coherence long before feeling a wall effect. This caveat should also be considered in any non-standard scenario of electroweak baryogenesis, where the wall thickness is larger than the mean free path.

Huet and Sather [5] have analyzed as well the finite temperature problem. These authors state that they confirm our conclusions. As we had done in ref. [4], they stress that the damping rate is a source for quantum decoherence, and use as well an effective Dirac equation which takes it into account. They discuss a nice physical analogy with the microscopic theory of reflection of light. They do not use wave packets to solve the scattering problem, but spatially damped waves.

FS [13] have expressed doubts on the technical reliability of both our work and that of Huet and Sather [5]. They claim that our schemes violate unitarity. This is incorrect, as particle number is always conserved in our approaches. The effective Dirac equation for a given quasi-particle contains indeed an imaginary component which parametrizes the damping rate. An effective description of the evolution of a subsystem of a larger entity does not have to be hermitian. In fact, consistency may imply an apparent lack of unitarity in a subensemble of a whole unitary system. We had explicitly discussed this point in the detailed version of our results [7]. We developed there a density matrix formalism containing a creation term of quasi-particles due to collisions with the medium, which exactly compensates disappearance by the same processes, see eq. (4.30) in [7]. The density of quasi-particles is always normalized to the equilibrium density. The omission of this normalization would lead to a suppression of the tree-level reflection probability for one flavour of order $\sim m^2/\gamma^2$, instead of our milder m/γ factor. The quasi-particles created by the medium are out of phase with respect to the ones destroyed, but total particle number, and thus unitarity, is preserved.

FS also object to our claim that the reflection amplitude is suppressed when integrated over a wave packet by the interference between the contribution of different momenta. They state that, as the reflection phase shift varies between 0 and π, the different contributions should still sum up to a significant contribution. This argument fails as the total phase to consider is the combination of the above mentioned one with the optical path length, i.e. the phase of the e^{ipz_0} factors, as may be seen in section 4.1.2 in [7]. Consequently, the phase shifts range between 0 and 2π resulting in a very strong destructive interference. The rest of the note by FS contains either comments which are unrelated to the main point under discussion, or unproved speculations on alternative scenarios. In fact, these authors have not demonstrated their implicit claim that the damping rate is irrelevant to the problem, neither have they proven us or Huet and Sather wrong in any concrete point of the calculations. And they have not included the effects of the damping rate in their explicit computation of the reflection properties. There is no point in being repetitive, and we refer the interested reader to the published work [4] [5] [6] [7].

It has also been argued that the effect of the damping term on the quasi-particle propagator may be cancelled by other diagrams which we would not take into account. In fact no such missing diagram was explicitly exhibited, but an analogy with the analysis of the polarization operator for the electromagnetic current in a quark gluon plasma [14] was suggested. In the latter case, the authors showed that an apparent violation of gauge invariance by the damping factor of the propagator is cancelled by vertex corrections. The damping rate contribution that we take into account is gauge invariant by itself, though. There are no symmetry arguments which can suggest such a cancellation, contrary to the case discussed in [14].

Pilar Hernandez acknowledges partial financial support from NSF-PHY92-18167 and the Milton Fund. C. Quimbay would like to thank COLCIENCIAS (Colombia) for financial support. This work was supported in part by the Human Capital and Mobility Programme, contract CHRX-CT93-0132.

References

[1] A.D. Sakharov JETP Lett. 6 (1967) 24.
[2] G.R.Farrar and M.E.Shaposhnikov, Phys. Rev. Lett. 70 (1993) 2833. G.R.Farrar and M.E.Shaposhnikov, CERN-TH.6732/93.
[3] A. Cohen, D. Kaplan, and A. Nelson Nucl. Phys. B373 (1992) 453.
[4] M.B. Gavela, P. Hernandez, J. Orloff, and O.Pène, Modern Physics Letters 9A 795 (1994).
[5] P. Huet and E. Sather, SLAC-PUB-6479 (1994).
[6] M.B. Gavela, M. Lozano, J. Orloff, and O.Pène, CERN-TH.7262/94, LPTHE Orsay-94/48, HD-THEP-94-19, FAMNSE-12-94., hep-ph/9406288. To be published in Nucl. Phys. B.
[7] M.B. Gavela, P. Hernandez, J. Orloff, O. Pène and C. Quimbay, CERN-TH.7263/94, LPTHE Orsay-94/49, HUTP-94/A015, HD-THEP-94-20, FTUAM-94/14, hep-ph/9406289. To be published in Nucl. Phys. B.
[8] E. Brateen and R.D. Pisarski, Phys.Rev. D46 (1992) 1829 and references therein. R. Kobes, G. Kunstatter and K. Mak, Phys. Rev. D 45 (1992)4632.
[9] V.V. Klimov, Sov. J. Nucl. Phys. 33 (1981) 934.
[10] H.A. Weldon, Phys.Rev. D26 (1982) 2789.
[11] E. Petitgerard, Z. Phys. C 54 (1992) 673.
[12] D. Seibert, CERN-TH-7034/93.
[13] G.R.Farrar and M.E.Shaposhnikov, RU-94-40, June 1994.
[14] V.V. Lebedev and A.V. Smilga, Phys. Lett. 253B (1991) 253.

*Paper presented at XXVII Int. Conf. on High Energy Physics: Session Pa-12
Glasgow, UK, 20–27 July 1994*

On a Minimal Standard Model Baryogenesis

M E Shaposhnikov[†‡]

† Theory Division, CERN, CH-1211 Geneva 23, Switzerland

Abstract

We consider the possibility that the baryonic asymmetry of the universe originated due to the minimal standard model interactions.

1. Introduction.

The minimal standard model (MSM) of electroweak (EW) interactions contains all 3 ingredients necessary [1] for the production of the baryonic asymmetry of the universe (BAU). Namely, the rate of the fermionic number non-conservation is large enough at high temperatures [2], CP-violation is provided by the KM mixing matrix, while strong deviations from thermal equilibrium are expected at the first order EW phase transition. The minimal standard model is a very constrained theory: only one parameter – the Higgs boson mass – remains unknown at present. This makes an explanation of the baryonic asymmetry in the framework of MSM be very difficult, since the slogan: "a new particle for an unexplained phenomenon" is not admitted by the rules of the game. The importance of the understanding of the MSM baryogenesis is clear - if it is not possible then we are forced to introduce some new physics, which is, hopefully, experimentally detectable. If the baryonic asymmetry may be explained in the MSM, we can considerably extend our understanding of the early universe and get a number of insights for particle physics. In this talk we consider the Higgs boson mass problem and the CP-violation problem of the MSM baryogenesis.

2. The Higgs boson mass problem.

The first order EW phase transition goes through the bubble nucleation [3]. Independently on the specific mechanism of the EW baryogenesis, the produced baryonic asymmetry must not be destroyed in anomalous reactions with B-non-conservation. So, sphaleron processes must be out of thermal equilibrium in the broken phase at the bubble nucleation temperature T_*. The non-equilibrium requirement puts a constraint on the effective sphaleron mass (accounting also for prefactor in the sphaleron transition rate) at $T = T_*$ [4], $M_{sph}(T_*) > 45T_*$, which in the MSM insures an upper limit on the Higgs mass [4], $M_H < M_{crit}$*. To determine M_{crit}, one should define the bubble nucleation temperature T_* and compute $M_{sph}(T_*)$. Both problems are far from being trivial. In particular, the first one cannot be solved with the help of perturbation theory which does not work for the description of the unbroken phase of the EW theory at high temperatures. The solution of the second problem in one-loop approximation requires the computation of the determinant of small fluctuations in the sphaleron background [5]. While the numerical computation of the determinant is possible [6], the way of going beyond 1-loop approximation is not clear yet.

The old estimates of the critical Higgs mass, which ignored the existence of the strong coupling regime in the unbroken phase and large $t - quark$ contribution to sphaleron determinant, gave quite a small value of M_{crit},

---

‡ On leave of absence from the Institute for Nuclear Research of the Russian Academy of Sciences, Moscow 117312, Russia. E-mail: mshaposh@nxth04.cern.ch.

* If the baryonic asymmetry produced is larger than the observed one, then this constraint is converted to a prediction of the Higgs boson mass, $M_H \simeq M_{crit}$ [4].

$M_{crit} \simeq 45\text{GeV}$ [4] or $M_{crit} \simeq 35\text{GeV}$ [7]. However, recently it was realized that non-perturbative effects [8] and the large mass of the top quark [9] can considerably change this estimate. The lattice simulations of the EW phase transition [10] allow to extract some non-perturbatiive information on the unbroken phase which suggests that M_{crit} increases. The accounting for a t-quark contribution further increases M_{crit}. Both effects may lift up M_{crit} to a value about 80 GeV, depending on a top quark mass$^{\|}$. While it seems that the EW baryogenesis is possible with the experimentally allowed mass of the Higgs boson, the exact determination of this bound requires more understanding of the dynamics of the unbroken hot phase of the EW plasma [8, 10, 11].

3.　The CP-problem.

The difficulties with the MSM baryogenesis from the side of CP-violation have been discussed in [4]. In the standard model CP-violation vanishes together with Jarlskog determinant [12], $d_{CP} = \sin(\theta_{12})\sin(\theta_{23})\sin(\theta_{13})\sin\delta_{CP}\cdot(m_t^2-m_c^2)(m_t^2-m_u^2)(m_c^2-m_u^2)\cdot(m_b^2-m_s^2)(m_b^2-m_d^2)(m_s^2-m_d^2)$, where θ_{ij} are the mixing angles, m_i are the quark masses. It seems, therefore, that the baryonic asymmetry $\Delta = n_B/s$ generated at the EW phase transition is at most $\Delta \sim d_{CP}/T_*^{12} \sim 10^{-20}$ – too small to explain the observed value $10^{-10} - 10^{-11}$. However, a number of dynamical mechanisms in which the baryonic asymmetry may be enhanced a lot, have been suggested.

(i) If there is a dynamical spontaneous CP-violation in the EW theory before [4] or during [13] the EW phase transition then the universe contains domains with different CP-parity at some stage if its evolution. The small explicit CP-violation breaks the degeneracy between the different CP-states, so that more energetically favorable domains "eat" ones with an opposite CP-parity. The fact that the universe lifetime at $T \sim 100$ GeV is macroscopical, gives an enhancement factor $\sim M_{Pl}/T_* \sim 10^{16}$ [4]. An interesting feature of this mechanism is that BAU does not depend on the magnitude of CP-violation but does depend on its sign [4, 13]. The spontaneous CP violation gives rise to a BAU which is naturally larger than the observed one, so that the Higgs mass should be tuned to M_{crit} [4]. We should stress, however, that the possibility of the spontaneous CP-breaking at high temperatures in EW theory is very speculative, and it is by no means proved (though not disproved).

(ii) In [14] it has been found that in a mechanism of the quasiparticle reflection from the bubble walls similar to one proposed in [15] there is an enhancement factor of the order $T_*^9/(m_b^6 m_s^3)$. In this mechanism the moving bubble walls are more transparent for quarks than for antiquarks; sphaleron processes, rapid in the unbroken phase destroy antiquarks, while baryonic number inside the bubbles is conserved, giving rise to BAU. The enhancement factor comes from the observation that in a small fraction of the phase space of incoming quarks (corresponding to a total reflection of quasiparticles) they interact strongly with the bubble walls, so that perturbative "no-go" CP-argument breaks down. The estimate of the asymmetry is quite uncertain at present, $\Delta \sim 10^{-10}\text{--}10^{-18}$, but gives the correct sign of BAU [14]. The uncertainties come mainly from our poor knowledge of the details of the EW phase transition together with the lack of of perturbative computability in the unbroken hot phase.

We would like also to make some comments on recent papers [16, 17] claiming that strong interactions of quarks in the plasma break down the quantum coherence in quark reflection from the bubble walls and reduce the baryonic asymmetry found in [14] by about 15 orders of magnitude. To prove this statement, authors adopt an ad hoc procedure for the computation of the reflection coefficients, inserting an imaginary part of the thermal quark mass operator into Dirac equation. This is not satisfactory from many points of view, but we will limit ourselves with a few [18]. First, this procedure violates quantum mechanics and unitarity (to restore unitarity the authors are forced to introduce by hand an extra "creative" term into their kinetic equation). In addition, it contradicts to kinetic approach, in which matrix elements are to be computed with the unitary S-matrix and different irreversible phenomena appear through the solution of kinetic equation rather than violation of quantum mechanics. At last, it ignores the fact that flavour coherence, essential for BAU computation, exists a time large compared with a typical mass scale of the problem [18]. Thus, this method cannot be considered as reliable, so that the the the claims of [16, 17] are not justified by the work reported in them.

4.　Conclusion.

Clearly, in the absence of a "factor of 2" computation it is too early to say whether MSM can or cannot accommodate BAU. However, theoretical ideas discussed above show that MSM cannot be discounted as a contender for explaining this phenomenon.

$\|$ The number quoted in [9] (66GeV) is derived with an assumption that the EW phase transition is of the second order. The first order nature of the EW phase transition changes this estimate.

References

1　A.D. Sakharov, JETP Lett. **5** (1967) 24.
2　V.A. Kuzmin, V.A. Rubakov, and M.E. Shaposhnikov, Phys. Lett. **155B** (1985) 36.

3 D.A. Kirzhnitz and A.D. Linde, Phys. Lett. **72B** (1972) 471,A.D. Linde, *Particle physics and inflationary cosmology* (Chur, Switzerland: Harwood 1990).

4 M.E. Shaposhnikov, JETP Lett. **44** (1986) 465,Nucl. Phys. **B287** (1987) 757,Nucl. Phys. **B299** (1988) 797,A. Bochkarev and M. Shaposhnikov, Mod. Phys. Lett. **A2** (1987) 417,A. Bochkarev, S. Khlebnikov and M. Shaposhnikov, Nucl. Phys. **B329** (1990) 493.

5 P. Arnold and L. McLerran, Phys. Rev. **D36** (1987) 581.

6 L. Carson et al., Phys. Rev. **D42** (1990) 2127.

7 M. Dine et al., Phys. Rev. **D46** (1992) 550.

8 M. Shaposhnikov, Phys. Lett. **B316** (1993) 112.

9 D. Diakonov et al., Phys. Rev. **D49** (1994) 6864;RUB-TPII-05/94 (hep-ph/9407238).

10 K. Kajantie, K. Rummukainen and M. Shaposhnikov, Nucl. Phys. **B407** (1993) 356,K. Farakos et al., CERN-TH.6973/94 (hep-ph/9404201), CERN-TH.7244/94 (hep-ph/9405234).

11 B. Bunk et al., Phys. Lett. **B284** (1992) 371,Nucl. Phys. **B403** (1993) 453,F. Csikor et al., DESY-94-088 (hep-lat/9405021).

12 C. Jarlskog, Phys. Rev. Lett. **55** (1985) 1039.

13 S. Nasser and N. Turok, PUPT-94-1456 (hep-ph/9406270).

14 G. Farrar and M. Shaposhnikov, Phys. Rev. Lett. **70** (1993) 2833,CERN-TH.6734/93 (hep-ph/9305275), to appear in Phys. Rev. D.

15 A. Cohen, D. Kaplan and A. Nelson, Nucl. Phys. **B373** (1992) 453,Ann. Rev. Nucl. Part. Sci. **43** (1993) 27.

16 B. Gavela et al., Mod. Phys. Lett. **9A** (1994) 795,CERN-TH.7262/94 (hep-ph/9406288), CERN-TH.7263/94 (hep-ph/9406289).

17 P. Huet and E. Sather, SLAC-PUB-6479 (hep-ph/9404302).

18 G. Farrar and M. Shaposhnikov, RU-94-40 (hep-ph/9406387).

Paper presented at XXVII Int. Conf. on High Energy Physics: Session Pa-12
Glasgow, UK, 20–27 July 1994

Electroweak Phase Changes and Baryogenesis in Two Higgs Doublet Models

A. T. Davies, C. D. Froggatt, G. Jenkins and R. G. Moorhouse

Department of Physics and Astronomy, University of Glasgow, Glasgow G12 8QQ, U.K.

presented by C. D. Froggatt

Abstract

A strongly first order electroweak phase transition is required in order that any baryon asymmetry be not washed out by sphaleron transitions. We investigate perturbatively the extent to which baryon washout may be evaded in a general two Higgs doublet model; we find that this constraint rules out about 95% of otherwise acceptable Higgs potentials although the presence of a soft CP violating term makes it somewhat easier to satisfy the required conditions. The spectrum of Higgs particles for these baryon preserving cases is presented. The Minimal Supersymmetric Standard Model is considered as a special case; here we find baryon preservation is only possible in a region ($tan\beta < 1$) disfavoured by supersymmetric grand unification and a heavy top quark mass.

1. Introduction

Electroweak baryon number violation [1] occurs due to sphaleron transitions between topologically distinct vacuum states. In order to avoid the washout of any existing baryon asymmetry in the early Universe immediately after the electroweak phase transition, the height of the energy barrier between vacua must be sufficiently large to suppress the thermal sphaleron transition rate. This leads to a baryon preservation condition, which we take in the approximate form

$$\frac{v(T_c)}{T_c} \geq 1 \qquad (1)$$

where $v(T_c)$ is the vacuum value of the Standard Model (SM) Higgs field at the critical temperature T_c for the phase transition. This constraint has been evaluated perturbatively using the temperature dependent effective potential, giving the SM Higgs mass bound $m_H \leq 35$ Gev which is inconsistent with the LEP experimental bound $m_H \geq 65$ Gev. Here we consider perturbatively the baryon preservation constraint on two Higgs doublet models and the Minimal

Supersymmetric Standard Model (MSSM).

2. Two Higgs Doublet Models

We adopt the usual theory where the down quarks (d_i) only couple to each other through the Higgs doublet Φ_1, the up quarks (u_i) only couple to each other through Φ_2, and there is a symmetry of the hard (dimension four) couplings under the discrete transformation $\Phi_2 \to -\Phi_2, (u_i)_R \to -(u_i)_R$. This symmetry is softly broken, without inducing tree level flavour changing neutral currents, by the CP violating coupling:

$$\mu_3^2 \Phi_1^\dagger \Phi_2 + \mu_3^{2*} \Phi_2^\dagger \Phi_1 \qquad (2)$$

We restrict the basis space of the Higgs potential parameters so that the potential is bounded below and that at its minimum:

$$\langle \Phi_1 \rangle = \frac{1}{\sqrt{2}} \begin{pmatrix} 0 \\ v_1 e^{i\theta} \end{pmatrix}, \langle \Phi_2 \rangle = \frac{1}{\sqrt{2}} \begin{pmatrix} 0 \\ v_2 \end{pmatrix} \qquad (3)$$

where v_1 and v_2 are real and $v = \sqrt{v_1^2 + v_2^2} = 246$ GeV. The Higgs mass eigenvalues are required to be greater

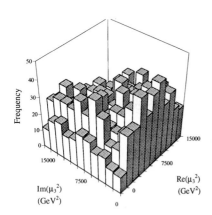

Figure 1. Frequency distribution of baryon number preserving cases in the complex μ_3^2 plane for the two Higgs doublet model with $m_t = 175$ GeV. Each block represents 500 initial cases. Note the low success rate (at about 3%) around $\mu_3^2 = 0$.

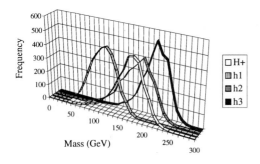

Figure 2. The frequency distribution of the scalar masses for the baryon preserving cases. The neutral scalars are denoted h_1, h_2 and h_3 in order of increasing mass. The high mass cutoff is primarily due to the choice of basis parameter space and Eq.(5). The CLEO measurement of $b \rightarrow s\gamma$ suggests a heavy charged Higgs H^+ in conflict with at least half of the above distribution.

than 40 Gev to satisfy experimental bounds. In order that perturbation theory may apply, we take the Φ^4 coupling constants to satisfy $|\lambda_i| < \frac{1}{2}$. Also assuming the validity of the renormalisation group equations up to $\Lambda \simeq 10^{15}$ Gev and a top quark mass $m_t \geq 150$ GeV leads to the condition $\tan\beta = v_2/v_1 > 0.9$.

At each point on an 11×11 grid of $\mu_3^2 = \mu_R^2 + i\mu_I^2$, with

$$0 \leq \mu_R^2, \mu_I^2 \leq 1.5 \times 10^4 GeV^2 \qquad (4)$$

we take a random sample of 500 points in the basis parameter space †. We then study the high temperature expansion of the one loop effective potential $V(\Phi, T_c)$ and determine the critical temperature T_c where the gauge symmetry preserving minimum at $\Phi = 0$ becomes unstable. The minimum of $V(\Phi, T_c)$ and the vacuum

† A previous statistical analysis [2] of the $\mu_3^2 = 0$ case was flawed by an invalid gauge choice.

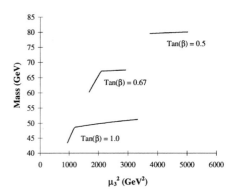

Figure 3. Lines showing the lightest scalar mass (m_h) as a function of μ_3^2 in baryon number preserving cases, for 3 values of $\tan\beta$ with $m_t = 150$ GeV and $TS = 1500$ GeV in the MSSM.

values $v_1(T_c)$, $v_2(T_c)$ and $\theta(T_c)$ are found. Hence $v(T_c)$ in the baryon preservation condition Eq.(1) is determined. We also require all the temperature dependent masses $m(T)$ to satisfy

$$\frac{m(T_c)}{T_c} < 1.6 \qquad (5)$$

so as to ensure the validity of the high T expansion.

The number of baryon preserving cases for each grid point is shown in Fig.1 and the distribution of the scalar masses in all the allowed cases is shown in Fig.2.

3. Minimal Supersymmetric Standard Model

We break supersymmetry in the simplest way by taking a single threshold TS above which supersymmetry is exact and below which there are only the SM particles. We vary TS between 0.5 and 2.5 Tev. The λ_i are determined by supersymmetry at TS in terms of the electroweak gauge couplings, and using the RGE, scaled down to 246 GeV. For a given m_t, we have a theory with only two free real parameters, μ_3^2 and $\tan\beta$.

The baryon preservation condition rejects $\tan\beta > 1$ as it implies too low scalar masses; this is in essential agreement with [3]. For $\tan\beta < 1$ and $TS > 1$ Tev the constraint can be satisfied and in Fig.3 we show, for TS = 1.5 Tev, allowed lines of constant $\tan\beta$ in the μ_3^2, m_h-plane. Note however that these solutions are inconsistent with a SUSY-GUT desert and require new interactions to be introduced at a scale $\Lambda < 10^6$ (10^5) Gev for $\tan\beta = 2/3$ (1/2).

References

[1] A.G. Cohen, D.B. Kaplan and A.E. Nelson, Annu. Rev. Nucl. Part. Sci. **43** (1993) 27.
[2] N. Turok and J. Zadrozny, Nucl. Phys. **B369** (1992) 729.
[3] A. Brignole, J.R. Espinosa, M. Quiros and F. Zwirner, Phys. Lett. **B324** (1994) 181.

Perturbative study of the electroweak phase transition

Zoltán Fodor*

Deutsches Elektronen-Synchrotron, DESY, 22603 Hamburg, Germany

Abstract

The electroweak phase transition is studied at finite temperature. The effective action is given to higher orders, including wave function correction factors and the full g^4, λ^2 effective potential. An upper bound for the Higgs mass $m_H \approx 70\ GeV$ is concluded for the reliability of the perturbative approach. A gauge invariant treatment of the phase transition is presented.

1. Introduction

At high temperatures (T) the spontaneously broken electroweak symmetry is restored. Since the baryon-number violating processes are unsuppressed at high T, there is a possibility to understand the observed baryon asymmetry within the standard model [1]. A departure from thermal equilibrium, a sufficiently strong first order phase transition via bubble nucleation is needed.

In Sect. 2 the finite T wave function corrections of the SU(2)-Higgs model to one-loop order [2] and the effective potential to order g^4, λ^2 will be studied [3]. This gives a range of Higgs boson masses (m_H) for which the derivative expansion of the effective action is reliable. Sect. 3 contains the gauge-invariant treatment of the finite T electroweak effective potential [4]. This is of particular importance for comparison with lattice simulations [5], where the expectation value of $\Phi\Phi^\dagger$ is well suited to characterize the broken phase, and the corresponding effective potential has been evaluated [6].

2. The effective action at finite temperature

2.1. The wave function correction term

Consider the SU(2)-Higgs model at finite T, described by the lagrangian $\mathcal{L} = W^a_{\mu\nu} W^a_{\mu\nu}/4 + (D_\mu \Phi)^\dagger D_\mu \Phi + V_0(\varphi^2)$, where $V_0(\varphi^2) = m^2\varphi^2/2 + \mu\lambda\varphi^4/4$, $\varphi^2 = 2\Phi^\dagger\Phi$.

* On leave from Institute for Theoretical Physics, Eötvös University, Budapest, Hungary

D_μ and $W^a_{\mu\nu}$ are the covariant derivative and the Yang-Mills field strength, respectively. In this section Landau gauge is used and the effects of the three generations of fermions $(m_t = f_t v/\sqrt{2})$ have been included.

To get the effective action $\Gamma_\beta[\Phi]$ at finite temperature a systematic expansion is needed where in all propagators the tree-level masses are replaced by one-loop plasma masses to order g^2 and λ.

At one-loop order this improved perturbation theory yields the effective potential to order $g^3, \lambda^{3/2}$,

$$V_{eff}(\varphi^2, T) = \frac{1}{2}\left(\frac{3g^2}{16} + \frac{\lambda}{2} + \frac{1}{4}f_t^2\right)(T^2 - T_b^2)\varphi^2$$

$$+ \frac{\lambda}{4}\varphi^4 - (3m_L^3 + 6m_T^3 + m_\varphi^3 + 3m_\chi^3)\frac{T}{12\pi}, \qquad (1)$$

which is equivalent to the result of the ring summation [7]. Here $m_L^2 = 11g^2T^2/6 + g^2\varphi^2/4$, $m_T^2 = g^2\varphi^2/4$, $m_\varphi^2 = (3g^2/16 + \lambda/2 + f_t^2/4)(T^2 - T_b^2) + 3\lambda\varphi^2$, $m_\chi^2 = (3g^2/16 + \lambda/2 + f_t^2/4)(T^2 - T_b^2) + \lambda\varphi^2$ and $T_b^2 = (16\lambda v^2)/(3g^2 + 8\lambda + 4f_t^2)$.

The strength of the electroweak phase transition is rather sensitive to the nonperturbative magnetic mass of the gauge bosons. In Landau gauge the one-loop gap equations yield $m_T = g^2T/(3\pi)$ at $\varphi = 0$. In order to estimate its effect we will replace [8] the previous definition of m_T by $m_T^2 = \gamma^2 g^4 T^2/(9\pi^2) + g^2\varphi^2/4$ and compute sensitive quantities for different values of γ.

V_{eff} of (1) has degenerate local minima at $\varphi = 0$ and $\varphi = \varphi_c > 0$ at a critical temperature T_c. The evaluation of the transition rate requires

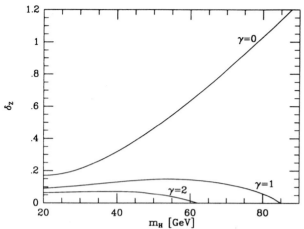

Figure 1. The one-loop wave function correction δ_Z as a function of m_H for different values of γ.

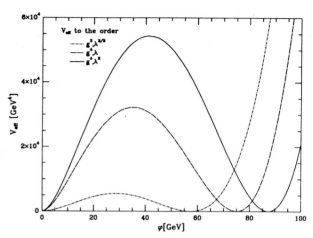

Figure 2. Different approximations of $V_{eff}(\varphi, T_c)$ for $m_H = 70\ GeV$.

knowledge of a stationary point of the free energy which interpolates between the two local minima. The effective action can be expanded in powers of derivatives, and for time-independent fields one has $T \cdot \Gamma_\beta[\Phi] = \int d^3x [V_{eff}(\varphi^2, T) + (\delta_{IJ} + Z_{IJ}(\Phi, T))\vec{\nabla}\varphi_I \vec{\nabla}\varphi_J/2 + \ldots]$. Using the inverse scalar propagator in the homogeneous scalar background field Φ one obtains on the one-loop level $Z_{IJ}(\Phi, T) = Z_\varphi(\varphi^2, T)P_{IJ}^\varphi + Z_\chi(\varphi^2, T)P_{IJ}^\chi$, where $Z_\varphi = T[\lambda \bar{m}^2(3/m_\varphi^3 + 1/m_\chi^3)/4 - 2g^2/(m_\chi + m_T) + g^2m^2(1/m_L^3 + 10/m_T^3)/16]/(4\pi)$ and $Z_\chi = T[2\lambda \bar{m}^2/(m_\varphi + m_\chi)^3 - 2g^2/(m_\chi + m_T) - g^2/(m_\varphi + m_T)]/(6\pi)$ with $P_{IJ}^\varphi = \varphi_I\varphi_J/\varphi^2$, $P_{IJ}^\chi = \delta_{IJ} - \varphi_I\varphi_J/\varphi^2$, $\varphi^2 = \sum_{I=1}^4 \varphi_I\varphi_I$, $\bar{m}^2 = \lambda\varphi^2$ and $m^2 = g^2\varphi^2/4$.

Note, that despite the divergence of Z_φ at $\varphi \sim 0$ the correction to the surface tension $\sigma = \int_0^{\varphi_c} d\varphi \sqrt{2(1 + Z_\varphi(\varphi^2, T_c))V_{eff}(\varphi^2, T_c)}$ is finite.

A measure for the size of the one-loop correction to the Z-factor is (Fig. 1) the ratio $\delta_Z = \int d^3x Z_{\bar{\varphi}}(\vec{\nabla}\bar{\varphi})^2/\int d^3x(\vec{\nabla}\bar{\varphi})^2$, where $\bar{\varphi}$ is the saddle point solution at the nucleation temperature calculated from (1). For $\gamma = 0$ the perturbative expansion becomes unreliable at $m_H \sim 80$ GeV. The magnetic mass as an infrared cutoff ($\gamma = 1, 2$) could improve the convergence.

The above results are based on Ref. [2], where additional details can also be found.

2.2. The effective potential to order g^4, λ^2

The principal method [9] of the calculation is based on the Dyson-Schwinger equation for the derivative of the potential $\partial V/\partial\varphi$. The calculation has been done in an alternative way too, using the resummation [10] method of P. Arnold and O. Espinosa, who calculated the effective potential to order g^4, λ.

The full result of order g^4, λ^2 predicts a stronger first order phase transition than the lower order results. We plot the potential using different approximations

for the $SU(2)$ Higgs-model at their respective T_c (Fig. 2). The expectation value of the Higgs field does not change dramatically, but there is an order of magnitude difference between the heights of the barrier. No convergence of the perturbation series can be claimed for these parameters.

The surface tension, $\sigma = \int_0^{\varphi_+} d\varphi \sqrt{2V(\varphi, T_c)}$, may be seen as a measure of the strength of the phase transition (Fig. 3). The g^4, λ^2 result gives a radiatively induced quartic term and a better approximation of the temperature integrals, thus ensures that σ does not grow for small m_H. For large m_H the higher order result produces an increase in σ.

The full standard model calculation with zero temperature renormalization has also been done. The qualitative behaviour of the potential is essentially the same as for the $SU(2)$-Higgs model.

As it has been shown in the previous subsection wave function correction terms suggest that the perturbative approach becomes unreliable for large Higgs masses. In

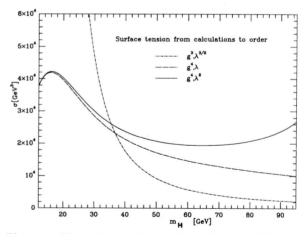

Figure 3. The surface tension calculated from the different potentials as a function of m_H.

this subsection the analysis of the g^4, λ^2 contributions to V_{eff} led to a very similar conclusion.

The results of this subsection are from Ref. [3], where the details of the calculation and the full standard model analysis can also be found.

3. Gauge invariant treatment

In this section the effective potential for the composite field $\rho = 2\Phi^\dagger\Phi$ will be calculated [4]. For simplicity, the Higgs model in three dimensions is studied [11].

The SU(2)-Higgs model in three dimensions is described by the lagrangian $\mathcal{L} = W_{\mu\nu}^a W_{\mu\nu}^a/4 + (D_\mu\Phi)^\dagger D_\mu\Phi + V_0(\varphi^2)$, where $V_0(\varphi^2) = m^2\varphi^2/2 + \mu\lambda\varphi^4/4$, $\varphi^2 = 2\Phi^\dagger\Phi$. Here $W_{\mu\nu}^a$ is the ordinary field strength tensor and $D_\mu = \partial_\mu - i\sqrt{\mu}gW_\mu^a\tau^a/2$ is the covariant derivative; μ is the mass scale.

To obtain the effective potential for the field ρ, one evaluates the "free energy" in the presence of an external source J; $\exp[-\Omega W(J)] = \int DW D\Phi D\Phi^\dagger \exp[-S - \int d^3x 2\Phi^\dagger\Phi J]$, where Ω is the total volume. For constant J one obtains $V(\rho)$ as a Legendre transform,

$$\partial W(J)/\partial J = \rho \,, \quad V(\rho) = W(J(\rho)) - \rho J \,. \quad (2)$$

$W(J)$ can be calculated in the semiclassical or loopwise expansion. The equation for a spatially constant stationary point, $(m^2 + 2\mu\lambda\Phi_c^\dagger\Phi_c + 2J)\Phi_c = 0$, has two solutions, which correspond to the symmetric and the broken phase, respectively, $\Phi_s = 0$ and $\Phi_b = \Phi_0[-(m^2 + 2J)/(2\mu\lambda)]^{1/2}$, where $|\Phi_0| = 1$. The determinants of fluctuations around the two stationary points depend on the masses of vector bosons, Higgs (φ) and Goldstone (χ) bosons. In the broken phase ($\Phi_c = \Phi_b$) one has, in any covariant gauge, $m_W^2 = -g^2(m^2 + 2J)/(4\lambda)$, $m_\varphi^2 = -2(m^2 + 2J)$, $m_\chi^2 = 0$, whereas in the symmetric phase ($\Phi_c = \Phi_s$) the masses are given by $m_W^2 = 0$, $m_\varphi^2 = m_\chi^2 = m^2 + 2J$.

The one-loop $W(J)$ in covariant gauge is

$$W_1(J) = \frac{1}{2}\int \frac{d^3k}{(2\pi)^3}\left(6\ln\left(k^2 + m_W^2\right) + \ln\left(k^2 + m_\varphi^2\right)\right.$$
$$\left. + 3\ln\left(k^4 + k^2 m_\chi^2 + \alpha m_W^2 m_\chi^2\right) - 6\ln k^2\right)\,, \quad (3)$$

where α is the gauge parameter. This expression is gauge independent and the same result for $W_1(J)$ is obtained in R_ξ-gauge.

Subtracting linear divergencies by means of dimensional regularization and performing the Legendre transformation according to eq. (2) gives

$$V(\rho) = V_b(\rho)\Theta(\rho) + V_s(\rho)\Theta(-\rho)\,, \quad (4)$$

where $V_b(\rho) = m^2\rho/2 + \mu\lambda\rho^2/4 - [6(\mu g^2\rho/4)^{3/2} + (2\mu\lambda\rho)^{3/2}]/(12\pi)$ and $V_s(\rho) = m^2\rho/2 - \pi^2\rho^3/6$. Here the couplings depend on the renormalization scale, i.e., $g = g(\mu)$, $\lambda = \lambda(\mu)$, $m^2 = m^2(\mu)$.

The Landau gauge effective potential for the field Φ

$$V_{LG}(\varphi^2) = \frac{m^2\varphi^2}{2} + \frac{\mu\lambda\varphi^4}{4} - \frac{6m_W^3 + m_\varphi^3 + 3m_\chi^3}{12\pi}\,, \quad (5)$$

with $m_W^2 = \mu g^2\varphi^2/4$, $m_\varphi^2 = m^2 + 3\mu\lambda\varphi^2$, $m_\chi^2 = m^2 + \mu\lambda\varphi^2$.

Comparing the two potentials (4) and (5) the first difference is the range of the fields. For (5) one has $0 \le \varphi^2 < \infty$, whereas for (4) the field varies in the range $-\infty < \rho < \infty$. In (5) the symmetric phase is represented by the point $\varphi = 0$, whereas in (4) by the half-axis $\rho \le 0$. At small values of ρ the potential increases very steeply. The second difference is that the non-analytic terms of the gauge invariant potential do not depend on m^2. Hence, this potential can also be used for $m^2 < 0$, where the symmetric phase is unstable.

We have performed the above calculation for the SU(2)-Higgs model at finite T. The gauge invariant potential [4] is $V(\rho, T) = V_s(\rho, T)\Theta(\rho) + V_b(\rho, T)\Theta(-\rho)$, where $V_b(\rho, T) = m^2(T)\rho/2 + \lambda\rho^2/4 - T[6(g^2\rho/4)^{3/2} + (2\lambda\rho)^{3/2}]/(12\pi)$ and $V_s(\rho, T) = m^2(T)\rho/2 - \pi^2\rho^3/(6T^2)$. Contrary to the conventional potential (neglect the fermions in $V_{eff}(\varphi^2, T)$ of eq. 1), $V(\rho, T)$ is valid at temperatures above and below T_b.

We have evaluated several observables for the conventional and for the gauge invariant effective potentials. The critical temperatures are different, but very similar. For Higgs masses between 30 GeV and 120 GeV the ratio $(T_c - T_b)/T_b$ differs by at most 40%. The latent heat differs by about 70% at $m_H = 120$ GeV.

References

[1] V. A. Kuzmin, V. A. Rubakov and M. E. Shaposhnikov, Phys. Lett. **B155** (1985) 36.

[2] D. Bödeker, W. Buchmüller, Z. Fodor and T. Helbig, Nucl. Phys. **B423** (1994) 171.

[3] Z. Fodor, A. Hebecker, DESY-94-025 (1994), Nucl. Phys. B, in press.

[4] W. Buchmüller, Z. Fodor and A. Hebecker, Phys. Lett. **B331** 131 (1994).

[5] B. Bunk et al., Nucl. Phys. **B403** (1993) 453; K. Kajantie, K. Rummukainen, M.E. Shaposhnikov, Nucl. Phys. **B407** (1993) 356; K. Farakos, K. Kajantie, K. Rummukainen, M.E. Shaposhnikov, CERN-TH.7244/94 (1994); F. Csikor, Z. Fodor, J. Hein, K. Jansen, A. Jaster, I. Montvay, Phys. Lett. **B334** (1994) 405; F. Karsch, T. Neuhaus, A. Patkos BI-TP 94/27, Z. Fodor, these proceedings.

[6] M. Lüscher, unpublished notes (1988).

[7] M. E. Carrington, Phys. Rev. **D45** (1992) 2933.

[8] W. Buchmüller, Z. Fodor, T. Helbig and D. Walliser, Ann. Phys. (NY) **234** (1994) 260.

[9] C.G. Boyd, D.E. Brahm and S.D.H. Hsu, Phys. Rev. **D48** (1993) 4963; A. Hebecker, Z. Phys. **C60** (1993) 271.

[10] P. Arnold and O. Espinosa, Phys. Rev. **D47** (1993) 3546.

[11] A. Jakovác, K. Kajantie, A. Patkós, Phys. Rev. **D49** (1994) 6810; K. Farakos, K. Kajantie, K. Rummukainen, M.E. Shaposhnikov, CERN-TH.6973/94 (1994); M. Laine, Phys. Lett. **B335** (1994) 173.

Hot standard model, metastable states and CP violation

C. P. Korthals Altes[†‡]

† Centre Physique Théorique au C.N.R.S.
B.P.907, Campus de Luminy, F13288 Marseille, France

Abstract

The effective potential of the hot standard model is analysed in terms of the phase of the Wilson line. Apart from stable states there are metastable states in the weak hypercharge direction. The latter are characterised by two properties: they are very long lived compared to the onset of the electroweak phase transition, and violate CP spontaneously. We give a qualitative description of how this novel source of CP violation works at the transition.

1. Introduction

This work got its motivation from two main sources. Firstly the last few years have seen an upsurge in the interest in the broken centergroup symmetry at high temperature T[1]. The centergroup of a non abelian gauge group gets spontaneously broken above a critical temperature T_c. This is signalled by the free energy as a function of the phase of the Wilson line showing degenerate minima at the centergroup values of the phases[2]. Subsequently the domain walls and the surface tension were computed in weak coupling[3]. As soon as particles in the fundamental representation are coupled into the system the degenerate minima disappear but reappear under certain circumstances as metastable minima. These metastable minima violate C and CP spontaneously.

On the other hand there are recent attempts[4] to compute the baryon asymmetry of the universe in the standard model(SM). The main difficulty is the small amount of CP violation available in the SM. In this talk I will first discuss the potential as a function of the Wilson line (section 2), then show that the metastable states are very long lived (section 3), by and large long enough to survive till the electro-weak transition. If the universe found itself in this metastable state say right after the GUT transition, then it could solve the obstacle of the

small amount of CP violation. This is qualitatively explained in section 4. We are well aware of certain difficulties[5] of the thermodynamical interpretation of the free energy. The metastable states we are discussing below don't suffer from them.

2. The potential

At a nonzero temperature T in the imaginary time formalism, consider the Wilson line which runs in the direction of imaginary time, $\Omega(x) = \exp(ig \int_0^{1/T} A_0(x,\tau)d\tau)$. In an abelian theory Ω is just a phase factor and so automatically gauge invariant under strictly periodic gauge transformations. In a nonabelian theory Ω is a matrix, where only the eigenvalues are gauge invariant. These eigenvalues lie in the space of the mutually commuting generators, which is the Cartan subalgebra of the group. To parametrize a theory where $\langle \Omega \rangle \neq 1$, at one loop order it suffices to calculate the effective potential in a background field of constant A_0. Notice that we deal not just with the sum of the eigenvalues, as arises for the Polyakov line $= tr(\Omega)$, but all eigenvalues.

In the case of the strong interaction colour group the potential as a function of the Wilson line is very well known[2], up to and including two loop corrections[6]. In the absence of quarks there is a Z(3) symmetry, that causes the potential to possess degenerate minima in the

‡ E-mail: altes@cptsu4.univ-mrs.fr

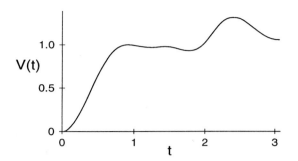

Figure 1. The potential for the standard model

$Z(3)$ centergroup values of the Wilson line. Two regions of space with different centergroup values are separated by a domain wall. In a semi classical approximation one can compute profile and surface tension of the wall. However the presence of quarks lifts the degeneracy. If not too many quarks are coupled, then the degenerate minima become meta stable minima, with a decay rate that makes them disappear long before the electro-weak phase transition sets in[7].

It is very important to realise[8] that at temperatures well above the electro-weak transition there is no reason to forget the other gauge groups (and hence the leptons and the Higgs) of the standard model. The Wilson line now contains the fourth component of all vector potentials in the SM. This is a four dimensional space: one coordinate for the $U(1)$ of hypercharge, one for the Cartan subalgebra of weak $SU(2)$, and two for the Cartan subalgebra of $SU(3)$ color. We give the timelike component of each vector potential a constant expectation value,

$$\mathcal{A}_0 = \frac{2\pi T}{g_{st}} \begin{pmatrix} q/3 + r/2 & 0 & 0 \\ 0 & q/3 - r/2 & 0 \\ 0 & 0 & -2q/3 \end{pmatrix},$$

$$A_0 = \frac{2\pi T}{g} \begin{pmatrix} s/2 & 0 \\ 0 & -s/2 \end{pmatrix}, \quad B_0 = \frac{2\pi T}{g'} t, \quad (1)$$

$\mathcal{A}_0$ is the field for $SU(3)$ color, with coupling constant g_{st}, A_0 is the field for weak $SU(2)$, with coupling g, and B_0 is the field for hypercharge $U(1)$, with coupling g'.

Including them gives the potential shown in the figure. We have shown only the weak hypercharge direction, since a rather involved argument shows that the only metastable minima are to be found on that axis. Just as in the case of the strong interactions alone, it is the various fractional charges that produce the metastable minima. They are located at:

$$t_1 = (0, 0, 0, 1.28751...) \quad, \quad t_2 = (0, 0, 0, 1.74843...) .$$
$$(2)$$

3.   Lifetimes of the metastable minima

The lifetimes are computed by well-known methods[9]. For the minima t_1 and t_2 we find[8] that the temperature at which tunneling takes place is well below 10^{-39} GeV. Thus at $T_e w$ the metastable states do survive, in contrast with the purely strong interaction case[7]. The reason for this longevity is two-fold: firstly the shoulder in the potential of fig 1 is more pronounced, and second the weak hypercharge coupling is smaller than the colour coupling. Note, that under CP the fourth component of the vector potential is odd. Thus the two metastable minima are CP non-invariant. This spontaneous breaking is a purely thermal effect, and is independent of the CP violation in the microscopic action through the CKM matrix. The metastable minima are also present when the number of families is smaller than three.

4.   The electro-weak transition and CP violation

The electro-weak transition changes the potential in fig 1. It can be argued[8] that, as a consequence of a non-zero Higgs expectation value, the phase in the Z_0 direction is necessarily zero. We are left with only three phases for the Wilson-line, one representing the electromagnetic phase and the other two the strong $SU(3)$ phases. Assuming that the transition is first order, the metastable vacuum t_1 (or t_2) will grow bubbles of non-zero Higgs vacuum. Inside the bubbles the non-zero Higgs expectation value is compatible with all phases equal to zero. Outside the bubbles the metastable vacuum is still present. Fermions in the plasma can easily seen to localise on the wall[10]. But if a given fermion species localises, its CP conjugate can *not!* This is one of the manifestations of the spontaneous CP breaking.

Whether this might help to solve the baryon asymmetry problem, is presently under investigation[11].

References

[1] L. MacLerran and B. Svetitsky, Phys. Rev. D24 (1981) 450; J.Kuti. J.Polonyi and K.Szlachnanyi, Phys.Lett. B96 (1981) 199.

[2] D. J. Gross, R. D. Pisarski, and L. G. Yaffe, *Rev. Mod. Phys.*, 53:43 (1981); N. Weiss, *Phys. Rev.* D24:475 (1981) and D25:2667 (1982).

[3] T. Bhattacharya, A. Gocksch, C. P. Korthals Altes, and R. D. Pisarski, *Phys. Rev. Lett.* 66:998 (1991); *Nucl. Phys.* B383:497 (1992).

[4] G.R.Farrar, M.E.Shaposhnikov, CERN-TH 6734/93 and references therein.

[5] V. M. Belyaev, I. I. Kogan, G. W. Semenoff, and N. Weiss, *Phys. Lett.* B277:331 (1992), A. V. Smilga, Bern University preprint BUTP-93-03, (May, 1993).

[6] V. M. Belyaev, *Phys. Lett.* B254:153; C.P.Korthals Altes, Nucl. Phys. B420(1994) 637.

[7] V. Dixit and M. C. Ogilvie, *Phys. Lett.* B269:353 (1991), J. Ignatius, K. Kajantie and K. Rummukainen, *Phys. Rev. Lett.* 68:737 (1992).

[8] C. P. Korthals Altes, K. Lee and R. D. Pisarski *Phys.Rev.Lett.* 73,1572,(1994).

[9] S. Coleman, *Phys. Rev.* D15:292 (1977).

[10] C. P. Korthals Altes, N.J.Watson, in preparation.

[11] C.P. Korthals Altes, K. Lee, R. D. Pisarski and N.J.Watson, in preparation.

Parallel Session Pa-13

Non-Accelerator Experiments

Conveners: A. Suzuki (Tohoku University)
M. Spiro (DAPNIA)

Scientific secretaries: F. Thomson
S. Dorris (reserve)

Breakthrough into the sub-eV neutrino mass range: status of the Heidelberg-Moscow double beta decay experiment with enriched ^{76}Ge

A. Balysh[b], M. Beck[a], S.T. Belyaev[b,*], J. Bockholt[a], A. Demehin[b], M. Eskef[a], D. Glatting[a],
A. Gurov[b], G. Heusser[a], J. Hellmig[a], M. Hirsch[a], Ch. Hoffmann[a],
H.V. Klapdor-Kleingrothaus[a,*], I. Kondratenko[b], D. Kotel'nikov[b], V.I. Lebedev[b], B. Maier[a],
A. Müller[c], F. Petry[a], E. Scheer[a], H. Strecker[a], M. Völlinger[a], K. Zuber[d]

[a]Max-Planck-Institut für Kernphysik, P.O. BOX 103980, 69029 Heidelberg, Germany
[b]Russian Scientific Center-Kurchatov Institute, 123182 Moscow, Russia
[c]INFN Gran Sasso, 67010 Assergi, Italy
[d]Institut für Hochenergiephysik, Schröderstr.90, 69120 Heidelberg, Germany

Presented by K. Zuber

Abstract

Recent results of the Heidelberg-Moscow double beta decay experiment are presented. After 8.6 kg·a of measuring time no signal is seen for the neutrinoless decay mode. A half-life limit of $T_{1/2}^{0\nu\beta\beta} > 5.1 \cdot 10^{24}$ a is deduced which converts into a neutrino mass limit of $\langle m_{\nu_e} \rangle < 0.68$ eV (90% CL). The experiment thus is the first one penetrating into the sub-eV range for the neutrino mass. For the 2ν mode a half life of $T_{1/2}^{2\nu\beta\beta} = (1.53 \pm 0.04_{stat} \pm 0.13_{sys}) \cdot 10^{24}$ a is derived. More than 10000 2ν double beta events are observed. This is the first high statistics observation of this nuclear decay mode. Limits on more exotic decay modes are also presented. Concerning dark matter the experiment now gives the sharpest limits for the observation of WIMPs.

1. Introduction

Neutrino physics has entered an era of new actuality. Several possible indications of physics beyond the Standard Model (SM) of particle physics are at present discussed: The lack of solar neutrinos, the atmospheric ν_μ deficit and mixed dark matter models could all be explained by nonvanishing ν-masses. Recent extended SO(10) scenarios with an S_4 horizontal symmetry which could explain these observations would predict degenerate ν-masses within 1-2 eV [1]. At present $\beta\beta$-decay research may play a decisive role, since with second generation $\beta\beta$ experiments like the Heidelberg-Moscow experiment using large amounts of enriched $\beta\beta$-emitter material such a prediction can be tested in very near future.

The following decay modes for double beta decay of a nucleus $^Z_A X$ are usually considered:

$$2\nu\beta\beta: \quad ^Z_A X \rightarrow \ ^{Z+2}_A X + 2e^- + 2\bar{\nu}_e \quad (1)$$
$$0\nu\beta\beta: \quad ^Z_A X \rightarrow \ ^{Z+2}_A X + 2e^- \quad (2)$$
$$0\nu\chi\beta\beta: \quad ^Z_A X \rightarrow \ ^{Z+2}_A X + 2e^- + \chi \quad (3)$$
$$0\nu2\chi\beta\beta: \quad ^Z_A X \rightarrow \ ^{Z+2}_A X + 2e^- + 2\chi \quad (4)$$

A positive evidence of processes (2)-(4) would require massive Majorana neutrinos, in addition a contribution from right-handed weak currents is possible. The quantity which can be extracted out of process (2) is the effective Majorana mass given by

$$\langle m_{\nu_e} \rangle = \sum_i | U_{ei}^2 m_i | \quad (5)$$

where m_i are the mass eigenstates. Though there exists the possibility for destructive interference, in most grand unified models the effective mass seems

---

* Spokesman of the Collaboration.

to be equal to the electron neutrino mass eigenstate [2].

Process (3) would reflect breaking of a global (B-L) symmetry. The Majoron χ would be the Goldstone-boson associated with this symmetry breaking. Process (4) with the emission of two majorons seems possible in the case of supersymmetric models [3], and the same spectral shape for the sum energy of the electrons is expected if the majoron carries a leptonic charge [4]. The isotope under study at the Heidelberg-Moscow experiment [5] is ^{76}Ge in form of low-level semiconductor detectors. Further topics which can be investigated with such detectors are, for example, charge non-conservation [6] and dark matter [7].

2.   The experiment

The Q-value of the decay to ^{76}Se is $Q = 2038.56$ keV. The experiment has 16.9 kg of Ge enriched to 86% in ^{76}Ge at hand (natural abundance of ^{76}Ge is 7.8 %). At present five enriched HP-detectors have been built from this material with a total mass of 11 kg of Ge. Table 1 gives some characteristics of the three detectors at present in regular operation at the Gran Sasso Laboratory. The given background B is determined between 2000-2080 keV. The next two detectors will be installed in fall 1994. The whole experiment is located underground in the Gran Sasso Laboratory in Italy (shielding depth is about 3500 m.w.e.). The detec-

Detector	Active mass [Kg]	Enrichment [%]	Background [C/(Kg.KeV.A)]
Enr.1	0.920	86	0.16
Enr.2	2.758	86	0.21
Enr.3	2.324	88	0.22

Table 1. A comparison of the different detectors used in the experiment.

tors are built in a 10 cm shield containing ultrapure LC2-lead surrounded by another 20 cm box of very pure Boliden lead. The whole setup is plugged in an air-free box which is flushed with high purity nitrogen. All parts of the detector cryostats are well selected and cleaned and have specific activities of less than 10 μBq/kg. To check the stability of the experiment a calibration is done every week with a

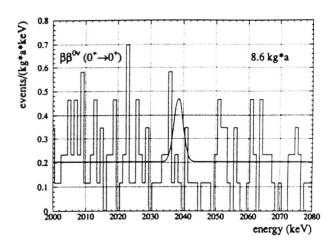

Figure 1. The energy range between 2000-2080 KeV of the spectrum seen after 8.6 Kg.A of measurement. The dotted curve shows the peak exculded with 90% CL.

^{232}Th source.

3.   Results

3.1.   2ν double beta decay

Fig.1 shows the region of interest of the $\beta\beta$-spectrum after a measuring time of 8.6 kg·a. No line is seen so far. For a signal hidden in the background a half-life limit for this decay mode of $T_{1/2}^{0\nu} > 5.1(8.6) \cdot 10^{24}$ a (90% and 68% CL) can be derived. Using the matrix-elements given by [8] this can be converted into a limit for the neutrino mass of

$$< m_{\nu_e} > < 0.68(.52) \text{ eV} \quad 90\%(68\%) \text{ CL} \quad (6)$$

This is the most stringent limit for a neutrino mass coming out of double beta decay so far.

A transition to the first excited state would be dominated by right-handed currents and not by the mass-term like the ground state transition. For this transition we obtain a half-life limit to the first excited state of $T_{1/2}^{(0^+ \to 2^+)}(^{76}Ge) > 6.5 \cdot 10^{23}$ a (90% CL).

3.2.   2ν double beta decay

In contrast to the neutrinoless decay the 2ν-mode has been observed in several isotopes, and there

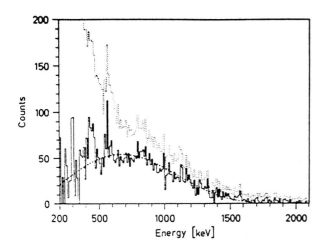

Figure 2. Remaining spectrum of enriched detector 2 after subtraction of all known background components (solid histogram, measuring time 19.2 mol.a). It is well fitted by a 2ν-spectrum (dashed line). Also shown is the measured spectrum stripped of all identified peaks (dotted histogram).

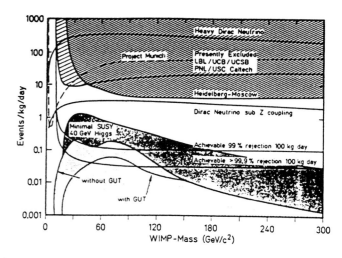

Figure 3. Exclusion limits for WIMPs with Ge detectors (dashed area). The increase of the sensitivity expected from some future [11] enriched ^{73}Ge cryo detectors is also indicated (curves 99 and 99.9%). Also shown are theoretical expectations for spin-dependently interacting WIMPs from different GUT models.

is also some evidence for an observation in ^{76}Ge. This decay mode can give information on nuclear structure. With the help of a Monte-Carlo simulation we subtracted all background components which can be identified, localized and quantitatively determined. The remaining counts are well fitted by a $2\nu\beta\beta$-spectrum (Fig. 2). Using a maximum likelihood fit, we derive a half life of $T_{1/2}^{2\nu} = (1.53 \pm 0.04_{,stat} \pm 0.13_{,sys}) \cdot 10^{21}$a after a measuring time of 49.6 mol·a (see also [9]). The number of $\beta\beta$ events is about 13500 and this decay is the main component of the measured spectrum in the region 500-1500 keV.

3.3. Majoron-accompanied double beta decay

For Majoron-accompanied $0\nu\beta\beta$ decay we look by further subtraction of the $2\nu\beta\beta$ spectrum from the 'remaining spectrum' of Fig. 2. We obtain a half-life limit for this decay mode of $T_{1/2}^{0\nu\chi} > 7.81 \cdot 10^{21}$ a (90 % CL). This half-life limit can be converted into a limit for the neutrino-majoron-coupling constant $\langle g_{\nu\chi}\rangle$, since

$$T_{\frac{1}{2}}^{-1}[a^{-1}] = \mid M_{GT} - M_F \mid^2 F^{0\nu\chi} \mid \langle g_{\nu\chi}\rangle \mid^2 \quad (7)$$

where

$$\langle g_{\nu\chi}\rangle = \sum_{ij} g_{\nu\chi} U_{ei} U_{ej} \quad (8)$$

resulting in $\langle g_{\nu\chi}\rangle < 2.4 \cdot 10^{-4}$. For details see [10]. The set of matrix elements given by [8] is used. An investigation of the $0\nu2\chi\beta\beta$-mode results in a half-life limit of $T_{1/2}^{0\nu\chi\chi} > 7.05(8.54) \cdot 10^{21}$ a (90 % CL and 68 %CL).

3.4. Dark Matter

Looking at dark matter interactions via coherent scattering of WIMPs off Ge nuclei requires sensitivity at low energies. By complementarily using an enriched ^{73}Ge detector, one would have a clear separation between spin-independent and spin-dependent interaction (^{73}Ge is the only germanium isotope with spin). After 165 kg·d of measurement with a lower threshold of 10 keV we obtained the exclusion plot shown in Fig. 3. The background is lower by a factor of 5-7 than that of other Ge-experiments dedicated to dark matter search, therefore improving the limits for heavier WIMPs [7, 12].

4. Conclusion and future

Using about 10 kg of enriched material, the final goal of the Heidelberg-Moscow experiment will be a

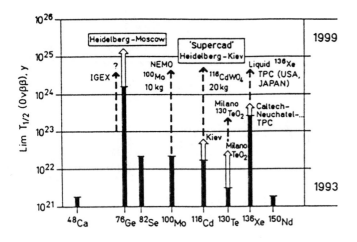

Figure 4. Present situation and perspectives of the most promising $\beta\beta$ experiments. Only for the isotopes shown $0\nu\beta\beta$ half life limits $> 10^{21}$ A have been obtained. The thick solid lines correspond to the present situation, 1993, open bars and dashed lines to 'safe' and 'less safe' expectations for 1999 .

References

[1] D.G. Lee and R.N. Mohapatra, preprint: UMD-PP-94-95.

[2] P. Langacker, in Neutinos; Ed. H.V. Klapdor (Springer 1988).

[3] R.N. Mohapatra and E. Takasugi, Phys. Lett. **B211** (1988) 192.

[4] C.P. Burgess and J.M. Cline, Phys. Lett. **B298** (1993) 141.

[5] H.V. Klapdor-Kleingrothaus, Prog. Part. Nucl. Phys. **32** (1994) 261.

[6] A. Balysh *et al.*, Phys. Lett. **B298** (1993) 278.

[7] M. Beck *et al.*, Phys. Lett. **B** to appear.

[8] A. staudt, K. Muto and H.V. Klapdor-Kleingrothaus, Europhys. Lett. **13** (1990) 31;
M. Hirsch *et al.*, Zeit. Phys. **A345** (1994) 163;
M. Hirsch *et al.*, Phys. Rep. **242** (1994) 403.

[9] A. Balysh *et al.*, Phys. Lett. **B322** (1994) 176.

[10] M. Beck *et al.*, Phys. Rev. Lett. **70** (1993) 2853.

[11] B. Sadoulet, Nucl. Phys. **B** (Proc. Suppl.) **35** (1994) 117.

[12] M. Beck *et al.*, Nucl. Phys. **B** (Proc. Suppl.) **35** (1994) 150.

[13] R.S. Raghavan, Phys. Rev. Lett. **10** (1994) 1411.

[14] M.K. Moe, Phys. Rev. **C44** (1991) R931.

half-life limit of $T_{1/2}^{0\nu} > 10^{25}$a corresponding to neutrino masses down to about 0.1 eV. Thus it will be possible to check beyond the mentioned $SO(10)xS_4$ model some other left-right symmetric see-saw models. The sensitivity of running and planned experiments till the end of the century is shown in Fig. 4. It is obvious that for making a significant step beyond the limit of about 0.1 eV in reach of the present most sensitive experiments, *very* large increases of set-ups are necessary (see e.g. [13, 14])

Acknowledgement

The experiment is supported by the Bundesministerium für Forschung und Technologie, the State Committee of Atomic Energy of Russia and the INFN. We thank the INFN Gran Sasso and especially Profs. P. Monacelli, E. Bellotti and N. Cabibbo for their generous support.

The Milano-Gran Sasso experiment on double beta decay using thermal detector array

A. Alessandrello, C. Brofferio, D.V. Camin, O. Cremonesi, E. Fiorini, E. Garcia, A. Giuliani, P. de Marcillac†, A. Nucciotti, M. Pavan, G.Pessina, E. Previtali and L. Zanotti

Dipartimento di Fisica dell'Universita' di Milano e Sezione di Milano dell'INFN,
Via Celoria 16, 20133 Milan, IT
† CEE Fellowship@LNGS, INFN, I-67010, IT

Abstract

Since more than 8 years our group is developing cryogenic thermal detectors (bolometers) for several experimental purposes like $\beta\beta$ decay, dark matter or direct detection of ν mass via β spectra endpoint. In particular, to study ^{130}Te $\beta\beta$ decay, an array of four 334 g TeO$_2$ monocrystal detectors was operating for about 620 h in the Gran Sasso Laboratory using a dilution refrigerator especially made for rare decay experiments, while a single detector of 334 g was measured for about 18 months (10510 h of effective running time). The energy spectrum collected gives a limit on the 0ν-^{130}Te $\beta\beta$ decay of 2.1x10^{22} y at 90% of confidence level, definitively excluding a significant contribution of neutrinoless mode to the rate of double beta decay found in geochemical experiments.

1. Introduction

Double beta decay (DBD) is a rare radioactive transition of an even-even nucleus (A,Z) to its isobar (A,Z+2) with the contemporary emission of two electrons [1]. According to the standard electroweak theory this process occurs with the emission of two electron antineutrinos (2ν-DBD). Neutrinoless DBD (0ν-DBD) where only two electrons are emitted would violate the lepton number conservation. A third process involving no neutrinos but a massless Goldstone boson, called majoron (majoron DBD), has also theoretically been considered [1].

In 0ν-DBD the two electrons would share the whole transition energy and a peak would appear in their sum energy spectrum. The phase space available to this process would be much larger than for the other two decay channels, favouring thus in principle the detection of even a tiny lepton number vbiolation.

^{130}Te DBD was searched in geochemical experiments, looking for an excess of the ^{130}Xe isotope in ores containing ^{130}Te. This method is very powerful due to the very long integration time, but it does not allow to isolate the contibution of the three decay channels. The situation for the DBD active tellurium isotope is still controversial. While the results on DBD of ^{128}Te seem now well established [2] with a $\tau_{1/2}$ of (7.3 ± 0.3)x10^{24}y, evidence is confirmed for DBD of ^{130}Te, but the measured $\tau_{1/2}$ ranges from 0.7x10^{21} to 2.7x10^{21}y[2, 3].

2. Experimental details

The use of thermal detectors to search for 0ν-DBD in the *calorimetric* (source $\equiv$ detector) approach has been suggested since 1984[4]. The source for DBD should be a large crystal of a pure dielectric and diamagnetic compound, operated at low temperatures. The heat capacity of such a crystal follows the Debye law $(C_{th}(T) \div (\frac{T}{T_{\Theta}})^3)$, where T_{Θ} is the crystal Debye temperature. At the usual bolometer working temperature (around 10 mK), C_{th} is so low that the energy released by a particle crossing the absorber gives

Det.: N°	Oper. Temp. (mK)	τ_{fall} (msec)	gain (mV/MeV)	ΔE_{FWHM} keV
0	10.5	700	0.230	12
1	11.0	270	0.220	45
2	12.1	350	0.110	9
3	13.0	1270	0.065	14
4	21.1	450	0.019	38

Table 1. TeO$_2$ bolometers main characteristics

on an adequate sensor (for example NTD Ge thermistor) a detectable increase of the temperature[5].

The single detector (Det.0) consists of a TeO$_2$ monocrystal (334 g - 3x3x6 cm^3), fastened to an OFHC copper frame by means of 13 spring loaded tips and with a NTD Ge thermistor glued on it [6]; while in the four crystals array (Det.1-4) each crystal has the same dimension and the same kind of sensor as before, but we substituted the tips, which showed a small contamination of ^{232}Th, with a teflon ring[5].

These detectors worked in two different dilution refrigerators, both installed in the Gran Sasso Laboratory, with similar characteristics and operating temperatures (with the only exception of Det.4, Tab. 1). A detailed description of both the apparatus and of the various electronic chains is given elsewhere[5, 6].

However from Tab. 1 one can see that the detector performances are different. The main differences are:

[1] τ_{fall}, due to the different thermal conductance between the absorber and the heat sink given by an additional copper strip present in Det.1, 2, 4;

[2] the noise of Det.1, due to an unpredictable deterioration of the performances of the read-out electronic chain;

[3] the temperature and the signal height of Det.4 due to a bad thermal coupling between the absorber and the sensor given by an unwilled grease contamination of the sensor surface.

For a better description of the detectors characteristics see ref. [5].

3. Results and Conclusions

As one can see in fig. 1, where the spectra of Det.0 and 2 are superimposed in the region of 0ν-DBD of ^{130}Te, the background in the new mounting, without the tips, seems to be unchanged: $(1.65 \pm 0.35) \times 10^{-4}$ c/keV/h in Det.2 compared to $(1.3 \pm 0.1) \times 10^{-4}$c/keV/h in Det.0; despite the fact that total lead+copper shield is more efficient for Det.0 than Det.2 (the low energy background is lower). In the mounting without the tips, however, the α background seems to be at least 3 times

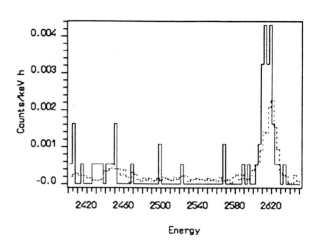

Figure 1. Spectra of Det.0 (dashed lines) and 2 in the region of 0ν-DBD of ^{130}Te

lower, apart for the 5410 MeV ^{210}Po α line (^{210}Po is a natural contaminant for Te).

No statistically significant peak appears in the region of 0ν-DBD of ^{130}Te. There is however in Det.0 an enhancement of 9.4±7 events at energy of 2521±5 keV still not observable in the other detectors. On the basis of the maximum likelihood method we can set a lower limit of $2.1(3.5) \times 10^{22}$ y for $\tau_{1/2}$ of the 0ν-DBD of ^{130}Te at 90%(68%) confidence level, using only Det.0, because the actual limit coming from the array detectors is still too low due to the shorter measurement time and the worse resolution in at least two detectors (1 and 4). This limit excludes that the 0ν-channel contributes more than 13% at 90% c.l. to the integral DBD using the higher geological $\tau_{1/2}$ [2].

In the near future we are going to set-up another array of 6 detectors and to improve the electronic chain of Det.1. With 10 detectors we hope to reach in one year of continuos measurements, having the present background, a lower limit of about 1×10^{23} on $\tau_{1/2}$ of the 0ν-DBD of ^{130}Te. Next year around July 4 crystals isotopically enriched in ^{130}Te (2) and in ^{128}Te (2) should be available to search for 2ν-DBD of ^{130}Te.

References

[1] M.K. Moe, Int. J. of Modern Physics, Phys. Rev. **E2** (1993) 507,and references therein

[2] M.T.F. da Cruz *et al.*, submitted to Phys. Rev., and T. Bernatowitz *et al.*, Phys. Rev., Phys. Rev. **C47** (1993) 806

[3] O.K. Manuel, J. Phys. G., Phys. Rev. **17** (19S221) 91

[4] E. Fiorini and T.O. Niinikoski, Nucl.Instrum.and Meth., Phys. Rev. **224** (1984) 83

[5] A. Alessandrello *et al.*, *"First Tests on Large Mass, Low Temperature Array Detector"*, presented at 6th Pisa Meeting on Avanced Detectors, May 1994, La Biodola, IT

[6] A. Alessandrello *et al.*, Physics Letters in the press

Paper presented at XXVII Int. Conf. on High Energy Physics: Session Pa-13
Glasgow, UK, 20–27 July 1994

Search for inclusive double beta decay of ^{96}Zr and ^{150}Nd to excited states of ^{96}Mo and ^{150}Sm.

C. Arpesella§, A.S. Barabash¤*, E. Bellotti‡, C. Brofferio‡*, E. Fiorini‡, P.P. Sverzellati‡, V.I. Umatov°*

§ Laboratori Nazionali del Gran Sasso, INFN, Assergi, Italy
¤Institute of Theoretical and Experimental Physics, Moscow, Russia
‡ Dept. of Physics, University of Milano, and INFN, Milano, Italy
° Lebedev Physical Institute, Moscow, Russia

* Authors of the search for inclusive double beta decay of ^{96}Zr to excited states of ^{96}Mo only.

Abstract

Double beta decay to excited states of daughter nuclei is poorly studied. Measurements were performed at Laboratori Nazionali del Gran Sasso with a germanium detector, by searching for the de-excitation gamma rays of the daughter nuclides. New lower limits on the half-lives for double beta decay of ^{96}Zr and ^{150}Nd to excited states of ^{96}Mo and ^{150}Sm have been obtained.

1. Introduction

Double beta decay is extremely investigated both from the point of view of theory and experimentally. Neutrinoless decay has intrigued theoreticians and experimentalists in elementary particle physics towards searches beyond the standard model, because of its implications on the lepton number conservation and neutrino properties [1]. Neutrinoless decay, which would violate the lepton number conservation, can be the consequence of a finite neutrino mass and/or of the presence of right-handed weak currents.

The detection of $\beta\beta$ decay to the 0^+_1 excited state gives similar informations about $\beta\beta$ decay as the observation of the decays to the ground 0^+_{gs} state. The energy released in $\beta\beta$ decay to the excited levels is less than for the ground state transition, so the phase space is substantially less. It has been recently shown [2] that the suppression factor respect to the transition to 0^+_{gs} may be not so large, at least for the one-phonon excited states within the framework of the QRPA. In ref.[3] half lives for $(2\nu)\beta\beta$ transitions in ^{96}Zr, ^{100}Mo and ^{150}Nd to the first 0^+_1 excited states of the daughter nuclei were estimated to be of the order of 10^{20} - 10^{21} years, thanks to their large transition energies (2202, 1903 and 2627 keV respectively), thus showing that this type of decay can be detected by present low-background detectors.

A possible signature for $\beta\beta$ decay to excited levels is the emission of de-excitation gamma rays from the daughter nuclide. Since the energy of the gamma rays is well defined, a good background rejection can be achieved if the detector has a high energy resolution, as , for instance, germanium diodes have.

2. Experimental setup and results for ^{96}Zr

The results of the search for $\beta\beta$ decay of the ^{96}Zr to excited states of ^{96}Mo are the subject of a paper submitted to Europhysics Letters [4] and the authors refer to it for this analysis.

3. Experimental setup and results for ^{150}Nd

A preliminary search was also carried out on $\beta\beta$ decay of ^{150}Nd to excited states of ^{150}Sm. In this case single β decay is energetically forbidden and the transition energies available for the decay to the first excited levels of ^{150}Sm are particularly high ($Q_{\beta\beta}$ = 2627 kev for the transition to the 0^+_1 excited level of ^{150}Sm). ^{150}Nd is present in natural neodymium with 5.64% atomic percentual abundance, which makes an experiment using natural neodymium , meaningful. This measurement, with 5106.7 hour of effective running time, was carried out using eighteen rods of natural metallic neodymium , 6185 g of total mass, each sealed in a very thin paraffin foil to avoid oxidation and placed around a germanium detector in the low background facility at Laboratori Nazionali del Gran Sasso [5]. The detector used is a High Purity Ge diode, 518 cm^3 volume, 113% relative efficiency. A shielding of OFHC copper and low activity lead with 7 and 25 cm minimum thickness, respectively, was mounted all around the detector to minimize background radiation. To avoid radon contamination, a plastic cover, into which nitrogen vapours were flushed, surrounded the shielding. This protection was changed during the experiment; in the final version of the set up a sealed acrylic box surrounded the lead shielding and a slight overpressure of argon was kept.

Radon concentration in the shielding was reduced by a factor 4 respect to the initial situation.

By analysing the spectra, gamma lines from natural radioactive series and other radionuclides have been observed in the samples and contaminations have been computed from their intensities.

3.1 Contaminations from ^{40}K

A small contamination has been found, corresponding to 3 $\cdot 10^{-6}$ Bq/g (10^{-11} g/g) and a concentration of 10^{-7} g/g of natural potassium.

3.2 Rare Earths

Due to the difficulty in purifing rare earths, the presence of radioactive lantanium and lutetium is expected. ^{138}La decays via E.C. (67.9% of the cases) to ^{138}Ba with the emission of a 1435.9 γ ray or beta decays to ^{138}Ce (32.1%) followed by a 789 keV γ ray. These two lines have been observed: the activity has been calculated from their mean value, thus giving a contamination of $3.6 \cdot 10^{-6}$ Bq/g ($4.15 \cdot 10^{-9}$ g/g) and a concentration of $4.66 \cdot 10^{-6}$ g/g of natural La.

^{176}Lu beta decays of ^{176}Hf, with the emission of four γ rays. A strong and well identified signal has been observed at 201.8 keV (84.4%) and 306.9 keV (93%) and the contamination results to be $2.7 \cdot 10^{-5}$ Bq/g ($1.3 \cdot 10^{-8}$ g/g), and a concentration of $5 \cdot 10^{-7}$ g/g of natural Lu.

3.3 Thorium

The secular equilibrium is broken: the concentration of ^{228}Ac results to be $2.9 \cdot 10^{-6}$ Bq/g, while the one of ^{212}Pb is $2.8 \cdot 10^{-5}$ Bq/g. Such a situation could be the consequence of a quite complete removal of radium from the sample during its preparation.

3.5 Uranium.

Gamma lines from ^{234m}Pa and ^{234}Pa have been detected and correspond to an activity of $1.85 \cdot 10^{-3}$ Bq/g of ^{238}U. Again the secular equilibrium is broken. The activity of the radionuclides descending from ^{226}Ra is dominated by radon and radon daughters in the air and inside the shielding. In the final shielding version, the radon rate has been reduced by a factor 4.

No evidence is found for any of the de-excitation gamma-lines expected for $\beta\beta$ decay of ^{150}Nd to excited states of ^{150}Sm. We concentrated our analysis to the search for the 333.9 keV gamma line for the 0^+_{gs} --- 2^+_1 decay and the 406.5 keV gamma line for 0^+_{gs} --- 0^+_1 decay. In the energy region around 333.9 keV, gamma lines from ^{227}Th (334.5 keV) and ^{228}Ac (332.9 keV) have been found and their contribution has been subtracted, by knowing ^{227}Th and ^{228}Ac contamination independently from other gamma lines. In the energy region around 406.5 keV, the contribution of ^{211}Pb with a gamma line at 404.8 keV has been subtracted.

The lower limits on the half lives of ^{150}Nd established are summarized in table 1 and compared with the previous published results[6]. The improvement results in limits more than one order of magnitude better than the previous ones.

4. Conclusions

We remind that the half life for $(0^+_{gs} --- 0^+_{gs})$ $(2\nu)\beta\beta$ decay of ^{150}Nd to ^{150}Sm has been recently measured to be $T_{1/2} = (1.7 ^{+1.0}_{-0.5} \pm 0.35) \times 10^{19}$ y [7]. On the basis of the expected dependence on the phase space, it appears that the present value is very close to the expected one and could be used to limit possible values of the nuclear matrix element.

The result obtained on natural neodymium has convinced us to improve the measurement by studing in order to reduce the background level. For this reason, studies for the purification of the material will be carried on. If a substantial improvement in the background will be reached, a further measurement with a sensitivity an order of magnitude higher than the present one will be performed.

$\beta\beta$ transition	efficiency	$t_{1/2}$ (90%C.L.) (this work)	$t_{1/2}$ (90%C.L.) (previous work [8])
$0^+ ---> 2^+_1$	2.34 %	$\geq 5.6 \times 10^{19}$ y	$\geq 1.0 \times 10^{18}$ y
$0^+ ---> 0^+_1$	2.659%	$\geq 7.3 \times 10^{19}$ y	$\geq 1.5 \times 10^{18}$ y

Table 1. lower limits on the half lives for $\beta\beta$ decay of ^{150}Nd to ^{150}Sm established in the present study, compared with previous direct measurements [8] of the same decay.

Acknowledgement

We wish to thank O.Cremonesi for assistance in the data analysis with particular regard to the Monte Carlo code for the estimation of the efficiencies. We also express our gratitude to B.Romualdi and E.Tatananni for their efficient and generous help in the preparation of the detector shielding.

References

[1] T.Tomoda. Rep.Prog.Phys., **54** (1991) 53, A.Morales, Nucl.Phys.B **S28a** (1992) 181, M.K.Moe and P.Vogel: Double beta decay, UCI-Neutrino 94-5, February 1994- to be published in Ann. Rev. of Nucl. and Part. Science

[2] J.Suhonen and O. Civitarese, Phys.Lett. **B308** (1993) 212

[3] A.S.Barabash, Soviet Phys.JETP **51** (1990) 207

[4] C. Arpesella et al., Europhys. Lett. **27** (1994) 29

[5] C. Arpesella et al., "A low background counting facility at LNGS", INFN/LNGS note 92/35, 1992

[6] W.C.Haxton, and G.J.Stephenson, Progr. Part. Nucl. Phys.,**12** (1984) 409

[7] V.A.Artem'ev et al., JETP Lett., **58** (1993) 262

[8] E. Bellotti et al., Lett. Nuovo Cimento, **33** (1982)273

Observation of ^{150}Nd $2\beta2\nu$ decay in the Time Projection Chamber experiment

V. Artemiev[†], E. Brachman[†], A. Karelin[†], V. Kirichenko[†], A. Klimenco[§], O. Kozodaeva[†], V. Lubimov[†], A. Mitin[†], S. Osetrov[§], V. Paramokhin[†], A. Pomansky[§], A. Smolnikov[§], T. Tsvetkova[†], S. Vasilev[§], O. Zeldovich[†]

† Institute of Theoretical and Experimental Physics, 117279, Moscow, Russia
§ Institute for Nuclear Research, 117312, Moscow, Russia

Presented by O. Zeldovich

Abstract

A positive effect in an experiment to search for two-neutrino $\beta\beta$-decay of ^{150}Nd using the Time Projection Chamber (TPC) is obtained. The half life time $T_{1/2}(2\beta2\nu) = [1.88^{+0.69}_{-0.39}(stat.) \pm 0.19(syst.)] \times 10^{19}$ years is obtained from the analysis of data accumulated with samples of ^{150}Nd (92% enrichment) and ^{nat}Nd (natural isotopic abundance).

1. Introduction

In the Institute of Theoretical and Experimental Physics there is prepared the track experiment with the large (3m*3m*1.5m) Time Projection Chamber (TPC) in magnetic field to search for neutrinoless double beta decay of different isotopes [1].

A prototype TPC (1.0m*0.8m*0.4m) was constructed to test the method, to study the background and to investigate two neutrino 2β–decay of different isotopes.

^{136}Xe was studied first. It was obtained the half-life limit of $T_{1/2}(2\beta2\nu) > 0.9*10^{20}$ years during the 400 hours measurement time in the conditions of ordinary earth laboratory without large passive shielding [2]. This sensitivity and background rejection factor more than 10^7 were reached due to track information and full identification of events in TPC.

2. Experimental situation

The isotope ^{150}Nd is one of the most perspective for investigation of 2β0ν decay due to its large transition energy (3.37 MeV) and coulomb factor. The experimental study of allowed two neutrino decay can give some confidence for the theoretical calculation of nuclear matrix element.

There were only few studies of ^{150}Nd 2β2ν decay [3,4,5]. The same sample of Nd, enriched by isotope 150, was used in all these experiments. The preliminary results did not agree. Baksan group obtained only the

half-life limits $T_{1/2} > 1.8*10^{19}$ years and $T_{1/2} > 1.1*10^{19}$ years [3,5]. Irvine group observed the positive effect with $T_{1/2} \sim .9*10^{19}$ years [4]. So, the sensitivity about 10^{20} years was reached at ITEP detector, we decided to study ^{150}Nd 2β2ν decay with Baksan sample (50g of Nd_2O_3 powder enriched to 92% by isotope ^{150}Nd) in TPC. The result, related to first 600 hours measurement time was published [6].

3. Detector

Schematic view of TPC in magnetic field is shown on Fig. 1 and described elsewhere [1,2]. Two samples of Nd were placed on maylar film simultaneously. One sample was enriched by ^{150}Nd and contained 40g of isotope, second sample was with natural isotopic composition and contained only 2.5g of isotope. The thickness of the sources were 25mg/cm^2.

The kinematic parameters of two electrons and their direction or sign were defined in the large volume by the multiwire detectors, instaled at the end of the drift path. The smaller volume operated as active protection against the electrons from bottom cover.

The energy resolution of the detector was studied with radioactive sources ^{207}Bi [1]. The measurement gave the value of 100 keV for the energy of IC-electrons 0.5 MeV and 1.0 MeV.

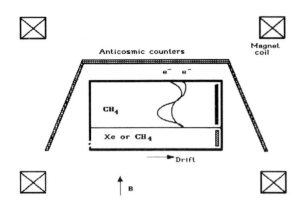

Figure 1. The TPC (1.0m×0.8m×0.4m) in an 800 Gauss magnetic field

4. Background study

TPC in magnetic field rejected all events with two electrons of the opposite helicity (electron from the upper cover reflected in the sources, e^-e^+-pair production) and electrons from the lateral walls.

Only two types of background can not be reject by the track information in our detector.

The first one is the double Compton and Compton Moller scattering of external γ–radiation in the sources. We used two sources simultaneously to subtract the external background.

	^{150}Nd	^{nat}Nd
^{238}U	< 1.2	< 1.2
^{232}Th	< 2	< 3

Table 1. The expected counts for working sources from radioactive impurities

The next background is due to the radioactive impurities in the sources. The electrons from beta decay of ^{214}Bi, ^{214}Pb, (U-family) and ^{208}Tl (Th-family) were followed by internal conversion electrons. The presence of these isotopes in the sources could be registered by measuring of the (β–α) delayed coincidences from the decay of ^{212}Bi, ^{214}Bi. For our working sources we obtained only limits on (β–α) delayed counts. To estimate the possible background we made some additional measurements with special sources contained of ^{238}U (0.45g/g) and ^{232}Th (075g/g) sand. The total mass of each source was about 21g. We measured (β–α) counts and 2β-events for these special sources. Using well known ratio of 2β-events to (β–α) counts and the limits on the (β–α) counts of the working sources, we experimentally obtained the possible

background counts for both sources (^{150}Nd and ^{nat}Nd). The limits for 1000 hours measurement times were presented in the table.

5. Search for 2β2ν decay

The time of measurement, related to the mass of 51.5g of Nd_2O_3 were 1260 hours for ^{150}Nd and 910 hours for ^{nat}Nd. After 'on-line' and ' off-line' processing selected 2β–events were viewed by physicists.

The sum-energy spectra of two electron events for both sources were presented on figs. 2&3. The difference between the counts from ^{150}Nd and ^{nat}Nd gave the positive effect 23 events for the energy range from 0.9 MeV to 2.5 MeV. The efficiency of TPC for detection of ^{150}Nd 2β–decay was 2.8% according to Monte-Carlo calculations.

The systematic error, connected with the uncertainties of processing procedure, was measured experimentally using the special samples with U and Th as sources of 2β–events. The absolute normalization for these measurements was made by low background Ge-spectrometer. The half-life time is

$$T(2β2ν)=[1.88+0.69-0.39stat.\pm0.19syst]*10^{19} \text{ years.}$$

So there was not difference between the natural and enriched sources at the energy range from 2.3 MeV to 3.5 MeV we derived the next limits (90% C.l.):

$$T(0ν)^{<m>} >1.9*10^{20} \text{ years, } <m_ν> < 13 \text{ eV,}$$
$$T(0ν,\chi)>1.55*!0^{20} \text{ years, } <g_{ν\chi}> < 1.35*10^{-4}.$$

There was used the matrix element from the work[7].

Only the limit for the Majoron coupling constant could be compared with the best world data [8].

Our result agreed well with the theoretical calculation of 2β2ν decay, using the Operator Expansion Method (OEM)[9], $T_{1/2}(2β2ν)=1.66*10^{19}$ years.

6. Future experiment

The TPC with volume 13 m^3 must be installed in the magnet with diameter 5.5 m. The work for the installation of the magnet is starting now. TPC box, the multiwire detectors and the proportional counters of the active protection from cosmic radiation were completed and tested.

TPC can use up to 10 kg of different isotopes as in gaseous (^{136}Xe - we have it), so in solid form (for example ^{100}Mo, ^{150}Nd).

The sensitivity $T_{1/2}> 10^{24}$ years and the limit on the neutrino mass $<m_ν> < 1eV$ can be achieved during the one year measurement time.

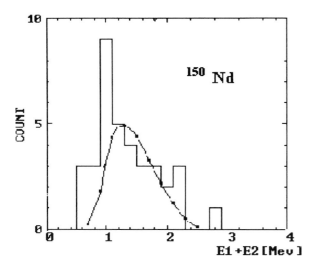

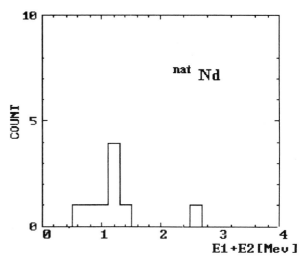

Figure 2. The sum-energy spectrum of two electrons from the source enriched in the isotope ^{150}Nd (1260h, 36eV). The solid line is the Monte Carlo calculation of $2\beta2\nu$.

Figure 3. The sum-energy spectrum of two electrons from the source with the natural isotopic abundance (910h, 9eV).

7. Conclusions

Two neutrino decay of ^{150}Nd was observed. The detail publication is in preparation.

The work with prototype showed that TPC in the magnetic field possesses of the powerful background rejection criteria.

We hope to reach the high sensitivity with large TPC, using up to 10kg of the different isotopes, in the conditions of the earth laboratory.

References

[1] V.A. Artemiev *et al.*, Nucl. Instr. Meth. **A303** (1991) 309.

[2] V.A. Artemiev *et al.*, Phys. Lett. **B280** (1992) 159.

[3] A.A. Klimenco *et al.*, Nucl. Instr. Meth. **B17** (1986) 445.

[4] S.R. Elliot *et al.*, in Proc. of XV Int. Conf. on Neutrino Phys. and Astrophys. (Neutrino '92); Ed. A. Morales.

[5] S.I. Vasiliev *et al.*, in Proc. III Int. Symp. on Weak and Electromagnetic Ints. in Nucl. (WEIN '92); Ed. T. Vylov (World Scientific 1993).

[6] V.A. Artemiev *et al.*, Pis'ma Zh. Eksp. Teor. Fiz. **58** (1993) 256.

[7] A. Staudt, K. Muto and H.V. Kleingrothaus, Europhys. Lett. **13** (1990) 31.

[8] M. Moe and P. Vogel, preprint: UCI-Neutrino 94-5.

[9] M. Hirsh *etal.*, preprint: MPIH V-4-93.

First results of the Troitsk experiment on the search for electron antineutrino rest mass in tritium beta-decay

S.N.Balashov [§], A.I.Belesev [†] A.I.Bleule [†], E.V.Geraskin [†], A.A.Golubev [†], N.A.Golubev [†],
O.V.Kazachenko [†], E.P.Kiev [†], Yu.E.Kuznetsov [†], V.M.Lobashev [†], B.M.Ovchinnikov [†],
V.I.Parfenov [†], I.V.Sekachev [†], A.P.Solodukhin [†], N.A.Titov [†], I.E.Yarykin [†], Yu.I.Zakharov [†]
P. E. Spivak [§‡]

[†] Institute for Nuclear Research of Russian Acad. of Sciences, Russia
[§] Institute for Nuclear Physics - R.S.C. "Kurchatov institute", Russia

Abstract

First results of investigation of tritium beta-spectrum near its end-point, carried out in INR RAS - INP("KI") (Troitsk) experiment, are presented. Experimental set-up includes an integral electrostatic spectrometer with adiabatic magnetic collimation and a gaseous tritium source of electrons. Fit of data gives value for m_ν^2 equal to $-18 \pm 6 eV^2$. Study of beta-spectrum in the region $7 - 15\,eV$ below its end-point provides indication that the effect of negative m_ν^2 may be explained by a spike-like (in differential spectrum) structure corresponding integrally to about 6×10^{-11} of total decay probability. The obtained upper limit for m_ν equals $4.5\,eV$ at 95% C.L.

We report here first results of the experiment on search for electron antineutrino rest mass in tritium beta decay. The experiment is being carried out at the Institute for Nuclear Research of Russian Academy of Sciences in the city of Troitsk of the Moscow region. The main features of the experiment are the use of integral electrostatic spectrometer with adiabatic magnetic collimation and gaseous tritium source of electrons. The main ideas of this experiment were first proposed in [1]. Some description of the experimental set-up was given in [2] and will be published in detail elsewhere. Spectrometer device based on similar principles was independently developed in Mainz, the main distinction being the use of frozen tritium source of electrons [3]. In our measurements the energy resolution was adjusted to be equal to $3.7\,eV$ (FW) at $18.6\,keV$. The spectrometer luminosity was $0.27 cm^2$ and the effective surface density of $T_2 + TH + H_2$ was maintained

‡ Deceased.

at the level of about $1 - 1.7 \times 10^{17}\,atoms/cm^2$.

Measurements of spectra were carried out changing the spectrometer potential by steps in the range from $18175\,V$ to $18770\,V$.

The measurement of the spectrometer resolution function and energy losses in tritium was made using an electron gun with photoemission induced by ultraviolet lamp. The accuracy of the energy losses factor measurement was estimated as 5%.

The fitting procedure at first step included 4 free parameters: normalization factor, the background, the end-point energy, and m_ν^2. The lower limit of the fit interval of the spectrum (E_{low}) was changed from 18175 eV to 18500 eV (for fitting results see table 1). Backward scattering and deflection efficiency energy dependence were not included into the analysis because it was shown that their influence on the result of fit is insignificant.

It is seen from the table that value of m_ν^2 is definitely

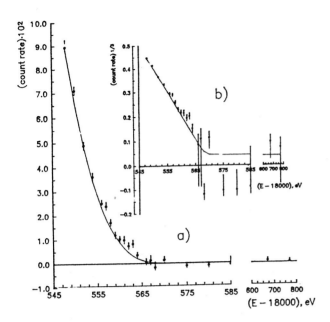

Figure 1. Part of the tritium spectrum (a) and Curie-plot (b) near the end point.

negative for all E_{low} and there is a rise of negative value both at the lowest and highest E_{low}. The source of the first one is an increase of intensity of about 1% at $18175\,eV$ revealing when spectrum fitted with $E_{low} > 18350\,eV$ is extrapolated down to $18175\,eV$, similar effect was observed in [3]. Formally, it is possible to fit this increase by β-decay transition to the some "missed" final state with excitation energy $100 - 150\,eV$ and probability of a few percent.

E_{low} (eV)	18175	18300	18350	18400	18450	18500
m_ν^2 (eV²)	−37.5 ±4.3	−19.3 ±4.8	−20.2 ±5.3	−18.6 ±6.1	−25.5 ±7.3	−35.7 ±10.2
E_0–18 KeV	573.15 ±0.08	573.60 ±0.10	573.55 ±0.11	573.60 ±0.12	573.35 ±0.18	572.95 ±0.38
$\frac{\chi^2}{d.o.f}$	$\frac{83.0}{42}$	$\frac{39.70}{39}$	$\frac{39.30}{37}$	$\frac{37.40}{35}$	$\frac{33.50}{33}$	$\frac{30.00}{31}$

Table 1. Results of the fit for m_ν^2 and E_0

Examination of the spectra presented in Fig. 1 draws attention to the group of points below $18564\,eV$, that is about $7\,eV$ below the end point. These several points seem to form some step starting from about $18563\,eV$ and extending to lower energy that is looking like a spike in differential spectra. Taking

into account this observation, we made an attempt to check possible connection between this step-like structure and the effect of negative m_ν^2 by subtraction of step-like functions starting at $18563\,eV$ with different magnitudes. Fitting procedure described above was carried out for the each step magnitude. It proved to be that the dependence of χ^2 on the magnitude of the step clearly exhibit a parabolic shape with the minimum at about $2.5 - 3\,mHz$. The m_ν^2-dependence on the magnitude of the step forms more or less linear function with all the graphs crossing the axis corresponding to $m_\nu^2 = 0$ around the point $2.5\,mHz$.

The existence of the minimum of χ^2 just around $m_\nu^2 \approx 0$ appears to be an important indication of connection of this step-like structure in original spectrum with the phenomenon of negative m_ν^2 for the fitting interval with $E_{low} > 18350\,eV$.

If we postulate $m_\nu^2 = 0$, leaving the other parameters free, we obtain step magnitude being equal to $2.61 \pm 0.63\,mHz$ corresponding to B.R.=$(6.3 \pm 1.5) \times 10^{-11}$ of the total decay rate.

With m_ν^2 and step magnitude taken as a free parameters we may obtain upper limit for m_ν^2. Step magnitude and m_ν^2 are strongly correlated and this leads to a significant increase of upper limit for m_ν^2. For most restrictive case (E_{low} equals $18350\,eV$) one can deduce the upper limit

$$m_\nu^2 < 20\,eV^2, \text{ or } m_\nu < 4.5\,eV \text{ at } 95\% \text{ C.L.}$$

This limit is essentially lower than those published up to now and involves a new kind of systematics which was not seen previously.

We do not include other uncertainty factors like electron energy loss inaccuracy because its influence on m_ν^2 limit is relatively small.

The spike-like structure in tritium beta spectrum of B.R. $\sim 10^{-10}$ could not be seen in the previous experiments [3, 4] due to insufficient statistical accuracy and cannot be reasonably understood on the basis of usual beta-decay processes. Admixture of some unknown radioactivity was rejected by special control experiment.

At the moment it seems to be early to discuss some exotic explanations of spike-like effects in tritium decay until this phenomenon is studied more carefully. It is possible in near future to improve both statistical and systematical accuracy of this experiment at least by a few times thus making the situation clearer.

References

[1] V.M. Lobashev and P.E. Spivak, Moscow preprint: INR P-0291 (1983); and Nucl. Instr. Meth. **A240** (1985) 305.
[2] S. Balashov *et al.*, Proceedings of WEIN-89 (Montreal 1989), p.295 (Edition Frontieres).
[3] Ch. Weinheimer *et al.*, Phys. Lett. **B300** (1993) 210.
[4] R.G.H. Robertson *et al.*, Phys. Rev. Lett. **67** (1991) 957.

A Measurement of the Beta Spectrum of ^{63}Ni using a New Type of Calorimetric Cryogenic Detector

R J Gaitskell, L C Angrave, N E Booth, A D Hahn, G L Salmon and A M Swift

Department of Physics, University of Oxford, Nuclear Physics Laboratory, Keble Road,
Oxford OX1 3RH, UK

Abstract

A beta spectrometer has been developed using a new type of cryogenic particle detector. The detectors consist of series arrays of superconducting tunnel junctions (SASTJs) fabricated on single crystals of InSb operated at 100mK. Two detectors are used to completely enclose a beta electron source and are able to make fully calorimetric measurements of beta decay, eliminating both back scattering and final state effects. Preliminary results from a precision measurement of the beta spectrum of a ^{63}Ni source are reported.

1. Introduction

We report on the preliminary results from a measurement of the beta spectrum of a ^{63}Ni source using a new type of cryogenic detector. The technique allows the direct measurement of the Ni spectrum over its entire energy range. A Kurie plot of the raw data, from a run over a period of 14days, is shown in Fig.1 acquired at a live count rate of 50Hz and contains 4×10^7 counts. The FWHM resolution of the detectors for this run was 1.3keV. The structure below 4keV is due to trigger threshold effects. The apparent end-point energy is slightly above 67 keV. The problems associated with energy calibration are discussed in §2.

The original goal of this experiment was to confirm or disprove the existence of a neutrino of mass 17 keV/c^2 by a new calorimetric technique. The evidence for this neutrino has now disappeared, in part due to a re-analysis of the data which provided the most compelling positive evidence[1] and also from experiments which showed that this positive evidence was due to instrumental effects[2].

In the present work, we have demonstrated that this new cryogenic technique, which obviates the problems of back-scattering and final-state atomic effects, is capable of making a precision measurement of a beta spectrum at the level of order 1%. These (and other cryogenic based detectors) will be used for future investigations of some of the more pressing problems in particle physics such as a search for dark matter WIMPs. (See [3] for a review of the field.)

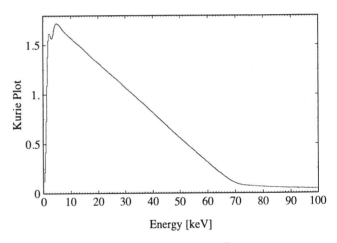

Figure 1. Kurie plot of the raw beta spectrum of ^{63}Ni. The plot contains 4×10^7 counts recorded over a period of 14 days.

2. Experimental Overview

The Ni source was deposited on the inside face of one of the detectors as an electroplated mono–layer and is totally enclosed by the two detector channels. This provides the ideal geometry for a calorimetric measurement. Pulses due to the beta electrons were recorded from both detectors. Further details of the detectors and detection mechanism are discussed elsewhere [4, 5]. In order to check the integrity of the data taken over long periods of time, the gain and linearity were monitored using pulses from a high stability LED which illuminated the detectors via an optical fibre.

We have found that the bias conditions of the devices can be subject to inherent instabilities. A change in the bias points alters the dynamic resistance or the tunnelling probability associated with the tunnel junctions, and therefore the intrinsic gain.

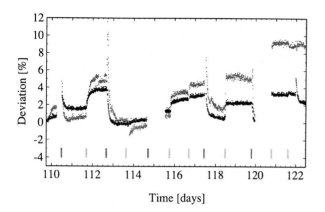

Figure 2. Plot of the variation of the gain of the two detector channels to LED calibration pulses (~60keV) over a period of two weeks.

For the run shown in Fig. 1 optimal bias points were chosen to minimise the instability. Figure 2 shows the variation of the detector gain over the period of two weeks. Most of the abrupt changes occur at the times indicated at the bottom of the figure when the dilution refrigerator is topped up with liquid nitrogen or liquid helium.

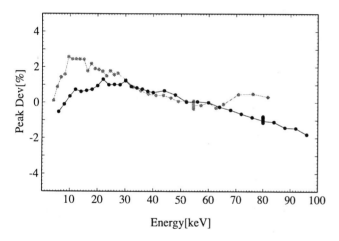

Figure 3. Typical plot of deviation from linearity of each of the two detector channels measured using a variable LED calibration pulse.

A plot of the deviations from linearity of the two channels is shown in Fig. 3 which was taken at a time during the run shown in Fig. 2. The details of the non-linearity were found to vary with the bias point of the detector. The monitoring system permits us to adjust the Ni spectrum data accordingly, and to discard blocks where the instabilities are beyond an acceptable limit.

External gamma sources of ^{241}Am (59.5keV) and ^{57}Co (122 and 136 keV) which span the end-point (67 keV) of the continuous ^{63}Ni spectrum were used to attempt to calibrate the absolute energy scale of the spectrometer. We have evidence that electrons give a larger pulse height

(~few%) than γ-rays of the same energy in the detectors. At present we are continuing to study these and related effects which affect the precise energy calibration of the detectors. Including a ^{109}Cd internal conversion source together with the beta source will allow us to determine a more precise energy calibration for the electron events and yield an electron response function.

3. Analysis of Kurie Plot

If we optimise the energy calibration of the two channels then it is possible to look at the shape of the Kurie plot when compared with the theoretical shape (including the effects of pile–up and background). Figure 4 shows the deviation of the Kurie plot, $\Delta K/K$, from a straight line fit in the region 51–60keV. Although the data taking is not yet complete, and the analysis is at a preliminary stage, it can be seen from the magnitude of the error bars that we are now at the stage where the statistics are nearly sufficient to test a neutrino admixture hypothesis at the 1% level.

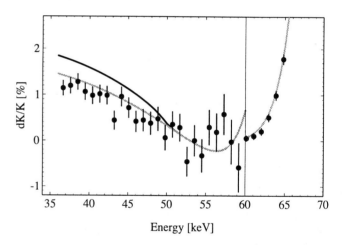

Figure 4. Relative deviation of the experimental Kurie spectrum from a straight line fit (51 to 60keV). The scale is compressed by a factor of 10 above 60keV. The grey line is the expected deviation based on the theoretical beta spectrum combined with pile–up/background effects. The black line is the deviation assuming an additional 1% admixture of a 17–keV neutrino.

References

[1] A. Hime, Phys. Lett. **299**, 165 (1993).
[2] M. G. Bowler and N. A. Jelley, Phys. Lett. **B 331**, 193 (1994).
[3] S. E. Labov and B. A. Young, eds., *Fifth International Workshop on Low Temperature Detectors*, J. Low Temp. Phys., **93** (1993).
[4] D. J. Goldie, A. M. Swift, N. E. Booth and G. L. Salmon, Nucl. Instr. and Meth. **A344**, 592 (1994).
[5] A. M. Swift, D. J. Goldie, N. E. Booth, P. L. Brink, R. J. Gaitskell, A. D. Hahn and G. L. Salmon, Nucl. Phys. **B (Proc. Suppl.) 35**, 405 (1994).

A detector for the study of neutrino-electron scattering at a nuclear reactor

J. Busto

Institut de Physique- University de Neuchâtel, Rue A.L. Breguet - 1
CH 2000 Neuchâtel, Switzerland

On behalf of the MUNU Collaboration

Abstract

In MUNU collaboration we are preparing a detector for the measurement of the neutrino magnetic moment studying the $\bar{\nu}_e e^-$ scattering at a nuclear reactor. This detector, $1\ m^3$ TPC surrounded by an anti-Compton scintillator, made with radiochemical clean materials, should be able to extend down the neutrino magnetic moment limits to $2 - 3 \cdot 10^{-11}$ Bohr magnetons, much better than in previous experiments.

1. Introduction

The neutrino magnetic moment matrix $\mu_{\ell,\ell'}(\ell, \ell' = e, \mu, \tau)$, like $m_{\ell,\ell'}$, is fundamental and its experimental study may provide insight on new physics.

Even if in the minimal standard model, neutrinos are massless Dirac particles and have vanishing magnetic moments, models motivated by the solar neutrino problem predict values as larges as $10^{-10}\mu_B$ by $\bar{\nu}_L \to \bar{\nu}_R$ spin flip in the solar medium [1,2]. Neutrino precesion in more general stelar medium, provides limits betwen 10^{-11} to $10^{-12}\mu_B$. In MUNU collaboration we expect to reach limits of the order of $10^{-11}\mu_B$, quite competitive with astrophysics limits, studying the $\bar{\nu}_e e^-$ scattering.

The differential cross section of this process is given by: [3]

$$\frac{d\sigma}{dT} = \frac{2G_F^2 m_e}{\pi}[g_R^2 + g_L^2(1 - \frac{T}{E})^2 - g_L g_R \frac{m_e T}{E^2}] + \frac{\pi\alpha^2 \mu^2}{m_e^2 \mu_B^2} \frac{(1 - T/E)}{T} \tag{1}$$

where T is the kinetic energy of the electron and

$$g_L = \frac{1}{2} + \sin^2\theta_W; \quad g_R = \sin^2\theta_W. \tag{2}$$

The terms on the first line are due essentially to W and Z exchange, and the second part comes from the magnetic moment interaction.

As we can see, the contribution of magnetic moment lead to the enhancement of this cross section compared to that of the usual weak interaction in particular for low energy scattering (fig. 1).

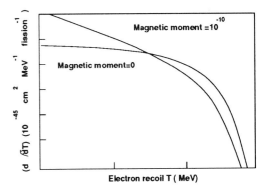

Figure 1. The distribution of recoil electrons folded over the reactor spectrum [5].

2. The experiment

The apparatus is a $1m^3$ time projection chamber (TPC) filled with CF_4 gas at 5 bar, serving as electron traget, and surrounded by an anti-Compton scintillator (fig. 2) [4]. The use of a gaseous detector should be helpful to identify the direction of single electrons originating from inside a predefined fiducial volume, keeping the background low. The gas used, should have low Z to minimize multiple scattering, and have high electron density. The most attractive appears CF_4 which has a very high density (3.68 g/l at 1 bar and thus a very high electron density, $1.06 \times 10^{21} cm^{-3}$). On the other hand, the absence of any free proton in the gas, eliminates the background reaction $\bar{\nu}p \to e^+ n$.

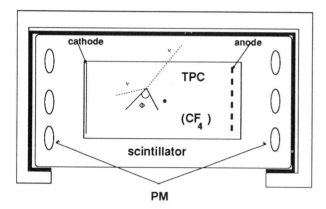

Figure 2. A sketch of the MUNU detector.

The TPC, an acrylic vessel of 90 cm diameter and 158 cm long, will be immersed in a stainless steel tank filled with a mineral oil based liquid scintillator (NE235H or equivalent). The scintillator will serve to veto the cosmic muons and as anti-Compton detector. The veto thickness is 60 cm for the ends, and 50 cm on the cylindrical periphery.

Top and bottom lid of the vessel will be instrumented with 48 low activity photomultipliers. With this arrangement we expect a good good photomultiplier coverage, and reach an anti-Compton efficiency of order 99% as well as a threshold around 100 keV.

The steel vessel, a cylinder 2.80 m long and 2 m in diameter, will be pressurized so as to have a small pressure difference between the inside and the outside of the lucite vessel.

The whole detector will be sourrunded with 15 cm of low activity Pb reducing the local activities, and with of 10 cm of borated polyethylene to reduce the neutron flux.

The experiment will be installed at the 2.8 GW reactor N° 5 of the Bugey nuclear power plant near Lyon in France.

3. Background and rates

The expected rates at 18.6 m from the Bugey reactor (neutrino flux $\sim 10^{13} \nu \cdot cm^{-2} \cdot s^{-1}$) calculated for recoil energies between 500 keV and 1 MeV are 5.3 events/day if $\mu = 0$ and 8.1 events/day if $\mu = 10^{-10} \mu_B$. The corresponding rates above 1 MeV are 4.2 and

5.3 events/day, respectively. These rates have to be compared to the background rates, which are estimated in the following.

We define as background a fully contained event which has a minimun energy deposition of 500 keV in the gas, together with a maximum energy deposition of 100 keV in the anti-Compton liquid scintillator. Two main sources of background have been considered: μ induced radioactivity, and natural radioactivity.

Muon capture in the TPC gas produces radioactive isotopes like ^{19}O, ^{18}N, and ^{12}B. On the other hand his interaction in the the iron and lead shielding induce a neutron flux in the detector. Nevertheless, the used of delayed tiggers, neutron CH_2 absorber, and other tracking conditions should be able to reduce this background to the level of of 1.4 event/day.

Estimating the background from natural radioactivity (Th, U, K, ^{60}Co, etc) is more difficult as it it depends on the purity of the materials that we will eventually get. Thus, all detector components will be low activity materials. For instance, mineral oil and acrylic, can be procured with a concentration in Th and U well below 10^{-12} g/g. Based on measurements, simulation and on the experience gathered by the Neuchâtel group with the Gotthard TPC, we estimate a background from natural radioactivity of 1.76 events/day. Thus the total background rate is estimated to 3 events/day compared to the signal rate of $\sim$ 10 events/day. The background will be measured continuously (with reactor on) by monitoring events with a backward emitted electron.

Taken into account the expected signal and background rates, and differents uncertainties (5% for systematics and 3% for statistics), we expect a sensitivity of $3 \times 10^{-11} \mu_B$, decreasing to $4 \times 10^{-11} \mu_B$ if the background contibution is four times higher than anticipated. In the absence of a sizeable magnetic moment, this experiment can measure the Weinberg angle in a purely leptonic process at very low energy with a relative precision of about $\pm$ 5%.

The experiment has been approved and is funded. It will be first installed in 1994 at the ISN in Grenoble so that backgrounds can be studied and hopefully reduced in a convenient environment.

References

[1] M.B. Voloshin, Sov. J. Nucl. Phys. **48** (1988) 512;
    K.S. Babu and R.N. Mohapatra,Phys. Rev. Lett. **63** (1989) 228
[2] P.I. Krastsev and A.Yu Smirnov, Z. Phys. **C49** (1991) 675;
    S.T. Petcov *et al.*, Phys. Lett. **B303** (1993) 85;
    J. Pulido Phys. Rev. **D48** (1993) 1492
[3] B.W. Lee and R.E. Shrock, Phys. Rev. **D16** (1977) 1444;
    W. Marciano and A.I. Sanda, Phys. Lett. **B67** (1977) 303
[4] C. Broggini *et al.*, MUNU-Proposal (1993).
[5] P. Vogel and J. Engel, Phys. Rev. **D39** (1989) 3378.

Neutrino mass and magnetic moment from neutrino–electron scattering

J. Bernabéu[†], S.M. Bilenky[‡], F.J. Botella[†], J.A. Peñarrocha[†] and J. Segura[†]

† Departament de Física Teórica, Universitat de València and
IFIC, Centre Mixt Univ. València-CSIC, E-46100 Burjassot, Spain
‡ INFN, Torino, Italy and JINR, Dubna, Russia

Presented by J. Segura

Abstract

We study both the elastic ($\nu e \to \nu e$) and the radiative process ($\nu e \to \nu e \gamma$) and discuss how these processes can shed light on some current topics in neutrino physics such as a neutrino magnetic moment and neutrino oscillations.

1. Introduction.

The neutrino-electron process plays a crucial role in the study of electroweak interactions. It gives relevant information about possible deviations from S.M. as, for instance, the existence of a large neutrino magnetic moment.

The differential cross section for $\bar{\nu}_i e^- \to \bar{\nu}_i e^-$ including the neutrino magnetic moment contribution [1] and neglecting neutrino mass can be written as the sum of the S.M. cross section $d\sigma^W/dT$ plus the magnetic moment contribution $d\sigma^M/dT$ which, in the LAB frame reads

$$\frac{d\sigma^M}{dT} = \frac{\pi\alpha^2}{m_e^2}\left(\frac{\mu_\nu}{\mu_B}\right)^2 \frac{(1 - T/E_\nu)}{T} \qquad (1)$$

being T the kinetic energy of the recoil electron.

In the laboratory experiments on neutrino magnetic moment, the sensitivity to μ_ν is connected with the fact that at low enough values of $Q^2 = 2m_e T$ the contribution of the electromagnetic amplitude to the cross section of the process becomes comparable to the contribution of the weak amplitude. It is thus extremely important to minimize the detection threshold on T.

2. Neutrino magnetic moment and the radiative process.

Contrary to the elastic scattering case, the process $\nu(\bar{\nu}) + e \to \nu(\bar{\nu}) + e + \gamma$, though including an additional power of α, allows to reach $Q^2 = 0$ at fixed values of the recoil energies. In fact, $Q^2 = 0$ can be reached for the maximal opening angle between electron and photon in the final state. Whatever the experimental limit on the total recoil energies ν could be, this process is able to lead to lower values of Q^2 than the elastic one, as shown by the ratio $x = Q^2/(2m_e\nu)$ varying from 1 to 0 ($\nu = T + E_\gamma$, being E_γ the photon energy).

With this motivation we have performed a detailed analytical calculation [2] of the cross section for this process both for the weak and the magnetic contribution.

Fig.1 gives the ratio of the inclusive cross section $d^2\sigma^M/d\nu dx$ over $d^2\sigma^M/d\nu dx$ for the scattering with $\bar{\nu}_e$ at $E_\nu = 1MeV$. This result confirms, as shown by the analytic results, that the highest sensitivity is obtained for the lowest values of ν and, by going down to low values of x, the sensitivity is higher than for the elastic scattering case with $x = 1$.. Then we see that, although the absolute cross sections are small (for instance, $\sigma_M/\sigma_W = 4.4$, $\sigma_M = 2.7\,10^{-47}cm^2$

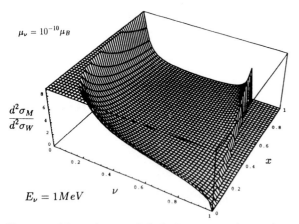
$\mu_\nu = 10^{-10}\mu_B$

$\dfrac{d^2\sigma_M}{d^2\sigma_W}$

$E_\nu = 1MeV$

ν

x

Figure 1. Magnetic to weak inclusive cross sections ratio. The flat region on the right is out of phase space boundaries.

for $\mu_\nu = 10^{-10}\mu_B$ integrating over $\nu < 0.5 MeV$, $x < 0.5$) , the standard model contribution is suppressed in these circumstances more strongly than in the elastic scattering case, thus giving a favourable ratio. The general features are not highly sensitive to the incoming neutrino energy within the range of the reactor antineutrino spectrum.

For $x \to 1$ and $\nu \to 2E_\nu^2/(2E_\nu + m_e)$ one can see from Fig. 1 that the ratio of cross sections increases. This effect is a consequence of a cancellation in the elastic weak cross section for forward electrons.

3.   The dynamical zero in $\bar\nu_e e^-$ elastic scattering.

In the LAB frame, the backward antineutrino (forward electron) cross section for $\bar\nu_i e^- \to \bar\nu_i e^-$ can be written as [3]

$$\left(\frac{d\sigma_{\bar\nu_i}}{dT}\right)_b = \frac{G^2 m}{2\pi}\left[g_R^i - g_L^i \frac{m}{2E_\nu + m}\right]^2 \qquad (2)$$

which vanishes for $\bar\nu_e$ at

$$E_\nu = m_e \frac{g_L^e - g_R^e}{2g_R^e} = \frac{m_e}{4sin^2\theta_W} \cdot \qquad (3)$$

Therefore for the antineutrino energy E_ν given by Eq. (3) and forward electrons the differential cross section for $\bar\nu_e e^- \to \bar\nu_e e^-$ vanishes exactly at leading order [3]. This is the only point in phase space where the differential cross section for $\bar\nu_e$ vanishes. For any other kind of (anti)neutrino specie ($\nu_{i=e,\mu,\tau}$, $\bar\nu_{i=\mu,\tau}$) there is no such kind of cancellation.

This kinematical configuration must be a good place to study new physics. The electron recoil energy for forward electrons corresponding to the dynamical zero $T \simeq 2m_e/3$ is within the range of the proposed detectors to measure recoil electrons[4]. The neutrino energy for the dynamical zero is on the peak of

any typical antineutrino reactor spectra [1, 5], being precisely $\bar\nu_e$ the flavour which is produced copiously in nuclear reactors. Although the dynamical zero appears for a given E_ν, the convolution of the cross section with the antineutrino spectrum still keeps the effect for the planned detectors that select neutrino energies by measuring T and the recoil angle of the electron (θ). The kinematical region where the dynamical zero lies is thus in principle reachable by experiment and profit could be taken from the existence of such effect to study the neutrino magnetic moment, since, for forward $\bar\nu_e$ with $T \simeq 2m_e/3$ the magnetic moment contribution could become dominant[3].

4.   A novel kind of neutrino oscillation experiment.

The fact that the weak cross section for $\bar\nu_e$ behaves in such a peculiar way in contrast to the other neutrino species suggests a second phenomenological implication: measuring neutrino oscillations.[6]

Suppose we have a source of electron-antineutrinos $\bar\nu_e(0)$ (a nuclear reactor for example) and we measure the differential cross section for the process $\bar\nu_e(x)e^- \to \bar\nu_e(x)e^-$ at a distance x from the source. If vacuum oscillations take place we will have

$$\frac{d\sigma^\nu}{dT}\bigg|_x = \sum_{i=e,\mu,\tau} P_{\bar\nu_i}(x)\frac{d\sigma^{\bar\nu_i}}{dT} \qquad (4)$$

where $P_{\bar\nu_i}(x)$ is the transition probability from $\bar\nu_e$ to $\bar\nu_i$ at a distance x from the source. In the particular case of considering only two flavour ($\bar\nu_e \leftrightarrow \bar\nu_\mu$) oscillation we have:

$$\frac{d\sigma^\nu}{dT}\bigg|_x = \frac{d\sigma^{\bar\nu_e}}{dT} + \left(\frac{d\sigma^{\bar\nu_\mu}}{dT} - \frac{d\sigma^{\bar\nu_e}}{dT}\right)P_{\bar\nu_\mu}(x) \qquad (5)$$

where

$$P_{\bar\nu_\mu}(x) = sin^2 2\phi\, sin^2\left(\frac{\Delta m^2 x}{4E_\nu}\right) \qquad (6)$$

being ϕ the vacuum mixing angle and Δm^2 the difference of the squared masses of the mass eigenstates.

From Eq. (5) it is quite evident that by measuring $d\sigma^\nu/dT$ at the kinematical configuration where $d\sigma^{\bar\nu_e}/dT$ vanishes, the signal will be proportional to the oscillation probability times the $\bar\nu_\mu e^- \to \bar\nu_\mu e^-$ cross section thus simulating an "appearance" experiment.

There are some features of this appearance-like experiment which distinguish it from the usual appearance experiments. First, by measuring events on the dynamical zero we are sensitive to oscillations

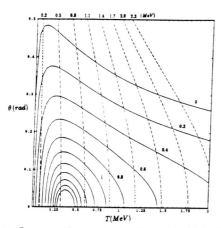

Figure 2. Isocurves for constant values of $log(d\sigma^{\nu_\mu}/d\sigma^{\nu_e})$ and for constant E_ν values in MeV (dashed lines) in the plane (T, θ).

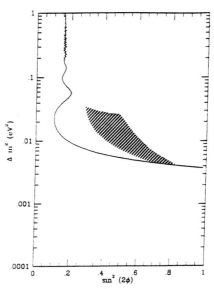

Figure 3. Would-be exclusion plot obtained by imposing $\int d\sigma^{\bar\nu}/\int d\sigma^{\bar\nu_e} < 1.5$ integrating the cross sections over a typical reactor spectrum in the kinematical region where $d\sigma_{\bar\nu_\mu}/d\sigma_{\bar\nu_e} \geq 5$. The detector is 20 meters away from the reactor. The shaded zone corresponds to the allowed region for atmospheric $\nu_e \leftrightarrow \nu_\mu$ oscillations.

$\bar\nu_e \rightarrow \bar\nu_x$, where $\bar\nu_x$ is any non-sterile neutrino. The detection is not via purely charged current processes; on the contrary any signal of oscillation would be detected via neutral currents $(\bar\nu_\mu(\bar\nu_\tau)e^- \rightarrow \bar\nu_\mu(\bar\nu_\tau)e^-)$. Hence there is no energy threshold; this experiment would use neutrinos with energies around 0.5 MeV, thus being in principle more sensitive to low Δm^2 values than in the standard appearance experiments.

In a reactor the antineutrino spectrum is continuous so in Fig.2 we have plotted (dashed lines) the curves for constant neutrino energies in the plane (T, θ). The solid lines represent the curves for constant ratio $d\sigma_{\bar\nu_\mu}/d\sigma_{\bar\nu_e}$. From this figure it is quite evident that far from the dynamical zero there still remain important effects associated to its presence. As an illustration of the exclusion plots that one could obtain from the observable (5) we have integrated it over a typical reactor spectrum in the kinematical region where $d\sigma_{\bar\nu_\mu}/d\sigma_{\bar\nu_e} \geq 5$ and imposed that the ratio $\int d\sigma^{\bar\nu}/\int d\sigma^{\bar\nu_e}$ is less than 1.5. With the detector placed at 20 meters, the would-be exclusion plot we get is represented in Fig. 3. Inside the excluded region we have inserted the by now allowed region of oscillations coming from atmospheric neutrino experiments [7]. Taking into account the original MUNU proposal [4], the numbers we have considered correspond roughly to detect a few (~ 10) events per year if no oscillations are present placing an upper bound (with oscillations) around 15 events. Fig. 3 has been drawn supposing a complete knowledge of the neutrino spectrum. From Fig. 2 it is evident that by measuring the cross section at different kinematical points with the same neutrino energies we can avoid uncertainties from the neutrino flux. Note that for points with different (θ, T) but corresponding to the same energy E_ν the dependence of $\frac{d\sigma^\nu}{dT}(\theta, T)$ on Δm^2 and ϕ is different, so that performing ratios the dependence on the flux

can be cancelled out without cancelling the effect. If this ratio is performed by integrating over a reasonable kinematical region we have checked that errors coming from the flux uncertainty can be reduced to a few percent.

Acknowledgements

This paper has been supported by CICYT under Grant AEN 93-0234 . We are indebted to J. Busto, D. Koang, , M.C. Gonzalez-García, F. Halzen, L.M. Sehgal and S.K. Singh for discussions about the topics of this paper.

References

[1] P. Vogel and J. Engel, Phys. Rev. D39(1989)3378.
[2] J. Bernabéu et al.,Preprint FTUV/94-22, IFIC/94-20, to appear in Nucl. Phys. B.
[3] J. Segura et al.,Phys. Rev. D49(1994)1633.
[4] C. Broggini et al. (MUNU),Report No. LNGS 92/47, 1992; J. Busto in these proceedings.
[5] K. Schereckenbach et al., Phys. Lett. B160(1985)325.
[6] J. Segura et al.,Preprint FTUV/94-34, to appear in Phys. Lett. B.
[7] K.S Hirata et al. (Kam-II), Phys. Lett B280(1992)146; R. Becker-Szendy et al. (IMB) , Phys. Rev. D46(1992)3720; Ch. Berger et al. (Fréjus), Phys. Lett. B245(1990)305, Phys. Lett. B227 (1989)489; E. Kh. Akhmedov, Preprint FTUV/94-9,IFIC/94-6.

Upward-Going Muons in MACRO

Douglas G. Michael

California Institute of Technology, Pasadena, Ca. 91125 USA

For the MACRO Collaboration

Abstract

Roughly 5 million muon events from six months of running with the lower half of the MACRO detector combined with 2.5 years of running with 1/6 of the lower detector have been analyzed looking for upward-going muons by using time information in the scintillator counters. The total number of upgoing muons observed in these running periods was $74 \pm 9_{\text{stat}} \pm 8_{\text{sys}}$ which compares to an expected number of events of $101 \pm 15_{\text{sys}}$. The flux of upgoing muons as a function of zenith angle is shown compared to MC expectation.

1. Introduction

The flux of muon neutrinos in the energy region from a few GeV up to hundreds of GeV can be inferred from measurements of upgoing muons in underground detectors. Measurements of the flux of upgoing muons with sufficiently large energies to penetrate through detectors have been made by the Baksan [1], Kamiokande [2] and IMB [3] detectors with no apparent discrepancy with expectations from calculation. MACRO's large area, low downgoing muon rate (about 10^{-6} of the surface rate), symmetric construction for upgoing versus downgoing events and fully automated analysis make it an excellent tool for measurement of the flux of upgoing muons resulting from interactions of ν_μ's underneath the detector. Here, we report on the first measurement of the upgoing muon flux with MACRO using the first 6 months of running with the full length of the lower structure of the detector and 2.5 years of running with 1/6 of the lower detector.

2. The MACRO Detector

The MACRO lower detector consists of a large rectangular box, 72m × 12m × 5m, with an outer shell of liquid scintillator counters with 10 horizontal layers of plastic streamer tubes distributed inside of the box. In addition to the horizontal layers, vertical layers of streamer tubes are also included along the sides of the detector. Tracking for muons is done using the streamer tubes which provide angular resolution (dominated by the muon multiple scattering) of less than about 1°. The scintillator counters have time resolution of about 500 ps which allows upgoing muons to be distinguished from downgoing muons which are about 10^5 times more prevalent at the depth of the Gran Sasso laboratory. (See [4] for more details of the detector hardware.) Because the configuration for the bottom half of MACRO used for this data acquisition is long and wide but relatively narrow in the vertical direction, the acceptance for small zenith angles is about 4 times that for large zenith angles.

3. Analysis

The data used for this measurement came from two different running periods. The first period used one supermodule and lasted from March of 1989 until November of 1991. During this time (1.4 live-years), approximately 2.3×10^6 muon events were recorded. The second running period is from December of 1992 until June of 1993 using 6 supermodules with 0.42 live-years

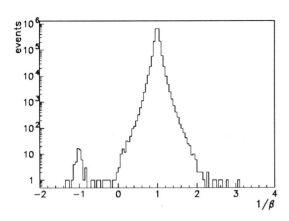

Figure 1. Distribution of $1/\beta$ after analysis cuts for the 6 supermodule running.

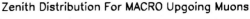

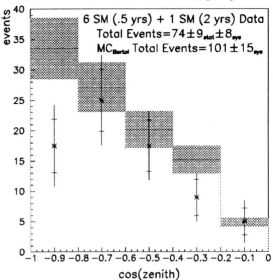

Figure 2. Distribution of cos(zenith) for upgoing events from the combined 6 supermodule and 1 supermodule running. The extensions to the statistical error bars are the point-by-point estimates of the systematic error. The Monte Carlo expectation using the Bartol flux is shown in the shaded regions with a $\pm 15\%$ systematic error range.

during which some 3×10^6 muon events were recorded.

The direction that muons travel through MACRO is determined by the time-of-flight between two different layers of scintillator counters. Only muons with pathlength in the detector greater than 3 m are used in the analysis to ensure that the time-of-flight is large compared to the time resolution. Some additional cuts are imposed to remove non-Gaussian tails in the timing resolution caused by nearly coincident radioactivity and showering events. The total effect from these cuts on acceptance (beyond the purely geometric requirements of a track from the streamer tubes and hit scintillator counters) is 6%. The acceptance is checked using downgoing muons.

Figure 1 shows the $1/\beta$ distribution after the analysis cuts are made for the 6 supermodule data. The cuts mostly affect only the non-Gaussian tails of the distribution. Some of the events in the region $1/\beta > 2.0$ result from downgoing muons which have stopped in the detector near the bottom layer with the decay products going into the bottom scintillator layer. After the cuts are applied, a clear peak of events is visible centered on $1/\beta = -1$. After the cuts are applied, a clear peak of events is visible centered on $1/\beta = -1$. Events with $-1.25 < 1/\beta < -.75$ are defined to be upgoing muon events. This range corresponds to a 4 σ assuming a Gaussian distribution for $1/\beta$ for the upgoing muons. There are 51 events which satisfy this definition for the 6 supermodule data. A similar analysis on the data with one supermodule resulted in a total of 26 events.

4. Monte-Carlo Simulation and Acceptance Calculation

The Monte Carlo simulation consists of three parts. First, a flux of muons at the detector coming from atmospheric neutrino interactions is calculated. Second, the acceptance for these muons is calculated for the geometry of the detector in a particular running period. Finally, an efficiency factor is applied to the expected number of events based on various electronic efficiencies which have been explicitly measured using downgoing muons. Four different calculations of the atmospheric neutrino flux have been used. These are the so-called 'Bartol' Flux [5], Butkevich et al. [6], Mitsui et al. [7] and Volkova [8]. The cross-sections for the neutrino interactions have been calculated using the Morfin and Tung parton distributions set S1 [9]. The resulting cross-section for ν interactions has good agreement with the average result calculated by the Particle Data Group [10] in the high-energy region where the best cross section measurements are available. No corrections to the cross section for quasi-elastic scattering have been applied but the effect that these may have on the total number of expected upgoing events is under further study. This could result in a small increase in the total number of upgoing events that are expected.

The variation in the expected rate of upgoing muons from these fluxes is about 10%. The estimated systematic error on the upgoing muon flux is 15%.

The detector has been simulated using both

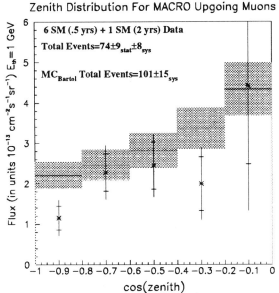

Figure 3. Distribution of cos(zenith) for the upgoing muon flux with energy greater than 1 GeV for the combined data from the 6 supermodule and 1 supermodule running. The extensions to the statistical error bars are the point-by-point estimates of the systematic error. The Monte Carlo expectation using the Bartol flux is shown in the shaded regions with a $\pm 15\%$ systematic error range.

a GEANT [12] based acceptance program and a simpler geometric model of the detector which includes all relevant dimensions of scintillator boxes and streamer tubes. By comparing different calculations of acceptance and measurements on the large sample of downgoing muons, it is estimated that the systematic uncertainty on the acceptance calculation is 5%.

5. Results

Figure 2 shows the zenith angle distribution of upgoing muon events for the combined data set for 6 supermodules and 1 supermodule compared to the Monte Carlo expectation using the Bartol neutrino flux. The error bars on the data show the statistical errors with an extension for the systematic error which is calculated separately for each point. The range for the Monte Carlo expectation reflects the $\pm 15\%$ systematic uncertainty in that prediction. A background subtraction of a total of 3 events has been applied to the data on a bin-by-bin basis according to the observed angular distribution of background events which are not in the $1/\beta = -1$ peak. The total number of upgoing muons observed in these running periods (after background subtraction) was $74 \pm 9_{\text{stat}} \pm 8_{\text{sys}}$ which compares to an expected number of events of $101 \pm 15_{\text{sys}}$ using the Bartol neutrino flux.

The shape of the distribution in figure 2 primarily reflects the acceptance of the detector given the

geometric acceptance for this running. By using the Monte Carlo expectations for the flux of muons at a particular angle, it is possible to remove the acceptance of the detector and present the data as a flux above a certain muon energy value. Figure 3 shows the zenith angle distribution as a flux of muons with energy greater than 1 GeV (which is the approximate threshold energy for muons to penetrate through the detector).

Overall, the measured flux is somewhat less than the prediction based on the Bartol flux of neutrinos. If all of the experimental and Monte Carlo systematic error are added in quadrature and subtracted from the Monte Carlo prediction, then the integrated number of events in all zenith bins agree between the data and Monte Carlo to within 1.1 σ. However, the dominant error in this calculation is the systematic error on the Monte Carlo prediction of the upgoing muon flux. The probability of measuring the observed number of events given that the central value of the Monte Carlo predicted upgoing muon flux is correct is 6%. The systematic uncertainty in the Monte Carlo prediction is dominated by the uncertainty in the calculation of normalization of the flux of the atmospheric neutrinos. Taking into account the other uncertainties in the upgoing muon flux (cross-section, rock and muon energy loss) the probability of measuring the observed number of events given that the central value of the Bartol neutrino flux is correct is 14%.

The experimentally detected rate is compared to hypotheses that assume the predicted rate is attenuated by neutrino oscillation between ν_μ and some other ν that is undetected (assuming effectively only two flavors mix). Taking the systematic error on the predicted flux into account, the MACRO data are consistent (at the 90% confidence level) with the hypothesis that no oscillations occur. Inclusion of quasi-elastic scattering as part of the total cross section for producing through-going muons may make the data slightly less consistent with a no oscillation hypothesis. Although consistent with no oscillations, the region in parameter space which is most consistent with the MACRO data corresponds to the region of parameter space suggested by the contained event analysis of Kamiokande.

[1] Boliev, M., *et al.*, Third International Workshop on Neutrino Telescopes, Venice, 1991.
[2] Totsuka, Y., Nuc. Phys. B Proceedings Suppl 31 (1993) 428.
[3] Becker-Szendy, R., *et al.*, Phys. Rev. Lett. **69(7)** (1992) 1010.
[4] Ahlen, S.P., *et al.*, Nucl. Inst. Meth. **A324** (1993) 337.
[5] T.K. Gaisser, private communication.
[6] Butkevich, A.V., *et al.*, Yad. Fiz. **50** (1989) 142.
[7] Mitsui, K. *et al.*, Nuovo Cimento **9c** (1986) 995.
[8] Volkova, L.V., Yad. Fiz. **31** (1980) 1510.
[9] Morfin, J.G. and Tung W.K., Z.Phys.**C52** (1991) 13.
[10] Aguilar-Benitez, M., *et al.*, Phys. Rev. **D45**, Part 2, June, 1992.
[11] Lohmann, W., *et al.*, CERN-EP/85-03, Mar, 1985.
[12] Brun, R. *et al.*, CERN report DD/EE84-1, 1987.
[13] W. Frati *et al.*, Phys. Rev., **D48** (1993) 1140.

Paper presented at XXVII Int. Conf. on High Energy Physics: Session Pa-13
Glasgow, UK, 20–27 July 1994

Results from SAGE II

Jeffrey S. Nico

Los Alamos National Laboratory,
P-3, MS D449
Los Alamos, NM 87545 USA

On behalf of the SAGE Collaboration

Abstract

The Russian-American Gallium solar neutrino Experiment (SAGE) began the second phase of operation (SAGE II) in September of 1992. Monthly measurements of the integral flux of solar neutrinos have been made with 55 tonnes of gallium. The K-peak results of the first nine runs of SAGE II give a capture rate of 66^{+14}_{-13} (stat) $^{+5}_{-7}$ (sys) SNU. Combined with the SAGE I result of 73^{+18}_{-16} (stat) $^{+5}_{-7}$ (sys) SNU, the capture rate is 69^{+11}_{-11} (stat) $^{+5}_{-7}$ (sys) SNU. This represents only 52%-56% of the capture rate predicted by different Standard Solar Models.

1. Introduction

At present, all four operating solar neutrino experiments have reported significant deficits of the flux of solar neutrinos relative to standard solar model (SSM) predictions. Numerous non-standard solar models [1,2] have been suggested, but none have been able to reproduce the observed ^{8}B flux without running into difficulties accounting for other observed features of the Sun. New particle physics [1,2], such as neutrino matter oscillations, have been invoked to provide an explanation of the "solar neutrino problem". Analyses [3,4] of the consistency of the chlorine and Kamiokande II results conclude that the results are inconsistent with any astrophysical explanations and are better described by Mikheyev-Smirnov-Wolfenstein (MSW) neutrino oscillations. However, given the uncertainties in the SSMs, it does not seem possible to rule out an astrophysical origin of the solar neutrino problem [5].

The ^{71}Ga (ν_e, e$^-$)^{71}Ge reaction [6] provides the only feasible means at present to measure low-energy solar neutrinos. The SSM calculations show that the dominant contribution to the capture rate in ^{71}Ga arises from the p-p neutrinos (71 ± 4 SNU where 1 Solar Neutrino Unit = 10^{-36} captures/target atom/s), while the total predicted rate in the SSMs is $122.5 - 131.5$ SNU [7,8].

2. The Baksan Gallium Experiment

The detector is situated in a specially built underground laboratory at the Baksan Neutrino Observatory in the Northern Caucasus Mountains. The experimental layout and the chemical and counting procedures have been described previously [9] and are not discussed here. The SAGE II counting system underwent several upgrades in the summer of 1992. These upgrades included replacing several components of the detector with ultrapure materials, use of a 1 GHz transient digitizer, and implementation of extensive noise suppression techniques. Eighteen additional solar neutrino runs have been made since September 1992, most of which include 1 GHz transient digitization of the pulse waveform. As a result of the upgrades to the counting system, the signal to background in SAGE II improved substantially relative to SAGE I. The K-peak background rate ranged from an initial value of 0.116±0.019 to 0.064±0.010 cts/d at the end of SAGE I.

Exposure Date	Ga Mass (tonnes)	^{71}Ge Events	K Peak Events	Best Fit SNU	68% CL (SNU)	Nw^2	Probability (%)
Sept 92	55.600	1.9	3	43	12-83	0.134	27
Oct 92	55.482	2.2	4	39	12-71	0.060	62
Nov 92	55.377	5.0	5	102	56-150	0.077	69
Dec 92	55.263	4.9	10	83	40-132	0.061	51
Jan 93	55.136	7.4	9	125	65-172	0.126	30
Feb 93	55.026	3.0	3	56	14-80	0.203	69
Apr 93	48.220	2.3	5	46	15-85	0.053	22
May 93	48.171	2.5	5	57	19-104	0.022	99
Jun 93	54.656	2.3	4	45	8-83	0.089	41

Table 1. Statistical analysis of the first nine runs from SAGE II. The analysis of the SAGE I runs are found in Ref. [9].

By comparison, the first nine runs of SAGE II presented here have a background rate of 0.013 ± 0.003 cts/d. In the SAGE II data, we are able to measure both the ^{71}Ge K and L peaks. Analysis of the L peak is proceeding, and results will be forthcoming.

The proportional counter containing the extraction sample is typically calibrated at one month intervals using an external ^{55}Fe source. The ^{71}Ge K-peak acceptance window is then determined by extrapolation from the ^{55}Fe peak. The extrapolation procedure was verified by filling a PC with ^{71}GeH$_4$ together with the standard counter gas. In SAGE II, we have also employed a Cd-Se fluorescence source which provides peaks at 11.2 keV (Se K-peak fluorescence), 6.9 keV (Xe escape peak), 6.4 keV (fluorescence from the Fe cathode), and 1.4 keV (Se L-peak fluorescence). We now also routinely measure the resolution integrated over the full counter volume using a Cd source in order to check the uniformity of the counter response.

A standard analysis procedure [9] for event selection was developed with two primary goals in mind: minimizing the efficiency uncertainty over the course of counting and keeping the background rate constant. Several cuts are made on the data. First, a cut is made to eliminate periods of noise bursts in the data. This results in the exclusion of a small fraction of a percent of the counting time. Second, cuts are made on energy and inverse rise time that accept 2 FWHM (98.15% acceptance) in energy centered symmetrically around the ^{55}Fe peak, and 95% of the inverse rise time distribution, with 1% being cut on fast rise time pulses (i.e., noise) and 4% cut on slow rise time pulses (i.e., background). Third, any event that has associated NaI activity is eliminated. Fourth, a cut was made to eliminate possible backgrounds from Rn daughters on the external surfaces of the PCs. Removing all data within 1.0 hour of a shield opening eliminates any observable excess of such events in the K-peak acceptance window.

A maximum likelihood analysis [10] is carried out

on the remaining events by fitting the time distribution to a ^{71}Ge exponential decay (11.43 day half life) plus a constant rate background. The results of the maximum likelihood analysis for the first nine runs of SAGE II are given in Table 1. We note that the number of ^{71}Ge events obtained by summing the individual runs (76.8 events) differs slightly from that (71.4 events) obtained by an analysis of the combined data. This is due to the constraint in the combined fit that all runs yield a common value of the capture rate. The good agreement is an indication of the consistency of the individual runs with the final result.

Figure 1 shows the individual run results along with the combined result. The 20 solar neutrino runs are consistent with the predicted statistical distribution of signals from 1000 Monte Carlo simulations of each extraction using the combined fit parameters and the constants of each data set. In addition, both the half-life for the decay measured from the combined data sets and the energy spectrum are in good agreement with the known properties of ^{71}Ge decay. The contributions to the systematic error are summarized in Table 2.

An experiment using a neutrino source is planned in order to test the overall extraction efficiency in situ. A suitable neutrino calibration source can be made using ^{51}Cr , which decays by electron capture, emitting monoenergetic neutrinos of 751 keV and 426 keV. Preparations are underway to carry out a full-scale experiment with a 1-MCi ^{51}Cr source in 1994.

3. Results and Conclusions

The best fit value for the capture rate and the uncertainties for the combined 1990-93 solar neutrino data are

$$^{71}\text{Ga Rate} = 69^{+11}_{-11} \text{ (stat) } ^{+5}_{-7} \text{ (syst) SNU.}$$

This assumes that the extraction efficiency for ^{71}Ge atoms produced by solar neutrinos is the same as that measured using natural Ge carrier. The result

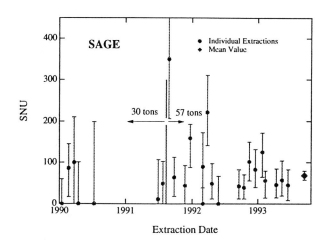

Figure 1. Results from SAGE for measurements from 1990 - 1993. Also shown is the current SAGE mean value from all runs reported. The error is derived by adding the quoted statistical and systematic uncertainties in quadrature.

Systematic	Contribution (SNU)
Chemical extraction efficiency	±2.5
Counting efficiency	+2.9/ − 2.1
K-peak acceptance	+3.5/ − 0.7
Backgrounds	−3.5
Radon	−5.9
Total	+5.2/ − 6.9

Table 2. Systematic uncertainties (1-σ) for the combined 1990-93 data sets.

corresponds to 71.4 counts assigned to ^{71}Ge decay, compared to the Bahcall-Pinsonneault and Turck-Chieze and Lopes SSM prediction of 136.1 and 126.8 counts, respectively

The measurements made by SAGE from January 1990 through June 1993 have observed fewer ^{71}Ge atoms than predicted by the SSMs. From the 1990-93 data, SAGE observes only 52% and 56% of the predicted Bahcall-Pinsonneault and Turck-Chieze rates, respectively. Taken alone, the SAGE result appears to favor a non-astrophysical solution of the solar neutrino problem, but cannot rule out an astrophysical solution. The solar neutrino experiments are consistent with two possible MSW solutions. The "non-adiabatic" solution ($\Delta m^2 \approx 6 \times 10^{-6} eV^2$ and $sin^2 2\theta \approx 7 \times 10^{-3}$) is the favored solution and represents a strong suppression of ^{7}Be neutrinos, a significant suppression of ^{8}B neutrinos, and essentially no suppression for the p-p neutrinos. Alternately, for the large-mixing angle solution ($\Delta m^2 \approx 10^{-5} eV^2$ and $sin^2 2\theta \approx 0.8$), it may be that all solar neutrinos are suppressed approximately the same, roughly independent of energy. With the improved precision from the combined 1990-93 SAGE data, SAGE is seeing approximately the rate predicted for the p-p neutrinos alone. With the ability to count both the K and L peaks with 55 tonnes of gallium, SAGE expects to reach a precision within the next two years that should provide a strong test for astrophysical solutions to the "solar neutrino problem".

The SAGE collaboration wishes to thank A.E. Chudakov, G.T. Garvey, M.A. Markov, V.A. Matveev, J.M. Moss, S.P. Rosen, V.A. Rubakov, and A.N. Tavkhelidze for their continued interest in our work and for stimulating discussions. We are also grateful to J.N. Bahcall, R.G.H. Robertson, A. Yu. Smirnov, and many members of the GALLEX collaboration for useful discussions. We acknowledge the support of the Russian Academy of Sciences, the Institute for Nuclear Research of the Russian Academy of Sciences, the Russian Ministry of Science and Technology, the Russian Foundation of Fundamental Research, the Division of Nuclear Physics of the Department of Energy, the National Science Foundation, Los Alamos National Laboratory, and the University of Pennsylvania.

References

[1] J.N. Bahcall, Neutrino Astrophysics Cambridge Univ. Press (1994).
[2] T.J. Bowles and V.N. Gavrin, Ann. Rev. Nucl. Part. Sci **43** (1993) 117.
[3] H.A. Bethe and J.N. Bahcall, Phys. Rev. **D44** (1991) 2962.
[4] S.A. Bludman, N. Hata, D.C. Kennedy, and P.G. Langacker, Phys. Rev. **D47** (1993) 2220.
[5] S. Turck-Chieze, Nucl. Phys. **B31** (1993) 129.
[6] V.A. Kuzmin, Zh. Eksp. Teor. Fiz. **49** (1965) 1532 and Sov. Phys. JETP **22** (1966) 1051.
[7] J.N. Bahcall and M.H. Pinsonneault, Rev. Mod. Phys. **64** (1992) 885.
[8] S. Turck-Chieze and I. Lopes, Astrophys. Jour. **408** (1993) 347.
[9] J.N. Abdurashitov et al., (SAGE Collaboration) Phys. Lett. B **328** (1994) 234.
[10] B.T. Cleveland, Nucl. Instr. Meth. **214** (1983) 451.

Status of the GALLEX Solar Neutrino Project

Helmut Lalla

Laboratori Nazionali del Gran Sasso (INFN),
S.S.17/bis Km.18+910, I-67010 Assergi (AQ), Italy

For the GALLEX collaboration[†]

Abstract

The GALLEX experiment monitors the solar neutrino flux since May 1991. After two years of data taking the result is $79 \pm 10[stat] \pm 6[syst]\, SNU$ (1σ). This result indicates a deficit in respect to the theoretical Standard Solar Model predictions but is still compatible with the full predicted flux of *p-p* neutrinos. Many efforts are made by the GALLEX collaboration to exclude any kind of unknown systematic error. They culminate in the exposure of the target to an artificial ^{51}Cr neutrino source to be performed this summer.

1. Introduction

The GALLEX collaboration [1, 2, 3, 4] measures the solar neutrino flux since May 1991. It makes use of the neutrino capture reaction

$$\nu_e + {}^{71}Ga \longrightarrow {}^{71}Ge + e^-$$

with a threshold of $233\,keV$ which makes the observation of the solar *p-p* neutrinos possible. The *p-p* neutrinos come from the basic solar fusion reaction

$$p + p \longrightarrow d + e^+ + \nu_e \qquad (E_\nu \leq 420\,keV)$$

and according to the Standard Solar Model [5, 6] form the bulk of the solar neutrinos, i.e. ca. 90%. Their flux is hardly sensitive to solar model fine tuning and given by the energy output of the Sun, if one accepts *p-p* fusion to be the principal mean of energy production in the Sun. Therefore the determination of the *p-p* neutrino flux represents a formidable test as to whether the deficit of higher energy solar neutrinos observed by both the Homestake [7] and Kamiokande [8] experiments is to be explained by errors in the Standard Solar Model or by new properties of the neutrino itself, most likely

matter enhanced neutrino oscillations (MSW effect [9]). A GALLEX result well below $80\,SNU$[‡] as compared to the Standard Solar Model expectation of $132^{+7}_{-6}\,SNU$ [6] could not be explained by a change in the solar model alone and would thus force the introduction of new neutrino physics.

2. Experimental procedure

The GALLEX target is a $101\,t$ hydrochloric aqueous solution of $GaCl_3$ containing $30.3\,t$ of gallium in its natural composition, i.e. $(1.044 \pm 0.008) \cdot 10^{29}$ atoms of the isotope ^{71}Ga. Contained all in one $54\,m^3$ tank the target is situated underground inside hall A of the Laboratori Nazionali del Gran Sasso (Italy) [10], where it is protected by a rock overburden of 3700 m.w.e. against the production of germanium by cosmic radiation. According to the Standard Solar Model we expect a capture rate of $1.18^{+0.06}_{-0.05}$ solar neutrinos per day in the GALLEX target.

In order to extract the produced ^{71}Ge, the liquid is sparged with a stream of nitrogen at room temperature, typically $2500\,m^3$ in $12\,h$ [11]. This is done currently

---

[†] see reference [4]

[‡] $1\,SNU = 1$ neutrino capture per second and 10^{36} target atoms

every four weeks, desorbing more than 99% of the germanium in the form of $GeCl_4$ including $1\,mg$ of germanium with a composition of stable isotopes. This stable germanium has been introduced into the target after the previous extraction and serves for monitoring the extraction procedure. The desorption gas containing the $GeCl_4$ is then led into absorber columns, where it is scrubbed with water leading to the quantitative absorption of the $GeCl_4$ in $30\,l$ of water. After several concentration steps the $GeCl_4$ is converted to GeH_4 gas, purified via gaschromatography and finally filled together with xenon into one miniaturized proportional counter [12] as counting gas [13]. The total efficiency of this extraction, conversion and filling process is about 96%. It is determined by measuring the GeH_4 volume when filling the counter.

The proportional counter is then brought into the GALLEX counting station [14], where it is shielded against background radiation by layers of lead and either copper or alternatively a $NaI(Tl)$ anticoincidence counter. The radon concentration in the atmosphere around the proportional counters is kept at a very low level ($\sim 0.5\,Bq/m^3$) by closing the station air tight and by flushing with a small but constant stream of nitrogen.

The ^{71}Ge is counted by means of observing its decay ($T_{1/2} = 11.4\,d$) via electron capture back to ^{71}Ga. Only the reorganisation of the electron shells in the ^{71}Ga atom produces ionisation in the counter via the emission of X-rays and Auger electrons. The energy spectrum shows two peaks, the L-peak at $1.17\,keV$ and the K-peak at $10.37\,keV$ named after the corresponding electron shells.

Calibrations with a cerium X-ray source [15] are performed every 8 weeks to verify the stability of the counting gas and the electronics. The calibration spectrum features three peaks at $1.03\,keV$, $5.09\,keV$ and $9.75\,keV$ covering the range given by the two ^{71}Ge peaks. Therefore the calibrations allow to find the position of two very confined acceptance windows (dubbed the L- and the K-window) in the energy-risetime plane of the pulses, which correspond to the two ^{71}Ge peaks and where ca. 66% of the ^{71}Ge decays are expected to appear. The background in these two acceptance windows is typically $0.05 - 0.1\,cpd$ (counts per day), whereas the signal has been determined to be around $0.3\,cpd$ at the start of counting. The calibrations also permit to find any unlinearity in the energy spectrum and to determine the energy resolutions for the ^{71}Ge peaks. The validity of the method has been tested many times by filling counters with ^{71}Ge.

The counter background can change when a counter is filled and must therefore be determined individually for each extraction ("run"). For this reason every run is counted for 6 months. Then the resulting time sequence of accepted events is used to determine via a statistical maximum-likelihood analysis [16] the production rate of ^{71}Ge in the GALLEX target. For the overall result of the experiment, we do not make use of the individual run results but perform a combined analysis with the data of all the runs.

After counting the germanium is recovered and analysed via mass spectroscopy for its isotopic composition. This enables us to determine the carry-over from previous extractions, i.e. the amount of germanium left in the target at the previous extraction and extracted in the analysed run.

3. Systematic error checks

3.1. The ^{51}Cr neutrino source

The GALLEX experimental procedure is well monitored. The extraction of the germanium, the conversion to GeH_4 and the counter filling procedure are monitored with the help of the germanium carrier. The question of hot chemistry effects, i.e. a chemically different behavior of germanium produced in nuclear reactions as compared to that introduced as a carrier, has been tackled by various tests, e.g. featuring the production of germanium via the reaction $^{69}Ga(p,n)^{69}Ge$ or via the decay of ^{71}As to ^{71}Ge. No effect has been detected. On the counting side the calibrations allow a very precise control of the counting efficiency.

Nevertheless it has been decided to do an overall performance test with an artificial ^{51}Cr neutrino source [17]. ^{51}Cr decays via electron capture ($T_{1/2} = 27.7\,d$) to stable ^{51}V and emits neutrinos with energies of $746\,keV$ (90%) and $426\,keV$ (10%), close to the energies of the p-p neutrinos ($E \leq 420\,keV$) and of the ^7Be neutrinos (90%: $861\,keV$, 10%: $383\,keV$), which together are expected to sustain 84% of the ^{71}Ge production in the GALLEX target.

$40\,kg$ of chromium enriched in ^{50}Cr (38.6%) had been acquired from the Kurchatov institute (Moscow) in the form of CrO_3. It was then transformed electrolytically into metallic chromium at Saclay. In order to obtain the ^{51}Cr the chromium was irradiated with neutrons for 24 days at the Siloe nuclear reactor (Grenoble). At the end an artificial neutrino source with an activity of about $64\,PBq$ ($1.7\,MCi$) has been obtained. The source was finally inserted in the central thimble of the GALLEX target tank, where initially it should produce about 15 times more ^{71}Ge than the Sun. It is planned to expose the GALLEX target to this neutrino source for ca. four months starting on June, 24th. Then the source will be removed and solar neutrino recording resume. During the source exposure 10 extractions are planned to be performed. We expect to observe ca. 185 decays of ^{71}Ge produced by the source. First preliminary results are not expected before late autumn this year. The precision of the test is expected to be about 10%, similar to the projected precision of the GALLEX experiment itself. The test is meant as a check for unknown systematic errors and not as a calibration of the experiment. Its result will therefore not enter as a parameter into the determination of the solar neutrino flux.

3.2. Blank runs

There is a number of systematic effects which cannot be tested with a neutrino source and must be checked by other means. Important are effects due to counter background components which are not constant in time. The most integral test for this kind of systematic effects is the performance of blank runs. Since a beam off condition is not possible, we define a blank run to be a run which has the minimal technically possible exposure time, i.e. one day. All other parameters remain the same as for the solar neutrino runs, all performed steps from the introduction of the carrier until the counting are done the same way. Currently one such blank run is performed immediately after each solar neutrino run, a $27\,d$ exposure. The combined result of these blank runs after correcting for the one day exposure time gives the expected null result: $-1 \pm 7\,SNU$ for 19 blank runs [4].

4. Results and discussion

The results of the first 30 GALLEX runs have been published in [4]. The final result for the period GALLEX-I (15 solar neutrino runs covering 324 days from May 1991 to April 1992) is $81 \pm 17\,[stat] \pm 9\,[syst]\,SNU$. The preliminary result for the first 15 runs of the period GALLEX-II (406 days from August 1992 to October 1993) is $78 \pm 13\,[stat] \pm 5[syst]\,SNU$. The reduction of the systematic error in GALLEX-II with respect to GALLEX-I is mainly due to the fact that the ^{68}Ge background ([2, 3]) has virtually disappeared. The combined result of 30 solar neutrino runs covering the periods GALLEX-I and part of GALLEX-II is $79 \pm 10\,[stat] \pm 6\,[syst]\,SNU$.

This means that now also GALLEX confirms the existence of a deficit in the solar neutrino flux in comparison with the expectation of the Standard Solar Model $132^{+7}_{-6}\,SNU$. Yet the deficit is not big enough to conclude, that there is a deficit also for p-p neutrinos which would require new neutrino physics. Thus the question whether errors in the solar models or the existence of neutrino oscillations are responsible for the solar neutrino deficit is left open. Astrophysical explanations of the Solar Neutrino Problem remain possible. However in the framework of astrophysical solutions, i.e. assuming a full p-p flux, it is now difficult to accomodate the ^7Be neutrino flux as expected by the Standard Solar Model.

If one seeks to explain the result in terms of matter enhanced neutrino oscillations (MSW effect), then GALLEX together with the Homestake and Kamiokande experiments favours the small angle solution at $\delta m^2 \approx 7 \cdot 10^{-6}\,eV^2$ and $\sin^2(2\theta) \approx 5 \cdot 10^{-3}$ in the $\delta m^2 - \sin^2(2\theta)$-plane. Less likely (i.e. having a large χ^2) but still possible is the large angle solution at $\sin^2(2\theta) \approx 0.6 - 0.8$.

5. Conclusion and outlook

The GALLEX collaboration is measuring the solar neutrino flux since May 1991. Great efforts have been taken to exclude any unknown systematic errors. They culminate in a test exposing the GALLEX target to an artificial neutrino source using ^{51}Cr. This test is performed this summer. After two years of measurements the measured solar neutrino flux is $79 \pm 10\,[stat] \pm 6\,[syst]\,SNU$. GALLEX confirms with this result the existence of a solar neutrino deficit. However the deficit is not big enough to enforce the introduction of new neutrino physics.

GALLEX is planned to continue measuring the solar neutrino flux until the end of 1996. By this time the total error is expected to have reached 10% or better. A decision for a further continuation of the experiment will not be taken before the outcome of the chromium source test is known. However, if the experiment is to continue after 1996, major funding efforts have to be undertaken.

References

[1] T. Kirsten, Nucl. Phys. **B19** (1991) 77.
[2] P. Anselmann *et al.*, Phys. Lett. **B285** (1992) 376.
[3] P. Anselmann *et al.*, Phys. Lett. **B314** (1993) 445.
[4] P. Anselmann *et al.*, Phys. Lett. **B327** (1994) 377.
[5] J. N. Bahcall, *Neutrino Astrophysics*, Cambridge University Press (1989).
[6] J. N. Bahcall, M. H. Pinsonneault, Rev. Mod. Phys. **64** (1992) 885.
[7] R. Davis, Jr., K. Lande, C. K. Lee, B. T. Cleveland, J. Ullman, Proc. 121st IAU Colloquium, Kluwer Academic Publishers, Dordrecht (1990).
[8] K. S. Hirata *et al.*, Phys. Rev. Lett. **65** (1990) 1297.
[9] S. P. Mikheyev, A. Yu. Smirnov, in: Progress in Particle and Nuclear Physics, Vol. 23, Pergamon Press (1989).
[10] L. Zanotti, J. Phys. G. **17** (1991) 373.
[11] E. Henrich, Interdisciplinary Science Reviews, Vol. 18, No. 3 (1993).
[12] R. Wink et al., Nucl. Instr. Meth. **A239** (1993) 541.
[13] C. Schlosser, PhD thesis, University of Heidelberg, (1992).
[14] G. Heusser, Proc. 2nd Int. Conf. Trends in Astroparticle Physics, Aachen (1991).
[15] A. Urban, PhD thesis, Technical University of Munich, (1989).
[16] B. Cleveland, Nucl. Instr. Meth. **214** (1983) 451.
[17] M. Cribier *et al.*, Nucl. Instr. Meth. **A265** (1988) 574.

Paper presented at XXVII Int. Conf. on High Energy Physics: Session Pa-13
Glasgow, UK, 20–27 July 1994

Recent results from the KAMIOKANDE

Masayuki Nakahata

Institute for Cosmic Ray Research, University of Tokyo, Tanashi, Tokyo 188, Japan

for the Kamiokande collaboration

Abstract

Recent results on atmospheric neutrinos from the Kamiokande are presented. The atmospheric neutrino events in the multi-GeV energy range are studied. The observed ratio of μ-like to e-like events relative to the expectation from the Monte Carlo simulation, $(\mu/e)_{data}/(\mu/e)_{MC} = 0.57 ^{+0.08}_{-0.07}$(stat.) ± 0.07(syst.), is significantly less than unity. The results suggest small flux ratio of $(\nu_\mu + \bar{\nu}_\mu)/(\nu_e + \bar{\nu}_e)$. The zenith-angle dependence of the ratio is also studied. The implication on neutrino oscillations is discussed.

1. Introduction

Atmospheric neutrinos have been studied by underground experiments. Kamiokande [1], IMB [2] and Soudan-II [3] (prelim.) observed that the μ/e ratio of atmospheric neutrino interactions with energies of about 1 GeV (or less) is significantly smaller than expectation. It suggests that the $(\nu_\mu + \bar{\nu}_\mu)/(\nu_e + \bar{\nu}_e)$ ratio of the atmospheric neutrinos is smaller than expected. Based on the small ν_μ/ν_e ratio, the possibilities of neutrino oscillations and proton decays into $e^+\nu\nu$ are discussed in refs.[1] and [4], respectively.

The analysis of the Kamiokande was devoted on the fully-contained atmospheric neutrino interactions with visible energy (E_{vis}) less than 1.33 GeV (called as 'sub-GeV' data from now on). Here, the data of neutrino interactions in the 'multi-GeV' energy range is presented. They consist of (1) fully-contained events with E_{vis} larger than 1.33 GeV, and (2) partially-contained events which have their interaction vertex in the fiducial volume and at least one visible track exiting from the inner-detector. The averaged neutrino energy of the multi-GeV data is estimated to be 5~7 GeV, which is about ten times as large as the one of the sub-

GeV data. Hence, the new analysis on the multi-GeV data provides independent information on atmospheric neutrinos and neutrino oscillations.

The Kamiokande is a water Cherenkov detector located 1000 m underground in the Kamioka mine in Japan [5]. The inner volume of the detector is viewed by 1000 20-inch photomultipliers(PMTs). The first stage of the experiment (Kamiokande-I (KAM-I)) was started in 1983 for the detection of nucleon decays and atmospheric neutrino interactions. The detector was upgraded between 1985 and 1986 for the measurement of solar neutrinos. The upgraded detector (Kamiokande-II (KAM-II)) had a 4π anti-counter and a dead-time-free electronics which takes pulse height and timing information of each PMT. After taking solar neutrino data for 1040 live-detector days, the detector was further upgraded in 1990 (Kamiokande-III (KAM-III)). In the upgrade from KAM-II to KAM-III, a reflective mirror was put around each PMT, which increased the light collection efficiency by 27 %. The energy and vertex position resolutions were improved by the increased light yield. More details of the detector are described in ref.[5]. In the analysis of the multi-GeV neutrino interactions, the data of KAM-II and KAM-III are used.

---

† E-mail: nakahata@icrkm4.icrr.u-tokyo.ac.jp.

2.   Event selection

The details of the selection criteria are described in Ref.[6]. Only a brief summary of the selection is described here. The selection criteria for fully contained events with E_{vis} higher than 1.33 GeV are: (1) $E_{vis} > 1.33$ GeV, (2) no anti-counter signal, and (3) the vertex position of the event should be at least 1 m inside the PMT plane. The fiducial volume for these events is 1.35 kton. We have observed 195 such fully contained events during 8.2 kton·yr of detector exposure. All single Cherenkov ring events in the sample are subjected to the particle identification and each event is classified as e- or μ-like. In case of multi-ring events, the particle identification is applied, if the most energetic ring contributes more than 80 % of the total visible energy. According to the Monte Carlo simulation, the purity of charged current(CC)ν_μ and CCν_e in the selected μ-like and e-like events are estimated to be greater than 95 % and 90 %, respectively.

The selection criteria for the partially-contained events are (1) total p.e. numbers of the inner detector > 1500 ($E_{vis} > 440$MeV), (2) elimination of cosmic-ray muons, (3) at most one cluster of hit PMTs in the anti-counter, and (4) reconstructed vertex position should be at least 1.5 m inside the PMT plane. The fiducial volume for these events is 1.04 kton. The detection efficiency of the partially contained events is estimated to be 92 %. We have observed 118 partially-contained events during 6.0 kton·yr of detector exposure. The partially-contained events are dominated by multi-GeV CC ν_μ interactions, because muons with a few GeV of energy cannot be contained in the detector. Hence, all partially-contained events except for single-ring e-like events are assigned as μ-like. The purity of the CC ν_μ interactions in the μ-like sample is estimated to be 94 %.

3.   Results

The observed multi-GeV atmospheric neutrino events are summarized in Table 1 together with Monte Carlo simulations. We have compared the data with two Monte Carlo simulations based on independent flux calculations. One is calculated by Honda *et al.* [7] (flux A) and another by Gaisser *et al.* [8] for neutrino energy $E_\nu < 3$ GeV and by Volkova [9] for $E_\nu > 10$ GeV (flux B, they are smoothly connected for E_ν between 3 and 10 GeV). The ratio of μ-like and e-like events is calculated by combining the multi-GeV fully-contained and partially-contained events. From Table 1, one can calculate

$$\frac{(\mu/e)_{\text{data}}}{(\mu/e)_{\text{MC}}} = 0.57 \begin{array}{c} +0.08 \\ -0.07 \end{array} \text{ (stat.) } \pm 0.07 \text{(syst.)}$$

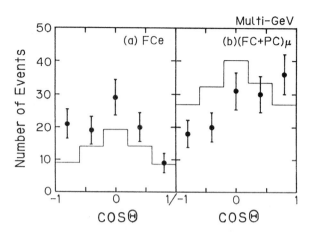

Figure 1. Zenith-angle distribution for the (a) e-like and (b) μ-like events. The circles with errors show the observed data and the histograms show Monte Carlo simulation. $\cos\theta = 1$ corresponds to the downward-going direction.

based on flux A. The result suggests that the atmospheric $(\nu_\mu + \bar{\nu}_\mu)/(\nu_e + \bar{\nu}_e)$ ratio is smaller than expected also for the multi-GeV data. The result agrees well with that obtained in the sub-GeV data.

Figure 1 shows the zenith-angle distribution for the (a) e-like events, and (b) μ-like events. The e-like events have a small excess of events for the upward and horizontal-going directions and the μ-like events have a small deficit of events in the same directions. The zenith-angle dependence of the $(\mu/e)_{data}/(\mu/e)_{MC}$ is shown in figure 2. It shows non-uniform distribution.

One of the possible explanations of the small $(\mu/e)_{data}/(\mu/e)_{MC}$ ratio and the non-uniform zenith-angle dependence is the neutrino oscillation. The allowed regions of the neutrino oscillation parameters are shown in figure 3 for $\nu_\mu \leftrightarrow \nu_e$ and $\nu_\mu \leftrightarrow \nu_\tau$ oscillations. The region of $\sin^2 2\theta > 0.6$ and $\Delta m^2 = 7 \times 10^{-3} - 8 \times 10^{-2}$eV^2 is allowed for $\nu_\mu \leftrightarrow \nu_e$ oscillation, and $\sin^2 2\theta > 0.7$ and $\Delta m^2 = 5 \times 10^{-3} - 3 \times 10^{-2}$eV^2 for $\nu_\mu \leftrightarrow \nu_\tau$ oscillation. The zenith-angle distributions of $(\mu/e)_{data}/(\mu/e)_{MC}$ ratio are calculated by assuming neutrino oscillations and they are shown in figure 2 by dotted and dashed histograms.

4.   Summary

The atmospheric $(\nu_\mu + \bar{\nu}_\mu)/(\nu_e + \bar{\nu}_e)$ ratio was studied for the data in the multi-GeV energy range. The observed $(\mu/e)_{data}/(\mu/e)_{MC}$ ratio, $0.57 \begin{array}{c} +0.08 \\ -0.07 \end{array} \pm 0.07$, is significantly smaller than unity. Non-uniform zenith-angle dependence of the $(\mu/e)_{data}/(\mu/e)_{MC}$ ratio is observed. The small μ/e ratio and the zenith-angle dependence are discussed assuming neutrino oscillations.

	Data	ν MC	
		Flux A	Flux B
Fully-contained ($E_{vis} > 1.33$ GeV)			
Total	195	181.0	189.1
e-like	98(73+25)	66.5(45.9+20.7)	70.8(49.1+21.6)
μ-like	31(20+10)	37.8(25.8+12.0)	40.4(27.3+13.2)
Partially-contained			
Total	118	135.5	136.6
e-like	-	-	-
μ-like	104	124.4	125.4
Total			
e-like	98	66.5	70.8
μ-like	135	162.2	165.8
$(\mu/e)_{data}/(\mu/e)_{MC}$		$0.57 {}^{+0.08}_{-0.07}$	$0.59 {}^{+0.08}_{-0.07}$

Table 1. Summary of multi-GeV atmospheric data (8.2 kton·yr and 6.0 kton·yr for fully-contained and partially-contained events, respectively). The numbers in the parentheses show numbers of single and multi-ring events.

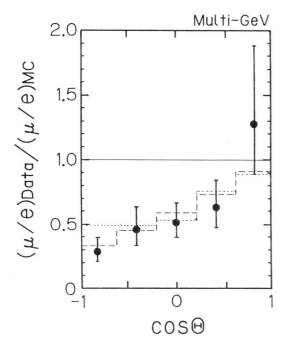

Figure 2. Zenith-angle dependence of $(\mu/e)_{data}/(\mu/e)_{MC}$ ratio. The circles with errors show the data and the dashed and dotted histograms show Monte Carlo simulations with neutrino oscillations for $\nu_\mu \leftrightarrow \nu_e$ ($\sin^2 2\theta = 1.0$, $\Delta m^2 = 1.8 \times 10^{-2}$eV^2) and $\nu_\mu \leftrightarrow \nu_\tau$ ($\sin^2 2\theta = 1.0$, $\Delta m^2 = 1.6 \times 10^{-2}$eV^2), respectively.

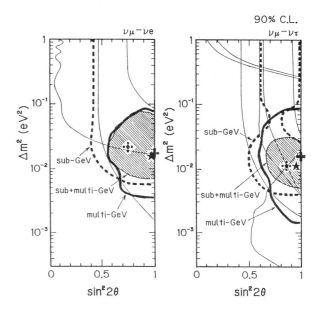

Figure 3. Allowed regions of neutrino oscillation parameters (90 % C.L.). The thick and thick-dotted curves show the allowed regions as obtained from the multi-GeV and sub-GeV data, respectively. The allowed regions as obtained by combining the sub- and multi-GeV data are shown by the hatched regions.

References

[1] K.S. Hirata et al., Phys. Lett. **B205** (1988) 416;Phys. Lett. **B280** (1992) 146.

[2] D. Casper et al., Phys. Rev. Lett. **66** (1991) 2561;R. Becker-Szendy et al., Phys. Rev. **D46** (1992) 3720.

[3] P. Litchfield, Proc. of the International Workshop on ν_μ/ν_e Problem in Atmospheric Neutrinos, Laboratori Nazionale del Gran Sasso, Italy, March 1993, P114.

[4] W.A. Mann, T. Kafka, W. Leeson, Phys. Lett. **B291** (1992) 200.

[5] K.S. Hirata et al., Phys. Rev. **D44** (1991) 2241;Phys. Rev. **D45** (1992) 2170(E).

[6] Y. Fukuda et al., accepted by Phys. Lett., ICRR-Report-321-94-16; N. Sato et al., Phys. Rev. **D44** (1991) 2220

[7] M. Honda et al., Phys. Lett. **B248** (1990) 193;M. Honda, private communication.

[8] G. Barr, T.K. Gaisser and T. Stanev, Phys. Rev. **D39** (1989) 3532.

[9] L.V. Volkova, Sov. J. Nucl. Phys. **31** (1980) 784.

Paper presented at XXVII Int. Conf. on High Energy Physics: Session Pa-13
Glasgow, UK, 20–27 July 1994

Semi-Empirical Bounds on Solar Neutrino Experiments

Waikwok Kwong and S. P. Rosen

Department of Physics, University of Texas at Arlington
Arlington, Texas 76019-0059

Abstract

The Kamiokande measurement of ^{8}B neutrinos is used to set a lower bound on the contribution to the ^{37}Cl and ^{71}Ga experiments. Implications for ^{7}Be neutrinos are discussed.

Energetic ^{8}B neutrinos from the sun have been detected in the Kamiokande experiment [1] at about one half the rate predicted by the Standard Solar Model (SSM) [2]. These neutrinos also interact with the ^{37}Cl and ^{71}Ga detectors so it is necessary to understand their contribution to these signals. By comparing this contribution to the total signal, we can extract information about other parts of the solar neutrino spectrum, especially ^{7}Be.

Even allowing for neutrino flavor oscillations, the Kamiokande experiment imposes a bound on the ^{37}Cl signal [3] that does not leave much room for a significant contribution from ^{7}Be neutrinos. This is not inconsistent with the latest results from the ^{71}Ga experiments [4, 5], and so we refine the solar neutrino problem to be: Where have all the ^{7}Be neutrinos gone?

The basic physical processes in the Kamiokande and in the ^{37}Cl and ^{71}Ga experiments are different, the former being neutrino–electron scattering, with cross section $\sigma(\nu_e e; E_\nu)$, and the latter being neutrino capture on nuclei, with cross sections $\sigma(^{37}\text{Cl}; E_\nu)$ and $\sigma(^{71}\text{Ga}; E_\nu)$. Therefore we must use a semi-empirical method to relate them to one another. The calculated signal involves the convolution over $\phi(E_\nu)$, the SSM spectrum of ^{8}B neutrinos with energy E_ν, and the experimental cross section σ. We plot in Fig. 1 the normalized shapes of the various $\phi\sigma$ as functions of E_ν.

The normalized functions for Kamiokande and ^{37}Cl are remarkably similar to one another. This is due to the high detection threshold and finite energy resolution for Kamiokande. We therefore write

$$\frac{\phi\sigma(^{37}\text{Cl}; E_\nu)}{\int \phi\sigma(^{37}\text{Cl}; E_\nu)dE_\nu} = \alpha \frac{\phi\sigma(\nu_e e; E_\nu)}{\int \phi\sigma(\nu_e e; E_\nu)dE_\nu} + r(E_\nu),$$

$$(1)$$

where α is a constant maximized so that the remainder function $r(E_\nu)$ is everywhere positive. The largest value of α is 0.93, and so we obtain

$$\phi\sigma(^{37}\text{Cl}; E_\nu) \geq 0.93 \frac{R_{\text{SSM}}(^8\text{B}; ^{37}\text{Cl})}{R_{\text{SSM}}(\text{Kam})} \phi\sigma(\nu_e e; E_\nu), \quad (2)$$

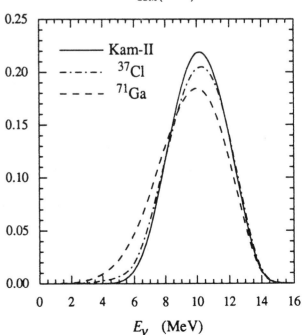

Figure 1. Normalized shapes $\phi\sigma/\int \phi\sigma \, dE_\nu$.

where $R_{SSM}(^8B; ^{37}Cl)$ is the contribution of ^8B neutrinos to the SSM signal in the ^{37}Cl experiment.

The actual quantity measured in these experiments involves the product of $\phi\sigma$ with an electron-neutrino "survival probability" $P(E_\nu)$ which, in general, may be a function of the neutrino energy E_ν. If $P(E_\nu)$ represents a reduction of the ^8B spectrum, or an oscillation into a sterile neutrino, then we find

$$\int \phi\sigma(^{37}Cl; E_\nu)P(E_\nu)\,dE_\nu$$
$$\geq 0.93 \frac{\int \phi\sigma(\nu_e e; E_\nu)P(E_\nu)\,dE_\nu}{R_{SSM}(Kam)} R_{SSM}(^8B; ^{37}Cl) \quad (3)$$

or

$$R(^8B; ^{37}Cl) \geq 0.93\,(0.51 \pm 0.07)\,(6.2\ SNU)$$
$$= (2.94 \pm 0.40)\ SNU\ , \quad (4)$$

where we have used the most recent result from the Kamiokande experiment [1]. This is barely consistent with the twenty-year average of the Davis value [3] $\langle R_{Davis}\rangle = 2.55 \pm 0.30$ SNU. Note that the bound in (4) also holds in the simple case of a reduction of the total ^8B flux with no change in the spectral shape.

Now, consider the case of oscillations of solar ν_e into ν_μ or ν_τ. The signal observed in Kamiokande is then

$$R(Kam)$$
$$= \int \left[\phi\sigma(\nu_e e; E_\nu)P(E_\nu) + [1 - P(E_\nu)]\,\phi\sigma(\nu_\mu e; E_\nu)\right]dE_\nu$$
$$= \int \phi\sigma(\nu_e e; E_\nu)[0.852\,P(E_\nu) + 0.148]\,dE_\nu \quad (5)$$

where we have put $\sigma(\nu_\mu e; E_\nu) = 0.148\,\sigma(\nu_e e; E_\nu)$, an extremely good approximation in this energy range. We can now write in the case of flavor oscillations

$$R(^8B; ^{37}Cl)$$
$$\geq 0.93 \frac{\int \phi\sigma(\nu_e e; E_\nu)P(E_\nu)\,dE_\nu}{R_{SSM}(Kam)} R_{SSM}(^8B; ^{37}Cl)$$
$$= 0.93 \frac{(0.51 \pm 0.07) - 0.148}{0.852}(6.2\ SNU)$$
$$= (2.45 \pm 0.47)\ SNU\ . \quad (6)$$

When compared with the Davis result, our bounds on the energetic ^8B neutrino contribution in (4) and (6) do not leave much room for the 1.8 SNU coming from all other sources, or the 1.1 SNU from ^7Be neutrinos alone. Indeed, the contribution X from all other sources is given in the two cases we have considered by

$$R(X, ^{37}Cl) \leq \begin{cases} -0.39 \pm 0.50\ SNU & (\text{no osc.}) \\ +0.10 \pm 0.56\ SNU & (\text{with osc.}) \end{cases} \quad (7)$$

The 95% confidence limits are 0.43 SNU (no osc.) and 1.02 SNU (with osc.) Assuming that the ^7Be contribution is approximately 1.2/1.8, or 2/3 of this, we

find $R(^7Be, ^{37}Cl) < 0.29$ SNU (no osc.) and < 0.68 SNU (with osc.) This result is consistent with the prediction of the nonadiabatic MSW solution [6, 7, 8]. If we had used another SSM, e.g., that of [9], which gives a smaller ^8B flux, the bound of (4) would remain unchanged while that of (6) would actually increase, giving an even more stringent bound on the remaining sources.

For the ^{71}Ga experiments we obtain an inequality similar to (2) but with $\alpha = 0.81$:

$$R(^8B, ^{71}Ga) \geq \begin{cases} 5.7 \pm 0.8\ SNU, & (\text{no osc.}) \\ 4.7 \pm 0.9\ SNU, & (\text{with osc.}) \end{cases} \quad (8)$$

Comparing with the combined result of 77 ± 10 SNU from the two gallium experiments [4, 5], we find that the sum of the signals from pp neutrinos, ^7Be neutrinos, and other non-^8B sources (X) is very close to the SSM prediction of 71 SNU for pp neutrinos alone: $R(X, ^{71}Ga) \leq 72 \pm 10$ SNU (no osc.) and $\leq 73 \pm 10$ SNU (with osc.)

Scaling up the ^7Be bounds from ^{37}Cl by the ratio of the capture cross sections on ^{71}Ga and ^{37}Cl, we find the maximum contribution of the ^7Be neutrino to the ^{71}Ga signals to be < 9.7 SNU (no osc.) and < 20.3 SNU (with osci.). If the pp neutrinos are present in full SSM strength, the ^7Be signal must be very much less than these bounds. On the other hand if the ^7Be signal is close to the maximum allowable value, the pp neutrinos must be reduced to about 65% of the SSM prediction. It will be interesting to test these bounds by direct observation of the ^7Be, or pp neutrinos themselves [10].

This work was supported in part by the U. S. Department of Energy grant DE-FG05-92ER40691.

References

[1] See M. Nakahata, Pa-13b, these proceedings.

[2] J. N. Bahcall and M. Pinsonneault, Rev. Mod. Phys. **64**, 885 (1992); J. N. Bahcall, *Neutrino Astrophysics* (Cambridge University Press, New York, 1993).

[3] K. Lande *et al.*, in Proc. of the 16th Int. Conf. on Neutrino Physics and Astrophysics, Eilat, Isreal, May 29–June 2, 1994.

[4] GALLEX Collab., P. Anselmann *et al.*, Phys. Lett. B **327**, 377 (1994).

[5] SAGE Collab., J. N. Abdurashitov *et al.*, Phys. Lett. B **328**, 234 (1994).

[6] V. Barger, R. J. N. Phillips, and K. Whisnant, Phys. Rev. D **43**, 1110 (1991); X. Shi *et al.*, Phys. Rev. D, Aug. 15, 1994.

[7] H. A. Bethe and J. N. Bahcall, Phys. Rev. D **44**, 2962 (1991).

[8] For recent discussions of MSW solutions, see S. Bludman, N. Hata, D. Kennedy, and P. Langacker, Phys. Rev. D **47**, 2220 (1993); N. Hata and P Langacker, University of Pennsylvania Preprint No. UPR-0592T (Nov. 1993); P. I. Krastev and S. Petcov, Phys. Lett. B **299**, 99 (1993); and L. Krauss, E. Gates, and M. White, Phys. Rev. Lett. **70**, 375 (1993).

[9] Turck-Chièze and I. Lopes, Astrophys. J. **408**, 347 (1993); Turck-Chièze *et al.*, Phys. Rep. **203**, 57 (1993).

[10] See, *e.g.*, Borexino Collab., G. Ranucci, Nucl. Phys. B (Proc. Suppl.) **32**, 149 (1993); and S. R. Bandler *et al.*, Phys. Rev. Lett. **68**, 2429 (1993).

Paper presented at XXVII Int. Conf. on High Energy Physics: Session Pa-13
Glasgow, UK, 20–27 July 1994

Lithium Iodide for solar neutrino detection

C.Y. Chang[†], F.T. Avignone[‡], C.C. Chang[†], G. Gollins[†], G. Giacomelli[||], D.M. Mustillo[†],
J.R. Swider[†] and W.B. Walters[†]

† The university of Maryland, USA
‡ The university of South Carolina, USA
|| University of Bologna, Italy

Abstract

The energy resolution of LiI(Eu) is measured to be 6 % for ^{60}Co 1.17 and 1.33 MeV γ rays. This excellent energy resolution coupled with its low E_{det-th} and favourable nuclear and physical-chemical properties makes LiI(Eu) a unique and desirable medium for solar ν detection.

1. The Solar Neutrino Problem

New results[1] on the measured solar neutrino flux from **SAGE, GALLEX** and **Kamiokande** are all converging to about one-half the rates predicted by the standard solar model of Bahcall and Pinsonneault(SSM)[2]. The discrepancy between experimental observation and the prediction of the SSM lies typically between 3 to 4 σ in significance, which makes the Cl-Ar result[3], with .29 the rate of SSM and a 6 σ significance, outstanding. Since the same ^8B neutrinos must have interacted with both ^{37}Cl and Kamiokande, Kwong and Rosen argued the consistency between the two experiments as if there is no ^7Be neutrino at all. As they put it: "Where have all the ^7Be neutrinos gone?"[4].

2. LiI(Eu) For Solar Neutrino Detection

In a previous communication[5], we have arqued that europium activated lithium iodide (LiI(Eu)) is of most unique and suitable for real time solar neutrino detection, because it has the following favourable chemical-physical proporties and nuclear structures.

2.1. Simple Isotopic Abundance

Natual lithium has an isotopic abundance of $(7.5\pm0.2)\%$ vs 92.5% in ^6Li and ^7Li. Iodine is 100% in ^{127}I. Simple isotopic abundance enhances the effectiveness of the

material as a solar neutrino target. LiI(Eu) is a material in which all elements, nuclei and electrons, are targets for solar neutrinos.

2.2. Large Number of SNU's

Superallowed nuclear transitions available in ^7Li and ^{127}I nuclei provide sensitivity for a large number of Solar Neutrino Units($SNU^\dagger$). Neutrinos can be detected by measuring the recoil e^-'s in $^7Li(\nu_e, e^-)^7Be$ and $^{127}I(\nu_e, e^-)^{127}Xe$ via CC interactions, and/or the characteristic γ rays from de-excitation of the target nuclei in $^7Li(\nu_x, \nu_x)^7Li^*$ and $^{127}I(\nu_x, \nu_x)^{127}I^*$ via NC interactions. The NC reaction allows a determination of the total flux and the solar ν_x energy spectrum independent of its type. With the threshold energies of 0.862, .789, .478 and 0.05 MeV for the four reactions listed above respectively, one would expect 51.8, 30 (or 130?), and 10 SNUs for the first three reactions, and a large number of SNUs for the fourth reaction from pp neutrinos where no theoretical calculation can be found in literature. As shown in Fig. 1, solar neutrinos can also be detected via $e^-(\nu_e, \nu'_e)e'^-$ scattering with $T_{\nu_e} \geq E_{det-th}$, where T_{ν_e} is the kinetic energy of the recoil electron, and E_{det-th} is the detector energy threshold. For $E_{det-th} = 100$ keV, more than 3000 SNUs are expected for the electrons in LiI(Eu). In this estimation, pure ν_e is assumed and that the effects of atomic binding of the electrons and of radiative and electroweak corrections are neglected.

† A SNU is defined as 10^{-36} events per target atom per sec.

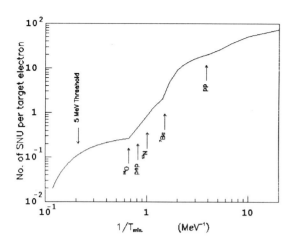

Figure 1. Fig. 1 Solar neutrino event rate expected from $e^-(\nu_e, \nu_e')e'^-$ scattering with $T_{\nu_e} \geq T_{min}$

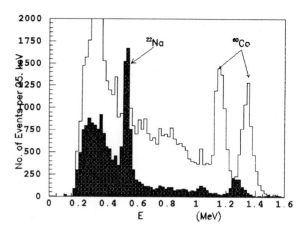

Figure 2. Fig. 2 LiI(Eu) energy calibrations with ^{60}Co and ^{22}Na sources.

2.3. *Energy Resolution and E_{det-th} of LiI(Eu)*

The energy resolution and E_{det-th} of LiI(Eu) has been systematically studied at Maryland. Figure 2 shows typical energy spectra from LiI(Eu) exposed to ^{60}Co and ^{22}Na sources. The 1.17 and 1.33 MeV ^{60}Co peaks (open histogram) are well resolved. The energy resolution, σ_E/E, is measured to be 6 % for the observed γ rays. The 0.511 MeV peak from the e^+e^- annihilation with the ^{22}Na source(the dark histogram) clearly distinguishs itself from its Compton background. We observed (not shown in the figure) that the E_{det-th} of LiI(Eu) is below the electronic noise of 50 keV with the current setup. This is very important, because νe^- scattering plays an important role in determining the the total fluxes of the pp and ^7Be neutrinos, which are considered as the central issue of the solar neutrino problem. For the non-radiochemical experiments with $E_{det-th} \geq 50 keV$, 42.4 of the 69.0 SNU's per target electron from pp neutrinos and similarly 23.5 of the 25.9 from the ^7Be neutrinos can be detected. On the other hand, for instance, with 250 keV detection threshold, only 0.01 of 69.0 SNU's per target electron from pp and 14.8 of 25.9 from ^7Be can be detected(see Figure 2).

2.4. *Self Monitoring*

With a ^6Li enriched LiI(Eu) detector, the characteristic 4 MeV neutron induced peak from the $^6Li(n,\alpha)t$ reaction can be used to monitor and calibrate the background or cosmic muon induced neutrons.

3. Impurities Studies

To investigate the radioactivies contributed by the environment and from the impurities inside the detector, we have measured the radioactivity of an 8" PMT of Sudbury design. The measurement was carried out in the low-background counting facility at the Reactor Laboratory at the National Institute of Standards and Technology[6]. Gamma-ray peaks origininating from the decay of ^{40}K, as well as ^{214}Bi and ^{208}Tl from actinide decay chains were observed. As anticipated, ^{40}K is the most prominent radioactive impurity in the PMT's. Our study shows ^{40}K activity to be an order of magnitude above background, increasing from 4.87×10^{-4} to 3.28×10^{-3} counts/sec in background counting in the counting facility when the SNO PMT is introduced. Similar studies with LiI(Eu) and NaI(Tl) crystals are in progress.

4. Summary

With excellent energy resolution coupled with low E_{det-th} and favourable nuclear and physical-chemical properties, we have demonstrated that LiI(Eu) is potentially a powerful, unique and desirable medium for solar ν detection.

References

[1] SAGE Collaboration: J.N. Abdurashitov *et al.*, Phys. Lett. **B328** (1994) 234;
GALLEX Collaboration: P. Anselmann *et al.*, Phys. Lett. **B328** (1994) 377;
Kamiokande Collaboration: K. Hirata *et al.*, Phys. Rev. **D44** (1991) 2241; see also, M. Nakahata, these proceedings.

[2] J.N. Bachall and P. Pinsonneault, Rev. Mod. Phys. **64** (1992) 885.

[3] R. Davies, Proc. of Workshop on Neutrino Telescopes (Venice 1994), p.47.

[4] W. Kwong and S.P. Rosen, Phys. Rev. Lett. **73** (1994) 369.

[5] C.C. Chang, C.Y. Chang and G. Gollin, Nucl. Phys. **B35** (1994) 464.

[6] R.M. Lindstrom *et al.*, Nucl. Instr. Meth. **299A** (1990) 425.

The Counting Test Facility of the Borexino experiment

G. Bellini and M. G. Giammarchi*

Dipartimento di Fisica dell'Università and Isituto Nazionale di Fisica Nucleare, Milano (Italy)

On behalf of the Borexino Collaboration[1]

Abstract

The first phase of the Borexino experiment is a low background Counting Test Facility (CTF) set up in the LNGS hall C. The purpose of this detector is the ultrahigh sensitivity measurement of residual U,Th,^{14}C,Be contamination from construction and shielding materials, surfaces, and the scintillator for Borexino. The detector is designed for reaching and measuring a purity of 10^{-16} g/g ^{238}U equivalent in the scintillator, which is the level required in Borexino.

1. Introduction

The main motivation of the Borexino experiment is the study of Solar Neutrino Physics. The longstanding *Solar Neutrino Problem* consists in the discrepancy of the neutrino fluxes predicted by the Standard Solar Model (SSM) [2,3,4] with respect to the ν fluxes measured by the Homestake[5], Kamiokande[6], GALLEX[7] and SAGE[8] experiments.

A general analysis of possible astrophysical solutions of the Solar Neutrino Problem has been done using the combined results of the experiments and the solar luminosity constraint[9,10,11]. This essentially model independent analysis favors the combination $\phi(Be) = 0$, $\phi(B) \simeq 0.37\phi_{SSM}(B)$ (see fig. 1 from ref. [10]), which is physically implausible since the generation of a ^{8}B ν flux from the Sun derives from the $^7Be + p \rightarrow^8 B + \gamma$ reaction.

While this result is incompatible with the SSM, it is difficult to explain even in the context of non-standard astrophysical models of the Sun (low Z, WIMP, low opacity, large S$_{11}$,...) because these models will decrease the ^{8}B neutrino flux more than the ^{7}Be ν flux, due to the structure of the energy generating reactions in the Sun (fig. 1). It is therefore concluded that an astrophysical solution is disfavoured by experiments provided that the

* Presented by M.G. Giammarchi.

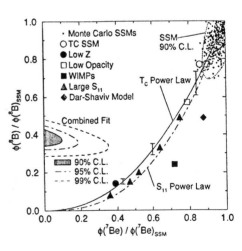

Figure 1. $\phi(Be) - \phi(B)$ plot from [10] which shows the regions allowed by the combined fit to the experiments at different C.L. together with predictions from the Standard Solar Model and a variety of non-standard Solar Model.

$\nu_e +^{37} Cl \rightarrow^{37} Ar + e^-$ cross section is not overestimated and systematic effects in Kamiokande and Homestake are well understood[11].

It is clear the importance of a direct measurement of the ^{7}Be neutrino flux from the Sun, which is the main goal of Borexino.

2. Borexino

Borexino is a Ultrahigh Purity Real Time detector for low energy neutrino spectroscopy[12]. It is an unsegmented scintillation counter consisting of ~300 tons of liquid organic scintillator *viewed* by 1700 photomultipliers and surrounded by an Aromatic Liquid/Water shielding. The detector features a stainless steel cylinder (17 *m* diameter, 17 *m* high) filled with water. Inside the tank another steel sphere supports the photomultipliers and contains an Aromatic Liquid buffer in which a nylon-made transparent Inner Vessel will be located. The Inner Vessel has a radius of 4.25 *m* and contains 300 tons of ultrapure scintillator.

This conceptual design features spherical shells of increasing purity and defines a central (≥100 tons) Fiducial Volume in which any background is negligible compared with the contamination of the scintillator itself. The detector gives the calorimetric measurement of the energy released and the position in space for each event. The estimated scintillator radiopurity of $10^{-15}/10^{-16}$ g^{238}U/g allows a design analysis threshold of 250 keV which makes the detector real-time sensitive to ^{7}Be neutrinos.

The main experimental goal of the experiment can be summarized as follows:

- The observation of the monoenergetic electron neutrinos from the ^{7}Be decay in the Sun (E=0.86 MeV) through the elastic scattering reaction $\nu_e e^- \rightarrow \nu_e e^-$. The threshold allows to observe this reaction at the 18000 SSM events/year level.
- The study of temporal variations of the ^{7}Be signal to study possible day/night effects and to detect seasonal variations related to the Sun origin and/or possible vacuum oscillations.
- The study of the ^{8}B solar neutrinos spectral shape.
- Appearance studies of $\bar{\nu}$'s from the Sun.
- $\bar{\nu}_e e^-$ scattering with a laboratory source.

3. The Counting Test Facility

The CTF[13] is a smaller scale Borexino-like detector which features a 4 ton liquid scintillator sphere immersed in 1000 tons of pure water and viewed by 100 photomultipliers suspended on a steel support structure (fig. 2). The external tank is in coated carbon steel, while the support structure is in stainless steel and the scintillator container is a 0.5 *mm* thick nylon membrane vessel (Inner Vessel).

Water is kept at a purity of 10^{-13} g^{238}U/g by a Water Purification system, while a Scintillator purity of 10^{-16} g^{238}U/g will be reached by a variety of continuous processes (mainly water extraction, distillation and gas stripping). The high purity of the materials together with the performance in timing (few *nsec*), space and

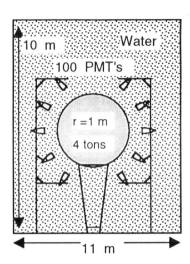

Figure 2. Conceptual design of the Counting Test Facility.

energy resolution of the system ($\sigma_E/E = 30\%$ at 100 keV) will allow the study of residual backgrounds both spectroscopically (as is the case for ^{14}C and ^{7,10}Be isotopes) and through the delayed coincidences method (for U,Th contamination, for which the predicted sensitivity is $\sim 10^{-16}$ g/g).

The CTF will be one of the facilities with lowest background in the world; the total background estimate in a 1 ton Fiducial Volume is of ~100 counts/day in the ≥250 kev energy range.

References

[1] Borexino Author List: G. Alimonti, C. Arpesella, M. Balata, G. Bellini, J. Benziger, S. Bonetti, F.P. Calaprice, M. Campanella, G. Cecchet, A. de Bari, M. Deutsch, F. Elisei, F. von Feilitzsch, M. G. Giammarchi, D. Giugni, T. Goldbrunner, A. Golubchikov, G. Heusser, M. Laubenstein, S. Magni, I. Manno, F. Masetti, U. Mazzucato, E. Meroni, L. Oberauer, G. Mantovani, G. Manuzio, A. Perotti, A. Preda, P. Raghavan, R.S. Raghavan, G. Ranucci, R. Scardaoni, S. Schönert, O. Smirnov, R. Tartaglia, G. Testera, S. Vitale, B. Vogelaar, O. Zaimidoroga.

[2] J.N. Bahcall, Neutrino Astrophysics, (Cambridge University Press, Cambridge, 1989).

[3] S. Turck-Chieze, W. Däppen, E. Fossat, J. Provost, E. Schatzmann, D. Vignaud, Phys. Rep. 230 (1993) 57.

[4] J.N. Bahcall, M. Pinsonneault, Rev. Mod. Phys. 64 (1992) 885.

[5] R. Davis, VI° Neutrino Telescopes Conf., Venice,1994.

[6] A. Suzuki, VI° Neutrino Telescopes Conf., Venice, 1994.

[7] P. Anselmann et al. Phys. Lett. B, 327 (1994) 377.

[8] V.N. Gavrin, VI° Neutrino Telescopes Conf., Venice, 1994.

[9] V. Castellani, S. Degl'Innocenti, G. Fiorentini, Astron. and Astrophys., 271 (1993) 601.

[10] S. Bludman, N. Hata, P. Langacker, UPR-0572T preprint, 1993.

[11] V. Berezinsky, VI° Neutrino Telescopes Conf., Venice, 1994.

[12] C. Arpesella et al., Borexino proposal, (ed. G. Bellini et al.), University of Milano, 1991.

[13] M.G. Giammarchi, VI° Neutrino Telescopes Conf., Venice, 1994.

Paper presented at XXVII Int. Conf. on High Energy Physics: Session Pa-13
Glasgow, UK, 20–27 July 1994

The steady vanishing of the three solar neutrino problems

Douglas R.O. Morrison

CERN, Geneva 23, Switzerland

Abstract

Three problems have been claimed for solar neutrinos. Firstly it has been said for over 20 years, that the flux of high energy neutrinos was substantially less than that predicted from solar evolutionary models. Secondly it was claimed that there were violent fluctuations in the high energy neutrino flux and that their periodicity was close to that of the sunspot cycle. Thirdly, recently evidence was presented that low energy neutrinos may also have a flux deficit. The second problem is shown to be in disagreement with more recent experimental results after 1986. The other two problems of flux are shown to be vanishing with time. This is not from a single cause but from a series of improvements of the input data to the models, to a better appreciation of the errors which had sometimes been significantly under-estimated, and also some of the experimental values have increased with time indicating a learning curve for some of these very difficult experiments with very low statistics. Finally it is concluded that the evidence for any solar neutrino problem is "not compelling".

1. Introduction

Four experiments have made measurements of solar neutrinos. Three are radio-chemical where the neutrinos give a (ν,e) interaction producing a radioactive element whose decay is observed. Since 1967 Davis et al. have measured decays of ^{37}Ar produced from the ^{37}Cl isotope in 615 tons of carbon tertrachloride. The conversion of ^{71}Ga to ^{71}Ge has been studied since 1990 by the SAGE Collaboration and since 1991 by the GALLEX collaboration. Since 1987 the Kamiokande group have studied Cerenkov radiation produced by neutrino interactions in a 3000 ton water detector.

These results have been compared with calculations of neutrino flux based on models which follow the evolution of the Sun from its beginning as a star 4.5 Gyears ago until the present where they are required to match contemporary values of the Sun's luminosity, radius and mass.

To see if there is a significant discrepancy between the experimental results and the model calculations, it is essential to study the assumptions and the input

data to the calculations. It will be shown that the errors chosen have unfortunately been unreasonably small which tends to make small discrepancies appear significant. In a series of papers [1] since 1990, it has been shown that the evidence for any discrepancy is "not compelling".

The complete version of this paper is available as a CERN preprint [2].

2. Solar evolutionary model

The model sometimes called the standard solar model, SSM, is an evolutionary one and takes a series of shells of different radii and follows them from the Sun's start 4.5 Gyr ago to the present. An essential input is the composition of the Sun 4.5 Gyr ago - in general this is in agreement with selected meteorites believed to have the same age except that it is too low by a factor of a hundred for ^{7}Li abundance and by a factor of two for ^{9}Be [1].

There are many assumptions and pieces of input data to the model - here we will consider only the most crucial ones. The high energy neutrinos measured by Kamiokande and mainly (80%) by the Chlorine experiment, come from Boron-8 decay, hence the cross section for the reaction $^7Be(p.\gamma)^8B$ which produces ^8B is crucial. An essential point is that the reaction $^7Be(p,\gamma)^8B$ is not measured at the energy range of about 1 to 10 keV which is important in the Sun, but at much higher energies. The lowest energy measured is 117 keV where the cross section is only 3 nb and falling very quickly because of the barrier penetration factor. This makes extrapolation difficult, so the astrophysical S-factor is used which separates off most of the barrier penetration effect and leaves nuclear effects, which it is hoped vary slowly at these very low energies. For this reaction, it is called S_{17}. The values measured for S_{17} have varied wildly and at present the only good direct measurement of S_{17} is by Filippone et al. [3] which gave an extrapolated value of about 20 keV-b which is lower than the value of 22.4 keV-b taken by Bahcall and Pinsonneault [4] and by Turck-Chieze and Lopez [5]. Recently Motobayashi et al. [6] measured Coulomb dissociation in the inverse reaction, $^8B(\gamma,p)^7Be$ and found values of S_{17} which were 20 to 30% lower than 22.4 keV-b. An additional problem of how to extrapolate from the measured region down to the astrophysical region was described by Rusager and Jensen [7]. They pointed out that neutron-rich nuclei have been found to have a neutron halo, and since ^8B is proton-rich (5 p and 3 n), it should correspondingly have a proton halo. This is important since while the radius of ^8B is normally taken to be about 2.5 fm, the solar interactions take place at a radius of about 40 to 50 fm. They concluded that the extrapolated S_{17} value from Filippone et al. should be reduced to 12 to 17 keV-b. Summarizing, the value of S_{17} used should be reduced by at least 25%, probably more, and the error on S_{17} must be large. Dar and Shaviv [8] have shown that the S_{34} value for the production of ^7Be in the reaction $^3He(^4He,\gamma)^7Be$, should also be lowered and this would decrease the flux of ^8B neutrinos further.

While the flux of neutrinos from most reactions in the Sun is a smooth function of energy, the cross section for the reaction $^{37}Cl(\nu,e)^{37}Ar$ reaction is not smooth as it depends on the energy levels of of the ^{37}Ar nucleus. Fortunately the energy levels of the isobaric analogue states, ^{37}K and ^{37}Ca are known [9] so that the calculation has little error. Unfortunately since ^{71}Ge is neutron-rich, the isobaric analogue nucleus does not exist so that the energy levels are poorly known and the cross section for the reaction $^{71}Ga(\nu,e)^{71}Ge$ cannot be as safely calculated. This means that rates calculated for gallium experiment could easilyhave much larger errors of tens of percent.

3. Choice of reference solar evolutionary model

The errors chosen by Bahcall et al. [4] are abnormally small - one of the main reasons being the use of a 'rule of thumb' [10] that for unknown theoretical (systematic) errors, the variation with time is taken - but if the same assumption is always taken, the time variation falls to zero! For ^8B neutrinos the errors of greater than 25% given by Turck-Chieze and Lopez [5] are preferable. For the gallium experiments, Refs. [4] and [5] quote about 6% but due to the lack of knowledge of the ^{71}Ge energy levels, this is probably appreciably too small. Hence here for the Chlorine and Kamiokande experiments, the values of Ref. [5] are taken but lowered by 25% to take into account the new Riken measurement (apart the problem of proton-rich ^8B).

Recently Kovetz and Shaviv [11] have made a new solar model calculation which appears to have advantages over previous calculations. Dar and Shaviv [8] used these calculations and added some recent data to show that Standard Solar Models are consistent with the safest experimental measurements.

4. Experimental results

It was claimed that there were significant fluctuations (five standard deviations) of the neutrino flux measured in the Chlorine experiment which correlated with the inverse of the sunspot activity. This periodicity of some ten years appeared to be in contradiction with the typical time for diffusion from the core of the sun to its surface of ten million years.

It was said that the rates at the solar minimum of solar cycles 21 and 22 were 4.1 ± 0.9 and 4.2 ± 0.7 SNU while at the solar maxima, they were 0.4 ± 0.2 and 1.2 ± 0.6 SNU. The value of 0.4 ± 0.2 SNU for the runs 61 to 66, that is, a years running, is surprisingly low - it can be compared to the average value from 1970 to 1992, [12] of 2.55 ± 0.25 SNU and it can be seen that the difference of 2.15 ± 0.30 is a seven standard deviation effect for this year alone.

It should also be noted that after two years running, the Chlorine experiment was reported [12] to have an upper limit of one SNU - again this seems in contradiction with 2.55 ± 0.25 SNU.

Now the Kamiokande experiment has been measuring since 1986 and finds no evidence of any significant variation of flux, not with the solar cycle nor on any other time scale. Also since the 1984-86 shutdown, the Chlorine experiment has not shown evidence for the dramatic variations found before the shutdown. It is concluded that the most likely explanation is that there were some learning problems with the very difficult pioneeering Chlorine experiment but that their data since

1986 which find no variation, are correct.

For Chlorine, the reference model of Turck-Chieze and Lopez [5] reduced by 25% for S_{17}, is 4.8 ± 1.1 SNU which is to be compared with the experimental value for runs since 1986, of 2.9 ± 0.3 SNU - the difference of 1.9 ± 1.1 SNU is less than a two standard deviation effect.

The recent result from Kamiokande for 1670 days running, gives a neutrino flux of $(2.89 + 0.22 - 0.21 \pm 0.35) \cdot 10^6$ cm^2/s. The Turck-Chieze and Lopez [5] value, reduced by 25% for S_{17}, is $(3.3 \pm 0.8) \cdot 10^6$ cm^2/s which is an agreement to half a standard deviation, so the Kamiokande result can be considered to be consistent with the model.

It may be concluded that there is no compelling evidence of a problem with the flux rate of high energy neutrinos.

With its low threshold, the gallium experiments dominantly measure low energy neutrinos, in particular from the pp reaction. The first result from SAGE on their 5 selected 1990 runs, gave a very low rate which was published as 20 SNU with an upper limit of 72 SNU (since re-evaluted as $(40 + 31 - 38)$. However their runs in 1991, 1992 and 1993 gave $(100+31-38)$, $(62+29-27)$ and $(76 + 21 - 19)$SNU resp. [13] and these are in good agreement with the GALLEX value of $(79 \pm 10 \pm 6)$ SNU [14]. These values are some three standard deviations lower than theoretical values of 132 [4], 122.5 [5], and 113 [8] SNU with errors of about 6 to 7%. This could be considered a possible problem but as discussed above, the errors of the models are probably much larger since the cross sections for the ^{71}Ga$(\nu,e)^{71}$Ge reaction energy level by energy level are not well known since the isobaric analogues do not exist.

5. Conclusions

In general the solar evolutionary model works well but the errors on the neutrino fluxes and rates have often been seriously underestimated.

The suggestion that the neutrino flux may vary as the inverse of the sunspot activity appears excluded experimentally.

The neutrino fluxes measured by the four experiments are not compellingly different from the model predictions when all reasonable errors are included.

Better statistics and better energy resolution from future experiments would be welomed. Also better information on reaction cross sections is needed.

Acknowledgements

In addition to those acknowledged in Ref. [2], special thanks are due to P.G. Hansen and P. Van Duppen.

References

[1] a) D.R.O. Morrison, Int. Conf. on High Energy Phys., Singapore, Eds. K.K. Phua and Y. Yamaguchi (1990) 676-680;
b) Particle World **3** (1992) 30;
c) Int. J. of Mod. Phys. **D1** (1992);
d) CERN–PPE/93-196, and XXIII Int. Symp. on Multiparticle Dynamics, Aspen, Sept. 1993 and 3rd Nestor Workshop, Pylos, October 1993.

[2] D.R.O. Morrison, CERN preprint CERN–PPE/94-125, and to be publ. in Uzpekhi.

[3] B.W. Filippone et al., Phys. Rev. Lett. **50** (1983) 412, and Phys. Rev. **C28** (1983) 2222.

[4] J.N. Bahcall and M.H. Pinsonneault, Rev. Mod. Phys. **64** (1992) 885.

[5] S. Turck-Chieze and I. Lopez, Astrophys. J. **408** (1993) 347.

[6] T. Motobayashi, to be publ. Phys. Rev. Lett. (1994).

[7] K. Russager and A.S. Jensen. Aarhus preprint, IFA-93-1 (1993).

[8] A. Dar and G. Shaviv, subm. to Phys. Rev. Lett.

[9] A. Garcia et al., Phys. Rev. Lett. **67** (1991) 365.

[10] J.N. Bahcall, "Neutrino Astrophysics", CUP, 1989, page 172.

[11] A. Kovetz and G. Shaviv, Ap. J. to be publ, May 1994.

[12] K. Lande, report to Rochester Conf. on High Energy Physics, Glasgow, July 1994.

[13] SAGE, V.N. Gavrin, Neutrino '94 Conf. Eliat, May 1994.

[14] GALLEX, P. Anselmann et al. Phys. Lett. **B327** (1994) 377.

Parallel Session Pa-14

Flavour Production on Hadronic Targets

Conveners: M. Purohit (Princeton University)
              S. Dawson (BNL)

Scientific secretaries: M. Peardon
                         V. Jamieson (reserve)

Charmonium Production, b Quark and B Meson Production and $b\bar{b}$ Correlations at CDF

K. Byrum[†‡]

† Argonne National Laboratory, Argonne, Illinois 60439 USA

Abstract

We present results on charmonium production, b quark and B meson production and $B\bar{B}$ correlations using data taken with the CDF detector at Fermilab in $p\bar{p}$ collisions at $\sqrt{s} = 1.8$TEV during the 1992-93 collider run.

1. Introduction

Understanding the production processes of heavy quarks in high energy hadronic collisions is fundamental for testing the theory of perturbative QCD in the next to leading order (NLO) calculation. Calculations of the b quark and B meson production cross sections at NLO have been performed by many authors [1,2,3,4,5,6] and are predicted to have large uncertainties due to choices in the renormalization scale μ, the b quark mass and the partonic distribution functions. While earlier UA1 results [7,8] were at reasonable agreement with NLO QCD calculations at $\sqrt{s} = 630$GeV, the 1989 CDF results tended to be roughly a factor of two higher than the theoretical central values [9]. In this paper, we use the 1992-93 data to refine our earlier cross section measurements.

We begin with a discussion of the CDF detector components relevant for the results shown here and also briefly describe the triggers used to collect this data. We start our physics discussion with a description of the theory of charmonium production and present measurements of the inclusive J/ψ and $\psi(2s)$ differential cross sections. We next present differential B meson cross sections using fully reconstructed $B^{\pm} \to J/\psi K^{\pm}$ and $B^0 \to J/\psi K^{*0}$ events and partially reconstructed $\bar{B} \to D^0\mu^- X$ events. We next present the b quark cross section using some of the above channels along with the

inclusive $B \to \mu^- X$ channel. Finally, we conclude with results that study the correlated $b\bar{b}$ cross section as a function of the azimuthal angle between the b and $\bar{b}$. In this paper, reference to any particular state implies the charge conjugate state as well.

1.1. Detector Description

The CDF detector is described in detail elsewhere [10]. We describe here only those components relevant for the results presented. The CDF coordinate system defines the beam line to be the z direction. R is the radial distance from the beam line and ϕ is the azimuthal angle.

Two tracking systems inside a 1.4T solenoidal magnetic field provide the $R - \phi$ momentum analysis for charged particles. The Silicon Vertex Detector (SVX) [11] is a four layer silicon microstrip device with a radii ranging from 3 to 8cm and covering the luminous region of $|z| <$26cm. The hit resolution is 13 μm and the impact parameter resolution is $(13 + 40/p_T)\mu$m. The rms size of the beam spot is 35μm so that not all events at CDF have vertices within the fiducial volume of the SVX. The Central Tracking Chamber (CTC) [12] is an 84-layer cylindrical drift chamber with radii ranging from 309 to 1320cm and covers the pseudorapidity range of $|\eta| <$1.1. The momentum resolution for the CTC alone is $\Delta p_T/p_T$=.0066+.0014p_T and for the combined SVX-CTC system is $\Delta p_T/p_T$=.0066+.0009p_T

Outside the solenoid are the central electromagnetic

‡ E-mail: byrum@fnald.fnal.gov.

(CEM) and hadronic (CHA) calorimeters which provide five absorption lengths of material before the Central Muon Chambers (CMU). The CMU is a four-layer "limited streamer" chamber covering 85% of the azimuthal region for $|\eta| < 0.6$. Muons with p_T below ≈ 1.4 GeV/c range out in the calorimeters. Behind the CMU system are three absorption lengths of steel followed by the Central Muon Upgrade chambers (CMP). The CMP is a four-layer drift chamber covering 53% of the azimuthal region for $|\eta| < 0.6$. Both of these chambers reconstruct short tracks of up to four hits called "stubs".

1.2. Triggers

The CDF trigger [13] consists of three levels. For discussions in this paper, I will describe only the muon b triggers. In the first level of triggering (L1), we require one central muon stub with $p_T > 6$GeV/c for the inclusive muon trigger and two or more central muon stubs with $p_T > 3$GeV/c for the dimuon trigger. At the second level of triggering (L2), the Central Fast Tracker (CFT) [14] is run. The CFT is a hardware track finder with a transverse momentum resolution of $\Delta p_T / p_T^2 = 3.5\%$. The L2 tracks are matched to the muon L1 stubs to within $5°$. The inclusive muon events require CFT tracks with $p_T > 9.2$GeV/c. The dimuon events require one stub have a matching CFT track with $p_T > 3$GeV/c. The third level of triggering (L3) [15,16] consists of a 1000 MIP microprocessor farm from which the offline reconstruction software is run. The L3 thresholds for the muons are matched to their L2 values.

2. Charmonium Production

The theory of charmonium production in hadronic collisions has been studied within the perturbative QCD model for quite awhile [17,18,19,20,21,22]. At the energies of the Tevatron, the production of J/ψ and $\psi(2s)$ is expected to be dominated by the lowest order two to two subprocesses [6]. Direct charmonium production is described by the processes $gg, q\bar{q}, gq \rightarrow \chi g$ followed by the decay $\chi \rightarrow J/\psi, \gamma$ Production through the decay of a B meson is described by the processes $gg, q\bar{q} \rightarrow b\bar{b}$ and $gq \rightarrow b\bar{b}g$ followed by the decay $b \rightarrow \bar{B} \rightarrow J/\psi X$. Only at $O(\alpha^3)$ can the J/ψ and $\psi(2s)$ be produced directly due to spin parity conservation.

If one assumes this theoretical description, J/ψ production should be dominated by χ and B production while the $\psi(2s)$ production should be dominated by B production. More recently, it has been suggested that there exist a class of higher order processes which are less suppressed than the leading order ones at large p_T [23,24,25]. These higher order processes can contribute to charmonium production when a high p_T gluon or

charm quark fragments into charmonium states.

Studies of the charmonium production at CDF produce our lowest p_T b cross section measurements. In our earlier measurements [26], we relied on the theoretical assumption described above to measure f_b, the fraction of inclusive J/ψ and $\psi(2s)$ events from B decays. With the addition of the SVX, we are now able to measure secondary vertices and separate those J/ψ and $\psi(2s)$ events produced via prompt charmonium production from those events produced from B decays in a model independent way [27].

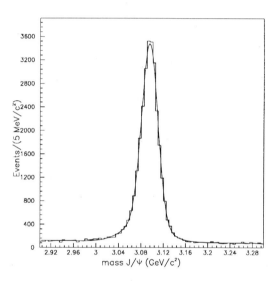

Figure 1. The J/ψ Invariant Mass distribution.

We reconstruct our J/ψ and $\psi(2s)$ events through the decay to muons and require the muons pass all three levels of trigger. We also require $p_T^{\psi,\psi(2s)} > 4$GeV/c and $|\eta^{\psi,\psi(2s)}| < .6$ and the invariant mass of the dimuon pair be within 50 MeV of the world $J/\psi, \psi(2s)$ average. Figure 1 shows the invariant mass distribution for the J/ψ events. Figure 2 shows the pseudo $c\tau$ lifetime distribution for the inclusive $\psi(2s)$ where $c\tau = L_{xy} * M_B / (p_T * F^c)$. L_{xy} is the projection of the decay length onto the $J/\psi, \psi(2s)$ transverse momentum and F^c is a Monte Carlo correction factor that relates the $J/\psi, \psi(2s)$ transverse momentum to the transverse momentum of the parent. Events in figure 2 are further required to have both muons be reconstructed as good quality SVX tracks. The B fraction is determined from a fit over this distribution.

Figure 3 shows the differential J/ψ cross section as a function of the $p_T(J/\psi)$ for $|\eta| < .6$ and $J/\psi \rightarrow$

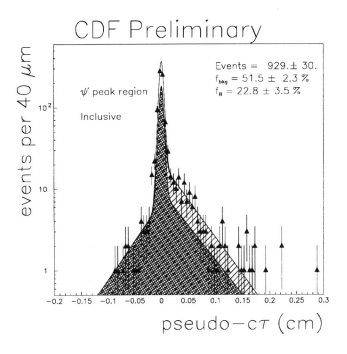

Figure 2. The $\psi(2s)$ Lifetime Pseudo $c\tau$ distribution. The dark region is the background shape and the slashed region is the B component, plus the background shape. The clear region shows an excess of prompt events.

$\mu\mu$. Three sets of data points are shown, the prompt component, the component from B decays and the total. The data points are each compared to theory curves. The excess over the predicted total cross section is primarily due to the prompt component. Even though the contribution from gluon fragmentation [23,24,25] has been included in the theory curves, the prompt theory still does not adequately describe the data.

The NLO theory curves [1] for the B component use MRSD0 structure functions with a renormalization scale of $\mu = \mu_0 = \sqrt{M_b^2 + p_T^2}$. The measured values are roughly a factor of two higher than the theoretical predictions. With a choice of the renormalization scale set to $\mu = \mu_0/4$, there is better agreement between the theory curves and the measured data. Motivations for choosing different renormalization scales is a separate topic of this conference [28].

The differential cross section for the $\psi(2s)$ is shown in Figure 4. Theoretical curves are shown for the prompt component and for the B component. The predicted prompt cross section is more than an order of magnitude lower than the observed data. The B production NLO theory [1] with the renormalization scale $\mu = \mu_0$ is again roughly a factor of two lower than the $\psi(2s)$ data points.

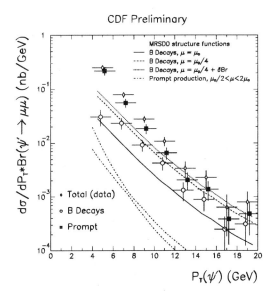

Figure 4. $d\sigma/dp_T(|\eta| < .6)J/\psi(2s) \to \mu\mu$ (nb/GeV).

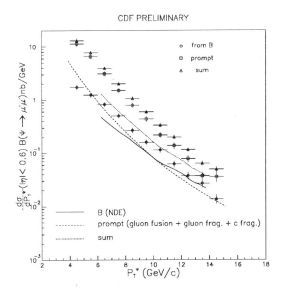

Figure 3. $d\sigma/dp_T(|\eta| < .6)J/\psi \to \mu\mu$ (nb/GeV).

The discrepancy between the data and the theory of prompt charmonium production is currently under study [29]. Higher order diagrams such as $gg \to J/\psi gg$ are being calculated and these contributions, for which the hard-scattering cross section has a p_T dependence, are expected to be intermediate between the LO and NLO corrections. Experimentally, CDF is in the midst of Run 1b and has already accumulated approximately $20pb^{-1}$ of new data. In the coming months, we plan to extend our measurements to the Υ system and should have differential cross sections for all three triplet S states by the end of the year. Additionally, we plan to search for excited χ states from which the $\psi(2s)$ could decay through the decay chain $\chi \rightarrow \psi(2s)\gamma$ by searching for the presence of an associated photon with the $\psi(2s)$.

3.   B Meson Production

We measure the differential $B^{\pm}$ and B^0 cross sections [30] as a function of the transverse momentum by fully reconstructing the B meson decays, $B^{\pm} \rightarrow J/\psi K^{\pm}$ and $B^0 \rightarrow J/\psi K^{*0}$, where the J/ψ is required to decay to two muons, and the K^{*0} is required to decay to $K^{\pm}\pi^{\mp}$. The reconstructed J/ψ is required to pass all three levels of the dimuon trigger and the invariant mass is required to be within 3σ of the J/ψ mass world average. SVX track information is used if available, otherwise CTC track information is used. Since kaons from $B^{\pm}$ decays have a harder p_T spectrum than particles from the underlying event, $p_T(K^{\pm,*0}) > 1.25$GeV/c. The B meson is required to have $p_T(B) > 6.$GeV/c. The invariant $K - \pi$ mass is required to be within 50MeV of the mass of the K^{*0} and only the combination closest to the world average K^{*0} mass of 896.1 MeV/c^2 is used to avoid double counting. A confidence level cut of $P(\chi^2) > .005$ is applied to the fit which constrains the decay tracks to come from a common vertex and requires the invariant dimuon mass to equal the J/ψ mass. There is also a cut on the proper decay length, $c\tau > 100\mu$m where $c\tau = L_{xy} * M_b/p_T$. This cut removes about 75% of the background while less than 20% of the signal is lost.

The $J/\psi K^{\pm}$ events are divided into 4 bins in p_T, 6-9,9-12,12-15 and >15 and the $J/\psi K^{*0}$ events are divided into 3 bins in p_T, 7-11,11-15 and >15. The choice of bin size leads to comparable statistical and systematic uncertainties. Only integrated cross-sections are determined for the last bins. Figure 5 shows the $B^{\pm}$ meson invariant mass distribution in the different bins of p_T.

We also measure the B cross section using the partially reconstructed decay $B \rightarrow \mu^- D^0 X$ where $D^0 \rightarrow K^- \pi^+$ and the decay $B \rightarrow \mu^- D^{*+} X$ where $D^{*+} \rightarrow D^0 \pi^+$ and $D^0 \rightarrow K^- \pi^+$ [31]. The muon is required to pass all three levels of trigger with $p_T > 7.6$GeV/c. For reconstructing the D mesons, charged tracks are assigned kaon and pion masses and the invariant $K^- \pi^+$ and $K^- \pi^+ \pi_b^+$ masses are computed for tracks satisfying $p_T^{K,\pi} > 1.5$GeV/c and $p_T^{K,\pi}$(Max)>3.0GeV/c. Events

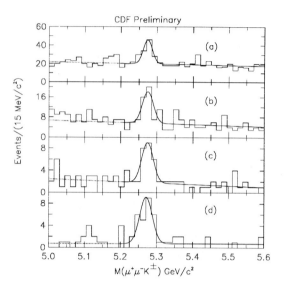

Figure 5. $B^{\pm}$ meson invariant mass distribution from the decay $B^{\pm} \rightarrow J/\psi K^{\pm}$ for the following momentum ranges: (a) 6-9 GeV/c, (b) 9-12 GeV/c, (c) 12-15 GeV/c, and (d) >15 GeV/c.

with $M(K\pi\pi) - M(K\pi) < 153$MeV are tagged as D^* candidates. For D^0 events, if the charge of the kaon matches the charge of the muon, the event is tagged as a "right-sign" combination, otherwise the event is tagged as a "wrong-sign" combination. For D^* events, "right-sign" combinations are those events where the sign of the π_b is opposite to the sign of the lepton and conversely for "wrong-sign" combinations. The invariant mass distribution of the "wrong-sign" combinations is used as a measure of the background. Figure 6 shows the invariant mass distribution for the "right-sign" and "wrong-sign" $K\pi$ combinations.

The differential cross section of the B meson is shown in Figure 7 compared to a NLO calculation [1] convoluted with Peterson fragmentation [32]. MRSD0 structure functions are used with $\mu = \mu_0 = \sqrt{M_b^2 + p_T^2}$. Not shown in this figure is a common systematic uncertainty due to the branching ratio of $\pm 24\%$ for the $J/\psi K^{*0}$ points and $\pm 15\%$ for the $J/\psi K^-$ points.

4.   b Quark Production

The b quark cross section is measured using the inclusive muon channel $B \rightarrow \mu X$ by determining F_b, the fraction of muons originating from B decays [33]. F_b is determined using the muon track impact parameter

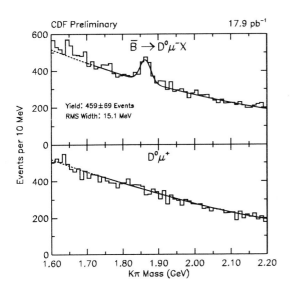

Figure 6. The invariant mass distribution for the decay D^0 from $B \to \mu D^0 X$ for a.) "right-sign" combinations and b.) "wrong-sign" $K\pi$ combinations.

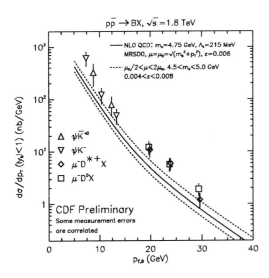

Figure 7. $d\sigma/dp_T(|\eta| < 1)(p\bar{p} \to BX)$. Not shown in this figure is a common systematic uncertainty due to the branching ratio of $\pm24\%$ for the $J/\psi K^{*0}$ points and $\pm15\%$ for the $J/\psi K^-$ points.

measured in the SVX. This method relies on the fact that B mesons have long lifetimes compared to the vertex resolution of the SVX detector. Using the impact parameter, it is easy to distinguish the long-lived B and C mesons from the prompt background.

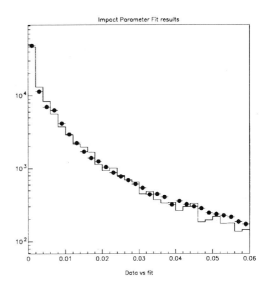

Figure 8. For 9 GeV muons, we show the impact parameter distribution (cm) overlaid with the fit results. The data are shown as the points and the boxed distribution is the sum of the input spectrums. The fraction of muons from B decays in the sample is $36 \pm 2.4\%$ where the error is statistical only.

For this measurement, good quality muons are required to pass all three levels of the trigger with $p_T > 9\text{GeV}/c$. The data is assumed to be a composition of a bottom component plus a charm component plus a background component. Monte Carlo data is used to parameterize the impact parameter distribution for the bottom and charm component and the background is parameterized using tracks from a sample of jet triggered data. Figure 8 shows the result of a binned maximum likelihood fit using the three input distributions and compared to the inclusive muon data.

The b quark cross section measurements are shown in Figure 9. The theory curves are based on the NLO calculation by Nason, Dawson and Ellis [1] convoluted with Peterson fragmentation [32]. The NLO theory uses MRSD0 structure functions, $\mu = \mu_0 = \sqrt{M_b^2 + p_T^2}$ and $M_b = 4.75\text{GeV}$. The dashed lines correspond to the upper and lower allowed predictions with variations in μ and M_b. The various data points have been derived

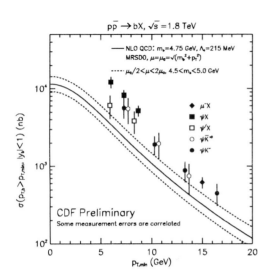

Figure 9. $\sigma(|\eta| < 1.)p\bar{p} \to bX$

For this measurement, good quality muons are required to pass all three levels of the trigger with $p_T > 9\,\text{GeV/c}$ and the event vertex is required to be less than 30cm to select events within the SVX fiducial volume. The events are further required to have a jet with uncorrected $E_t > 10\,\text{GeV}$ which contains at least 2 good quality tracks. The space angle between the muon and jet is required to be greater than $\Delta R_{jt,\mu} > 1.0$ to ensure the muon is not associated with the jet and the jet is required to be within $\eta < 1.5$. The fit method is identical to the inclusive muon analysis described in section 4. The data is described as a combination of bottom plus charm plus background and a binned maximum likelihood fit is performed on the jet probability distribution using three input distributions and the data.

Figure 10 shows the distribution of the cross section as a function of the azimuthal angle between the jet and the muon, overlaid with a theoretical prediction. The theory curve uses the Mangano-Nason-Ridolfi calculation [3] with $M_b = 4.75$, MRSB structure functions and $\mu = \mu_0$ for $|\eta^{b1}| < 1$, $p_T^{b1} > 15\,\text{GeV}$, $|\eta^{b2}| < 1.5$ and $p_T^{b2} > 10\,\text{GeV}$. From this distribution, we note that the shapes of the theoretical prediction and the data agree well with each other.

by using the measured integrated cross sections (from the specific channels mentioned earlier in this text) normalized to a b quark acceptance of $p_T^b > p_T(\text{min})$ and $|y| < 1.0$. The points are plotted at the $p_T(\text{min})$ value.

As with the differential cross section distributions, the data lie approximately a factor of 2 above the central theory curve. The biggest difference between the results presented here and our earlier measurements [9] is that the J/ψ and $\psi(2s)$ points have come down. This is due to the fact that the measured f_b is smaller than the theoretical number assumed in the 1988-1989 analysis.

5. $B\bar{B}$ Correlation Studies

We also present a measurement of the correlated b quark cross section, where one b is detected from the lepton from semileptonic decay and the other b is detected with secondary vertexing techniques [34]. The secondary vertex technique [35,36] uses a prescribed algorithm requiring the presence of a jet with uncorrected $E_t > 10\,\text{GeV/c}$ and answers the question "Is the ensemble of tracks in a jet consistent with being from the primary vertex?". The algorithm assigns a probability between 0 and 1 to each jet which has at least two good tracks with a probability value near 1 indicating that the jet is very consistent with being primary, while a probability near 0 indicates the jet is very inconsistent with being primary.

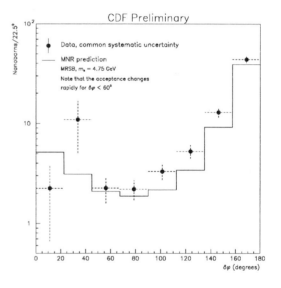

Figure 10. The distribution of the cross section as a function of the azimuthal angle between the jet and the muon, overlaid with a theoretical prediction. There is a common systematic uncertainty of +18.3 - 15.4 % not included in the experimental points.

References

[1] P.Nason,S.Dawson and R.Ellis, Nucl. Phys. **B303** (1988) 607; **B327** (1989) 49; **B335** (1990) 260.

[2] W.Beenakker,W.Van Neervan,R.Meng,G.Schuler and J.Smith, Nucl. Phys. **B351** (1991)

[3] M.Mangano,P.Nason and G.Ridolfi, Nucl. Phys. **B373** (1992) 295; **B405** (1993) 507.

[4] E.Levin,M.Ryskin,Y.Shabelski, and A.Shuvaev, DESY 91-065, (June 1991), ISSN 0418-9833.

[5] G.Altarelli,M.Diemoz,G.Martinelli, and P.Nason, Nucl. Phys. **B308** (1988) 724.

[6] E.Berger and R.Meng Argonne Preprint: ANL-HEP-PR-92-11 (1992), Phys. Rev. D Vol **49**, No. 7, (1994) 3248.

[7] M.L.Mangano, IFUP-TH (Feb. 1993)

[8] UA1 Collaboration: C.Albajar *et al.*, Phys. Lett. **256B** (1991), 121.

[9] CDF Collaboration: F. Abe *et al.*, Phys. Rev. Lett. **69** (1992) 3704, **71** (1993) 500, **71** (1993) 2537, **71** (1993) 2396, FERMILAB-PUB-93-131-E (June 1993)submitted to Phys. Rev. D.

[10] CDF Collaboration: F. Abe *et al.*, Nucl. Instr. Meth. **A271** (1988) 387.

[11] D. Amidei *el al.* Nucl. Instr. Meth. **A289** (1990) 388.

[12] F. Bedeschi *el al.* Nucl. Instr. Meth. **A268** (1988) 50.

[13] D. Amidei *el al.* Nucl. Instr. Meth. **A269** (1988) 51.

[14] G. Foster *el al.* Nucl. Instr. Meth. **A269** (1988) 93.

[15] J.Carroll *el al.* Nucl. Instr. Meth. **A300** (1991) 552.

[16] U.Joshi *el al.* Nucl. Phys. B. **23A** (1991) 365.

[17] E.Berger and D.Jones, Phys. Rev. **D23** (1981) 1521.

[18] R.Baier and R. Ruckl, Z. Phys. **C19** (1983) 251.

[19] B.Humpert, Phys. Lett. **184B** (1987) 105.

[20] R.Gastmans,W.Troost and T.Wu, Nucl. Phys. **B291** (1987) 731.

[21] E.Glover,A.Martin and W.Stirling, Z. Phys. **C38** (1988) 473

[22] E.Glover,F.Halzen and A.Martin, Phys. Lett. **185B** (1987) 441.

[23] E.Braaten and T.Yuan, Phys. Rev. Lett. **71** (1993 1673. FERMILAB-PUB-94-0400-T

[24] M. Doncheski, S.Fleming and M. Mangano, FNAL-CONF-93-348-T; FNAL-PUB-94-135-T, hep-ph-9405407.

[25] M.Cacciari and M.Greco, FNT-T-94/24, hep-ph/94405241.

[26] CDF Collaboration: F.Abe *el al.* Phys. Rev. Lett **69** (1992) 3704, **71** (1993) 2537

[27] CDF Collaboration: F.Abe *el al.* FERMILAB-Con-94-136-E.

[28] M.Mangano, to appear in the ICHEP94 proceedings, 20-27 July 1994; Glasgow, Scotland.

[29] M.Mangano, *Phenomenology of B Quark Production in Hadronic Collisions* to appear in the Proceedings of the XXIX Rencontres de Moriond, 19-26 March 1994; Meribel, France.

[30] CDF Collaboration: F.Abe *el al.* FERMILAB-Con-94-141-E.

[31] CDF Collaboration: F.Abe *el al.* FERMILAB-Con-94-134-E.

[32] C.Peterson,D.Schlatter,I.Schmitt and P.Zerwas, Phys. Rev. **D27** (1983) 105.

[33] T.Song, *el al.* CDFNOTE 2004.

[34] CDF Collaboration: F.Abe *el al.* FERMILAB-Con-94-129-E.

[35] D.Gerdes, *el al.* CDFNOTE 2023.

[36] D.Amidei, *el al.* CDFNOTE 2091.

B-Physics Results from D0

D. Hedin[†‡] and L. Markosky[§||]

† Northern Illinois University,
DeKalb, Illinois, USA
§ University of Arizona,
Tucson, Arizona, USA

For the D0 Collaboration at Fermilab

Abstract

We report on preliminary measurements of the inclusive single muon and dimuon cross sections in $p\bar{p}$ collisions at $\sqrt{s} = 1.8$ TeV using the D0 detector at the Fermilab collider. From these results, we extract the cross section for b-quark production for the kinematic range $|y_b| < 1.0$ and $6 < p_t^b < 50$ GeV/c. We also report measurements on the J/ψ and Υ production cross sections, sources of J/ψ production, and correlations between muons in dimuon events.

1. Introduction

The D0 experiment at the Fermilab Tevatron has measured the inclusive single muon and dimuon cross sections for $|\eta_\mu| < 0.8$ in $p\bar{p}$ collisions at $\sqrt{s} = 1.8$ TeV using data taken during the 1992-93 collider run. The b-quark cross section is extracted using these measurements and found to be in good agreement with next-to-leading order QCD predictions. The inclusive J/ψ and Υ cross sections in the central region have also been measured and sources of J/ψ production are discussed.

The D0 detector has been described elsewhere [1]. It consists of inner tracking chambers used to measure the primary vertex and to help identify electrons and muons, uranium-liquid argon calorimeters to detect electrons, photons and jets, and iron toroids and drift chambers to detect muons. The combined calorimeter plus toroid thickness varies from about 14 λ in the central region to 19 λ in the end. This thickness reduces the punchthrough backgrounds to less than 1% of prompt muon production and also allows for

clean muon identification within hadronic jets. Muon momentum is measured using the toroid and has a resolution of $\sigma(p)/p = 0.18(p-2)/2 \oplus 0.008p$ (p in GeV/c).

2. Measurement of the b-quark Production Cross Section

We have measured b-quark production cross section using the semileptonic decays $b \rightarrow \mu + X$ and $b\bar{b} \rightarrow \mu\mu + X$. For this paper, only results from the central region with $|\eta_\mu| < 0.8$ are presented. Events were collected using three different triggers, giving a single muon, a muon plus jet, and a dimuon data sample. Each trigger required a level 0 trigger which indicated that an inelastic collision had occured. Level 1 muon triggers used 60 cm wide hodoscopic elements formed from the muon drift chambers, and required 2 or 3 layers of chambers to have hits consistent with a muon produced in the interaction region. The minimum energy of muons exiting the toroid is about 3.2 GeV and the level 1 muon trigger became fully efficient at 5 GeV. At level 2, muons and jets are identified using a software filter composed of the initial part of the offline reconstruction. Single muon

‡ E-mail: Hedin@fnald0.fnal.gov
|| E-mail: Leigh@fnald0.fnal.gov

triggers require one or more level 1 and level 2 muon triggers while the dimuon triggers require two or more at each level. The muon plus jet trigger also required calorimeter energy in a level 1 trigger tower of 0.2 by $0.2 \, \Delta\eta - \Delta\phi$ to be ≥ 3 GeV.

Good muons were selected offline by requiring each muon to have hits in all three layers of the muon system for the single muon cross section analyses (this requirement is relaxed by one for the dimuon cross section). Additionally each muon was required to have at least 1 GeV of associated calorimeter energy, possess a matching track in the central tracking chamber, point back to the interaction vertex in the bend and non-bend views, and traverse a minimum field integral of 0.6 GeV/c in the toroids.

All muons were required to have $|\eta^\mu| < 0.8$. Additional kinematic cuts applied were $3.5 < p_t^\mu < 60$ GeV/c for the single muon cross section and $p_t^\mu > 6.0$ GeV/c and $E_t^{jet} > 12$ GeV for the muon plus jets cross section. Dimuons were required to have $4 < p_t^\mu < 25$ GeV/c and mass $6 < M_{\mu\mu} < 35$ GeV/c^2.

Cosmic ray contamination was estimated by fitting the crossing time distribution in the muon chambers (called floating T0) to distributions of known beam produced muons and cosmic rays. In all analyses the remaining cosmic ray contamination is approximately 10%. After all cuts the number of single muon events is 19000 from 93 nb^{-1} of data. For muons plus jets the corresponding numbers are 4300 events from 197 nb^{-1} of data. For dimuons, 550 events from 6.4 pb^{-1} of data passed all cuts.

Trigger and offline selection efficiencies were determined by passing Monte Carlo events through the full D0 detector, trigger simulation, and reconstruction packages. In all cases the efficiencies were cross checked using appropriate data samples.

The resulting single muon cross section in shown in Figure 1. Also shown are the ISAJET Monte Carlo predictions for the predominant processes giving single muons. The sum of all contributions is in good agreement with the data.

The resulting dimuon cross section plotted as a function of the highest p_t^μ of the pair is shown in Figure 2. Also shown are the ISAJET Monte Carlo predictions for the predominant processes giving dimuons. The sum of all contributions is again in good agreement with the data.

In order to extract the b-quark cross section one must estimate that fraction of the inclusive muon or dimuon spectrum coming from b-quark decays. The b-quark decay fraction is found using the ISAJET results for the known background contributions to b-quark production. For the single muon and muon plus jets analyses, the b-quark fraction was cross checked by fitting the p_t^{rel} distribution in the data as the sum

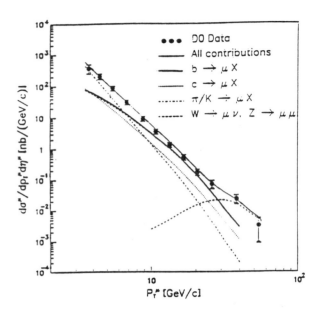

Figure 1. The single muon cross section vs. p_t^μ for muons with $|\eta| < 0.8$.

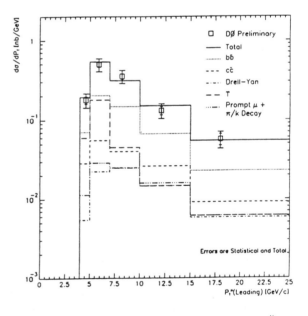

Figure 2. The dimuon cross section vs. the highest p_t^μ of the pair, for muons with $|\eta| < 0.8$.

of p_t^{rel} distributions from b-quark decay and c-quark plus π/K decay. The quantity p_t^{rel} is the transverse momentum of the muon relative to the associated jet axis where the jet momentum also includes the muon momentum. The b-quark fraction found with this fitting procedure is in good agreement with the b-quark fraction determined via Monte Carlo alone. Once the fractions of the single muon and dimuon inclusive cross sections coming from b-quark decay is determined, the integrated inclusive b-quark cross section can be extracted following the method of UA1 and CDF in order to facilitate

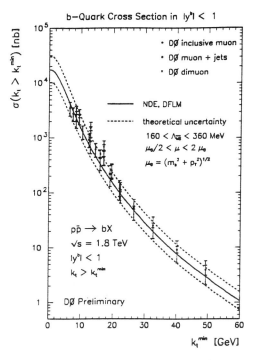

Figure 3. The *b*-quark cross section vs. k_t^{min} for the single muon, single muon plus jet, and dimuon analyses.

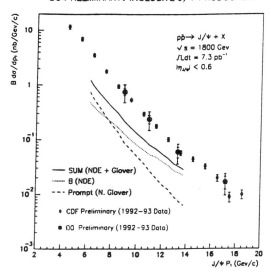

Figure 4. Inclusive J/ψ cross section a function of p_t^ψ.

comparison [2, 3]. The resulting *b*-quark cross section is plotted in Figure 3 from the inclusive muon, muon plus jet, and dimuon cross section data. The results are consistent with the next-to-leading order (NLO) QCD calculations of Nason *et al.* [4].

3. Inclusive J/ψ Cross Section and Production Mechanisms

To select J/ψ candidates, each muon was required to pass similar track quality criteria as in the dimuon cross section analysis described above. The dimuon was required to have oppositely signed muons, invariant mass in the range $2 < M^{\mu\mu} < 4.0$ GeV/c^2, and $|\eta_\psi| <$ 0.6. The number of J/ψ after all cuts was estimated by fitting the invariant dimuon mass distribution to the sum of a Gaussian centered at the J/ψ mass and a polynomial background (consisting mostly of sequential *b*-quark decays). The total number of J/ψ given by the fit was 450 ± 20 from data runs having a total integrated luminosity of 7.2 pb^{-1}. The overall J/ψ detection efficiency is a combination of trigger and offline efficiencies, and was determined using complete detector and trigger simulations. The number of J/ψ's in each p_t^ψ bin was determined from the fit described above. The inclusive cross section times branching ratio shown in Figure 4 was obtained by dividing the data bin by bin by the J/ψ detection efficiency and the integrated luminosity. The D0 data points are in good agreement with the CDF data [5]. Also shown are the

theoretical estimates for J/ψ production from *b*-quark decay and direct charmonium production [6, 7]. The measured inclusive ψ cross section lies well above the prediction for the sum of these two processes, indicating contributions from further processes not modelled by the theory. Additional diagrams such as gluon and charm fragmentation into J/ψ and χ_c [8] have been proposed to account for this discrepancy.

3.1. Fraction of J/ψ from b-quark decay.

The fraction of J/ψ's from *b*-quark decay was estimated using trimuon events. A fit was made to the invariant mass spectrum of the dimuon sample in the range $1 < M^{\mu\mu} < 5$ GeV/c^2, as the sum of signal (J/ψ) and background (sequential decays) distributions. Next the dimuon invariant mass is formed using trimuon events (J/ψ plus muon (*b*-quark) tag). Using the shapes obtained from fitting the dimuon sample, the identical fit was performed on the trimuon events, and the relative proportions of signal and background extracted. The number of J/ψ predicted from the fit is $2.5^{+3.3}_{-2.5}$. ISAJET Monte Carlo studies were then used to determine the fraction of J/ψ plus muon tag events in inclusive J/ψ events from $b\bar{b}$ production. From this, an upper limit for the J/ψ fraction from *b*-quark decay at the 95% CL was determined to be 50%.

3.2. Fraction of J/ψ from direct charmonium.

J/ψ's from direct charmonium production arise primarily through the decay of χ_c. The muons from χ_c are expected to be isolated, and are accompanied by a low E_t photon. Isolated J/ψ's were chosen from the J/ψ sam-

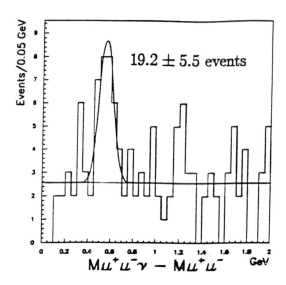

Figure 5. $M_{\mu\mu\gamma} - M_{\mu\mu}$ for the $\chi_c \longrightarrow J/\psi X$ sample.

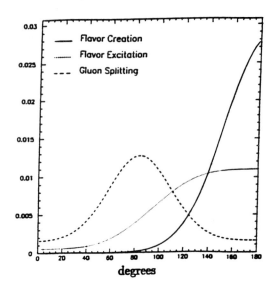

Figure 6. Azimuthal opening angle of muons from $b\bar{b}$ decay for LO and NLO production mechanisms.

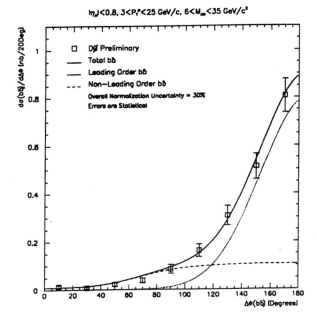

Figure 7. $b\bar{b}$ cross section as a function of azimuthal opening angle of the muons. Curves are ISAJET predictions for LO and NLO contributions.

ple by requiring no jet be found in a cone of $\Delta r < 1.0$ in $\eta - \phi$ space about each muon. Events with photons were tagged by requiring the presence in the event of an electromagnetic calorimeter cluster of energy $E_\gamma > 0.6$ GeV. Figure 5 shows the distribution of mass difference, $M^{\mu\mu\gamma} - M^{\mu\mu}$, with a peak at roughly 0.55 GeV. The number of χ_c's predicted from the fit (after background subtraction) is 19.2 ± 5.5. Dividing this number by the photon detection efficiency (0.21) and isolation efficiency (0.33) gives the fraction of J/ψ with $p_t > 8$ GeV/c and $|\eta| < 0.6$ from χ_c decay as $0.41 \pm 0.14 \pm 0.10$. This is in good agreement with the CDF result [9] for $p_t^\psi > 6$ GeV/c and $|\eta^\psi| < 0.5$.

4. $b\bar{b}$ Correlations

The angular separation of the leptons from $b\bar{b}$ decay is related to the particular mechanism involved in producing the b's. Figure 6 shows the distributions in azimuthal opening angle between the muons in $b\bar{b}$ decay for the leading order process of flavor creation compared to two NLO diagrams, gluon splitting and flavor excitation. Here we adopt the phenomenological model of ISAJET. Measurements of angular correlations of the leptons can be used to separate leading from NLO contributions to the $b\bar{b}$ cross section, and test the QCD predictions for these contributions.

The data and selection criteria for this measurement were the same as for the $b\bar{b}$ cross section measurement. ISAJET Monte Carlo was used to provide shapes to fit the LO and NLO contributions to the dimuon cross section as a function of $\Delta\phi$ of the muons. It was also used to estimate the b fraction in each $\Delta\phi$ bin. Figure

7 shows the $b\bar{b}$ cross section as function of the dimuon opening angle fit to the ISAJET predictions for the LO and NLO (sum of flavor excitation and gluon splitting) contributions. The fit predicts $71 \pm 8\%$ from LO and $29 \pm 5\%$ from NLO processes, in good agreement with the fractions in ISAJET of $71 \pm 1\%$ and $29 \pm 1\%$.

5. Inclusive Upsilon cross section

The data sample for the Υ analysis was selected from the same data as for the dimuon analyses described above. Since muons from Υ decay are expected to be isolated, at least one of the muons in each event was required to satisfy an isolation cut defined as the calorimeter energy deposited in a cone of $r = 0.2$ in $\eta - \phi$ space about the muon, minus the energy expected for minimum ionizing particle (divided by the energy uncertainty). A simultaneous maximum likelihood fit to three distributions: dimuon mass, energy deposition in a wide cone of $r = 0.6$ minus the energy in cone of $r = 0.2$ about the muon, and floating T0 (defined in section 3), was used to extract the number of Υ's from the background (QCD, Drell-Yan, and cosmic rays). The shapes used in the fit were derived from appropriate data samples, and in the case of the mass distribution, from Monte Carlo. The result of this fit is shown in Figure 8. The number of Υ's predicted in the sample from this fit was 95^{+15}_{-14}. Correcting for the acceptance, the offline cuts, and the trigger efficiency, and the integrated luminosity of the sample, the total cross section times branching fraction to muons was calculated to be:

$$\sigma \cdot B(\Upsilon \longrightarrow \mu\mu) = (9.5 \pm 1.1(\boldsymbol{stat}) \pm 4.3(\boldsymbol{sys})) \times 10^3 pb \tag{1}$$

Assuming the $\Upsilon(1S) : \Upsilon(2S)$ ratio to be 2 to 1, and using published Particle Data Group branching fractions [10, 11] the total branching fraction was calculated to be $2.09 \pm 0.19\%$. Using this figure, the total Υ production cross section was calculated to be

$$\sigma_\Upsilon = (4.5 \pm 0.5(\boldsymbol{stat}) \pm 2.1(\boldsymbol{sys})) \times 10^5 pb \tag{2}$$

The leading order theoretical prediction for the total cross section [12] is $(1.5 \pm 0.5) \times 10^5 pb$, a 2σ deviation from the D0 result.

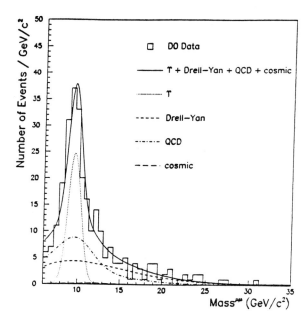

Figure 8. Result of simultaneous fit to the mass distribution in the Υ sample. Data is shown as a histogram. Curves are Monte Carlo signal and background (data) contributions.

References

[1] S. Abachi et al., Nucl. Instr. Meth. **A338** (1994) 185.

[2] C. Albajar et al., Phys. Lett. **B186** (1987) 237.

[3] F. Abe et al., Phys. Rev. Lett. **71** (1993) 2396.

[4] P. Nason, S. Dawson, R. K. Ellis, Nucl. Phys. **B303** (1988) 607; *ibid* **B327** (1989) 49; *ibid* **B335** (1990) 260.

[5] J. Mueller (these Proceedings).

[6] E. W. N. Glover, A. D. Martin, W. J. Stirling, Zeit. Phys. **C38** (1988) 473.

[7] F. Abe et al., Phys. Rev. Lett. **69** (1992) 3704.

[8] E. Braaten et al., FERMILAB-PUB-94/135-T (1994).

[9] F. Abe et al., Phys. Rev. Lett. **71** (1993) 2537.

[10] V. Papadimitriou, Proc. of the 1994 DPF meeting, 2–6 Aug. 1994, Albuquerque, NM, USA (to be published).

[11] *Review of Particle Properties*, Phys. Rev. **D45** (1992) .

[12] V. Barger, A. Martin, Phys. Rev. **D31** (1985) 1051.

Cross Section Measurement of D* and Elastic J/ψ Production at HERA

J N Lim ‡

McGill University, Dept. of Physics,
Montreal, Quebec, Canada

On behalf of the ZEUS collaboration

Abstract

This paper reports on the first observation of charmed mesons in the decay channel $D^{*+} \rightarrow (K^-\pi^+)\pi^+$ (+ c.c.) and a preliminary measurement of the cross section of D* and elastic J/ψ production at HERA using the ZEUS detector.

1. Introduction

We search for $c\bar{c}$ production at HERA by looking for the fragmentation products of the heavy flavour quarks which produce a $D^{*\pm}$ and give a preliminary cross section measurement for D* production using 486 nb^{-1} of data taken in 1993. The method relies on the kinematic constraints of the decay $D^{*+} \rightarrow D^0\pi^+$. The momentum of the pion coming from the D* is 40 MeV in the D* rest frame, giving a mass difference $\Delta M(M(D^0\pi) - M(D^0))$ of 145.42 MeV [1] which can be measured accurately. The D^0 is detected via the $D^0 \rightarrow K^-\pi^+$ (+c.c.) channel. Background from $b\bar{b}$ pairs is very small and we assume all the D* events originated directly from charm quarks.

We also present preliminary results of the cross section measurement of J/ψ in photoproduction in the reactions ep $\rightarrow$ eJ/ψp. The photon-proton center of mass energy ($W_{\gamma^* p}$) is confined to the kinematic region where the detector acceptance is well understood and the process is properly simulated. The present data sample contains photoproduction events with $Q^2 < 3$ GeV^2.

2. The ZEUS Detector

The ZEUS [2] detector has been described elsewhere. The components relevant to this analysis are the vertex and central-tracking detectors, the uranium-scintillator calorimeter, the barrel and rear muon detectors, the veto wall detector, a scintillator counter (C5) detector to veto beam-gas interactions and the luminosity monitor.

3. Monte Carlo Simulation

The Monte Carlo programs HERWIG [3] and PYTHIA [4] were used to model the expected hadronic final states in $c\bar{c}$ production. Elastic J/ψ production was simulated with the DIPSI[5] and the EPJPSI[6] generators.

4. D* Reconstruction and Results

Pairs of oppositely charged tracks with transverse momentum, $p_T > 0.5$ GeV, were combined and considered in turn to be a kaon or a pion. The combination was accepted as a possible D^0 candidate if the $K\pi$ invariant mass lay between 1.80 and 1.90 GeV. To reconstruct D* mesons, these D^0 candidates were combined with an additional track having $p_T > 0.16$ GeV and opposite charge to that of the kaon. No

‡ E-mail: lim@vxdesy.desy.de.

particle identification was used in this analysis. A cut of $p_T(D^*) > 1.7$ GeV was applied to reduce background and the pseudorapidity, $\eta = -\ln[\tan(\frac{\theta}{2})]$, was confined to the region, $|\eta(D^*)| < 1.5$, where the detector is well understood.

Figure 1 shows the ΔM signal with a peak at 145.5 ± 0.2 MeV and width of 1.0 ± 0.2 MeV. There are 74 ± 14 D^* events observed over a background of ~ 40 events. The $M(K\pi)$ distribution for events with $142 < \Delta M < 149$ MeV is shown in figure 2. The fit gives a D^0 mass of 1.85 ± 0.01 GeV, with a width of ~ 20 MeV and 72 ± 13 events.

The ΔM distribution was used to estimate the number of D^* events over the background. The efficiency was evaluated using both PYTHIA and HERWIG Monte Carlo with different structure function parametrisations. The total systematic error on the results was estimated to be 19 %.

For the kinematic range $p_T(D^*) > 1.7$ GeV and $|\eta(D^*)| < 1.5$ we obtained $\sigma(ep \rightarrow D^{*}X + c.c.)B(D^{*+} \rightarrow D^0\pi^+ \rightarrow (K^-\pi^+)\pi^+) = 1.5 \pm 0.3(stat) \pm 0.3(syst)$ nb.

Extrapolation outside the selected kinematic range, assuming different parton density parametrisations and a branching ratio $B(c \rightarrow D^{*+} \rightarrow D^0\pi^+ \rightarrow (K^-\pi^+)\pi^+)$ of 7.1×10^{-3} [7], gave a total charm cross section of $\sigma(ep \rightarrow c\bar{c}X) \sim 1.7\,\mu$b for MRSD-[8]/LAC1[9] and $\sim 1\,\mu$b for MRSD- with either GRV[10],ACFGP[11] or DG[12].

5. J/ψ Event Selection and Results

The J/ψ was identified in its leptonic decay modes. In the case of the muon channel, particle identification was accomplished by matching at least one of the final state tracks with calorimeter energy deposits corresponding to a minimum ionising particle and to matching hits in the muon detectors.   Electron identification was accomplished by matching final state tracks to calorimeter energy deposits consistent with that of an electron.

Events with exactly two well reconstructed tracks within $|\eta| < 1.5$ and transverse momenta greater than 0.5 GeV were accepted. In addition, the total energy in the calorimeter, apart from the energy deposited by the two lepton candidates from the J/ψ decay, was required to be less than 1.0 GeV. This criterion was imposed to select elastic events i.e., from the reaction ep $\rightarrow$ eJ/ψp, by ensuring that there was no other activity in the detector. These selection criteria, however, do not exclude the events where the proton dissociates diffractively and remains undetected in the beampipe.

The invariant mass spectra, displayed in figure 3, were then fitted with a Gaussian form and a polynomial background. The fitted mass for the J/ψ candidates

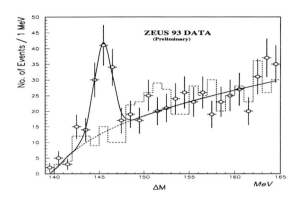

Figure 1. ΔM distribution for $p_T(D^*) > 1.7$ GeV and $|\eta(D^*)| < 1.5$. The dashed line is the plot for the wrong charge combinations.

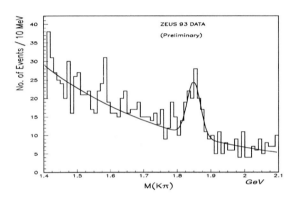

Figure 2. $K\pi$ invariant mass distribution for those candidates with $(142 < \Delta M < 149)$ MeV in the whole range of $M(K\pi)$. The fit consists of a gaussian plus an exponential background shape.

was 3.03 ± 0.02 GeV with a width of 80 ± 16 MeV in the electron channel, and 3.07 ± 0.02 GeV, with a width of 66 ± 12 MeV, for the muon channel, respectively. In the case of the electron channel, the shift of the fitted mass of the J/ψ from the nominal J/ψ mass (3.1 GeV) is attributed to energy loss in the material encountered by the electrons. This was also observed in the Monte Carlo. A fit which included a bremsstrahlung function gave a mass of 3.07 ± 0.02 GeV.

The selected range of W_{γ^*p} was 40 GeV $< W_{\gamma^*p} < 140$ GeV, where the observed acceptance on the average was well above 10%. A preliminary estimate of the systematic uncertainties was 21% for the electron and 30% for the muon channel. The photoproduction cross section, σ_{γ^*p}, is related to the electron proton cross section by a flux factor given by the Equivalent Photon Approximation [13].   The photoproduction cross sections, the integrated photon flux used in these calculations, and the electroproduction cross sections, σ_{ep}, are summarized in table 1. The photoproduction cross sections as a function of W_{γ^*p} are shown in figure 4 which includes earlier J/ψ measurements [14].

$W_{\gamma^* p}$ (GeV)	40-140	
channel	$e^+ e^-$	$\mu^+ \mu^-$
Int. Luminosity (nb^{-1})	496	490
acceptance	25.2%	17.7%
signal events	58 ± 9	35 ± 6
$\sigma_{ep \to J/\psi \, ep}$(nb)	$7.4 \pm 1.2 \pm 1.6$	$6.7 \pm 1.2 \pm 2.0$

channel	$e^+ e^-$	
$W_{\gamma^* p}$ range (GeV)	40-75	75-140
acceptance	26.8%	22.8%
signal events	32 ± 7	24 ± 6
$\sigma_{ep \to J/\psi \, ep}$(nb)	$3.8 \pm 0.8 \pm 0.8$	$3.4 \pm 0.8 \pm 0.7$
Int. photon flux	0.061	0.049
$\sigma_{\gamma p \to J/\psi \, p}$(nb)	$62 \pm 13 \pm 13$	$70 \pm 16 \pm 13$

channel	$\mu^+ \mu^-$	
$W_{\gamma^* p}$ range (GeV)	40-90	90-140
acceptance	14.9%	23.4%
signal events	16 ± 4	19 ± 5
$\sigma_{ep \to J/\psi \, ep}$(nb)	$3.7 \pm 0.9 \pm 1.1$	$2.8 \pm 0.7 \pm 0.8$
Int. photon flux	0.077	0.033
$\sigma_{\gamma p \to J/\psi \, p}$(nb)	$48 \pm 12 \pm 14$	$84 \pm 21 \pm 24$

Table 1. Cross section for $ep \to e\, J/\psi\, p$ and $\gamma p \to J/\psi\, p$

6. Summary

A sample of ≈ 74 events containing $D^*(2010)$ was isolated in ep collisions at HERA using the ZEUS detector. The preliminary cross section for the kinematic region { $p_T(D^*) \geq 1.7$ GeV , $|\eta(D^*)| < 1.5$ } was found to be $1.5 \pm 0.3(stat) \pm 0.3(syst)$ nb. Extrapolation outside the selected kinematic range, gave a total charm cross section of $\sigma(ep \to c\bar{c}X) \sim 1.7\,\mu$b assuming MRSD-/LAC1 and $\sim 1\,\mu$b for MRSD-/GRV. The sensitivity in the present analysis to the proton and photon structure functions is limited due to the requirement of $|\eta(D^*)| < 1.5$.

The results of a preliminary measurement of $ep \to eJ/\psi p$ cross section for $Q^2 \leq 3$ GeV^2 and $40 \leq W_{\gamma^* p} \leq 140$ GeV are $7.4 \pm 1.2 \pm 1.6$nb^{-1} for the electron channel and $6.7 \pm 1.2 \pm 2.0$nb^{-1} for the muon channel, respectively. It should be noted that a fraction of the events where the proton diffractively dissociates could be contained in the final data sample.

References

[1] Review of Particle Properties, Phys. Rev. **D50** (1994) .

[2] ZEUS Collab., The ZEUS Detector, Status Report, DESY (1993).
ZEUS Collab., M. Derrick et al., Phys. Lett. **B293** (1992) 465.

[3] G. Marchesini et al., Computer Phys. Comm. **67** (1992) 465.
B.R. Webber, HERWIG at HERA DESY 92-028, Proc. of the Workshop "Physics at HERA", Vol III., Oct 1991, p. 1354.
L. Stanco, ibidem, p. 1363.

[4] T. Sjoestrand, Zeit. Phys. **C42** (1989) 301 and in Proc. of the Workshop on Physics at HERA, DESY Vol III (1992) 1405.

[5] M. Ryskin, Zeit. Phys. **C57** (1993) 89.

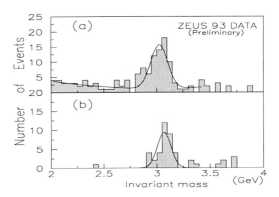

Figure 3. Invariant mass of J/ψ candidates. (a) $e^+ e^-$ and (b) $\mu^+ \mu^-$ mode. The superimposed curves are (a) a Gaussian and a second order polynomial, and (b) a Gaussian.

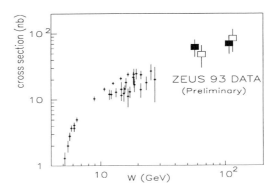

Figure 4. A compilation of $\sigma(\gamma p)$ values as a function of $W_{\gamma^* p}$ for $\gamma p \to \psi N, \gamma p \to \psi p$. The squares show the results of the present paper. Solid squares are for the $e^+ e^-$ and open squares for the $\mu^+ \mu^-$ mode.

[6] H. Jung, DESY 92-028, and in Proc. of the Workshop "Physics at HERA", Vol III., Oct 1991, p. 1488.

[7] F. Butler et al., (CLEO Collaboration), Phys. Rev. Lett. **69** (1992) 2041;
D.S. Akerib et al., (CLEO Collaboration), Phys. Rev. Lett. **71** (1993) 3070;
H. Albrecht et al., (ARGUS Collaboration), DESY 94-094 preprint.

[8] A.D. Martin, R.G. Roberts and W.J. Stirling, Phys. Rev. **D47** (1993) 867.

[9] H. Abramowicz, K. Charchula and A. Levy, Phys. Lett. **B269** (1991) 458.

[10] M. Glück,E. Reya and A. Vogt, Phys. Rev. **D46** (1992) 1973.

[11] P. Aurenche et al., Zeit. Phys. **C56** (1992) 589.

[12] M. Drees and K. Grassie, Zeit. Phys. **C28** (1985) 451.

[13] V.N. Gribov, V.A. Kolkunov, L.B. Okun, V.M. Shekhter, Sov. Phys. JEPT **14** (1962) 1308.
B. Burow, Ph.D. Thesis, Graduate Dept. of Physics, University of Toronto, Canada (1994) available as Internal Report DESY F35D-94-01 February 1994.

[14] A. Baldini et.al., Landolt-Bornstein, Group I, Vol 12b, Springer-Verlag, ed. H.Schopper.
S. Holmes, W. Lee & J. Wiss, Ann. Rev. Nucl. Part. Sci. **35** (1985) 397.

Studies of Charm Production with the H1 Detector at HERA and Observation of Elastic Vector Meson Photoproduction at HERA

C. Kleinwort

University Hamburg

Representing the H1 Collaboration

Abstract

Photoproduction with quasi-real photons in collisions of $26.7\,GeV$ electrons with $820\,GeV$ protons has been studied with the H1 detector at HERA. Requiring exactly two leptons (e^+e^- or $\mu^+\mu^-$) in the detector, a total photoproduction cross-section of $\sigma(\gamma p \to J/\psi + X) = (56 \pm 13 \pm 14)\,nb$ is derived at an average $W_{\gamma p} = 90\,GeV$. The distribution of the squared momentum transfer below $0.75\,GeV^{-2}$ was fitted to an exponential yielding a slope parameter of $b = -(4.7 \pm 1.9)\,GeV^{-2}$. From events with a muon in the central part of the detector a total photoproduction cross-section of $\sigma(\gamma p \to c\bar{c} + X) = (3.6 \pm 0.8 \pm 1.8)\,\mu b$ is obtained at an average $W_{\gamma p} = 114\,GeV$. Finally a signal for $D^{*\pm} \to D^0 \pi_s^{\pm}, D^0 \to K^{\pm}\pi^{\mp}$ is presented.

1. Introduction

The investigation of the production of heavy quarks by real or virtual photons allows one to probe strong interaction physics in kinematical regions in which the physics descriptions range from nonpertubative phenomelogic approaches to pertubative QCD.

At small p_t the vector-meson-dominance model may be used to describe the photon-proton scattering: the incident photon fluctuates into a virtual vector meson exchanging a pomeron with the proton. The proton may hereby scatter elasticly (figure 1(a)) or dissociate diffractively (figure 1(b)).

In QCD inspired models heavy quark photoproduction can be interpreted as photon-gluon fusion (figure 1(c)) giving access to the proton gluon structure function or 'resolved' photoproduction (figure 1(d)), where a hadronic photon component (quark or gluon) interacts with a parton from the proton.

For vanishing Q^2 HERA can be seen as a wideband source of quasi-real photons increasing the accessible photon-proton invariant mass from up to $20\,GeV$ at fixed target machines to $W_{\gamma p} \approx 100\,GeV$.

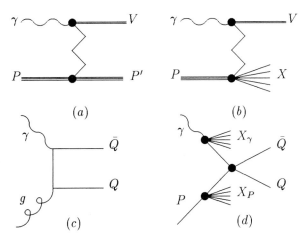

Figure 1. Mechanisms for heavy quark photoproduction

2. Experimental setup

The results presented are based on the data taken in 1993 with the H1 detector [1] at the electron-proton collider HERA. The beam energies were $E_p = 820\,GeV$ and $E_e = 26.7\,GeV$.

3. J/ψ analysis [†]

Strategy: The J/ψ mesons are identified by their decay into leptons (e or μ) and only the decay leptons are allowed to be visible in the detector. This restricts the analysis to 'elastic' J/ψ-production containing a mixture of true elastic events and those where the proton breaks up into fragments remaining in the beam pipe.

Data selection: An integrated Luminosity of $259\,nb^{-1}$ ($284\,nb^{-1}$) was used for the μ (e) analysis.

Tracks originating from the interaction region with transverse momenta $p_t > 200\,MeV$ are selected in the central polar region ($20° \leq \theta \leq 160°$). A track is identified as a muon by a matching track segment in the muon system or a minimum ionizing particle signature in the liquid argon calorimeter and as a electron by a matching electromagnetic cluster. A track pair consistent with $\mu^+\mu^-$ or e^+e^- and an invariant mass $> 1.5\,GeV$ is required. No other tracks or energy depositions are allowed. Background from beam-gas interactions or cosmic ray muons is removed.

The final sample contains 48 (40) muon (electron) pair events with 22 (10) in a region of $\pm 225\,MeV$ around the nominal J/ψ mass. The main background is from QED lepton pair production by two virtual photons. A Monte Carlo simulation predictes 3 ± 1 events per channel in the above region. This number is consistent with the observed mass distribution in figure 2.

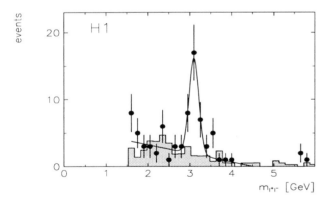

Figure 2. Mass distribution for $ep \rightarrow \ell^+\ell^-$. The curve is a fit of a Gaussian plus linear background. Shaded is the Monte Carlo expectation for QED lepton pairs.

Acceptance and efficiencies: Monte Carlo techniques with different production mechanisms were used to determine the acceptance and efficiencies. With the leptons in the central polar region, $30\,GeV < W_{\gamma p} < 180\,GeV$ and $Q^2 < 4\,GeV^2$ the acceptance is $63 \pm 4\%$. The combined trigger, reconstruction and selection efficiency amounts to $19.3 \pm 0.4\%$ for muons and $9.5 \pm 0.2\%$

[†] A paper (DESY preprint 94-153) has been submitted to Phys. Lett. B.

for electrons. The efficiencies were checked against data and agree between simulation and data within 5–10%.

Results: With 19 (7) muon (electron) candidate events, the integrated luminosity, acceptance, efficiencies and a leptonic J/ψ branching ratio of 6% a cross-section of $\sigma(ep \rightarrow J/\psi + X) = (8.8 \pm 2.0 \pm 2.2)\,nb$ is obtained. The systematic error of 25% is dominated by the uncertainties of the background subtraction (8%), acceptance (6%), efficiencies (17%), leptonic branching ratio (5%) and luminosity mesurement (5%).

The total photoproduction cross-section is derived by integrating the photon flux for $30\,GeV < W_{\gamma p} < 180\,GeV$ and $Q^2_{max} = 4\,GeV^2$ according to [3]. The resulting $\sigma(\gamma p \rightarrow J/\psi + X) = (56 \pm 13 \pm 14)\,nb$ at a mean $W_{\gamma p}$ of $\approx 90\,GeV$ is shown in figure 3 together with earlier measurement at lower values of $W_{\gamma p}$ [2].

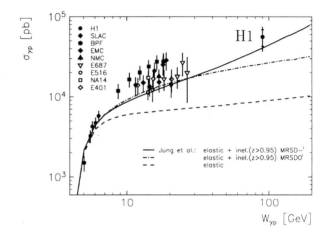

Figure 3. Total cross-section for $\gamma p \rightarrow J/\psi + X$. The inner error bar of the H1 point is purely statistical, the outer one contains statistical and systematic errors added in quadrature. The data at lower center-of-mass energies are from previous experiments [2]; they were corrected with the new J/ψ decay branching ratio of [6] and include systematic errors (added in quadrature). The thick full line shows the QCD model by Jung et al. [4] with the MRSD$-'$ parton density functions [5], the dash-dotted line with MRSD0$'$ (inelastic contribution for $z > 0.95$). The dotted line represents the purely elastic contribution in the QCD model.

The dependence of the cross-section on the momentum transfer t between photon and J/ψ was studied with the p_t^2 distribution ($t \approx -p_t^2$ for small Q^2 and proton deflection angle). For $p_t^2 < 0.75\,GeV^2$ a fit $d\sigma/dt = A \cdot \exp(b \cdot p_t^2)$ to the data yields a slope of $b = -(4.7 \pm 1.9)\,GeV^{-2}$.

4.   Inclusive muon analysis[‡]

Strategy: The production of c and b quarks is tagged with high p_t muons in the central region of the detector.

[‡] The results are still preliminary.

Data selection: An integrated luminosity of $410\,nb^{-1}$ has been analyzed.

Events with a reconstructed muon in the central part of the muon system are selected. At least one track originating from the interaction region with transverse momenta $p_t > 1.5\,GeV$ in the polar region $30° \leq \theta \leq 130°$ linked to a track segment in the muon system is required. Cosmic ray muons are rejected and after a visual scan 484 events are accepted.

Background: The background is dominated by muons from $\pi^{\pm}$, $K^{\pm}$ decays and fake muons and has been studied with independent data samples: All tracks in the above p_t and θ region are taken as $\pi^{\pm}$ or $K^{\pm}$ (ratio 2:1–4:1) and the detailed detector simulation is used to regenerate the response in the muon system. This leads to a background of 279 ± 33 events to the inclusive muon sample. According to Monte Carlo studies another 17 events can be attibuted to production of J/ψ mesons decaying into muons.

Efficiencies: The trigger, reconstruction and selection efficiencies have been studied with Monte Carlo techniques and checked against data. The combined efficiency amounts to $23.3 \pm 3.0\%$.

Results: The accepted cross-section is $\sigma_{acc}(ep \rightarrow \mu + X) = (2.03 \pm 0.43 \pm 0.70)\,nb$. The systematic error is dominated by the uncertainties of trigger efficiency (20%), background subtraction (20%) and the visual scan (14%).

Monte Carlo studies with various sets of structure functions predict $\sigma_{acc} \approx 2.0(0.1)\,nb$ for c (b) quark production. The acceptance for the c quark starts at a $W_{\gamma p}$ of several $10\,GeV$ and amounts to $1.1 \pm 0.4\%$ for $W_{\gamma p} > 10\,GeV$. With an $c\bar{c} \rightarrow \mu + X$ branching ratio of $18 \pm 2\%$ this results into $\sigma(ep \rightarrow c\bar{c} + X) = (0.99\pm0.21\pm0.50)\,\mu b$. The different choices of structure functions lead to an additional systematic error of 35% due to the acceptance.

The total photoproduction cross-section is derived by integrating the photon flux for $W_{min} = 10\,GeV$. The resulting $\sigma(\gamma p \rightarrow c\bar{c} + X) = (3.6 \pm 0.8 \pm 1.8)\,\mu b$ at a mean $W_{\gamma p}$ of $\approx 114\,GeV$ is shown in figure 4 together with earlier measurement at lower values of $W_{\gamma p}$[7] and QCD calculations by Ellis and Nason [8].

5. D^* analysis[††]

The production of c quarks is studied by tagging $D^{*\pm}$ mesons in the decay chain $D^{*\pm} \rightarrow D^0 \pi_s^{\pm}, D^0 \rightarrow K^{\pm}\pi^{\mp}$. Candidates are built from 3 tracks in the central tracker with some minimum p_t and using the specific energy loss for particle identification. With $|m(K\pi)-m(D^0)| < 50\,MeV$, less than 10 tracks in total and more backward

††Analysis is in early stage, results are preliminary.

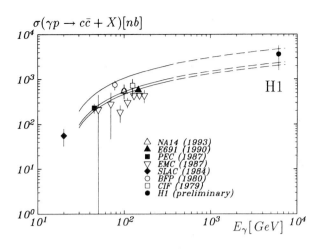

Figure 4. Total cross-section for $\gamma p \rightarrow c\bar{c} + X$. The solid curves show QCD calculations by [8] for m_c=1.5 GeV and the dashed extrapolations to HERA energies using a logarithmic rise.

than forward going tracks 21.6 ± 9.0 candidates are observed in the $m(K\pi\pi_s) - m(K\pi)$ distribution in figure 5 for an integrated luminosity of $280\,nb^{-1}$.

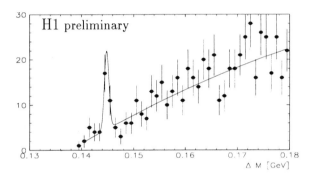

Figure 5. $m(K\pi\pi_s) - m(K\pi)$

References

[1] I. Abt et al., H1, DESY preprint 93-103 (1993)

[2] U. Camerini et al., Phys. Rev. Lett. **35** (1975) 483
J. Clark et al., BPF, Phys. Rev. Lett. **43** (1979) 187
J.J. Aubert et al., EMC, Nucl. Phys. **B213** (1983) 1
M. Arneodo et al., NMC, Phys. Lett. **B332** (1994) 195
P.L. Frabetti et al., E687, Phys. Lett. **B316** (1993) 197
B.H. Denby et al., FTPS, Phys. Rev. Lett. **52** (1984) 795
R. Barate et al., NA-14, Zeit. Phys. **C33** (1987) 505
M. Binkley et al., E401, Phys. Rev. Lett. **48** (1982) 73

[3] V.M. Budnev et al., Phys. Rep. **C15** (1975) 181

[4] H. Jung et al. Zeit. Phys. **C60** (1993) 721

[5] A.D. Martin et al., Phys. Lett. **B306** (1993) 145

[6] M. Aguilar-Benitez et al., PDG, Phys. Rev. **D45** (1992)

[7] M.P. Alvarez et al., NA-14, Zeit. Phys. **C60** (1993) 53
J.C. Anjos et al., E691, Phys. Rev. Lett. **65** (1990) 2503
M. Adamovich et al., PEC, Phys. Lett. **B187** (1987) 437
M. Arneodo et al., EMC, Zeit. Phys. **C35** (1987) 1
K. Abe et al., SLAC, Phys. Rev. **D30** (1984) 1
A.R. Clark et al., BFP, Phys. Rev. Lett. **45** (1980) 682
M.S. Atiya et al., CIF, Phys. Rev. Lett. **43** (1979) 414

[8] R.K. Ellis, P. Nason, Nucl. Phys. **B312** (1989) 551

Study of charmed meson states photoproduced at high energy at Fermilab

G.Bellini and D.Pedrini

Dipartimento di Fisica dell'Università and I.N.F.N. Milano, Via Celoria 16, 20133 Milan, Italy

On behalf of the E687 collaboration[†]

Abstract

The E687 collaboration collected 10^5 charmed particles with a photon beam of 220 GeV mean energy at Fermilab. Many results have been obtained on the charmed mesons. Here we present a study of the production mechanism and correlations using the double D events, the hadronic decays with a particular emphasis on the Cabibbo suppressed processes, a 3-body amplitude analysis using the Dalitz plot technique, a new measurement of the semileptonic decay $D^0 \rightarrow K^-\mu\nu$ and new limits on the CP violation in the charm decays

1. Study of the photoproduction mechanism

Correlations between two fully reconstructed D's can be used to test photoproduction models. The acoplanarity angle $\Delta\phi$ is the angle between the D and the $\overline{D}$ momentum vectors in the plane transverse to the photon direction. At the leading order the acoplanarity is expected to be π radians and the p_t^2 of the $D\overline{D}$ pair 0. The $\Delta\phi$ and p_t^2 distributions from our sample of 325 ± 23 fully reconstructed $D\overline{D}$ pairs show good agreement with the NLO QCD prediction of FNMR[1]. When the NLO result is supplemented with a fragmentation model and an intrinsic k_t kick, the agreement with our data is improved.

† Coauthors: P.L.Frabetti **Bologna**; J.P.Cumalat, C.Dallapiccola, J.F.Ginkel, S.V.Greene, W.E.Johns, M.S.Nehring **Colorado**; J.N.Butler, H.W.K.Cheung, S.Cihangir, I.Gaines, P.H.Garbincius, L.Garren, S.A.Gourlay, D.J.Harding, P.Kasper, A.Kreymer, P.Lebrun, S.Shukla, M.Vittone **Fermilab**; S.Bianco, F.L.Fabbri, S.Sarwar, A.Zallo **Frascati**; R.Culbertson, R.Gardner, R.Greene, J.Wiss **Illinois**; G.Alimonti, B.Caccianiga, L.Cinquini, M.Di Corato, M.Giammarchi, P.Inzani, F.Leveraro, D.Menasce, E.Meroni, L.Moroni, L.Perasso, A.Sala, S.Sala, D.Torretta **Milano**; D.Buchholz, D.Claes, B.Gobbi, B.O'Reilly **Northwestern**; J.M.Bishop, N.M.Cason, C.J.Kennedy, G.N.Kim, T.F.Lin, D.L.Puseljic, R.C.Ruchti, W.D.Shephard, J.A.Swiatek, Z.Y.Wu **Notre Dame**; V.Arena, G.Boca, C.Castoldi, G.Gianini, S.Malvezzi, S.P.Ratti, L.Viola, P.Vitulo **Pavia**; A.Lopez **Puerto Rico**; G.P.Grim, V.S.Paolone, P.M.Yager **Davis**; J.R.Wilson **South Carolina**; P.D.Sheldon **Vanderbilt**; F.Davenport **North Carolina**; J.F.Filaseta **Northern Kentucky**; G.R.Blackett, M.Pisharody, T.Handler **Tennessee**; B.G.Cheon, S.Kang, K.Y.Kim **Korea**

2. Hadronic decays

The hadronic decays of the D mesons are remarkable because they address important questions about the non-spectator contributions to the charm decays and the Final State Interactions (FSI). In particular the E687 collaboration studied some rare decays, as $D^0 \rightarrow K^-K^+K^-\pi^+$, $D^0 \rightarrow K_s^0 K_s^0 K_s^0$ and several Cabibbo suppressed decays, as $D^0 \rightarrow \pi^-\pi^+$, $D^0 \rightarrow K^-K^+$, $D^0 \rightarrow \pi^-\pi^-\pi^+\pi^+$, $D^0 \rightarrow K^-K^+\pi^-\pi^+$, $D^0 \rightarrow K^0\overline{K^0}$, $D^+(D_s) \rightarrow 5\pi$ (throughout this paper the charge conjugate state is implied when a decay mode of a specific charge is stated).

The ratio $\Gamma(D^0 \rightarrow K^-K^+)/\Gamma(D^0 \rightarrow \pi^-\pi^+)$ is interesting because the theoretical models predict a value around 1.4, while the experiments measure 2.5. Our measurement[2] confirms a large value for this branching ratio. There are several theoretical explanations for this disagreement: one involves FSI which shift the relative rates into the various two body channels differently for $\pi\pi$ and KK final states altering the ratio; another invokes penguin diagrams which interfere constructively with the spectator decay for KK but destructively for $\pi\pi$.

B.R.	$\dfrac{\Gamma(D^0 \to 4\pi)}{\Gamma(D^0 \to K3\pi)}$	$\dfrac{\Gamma(D^0 \to 2K2\pi)}{\Gamma(D^0 \to K3\pi)}$
E691	$.096 \pm .018 \pm .007$	$.028^{+.008}_{-.007}$
CLEO	$.102 \pm .013$	$.0314 \pm .010$
ARGUS		$.041 \pm .007 \pm .005$
E687	$.097 \pm .006 \pm .002$	$.034 \pm .004 \pm .002$

B.R.	$\dfrac{\Gamma(D^0 \to 3K\pi)}{\Gamma(D^0 \to K3\pi)}$	
E687	$.0028 \pm .0007 \pm .0002$	

Table 1. Four body B.R. and comparison with previous results

The measured 4-body decays of D^0 are shown in Fig.1 and the branching ratios relative to $D^0 \to K^-\pi^+\pi^-\pi^+$ are reported in Table 1.

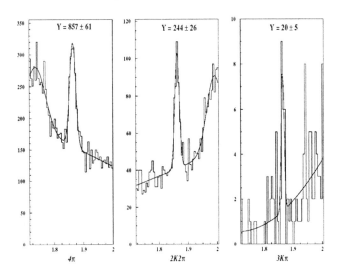

Fig. 1: Charged 4-body decay modes of D^0

Our results constitute a significant improvement with respect to the previous ones.

The 4-body branching ratio $\Gamma(D^0 \to 2K2\pi)/\Gamma(D^0 \to 4\pi) = 0.35 \pm 0.05 \pm 0.02$ as measured by our collaboration shows an opposite direction with respect to the 2-body branching ratio $\Gamma(D^0 \to 2K)/\Gamma(D^0 \to 2\pi) = 2.53 \pm 0.46 \pm 0.19$. This result supports the interpretation that Cabibbo suppressed decays occur more or less equally with and without strangeness at the quark final-state level, although the hadronic 2-body and 4-body final states do not separately show this symmetry[3].

Our measurements of the relative branching ratios of $D^0 \to K^0\overline{K^0}$ and $D^0 \to 3K^0_s$ are reported in Table 2. These results support the importance of the FSI in the charm decays. In fact, simple spectator diagrams do not contribute to either of these decay modes, and thus they can provide information on the importance of other processes. The decay $D^0 \to 3K^0_s$ is Cabibbo allowed and could result from W-exchange or FSI. For the decay $D^0 \to K^0\overline{K^0}$ there are two W-exchange diagrams which

B.R.	$\dfrac{\Gamma(D^0 \to \overline{K^0K^0})}{\Gamma(D^0 \to K^0\pi^+\pi^-))}$	$\dfrac{\Gamma(D^0 \to K^0_sK^0_sK^0_s)}{\Gamma(D^0 \to K^0\pi^+\pi^-))}$
ARGUS	$< .016$ (90% C.L.)	$.017 \pm .007 \pm .005$
CLEO	$.021^{+0.011+.002}_{-.008-.002}$	$.016 \pm .005$
E687	$.039 \pm .013 \pm .013$	$.035 \pm .012 \pm .006$

Table 2. Multi K^0_s B.R. and comparison with other measurements

cancel almost exactly due to the GIM mechanism, and thus the decay would occur primarily through FSI.

E687 reports the first significant evidence of $D^+, D_s \to 5\pi$; the signals are shown in Fig.2 with and without the out-of-target cut. We studied, in fact, very carefully the signals inside and outside the target to reduce the contamination of the secondary interactions and to limit the multiple Coulomb scattering.

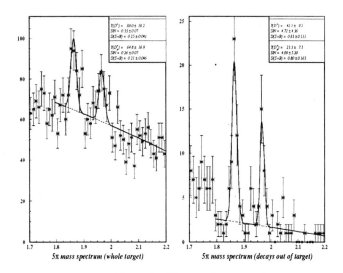

Fig. 2: 5π mass with and without the out-of-target cut

3. Dalitz plot analysis

A detailed Dalitz plot analysis has been performed on the decays of charmed mesons into 3-body final states. The phenomenological amplitude used to fit the data is a sum of Breit-Wigner terms with appropriate angular factors and a constant term to represent the assumed uniform non-resonant contribution. The $K\pi\pi$ Dalitz plot analysis has already been completed[4]. The isospin amplitudes, I = 1/2 and 3/2, have been computed using the branching fractions obtained from this analysis in the modes $D^0 \to K^{*-}\pi^+$, $D^0 \to K^{*0}\pi^0$ and $D^+ \to K^{*0}\pi^+$. A ratio $|A_{1/2}|/|A_{3/2}| = 5.9 \pm 0.3 \pm 0.3$ and a phase shift $\delta_{1/2} - \delta_{3/2} = 95 \pm 16 \pm 21°$ have been measured; this phase difference indicates the importance of FSI in charm decays.

Fig.3 shows the $D^+(D_s) \to K^- K^+ \pi^+$ signals along with their Dalitz plots. The results are still preliminary, however the D_s Dalitz plot shows clearly that the $KK\pi$ decay is dominated by the $\phi\pi$ and the $\overline{K^{*0}}K$ channels. The non-ϕ and non-$\overline{K^{*0}}$ events may be attributed either to the non-resonant or to the $f_0(975)\pi$ channel.

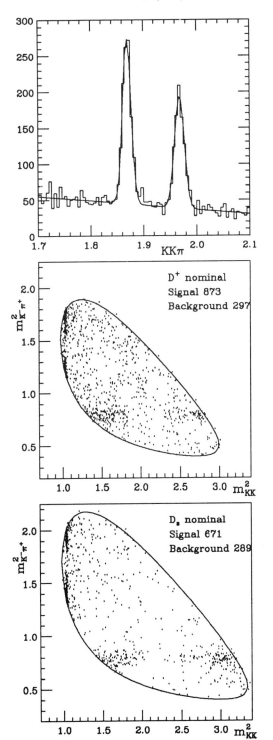

Fig. 3: $D^+, D_s \to K^- K^+ \pi^+$ signals and Dalitz plot

Mode	Asymmetry	90% C.L. limit
$D^0 \to K^- K^+$	$.024 \pm .084$	$-11\% < A_{CP} < 16\%$
$D^+ \to K^- K^+ \pi^+$	$-.031 \pm .068$	$-14\% < A_{CP} < 8.1\%$
$D^+ \to K^{*0} K^+$	$-.12 \pm .13$	$-33\% < A_{CP} < 9.4\%$
$D^+ \to \phi\pi^+$	$.066 \pm .086$	$-7.5\% < A_{CP} < 21\%$

Table 3. CP violating asymmetry and 90% C.L. limits

4.   The semileptonic decay $D^0 \to K^- \mu^+ \nu$

A new measurement of the semileptonic decay $D^0 \to K^- \mu^+ \nu$ has been performed relaxing the D^* tag requirement to increase statistics. The preliminary results from the non-tagged signal are : $\Gamma(D^0 \to K^- \mu^+ \nu)/\Gamma(D^0 \to K^- \pi^+) = 0.860 \pm 0.028^{+0.042}_{-0.039}$, $M_{pole} = 1.98^{+0.13+0.04}_{-0.10-0.10}$ and $f_+(0) = 0.730^{+0.020+0.029}_{-0.021-0.033}$. Our results agree within 2σ with a recent CLEO measurement[5], but we are unable to rule out a significant f_- contribution to the semimuonic branching fraction.

5.   CP violation in charm meson decays

Recent theoretical calculations have shown that sizeable CP violation effects could occur in the charm meson decays within the standard model. A signature for CP violation would be an asymmetry (A_{CP}) in the decay rate of a charm decay mode and its conjugate. The only existing limit for CP violation in charm meson decay is for the Cabibbo suppressed mode $D^0 \to K^- K^+$: $A_{CP} < 45\%[6]$. Our results are summarized in Table 3 [7]. All measured asymmetries are consistent with zero.

6.   Conclusions

We have presented several new measurements of rare charm meson decays. The high statistics data samples, now available, are giving quantitative constraints to the theoretical models; for example our recent results support the importance of the final state interactions in the charm meson decays.

References

[1] S. Frixione, M. Mangano, P. Nason, G. Ridolfi, Nucl. Phys. **B412** (1994) 225;*ibid.* "Charm and Bottom production: Theoretical Results Versus Experimental Data" CERN-TH.7292/94
[2] P.L. Frabetti *et al.*, Phys. Lett. **B321** (1994) 295.
[3] J.C. Anjos *et al.*, Phys. Rev. Lett. **D43** (1991) R635.
[4] P.L. Frabetti *et al.*, Phys. Lett. **B331** (1994) 217.
[5] A. Bean *et al.*, Phys. Lett. **B317** (1993) 647.
[6] J.C. Anjos *et al.*, Phys. Rev. Lett. **D44** (1991) R3371.
[7] P.L. Frabetti *et al.*, Fermilab preprint : FERMILAB-PUB-94-71-E.

New Preliminary Results on the Physics of
Charm Hadroproduction Subprocesses

Jeffrey A. Appel[†‡]

† Fermi National Accelerator Laboratory, Batavia, IL 60510 USA*

Abstract

This paper reviews the results and physics of two contributed papers to ICHEP94. Both papers relate to charm meson hadroproduction at Fermilab fixed target energies. The first (from E769) addresses the total forward cross section for charm mesons ($D^{\pm}$ and $D_s^{\pm}$) produced by $\pi^{\pm}$, $K^{\pm}$, and proton beams. The second paper (from E791) deals with the asymmetries in the differential cross sections for charged D mesons produced in the forward direction by π^- beam.

The physics most directly related to the results of the E769 paper are the gluon distributions in the incident hadrons as well as perturbative QCD calculations of charm quark production and the charm quark mass. The E791 results address the details of the hadronization process after production of the charm quarks.

1. Introduction

QCD subprocess cross-sections for the creation of $c\bar{c}$ pairs in high-energy parton interactions have been calculated perturbatively up to next-to-leading order (NLO). Convolution of these with the quark and gluon distribution functions of mesons and baryons allows for calculation of the total rate of charm production in hadronic collisions [1]. Fragmentation to particular charm final states, however, cannot be treated perturbatively, thus complicating the calculation of hadroproduction cross-sections for charm particles. For example, enhanced production in the forward hemisphere of particles which share a quark with the projectile particle (the leading-particle effect) is a feature of some phenomenological models [2,3] and indeed has been observed at levels not attributable to the underlying perturbative process of charm quark production [4-6]. Fermilab experiments E769 and E791 have new results [7,8 respectively] on these topics.

‡ E-mail: appel@fnal.gov.
* Work supported by the U.S. Department of Energy under contract No. DE-AC02-76CH03000.

2. Comparison of Experiments E769 and E791

Table 1 gives a comparison of the major differences between E769 and E791. Both experiments took data using the Tagged Photon Spectrometer at Fermilab. The earlier experiment E769 focused on production issues, including dependence on incident particle type. This provides comparisons among charged pions, charged kaons and protons. The major upgrade for E791 was a massive increase in data handling capability [9] and higher beam energy, but without the E769 trigger enhancement of minority beam particles. E791 used only negative beam, while E769, in addition to its negative beam measurements, has made the first measurements of charm production with positive pions and positive kaons.

3. Forward $D^{\pm}$ and $D_s^{\pm}$ Cross-sections

E769's preliminary measurements of the $D^{\pm}$ and $D_s^{\pm}$ production cross-sections are listed in Table 2. Errors quoted for the $D^{\pm}$ are statistical and systematic, in that order; only statistical errors are shown for the $D_s^{\pm}$.

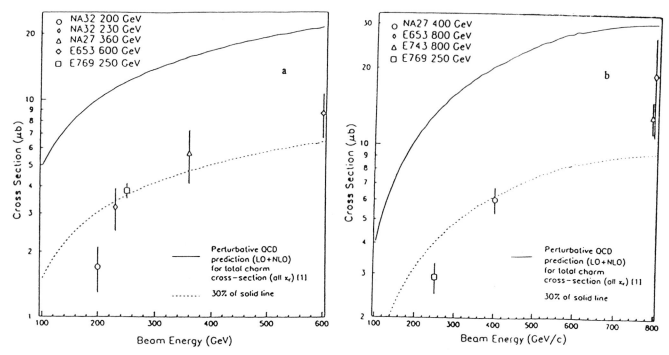

Figure 1. Measurements of (a) $\sigma_{x_F>0}(\pi^- N \to D^\pm X)$ and (b) $\sigma_{x_F>0}(pN \to D^\pm X)$ versus beam energy. The curves are for total charm quark production, i.e., all x_F.

Description	Experiment E769	Experiment E791
Years Data Taken	1987-8	1991-2
Beam Energy	250 GeV	500 GeV
Beam Particle ID	Cerenkov,TRD	none
Targets	W,Cu,Al,Be	Pt,C
No. of Events	400 M	20,000 M
Data Set Size	1.5 TBytes	50 TBytes
Recon. Decays	4,000	>200,000

Table 1. Comparisons of Fermilab experiments E769 and E791.

Beam, B	$\sigma_{x_F>0}(BN \to D^\pm X)$	$\sigma_{x_F>0}(BN \to D_s^\pm X)$
π^-	$3.8 \pm 0.3 \pm 0.2$	1.9 ± 0.4
π^+	$3.9 \pm 0.4 \pm 0.4$	2.9 ± 0.9
K^-	$2.8 \pm 0.5 \pm 0.8$	3.5 ± 1.3
K^+	$3.1 \pm 0.4 \pm 0.4$	2.8 ± 1.1
p^+	$2.9 \pm 0.4 \pm 0.2$	$< 1.9(90\%c.l.)$

Table 2. Each cross section is in microbarn/nucleon and is for the sum of mesons observed in the forward hemisphere, the particles and the antiparticles.

Branching fractions from the 1992 Review of Particle Properties [10] were used; their errors are not included.

For both the $D^\pm$ and $D_s^\pm$, no significant differences in beam particle and antiparticle-induced cross-sections are observed. Also consistent with being equal are the π and K induced cross-sections, suggesting that the gluon distribution functions of the two mesons are similar. Additionally, fragmentation of charm to $D_s^\pm$

is not greatly suppressed with respect to $D^\pm$ at this energy. Nor is $D_s^\pm$ production enhanced by having the appropriate strange quark in the projectile. This lends support to the dominance of gluon-gluon fusion in the theory.

In Figures 1(a) and 1(b), respectively, E769 results for π^- and p induced $D^\pm$ production are displayed alongside previous measurements. Assuming a constant $D^\pm$ fragmentation rate, the energy dependence of $D^\pm$ production can be compared to the theoretical predictions for all charm, as shown in the figures. Given this, it appears that the steepness of the data points vs energy with respect to the theoretical curves points to too hard gluon distributions and/or too low an effective charm quark mass in the parameterizations used in the theoretical calculations.

4.   Production Asymmetries

Previous experiments [4,6] have seen asymmetries in the hadronic production of charmed mesons. Mesons which have a light quark in common with the incoming beam ("leading particles") have a harder momentum spectrum than those which do not ("non-leading particles"). In the case of E791, with its π^- ($d\bar{u}$) beam, the D^- ($d\bar{c}$) is leading and the D^+ ($\bar{d}c$) is non-leading.

Next to leading order PQCD calculations [1] predict, for a π^- beam, only a very small excess in $\bar{c}$ quarks relative to c quarks in the very forward direction. This effect is much smaller than that seen in data.

Another possible explanation of the asymmetry is inherent in the Lund "string fragmentation" model [11]. In this model, forward momentum is added to the produced heavy quarks as they combine with the remnant light quarks from the incoming beam particle. As implemented in the model, the string connections cause the leading particles to have a harder momentum spectrum than non-leading particles. However, unlike the data, the default parameters in the model give a large asymmetry, even at low momentum. The shape matches the asymmetry better if the number of D^+ produced is forced to match the number of D^-.

A third possible source of asymmetry is intrinsic charm [3]. Here, a virtual $c\bar{c}$ pair in the incoming beam particle is knocked onto the mass shell in a small percentage of the interactions. The recent publication in reference 3 compares its predicted results to past data and predicts asymmetries as a function of transverse momentum. The prediction for the asymmetry versus longitudinal momentum matches the data. However, equality of the overall D^+ and D^- production is put into the prediction by hand and the prediction depends on selected phenomenological parameters.

One can also study production asymmetries for D^0's and D^*'s. For the D^0's, however, a large fraction of the D^0's (typically 1/3 of those observed) are produced by the $D^{*+} \to D^0 \pi^+$ decay process. The original D^{*+} is actually a *non*-leading particle. Therefore, the observed D^0's come from a mixture of leading and non-leading processes, making the study more complex.

A produced charm meson may be described by its x_F, the scaled longitudinal momentum (Feynman x), and its P_t, transverse momentum. In order to show small differences in distributions in different x_F and P_t regions, an asymmetry parameter is calculated for each region. For a π^- beam, this parameter, A, is defined as:

$$A \equiv \frac{N_{D^-} - N_{D^+}}{N_{D^-} + N_{D^+}}$$

where N_D is the number of that meson produced within that x_F or P_t bin. (Note that since the acceptance for D^+ and D^- is nearly the same in the detectors, A is independent of the acceptance values.)

The new preliminary E791 $D^\pm$ forward asymmetries are very similar to the earlier WA82 and E769 published results. However, E791 has more than an order of magnitude more data, even in the reported 1/3 of their total data sample (9363 ± 96 $D^\pm$ vs 863 ± 32 $D^\pm$ from WA82 and 919 ± 37 $D^\pm$ and 600 ± 30 $D^{*\pm}$ from E769). Thus, E791 can examine, for example, the P_t^2 asymmetry distribution in restricted regions of x_F. PYTHIA-LUND predicts a slight increase in A with increasing P_t^2. The intrinsic charm model predicts a maximum at P_t^2 of zero, decreasing with P_t^2. The effect would be strongest in mesons with large values of x_F in

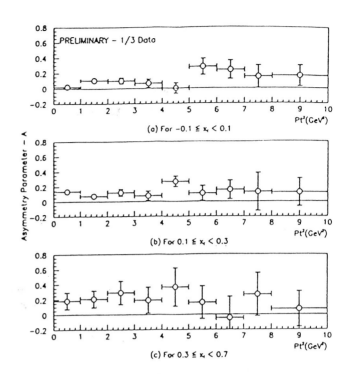

Figure 2. Asymmetry vs P_t^2 in various regions of x_F.

both models. Figure 2 shows the value of A vs P_t^2 for different regions of x_F. The data does not match either prediction.

5. Acknowledgements

I am very indebted to my colleagues on E769 and E791 their help and for allowing me to report on the results of their work and especially to Tom Carter and Andrew Wallace.

References

[1] P. Nason, S. Dawson, and K. Ellis, Nucl. Phys. **B327** (1989) 49.

[2] B.L. Combridge, Nucl. Phys. **B151** (1979) 429.

[3] S.J. Brodsky *et al.*, Phys. Lett. **93B** (1980) 451 and R. Vogt and S.J. Brodsky SLAC-PUB-6468 (1994).

[4] WA82 Collaboration, M. Adamovich *et al.*, Phys. Lett. **B305** (1993) 402.

[5] E769 Collaboration, G.A. Alves *et al.*, Phys. Rev. Lett. **69** (1992) 3147 and Phys. Rev. **D49** (1994) R4317.

[6] E769 Collaboration, G.A. Alves *et al.*, Phys. Rev. Lett. **72** (1994) 812 and **72** (1994) 1946.

[7] E769 Collaboration: A. Wallace *et al.*, Fermilab preprint: FERMILAB-Conf-94-184-E (submitted paper gls0679).

[8] E791 Collaboration: T. Carter *et al.*, Fermilab preprint: FERMILAB-Conf-94-185-E (submitted paper gls0662).

[9] S. Amato *et al.*, Nucl. Instr. Meth. **A324** (1993) 535.

[10] Particle Data Group, K. Hikasa *et al.*, Phys. Rev. **D45** (1992) II.12.

[11] T. Sjostrand CERN-TH.6488-92 (PYTHIA 5.6 Manual) (FNAL PM0087).

CHARMONIUM PRODUCTION
IN 800 GeV/c pSi INTERACTIONS.

The E-771 collaboration

T. Alexopoulos[1], L. Antoniazzi[2], M. Arenton[3], H.C. Ballagh[4], H. Bingham[4], A. Blankman[5],
M. Block[6], A. Boden[7], G. Bonomi[2], S.V. Borodin[5], J. Budagov[8], Z.L. Cao[3], G. Cataldi[9],
T.Y. Chen[10], K. Clark[11], D. Cline[7], S. Conetti[3], M. Cooper[12], G.Corti[3], B. Cox[3], P. Creti[9],
C. Dukes[3], C. Durandet[1], V. Elia[9], A.R. Erwin[1], E. Evangelista[9], L. Fortney[13], V. Golovatyuk[3],
E. Gorini[9], F. Grancagnolo[9], K. Hagan-Ingram[3], M. Haire[14], P. Hanlet[3], M. He[15], G. Introzzi[2],
M. Jenkins[11], J. Jennings[1], D. Judd[14], W. Kononenko[5], W. Kowald[13], K. Lau[16], T. Lawry[3],
A. Ledovskoy[3], G. Liguori[2], J. Lys[4], P.O. Mazur[17], A. McManus[3], S. Misawa[4], G.H. Mo[16],
C.T. Murphy[17], K. Nelson[3], M. Panareo[9], V. Pogosian[3], S. Ramachandran[7], M. Recagni[3],
J. Rhoades[7], J. Segal[3], W. Selove[5], R.P. Smith[17], L. Spiegel[17], J.G. Sun[3], S. Tokar[18], P. Torre[2],
J. Trischuk[19], L. Turnbull[14], I. Tzamouranis[3], D.E. Wagoner[14], C.R. Wang[15], C. Wei[13], W. Yang[17],
N. Yao[10], N.J. Zhang[15], S.N. Zhang[5] and B.T. Zou[13]

1. University of Wisconsin, Madison, Wisconsin, USA; 2. Pavia INFN and University, Pavia, Italy; 3. University of
Virginia, Charlottesville, Virginia, USA; 4. University of California at Berkeley, Berkeley, California, USA; 5. University of
Pennsylvania, Philadelphia, Pennsylvania, USA; 6. Northwestern University, Evanston, Illinois, USA; 7. University of
California at Los Angeles, Los Angeles, California, USA 8. JINR, Dubna, Russia; 9. Lecce INFN and University, Lecce, Italy;
10. Nanjing University, Nanjing, People's Republic of China; 11. University of South Alabama, Mobile, Alabama, USA;
12. Vanier College, Montreal, Quebec, Canada; 13. Duke University, Durham, North Carolina, USA; 14. Prairie View A&M,
Prairie View, Texas, USA; 15. Shandong University, Jinan, Shandong, People's Republic of China; 16. University of
Houston, Houston, Texas, USA; 17. Fermilab, Batavia, Illinois, USA; 18. Comenius University, Bratislava, Slovakia;
19. McGill University, Montreal, Quebec, Canada

Abstract

We report on the analysis of high mass opposite sign dimuon states produced in pSi interactions at
$\sqrt{s} = 38.7$ GeV. These data have been collected with an open geometry fixed target spectrometer
in the Fermilab Experiment E771. J/ψ and $\psi(2S)$ total cross sections and x_f and p_t differential
cross sections have been measured and compared with extrapolations from data at lower energies.
Evidence for possible production of a $^3D_2$ state of charmonium is also presented.

1. Introduction

The hadronic production of charmonium has been, and
still is, an important test of QCD. Given the energy
scale of this process and the relatively small coupling
constant, perturbative QCD is expected to produce a
reliable description of the production. The leading
processes at Fermilab Tevatron fixed target energies are
gluon-gluon (at low x_F) and q-q̄ fusion (at high x_F),
with the cautionary note that direct J/ψ production
should not proceed from a simple two gluon diagram.

In this paper we present data from FNAL E771
on the production of some charmonium states in p-Si
interactions at 800 GeV/c.

2. E771 experimental setup

The E771 spectrometer[1] consisted of 31 wire planes positioned upstream and 28 planes located downstream of a 0.821 GeV/c p_t kick analysis magnet. The spectrometer included a 12 plane silicon microstrip vertex detector and an electromagnetic calorimeter, neither of which were used in the following analysis. A muon detector was located downstream of the tracking chambers, consisting of three planes of scintillator and Resistive Plate Counters[2] (RPCs) interspersed among three steel and concrete shielding walls.

The average beam intensity during the E771 data run was approximately 4×10^7 protons/s, impinging on a target of 12 silicon foils (each foil 2 mm thick) spaced 4 mm apart. Selective single and dimuon triggers were implemented, where a muon was defined by the triple coincidence of signals in corresponding sets of pads in the three RPC planes[3].

3. Data Analysis

The sample of 1.27×10^8 dimuon triggers accumulated on tape was analyzed to search for muon candidates,first identified in the muon detector using the RPC pads and scintillators. Track segments downstream of the analysis magnet were then reconstructed within a search window defined by the RPC muon tracks. Track segments upstream of the analysis magnet were reconstructed and matched to downstream muon segments to form momentum-determined muon tracks. Opposite sign dimuon pairs were required to originate from a common vertex. In a given event only the dimuon pair forming the best common vertex was selected for further studies.

The dimuon mass spectrum of these best pairs is shown in Fig. 1.

4. J/ψ and $\psi(2S)$ Total Cross Sections

Superimposed on the dimuon mass spectrum in Fig. 1 is a fit to the data using the sum of two Gaussians for the J/ψ peak, a single Gaussian for the $\psi(2S)$ peak and an exponential for the background. Two Gaussians produce a better fit to the J/ψ state since a sizable fraction of the muons inhabit regions of the detector with high track density producing non-Gaussian tails. From the fit of Fig. 1 we obtain $N_{J/\psi} = 12733 \pm 208$ and $N_{\psi(2S)}=207\pm23$ for the background subtracted number of events in the J/ψ and $\psi(2S)$ peaks, respectively.

To determine overall reconstruction efficiencies and acceptance, we generated 8×10^5 Monte Carlo J/ψ decays into dimuons. The dimuons were propagated through a GEANT simulation of the E771 detector. The hit information from this simulation was superimposed onto data events to provide a realistic estimate of

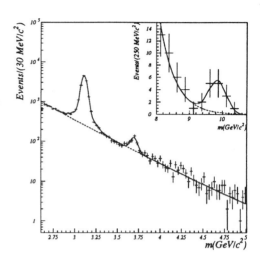

Figure 1. Mass spectrum (fit described in text). In the small frame the Υ region is showed together with an exponential fit to the background.

the background from noise and other tracks associated with the events. The superimposed events were then processed with the same programs as those used on the data.

The total J/ψ inclusive cross section per nucleon, evaluated assuming an atomic weight dependence of $A^\alpha = A^{0.920\pm0.008}$[4], was determined to be $330 \pm 5 \pm 35$ nb/nucleon, where the first error is statistical and the second is systematic.

Applying a similar technique to the $\psi(2S)$ we determined the inclusive $\psi(2S)$ production cross section to be $36 \pm 4 \pm 10$ nb/nucleon.

We have compared our J/ψ $Br\cdot\sigma$ to that of previous experiments (Fig. 2) as a function of $\sqrt{s}$. The data have been fit[5] to the threshold production parameterization

$$Br \cdot \sigma(J/\psi \to \mu^+\mu^-) = \sigma_0 \cdot (1 - M_{J/\psi}/\sqrt{s})^N, \quad (1)$$

with $\sigma_0 = (59 \pm 6)$ nb/nucleon and $N = 11.7 \pm 0.5$.

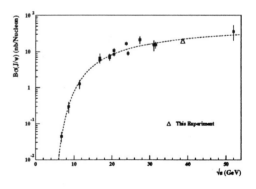

Figure 2. Threshold production parametrization $Br \cdot \sigma(J/\psi)$ vs c.m. energy. The parametrization is described in the text. The data points are from [5], [6] and references therein.

5. Differential Cross Sections

The x_F and p_T differential cross sections for J/ψ, corrected for acceptance and normalized by luminosity, are shown in Fig. 3a and 3b. The parametrization used to fit the x_F curve is:

$$\frac{d\sigma}{dx_F} \propto (1 - |x_F|)^c. \tag{2}$$

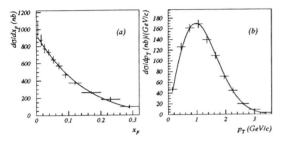

Figure 3. J/ψ x_F (a) and p_T (b) distribution fitted with the parametrization described in the text.

Our fitted value $c=6.8 \pm 0.3$ (the error is statistical) is in good agreement with an extrapolated value of $c=6.2 \pm 2.6$, obtained from a parameterization[5] of the energy dependence of the c parameter based on data from other experiments.

The J/ψ cross section as a function of transverse momentum (p_T), has been fit to the expression:

$$\frac{d\sigma}{dp_T} \propto p_T \cdot \exp\left(-bp_T^2\right). \tag{3}$$

The fitted values of the b parameter and of the mean and mean squared of the transverse momentum obtained are respectively $b=0.54 \pm 0.02$, $< p_T >=1.20 \pm 0.02$ and $< p_T^2 >=1.85 \pm 0.06$. The energy dependence parameterization of Ref.5, extrapolated to our $\sqrt{s}=38.7$ energy, gives $< p_T >=1.17 \pm 0.05$ in good agreeement with our data.

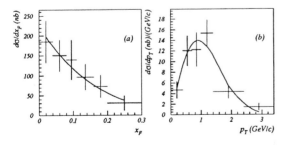

Figure 4. $\psi(2S)$ x_F (a) and p_T (b) distribution fitted with the parametrization described in the text.

We have also investigated the x_F and p_T differential cross sections for the $\psi(2S)$. The distributions, obtained

in the same manner as those of the J/ψ, are shown in Fig. 4. In analogy with the J/ψ, we used the form of Eq. (2) to fit the x_F distribution and the form of Eq. (3) to fit the p_T curve. The fitted values of the c and b parameters are respectively $c=6.2 \pm 1.i$ and $b=0.6 \pm 0.2$.

6. Search for a New Charmonium State

Finally, we have examined the $J/\psi\pi\pi$ mass combinations, looking for a confirmation of a possible $^3D_2$ charmonium state, which has been tentatively observed by a previous experiment[7] at a mass of $3.836\ Gev/c^2$. Fig. 5 shows the $J/\psi\pi\pi$ mass spectrum for opposite sign as well as same sign dipions. In the opposite sign sample, a double peak structure appears to be present, where the first peak is identified with the $\psi(2S)$ decay into $J/\psi\pi\pi$, while the second peak seems to agree with the observation of Ref. 7. If confirmed, this preliminary result will eventually be analyzed to produce a value of $Br \cdot \sigma$ for the new charmonium level.

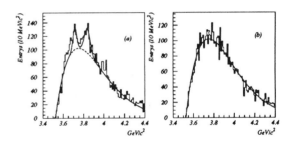

Figure 5. a) Invariant $J/\Psi\pi^+\pi^-$ mass. b) Invariant $J/\Psi\pi^\pm\pi^\pm$ mass.

7. Acknowledgments

We acknowledge the invaluable help of the Fermilab staff including the Research and Computing Division personnel. This work is supported by the U.S. Department of Energy, the National Science Foundation, the Natural Science and Engineering Research Council of Canada, the Instituto Nazionale di Fisica Nucleare of Italy and the Texas Advanced Research Program.

References

[1] T.Alexopoulos *et al*, Nucl. Phys., B27 257 (1992).
[2] G.Cataldi *et al.*, Nucl. Instr. and Meth., A337 350 (1994).
[3] L. Antoniazzi *et al.*, FNAL E771 Fast Muon Trigger, To appear in Nucl. Instr. and Meth.
[4] M.R. Adams *et al.*, Phys. Rev. Lett., B66 133 (1991).
[5] V.Abramov *et al.*, E672/706 Collaboration, FERMILAB-PUB-91/62-E (1991).
[6] L.Antoniazzi *et al.*, Phys. Rev., D46 4828 (1992).
[7] L.Antoniazzi *et al.*, to appear in Phys. Rev. D.

Production of Charmed Baryons in the CERN Hyperon Beam Experiment WA89

Roland Werding[‡]

Max-Planck-Institut für Kernphysik, Heidelberg, Germany

Representing the WA89 Collaboration[†]

Abstract

Recent results on charmed baryon production in $330\,\mathrm{GeV}/c\ \Sigma^- N$ interactions are given. Inclusive cross sections in the forward direction for Λ_c^+, Σ_c^0 and D^- indicate a leading particle effect. The x_F distributions for the Λ_c^+, Σ_c^0 and Ξ_c^+ baryons are compared to LUND model predictions, deviations from which are discussed. The charmed strange baryons Ξ_c^+ and Ξ_c^0 have been reconstructed in several decay channels; a preliminary determination of the Ξ_c^+ lifetime and evidence for the $\Xi_c^{+\prime}$ and Ω_c^0 are presented.

1. Introduction

The fixed target experiment WA89 aims at the study of the production and decay properties of charmed baryons using the high energy hyperon beam ($2 \times 10^5 \Sigma^-/$ spill) at the CERN SPS. Assuming leading particle effects to provide an enhanced production in the forward direction, this allows the study of charmed states containing strangeness in addition. Furthermore, flavour dependencies can be investigated by the comparison of charmed and charmed-strange baryons in the forward kinematic region. Leading particle effects due to an overlap of the quark content between projectile and final states have already been observed in the D meson sector [1] but are not yet observed for the hadroproduction of charmed baryons.

2. Event selection

The event reconstruction heavily relies on a silicon vertex detector for tracking and particle identification. The momentum measurement is performed by means of the Omega spectrometer. A detailed description of the experimental setup is given in [2]. Charm events are identified by the reconstruction of an isolated decay vertex and requiring the momentum vector of the charmed particle to point back to the interaction vertex. Final state hyperons are identified by detecting their decay products, and invariant mass criteria are used for particle identification, while for long-lived charged particles the RICH detector serves for their identification where possible.

The experimental setup is dedicated to the reconstruction of charmed particles produced in the forward direction. The total efficiency for charmed baryons is at the level of a few percent for $x_F > 0.15$; below this the detector acceptance drops rapidly. For the transverse momentum p_T almost no efficiency dependence exists up to $p_T \simeq 5\,\mathrm{GeV}/c$.

‡ E-mail: rwe@vsnhdl.cern.ch
† Bristol University - CERN Geneva - Genova University/INFN - ISN Grenoble - MPI für Kernphysik, Heidelberg - Heidelberg University - Institute of Nuclear Physics, Mainz University - Moscow Lebedev Institute.

3.   Spectral distributions

The invariant mass spectra of the final states $pK^-\pi^+$, $pK^-\pi^+\pi^-$, and $\Lambda K^+\pi + \pi+$ show clear signals for the charmed baryons Λ_c^+, Σ_c^0 and Ξ_c^+ respectively (fig. 1, upper row). The peak for the charmed strange baryon Ξ_c^+ was extracted from about 12% of the 1993 data, while the first two signals correspond to the full data sample from 1991. Table 1 summarizes the signal parameters. Based on these data samples, efficiency-corrected differential x_F distributions were measured (fig. 1, lower row). The spectral shapes are fitted according to the parametrization $dN/dx_F \propto (1 - x_F)^n$.

The production spectrum for Λ_c^+ seems to be more steeply falling towards higher x_F than in the case of π beams ($n \simeq 3.7 \pm 0.7$) [3]; this could be attributed to the harder quark and gluon momentum distributions inside mesons as compared to baryons. For the Σ_c^0 this constitutes the first n-value measurement. The Ξ_c^+ measurement agrees with a measurement using a neutron beam [4] but not with the previous hyperon beam measurement [5], which had obtained a flatter distribution for $x_F > 0.6$. None of the observed x_F distributions shows a rise towards high x_F, thus leaving no room for a strong diffractive component.

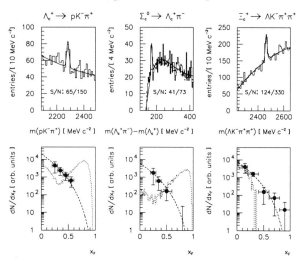

Figure 1. Upper row: invariant mass spectra for $\Lambda_c^+ \rightarrow pK^-\pi^+$, $\Sigma_c^0 \rightarrow \Lambda_c^+\pi^-$ and $\Xi_c^+ \rightarrow \Lambda K^-\pi^+\pi^+$; signal to noise ratios are quoted. Lower row: background and acceptance corrected x_F distributions; solid points represent data; the dashed line shows the results of a fit while the dotted lines stem from PYTHIA simulations; the distributions are not normalized.

As a consistency check we have also measured the differential distribution for D^- mesons, which agrees well with results from pN interactions [6], whereas data from π beams produce a less steep x_F spectrum again [7]. The p_T dependencies of all data samples commonly parametrized by $dN/dp_T \propto \exp(-b\,p_T^2)$ are consistent with the expectation of $b \simeq 1$ GeV$^{-2}c^2$. The values for n can be compared to the QCD prediction

	Mass [MeV/c^2]	S/B	n
Λ_c^+	2281.7 ± 2.3	65/150	$4.9 \pm 1.2 \pm 0.4$
Σ_c^0	$169.5 \pm 1.1^*$	41/73	$4.6 \pm 2.3 \pm 0.6$
Ξ_c^+	2462.2 ± 1.6	124/330	$4.7 \pm 1.6 \pm 0.6$
D^-	1866.5 ± 153	70/120	$5.1 \pm 1.9 \pm 0.4$

Table 1. Parameters of the observed charm signals; * in the case of Σ_c^0 the measured mass difference to Λ_c^+ is quoted.

$n = 6.9$ for the production of free charm quarks in pN reactions [8]. The small differences might indicate hadronization effects. The full reaction mechanism for baryon production should be reproduced by any model containing hadronization, as is done qualitatively by the LUND model for mesons [1]. In the baryon sector we see an obvious deviation in the differential shapes of data from PYTHIA simulations, especially in the forward direction, as demonstrated in figure 1 [9]. The Σ_c^0 has two d-quarks in common with the projectile and the Λ_c^+ can be a direct product of the strong Σ_c^0 decay, whereas the Ξ_c^+ shares only an s-quark with the beam particle. Thus the results point to an overestimation of the leading particle effect induced by the diquark mechanism.

4.   Production ratios and cross sections

By using absolute branching ratios from the PDG, inclusive cross sections are obtained assuming a linear dependence on the target nucleon number (table 2). The D^- cross section is in agreement with other experiments using baryon beams [6]. In the forward region we observe a Λ_c^+ baryon production, which is comparable to D^- mesons. Such an enhanced Λ_c^+ production as compared to D^- mesons has also been measured in pp interactions [6]. This is in contrast to the dominant meson production in e^+e^- or π induced interactions, where quarks for two associated baryons have to be generated.

The large cross section ratio $\sigma(\Sigma_c^0)/\sigma(\Lambda_c^+)$ of 0.45 given in table 3 indicates that genuine Λ_c^+ production is suppressed over production through the leading Σ_c^0. For the understanding of the other measured charm production ratios, leading effects seem to play

	σ [μb /nucleon]	x_F
Λ_c^+	$9.3 \pm 4.3 \pm 2.5$	> 0.2
Σ_c^0	$4.8 \pm 2.6 \pm 1.5$	> 0.2
D^-	$2.9 \pm 0.8 \pm 0.6$	> 0.1

Table 2. Inclusive cross sections.

an important role too. This is demonstrated by the favoured production of Σ_c^0 and D^- as compared to Σ_c^{++} and D^+. PYTHIA predictions also listed in table 3 tend to reproduce the meson/meson and baryon/baryon ratios; especially the Λ_c^+ production through the Σ_c^0 agrees well with the data. However the Λ_c^+/D^- ratio is underestimated.

5. Charmed strange baryons

Using the 1991 data sample we have reconstructed the charmed strange baryons Ξ_c^+ and Ξ_c^0 in the modes $\Lambda K^- \pi^+ \pi^+$, $\Xi^- \pi^+ \pi^+$ and $\Lambda K^- \pi^+, \Xi^- \pi^+$ respectively [2]. The statistically most significant decay mode $\Xi_c^+ \to \Lambda K^- \pi^+ \pi^+$, was used to determine the Ξ_c^+ lifetime by a binned maximum likelihood method. Applying corrections for the reconstruction efficiency we obtain

$$\tau(\Xi_c^+) = 0.32^{+0.08}_{-0.06}(stat.) \pm 0.05(syst.) \text{ ps},$$

which is consistent with other lifetime measurements [4, 10]. Using these Ξ_c^+ candidates, we have searched for the undiscovered $\Xi_c^{+\prime}$ state. While the well established Ξ_c^+ has an antisymmetric spin wave function in the two light quarks (su), the primed multiplet partner has a symmetric one. The spin-spin interaction generates a mass splitting of about 100 MeV/c^2, which leads to the expectation of a radiative decay $\Xi_c^{+\prime} \to \Xi_c^+ \gamma$. Figure 2 shows the mass difference spectrum for both observed Ξ_c^+ decay modes, $\Lambda K^- \pi^+ \pi^+$ and $\Xi^- \pi^+ \pi^+$ separately and combined. About 11 events above background give evidence for the state $\Xi_c^{+\prime}$.

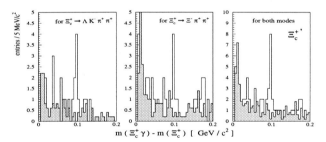

Figure 2. First evidence for $\Xi_c^{+\prime} \to \Xi_c^+ \gamma$, shown for two Ξ_c^+ decay modes separately and merged. The hatched distributions show the background from sidebands of the Ξ_c^+ mass distributions.

	ratio	x_F	PYTHIA
Λ_c^+/D^-	11.3 ± 7.1	> 0.2	0.58
Σ_c^0/Λ_c^+	$0.45 \pm 0.31 \pm 0.10$	> 0.2	0.32
Σ_c^{++}/Σ_c^0	< 0.52 (90% CL)	> 0.2	0.03
D^+/D^-	$0.47 \pm 0.14 \pm 0.05$	> 0.1	0.84

Table 3. Charmed particle production ratios compared to predictions from PYTHIA simulations.

6. Summary and outlook

We have measured the characteristics of charmed baryon production in a Σ^- hyperon beam in the forward kinematic region. The measured differential dependences as well as the total cross sections are comparable to the values obtained for proton beams. Indications for leading particle effects have been found for the Σ_c baryon and D meson states. Comparisons of the baryon data with PYTHIA simulations point to a conceptual problem of the PYTHIA model concerning the description of the final state interaction for baryon production. In the charmed strange baryon sector the states Ξ_c^+ and Ξ_c^0 have been reconstructed in several decay modes, and the Ξ_c^+ lifetime has been determined. Based on the available Ξ_c^+ data from 1991, evidence for the symmetric state $\Xi_c^{+\prime}$ has been found. First results obtained from the 1993 data sample, which was taken after a major detector upgrade, look very promising. Using about 12% of the data sample, the largest Ξ_c^+ signal seen so far was found. Thus in the full sample we expect to find several hundreds of charmed strange baryons per decay channel. Very preliminary results on the double strange charmed baryon Ω_c^0 show evidence for the observation of the three decay channels $\Xi^- K^- \pi^+ \pi^+$, $\Omega^- \pi^+$ and $\Omega^- \pi^+ \pi^+ \pi^-$ (fig. 3). In this year's (1994) run we expect to record another 200 million events with the same sensitivity to charm.

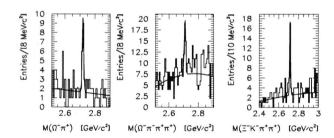

Figure 3. Invariant mass spectra $\Omega^- \pi^+$, $\Omega^- \pi^- \pi^+ \pi^+$ and $\Xi^- K^- \pi^+ \pi^+$ showing evidence for the Ω_c^0 state.

References

[1] M. I. Adamovich et al., Phys. Lett. **B305** (1993) 402; G. A. Alves et al., Phys. Rev. Lett. **72** (1994) 812
[2] WA89 Collaboration, CERN-PPE 94-86
[3] S. Barlag et al., Phys. Lett. **B247** (1990) 113
[4] P. Coteus et al., Phys. Rev. Lett. **59** (1987) 1530
[5] S. F. Biagi et al., Zeit. Phys. **C28** (1985) 175
[6] M. I. Adamovich et al., CERN-PREp91-055; M. Aguilar-Benitez et al., Zeit. Phys. **C49** (1991) 321
[7] G. A. Alves et al., Phys. Rev. Lett. **69** (1992) 3147; S. Barlag et al., Zeit. Phys. **C49** (1991) 555
[8] P. Nason et al., CERN-TH-94-7134
[9] H. U. Bengtson et al., Comp. Phys. Comm. **46** (1987) 43
[10] S. F. Biagi et al., Phys. Lett. **B150** (1985) 230; S. Barlag et al., Phys. Lett. **B233** (1989) 522; P. L. Frabetti et al., Phys. Rev. Lett. **70** (1993) 2058

Paper presented at XXVII Int. Conf. on High Energy Physics: Session Pa-14
Glasgow, UK, 20–27 July 1994

A measurement of beauty production cross section

Leonardo Rossi

University and INFN Genova (Italy)

representing the **BEATRICE Collaboration:**

M. Adamovich[6], M. Adinolfi[3], Y. Alexandrov[6], C. Angelini[7], C. Bacci[10], D. Barberis[3], D. Barney[5], J. Batten[5],

W. Beusch[2], C. Bruschini[3], R. Cardarelli[9], A. Cardini[7], V. Casanova[3], F. Ceradini[10], G. Ciapetti[8], M. Dameri[3],

G. Darbo[3], A. Di Ciaccio[9], A. Duane[5], J.P. Dufey[2], Ph. Farthouat[2], V. Flaminio[7], A. Forino[1], B.R. French[2],

A. Frenkel[8], C. Gemme[3], R. Gessaroli[1], K. Harrison[3], R. Hurst[3], A. Kirk[2], F. Lacava[8], C. Lazzeroni[7],

L. Malferrari[1], S. Maljukov[4], G. Martellotti[8], P. Martinengo[2], P. Mazzanti[1], J.G. McEwen[11], I. Minashvili[4],

P. Nechaeva[6], A. Nisati[8], D. Orestano[8], B. Osculati[3], M. Passaseo[8], G. Penso[8], E. Petrolo[8], L. Pontecorvo[8],

A. Quareni[1], P. Ragni[8], H. Rotscheidt[2], V. Ryzhov[2], C. Roda[7], L. Rossi[3], N. Russakovich[4], C. Salvo[3],

R. Santonico[9], G. Schuler[2], A. Semenov[4], A. Solovjev[4], M. Torelli[8], S. Veneziano[8], M. Verzocchi[8], D. Websdale[5],

M. Weymann[2], L. Zanello[8], M. Zavertyaev[6]

Bologna[1], CERN[2], Genova[3], JINR-Dubna[4], London ICSTM[5], Moscow LPI[6],

Pisa[7], Roma I[8], Roma II[9], Roma III[10], Southampton[11]

Abstract

We present a measurement of the beauty production cross section in interactions of 350 GeV/c π^- on a copper target.

1. Introduction and apparatus

Experiment WA92 [1], which took data at the Ω spectrometer at the CERN SPS, has been designed to study the hadroproduction and the decays of particles containing b quarks. Two factors are important for finding a beauty signal in a fixed-target environment: the selectivity of the trigger and the reconstruction efficiency for decay vertices. A large acceptance for beauty particles and high background rejection have been achieved by WA92. The apparatus and its performance are described elsewhere [2]

We here simply recall the description of the Decay Detector (DD), which is a sort of "electronic bubble chamber" able to visualize the complex topologies (i.e. chained decays) typical of beauty decays. The DD is made of 17 planes of Si microstrip detectors with $10\,\mu$m pitch covering an area of $5 \times 5\,$mm^2. The spacing along the beam direction is $1.2\,$mm for the first 14 planes and $5\,$mm for the following ones; the first 6 detectors are $150\,\mu$m thick and the rest $300\,\mu$m thick. Thirteen planes measure the Z (vertical) coordinate, 2 the Y (horizontal) coordinate and 2 are inclined for projection matching. All strips are individually read out into 8-bit ADC's; with thresholds set for each strip at 4 times the pedestal RMS we obtain efficiencies of 93% and 97% for the thin and thick planes respectively with a noise level of 10^{-3} per strip. The single-point resolution is 2 to 3 μm and the two-track resolution is $\simeq 30\,\mu$m.

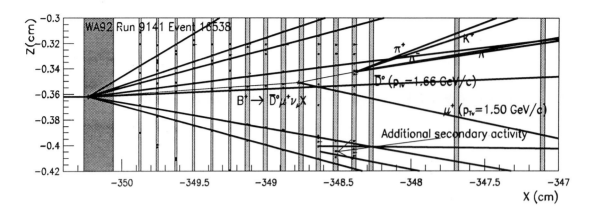

Figure 1. *Display of a beauty candidate event, 1992 data, Cu target.*

Most secondary vertices reconstructed in the decay detector region are hadronic interactions in the silicon planes which are characterized by large energy release due to nuclear fragments and slow tracks. Thanks to the analogue read-out we could implement cuts based on the distance between the reconstructed vertex position and the centroid of the large energy deposits, these reject 91% of the vertices due to secondary interactions while loosing only 3% of K_s^0 and Λ^0 and 8% of $D^{0,\pm}$ decays.

2. Measurement of beauty cross section

This analysis is based on $40 \cdot 10^6$ events; among these the reconstruction program finds $6 \cdot 10^6$ events with a secondary vertex, containing an estimated sample of 350 beauty events (assuming a cross-section of 5 nb/nucleon and $\sigma_b \propto A$). The cut on hadronic interactions reduces the data sample to 10^6 events. The events are then separated into 2 streams to be analyzed with a graphical display program, in order to exploit the visualizing capabilities of the decay detector:

- events with ≥ 3 secondary vertices in the decay detector region (multivertex events);
- events with ≥ 2 secondary vertices and a high P_t muon associated to one of them (μ events).

These strict selection criteria give $\simeq 2000$ events. The use of the DD information in the graphical analysis of these events has significantly enhanced the S/N ratio through the rejection of the background due to multiple interactions and to pattern recognition errors. We are finally left with 25 multivertex events and 31 μ events (one of them is shown in figure 1). Simulation indicates that the dominant background in these samples is due to charm decays. We reduce it to less than 0.5 ev @

90% CL by asking that at least one secondary track satisfy the requirement $P_{tv} \geq 1.0\ GeV/c$,where P_{tv} is the transverse momentum of a track relative to the line of flight of the secondary vertex to which is associated.

The cut reduces our sample to 5 multivertex and 9 muon events. Once correcting for the acceptance (respectively : 0.28±0.02% and 0.62±0.02%) we obtain : $\sigma(B_{mvtx}) = 7.6 \pm 3.4$ nb and $\sigma(B_\mu) = 6.3 \pm 2.1$ nb and, combining the results, we finally obtain : $\sigma(B) = 6.6 \pm 1.8(stat) \pm 2.0(syst)$ nb per nucleon(N) which is in good agreement with next-to-leading order perturbative QCD calculations [3].

As a check we have also measured the production cross section for D^0, $D^{\pm}$ and J/ψ. We obtain : $\sigma(D^0) = 9.6 \pm 2.4\ \mu b/N$ and $\sigma(D^+) = 4.8 \pm 1.3\ \mu b/N$ (both for $x_F > 0$) while $\sigma(J/\psi) = 300\pm20$ nb/N (all x_F). The above results, on open and hidden charm, are in good agreement with other experiments.

3. Conclusions

The cross section for the production of beauty hadrons in interactions of 350 GeV/c π^- on a copper target has been measured. The value presented, which is still preliminary, has been extracted using 20% of the WA92 statistics. The agreement with QCD calculations is good.

References

[1] M. Adamovich et al., *Nucl. Phys.* **B 27** (1992) 251-256.
[2] D.Barberis et al., Proc. CHARM2000 Workshop, Fermilab, USA, June 7-9,1994, 213-220.
[3] G.Ridolfi et al., Proc. Workshop on heavy quarks at fixed target, Frascati, Italy, May 31st-June 2nd 1993, 81-98.

Paper presented at XXVII Int. Conf. on High Energy Physics: Session Pa-14
Glasgow, UK, 20–27 July 1994

Charm Production at 70 GeV in Proton - Proton Interactions

The SVD Collaboration presented by M.Shafranov # !

\#   Joint Institute for Nuclear Research, Dubna, Russia.
Nuclear Physics Institute, Moscow State University, Russia.
Institute of High Energy Physics, Serpukhov, Russia.
Institute of High Energy Physics, Tbilisi State University, Georgia.

Abstract

Measuring of the charmed particles production cross section   at the energies of 70 GeV is performed at the accelerator of the IHEP in Serpukhov (experiment SERP-161).
Experiment SERP-161 is held at the set-up SVD - spectrometer with a vertex detector. A   liquid hydrogen bubble chamber is used as a vertex detector. The expansion frequency at the necessary quality of pictures and resolution is up to 30 Hz and limited only by the photography system. At present about 300000 stereo-pictures have been taken with a trigger of the first level   (output from the beam). The selection of the events is done in thecharm box, $5 \times 5 \, m \, m^2$, while looking through the pictures. The estimate of the upper limit of the   cross section of the charm produktion is 4 microbarn.

The main results on the charm production in hadron-hadron interactions were received in CERN and FNAL with the extracted beams at the energy interval $15 < \sqrt{s} < 40$ [1]. It was shown that the energy dependence of $\sigma(\overline{cc})$ agrees with the results of calculations in terms of perturbative QCD only qualitatively. In QCD calculations of the absolute value of $\sigma(\overline{cc})$ there is   large enough indefinitness - 4-5 times,   caused by an unknown contribution of the higher order expansion terms and uncertainty in determination of the charmed quark structure functions and the estimation of quark mass [2]. The study of the charmed hadron spectra depending on Feynman longitudinal variable, has indicated on the existance of the leading effect of the particles with the valence quarks of the primary hadron [3]. This effect, as well as some others [4], can be treated as the indication on existence of the wave functions of hadrons in the states with *intrinsic charm.* These states can lead to the charmed hadron production in soft interactions.

The experimental data on the charm of mesons and barions hadroproduction at CM energies below 15 GeV,

are still very scarce. The information on the charm production at IHEP accelerator comes only from the nC interaction at neutron energy of 58 GeV[5]. But these results on the charm production cross section are not confirmed in the *beam-dump experiment* at 70 Gev[6].
Therefore the study of charm production at energies near the threshold is   very important and fruitful. It is possible to measure the cross section of charm production using the high resolution vertex detector combined with the charged and neutral particles spectrometer.

The experiment aimed at measuring of the charmed particle production in proton-proton interactions at energies of 70 GeV, is performed at the accelerator of the IHEP in Serpukhov with the help of the Vertex Detector Spectrometer (SVD) [7].   SVD is shown in Figure 1.
The spectrometer (Fig. 1) consists of the vertex detector, magnetic spectrometer, and electromagnetic calorimeter. The rapid cycling liquid hydrogen bubble chamber (HBC) is used as a precision vertex detector. The working volume

of the bubble chamber has dimensions $15 \times 7 \times 5 \, cm^3$ The tracks with a density of 150 bubbles/cm and bubble diameters of 25 mcm, were obtained at the temperature of liquid hydrogen - $29.8 K^0$ [8]. The coordinate measurement system of the magnetic spectrometer consists of 19 planes of MWPC located inside the magnet.

! E-mail: mshafran@lhe08.jinr.dubna.su.

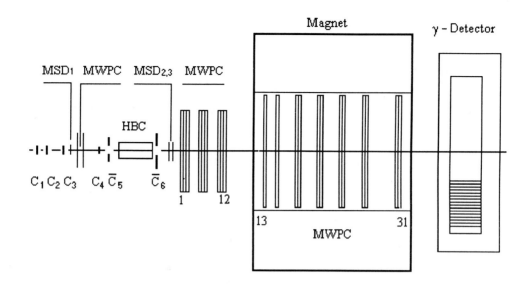

Fig. 1. Layout of the SVD spectrometer. C1 - C6 -scintillation counters; MWPC -proportional chambers; HBC- hydrogen bubble chamber, MSD- microstrip silicon detectors.

The magnet has the aperture of $1.8 \times 1.3 m^2$. The length of the pole along the proton beam is $3\ m$. The MWPC are stacked in 5 triplets UYV and 2 doublets, YV and YU. The wires are inclined with the angle of 11.5^0 (U,V - planes).The dimensions of these chambers are $1.3 \times 1.8 m^2$, their pitch is equal to $2mm$. 12 planes of MWPC are placed between the vertex detector and the magnet. They are stacked in three quadruplets UYVZ. These MWPC have the working area of $1.0 \times 1.0\ m^2$. The electromagnetic hodoscope calorimeter consists of 2048 Cherencov counters. The lead - glass radiators have the dimensions $3.8 \times 3.8 \times 50\ c\ m^3$. The trigger system consists of 6 scintillation counters and 3 planes of the silicon microstrip detectors (MSD).

Photographing of the fiducial volume was performed after the first level (output from the beam) trigger signal. About 300000 pictures were taken. The standard scanning procedure was used there. The upper limit of the charm production cross section was previously estimated only after analysis of the scanning data, using 150000 bubble chamber pictures without information from the magnetic spectrometer. 69000 interactions were found in the fiducial volume. It means that the sensitivity of the experiment was equal to 2 events per microbarn.

The selection of the events with the secondary activity was done in a charm box, 500 events of the C1, C3, V2 decays were registered among all the selected events with the secondary activity . The number of such events for K, Λ, Σ - decays, simulated with PYTHIA program, approximately corresponds to the experimentally found value.

Taking into account the efficiency of the visible charm decay registration in the charm box region, the upper limit of the cross section of the charm production was found to be 4 microbarn.

References

[1] J.A.Appel, Annu. Rev. Nucl. Part. Sci., **42** (1992) 367.
[2] P.Nason et al., Preprint CERN-TH 7134/94 (1994).
[3] M.Augilar-Benitez et al., Z. Phys., **C31** (1986) 491.
[4] J.Badier et al., Z. Phys., **C20** (1983) 102.
[5] A.N.Aleev et al., Z. Phys. **C37** (1988) 243.
[6] J.Blumlein et al., Phys. Lett., **B279** (1991) 405.
[7] A.M.Andriishchin et al., Preprint IPHE 84-3 (1984).
[8] E.N. Ardashev et al., Preprint IHEP 93-99 (1993).

A Test of Internal Halo Targets for Heavy Flavour Hadro-Production at the HERA Proton Ring

Klaus Ehret[†‡]

† Max-Planck-Insitut für Kernphysik, Postfach 103980, D-69029 Heidelberg, Germany

Abstract

The main goal of the proposed HERA-B experiment [1] is the detection of CP-violation in the B system by studying the decay $B^0 \rightarrow J/\Psi K_S^0$. As a source of the B-mesons an internal halo target in the HERA proton ring will be used. The detection of CP-violation requires interaction rates up to 50 MHZ. This paper discusses the principle of halo targets and the results of several test measurements carried out at the 820 GeV HERA proton ring, which demonstrates the possibility to obtain the required rates parallel to the HERA ep luminosity operation.

1. Introduction

It appears very promising to study the origin of CP violation with decays of neutral B mesons. But there exist only a few decay channels, all of them with small branching ratios, which can exhibit CP asymmetries. HERA-B [1] [2] will measure $\sin(2\beta)$, which is expected to be between 0.2 and 0.9, by comparing the decay rates of B^0 and $\bar{B}^0$ into the CP eigenstate $J/\Psi K_S^0$.

Besides the proposed e^+e^-B factories, internal targets in the halo of a stored proton beam provide a source of B mesons. For the planned HERA-B experiment thin wires or ribbons are positioned around the beam at a distance of $4-8$ r.m.s. Such a target is mechanically stable and easy to operate, gives a well localized main vertex and with several wires one can distribute the required multiple interactions per bunch on different wires.

At the 820 GeV HERA proton ring, with a center of mass energy ($\sqrt{s} \approx 40$ GeV) not far above the B-threshold, the background dominates B production by six orders of magnitude. Together with branching ratios, tagging and experimental efficiencies one ends up with about $3 \cdot 10^{-12}$ detected $B^0 \rightarrow J/\Psi K_S^0$ decays per interaction. Therefore one needs 40 MHz interaction rate assuming 10^7 s running time per year, to get the desired 1000 $B^0 \rightarrow J/\Psi K_S^0$ events per year to measure $\sin(2\beta)$ with an accuracy of 0.13. In the last two years several measurements have been carried out to study whether it is possible to achieve the desired rates and not to disturb the other HERA experiments with the

parallel operation of an internal halo target at high rates.

2. Required Target Performance

HERA will operate at a bunch frequency of 10 MHz. Therefore several target interactions per bunch are required to get the desired rates. Assuming the design current of the HERA proton ring (160 mA) and a typical lifetime of 100 h the natural loss rate is 60 MHz. If only using this natural loss, one needs a highly efficient target which absorbs more than 60% of the protons drifting outwards. The protons have to pass the target several hundred times before an interaction takes place. Therefore small drift velocities in the halo are required. Also a large aperture is necessary for efficient competition with scrapers and low β-functions to minimize emittance blow up in the halo due to multiple scattering.

3. Halo Target Test Measurements

For the 1993 measurements a setup with different scintillator counters (Figure 1) and four ribbons as target on two moveable forks surounding the beam (Figure 2) located in the straight west right section of the HERA ring was used. HERA was operating with 90 proton bunches and typical currents of 15 mA. A complete description of these measurements and detailed discussions of the results are given in [3].

Figure 3 shows a typical target scan. If the target leaves the collimator shadow at about 12σ the trigger

‡ E-mail: ehret@desy.de.

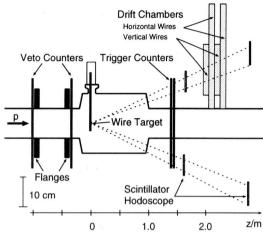

Figure 1. Sketch of the experimental set-up. The trigger counters are nearly full efficient for interactions in the target.

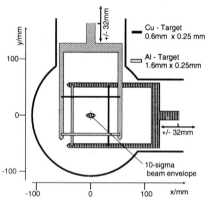

Figure 2. Arrangement of target ribbons on moveable forks.

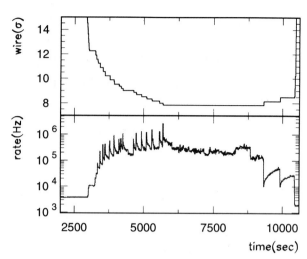

Figure 3. Target distance to beam center (measured in r.m.s. beam widths) and trigger rate as function of time.

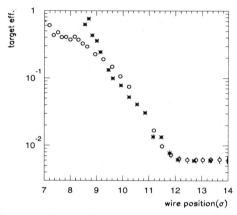

Figure 4. Target efficiency ϵ_{tar} as function of the distance to the beam center (measured in r.m.s. beam widths).

rate suddenly starts to rise. With each step towards the beam center the target scrapes away a part of the beam halo. This leads to a sharp rise in the rate which decays then within a few minutes to a new steady state. At a distance of about 8σ the rate remained at 200–300 kHz for about one hour. After retracting the target the rate drops suddenly and rises again until the halo is refilled.

In Figure 4 the target efficiency ϵ_{tar}, which is defined by the ratio of the interaction rate in the target to the proton loss rate, is shown for two different wire scans. ϵ_{tar} rises after the wire has left the collimator shadow at 12σ and becomes the dominating absorber if the target is moved closer into the beam. Efficiencies well above 50% have been reached.

At only 30% of the nominal bunch current already more than 2.5 interactions per bunch crossing were observed without any disturbance of the ep luminosity operation. The track direction reconstructed in the small drift chambers gives clear evidence that the observed interactions come from the halo target. Variations and fluctuations of the rate on several time scales have been studied. Only the bunch to bunch variations, caused by timing problems at the injection,

are large for some fills. However solutions to improve the injection are still under study.

4.   Conclusion

The measurements demonstrate the feasibility of internal halo target at the HERA proton ring, and indicate that the required rates for a dedicated B Experiment can be achieved in parallel running to ep luminosity operation. The measurements will continue with an improved setup to study more in detail, e.g., event topology and vertex distributions along the target.

References

[1] T. Lohse *et al.*, *HERA-B An Experiment to Study CP Violation in the B System Using an Internal Target at the HERA Proton Ring*, Proposal: DESY-PRC 94/02 (1994).

[2] W. Hofmann, *CP violation using an internal Halo target at HERA-B* , this conference.

[3] C. Hast *et al.*, *Test of Internal Halo Target in the HERA Proton Ring*, DESY 94-119 (1994).

Parallel Session Pa-15

Non-Perturbative Methods

Conveners: N. Manton (DAMTP/Cambridge)
V. Khoze (SLAC)

Scientific secretaries: S. Ryan
H. Hoeber (reserve)

Paper presented at XXVII Int. Conf. on High Energy Physics: Session Pa-15
Glasgow, UK, 20–27 July 1994

Sphaleron transitions at high temperatures and the upper bound for the Higgs mass

Dmitri Diakonov*, Maxim Polyakov*, Pavel Pobylitsa*,
Peter Sieber°, Jörg Schaldach°, and Klaus Goeke°

* St. Petersburg Nuclear Physics Institute, Gatchina, St.Petersburg 188350, Russia
° Inst. für Theor. Physik II, Ruhr-Universität Bochum, D-44780 Bochum, Germany

Abstract

We calculate the decrease of the baryon number after the electroweak phase transition due to thermal fluctuations above the sphaleron barrier. We consider not only the classical Boltzmann factor but also fermionic and bosonic 1-loop contributions which can considerably suppress the rate. The condition that the initial baryon asymmetry must not be washed out by sphaleron transitions leads, in the minimal standard model, to an upper bound for the Higgs mass of about 63 GeV.

1. Introduction

The fact that the potential energy of the Yang–Mills fields is periodic in a certain topological functional of the gauge fields, called the Chern–Simons number N_{CS}, was found quite a long time ago by Faddeev [1] and Jackiw and Rebbi [2]. Field configurations with integer N_{CS} have zero static energy, they correspond to topologically distinct vacua of the theory. In the electroweak theory those vacua are separated by a barrier whose height is of the order of m_W/α, where m_W is the W-boson mass and $\alpha = g^2/(4\pi)$ is the $SU(2)$ gauge coupling constant.

The static configuration of the Yang–Mills (YM) and Higgs (H) field corresponding to the top of the barrier and having $N_{CS} = \frac{1}{2}$ was first found by Dashen, Hasslacher and Neveu [3] and, in the context of the electroweak theory, rediscovered by Klinkhamer and Manton [4] and named sphaleron.

Transitions from one vacuum to a topologically distinct one over this barrier cause a change in the baryon and lepton number by one unit per fermion generation due to the axial anomaly [5]. Hence, this transition is a baryon and lepton number violating process and therefore of great physical significance. Although it is very strongly suppressed under ordinary conditions [5], its rate can become large at high densities [6, 7], high temperatures [8, 9, 10] or maybe, at high particle energies. In particular, the transitions should have occurred in the early universe immediately after the electroweak phase transition. Whatever was the mechanism leading to the baryon asymmetry of the universe at earlier times, these transitions might have washed out any initial baryon excess over antibaryons if their rate is large enough [8, 9, 11]. In order to understand the presently observed baryon excess we therefore need an exact determination of the transition rate.

The dominant contribution to this rate is given by the classical Boltzmann factor $e^{-E_{class}/T}$ where T is the temperature, and E_{class} is the classical energy of the sphaleron. Quantum corrections arise from bosonic and fermionic fluctuations about the sphaleron; there are also prefactors due to negative and zero bosonic fluctuation modes [10]. In [9, 10] the rate was calculated considering the classical contribution and the factors due to zero and negative modes only; in [12, 13, 14] the bosonic determinant over non-zero modes was also taken into account. However, the results of these investigations differ by orders of magnitude and are valid only in the limit of high temperatures, which numerically is not necessarily fulfilled. We have therefore recalculated the rate including both bosonic and fermionic fluctuations for arbitrary temperature [7, 15] and found that

- fermionic fluctuations can suppress the rate considerably, depending on the masses of the top quark and the Higgs boson. Close to the critical temperature of the electroweak phase transition they can become as important as the classical contribution,
- bosonic fluctuations also suppress the rate provided the Higgs mass is not too large, but in general they are less important than the fermionic fluctuations,
- using the recently found value of the top quark mass of 174 GeV the total rate is low enough to prevent the baryon number dissipation if the mass of the Higgs is lower than about 63 GeV. The numerical results apply to the minimal standard model with only one Higgs doublet. Therefore, if the neutral Higgs boson is not found below that value, it would rule out the minimal standard model.

2. Loop corrections to the sphaleron transition rate

We consider the minimal version of the standard electroweak theory with one Higgs doublet which is Yukawa coupled to left handed fermion doublets and to right handed singlets; in the following we write only one doublet and one pair of singlets for brevity. We neglect the Weinberg angle, i.e. we work with a pure $SU(2)$ gauge theory. This idealization does not seem to be significant [16]. The Lagrangian is thus

$$
\mathcal{L} = -\frac{1}{4g^2} F^a_{\mu\nu} F^{a\,\mu\nu} + (D_\mu \Phi)^\dagger (D^\mu \Phi)
$$
$$
- \frac{\lambda^2}{2} \left(\Phi^\dagger \Phi - \frac{v^2}{2} \right)^2 + \bar{\psi}_L i\gamma^\mu D_\mu \psi_L \quad (2.1)
$$
$$
+ \bar{\chi}_R i\gamma^\mu \partial_\mu \chi_R - \bar{\psi}_L M \chi_R - \bar{\chi}_R M^\dagger \psi_L
$$

with $F^a_{\mu\nu} = \partial_\mu A^a_\nu - \partial_\nu A^a_\mu + \varepsilon^{abc} A^b_\mu A^c_\nu$ and the covariant derivative being defined as $D_\mu = \partial_\mu - \frac{i}{2} A^a_\mu \tau^a$. M is a 2×2 matrix composed of the Higgs field components $\Phi = \binom{\phi^+}{\phi^0}$, and the Yukawa couplings h_u, h_d:

$$
M = \begin{pmatrix} h_u \phi^{0*} & h_d \phi^+ \\ -h_u \phi^{+*} & h_d \phi^0 \end{pmatrix}. \quad (2.2)
$$

ψ_L means the $SU(2)$ fermion doublet $\binom{u_L}{d_L}$, and with χ_R we denote the pair of the singlets u_R, d_R.

The transition rate per volume V of the system going from one vacuum into a topologically distinct one is given by the semi-classical Langer–Affleck formula [17, 18, 19] which, applied to the model [10], reads

$$
\gamma = \frac{\Gamma}{V} = \frac{\omega_-}{2\pi} \frac{\mathcal{N}_{0,-}}{V} \kappa_{\text{bos}} \, \kappa_{\text{ferm}} \, \exp(-E_{\text{class}}/T), \quad (2.3)
$$

with ω_- being the frequency of the negative bosonic mode and $\mathcal{N}_{0,-}$ the jacobian factor due to the negative and the zero bosonic modes. E_{class} is the classical energy of the sphaleron configuration,

$$
E_{\text{class}} = \int d^3\mathbf{r} \left[\frac{1}{4g^2}(F^a_{ij})^2 + (D_i \Phi)^\dagger (D_i \Phi) \right.
$$
$$
\left. + \frac{\lambda^2}{2} \left(\Phi^\dagger \Phi - \frac{v^2}{2} \right)^2 \right] = \mathcal{O}\left(\frac{m_W}{\alpha} \right) \quad (2.4)
$$

The determinants κ_{bos}, κ_{ferm} correspond to bosonic and fermionic fluctuations; they are divergent and have to be renormalized which we perform using a proper time regularization scheme. The divergent parts are combined with the classical energy, which yields the physical parameters normalized at the scale of m_W. The major part of their temperature dependent contribution can also be absorbed by the classical energy, leading to temperature dependent masses (see e.g. [20]):

$$
\frac{m_W(T)}{m_W} = \frac{m_H(T)}{m_H} = \frac{m_F(T)}{m_F} = \frac{E_{\text{class}}(T)}{E_{\text{class}}}
$$
$$
= q(T) \equiv \sqrt{1 - \frac{T^2}{T_c^2}}, \quad (2.5)
$$

where T_c is the 1-loop critical temperature of the phase transition given by

$$
T_c = \frac{1}{g} \sqrt{\frac{24\,m_W^2\,m_H^2}{3\,m_H^2 + 9\,m_W^2 + 4\sum_{\text{doubl.}} m_F^2}}. \quad (2.6)
$$

In a realistic model all fermion masses except the top mass are negligible, so that $\sum_{\text{doubl.}} m_F^2 = \frac{3}{2} m_t^2$. After performing this renormalization we find

$$
\frac{\mathcal{N}_{0,-}}{V} = \frac{4\pi^2 m_W(T)^8}{g^6 T^4 m_W} (N_{\text{rot}} N_{\text{trans}})^3
$$
$$
\left[\sin\left(\frac{\omega_- m_W(T)}{2T m_W} \right) \right]^{-1}, \quad (2.7)
$$

with N_{rot}, N_{trans} being the jacobians of the zero modes [12]. The determinants can be written in the following form:

$$
\kappa_{\text{ferm}} = \frac{\prod_n \cosh\left(\frac{\varepsilon_n m_W(T)}{2T\,m_W} \right)}{\prod_n \cosh\left(\frac{\varepsilon_n^0 m_W(T)}{2T\,m_W} \right)} \quad (2.8)
$$

$$
\kappa_{\text{bos}} = \left(\frac{2T}{m_W(T)} \right)^7 \frac{\prod_n \sinh\left(\frac{\omega_n^0 m_W(T)}{2T\,m_W} \right)}{\prod_n'' \sinh\left(\frac{\omega_n m_W(T)}{2T\,m_W} \right)}
$$
$$
\frac{\prod_n \sinh\left(\frac{\omega_n^{\text{FP}} m_W(T)}{2T\,m_W} \right)}{\prod_n \sinh\left(\frac{\omega_n^{\text{FP},0} m_W(T)}{2T\,m_W} \right)}. \quad (2.9)
$$

Here ϵ_n are the eigenvalues of the fermionic fluctuation operator $\delta^2 S_{\text{eff}}/\delta\psi\delta\bar{\psi}$ [7], ω_n are the eigenvalues of the bosonic fluctuation operator [12, 14], using the background gauge for the fluctuations, and ω_n^{FP} are the corresponding eigenvalues of the Faddeev-Popov operator. The double primed product $\prod''$ means that negative and zero mode frequencies are removed. If we assume the hedgehog ansatz

$$A_i^a(\mathbf{r}) = \varepsilon_{aij}n_j\frac{1-A(r)}{r}+(\delta_{ai}-n_an_i)\frac{B(r)}{r}+n_an_i\frac{C(r)}{r},$$

$$\Phi(\mathbf{r}) = \frac{v}{\sqrt{2}}\left[H(r)+iG(r)\,\mathbf{n}\cdot\boldsymbol{\tau}\right]\binom{0}{1}, \qquad (2.10)$$

for the classical sphaleron field, the fluctuation operators become block diagonal with respect to the "grand spin" K and can be numerically diagonalized for each K separately. More details can be found in [7, 15]. Hence it is possible to evaluate the rate $\gamma(T)$ numerically for given values of m_H/m_W and m_t/m_W as a function of the temperature.

In order to get a feeling for the dependence of the determinants on these mass parameters note that for large values of m_t/m_W the aggregate energy density of the Dirac sea in the sphaleron background behaves as $(h\Phi)^4\ln(h\Phi/m_W)$ which should be integrated over the space where the Higgs field differs from its vacuum expectation value, that is over the spread of the sphaleron being of the order $[\min(m_H, m_W)]^{-1}$. Therefore, for $m_H < m_W < m_t$ we estimate

$$\ln(\kappa_{\text{ferm}}) \;\propto\; N_c\frac{(m_t/m_W)^4\ln(m_t/m_W)}{(m_H/m_W)^3}, \quad (2.11)$$

$$\ln(\kappa_{\text{bos}}) \;\propto\; \frac{1}{(m_H/m_W)^3}, \qquad (2.12)$$

with $N_c = 3$ being the number of colours. Actually, eqs. (2.11, 2.12) give the quantum corrections to the classical sphaleron energy E_{class} (2.4). Though parametrically they are α times smaller than E_{class}, numerically the fermion sea contribution to the sphaleron energy appears to be large, especially for large top masses m_t and relatively small Higgs masses m_H. It is mainly the fermionic factor κ_{ferm}, which was put to unity in the previous work [9, 12, 13, 14], that leads to a significant additional suppression of the baryon dissipation rate, see below.

3. The baryon dissipation rate

Sphaleron transitions can increase and decrease the baryon number. If the baryon number B were zero, the transitions in both directions would happen equally often and cancel each other. In the case $B \neq 0$ one has to introduce a chemical potential favouring transitions which erase the baryon asymmetry, in accordance with

the le Châtelier principle. This has been done in [9, 10], and for fermions with small masses we obtain:

$$\frac{1}{B}\frac{dB}{dt} = -\frac{13}{2}N_g\frac{\gamma(T)}{T^3}, \qquad (3.1)$$

where $N_g = 3$ is the number of fermion generations. Since the top mass is actually not small the prefactor $\frac{13}{2}$ should be replaced by a slightly bigger number. This effect, however, is negligible compared to the other factors so we do not consider it further.

Standard cosmology yields a relation between time and temperature [21]:

$$t = C\,T^{-2}, \qquad (3.2)$$

with the constant $C \approx 5\cdot10^{15}\,m_W$ depending on the Planck mass and the number of degrees of freedom of the thermalized particles. Hence we obtain

$$\frac{1}{B}\frac{dB}{dT} = 13\,C\,N_g\,\frac{\gamma(T)}{T^6}, \qquad (3.3)$$

which can be integrated to

$$B(T) = B(T_c)\exp\left\{-13\,C\,N_g\int_T^{T_c}\frac{\gamma(T)}{T^6}\,dT\right\} \quad (3.4)$$

$$= B(T_c)\exp\left\{\frac{-13\,C\,N_g}{T_c^5}\int_0^{q(T)}\frac{q\,\gamma(q)}{(1-q^2)^{7/2}}\,dq\right\},$$

where $q(T)$ was defined in eq. (2.5). Thus, we can evaluate the ratio $B(0)/B(T_c)$ of the present baryon number to the one immediatly after the phase transition, which is supposed to be of the order of 10^{-5} [9]. This condition implies an upper bound on the Higgs mass which will be discussed in the last section.

4. Results

For our numerical calculations we fixed the coupling constant to its physical value $g = 0.67$ and the top quark mass to $m_t = 2.1\,m_W$, according to its recently stated value of 174 GeV. The only free parameter left is the Higgs mass m_H.

Figure 1 shows the logarithms of the different contributions to the transition rate γ (2.3): the classical part $e^{-E_{\text{class}}(T)/T}$, the prefactor $\omega_-\,\mathcal{N}_{0,-}/(2\pi V)$, and the bosonic and fermionic fluctuations κ_{bos} and κ_{ferm}, which have all been discussed in the second section. Obviously, the loop corrections, especially the fermionic ones yield a strong suppression of the total transition rate. If the temperature approaches the critical value of the electroweak phase transition, all masses disappear, and the transition rate goes to zero fast due to the vanishing prefactor. It should be mentioned that the one-loop approximation we are dealing with breaks down in the near vicinity of the phase transition. However, the integral in (3.4) is strongly dominated by a small region around the maximum of the transition rate $\gamma(q)$, which is separated from the phase transition itself (see Figure 1).

Figure 1 was calculated for $m_H = 0.8\,m_W$, for other values of m_H the qualitative behaviour of the curves is basically the same, only the numbers change a bit.

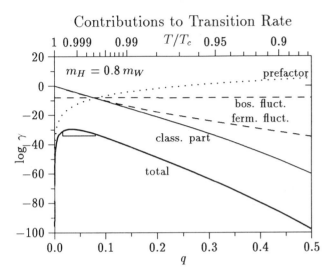

Figure 1. Classical and loop contributions to the sphaleron transition rate per volume, $q = \sqrt{1 - (T/T_c)^2}$, $T_c = 0.957\,m_W$, $m_H = 0.8\,m_W$. The interval which actually contributes to the integral (3.4) is marked.

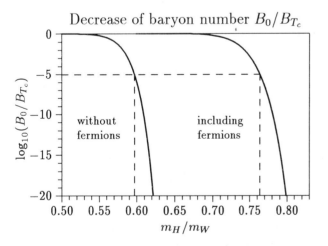

Figure 2. Total decrease of the baryon number via the sphaleron transition in dependence on the Higgs mass, with and without fermionic contributions.

According to eq. (3.4) we calculated the quotient B_0/B_{T_c} of the present baryon number B_0 and the initial one B_{T_c}. Figure 2 shows the ratio for different values of m_H. If we assume that the initial baryon number B_{T_c} was not larger than about $10^5\,B_0$ [9], we find an upper bound of the Higgs mass of about $0.76\,m_W \approx 63\,\text{GeV}$. Figure 2 exhibits a very sharp dependence on m_H: even if we assume an apparently unrealistic initial baryon excess $B_{T_c} \approx 1$, we get from the present-day asymmetry $B_0 \approx 10^{-10}$ that the Higgs mass does not exceed the value of $m_H \approx 0.78\,m_W \approx 65\,\text{GeV}$.

In order to demonstrate the significance of the fermionic fluctuations, which have not been taken into account previously, we calculated the transition rate and the resulting decrease of the baryon number also without the fermionic contribution. Figure 2 shows that in this case the upper bound for the Higgs mass would be as low as about 49 GeV.

Acknowlegdments

We acknowledge the support of the Deutsche Forschungs-gemeinschaft, of the International Science Foundation, and of the Alexander von Humboldt Foundation.

References

[1] L.D.Faddeev, *"Looking for multi-dimensional solitons"*, in: Non-local Field Theories, Dubna (1976)

[2] R.Jackiw and C.Rebbi, Phys. Rev. Lett. **37** (1976) 172

[3] R.Dashen, B.Hasslacher and A.Neveu, Phys. Rev. **D10** (1974) 4138

[4] N.Manton, Phys. Rev. **D28** (1983) 2019; F.R.Klinkhamer and N.S.Manton, Phys. Rev. **D30** (1984) 2212

[5] G.'t Hooft, Phys. Rev. Lett. **37** (1976) 8

[6] V.Rubakov and A.Tavkhelidze, Phys. Lett. **B165** (1985) 109; V.Rubakov, Prog. Theor. Phys. **75** (1986) 366; V.Matveev, V.Rubakov, A.Tavkhelidze and V.Tokarev, Nucl. Phys. **B282** (1987) 700

[7] D.Diakonov, M.Polyakov, P.Sieber, J.Schaldach and K.Goeke, Phys. Rev. **D49** (1994) 6864

[8] V.Kuzmin, V.Rubakov, and M.Shaposhnikov, Phys. Lett. **B155** (1985) 36, **B191** (1987) 171

[9] A.I.Bochkarev, M.E.Shaposhnikov, Mod. Phys. Lett. **A2** (1987) 417

[10] P.Arnold and L.McLerran, Phys. Rev. **D36** (1987); *ibid.* **37** (1988) 1020

[11] M.Shaposhnikov, Nucl. Phys. **B287** (1987) 757; **B299** (1988) 797

[12] L.Carson and L.McLerran, Phys. Rev. **D41** (1990) 647

[13] L.Carson, X.Li, L.McLerran, and R.-T.Wang, Phys. Rev. **D42** (1990) 2127

[14] J.Baacke and S.Junker, Phys. Rev. **D49** (1994) 2055

[15] D.Diakonov, M.Polyakov, P.Pobylitsa, P.Sieber, J.Schaldach and K.Goeke, *submitted to* Phys. Rev. **D**

[16] J.Kunz, B.Kleihaus and Y.Brihaye, Phys. Rev. **D46** (1992) 3587

[17] J.Langer, Ann. Phys. (N.Y.) **41** (1967) 108; *ibid.* **54** (1969) 258

[18] I.Affleck, Phys. Rev. Lett. **46** (1981) 388

[19] S.Khlebnikov and M.Shaposhnikov, Nucl. Phys. **B308** (1988) 885

[20] D.A.Kirzhnitz and A.D.Linde, Ann. Phys. **101** (1976) 195

[21] S.Weinberg, *Gravitation and Cosmology*, John Wiley & Sons, 1972

Gradient approach to the sphaleron barrier

Guido Nolte[†] and Jutta Kunz[†‡]

† Fachbereich Physik, Universität Oldenburg, Postfach 2503
D-26111 Oldenburg, Germany
‡ Instituut voor Theoretische Fysica, Rijksuniversiteit te Utrecht
NL-3508 TA Utrecht, The Netherlands

Abstract

We apply a gradient approach to obtain a path over the sphaleron barrier and demonstrate the fermionic level crossing phenomenon. Neglecting the mixing angle dependence and assuming that the fermions of a doublet are degenerate in mass we employ spherically symmetric ansätze for the fields. The metric on the space of field configurations is motivated by requiring a maximal tunneling rate. The gradient path over the barrier is smooth, even for large values of the Higgs boson mass or of the fermion mass, where the extremal energy path bifurcates.

1. Introduction

In 1976 't Hooft [1] observed that the standard model does not absolutely conserve baryon and lepton number due to the Adler-Bell-Jackiw anomaly. Investigating the topological structure of the configuration space of the Weinberg-Salam theory, Manton predicted the existence of a static, unstable solution of the field equations, a sphaleron [2,3], representing the top of the energy barrier between topologically distinct vacua.

While the barrier between topologically distinct vacua is traversed, the Chern-Simons number changes continuously from $N_{CS} = 0$ in one vacuum sector to $N_{CS} \pm 1$ in the neighbouring vacuum sectors, passing through the sphaleron at $N_{CS} = \frac{1}{2}$ [4,5]. However, for large values of the Higgs boson mass, energetically lower, asymmetric sphaleron solutions appear, the bisphalerons [6,7]. The minimum energy path over the barrier [4] then develops bifurcations [5].

As the barrier is traversed one occupied fermion level crosses from the positive continuum to the negative continuum or vice versa, leading to the change in fermion number. Considering the minimum energy path over the barrier [4], the fermionic level crossing along the barrier was demonstrated recently in the background

field approximation [8,9], under the assumption, that the fermions of a doublet are degenerate in mass. This assumption, violated in the standard model, allows for spherically symmetric ansätze for all of the fields, when the mixing angle dependence is neglected (which is an excellent approximation [10,11]). An analogous, but selfconsistent calculation led to similar results [12]. Only for heavy fermions it led to strongly deformed barriers, eventually giving rise to new sphalerons [12].

2. Gradient Approach

Approximations to the sphaleron barrier can be obtained by constructing families of field configurations for the gauge and Higgs boson fields, which interpolate smoothly from one vacuum sector to another.

In the limit of vanishing mixing angle the general static, spherically symmetric ansatz for the gauge and Higgs boson fields is given by [13]

$$V_0^a = 0 \,, \tag{1}$$

$$V_i^a = \frac{1 - f_A(r)}{gr} \varepsilon_{aij}\hat{r}_j$$
$$+ \frac{f_B(r)}{gr}(\delta_{ia} - \hat{r}_i\hat{r}_a) + \frac{f_C(r)}{gr}\hat{r}_i\hat{r}_a \,, \tag{2}$$

$$\Phi = \frac{v}{\sqrt{2}}\Big(H(r) + i\vec{\tau}\cdot\hat{r}K(r)\Big)\begin{pmatrix} 0 \\ 1 \end{pmatrix} , \qquad (3)$$

and involves the five radial functions $f_A(r)$, $f_B(r)$, $f_C(r)$, $H(r)$ and $K(r)$.

The ansatz is form-invariant under a spherically symmetric gauge transformation with the unitary matrix

$$U(\vec{r}) = \exp(i\frac{\Theta(r)}{2}\vec{\tau}\cdot\hat{r}) . \qquad (4)$$

The minimum energy path ('extremal path') over the sphaleron barrier, is obtained from the functional

$$W(f) = E(f) + \frac{8\pi^2 M_W}{g^2}\xi N_{\mathrm{CS}}(f) , \qquad (5)$$

where ξ is a dimensionless lagrange multiplier. For large values of the Higgs boson mass, when bisphalerons come into play, the extremal path does not culminate at the bisphaleron. Instead the extremal path develops bifurcations and culminates at the energetically higher sphaleron [5]. Bifurcations also occur along the extremal path, when fermions with very large masses are coupled selfconsistently to the boson fields [12]. This indicates the need for another approach to the sphaleron barrier.

Here we consider the gradient approach to the sphaleron barrier. To define the gradient approach, we need a metric on the space of field configurations. This metric is naturally provided, when considering the tunneling amplitude $\exp(-R_0)$ [14]

$$R_0 = \int_a^b d\lambda\sqrt{2m(\lambda)(V(\lambda) - E)} , \qquad (6)$$

where E is the energy of the classical turning points a and b, V is the potential energy as a function of the arbitrary pathparameter λ, and

$$
\begin{aligned}
m(\lambda) =\ & \frac{8\pi}{g^2 M_W}\int dx\Big[\Big(\frac{df_A}{d\lambda}\Big)^2 + \Big(\frac{df_B}{d\lambda}\Big)^2 + \frac{1}{2}\Big(\frac{df_C}{d\lambda}\Big)^2 \\
& + 2x^2\Big(\frac{dH}{d\lambda}\Big)^2 + 2x^2\Big(\frac{dK}{d\lambda}\Big)^2\Big]
\end{aligned}
\qquad (7)
$$

is the so called effective mass. Defining a trial distance $\hat{d}(f,\tilde{f})$ of two gauge configurations $f = (f_A, f_B, f_C, H, K)$ and $\tilde{f} = (\tilde{f}_A, \tilde{f}_B, \tilde{f}_C, \tilde{H}, \tilde{K})$ at two 'times' to be

$$
\begin{aligned}
\hat{d}^2 = \frac{16\pi}{g^2}\int dx\Big[&(f_A - \tilde{f}_A)^2 + (f_B - \tilde{f}_B)^2 + \frac{1}{2}(f_c - \tilde{f}_c)^2 \\
& + 2x^2(H - \tilde{H})^2 + 2x^2(K - \tilde{K})^2\Big] ,
\end{aligned}
\qquad (8)
$$

we obtain R_0 as a line integral along the path in configuration space

$$R_0 = \int_a^b \hat{d}f\sqrt{\frac{V(f) - E}{M_W}} . \qquad (9)$$

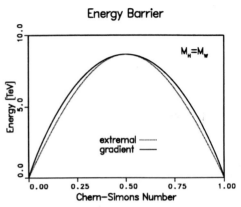

Figure 1. Energy as a function of Chern-Simons number for the extremal and gradient path

This trial metric is gauge invariant under equal residual gauge transformations of f and $\tilde{f}$, but not under different gauge transformations.

Given an old configuration $\tilde{f}$, we are now looking in the gradient approach for the new neighbouring configuration in the direction of steepest descent in the metric $\hat{d}$. Since the energy of f is gauge-invariant, in the direction of steepest descent we must have for f and $\tilde{f}$

$$\hat{d}(f,\tilde{f}) = \min_\Phi \hat{d}(f_\Phi, \tilde{f}) , \qquad (10)$$

where f_Φ is a gauge transform of f with the 'gauge function' Φ. This minimization with respect to Φ can be incorporated directly into the definition of the metric by defining

$$d(f,\tilde{f}) = \min_\Phi \hat{d}(f_\Phi, \tilde{f}) . \qquad (11)$$

This new metric is now manifestly gauge invariant under independent residual gauge transformations of f and $\tilde{f}$. Hence we are now free to choose the configurations to be in the gauge $f_C = 0$ everywhere. R_0 is again given by Eq. (9) with $\hat{d}$ replaced by d.

Now we construct the path as follows. For a given point $\tilde{f}$ in configuration space we find the new point f by varying the functional W

$$W(f) = E(f) + \frac{1}{4}\xi M_W d^2(f, \tilde{f}) , \qquad (12)$$

where ξ is a lagrange multiplier, and then solving the resulting set of differential equations.

Let us now turn to the results. In Fig. 1 we show the energy as a function of N_{CS}. With respect to the Chern-Simons number the minimal energy path yields a steeper barrier than the gradient path. As seen in Fig. 2, the picture reverts when we consider the energy as a function of the pathlength l, defined by the metric d. (Note, that l is shifted such that the energy as a function of l is always peeked around zero.)

The gradient method always produces smooth barriers, independent of the value of the Higgs boson

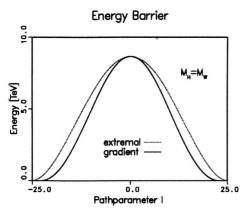

Figure 2. Energy as a function of the pathparameter l for the extremal and gradient path

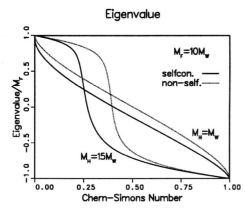

Figure 3. Eigenvalue along the barrier for two Higgs boson masses

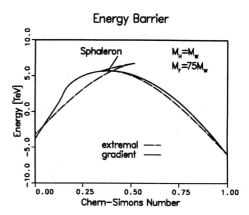

Figure 4. Energy as a function of Chern-Simons number in a selfconsistent calculation

where we include the fermion backreaction in the equations for the bosonic fields. In Fig. 3 we show the eigenvalue as a function of the Chern-Simons number. In contrast with the extremal path [9], the eigenvalue is now a monotonically decreasing function of the Chern-Simons number for all values of the Higgs boson mass.

Similarly, in the case of extremely heavy fermions coupled selfconsistently to the bosons, where the extremal energy barrier developed bifurcations, giving rise to new sphaleron solutions [12], the gradient path over the barrier is smooth and monotonically decreasing on both sides of the sphaleron, as seen in Fig. 4.

References

[1] G. 't Hooft, Phys. Rev. Lett. **37** (1976) 8.
[2] N.S. Manton, Phys. Rev. **D28** (1983) 2019.
[3] F.R. Klinkhamer and N.S. Manton, Phys. Rev. **D30** (1984) 2212.
[4] T. Akiba, H. Kikuchi and T. Yanagida, Phys. Rev. **D38** (1988) 1937.
[5] Y. Brihaye, S. Giler, P. Kosinski and J. Kunz, Phys. Rev. **D42** (1989) 2846.
[6] J. Kunz and Y. Brihaye, Phys. Lett. **B216** (1989) 353.
[7] L.G. Yaffe, Phys. Rev. **D40** (1989) 3463.
[8] J. Kunz and Y. Brihaye, Phys. Lett. **B304** (1993) 141.
[9] J. Kunz and Y. Brihaye, Phys. Rev. **D50** (1994) 1051.
[10] B. Kleihaus, J. Kunz and Y. Brihaye, Phys. Lett. **B273** (1991) 100.
[11] J. Kunz, B. Kleihaus and Y. Brihaye, Phys. Rev. **D46** (1992) 3587.
[12] G. Nolte and J. Kunz, Phys. Rev. **D48** (1993) 5905.
[13] R.F. Dashen, B. Hasslacher and A. Neveu, Phys. Rev. **D12** (1974) 4138.
[14] K. Bittar and S.-J. Chang, Phys. Rev. **D17** (1978) 486.

mass. In particular the bisphaleron barrier has no bifurcations and culminates at the bisphaleron. The transition amplitude in the gradient approach is fairly independent of the Higgs boson mass, e. g. for $M_H = 15 M_W$ we find $R_0 = 1.525$ (1.533) in units of $\frac{8\pi^2}{g^2}$ for the bisphaleron (symmetric sphaleron).

3. Fermions

To retain spherical symmetry we consider only fermion doublets degenerate in mass. The corresponding spherically symmetric ansatz for the fermion eigenstates is the hedgehog ansatz,

$$q_L(\vec{r}, t) = e^{-i\omega t} M_W^{\frac{3}{2}} \left[G_L(r) + i\vec{\sigma} \cdot \hat{r} F_L(r) \right] \chi_h \, , \quad (13)$$

$$q_R(\vec{r}, t) = e^{-i\omega t} M_W^{\frac{3}{2}} \left[G_R(r) - i\vec{\sigma} \cdot \hat{r} F_R(r) \right] \chi_h \, , \quad (14)$$

where the normalized hedgehog spinor χ_h satisfies the spin-isospin relation

$$\vec{\sigma} \chi_h + \vec{\tau} \chi_h = 0 \, . \quad (15)$$

We calculate the fermion eigenvalue in the background field of the gradient barrier as well as selfconsistently,

*Paper presented at XXVII Int. Conf. on High Energy Physics: Session Pa-15
Glasgow, UK, 20–27 July 1994*

New Electroweak Instanton and Possible Breakdown of Unitarity

F. R. Klinkhamer

Institut für Theoretische Physik, Universität Karlsruhe,
D–76128 Karlsruhe, Germany

Abstract

Potential implications of a new constrained instanton solution in the electroweak standard model are discussed. Notably, there may be a non-perturbative unitarity violating contribution to the total cross-section at high collision energies.

1. Introduction

In the last year we have given for the electroweak standard model :

1. an explicit construction of a new static, but unstable, classical solution, the sphaleron S* [1] ;
2. an existence "proof" (and construction method) for the related constrained instanton I* [2] .

Roughly speaking, S* is a constant time slice through I*, just like the well-known sphaleron S [3] resembles a constant time slice of the BPST instanton I [4].
The outline of this talk is as follows. First we recall a few pertinent facts about these two new classical solutions. Then we make some remarks on the potential physics implications, focussing on the role of the new instanton I*. Specifically, we mention the asymptotics of perturbation theory and the apparent violation of unitarity at high energies.

2. Classical solutions

The sphaleron S* has the following characteristics [1] :

1. axial symmetry of the fields ;
2. vanishing Higgs field at two points on the symmetry axis, separated by a distance $d_{S^\star}$;
3. chiral fermion zeromodes (related to the global $SU(2)$

anomaly), localized at either point of vanishing Higgs field, depending on the chirality ;
4. energy $E_{S^\star} \sim 2\, E_S \sim 20\, \text{TeV}$ and $d_{S^\star} \sim 4\, M_W^{-1}$.

The instanton I* has not yet been constructed in all detail, but at least the following properties are clear [2], starting with a technical preliminary :

0. constraint needed to fix the scale (ρ) of the solution ;
1. axial symmetry of the fields ($U(1)$-equivariance) ;
2. Higgs zeros seperated by a distance $d_{I^\star}$;
3. localized chiral fermion zeromodes ;
4. action $A_{I^\star} \sim 2\, A_I \sim \left(16\, \pi^2/g^2 \right) \left(1 + \mathrm{O}(\rho^2 M_W^2) \right)$ and distance parameter $d_{I^\star} \sim M_W^{-1} \left(2 + \mathrm{O}(\rho\, M_W) \right)$;
5. resemblance to a very loose di-atomic molecule for scales $\rho << M_W^{-1}$.

3. Perturbation theory

The instanton I* sits at the top of a non-contractible loop of 4-dimensional euclidean configurations and is assumed to have only one negative mode. In a way I* is like the sphaleron of a 5-dimensional theory. (Note that I* is not a "bounce" solution [5], because of the absence of a "turning point" with vanishing field derivatives.)

Following Lipatov [6] we see that I* determines the asymptotics of electroweak perturbation theory

$$c_k \, g^{2k} \propto \frac{k!}{(A_{I^*})^k} \sim \frac{k!}{(16\,\pi^2)^k}\, g^{2k} \,, \qquad (1)$$

where c_k are the coefficients calculated for an arbitrary Green's function. The same behaviour has actually been verified for the groundstate energy in a quantum mechanical model [7].

The result (1) on the asymptotics can be rephrased [8] by saying that the solution I^* gives a singularity at $z \sim 16\,\pi^2$ in the Borel plane (variable z corresponding to g^2).

4. Unitarity

A straightforward calculation [2, 9] of the two-fermion forward elastic scattering (FES) amplitude gives from the euclidean path integral (the dominant contribution being close to $\rho = 0$)

$$F(s,0)^{\text{non-pert}} \propto \exp\left[\sqrt{s}\, d_{I^*}(0) - A_{I^*}(0)\right] \,, \qquad (2)$$

with $F(s,t)$ the scattering amplitude as a function of the Mandelstam variables. This behaviour follows from inserting the I^* fields into the euclidean path integral for the 4-point Green's function and integrating over the collective coordinates. The first term in the exponent (2) comes from the Fourier transform of the fermion zeromodes, which are asymmetric with a distance parameter d_{I^*}, and the analytic continuation from euclidean to minkowskian space-time. The second term is simply the instanton action.

Remark that our calculation is similar to an earlier one with an *approximate* solution $I\bar{I}$ [10, 11]. We use, instead, the only known *exact* solution (I^*) relevant to the problem.

The non-perturbative contribution (2) is generic to all FES amplitudes and violates unitarity at

$$\left(\sqrt{s}\right)_{\text{threshold}} \sim \frac{A_{I^*}(0)}{d_{I^*}(0)} = \left(\frac{A_{I^*}(0)}{16\,\pi^2/g^2}\right)\left(\frac{2\,M_W^{-1}}{d_{I^*}(0)}\right)\tilde{E}_{S^*} \,, \qquad (3)$$

with the definition

$$\tilde{E_{S^*}} \equiv 2\,\pi\, M_W/\alpha_w \sim E_{S^*} \,.$$

The point is that by the optical theorem (unitarity) the imaginary part of the FES amplitude should be related to the total cross-section, with the Froissart bound (unitarity and analyticity) $\sigma^{\text{total}} < O(\log^2 s)$, and this bound is rapidly violated by the exponential increase with center of mass energy $\sqrt{s}$ as given by (2). More directly, the exponential behaviour (2) violates the

polynomial boundedness condition $|F(s,0)| < s^N$, with N a finite power, see for example [12].

Clearly this is a serious problem for electroweak field theory which *must* be solved. We see three possible solutions :

1. unitarity restoration together with the Feynman perturbation series ;
2. inapplicability of the conventional euclidean path integral formalism, cf. [13] ;
3. modification of the standard model .

Elsewhere we hope to elaborate on the first, most conservative, alternative. Here we only remark that this possible solution may provide us with additional constraints on the parameters of the theory.

If, however, there is a significant B+L violating part to σ^{total} from (2), then solutions 2 and/or 3 may be forced upon us.

5. Conclusions

New classical solutions of the electroweak field equations have been discovered recently, the sphaleron S^* and the instanton I^*. In this talk we have argued that these classical solutions play a role in some of the most fundamental questions of electroweak field theory, viz. the meaning of perturbation theory and unitarity.

Acknowledgements

The author would like to acknowledge the continued hospitality of CHEAF and NIKHEF-H. He also thanks M. Veltman for valuable discussions.

References

[1] F. Klinkhamer, Nucl. Phys. **B410** (1993), 343.
[2] F. Klinkhamer, Nucl. Phys. **B407** (1993), 88.
[3] F. Klinkhamer and N. Manton, Phys. Rev. **D30** (1984), 2212
[4] A. Belavin, A. Polyakov, A. Schwartz and Yu. Tyupkin, Phys. Lett. **59B** (1975), 85
[5] S. Coleman, Phys. Rev. **D15** (1977), 2929
[6] L. Lipatov, Sov. Phys. JETP **45** (1977), 216.
[7] V. Rubakov and O. Shvedov, *Sphalerons and large order behaviour of perturbation theory in lower dimension*, preprint hep-ph/9404328.
[8] G. 't Hooft, in *The whys of subnuclear physics*, Ed. A. Zichichi (Plenum 1979).
[9] F. Klinkhamer, Nucl. Phys. **B376** (1992), 255.
[10] M. Porrati, Nucl. Phys. **B347** (1990), 371.
[11] V. Khoze and A. Ringwald, Nucl. Phys. **B355** (1991), 351
[12] R. Eden, *High energy collisions of elementary particles* (Cambridge 1967).
[13] M. Veltman, *Perturbation theory and relative space*, preprint hep-ph/9404358.

CORE – A New Method for Solving Hamiltonian Lattice Systems

Colin J. Morningstar[†] and Marvin Weinstein[‡]

† Department of Physics & Astronomy, University of Edinburgh, Edinburgh EH9 3JZ, Scotland
‡ Stanford Linear Accelerator Center, Stanford University, Stanford, California 94309

Abstract

The COntractor REnormalization group (CORE) approximation, a new method for solving Hamiltonian lattice systems, is introduced. The approach combines variational and contraction techniques with the real-space renormalization group approach and is systematically improvable. Since it applies to lattice systems of infinite extent, the method is suitable for studying critical phenomena and phase structure; systems with dynamical fermions can also be treated. The method is tested using the 1+1-dimensional Ising model.

1. Introduction

Perturbative methods are inadequate for investigating many current problems in high energy and condensed matter physics, such as the confinement of quarks and gluons in QCD. Thus, the development of new nonperturbative tools is important. The COntractor REnormalization group (CORE) approximation, a new nonperturbative method for studying Hamiltonian lattice systems, is presented in this talk. The method is a hybrid of contraction, variational, cluster, mean-field, and block renormalization-group techniques. It is systematically improvable and applies to lattice systems of infinite extent, enabling direct study of phase structure and critical phenomena. Dynamical fermions can be treated without problem.

We briefly describe the method, then apply two variants of the CORE approximation to the 1+1-dimensional Ising model.

2. Description of the Method

The success of any variational calculation, especially one involving an infinite number of degrees of freedom, depends crucially on choosing a good trial state. An algorithm for building trial states suitable for lattice systems is the Hamiltonian real-space renormalization group (RSRG) method [1]. In this approach, the lattice is partitioned into blocks including a few sites and the block-Hamiltonians are diagonalized. The Hilbert space is then *thinned* by discarding all high-energy states, retaining only those states which can be constructed from tensor products of some small subset of low-lying block eigenstates, and an effective Hamiltonian which describes the mixing of the remaining states is computed. This thinning process is repeated again and again until the effective Hamiltonian takes a fixed form which can be diagonalized.

Unfortunately, simple RSRG truncation procedures often have difficulties accurately describing the long-wavelength modes on the full lattice because they badly underestimate the block-to-block mixings. Past approaches to overcoming this problem have concentrated on using larger blocks, increasing the number of states retained per block, or introducing more sophisticated truncation schemes. The CORE approximation is a new approach to this problem which emphasizes simplicity and versatility; it frees one from the need to develop clever truncation schemes and allows the use of manifestly gauge-invariant RSRG schemes when studying lattice gauge theories.

The basic idea of the CORE approach is to steer the RSRG iteration using contraction techniques. An important part of this steering process is reliably approximating the expectation value

$$\mathcal{E}(t) = \frac{\langle \Phi_{\text{var}} | e^{-tH} H e^{-tH} | \Phi_{\text{var}} \rangle}{\langle \Phi_{\text{var}} | e^{-2tH} | \Phi_{\text{var}} \rangle}, \tag{1}$$

which tends to the lowest eigenvalue ϵ_0 of Hamiltonian H as $t \to \infty$, assuming the trial state $|\Phi_{\text{var}}\rangle$ has non-vanishing overlap with the ground state of H. Since e^{-tH} cannot be computed exactly, it is replaced in the CORE method by an operator $T(t)$ which closely approximates e^{-tH} for t in some range $0 < t < t_{max}$ and which can be easily evaluated. A procedure for constructing such an operator has been described in Ref. [2]. In this procedure, one expresses e^{-tH} as a symmetric product of explicitly computable terms; for example, if $H = H_1 + H_2$, where e^{-tH_1} and e^{-tH_2} can be evaluated exactly, then

$$e^{-tH} = e^{-tH_1/2} e^{-tH_2/2} e^{C_3(t)} e^{-tH_2/2} e^{-tH_1/2}, \tag{2}$$

where $C_3(t)$ is order t^3 or higher. To construct $T(t)$, one then either replaces $e^{C_3(t)}$ by the identity operator or retains low-order terms in $C_3(t)$, rewriting their exponential again as a symmetric product of computable terms. A given contractor $T(t)$ can also be improved by using $T_p(t) = [T(t/p)]^p$.

Having chosen a contractor $T(t)$, a variational best estimate for ϵ_0 can be obtained by minimizing

$$\mathcal{E}_T(t) = \frac{\langle \Phi_{\text{var}} | T(t) H T(t) | \Phi_{\text{var}} \rangle}{\langle \Phi_{\text{var}} | T(t)^2 | \Phi_{\text{var}} \rangle} \tag{3}$$

with respect to t and any parameters in $|\Phi_{\text{var}}\rangle$. For a trial state $|\Phi_{\text{var}}\rangle = \sum_{j=1}^{n} \alpha_j |\phi_j\rangle$, where $\{|\phi_j\rangle\}$ is any set of orthonormal states, minimizing $\mathcal{E}_T(t)$ with respect to the α_j parameters is equivalent to solving the generalized eigenvalue problem

$$\det \left([\![T(t) H T(t)]\!] - \lambda [\![T(t)^2]\!] \right) = 0, \tag{4}$$

where $[\![\dots]\!]$ denotes truncation to the subspace spanned by the $|\phi_j\rangle$ states. Hence, we can replace the problem of finding the best trial state by that of diagonalizing the *effective Hamiltonian*

$$H_{\text{eff}}(t) = [\![T(t)^2]\!]^{-1/2} [\![T(t) H T(t)]\!] [\![T(t)^2]\!]^{-1/2}. \tag{5}$$

Developing *this* operator in the RSRG iteration instead of $[\![H]\!]$ is the key innovation of the CORE approach.

The effective Hamiltonian cannot be exactly determined. The last step in the CORE approach is to apply *cluster* techniques to approximate $H_{\text{eff}}(t)$ (see Ref. [3] and references cited therein). Essentially, this involves evaluating $H_{\text{eff}}(t)$ on increasingly-larger, connected sublattices and using the principle of inclusion-exclusion to appropriately combine the results for the full lattice.

In summary, CORE is an iterative blocking and thinning process, developing the low-lying physics in a

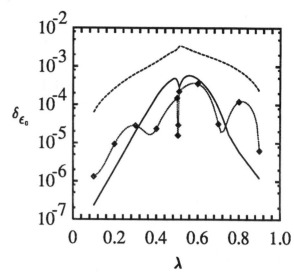

Figure 1. Fractional error δ_{ϵ_0} in the ground-state energy density estimates against λ. Results using T_1^2 (dashed curve), T_1^{16} (solid), and T_2^{12} (diamonds with dotted curve) are shown.

sequence of effective sub-Hamiltonians $H_{\text{eff}}^{(n)}(t_n^*)$ using the recursion relation

$$H_{\text{eff}}^{(n+1)}(t) = R_n(t) [\![T^{(n)}(t) H_{\text{eff}}^{(n)}(t_n^*) T^{(n)}(t)]\!] R_n(t), \tag{6}$$

where $R_n(t) = [\![T^{(n)}(t)^2]\!]^{-1/2}$, the contractor $T^{(n)}(t)$ approximates $\exp[-tH_{\text{eff}}^{(n)}(t_n^*)]$, and t_n^* is a best value for t selected for each RG iteration in some manner: minimizing $H_{\text{eff}}^{(n)}(t)$ in a simple product state is one possibility. As the recursion proceeds, the effective Hamiltonian evolves eventually into a simple form which can be easily diagonalized, yielding estimates of the ground state energy and the energies of some low-lying excited states.

CORE can also be used to estimate the vacuum expectation value of an extensive operator O. Using the same RSRG transformations as for H, one first computes the sequence of effective operators $O_{\text{eff}}^{(n)}(t_n^*)$. Once H_{eff} has evolved sufficiently such that its ground state can be found, the matrix element of O_{eff} in the ground state of H_{eff} then yields the desired expectation value.

3. The 1+1-Dimensional Ising Model

The Ising model in $1 + 1$ dimensions is often used as a testing ground for new calculational methods. Its Hamiltonian is given by

$$H_{\text{Ising}} = -\sum_j [c_\lambda \sigma_z(j) + s_\lambda \sigma_x(j)\sigma_x(j+1)], \tag{7}$$

where j labels the sites in the infinite chain, $c_\lambda = \cos(\lambda\pi/2)$, and $s_\lambda = \sin(\lambda\pi/2)$, for $0 \le \lambda \le 1$. A second-order phase transition occurs in this model at $\lambda = 1/2$.

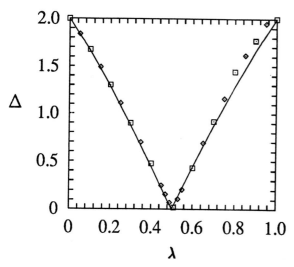

Figure 2. Mass gap estimates Δ against λ. The diamonds and squares indicate CORE estimates obtained using T_1^{16} and T_2^{12}, respectively. The exact mass gap appears as a solid curve.

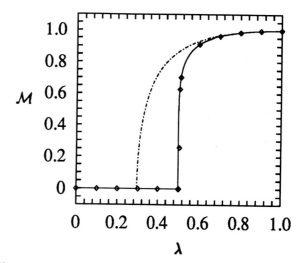

Figure 3. Magnetization $\mathcal{M}$ against λ. The diamonds indicate CORE estimates obtained using T_2^{12}, the solid curve shows the exact magnetization, and the dot-dashed curve shows the estimates from mean-field theory.

When $\lambda < 1/2$, the order parameter $\langle \sigma_x(j) \rangle = 0$ and the ground state is unique. For $\lambda > 1/2$, spontaneous symmetry breaking occurs and the order parameter takes values $\langle \sigma_x(j) \rangle = \pm(1 - \cot^2(\lambda\pi/2))^{1/8}$.

We tested the CORE approximation in two different applications to the Ising model. In both applications, the Hilbert space was thinned to the lowest two eigenstates in each block, the cluster expansion of $H_{\text{eff}}(t)$ was truncated after three-block clusters, and t was fixed by minimizing the expectation value of H_{eff} in a mean-field state. Two-site blocking was used in the first application, and blocks containing three sites were used in the second application. The contractor for the first application was $T_1(t) = S_1^\dagger(t)S_1(t)$, with $S_1(t) = \prod_\alpha \{\prod_j [1 + \tanh(c_\alpha t/2)O_\alpha(j)]\}$, where c_α are couplings, α labels the different types of operators $O_\alpha(j)$, such as $\sigma_z(j)$ and $\sigma_x(j)\sigma_x(j+1)$, and j is a site label. The second contractor used was $T_2(t) = S_2^\dagger(t)S_2(t)$ with $S_2(t) = \exp(-tV/2)\exp(-tH_b/2)$, where H_b contains all intra-block interactions and V contains all inter-block operators (those which cross block boundaries). Note that $\exp(-tH_b/2) = \prod_p \exp(-tH_b(p)/2)$ and $\exp(-tV/2) = \prod_p \exp(-tV(p)/2)$, where p labels the blocks. Calculations were done using $T_1^n(t/n)$ and $T_2^n(t/n)$ for various values of n.

Fractional errors $\delta_{\epsilon_0} = |(E_0 - \epsilon_0)/\epsilon_0|$ in the ground-state energy estimates E_0 from both variants of the CORE approach are shown in Fig. 1. Selected estimates for the mass gap Δ and magnetization $\mathcal{M} = |\langle \sigma_x(j) \rangle|$, for some site j, are compared to the exactly-known results in Figs. 2 and 3. Considering that only the first three terms in the cluster expansion are included in the calculations, the accuracy of the results is striking. The

CORE approximation reproduces the correct location of the critical point with remarkable precision. Including more terms in the cluster expansion should significantly improve these results.

4. Conclusion

We believe that the CORE approximation will prove to be a powerful tool for studying nonperturbative systems. An exciting feature of the method is that it can be used to analyze systems containing dynamical fermions, systems which resist treatment by present stochastic means. We are presently extending the method for use with lattice field theories.

Acknowledgement

This work was supported by the NSERC of Canada, the U. S. DOE, Contract No. DE-AC03-76SF00515, and the UK SERC, grant GR/J 21347.

References

[1] S. Drell, Marvin Weinstein, and S. Yankielowicz, Phys. Rev. D **16**, 1769 (1977); S. D. Drell, Benjamin Svetitsky, and Marvin Weinstein, *ibid.* **17**, 523 (1978); S. D. Drell and Marvin Weinstein, *ibid.* **17**, 3203 (1978); D. Horn and S. Yankielowicz, Nucl. Phys. **B161**, 533 (1979); D. Horn, M. Karliner, and S. Yankielowicz, *ibid.* **B170**, 467 (1980); David Horn and Marvin Weinstein, Phys. Rev. D **25**, 3331 (1982).

[2] Marvin Weinstein, Phys. Rev. D **47**, 5499 (1993).

[3] Colin J. Morningstar, Phys. Rev. D **46**, 824 (1992); see also Domb, C., in *Phase Transitions and Critical Phenomena*, edited by C. Domb and M. S. Green (Academic Press, London, 1974), Vol. 3, p. 1.

Paper presented at XXVII Int. Conf. on High Energy Physics: Session Pa-15
Glasgow, UK, 20–27 July 1994

Symmetric Monopole Scattering

N S Manton

Department of Applied Mathematics and Theoretical Physics,
University of Cambridge,
Silver Street, Cambridge CB3 9EW, England

Abstract

Recent work on multi-monopole scattering is summarized. The outcome of a head-on collision of N monopoles with N-fold cyclic symmetry is described.

The slow motion of $SU(2)$ Bogomolny-Prasad-Sommerfield monopoles is well approximated by a geodesic motion on the moduli space (parameter space) of static solutions of the Bogomolny equation $B_i = D_i\Phi$. Here, B_i is the $SU(2)$ magnetic field and $D_i\Phi$ is the covariant gradient of an adjoint Higgs field. The scattering and bound orbits of two monopoles have been studied in some detail this way. The general motion of three or more monopoles would be very hard to describe, as N monopoles have $4N$ moduli, each monopole having a position and a phase.

However, some very symmetrical scattering processes have been understood recently [1]. These processes involve N monopoles in a simultaneous head-on collision, symmetric under the cyclic group C_N. Initially the monopoles are at the vertices of a regular N-gon in a plane, with phases round the N-gon $\{1, e^{2\pi ik/N}, e^{4\pi ik/N}, \ldots, e^{2(N-1)\pi ik/N}\}$ and k an integer in the range $0 \le k < N$. The monopoles are moving towards the centre of the N-gon at the same speed, but the phases are not changing. If $k = 0$ then the monopoles remain in the plane. They pass instantaneously through the (essentially unique) charge N static solution with circular symmetry, and emerge again at the vertices of an expanding N-gon, rotated by π/N relative to the initial one. This motion is analogous to that of N Nielsen-Olesen vortices in a plane. If $k \ne 0$, then a genuinely three-dimensional scattering takes place. After the collision, two clusters of monopoles emerge, moving in opposite directions along the line perpendicular to the ini-

tial N-gon passing through its centre. One cluster has charge k, the other charge $N - k$, and their speeds are proportional to, respectively, $N - k$ and k. As the clusters move far apart they approach in shape the circularly symmetric solutions of charges k and $N - k$, with the axis of symmetry along the line of motion. These scattering processes are symmetric with respect to reflection in the initial plane only if $k = \frac{N}{2}$ with N even, or $k = 0$. For other values of k, the reflection exchanges k and $N - k$.

It is conjectured that there exists a static charge three monopole solution with tetrahedral symmetry, and a static charge four solution with cubic symmetry. Instanton and Skyrmion solutions with these charges and symmetries are known to exist. If the conjecture is correct, then the three colliding monopoles with $k = 1$ or $k = 2$, as described above, would pass instantaneously through the tetrahedral solution, its orientation being opposite in the two cases. Similarly, four colliding monopoles with $k = 2$ would pass through the cubic solution.

Reference

[1] N.S. Manton and M.K. Murray, Symmetric Monopoles, DAMTP preprint 94-57, hep-th 9407102.

Paper presented at XXVII Int. Conf. on High Energy Physics: Session Pa-15
Glasgow, UK, 20–27 July 1994

No Z_N - bubbles in hot Yang-Mills theory

A.V. Smilga

ITEP, B.Cheremushkinskaya 25, Moscow 117259, Russia

Abstract

Pure Yang-Mills theory at high temperature is considered. We show that no distinct Z_N- phases separated by domain walls do exist in the physical Minkowski space. That means the absense of the spontaneous breaking of Z_N- symmetry in the physical meaning of this word.

1. Introduction.

It was shown some time ago that the pure YM theory undergoes a phase transition at some temperature $T_c \sim \Lambda_{QCD}$ [1, 2]. This phase transition exhibits itself in a radical change of the behaviour of the correlator

$$C(x) = < P(x)P^*(0) >_T \qquad (1)$$

where $P(x)$ is the Polyakov line

$$P(x) = \frac{1}{N_c}Tr\{\exp[ig\beta\hat{A}_0(x)]\} \qquad (2)$$

(we choose the gauge where $\hat{A}_0$ is time-independent; $\beta = 1/T$). Physically, this gauge transition corresponds to deconfinement: at low T, the interaction part of free energy of a test heavy quark-antiquark pair at distance R grows linearly with R whereas, for high T, it tends to zero at large distances.

There were scores of papers published since 1978 where it was explicitly or implicitly assumed that one can use the cluster decomposition for the correlator (1) at large T and attribute the meaning to the temperature average $< P >_T$. Under this assumption, the phase of this average can acquire N_c different values: $< P >_T = C \exp\{2\pi i k/N_c\}$, $k = 0,\ldots,N_c-1$ which would correspond to N_c distinct physical phases and to the spontaneous breaking of the discrete Z_N - symmetry. In recent [3], the surface energy density of the domain walls separating these phases has been evaluated.

We show, however, that the standard interpretation is wrong. In particular:

1 Only the correlator (1) has the physical meaning. The phase of the expectation value $< P >_T$ is not a physically measurable quantity. There is only *one* physical phase in the hot YM system.

2 The "walls" found in [3] should not be interpreted as physical objects living in Minkowski space but rather as Euclidean field configurations, kind of "planar instantons" appearing due to nontrivial $\pi_1[\mathcal{G}] = Z_N$ where G= $SU(N)/Z_N$ is the true gauge symmetry group of the *pure* YM system.

3 The whole bunch of arguments which is usually applied to nonabelian theories can be transferred with a little change to hot QED. The latter also involves planar instantons appearing due to nontrivial $\pi_1[U(1)] = Z$. These instantons should *not*, however, be interpreted as Minkowski space walls.

It is impossible to present an adequate discussion of this issue in this short note. The reader is referred to [4] where such a discussion is given. We can only briefly mention here some crucial points of our reasoning.

2. Continuum Theory.

A preliminary remark is that the situation when the symmetry is broken at high temperatures and restores at low temperatures is very strange and unusual. The opposite is much more common in physics. We are aware of only one model example where spontaneous symmetry breaking survives and can even be induced at high temperatures [5]. But the mechanism of this breaking is completely different from what could possibly occur in the pure Yang-Mills theory.

Speaking of the latter, we note first that there is no much sense to speak about the spontaneous breaking of Z_N - symmetry because such a symmetry is just not there in the theory. As was already mentioned, the true gauge group of pure YM theory is $SU(N)/Z_N$ rather than $SU(N)$. This is so because the gluon fields belong to the adjoint colour representation and are not transformed at all under the action of the elements of the center Z_N of the gauge group $SU(N)$.

$<P>_T$ as such is not physical because it corresponds to introducing a single fundamental source in the system: $<P>_T = \exp\{-\beta F_T\}$ where F_T is the free energy of a single static fundamental source [6]. But one cannot put a single fundamental source in a finite spatial box with periodic boundary conditions [7]. This is due to the Gauss law constraint: the total colour charge of the system "source + gluons in the heat bath" should be zero, and adjoint gluons cannot screen the fundamental source. This observation resolves the troubling paradox: complex $<P>_T$ would mean the complex free energy F_T which is meaningless.

The "states" with different $<P>_T$ could be associated with different minima of the effective potential [8]

$$V_T^{eff}(A_0^3) = \frac{\pi^2 T^4}{12}\left\{1 - \left[\left(\frac{gA_0^3}{\pi T}\right)_{mod.2} - 1\right]^2\right\}^2 \quad (3)$$

For simplicity, we restrict ourselves here and in the following with the $SU(2)$ case.

This potential is periodic in A_0^3. The minima at $A_0^3 = 4\pi nT/g$ correspond to $P = 1$ while the minima at $A_0^3 = 2\pi(2n+1)T/g$ correspond to $P = -1$. There *are* also planar (independent of y and z) configurations which interpolate between $A_0^3 = 0$ at $x = -\infty$ and $A_0^3 = 2\pi T/g$ at $x = \infty$. These configurations contribute to Euclidean path integral and are topologically non-equivalent to the trivial configuration $A_0^3 = 0$ (Note that the configuration interpolating between $A_0^3 = 0$ and $A_0^3 = 4\pi T/g$ *is* topologically equivalent to the trivial one. Such a configuration corresponds to the equator on $S^3 \equiv SU(2)$ which can be easily slipped off. A topologically nontrivial configuration corresponds to a meridian going from the north pole of the sphere to its south pole and presents a noncontractible loop on $SU(2)/Z_2$). Actually, such configurations were known for a long time by the nickname of 't Hooft fluxes [9].

Minimizing the surface action density in a nontrivial topological class, we arrive at the configuration which is rather narrow (its width is of order $(gT)^{-1}$) and has the

action density

$$\sigma^{su(2)} = \frac{4\pi^2 T^2}{3\sqrt{3}g} + CgT^2 \quad (4)$$

(the constant C cannot be determined analytically in contrast to the claim of [3] due to infrared singularities characteristic for thermal gauge theories [10]). These topologically nontrivial Euclidean configurations are quite analogous to instantons. Only here they are delocalized in two tranverse directions and thereby the relevant topology is determined by $\pi_1[\mathcal{G}]$ rather than $\pi_3[\mathcal{G}]$ as for usual localized instantons. But, by the same token as the instantons cannot be interpreted as real objects in the Minkowski space even if they are static (and, at high T, the instantons with the size $\rho \gg T^{-1}$ become static), these planar configurations cannot be interpreted as real Minkowski space domain walls.

I want to elucidate here the analogy between nonabelian and abelian theories. The effective potential for standard QED at high temperature has essentially the same form as (3):

$$V_T^{eff}(A_0) = -\frac{\pi^2 T^4}{12}\left\{1 - \left[\left(\frac{eA_0}{\pi T} + 1\right)_{mod.2} - 1\right]^2\right\}^2 \quad (5)$$

It is periodic in A_0 and acquires minima at $A_0 = 2\pi nT/e$. Here different minima correspond to the same value of the standard Polyakov loop $P_1(x) = \exp\{ie\beta A_0(x)\}$. One can introduce , however, the quantity $P_{1/N}(x) = \exp\{ie\beta A_0(x)/N\}$ which corresponds to probing the system with a fractionally charged heavy source : $e_{source} = e/N$. Note that a fractional heavy source in a system involving only the fermions with charge e plays exactly the same role as a fundamental heavy source in the pure YM system involving only the adjoint colour fields. A single fractional source would distinguish between different minima of the effective potential. If $N \to \infty$, all minima would be distinguished, and we would get infinitely many distinct "phases".

But this is wrong. One cannot introduce a *single* fractional source and measure $<P>_T$ as such due to the Gauss law constraint. What can be done is to introduce a pair of fractional charges with opposite signs and measure the correlator $<P_{1/N}(x)P_{1/N}^*(0)>_T$. The latter is a physical quantity but is not sensitive to the phase of P. The same concerns the correlator $<P_{1/N}(x_1)...P_{1/N}(x_N)>_T$ which corresponds to putting N fractional same-sign charges at different spatial points.

Finally, one can consider the configurations $A_0(x)$ interpolating between different minima of (5). They are topologically inequivalent to trivial configurations and also have the meaning of planar instantons †. But not the meaning of the walls separating distinct physical phases. The profile and the surface action density of these abelian planar instantons can be found in the same way as it has been done in Ref.[3] for the nonabelian case. For configurations interpolating between adjacent minima, one gets

$$\sigma^{u(1)} = \frac{2\pi^2(2\sqrt{2}-1)T^2}{3\sqrt{6}e} + CeT^2\ln(e) \qquad (6)$$

where C is a numerical constant which *can* in principle be analytically evaluated.

There is a very fruitful and instructive analogy with the Schwinger model. Schwinger model is the two-dimensional QED with one massless fermion. Consider this theory at high temperature $T \gg g$ where g is the coupling constant (in two dimensions it carries the dimension of mass). The effective potential in the constant A_0 background has the form which is very much analogous to (3,5):

$$V^{eff}(A_0) = \frac{\pi T^2}{2}\left[\left(1 + \frac{gA_0}{\pi T}\right)^2 - 1\right]^2 \qquad (7)$$

It consists of the segments of parabola and is periodic in A_0 with the period $2\pi T/g$. Different minima of this potential are not distinguished by a heavy integerly charged probe but could be distinguished by a source with fractional charge. Like in four dimensions, there are topologically nontrivial field configurations which interpolate between different minima. These configurations are localized (for $d = 2$ there are no transverse directions over which they could extend) and are nothing else as high-T instantons. The minimum of the effective action in the one-instanton sector is achieved at the configuration [4, 11]

$$A_0(x) = \begin{bmatrix} \frac{\pi T}{g}\exp\left\{\frac{g}{\sqrt{\pi}}(x-x_0)\right\}, & x \leq x_0 \\ \frac{\pi T}{g}\left[2 - \exp\left\{\frac{g}{\sqrt{\pi}}(x_0-x)\right\}\right], & x \geq x_0 \end{bmatrix} \qquad (8)$$

the instanton (8) is localized at distances $x - x_0 \sim g^{-1}$ and has the action $S_I = \pi^{3/2}T/g$. But, in spite of that it is time-independent, it is the essentially Euclidean configuration and should not be interpreted as a "soliton" with the mass $M_{sol.?} = TS_I$ living in the physical Minkowski space.

3. Lattice Theory

The most known and the most often quoted arguments in favour of the standard conclusion of the spontaneous

† In the abelian case, there are infinitely many topological classes: $\pi_1[U(1)] = Z$.

breaking of Z_N-symmetry in hot Yang-Mills theory come from lattice considerations. Let us discuss anew these arguments and show that, when the question is posed properly, the answer *is* diferent.

Following Susskind [2], consider the hamiltonian lattice formulation where the theory is defined on the 3-dimensional spatial lattice and the time is continuous. In the standard formulation, the dynamic variables present the unitary matrices $V(r,n)$ dwelling on the links of the lattice (the link is described as the vector starting from the lattice node **r** with the direction **n**). The hamiltonian is

$$H = \sum_{links} \frac{g^2(E^a)^2}{2a} - \frac{2}{ag^2}\sum_{plaq.} Tr\{V_1V_2V_3V_4\} \qquad (9)$$

where a is the lattice spacing, g is the coupling constant and E^a have the meaning of canonical momenta $[E^a(r,n), V(r,n)] = t^aV(r,n)$. Not all eigenstates of the hamiltonian (9) are, however, admissible but only those which satisfy the Gauss law constraint. Its lattice version is

$$G^a(r) = \sum_n E^a(r,n) = 0 \qquad (10)$$

It is possible to rewrite the partition function of the theory (9, 10) in terms of the *dual variables* $\Omega_r \in SU(2)$ which are defined not at links but at the nodes of the lattice. Ω_r are canonically conjugate to the Gauss law constraints (10) and have the meaning of the gauge transformation matrices acting on the dynamic variables $V(r,n)$. In the strong coupling limit when the temperature is much greater than the ultraviolet cutoff $\Lambda_{ultr} \sim 1/a$, the problem can be solved analytically. The effective dual hamiltonian has 2 sharp minima at $\Omega_r = 1$ and $\Omega_r = -1$ and this has been interpreted as the spontaneous breaking of Z_2-symmetry.

Note, however, that the same arguments could be repeated in a much simpler and the very well known two-dimensional Ising model. Being formulated in terms of the physical spin variables σ, the theory exhibits the spontaneous breaking of Z_2-symmetry at low temperatures, and at high T the symmetry is restored. But the partition function of the Ising model can also be written in terms of the dual variables η defined at the plaquette centers [12]. Dual variables are ordered at high rather than at low temperatures. This obvious paradox is resolved by noting that the dual variables η are not measurable and have no direct physical meaning. The "domain wall" configurations interpolating between $\eta = 1$ and $\eta = -1$ *do* contribute in the partition function formulated in dual terms. But one cannot feel these configurations in any physical experiment.

And the same concerns the lattice pure YM theory . There *are* configurations interpolating between different

$\Omega r \in Z_2$ and contributing to the partition function, but they do not correspond to any real-time object and cannot be felt as such in any physical experiment.

Up to now we discussed the system with a standard lattice hamiltonian (9). Note, however, that one can equally well consider the lattice theory with the hamiltonian having the same form as (9) but involving not the unitary but the orthogonal matrices $V^{adj}(r, n) \in SO(3)$. Both lattice theories should reproduce one and the same continuous Yang-Mills theory in the limit when the inverse lattice spacing is much greater than all physical parameters (As far as I understand, there is no unique opinion on this issue in the lattice community. If, however, lattice hamiltonia involving unitary and orthogonal matrices would indeed lead to different field theories in the continuum limit, it would mean that the Yang-Mills field theory is just not defined until a particular procedure of ultraviolet regularization is specified. This assertion seems to me too radical, and I hesitate to adopt it.).

But in the strong coupling limit $T \gg \Lambda_{ultr.}$ the two lattice theories are completely different. The theory with orthogonal matrices has the same symmetry properties as the continuum theory, and there is no Z_2-symmetry whatsoever. The effective dual hamiltonian depending on the gauge transformation matrices $\Omega_r^{adj} \in SO(3)$ also has no such symmetry and there is nothing to be broken.

Earlier the lattice studies of the deconfinement phase transition have been performed exclusively with the standard lattice lagrangian involving unitary matrices. These studies suggest that the deconfinement phase transition occurs simultaneously with the spontaneous symmetry breaking in the dual hamiltonian $H^{eff}(\Omega_r^{fund.})$ [13] (We repeat that such a breaking is not a physical symmetry breaking because it does not lead to the appearance of domain walls detectable in experiment.). In our opinion, however, the additional Z_2-symmetry which the hamiltonian (9) enjoys is a nuisance rather than an advantage. It is a specifically lattice feature which is not there in the continuum theory. We strongly suggest to people who can do it to perform a numerical study of the deconfinement phase transition for the theory involving orthogonal matrices. In that case, no spontaneous Z_N breaking can occur. Probably, for finite lattice spacing, one would observe kind of crossover rather than the phase transition. The crossover is expected to become more and more sharp as the lattice spacing (measured in physical units) would become smaller and smaller.

It would be interesting also to try to observe the "walls" (i.e. the planar Euclidean instantons) for the orthogonal lattice theory. They should "interpolate" between $\Omega_r^{adj} = 1$ and $\Omega_r^{adj} = 1$ along a topologically nontrivial path. Like any other topological effect, these instantons should become visible only for a small enough lattice spacing (much smaller than the characteristic instanton size), and to detect them is definitely not an easy task. But using the orthogonal matrices is the only way to separate from lattice artifacts. The only available numerical study [14] was done for the theory with unitary matrices and too close to the strong coupling regime where these artifacts are desisive. Thereby, it is not conclusive.

Acknowledgement

I benefited a lot from numerous discussions with many people. An incomplete list includes P. Hasenfratz, C. Korthals-Altes, H. Leutwyler, M. Lüscher, L. McLerran, F. Niedermayer, L. Susskind, N. Weiss and U. Weiss. It is a pleasure to thank the organizers of this conference for their excellent and dedicated job and for kind hospitality.

References

[1] A.M. Polyakov, Phys. Lett. **72B** (1978) 477.

[2] L. Susskind, Phys. Rev. **D20** (1979) 2610.

[3] T. Bhattacharya *et al.*, Nucl. Phys. **B383** (1992) 497.

[4] A.V. Smilga, Ann. Phys., *to be published* .

[5] R.N. Mohapatra and G. Senjanovic, Phys. Rev. **D20** (1979) 3390.

[6] L. McLerran and B. Svetitsky, Phys. Rev. **D24** (1991) 450; J. Kuti, J. Polonyj and K. Szlachanyj, Phys. Lett. **98B** (1981) 199.

[7] E. Hift and L. Polley, Phys. Lett. **131B**(1983) 412.

[8] N. Weiss, Phys. Rev. **D24** (1981) 475.

[9] G. 't Hooft, Nucl. Phys. **B153** (1979) 141; Acta Physica Austriaca Suppl. **22** (1980) 53.

[10] A. Linde, Phys. Lett., **93B** (1980) 327; D.J. Gross, R.D. Pisarski and L.G. Yaffe, Rev. Mod. Phys. **53** (1981) 43.

[11] A.V. Smilga, Phys. Rev. **D49** (1994) 5480.

[12] H.A. Kramers and G.H. Wannier, Phys. Rev. **60** (1941) 252;L.P. Kadanoff and H. Ceva, Phys. Rev. **B3** (1971) 3918.

[13] J. Fingberg, U. Heller and F. Karsch, Nucl.Phys. **B392** (1993) 493 *and references therein*.

[14] K. Kajantie et al., Nucl. Phys. **B357** (1991) 693.

Paper presented at XXVII Int. Conf. on High Energy Physics: Session Pa-15
Glasgow, UK, 20–27 July 1994

Electroweak Strings and Monopoles

Tanmay Vachaspati [‡]

Isaac Newton Institute, 20 Clarkson Road, University of Cambridge,
Cambridge, CB3 0EH, UK.

Abstract

Some known properites of electroweak strings and monopoles are described.

1. Introduction

The standard model of the electroweak interactions does not contain topological magnetic monopoles or topological Nielsen-Olesen string solutions since the vacuum manifold is a three sphere whose first and second homotopy groups are trivial. Yet the model does contain non-topological magnetic monopoles[1] and two kinds of strings[2, 3]. These defects are very similar to their topological counterparts and possess novel properties that are likely to be relevant in a cosmological setting and perhaps in future collider experiments.

This article summarizes the various defects in the standard model and their known properties.

1.1. Z-strings

The Z-string is a cylindrically symmetric solution to the equations of motion of the standard model (bosonic sector only). The solution is[4, 5, 6]:

$$\Phi = \frac{\eta}{\sqrt{2}} f(r) e^{im\theta} \begin{pmatrix} 0 \\ 1 \end{pmatrix} , \qquad Z_\mu = -\frac{v(r)}{\alpha r} \delta_{\mu\theta} \quad (1)$$

where, (r, θ, z) are cylindrical coordinates and the other symbols are as given in Reference [6]. The functions $f(r)$ and $v(r)$ are the profile functions for the Nielsen-Olesen vortex[7].

The Z-flux through the string is:

$$F_Z = \frac{4\pi}{\alpha} = \frac{4\pi}{e} sin\theta_W \, cos\theta_W . \quad (2)$$

‡ Address from 1 January 1995: Department of Physics, Case Western Reserve University, Cleveland, OH 44106, U.S.A.

The mass per unit length of the string is:

$$\mu_Z \sim \pi\eta^2 . \quad (3)$$

A long segment of string is unstable[8, 9, 10] to fragmentation into smaller pieces in addition to the dynamical instability by which it can collapse. If one considers an infinite straight string, the time scale of instability towards fragmentation is set by m_W^{-1}. But if the string is relatively short, the fragmentation time scale could be longer. (This issue is currently under investigation.) The process of dynamical collapse is slowed down if the string segment has angular momentum. But then one must also include the possibility of radiative losses. Nambu[1] estimates the life-time of a string to radiative losses to be $\sim J/E$ where the string has energy E and angular momentum J.

Z-strings can carry baryon number in the following way[11]. Suppose we have two loops of Z-string that are linked once. Then,

$$\int d^3x \, \vec{Z} \cdot \vec{B}_Z = 2F_Z^2 \text{ (linking number)} \quad (4)$$

where the flux F_Z is given in eqn. (2). But this integral shows up on integrating the right-hand side of the anomaly equation for the baryonic current and any process that changes the value of this integral would be a baryon number violating process. Therefore, when the linking number of Z-string loops changes, baryon number violation occurs.

A segment of Z-string has fermionic zero modes. This means that the Z-string is superconducting[12].

1.2. W-strings

The W-string refers to the following string solution[3]:

$$\Phi(r,\theta) = \frac{\eta}{\sqrt{2}} f(r) \begin{pmatrix} e^{i\theta} \\ e^{-i\theta} \end{pmatrix},$$

$$W_\mu{}^1 = W_\mu{}^2 = B_\mu = 0, \quad W_\mu{}^3 = -\frac{v(r)}{gr}\delta_{\mu\theta} \tag{5}$$

The W-string has mass per unit length:

$$\mu_W \sim \mu_Z \tag{6}$$

but is somewhat more massive than the Z-string. For this reason, it is expected to be less stable than the Z-string. (See the paper by Klinkhamer and Olesen[10] for an explicit construction of an unstable mode of the W-string.)

Fermionic zero modes on W-strings have not been investigated so far. But W-strings do exhibit vector superconductivity of the type discussed by Everett[13, 3].

1.3. Monopoles and Dyons

The string solutions described above are not topological and so they can end. It is natural to ask what happens at the end of a string. It is not known how the W-string ends but it is known that the Z-string ends on magnetic monopoles[1]. Further, the magnetic monopole can be replaced by a dyon[14].

I would like to stress that the electroweak monopole is a genuine monopole. To make this absolutely clear, let us consider a Cabrera type experiment that might be used to search for such monopoles. Figure 1 shows a SQUID detector and an electroweak monopole together with the accompanying Z-string and antimonopole. The monopole then passes through the SQUID but the antimonopole passes from outside. This causes a jump in the SQUID current. Note that the intersection of the Z-string with the SQUID does not affect the electromagnetic current since the Z and A gauge fields are orthogonal. However, it could happen that the intersection of the Z-string with the SQUID would yield baryons via the anomaly equation.

The monopole mass can be estimated if one assumes that it is of the 't Hooft-Polyakov type: $M \sim (4\pi/g^2)m_W$. The electromagnetic flux is: $(4\pi/e)\sin^2\theta_W$. To understand the electroweak monopole better, it is crucial to realize that the monopole is actually entirely in the SU(2) sector of the theory and the SU(2) flux from the monopole is: $4\pi/g$. The U(1) hypercharge flux is conserved and the net hypercharge flux from the monopole is zero. With this realization, the dyon charge spectrum is found to be $(n+\theta/2\pi)e$ where n is an integer and we have included the possibility of a θ term in the action[14].

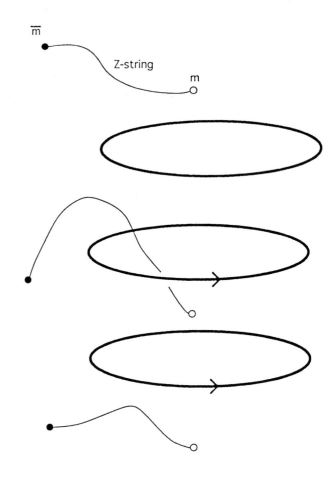

Figure 1. A SQUID detector with an electroweak monopole, Z-string and antimonopole.

References

[1] Y. Nambu, Nucl. Phys. **B130** (1977) 505.
[2] T. Vachaspati and M. Barriola, Phys. Rev. Lett. **69** (1992) 1867.
[3] M. Barriola, T. Vachaspati and M. Bucher, "Embedded Defects", Phys. Rev. D (1994) to be published; TUTP-93-7.
[4] N.S. Manton, Phys. Rev. **D28** (1983) 2019.
[5] T. Vachaspati, Phys. Rev. Lett. **68** (1992) 1977; 216(E) (1992).
[6] T. Vachaspati, Nucl. Phys. **B397** (1993) 648.
[7] H.B. Nielsen and P. Olesen, Nucl. Phys. **B61** (1973) 45.
[8] M. James, L. Perivolaropoulos and T. Vachaspati, Phys. Rev. **D46** (1992) R5232; Nucl. Phys. **B395** (1993) 534.
[9] M. James, DAMTP-HEP-94-13.
[10] F.R. Klinkhamer and P. Olesen, Nucl. Phys. **B422** (1994) 227.
[11] T. Vachaspati and G.B. Field, Phys. Rev. Lett. **73** (1994) 373.
[12] M.A. Earnshaw and W.B. Perkins, Phys. Lett. **B328** (1994) 337.
[13] A.E. Everett, Phys. Rev. Lett. **61** (1988) 1807.
[14] T. Vachaspati, "Electroweak Dyons", TUTP-94-10.

Paper presented at XXVII Int. Conf. on High Energy Physics: Session Pa-15
Glasgow, UK, 20–27 July 1994

Effective Heavy Meson Lagrangians from an Extended NJL Model

D. Ebert[†∥], T. Feldmann[†∥],
R. Friedrich[‡#] and H. Reinhardt[‡#]

†Institut fuer Physik, Humboldt–Universitaet, Invalidenstrasse 110, D–10115 Berlin, Germany
‡Institut fuer Theoretische Physik, Universitaet Tuebingen, Auf der Morgenstelle 14, D–72076 Tuebingen, Germany

Abstract

It is shown how chiral symmetry of light quarks and spin and flavour symmetry of heavy quarks can be combined in an extension of the NJL model. Besides the heavy quark masses, this introduces the four quark coupling constant between heavy and light quarks as an additional parameter. The bosonization procedure is worked out using a gradient expansion. The resulting effective lagrangian describes low–energy phenomena of heavy and light mesons.

1. Introduction

Recently, new important symmetries have been discovered for heavy quark flavors $Q = b, c, \ldots$ which considerably simplify the description of hadrons containing one heavy quark. These symmetries arise in the limit of infinite heavy quark masses $m_Q \to \infty$, where the heavy quark spin decouples from the light QCD degrees of freedom, and the dynamics of the light quarks within a heavy hadron is independent of the heavy quark flavor. Furthermore, corrections to the heavy quark limit are treated systematically in the Heavy Quark Effective Theory (HQET) [1]. This offers the possibility to extract Standard Model parameters for heavy quarks.

However, HQET is still defined in terms of quark and gluon degrees of freedom while for practical applications it would be desirable to reformulate it in terms of hadronic degrees of freedom, which unfortunately cannot exactly be accomplished.

For light quark flavors the Nambu–Jona–Lasionio (NJL) model has been successfully used to describe the dynamics of QCD. The properties of this model are governed by global chiral invariance and its spontaneous

breaking in the ground state. Indeed, employing appropriate bosonization techniques combined with a gradient expansion, the low energy dynamics of light pseudoscalar, vector and axial–vector mesons is described surprisingly well, embodying the soft–pion theorems, vector dominance, Goldberger–Treiman and KSFR relations and the integrated chiral anomaly [2, 3]. In addition, the bosonized NJL model also provides a natural explanation of how baryons can emerge as composite quark–diquark states or, in the case of large number of colors $N_c \to \infty$, as chiral solitons. For a recent review on these subjects see [4] and references therein.

In [5] we therefore proposed an extension of the NJL model (for related work see also [6, 7]) which includes chiral symmetry for light quarks and the heavy quark symmetries. The scale of chiral symmetry breaking reflects itself in a model–inherent cut–off Λ of about 1 GeV for both the light quark momenta as well as the heavy quark residual momentum $k^\mu = p^\mu - m_Q v^\mu$, where v^μ is the conserved velocity of an infinitely heavy quark and p^μ its total momentum.

In this talk we will discuss the bosonization of this model, reproducing basically the effective heavy and light meson lagrangians with heavy quark and chiral symmetries which have been introduced phenomenologically before [8].

∥ Supported by *Deutsche Forschungsgemeinschaft* under contract
Eb 139/1–1
♯ Supported by *Deutsche Forschungsgemeinschaft* under contract
Re 856/2–2

2. Extended NJL Model

In the extended NJL model under consideration we add to the free lagrangian of light (q) and heavy (Q_v) quarks of definite velocity v,

$$\mathcal{L}_0 = \overline{q}(i\slashed{\partial} - \widehat{m}_0)q + \overline{Q}_v(iv \cdot \partial)Q_v \quad ,$$

a four–quark interaction term which is motivated by the general quark–current structure of QCD and obeys chiral and heavy quark symmetries. After Fierz–rearrangement into the physical color–singlet channel this interaction between two light quarks (denoted by $\mathcal{L}_{int}^{ll}$), respectively one light and one heavy quark ($\mathcal{L}_{int}^{hl}$) is given by (summation over repeated indices is understood)

$$\mathcal{L}_{int}^{ll} =$$
$$2G_1 \left((\overline{q}\frac{\lambda_F^a}{2}q)^2 + (\overline{q}i\gamma_5\frac{\lambda_F^a}{2}q)^2 \right)$$
$$-2G_2 \left((\overline{q}\gamma^\mu\frac{\lambda_F^a}{2}q)^2 + (\overline{q}\gamma^\mu\gamma_5\frac{\lambda_F^a}{2}q)^2 \right) \quad , \qquad (1)$$

$$\mathcal{L}_{int}^{hl} =$$
$$G_3 \left((\overline{Q}_v i\gamma_5 q)(\overline{q}i\gamma_5 Q_v) - (\overline{Q}_v\gamma^\mu q)P_{\mu\nu}^\perp(\overline{q}\gamma^\nu Q_v) \right)$$
$$+G_3 \left((\overline{Q}_v q)(\overline{q}Q_v) - (\overline{Q}_v i\gamma^\mu\gamma_5 q)P_{\mu\nu}^\perp(\overline{q}i\gamma_5\gamma^\nu Q_v) \right) \qquad (2)$$

where $\lambda_F^a \in SU(3)_F$ and additional terms contributing to diquark channels are subleading in $1/N_c$ and have been discarded. We also discarded the interaction between two heavy quarks. Furthermore we have allowed for different couplings G_1, G_2 and G_3. In order to obtain expression (2) we have decomposed the interaction terms into longitudinal and transversal parts by means of projection operators $P_{\mu\nu}^\| = v_\mu v_\nu$, $P_{\mu\nu}^\perp = g_{\mu\nu} - v_\mu v_\nu$.

The bosonization procedure is standard [2, 3] and consists in introducing composite mesonic fields $(\overline{q}q)$, $(\overline{q}Q_v)$ into the generating functional which is given by the path integral

$$Z = \int \mathcal{D}q\mathcal{D}\overline{q}\mathcal{D}Q_v\mathcal{D}\overline{Q}_v e^{i \int d^4x(\mathcal{L}_0 + \mathcal{L}_{int}^{ll} + \mathcal{L}_{int}^{hl})} \quad , \qquad (3)$$

such that the lagrangian becomes bilinear in the quark fields and the latter can be integrated out.

We use a non–linear representation where

$$\xi = \exp(i\pi/F) \qquad (4)$$

is an element in the coset space $SU(3)_L \times SU(3)_R / SU(3)_V$. Here F is the bare decay constant, and $\pi = \pi^a\lambda_F^a/2$ represents the light octet of (pseudo)-Goldstone bosons associated to spontaneous breakdown of chiral symmetry through a non–vanishing vacuum expectation value of the scalar field Σ which is absorbed into the definition of light constituent quark masses m. Our model includes light vector mesons $V_\mu = V_\mu^a\lambda_F^a/2$ and axial vector mesons $A_\mu = A_\mu^a\lambda_F^a/2$.

In the heavy–light sector we can collect the pseudoscalar field Φ^5 and the vector field Φ^μ into a (super)field H which represents the $(0^-, 1^-)$–doublet of spin symmetry. Analogously the scalar field Φ and the axial–vector field $\Phi^{5\,\mu}$ are combined in the parity conjugate (super)field K

$$H = P_+(i\Phi^5\gamma_5 + \Phi^\mu\gamma_\mu) \quad , \quad v_\mu\Phi^\mu = 0 \quad , \quad (5)$$
$$K = P_+(\Phi + i\Phi^{5\,\mu}\gamma_\mu\gamma_5) \quad , \quad v_\mu\Phi^{5\,\mu} = 0 \quad , \quad (6)$$

where the projection operator on the heavy quark velocity is defined through $P_+ = (1 + \slashed{v})/2$. This is a shorthand notation, as these fields carry light flavor quantum numbers $H = H^a = (H^u, H^d, H^s)$, $K^a = (K^u, K^d, K^s)$ to form anti–triplets under chiral symmetry and the dependence on the heavy quark velocity $H = H_v$, etc. has not been quoted explicitly. Due to flavor symmetry of HQET these fields describe both B or D mesons. The details can be found in [5].

Performing the integration over heavy quark fields $Q_v(x)$ in (3) results in a trivial determinant which is absorbed into the normalization. Finally, integrating out the light quark fields leads to the following lagrangian

$$\mathcal{L} = -iN_c\,\text{Tr}\ln i\slashed{D}$$
$$-\frac{1}{4G_1}\text{tr}_\text{F}\left[\Sigma^2 - \widehat{m}_0(\xi\Sigma\xi + \xi^\dagger\Sigma\xi^\dagger)\right]$$
$$+\frac{1}{4G_2}\text{tr}_\text{F}\left[(V_\mu - \mathcal{V}_\mu^\pi)^2 + (A_\mu - \mathcal{A}_\mu^\pi)^2\right]$$
$$+\frac{1}{2G_3}\text{Tr}\left[(\overline{H} + \overline{K})(H - K)\right] \quad , \qquad (7)$$

where

$$i\slashed{D} = i\slashed{\partial} - \Sigma + \slashed{V} + \slashed{A}\gamma_5$$
$$-(\overline{H} + \overline{K})(iv \cdot \partial)^{-1}(H + K) \qquad (8)$$

is the Dirac operator for the light constituent quarks and we have defined the vector and axial–vector combinations

$$\mathcal{V}_\mu^\pi = \frac{i}{2}(\xi\partial_\mu\xi^\dagger + \xi^\dagger\partial_\mu\xi) \quad ,$$
$$\mathcal{A}_\mu^\pi = \frac{i}{2}(\xi\partial_\mu\xi^\dagger - \xi^\dagger\partial_\mu\xi) \quad .$$

To regularize the quark loops arising from (7) we shall use a universal proper–time cut–off Λ which will be fixed from the light meson data.

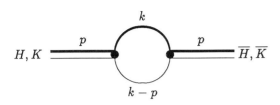

Figure 1. Self–energy diagram for heavy meson fields H, K.

3. The Effective Meson Lagrangian

Expanding the term $-iN_c \operatorname{Tr} \ln i\!\!\not{D}$ in (7) in powers of the meson fields leads to the familiar loop expansion given by Feynman diagrams with heavy and light mesons as external lines and heavy and light quarks in internal loops. For the light sector this has been done to derive an effective lagrangian in terms of π, ρ and A_1 fields [2, 3]. Comparison with experimental data fixes the parameters relevant for the heavy sector: the light constituent quark masses, $m^{u,d} = 300$ MeV, $m^s = 510$ MeV, and a universal cut–off $\Lambda = 1.25$ GeV.

In the heavy sector the loop expansion of the fermion determinant gives rise to the self–energy diagram for the heavy fields in Figure 1.

Expanding the corresponding self–energy part in powers of the external momentum $v \cdot p$, the effective meson lagrangian acquires in configuration space the desired form

$$
\begin{aligned}
\mathcal{L}_0^{heavy} &= -\operatorname{tr}_D \left[\widehat{\overline{H}}^i (iv \cdot \partial - \Delta M_H^i) \widehat{H}^i \right] \\
&+ \operatorname{tr}_D \left[\widehat{\overline{K}}^i (iv \cdot \partial - \Delta M_K^i) \widehat{K}^i \right] \quad , \quad (9)
\end{aligned}
$$

where the mass differences between heavy meson and heavy quarks are $\Delta M_{H,K}^i = M_{H,K}^i - m_Q$, and the heavy meson fields have been rescaled by Z–factors,

$$
\begin{aligned}
\widehat{H}^i &= (Z_H^i)^{-1/2} H^i \quad , \\
\widehat{K}^i &= (Z_K^i)^{-1/2} K^i \quad . \quad (10)
\end{aligned}
$$

The explicit expressions for the $Z_{H,K}^i$ and $\Delta M_{H,K}^i$ read

$$
Z_{H,K}^i = \left(I_3^i \pm 2m^i I_2^{ii} \right)^{-1} \quad , \quad (11)
$$

$$
\Delta M_{H,K}^i = Z_{H,K}^i \left(\frac{1}{2G_3} - I_1^i \mp m^i I_3^i \right) \quad , \quad (12)
$$

where the integrals I_1^i, I_2^{ii} and I_3^i are functions of m^i and Λ given in [5].

For applications in heavy–flavor decay processes it is necessary to know the strong interaction couplings between heavy mesons and light mesons V, A. The

loop expansion of the quark determinant yields such vertex terms and the low–momentum expansion around $v \cdot p_i = v \cdot p_j = 0$ leads to the following contributions to an effective lagrangian in terms of renormalized heavy and light fields

$$
\begin{aligned}
\mathcal{L}_{V/A}^{heavy} &= \\
& g_V^{ij} \lambda_1^{ij} \operatorname{tr}_D \left[\widehat{\overline{H}}^j \widehat{H}^i \right] v \cdot \widehat{V}^{ij} - g_V^{ij} \lambda_2^{ij} \operatorname{tr}_D \left[\widehat{\overline{K}}^j \widehat{K}^i \right] v \cdot \widehat{V}^{ij} \\
&+ g_V^{ij} \lambda_3^{ij} \operatorname{tr}_D \left[\widehat{\overline{H}}^j \widehat{H}^i \widehat{\mathcal{A}}^{ij} \gamma_5 \right] + g_V^{ij} \lambda_4^{ij} \operatorname{tr}_D \left[\widehat{\overline{K}}^j \widehat{K}^i \widehat{\mathcal{A}}^{ij} \gamma_5 \right] \\
&- g_V^{ij} \lambda_5^{ij} \operatorname{tr}_D \left[\widehat{\overline{K}}^j \widehat{H}^i \widehat{V}^{ij} \right] + h.c. \\
&+ g_V^{ij} \lambda_6^{ij} \operatorname{tr}_D \left[\widehat{\overline{K}}^j \widehat{H}^i \widehat{\mathcal{A}}^{ij} \gamma_5 \right] + h.c. \quad (13)
\end{aligned}
$$

where λ_n^{ij} are coupling parameters.

In our approach, the heavy mesons H, K couple to the fields π via $\pi - A_1$ mixing due to the coupling between A^μ and $\mathcal{A}^{\pi\,\mu}$. For concreteness, we quote the coupling between two members of the $(0^-, 1^-)$ multiplet $\widehat{H}^i$ with a pseudoscalar $\widehat{\pi}^{ij}$

$$
\mathcal{L}_\pi^{heavy} = g_{HHA}^{ij} \operatorname{tr}_D \left[\widehat{\overline{H}}^j \widehat{H}^i \mathcal{A}^{\pi\,ij} \gamma_5 \right] \quad (14)
$$

where the coupling constant is given by $g_{HHA}^{ij} = \lambda_3^{ij} (M_V^{ij})^2 / (M_A^{ij})^2$.

The electroweak decay constant of heavy mesons $f_{H,K}$ defined through†

$$
\begin{aligned}
\langle 0 | \bar{q} \gamma_\mu (1 - \gamma_5) Q_v | H_v(0^-) \rangle &= i f_H M_H v_\mu \quad , \\
\langle 0 | \bar{q} \gamma_\mu (1 - \gamma_5) Q_v | K_v(0^+) \rangle &= -f_K M_K v_\mu \quad , (15)
\end{aligned}
$$

can be related to the model parameters by a simple shift in the heavy meson fields,

$$
f_{H,K} \sqrt{M_{H,K}} = \frac{\sqrt{Z_{H,K}}}{G_3} \quad . \quad (16)
$$

We recover the familiar scaling of the weak decay constant of heavy mesons with the heavy mass in HQET due to heavy spin and flavor symmetry. The bosonized weak current is then represented by

$$
\begin{aligned}
J_{\mu L} &= \frac{\sqrt{M_H} f_H}{2} \operatorname{Tr} \left[\xi^\dagger \gamma_\mu (1 - \gamma_5) \widehat{H} \right] \\
&- \frac{\sqrt{M_K} f_K}{2} \operatorname{Tr} \left[\xi^\dagger \gamma_\mu (1 - \gamma_5) \widehat{K} \right] \quad , \quad (17)
\end{aligned}
$$

which coincides with expressions given on the basis of symmetry arguments in [8].

A similar calculation for currents between two heavy quarks determines the Isgur–Wise function [1] in our model. The details can be found in [5].

† The definition of $f_{H,K}$ corresponds to $f_\pi = \sqrt{2} F_\pi = 132$ MeV.

$G_3[\text{GeV}^{-2}]$	5	6	7	8	9	Exp. and others
$M_H^s - M_H^u$ [MeV]	240	190	150	120	90	100 [9]
f_B [MeV]	310	260	220	190	170	180 [10, 11]
f_{B_s}/f_B	1.1	1.1	1.1	1.1	1.1	1.1–1.2 [10, 11]
g_A	0.17	0.17	0.17	0.17	0.17	$g_A^2 < 0.5$ [12]
m_b [GeV]	4.5	4.7	4.9	5.0	5.1	$M_T/2 = 4.73$
m_c [GeV]	1.2	1.4	1.5	1.6	1.7	$M_{J/\Psi}/2 = 1.55$

Table 1. Heavy meson quantities as functions of the coupling constant G_3. The last column denotes experimental values and estimates and predictions of other approaches.

4.   Discussion and Conclusions

The extension of the NJL model has introduced heavy quarks in the infinite mass limit together with a new parameter, the four–quark coupling constant between heavy and light quarks G_3. The mass differences ΔM between a heavy meson and a heavy quark are then calculable within our model, such that heavy quark masses are estimated as $m_{b,c} = M_{B,D} - \Delta M$. Light meson physics fixes the parameters relevant for the heavy sector, like constituent quark masses $m^{u,d} = 300$ MeV, $m^s = 510$ MeV, together with a universal cut–off $\Lambda = 1.25$ GeV.

Several low–energy properties of heavy mesons follow in terms of G_3. We present some of our results in table 1 where the four–quark coupling is varied in a range of 5 GeV$^{-2} \leq G_3 \leq 9$ GeV^{-2}.

Reasonable estimates are obtained for the value $G_3 = 8.7$ GeV^{-2}, which reproduces simultaneously the $SU(3)_F$ splitting of masses and decay constants of heavy mesons as well as the theoretically favored estimate $f_B = 180$ MeV.

Note that the heavy quark scaling law $\sqrt{M_B}f_B = \sqrt{M_D}f_D$ is expected to have large $1/m_c$ corrections leading to a value of $f_D \approx 200$ MeV.

We have not presented here the values for the $(0^+, 1^+)$ heavy mesons, which can not be fitted simultaneously. We argue that this is due to the failure of the naive gradient expansion. Improvement in this direction is in progress [13].

References

[1] N. Isgur and M. Wise, Phys. Lett. **B232** (1989) 113; Phys. Lett. **B237** (1990) 527; E. Eichten and B. Hill, Phys. Lett. **B234** (1990) 511; B. Grinstein, Nucl. Phys. **B339** (1990) 253; H. Georgi, Phys. Lett. **B240** (1990) 447; T. Mannel, W. Roberts and Z. Ryzak, Nucl. Phys. **B368** (1992) 204.

[2] D. Ebert and M. K. Volkov, Yad. Fiz. **36** (1982) 1265; Z. Phys. **C16** (1983) 205; M. K. Volkov, Ann. Phys. (N.Y.) **157** (1984) 282.

[3] D. Ebert and H. Reinhardt, Nucl. Phys. **B271** (1986) 188.

[4] D. Ebert, H. Reinhardt and M. K. Volkov, *Effective Hadron Theory of QCD*, Progr. Part. Nucl. Phys. **33** (1994) 1.

[5] D. Ebert, T. Feldmann, R. Friedrich and H. Reinhardt, Prepr. DESY 94–098 (submitted for publication).

[6] W. A. Bardeen and C. T. Hill, Phys. Rev. **D49** (1993) 409.

[7] M.A. Novak, M. Rho and I. Zahed, Phys. Rev. **D48** (1993) 4370.

[8] G. Burdman and J. F. Donoghue, Phys. Lett. **B 280** (1992) 287; M. B. Wise, Phys. Rev. **D 45** (1992) 2188; R. Casalbuoni et al., Phys. Lett. **B 292** (1992) 371; Phys. Lett. **B 299** (1993) 139;

[9] Particle Data Group, *Review of Particle Properties*, Phys. Rev. **D 45** (1992).

[10] C. R. Allton et al., Nucl. Phys. **B349** (1991) 598; C. Alexandrou et al., Phys. Lett. **B256** (1991) 60; R. Sommer, DESY preprint 94–011 (1994).

[11] P. Colangelo, G. Nardulli, A. A. Ovchinnikov and N. Paver, Phys. Lett. **B269** (1991) 201; S. Narison, Phys. Lett. **B322** (1994) 247; CERN preprint TH. 7103/93; S. Narison and K. Zalewski, Phys. Lett. **B320** (1994) 369.

[12] S. Barlag et al. (ACCMOR collaboration), Phys. Lett. **B278** (1992) 480.

[13] D. Ebert, T. Feldmann, R. Friedrich, H. Reinhardt, in preparation.

Paper presented at XXVII Int. Conf. on High Energy Physics: Session Pa-15
Glasgow, UK, 20–27 July 1994

The ideas of gravitational effective field theory

John F. Donoghue

Department of Physics and Astronomy
University of Massachusetts Amherst, MA 01003 U.S.A.

Abstract

I give a very brief introduction to the use of effective field theory techniques in quantum calculations of general relativity. The gravitational interaction is naturally organized as a quantum effective field theory and a certain class of quantum corrections can be calculated.

We expect that there will be new interactions and new degrees of freedom at the Planck scale, if not sooner. Many discussions of quantum mechanics and gravity involve speculations about Planck scale physics. This talk describes a more conservative approach as we will use quantum mechanics and general relativity at ordinary energies, where we expect that they should both be valid. The goal is to argue that general relativity forms a fine quantum theory at ordinary energies, and to identify a class of "leading quantum corrections" which are the dominant quantum effects at long distance and which are reliably calculable. The apparent obstacle to such a program is the fact that the quantum corrections involve integration over all energy scales, including extreme high energies. The solution to this is the use of effective field theory. Because of the briefness of this report, the discussion here is necessarily superficial, but I will concentrate on the basic ideas of such an approach [1].

Effective field theory is a technique that allows one to separate the effects of high energy scales from low energy ones. In many cases, such as the theory of gravity, one does not know the correct high energy theory. However as a consequence of the uncertainty principle we do know that, when viewed at low energy, the high energy degrees of freedom do not propagate far. They can be integrated out of the theory leaving a local Lagrangian, although this Lagrangian will in general contain nonrenormalizable interactions. In contrast, the low energy degrees of freedom propagate long distances

and cannot be summarized by a local interaction. They must be included explicitly. From an unknown high energy theory, we are then led to write the most general Lagrangian containing the low energy particles which is consistent with the symmetries and vacuum structure of the theory. In the case of gravity interacting with a massive matter field we impose general covariance and find that

$$
\begin{aligned}
\mathcal{L} &= \mathcal{L}_{gr} + \mathcal{L}_{matter} \\
\mathcal{L}_{gr} &= \sqrt{-g}\left\{\Lambda + \frac{2}{\kappa^2}R + c_1 R^2 + c_2 R_{\mu\nu}R^{\mu\nu} + \dots\right\} \\
\mathcal{L}_{matter} &= \sqrt{-g}\left\{\frac{1}{2}\left(g^{\mu\nu}\partial_\mu\phi\partial_\nu\phi - m^2\phi^2\right)\right. \\
&\quad + d_1 R_{\mu\nu}\partial^\mu\phi\partial^\nu\phi \\
&\quad + \left. R\left(d_2\partial_\lambda\phi\partial^\lambda\phi - d_3 m^2\phi^2\right) + \dots\right\}
\end{aligned}
\tag{1}
$$

where $\Lambda \approx 0$ is related to the cosmological constant (we will set this equal to zero), $\kappa^2 = 32\pi G$, and c_i, d_i are unknown constants. The second key ingredient to effective field theory is the energy expansion, in which the many terms in the effective Lagrangian are ordered in powers of the low energy scale over the high energy scale. In gravity, since R involves two derivatives (which will become two factors of momentum q in matrix elements), the R^2 terms will be of order q^4 and hence much smaller than the R term at low enough energies. It is for this reason that we have essentially no phenomenological constraint on the R^2

terms (*i.e.* $c_1, c_2 < 10^{74}$) [2].

While it may seem relatively obvious that a classical Lagrangian can be ordered in an energy expansion, it is perhaps less obvious that quantum effects of the low energy particles can also be so ordered[3]. However, in loop diagrams the high momentum portions of the integration and all the ultraviolet divergences are also equivalent to local counterterms in a Lagrangian. For example the effect of gravitons at one-loop order has the high energy behavior (in dimensional regularization) of [4]

$$\mathcal{L}_{div} = \sqrt{-g} \frac{1}{8\pi^2(4-d)} \left(\frac{1}{120} R^2 + \frac{7}{20} R_{\mu\nu} R^{\mu\nu} \right). \quad (2)$$

This is probably not an accurate description of the full high energy behavior, but this does not matter because such quantum effects are not themselves observable and can be absorbed into renormalized values of the unknown constants c_i. However within the same Feynman diagrams there are also low energy quantum effects which correspond to the long range propagation of gravitons. These are reliable because they are independent of the unknown high energy theory, depending only on the massless degrees of freedom (gravitons) and their couplings at the lowest energies (which follow from the Einstein action). In calculations, the distinguishing characteristic is the analytic structure of the amplitudes. Effects which are able to be expanded in a power series in the momentum are thereby in a form that has the same structure as operators which arise in a local Lagrangian. These are then in most cases indistinguishable from possible effects from a high energy theory, which we argued above would be contained in the unknown coefficients of a local Lagrangian. However, non-analytic effects in the matrix element cannot come from a local Lagrangian, and only arise from long range propagation of light particles. One can use this distinction to separate out the low energy quantum effects. In most cases, the nonanalytic terms are larger numerically when one works at extremely low energies, so they are the leading long distance corrections. Effective field theory is a procedure which carries out these ideas in a straightforward way.

These ideas can perhaps best be explained by an example. The usual gravitational interactions between two masses can be obtained from the one graviton exchange potential

$$\frac{\kappa^2 m_1 m_2}{8q^2} \rightarrow -\frac{Gm_1 m_2}{r} \quad (3)$$

The effects of the R^2 terms in the effective Lagrangian appear at one higher power of q^2. Loop diagrams also give contribution at this order but the nonlocal effects

of low energy are represented by nonanalytic terms in momentum space, i.e., schematically

$$V(q) \sim \kappa^2 m_1 m_2 \left[\frac{1}{q^2} + (c_i + \kappa^2 \ell_i) \right.$$
$$\left. + \kappa^2 \left(a \sqrt{\frac{m^2}{-q^2}} + b\, ln(-q^2) \right) + \ldots \right] \quad (4)$$

where a, b and ℓ_i arise form the calculation of a set of one-loop diagrams. (ℓ_i is divergent and is absorbed into the renormalized value of the parameter c_i.) The coefficient of the nonanalytic terms (a, b) are finite and are a consequence of the low energy part of the theory. While most work in the field has focussed on the divergent portion, it is these latter finite terms which are the most predictive part of the diagrams. Note that at low enough momentum, the non-analytic terms are larger than the constant terms. In addition, they are distinguished by a different spatial dependence. When one forms a nonrelativistic potential one finds

$$V(r) \sim -Gm_1 m_2 \left[\frac{1}{r} + 4\pi \left(c_i + \kappa^2 \ell_i \right) \delta^3(x) \right.$$
$$\left. + \frac{2}{\pi} \frac{\kappa^2 am}{r^2} - \frac{2}{\pi} \frac{\kappa^2 b}{r^3} + \ldots \right] \quad (5)$$

The nonanalytic terms give power-law corrections while the local Lagrangian and high energy loop effects give a delta function. Thus the long distance quantum correction to the Newtonian potential is calculable. An explicit calculation [1] yields

$$V(r) = -\frac{Gm_1 m_2}{r} \left[1 - \frac{G(m_1 + m_2)}{rc^2} \right.$$
$$\left. - \frac{127 G\hbar}{30\pi^2 r^2 c^3} + \ldots \right] \quad (6)$$

The idea of a gravitational effective field theory extends well beyond this calculation. In general, effective field theory techniques will organize any given matrix element into the calculable effects of low energy and the unknown effects of the full high energy theory. Most commonly, the nonanalytic terms are the leading contributions at large distance. This division has not been commonly applied to the gravitational interactions and much of the standard wisdom of general relativity needs to be scrutinized through the eyes of effective field theory. The quantum corrections are numerically small in macroscopic phenomena, and I know of no such effects that can influence present day experimental relativity. However, these ideas may be useful in elucidating some of the theoretical issues of general relativity, and perhaps can be compared to the work being done in lattice simulations of quantum gravity.

As far as quantum mechanics are concerned, effective field theories are as natural as the more restrictive class of renormalizable field theories (and are perhaps even more natural). From this point of view, the quantum theory of gravity does not seem more problematic at ordinary energies than the rest of the Standard Model.

References

[1] J.F. Donoghue, Phys. Rev. Lett. **72**, 2996 (1994)
    J.F. Donoghue, UMHEP-408, gr-qc 9405057, to be published in Phys. Rev. D.
[2] K.S. Stelle, Gen. Rel. Grav. **9**, 353 (1978).
[3] J.F. Donoghue (to appear).
[4] G. 't Hooft and M. Veltman, Ann. Inst. H. Poincare **A20**, 60 (1974)

Parallel Session Pa-16

Weak Decays

Conveners: V. Sharma (University of Wisconsin)
M. Shapiro (LBL)

Scientific secretaries: M. Smith
A. Pilaftsis (reserve)

Paper presented at XXVII Int. Conf. on High Energy Physics: Session Pa-16 Glasgow, UK, 20–27 July 1994

Calculation of a weak nonleptonic matrix element using "Weinberg" sum rules

John F. Donoghue

Department of Physics and Astronomy
University of Massachusetts Amherst, MA 01003 U.S.A.

Abstract

There is a "toy" weak matrix element which can be expressed as an integral over the vector and axial vector spectral functions, $\rho_V(s) - \rho_A(s)$. I review our recent evaluation of these spectral functions, the study of four "Weinberg" sum rules and the calculation of this matrix element.

Weak nonleptonic matrix elements are notoriously difficult to calculate by any reliable method. E. Golowich and I have proposed a novel weak matrix element, not found in the standard model, which can be well calculated by a mixture of theoretical and phenomenological inputs[1]. In the process we had to update the status of the Weinberg sum rules[2]. This talk briefly reviews these developments.

Consider a weak matrix element formed using only vector currents

$$\tilde{\mathcal{H}}_w = \frac{g^2}{8} \int d^4x \, D_F(x, M_w) T \left(\bar{d}(x)\gamma_\mu u(x)\bar{u}(0)\gamma^\mu s(0) \right). \quad (1)$$

Aside from KM factors, this differs from the weak Hamiltonian of the Standard Model only in that the latter involves left handed (V-A) currents. However under chiral symmetry the Hamiltonian in Eq. 1 has a different transformation property since $8_V = 8_L \oplus 8_R$, where V, L, R refer to transformations under vectorial, left handed and right handed SU(3) respectively. The $8 \oplus 8$ direct product contains an $(8_L, 8_R)$ term

$$
\begin{aligned}
8 \otimes 8 &= (8_L, 8_R) + (8_L, 1_R) \\
&+ (1_L, 8_R) + (27_L, 1_R) + (1_L, 27_R). \quad (2)
\end{aligned}
$$

The $(8_L, 8_R)$ component is special because it is the only term which does not vanish in the chiral limit

$(m_q \to 0, p \to 0)$. The value of a $K \to \pi$ matrix element in the chiral limit (which we adopt hence forth) is then calculable using the soft pion theorem to remove the pseudoscalars

$$
\begin{aligned}
&\langle \pi(p) \mid \tilde{\mathcal{H}}_w \mid K(p) \rangle \\
&= \frac{-g^2}{F_\pi^2} \int d^4x \, D_F(x, M_w) \\
&\quad \langle 0 \mid T \left(V_\mu(x)V^\mu(0) - A_\mu(x)A^\mu(0) \right) \mid 0 \rangle \\
&= \frac{-g^2}{F_\pi^2} \int d^4x \, D_F(x, M_w) \left[\pi_V(x) - \pi_A(x) \right] \quad (3)
\end{aligned}
$$

where $\pi_{V,A}$ are the vector and axial polarization tensors. After writing these in terms of the spectral densities, one obtains

$$\langle \pi(p) \mid \tilde{\mathcal{H}}_w \mid K(p) \rangle = \frac{G_F}{\sqrt{2}} A \quad (4)$$

where

$$A = M_w^2 \int ds \frac{s^2}{s - M_w^2} \ln \left(s/M_w^2 \right) \left[\rho_V(s) - \rho_A(s) \right] \quad (5)$$

This is similar to four other sum rules.

$$\int \frac{ds}{s} \left[\rho_V(s) - \rho_A(s) \right] = -4\bar{L}_{10}$$

$$\int ds\, [\rho_V(s) - \rho_A(s)] = F_\pi^2$$

$$\int ds\, s\, [\rho_V(s) - \rho_A(s)] = 0$$

$$\int ds\, s\, ln(s)\, [\rho_V(s) - \rho_A(s)]$$

$$= -\frac{16\pi^2 F_\pi^2}{3e^2} \left(m_\pi^2 - m_\pi^2\right) \qquad (6)$$

valid in the chiral limit. Here the second and third of these are the original two Weinberg sum rules[3]. The first sum rule above involves the chiral coefficient $\bar{L}_{10} = -(9.1 \pm 0.3) \times 10^{-3}$ which is measured in radiative pion decay. This sum rule originates in work of Das et al and was given in its present, more general, form by Gasser and Leutwyler[4]. The final sum rule comes from the calculation of the electromagnetic contribution to the mass difference of neutral and charged pions[5] at lowest order in the chiral expansion. Although these were first derived before QCD, they rely on assumptions about the short distance properties that can only be proven through the use of QCD in the chiral limit. Note that the last two sum rules are no longer valid if the quark masses are turned on. This set of sum rules represents a beautiful interplay of the chiral and short distance properties of QCD.

The spectral functions can be constructed fairly reliably. This is not the place to discuss all aspects [see Ref. 2], but the low energy portion is known from chiral symmetry and the high energy effects are small and amenable to treatment by perturbative QCD. The intermediate energy contributions are not theoretically calculable at present, but fortunately these may be extracted from e^+e and τ decay data. The vector spectral function starts out with two-pion and four-pion contributions, and relatively quickly approaches a constant value. The axial spectral function has three and five pion contributions and approaches the same constant. The difference between them goes to zero as s^{-3}, which vanishes so rapidly that there is not much contribution to the sum rules from high energy. There are minor uncertainties in the data, and we adjust the spectral functions within the range of experimental uncertainties in order to fit the data while accommodating the four Weinberg sum rules. The resulting forms for ρ_V and ρ_A separately and for the difference are given in Ref 2. While this procedure does not prove the Weinberg sum rules are required by the data, they certainly are easily compatible with the set of experimental information. The fact that it is easy to satisfy the Weinberg sum rules within the constraints of theory and data is very nontrivial and is a credit to the complex theoretical ideas that went into their formulation.

When applied to the weak matrix element we obtain

$$A = -0.062 \pm 0.017 GeV^6$$

$$\langle \pi(p) \mid \tilde{\mathcal{H}}_w \mid K(p) \rangle = 5.3 \times 10^{-7} GeV^2 \qquad (7)$$

In contrast, the "vacuum saturation" approximation would yield

$$A_{vac-sat} = -0.033 GeV^6 \qquad (8)$$

and the real weak matrix element extracted from $K \to 2\pi$ using chiral symmetry

$$\frac{\langle \pi(p) \mid \mathcal{H}_w \mid K(p) \rangle}{\mid V_{ud} V_{us}^* \mid} = 1.7 \times 10^{-7} GeV^2 \qquad (9)$$

We see a modest enhancement of the matrix element.

This calculation has not uncovered the mechanism for the $\Delta I = \frac{1}{2}$ rule, as the $(8_L, 8_R)$ operator automatically does not have the freedom to have a $\Delta I = \frac{1}{2}$ enhancement, requiring $A_{3/2} = \frac{2}{3} A_{1/2}$ always. However inspection of the details of the calculation does reveal a hint as to why it is so difficult to calculate nonleptonic amplitudes. There is very little contribution from either the high or low energy ends, where theory is useful. Most of the strength comes from intermediate energies, which are generally not under theoretical control. While we cannot apply this matrix element to Standard Model phenomenology, it should prove possible to use it as a test of lattice calculational methods. In addition, it is possible that this calculational technique may be extended to study more realistic matrix elements.

References

[1] J.F. Donoghue and E. Golowich, Phys. Lett. **B312**, 406 (1993) hep-ph 9307263.

[2] J.F. Donoghue and E. Golowich, Phys. Rev. **D49**, 1513 (1994) hep-ph 9307262.

[3] S. Weinberg, Phys. Rev. Lett. **18**, 507 (1967).

[4] T. Das, V. Mathur and S. Okubo, Phys. Rev. Lett. **19**, 859 (1967);
J. Gasser and H. Leutwyler, Nucl. Phys. **B250**, 465(1985).

[5] T. Das, G.S. Guralnik, V.S. Mathur, F.E. Low and J.E. Young, Phys. Rev. Lett. **18**, 759 (1967).

Paper presented at XXVII Int. Conf. on High Energy Physics: Session Pa-16
Glasgow, UK, 20–27 July 1994

QCD Analysis of Inclusive $\Delta S = 1, 2$ Transitions: The $|\Delta I| = 1/2$ Rule

A Pich

Departament de Física Teòrica and IFIC, Universitat de València – CSIC,
Dr. Moliner 50, E-46100 Burjassot, València, Spain

Abstract

The interplay of QCD in $\Delta S = 1, 2$ non-leptonic weak transitions can be rigorously analyzed, at the inclusive level, by studying the 2–point functions associated with the corresponding $\Delta S = 1, 2$ effective Hamiltonians. The next-to-leading order calculation of these correlators shows a huge ($\gtrsim 100\%$) gluonic enhancement of the $|\Delta I| = 1/2$ channel, providing a qualitative understanding of the $|\Delta I| = 1/2$ rule within QCD.

1. Introduction

The origin of the empirically observed enhancement of strangeness-changing non-leptonic weak amplitudes with isospin transfer $|\Delta I| = 1/2$ is a long-standing question in particle physics. The short-distance analysis of the product of weak hadronic currents results in an effective $\Delta S = 1$ Hamiltonian

$$\mathcal{H}_{\text{eff}}^{\Delta S=1} = \frac{G_F}{\sqrt{2}} V_{ud} V_{us}^* \sum_i C_i(\mu^2) Q_i, \qquad (1)$$

which is a sum of local four-quark operators Q_i, constructed with the light (u, d, s) quark fields only, modulated by Wilson coefficients $C_i(\mu^2)$ which are functions of the heavy (t, Z, W, b, c) masses and an overall renormalization scale μ.

In the absence of strong interactions, $C_2(\mu^2) = 1$ and all other Wilson coefficients vanish. The operator Q_2 can be decomposed as $Q_2 = (Q_+ + Q_-)/2$, where $Q_- \equiv Q_2 - Q_1$ is a pure $|\Delta I| = 1/2$ operator and $Q_+ \equiv Q_2 + Q_1$ induces both $|\Delta I| = 1/2$ and $|\Delta I| = 3/2$ transitions. The standard electroweak model gives then rise to $|\Delta I| = 1/2$ and $|\Delta I| = 3/2$ amplitudes of nearly equal size, while experimentally the ratio between both amplitudes is a factor of twenty. To solve this big discrepancy, QCD effects should be enormous.

The leading α_s corrections indeed give, for μ-values around 1 GeV, an enhancement by a factor two to three of the Q_- Wilson coefficient with respect to the Q_+ one. Moreover, the gluonic exchanges generate the additional $|\Delta I| = 1/2$ operators Q_i (i=3,4,5,6), the so-called "Penguins". Nevertheless, this by itself is not enough to explain the experimentally observed rates, without simultaneously appealing to a further enhancement in the hadronic matrix elements of at least some of the isospin–1/2 four-quark operators.

The evaluation of hadronic matrix elements is unfortunately very difficult, since it involves non-perturbative dynamics at low energies. The problem gets, moreover, complicated by the μ-dependence of the matrix elements, which should exactly cancel the corresponding renormalization-scale dependence of the Wilson coefficients. In order to get meaningful results, a full QCD calculation is required; this is a highly non-trivial task.

The problem becomes much easier at the inclusive level, where the properties of $\mathcal{H}_{\text{eff}}^{\Delta S=1}$ can be analyzed through the 2–point function

$$\Psi(q^2) \equiv i \int dx\, e^{iqx} \left\langle 0 \right| T\{ \mathcal{H}_{\text{eff}}^{\Delta S=1}(x)\, \mathcal{H}_{\text{eff}}^{\Delta S=1}(0)^\dagger \} \left| 0 \right\rangle$$
$$= \left(\frac{G_F}{\sqrt{2}} \right)^2 |V_{ud} V_{us}^*|^2 \sum_{i,j} C_i(\mu^2)\, C_j^*(\mu^2)\, \Psi_{ij}(q^2)\,.$$
$$(2)$$

This vacuum-to-vacuum correlator can be studied with perturbative QCD methods, allowing for a consistent combination of Wilson coefficients $C_i(\mu^2)$ and 2–point functions of the 4–quark operators, Ψ_{ij}, in such a way that the renormalization scheme and scale dependences exactly cancel (to the computed order). The associated spectral function,

$$\frac{1}{\pi} \text{Im}\,\Psi(q^2) = (2\pi)^3 \sum_\Gamma \int d\Gamma\, |\langle 0|\mathcal{H}_{\text{eff}}^{\Delta S=1}|\Gamma\rangle|^2\, \delta^4(q - p_\Gamma),$$
$$(3)$$

is a quantity with definite physical information; it describes in an inclusive way how the weak Hamiltonian couples the vacuum to physical states Γ of a given invariant mass. General properties like the observed enhancement of $|\Delta I| = 1/2$ transitions can be then rigorously analyzed at the inclusive level.

A detailed analysis of two-point functions associated with $\Delta S = 1$ and $\Delta S = 2$ operators was presented in Ref. [1], where the $\mathcal{O}(\alpha_s)$ corrections to the correlators Ψ_{ij} were calculated. The next-to-leading order (NLO) corrections to the $|\Delta I| = 1/2$ 2–point functions were found to be very large, confirming the QCD enhancement obtained in a previous approximate calculation [2]. Those results were, however, incomplete because the NLO corrections to the Wilson-coefficients of "Penguin" operators were still not known.

The recent calculation of $\mathcal{H}_{\text{eff}}^{\Delta S=1}$ at NLO [3, 4] has allowed us to improve the results of Ref. [1], matching matrix elements and Wilson coefficients consistently at NLO [5]. Previously missing contributions from evanescent operators have been also incorporated [5]. In order to have a check of the results, the calculation has been performed in two different renormalization schemes for γ_5 (naively anticommuting γ_5 and 't Hooft–Veltman), and the scale- and scheme-independence of the final physical quantities has been verified.

2. Approximate results

The full calculation of $\Psi(q^2)$ is rather involved due to the fact that there are several operators which mix under renormalization. One needs to compute, at the four-loop level, all possible 2–point functions Ψ_{ij}; i.e. a 6×6 (12×12 at intermediate steps to include the contributions of evanescent operators) matrix correlator which must be renormalized in matrix form, and later convoluted with the NLO Wilson coefficients as indicated in Eq. 2.

It is possible to obtain some simplified results by using two different approximations which eliminate the mixing among operators, while keeping at the same time the important physical effects [2]:

i) If "Penguins" are neglected, the operators $Q_\pm$ are multiplicatively renormalizable. The corresponding scheme- and scale-independent spectral functions $\Phi_{\pm\pm}(s) \equiv C_\pm^2(\mu^2) \frac{1}{\pi} \text{Im}\,\Psi_{\pm\pm}(s, \mu^2)$ are found to be [5]:

$$\Phi_{++}(s) \sim \frac{8}{15} \frac{s^4}{(4\pi)^6} \alpha_s(s)^{-4/9} \left[1 - \frac{3649}{1620} \frac{\alpha_s(s)}{\pi} \right],$$
$$(4)$$

$$\Phi_{--}(s) \sim \frac{4}{15} \frac{s^4}{(4\pi)^6} \alpha_s(s)^{8/9} \left[1 + \frac{9139}{810} \frac{\alpha_s(s)}{\pi} \right].$$
$$(5)$$

ii) The interesting "Penguin" operator Q_6 can be isolated, by noting that in the large N_c limit (N_c = number of colours) the anomalous dimension matrix γ_{ij} of the set of operators Q_i becomes zero, but for γ_{66}; i.e. in this limit there is no mixing among operators and only Q_6 gets renormalized. The $\mathcal{O}(\alpha_s^2)$ correction can also be easily computed in this limit [1]:

$$\Phi_{66}(s) \sim \frac{3}{5} \frac{s^4}{(4\pi)^6} \alpha_s(s)^{18/11} \left[1 + \frac{117501}{4840} \frac{\alpha_s(s)}{\pi} \right.$$
$$\left. + 470.72 \left(\frac{\alpha_s(s)}{\pi} \right)^2 \right].$$
$$(6)$$

The NLO corrections to the $|\Delta I| = 1/2$ correlators turn out to be very big and positive, while for Φ_{++} the correction is moderate and negative. Taking $\alpha_s(s)/\pi \approx 0.1$, we find a moderate suppression of Φ_{++} by roughly 20%, whereas Φ_{--} acquires a huge enhancement of the order of 100%. The correction is even bigger for the "Penguin" correlator Φ_{66}: 240% at NLO and 700% at next-to-next-to-leading order! The perturbative calculation blows up in the $|\Delta I| = 1/2$ sector, clearly showing a dynamical gluonic enhancement of the $|\Delta I| = 1/2$ amplitudes.

3. Exact results

Following the notation of Refs. [3], the Wilson-coefficient functions can be decomposed as $C_i(s) = z_i(s) + \tau\, y_i(s)$, where $\tau \equiv -\left(V_{td}V_{ts}^*\right)/\left(V_{ud}V_{us}^*\right)$. The coefficients $z_i(s)$ govern the real part of the effective Hamiltonian, while $y_i(s)$ parametrize the imaginary part and govern, e.g., the measure for direct CP-violation in the K-system, ε'/ε. We can then form two different scale- and scheme-invariant spectral functions,

$$\widehat{\Phi}_z(s) = \sum_{i,j} z_i(\mu^2)\frac{1}{\pi}\mathrm{Im}\Psi_{ij}(s,\mu^2)\,z_j(\mu^2)\,, \quad (7)$$

$$\widehat{\Phi}_y(s) = \sum_{i,j} y_i(\mu^2)\frac{1}{\pi}\mathrm{Im}\Psi_{ij}(s,\mu^2)\,y_j(\mu^2)\,, \quad (8)$$

corresponding to z_i and y_i respectively.

Since we are mainly interested in the size of the radiative corrections, let us write $\widehat{\Phi}_{z,y}(s)$ as

$$\widehat{\Phi}_{z,y}(s) = \widehat{\Phi}_{z,y}^{(0)}(s) + \widehat{\Phi}_{z,y}^{(1)}(s)\,, \quad (9)$$

where the superscripts (0) and (1) refer to the leading and next-to-leading order respectively. The exact results obtained [5] for the ratios $\widehat{\Phi}_z^{(1)}/\widehat{\Phi}_z^{(0)}$ and $\widehat{\Phi}_y^{(1)}/\widehat{\Phi}_y^{(0)}$ are plotted in Fig. 1, for $\Lambda_{\overline{MS}}^{(3)} = 200,\ 300,$ and 400 MeV.

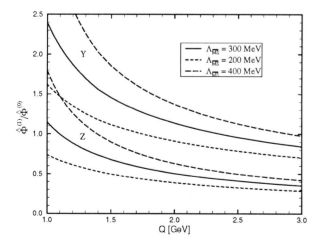

Figure 1. The ratios $\widehat{\Phi}_z^{(1)}/\widehat{\Phi}_z^{(0)}$ and $\widehat{\Phi}_y^{(1)}/\widehat{\Phi}_y^{(0)}$.

From Fig. 1, we can see that in the region $Q = 1-3\,\mathrm{GeV}$, and for a central value $\Lambda_{\overline{MS}}^{(3)} = 300\,\mathrm{MeV}$, the radiative QCD correction to $\widehat{\Phi}_z$ ranges approximately between 40% and 120%, whereas in the case of $\widehat{\Phi}_y$ we find a correction of the order of 100%–240%. As

explicitly shown by the approximate results of the previous section, the large α_s corrections correspond to the $|\Delta I| = 1/2$ part of the effective weak Hamiltonian. In fact, the corrections to the $|\Delta I| = 3/2$ correlator are exactly given by Eq. 4 ("Penguins" only give $\Delta I = 1/2$ contributions), and therefore are quite moderate.

In the case of $\Delta S = 2$ transitions, there is only one 4–quark operator. Since the $\Delta S = 2$ and $|\Delta I| = 3/2$ operators belong to the same representation of the (flavour) $SU(3)_L \otimes SU(3)_R$ group, the NLO corrections to the $\Delta S = 2$ correlator are also exactly given by Eq. 4.

4. Summary

The short-distance behaviour of the $\Delta S = 1$ correlators clearly shows a dynamical enhancement of the $|\Delta I| = 1/2$ channel, as a consequence of the interplay of gluonic corrections. The structure of the radiative corrections also allows for a deeper understanding of the underlying dynamical mechanism [5]: large corrections appear wherever quark-quark correlations can contribute. This explains why the phenomenological description of the $|\Delta I| = 1/2$ rule in terms of intermediate effective diquarks [6] was so successful.

A full QCD calculation has been possible because of the inclusive character of the defined 2–point functions. Although only qualitative conclusions can be directly extracted from these results, they are certainly important since they rigorously point to the QCD origin of the infamous $|\Delta I| = 1/2$ rule.

Acknowledgments

I would like to thank M. Jamin for a very enjoyable collaboration. This work has been supported in part by CICYT (Spain) under Grant No. AEN-93-0234.

References

[1] A. Pich and E. de Rafael, Nucl. Phys. **B358** (1991) 311.

[2] A. Pich, Nucl. Phys. B (Proc. Suppl.) **7A** (1989) 194.

[3] A. J. Buras *et al.*, Nucl. Phys. **408** (1993) 209; ibid **400** (1993) 37, 75; ibid **B370** (1992) 69; add. ibid. **B375** (1992) 501; ibid **347** (1990) 491; ibid **333** (1990) 66.

[4] M. Ciuchini *et al.*, Nucl. Phys. **B415** (1994) 403; Phys. Lett. **B301** (1993) 263.

[5] M. Jamin and A. Pich, Nucl. Phys. **B425** (1994) 15.

[6] M. Neubert and B. Stech, Phys. Rev. **D44** (1991) 775, and references therein.

Paper presented at XXVII Int. Conf. on High Energy Physics: Session Pa-16
Glasgow, UK, 20–27 July 1994

Measurement of the Michel Parameters in τ-Decays and the Helicity of the ν_τ

D. Wegener

Institute of Physics, University of Dortmund

Abstract

Recent measurements of the Michel parameters in τ-decays determined in correlation studies are discussed. The results are in good agreement with the predictions of the standard model.

1. Introduction

The study of the 3rd lepton family allows sensitive tests of the standard model. Up to now impressive agreement between theoretical predictions and experimental results averaged over the allowed helicity configurations is observed [1]. Investigations of the Lorentz structure of the τ- interaction provide a further sensitive test of the standard model. In this review the recent progress in this field [2, 3, 5, 6, 7, 8] is discusssed.

The most general matrix element for leptonic τ-decays is given by the expression

$$M \sim \sum_{\gamma\epsilon\mu} g^{\gamma}_{\epsilon\mu} < l_\epsilon \mid \Gamma^\gamma \mid \nu_l >< \nu_\tau \mid \Gamma_\gamma \mid \tau_\mu > \quad (1)$$

γ labels the scalar, vector, axial vector and tensor interaction while ϵ, μ indicate the allowed helicity states of the charged lepton. The helicity of the neutrino is fixed for the different interactions [9]. In the τ-rest-frame the energy distribution of the charged lepton is given by the expression $(\sqrt{(s)} \ll m_Z)$

$$\frac{d\Gamma}{dz} \sim x^2 \{12(1-x) + \rho(\frac{32x}{3} - 8) + \eta \frac{m_l}{m_\tau} \frac{24(1-x)}{x}\} \quad (2)$$

$$x = \frac{2E_l}{m_\tau} \quad (3)$$

The Michel parameters ρ, η, ξ, δ are functions of 10 complex coupling constants [10]. According to eq.(6) the latter two are only relevant if the τ-lepton is polarized i. e. at LEP energies. The standard model assumes a pure V-A structure of the charged current and predicts for leptonic decays $\rho = \delta = 0.75$, $\eta = 0$, $\xi_l = 1$.

The expression (2) can be generalized to describe the decay spectrum of a hadron. If the τ-lepton is in a pure helicity state $h(\tau^\pm)$ the following relation holds:

$$\frac{d\Gamma}{dz} \sim F(z) \pm h(\tau^\pm)\xi G(z) \quad (4)$$

For hadronic decays the functions $F(z), G(z)$ are exclusively fixed by kinematics while for leptonic decays the functions in addition depend on the Michel parameters: $F(z, \rho, \eta), G(z, \delta)$. For hadronic τ-decays different from ρ-decay z can be derived from the normalized lab - energy $\frac{Ex}{E_\tau}$, for ρ- mesons the decay angle of the charged π-meson with respect to the τ direction in the lab system is used:

$$z = \frac{m_\rho}{\sqrt{m_\rho^2 - 4m_\pi^2}} \frac{E_{\pi^+} - E_{\pi^0}}{\mid \vec{p_\rho} \mid} \quad (5)$$

For hadronic final states the standard model predicts $\xi_h =< h(\nu_\tau) >= -1$ and for leptonic decays of the τ one gets $\xi_l = 1$. Assuming a pure vector neutral current interaction for the production of the τ-leptons one expects a strong spin correlation of the produced $\tau^\pm$ leptons which implies a correlation of the lab-energies of the corresponding charged decay particles. The correlated energy spectra of the decay particles is given by the expression [11]

$$\frac{d^2\Gamma}{dz_i dz_j} \sim F_i F_j + \xi_i\xi_j G_i G_j - p\{\xi_i G_i F_j + \xi_j G_j F_i\} \quad (6)$$

Parameter	ALEPH	L3	ARGUS	CLEO	PDG
ρ_l	$0.798 \pm 0.032 \pm 0.026$		$0.735 \pm 0.036 \pm 0.020$		0.74 ± 0.04
ξ_l	$+1.13 \pm 0.17 \pm 0.07$	1.28 ± 0.58	$0.90 \pm 0.15 \pm 0.10$		0.90 ± 0.18
δ_l	$0.79 \pm 0.17 \pm 0.06$	0.38 ± 0.6			
η_l			$0.03 \pm 0.18 \pm 0.12$		
ξ_h	$-0.951 \pm 0.051 \pm 0.028$		$1.022 \pm 0.028 \pm 0.030$	$0.99 \pm 0.06 \pm 0.1$	$-1.25^{+0.27}_{-0.24}$

Table 1. Michel parameters as determined in recent experiments [2, 3, 4, 5, 6, 7, 1] . If a sign explicetely is given it has been measured.

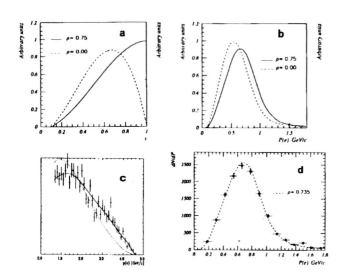

Figure 1. Electron energy spectra for the decay $\tau^- \to e^- \bar{\nu}_e \nu_\tau$. In a) - c) the spectra for $\rho = 0.75$ (full line) and $\rho = 0$ (broken line) are compared in different reference frames: a) τ-rest-frame, b) τ-pseudo-rest-frame, c) lab-system. In d) the measured spectrum in the τ-pseudo-rest- frame is compared with the theoretical expectation for $\rho = 0.735$.

i,j label the kind of particle, p is the mean polarization of the τ^--lepton which at the Z-pole is approximately $p \approx -\frac{g_V}{g_A}$. At low energies $\sqrt{s} = 10 GeV$ one expects p=0. The measured polarisation asymmetry and the left-right asymmetry determined at SLD fix the average τ^- polarization to $p < 0$.

2.   Single particle spectra

The ARGUS collaboration [2] has presented the results of a new analysis of the energy spectra for the decays $\tau^- \to e^- \bar{\nu}_e \nu_\tau$ and $\tau^- \to \mu^- \bar{\nu}_\mu \nu_\tau$. As demonstrated by figs.1a,c the sensitivity of the spectra with respect to ρ, η is diluted when the theoretical distribution (2) is transformed from the τ-rest-system into the lab-system. ARGUS has developed a new method to reduce the influence of this transformation. They select τ-events which decay in the 1-3 topology. The direction of the $3\pi^\pm(\pi^0)$ system is used to approximate the τ-direction. Since the energy of the produced τ-lepton is known, one

can reconstruct the lepton spectrum in this pseudo-rest-system. As follows from figs.1a,b the shape of the lepton spectrum is roughly a factor 1.5(2) more sensitive to the Michel parameter $\rho(\eta)$ in this reference frame than in the lab-system (fig.1c). A common fit to the $e(\mu)$-spectrum allows to determine ρ_l and η_l if lepton universality is assumed. The results of the ARGUS analysis are collected in table 1. They are in good agreement with the PDG 1994 world average [1]. Note however the improved precision achieved with the new method. The results are in perfect agreement with the standard model predictions. A. Stahl [8] has derived the Michel parameter η from the difference of the leptonic branching ratios of the τ-lepton which have recently been measured with high precision [1]. He derives a value $\eta = 0.01 \pm 0.05$. This result is in good agreement with the standard model prediction

3.   Correlation studies

New results on energy-energy correlations have been presented at this conference. L3 [6] has measured energy-energy correlations of the $e\mu$ final state, while CLEO studied the $\pi^+\pi^-$ final state [7] exploiting its high statistic sample of $1.6 * 10^6$ events. Both groups use eq. (6), note however that for the CLEO analysis p=0 holds. Hence only ξ_π^2 and $| h(\nu_\tau |$ respectively are measured. Both groups find good agreement with the standard model prediction. (table 1).

ALEPH has performed an extensive correlation study [5] of 13 channels with e, μ, π, ρ and other hadrons respectively in the final state. Their selection efficiency is of the order of 50%, the background from non-τ events is small while the background from other τ-decays is of the order of 8%. Assuming $\eta = 0$ -note that the results anyway are not sensitive to this Michel parameter because of the $\frac{m_l}{m_\tau}$ factor in eq (2) - they get for the mean polarization of the τ-lepton $p_\tau = -0.135 \pm 0.02$ in good agreement with previous studies of the $\tau - polarization$ [1]. Assuming lepton universality one gets the Michel parameters collected in table 1. Note that δ_l has been measured for the first time.

ARGUS has studied $\rho^+\rho^-$ correlations [3]. In contrast to the ALEPH experiment they have used the full available information of the final state. The matrix element is given by the expression [12]

$$| M |^2 = A(\vec{\alpha}) + \xi_\rho^2 B(\vec{\alpha}) \qquad (7)$$

$$\xi_\rho^2 = -h(\nu_\tau)h(\bar{\nu}_\tau) = \frac{2g_A g_V}{g_A^2 + g_V^2} \qquad (8)$$

where $\vec{\alpha}$ is a vector with 9 angles and 2 invariant masses as components. Applying a likelihood fit and correcting for efficiency, background and initial state radiation they get

$$| \xi_\rho |= 1.022 \pm 0.028 \pm 0.030 \qquad (9)$$

$$h(\nu_\tau) = -h(\bar{\nu}_\tau) \qquad (10)$$

Also this high precision result is in good agreement with the standard model prediction. ARGUS in addition has analyzed the data sample using only the energy-energy correlation of the ρ mesons. The power of the new method is demonstrated by the fact that for their statistics the full information improves the precision of $| \xi_\rho |$ by a factor of ≈ 8 [13].

4. Summary

New results of the Michel parameters ρ, η, δ, ξ have been derived. Compared to the 1994 summary of the PDG [1] an appreciable improvement is observed. The results are collected in table 1. In the near future further progress is to be expected since CLEO is increasing its already at present impressive statistics and the LEP experiments up to now analyzed only a part of their data. Moreover the ARGUS collaboration in a pioneering contribution [3] has shown that further apreciable improvements of the precision can be achieved if one exploits the full information available for the decays.

Acknowledgements

I thank the members of the ARGUS collaboration for many fruitful discussions. This work was supported by the Bundesministerium fuer Forschung und Technologie of the Federal Repubblic of Germany under contract number 05-6DO57P(6).

References

[1] Particle Data Group Phys. Rev. **D50** (1994) 1175
[2] H. Albrecht *et al.* DESY 94 - 100 ,contr paper #0189
[3] H. Albrecht *et al.* DESY 94 - 120 ,contr paper #0190
[4] H. Albrecht *et al.* Phys. Lett. **B316** (1993) 608
[5] The ALEPH Collaboration, contributed paper #0573
[6] The L3 Collaboration, contributed paper #0639
[7] J. Bartelt *et al.*, Cornell preprint CLEO CONF 94-21 ,contr paper #0156
[8] A. Stahl Phys. Lett. **B324** (1994) 121
[9] W. Fetscher, H.J. Gerber and K.F. Johnson Phys. Lett. **B173** (1986) 102
[10] W. Fetscher Phys. Rev. **D42** (1990) 1544i
[11] D. Bustulic *et al.* Phys. Lett. **B321** (1994) 168
[12] H. Thurn and H. Kolanoski Zeit. Phys. **C60** (1993) 277
[13] H. Thurn , PhD thesis, Dortmund 1994

Measurements of the τ Mass, Lifetime and Leptonic Branching Ratio

J Timmermans[†]

NIKHEF, P.O.Box 41882, 1009 DB Amsterdam, The Netherlands

Abstract

Recent results on τ mass, lifetime and leptonic branching ratios are presented. The measurements are in agreement with $\tau - \mu$ universality at the level of 0.4%.

1. Introduction

The partial width for the *leptonic* decay $\tau^- \to l^- \bar{\nu}_l \nu_\tau$ is given by [1]

$$\Gamma_l = \frac{G_\tau G_l}{192\pi^3} m_\tau^5 f\left(\frac{m_l^2}{m_\tau^2}\right)(1 + \delta_{QED})(1 + \delta_{EW}) \quad (1)$$

where:

$$G_l = \frac{g_l^2}{4\sqrt{2}M_W^2} \quad (2)$$

is the Fermi constant, g_l is the coupling strength of the charged current to the lepton l, and m_τ is the τ mass. The function $f(x) = 1 - 8x + 8x^3 - x^4 - 12x^2 lnx$ is a phase space suppression factor: $f(m_e^2/m_\tau^2) = 1.0$ and $f(m_\mu^2/m_\tau^2) = 0.9726$. The QED corrections

$$1 + \delta_{QED} = 1 + \frac{\alpha(m_\tau)}{2\pi}\left(\frac{25}{4} - \pi^2\right) = 0.9957 \quad (3)$$

and the effects of the W mass

$$1 + \delta_{EW} = 1 + \frac{3}{5}\frac{m_\tau^2}{M_W^2} = 1.0003 \quad (4)$$

are small. Comparing Equation (1) with a similar expression for the decay $\mu^- \to e^- \bar{\nu}_e \nu_\mu$ provides the following test of lepton universality in the Standard Model:

$$\left(\frac{g_\tau}{g_\mu}\right)^2 = \left(\frac{\tau_\mu}{\tau_\tau}\right) Br(\tau^- \to e^- \bar{\nu}_e \nu_\tau) \left(\frac{m_\mu}{m_\tau}\right)^5 \quad (5)$$

† E-mail: timmermans@nikhef.nl

where τ_μ, τ_τ are the lifetime of the μ and τ respectively, $Br(\tau^- \to e^- \bar{\nu}_e \nu_\tau)$ is the electronic τ decay branching ratio and m_μ is the μ mass.

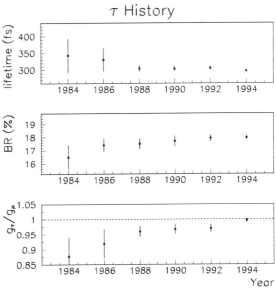

Figure 1. PDG values for lifetime, electron branching ratio and g_τ/g_μ vs. year

Up to 1992 there existed a discrepancy at the 2-2.3 standard deviation level between the measured value for the ratio of the coupling constants g_τ/g_μ and the Standard Model value of 1. Figure 1 shows the PDG values for the τ lifetime, the electronic branching ratio and the calculated value of g_τ/g_μ for the years 1984-1994. Before 1992 the PDG value for the τ mass was 1784 ± 3 MeV, mainly coming from the DELCO experiment [2]. During 1992, new and more precise results on the τ mass became available, moving the value away from the previous average by 2.2 standard deviations. Together with new measurements on τ lifetime and leptonic branching ratios during 1993 a 'PDG94' value (prior to this Conference) of $g_\tau/g_\mu = 0.996 \pm 0.007$ is obtained, consistent with lepton universality in the charged couplings.

In this report I will review the new results (since the Dallas Conference in 1992) on τ mass, lifetime and leptonic branching ratios and use these to test again the lepton universality.

2. τ mass

The ARGUS Collaboration has measured the τ mass from the τ pseudomass distribution in the decays $\tau^- \rightarrow \pi^-\pi^-\pi^+\nu_\tau$ (11k events) [3]. The BES Collaboration at BEPC fits the energy dependence of the cross section $e^+e^- \rightarrow \tau^+\tau^-$ near threshold. Their original measurement was based on 14 events of the type $\tau\tau \rightarrow e\mu(+4\nu)$ [4]. At this Conference, the results of a re-analysis of their full data sample were reported [5]: 64 events in the decay categories $ee(4)$, $e\mu(18)$, $e\pi(19)$, $eK(2)$, $\mu\mu(3)$, $\mu\pi(5)$, $\mu K(3)$, $\pi\pi(4)$ and $\pi K(6)$. The CLEO Collaboration published in 1993 a τ mass measurement based on hadronic τ decays $e^+e^- \rightarrow \tau^+\tau^- \rightarrow \pi^+\pi^-n\pi^0(+2\nu_\tau)$ with $1 \leq n \leq 3$. Exploiting the unique kinematics of these decays, the τ mass is obtained from the distribution ($\sim$30k events) of the 'minimum kinematically possible τ mass for the event' [6]. The DELPHI Collaboration reported a preliminary value for the τ mass, also from the pseudomass distribution in 3π decays. The data come from 3580 $\tau\tau$ events collected at LEP during 1991-1993.

The results of these measurements are summarised in Table 1 and in Figure 2 together with the PDG92 value. All the new measurements are consistent and lower than the previous world average. The *new* world average is: $m_\tau = 1777.02 \pm 0.25$ MeV.

Experiment	m_τ [MeV]
BES [5]	$1776.96 \, ^{+0.18}_{-0.19} \, ^{+0.20}_{-0.16}$
ARGUS [3]	$1776.3 \pm 2.4 \pm 1.4$
CLEO [6]	$1777.8 \pm 0.7 \pm 1.7$
DELPHI	$1778.7 \pm 3.1 \pm 1.3$

Table 1. Summary of τ mass results

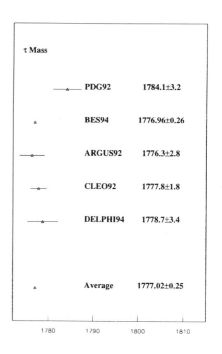

Figure 2. τ mass measurements

3. τ lifetime

Four different methods have been used so far for the determination of the τ lifetime:

1 the *decay length* (DL) method in the 1 prong - 3 prong topology.

2 the *impact parameter* (IP) method. The IP suffers from the uncertainty in the τ direction and in the τ production point.

3 the *impact parameter difference* (IPD) method. The IPD is insensitive to the τ direction, but the uncertainty on the τ production point enters twice.

4 the *impact parameter sum* or *missed distance* (MD) method. The missed distance is independent of the τ production point, but is again sensitive to the unknown τ direction.

New results were presented to this Conference by several groups. The CLEO Collaboration reported on the τ lifetime measurement using the DL method in the 1-3 topology, but also for the first time with rather large statistics (1481 events) in the 3-3 topology [7]. The OPAL Collaboration has final results from their data collected during 1992 and 1993 at LEP. They used the DL and IP methods [8]. The ALEPH Collaboration reported results from their 1992 data, using the DL, IPD, MD and newly an impact parameter sum method (MD') where the dependence on the momenta of the

Experiment	Method	τ_τ [fs]
OPAL [8]	IP	$287.2 \pm 3.4 \pm 2.0$
	DL	$288.9 \pm 3.6 \pm 1.7$
	Comb. 1992-1993	$288.1 \pm 2.5 \pm 1.3$
	Comb. 1990-1993	$288.8 \pm 2.2 \pm 1.4$
ALEPH [9]	MD'	$298.5 \pm 3.4 \pm 4.5$
	MD	$295.0 \pm 3.9 \pm 4.4$
	IPD	$288.1 \pm 5.4 \pm 1.2$
	DL	$290.0 \pm 5.8 \pm 2.1$
	Comb. 1992	$291.9 \pm 3.2 \pm 1.8$
	Comb. 1990-1992	$292.5 \pm 2.8 \pm 1.5$
CLEO [7]	DL 1-3	$291 \pm 4 \pm 7$
	DL 3-3	$285 \pm 13 \pm 10$
	IP [13]	$294 \pm 7 \pm 12$
SLD [10]	DL 1-3	$272 \pm 17 \pm 3$
	IP	$289 \pm 12 \pm 6$
DELPHI [11]	Comb. 1991-1992	$298 \pm 4 \pm 3$
L3 [12]	IP + DL	$293 \pm 9 \pm 12$

Table 2. Summary of τ lifetime results

daughter tracks is taken into account in the fitting function [9]. The SLD Collaboration at SLC has given their first τ lifetime results using the DL and IP method. The relatively small systematic errors reflect the small beam spot size (7 μm) [10]. A summary of these results, together with values from the DELPHI and L3 Collaborations presented at the 1993 Lepton-Photon Conference [11] are given in Table 2 and Figure 3.

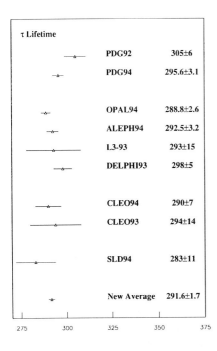

Figure 3. τ lifetime measurements

Wasserbaech [14] has shown that due to the correlation between the impact parameter and the τ

Experiment	$Br(\tau^- \to e^- \bar{\nu}_e \nu_\tau)$	$Br(\tau^- \to \mu^- \bar{\nu}_\mu \nu_\tau)$
ALEPH [17]	$17.48 \pm 0.15 \pm 0.06$	$17.05 \pm 0.14 \pm 0.06$
DELPHI [18]	$17.61 \pm 0.22 \pm 0.40$	$17.47 \pm 0.19 \pm 0.27$
L3 [11]	$17.86 \pm 0.25 \pm 0.23$	$17.26 \pm 0.25 \pm 0.23$
OPAL [11]	$17.5 \pm 0.3 \pm 0.3$	$16.8 \pm 0.3 \pm 0.3$
CLEO [15]	$17.97 \pm 0.14 \pm 0.23$	
ARGUS [16]	$17.5 \pm 0.3 \pm 0.5$	$17.4 \pm 0.3 \pm 0.5$

Table 3. Summary of τ leptonic branching ratios [%]

decay angle, small positive lifetime biases exist, that not all experiments have subtracted. This affects the 1994 PDG average by -0.8 fs. Another 0.2 fs downward correction on the average results from the new τ mass when applied to the older lifetime measurements using the decay length method. The PDG94 value in Figure 3 contains these corrections. The *new* world average for the τ lifetime is: $\tau_\tau = 291.6 \pm 1.7$ fs.

4. τ leptonic branching ratios

Since the 1992 Dallas Conference several measurements of the branching ratios $Br(\tau^- \to e^- \bar{\nu}_e \nu_\tau)$ and $Br(\tau^- \to \mu^- \bar{\nu}_\mu \nu_\tau)$ were reported [11][15][16]. At this Conference there were new results from ALEPH based on their 1991-1992 data sample [17] and DELPHI for their 1990-1992 data [18]. The results are summarised in Table 3, Figure 4 and Figure 5. There is good agreement between the various measurements. The *new* world averages are: $Br(\tau^- \to e^- \bar{\nu}_e \nu_\tau) = (17.67 \pm 0.11)\%$ and $Br(\tau^- \to \mu^- \bar{\nu}_\mu \nu_\tau) = (17.15 \pm 0.11)\%$.

5. Universality test

From Equation (1) and the measured electron and muon branching ratios, one obtains for the ratio of the coupling constants:

$$\frac{g_\mu}{g_e} = \left(\frac{Br(\tau^- \to \mu^- \bar{\nu}_\mu \nu_\tau)}{0.9726 \cdot Br(\tau^- \to e^- \bar{\nu}_e \nu_\tau)} \right)^{1/2} = 0.999 \pm 0.005 \tag{6}$$

in agreement with the more precise measurements from the branching ratios $\pi \to e\nu$ and $\pi \to \mu\nu$ [19][20], which yield an average value of $g_\mu/g_e = 1.0017 \pm 0.0016$.

Inserting the new world averages for the τ mass, lifetime and electron branching ratio in Equation (5) gives:

$$\frac{g_\tau}{g_\mu} = 0.995 \pm 0.004 \tag{7}$$

in agreement with $\tau - \mu$ universality in the charged current. The new result is plotted in Figure 6 together with the points obtained from the PDG92 and PDG94 values, showing the improvement in this measurement over the last few years.

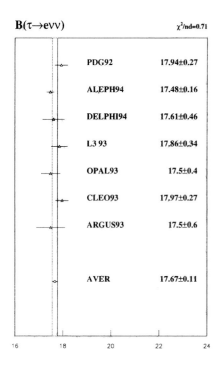

Figure 4. Measurements of electron branching ratio [%]

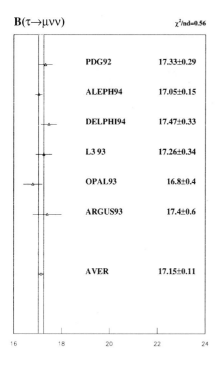

Figure 5. Measurements of muon branching ratio [%]

Acknowledgments

I would like to thank Luc Pape, William Trischuk and Steve Wasserbaech for their help in preparing this review.

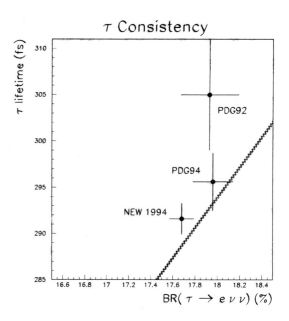

Figure 6. The new value of the τ lifetime vs. the electron branching ratio. The band shows the constraint from the new τ mass average if universality is assumed.

References

[1] W. Marciano and A. Sirlin, Phys. Rev. Lett. **61** (1988) 1815.
[2] DELCO Collaboration: W. Bacino *et al.*, Phys. Rev. Lett. **41** (1978) 13.
[3] ARGUS Collaboration: H. Albrecht *et al.*, Phys. Lett. **B292** (1992) 221.
[4] BES Collaboration: J. Bai *et al.*, Phys. Rev. Lett. **69** (1992) 3021.
[5] BES Collaboration, contribution to this Conference.
[6] CLEO Collaboration: R. Balest *et al.*, Phys. Rev. **D47** (1993) R3671.
[7] CLEO Collaboration, contribution to this Conference.
[8] OPAL Collaboration, contribution to this Conference.
[9] ALEPH Collaboration, contribution to this Conference.
[10] SLD Collaboration, contribution to this Conference.
[11] A.S. Schwarz, Proc. of the XVI Int. Symp. on Lepton and Photon Interactions, Cornell 1993,p.671; Eds. P. Drell and D. Rubin (AIP 1994).
[12] L3 Collaboration: O. Adriani *el al.*, Phys. Rep. **236** (1993) 1.
[13] P. Weber, Proc. of the Int. Europhysics Conf. on High Energy Physics, Marseille 1993,p.479; Eds. J. Carr and M. Perrottet (Editions Frontieres 1994)
[14] S.R. Wasserbaech, Phys. Rev. **D48** (1993) 4216
[15] CLEO Collaboration: D.S. Akerib *et al.*, Phys. Rev. Lett. **69** (1992) 3610; *ibid.* **71** (1993) 3395.
[16] C. Hast, Proc. of the Int. Europhysics Conf. on High Energy Physics, Marseille 1993,p.481; Eds. J. Carr and M. Perrottet (Editions Frontieres 1994)
[17] ALEPH Collaboration, contribution to this Conference.
[18] DELPHI Collaboration, contribution to this Conference.
[19] D.I. Britton *et al.*, Phys. Rev. Lett. **68** (1992) 3000.
[20] G. Czapek *et al.*, Phys. Rev. Lett. **70** (1993) 17.

Tau decays into kaons

R. Alemany

Laboratoire de l'Accélérateur Linéaire, IN2P3 - CNRS
Université de Paris-Sud, 91405 Orsay, France

Abstract

A summary of recent measurements of τ branching ratios into charged and/or neutral kaons is presented. The substantial improvement achieved in the strange sector of τ decays allows to discuss the internal consistency of these results and the new possibilities offered by these measurements. The results quoted in this paper should be considered preliminary unless stated otherwise.

1. Introduction

The τ lepton provides a potential probe of the strange sector of the weak charged current. However, as the strange currents are suppressed with respect to the non-strange currents by the Cabibbo-Kobayashi-Maskawa (CKM) matrix elements, large and clean data samples are needed in order to study the tau decays into kaons. These decays containing kaons provide information on the $SU(3)_f$ symmetry properties and bring information about their dynamics which is interesting by itself and also for other measurements in tau physics such as polarization, α_s,... Apart from the well known K and K^* modes, other channels with additional kaons and/or pions are expected. However the theoretical calculations for the processes governing these decays are of a limited accuracy. In the next sections the available measurements of branching ratios involving kaons in the final state are reviewed. The present experimental status provides a rather complete description of the strange sector of tau decays.

2. Kaon identification

The measurements of the τ branching ratios into kaons reported here are based on charged and neutral kaon identification. Presently, charged kaons have been identified by either means of a Ring Imaging Cherenkov detector (DELPHI) or using the energy loss in a tracking

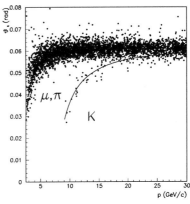

Figure 1. Measured Cherenkov angle versus momentum for single prong τ decays from the DELPHI detector.

chamber, the so-called dE/dx (OPAL, ALEPH and CLEO).

The Cherenkov angle for one prong τ decays as measured by DELPHI is shown in figure 1. This technique allows an unambiguously kaon identification to be performed over a large momentum range.

Requiring the dE/dx measurement of a tracking chamber to be within 2-3 σ of the expectation value for a kaon provides a kaon tagging. The kaon fraction in a given sample can also be derived by fitting the observed ionization loss distribution to a linear combination of pion and kaon expected distributions. The difference between the dE/dx measurement and the expectation

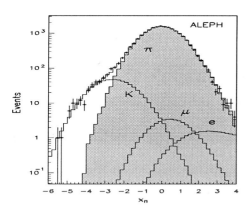

Figure 2. Fitted x_π distribution in one prong hadronic τ decays. The points correspond to data, the solid lines show the π, e and μ contributions and the fitted K component.

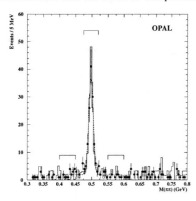

Figure 3. $\pi^+\pi^-$ invariant mass distribution of the vertex tracks in the K_S^0 sample. The points(solid line) correspond to data (Monte Carlo).

value for a pion over the experimental resolution (x_π) is shown in figure 2 by ALEPH. With this procedure a good understanding of the calibration of the dE/dx is needed, and independent data samples are commonly used in order to correct possible angular and momentum dependence effects.

The results on neutral kaons reported at this conference are based on the identification of both K_S^0 and K_L^0 components. The K_S^0 decaying to $\pi^+\pi^-$ is identified by requiring good quality vertices and by constraining the reconstructed invariant mass of the pion pair to be consistent with m_{K^0}, as illustrated in figure 3.

In addition, the K_L^0 component is identified in ALEPH using the hadronic calorimeter, by requiring a large energy deposition not connected to the hadronic shower of a charged particle.

3.   Review of measurements

3.1.   *Inclusive decays into charged and neutral kaons*

Inclusive strange pseudoscalar decays of the τ to

Experiment	$Br(\tau \to K\ \nu_\tau + neutrals)$ (%)
CLEO	$1.60 \pm 0.12 \pm 0.19$
DELPHI	1.54 ± 0.24
ALEPH	$1.60 \pm 0.07 \pm 0.12$
PDG92	1.68 ± 0.24
New Average	1.60 ± 0.097

Table 1. Inclusive branching ratio measurements involving one charged kaon.

Experiment	$Br(\tau \to K^0 h^-\ \nu_\tau + neutrals)$ (%)
OPAL	$1.72 \pm 0.16 \pm 0.1$
ALEPH	$2.34 \pm 0.18 \pm 0.16$
PDG92	1.30 ± 0.30
New Average	1.83 ± 0.13

Table 2. Inclusive branching ratio measurements involving one neutral kaon.

Experiment	$Br(\tau \to K\ \nu_\tau)$ (%)
DELPHI	0.85 ± 0.18
ALEPH	$0.64 \pm 0.05 \pm 0.05$
OPAL	1.00 ± 0.3
CLEO	$0.66 \pm 0.07 \pm 0.09$
PDG92	0.67 ± 0.23
New Average	0.68 ± 0.056

Table 3. Exclusive branching ratio measurements involving only one charged kaon.

a single charged track identified as a kaon have been measured by CLEO, DELPHI and ALEPH. The results are given in table 1 [1, 2, 3]. These measurements include contributions from decays with additional neutrals, i.e. π^0 and/or K^0.

The OPAL [4] and ALEPH collaborations provided inclusive measurements using three prong τ decays events where a $K_S^0 \to \pi^+\pi^-$ is reconstructed. The results are given in table 2. These inclusive branching ratios are obtained with an error significantly smaller than the ones of previous measurements.

3.2.   *Exclusive decay into a charged kaon*

Several new measurements from the CLEO and LEP collaborations have significantly improved the precision of the exclusive tau decay into a charged kaon. Table 3 shows the new measurements corrected for the K^0 component. The PDG92 value, being not corrected, is not included for this reason in the new average.

An additional test of the $\tau - \mu$ universality can be performed using the precise prediction for the ratio $R_\pi^K = Br(\tau \to K\nu_\tau)\ /\ Br(\tau \to \pi\nu_\tau)$ that can be obtained from the branching ratios of the decays $K \to \mu\nu_\mu$ and $\pi \to \mu\nu_\mu$ and from the lifetimes of the charged pion and kaon. The theoretical prediction, including

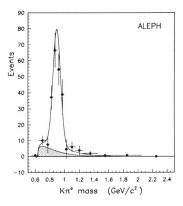 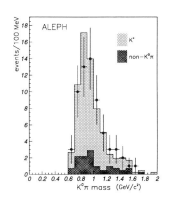 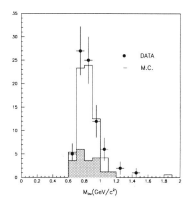

Figure 4. $K\pi$ invariant mass distributions from ALEPH. From left to right, the first figure shows data points for the $K\pi^0$ final state as obtained from the dE/dx fit in each mass bin; the solid line corresponds to the Monte Carlo expectation for that mode while the shaded area to the expected background. The central figure corresponds to the $K_L^0\pi$ system where the Monte Carlo signal and background expectations are also shown. The last figure shows the invariant mass distribution for the $K_S^0\pi$ system.

Experiment	$Br(\tau \to K^* \, \nu_\tau)$ (%)	Mode
DELPHI	1.71 ± 0.69	$K\pi^0$
ALEPH	$1.46 \pm 0.12 \pm 0.09$	$K_S^0\pi, K\pi^0, K_L^0\pi$
ARGUS	$0.97 \pm 0.15 \pm 0.12$	$K_S^0\pi$
CLEO	1.32 ± 0.15	$K_S^0\pi, K\pi^0$
PDG92	1.56 ± 0.26	
New Average	1.33 ± 0.087	

Table 4. $\tau \to K^* \, \nu_\tau$ branching ratio measurements.

Experiment	$Br(\tau \to K^* \, \nu_\tau + neutrals)$ (%)
OPAL	$1.73 \pm 0.24 \pm 0.13$
ARGUS	$1.19 \pm 0.15 \pm 0.14$
PDG92	1.43 ± 0.17
New Average	1.41 ± 0.12

Table 5. $\tau \to K^* \, \nu_\tau + neutrals$ branching ratio measurements.

radiative corrections, is $R_\pi^K = 6.62 \pm 0.04$ %. † From the $Br(\tau \to \pi\nu_\tau)$ value given in ref [5], the ratio R_π^K is measured to be 6.0 ± 0.5 % in good agreement with the above prediction and close to the suppression that one would simply expect in the weak vertex by the corresponding CKM matrix elements.

3.3. Decays into vector strange final states $K\pi$

Branching ratios of strange vector-decays of the tau have also been measured by several experiments with a noticeably improved precision with respect to previous measurements. In the past, the $\tau \to K^*\nu_\tau$ branching ratio was measured in the three prong topology resulting from $K^* \to K_S^0\pi^-$ with the subsequent decay of the K_S^0 into two charged pions. The new results from CLEO and ALEPH collaborations [6, 7] include the $K\pi^0$ and $\pi K_L^0, K\pi^0$ modes respectively. Combining these results assuming isospin invariance one obtains the values quoted in table 4. Figure 4 shows the invariant mass spectrum for the $K\pi$ system, which is dominated by the $K^*(892)$ resonance, in the three modes detected by ALEPH.

Furthermore, table 5 shows the inclusive strange vector decay measurements. Together with the above measurements, they limit the branching ratio of the τ to a K^* plus additional neutrals to the 0.08 ± 0.15 % level.

The ratio of $Br(\tau \to K^*\nu_\tau)$ to $Br(\tau \to \rho\nu_\tau)$ can be compared to the theoretical predictions based on QCD sum rules [8, 9]. In particular, a value of 0.048 ± 0.001 is obtained from the DMO sum rule, in excellent agreement with the experimental value of 0.0525 ± 0.0034.†

3.4. Decays into strange axial-vector final states $K\pi\pi$

The experimental situation for the decay into strange axial-vector final state $K\pi\pi$ and Cabibbo allowed decays involving a $K\overline{K}$ pair (described in the next section) has been greatly improved and several new modes are measured for the first time. This results in a complete description of the strange sector in tau decays.

The TPC/2γ collaboration has recently published the branching fraction for the decay $\tau^- \to K^-\pi^+\pi^- \, \nu_\tau + neutrals$, obtaining [11]

$$\mathrm{Br}(\tau^- \to K^-\pi^+\pi^- \, \nu_\tau + neutrals) = 0.58 \pm 0.14 \% \quad (1)$$

---

† The radiative corrections, as described by Decker and Finkemeier, are taken into account.

† For $Br(\tau \to \rho\nu_\tau)$ the last published result from CLEO is used [10].

Experiment	$Br(\tau \to \pi K^0 \pi^0 \ \nu_\tau)$ (%)	Mode
CLEO	$0.39 \pm 0.06 \pm 0.06$	K_S^0
ALEPH	$0.33 \pm 0.14 \pm 0.07$	K_L^0
New Average	0.38 ± 0.075	

Table 6. $\tau \to \pi K^0 \pi^0 \ \nu_\tau$ branching ratio measurements.

Experiment	$Br(\tau \to K \pi^0 \pi^0 \ \nu_\tau)$ (%)
CLEO	$0.14 \pm 0.10 \pm 0.03$
ALEPH	$0.04 \pm 0.03 \pm 0.02$
New Average	0.05 ± 0.034

Table 7. $\tau \to K \pi^0 \pi^0 \ \nu_\tau$ branching ratio measurements.

which is slightly higher than the previous DELCO measurement [12]. The TPC/2γ study of the invariant mass distributions in the $K^- \pi^+ \pi^-$ decay is consistent with K_1 dominance and the value

$$\mathrm{Br}(\tau \to K_1 \ \nu_\tau) \ = \ 1.17 \pm_{0.37}^{0.41} \ \% \qquad (2)$$

is obtained with an indication from the 23 candidate events that the branching fraction for $K_1(1400)$ is higher than for $K_1(1270)$.

ARGUS is reporting a preliminary exclusive measurement for the mode $\tau \to K^- \pi^+ \pi^- \ \nu_\tau$ equal to

$$\mathrm{Br}(\tau \to K^- \pi^+ \pi^- \ \nu_\tau) \ = \ 0.33 \pm 0.11 \pm 0.13 \ \% \ (3)$$

By reconstructing the K^{*0} in its charged decay mode, the branching ratio $\tau \to \overline{K^{*0}} \pi^- \ \nu_\tau$ is measured to be

$$\mathrm{Br}(\tau \to \overline{K^{*0}} \pi^- \ \nu_\tau) \ = \ 0.21 \pm 0.09 \pm 0.05 \ \% \ (4)$$

The CLEO and ALEPH collaborations [6, 7] have measured the decay rate of $\tau \to \pi K^0 \pi^0$ as given in table 6. In addition, the CLEO study of invariant mass distribution for the 443 $h^- K_S^0 \pi^0$ observed events, indicates that this decay proceeds preferentially through $K_1(1270)$ rather than $K_1(1400)$ as shown in figure 5. Further studies of these resonant substructures are required for the understanding of $SU(3)_f$ symmetry breaking.

The ALEPH and CLEO collaborations have also measured the branching ratio of $Br(\tau \to K \pi^0 \pi^0 \ \nu_\tau)$. These results are quoted in table 7 and are in agreement within the errors.

3.5. Cabibbo allowed decays with $K\overline{K}$ pairs

The decay rate of $\tau \to K K^0 \ \nu_\tau$ has been measured by the CLEO collaboration [13] identifying the K^0 through

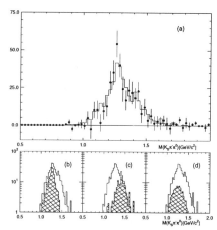

Figure 5. a) $\pi^- K^0 \pi^0$ invariant mass distribution from CLEO after background subtraction. The solid line is the result of a fit to the Monte Carlo predicted distributions for $K_1(1270)$, $K_1(1400)$ and a fixed (the CLEO measurement of table 9 is used) $K^- K_S^0 \pi^0$ contribution. The hatched areas in figures b), c) and d) show the $K_1(1270)$, $K_1(1400)$ and $K^- K_S^0 \pi^0$ contributions respectively.

Experiment	$Br(\tau \to K K^0 \ \nu_\tau)$ (%)	Mode
CLEO	$0.123 \pm 0.023 \pm 0.023$	$K_S^0 \pi$
ALEPH	$0.29 \pm 0.12 \pm 0.03$	$K_L^0 \pi$
New Average	0.13 ± 0.031	

Table 8. $\tau \to K K^0 \ \nu_\tau$ branching ratio measurements.

its K_S^0 component and by the ALEPH collaboration through its K_L^0 component. In spite of the higher ALEPH value both results are compatible within the present accuracy as shown in table 8 and are in agreement with theoretical estimates which predict a decay rate close to 0.16% [14, 15].

An inclusive measurement of the $K^- K^+ \pi^-$ final state is given by TPC/2γ [11]

$$\mathrm{Br}(\tau \to K^- K^+ \pi^- \ \nu_\tau + neutrals) = 0.15 \pm 0.08 \ \% \ (5)$$

while ARGUS provided an exclusive measurement for the same final state but with the K^{*0} resonant production reconstructed from its charged decay $K^+ \pi^-$

$$\mathrm{Br}(\tau \to K^- K^* \ \nu_\tau) \ = \ 0.18 \pm 0.05 \pm 0.04 \ \% \ (6)$$

These measurements are in good agreement with the previous results from DELCO and CLEO [12, 16].

Table 9 shows the CLEO and ALEPH measurements of the branching ratio of the decay $\tau \to K \overline{K^0} \pi^0 \ \nu_\tau$ with the detection of the K^0 through its short and long components by CLEO and ALEPH, respectively.

Finally, the CLEO collaboration [17] has provided a measurement of the decay rate $\tau \to \pi K^0 \overline{K^0} \ \nu_\tau$

$$\mathrm{Br}(\tau \to \pi K^0 \overline{K^0} \ \nu_\tau) = 0.083 \pm 0.017 \pm 0.017 \ \% \ (7)$$

Experiment	$Br(\tau \to K\overline{K^0}\pi^0 \nu_\tau)$ (%)	Mode
CLEO	$0.129 \pm 0.05 \pm 0.032$	$K_S^0\pi$
ALEPH	$0.05 \pm 0.05 \pm 0.01$	$K_L^0\pi$
New Average	0.084 ± 0.039	

Table 9. $\tau \to K\overline{K^0}\pi^0 \nu_\tau$ branching ratio measurements.

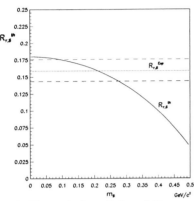

Figure 6. Theoretical prediction of $R_{\tau,s}$ as a function of the s quark mass contrasted with the experimental value 0.159 ± 0.015

using events where the two K^0's are short. This measurement is sensitive to both K^0 types if the decay proceeds through $\overline{K^{*-}}K^0$ or $K^{*0}K^-$ resonant states; it is not if the decay involves $\pi\rho$ resonant states, for instance, since, in that case, only the combination $K_S^0 K_L^0$ is allowed.

4. Discussions of the results

From the results reported in section 3.4 concerning the different strange axial-vector $K\pi\pi$ decay rates it is possible to perform some internal consistency test using isospin invariance.

In particular, since the $K_1(1270)$ decay is equally dominated by the intermediate states $K\rho$ and $K^*\pi$ and since the $K_1(1400)$ state is dominated by $K^*\pi$, it follows from isospin invariance that one can compute the expected fraction of the decay rates $K^-\pi^+\pi^-$, $K^-\pi^0\pi^0$ and $\overline{K^0}\pi^-\pi^0$ entering in the total branching ratio for the $K_1(1270)$ and $K_1(1400)$ resonant states. Following this procedure the branching ratio for the sum of the states $K_1(1270)$ and $K_1(1400)$ is obtained equal to

$$Br(\tau \to K_1 \nu_\tau) = 0.77 \pm 0.12 \% \qquad (8)$$

which is in good agreement with the value measured by TPC/2γ.

Following ref [18] (and references therein) one defines $R_{\tau,s}$, the Cabibbo-suppressed τ decay width normalized to the electronic one. The experimental value of $R_{\tau,s}$

can be computed from the previous results shown in tables 3,4,6 and 7 and (3); one obtains

$$R_{\tau,s} = 0.159 \pm 0.015 \qquad (9)$$

Figure 6 shows the theoretical prediction of $R_{\tau,s}$, computed according to ref [18], as a function of the s quark mass for a given value of $\alpha_s(m_\tau)$; 0.37 here, but the theoretical prediction depends only weakly on this choice. In spite of the relatively poor precision with which $R_{\tau,s}$ is presently determined some valuable information can already be derived on the s quark mass. More accurate measurements of the Cabibbo-suppressed τ decays will permit a more profitable exploitation of the $R_{\tau,s}$ properties.

5. Conclusions

The experimental situation on the strange sector of τ decays has been greatly improved. More precise measurements are available and new decay modes have been measured. The nice complementarity among experiments allows a rather complete description of the strange sector to be provided.

The inclusive and the sum of the exclusive rates show no evidence for missing modes with the present experimental accuracy:

$$Br(\tau \to K \nu_\tau + 0\pi^0 + 0K^0)$$
$$-\sum_i Br_i(\tau \to K \nu_\tau \cdots) = 0.136 \pm 0.15 \% \quad (10)$$

$$Br(\tau \to K^0 \nu_\tau + 0\pi^0 + 0K^0)$$
$$-\sum_i Br_i(\tau \to K^0 \nu_\tau \cdots) = 0.34 \pm 0.23 \% \quad (11)$$

I would like to express my gratitude to M. Davier and to F. Le Diberder for very useful discussions and comments during the preparation of this talk.

References

[1] DELPHI Col.: P. Abreu *et al.*, CERN-PPE/94-88 .
[2] CLEO Col.: M. Battle *et al.*, CLNS 94/1273 .
[3] ALEPH Col.: D. Buskulic *et al.*, CERN-PPE/94-58 .
[4] OPAL Col.: R. Akers *et al.*, CERN-PPE/94-108 .
[5] M.Davier, Proceedings of the 2nd International Workshop on τ Lepton Physics, Columbus, ed. World Scientific.
[6] CLEO Col.: M. Athanas *et al.*, CLEO CONF 94-23 .
[7] ALEPH Col.: D. Buskulic *et al.*, CERN-PPE/94-59 .
[8] E. Floratos *et al.*, Nucl. Phys. **B155** (1979) .
[9] T. Das *et al.*, Phys. Rev. Lett. **18** (1967) 761 .
[10] CLEO Col.: M. Artuso *et al.*,Phys. Rev. Lett. **72** (1994) .
[11] TPC/2γ Col.: D. Bauer *et al.*, Phys. Rev. **D50** (1994) R13 .
[12] DELCO Col.: G. Mills *et al.*,Phys. Rev. Lett. **54** (1985) 624.
[13] CLEO Col.: J. Gronberg *et al.*, CLEO CONF 94-24 .
[14] S. Narison and A. Pich, Phys. Lett. **B257** (1991) 437.
[15] S. Eidelman *et al.*, Phys. Lett. **B304** (1993) 359.
[16] CLEO Col: M. Goldberg *et al.*,Phys. Lett. **251B** (1990) 223.
[17] CLEO Col.: R. Balest *et al.*, CLEO CONF 94-25 .
[18] E. Braaten *et al.*, Nucl. Phys. **B373** (1992) .

Paper presented at XXVII Int. Conf. on High Energy Physics: Session Pa-16
Glasgow, UK, 20–27 July 1994

The Decay of the Tau to One-Prong Modes

Randall J. Sobie[†]

The Institute of Particle Physics of Canada
and
The University of Victoria, Department of Physics and Astronomy
P.O. Box 3055, Victoria, British Columbia, V8W 3P6 Canada

Abstract

The observed inconsistency between the inclusive and exclusive τ 1-prong branching ratios (1-prong problem) is shown to be resolved with new measurements of the $\tau \rightarrow h^- \geq 1\pi^0 \nu_\tau$ branching ratios.

1. Introduction

Current compilations of τ branching ratio measurements suggest an inconsistency when the inclusive single-charged-particle or 1-prong decay mode ($85.94 \pm 0.23\%$) is compared with the sum of all the exclusive 1-prong decay modes ($82.0 \pm 1.2\%$) [1]. In this paper we divide the exclusive 1-prong measurements into the channels that have been well measured ($e^-\nu\nu$, $\mu^-\nu\nu$ and $h^-\nu$, where h is either a π^- or K^-) and those channels where precision measurements are only now appearing ($h \geq 1\pi^0\nu$). We then compare those measurements with the recent results on the inclusive 1-prong branching ratio.

The branching ratio averages presented in this paper are calculated using data published after 1990. This arbitrary cutoff is only meant to show the reader the recent improvement in τ branching ratio measurements.

2. Branching Ratio Measurements

2.1. Inclusive 1-prong measurements

In Figure 1 we present the inclusive 1-prong branching ratios. The newer measurements are now converging and an average of $(84.97 \pm 0.16)\%$ is obtained using the data published after 1990. Note that the new average is

significantly lower than the 1992 PDG average [1].

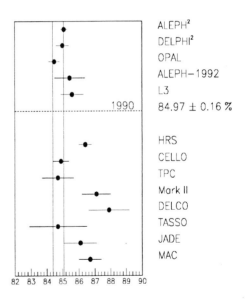

Figure 1. The inclusive 1-prong branching is shown. **The error bars shown are the combined statistical and systematic errors.** The superscipt (2) indicates a contribution to this conference.

† E-mail: sobie@monty.phys.uvic.ca

2.2. $e^-\nu\nu$, $\mu^-\nu\nu$ and $h^-\nu$ measurements

The precision on these branching ratio measurements has gradually improved, with little change in their average value. The average of the recent data gives $B_{e\nu\nu} = (17.96 \pm 0.20)\%$, $B_{\mu\nu\nu} = (17.26 \pm 0.35)\%$ and $B_{h\nu} = (12.72 \pm 0.39)\%$.

2.3. $h \geq 1\pi^0\nu$ measurements

A significant number of new measurements of the $h\pi^0$, $h2\pi^0$, $h \geq 2\pi^0$, $h3\pi^0$, $h \geq 3\pi^0$, and $h4\pi^0$ have been made. This can be partly attributed to the increase in the size of the τ data samples but also due to the improved identification of π^0's in the detectors. In addition, the measurement of the branching ratios using inclusive or quasi-inclusive techniques has reduced or eliminated the need for prior knowledge of the τ branching ratios.

The measured branching ratios for the $\tau \to h^-\pi^0\nu_\tau$ are shown in Figure 2. One observes that a large number of new measurements have been made over the past few years and also that there is a trend toward a higher value.

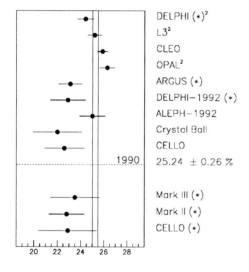

Figure 2. The $\tau^- \to h^-\pi^0\nu_\tau$ branching ratios are presented. Those results labelled with an $\star$ have been corrected for $K^-\pi^0$ contributions. The superscipt (2) indicates a contribution to this conference.

Many new results on the other branching ratios have also been made which unfortunately cannot be reproduced here. However, a large number of experiments measure the $\tau \to h^- \geq 1\pi^0\nu_\tau$ branching ratio, either directly or from the sum of individual measurements. In Figure 3 we plot those results and find excellent agreement between all experiments. Note that the uncertainties shown include both the statistical and systematic error.

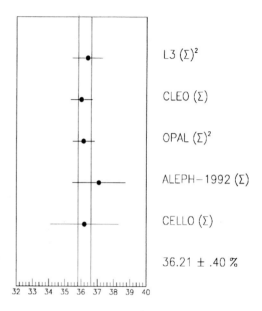

Figure 3. The $\tau \to h^- \geq 1\pi^0\nu_\tau$ branching ratios are presented. The label Σ indicates that the branching ratio was calculated by adding individual branching ratios. The superscipt (2) indicates a contribution to this conference.

3. Discussion

In the following table we present the branching ratios for the sum of the $e^-\nu\nu$, $\mu^-\nu\nu$ and $h^-\nu$ channels and the sum of the $h \geq 1\pi^0\nu$ channels. The sum of those values, together with an additional $0.5 \pm 0.1\%$ contribution for the $\pi^-K_L^0$ mode, is consistent with the inclusive 1-prong branching ratio. The 1992 PDG numbers are also given in the table for comparison.

We have shown that the inclusive and exclusive τ branching ratio are now in excellent agreeement. This 1-prong problem has been resolved by improved measurements of the $h \geq 1\pi^0\nu$ branching ratios and the inclusive 1-prong branching ratio.

	1994 Glasgow	1992 PDG Averages
$B(e\,\mu\,h)$	$47.94 \pm 0.56\%$	$47.8 \pm 0.5\%$
$B(h \geq 1\pi^0\nu)$	$36.21 \pm 0.40\%$	$34.2 \pm 1.0\%$
$B(\pi^-K_L^0)$	$0.50 \pm 0.10\%$	$0.5 \pm 0.1\%$
Total	$84.65 \pm 0.70\%$	$82.5 \pm 1.1\%$
$B(\text{1-prong})$	$84.97 \pm 0.16\%$	$85.94 \pm 0.23\%$

References

[1] Particle Data Group, K. Hikasa *et al*, Phys. Rev. **D45** (1992) 1.

[2] Contribution to this conference.

Paper presented at XXVII Int. Conf. on High Energy Physics: Session Pa-16
Glasgow, UK, 20–27 July 1994

The V–A×V–A Structure of B-decays and Missing Energy Measurements

Michael Dittmar

Eidgenössiche Technische Hochschule,
ETH Zürich, CH-8093 Zürich, Switzerland

Abstract

The sensitivity of the neutrino energy spectrum to the polarisation of the weak charged current in semileptonic B–hadron decays is discussed. First preliminary results of the neutrino energy spectrum from L3 show good agreement between the W polarisation in the data and B–hadron decay models with a V–A×V–A decay structure. This measurement excludes a V+A×V–A decay structure with a significance of about five standard deviations. New branching ratio measurements from ALEPH and L3 for the decays $b \to \nu X$ and $b \to \tau \nu X$ are also discussed.

1. The neutrino energy spectrum in B–decays

As the direct measurement of neutrinos from semileptonic B–decays is essentially impossible, little theoretical and experimental attention has been put into details of the neutrino energy spectrum. Recently, the feasibility of an indirect neutrino measurement in e^+e^- collisions, using the difference between the beam energy and the observed jet energy, has been discussed in the context of semileptonic B–decays [1]. It was shown, that such a measurement at LEP, allows to study details of the underlying structure of the weak charged current in B–hadron decays. For example, the simultaneous measurement of the charged lepton and the neutrino would allow to distinguish clearly between the free quark B–hadron decay model with a V–A×V–A structure and the exotic V+A×V–A structure. While the charged lepton spectra can be described by almost any model, a strong difference would show up in the average neutrino energy. The neutrino energy in the V+A case would be about 1.1 GeV larger than in the V–A case, using realistic charged lepton selection criteria. With an inclusive measurement of the neutrino alone, the average neutrino energy would be about 1.7 GeV larger for the V+A structure. The possibility that hadronic corrections in B–hadron decays would destroy any polarisation of the virtual W, like in the decay $K \to \pi e \nu$, would result in a roughly 500 MeV harder neutrino spectrum. Such large differences should clearly be observable if an energy calibration ac-curacy of about 100–200 MeV can be obtained.

This neutrino energy measurement has now been performed by the L3 collaboration using the data collected between 1991 and 1992. Requiring that the events show a two jet structure and that the jets are pointing to the hermetic barrel region of the experiment, a total of 350k hadronic Z^0 decays could be analysed.

Starting from these two jet events, the neutrino energy is obtained from the difference between the beam energy and the jet energy, which is determined from the energy deposit in the electromagnetic and hadron calorimeter. Using a technique, which separates hadronic and electromagnetic showers in the calorimeter and a correction for the energy dependent calorimeter response to hadrons, 45 GeV jets are measured with a gaussian energy resolution with a sigma of about 4.3 GeV in the data and 4.6 GeV in the Monte Carlo simulation [2], [3]. The jet energy scale has been determined with the following procedure. First the energy in the Monte Carlo simulation is calibrated such that the average neutrino energy in semileptonic B–hadron decays is correctly reproduced. In the next step, the average jet energy is determined from a gaussian fit in the energy range between 40–70 GeV, a region which is essentially independent of neutrinos. The data are calibrated such that this average jet energy agrees with the one in the Monte Carlo. The stability of this calibration is found to be better than 50 MeV using different data taking periods. A possible difference of the flavour dependence between data and the simulation for the jet energy response has been studied with b–quark enriched or depleted event samples and was found to be smaller than 120 MeV.

Semileptonic B–hadron decays are selected using electrons (muons) candidates with an energy above 3 GeV (4 GeV) and a transverse momentum of more than 1.4 GeV with respect to the closest hadronic jet. With these criteria, about 5000 inclusive electron and 10000 muon events are selected. The obtained purity of correctly identified semileptonic B–hadron decays is found to be 78.4% for the electron sample and 69% for the muon sample.

The observed p and p_t charged lepton spectra in the data are reproduced by the simulation, if the weak semileptonic B–hadrons are generated with an average energy of 72% of the beam energy using the Peterson fragmentation function [4] and if the B–hadron decays are simulated with a virtual W polarization according to the V–A×V–A structure. Alternatively, the charged lepton spectra can also be described with a V+A×V–A B–hadron decay structure and a roughly 5% harder fragmentation function.

The neutrino energy spectra obtained from the missing energy of the jet associated to the charged lepton, are shown in figure 1 for the electron tagged events and in figure 2 for muon tagged events. The data are well described by a Monte Carlo with a V–A×V–A decay structure. The difference in the average neutrino energy in the data and in the Monte Carlo (with a V–A×V–A structure) ΔE_ν is found to be –90 ± 160 MeV (stat.) for the electron sample and +10 ± 110 MeV (stat.) for the muon sample. Systematic uncertainties of the measured neutrino spectrum arise mainly from three sources. These are the uncertainties due to the jet energy calibration, the purity of the inclusive charged lepton sample and efficiency uncertainties of the charged lepton selection. The resulting total systematic error of the average neutrino energy, adding the different contributions in quadrature, is found to be 220 (200) MeV for the neutrino energy associated to the $b \rightarrow e(\mu)\nu X$ decays. Comparing the data with a V+A×V–A decay simulation, one finds that the average neutrino energy in the data is too soft by 890 MeV (for the electron sample) and 690 MeV (for the muon sample) with the above statistical and systematic errors. Combining the two measurements, the exotic possibility of a V+A×V–A decay structure is excluded with a significance of about 5 standard deviations. The alternative, of a pointlike B–hadron decay structure with unpolarized virtual W's with a V× V–A structure would result in a roughly 400 (350) MeV larger average neutrino energy and is clearly disfavoured by the data.

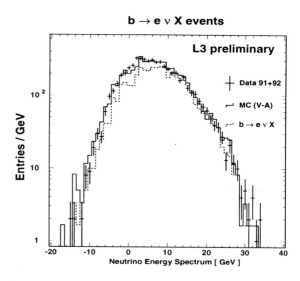

Figure 1. The neutrino energy spectrum in $b \rightarrow e^{\pm}\nu X$ events.

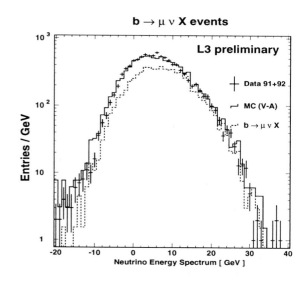

Figure 2. The neutrino energy spectrum in $b \rightarrow \mu^{\pm}\nu X$ events.

2.   Results of $b \rightarrow \nu X$ and $b \rightarrow \tau\nu X$

Inclusive branching ratio (BR) measurements depend on the assumed lepton energy spectra. As predictions for these spectra vary for the different B–hadron decay models, it is important to constrain these models using many different types of measurements. Obviously, once the neutrino energy spectrum can be obtained from the missing energy in b–flavoured jets, a BR$(b \rightarrow \nu X)$ can be measured. Such a measurement is interesting, as inconsistencies between the BR measurement of $b \rightarrow \nu X$ and $b \rightarrow \ell X$ could be used to distinguish between B–decay models. For such a measurement one has to assume that the inclusive semileptonic B–hadron decays $(b \rightarrow \ell\nu X)$, with ℓ being electron, muon and τ, occur in a certain ratio. Because of the large τ mass, the $\text{BR}(b \rightarrow \tau\nu X)$, is expected to be smaller by a factor of 0.26 ± 0.03 [5] and 0.22 ± 0.02 [6] than the other semileptonic BR's. According to these estimates, one can assume that the inclusive leptons are produced in the ratios $1{:}1{:}0.25$ ($\pm$ 0.05).

L3 has performed a measurement of $\text{BR}(b \rightarrow \nu X)$ using the missing energy spectrum in lifetime tagged $b\bar{b}$ events. The observed visible energy distribution in the data event sample is shown in figure 3, the result of the fit and the estimated neutrino contribution are also shown.

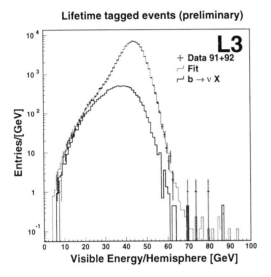

Lifetime tagged events (preliminary)

Figure 3. The jet energy in tagged $b\bar{b}$ events.

For this fit, the shape of the hadronic background has been determined from the data using b–quark depleted event selections. The shape of the neutrino energy spectrum is from the Monte Carlo, where semileptonic B–decays were simulated with a V–A×V–A structure and the relative BR's were fixed with the above ratios. Using this procedure, L3 finds a $\text{BR}(b \rightarrow \nu X)$ of $22.7 \pm 0.8\% \pm 1.5\%$ (preliminary). The dominant systematic errors of this measurement are from the uncertainty in the b–purity of the lifetime event sample and from the uncertainties of the predicted neutrino energy spectrum. The purity uncertainty has been estimated to be smaller than 2.5%, using the observed $\text{BR}(Z^0 \rightarrow b\bar{b})$. The uncertainty of the assumed neutrino energy spectrum was determined to be accurate within $\pm$ 200 MeV, using the results of the analysis, described in the previous section. A change of either the purity or the neutrino energy spectrum with the above errors would change the above BR by roughly $\pm$ 1%. This measurement can be transformed into a result for BR $(b \rightarrow e(\mu)\nu X)$ of $10.1 \pm 0.4(\text{stat.}) \pm 0.7(\text{syst.})\%$.

Instead of fixing the ratio between the different semileptonic decays, one can constrain the directly measurable $\text{BR}(b \rightarrow e(\mu)\nu X)$. The $b \rightarrow \tau\nu X$ component can be enhanced using a hard veto against jets which contain electron or muon candidates. A remaining excess of the jets with large missing energy can than be associated to the decay $b \rightarrow \tau\nu X$.

Such a measurement has first been performed by the ALEPH collaboration in 1982 and has been updated for this conference using the 1991 to 1993 data sample [7]; a similar measurement has also been presented by L3 [8]. Both groups have assumed a value of $11\% \pm 0.5\%$ for the $\text{BR}(b \rightarrow e\nu X)$. As theoretical calculations exist for the ratio $\text{BR}(b \rightarrow \tau\nu X)/\text{BR}(b \rightarrow e\nu X)$, we prefer to give the measured ratios instead of the obtained BR's. Both results are in agreement with the above given non exotic theoretical estimations. ALEPH obtains a ratio of $0.284 \pm 0.033(\text{stat.}) \pm 0.034(\text{syst.})$; the one from L3 is $0.218 \pm 0.064(\text{stat.}) \pm 0.057$ (syst.) (L3).

3. Summary

First preliminary measurements of the neutrino energy spectrum in B–hadron decays from L3 show a polarisation of the virtual W, which is in good agreement with a V–A×V–A B–decay structure. The exotic V+A×V–A structure can be excluded with roughly five standard deviations.

The preliminary L3 result of $\text{BR}(b \rightarrow \nu X)$, with a competitive relative accuracy of better than 10%, is consistent with direct BR measurements using inclusive electrons or muons and supports the V–A×V–A B–hadron decay structure. The results from ALEPH and L3 for the ratio $\text{BR}(b \rightarrow \tau\nu X)/\text{BR}(b \rightarrow \tau\nu X)$ are found to be in agreement with expectations, but the experimental and theoretical errors are still too large to establish an excess or to exclude certain models.

[1] M. Dittmar and Z. Wąs, Phys. Lett. **B332** (1994) 168.
[2] T. Sjöstrand, Comput. Phys. Commun. **27** (1982) 243; and "PYTHIA 5.6 and JETSET 7.3: Physics and manual", CERN preprint CERN-TH.6488/92.
[3] The L3 detector simulation is based on GEANT Version 3.14; see R. Brun *et al.*, GEANT 3, CERN DD/EE/84-1 (Revised), September 1987 and the GHEISHA program (H. Fesefeld, RWTH Aachen Report PITHA85/02 (1985) for the simulation of hadronic interactions.
[4] C. Peterson *et al.*, Phys. Rev. **D27** (1983) 105.
[5] P. Heiliger and L.M. Sehgal, Phys. Lett. **B229** (1989) 409.
[6] A. Falk *et al.*, Phys. Lett. **B326** (1994) 145.
[7] ALEPH Collaboration: D. Buskulic *et al.*, Phys. Lett. **B298** (1993) 479; andICHEP94 Ref. 0582.
[8] L3 Collaboration: M. Acciarri *et al.*, Phys. Lett. **B332** (1994) 201.

QCD Corrections to Inclusive Distributions of Leptons in Decays of Polarised Heavy Quarks*

Marek Jeżabek [‡]

Institute of Nuclear Physics, ul.Kawiory 26a, PL-30055 Cracow, Poland

Abstract

Compact analytic expressions have been obtained for the first order perturbative QCD corrections to the inclusive spectra of the leptons in the semileptonic decays of polarised heavy quarks.

Charmed and beautiful Λ baryons from Z^0 decays can be viewed as sources of highly polarised charm and bottom quarks. Charged leptons and neutrinos from Λ_b and Λ_c decays can be used in the polarisation studies for the corresponding heavy quarks. Thus our results are applicable for the b quark polarisation measurements at LEP.

Short lifetime enables polarisation studies for the top quark. The angular-energy spectra of the charged leptons are particularly useful in this respect whereas the distributions of the neutrinos are sensitive to deviations from the V-A structure of the charged weak current in the decay.

1. Introduction

Inclusive semileptonic decays of polarised charm and bottom quarks play important role in present day particle physics. With increasing statistics at LEP and good prospects for B-factories quantitative description of these processes may offer the most interesting tests of the standard quantum theory of particles. In fact the first measurement of b quark polarisation at LEP has been presented by the ALEPH collaboration at this conference [1]. At the high energy frontier semileptonic decays of the top quark will be instrumental in establishing its properties [2, 3, 4, 5].

In this article I present the results of calculations of the first order perturbative QCD corrections to semileptonic decays of polarised heavy quarks. Some of these results have been published in [6, 7]. In [8] compact analytic formulae have been obtained for the distributions of the charged lepton and the neutrino. These formulae agree with those given in [6] for the joint

* Work partly supported by KBN under contract 2P30225206 and by DFG under contract 436POL173193S.

‡ E-mail: jezabek@chopin.ifj.edu.pl

angular and energy distribution of the charged lepton in top quark decays and are much simpler.

2. The formula and cross checks

The QCD corrected triple differential distribution of the charged lepton for the semileptonic decay of the polarised quark with the weak isospin $I_3 = \pm 1/2$ can be written in the following way [8]:

$$
\frac{d\Gamma^\pm}{dx\,dy\,d\cos\theta} \sim \left[\, F_0^\pm(x,y) + S\cos\theta\, J_0^\pm(x,y) \,\right] \\
- \frac{2\alpha_s}{3\pi}\left[\, F_1^\pm(x,y) + S\cos\theta\, J_1^\pm(x,y) \,\right]
$$

$$(1)$$

In the rest frame of the decaying heavy quark θ denotes the angle between the polarisation vector $\vec{s}$ of the heavy quark and the direction of the charged lepton, $S = |\vec{s}|$, $x = 2Q\ell/Q^2$ and $y = 2\ell\nu/Q^2$ where Q, ℓ and ν denote the four-momenta of the decaying quark, charged lepton and neutrino. Eq.(1) describes also the triple differential distribution of the neutrino for $I_3 = \mp 1/2$. In this case, however, $x = 2Q\nu/Q^2$ and θ denotes the angle between $\vec{s}$ and the three-momentum of the neutrino. The functions $F_0^\pm(x, y)$ and $J_0^\pm(x, y)$ corresponding to Born approximation read:

$$F_0^+(x, y) = x(x_m - x) \tag{2}$$

$$J_0^+(x, y) = F_0^+(x, y) \tag{3}$$

$$F_0^-(x, y) = (x - y)(x_m - x + y) \tag{4}$$

$$J_0^-(x, y) = (x - y)(x_m - x + y - 2y/x) \tag{5}$$

where $x_m = 1 - \epsilon^2$, $\epsilon^2 = q^2/Q^2$ and q denotes the four-momentum of the quark originating from the decay. The functions $F_1^\pm(x, y)$ and $J_1^+(x, y)$ correspond to the first order QCD corrections and are given in [8].

Non-trivial cross checks are fulfilled by the polarisation independent parts of the distributions (1):

- the distributions $d\Gamma^\pm/dx\,dy$ agree with the results for unpolarised decays which were obtained in [9]. The present formulae are simpler.

- in the four-fermion (Fermi) limit integration over y can be performed numerically. The resulting distributions $d\Gamma^\pm/dx$ also agree with those of [9]. Recently the results of [9] have been confirmed [10]. Thus an old conflict with other calculations [11] is solved and the agreement with [9] can be considered as a non-trivial cross check. Moreover, the analytic result of [9] for $d\Gamma^+/dx$ and $\epsilon = 0$ has been also confirmed [12].

- $$d\Gamma^+/dy = d\Gamma^-/dy$$

and the analytic formula for this distribution exists [13] which at the same time describes the lifetime of the top quark as a function of its mass. This formula has been confirmed by a few groups, c.f. [14] and references therein.

- in the four-fermion limit the result for the total rate Γ derived from eq.(1) agrees with the results of [15] and the analytical formula of [16].

3.   Applications

3.1.   *Polarised bottom and charm quarks*

Polarisation studies for heavy flavors at LEP are a new interesting field of potentially fundamental significance, see [17, 1] for recent reviews. According to the Standard Model $Z^0 \to b\bar{b}$ and $Z^0 \to c\bar{c}$ decays can be viewed as sources of highly polarised heavy quarks. The degree of longitudinal polarisation is fairly large, amounting to $\langle P_b \rangle = -0.94$ for b and $\langle P_c \rangle = -0.68$ for c quarks [2]. The polarisations depend weakly on the production angle. QCD corrections to Born result are about 3% [18]. The real drawback is that due to hadronisation the net longitudinal polarisation of the decaying b and c quarks is drastically decreased. In particular these

b quarks become depolarised which are bound in B mesons both produced directly and from $B^* \to B\gamma$ transitions. The signal is therefore significantly reduced. Only those b's (a few percent) which fragment directly into Λ_b baryons retain information on the original polarisation [19]. Polarisation transfer from a heavy quark Q to the corresponding Λ_Q baryon is 100% [20] at least in the limit $m_Q \to \infty$. Thus, a large net polarisation is expected for heavy quarks in samples enriched with these heavy baryons.

It has been proposed long ago [21] that distributions of charged leptons from semileptonic decays of beautiful hadrons can be used in polarisation studies for b quarks. Some advantages of neutrino distributions have been also pointed out [7, 22, 23]. Recently there has been considerable progress in the theory of the inclusive semileptonic decays of heavy flavor hadrons. It has been shown that in the leading order of an expansion in inverse powers of heavy quark mass $1/m_Q$ the spectra for hadrons coincide with those for the decays of free heavy quarks [24] and there are no Λ_{QCD}/m_Q corrections to this result away from the energy endpoint. Λ_{QCD}^2/m_Q^2 corrections have been calculated in [25, 26] for B mesons and in [26] for polarised Λ_b baryons. For some decays the results are similar to those of the well-known $ACCMM$ model [27]. The corrections to charm decays are larger than for bottom and convergence of $1/m_Q$ expansion is poorer [28]. Perturbative first order QCD corrections contribute 10-20% to the semileptonic decays and for bottom are much larger than the nonperturbative ones.

3.2.   *Polarised top quarks*

The analysis of polarised top quarks and their decays has recently attracted considerable attention, see [4, 5] and references cited therein. The reason is that this analysis will result in determination of the top quark coupling to the W and Z bosons either confirming the predictions of the Standard Model or providing clues for physics beyond. The latter possibility is particularly intriguing for the top quark because m_t plays an exceptional role in the fermion mass spectrum.

A number of mechanisms have been suggested that will lead to polarised top quarks. Studies at a linear electron-positron collider are particularly clean for precision tests. However, also $\gamma\gamma$ collisions with circular polarised photons and subsequent spin analysis of top quarks might reveal new information. Related studies may be performed in hadronic collisions which in this case are mainly based on the correlation between t and $\bar{t}$ decay products. However, single top production through Wb fusion at LHC may also be a useful source of polarised top quarks. Electron-positron collisions are the most efficient and flexible reactions producing polarised top quarks. A small component of polarisation transverse to the production plane is induced by final state interactions. The longitudinal polarisation P_L is large. P_L varies strongly with the production angle. Averaging over the production angle leads therefore to a significant reduction of P_L with typical values of $\langle P_L \rangle$ around -0.2 [18].

All these reactions lead to sizable polarisation and can be used to obtain information on the production mechanism. However, two drawbacks are evident: production and decay are mixed in an intricate manner, and furthermore the degree of polarisation is relatively small and depends on the production angle. Top quark production with longitudinally polarised electron beams and close to threshold provides one important exception: the restricted phase space leads to an amplitude which is dominantly S-wave such that the electron (and positron) spin is directly transferred to the top quark. Close to threshold and with longitudinally polarised electrons one can study decays of polarised top quarks under particularly convenient conditions: large event rates, well identified rest frame of the top quark, and large degree of polarisation. Moreover, short lifetime of top quark practically eliminates nonperturbative corrections due to hadronisation.

In the rest frame of the decaying t quark distributions of the decay products are sensitive to its polarisation. Eq.(3) implies that in Born approximation the double differential angular-energy distribution of the charged lepton is the product of the energy distribution and the angular distribution. The latter distribution is of the following form

$$\frac{dN}{d\cos\theta} = \frac{1}{2}\left[1 + S\cos\theta\right] \qquad (6)$$

QCD corrections essentially do not spoil factorisation of the charge lepton distribution [6]. It is noteworthy that for $S=1$ the angular dependence in (6) is maximal because any larger coeffecient multiplying $\cos\theta$ would be in conflict with positivity of the decay rate. Thus the polarisation analysing power of the charged lepton energy-angular distribution is maximal †.

It follows from eqs. (4) and (5) that already in Born approximation there is no factorisation for the neutrino energy-angular distribution. Neutrino distributions are therefore less sensitive to the polarisation of the decaying top quark than charge lepton distributions On the other hand it has been shown [29] that the angular-energy distribution of neutrinos from the polarised top quark decay will allow for a particularly sensitive test of the V-A structure of the weak charged current. The

effect of QCD correction can mimic a small admixture of V+A interaction. Therefore, inclusion of the radiative QCD correction to the decay distributions is necessary for a quantitative study.

Acknowledgements

I thank Andrzej Czarnecki, Hans Kühn and Jürgen Körner for collaborations on research reported in this article. I would like to gratefully acknowledge helpful correspondence with Professors N. Cabibbo, G. Corbo and L. Maiani.

References

[1] P. Roudeaud, *Heavy Quark Physics*, in these proceedings.
[2] J.H. Kühn and P.M. Zerwas, in *Heavy Flavours*, eds. A.J. Buras and M. Lindner, (World Scientific, Singapore, 1992), p.434.
[3] J.H. Kühn et al., DESY Orange Report 92-123A (1992), vol.I,p.255.
[4] J.H. Kühn, "Top Quark at a Linear Collider", in *Physics and Experiments with Linear e^+e^- Colliders*, eds. F.A. Harris et al., (World Scientific, Singapore, 1993), p.72.
[5] M. Jeżabek, *Top Quark Physics*, in proceedings of Zeuthen workshop *Physics at LEP 200 and Beyond*, to appear in Nucl. Phys. **B** (1994) Suppl.; Karlsruhe preprint TTP94-09.
[6] A. Czarnecki, M. Jeżabek and J.H. Kühn, Nucl. Phys. **B351** (1991) 70.
[7] A. Czarnecki, M. Jeżabek, J.G. Körner and J.H. Kühn, Phys. Rev. Lett. **73** (1994) 384.
[8] A. Czarnecki and M. Jeżabek, preprint TTP 93-40, Karlsruhe, 1994, hep-ph/9402326, Nucl. Phys. **B** (1994) in print.
[9] M. Jeżabek and J.H. Kühn, Nucl. Phys. **B320** (1989) 20.
[10] N. Cabibbo, G. Corbo and L. Maiani, private communication.
[11] N. Cabibbo, G. Corbo and L. Maiani, Nucl. Phys. **B155** (1979) 93; G.Corbo, Nucl. Phys. **B212** (1983) 99.
[12] C. Greub, D. Wyler and W. Fetscher, Phys. Lett. **B324** (1994) 109.
[13] M. Jeżabek and J.H. Kühn, Nucl. Phys. **B314** (1989) 1.
[14] M. Jeżabek and J.H. Kühn, Phys. Rev. **D48** (1993) R1910.
[15] N. Cabibbo and L. Maiani, Phys. Lett. **B79** (1978) 109.
[16] Y. Nir, Phys. Lett. **B221** (1989) 184.
[17] B. Mele, preprint n.1009, Rome, 1994.
[18] J.G. Körner, A. Pilaftsis and M.M. Tung, preprint MZ-TH/93-3, Zeit. Phys. C (1994) in print.
[19] J.D. Bjorken, Phys. Rev. **D40** (1989) 1513.
[20] F.E. Close, J.G. Körner, R.J.N. Phillips and D.J. Summers, J. Phys. G. **18** (1992) 1716.
[21] G. Köpp, L.M. Sehgal and P.M. Zerwas, Nucl. Phys. **B123** (191977) 77; B. Mele and G. Altarelli, Phys. Lett. **B299** (1993) 345.
[22] G. Bonvicini and L. Randall, preprint CERN-PPE/94-07, to appear in Phys. Rev. Lett. (1994) .
[23] M. Dittmar and Z. Wąs, Phys. Lett. **B332** (1994) 168; M. Dittmar, in these proceedings.
[24] J. Chay, H. Georgi and B. Grinstein, Phys. Lett. **B247** (1990) 399.
[25] I. Bigi, M. Shifman, N. Uraltsev and A. Vainshtein, Phys. Rev. Lett. **71** (1993) 496.
[26] A.V. Manohar and M.B. Wise, Phys. Rev. **D49** (1994) 1310.
[27] G. Altarelli et al, Nucl. Phys. **B208** (1982) 365.
[28] M. Shifman, in these proceedings.
[29] M. Jeżabek and J.H. Kühn, Phys. Lett. **B329** (1994) 317.

---

† This is reversed for b decays and the polarisation analysing power is maximal for the neutrino distributions because the formulae for the neutrino distributions in down-type quark decay describe the charged lepton distributions for an up-type quark.

Measurements of the Branching Ratio of $B \to X\ell\nu$

Nobuhiko Katayama[‡]

Laboratory of Nuclear Study, Cornell University, Ithaca, N.Y., 14853, U.S.A.

On behalf of the CLEO collaboration

Abstract

We report preliminary measurements of $\mathcal{B}(B \to X\ell\nu)$ that have been made with single and dilepton events from data collected with the CLEO-II detector. In the dilepton events we used charge and kinematic correlations to obtain the electron spectrum of B decays. We also measure the B^+ and B^o semileptonic branching fractions using tagging. Assuming equal semileptonic partial decay widths, their ratio is equivalent to the ratio of lifetimes.

1. Introduction

The semileptonic branching fraction of the B meson has been a persistent puzzle in heavy flavor physics. While experimental measurements have consistently been smaller than 11%, theoretical expectations have remained at 12.5% or higher [1]. The most precise measurements have been based on analyses of the inclusive lepton momentum spectrum at the $\Upsilon(4S)$ resonance. In this paper, we describe a measurement which has achieved a statistical precision of better than 0.5%. The measurement is limited by significant systematic uncertainties. The contribution of primary decays $(B \to X\ell\nu)$ must be separated from that of secondary charm decays $(b \to c \to Y\ell\nu)$ by fitting the spectrum to the predictions of theoretical models. Results obtained with different models span a range that is greater than the experimental error.

Recently the ARGUS collaboration presented an elegant analysis that reduces the model dependence by using dilepton events [2]. In this paper we describe a similar analysis based on a ten times larger data sample.

The lifetime of B^+ is predicted to be slightly longer than that of B^o. Assuming that the semileptonic partial decay widths are equal the B^+ semileptonic branching fraction should be larger than B^o. We report

‡ E-mail: nk@lns62.lns.cornell.edu.

the separate measurements of charged and neutral B semileptonic branching fractions and their ratio.

2. $\mathcal{B}(B \to X\ell\nu)$ from Single Lepton Spectrum

Our data sample was collected with the CLEO-II detector at the Cornell Electron Storage Ring (CESR). The CLEO-II detector has previously been described in detail [3]. Figure 1 shows the electron and muon spectra from the B decays observed with 0.94 fb^{-1} of the $\Upsilon(4S)$ resonance data. The inclusive spectra contain contributions from primary B decays and from secondary B decays $B \to DX$ followed by $D \to Y\ell\nu$. By fitting to theoretical models, we extract the average B semileptonic branching fraction. A fit to ISGW model[4] with a floating D^{**} fraction yields $\mathcal{B}(B \to X\ell\nu) = (10.98 \pm 0.10 \pm 0.33)\%$. for a D** fraction of $21 \pm 2\%$. Using the ACCMM model[5], we obtain $\mathcal{B}(B \to X\ell\nu) = (10.65 \pm 0.05 \pm 0.33)\%$. The systematic error in this result includes a 1% uncertainty in our electron identification efficiency, a 2% uncertainty in the tracking efficiency.

3. $\mathcal{B}(B \to X\ell\nu)$ with Lepton Tags

The data sample for this analysis consists of an integrated luminosity of 2.07 fb^{-1} at the $\Upsilon(4S)$

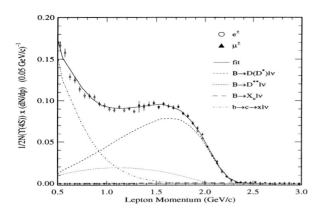

Figure 1. Fit to the lepton spectrum of the ISGW model with a floating D^{**} fraction.

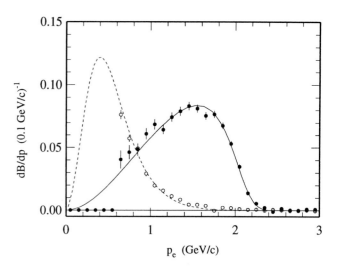

Figure 2. Spectra of electrons from primary decays $B \to Xe\nu$ (filled circles) and secondary decays $b \to c \to y\ell\nu$ (open circles) from the analysis of $B\bar{B}$ events tagged by a high-momentum lepton. The curves show the results of fits to the ACCMM model.

resonance. In each event the presence of a lepton with a momentum above 1.4 GeV/c was required, since high-momentum leptons at the $\Upsilon(4S)$ are predominantly from $b \to c\ell\nu$ transitions. We then looked for an additional electron accompanying this tag, with a minimum momentum requirement of 0.6 GeV/c to allow measurement of most of the B-meson semileptonic decay spectrum. When the other B decays semileptonically, the daughter electron usually has a charge that is opposite to that of the tag. When the second electron is from the semileptonic decay of a charmed particle produced in the decay of the other B, the charge is usually the same as the tag's. Secondary electrons from charm decay on the same side as the tag lepton can also contribute. In this case the charges are opposite, and events of this type complicate the charge-correlation pattern. To suppress electrons from the same B and retain those from the opposite B, we imposed the "diagonal" cut, $p_e + \cos\theta_{\ell e} > 1$, on the unlike-sign sample. This requirement suppresses the same-B background by a factor of 25, while keeping 67% of the signal.

After corrections for fakes, leptons from J/ψ and $\pi^0 \to e^+e^-\gamma$ decays, from decays of τ's produced in $B \to X\tau\nu$ and false tags by secondary leptons above 1.4 GeV/c, the unlike- and like-sign electron momentum spectra can be expressed algebraically in terms of the primary and secondary branching fractions as

$$\frac{dN(\ell^\pm e^\mp)}{dp} = N_\ell \eta(p) \left[\frac{d\mathcal{B}(b)}{dp}(1-\chi) + \frac{d\mathcal{B}(c)}{dp}\chi \right] \epsilon(p),$$
(1)

$$\frac{dN(\ell^\pm e^\pm)}{dp} = N_\ell \eta(p) \left[\frac{d\mathcal{B}(b)}{dp}\chi + \frac{d\mathcal{B}(c)}{dp}(1-\chi) \right],$$
(2)

where $\eta(p)$ is the efficiency of electron identification and $\epsilon(p)$ is the efficiency of the diagonal cut that we applied to the unlike-sign electrons. The number of tag leptons in the $B\bar{B}$ data sample was $N_\ell = 247811 \pm 771$.

The effect of neutral B-meson mixing is parameter-

ized by $\chi = f_0\chi_0$, where χ_0 is the $B^0\bar{B}^0$ mixing parameter and f_0 is the fraction of $\Upsilon(4S)$ decays which produce neutral B mesons, χ has been directly measured to be 0.079 ± 0.012[6]. The error includes both statistical and systematic components, but the measurement is immune to uncertainty in f_0. Eqs. 1 and 2 have been solved to obtain the primary and secondary electron spectra shown in Fig. 2.

By integrating the primary spectrum from 0.6 GeV/c to 2.5 GeV/c we calculate the partial branching ratio $\mathcal{B}(B \to Xe\nu, p_e > 0.6 \text{ GeV/c}) = (9.76 \pm 0.16)\%$, where the error is only statistical. This result is almost completely model-independent. The fraction of undetected electrons below 0.6 GeV/c, determined using models of ACCMM and ISGW is only $(5.8 \pm 0.5)\%$. With this extrapolation, we obtain the semileptonic branching fraction of B mesons $\mathcal{B}(B \to Xe\nu) = (10.36 \pm 0.17 \pm 0.40)\%$. The systematic error in this result includes a 1% uncertainty in our electron identification efficiency, a 2% uncertainty in the tracking efficiency, and the uncertainty in the mixing parameter χ.

Neglecting the contribution from V_{ub}, the B-meson inclusive branching fraction is related to the CKM matrix element V_{cb}:

$$\Gamma(B \to X\ell\nu) = \gamma_c |V_{cb}|^2,$$
(3)

where the factor γ_c must be obtained from theory. With both ACCMM and ISGW models ($\gamma_c = 40 \pm 8 \ ps^{-1}$ and $41 \pm 8 \ ps^{-1}$, respectively) and the average lifetime for charged and neutral B mesons of $1.49 \pm 0.05 \ ps$ [7] we obtain $|V_{cb}| = 0.042 \pm 0.001 \pm 0.004$. In this result the first error combines all of the experimental uncertainties, both statistical and systematic. It is much smaller than

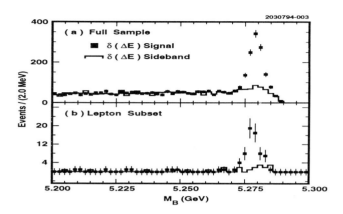

Figure 3. $B^- \to$ hadrons tags

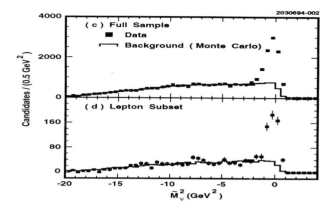

Figure 4. $\overline{B^0} \to D^{*+}\ell^-\overline{\nu}$ tags

the second error, which is an estimated 10% theoretical uncertainty in the computation of γ_c.

4. $\mathcal{B}(B^+ \to X\ell\nu)$ and $\mathcal{B}(B^o \to X\ell\nu)$ from tagging

We measure the B^+ semileptonic branching fraction in a sample of fully reconstructed B^- decays. We reconstruct B^- in eight different modes: $D^{(*)}\pi^-$, $D^{(*)}\rho^-$, $D^{(*)}a_1^-$, and $K^{(*)}J/\psi$. The candidate momenta and energies, $\vec{p}_B$ and E_B, of the measured components are used to calculate the beam-constrained mass $M_B = \sqrt{E_{\text{beam}}^2 - |\vec{p}_B|^2}$ and the normalized energy difference between the B and the beam energy $\delta(\Delta E) = (E_{\text{beam}} - E_B)/\sigma(\Delta E)$, where $\sigma(\Delta E)$ is the expected resolution on $E_{\text{beam}} - E_B$. For signal, M_B peaks at the B mass, and $\delta(\Delta E)$ is a normal Gaussian. Figure 3(a) shows the M_B distribution for the B^- tags in the $\delta(\Delta E)$ signal (points) and sideband (histogram) regions. We find 834 ± 42 tags using 1.35 fb^{-1} of on-resonance data.

Additional leptons are selected in the range 1.4–2.4 GeV/c. The leptons are from the semileptonic decay of the remaining B mesons in the events. After the fake and secondary lepton subtractions and correction for efficiencies, we obtain 97.2 ± 20.8 $e^\pm$ and 73.0 ± 19.8 $\mu^\pm$ candidates and $\mathcal{B}(B^+ \to X\ell\nu) = (10.1 \pm 1.8 \pm 1.4)\%$. This is the first measurement of the B^+ semileptonic branching fraction.

While we find 515 ± 31 fully reconstructed B^o events using the hadronic tagging, we use two more tagging methods for B^o. In the two techniques, B^os are partially reconstructed as $B^o \to D^{*-}\pi^+$ or $B^o \to D^{*-}\ell^+\nu$, $D^{*-} \to D^o\pi^-$, where D^o is unseen. We reconstruct 822 ± 53 tags using partially reconstructed $B^o \to D^{*-}\pi^+$ decays. In the $B^o \to D^{*-}\ell^+\nu$ partial reconstruction we utilizes leptons which have momentum > 1.8 GeV/c to suppress feed-down from $B^o \to \bar{D}^{**}\ell^+\nu$ decays. The squared neutrino mass M_ν^2 is calculated assuming that the B is at rest. Figure 4(c) shows the M_ν^2 distribution, which give 7119 ± 139 tags. We find the lepton subsets

for three tags and measure $\mathcal{B}(B^o \to X\ell\nu)$ separately. We then average three measurements weighting each by the statistical and uncorrelated systematic errors to obtain $\mathcal{B}(B^o \to X\ell\nu) = (10.9 \pm 0.7 \pm 1.1)\%$.

Assuming the semileptonic partial widths are equal, we obtain the ratio of lifetimes, $\tau_+/\tau_o = 0.93 \pm 0.18 \pm 0.12$.

5.   Conclusions

In conclusion, we have made new measurements of $\mathcal{B}(B \to X\ell\nu)$. Using the inclusive spectrum, we obtain a preliminary result of $\mathcal{B}(B \to X\ell\nu) = (10.98 \pm 0.10 \pm 0.33)\%$ for the ISGW model and $(10.65 \pm 0.05 \pm 0.33)\%$ for ACCMM. Using the lepton tag method, our preliminary measurement is $\mathcal{B}(B \to Xe\nu) = (10.36 \pm 0.17 \pm 0.40)\%$. They are in agreement with other recent measurements, and significantly below theoretical expectations. The latter measurement is largely independent of theoretical models, and is insensitive to possible non-$B\bar{B}$ decays of the $\Upsilon(4S)$. Using three tagging techniques, we have also measured $\mathcal{B}(B^+ \to X\ell\nu) = (10.1 \pm 1.8 \pm 1.4)\%$ and $\mathcal{B}(B^o \to X\ell\nu) = (10.9 \pm 0.7 \pm 1.1)\%$ and the ratio of lifetimes, $\tau_+/\tau_o = 0.93 \pm 0.18 \pm 0.12$.

6.   References

[1] G. Altarelli and S. Petrarca, Phys. Lett. **B 261** (1991), 303; I. Bigi, B. Blok, M.A. Shifman and A. Vainshtein, Phys. Lett. **B 323**, 408 (1994).
[2] H. Albrecht *et al.* (ARGUS), Phys. Lett. **B 318**, 397 (1993).
[3] Y. Kubota *et al.* (CLEO), Nucl. Instr. Meth. **A 320**, 66 (1992).
[4] N. Isgur, D. Scora, B. Grinstein and M.B. Wise Phys. Rev. D **39**, 799 (1989).
[5] G. Altarelli, N. Cabibbo, G. Corbo, L. Maiani and G. Martinelli, *Nucl. Phys.* **B208** (1982) 365.
[6] J. Bartelt *et al.* (CLEO), Phys. Rev. Lett. **71**, 1680 (1993).
[7] W. Venus, Proc. of XVI Int. Symp. on Lepton-Photon Interactions, Eds. P. Drell and D. Rubin, AIP Press, New York (1994).

Paper presented at XXVII Int. Conf. on High Energy Physics: Session Pa-16
Glasgow, UK, 20–27 July 1994

Theory of Semi– and Nonleptonic Decays of Heavy Mesons

Patricia Ball[†]

† Physik–Department, TU München, D–85747 Garching, Germany

Abstract

I review some of the recent developments in the theoretical description of weak inclusive decays of heavy mesons. The topics cover the value of $|V_{cb}|$ as extracted from semileptonic inclusive decays and a short discussion of the theoretical errors. I also present the results of a recent calculation of next–to–leading order corrections to nonleptonic inclusive B decays which allows an improved prediction of the semileptonic branching ratio of B mesons.

1. Outline of Theoretical Foundations

During the recent two years, the theoretical description of inclusive decays of heavy hadrons has experienced considerable progress. For quark masses $m_Q \gg \Lambda_{QCD}$, the well–known short–distance expansion technique yields an expansion in inverse powers of the heavy quark mass, the so–called heavy quark expansion (HQE) [1]. The starting point for the HQE of, e.g., the decay rate of a B meson into a final state X is its representation as imaginary part of the relevant forward–scattering amplitude:

$$\Gamma(B \to X) = \frac{1}{m_B} \operatorname{Im} i \int d^4x \, \langle B|T\mathcal{L}_W(x)\mathcal{L}_W(0)|B\rangle. \quad (1)$$

Here $\mathcal{L}_W$ is the effective weak Lagrangian mediating the decay $B \to X$. As shown in [1], for a very heavy b quark mass m_b, a short distance expansion of Eq. (1) yields:

$$\Gamma(B \to X) = \frac{G_F^2 m_b^5}{192\pi^3} |CKM|^2 \left\{ C_0^{(X)}(\alpha_s(\mu)) \frac{\langle B|\bar{b}b|B\rangle}{2m_B} \right.$$
$$\left. + C_2^{(X)}(\alpha_s(\mu)) \frac{1}{m_b^2} \frac{\langle B|\bar{b}g_s\sigma_{\mu\nu}F^{\mu\nu}b|B\rangle}{2m_B} + \mathcal{O}\left(\frac{1}{m_b^3}\right) \right\} (2)$$

Here CKM denotes the appropriate CKM matrix elements, the $C_i^{(X)}$ are short–distance Wilson–coefficients, which depend on the parton model process underlying the decay $B \to X$. b is the b quark field in full QCD, m_B is the mass of the B meson and $F^{\mu\nu}$ the gluonic field–strength tensor.

Without going into too much details, let me mention just a few general features of the above expansion. First we remark that HQE strongly resembles deep inelastic scattering with the difference that the value of the expansion parameter m_b is fixed and cannot be controlled by the experimenter, so that higher twist effects in $1/m_b$ are important. On the other hand, the corresponding hadronic matrix elements can be expressed as moments of a universal distribution function [2, 3] and are thus measurable, at least in principle, cf. [4].

The first term in the above series, $\langle B|\bar{b}b|B\rangle$, just reproduces the free quark decay process; non–perturbative corrections to that picture are suppressed by terms of $\mathcal{O}(1/m_b^2)$ or higher. There are no terms of order $1/m_b$, since all possible gauge–invariant operators of suitable dimension either vanish or can be reduced to $\bar{b}b$ by the equations of motion.

The Wilson coefficients $C_j^{(X)}(\alpha_s(\mu))$ encode the short distance behaviour of Eq. (1) and are calculable within perturbation theory; they depend on the parton content of X, the renormalization scale μ and the renormalization scheme. In particular, $C_0^{(X)}$ contains the radiative corrections to the free quark decay and has been studied for various processes [5, 6, 7, 8, 9].

Let me also mention some words of caution. In order to separate clearly the expansion in $1/m_Q$ from the one in α_s, the HQE has to be done in terms of the *pole mass.* This mass definition, however, is unphysical and contradicts the confinement property of QCD. It has been shown, that this contradiction reflects itself in an intrinsic ambiguity of the definition of the pole mass which is said to be caused by a "renormalon" [10]. Although it was shown in [11] that the renormalon cancels in the semileptonic rate, at least up to order $1/m_b^2$, there is still a number of questions to be answered as far as nonleptonic and exclusive decays are concerned.

2. Applications I: $|V_{cb}|$ from Semileptonic Inclusive Decays

One immediate application of the HQE is the extraction of $|V_{cb}|$ from semileptonic inclusive decays. The decay rate $\Gamma(B \to X_c e\nu)$, of the generic form of Eq. (2), contains to order $1/m_b^2$ five unknown parameters: V_{cb}, m_b, m_c and two hadronic matrix elements:

$$2m_B \lambda_1 = \langle B | \bar{b}_v (iD)^2 b_v | B \rangle,$$
$$6m_B \lambda_2 = \langle B | \bar{b}_v \frac{g}{2} \sigma_{\mu\nu} F^{\mu\nu} b_v | B \rangle, \qquad (3)$$

where b_v is defined as $b_v = e^{im_b vx} b$ and v_μ is the four-velocity of the B meson.

Whereas λ_2 is directly related to the observable spectrum of beautiful mesons,

$$\lambda_2 \approx \frac{1}{4} (m_{B^*}^2 - m_B^2) = 0.12 \, \text{GeV}^2, \qquad (4)$$

the quantity λ_1 is difficult to measure, cf. [4]. Physically, $-\lambda_1/(2m_b)$ is just the average kinetic energy of the b quark inside the meson. At present, only a QCD sum rule estimate is available, according to which $\lambda_1 \simeq -0.6$ GeV^2 [12]. This result has been met with caution (see, e.g. [13]), since it corresponds in fact to a surprisingly large momentum of the b quark inside the meson of order $(700–800) \, \text{MeV}$. However, in a recent series of papers, cf. [4, 3], an upper bound on λ_1 was derived, to wit $\lambda_1 \leq -0.4 \, \text{GeV}^2$, which is in nice agreement with the QCD sum rule prediction. For a further discussion of the present status of λ_1, I refer to [14].

The next step is to fix m_b and m_c. Here one makes use of the fact that in the framework of HQE the *difference* between m_b and m_c is given by

$$m_b - m_c = m_B - m_D + \frac{\lambda_1 + 3\lambda_2}{2} \left(\frac{1}{m_b} - \frac{1}{m_c} \right) + \mathcal{O}\left(\frac{1}{m_Q^2} \right). \qquad (5)$$

Thus either m_b or m_c remain to be fixed. Shifman et al. [15] took $m_b = (4.8 \pm 0.1) \, \text{GeV}$ from spectroscopy. With $\lambda_1 = -0.5 \, \text{GeV}^2$ and for a B lifetime $\tau_B = 1.49 \, \text{ps}$, they get $|V_{cb}| = 0.0415$. In [16, 17, 18, 19] m_c was determined from the experimental value of $B(D \to X e\nu)$ via Eq. (2) with m_b replaced by m_c.

Although this procedure has the advantage that both m_b and m_c are obtained by the same method, the validity of the HQE for the charm quark is not beyond controversy. The b quark mass obtained is typically larger than $5 \, \text{GeV}$ and thus considerably larger as m_b from spectroscopy. On the other hand, the b quark mass used by Shifman et al. seems to underestimate the intrinsic renormalon ambiguity mentioned in the last section. But even using the same method, [16] and [17] obtain different results: $|V_{cb}| = 0.046 \pm 0.008$ and ≈ 0.042, respectively (both numbers rescaled using $\tau_B = 1.49 \, \text{ps}$). Ref. [19] takes into account the scheme-dependence of the free quark decay contribution and using running $\overline{\text{MS}}$ masses instead of pole masses obtains $|V_{cb}| = 0.036 \pm 0.005$. Since the decay rates only differ in terms of $\mathcal{O}(\alpha_s^2)$, these results show that at present the theoretical error due to scale- and scheme-dependence is of paramount importance in exploiting inclusive decays of heavy mesons and for $|V_{cb}|$ amounts to nearly 20%.

3. Applications II: the Semileptonic Branching Ratio of B Mesons

The semileptonic branching ratio of B mesons is defined by

$$B(B \to X e\nu) = \frac{\Gamma(B \to X e\nu)}{\Gamma_{tot}} \qquad (6)$$

with

$$\Gamma_{tot} = \sum_{\ell = e, \mu, \tau} \Gamma(B \to X \ell \nu_\ell) + \Gamma(B \to X_c) + \Gamma(B \to X_{c\bar{c}}). \qquad (7)$$

The explicit formulas for the decay rates can be found in [1]. The radiative corrections to $\mathcal{O}(\alpha_s)$ to the semileptonic decay $b \to ce\nu$ were calculated in [5, 7, 8], the corrections to $b \to cud$ with a massless c quark in [6], with a massive c quark in [9]; the complete corrections to $b \to ccs$ are not known to date, but can partly be obtained from Ref. [7].

The experimental branching ratios are $B(B \to X e\nu) = (10.43 \pm 0.24)\%$ (world average) [20] and $B(B^0 \to X e\nu) = (10.9 \pm 0.7 \pm 1.1)\%$, the most recent result obtained by CLEO [21].

There exists a number of theoretical analyses of $B(B \to X e\nu)$ using different methods and obtaining different results. In [22], e.g., the branching ratio was investigated in a purely perturbative framework using the full radiative corrections for $b \to ce\nu$ [5, 8], but with $m_c = 0$ in the corrections to $b \to cud$ and $b \to ccs$ [6]. In Ref. [23], the same analysis was repeated taking into account non-leading terms in the HQE. Finally, in [9, 24] also the full radiative corrections to $b \to cud$ were calculated and those parts of the corrections to $b \to ccs$ available from [7] were taken into account. Also the

$\alpha_s(m_Z)$	Parton Model [22] pole masses	HQE [23] pole masses	HQE [9, 24] pole masses	$\overline{MS}$ masses
0.110	0.132	0.130	0.121	0.111
0.117	0.128	0.126	0.116	0.103
0.124	0.124	0.121	0.111	0.097

Table 1. $B(B \to Xe\nu)$ in different models depending on $\alpha_s(m_Z)$. Input parameters: $m_b = 4.8\,\mathrm{GeV}$, $m_c = 1.3\,\mathrm{GeV}$ (pole masses) corresponding to $\lambda_1 = -0.6\,\mathrm{GeV}^2$. Renormalization scale: $\mu = m_b$. In the phase–space factor of $\Gamma(b \to ccs)$ $m_s = 0.2\,\mathrm{GeV}$ is used. Only in [9, 24] full radiative corrections to the nonleptonic B decay modes were taken into account.

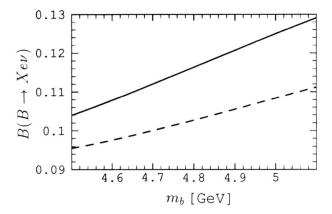

Figure 1. $B(B \to Xe\nu)$ as function of the pole mass m_b for $\mu = m_b$. Solid line: B calculated using pole masses, dashed line: B calculated using running $\overline{MS}$ quark masses.

effect of scheme–dependence was estimated by changing the definition of the quark mass. For the same set of input parameters, the results are given in Table 1. The table shows that the introduction of nonperturbative correction terms by Bigi et al. reduces $B(B \to Xe\nu)$ by 0.3% with respect to the free quark decay model, and that the account for the c quark mass in the radiative corrections yields an additional –0.9%, which again shows the importance of *perturbative* corrections to the HQE. The scheme–dependence, however, is still tremenduous and amounts to an uncertainty in $B(B \to Xe\nu)$ of more than 1%. Whereas Refs. [22, 23] concluded that $B(B \to Xe\nu) > 12.5\%$, Refs. [9, 24] find

$$B(B \to Xe\nu) = (11.0 \pm 1.8 \pm 1.0)\%, \qquad (8)$$

where the first error combines uncertainties in $\alpha_s(m_Z)$, m_b ($4.5\,\mathrm{GeV} < m_b < 5.1\,\mathrm{GeV}$), the hadronic corrections, the renormalization scale and the uncertainty in the radiative corrections to $b \to ccs$. The second error is a "guestimate" of the theoretical error due to scheme–dependence. The combined effect of complete radiative corrections, new results on $\alpha_s(m_Z)$ [25] and the consideration of different definitions of the quark mass thus lowers the theoretical branching ratio, which now agrees with the experimental one within the errors and seriously restricts any possible "new physics" in

nonleptonic B decays. A more detailed analysis is in preparation [24].

References

[1] I. Bigi, N. Uraltsev and A. Vainshtein, Phys. Lett. **B293** (1992) 430; *Erratum ibid.* **B297** (1993) 477; I. Bigi *et al.*, Phys. Rev. Lett. **71** (1993) 496; A. Manohar and M.B. Wise Phys. Rev. **D49** (1994) 1310; B. Blok *et al.*, Phys. Rev. **D49** (1994) 3356; T. Mannel, Nucl. Phys. **B413** (1994) 396.
[2] M. Neubert, Phys. Rev. **D49** (1994) 3392; T. Mannel and M. Neubert, Phys. Rev. **D50** (1994) 2037; I. Bigi et al., Int. J. Mod. Phys. **A9** (1994) 2467.
[3] I. Bigi *et al.*, Minneapolis preprint: TPI–MINN–94/12–T (hep–ph/9405410).
[4] I. Bigi *et al.*, Minneapolis preprint: TPI-MINN–94/25–T (hep–ph/9407296).
[5] N. Cabibbo and L. Maiani, Phys. Lett. **B79** (1978) 109.
[6] G. Altarelli *et al.*, Nucl. Phys. **B187** (1981) 461; G. Buchalla, Nucl. Phys. **B391** (1993) 501.
[7] Q. Hokim and X.Y. Pham, Phys. Lett. **B122** (1983) 297; Ann. Phys. **155** (1984) 202.
[8] Y. Nir, Phys. Lett. **B221** (1989) 184.
[9] E. Bagan *et al.*, TU München preprint: TUM–T31–67/94/R (hep–ph/9408306).
[10] I. Bigi *et al.*, Phys. Rev. **D50** (1994) 2234; M. Beneke and V.M. Braun, MPI München preprint: MPI–PhT/94–9 (hep–ph/9402364) (to appear in Nucl. Phys. **B**).
[11] M. Beneke, V.M. Braun and V.I. Zakharov, MPI München preprint: MPI–PhT/94–18 (hep–ph/9405304).
[12] P. Ball and V.M. Braun, Phys. Rev. D **49** (1994) 2472.
[13] M. Neubert, Phys. Lett. B **322** (1994) 419.
[14] M. Neubert, Talk given at QCD 94, Montpellier, France, 7–13 July 1994.
[15] M. Shifman, N. Uraltsev and A. Vainshtein, Minneapolis preprint: TPI–MINN–94/13–T (hep–ph/9405207).
[16] M. Luke and M. Savage, Phys. Lett. **B321** (1994) 88.
[17] I. Bigi and N. Uraltsev, Z. Phys. **C62** (1994) 623.
[18] Z. Ligeti and Y. Nir, Phys. Rev. **D49** (1994) 4331.
[19] P. Ball and U. Nierste, TU München preprint: TUM–T31–56/94/R (hep–ph/9403407) (to appear in Phys. Rev. **D**).
[20] Particle Data Group: M. Aguilar-Benitez *et al.*, Phys. Rev. **D50** (1994) 1173.
[21] CLEO Collaboration: M.Athanas *et al.*, Cornell preprint: CLNS 94–1286 (hep–ex/9406004).
[22] G. Altarelli and S. Petrarca, Phys. Lett. **B261** (1991) 303.
[23] I. Bigi *et al.*, Phys. Lett. **B323** (1994) 408.
[24] E. Bagan *et al.*, TU München preprint: TUM–T31–68/94 (in preparation).
[25] S. Bethke, Talk given at QCD 94, Montpellier, France, 7–13 July 1994.

Paper presented at XXVII Int. Conf. on High Energy Physics: Session Pa-16
Glasgow, UK, 20–27 July 1994

A Study of $B^- \rightarrow (D^{*+}\pi^-)\ell^-\bar{\nu}$ at LEP

Massimo Carpinelli‖

Dipartimento di Fisica dell'Università e INFN Sezione di Pisa, 56010 Pisa, Italy

Abstract

In a sample of 1.5 million hadronic decays of the Z collected by the ALEPH detector, a search for the decay $B \rightarrow D_1\ell^-\bar{\nu}X$ and $B \rightarrow D_2^*\ell^-\bar{\nu}X$ is carried out. The result is $\mathrm{Br}(b \rightarrow B) \cdot (\mathrm{Br}(B \rightarrow D_1\ell^-\bar{\nu}X) \cdot (\mathrm{Br}(D_1 \rightarrow D^{*+}\pi^-) = (2.08 \pm 0.59\,(\text{stat.}) \pm 0.34\,(\text{syst.})) \cdot 10^{-3}$ and a 95% confidence level upper limit of $1.92 \cdot 10^{-3}$ is obtained for the corresponding D_2^* decays. A topological search, sensitive to the production of all the $\ell = 1$ charm mesons (wide and narrow resonances) and of non-resonant $D^{*+}\pi^-$ is also carried out. The result is: $\mathrm{Br}(b \rightarrow B) \cdot (\mathrm{Br}(B \rightarrow D^{*+}\pi^-\ell^-\bar{\nu}X) = (4.0 \pm 1.1\,(\text{stat.}) \pm 0.8(\text{syst.})) \cdot 10^{-3}$. The results include the first direct evidence of non-resonant $D^*\pi$ production in semileptonic B decay.

The OPAL collaboration made the first observation of semileptonic B decays into charged narrow resonances of $\ell = 1$ charm mesons.

1. Introduction

The composition of the inclusive semileptonic branching ratio in terms of exclusive ones is a long-standing problem which affects a number of experimental studies and theoretical models. Experimentally, $40 \pm 9\%$ [1] of the inclusive rate is not accounted for by the decays $B \rightarrow D\ell^-\bar{\nu}$ and $B \rightarrow D^*\ell^-\bar{\nu}$. Possible explanations are: direct four-body decays, such as $B \rightarrow D^*\pi\ell^-\bar{\nu}$ and decays to $\ell = 1$ charm mesons. From HQET [2], four such states are expected: two are the observed [1, 4] narrow resonances $D_1(2420)$ and $D_2^*(2460)$, having the angular momentum of the light quark J_{lq} of $3/2$, and two are wide resonances, with J_{lq} of $1/2$, not yet observed.

2. $B \rightarrow D_1\ell^-\bar{\nu}X$

The decays of the Z at LEP provides a source of boosted B mesons and the tracking resolution of the ALEPH detector [5] provides the capability of differentiating a track originating at the primary interaction point from a track originating at the B decay point. The decay $B \rightarrow D_1\ell^-\bar{\nu}X$ is identified in events where a D^{*+}

and a lepton are found in the same hemisphere of an hadronic Z decays The D^{*+} mesons are reconstructed in the channel $D^0\pi^+$, followed by $D^0 \rightarrow K^-\pi^+$ or $D^0 \rightarrow K^-\pi^+\pi^-\pi^+$. Having selected a clean $D^{*+}\ell^-$ sample, (133 ± 17 with a background of 1.7 ± 0.7 in the $K^-\pi^+$ channel and 179 ± 14 with a background of 20.5 ± 2.3 in the $K^-\pi^+\pi^-\pi^+$) a pion of the same sign of the lepton is added to build the D_1 and D_2^* resonances. The added pion is required to come from the $D^{*+}\ell^-$ vertex and not to be compatible with the primary vertex. The background is from the decay $B^0 \rightarrow D^{*+}\ell^-\bar{\nu}$ where a fragmentation track is poorly measured and assigned to the $D^{*+}\ell^-$ vertex. The distribution of Δm^*, which is the difference between the measured mass of the $D^{*+}\pi_{**}^-$ and the D^{*+} as found in the data with this selection procedure is shown in figure 1. The D_1 component contains 16.8 ± 5.0 events, and there is no significant D_2^* signal. The result is $\mathrm{Br}(b \rightarrow B) \cdot \mathrm{Br}(B \rightarrow D_1\ell^-\bar{\nu}X) \cdot \mathrm{Br}(D_1 \rightarrow D^{*+}\pi^-) = (2.08 \pm 0.59(\text{stat.}) \pm 0.34(\text{syst.})) \cdot 10^{-3}$. A 95% confidence level upper limit of $1.92 \cdot 10^{-3}$ is obtained for

---

† The procedure is described in more detail in reference [3]

‡ The symbol π_{**}^- indicates the pion from the $\ell = 1$ charm meson decays

‖ E-mail: carpinelli@pisa.infn.it.

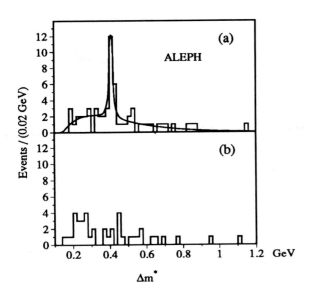

Figure 1. Distribution of Δm^*, for both the same sign and opposite sign samples. The same sign sample is fit to a background plus a Breit Wigner.

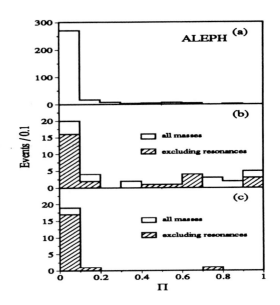

Figure 2. Probability of originating from the $D^{*+}\ell^-$ vertex, Π, for pions in: (a) simulated background events; (b) signal candidates in data; (c) opposite sign pions in the data.

the corresponding D_2^* decays.

3. $B \to D^{*+}\pi^-\ell^-\bar{\nu}X$

In contrast to the previous cases, the resonant structure cannot be used to extract the signal in $B \to D^{*+}\pi^-\ell^-\bar{\nu}X$. Nevertheless, the topology of this decay mode is sufficient for its identification. The event selection use the previous $D^{*+}\ell^-$ sample but more stringent requirement are made on the position of the π^-_{**} relative to the $D^{*+}\ell^-$ vertex. The distribution of the impact parameter of the π^-_{**} with respect to the $D^{*+}\ell^-$ vertex divided by its resolution, δ/σ_δ, for simulated signal events is parametrized with a 3d-gaussian plus an exponential term. This parametrization, R_δ is used to calculate an integrated probability according to $\Pi = \int_{\delta/\sigma_{delta}}^{\infty} R_\delta(x)dx$. By construction the distribution of this probability is uniform between 0 and 1 for signal events, while background events have a disitribution peaked toward low values of Π This can be seen with simulated events in figure 2(a). The distribution of the signal probability, shown in figure 2(b), has a clear excess of 18 events with a high probability ($\Pi > 0.2$) in the same sign sample, and no corresponding excess in the opposite sign sample is seen. Excluding the D_1 mass region nine events are found in the same sign sample, as shown in figure 2(b). This is the first evidence of wide $\ell = 1$ charm meson production in semileptonic B decay. The signal is estimated from the events with $\Pi > 0.2$, after background subtraction. The number of background events, N_{bg}, in the signal region is $N_{bg} =$

$f_{\Pi>0.2}/(1-f_{\Pi>0.2}) \cdot N_{ssb}$ where $f_{\Pi>0.2}$ is the fraction of hadronization pions in the signal region, and N_{ssb} is the number of same sign background events having $\Pi < 0.2$. $f_{\Pi>0.2} = 0.100 \pm 0.017$ is found in the simulation. With this procedure a signal of 15.8 ± 4.3 events is found. The branching ratio for the semileptonic B decays into $l = 1$ charm mesons is: $\mathrm{Br}(b \to B) \cdot (\mathrm{Br}(B \to D^{*+}\pi^-\ell^-\bar{\nu}X) = (4.0 \pm 1.1 \,(\text{stat.}) \pm 0.8(\text{syst.})) \cdot 10^{-3}$.

4.   Charged $\ell = 1$ charm states

The D_1 and D_2^* states have charged isospin partner. The OPAL collaboration has made a search for narrow $\ell = 1$ charmed mesons in semileptonic B decays using the decay channels $D_2^{*0} \to D^+\pi^-$, $(D_1^0$ or $D_2^{*0}) \to D^{*+}\pi^-$ and $D_2^{*-} \to D^0\pi^-$, finding $44 \pm 8^{+3}_{-7}$ $(D_1^0$ or $D_2^{*0})$ and $48 \pm 10^{+3}_{-6}$ D_2^{*-} events. The latter results is the first evidence for semileptonic B decays to charged $\ell = 1$ charm narrow resonances.

References

[1] Particle Data Group, Phys. Rev. D **50** (1994) 1173
[2] M.Neubert, SLAC preprint SLAC-PUB-6263 (1993) and the refernces therein.
[3] ALEPH Coll., D. Buskulic *et al.* , Phys. Lett. **B307** (1993) 194
[4] CLEO Coll., P. Avery *et al.* , CLEO 94-10, CLNS 94/1280
[5] ALEPH Coll., D. Decamp *et al.* , Nucl. Instr. Methods. **A294** (1990) 121

Paper presented at XXVII Int. Conf. on High Energy Physics: Session Pa-16
Glasgow, UK, 20–27 July 1994

Light Flavor Dependence of the Isgur-Wise Function

Tao Huang[a,b] and Chuan-Wang Luo[b]

a. CCAST (World Laboratory), P.O.Box 8730, Beijing 100080, China
b. Institute of High Energy Physics, P.O.Box 918(4), Beijing 100039, China
(presented by T.Huang)

Abstract

We present an investigation on the ligh flavor dependence of the Isgur-Wise function for $B_a \to D_a$ and $B_a \to D_a^*$ in the framework of QCD sum rules. It is found that the Isgur-Wise function for B_s decay falls faster than that for $B_{u,d}$ decay, which is contrary to the recent prediction of heavy meson chiral perturbation theory. SU(3) symmetry breaking effects in the mass and the decay constant are also estimated.

As a heavy quark goes into the infinite mass limit, all form factors for $B \to D$ and $B \to D^*$ can be expressed in terms of a single universal function [1], the so-called Isgur-Wise function. The Isgur-Wise function represents the nonperturbative dynamics of weak decays of heavy mesons. It depends not only on the dimensionless product $v \cdot v'$ of the initial and final mesonic velocities, but also on the light quark flavor of the initial and final mesons [1, 2, 3, 4]. Here, we apply QCD sum rule approach [3, 4] to study its light quark flavor dependence.

In HQET, the low energy parameter $F_a(\mu)$ of heavy meson $M_a(\bar{q}Q)$ is defined by [3]

$$< 0|\bar{q}\Gamma h_Q|M_a(v) > = \frac{F_a(\mu)}{2} Tr[\Gamma M(v)]. \quad (1)$$

In the leading order, the decay constant $f_{M_a} \simeq F_a(\mu)/\sqrt{m_{M_a}}$. It should be emphasized that here and below, the subscript $a = u, d, s$ specifies the light antiquark $\bar{q} = \bar{u}, \bar{d}, \bar{s}$ of the heavy meson $M_a(\bar{q}Q)$.

Starting from the two-point correlation function in HQET,

$$\pi_5(\omega) = i \int d^4x e^{ik \cdot x} < 0|TA_5^{(v)}(x), A_5^{(v)+}(0)|0 >, \quad (2)$$

where $A_5^{(v)} = \bar{q}\gamma_5 h_Q$ and $\omega = 2k \cdot v$, one obtains the sum rule for $F_a(\mu)$

$$F_a^2(\mu)e^{-2\bar{\Lambda}_a/T} = \frac{3}{8\pi^2} \int_{2m_q}^{\omega_a^c} ds\sqrt{s^2 - 4m_q^2}[2m_q + s]e^{-s/T}$$

$$- < \bar{q}q > [1 - \frac{m_q}{2T} + \frac{m_q^2}{2T^2}] - \frac{< \frac{\alpha_s}{\pi}GG > m_q}{4T^2} \cdot$$

$$[0.077 - ln\frac{T}{\mu}] + \frac{g_s < \bar{q}\sigma Gq >}{4T^2} + \frac{4\pi\alpha_s}{81T^3} < \bar{q}q >^2 \cdot \quad (3)$$

Taking the derivative with respect to the inverse of T, one can obtain the corresponding sum rule for $\bar{\Lambda}_a$.

The Isgur-Wise function $\xi_a(v \cdot v', \mu)$ is defined by the matrix element at the leading order in $\frac{1}{m_Q}$ [3],

$$< M_a(v')|\bar{h}_{Q_2}(v')\Gamma h_{Q_1}(v)|M_a(v) > =$$
$$-\xi_a(v \cdot v', \mu)Tr[\bar{M}(v')\Gamma M(v)]. \quad (4)$$

In the same way as above, it is not difficult to get the sum rule for the Isgur-Wise function

$$\xi_a(y, \mu) = \frac{K(T, \omega_a^c, y)}{K(T, \omega_a^c, 1)}, \quad (5)$$

where

$$K(T, \omega_a^c, y) = \frac{3}{8\pi^2}(\frac{2}{1+y})^2 \int_{m_q\sqrt{2(1+y)}}^{\omega^c} d\alpha[\alpha + (1+y) \cdot$$

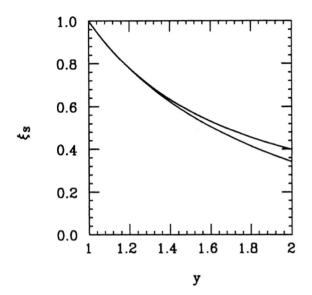

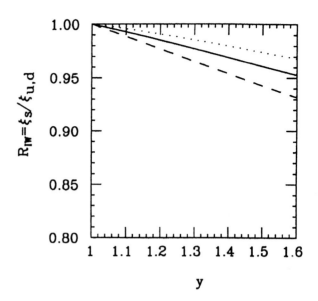

Figure 1. The Isgur-Wise function ξ_s as a function of y. The band corresponds to variations of ω_s^c in 1.8 GeV $\sim$ 2.4 GeV and T in 0.7 GeV $\sim$ 0.9 GeV.

Figure 2. The ratio $R_{IW} = \xi_s/\xi_{u,d}$ as a function of y at T=0.8 GeV ($\omega_s^c = \omega_{u,d}^c + 0.1$ GeV): Dashed line: $\omega_{u,d}^c = 1.7$ GeV, Solid line: $\omega_{u,d}^c = 2.0$ GeV, Dotted line: $\omega_{u,d}^c = 2.3$ GeV.

$$\cdot m_q]\sqrt{\alpha^2 - 2(1+y)m_q^2}\,e^{-\alpha/T} - <\bar{q}q>[1 - \frac{m_q}{2T}$$
$$+\frac{m_q^2}{4T^2}(1+y)] + <\frac{\alpha_s}{\pi}GG>[\frac{y-1}{48T(1+y)}$$
$$-\frac{m_q}{4T^2}(0.077 - \ln\frac{T}{\mu})] + \frac{g_s<\bar{q}\sigma Gq>}{4T^2}\frac{2y+1}{3} +$$
$$\frac{4\pi\alpha_s<\bar{q}q>^2}{81T^3}y. \tag{6}$$

In the above derivation, we have used the sum rule for $F_a(\mu)$.

In the numerical analysis of sum rules, we take the parameters such as condensates and m_q as in [3, 4] and set the scale $\mu = 1$ GeV. For the continuum model $\omega^c = \sigma(y)\omega_a^c$, we use the experiment preferred model $\sigma(y) = \frac{y+1}{2y}$ as in [3].

Evaluations of sum rules for F_a and $\bar{\Lambda}_a$ give

$$\bar{\Lambda}_s \simeq 0.62 \pm 0.07 GeV, \quad F_s \simeq 0.36 \pm 0.05 GeV^{3/2}, \tag{7}$$
$$\bar{\Lambda}_{u,d} \simeq 0.55 \pm 0.07 GeV, \quad F_{u,d} \simeq 0.32 \pm 0.05 GeV^{3/2}. \tag{8}$$

However, in order to reduce the errors, writing the mass difference $\Delta M = m_{M_s} - m_{M_{u,d}} = \bar{\Lambda}_s - \bar{\Lambda}_{u,d}$ and the ratio $R_F = F_s/F_{u,d}$ with the corresponding sum rules, one gets $\Delta M = 69 \pm 5$ MeV, which is in good agreement with the recent experiment results [5, 6] $m_{B_s} - m_B = 90 \pm 6$ MeV, $m_{D_s} - m_D = 99.5 \pm 0.6$ MeV, and the ratio $R_F = 1.13 \pm 0.01$.

In Fig.1, the Isgur-Wise function ξ_s is shown as a function of y. Obviously, the dependence on the parameters ω_s^c and T is very weak. At the center of the sum rule window T=0.8GeV, we obtain the slope parameter ϱ_a^2 defined as $\varrho_a^2 = -\xi_a'(y = 1, \mu)$

$$\varrho_s^2 = 1.09 \pm 0.04, \tag{9}$$

the uncertainty is due to the variation of ω_s^c. One can compare with

$$\varrho_{u,d}^2 = 1.01 \pm 0.02. \tag{10}$$

and find that SU(3) breaking effects in the slope parameter is not large but the important thing is

$$\varrho_s^2 > \varrho_{u,d}^2. \tag{11}$$

This result just indicates that the Isgur-Wise function ξ_s falls faster than the Isgur-Wise function $\xi_{u,d}$ as shown below.

In Fig.2, we show $R_{IW} = \xi_s/\xi_{u,d}$ as a function of y at $T = 0.8$ GeV for different $\omega_{u,d}^c = 1.7 \sim 2.3$ GeV and $\omega_s^c = \omega_{u,d}^c + 0.1$ GeV. One can find that the ratio R_{IW} displays a soft dependence on $\omega_{u,d,s}^c$. At $y = 1.6$ ($q^2 = 0$ for $B_{u,d} \to D_{u,d} + l\nu$), we get from the sum rule

$$R_{IW} \simeq (95 \pm 2)\%, \tag{12}$$

where the uncertainty is ascribed to the uncertainty in $\omega_{u,d,s}^c$ and T.

In the evaluations of sum rules for ξ_a and R_{IW}, the continuum model is chosen as $\sigma(y) = \frac{y+1}{2y}$. This may cause large errors in ξ_a and R_{IW}. As discussed in [3], one knows

$$\sigma_{min} = \frac{y+1-\sqrt{y^2-1}}{2} \le \sigma(y) \le \sigma_{max} = 1, \tag{13}$$

and the model σ_{max} and σ_{min} respectively constituents the upper bound and the lower bound for ξ_a. However, for R_{IW}, the model σ_{max} and σ_{min} just give the lower bound and the upper bound respectively. Although different continuum model gives different value for R_{IW}, one can find that all of these values clearly give

$$R_{IW} < 1 \quad , \quad \text{for } y \neq 1. \tag{14}$$

Therefore we conclude that $R_{IW} < 1$ (for $y \neq 1$) is independent of the model choice $\sigma(y)$.

In summary, it is very interesting to find that the Isgur-Wise function for $B_s \rightarrow D_s$ falls faster than the Isgur-Wise function for $B_{u,d} \rightarrow D_{u,d}$, which is just contrary to the prediction of the heavy meson chiral perturbation theory where only SU(3) breaking chiral loops are calculated [2]. Our result $R_{IW} \leq 1$ agrees with that of other calculations [7]. It is expected that the future experiments can test this result and reveal the underlying mechanism of SU(3) breaking effects.

References

[1] N.Isgur and M.B.Wise, Phys. Lett. **B232** (1989) 113; Phys. Lett. **237B** (1989) 527.
[2] E.Jenkins and M.J.Savage, Phys. Lett. **B281** (1992) 331.
[3] M.Neubert, Phys. Rev. **D45** (1992) 2451.
[4] T.Huang and C.W.Luo, BIHEP-TH-94-10 (hep-ph/9408303), to appear in Phys. Rev. **D50** (1994) No7.
[5] D.Buskulic et.al., Phys. Lett. **B311** (1993) 425.
[6] Particle Data Group, Phys. Rev. **D45** (1992) Part II.
[7] M.Neubert and V.Rieckert, Nucl. Phys. **B382** (1992) 97;
    F.Close, these Proceedings;
    J.Shigemitsu, these Proceedings.

Flavour Dependence of Form Factors in Heavy Meson Decays

F. E. Close

Rutherford Appleton Laboratory,
Chilton Didcot, Oxon OX11 0QX, Great Britain

Abstract

Recently we have shown that due account of Wigner spin rotations is needed to match the ISGW model consistently onto HQET. We now discuss the flavour dependence of this procedure. We find that for finite mass "heavy" quarks the universal function $\xi(y = 1) \approx 1$ but the slope is proportional to the energy of the spectator quarks, and ratios of form factors are corrected in a non-trivial way. Predictions for heavy quarks, such as in $B_c \to \psi(\eta_c)$ and to mixed systems, such as $D \to K$ and $B \to \pi$ show a systematic mass dependence that may be confronted with data.

The ISGW model [1] is widely used in describing heavy quark transition form factors at low (zero) recoil ($y = v \cdot v' \approx 1$). It describes the spectroscopy of heavy flavoured mesons in terms of quarks in a Coulomb plus linear potential and uses variational solutions to the Schrodinger equation based on harmonic oscillator wavefunctions. In recent works [2]–[6] we have shown that computation of current induced transition matrix elements in this model (and indeed any quark model) requires considerable care even when $M_Q \to \infty$, due to the nontrivial recoil and spin rotation structure for light spectator antiquark systems.

In ref [2] it was shown that that such quark models can be applied to electromagnetic and weak (semileptonic) transitions in a *limited region of phase space* and that consistency requires the transition amplitudes be calculated to $O(v^2/c^2)$ or [3] $O(v \cdot v' - 1)$. In particular it is important to keep account of the Wigner rotation of spins [7].

Many quark model calculations of form factors had historically been either inconsistent in their restriction to $O(v/c)$ and/or in their application to data in regions of phase space where the approximations of the model fail. Ref [2] showed that the Coulomb plus linear quark model with harmonic oscillator variational wavefunctions is empirically successful for light hadrons though only within a (very) limited range. In ref [4] we

applied these ideas to heavy-heavy transitions ($B \to D$) and found that when these Wigner rotations are consistently accounted for the ISGW extended model, with parameters determined from a fit to heavy flavour spectroscopy, describes dynamical transitions not just at zero recoil but also is consistent with the leading behaviour for non zero recoil.

As knowledge of the form factors in this limit is important in extrapolating to zero recoil (e.g. when extracting CKM matrix elements) it is natural to consider the implications of the above approach for the full range of heavy and light flavours[8]. Of particular interest will be the emerging data on the decay $B_c \to J/\Psi(\eta_c)e\nu$ where both active and spectator quarks are relatively heavy. Although $M_b \to \infty$ is still assumed, consistency requires that mass corrections for the c-quark are included, both in its role as active participant and, for the $\bar{c}$, as spectator. The explicit derivation of these corrections then provides us with a tool for calculating transition elements for $B \to D$, $D \to K$ and even $B \to \pi$ in a limited kinematic range.

In the zero–recoil frame

$$\langle P(v)|\Gamma_0|P(v)\rangle \; = \; 2v_0\xi_1(y = 1) \tag{1}$$

while for the pseudoscalar to vector meson transition:

$$\langle V(v',\epsilon)|A_\mu|P(v)\rangle = \rho_1(y)\epsilon_\mu^* +$$

$$\rho_2(y)(\epsilon^* \cdot v)v_\mu + \rho_3(y)(\epsilon^* \cdot v)v'_\mu$$

$$\langle V(v',\epsilon)|V_\mu|P(v)\rangle = i\eta(y)\epsilon_{\mu\alpha\beta\gamma}v^\alpha\epsilon^{*\beta}v'^\gamma \qquad (2)$$

In the ISGW model [1] variational solutions to the Schrödinger problem were found based on harmonic oscillator wavefunctions. The parameter in this gaussian wavefunction which was optimized by a fit to spectroscopy is the oscillator strength $\beta \equiv \sqrt{m\Delta E}$ for particle mass m with excitation energy ΔE. Empirically ΔE is approximately flavour independent [8].

In general the data behave in the following way: If HQET predicts a nonzero value for a form factor at a special point, i.e. the zero–recoil point, the modifications induced by mass effects are not significant. However, values which are not restricted by HQET (such as the slope of the form factor, coefficient of ϵ) do show a very strong dependence on the spectator quark mass; for example, the slope of ξ_1 turns out to be nearly proportional to the mass of the spectator quark. This finds its cause in the non–relativistic prediction, where $\rho^2 = \frac{m^2}{2\beta^2} = \frac{m}{2\Delta E}$, together with the empirical flavour independence of ΔE. Deviations to this linear dependence on the spectator quark mass are induced by relativistic effects.

In figure 1 we plot the form factor ξ_1 as a function of $(y-1)$ for different meson transitions in a limited range where ξ_1 exhibits a linear dependence in $(y-1)$. Note that the slopes for $B \to \pi$, $D \to K$ and $B \to D$ are approximately parallel, reflecting their common light spectator (anti)quark; $D_s \to \bar{s}s$ is analogously parallel to $B_s \to D_s$, though with a larger slope due to the heavier strange quark mass and $B_c \to \eta_c$ has the steepest slope due to the massive charmed spectator.

As noted already in ref[4], the consistent description of Wigner rotations and associated recoil effects played

a non-trivial role in this application and it was their neglect which was a reason why early application of the ISGW model appeared to fail. The quantitative role of these effects is rather sharply seen if one compares the predictions of (i) HQET   (ii) the ISGW naive model (iii) the ISGW model as applied here to the functions R_1 and R_2 which were proposed by Neubert [10] as a measure of symmetry breaking effects. They read (in our parametrization of the form factors):

$$R_1(y) = 2\frac{\eta(y)}{\rho_1(y)}\left(1 + \tfrac{1}{2}(y-1)\right)$$

$$R_2(y) = -2\frac{\rho_2(y)+r\rho_3(y)}{\rho_1(y)}\left(1 + \tfrac{1}{2}(y-1)\right) \qquad (3)$$

where $r = M_{D^*}/M_B$. In the HQET limit $R_1 = R_2 = 1$, however finite mass corrections as well as QCD correction terms modify this result.

In the ISGW model, the ratios $\eta(y)/\rho_1(y)$ and $(\rho_2(y) + r\rho_3(y))/\rho_1(y)$ are constant, so that the y dependences of R_1 and R_2 are that of the common factor $(1 + \tfrac{1}{2}(y-1))$.

In our computation the velocity dependence is more subtle. We find

$$R_1(y) = 1.15 - 0.07(y-1) + \mathrm{O}((y-1)^2)$$

$$R_2(y) = 0.91 + 0.04(y-1) + \mathrm{O}((y-1)^2) \qquad (4)$$

which in sign as well as in magnitude show the same behaviour as the estimates based on QCD sum rules, given in table III of [10] and updated in [9] and [11] which were determined to $O(1/m_Q)$:

$$R_1(y) = 1.23 - 0.19(y-1) + \mathrm{O}((y-1)^2)$$

$$R_2(y) = 0.79 + 0.15(y-1) + \mathrm{O}((y-1)^2) \qquad (5)$$

Note in particular that as $y \to 1$ the two approaches agree that $R_1(1) > 1$, $R_2(1) < 1$ and that $R_1(y > 1)$ decreases with y.

References

[1] N. Isgur, D. Scora, B. Grinstein, M. Wise, Phys. Rev. D39 (1989) 799
[2] F. E. Close and Z. Li, Phys. Rev. D42 (1990) 2194, ibid 2207
[3] F. E. Close and Z. Li, Phys. Lett. B289 (1992) 143
[4] F. E. Close and A. Wambach , Nucl. Phys. B412 (1994) 169
[5] A. Wambach, OUTP 93–28P, hep-ph 9312227
[6] A. Wambach, OUTP 94–01P, hep-ph 9403207, to appear in Z. Phys. C
[7] S. Brodsky and J. Primack, Ann.Phys 52 (1969) 315
[8] F. E. Close and A. Wambach RAL-94-041
[9] For a review see: M. Neubert, Heavy Quark Symmetry, SLAC-PUB-6263, hep–ph 9306320, to be published in Physics Reports
[10] M. Neubert, Phys. Rev. D46 (1992) 3914
[11] M. Neubert, private communication

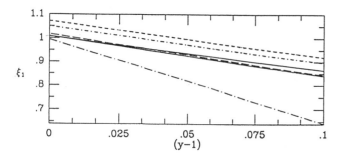

Figure 1. The form factor ξ_1 is plotted for different meson transitions. From top to bottom they are: $B \to \pi$ (short dash), $D \to K$ (dot – short dash), $D_s \to \bar{s}s$ (long dash), $B_s \to D_s$ (dotted), $B \to D$ (solid), $B_c \to \eta_c$ (dot – long dash)

Measurement of the Form Factors for $\overline{B^0} \to D^{*+} \ell^- \overline{\nu}$

R K Kutschke

Department of Physics, University of California
Santa Barbara, CA 93016, USA

Representing the CLEO Collaboration

Abstract

Using a sample of 2.2×10^6 $B\overline{B}$ pairs collected by the CLEO-II detector at the Cornell Electron Storage Ring, we have studied the form factors for the process $\overline{B^0} \to D^{*+} \ell^- \overline{\nu}$. We have obtained preliminary results for the form factor ratios, $R_1 = 1.30 \pm 0.36 \pm 0.16$ and $R_2 = 0.64 \pm 0.26 \pm 0.12$, and for the form factor slope, $\rho^2 = 1.01 \pm 0.15 \pm 0.09$.

The decay $B \to D^* \ell \nu$ is a key process for measuring the magnitude of the CKM matrix element V_{cb} and for testing theoretical predictions for form factors in semileptonic decays. This decay has a large branching fraction and very little background, which makes it well-suited, experimentally, for the detailed studies of the kinematic distributions that are required for the measurement of the form factors. This analysis is described in more detail elsewhere [1].

With the recent development of heavy quark effective theory (HQET) [2], there has been important progress in the theoretical understanding of the process $\overline{B^0} \to D^{*+} \ell^- \overline{\nu}$. HQET relates the three form factors $A_1(q^2)$, $V(q^2)$, and $A_2(q^2)$, that describe the decay $\overline{B^0} \to D^{*+} \ell^- \overline{\nu}$, to one form factor, the Isgur-Wise function, $\xi(q^2)$:

$$
\begin{aligned}
V(q^2) = A_2(q^2) &= A_1(q^2)\left[1 - \frac{q^2}{(m_B + m_{D^*})^2}\right]^{-1} \\
&= R^{*-1}\xi(q^2).
\end{aligned} \tag{1}
$$

Here q^2 is the invariant mass squared of the $\ell^- \overline{\nu}$ system and $R^* = 2\sqrt{m_B m_{D^*}}/(m_B + m_{D^*}) \approx 0.89$. In HQET, ξ is normally written as a function of of w,

$$
w = (m_B^2 + m_{D^*}^2 - q^2)/2m_B m_{D^*} = E_{D^*}/m_{D^*}. \tag{2}
$$

HQET cannot predict $\xi(w)$ over the full range of w, but it does predict the absolute normalization in the zero-recoil configuration, $\xi(w = 1) = 1$. In our fits we assume that the Isgur-Wise function has the form $\xi(w) = 1 - \rho^2(w - 1)$, where ρ^2 is called the slope of the Isgur-Wise function, or simply the form factor slope. The linear form is expected to be a good approximation over the range of w available in the decay $B \to D^* \ell \nu$.

Following Neubert [3], we define the form factor ratios

$$
R_1 \equiv \left[1 - \frac{q^2}{(m_B + m_{D^*})^2}\right] \frac{V(q^2)}{A_1(q^2)} \tag{3}
$$

$$
R_2 \equiv \left[1 - \frac{q^2}{(m_B + m_{D^*})^2}\right] \frac{A_2(q^2)}{A_1(q^2)}. \tag{4}
$$

These form factor ratios are slightly different from those used in studies of $D \to K^* \ell \nu$ and are defined in such a way that, in the limit of heavy-quark symmetry, they are constant. Moreover, in that limit, both form factor ratios are expected to be unity. The b and c quarks, however, are not infinitely heavy and corrections to the form factor ratios have been estimated by Neubert [3], who finds $R_1 \approx 1.3$ and $R_2 \approx 0.8$. Lattice QCD and QCD sum rules predict that ρ^2 falls in the range from 0.5 to 2.

In order to extract the three parameters R_1, R_2, and ρ^2, we perform a fit to the joint four-dimensional distribution of the four kinematic variables which describe for the decay chain $\overline{B^0} \to D^{*+} \ell^- \overline{\nu}$,

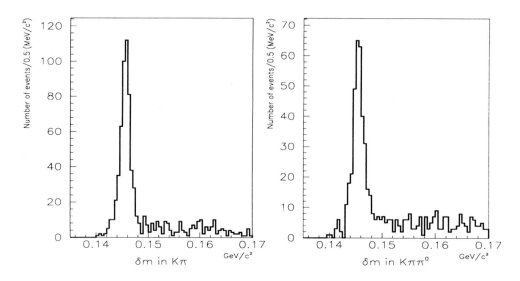

Figure 1. The distribution of $\delta m = M(D^{*+}) - M(D^0)$ for $D^0 \rightarrow K^-\pi^+$ candidates (left) and $D^0 \rightarrow K^-\pi^+\pi^0$ candidates (right) after all analysis cuts except the δm cut.

$D^{*+} \rightarrow D^0\pi^+$. These kinematic variables are q^2, $\cos\theta_\ell$, $\cos\theta_V$, and χ, where θ_ℓ is the lepton decay angle in the W rest frame, θ_V is the D^0 decay angle in the D^{*+} rest frame, and where χ is the azimuthal angle, in the $\overline{B^0}$ rest frame, between the decay planes of the D^{*+} and the W.

The D^* is reconstructed in the mode $D^{*+} \rightarrow D^0\pi^+$ with $D^0 \rightarrow K^-\pi^+$ or $D^0 \rightarrow K^-\pi^+\pi^0$. Lepton candidates are either electrons or muons. The $D^*\ell$ candidates are required to be kinematically consistent with coming from the decay $B \rightarrow D^*\ell\nu$, where the B meson is slow and a neutrino is missing. In order to minimize the uncertainty in the modeling of the backgrounds in the form factor fit, the cuts used in the analysis are designed to suppress the backgrounds strongly. For the two modes in which the D^0's are reconstructed, figure 1 shows the distribution of $\delta m = m_{D^0\pi^+} - m_{D^0}$, after all cuts except that on δm. The signal region in δm is ± 2 MeV/c^2 around the nominal value, which is approximately a 2σ cut. To study the background from fake D^*'s, which is the dominant background in both D^0 channels, we select combinations from the sideband region $0.15 < \delta m < 0.17$ GeV/c^2. After all event selection criteria are applied we have 783 events with a 16% background contamination.

We then fit the uncorrected, experimental joint four-dimensional distribution using an unbinned maximum likelihood fit. This distribution is modelled as the convolution of the true four-dimensional distribution with the full smearing and acceptance function of the detector. We use a method that was originally developed by the E691 collaboration in their measurement of the $D \rightarrow K^*\ell\nu$ form factor ratios.

Instead of parameterizing the smearing and acceptance of the detector, this method uses a technique of reweighting Monte Carlo events to evaluate the likelihood function numerically. In figure 2, the quality of the fit is shown in the four 1-dimensional projections. The plots show that the fit describes the data well in all four projections. The last plot, f), shows an example of a 2-dimensional projection, χ vs. $\cos\theta_V$. The dominant structure in this plot, the enhancement in the upper-left and lower-right quadrants and the depletion in the other two quadrants, is due to an interference term of the form $\sin\theta_V \cos\theta_V \cos\chi$. If parity were conserved in the decay $b \rightarrow cW$, the coefficient of this term would be zero. The observed structure is in agreement with the expectations from the standard model. If the $b \rightarrow c\ell\nu$ process had a $V + A$ coupling at the $b \rightarrow cW$ vertex, we would expect the pattern of enhanced and depleted regions to be reversed, which is in disagreement with the data. (The observed pattern is also consistent with the hypothesis that both the $b \rightarrow cW$ and the $W \rightarrow \ell\nu$ vertices have a $V + A$ coupling.)

Table 1 shows the result of the fit for R_1, R_2, and ρ^2. Since the errors on these quantities are highly correlated, we also present the off-diagonal elements of the correlation matrix. Several sources of systematic errors have been investigated. The dominant sources of systematic errors arise from the uncertainty in the modelling of backgrounds and from the fitting method itself. Our value of $\rho^2 = 1.01 \pm 0.15 \pm 0.09$ is in agreement with the measurement of $\hat{\rho}^2 = 0.84 \pm 0.13 \pm 0.08$, obtained as part of the CLEO measurement [4] of $|V_{cb}|$. Using the values of R_1 and R_2 reported above, Neubert [5] estimates that $\hat{\rho}^2 - \rho = -0.3 \pm 0.2$.

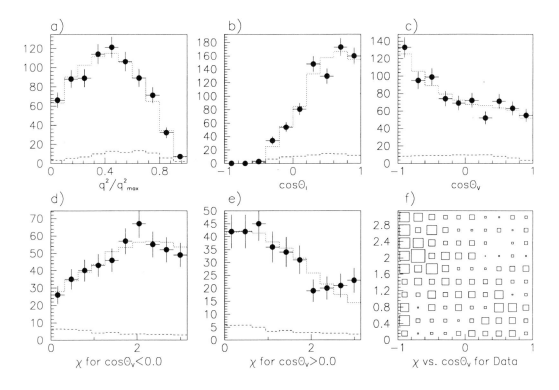

Figure 2. In plots a) through e), the data are shown with error bars, the full fit as the dotted line, and the contribution of the backgrounds as the dashed line. In a) through c), the one dimensional projections onto the q^2, $\cos\theta_\ell$, and $\cos\theta_V$ axes are shown. Plots d) and e) show the projection onto the χ axis for low and high values of $\cos\theta_V$. The two-dimensional projection of the experimental data onto the plane χ vs. $\cos\theta_V$ is shown in f); the density of points is proportional to the size of the boxes.

	Fit Parameters	Correlation Coefficients	
R_1	$1.30 \pm 0.36 \pm 0.16$	$C(R_1 R_2)$	-0.83
R_2	$0.64 \pm 0.26 \pm 0.12$	$C(R_1 \rho^2)$	0.63
ρ^2	$1.01 \pm 0.15 \pm 0.09$	$C(R_2 \rho^2)$	-0.82

Table 1. The preliminary result of the three parameter fit. The first error is statistical and the second is systematic.

ρ^2	R_1	R_2	$C(R_1 R_2)$
0.50	$0.77 \pm 0.21 \pm 0.16$	$1.11 \pm 0.10 \pm 0.10$	-0.67
0.75	$0.99 \pm 0.24 \pm 0.16$	$0.93 \pm 0.12 \pm 0.10$	-0.68
1.00	$1.29 \pm 0.27 \pm 0.16$	$0.65 \pm 0.15 \pm 0.10$	-0.73
1.25	$1.75 \pm 0.34 \pm 0.17$	$0.20 \pm 0.20 \pm 0.11$	-0.77

Table 2. The preliminary results of the two parameter fits for different slopes, ρ^2. The first error is statistical and the second is systematic. The correlation, $C(R_1 R_2)$, between the errors on R_1 and R_2 is strong.

Table 2 shows the results from a series of fits for R_1 and R_2, in which the slope, ρ^2, was fixed to a series of values. If theoretical calculations of ρ^2 become sufficiently precise, this table shows the

expected improvement in the precision with which the form factor ratios, especially R_2, will be known.

In conclusion, we have performed the first simultaneous measurement of R_1, R_2, and ρ^2 for the decay $\overline{B^0} \to D^{*+}\ell^-\overline{\nu}$. We make a precise measurement of ρ^2, even with R_1 and R_2 floating. The measurements of R_1 and R_2 are in agreement with the predictions of heavy-quark symmetry and in slightly better agreement with the estimated corrections to this limit. The measurement of ρ^2 is within the range of predictions from lattice QCD and QCD sum rules.

References

[1] P. Avery *et al.* (CLEO), *Measurement of the Form Factors for $\overline{B^0} \to D^{*+}\ell^-\overline{\nu}$*, ICHEP94 paper GLS0144, 1994.

[2] N. Isgur and M.B. Wise, Phys. Lett. B **232**, 113 (1989); **237**, 527 (1990); H. Georgi, Phys. Lett. B **240**, 447 (1990).

[3] M. Neubert, *Heavy Quark Symmetry*, SLAC–PUB–6263, June 1993, to appear in Physics Reports.

[4] B. Barish *et al.* (CLEO), *Measurement of the $B \to D^*\ell\nu$ Branching Fractions and $|V_{cb}|$*, CLEO Preprint CLNS 94/1285. ICHEP94 paper GLS0251, 1994.

[5] M. Neubert, *Theoretical Update on the Model-Independent Determination of $|V_{cb}|$ Using Heavy Quark Symmetry*, Preprint CERN-TH 7395/94, hep-ph/9408290, 1994.

Measurement of the Branching Ratio for $B \to D^* l \nu$ and V_{cb}

T.E. Browder[†,*]

† Department of Physics, University of Hawaii, Honolulu, HI 96822, U.S.A.

On behalf of the CLEO Collaboration

Abstract

Using data collected by the CLEO II experiment at the Cornell Electron Storage Ring (CESR), the branching ratio for the reaction $B \to D^* l \nu$ is determined. We find $\mathcal{B}(\bar{B}^0 \to D^{*+} l \nu) = 4.49 \pm 0.32 \pm 0.39\%$ and $\mathcal{B}(B^- \to D^{*0} l \nu) = 5.13 \pm 0.54 \pm 0.64\%$ assuming equal production of $B^+ B^-$ and $B^0 \bar{B}^0$ meson pairs at the $\Upsilon(4S)$ resonance. This assumption concerning production is also tested and found to be valid. The branching ratio measurements can be used to determine model dependent values of $|V_{cb}|$. Using measurements of the differential spectrum for this decay, and a method inspired by heavy quark effective theory (HQET), a value for the KM matrix element V_{cb} is determined with minimal model dependence. The value obtained is $|V_{cb}| \xi(1) \eta_A = 0.0351 \pm 0.0019 \pm 0.0018 \pm 0.008$, where $\xi(1)$ is the value of the universal form factor at zero recoil and η_A is a factor (close to unity) which accounts for QCD corrections. Systematic effects and the small model dependence in the final value of V_{cb} are discussed.

1. Introduction

The determination of Cabibbo-Kobayashi-Maskawa matrix elements is one of the central experimental problems in heavy quark physics. The element V_{cb} is the focus of study in this report. This element can be determined from measurements of the branching ratio for inclusive semileptonic decays, as discussed in the contribution of N. Katayama, or from measurements of exclusive semileptonic B decay modes. The measurements of the inclusive semileptonic branching ratio are now quite precise with experimental uncertainty below ($\sim$ 5%) however the conversion of the resulting semileptonic width to $|V_{cb}|$ has a fairly large theoretical uncertainty. Estimates of this uncertainty range from 5% to 20%. By constrast, it is widely believed that measurements of exclusive semileptonic modes can be used to extract $|V_{cb}|$ with smaller theoretical uncertainty. The mode $B \to D^* l \nu$ is preferred experimentally to the mode $B \to D l \nu$ since

the addition of the D^* constraint allows the isolation of a large and clean experimental signal. CLEO II can observe clean signals in both $\bar{B}^0 \to D^{*+} l^- \nu$ and $B^- \to D^{*0} l^- \nu$ with $D^* \to D^0 \pi$ and $D^0 \to K^- \pi^+$. The pion from the D^* has a momentum below 225 MeV in the laboratory and is referred to as the slow pion (or π_s).

2. Determination of the $B \to D^* l \nu$ Branching Ratios

A data sample with an integrated luminosity of 1.55 fb^{-1} recorded on the $\Upsilon(4S)$ resonance is used to obtain the signal. In the decay of the $\Upsilon(4S)$ resonance, B mesons are produced in pairs with momenta of about 330 MeV. The signal is isolated using the kinematic constraints from production at threshold. The effective mass of the neutrino in the decay $B \to D^* l \nu$ is given by

$$m_\nu^2 = (E_B - E_{D^* l})^2 - |p_B|^2 - |P_{D^* l}|^2 + 2|p_B||p_{D^* L}|\cos\Theta$$

* E-mail: teb@uhhepj.phys.hawaii.edu

where (E_B, p_B) is the B meson 4-momentum, (E_{D*l}, p_{D*l}) is the sum of the $D*$ and lepton 4-momenta, and Θ is the angle between the 3-momenta p_{D*l} and p_B. The first three terms in the expression for m_ν^2 are the missing mass squared, denoted MM^2. The factor multiplying $\cos\Theta$ will be denoted C. For lepton momenta above 1.4 GeV, correctly reconstructed $B \to D*l\nu$ decays must lie in a triangular region in the plane of MM^2 and C. A cut on the $D* - D$ mass difference is imposed, and the D^0 invariant mass spectrum (shown in Figure 1) is fitted to extract the number of B candidates. The largest background is due to combinations of fake $D*$s and real leptons. This background is subtracted using the sidebands of the $D* - D$ mass difference. There is also a small background from random combinations of real $D*$s and leptons which can be estimated from data. A small correction for background from non-resonant processes (continuum) and misidentified leptons is also included. The resulting signal yield is due to $B \to D*(X)l\nu$ events. After removing all backgrounds, we find $376 \pm 27 \pm 16$ $\bar{B}^0 \to D*+l^-\nu$ events and $302 \pm 32 \pm 13$ $B^- \to D*^0l^-\nu$ events.

Unlike collider experiments, the background from $B \to D**l\nu \to D*(\pi)l\nu$ where the (π) from the $D**$ decay is not detected is small. This background is determined by examining $D*$ lepton combinations with p(lepton) in the range $0.8 - 1.4$ GeV in the portion of $C\text{-}MM^2$ plane which is preferentially populated by $B \to D**l\nu$ decays. We find a modest excess in this region which corresponds to an upper limit of $\mathcal{B}(B \to D**l\nu) < 2.8\%$ at the 95 % confidence level.

Assuming equal production of charged and neutral B meson pairs at the $\Upsilon(4S)$ resonance, and using the CLEO II D and $D*$ branching fractions, we obtain $\mathcal{B}(\bar{B}^0 \to D*+l\nu) = 4.49 \pm 0.32 \pm 0.39\%$ and $\mathcal{B}(B^- \to D*^0l\nu) = 5.13 \pm 0.54 \pm 0.64\%$. The dominant systematic error is due to the uncertainty in the slow pion detection efficiencies.

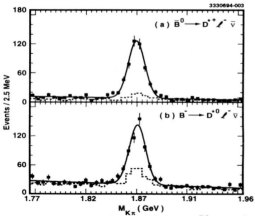

3330694-003

Figure 1. The $M_{K^-\pi^+}$ mass distributions for a) $\bar{B}^0 \to D*+l^-\nu$ and for b) $B^- \to D*^0l^-\nu$

By comparing the branching ratios for $\bar{B}) \to D*+l^-\nu$ and $B^- \to D*^0l^-\nu$ and using measurements of the ratio of lifetimes from collider experiments, we find that f_{+-}/f_{00} the ratio of the production of B^+B^- and $B^0\bar{B}^0$ meson pairs at the $\Upsilon(4S)$ resonance is $f_{+-}/f_{00} = 1.04 \pm 0.13(stat) \pm 0.12(sys) \pm 0.10$ (lifetime ratio). This confirms to an accuracy of about 15% the initial assumption that the production of charged and neutral B meson pairs are equal. The small value of the $B^+ - B^0$ mass difference, 0.2 ± 0.3 MeV, also supports this conclusion[2].

Using measurements of the B^+ and B^0 lifetimes, and the assumption of isospin invariance, we can combine the two branching fraction measurements to obtain the width $\Gamma(B \to D*l\nu) = [29.9 \pm 1.9 \pm 2.7 \pm 2.0]$ ns $^{-1}$. This can be translated into a value for $|V_{cb}|$ using the models of Isgur, Scora, Grinstein and Wise (ISGW), Bauer, Stech and Wirbel (BSW), Korner and Schuler (KS) or Neubert. The values obtained for $|V_{cb}|$ are: $0.0348 \pm 0.0011 \pm 0.0016$, $0.0375 \pm 0.0012 \pm 0.0017$, $0.0344 \pm 0.0011 \pm 0.0015$ and $0.0322 \pm 0.0010 \pm 0.0014$ respectively. The detection efficiencies have be determined separately for each model. The variation from this source is about 3%.

3. Extraction of V_{cb} from Differential Decay Spectrum

In the Heavy Quark Effective Theory (HQET), the decay rate for $B \to D*l\nu$ as a function of y (which is $\gamma_D^* = E_{D*}/m_{D*}$ in the B rest frame) can be expressed in terms of a single unknown form factor $\xi(y)$. According to the celebrated result called Luke's theorem [5], at the point of zero recoil for the $D*$ meson (i.e. $y = 1$), this universal form factor is absolutely normalized up to corrections of order $1/m_Q^2$ (where m_Q is the c quark or b quark mass).

The decay rate

$$d\Gamma/dy = \mathcal{G}(y)\eta_A^2|V_{cb}|^2\xi^2(y) \qquad (1)$$

where $\mathcal{G}(y)$ is a known function, $\eta_A = 0.986 \pm 0.006$ accounts for QCD corrections and $\xi(y)$ is the universal form factor. After subtracting background and and correcting for efficiency the experimental distribution of $d\Gamma/dy$ is divided by the factor $\mathcal{G}(y)$ to give a distribution whose intercept is $|V_{cb}|^2\xi^2(1)$. In the limit of heavy quark symmetry, the intercept is the physical quantity of interest, $|V_{cb}|^2$. In principle, the value obtained in this manner has no model dependence.

The $d\Gamma/dy$ distribution is extracted after subtracting backgrounds from fake $D*$ and random $D*$ lepton combinations. This distribution is then corrected for efficiency. After dividing through by $\mathcal{G}(\dagger)$ we obtain the distribution shown in Figure 2. Experimentally, since we have poor statistics at the point of zero recoil, we use the available data over the entire y range and extrapolate to $y = 1$. Most of the functional forms proposed for $\xi(y)$ are roughly linear near $y = 1$. Thus the experimental distribution is fitted to the functional form $|V_{cb}|^2(1 - \hat{\rho}^2(y - 1))$. After properly accounting for the smearing in y due to the motion of the B meson[3], we obtain:

$$|V_{cb}|\xi(1)\eta_A = 0.0351 \pm 0.0019 \pm 0.0018 \pm 0.008 \quad (2)$$

The first error is statistical. The second error is the experimental systematic uncertainty. The dominant experimental systematic error is the uncertainty in the slow pion detection efficiencies. There is also a significant error from the uncertainty in high energy measurements of the B meson lifetimes which is the third error quoted.

There are two significant uncertainties in the final determination of $|V_{cb}|$. These arise from the model dependence in the calculation of the $1/m_c^2$ corrections to $\xi(1)$ and the lack of knowledge of the functional form of the function $\xi(y)$ which is used for the extrapolation. There are now four calculations of $\xi(1)$ to order $1/m_c^2$ from Neubert [7],[8], Mannel[9] and from Shifman, Uraltsev and Vainshtein[10]. For example, using $\xi(1)\eta_A = 0.97 \pm 0.04$ from Neubert, we obtain $|V_{cb}| = 0.0362 \pm 0.0019 \pm 0.0020 \pm 0.0014$ where the first error is statistical, the second is experimental systematic and the third is error from the quoted uncertainty in $\xi(1)$. Other recent estimates of this product obtained using QCD sum rules are 0.93 ± 0.03[8], 0.96 ± 0.03[9], and 0.89 ± 0.03[10]. The model dependence from the normalization is about 7% but may be reduced in the near future.

We have investigated the uncertainty in the shape of $\xi(y)$ using many of the functional forms proposed in the literature[4]. We find the systematic error from this source is less than 5% in $|V_{cb}|$.

We note that the values of the form factor intercepts obtained by CLEO are consistent with heavy quark symmetry (HQS) at the present level of experimental precision. This supports the hypothesis that deviations from HQS are small.

4. Slope of $\xi(y)$

The universal form factor $\xi(y)$ is a quantity which cannot be derived in pertubation theory. To obtain this function, we must depend on models or on lattice calculations. From the fit to $d\Gamma/dy$ with a linear form, we obtain

$$\hat{\rho}^2 = 0.84 \pm 0.12 \pm 0.08 \quad (3)$$

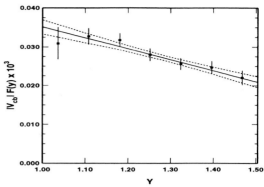

Figure 2. $d\Gamma/dy$ distribution corrected for detection efficiency and kinematic factors.

A fit using a quadratic form for $\xi(y)$ gives slightly different results for $\hat{\rho}^2$. The magnitude of the quadratic term is very poorly determined. The value of $\hat{\rho}^2$ is consistent with most quark models, QCD sum rules, and with lattice calculations.

Note that the quantity $\hat{\rho}^2$ and the quantity ρ^2 discussed in the contribution of Kutschke are slightly different. The former is calculated assuming HQS. An approximate relation between the two values is $\hat{\rho}^2 \approx \rho^2 - 0.1$. The two values agree well.

5. Acknowledgements

I would like to thank Daniela Bortoletto, Persis Drell, Arne Freyberger, Xu Fu, and Maurice Garcia-Sciveres for their contributions to the work described here. I also thank David Cassel, Jeff Richman, and Anders Ryd for informative discussions.

References

[1] B. Barish et al., *Measurement of the $B \to D^*l\nu$ Branching Fractions and V_{cb}*, Cornell preprint CLNS 94/1285, submitted to Physical Review D.

[2] T.E. Browder, K. Honscheid, and S. Playfer, CLNS 93/1261, contribution to B Decays (ed. S. Stone) World Scientfic, 1994.

[3] M. Garcia Sciveres, Ph.D. Thesis, Cornell University 1994 (unpublished).

[4] X. Fu, Ph.D. Thesis, University of Oklahoma 1995 (unpublished).

[5] M.E. Luke, Phys. Lett. B 252, 447 (1990).

[6] The known quantity $\mathcal{G}(y)$ is given by

$$\frac{G_F^2}{48\pi^3}m_{D^*}^3(m_B - m_{D^*})^2$$

$$\times \sqrt{y^2 - 1}[4y(y+1)\frac{1 - 2yr + r^2}{(1-r)^2} + (y+1)^2]$$

where $r = m_{D^*}/m_B$.

[7] M. Neubert, SLAC report No. SLAC-PUB-6263 to appear in Physics Reports.

[8] M. Neubert, CERN report CERN-TH.7395/94, submitted to Physics Letters B.

[9] T. Mannel, Phys. Rev. **D50** (1994) 428.

[10] M. Shifman, N. Uraltsev, and A. Vainshtein, University of Minnesota report No. TPI-MINN-94/13-T.

A Measurement of $|V_{cb}|$ from $\overline{B}^0 \to D^{*+}\ell^-\overline{\nu}_\ell$

Ian J. Scott[†‡]

† Physics Dept., University of Wisconsin, Madison, Wisconsin 53706, USA

ALEPH collaboration

Abstract

In a sample of approximately 1.6 million hadronic decays of Z bosons recorded with the ALEPH detector at LEP, $\overline{B} \to D^{*+}\ell^- X$ candidates have been identified. From this sample, the differential width $d\Gamma(\overline{B}^0 \to D^{*+}\ell^-\overline{\nu}_\ell)/dq^2$ has been measured. From a fit to this spectrum the product of the CKM matrix element $|V_{cb}|$ and the normalization of the decay form factor at the point of zero recoil of the D* meson $\mathcal{F}(1)$ has been measured to be

$$\mathcal{F}(1)|V_{cb}| = (36.4 \pm 4.2_{stat} \pm 3.1_{syst}) \times 10^{-3}.$$

A value for $|V_{cb}|$ has been extracted using theoretical calculations of the form factor normalization.

1. Introduction

Recent developments in Heavy Quark Effective Theory (HQET) have raised hopes for a precise and a model-independent measurement of $|V_{cb}|$ using exclusive decays such as $\overline{B}^0 \to D^{*+}\ell^-\overline{\nu}_\ell$ (For a review, see for example [2] and references therein). The expression for the differential partial width is [3]:

$$
\begin{aligned}
\frac{d\Gamma}{dy} &= \frac{1}{\tau_{B^0}} \frac{d\mathcal{B}(\overline{B}^0 \to D^{*+}\ell^-\overline{\nu}_\ell)}{dy} \\
&= \frac{G_F^2}{48\pi^3\hbar} m_{D^{*+}}^3 (m_{B^0} - m_{D^{*+}})^2 \mathcal{F}^2(y)|V_{cb}|^2 \\
&\times \sqrt{y^2 - 1} \\
&\times \left[4y(y+1)\frac{1 - 2yr + r^2}{(1-r)^2} + (y+1)^2 \right], \quad (1)
\end{aligned}
$$

where $r = m_{D^{*+}}/m_{B^0}$ and

$$y = \frac{m_{B^0}^2 + m_{D^{*+}}^2 - q^2}{2m_{B^0}m_{D^{*+}}}.$$

‡ E-mail: VXCERN::IJSCOTT
§ This analysis is described in more detail in [1].

The variable q^2 is the square of the four-momentum transfer in the decay. The unknown quantities in this expression are $|V_{cb}|$ and $\mathcal{F}(y)$. The function $\mathcal{F}(y)$ is not specified by HQET but its magnitude at maximum q^2 ($y = 1$) is normalized to one in the heavy quark limit. While the QCD corrections can be estimated at this point, the experimental data are statistically deficient due to the vanishing rate. Consequently, $|V_{cb}|$ is presently measured from the $d\Gamma/dy$ spectrum by an extrapolation to $y = 1$.

So far all such measurements of $|V_{cb}|$ have come from the ARGUS and CLEO experiments at the $\Upsilon(4S)$ resonance where the B mesons are produced with momentum of 325 MeV [3, 4]. At maximum q^2 the D*⁺ are produced at rest and subsequently decay into a D meson and a pion with momentum of about 40 MeV and can only be reconstructed with substantially reduced efficiency. In contrast, at the Z resonance, the B hadrons are produced with a large boost ($\beta\gamma \approx 6$). Consequently, the pion from the D*⁺ decay has a typical momentum of about 1 GeV. This feature of B meson production at the Z resonance allows access to the entire $d\Gamma/dy$ spectrum in

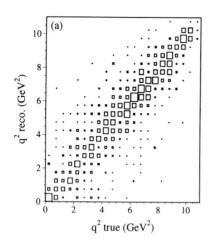

Figure 1. Monte Carlo simulation of the reconstructed q^2 vs. the input q^2 for $\overline{\text{B}}^0 \to \text{D}^{*+}\ell^-\overline{\nu}_\ell$ events.

$\overline{\text{B}}^0 \to \text{D}^{*+}\ell^-\overline{\nu}_\ell$ decays with approximately equal (and high) efficiency.

2. q^2 Reconstruction

Equation 2 expresses the q^2 in terms of the neutrino energy E_ν and the angle ϕ between the planes formed by the D* and the lepton and by the B and the neutrino:

$$
\begin{aligned}
q^2 &= m_\ell^2 + p_\ell \cos\theta_\ell (M_\text{B}^2 - m^2)/P \\
&+ 2E_\nu \left(E_\ell - p_\ell \cos\theta_\ell E/P \right) \\
&+ 2p_\ell \sin\theta_\ell E_\nu \sin\theta_\nu \cos\phi \, ,
\end{aligned} \tag{2}
$$

where m, P, and E are the mass, momentum and energy of the reconstructed D$^{*+}\ell^-$ and M_B is the B meson mass. The variables θ_ℓ and θ_ν are respectively the opening angles of the lepton and the neutrino with respect to the axis defined by the D$^{*+}\ell^-$ system. The variable θ_ν can be expressed as a function of E_ν, which is estimated from the center of mass energy and the visible energy in the hemisphere containing the D$^{*+}\ell^-$ candidate. The angle ϕ is calculated from the B-meson direction as measured by the production and decay vertices. Figure 1 shows a Monte Carlo simulation of the reconstructed q^2 resolution [5]. The resolution is approximately $1.4\,\text{GeV}^2$, which corresponds to about 13% of the allowed q^2 range.

The opening angle θ_B between the reconstructed B meson direction and the D$^{*+}\ell^-$ direction can be used in conjunction with the measured neutrino energy to reconstruct the missing squared mass MM^2 of the system recoiling against the D$^{*+}\ell^-$:

$$
MM^2 = M_\text{B}^2 + m^2 - 2\left(E + E_\nu \right)\left(E - \beta P \cos\theta_\text{B} \right) ,
$$

Channel	Branching Ratio	Reference
$\mathcal{B}(b \to \overline{\text{B}}^0)$	37±3%	[6]
$\mathcal{B}(\text{B}^- \to \text{D}^{*+}\pi^-\ell^-\overline{\nu})$	0.36±0.12%	[1]
$\mathcal{B}(\overline{\text{B}} \to \text{D}^{*+}X_c, X_c \to \ell^-\overline{\nu}Y)$	0.32±0.06%	[1]
$\mathcal{B}(\overline{\text{B}}^0 \to \text{D}^{*+}\tau^-\overline{\nu}_\tau)$	2.34±0.39%	[1]
$\mathcal{B}(\text{D}^{*+} \to \text{D}^0\pi^+)$	68.1±1.3%	[7]
$\mathcal{B}(\text{D}^0 \to \text{K}^-\pi^+)$	4.01±0.14%	[7]
$\mathcal{B}(\text{D}^0 \to \text{K}^-\pi^+\pi^-\pi^+)$	8.1±0.5%	[7]
$\mathcal{B}(\text{D}^0 \to \text{K}^0_\text{S}\pi^+\pi^-)$	1.8±0.2%	[7]
$\times\mathcal{B}(\text{K}^0_\text{S} \to \pi^+\pi^-)$		

Table 1. Summary of the branching fractions used in this analysis.

where $\beta = \sqrt{1 - 1/\gamma^2}$ and $\gamma = (E + E_\nu)/M_\text{B}$. This is useful in rejecting background with additional particles coming from the B decay vertex.

3.   Event Selection and Sample Composition

The decay $\overline{\text{B}} \to \text{D}^{*+}\ell^-\overline{\nu}X$ was identified in events where a D^{*+} and a lepton were found in the same hemisphere of a hadronic Z decay. The D^{*+} candidates were reconstructed in the channel D$^{*+} \to \text{D}^0\pi^+$. The D^0 candidates were reconstructed in three decay modes; D$^0 \to \text{K}^-\pi^+$, D$^0 \to \text{K}^-\pi^+\pi^-\pi^+$ and D$^0 \to \text{K}^0_\text{S}\pi^+\pi^-$.

In order to suppress background events with extra particles originating from the B-hadron decay vertex (e.g. $\overline{\text{B}} \to \text{D}^{*+}\pi\ell^-\overline{\nu}$), additional event selection criteria were applied. In candidate events, tracks consistent within three standard deviations with the reconstructed D$^{*+}\ell^-$ vertex and having the same charge as the lepton candidate were identified. Events containing at least one such track were rejected. Furthermore, the reconstructed missing mass squared in the event was required to be less than $1\,\text{GeV}^2$. Finally, as the measurement precision of the B meson direction improves with the decay length, candidates were rejected if the D$^{*+}\ell^-$ vertex was less than 1 mm away from the interaction point. The selection results in a sample of 190±14 D$^{*+}\ell^-$ candidates with an estimated background of 35±6.

Table 3 lists the branching ratios used in this analysis, and Fig. 2 shows the reconstructed q^2 spectrum and the expected background.

4.   Measurement of $|V_{\text{cb}}|$

A binned χ^2 fit was performed to the background subtracted q^2 spectrum. The fitting function is given in Eq. 1, with the following assumed functional form for $\mathcal{F}(y)$ [3]:

$$
\mathcal{F}(y) = \mathcal{F}(1)(1 + a^2(1 - y)) .
$$

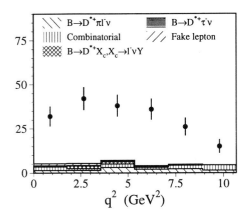

Figure 2. The reconstructed q^2 of events with estimated background.

The two free parameters in the fit are $\mathcal{F}(1)|V_{cb}|$ and a^2. The fit takes into account both resolution and efficiency as determined from a Monte Carlo simulation [5].

The fit gives a result of

$$|V_{cb}|\mathcal{F}(1)\sqrt{\tau_{B^0}/1.5\,\text{ps}} = (37.7 \pm 4.3) \times 10^{-3}$$
$$a^2 = 0.46 \pm 0.30 \,,$$

where the errors are statistical only. The χ^2 of the fit is 1.6 for 4 degrees of freedom.

The measured B^0 lifetime of $\tau_{B^0} = 1.61 \pm 0.09\,\text{ps}$ [8] is used to obtain

$$|V_{cb}|\mathcal{F}(1) = (36.4 \pm 4.2_{\text{stat}} \pm 1.0_{\text{lifetime}}) \times 10^{-3} \,,$$

where the first error is statistical and the second error is due to the lifetime uncertainty.

Using $\mathcal{F}(1) = 0.93 \pm 0.03$ [9] we obtain

$$|V_{cb}| = (39.1 \pm 4.5_{\text{stat}} \pm 1.1_{\text{lifetime}} \pm 1.3_{\text{theory}}) \times 10^{-3} \,,$$

where the the third error is the quoted theoretical uncertainty in $\mathcal{F}(1)$.

Plotting the reconstructed q^2 spectrum as a function of y and factoring out known q^2 dependent terms, a graph can be made where the intercept at $y = 1$ is given by $\mathcal{F}(1)|V_{cb}|$ and the slope is a^2. In practice finite q^2 resolution distorts the shape, destroying the simple interpretation. The graph does provide a qualitative description of the data, as is shown in Fig. 3.

The background-subtracted data sample can also be used to extract a measurement of $\mathcal{B}(\overline{B}^0 \to D^{*+}\ell^-\overline{\nu}_\ell)$:

$$\mathcal{B}(\overline{B}^0 \to D^{*+}\ell^-\overline{\nu}_\ell) = (5.07 \pm 0.48)\% \,,$$

where the quoted error is statistical only.

5. Systematic Uncertainties and Summary

Uncertainties due to branching ratios and the B^0 lifetime are determined from the effect of varying

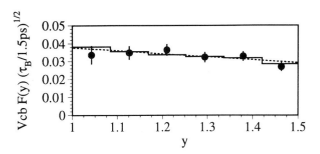

Figure 3. $|V_{cb}|\mathcal{F}(y)\,(\tau_{B^0}/1.5\,\text{ps})^{1/2}$ vs. the reconstructed y. See text for details. The solid curve is the fit. The dashed curve is the fitted function without taking into account resolution.

Source	$\Delta\mathcal{B}/\mathcal{B}$	$\Delta|V_{cb}|/|V_{cb}|$	Δa^2
$\mathcal{B}(b \to B^0)$	8.2%	4.1%	–
$\mathcal{B}(\overline{B} \to D^{*+}\pi\ell^-\overline{\nu})$	3.0%	2.4%	0.03
$\mathcal{B}(D^{*+} \to D^0\pi^+)$	1.9%	1.0%	–
$\mathcal{B}(D^0 \to K^-\pi^+)$	1.4%	0.7%	–
$\mathcal{B}(D^0 \to K^-\pi^+\pi^-\pi^+)$	3.4%	1.7%	–
$\mathcal{B}(D^0 \to K_S^0\pi^+\pi^-)$	0.6%	0.3%	–
τ_{B^0}	–	2.8%	–
Absolute efficiency	10%	5%	–
Efficiency shape	–	3.6%	0.13
Total	13.9%	8.5%	0.13

Table 2. Summary of systematic uncertainties.

the values within quoted errors. The error on the absolute efficiency is the estimated from the statistical uncertainty due to the finite Monte Carlo sample. The systematic uncertainties are summarized in Table 2.

Including the systematic uncertainties, the following quantities have been measured:

$$\mathcal{B}(\overline{B}^0 \to D^{*+}\ell^-\overline{\nu}_\ell) = (5.07 \pm 0.48_{\text{stat}} \pm 0.70_{\text{syst}})\%$$
$$\mathcal{F}(1)|V_{cb}| = (36.4 \pm 4.2_{\text{stat}} \pm 3.1_{\text{syst}}) \times 10^{-3}$$
$$|V_{cb}| = (39.1 \pm 4.5_{\text{stat}} \pm 3.3_{\text{syst}} \pm 1.3_{\text{theo}}) \times 10^{-3}$$
$$a^2 = 0.46 \pm 0.30_{\text{stat}} \pm 0.13_{\text{syst}} \,.$$

References

[1] ALEPH Collab.: D. Decamp *et al.*, **GLS0605**. Submitted paper to ICHEP94.

[2] M. Neubert, SLAC preprint: SLAC-PUB-6263 (1993).

[3] CLEO Collab.: B. Barish *et al.*, preprint CLNS 94/1285.

[4] ARGUS Collab.: H. Albrecht *et al.*, Z. Phys. C **57** (1993) 533.

[5] Throughout this analysis, JETSET 7.3 program was used to generate $Z \to q\overline{q}$ events. T. Sjöstrand and M. Bengtsson, Comp. Phys. Com. **46**, (1987) 43.

[6] ALEPH Collab.: D. Decamp *et al.*, Phys. Lett. B **322** (1992) 441.

[7] Particle Data Group: K. Hikasa *et al.* Phys. Rev. D **50** (1994).

[8] P. Roudeau, these proceedings.

[9] M. Neubert, CERN preprint CERN-TH.7395/94

$|V_{cb}|$ from OPE Sum Rules for Heavy Flavor Transitions

Mikhail Shifman

Theoretical Physics Institute, University of Minnesota, Minneapolis, MN 55455, USA

Abstract

Recent progress on the determination of $|V_{cb}|$ within the heavy quark expansion is reported. Both exclusive and exclusive approaches are discussed.

1. Introduction

The main topic today is determination of V_{cb}, the CKM matrix element. We have just heard two experimental talks devoted to measurements of this fundamental parameter. My aim is to discuss the theoretical basis.

Two basic methods allowing one to determine V_{cb} from experimental data exist at present: exclusive and inclusive. In the first case one studies the exclusive $B \to D^* l\nu$ decays selecting slow D^*'s (the so called small velocity or SV limit). Extrapolation of the amplitude to the point of zero recoil yields $|V_{cb}|F_{B\to D^*}$(zero recoil), where $F_{B\to D^*}$ is an effective $B \to D^*$ transition form factor. In the SV limit this form factor is close to unity as a consequence of the heavy quark symmetry [1, 2]; deviations from unity are quadratic in the inverse heavy quark mass, $1/m_{b,c}^2$ [2, 3]. The task of the theorists is to calculate these deviations.

In the inclusive approach one deals with the total semileptonic decay rate of B mesons which is proportional to $|V_{cb}|^2 m_b^5$ times a function of m_c/m_b. The main question is what the quark masses actually are. The task of the theorists is to answer this question.

So far, theoretical uncertainties quoted in the talks devoted to determination of $|V_{cb}|$ dominate all other error bars. Reducing them to a level significantly lower than the experimental uncertainties is a major challenge. I am going to report today on recent progress in this direction [4, 5]. The basic theoretical tool is a systematic QCD-based expansion of relevant transition operators in the inverse heavy quark masses developed in the eighties and the very beginning of the nineties.

2. Exclusive method

Let me first briefly explain how one can predict deviation of $F_{B\to D^*}$ at zero recoil from unity. To this end we derive a sum rule for the transitions $B \to D^*$ and $B \to$ vector excitations generated by the axial-vector current, $A_\mu = \bar{b}\gamma_\mu\gamma_5 c$. If the momentum carried by the lepton pair is denoted by q, the zero recoil point is achieved if $\vec{q} = 0$. To obtain the sum rule we consider the T product

$$h_{\mu\nu} = i \int d^4x e^{-iqx} \frac{1}{2M_B} \langle B|T\{A_\mu^\dagger(x)A_\nu(0)\}|B\rangle \quad (1)$$

where the hadronic tensor $h_{\mu\nu}$ can be systematically expanded in $\Lambda_{\text{QCD}}/m_{b,c}$. For our purposes it is sufficient to keep the terms quadratic in this parameter and to consider only one out of five possible kinematical structures, namely h_1, the only structure surviving for the spatial components of the axial-vector current, see e.g. [6, 7].

Next we use the standard technology of the sum rule approach. Let us define

$$\epsilon = M_B - M_{D^*} - q_0 = \Delta M - q_0. \quad (2)$$

If ϵ is positive we sit right on the cut. The imaginary part of the amplitude (1) is the sum of the form factors squared (taken at zero recoil). The sum runs over all possible intermediate states, D^* and excitations. We want to know the first term in the sum, $|F_{B\to D^*}|^2$. Alas, the present-day QCD does not allow us to make calculations directly in this domain.

On the other hand, if ϵ is negative we are below the cut, in the Euclidean domain. Here the amplitude (1) can be calculated as an expansion in $1/m_{b,c}$ provided that $|\epsilon| \gg \Lambda_{QCD}$. To get a well-defined expansion in $1/m_{b,c}$ we must simultaneously assume that $\epsilon \ll m_{b,c}$.

The non-perturbative corrections we are interested in are due to the fact that both, the c quark propagator connecting the points 0 and x in Eq. (1) and the external b quark lines, are not in the empty space but are, rather, submerged into a soft-gluon medium, a light cloud of the B meson. Two parameters characterizing the properties of this soft medium are relevant for our analysis. A chromomagnetic parameter

$$\mu_G^2 = \frac{1}{2M_B}\langle B|\bar{b}\,\frac{i}{2}\sigma_{\mu\nu}G^{\mu\nu}\,b|B\rangle = \frac{-1}{2M_B}\langle B|\bar{b}\,\vec{\sigma}\vec{B}\,b|B\rangle \tag{3}$$

measures the correlation between the spin of the b quark inside B and the chromomagnetic field $\vec{B}$ created by the light cloud. The second parameter is $\mu_\pi^2 = (2M_B)^{-1}\langle B|\bar{b}(i\vec{D})^2 b|B\rangle$ measuring the average spatial momentum squared of the b quark. The both parameters are proportional to Λ_{QCD}^2. That's all we need for the leading non-perturbative term.

If the amplitude (1) is considered in the Euclidean domain far below the cut (i.e. $-\epsilon \gg \Lambda_{QCD}$) the distance between the points 0 and x is short and we can expand h_1 in $\Lambda_{QCD}^2/m_{b,c}^2$. Actually, the whole amplitude contains more information than we need; the sum rule sought for is obtained by considering the coefficient in front of $1/\epsilon$ in h_1. In this way we arrive at the following prediction:

$$F_{B\to D^*}^2 + \sum_{i=1,2,\ldots} F_{B\to excit}^2 =$$

$$1 - \frac{1}{3}\frac{\mu_G^2}{m_c^2} - \frac{\mu_\pi^2 - \mu_G^2}{4}\left(\frac{1}{m_c^2} + \frac{1}{m_b^2} + \frac{2}{3m_c m_b}\right), \tag{4}$$

where the sum on the *lhs* runs over excited states with the appropriate quantum numbers, up to excitation energies $\sim \epsilon$. (In other words, ϵ plays the role of the normalization point. Higher excited states are dual to the graphs with the hard gluon in the intermediate state are neglected together with the latter). All form factors in Eq. (4) are taken at zero recoil.

Let us now transfer the contribution of the excited states to the right hand side and account for the fact [9, 8, 4] that $\mu_\pi^2 > \mu_G^2$. Then we get a lower bound on the deviation of $F_{B\to D^*}$ from unity,

$$\eta_A - F_{B\to D^*} > \frac{\mu_G^2}{6m_c^2}. \tag{5}$$

Here we included the perturbative one-loop correction [2] so that $1 \to \eta_A$,

$$\eta_A = 1 + \frac{\alpha_s}{\pi}\left(\frac{m_b + m_c}{m_b - m_c}\log\frac{m_b}{m_c} - \frac{8}{3}\right) \approx 0.975. \tag{6}$$

Using the known value of μ_G^2 and $m_c = 1.3$ GeV (see below) we conclude that $F_{B\to D^*} < 0.94$.

Including the $\mu_\pi^2 - \mu_G^2$ term and the contribution from the excited states lowers the prediction for $F_{B\to D^*}$ making deviation from unity more pronounced. If μ_π^2 is taken from the QCD sum rule calculation [10] the estimate of $F_{B\to D^*}$ is reduced to 0.92. As far as the excited states are concerned a rough estimate of the $D\pi$ intermediate state can be given [5] implying that

$$F_{B\to D^*} = 0.89 \pm 0.03. \tag{7}$$

The error bars here reflect only the uncertainty in the excited states. The parameters μ_π^2, μ_G^2, m_c and η_A have their own error bars which I can not discuss here due to time/space limitations.

The corrections $\mathcal{O}(1/m_{b,c}^2)$ to the form factors at zero recoil have been discussed previously [11, 12] within a version of the heavy quark expansion. In this version, instead of the excited state contribution, one deals with certain non-local correlation functions which are basically unknown. About the excited states we can at least say that their contribution has definite sign and, moreover, we have a rough idea of its magnitude. This is not the case for the expansion parameters appearing in [11, 12]. It is not surprising then that even the sign of deviation of $F_{B\to D^*}$ from unity was not understood in Ref. [11], and its absolute value was underestimated.

It is curious to note that the sum rule (4) has been recently questioned in Ref. [13] whose authors observe an infrared contribution (due to the so called renormalons) allegedly defying the operator product expansion. The whole situation reminds *perpetuum mobile* searches. Each time a new project is put forward always a little hurdle here or there can be found, a crucial mistake. Sure enough, this is also the case with Ref. [13]. The renormalon contribution is calculated only in the b to c on-shell matrix element. Two other graphs in the amplitude (1), with the gluons in the intermediate state, producing the renormalon contribution of the same order, are simply omitted.

3. Inclusive approach

The CKM matrix element $|V_{cb}|$ can be alternatively determined from the inclusive semileptonic width $\Gamma(B \to X_c l\nu)$. The theoretical expression for the widths is well-known in the literature including the α_s and the leading non-perturbative correction, and to save space I will not quote it here. Usually people believe that the theoretical uncertainty is rather large since the expression for $\Gamma(B \to X_c l\nu)$ is proportional to m_b^5, and even a modest uncertainty in m_b is seemingly strongly amplified due to the fifth power.

The key observation is as follows. If one carefully examines the formula for $\Gamma(B \to X_c l\nu)$ one observes that it depends essentially on the difference of the quark masses, $m_b - m_c$. This is due to the fact that in a large part of the phase space we are not far from the SV limit, and in the SV limit $\Gamma(B \to X_c l\nu)$ depends *only* on the difference $m_b - m_c$. For the actual values of $m_{b,c}$ the residual dependence on the individual quark masses is very weak.

Now, the quark mass difference is known to a much better accuracy than the individual masses,

$$m_b - m_c = \overline{M_B} - \overline{M_D} + \mu_\pi^2 \cdot \left(\frac{1}{2m_c} - \frac{1}{2m_b}\right) + ..., \quad (8)$$

where $\overline{M_B} = (M_B + 3M_{B^*})/4$ and the same for $\overline{M_D}$.

What is suggested? One should *not* allow m_c to change independently; this parameter must be tied up to m_b through Eq. (8). This simple step dramatically reduces the uncertainty in the theoretical prediction for $\Gamma(B \to X_c l\nu)$.

For the b mass normalized not far from the would-be mass shell it is reasonable to accept $m_b = 4.8 \pm 0.1$ GeV. The central value follows from the QCD sum rule analysis of the Υ system [14]. To be on a safe side the original error bars are multiplied by a factor of 4. The central value of m_b above implies $m_c \approx 1.30$ GeV (see below) which matches very well with an independent determination of the c quark mass.

In this way we get numerically [5]

$$|V_{cb}| = 0.0415 \left(\frac{1.49\text{ps}}{\tau_B}\right)^{1/2} \left(\frac{\text{Br}_\text{sl}(B)}{0.106}\right)^{1/2} \quad (9)$$

where we used the central value 4.80GeV for m_b and the value of the strong coupling $\alpha_s = 0.22$; the expectation value of μ_π^2 is also set equal to its central value, $\mu_\pi^2 = 0.54\text{GeV}^2$.

What theoretical error bars in Eq. (9) are expected? First, the variation of m_b (or, alternatively, m_c) in the range ± 100MeV results only in a $\mp 1.6\%$ relative variation of $|V_{cb}|$ if other parameters are kept fixed! The most sizable uncertainty arises in this approach due to dependence of $m_b - m_c$ on the value of μ_π^2. Again, to be on a safe side, we double the original theoretical error bars [10] in this parameter and allow it to vary within the limits $0.35\text{GeV}^2 < \mu_\pi^2 < 0.8\text{GeV}^2$. This uncertainty leads to the change in $|V_{cb}|$ of $\mp 2.8\%$. It seems obvious that the interval above overestimates the existing uncertainty in μ_π^2.

It is worth noting that the value of μ_π^2 can, and will be measured soon via the shape of the lepton spectrum in $b \to cl\nu$ inclusive decays [4] with theoretical accuracy of at least 0.1GeV^2.

Finally there is some dependence on the value of the strong coupling. Numerically the uncertainty constitutes about $\pm 1\%$ when α_s is varied between 0.2 and 0.25. This must and will be reduced by

explicit calculation of the next loop correction, which is straightforward (though somewhat tedious in practice).

Therefore, the above numerical estimates imply that already at present the theoretical uncertainty in the "inclusive" value of $|V_{cb}|$ does not exceed $\sim \pm 5\%$ and is quite competitive with the existing experimental uncertainties in this quantity. It seems possible to further reduce this error to 4 or even 3% by measuring μ_π^2 and calculating the two-loop perturbative correction to the width.

4. Numerical results

Thus, from the inclusive method we get $|V_{cb}| = 0.042 \pm 0.002_\text{theor} \pm$ experimental error. In the exclusive method experimentalists extrapolate to the point of zero recoil and obtain $|V_{cb}|F_{B \to D^*}$(zero recoil). If our central value is taken as an estimate of $F_{B \to D^*}$ then, in order to get $|V_{cb}|$ from the experimental extrapolation to zero recoil, one must multiply the experimental number by 1.1, quite a noticeable correction. This leads to the values of $|V_{bc}|$ from 0.039 (CLEO) to 0.043 (ARGUS) $\pm$ experimental error. The ALEPH result lies in between. Theoretical uncertainty in $F_{B \to D^*}$ at the level of 3 to 4% is translated in the uncertainty in $|V_{bc}|$ at the level ± 0.001 to ± 0.002, i.e. slightly better although comparable to the uncertainty one obtains in the inclusive method today.

With great satisfaction I state that the both methods nicely converge in the problem of V_{cb}.

This work was supported in part by DOE under the grant number DE-FG02-94ER40823.

References

[1] S. Nussinov and W. Wetzel, Phys. Rev. **D36** (1987) 130.
[2] M. Voloshin and M. Shifman, Yad. Fiz. **47** (1988) 801 [Sov. J. Nucl. Phys. **47** (1988) 511].
[3] M.E. Luke, Phys. Lett., **B252** (1990) 447.
[4] I.Bigi, M. Shifman, N. Uraltsev and A. Vainshtein, University of Minnesota preprint TPI-MINN-94/12-T.
[5] M. Shifman, N. Uraltsev and A. Vainshtein, University of Minnesota preprint TPI-MINN-94/13-T.
[6] J. Chay, H. Georgi and B. Grinstein, Phys. Lett. **B247** (1990) 399.
[7] B. Blok, L. Koyrakh, M. Shifman and A. Vainshtein, Phys. Rev. **D49** (1994) 3356.
[8] M. Voloshin, University of Minnesota Preprint TPI-MINN-94/18-T.
[9] I. Bigi, M. Shifman, N. Uraltsev, A. Vainshtein, Int. Journ. Mod. Phys. **A9** (1994) 2467.
[10] P. Ball and V. Braun, Phys. Rev. **D49** (1994) 2472.
[11] A.F. Falk, M. Neubert, Phys. Rev. **D 47** (1993) 2965.
[12] T. Mannel, CERN Preprint CERN-TH.7162/94.
[13] M. Neubert and C. Sachrajda, CERN Preprint CERN-TH.7312/94.
[14] M. Voloshin, Moscow Preprint ITEP-21-1980; M. Voloshin and Y. Zaitsev, Sov. Phys. Usp. **30** (1987) 553.

Paper presented at XXVII Int. Conf. on High Energy Physics: Session Pa-16
Glasgow, UK, 20–27 July 1994

Theoretical Uncertainties in the Extraction of $|V_{cb}|$ from $\bar{B} \to D^* \ell \, \bar{\nu}$ Decays near Zero Recoil

Matthias Neubert*

Theory Division, CERN, CH-1211 Geneva 23, Switzerland

Abstract

I discuss the theoretical uncertainties in the extraction of $|V_{cb}|$ from a measurement of the $\bar{B} \to D^* \ell \, \bar{\nu}$ decay rate close to zero recoil. In particular, I combine previous estimates of the $1/m_Q^2$ corrections to the normalization of the hadronic form factor at zero recoil with sum rules derived by Shifman *et al.* to obtain a new prediction with less uncertainty. I also give a prediction for the slope of the form factor $\widehat{\xi}(w)$ at zero recoil: $\widehat{\varrho}^2 = 0.7 \pm 0.2$. Using the most recent experimental results, I obtain the model-independent value $|V_{cb}| = 0.0395 \pm 0.0030$.

1. Introduction

With the discovery of heavy quark symmetry (for a review see Ref. [1] and references therein), it has become clear that the study of exclusive semileptonic $\bar{B} \to D^* \ell \, \bar{\nu}$ decays close to zero recoil allows for a reliable determination of the Cabibbo–Kobayashi–Maskawa matrix element V_{cb}, which is free, to a large extent, of hadronic uncertainties [2]–[4]. Model dependence enters this analysis only at the level of power corrections, which are suppressed by a factor of at least $(\Lambda_{\text{QCD}}/m_c)^2$. These corrections can be investigated in a systematic way using the heavy quark effective theory [5]. They are found to be small, of the order of a few per cent.

Until recently, this method to determine $|V_{cb}|$ was limited by large experimental uncertainties of about 15–20%, which were much larger than the theoretical uncertainties in the analysis of symmetry-breaking corrections. However, three collaborations have now presented results of higher precision [6]–[8]. It is thus important to reconsider the status of the theoretical analysis, even more so since the original calculation of power corrections in Ref. [9] has become the subject of controversy [10].

* E-mail: neubert@cernvm.cern.ch

The differential decay rate for the process $\bar{B} \to D^* \ell \, \bar{\nu}$ is given by [1]

$$\frac{d\Gamma}{dw} = \frac{G_F^2}{48\pi^3} (m_B - m_{D^*})^2 \, m_{D^*}^3 \, \sqrt{w^2 - 1} \, (w+1)^2$$
$$\times \left[1 + \frac{4w}{w+1} \, \frac{m_B^2 - 2w \, m_B m_{D^*} + m_{D^*}^2}{(m_B - m_{D^*})^2} \right]$$
$$\times |V_{cb}|^2 \, \eta_A^2 \, \widehat{\xi}^2(w), \tag{1}$$

where

$$w = v_B \cdot v_{D^*} = \frac{m_B^2 + m_{D^*}^2 - q^2}{2 m_B m_{D^*}} \tag{2}$$

denotes the product of the meson velocities. I have factorized the hadronic form factor for this decay into a short-distance coefficient η_A and a function $\widehat{\xi}(w)$, which contains the long-distance hadronic dynamics. Apart from corrections of order $1/m_Q$, this function coincides with the Isgur–Wise form factor [3, 11]. Luke's theorem determines the normalization of $\widehat{\xi}(w)$ at zero recoil $(w = 1)$ up to second-order power corrections [4, 12]:

$$\widehat{\xi}(1) = 1 + \delta_{1/m^2}. \tag{3}$$

The strategy is to obtain the product $|V_{cb}| \, \eta_A \, \widehat{\xi}(w)$ from a measurement of the differential decay rate, and to extrapolate it to $w = 1$ to extract

$$|V_{cb}| \, \eta_A \, (1 + \delta_{1/m^2}) = |V_{cb}| \left\{ 1 + O(\alpha_s, 1/m_Q^2) \right\}. \tag{4}$$

The task of theorists is to provide a reliable calculation of η_A and δ_{1/m^2} in order to turn this measurement into a precise determination of $|V_{cb}|$.

2. Calculation of η_A

The short-distance coefficient η_A takes into account a finite renormalization of the axial vector current in the region $m_b > \mu > m_c$. Its calculation is a straightforward application of QCD perturbation theory. At the one-loop order, one finds [2, 13]

$$\eta_A = 1 + \frac{\alpha_s}{\pi} \left(\frac{m_b + m_c}{m_b - m_c} \ln \frac{m_b}{m_c} - \frac{8}{3} \right). \qquad (5)$$

The scale of the running coupling constant is not determined at this order. Choosing α_s between $\alpha_s(m_b) \simeq 0.20$ and $\alpha_s(m_c) \simeq 0.32$, and using $m_c/m_b = 0.30 \pm 0.05$, one obtains values in the range $0.95 < \eta_A < 0.98$. The scale ambiguity leads to an uncertainty of order $\Delta\eta_A \sim [(\alpha_s/\pi) \ln(m_b/m_c)]^2 \sim 2\%$.

The calculation can be improved by using the renormalization group to resum the leading and next-to-leading logarithms of the type $[\alpha_s \ln(m_b/m_c)]^n$, $\alpha_s[\alpha_s \ln(m_b/m_c)]^n$, and $(m_c/m_b)[\alpha_s \ln(m_b/m_c)]^n$ to all orders in perturbation theory [14]–[17]. A consistent scheme for a next-to-leading-order calculation of η_A has been developed in Ref. [18]. The result is

$$\eta_A = x^{6/25} \left\{ 1 + 1.561 \frac{\alpha_s(m_c) - \alpha_s(m_b)}{\pi} - \frac{8\alpha_s(m_c)}{3\pi} \right.$$
$$+ \frac{m_c}{m_b} \left(\frac{25}{54} - \frac{14}{27} x^{-9/25} + \frac{1}{18} x^{-12/25} + \frac{8}{25} \ln x \right)$$
$$\left. + \frac{2\alpha_s(m)}{\pi} \frac{m_c^2}{m_b(m_b - m_c)} \ln \frac{m_b}{m_c} \right\}, \qquad (6)$$

where $x = \alpha_s(m_c)/\alpha_s(m_b)$, and $m_b > m > m_c$. The numerical result is very stable under changes of the input parameters. For $\Lambda_{\overline{\text{MS}}} = (0.25 \pm 0.05)$ GeV (for 4 flavours) and $m_c/m_b = 0.30 \pm 0.05$, one obtains $\eta_A = 0.985 \pm 0.006$. The uncertainty arising from next-to-next-to-leading corrections is of order $\Delta\eta_A \sim (\alpha_s/\pi)^2 \sim 1\%$. Taking this into account, I think it is conservative to increase the error by a factor 2.5 and quote

$$\eta_A = 0.985 \pm 0.015. \qquad (7)$$

3. Anatomy of δ_{1/m^2}

Hadronic uncertainties enter the determination of $|V_{cb}|$ at the level of second-order power corrections, which are expected to be of order $(\Lambda_{\text{QCD}}/m_c)^2 \sim 3\%$. For a precision measurement, it is important to understand the structure of these corrections in detail. Falk and

myself have derived the exact expression [9]

$$\delta_{1/m^2} = -\left(\frac{1}{2m_c} - \frac{1}{2m_b} \right) \left(\frac{\ell_V}{2m_c} - \frac{\ell_P}{2m_b} \right)$$
$$+ \frac{1}{4m_c m_b} \left(\frac{4}{3} \lambda_1 + 2\lambda_2 - \lambda_{G^2} \right), \qquad (8)$$

which depends upon five hadronic parameters: ℓ_P and ℓ_V parametrize the deficit in the "wave-function overlap" between b- and c-flavoured pseudoscalar (P) and vector (V) mesons, for instance

$$\langle D(v) | c^\dagger b | B(v) \rangle \propto 1 - \left(\frac{1}{2m_c} - \frac{1}{2m_b} \right)^2 \ell_P. \qquad (9)$$

The parameter $-\lambda_1 = \langle \vec{p}_Q^2 \rangle$ is proportional to the kinetic energy of the heavy quark inside a heavy meson, $\lambda_2 = (m_{B^*}^2 - m_B^2)/4 \simeq 0.12$ GeV^2 is determined by the vector–pseudoscalar mass splitting, and λ_{G^2} parametrizes certain matrix elements containing double insertions of the chromo-magnetic operator. With the exception of λ_2, estimates of these parameters are model-dependent. In Ref. [9], we made the simplifying assumptions that $\ell_P = \ell_V$, and that the corrections represented by λ_{G^2} are negligible. The latter one is based on the observation that these corrections involve a double insertion of an operator that breaks the heavy quark spin symmetry. Using then reasonable values such as $\ell_P = \ell_V = (0.35 \pm 0.15)$ GeV^2 and $-\lambda_1 = (0.25 \pm 0.20)$ GeV^2, one obtains $\delta_{1/m^2} = -(2.4 \pm 1.3)\%$. Here and in the following, I take $m_b = 4.80$ GeV and $m_c = 1.45$ GeV for the heavy quark masses. In Ref. [1], the error in the estimate of δ_{1/m^2} has been increased to $\pm 4\%$ in order to account for the model dependence and higher-order corrections. A very similar result, $-5\% < \delta_{1/m^2} < 0$, has been obtained by Mannel [19].

Recently, Shifman *et al.* have suggested an alternative approach to obtain an estimate of δ_{1/m^2}, which is based on bounds derived using sum rules and the operator product expansion [10]. These bounds imply the inequalities

$$\ell_P > \frac{1}{2}(-\lambda_1 - 3\lambda_2) \equiv \ell_P^{\min} > 0,$$
$$\ell_V > \frac{1}{2}(-\lambda_1 + \lambda_2) \equiv \ell_V^{\min} > 2\lambda_2,$$
$$\delta_{1/m^2} < -\left(\frac{1}{2m_c} - \frac{1}{2m_b} \right) \left(\frac{\ell_V^{\min}}{2m_c} - \frac{\ell_P^{\min}}{2m_b} \right)$$
$$+ \frac{1}{4m_c m_b} \left(\frac{4}{3} \lambda_1 + 2\lambda_2 \right)$$
$$< -\frac{\lambda_2}{2m_c^2} \simeq -2.9\%. \qquad (10)$$

The upper bound for δ_{1/m^2} implies that $\eta_A \hat{\xi}(1) < 0.956$. In Ref. [10], this number is quoted as 0.94. In the same reference, the authors give an "educated guess" $\eta_A \hat{\xi}(1) = 0.89 \pm 0.03$ corresponding to $\delta_{1/m^2} = -(9.6 \pm 3.0)\%$. However, the arguments presented to support this guess are not very rigorous.

It is possible to combine the above approaches to reduce the theoretical uncertainty in the estimate of δ_{1/m^2} [20]. The idea is to use the sum rules to constrain the hadronic parameters in (8) in a threefold way: (i) The first relation in (10) implies that

$$-\lambda_1 > 3\lambda_2 \simeq 0.36 \text{ GeV}^2\,, \tag{11}$$

excluding some of the values for the parameter λ_1 used in previous analyses. (ii) Comparing the third relation in (10) with (8) in the limit $m_b = m_c$, one finds that

$$\lambda_{G^2} > 0\,. \tag{12}$$

(iii) Finally, ℓ_P and ℓ_V are correlated in such a way that $\ell_V > \ell_P$ if λ_{G^2} is not too large. To illustrate this last point, let me define new parameters

$$\bar{\ell} = \frac{1}{2}\,(\ell_V + \ell_P)\,,$$

$$D = \frac{1}{2}\,(\ell_V - \ell_P) - \lambda_2\,. \tag{13}$$

In terms of these,

$$\delta_{1/m^2} = -\left(\frac{1}{2m_c} - \frac{1}{2m_b}\right)^2 \bar{\ell} - \left(\frac{1}{4m_c^2} - \frac{1}{4m_b^2}\right)(\lambda_2 + D)$$
$$+ \frac{1}{4m_c m_b}\left(\frac{4}{3}\,\lambda_1 + 2\lambda_2 - \lambda_{G^2}\right). \tag{14}$$

Using the inequalities (10), one can show that $\bar{\ell} > \frac{1}{2}(-\lambda_1 - \lambda_2)$ and $-D_{\max} < D < D_{\max}$, with [20]

$$D_{\max} = \begin{cases} S & ; \quad 0 < S \leq \lambda_{G^2}/2\,, \\ \sqrt{\lambda_{G^2}S - \lambda_{G^2}^2/4} & ; \quad S \geq \lambda_{G^2}/2\,, \end{cases} \tag{15}$$

where $S = \bar{\ell} + (\lambda_1 + \lambda_2)/2$. There are thus three effects, which decrease δ_{1/m^2} with respect to the estimate given in Ref. [9]: a large value of $(-\lambda_1)$, a positive value of λ_{G^2}, and the fact that for small λ_{G^2} the difference $(\ell_V - \ell_P)$ is centred around $2\lambda_2$ (i.e. D is centred around 0).

In evaluating (14), I will take $-\lambda_1 = 0.4$ GeV^2, which is consistent with the bound in (11) and with the value $-\lambda_1 = (0.5 \pm 0.1)$ GeV^2 obtained from QCD sum rules [21]. Varying $-\lambda_1$ in the range between 0.36 and 0.5 GeV^2 does not alter the results very much. The main uncertainty comes from the unknown values of the parameters $\bar{\ell}$ and λ_{G^2}. As a guideline, one may employ the constituent quark model of Isgur *et al.* [22], in which one uses non-relativistic harmonic oscillator wave functions for the ground-state heavy mesons, for instance $\psi_B(r) \sim \exp(-\frac{1}{2}\mu\omega r^2)$, where $\mu = (1/m_q +$

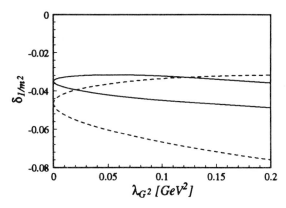

Figure 1. Allowed regions for δ_{1/m^2} as a function of λ_{G^2} for the two cases $\bar{\ell} = 0.2$ GeV^2 (solid) and 0.4 GeV^2 (dashed).

$1/m_b)^{-1}$ is the reduced mass. One then obtains $\bar{\ell} = \frac{3}{4}m_q^2 \simeq 0.2$ GeV^2, where I use $m_q \simeq 0.5$ GeV for the light constituent quark mass. However, this estimate of $\bar{\ell}$ is probably somewhat too low. Lattice studies of heavy-light wave functions suggest an exponential behaviour of the form $\psi_B(r) \sim \exp(-\kappa\mu r)$ [23], which leads to $\bar{\ell} = \frac{3}{2}m_q^2 \simeq 0.4$ GeV^2. Values much larger than this are unlikely, since I use a rather large constituent quark mass m_q. In fact, adopting the point of view that the sum rules for ℓ_P and ℓ_V are saturated to approximately 50% by the ground-state contribution [10], one would expect $\bar{\ell} \simeq (-\lambda_1 - \lambda_2) \simeq 0.28$ GeV^2, which seems a very reasonable value to me. In Fig. 1, I show the allowed regions for δ_{1/m^2} as a function of λ_{G^2} for two values of $\bar{\ell}$. I think it is reasonable to assume that λ_{G^2} is of a magnitude similar to λ_2 or smaller. Thus, I conclude that for all reasonable choices of parameters the results are in the range

$$-8\% < \delta_{1/m^2} < -3\%\,, \tag{16}$$

which is consistent with the previous estimates in Refs. [9, 10, 19] at the 1σ level. A more precise determination of the parameter $\bar{\ell}$ would help to reduce the uncertainty in this number.

4. Prediction for the slope parameter $\hat{\varrho}^2$

In the extrapolation of the differential decay rate (1) to zero recoil, the slope of the function $\hat{\xi}(w)$ close to $w = 1$ plays an important role. One defines a parameter $\hat{\varrho}^2$ by

$$\hat{\xi}(w) = \hat{\xi}(1)\left\{1 - \hat{\varrho}^2\,(w - 1) + \ldots\right\}. \tag{17}$$

It is important to distinguish $\hat{\varrho}^2$ from the slope parameter ϱ^2 of the Isgur–Wise function. They differ by corrections that break the heavy quark symmetry. Whereas the slope of the Isgur–Wise function is a universal, mass-independent parameter, the slope of the physical form factor depends on logarithms and inverse powers of the heavy quark masses. On the other hand, $\widehat{\varrho}^2$ is an observable quantity, while the value of ϱ^2 depends on the renormalization scheme. To illustrate this last point, let me neglect for the moment $1/m_Q$ corrections and work in the leading logarithmic approximation. Then the relation between the physical slope parameter $\widehat{\varrho}^2$ and the slope parameter $\varrho^2(\mu)$ of the regularized Isgur–Wise function is [20]

$$\widehat{\varrho}^2 = \varrho^2(\mu) - \frac{16}{81}\ln\frac{\alpha_s(m)}{\alpha_s(\mu)} \equiv \varrho^2 - \frac{16}{81}\ln\alpha_s(m), \quad (18)$$

where μ is the renormalization scale, and m is an undetermined (at this order) scale between m_b and m_c. The last equation can be used to define the μ-independent slope of the renormalized Isgur–Wise function (see Ref. [18] for the generalization of this definition to next-to-leading order). If next-to-leading logarithmic corrections are taken into account, the scale ambiguity related to the choice of m is resolved, and one obtains

$$\widehat{\varrho}^2 = \varrho^2 + (0.14 \pm 0.02) + O(1/m_Q). \quad (19)$$

The $1/m_Q$ corrections to this relation have been investigated and are found to be negative. However, any such estimate is model-dependent and thus has a large theoretical uncertainty. The result is $\widehat{\varrho}^2 \simeq \varrho^2 \pm 0.2$ [20]. Predictions for the renormalized slope parameter ϱ^2 are available from QCD sum rules including a next-to-leading-order renormalization-group improvement. One obtains $\varrho^2 \simeq 0.7 \pm 0.1$ [1, 24, 25]. I thus expect

$$\widehat{\varrho}^2 = 0.7 \pm 0.2. \quad (20)$$

5. Summary

Using the updated values $\eta_A = 0.985 \pm 0.015$ and $\delta_{1/m^2} = -(5.5 \pm 2.5)\%$, I obtain for the normalization of the hadronic form factor at zero recoil:

$$\eta_A\,\widehat{\xi}(1) = 0.93 \pm 0.03. \quad (21)$$

Three experiments have recently presented new measurements of the product $|V_{cb}|\,\eta_A\,\widehat{\xi}(1)$. When rescaled using the new lifetime values $\tau_{B^0} = (1.61 \pm 0.08)$ ps and $\tau_{B^+} = (1.65 \pm 0.07)$ ps [26], the results obtained from a linear fit to the data are

$$|V_{cb}|\,\eta_A\,\widehat{\xi}(1) = \begin{cases} 0.0347 \pm 0.0019 \pm 0.0020; & \text{Ref. [6]}, \\ 0.0364 \pm 0.0042 \pm 0.0031; & \text{Ref. [7]}, \\ 0.0385 \pm 0.0043 \pm 0.0028; & \text{Ref. [8]}, \end{cases} \quad (22)$$

where the first error is statistical and the second systematic. I will follow the suggestion of Ref. [27] and add 0.001 ± 0.001 to these values to account

for the curvature of the function $\widehat{\xi}(w)$. Taking the weighted average of the experimental results and using the theoretical prediction (21), I then obtain

$$\begin{aligned} |V_{cb}| &= 0.0395 \pm 0.0027\,(\text{exp}) \pm 0.0013\,(\text{th}) \\ &= 0.0395 \pm 0.0030, \end{aligned} \quad (23)$$

which corresponds to a model-independent measurement of $|V_{cb}|$ with 7% accuracy. This is by far the most accurate determination to date.

Neglecting $1/m_Q$ corrections, I have related the physical slope parameter $\widehat{\varrho}^2$ to the slope of the Isgur–Wise function and obtain the prediction $\widehat{\varrho}^2 = 0.7 \pm 0.2$. It compares well with the average value observed by experiments, which is $\widehat{\varrho}^2 = 0.87 \pm 0.12$ [6]–[8].

References

1 M. Neubert, SLAC preprint SLAC-PUB-6263 (1993), to appear in Phys. Rep.
2 M.B. Voloshin and M.A. Shifman, Yad. Fiz. **47**, 801 (1988) [Sov. J. Nucl. Phys. **47**, 511 (1988)].
3 N. Isgur and M.B. Wise, Phys. Lett. B **232**, 113 (1989); **237**, 527 (1990).
4 M. Neubert, Phys. Lett. B **264**, 455 (1991).
5 H. Georgi, Phys. Lett. B **240**, 447 (1990).
6 T. Browder (CLEO Collaboration), talk presented at this conference; B. Barish et al. (CLEO Collaboration), Cornell preprint CLNS 94/1285, submitted to this conference.
7 I. Scott (ALEPH Collaboration), talk presented at this conference; D. Decamp et al. (ALEPH Collaboration), paper gls0605, submitted to this conference.
8 H. Albrecht et al. (ARGUS Collaboration), Z. Phys. C **57**, 533 (1993).
9 A.F. Falk and M. Neubert, Phys. Rev. D **47**, 2965 and 2982 (1993).
10 M. Shifman, N.G. Uraltsev, and A. Vainshtein, Minnesota preprint TPI-MINN-94/13-T (1994); I. Bigi, M. Shifman, N.G. Uraltsev, and A. Vainshtein, Minnesota preprint TPI-MINN-94/12-T (1994).
11 A.F. Falk, H. Georgi, B. Grinstein, and M.B. Wise, Nucl. Phys. B **343**, 1 (1990).
12 M.E. Luke, Phys. Lett. B **252**, 447 (1990).
13 M. Neubert, Nucl. Phys. B **371**, 149 (1992).
14 H.D. Politzer and M.B. Wise, Phys. Lett. B **206**, 681 (1988); **208**, 504 (1988).
15 X. Ji and M.J. Musolf, Phys. Lett. B **257**, 409 (1991).
16 D.J. Broadhurst and A.G. Grozin, Phys. Lett. B **267**, 105 (1991).
17 A.F. Falk and B. Grinstein, Phys. Lett. B **247**, 406 (1990).
18 M. Neubert, Phys. Rev. D **46**, 2212 (1992).
19 T. Mannel, Phys. Rev. D **50**, 428 (1994).
20 M. Neubert, CERN preprint CERN-TH.7395/94 (1994), to appear in Phys. Lett. B.
21 P. Ball and V.M. Braun, Phys. Rev. D **49**, 2472 (1994), and private communication.
22 N. Isgur, D. Scora, B. Grinstein, and M.B. Wise, Phys. Rev. D **39**, 799 (1989).
23 A. Duncan, E. Eichten, and H. Thacker, Phys. Lett. B **303**, 109 (1993).
24 E. Bagan, P. Ball, and P. Gosdzinsky, Phys. Lett. B **301**, 249 (1993).
25 M. Neubert, Phys. Rev. D **47**, 4063 (1993).
26 F. DeJongh, talk presented at this conference.
27 R. Patterson, talk presented at this conference.

An Update of the CKM Matrix

Ahmed Ali[†‡¶] and David London[§‖]

† Theory Division, CERN, CH-1211 Geneva 23, Switzerland
§ Laboratoire de physique nucléaire, Université de Montréal
C.P. 6128, succ. centre-ville, Montréal, QC, Canada

Abstract

We update the constraints on the parameters of the quark flavour mixing matrix V_{CKM} in the standard model using the latest experimental and theoretical results as input. We present the 95% C.L. allowed region of the unitarity triangle and the corresponding ranges for the ratio $|V_{td}/V_{ts}|$ and for the quantities $\sin 2\alpha$, $\sin 2\beta$ and $\sin^2 \gamma$, which characterize CP-violating rate asymmetries in B-decays. The SM prediction for the B_s^0-$\overline{B_s^0}$ mixing ratio x_s is also presented.

1. Experimental and Theoretical Input

In ref. [1], we recently updated the profile of the Cabibbo-Kobayashi-Maskawa (CKM) matrix [2], in particular the CKM unitarity triangle. In performing this update, we included the improvements reported in the measurements of the B lifetime, the B_d^0-$\overline{B_d^0}$ mass difference ΔM_d, the CKM matrix elements $|V_{cb}|$ and $|V_{ub}/V_{cb}|$ from B decays, measured by the ARGUS, CLEO, CDF and LEP experiments, and the lower bound on the ratio $\Delta M_s/\Delta M_d$ reported by the ALEPH collaboration [3]. The CDF value for the top quark mass $m_t = 174 \pm 10^{+13}_{-12}$ GeV [4] was also included. We refer to ref. [1] for details and references to earlier work and confine ourselves here to giving the principal results.

In performing this update, we make use of the Wolfenstein parametrization [5] in which the CKM matrix can be written in terms of four parameters λ, A, ρ and η. The matrix element $|V_{us}|$ has been extracted from $K \to \pi e \nu$ and hyperon decays to be $|V_{us}| = \lambda = 0.2205 \pm 0.0018$ [6]. The parameter A is related to the CKM matrix element V_{cb}, which can be obtained from semileptonic decays of B mesons. Using methods based on heavy quark effective theory (HQET), we find

$$|V_{cb}| = 0.039 \pm 0.006 , \qquad (1)$$

which yields $A = 0.80 \pm 0.12$. We refer to ref. [1] for a full discussion of the experimental and theoretical inputs leading to the above values, and to ref. [7] for the latest developments in HQET.

The parameters ρ and η are constrained by the measurements of $|V_{ub}/V_{cb}|$, $|\epsilon|$ (the CP-violating parameter in the kaon system) and ΔM_d (B_d^0-$\overline{B_d^0}$ mixing induced mass difference). The ratio $|V_{ub}/V_{cb}|$ can be obtained by looking at the endpoint of the inclusive lepton spectrum in semileptonic B decays. There still exists quite a bit of model dependence in the interpretation of data and the present average is [8]

$$\left| \frac{V_{ub}}{V_{cb}} \right| = 0.08 \pm 0.03 , \qquad (2)$$

giving $\sqrt{\rho^2 + \eta^2} = 0.36 \pm 0.14$.

Turning to $|\epsilon|$, its experimental value is $|\epsilon| = (2.26 \pm 0.02) \times 10^{-3}$ [6]. In the SM, $|\epsilon|$ is given by

$$|\epsilon| = \frac{G_F^2 f_K^2 M_K M_W^2}{6\sqrt{2}\pi^2 \Delta M_K} \hat{B}_K A^2 \lambda^6 \eta \big(y_c \{\hat{\eta}_{ct} f_3(y_c, y_t) - \hat{\eta}_{cc}\}$$
$$+ \hat{\eta}_{tt} y_t f_2(y_t) A^2 \lambda^4 (1 - \rho)\big). \qquad (3)$$

‡ e-mail: alia@cernvm.cern.ch
¶ On leave of absence from DESY, Hamburg, FRG.
‖ e-mail: london@lps.umontreal.ca

Parameter	Value
λ	0.2205
$|V_{cb}|$	0.039 ± 0.006
$|V_{ub}/V_{cb}|$	0.08 ± 0.03
$|\epsilon|$	$(2.26 \pm 0.02) \times 10^{-3}$
ΔM_d	$(0.50 \pm 0.033) \, (\text{ps})^{-1}$
$\overline{m_t}(m_t(pole))$	$(165 \pm 16) \, \text{GeV}$
$\hat{\eta}_B$	0.55
$\hat{\eta}_{cc}$	1.10
$\hat{\eta}_{ct}$	0.36
$\hat{\eta}_{tt}$	0.57
$\hat{B}_K$	0.8 ± 0.2
$\hat{B}_B$	1.0 ± 0.2
f_{B_d}	$180 \pm 50 \, \text{MeV}$

Table 1. Parameters used in the CKM fits. Values of the hadronic quantities f_{B_d}, $\hat{B}_{B_d}$ and $\hat{B}_K$ shown are motivated by the lattice QCD results. In Fit 1, specific values of these hadronic quantities are chosen, while in Fit 2, they are allowed to vary over the given ranges.

Here, the $\hat{\eta}_i$ are QCD correction factors [9], $y_i \equiv m_i^2/M_W^2$, and the functions f_2 and f_3 are given in ref. [1].

The final parameter in the expression for $|\epsilon|$ is the renormalization scale independent parameter $\hat{B}_K$, which represents our ignorance of the hadronic matrix element $\langle K^0|\left(\overline{d}\gamma^\mu(1-\gamma_5)s\right)^2|\overline{K^0}\rangle$. The evaluation of this matrix element has been the subject of much work, summarized in ref. [10]. The present lattice-QCD estimates give $\hat{B}_K = 0.82 \pm 0.027 \pm 0.023$ [11]. In our fits we take $\hat{B}_K = 0.8 \pm 0.2$, although we also consider specific values of $\hat{B}_K$ ranging from 0.4 to 1.

The present world average of the B_d^0-$\overline{B_d^0}$ mixing parameter $x_d \equiv \Delta M_d/\Gamma_d$ is $x_d = 0.76 \pm 0.06$ [3]. The precision on ΔM_d alone is now quite competitive with the precision on x_d. The LEP-average $\Delta M_d = 0.513 \pm 0.036 \, (\text{ps})^{-1}$ has been combined with that derived from time-integrated measurements yielding the present world average [3]

$$\Delta M_d = 0.500 \pm 0.033 \, (\text{ps})^{-1} . \qquad (4)$$

In our fits we use this number instead of x_d.

The mass difference ΔM_d is calculated from the B_d^0-$\overline{B_d^0}$ box diagram, which is dominated by t-quark exchange:

$$\Delta M_d = \frac{G_F^2}{6\pi^2} M_W^2 M_B \left(f_{B_d}^2 \hat{B}_{B_d}\right) \hat{\eta}_B y_t f_2(y_t)|V_{td}^* V_{tb}|^2 , \qquad (5)$$

where $|V_{td}^* V_{tb}|^2 = A^2\lambda^6 \left[(1-\rho)^2 + \eta^2\right]$. Here, $\hat{\eta}_B$ is the QCD correction. In the fits presented here we use the value $\hat{\eta}_B = 0.55$, calculated in the $\overline{MS}$ scheme, following ref. [12]. Consistency requires that the top quark mass be rescaled from its pole (mass) value of $m_t = 174 \pm 16$ GeV to the value $\overline{m_t}(m_t(pole))$ in the $\overline{MS}$ scheme, which is typically about 9 GeV smaller.

For the B system, the hadronic uncertainty is given by $f_{B_d}^2 \hat{B}_{B_d}$, analogous to $\hat{B}_K$ in the kaon system. In

our fits, we take ranges for f_{B_d} and $\hat{B}_{B_d}$ which are compatible with recent lattice QCD results [13] and QCD sum rule results [14]:

$$f_{B_d} = 180 \pm 50 \, \text{MeV} ,$$
$$\hat{B}_{B_d} = 1.0 \pm 0.2 . \qquad (6)$$

Table 1 summarizes all input quantities to our fits.

2. The Unitarity Triangle

The allowed region in ρ-η space can be displayed quite elegantly using the so-called unitarity triangle. The unitarity of the CKM matrix leads to the relation $V_{ud}V_{ub}^* + V_{cd}V_{cb}^* + V_{td}V_{tb}^* = 0$. This can be recast as a triangle relation in the ρ-η plane, in which the base of the triangle goes from $(0,0)$ to $(1,0)$, and the apex is given by the coordinates (ρ, η). Thus, allowed values of ρ and η translate into allowed shapes of the unitarity triangle.

In order to find the allowed unitarity triangles, the computer program MINUIT is used to fit the CKM parameters A, ρ and η to the experimental values of $|V_{cb}|$, $|V_{ub}/V_{cb}|$, $|\epsilon|$ and ΔM_d. Since λ is very well measured, we fix it to its central value given above. We present here the results from two types of fits:

Fit 1: Here, only the experimentally measured numbers are used as inputs to the fit with Gaussian errors; the coupling constants $f_{B_d}\sqrt{\hat{B}_{B_d}}$ and $\hat{B}_K$ are given fixed values.

Fit 2: Here, both the experimental and theoretical numbers are used as inputs assuming Gaussian errors for the theoretical quantities. All errors are combined in quadrature.

We briefly summarize the results of Fit 1. The goal here is to restrict the allowed range of the parameters (ρ, η) for given values of the coupling constants $f_{B_d}\sqrt{\hat{B}_{B_d}}$ and $\hat{B}_K$. In ref. [1] we showed that certain values of $\hat{B}_K$ and $f_{B_d}\sqrt{\hat{B}_{B_d}}$ are disfavoured since they do not provide a good fit to the data. For example, fixing $\hat{B}_K = 1.0$, the fitting program was used to obtain the minimum χ^2 for various values of $f_{B_d}\sqrt{\hat{B}_{B_d}}$. The results are given in Table 2, along with the best fit values of (ρ, η). Using $\chi^2_{min} < 2.0$ as our "good fit" criterion (since we have two variables, ρ and η), we note that $f_{B_d}\sqrt{\hat{B}_{B_d}} < 120$ MeV and $f_{B_d}\sqrt{\hat{B}_{B_d}} > 290$ MeV give poor fits to the existing data. We also note that the χ^2 distribution has two minima, at around $f_{B_d}\sqrt{\hat{B}_{B_d}} = 160$ and 230 MeV. We do not consider this terribly significant, since the surrounding values of $f_{B_d}\sqrt{\hat{B}_{B_d}}$ also yield good fits to the data. In addition, we found that, for the lower value $\hat{B}_K = 0.4$, the allowed

$f_{B_d}\sqrt{\hat{B}_{B_d}}$ (MeV)	(ρ, η)	χ^2_{min}
110	$(-0.48, 0.10)$	3.24
120	$(-0.44, 0.12)$	1.77
130	$(-0.40, 0.15)$	0.85
140	$(-0.36, 0.18)$	0.33
150	$(-0.32, 0.21)$	7.6×10^{-2}
160	$(-0.28, 0.24)$	1.1×10^{-3}
170	$(-0.23, 0.27)$	2.4×10^{-2}
180	$(-0.17, 0.29)$	8.0×10^{-2}
190	$(-0.11, 0.32)$	0.12
200	$(-0.04, 0.33)$	0.13
210	$(0.03, 0.33)$	8.5×10^{-2}
220	$(0.09, 0.33)$	2.8×10^{-2}
230	$(0.15, 0.33)$	4.5×10^{-5}
240	$(0.21, 0.33)$	4.4×10^{-2}
250	$(0.25, 0.33)$	0.18
260	$(0.29, 0.33)$	0.43
270	$(0.33, 0.33)$	0.77
280	$(0.37, 0.33)$	1.21
290	$(0.40, 0.33)$	1.73
300	$(0.43, 0.32)$	2.34

Table 2. The "best values" of the CKM parameters (ρ, η) as a function of the coupling constant $f_{B_d}\sqrt{\hat{B}_{B_d}}$, obtained by a minimum χ^2 fit to the experimental data, including the renormalized value of $m_t = 165 \pm 16$ GeV. We fix $\hat{B}_K = 1.0$. The resulting minimum χ^2 values from the MINUIT fits are also given.

range of $f_{B_d}\sqrt{\hat{B}_{B_d}}$ is quite restricted, with generally higher values of χ^2 than for the cases of $\hat{B}_K$ in the range 0.6-1.0. This suggests that the data disfavour (though do not completely exclude) $\hat{B}_K \leq 0.4$ solutions. Details are given in ref. [1].

We now discuss Fit 2. Since the coupling constants are not known and the best we have are estimates given by the ranges in eq. (6), a reasonable profile of the unitarity triangle at present can be obtained by letting the coupling constants vary in these ranges. The resulting CKM triangle region is shown in Fig. 1. As is clear from this figure, the allowed region is enormous! Even so, it is still reduced compared to the previous such analyses, due to the knowledge of m_t. The preferred values of ρ and η obtained from this fit are

$$(\rho, \eta) = (-0.12, 0.34) \quad (\text{with } \chi^2 = 1.1 \times 10^{-3}) . \quad (7)$$

We have determined bounds on the ratio $|V_{td}/V_{ts}|$ from our fits. For 110 MeV $\leq f_{B_d}\sqrt{\hat{B}_{B_d}} \leq 290$ MeV, i.e. in the entire allowed domain, at 95 % C.L. we find

$$0.11 \leq \left|\frac{V_{td}}{V_{ts}}\right| \leq 0.36 . \quad (8)$$

The upper bound from our analysis is more restrictive than the current experimental upper limit following from the CKM-suppressed radiative penguin decays $BR(B \to \omega + \gamma)$ and $BR(B \to \rho + \gamma)$, which at present yield $|V_{td}/V_{ts}| \leq 0.64$-0.75 (90% C.L.) [15], depending

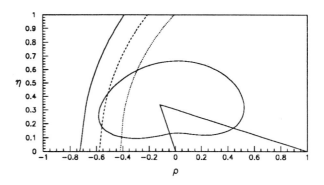

Figure 1. Allowed region in ρ-η space, from a simultaneous fit to both the experimental and theoretical quantities given in Table 1. The theoretical errors are treated as Gaussian for this fit. The solid line represents the 95% C.L. region. The triangle shows the best fit. The constraints in ρ-η space from the ALEPH bound on ΔM_s are presented for 3 choices of the SU(3)-breaking parameter: $\xi_s^2 = 1.1$ (dotted line), 1.35 (dashed line) and 1.6 (solid line). In all cases, the region to the left of the curve is ruled out.

on the model used for the SU(3)-breaking in the relevant form factors [16]. Furthermore, the upper bound is now as good as that obtained from unitarity, which gives $0.08 \leq |V_{td}/V_{ts}| \leq 0.36$, but the lower bound from our fit is slightly more restrictive.

Note that the matrix element ratio $|V_{ub}/V_{cb}|$ is very poorly determined. Our fits give:

$$0.03 \leq \frac{|V_{ub}|}{|V_{cb}|} \leq 0.137 . \quad (9)$$

It is important to reduce the present errors on the ratios $|V_{td}/V_{ts}|$ and $|V_{ub}/V_{cb}|$ in order to quantitatively test CKM unitarity.

3. B_s^0-$\overline{B_s^0}$ Mixing and the Unitarity Triangle

The B_s^0-$\overline{B_s^0}$ box diagram is also dominated by t-quark exchange, and the mass difference between the eigenstates ΔM_s is given by the analog of eq. (5),

$$\Delta M_s = \frac{G_F^2}{6\pi^2} M_W^2 M_{B_s} \left(f_{B_s}^2 \hat{B}_{B_s}\right) \hat{\eta}_{B_s} y_t f_2(y_t) |V_{ts}^* V_{tb}|^2 . \quad (10)$$

A measurement of ΔM_s can be used to give an additional constraint on the unitarity triangle. Taking the ratio of ΔM_d and ΔM_s, we find

$$\frac{\Delta M_s}{\Delta M_d} = \frac{\hat{\eta}_{B_s} M_{B_s} \left(f_{B_s}^2 \hat{B}_{B_s}\right)}{\hat{\eta}_{B_d} M_{B_d} \left(f_{B_d}^2 \hat{B}_{B_d}\right)} \left|\frac{V_{ts}}{V_{td}}\right|^2 . \quad (11)$$

All dependence on the t-quark mass drops out, leaving the square of the ratio of CKM matrix elements, multiplied by a factor which reflects $SU(3)_{flavour}$

breaking effects. Since we expect the QCD correction factor $\hat{\eta}_B$ to be equal to its B_d counterpart, the only real uncertainty in this factor is the ratio of hadronic matrix elements. In what follows, we take

$$\xi_s \equiv \frac{(f_{B_s}\sqrt{\hat{B}_{B_s}})}{(f_{B_d}\sqrt{\hat{B}_{B_d}})} = (1.16 \pm 0.1) . \qquad (12)$$

This is consistent with estimates from lattice QCD [13] and QCD sum rules [14].

The ALEPH lower bound $\Delta M_s/\Delta M_d > 11.3$ at 95% C.L. [3] can thus be turned into a bound on the CKM parameter space (ρ, η) by choosing a value for the SU(3)-breaking parameter ξ_s^2. We assume three representative values: $\xi_s^2 = 1.1$, 1.35 and 1.6, and display the resulting constraints in Fig. 1. From this graph we see that the ALEPH bound marginally restricts the allowed ρ-η region for small values of ξ_s^2, but does not provide any useful bounds for larger values. Of course, an actual measurement of ΔM_s would be very helpful in further constraining the CKM parameter space.

We now turn to the SM prediction for $x_s \equiv \Delta M_s/\Gamma_s$. The main uncertainty in x_s (or, equivalently, ΔM_s) is $f_{B_s}^2 \hat{B}_{B_s}$. Using the determination of A given previously, $\tau_{B_s} = 1.54 \pm 0.14$ (ps) and $\overline{m_t} = 165 \pm 16$ GeV, we obtain

$$x_s = (19.4 \pm 6.9)\frac{f_{B_s}^2 \hat{B}_{B_s}}{(230 \text{ MeV})^2} . \qquad (13)$$

The choice $f_{B_s}\sqrt{\hat{B}_{B_s}} = 230$ MeV corresponds to the central value given by the lattice-QCD estimates, and with this our fits give $x_s \simeq 20$ as the preferred value in the SM.

4.   CP Violation in the B System

It is expected that the B system will exhibit large CP-violating effects, characterized by nonzero values of the three angles α, β and γ in the unitarity triangle. These angles can be measured via CP-violating asymmetries in hadronic B decays. In the decays $\overset{(-)}{B_d} \to \pi^+\pi^-$, for example, one measures the quantity $\sin 2\alpha$, and in $\overset{(-)}{B_d} \to J/\psi K_S$, $\sin 2\beta$ is obtained. The CP asymmetry in the decay $\overset{(-)}{B_s} \to D_s^\pm K^\mp$ is slightly different, yielding $\sin^2 \gamma$.

These CP-violating asymmetries can be expressed straightforwardly in terms of the CKM parameters ρ and η. The 95% C.L. constraints on ρ and η found previously can be used to predict the ranges of $\sin 2\alpha$, $\sin 2\beta$ and $\sin^2 \gamma$ allowed in the standard model. The allowed ranges, obtained from Fit 1, are found in Table 3. In this Table we have assumed that the angle β is measured in $\overset{(-)}{B_d} \to J/\Psi K_S$, and have therefore included

$f_{B_d}\sqrt{\hat{B}_{B_d}}$	$\sin 2\alpha$	$\sin 2\beta$	$\sin^2 \gamma$
130	$0.36 - 0.96$	$0.17 - 0.41$	$0.08 - 0.48$
155	$0.15 - 1.0$	$0.26 - 0.62$	$0.23 - 1.0$
180	$-1.0 - 1.0$	$0.33 - 0.81$	$0.37 - 1.0$
205	$-1.0 - 1.0$	$0.40 - 0.93$	$0.20 - 1.0$
230	$-1.0 - 0.86$	$0.47 - 0.99$	$0.15 - 1.0$

Table 3. The allowed ranges for the CP asymmetries $\sin 2\alpha$, $\sin 2\beta$ and $\sin^2 \gamma$, corresponding to the constraints on ρ and η obtained in Fit 1. Values of the coupling constant $f_{B_d}\sqrt{\hat{B}_{B_d}}$ (in MeV) are stated. We fix $\hat{B}_K = 0.8$.

an extra minus sign due to the CP of the final state. Since the CP asymmetries all depend on ρ and η, the ranges for $\sin 2\alpha$, $\sin 2\beta$ and $\sin^2 \gamma$ shown in Table 3 are correlated. That is, not all values in the ranges are allowed simultaneously. This correlation can be seen in ref. [1].

Summarizing our results on CP violation, the ranges for the CP-violating rate asymmetries parametrized by $\sin 2\alpha$, $\sin 2\beta$ and and $\sin^2 \gamma$ are determined at 95% C.L. to be

$$-1.0 \le \sin 2\alpha \le 1.0 ,$$
$$0.17 \le \sin 2\beta \le 0.99 , \qquad (14)$$
$$0.08 \le \sin^2 \gamma \le 1.0 .$$

(For $\sin 2\alpha < 0.4$, we find $\sin 2\beta \ge 0.3$.)

References

[1] A. Ali and D. London, CERN-TH.7398/94.
[2] N. Cabibbo, Phys. Rev. Lett. **10** (1963) 531; M. Kobayashi and T. Maskawa, Prog. Theor. Phys. **49** (1973) 652.
[3] R. Forty, these proceedings.
[4] F. Abe *et al.* (CDF Collaboration) FERMILAB-PUB-94/097-E; FERMILAB-PUB-94/116-E.
[5] L. Wolfenstein, Phys. Rev. Lett. **51** (1983) 1945.
[6] K. Hikasa *et al.* (PDG), Phys. Rev. **D45** (1992) 1.
[7] M. Neubert, preprint CERN-TH.7395/94 (1994), and these proceedings; M. Shifman, N. G. Uraltsev and A. Vainshtain, Preprint TPI-MINN-94/13-T (1994), and M. Shifman, these proceedings; P. Ball, these proceedings.
[8] D. Cassel (private communication).
[9] A. J. Buras, M. Jamin and P. H. Weisz, Nucl. Phys. B347 (1990) 491; J. Flynn, Mod. Phys. Lett. **A5** (1990) 877; S. Herrlich and U. Nierste, Nucl. Phys. **B419** (1994) 292.
[10] A. Ali and D. London, J. Phys. G: Nucl. Part. Phys. **19** (1993) 1069; A. Pich and J. Prades, Valencia report FTUVC/94-37 (1994).
[11] R. Gupta *et al.*, Phys. Rev. **D47** (1993) 5113.
[12] A. J. Buras, M. Jamin and P. H. Weisz, in ref. [9].
[13] J. Shigemitsu, these proceedings.
[14] S. Narison, Phys. Lett. **B 322** (1994) 247; S. Narison and A. Pivovarov, Phys. Lett. **B327** (1994) 341.
[15] R. Patterson, these proceedings.
[16] A. Ali, V. M. Braun and H. Simma, CERN TH.7118/93 (1993); J. M. Soares, Phys. Rev. **D49** (1994) 283; S. Narison, Phys. Lett. B327 (1994) 354.

Parallel Session Pa-17

Experimental Techniques

Conveners: R. Klanner (DESY)
                N. Ellis (CERN)

Scientific secretaries: R. L. Bates
                                 M. Stavrianakou (reserve)

Paper presented at XXVII Int. Conf. on High Energy Physics: Session Pa-17
Glasgow, UK, 20–27 July 1994

ATLAS liquid argon calorimetry for LHC

P. Pétroff

LAL, Orsay

On behalf of the RD3 collaboration:
Alberta University, Alma-Ata, LAPP Annecy, Univ. Autònoma Barcelona, Brookhaven National Laboratory, CERN, DAPNIA-SPP Saclay, ISN Grenoble, Univ. Autònoma Madrid, CCP Marseille, Univ. and INFN Milano, University of Montreal, LAL Orsay, LPNHE Universités de Paris VI et VII, Royal Institute of Technology Stockholm, University of Victoria.

Abstract

The RD3 collaboration has proposed and tested a new liquid argon calorimeter geometry. The performances obtained on large-scale prototypes satisfy the physics requirements at LHC: a sampling term of $10\%/\sqrt{E_{(GeV)}}$ with a constant term of 0.7% and a position resolution of $4\,\text{mm}/\sqrt{E_{(GeV)}}$ in the direction perpendicular to the accordion waves.

1. Introduction

The electromagnetic (em) calorimetry of the future ATLAS experiment will combine the liquid argon (LAr) sampling technique with accordion geometry and a fast readout.

This technology has been pioneered since 1990 by the RD3 collaboration [1]–[4].

Accordion geometry allows a fast rise time of the ionization current by minimizing the charge transfer time from the detector to the readout chain. This fast response is obtained by a shaping of the signal, with a 20 ns shaping time (40 ns signal peaking time).

In accordion geometry, the electrodes and the converter plates have an accordion shape with waves along the LHC beam's direction. Readout towers are defined by cutting the electrodes in longitudinal strips through which the signal propagates to the calorimeter's front or back faces. This is a very favorable configuration for high-speed, low-noise and small cross-talk. Moreover, the absence of dead space between the towers gives a good hermeticity and allows high granularity.

2. Large-scale barrel prototype

A 2 m-long barrel prototype was built with a fully pointing structure, already conceived as a sector of the ATLAS em barrel calorimeter. The main point investigated was the capability of maintaining the energy resolution at the level of $10\%/\sqrt{E}$ over a large angular coverage and a constant term of less than 1%, while keeping a short shaping time.

2.1. Description of the "2m" prototype

This prototype corresponds to a pseudorapidity range $0 < \eta < 1.1$ and covers 27° in ϕ. It fully points towards the nominal LHC interaction centre (Fig. 1).

The stack consists of 73 converter plates interleaved with 72 readout electrodes.

The absorbers are made of 1.8 mm-thick lead plates up to $\eta = 0.7$. As the sampling frequency decreases with the increase in rapidity, the lead thickness is reduced to 1.2 mm above $\eta = 0.7$.

The electrodes are multilayered copper-kapton boards of 0.3 mm thickness, separated from the converter plates by a 1.9 mm gap of LAr. The width of the LAr gap and the sampling fraction are kept constant

Figure 1. View of the 2m accordion prototype during assembly

	2 m prototype	
	$\eta = 0.28$	$\eta = 0.90$
$a\%$	10.0 ± 0.3	10.4 ± 0.3
b (MeV)	282 ± 17	387 ± 16
$c\%$	0.35 ± 0.04	0.27 ± 0.08

Table 1. Energy resolution fit results

by gradually changing the angle of the accordion folds along the depth of the calorimeter from 87° to 111°. The final mechanical layout was guided by a detailed Monte Carlo simulation [5].

The granularity is $\Delta\eta \times \Delta\phi \simeq 0.018 \times 0.020$ in the first two samplings ($9X_0$ each) and twice as coarse in η in the last one ($7X_0$).

2.2. Results in beam tests

2.2.1. Linearity and energy resolution: The energy resolution and the linearity were studied with a CERN electron beam from 10 GeV to 300 GeV, in two benchmark positions: $\eta = 0.28$ and $\eta = 0.90$ in the region readout with Si preamplifiers, and $\eta = 0.50$ in the region equipped with GaAs hybrids.

The calorimeter response was found to be linear within $\pm 1\%$. The dependence of the energy resolution, in respect of the incident energy, was fitted with the form $\sigma/E = a/\sqrt{E} \oplus b/E \oplus c$ where the three addends are the sampling term, the electronic noise and the constant term, respectively; E is expressed in GeV. The results are presented in Table 1 and on Fig. 2.

The data demonstrate that the sampling term of the energy resolution can be kept under control as a function of rapidity by suitably reducing the composition of the converter plates.

2.2.2. Position resolution: The position resolution was determined by comparing the shower centre of

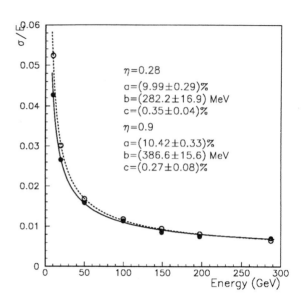

Figure 2. Energy resolution as a function of the incident energy for e^- hitting the calorimeter at $\eta = 0.28$ (closed circles) and $\eta = 0.90$ (open circles)

gravity with the extrapolated impact point provided by the beam chamber system. By fitting data with the expected $1/\sqrt{E}$ law (where E is in GeV) and after subtracting the contribution of the beam chambers, the position resolution was:

$$\sigma_\theta = (0.210 \pm 0.015) \oplus \frac{4.70 \pm 0.5}{\sqrt{E}} \text{ mm}$$

$$\sigma_\phi = (0.186 \pm 0.021) \oplus \frac{3.87 \pm 0.5}{\sqrt{E}} \text{ mm}$$

(Note that the constant term is dominated by the non-projectivity of the test beam).

2.2.3. Uniformity of response: Detailed Monte Carlo simulations give an understanding of the response of the accordion calorimeter as a function of the impact point. In ϕ, there is little (less than $\pm 1\%$) modulation, due to the accordion shape itself. In η there is a periodical modulation due to the limited containment of the shower in a fixed-sized cluster. These modulations are easily off-line corrected. A scan in uniformity was performed over a significant part of the prototype (~ 1 m^2). Figure 3 shows the relative response over the whole scanned region. It includes different e^- energies, and different front-end electronics. The resulting r.m.s. is 0.62%. This dispersion corresponds to a constant term of $0.7 \pm 0.05\%$.

A major part of this term can be attributed to known mechanical and non-uniform calibration sources.

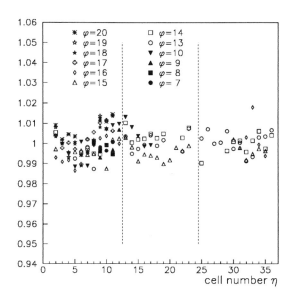

Figure 3. Mean energy reconstructed in the calorimeter for 287 GeV e^- as a function of the hit cell position in η for various rows in ϕ

3. End-cap prototype

Physics requires similar performances in both the barrel and the end-cap. It has been proposed to built an end-cap LAr prototype calorimeter with an accordion shape.

3.1. Description

The accordion end-cap calorimeter is designed to be ϕ symmetric while keeping the sampling fraction and the calorimeter density constant with the radius (see Fig. 4). Consequently the argon gap (1.2 mm to 1.9 mm) and the absorber thickness (lead 0.9 mm to 1.6 mm) increase with the radius. The detector geometry corresponds to a rapidity coverage from 2.16 to 2.89.

A constant response at short shaping time is obtained provided the drift time is also constant. This is achieved by radially increasing the high voltage. Typically the voltage grows from 0.8 kV to 2.2 kV.

The future ATLAS end-cap calorimeter will consist in two concentric wheels with 348 identical accordion-shaped absorbers, piled-up in phi, and interleaved with as many readout electrodes. The granularity is $\Delta \eta \times \Delta \phi = 0.03 \times 0.05$ rad.

3.2. Results in beam tests

3.2.1. Linearity and energy resolution: The prototype was scanned in η and ϕ. In η, the scan shows a dominant clustering effect with a period of one cell. A two-cell periodic effect can be seen at a level of less than

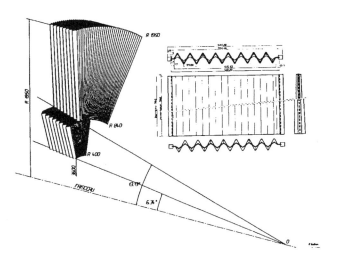

Figure 4. Schematic view of the end-cap calorimeter

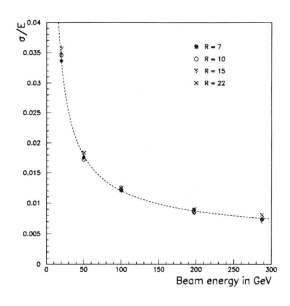

Figure 5. Energy resolution versus e^- beam energy at different η (radius) positions

1%, consequence of the discrete high voltage distribution.

As in the "2 m" prototype, a modulation in phi is observed (maximum $\pm$ 1.2%), well understood by the Monte Carlo simulation, and corrected off-line.

A good linearity between 20 – 287 GeV of $\pm 1\%$ is observed at different η positions (equivalent to a different radius). The energy resolution (see Figure 5) is given in Table 2 at different η values and for a 3 × 3 cluster.

The response uniformity is around 0.7% (very preliminary).

R (cell unit)	η (%)	Sampling (%)	Constant Term (%)	Noise (MeV)
7	2.7	10.0 ± 0.5	0.43 ± 0.06	492 ± 26
10	2.6	9.7 ± 0.5	0.44 ± 0.06	523 ± 27
15	2.4	10.5 ± 0.5	0.27 ± 0.09	532 ± 27
22	2.2	9.9 ± 0.5	0.50 ± 0.05	530 ± 22

Table 2. Energy resolution versus η

3.2.2. Resolution in position: By comparing the energy-weighted barycentre (3×3 cluster) with the extrapolated beam chambers impact point we obtain:

$$\sigma_\phi = \frac{4.9 \pm 0.5}{\sqrt{E}} \oplus (0.28 \pm 0.03) \oplus \left(\frac{23.7 \pm 2.8}{E}\right) \text{ mm}$$

$$\sigma_\theta = \frac{4.3 \pm 0.5}{\sqrt{E}} \oplus (0.19 \pm 0.04) \oplus \left(\frac{28.7 \pm 2.7}{E}\right) \text{ mm}$$
$$\eta = 2.7 \text{ (cell 7)}$$

$$\sigma_\theta = \frac{6.8 \pm 0.4}{\sqrt{E}} \oplus (0.21 \pm 0.05) \oplus \left(\frac{22.1 \pm 2.9}{E}\right) \text{ mm}$$
$$\eta = 2.2 \text{ (cell 22)}$$

The $1/E$ term comes from multiple scattering (1.4 m of foam between calorimeter and entrance face of cryostat). The position resolution improves at low radius where cell size is smaller.

4. Conclusion

The accordion technique is now a concept well validated by test beam results on large scale prototypes both for barrel and end-cap geometries. Its main features are:

- good energy linearity;
- energy and position resolution satisfying the physics requirement at LHC;
- good uniformity.

References

[1] B. Aubert et al., *Performance of a Liquid Argon Detector with an 'Accordion' Geometry*, Nucl. Instrum. Methods Phys. Res. **A309** (1991) p. 438.

[2] B. Aubert et al., *Performance of a Liquid Argon Calorimeter with Fast Readout*, Nucl. Instrum. Methods Phys. Res. **A321** (1992) p. 467.

[3] B. Aubert et al., *Performance of a Liquid Argon Calorimeter with a Cylindrical Geometry*, Nucl. Instrum. Methods Phys. Res. **A330** (1993) p. 405.

[4] B. Aubert et al., *Performance of a Liquid Argon Preshower Detector Integrated in an 'Accordion' Calorimeter*, Nucl. Instrum. Methods Phys. Res. **A330** (1993) p. 405.

[5] M. Lefèbvre, G. Parrour and P. Pétroff, *Electromagnetic Liquid Argon Accordion Calorimeter Simulation*, RD3 Internal Note **41** (unpublished).

Paper presented at XXVII Int. Conf. on High Energy Physics: Session Pa-17
Glasgow, UK, 20–27 July 1994

First High Resolution Results From a Cathode Strip Detector Based on Iarocci-type Plastic Chambers*

K. Lau, B. Mayes and J. Pyrlik

Physics Department and Institute for Beam Particle Dynamics,
University of Houston, Houston, Texas 77204-5506, USA

Abstract

We constructed a 1.0×0.5 m^2 three layer detector by combining inexpensive Iarocci-type PVC chambers with high precision 4 mm wide cathode strips photo-etched on circuit-board material. The detector was tested with cosmic rays and in a muon beam. By using an optimized reconstruction algorithm we were able to achieve spatial resolutions per layer below 50 μm. The angular and high voltage dependence of the resolution was found in good agreement with simple models and independent of gas mixtures.

1. Introduction

A Cathode Strip Chamber (CSC) is a proportional chamber which has a cathode that is segmented into strips oriented orthogonal to the wire. The avalanche near the wire induces image charges on the strips which are measured [1]. An algorithm is used to determine the track position from the strip charges [2]. Multiwire proportional chambers operated as CSCs using wire or strip cathodes have reached spatial resolutions of 50–60 μm [3]. Previous attempts to use Iarocci limited streamer chambers in CSCs achieved only resolutions of about 350 μm [4], which may have been caused by imprecise strips or a large non-uniformity in the graphite coating of the PVC leading to distortions in the strip charges.

The spatial resolution of CSCs is usually dominated by electronic noise in the charge measurement, and is given approximately by

$$\sigma_e = \sqrt{n_{st} - 1} \cdot \sigma_q/Q \cdot w, \tag{1}$$

where n_{st} is the number of strips used in the algorithm, σ_q/Q is the error in the charge measurement, and w is the strip pitch. A CSC with 5 mm pitch, a 0.5% charge error, and $n_{st} = 5$ could in principle achieve a resolution of 50 μm.

One of the drawbacks of CSCs is the strong dependence of the resolution on the incident angle of the track. At normal track incidence, $\alpha = 0$, all

avalanches develop in one spot on the wire; for $\alpha > 0$ the avalanches are spread out. The additional error on the track position can be approximated by

$$\sigma_\alpha = \frac{h \, \tan \alpha}{\sqrt{12 \, N_0/\cos \alpha}} = b \frac{\sin \alpha}{\sqrt{\cos \alpha}}, \tag{2}$$

where N_0 is the number of primary ionizations and h is the cell-height. In our case, $h = 9$ mm and $N_0 = 42$ [12], b is 400 μm and σ_α reaches about 50 μm at 7.5°.

We have pursued a new type of CSC [5, 6] combining mass-produced, moderate precision, Iarocci-style plastic streamer tubes with high precision photo-etched strips made on printed circuit boards. The tubes use thinner wires and are operated in the proportional mode.

2. Detector Construction

In order to determine the intrinsic spatial resolution of such a CSC, and to fully investigate the angular dependence of the resolution, we have constructed a three layer 0.5×1 m^2 prototype, see Fig. 1. We used low resistivity (4 kΩ/□) graphite coated PVC profiles made at the Streamer Chamber Assembly and Research Facility (SCARF) at the University of Houston [7]. Each layer consists of 12 sealed streamer chambers strung with 44.5 μm tungsten wires. Facing the open side of the chambers is a 1040×540 mm^2 circuit-board (1.53 mm FR-4 with 0.5 oz/ft^2 copper on both faces). The 100 strips, each 1 m long and 4 mm wide (5 mm pitch) on each board were produced by standard photo-etching techniques. Each strip-board is mounted

* This research was supported by the US Department of Energy (DOE), the Texas National Research Laboratory Commission (TNRLC), and the SSC Laboratory R&D program

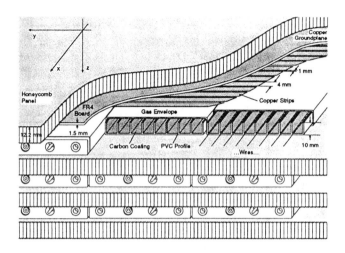

Figure 1. Assembly details of the CSC prototype.

on the underside of a 1/2″ honeycomb panel which also supports the next layer of chambers. A stripless fourth panel supports the lowest layer of chambers. The panels were aligned by 1/2″ steel pins inserted through precision holes, referenced to fiducial marks on the strip-boards, in the reinforced corners of each panel.

The middle ten strips of each layer were connected to low-noise charge amplifiers (gain ≈ 500), designed and built by a group at Dubna [10] and loaned to us. The signals were digitized by 11-bit charge-sensitive ADCs (LeCroy 2249W) using an integration time of 500 ns. The observed average amplifier noise was 6.5 ADC counts. The gain of the amplifiers was calibrated by signals from a pulse generator.

3.   Experiments

We have tested the prototype with cosmic rays at at the SSC Laboratory using the Texas Test Rig (TTR), a $3\times5\times5$ m^3 muon telescope [11]. The muons had a momentum of at least 1.3 GeV after penetrating a 1 m iron absorber. We operated the prototype with the flammable standard (ST) mixture of 75% isobutane and 25% argon and with a non-flammable (NF) mixture of 77.5% CO_2, 10.0% isobutane and 2.5% argon.

We have also tested the prototype in a 190 GeV muon beam at CERN, 50 m downstream of the SMC target 3 m away from the beam line. The detector was mounted with the strips vertically and the wires horizontally and could be rotated around a vertical axis. The trigger-rate from two 12.5×40.0 cm^2 scintillators, installed before and after the prototype was 800 Hz during spill. We took data runs of about 100 000 triggers that lasted approximately one hour, for different settings of chamber voltage, gas mixture, and incident angle.

Calibration runs of about 10 000 events were taken between data runs.

4.   Data Analysis

Using the information from the calibration runs, the raw data were corrected for pedestal (average 35 counts) and preamplifier gain. Several cuts were applied to extract events for resolution determination. The cuts ensured clusters of at least four strips with no overflowing ADC channels in all three layers. The final data samples used for the resolution analysis of each setting contained between 5000 and 15 000 events.

The muon trajectory is determined by the x-position (along the wire) of the avalanche in each of the three layers. We developed a weighted center-of-gravity (WCOG) method [9] that combines the simple weighted means determined from three (x_3) and four (x_4) strips in such a way that the result (x_w) is exact, when the avalanche is between two strips and when it is in the center of a strip:

$$x_w = \frac{x_3}{1 + \frac{2}{w}(x_3 - x_4)}. \qquad (3)$$

All x positions are relative to the highest strip measured in units of the strip pitch w. Using the least-square method a straight line is fitted through the three points and a single residual is determined. The WCOG method introduces a systematic error in the residuals, which is periodic in x, and reaches about ±80 μm at $x = \frac{1}{4}w$ and $x = \frac{3}{4}w$ which is clearly visible in a residual vs. x plot. We corrected this deviation using a three term fourier series, $\sum a_n \sin(\frac{2n\pi x}{w})$, with $a_1 = 80.0$, $a_2 = -6.2$ and $a_3 = 3.3$ μm. The relative alignment of the three layers was determined empirically, and was corrected by a 25 μm shift in x-direction of the middle plane.

5.   Results

Fig. 2 shows the distribution of residuals for two chambers voltages. The distributions were fitted to a four parameter Gaussian, yielding a σ of 41.6 and 21.9 μm. This σ has to be multiplied by a statistical factor of $\sqrt{6}$ in order to get the resolution per layer, σ_l. The best σ_l achieved is 53.3 ±0.9 μm with beam muons (Fig. 2) and 44.7 ±2.8 μm (not shown) for cosmics, both at 3300 V. The resolution σ_l at normal incidence as a function of the most probable pulse height is shown in Fig. 3. The data were divided in two groups, beam data (solid symbols) and cosmic data (open symbols). The points in each group are well described by a fit of the form $\sigma = \sqrt{\sigma_i^2 + \sigma_e^2}$, with an intrinsic term, σ_i, and an electronic noise term, σ_e, of the form given in eqn. (1), and proportional to $1/PH$. The beam data are a combination of the points for the ST and NF gases.

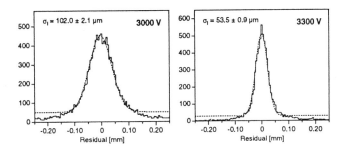

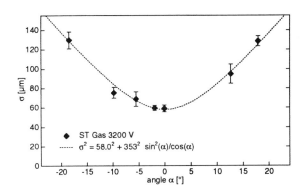

Figure 2. Distribution of residuals and Gauss-fit for beam data at normal incidence using the standard gas for 3000 and 3300 V.

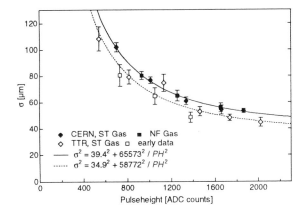

Figure 3. Resolution as a function of pulse height for beam and cosmic muons and results of two fits.

Figure 4. Resolution as a function of the incident angle α of the muon and results of a fit.

an inexpensive non-flammable mixture of 87.5% CO_2, 10.0% isobutane and 2.5% argon could be used. Due to the mass-producible plastic chambers and the industry made strips the overall construction and operating costs for this type of CSC are expected to be much lower than those of MWPC systems.

Acknowledgments

We thank R. Weinstein for the use of the SCARF facility. We are grateful to the staff at TTR, particularly to Yu. Bonushkin, A. Gonzales, and E. C. Milner. The assistance provided by the SMC and ATLAS collaborations for the CERN runs is acknowledged.

The data support the hypothesis that the resolution is only a function of the pulse height, and is independent of the gas mixture. The fits infer an intrinsic resolution of about 40 μm for the beam data and 35 μm for the cosmic data. An estimate of σ_e based on eqn (1) for our prototype, using $n_{st} = 3.5$ (we combine 3 and 4 strips), $\sigma_q = 6.5$ ADC counts, and $w = 5000$ μm, gives 51 400 μm/count, which is 14–28% smaller than the fit results, and supports the validity of the simple resolution model.

We have also studied angular effects. The spatial resolution as a function of the muon incident angle is shown in Fig. 4, for the standard gas at 3.2 kV. The curve is a fit with $\sigma = \sqrt{\sigma_0^2 + \sigma_\alpha^2}$ where σ_0 is the 0°-resolution and σ_α is of the form of eqn. (2). The fitted b value of 353 μm is 12% lower than our estimate of 400 μm based on our geometry. The results from refs. [3] seem to suggest b-parameters 2 to 3 times higher than the prediction of eqn. (2).

6. Conclusions

A spatial resolution of about 50 μm was achieved in a CSC prototype constructed with plastic streamer tubes and precision strips. This resolution is comparable to that of multi-wire-proportional CSCs. It was shown that

References

[1] For a recent review, see F. Sauli, NIM **156** (1978) 147.
[2] I. Endo *et al.*, NIM **188** (1981) 51; E. Gatti, A. Longoni, R.A. Boie, and V. Radeka, NIM **188** (1981) 327; J. Chiba *et al.*, NIM **206** (1983) 451.
[3] A. Breskin *et al.*, NIM **143** (1977) 29; G. Charpak *et al.*, NIM **148** (1978) 471; G. Charpak *et al.*, NIM **167** (1979) 455; L. S. Barabash *et al.*, NIM **A236** (1985) 271; H. van der Graaf *et al.*, NIM **A307** (1991) 220.
[4] J. Fujimoto *et al.*, NIM **A252** (1986) 53; G. D'Agostini *et al.*, NIM **A252** (1986) 431; G. Bauer *et al.*, NIM **A260** (1987) 101; Yu. Ye. Bonushkin, A. V. Korytov, and V. L. Malyshev, NIM **A300** (1991) 268.
[5] G. Mitselmakher, private communication; K. Lau, B Mayes, J. Pyrlik, and R. Weinstein, GEM TN-93-281 (unpublished).
[6] N. Khovansky *et al.*, LNS-94-52, 1994, (to be published).
[7] D. Hungerford *et al.*, NIM **A286**, (1990) 431; K. Lau, D. Parks, J. Pyrlik, and R. Weinstein, NIM **A320** (1992) 243.
[8] Iarocci, NIM **217** (1983) 30.
[9] K. Lau and J. Pyrlik, *An Optimized Algorithm for Centroid Finding in Cathode Strip Chambers*, UHIBPD-HEP-94-002, 1994 (to be published).
[10] M. O. Deighton, NIM **58** (1968) 201; R. A. Boie *et al.*, NIM **192** (1982) 365; P. D'Angelo *et al.*, NIM **193** (1982) 523.
[11] E. C. Milner, *Overview of the GEM Muon System Cosmic Ray Test Program at the SSCL*, SSCL-PRE-256 (1993).
[12] F. Sauli, *Principles of Operation of Multiwire Proportional and Drift Chambers*, CERN 77-09 (1977). Reprinted in *Experimental Techniques in High Energy Physics*, edited by T. Ferbel, Addison-Wesley, 1987.

Paper presented at XXVII Int. Conf. on High Energy Physics: Session Pa-17
Glasgow, UK, 20–27 July 1994

Gas microstrip Chambers for LHC

T. J. V. Bowcock

Oliver Lodge Laboratory, Department of Physics
Liverpool University, P.O. Box 147
Liverpool L69 3BX, England

Abstract

Gas Microstrip Detectors have been proposed for the forward region of the ATLAS detector at the Large Hadron Collider (LHC). The properties of Gas Microstrip Chambers fabricated on a thin silicon dioxide layer are discussed below. In particular their ageing and rate properties are presented.

1. Introduction

Gas Microstrip Chambers (MSGC's) are a technology that has been developed over the last few years for the space, medical and High Energy Physics communities[1,2,3,4,5]. In HEP we have concentrated on this technology because there are many favourable features that are most promising for the construction of tracking chambers: low mass and two-dimensional readout are only two of these. Here we present a brief review of our current understanding of a specific type of MSGC - that fabricated on a thin ion-implanted silicon dioxide layer - and try to assess the advantages and disadvantages of using MSGC's in the ATLAS experiment.

The MSGC's discussed below were fabricated on Si wafers by Hughes Microelectronics U.K. The detectors were of a parallel geometry (non-parallel or *keystone* designs have been built and tested and have been reported elsewhere[6]) and had the following properties. The pitch of the detectors was 200 microns. The anodes and cathodes were 1.4 microns thick aluminium. The anode width was 10 microns and the cathode width was 78 microns wide. The wafers were 100mm in diameter which enabled a detector of active area of 60mm by 60mm to be built. The anodes and cathodes were dry etched onto a 3 micron layer of CVD oxide. which was laid down on a 300μm thick Si wafer. The CVD was implanted with $4*10^{16}$ Boron ions per cm^2 in order to modify the resistance of the substrate. It has not yet been proven conclusively that the mechanism by which the surface is rendered conducting by ion bombardment is fully understood, but it is believed to be due to a very thin non-stoichiometric surface layer. Further details of the contruction of these detectors may be found in the literature.

2. Laboratory Tests

The detectors were assembled in as a controlled environment as possible - important for devices where surface resistance is crucial to their performace and then detectors were characterized in the laboratory. The tests of most interest here are the ones that are important for: 2D readout, high rates and accelerated ageing tests.

The detectors tested here had a 3mm gas gap between the anode-cathode structures and the drift plane (aluminized mylar). The gases chosen were DME and argon. The gain versus anode voltage for these detectors is shown in Figure 1.

The 2D readout capability has been discussed elsewhere[7]. Anode strips and the backplane were readout simultaneously. It was seen that the pulse heights are well correlated. Thus the use of a divided backplane would give 2D capability to a detector fabricated on a single substrate.

Since the LHC will operate at high rates we have studied the MSGC's in order to understand their behaviour in this regime. In particular we have made pulse height and current measurements from a few Hz to a few MHz. This was done using an X-ray generator with a Cu target that produced a small collimated (1mm^2) beam directed onto the MSGC drift plane at normal incidence. In this test the effect of the (slow)

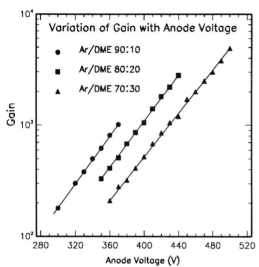

Figure 1: Shows the variation of gain of the MSGC counters with anode voltage for different gas mixtures.

amplifiers was seen at high currents. In order to overcome this problem a fast DAQ and amplifier system enabled us to look at the pulse shape at rates of up to 1MHz. The performance was extremely uniform as a function of rate as can be seen in Figure 2.

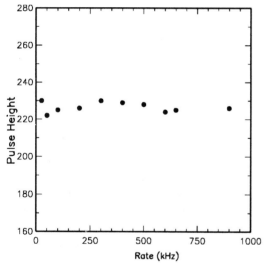

Figure 2: Shows the rate dependence of the of the gain of the MSGC chambers.

The intense X-ray source enabled us to make a first attempt at exposing the MSGC's to large integrated currents. The X-rays that interact in the gas create much more primary charge than a minimum ionizing particle. The combination of high flux and large

currents means that the charge collected (per cm of strip) is between 100 and 1000 times larger in the X-ray machine than at LHC. We should note that it is clear that this does not correctly duplicate the damage caused by charged and neutral particles (including neutrons) at LHC. The accumulated charge versus the relative gas gain is shown in Figure 3.

3. Test Beam Studies

These chambers have been run in a testbeam at CERN in order to study, amongst other details, the resolution. A run was taken in 1993 and has been followed by two runs in 1994. In our final configuration 8 planes of Si diode detectors were used to define the trajectory of charged particles through the MSGC chambers. Here we show a few results from the 1993 data (the higher statistics 1994 data is still under anlysis) that demonstrate a resolution of about 36 microns for normally incident tracks, Fig. 4 and the resolutions as a function of angle and gas mixture, Figure 5.

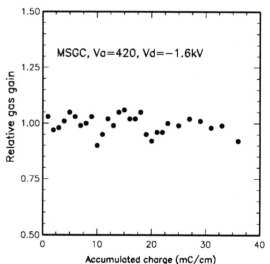

Figure 3: Gain in the accelerated ageing test for MSGC counters.

4. Simulation

In parallel with the development of the detectors a detailed simulation of the MSGC chambers has been developed. This combined an commercial electrostatics package (MAXWELL™ by ANSOFT) and a detailed simulation of the processes in the gas. This enables not only the fields to be predicted at every point on the chambers but also much more interesting measurable quantities like the cumulative anode signal versus time. This is crucial if MSGC's are to be used in LHC. This simulation has already predicted a shift in the measured charge weighted cluster centre compared to the actual *true* position. This shift can be corrected for in test beam data and gives an improvement in the resolution of about 4-5 microns.

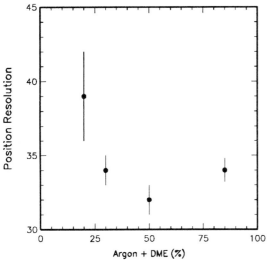

Figure 4: Resolution as a function of some gas mixtures for MSGC chambers.

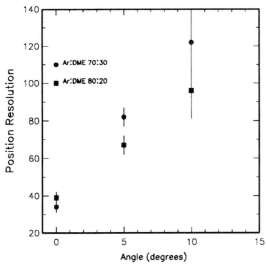

Figure 5: Resolution as a function of incident particle direction.

5. Summary

It is clear that MSGC technology is evolving rapidly. New substrates are being developed all the time. However many fundamental questions have yet to be fully answered:

- Ageing in a realistic LHC environment has to be demonstrated.
- Robustness: the detectors have to be impervious to micro-discharges and large neutron induced discharges.
- The correct electronics - which must depend on the exact type of detector chosen (simulation shows large dependencies on detector substrate technology) must be proven.
- The precise details of the gas and operating conditions need to be defined.
- Cost must be as low as possible.

For LHC applications the relatively low gain and slow rise times of the current designs is far from optimal. However it should be emphasized that for medium resolution tracking with very low amounts of material MSGC's may yet prove to be ideal.

Acknowledgments

It is a pleasure to thank my colleagues whose work is represented here, P.P. Allport, S. Biagi., P.S.L. Booth, J.N. Jackson, T. Jones, S. Kiourkos, I.J. Last, J. Richardson and N.A. Smith. In particular I thank D. King, A. Muir and E.J. Orme for their superb design and technical work.

References

[1] A. Oed, Nucl. Instr. Meth. **A263** (1988) 351.
[2] P. McIntyre, Nucl. Inst. Meth.
[3] F. Angelini, Nucl. Instr. Meth. **A315** (1992) 351.
[4] S.F. Baigi *et al.*, Nucl. Instr. Meth. **A323** (1992) 258.
[5] T. Bowcock, in Proc. XXVI Int. Conf. on HEP; Eds. J.R. Sanford (AIP Publishing, 1993).
[6] S. Kiorkos *et al.*, Nucl. Instr. Meth. **A348** (1994) 351
[7] F. Sauli, CERN-DRDC-93-34 (RD28).

Paper presented at XXVII Int. Conf. on High Energy Physics: Session Pa-17
Glasgow, UK, 20–27 July 1994

Performance of Microstrip Gas Chambers Passivated by Thin Semiconducting Glass and Plastic Films

M.R. Bishai[†], E.K.E. Gerndt[†], I.P.J. Shipsey[†], P.N. Wang[†] A.V. Bagulya[‡], V.M. Grishin[‡], M.A. Negodaev[‡] and P. Geltenbort[§]

† Purdue University, West Lafayette, IN 17907-1396, U.S.A.
‡ Lebedev Institute, Lenin Prospect 53, 117924 Moscow GSP-1, Russia
§ Institute Laue-Langevin, BP 156, F-38042 Grenoble Cedex 9, France

Abstract

Patterned Microstrip Gas chamber substrates were covered with ion-beam sputtered glass with electronic conductivity or a polymer which was subsequently irradiated with an ion-beam. The performance of several detectors is reported.

1. Introduction

In the Microstrip Gas Chamber (MSGC), the wires of a multiwire proportional chamber are replaced by metallic microstrips produced by lithography on a dielectric substrate [1]. The avalanche discharge in a MSGC near the anode strip develops very close to the surface of the dielectric substrate. This is one of the main disadvantages of the MSGC: the gain variation due to the accumulation of positive avalanche ions on the dielectric substrate limits the high rate capability of the detector. Several approaches have been proposed to solve this problem. If the substrate bulk resistivity is selected in the range $\rho \sim 10^9 - 10^{12}\Omega\cdot$cm effective neutralization of positive ions on the substrate surface up to a rate of $\sim 10^6$ particles/mm^2 can be achieved, but a substantial current between anode and cathode strips and, hence, noise and heat are also produced [2]. A similar behavior is observed on substrates with a surface layer of thickness $t \sim 1\mu$m modified to be semiconductive with a surface resistivity of $R_s \sim \rho/t \sim 10^{11} - 10^{14}\Omega/\square$, for example, by ion implantation [3][4]. More recently it was proposed to cover the substrate surface and microstrip pattern with a semiconductive film (figure 1), for example by thin (20-100 Å) copper or germanium layers [5]. The latter method also improves,

by passivation, the breakdown condition of the MSGC.

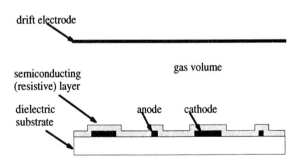

Figure 1. Microstrip gas chamber with surface fully passivated by thin semiconducting coating.

In this paper we investigate the performance of MSGC's with the substrate surface passivated by sputtering glass with electronic conductivity or spun-on polyimide followed by ion-implantation.

2. Preparation of Glass and Polymide Coatings

Plates of standard photomask glass ($\rho > 10^{16}\Omega.$cm) were used as MSGC substrates on which a microstrip pattern (chromium with a thickness of 0.1-0.15 μm), was prepared by electron beam lithography.

We passivated the MSGC substrate surface by ion-beam sputtering of glass with electronic conductivity. The sputtering was performed at the GELIS (Lebedev Institute) facility, which is an ion accelerator of elements with atomic numbers in the range Z = 1-54 with ion energies up to 50KeV. An accelerated beam of neon ions (10-15KeV) is incident on a glass target below which the MSGC substrate is mounted. The sputtering material consisted of 5mm thick plates, prepared according to the SSPC NIEES specifications [7]. Composition I is a multicomponent silicate glass with bulk resistivity $\rho \sim 10^9 - 10^{10}\Omega$.cm. An MSGC with a substrate made from this type of glass has already demonstrated long-term stable performance and promising high rate capability [6]. Phosphate glass of composition II has a volume resistivity $\rho \sim 10^9\Omega$.cm and an increased content of lead oxide, which is slightly reduced during the sputtering process.

For an ion beam current in the range of 0.5-1A and exposure time of 5-10 hours, the coating thickness, measured by an ellipsometer was in the range $t = 200 - 1000\text{Å}$.

An MSGC substrate with a microstrip pattern prepared as described above was covered with a very thin polyimide film (0.3 - 0.5μm) by spinning on a liquid polymer. The MSGC with the polymide coating was then irradiated by a hydrogen ion beam at about 30KeV. The range of hydrogen ions in polymide is about 1μm. The irradiation causes the formation of a semiconducting polymer matrix in the full thickness of the coating. An advantage of using polyimide rather than glass is that the preparation time is greatly reduced. At a beam current of about 1mA and exposure time of 100-200s (total dose $10^{15} - 10^{16}$ions/cm^2), the surface resistivity of the coating was in the range $10^{12} - 10^{14}\Omega/\square$

3. Detector Performance

Four detectors differing in geometry and conducting layer were transported to Purdue for further evaluation. A description of the four samples is given in table 1. Sample A and B have a 1 mm pitch suitable for applications in neutron physics. Sample C and D have a 200 micron pitch, well-suited for use in a High Energy Physics experiment.

The test assembly consisted of a stainless steel gas enclosure to house the MSGC. A thin aluminized mylar window in the enclosure provided the drift electrode and an enterance port for collimated ^{55}Fe photons. A gas system provided an Argon Isobutane 90/10 mixture regulated by mass flow controllers downstream of a purification stage. In all detectors groups of electrodes (anodes) are connected via a common readout pad. The

Sample	pitch: anode : cathode	conductive layer
A	1,000 : 12 : 500	glass I
B	1,000 : 12 : 500	glass II
C	200 : 10 : 90	glass I
D	200 : 10 : 90	kapton

Table 1. MSGC Sample

cathodes are grounded through 1MΩ. The response of the 40 OR'ed anodes of sample A to a ^{55}Fe source providing a few 10^3 photons/mm^2/s is shown in figure 2. Excellent energy resolution of about 15% at 6 KeV is obtained for a gain of about 1,000. The energy resolution as a function of gas gain is shown in figure 3. Full efficiency is reached above 500 V and gains of about 30,000 at 750 V were achieved without any sign of electrical breakdown (figure 4). Another factor of two in gain was obtained by varying the drift voltage. The need for a relatively high operating voltage and the fact that a large gain is achieved without breakdown is attributable to both the passivation provided by the conducting layer and the large distance between the anode and cathode microstrips.

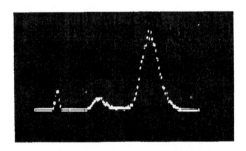

Figure 2. Response of sample A to a ^{55}Fe source.

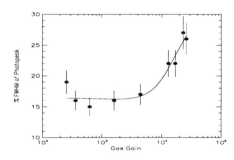

Figure 3. Energy resolution for different gas gains for sample A.

Detector B has the same geometry as sample A, however the semi-conducting layer is a glass based on P$_2$O$_5$ (composition II), that has a resistivity, for

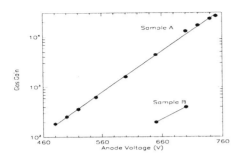

Figure 4. Gas gain as a function of anode voltage for samples A and B.

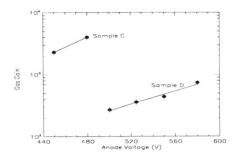

Figure 5. Gas gain as a function of anode voltage for samples C and D.

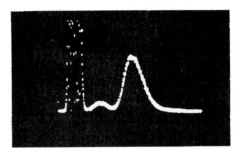

Figure 6. Response of sample D to a ^{55}Fe source.

this detector, several orders of magnitude less than composition I glass. As expected there is a significant gain suppression in this detector (figure 4), about a factor three, compared to detector A. This phenomenon was predicted in [8] and subsequently observed in ion-implanted plastic MSGC's by our group [4].

Detector C differs from detector A only in having a smaller pitch. At the same voltage, the gain of detector C is higher by more than an order of magnitude, compared to detector A (figure 5.). However the largest gain we were able to obtain, before breakdown, was 5,000 at 490 V. The lower maximum attainable gain of detector C is presumably related to the small anode cathode gap of only 50 microns.

Detector D has the same geometry as detector C but is covered in ion-implanted kapton rather than glass. The kapton has a resistivity several orders of magnitude less than glass I and in consequence gain suppression relative to detector C was expected and observed. Detector D has a gain suppressed by about a factor of 20 (figure 5). The spectrum obtained with detector D is shown in figure 6. For this figure the anodes are at 500 V, the gas gain is approximately 500 and the energy resolution is about 30 %. The poorer energy resolution compared to detector A, may be related to the thickness of the ion implanted Kapton layer, or the variation in the thickness of this layer.

4. Conclusion

From our measurements we conclude that MSGCs with thin semiconductive coatings of sputtered glass with electronic conductivity show encouraging performance at moderate rates. Our results on the performance of a MSGC with a thin conducting polyimide layer show that this technique is promising but needs further study. We are now working to systematically study the high rate performance and aging properties of thin conducting film MSGC's.

Acknowledgement

The authors would like to thank F.Sauli, M. Heidrich and V. Rigato for fruitful discussions. The Lebedev group performed this investigation in the framework of the collaboration for the Development of Microstrip Gas Chambers for Radiation Detection and Tracking at High Rates (CERN Research and Development Project RD-28). IPJS thanks the Young Investigator Program of the U.S. National Science Foundation and the SSC Fellowship Program of the Texas National Research Laboratory Commission. This work was supported in part under U.S. Department of Energy Contract No. (DE-FG02-91ER40681).

References

[1] A. Oed, Nucl.Instr.and Meth. A263 (1988)351.
[2] R. Bouclier *et al.* Nucl.Instr.and Meth. A332 (1993)100.
[3] F. Angelini *et al.* Nucl.Instr.and Meth. A314 (1992)450.
[4] I. Shipsey, in Proceedings of the European Physical Society Europhysics Conference, Marseille, France (1993).
[5] S. Brons *et al.* Preprint CERN-PPE/93-194 (1993).
[6] R. Bouclier *et al.* Preprint CERN-PPE/93-192 (1993).
[7] N.V. Petroiyh, "Electrical Properties and Structure of Iron Contained Glasses", Table I. Proceedings of the 10th International Glass Congress, Japan (1967)
[8] J. Florent *etal.* Nucl.Instr.and Meth. A329 (1993)125.

A Straw Transition Radiation Tracker for the LHC

M. Stavrianakou

University of Glasgow

on behalf of the RD6 collaboration

Abstract

The role and the performance of an integrated straw tracker and transition radiation detector (TRT), as proposed for the ATLAS experiment at the future Large Hadron Collider (LHC), have been extensively investigated by the RD6 collaboration, with Monte Carlo simulations, test beam studies of prototype detectors and laboratory tests of the various elements. Here, we summarize the properties of the straw tubes as detecting elements and we present test beam results which demonstrate the tracking and particle identification capabilities of the detector.

1. Introduction

In the inner detector of the proposed ATLAS experiment at the LHC, [1], 'continuous' tracking and electron identification using the phenomenon of transition radiation [2] in an integrated Straw Transition Radiation Tracker (TRT) [3, 4, 5, 6] are combined with 'precision' tracking in discrete layers.

The TRT occupies the outer ~ 40 cm of the inner detector cavity and covers 2.5 units in rapidity. The active detector elements are 4 mm in diameter proportional 'straw' chambers, arranged axially in the central 'barrel' region and radially in the forward and backward 'end-cap' regions. This orientation allows optimal use of the 2 T axial magnetic field of the inner detector. The straws are evenly distributed over the detector volume, so as to have low correlation between pile-up hits when searching for high-p_T tracks.

The transition radiation photons are produced in the 'radiator' which is polyethylene foam into which the straws are embedded in the barrel, and stacks of polypropylene foils stretched between the straw planes in the end-caps.

The role of the TRT will be to provide tracking and pattern recognition over $|\eta| < 2.5$ at the highest LHC luminosities for charged tracks with $p_T > 0.5$ GeV, particle identification over a wide η range, namely identification of electrons and high energy muons with the rejection of hadrons using transition radiation and of photon conversions and Dalitz pairs by finding the partners, and finally, level 2 trigger information to identify tracks of $p_T > 10$ GeV.

2. The Proportional 'Straw' Tubes

The active detector elements of the TRT are proportional straw tubes, [7, 8] 4 mm in diameter with 50 μm anode wire. They are made of 60 μm thick Kapton film, coated on both surfaces with a thin conductive layer of carbon and aluminum. The straws will be reinforced with C-fibres glued along the straw wall. Their mechanical and electrical properties have been thoroughly investigated and are well understood [7, 8]. The gas gain uniformity along the straw will be better than 5%.

With a gas mixture of 70% $Xe+20\%CF_4+10\%CO_2$ at a gas gain of 2.5×10^4 [9] the total charge collection time in the 2 Tesla field of the ATLAS inner detector is 38 ns.

The ageing studies have shown that there are no changes for fluences of 4×10^{14} cm^{-2} fast neutrons and 1.7×10^{15} cm^{-2} slow neutrons and ionizing doses of 80 Mrad i.e. more than 20 years of operation at the highest luminosity, no ageing for total integrated charge of up to 5 C/cm i.e. 8 years at design luminosity, no etching effects on the cathode for similar charge and no transient radiation ageing effects.

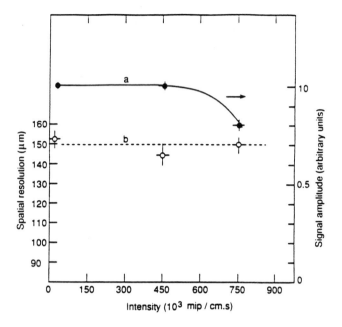

Figure 1. Amplitude of signal from ^{55}Fe (a) and drift-time accuracy (b) as a function of the charged particle rate per unit straw length.

Dedicated studies were performed to determine the influence of space charge effects on the gas gain and the spatial resolution. Fig.1 shows the drift-time accuracy and the amplitude of the signal from a ^{55}Fe source as a function of the charged particle rate per unit straw length. No deterioration of performance is observed for intensities of up to 6×10^5 particles per cm per second, i.e. twice the maximum intensities expected in ATLAS.

Under the LHC operating conditions, the TRT straw tubes will be continuously irradiated by charged particles and neutrons. The occupancy will be 34% in the 1 m long straws close to the beam in the barrel TRT and 15% in the endcap wheels, corresponding to 14 and 6 MHz counting rates respectively. Good performance of the straws for up to 12 MHz is maintained by ensuring ion tail cancellation.

3. Test Beam Studies

A TRT prototype consisting of 864 40 cm long, 4 mm diameter Kapton straws embedded in polyethylene foam radiator [10] was tested at the SPS. The straws were operated with 70% Xe 20% CF_4 10% CO_2 at a gas gain of 2.5×10^4. All straws were equipped with fast preamplifiers, shaping amplifiers, discriminators and ADCs; half of the channels were also equipped with

TDCs for drift time measurements inside the straws. The prototype was exposed to electron, pion and photon beams, and also 205 GeV pions on a Be target for performance in jet studies. Data were taken without and with magnetic field.

3.1. Tracking Performance of the TRT Prototype

Fig.2 shows an event display in the TRT in magnetic field.

For a tracking threshold of 250 eV and signal rise time $\sim$ 12 ns, the drift time accuracy per straw was $\sim$ 170 μm and the track reconstruction accuracy was 0.17 mrad in angle and 37 μm in position.

The measured momentum resolution in BL=0.3 Tm was $\Delta p_T/p_T = 4.2\times10^{-3}p_T$. This extrapolates to $\Delta p_T/p_T = 8\times10^{-4}p_T$ in the 2 Tm of the ATLAS inner detector.

The alignment accuracy with drift time measurements was $\sigma \simeq 70$ μm for 100 tracks per straw and with 400 μm external coordinate detector resolution; it can be improved to $\sim$ 40 μm for 30 μm external device accuracy.

By calculating fake track rates for different degrees of hit correlations using target run data and MC extrapolations to LHC, it has been shown that the TRT pattern recognition capabilities remain robust even at the highest LHC luminosities provided the number of crossed straws per track remains $\sim$ 40.

3.2. Particle Identification with the TRT prototype

The charged pion rejection, calculated by counting transition radiation clusters, i.e. energy depositions with energy above an optimal threshold of 6.5 keV, was of the order of $\sim 10^{-2}$ for 90% electron efficiency, for a configuration corresponding to $|\eta| = 1.2$ in ATLAS up to occupancies of $\sim$ 15%, fig.3. This rejection does not deteriorate for channel gain dispersions up to 15%.

It was shown that the rejection improves by $\sim$ 2 orders of magnitude as the detector thickness seen by the particle increases by a factor of 4, due to the larger number of crossed straws and the longer total path in the radiator; it also improves with increasing Xenon concentration, 70% being a practical upper limit for drift time and operational stability.

Converted photons, in the absence of magnetic field and using only TR-information, were rejected by factors of $\sim 10 - 40$ depending on the photon energy. Conversions produced in the TRT material were rejected by a factor of 60.

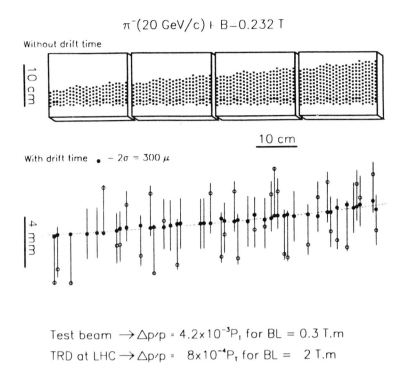

$$\pi^-(20 \text{ GeV/c}) \vdash \text{B}-0.232 \text{ T}$$

Without drift time

10 cm

10 cm

With drift time ● $- 2\sigma = 300 \mu$

4 mm

Test beam $\rightarrow \Delta p/p = 4.2 \times 10^{-3} P_1$ for BL = 0.3 T.m

TRD at LHC $\rightarrow \Delta p/p = 8 \times 10^{-4} P_1$ for BL = 2 T.m

Figure 2. TRT-prototype event display for the 1992 run in magnetic field. The lower part corresponds to the drift-time hits with a magnification of 25 along the vertical axis. The full/open circles represent the chosen/rejected coordinate as obtained from the drift-time measurement, once the track fit has been performed.

4. Conclusions

Kapton straw tubes reinforced with C-fibres will operate reliably in a magnetic field even at the highest LHC luminosities. No loss of performance due to ageing is expected for more than 10 years of operation at the design luminosity.

Using drift time measurements inside the straw tubes a $\sim 170~\mu$ m accuracy per straw can be achieved. The charged particle momentum resolution extrapolated to LHC (BL=2 Tm) is $\Delta p_T/p_T = 8 \times 10^{-4} p_T$.

The TRT pattern recognition capabilities remain robust even at the highest LHC luminosities provided the number of crossed straws per track remains ~ 40.

Charged hadron rejection factors of ~ 100 can be achieved up to occupancies of $\sim 15\%$.

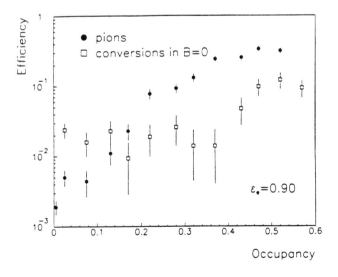

$\varepsilon_e = 0.90$

Figure 3. Efficiency for detecting 20 GeV pions and 20-150 GeV photon conversions as a function of straw occupancy.

References

[1] *ATLAS, Letter of Intent*, CERN/LHCC 92-4
[2] V.L. Ginzburg and I.M. Frank, Zh. Eksp. Teor. Fiz. 16 (1946) 15
[3] V.A. Polychronakos et al., CERN/DRDC/90-38, DRDC/P8
[4] V.A. Polychronakos et al., CERN/DRDC/91-47
[5] V. Commishau et al., CERN/DRDC/93-46
[6] J. T. Shank et al, Nucl. Instr. Meth. A309(1991)377/385
[7] V. Bondarenko et al., Nucl. Instr. Meth. A327(1993)386
[8] RD6 Collaboration, ATLAS Internal Note,INDET-NO-018
[9] B. Dolgoshein et al, CERN-EP/89-161, 12 December 1989
[10] V. Chernyatin et al., Nucl. Instr. Meth. A325(1993)441/445

Paper presented at XXVII Int. Conf. on High Energy Physics: Session Pa-17
Glasgow, UK, 20–27 July 1994

The DELPHI Microvertex Detector with Double Sided Readout

W. J. Murray

Rutherford Appleton Laboratory, Chilton, Didcot, Oxon., OX11 0QX, UK

On behalf of the DELPHI Collaboration

Abstract

The Silicon Strip Microvertex detector of the DELPHI experiment has been upgraded to read not only $R\phi$ coordinates but z as well, without increasing the material in the active volume. This has been achieved using double sided silicon detectors with a second metal layer routing the z signals to the ends.

1. Introduction

The DELPHI[1] experiment at LEP had a silicon microvertex detector installed from the beginning. Initially two layers of $R\phi$ readout, it was upgraded to three layers in 1991 when the radius of the beampipe was reduced to 5.5 cm. This detector is described in[2], and had a resolution of $\sqrt{(69/p_t)^2 + 24^2}\,\mu m$, with p_t in GeV/c.

The typical track P_t at LEP is 1 GeV/c, and so the momentum dependent term, which is due to multiple scattering in the beam pipe and detector material, dominates the resolution for many purposes. When considering a change to the detector it was therefore very important that the material was not increased.

The new detector described here has three layers like its predecessor, but the closest to, and furthest from, the beam are double sided. They have a second metal layer which routes the z signals to the end of the silicon, thus allowing the readout electronics to remain outside the active volume. Thus is achieves its goal of adding information about the previously unmeasured coordinate without degrading the excellent resolution obtained previously.

A $Z^0 \rightarrow b\bar{b}$ candidate can be seen in figure 1. The event display also shows the geometry of the detector in $R\phi$ and Rz projections.

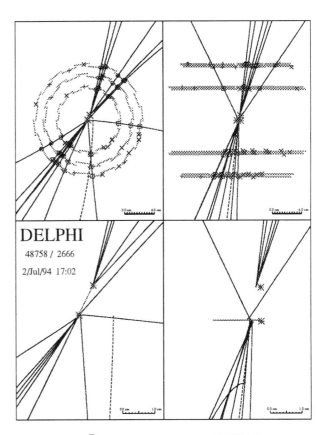

Figure 1. A $b\bar{b}$ candidate seen in the DELPHI Microvertex. The track extrapolations are *not* constrained by the vertex.

2. Detector Design

The $R\phi$ component of the silicon detectors is a capacitively coupled n type detector with p implants

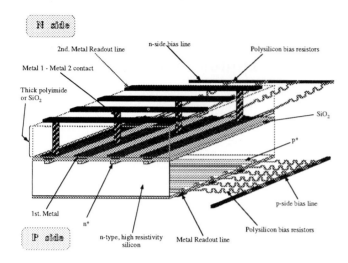

Figure 2. A cross section through a detector

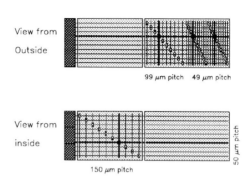

Figure 3. One of the half-modules (see section 3) of the closest layer to the interaction point.

and polysilicon biasing. For the z readout, n^+ strips are implanted, but there is a problem of electron accumulation at the interface between the silicon and Silicon dioxide. This creates a layer of mobile electrons which would allow excessive charge sharing between the strips. This layer is disturbed in two different ways: with 'p stops' for the outer layer and 'field plates' for the closer.

A schematic cross section through a detector can be seen in figure 2.

In the 'p stops' technique an implant of p^+ type silicon is placed between the n^+ strips, while in the 'field plates' solution the capacitively-coupled metal readout line, which is held at ground, is made wider than the implant. The field from the edges of this line also act to break the electron accumulation layer.

The $R\phi$ signals naturally appear at the ends of the silicon 'plaquette', but the z information appears at the sides. To read it out there would introduce extra material into the active region, and so it must be routed to the ends. This has been achieved by the use of a second metal layer. After the diodes and z strips have been produced the detector is passivated and contact holes are etched through it in a diagonal pattern (see figure 3. A second metal layer with the strips running in the $R\phi$ direction makes contacts through those holes and brings the signals to the ends of the plaquette.

This has the potential disadvantage of capacitive coupling between the two metal layers, and the passivation has to be thick enough to reduce this to a tolerable level. $5\mu m$ are found to be sufficient, and this is achieved using either just SiO_2 or polyimide.

The detector layout is shown in figure 3 for the closer layer modules. It can be seen that one detector has been 'flipped' with respect to the other. As signals in the p and n sides have opposite polarity, the sign of the signal

shows which detector it comes from, and this increases the information about the position of the particle. There is still an ambiguity on the z readout as to which of the ganged-together strips has been hit, which is three-fold in the worst case. This is resolved using information from the other tracking detectors in DELPHI.

The flipped design also helps to equalize the noise on the two sides, which is an advantage as the second metal layer increases the capacitance on the n side of the device.

3.   Construction

The plaquettes are assembled into modules each containing four detector elements. This is done by bonding the endmost detectors onto the 'hybrid' equipped with MX6 chips, testing this quarter-module, and if those tests are successful bonding a second plaquette onto the end. Then the two half modules are mechanically joined.

Each of the final three layers consists of 24 modules, but mechanically the construction is as two half shells, each with 12. The closest layer to the beam pipe uses double sided detectors with 384 readout channels and has three different pitches in z: 49 μm, 99 μm and 148 μm†. The inner layer is made of single sided detectors reclaimed from the previous detectors inner and outer layers, and has alternately 512 and 640 channels. The outer layer uses double sided detectors with 640 readout channels on each side and has two different pitches in z: 42 μm and 84 μm‡.

There are 1255952 readout channels in total.

---

† Supplied by SINTEF, Oslo.
‡ Supplied by Hammamatsu.

Layer	signal to noise	
	$R\phi$	z
Closer	11:1	13:1
Inner	12:1	—
Outer	17:1	17:1

Table 1. The signal to noise performance of the three layers.

4. Alignment

4.1. Survey

The survey is performed in two steps. Firstly, each module is measured, and the position of the strips is found with respect to two reference spheres, one at each end. Then, when the modules have been assembled into a complete half-shell, their relative positions are found.

The strip position measurement uses a camera† mounted on the 3D measuring device‡ used for previous detectors. The precision is $2\mu m$ at the focal plane.

The module survey is done exactly as it was in [2], using a touching probe mounted on the same measuring device as above. This gives $3\mu m$ accuracy for the sphere positions and $23\mu m$ for the radial positions of the modules.

4.2. Software Alignment

Software alignment uses tracks from hadronic Z^0 decays in the overlaps of the detector and inside a sector when there are three hits on the track. It also uses muon pair events, where the two muons are assumed to lie on the same helix.

An iterative procedure is followed, minimising each distribution in turn. To observe twists of one endring with respect to the other it is necessary to add more information, and the geometrically signed impact parameter of tracks on the beamspot is used, as are cosmic ray events. These are needed because they contain information about tracks which do not come from the centre of the detector.

5. Results

The detector has been operating reliably since the beginning of the 1994 data taking period. Around 2% of the modules exhibit problems which result in reduced efficiency, which is an acceptable level.

The signal to noise performance has been measured using hits which have been associated to tracks, and it is shown in table 1. With this signal to noise the hit efficiency is expected to be extremely good, but it has not been measured as yet.

† MONDO ltd., England
‡ POLI S.p.A., Italy

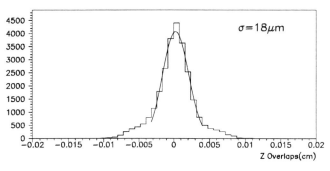

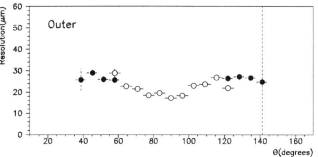

Figure 4. The resolution in z using hardware alignment; and the variation of the resolution with angle

The resolution achieved depends critically upon the alignment of the detector. This has been essentially completed in the $R\phi$ direction, where the problem is very similar to that faced in previous years. The precision reached is 6-8 μm. In the z direction the alignment has not yet been finalised, and the resolution shown in figure 4 uses alignment from the measuring machine described earlier.

The lower plot shows how the z resolution depends upon the track angle in the outer layer. The open circles refer to hits which have $42\mu m$ readout pitch, while the dark ones are from hits in regions where the strip pitch is $84\mu m$. By matching the readout pitch to the width of the clusters the resolution has been maintained out to higher angle.

6. Conclusions

The DELPHI Microvertex detector is performing as hoped. The upgrade has introduced effectively no material, and it is taking data reliably. Preliminary indications are that efficiency and resolution should be entirely satisfactory.

References

[1] P. AArnio et al. *The DELPHI detector at LEP* Nucl. Instr. Meth. **A303** (1991) 233
[2] N. Bingefors et al. *The DELPHI Microvertex detector* Nucl. Instr. Meth. **A328** (1993) 447

Paper presented at XXVII Int. Conf. on High Energy Physics: Session Pa-17
Glasgow, UK, 20–27 July 1994

Recent developements of RD2

F. Anghinolfi[§], P. Apsell[§], G. Bashindzhagyan[♯], J. Beringer[†], R. Bonino[¶], R. Bardos[*], K. Borer[†],
D. Campbell[††], A. Chilingarov[§♭], A.G. Clark[∥P], F. Fares[*], M. Fedotov[‡], H. Feick[+], E. Fretwurst[+],
G. Gorfine[*], C. Gößling[∥], E.H.M. Heijne[§], P. Jarron[§], H. Kambara[¶], E. Kuper[‡], D. La Marra[¶],
G. Lindstroem[+], A. Leger[¶], B. Lisowski[∥], M. Merkin[♯], G.F. Moorhead[*], P. Murray[††], E. Perrin[¶],
A. Reichold[∥], J.P. Richeux[¶], J.C. Santiard[§], T. Schultz[+], P. Seller[††], G. Stavropoulos[∥],
G.N. Taylor[*], S.N. Tovey[*], Y. Velikzhanin[‡], H. Verweij[§], X. Wu[¶]

† University of Bern, Switzerland
‡ Budker Institute of Nuclear Physics, Novosibirsk, Russia
§ CERN, Geneva, Switzerland
∥ Institut für Physik, Universität Dortmund, Germany
¶ DPNC, Université de Genève, Switzerland
+ Institut für Experimentalphysik, Hamburg, Germany
* School of Physics, University of Melbourne, Australia
♯ Moscow State university, Russia
†† Rutherford Appleton Laboratory, England
♭ on leave from the Budker Institute

Abstract

The RD2 collaboration is studying the major aspects of an outer silicon tracker to be developed as part of the ATLAS inner detector.

A particular attention, both from the layout and research point of view, is devoted to the effect of radiation on the behavior of silicon detectors.

A signal processing architecture is being developed to provide the data reduction speed, low power, high spatial density and robustness required by LHC operations. A new chip, ADAM, is under development with improved analog memory and front end amplifier, a complete memory management logic, a multiplexed 8 bit piece wise linear ADC and a digital buffer compatible with a simple daisy chain readout protocol.

Two complementary mechanical options are being followed to design a detector with several millions channels operated at low (0-10 C) temperature maintaining the required geometrical precision.

Prototype modules satisfying the full mechanics specifications are being developed implementing the ADAM chip and an optical readout scheme.

1. Introduction

The research program of the RD2 collaboration covers the major aspects of a silicon tracker for LHC [1], and is now focusing on the specific design of the ATLAS inner detector [2] The ATLAS silicon tracker will consist of several concentric planes for precision measurement, read by an electronics with less than 2000 ENC., and capable of resolving the bunch crossings at 40 MHz. The large number of channels imposes data reduction at the detector level. Radiation and limited access for service and maintenance requires the design of a very robust system with ample safety factors, intrinsic simplicity and reliability, and the flexibility to adjust system parameters in place.

2. Detectors

The effect of radiation damage on the depletion voltage, the leakage current and the charge collection efficiency has been extensively studied (see [3] for references) at various operating temperatures. The results of the measurements have been integrated into models for bulk damage in high resistivity silicon [4].

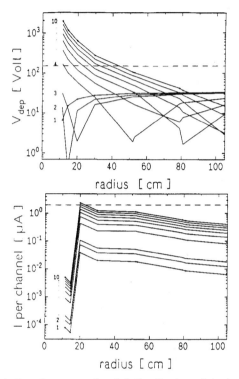

Figure 1. Development of radial distribution of depletion voltage (a)and leakage current per channel (b)

The radiation levels expected in the ATLAS inner detector have been calculated [5] and the results can be used to estimate the behavior of the detectors for various scenarios. A typical assumption is that during one year of operation the apparatus is constantly kept at 0 °C, except for one month of maintenance, and that the total beam time adds up to seven months. The effect on the depletion voltage and leakage current of 300 μm detectors are plotted in figure 1, assuming a luminosity of $10^{-33} \text{cm}^{-2}\text{s}^{-1}$ for the first three years and $10^{-34}\text{cm}^{-2}\text{s}^{-1}$ thereafter. The depletion voltage or the innermost layer at 30 cm starts to exceed the typical maximum of 150 V after seven years, while the leakage current, calculated taking into account the appropriate active volume, remains below 2.5 μA .

3.   The signal processing electronics

The aim of the RD2 signal readout concept[6,7] is to integrate into a single CMOS chip the preamplifier with the signal processing. Simplicity, insensitivity to time fluctuations of the charge deposition and full charge measurement determined the choice of a fast preamplifier capable of tolerating a leakage current up to 10μA.

In a system exposed for several years in a hostile environment, it is considered essential to monitor the response of each channel by transferring the full measurement of the charge deposition. Data from each channel is therefore stored in the analog memory at each bunch crossing. The memory controller retrieves, from the analog memory, data corresponding to a Level 1 trigger. For each trigger being processed, values from channels selected by the sparse data readout system are digitized on-chip to minimize cross talk and pickup. Finally, digitized data and channel addresses are stored in the output buffer, and made available for readout.

The components of this structure are functionally decoupled and the architecture has the flexibility to be modified in various directions:, including, for example, a separate bipolar front end amplifier.

Recent chip developments [6,7] have concentrated on increasing the functionality of the memory controller and on extending the analog memory depth to 128 cells. The simultaneous processing of multiple triggers has been demonstrated. Radiation hard versions of analog memory chips are being developed in the Thomson HSOI3MD CMOS on SOI[8] and in the HARRIS bulk CMOS radiation hard processes.

10 mV/square

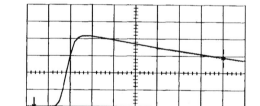

20 ns/square

Figure 2. NICON output for 1 mip input charge

Recently, we have developed a fast, low power ADC, CRIAD [3], and focused on the optimization of the front end amplifier and the analog memory structure for tracking applications. A new, faster CMOS front end amplifier, NICON, has been developed. The NICON has a rise time (10 - 90%) of 13 ns with 8 pF input capacitance (see Figure 2) and a noise of 800 e + 80 e/pF. after a gaussian shaping with 25 ns peaking time. The power consumption of the circuit is measured to be as low as 400 μW.

A new analog memory structure, DHARP, has been developed performing correlated double sampling on the NICON output. It will allow the storage of more than

90% of the charge within a single clock period at 40 MHz. These structures and the ADC are now being included into the new chip, ADAM[3], providing all the functionality required by LHC operation except for the sparse readout.

4. Mechanics

RD2 is studying a carbon fibre cylindrical structure with a coefficient of thermal expansion (cte) close to zero, which is appropriate for operation at low temperature. the cylindrical structure will support individual modules consisting of several detectors together with their associated electronics, cooling and readout. The design specifications require that the average radiation length per layer be less than $0.02 X_0$. This support is requested to provide a structural stability of less than 60 μm and an alignment precision in rφ and z respectively of ≤30μm and ≤60μm in order to guarantee that alignment uncertainties are well below the resolution of the silicon detectors.

Two solutions have been studied for the module design. One places the electronics along the longitudinal edge and makes contact with the strips via a kapton fanout. In the other design the electronics is placed radially, directly facing the strips. The module design emphasizes on the simplification of the assembly work. Detectors cut with a tolerance of 5mm can be assembled using high precision jigs, without the need for complicated optical alignment systems. Prototype modules demonstrated an assembly misplacement of 8 μm average.

5. Readout

A complete readout concept is also being developed around the ADAM architecture. In each board the ADAM chips will be connected in a token ring to a readout controller. The ROC receives the master clock and trigger signals from optical links and broadcasts them to the 8 chips on board. For each sample to be processed it starts a readout sequence by enabling the first chip in the ring to send on the bus data from the first available event. When data transmission is completed, each FE-chip sends the readout token to the following one, and the procedure continues until the token is back to the ROC. The ROC buffers and formats the data coming from the bus before transmitting it on the optical fibre.

6. Conclusions

A signal processing and readout architecture has been designed for an LHC silicon tracker. The major building blocks of the signal processing chip have already been developed and extensively tested. We aim at implementing a chip with an analog performance satisfying LHC specifications on prototype boards to be tested towards the end of 1994.

Acknowledgments

This development effort is part of the CERN R&D program for LHC and partially financed by CERN. Further financial support is acknowledged from UK Science and Engineering Research Council to the Rutherford Appleton Laboratory(RAL); from the Australian Research Council and the Department of Industry, Trade and Regional Development to the Melbourne group; from the Schweizerischen Nationalfonds zur Förderung der Wissenschaftlichen Forschung to the Bern and Geneva groups and from Bundesministerium für Forschung und Technologie to the Dortmund and Hamburg groups.

References

[1] A. Clark and G. Goessling (joint spokesmen), *A proposal to study a tracking/preshower detector for the LHC*, CERN/DRDC 90-27.
[2] ATLAS Collaboration, Letter of intent: CERN/LHCC/92-4.
[3] RD2 status report, CERN/DRDC 94-34.
[4] H. Feick *et al.*, in Proc. 6th Pisa Meeting on Advanced Detecors, Isola d'Elba 1994.
[5] G. Gorfine and G. taylor, ATLAS INDET 030 (1993).
[6] RD2 Collaboration, CERN/DRDC 93.
[7] K. Borer *et al.*, Nucl. Instr. Meth. **A344** (1994) 185.
[8] F. Faccio *et al.*, in Proc. IEEE-NSERC Conf., New Orleans 1992.

Paper presented at XXVII Int. Conf. on High Energy Physics: Session Pa-17
Glasgow, UK, 20–27 July 1994

A hybrid pixel detector for readout of scintillating fibres

C. Da Via, M. Campbell, E.H.M. Heijne, P. Middelkamp and G. Stefani

CERN, Geneva, Switzerland

Presented by C. Da Via on behalf of the RD19 Collaboration

Abstract

A pixel detector for visible photons has been developed for low-cost, high-speed readout of scintillating fibres and imaging applications. The device is a hybrid assembly of a high-resistivity silicon detector array, bump-bonded to a CMOS binary readout chip. Sensitivity to visible photons is obtained by modifying the rear metal contact on the detector. The 2-D hybrid array presently consists of 1006 pixels of 75 µm × 500 µm dimensions. Scintillating fibre ribbons are coupled to the detector array using one stage of light amplification provided by a micro-channel plate (MCP) image intensifier with fibre-optic faceplates. The device currently used has a maximum photon gain of ~ 1000 with a photocathode spectral sensitivity matched to the emission spectrum of SCSF-38 blue scintillating fibres. With this set-up, tracks from a ^{90}Sr collimated β-source in a five-layer ribbon of 500 µm diameter fibres have been clearly observed. A test has been performed in a high-energy particle beam and a maximum detection efficiency of 51% measured. Performance limitations are understood and plans made to improve the system.

1. Introduction

We have developed a novel readout system for scintillating fibres based on the combination of a silicon pixel detector and a micro-channel plate (MCP) image intensifier. Light emitted from the fibres is amplified in the MCP device and picked up by the photo-sensitive pixel detector. This system could offer considerable cost savings on multi-anode photo-multipliers.

Pixel detectors offer the combined advantages of very high spatial precision and high readout rate. In its present form, the pixel detector has a matrix of 1006 sensitive elements, each with dimensions of 75 µm × 500 µm [1]. Although it was designed for direct particle detection the detector can be adapted to make it sensitive to visible photons [2]. Obviously, the present rectangular shape of the pixel is not well adapted for fibre applications, but the aim of our study was to prove the feasibility of such an approach.

Firstly, we describe the set-up of the system along with its calibration. Following calibration we performed radioactive source measurements in the laboratory. As these gave encouraging results, we then made a test with a high energy particle beam in order to understand the detection efficiency of the system. Finally, we discuss the performance limits of the present system and how these could be overcome by the new approach.

2. System setup and calibration

Figure 1 shows the set-up we used to calibrate our system. The image intensifier is the 1450R from DEP [3]. At the input to the image intensifier is a type S20 photocathode with a peak sensitivity at 420 nm and a maximum quantum efficiency of 22%. This is followed by the MCP, which provides the amplification, and then by a type P46 phosphor screen. This screen emits light at 530 nm with a decay time (fast component) of ~ 100 ns.

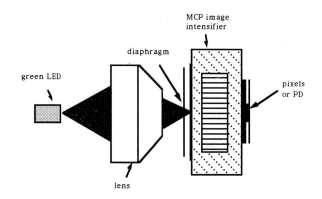

Figure 1. The set-up used for calibration of the MCP image intensifier. The diameter of the diaphragm is 300 µm.

A first test was performed in order to verify the gain of the MCP. The light from a green LED was focused through a diaphragm onto the photocathode of the image intensifier and the light output from the phosphor screen was detected by a calibrated photodiode. The same photodiode was later used to measure the incidental light, giving a direct measurement of the image intensifier photon-gain as a function of the applied voltage across the MCP. The results thus obtained are shown in Fig. 2. These correspond very well to the manufacturer's data sheet. The maximum gain obtained was ~ 1000 for an applied voltage of ~ 900 V. Our standard operating condition was for a gain of 800, corresponding to an applied voltage of 875 V.

We then replaced the photodiode with the photopixel matrix in order to be able to look at the image of the 300 μm diaphragm. The image thus obtained is shown in Fig. 3. The FWHM of the image covers four pixels in the short dimension, corresponding to the 300 μm diameter.

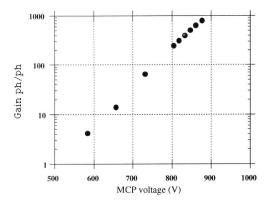

Figure 2. The gain versus applied voltage characteristic of the MCP image intensifier. This curve agrees well with the manufacturer's specifications.

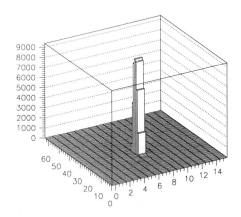

Figure 3. The accumulated profile of the diaphragm. The FWHM is 4 pixels, which corresponds to the 300 μm diaphragm hole.

3. Testing with a radioactive source

Having calibrated the system, we then attached the scintillating fibre ribbon as shown in Fig. 4. The fibres were Kuraray type SCSF-38 [4] with a diameter of

500 μm and a peak emission at 430 nm corresponding to the peak sensitivity of the S20 photocathode. The fibre length was 15 cm. The attenuation length of this kind of fibre has been measured at ~ 2 m. The ^{90}Sr β-source, which has a 2 mm collimator, was placed 6 cm from the image intensifier. Random triggers were given to the pixel detector and the beam profile shown in Fig. 5 was accumulated. We clearly observed the 2 mm collimation corresponding to 4 pixels in the long dimension, and that there are around 29 pixels hit in the short dimension, corresponding to the 2.1 mm thickness of the fibre ribbon. In this way we verified that the proposed set-up works.

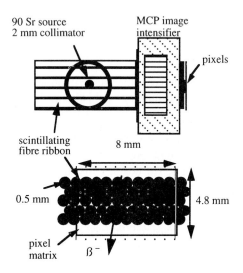

Figure 4. The set-up used for the radioactive source measurements.

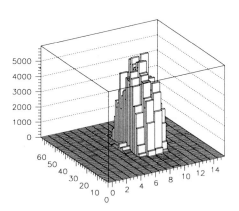

Figure 5. The accumulated beam profile for the collimated radioactive source.

4. Beam test results

In order to measure the detection efficiency of the system, we used the H6 test beam at the CERN SPS fixed target site. This facility provided 120 GeV/*c* pions acting as Minimum Ionizing Particles (MIPs). The only modification made to the set-up in Fig. 4 was that the fibre ribbon was replaced by a ribbon of 1.5 m length. The fibre ribbon was then inserted into the RD-19 pixel telescope described in [5]. The geometry of the telescope with the fibres added is shown in Fig. 6. The beam was defined by the crossover of scintillating fibres S3 and S4, which formed a 1 mm × 1 mm area. The distance between this crossover point and the image intensifier was 65 cm. Data was accumulated in all three planes, while the threshold current of the photopixel plane was varied.

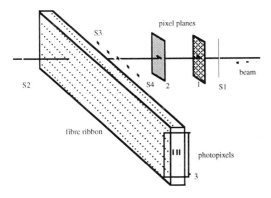

Figure 6. The RD 19 pixel telescope with the fibre ribbon added. Triggers are produced by the coincidence in scintillators S1, S2, S3 and S4. This forms a 1 mm × 1 mm area in pixel planes 1 and 2. The beam itself is, of course, much wider than this.

To make a first estimate of overall detection efficiency, we selected events with a track in planes 1 and 2 and looked for at least one correlated hit in plane 3. The curve of efficiency versus threshold is shown in Fig. 7. For reference, we added data from a 300 μm silicon pixel detector placed directly in the beam. We observed that the detection efficiency of the fibre set-up measured in this way is around 40%. As each incident particle crosses several fibres, we expected more than one hit in plane 3. Therefore, we defined a track in plane 3 as an event with two or more correlated hits. The track detection efficiency, also shown in Fig. 7, was at best 18%. A further test was made by increasing the MCP bias voltage to ~ 900 V in order to increase the gain of the MCP. In this case the detection efficiency had a maximum of 51.2% and the track detection efficiency a maximum value of 23%.

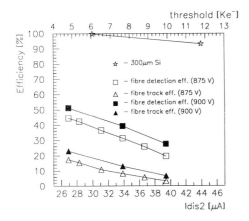

Figure 7. The efficiency versus threshold curve for the fibre ribbon. The 300 μm Si curve is added for reference.

This leads us to an analysis of the system's limitations. Typically, the number of photons produced by an MIP crossing a fibre and reaching its end is ~ 20 [6]. This means that at 875 V MCP bias one MIP will produce ~ 29 000 photons at the output of the image intensifier. We have corrected the gain measured in the green with the photocathode quantum efficiency at 430 nm. With a quantum efficiency in the green of 70% the pixel detector collects ~ 20 000 e^-. In the case of the MCP bias voltage of 900 V, the charge delivered to the pixel is typically ~ 25 000 e^-. In addition, light emitted from one fibre is spread over several pixels (the small pixel dimension is 75 μm whilst the fibres are 500 μm in diameter). As the lowest threshold of the pixel detector is around 8 000 e^-, the low-track detection efficiency is consistent with the limitations of our system.

A beam profile is shown in Fig. 8. The two columns corresponding to the 1 mm scintillator crossover are clearly evident. Compared with the source measurements there is a large number of background hits. These are not present when the beam is off, and can be explained by particle hits to the fibres outside our 1 mm × 1 mm coincidence.

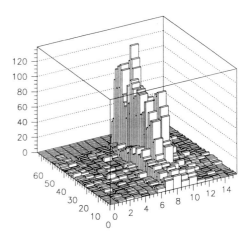

Figure 8. The accumulated beam profile in the fibre plane. The 1 mm wide coincidence is clearly evident. The hits outside the coincidence are due to untriggered particle tracks.

5. Conclusions and further work

We conclude that a system which combines silicon pixel detector and MCP image intensifier offers a very interesting alternative to multi-anode photo-multipliers for readout of scintillating fibres. While the advantages of a high spatial resolution are maintained, system cost is kept to a minimum. The pixel detector offers a much greater readout speed than that offered by CCDs. The image intensifier chosen behaved exactly according to the manufacturer's specifications. Tracks were detected by the pixel detector both using a radioactive source and a high-energy particle beam. The total detection efficiency is limited at present by the quantum efficiency of the photocathode, the minimum threshold of the pixel detector and the shape of the pixel itself.

There are several ways of optimizing this system in a future version. We are studying the use of an image intensifier produced by Intevac [7] which uses a GaAsP photocathode with a peak quantum efficiency of 39%. A new pixel readout chip is being developed with a lower minimum threshold. It would also be beneficial if the pixel dimensions were better matched to the fibre diameter.

There may be applications in medical imaging for such a system.

Acknowledgments

We would like to thank P.A. Giudici, R. Grabit and P. Knobel for their fundamental help in the technical aspects of the test. We would also like to acknowledge Prof. V. Cavasinni, B. De Gerolamo and Prof. V. Flaminio for their support, advice and assistance.

References

[1] F. Anghinolfi *et al.*, IEEE Trans. Nucl. Sci **NS-32** (1992) 650.
[2] C. Da Via *et al.*, CERN preprint: CERN/ECP 93-18; and in Proc. 3rd London Conf. on Position-Sensitive Detectors, Brunel Univ. 1993; Eds. P.R. Hobson, A. Farugi and G.H. Fraser (to appear in Nucl. Inst. Meth.).
[3] DEP Delft Electronicische Producten, Dwazziewegen 2, 9300 Ab Roden (Dr.), Holland.
[4] Kuraray Co. Ltd. Methacrylic Resin Division, Hatchobory 2-Chome, Chuo-ku, Tokyo 140, Japan.
[5] E.H.M. Heijne *et al.*, Nucl. Instr. Meth. **A349** (1994) 138.
[6] A, Cardini *et al.*, preprint: INFN PI/AE 94/08.
[7] INTEVAC, Eo Sensors Division, 601 California Ave., Palo Alto, California 94304-0883, USA.

Paper presented at XXVII Int. Conf. on High Energy Physics: Session Pa-17
Glasgow, UK, 20–27 July 1994

1171

Gallium Arsenide Microstrip Detectors*

J Ludwig[‡]

Fakultät für Physik, Universität Freiburg,
Hermann Herder Strasse 3, 79104 Freiburg, Germany

On behalf of the RD8 collaboration

Abstract

The interest in GaAs as a basic material for detection of elementary particles stems from the fact that it is intrinsically radiation hard and therefore well suited for deployment in regions of high radiation dose.

Measurements with microstrip- and pixel detectors of different pitch and strip width have been carried out with α sources and in pion beams. The thickness of detectors has been varied between 500 and 200 μm.

First results from detectors fabricated from Liquid Phase Epitaxial (LPE) material give up to 100 % collection efficiency.

The development of customized frontend electronics for the fast pulses encountered with GaAs detectors (risetime 100 ps) is underway.

1. Introduction

The anticipated radiation dose close to the beampipe at LHC experiments (radius of 10 cm) has been estimated to be a few times 10^{14} neutrons per cm^2. Gallium arsenide detectors and electronics have demonstrated their radiation hardness in excess of such rates [1].

2. Micro strip detectors

Microstrip detectors with different pitch and width of the strips have been fabricated to investigate uniformity of charge collection efficiency, energy resolution and coupling between strips. The length of the strips is limited to about 3 cm by the 2 inch wafer size used for these devices. Only 500 μm thick wafers have been used for these investigations.

In Fig. 1 the different geometries and the negative crosstalk are shown.

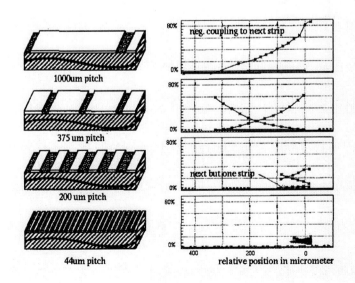

Fig.1: geometries and crosstalk for micro strips

As a general result it turned out that these devices

are not fully depleted. The depletion width as a function of applied voltage plateaus for α particles at values of about 200 to 300 μm. This corresponds to a charge collection efficiency of about 40 to 60 % at best (see Fig. 2).

3.   200 μm thin devices

Radiation length and therefore multiple scattering should be as small as possible for devices close to the beampipe to facilitate accurate vertex measurements. In order to have the same radiation length as a 400 μm silicon detector the GaAs device should have a thickness of 200 μm (density Si = 2.33, GaAs =5.32 g/cm^3). Besides the fact that most foundries slice there ingots into 400 - 500 μm wafers, we obtain with thinner detectors larger pulseheights then with thicker ones. As long as the detectors are not fully depleted (only about 200 μm in the case of a 500 μm detector), Ramo's theorem:

$$Q_{coll} = q \times \frac{x_{drift}}{d} \qquad (1)$$

q = charge created, x = drifted distance, d = thickness of detector
shows that we have to expect twice the pulseheight with a detector of half the thickness. This can be seen very clearly by comparison of Fig. 2 with 3.

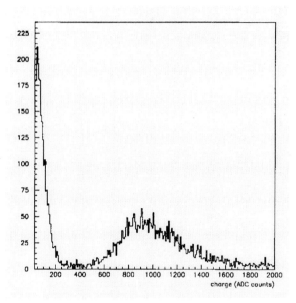

Fig.3: MIP spectrum for a 200 μm detector

4.   Pixel detectors

Pixel arrays are forseen as tracking devices at the innermost radii of general purpose detectors to allow unambiguous 3 coordinate spacepoint determination for tracks. A pixel size of 75 $\times$ 500 μm has been chosen by Ref. [2] to study the behaviour of silicon arrays, special connection techniques (ball bonding) and electronics for such devices. The electronics features a comparator, where the discrimination level can be set between 5000 and 15000 electrons.

Further details can be taken from [3].

Fig. 4 and 5 show the results obtained with a 300 μm silicon and a 200 μm GaAs detector. This very first pioneering attempt shows a very similar beam profile for both techniques. A total of 16 $\times$ 64 pixels have been ball bonded up to the readout. The failure rate was again extremely small (less then 10)and has encouraged us to proceed with the development of GaAs pixel arrays and electronics.

5.   LPE detectors

Deep level defects like EL2 have a concentration of a few 10^{16} cm^{-3} due to the growing technique applied to Liquid Encapsulated Czochralski (LEC) ingots. These defects are under normal conditions neutral but become ionized due to bending of energy bands if the GaAs is in

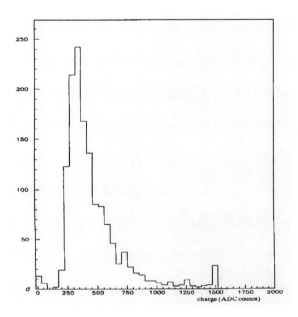

Fig.2: MIP spectrum for a 500 μm detector

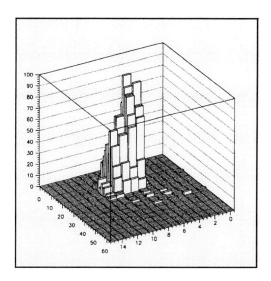

Fig.4: beam profile with Silicon pixel array

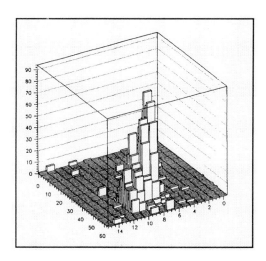

Fig.5: beam profile with GaAs pixel array

contact with a metal and a voltage is applied. The result is a high concentration of space charge in a limited and depleted region where almost the entire voltage drop takes place.

The way to obtain full depleted detectors at low voltages is therefore to obtain gallium arsenide material with low concentration of deep level defects. Liquid Phase Epitaxy (LPE) is a technique which allows growth of GaAs crystals without a higher percentage of arsenic than needed in the crystal. Therefore deep level defects

are absent and 100 percent charge collection efficiencies are possible at low applied voltages.

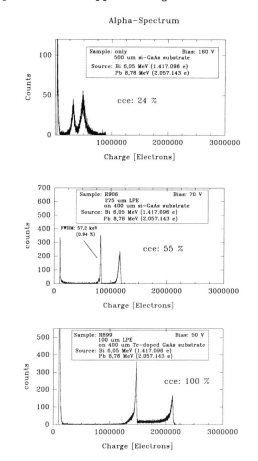

Fig.6: α spectra obtained with LEC and LPE detectors

6. Customized frontend GaAs electronics

GaAs electronic circuits based on HEMT (High Electron Mobility Transistors) technology have been successfully designed and tested. Up to now a preamplifier with shaper main amplifier have been realized. A device with integration of detector and electronics on one chip has also been operated in GaAs technology.

References

[1] M. Turala, Proc. of the 2nd Int. Meeting on Front End Electronics for Tracking Detectors at Future Colliders 1994, *The ATLAS Inner tracking Detector*, (Perugia, 19-21 May 1994).
RD8 collaboration: CERN DRDC 92-12 (1992).

[2] RD19 collaboration: E.H.M. Heijne et al., *First operation of a 72 k element hybrid silicon micropattern pixel detector array*, CERN ECP EH1 (1994).

[3] measurements by M.K. Campbell and C. da Via.

Paper presented at XXVII Int. Conf. on High Energy Physics: Session Pa-17
Glasgow, UK, 20–27 July 1994

Diamond Detectors for Future Particle Physics Experiments

John Hassard[‡]

Blackett Laboratory, Imperial College,
London SW7 2BZ, UK

Abstract

Diamond has recently been shown to be a viable contender for certain niche detector applications in the next generation of particle accelerators. This paper surveys the properties of diamond which make it interesting, the work achieved so far, the remaining unresolved issues and the possible routes diamond detector research may take in the future.

1. Introduction

We have developed particle strip detectors in Chemical Vapour Deposition (CVD) diamond. The key remaining issues are those of radiation hardness, the uniformity and maximisation of charge collection efficiency, and the optimisation of these detectors for the various applications which now suggest themselves.

We are getting an increasingly clear picture of radiation hardness - and results are so far very encouraging. The charge maximisation goal can be divided into the two tasks: maximising charge collection distance and optimising the ohmic contacts made to the detector. Great progress has been made in both areas. These issues require complementary characterisation and diagnostics techniques. These are briefly discussed below.

Diamond offers opportunities in particle detection because its very stiff lattice results in excellent mechanical and thermal properties and its very tightly bound atomic structure allows few free charge carriers and a most impressive voltage to be applied to a wafer. The resulting high carrier mobility suggests that as a simple ionisation detector material, intrinsic diamond offers many opportunities. Carbon's low Z points to detector applications in which multiple scattering is an issue. Initial results [1] are available. I conclude with an outline of possible future paths this research can take.

1.1. The key properties of diamond

We list diamond's key properties here:

Property	Value at 300K	xSi	xGaAs
Band Gap	5.45 eV	5	3.8
Energy/e-h pair	13 eV	3.3	3.1
Density	3.5 gm cm	1.3	0.66
Z	6	0.43	0.18
Rad length	12.03cm	1.3	5.2
Min. Ion. sig/100	3600 e/h	0.41	0.28
Min. Ion. sig/0.1% Xo	4500 e/h	0.54	1.5
Carr.Rec.Length	typically 80	n/a	n/a
Resistivity	up to 10^{13} Ω-cm	$\geq 10^7$	$\geq 10^4$
Sat. elec velocity	200-270 μm ns^{-1}	2.7	2.8
Carrier mobility (e)	1800 $cm^2 V^{-1} sec^{-1}$	1.4	0.21
Carrier mobility (h)	1200 $cm^2 V^{-1} sec^{-1}$	2.5	3
Dielectric Constant	5.7	smaller	smaller

Property	Value at 300K	Comment	
Thermal conductivity	20 W cm^{-1} K^{-1}	4 x Cu (ie the best)	
Thermal expansivity	0.8- 1.1 ppm K^{-1}	0.31xSi, 0.11x GaAs	
Optical transparency	$\geq 70\%$	0.33-5.45 eV	
Radiation Hardness	very impressive	work in progress	

‡ E-mail: hassard@vxcern

1.2. The Signal to Noise Issue

It has often been remarked that it is not intuitively obvious to expect a perfect insulator to be a good choice as a charge source. The issue is the huge bandgap - diamond will never produce signals as large as those of some alternative solid state detectors. However, if this disadvantage can be overcome, then diamond's other attractive features can become real assets. The charge collection efficiency depends largely on the charge collection distance - a measure of the distance a hole and an electron, created by an ionising particle, move apart before being trapped or annihilated. This distance has increased greatly over the last few years as a result of interplay largely between our US collaborators and industry, going from a fraction of one micron five years ago, to - in the best electronic grade diamonds - nearly $200\mu m$, exceeding that measured in good quality natural diamond. The technique is in part one of growing diamond with a low defect density, and with large crystallites. It was this realisation which has led to the whole field of intrinsic diamond electronic devices.

Once the collection distance in a CVD diamond is greater than a few tens of microns, the surface preparation and metallisation of the diamond is crucial in its operation as a detector. Again, this technology has improved greatly, but the optimum treatments are still being developed.

The other main issue is the noise in the detectors, arising from the device itself and the associated electronics. Diamond's main advantage lies in the negligible parallel shot noise owing to the exceptionally low leakage current. As will be discussed, the intrinsic noise in a given detector can be made very small indeed, and under certain circumstances it is expected that the total noise can be brought to below 100e noise even with integration times compatible with LHC running.

It can be shown that S/N of better than 15 will allow, for example, highly efficient vertex hit/track association, even in the difficult LHC environment. Our test beam results indicate that achieving the necessary signal can be realistically expected relatively soon. The problem will then be one almost entirely in the making of low noise fast electronics.

1.3. Diagnostics and Characterisation

It is fortunate that diamond can be studied in a wide range of techniques, many of which relate directly to the charge collection efficiency. For example, cathodoluminescence and photoluminescence and absorption spectroscopy tell us about impurities and defects directly, graphitisation can be studied with Raman and SEM/TEM techniques. A survey can be found [2].

2. Results in Particle Testbeams

Early on in the current research programme it was decided to demonstrate diamond's potential in a simple calorimeter[3] - one which would allow direct comparison with silicon active planes and with our expectations from simulations. The success of this detector gave confidence to push on to the next stage - a strip detector for tracking.

It is a measure of diamond's adaptability that some of the calorimeter diamond was recycled into the first testbeam studies[1]. In this work, the "Strasbourg Telescope"[4] allowed us to measure the position at which 50 GeV πs traversed a diamond detector plane; standard analysis techniques allows us to measure signal and noise separately, and the positional precision.

The diamond detectors in this work were planar 8mm x 8 mm x 300μ with 100 μ pitch strips, across the smallest dimension of which were applied voltages of up to nearly 200V. The detector strips were DC coupled to individual Viking[5] channels. Data were taken with normally incident particles, at a variety of bias voltages and with a 2 μsecond shaping time. Our analysis showed that at a bias voltage of 195V we get a S/N of 6.3±0.2 and a position precision slightly better than the digital value. This is equivalent to an efficiency of at least 86% - we made no correction for dead channels.

The subsequently calculated signal and noise values in electrons agreed with our expectations from independent measurements, and was equal to a median charge of 875±105 electrons signal. While this is clearly not adequate for real LHC detectors being roughly equivalent to the noise one might expect in a shaping time of 25ns in derived preamp technology, there are several steps we can take to improve the situation as will be oulined in the last section.

3. Radiation damage in Diamond Detectors

Radiation damage of diamond was studied intensively between 1950 and 1970[6, 7] but until two years ago, recent work has concentrated on the production of specific defects by photon and electron irradiation, using as diagnostic tools pulse height distributions, and electron spin resonance and electron spectroscopy[8]. Up to levels of irradiation to several Gy, the normalised gain in CVD diamond increases by about 50%. This priming effect is interpreted as being due to the removal of defects. The gain is then constant out to and beyond the limit of available data at about 100kGy.

Diamonds irradiated with 5 MeV alphas also exist - and show that out to fluences of 10^{12} negligible gain drop-off occurs. The gain then slowly falls until at about 10^{14} alphas, corresponding to about 7 MGy, the gain drops to 50% of its unirradiated value. While immensely encouraging, this is difficult to interpret quantitatively in terms of the LHC.

We have established a coherent programme of study into radiation damage, primarily using neutrons and pions. Quantitative results can be expected very soon.

Theoretical understanding of this problem is progressing rapidly. The production of primary defects – vacancies and interstitials – is quite well understood, as is their migration at high temperatures to form aggregated defects. However, very little is known about the effects that these defects have on the electrical properties of diamond. Damage by a neutrons of a dose comparable with that expected in the LHC appears to produce very little effect on the resistivity of natural diamond[9]. This work shows that even at 10^{19} neutrons cm^{-2} diamond has detection capabilities. Only by much more theoretical and experimental studies can detectors be designed with the best possible performance, and any possible degradation due to radiation damage minimised. But in a very short time it will be possible to know the broad effects of the likely radiation doses expected at LHC.

4. Future Directions in Diamond in Particle Physics

Those working with diamond have a wide range of goals which hopefully will achieve acceptance of diamond in the particle physics community. We aim to demonstrate that we can attain a charge collection distance of 100μ, which should result in 2400 electron signal. The limit to which we can aspire is well in excess of this number: the production technique and quality feedback loop between this collaboration and several diamond manufacturers and processors is a particularly strong and likely to bring further large improvements

We find the strip detector environment a sensible arena for his work, but recognise that there are strong possibilities in other detector configurations. For example, pixel devices read out by low noise amplifiers like those that have been developed for silicon detectors[10] are likely to be a successful solution for diamond. There is every expectation that we can achieve a S/N in excess of 30 and positional precisions of about 5 microns in shaping times reasonable for the LHC. Additionally, in the detector applications for which diamond appears to offer useful solutions, namely vertex detectors, the pixel approach has great advantages in pattern recognition.

We must work on the design and engineering of diamond detectors demanded in real detector applications. Diamond might be a possible choice in the HERA-B experiment, for example, and detailed studies are proceeding[11].

The possibilities for diamond are not restricted to detection. Diamond is already used extensively in thermal management, and it may be possible that it has some role in mechanical supports[12].

In conclusion, we have shown that diamond offers a compelling solution to the intense radiation and acute thermal problems presented by the LHC, particularly but not exclusively in vertexing. Definitive results in radiation hardness are being produced, and so far, all indications are extremely promising.

References

[1] DRDC P56 "Diamond Detectors", CERN report 1994.
[2] *The Properties of Natural and Synthetic Diamond*; Ed. J. Field (Academic Press 1992).
[3] R.J. Tesarek *et al.*, to appear in Nucl. Inst. Meth.
[4] C. Colledani *et al.*, "A high resolution beam telescope", CRN-LEPSI note.
[5] E. Nygard *et al.*, Nucl. Instr. Meth. **A301** (1991) 506.
[6] E.W.J. Mitchell in Physical Properties of Diamond, Ed. R. Berman (Clarendon 1965).
[7] D.W. Palmer in Properties of Diamond – a Data Review, Ed. G. Davis (IEE London 1994).
[8] C.D. Clark, A.T. Collins and G.S. Woods in [1].
[9] E.R. Vance, H.J. Milledge and A.T. Collins, J. Phys. **D5** (1972) L40.
[10] E. Heijne *et al.*, preprint: CERN ECP EH1.
[11] HERA-B progress report: DESY-PRTC 93/04.
[12] C. Hauviller, talk at The Workshop on Vertex Detection in CMS, PSI 1994.

Performance of the SLD CCD Pixel Vertex Detector and Design of an Upgrade*

M G Strauss

University of Massachusetts, Amherst, MA 01003, USA.

Representing the SLD Collaboration

Abstract

We present the performance of the SLD CCD pixel vertex detector (VXD2) after two years of running experience in the SLC e^+e^- beam environment and the design of a significantly improved upgrade (VXD3) to be installed in late 1995. The existing VXD2 has performed very reliably. A spatial resolution of ~ 5 μm in both the $R\phi$ and Z coordinates has been achieved. Impact parameter resolutions of 11 μm in the $R\phi$ view and 38 μm in the RZ view for high momentum tracks are observed from the data. The upgraded design has full three layer solid angle coverage to $|cos\theta| = 0.85$, using CCDs at a much larger size of 8.0×1.6 cm. Optimized geometry and reduced material will improve the impact parameter resolution by a factor of two compared with VXD2. This upgrade will greatly enhance the heavy flavor physics potential of SLD, allowing a unique exploration of the B_s mixing time evolution measurement in an interesting x_s region.

1. Introduction

The SLD Vertex Detector (VXD2) has been collecting data at the SLAC Linear Collider (SLC) since April 1992. Over the last two years, the SLD collaboration has demonstrated that a large array of charged coupled devices (CCDs) can effectively function as a charged particle tracking detector in a linear collider environment. The success of VXD2 has motivated the SLD collaboration to design and begin construction of an upgraded CCD based vertex detector (VXD3) which will be installed in late 1995, and will enhance the physics capabilities of the SLD detector.

2. VXD2 Overview

The design, construction, and initial performance of the SLD Vertex Detector has been described elsewhere [1, 2]. VXD2 consists of 480 CCDs installed in a cylindrical geometry around the SLC beam pipe. A CCD contains $\sim 400 \times 600$ pixels, each of size 22×22 μm. Eight CCDs are wire-bonded to an alumina mother board of thickness 250 μm to create a CCD "ladder" with an active area of about 8.5×92 mm^2. These ladders are arranged in four coaxial layers around the beam pipe with 13 (17) ladders in the two inner (outer) layers. The ladders are mounted in two half-cylindrical beryllium support structures with spring-loaded fixtures.

The CCDs are surrounded by a foam cryostat and are cooled to $-80°C$ by flowing N$_2$ gas through the detector. Cooling the detector suppresses dark currents and the loss due to radiation damage of CCD charge transfer efficiency. Electronic readout is accomplished by clocking the CCD charge to an output node at 1.85 MHz. All CCDs are read out continuously in parallel.

3. Operational Experience and Performance

Backgrounds in the detector come predominately from X-ray conversions and upstream tracks parallel to the

* Work supported in part by the U.S. Department of Energy under contracts DE-AC03-76SF00515 and DE-FG02-92ER40715.

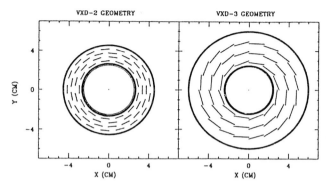

Figure 1. Cross sections of VXD2 and VXD3 showing beam pipe, beryllium support structure, and ladders.

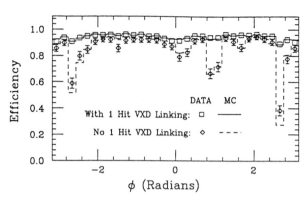

Figure 2. The effect of linking single VXD hits on the efficiency for correctly associating VXD hits with CDC tracks.

beam pipe axis. The parallel track backgrounds are suppressed by deleting clusters having a large number of hit pixels. Electronic noise is minimal, less than 1 hit/CCD for each event. Although all backgrounds add up to less than .01% occupancy in the detector, the ratio of background to signal hits in the detector is about one hundred to one for multi-hadronic events, so that the high granularity and unambiguous three-dimensional space point provided by the CCDs is essential for efficient pattern recognition.

Immediately after the installation of VXD2, it was discovered that two of the eighty ladders were inoperable due to faulty micro-connectors which connect the ladder to the local electronics cable. A few other CCDs also experienced electronics failures. Apart from these problems which occurred during installation, VXD2 has had only one other CCD failure during its operations. The CCDs, mechanical support structure, and electronics have proven to be extremely reliable and robust. In total, 95% of the 480 channels completely functional.

The CCDs in each layer of VXD2 cover about 60% of the ϕ angle around the beam pipe with layer 2 (4) covering the gaps in layer 1 (3), giving an average of 2.3 hits/track (Figure 1). One of the consequences of having a nonfunctional ladder is to create a region in ϕ containing only one active CCD. For these regions, a pattern recognition algorithm has been developed which supplements the usual technique [2] and allows tracks from the Central Drift Chamber (CDC) to be linked with a single Vertex Detector hit. Tracks found in the CDC are initially constrained to go through the primary vertex, which is determined to an accuracy of 7 microns perpendicular to the beam direction (XY) and 40 microns along the beam direction (Z). The position of these tracks on the CCD surface is interpolated, and a search is made for nearby VXD hits. Finally, a track candidate, including the initial CDC track and the single VXD hit, is fit. Efficiency for linking CDC tracks to

VXD hits is about 96% and uniform in ϕ, even in regions where the track has traversed only one CCD (Figure 2).

Tracking spatial resolution is measured using CDC tracks with three hits in VXD2. A fit is made to the track using only the VXD2 hits at the minimum and maximum radii. The residual between the third hit and the fitted track have widths $\sqrt{3/2}$ times the single CCD total tracking precision, including effects due to alignment errors. The global spatial resolution is measured to be 5 μm in XY and 6 μm in Z.

The two-track impact parameter has been measured for high momentum tracks using muon pairs from Z^0 decays. The tracks are extrapolated to the point of closest approach to the nominal interaction point and the distance between them is computed. Gaussian fits give single track resolutions of 11 μm in XY and 38 μm in RZ. Including a term for multiple scattering, the error on the impact parameter can be approximated by $\sigma_b(XY) = 11 \oplus \frac{70}{p \sin^{3/2}\theta}$ and $\sigma_b(RZ) = 38 \oplus \frac{70}{p \sin^{3/2}\theta}$, where σ_b is in microns, p is the momentum in GeV/c, and θ is the angle with respect to the beam axis.

4.   VXD Upgrade and Expected Performance

The basic components of VXD2 are CCDs having an active area of about 1 cm^2. This relatively small size placed many limitations on the design of the vertex detector since any detector containing more than 480 CCDs was considered to be too difficult to construct, with not enough space around the beam pipe to mount the local electronic boards. These design compromises included an average of fewer than three hits in the vertex detector for each track, layers which only cover $\sim$ 60% of the ϕ angle, a maximum $|\cos\theta|$ of 0.75 for multi-hit tracks, and a a small and ϕ-dependent lever arm ratio (the ratio of the distance between the inner and outer VXD hits to the distance between the inner VXD hit and the interaction point) which results in increased track resolution.

Parameter	VXD2	VXD3
# Layers	4	3
# Ladders	60	48
# CCDs	480	96
# Pixels (10^6)	110	307
CCD Active Size (cm)	1.3×0.9	8.0×1.6
Active z Length (cm)	9.2	15.9
⟨ # Hits/Track ⟩	2.3	3.2
% of ϕ Covered/Layer	60	100
2 Hit $\cos\theta_{max}$	0.74	0.90
3 Hit $\cos\theta_{max}$	-	0.85
Readout Rate (MHz)	2	10
Readout Time (msec)	160	< 100
L/L_R (%)/Layer‡	1.1	0.5
$\sigma_b(XY)$ (μm)†	$11 \oplus 70/p$	$9 \oplus 29/p$
$\sigma_b(RZ)$ (μm)†	$38 \oplus 70/p$	$14 \oplus 29/p$

Table 1. Comparison of VXD2 and VXD3 Specifications. ‡L/L_R is the fraction of a radiation length. †This expression is for tracks perpendicular to the beam pipe. p is in GeV/c.

In the last several years manufacturing methods have improved, allowing production of much larger CCDs which are being used to construct an upgraded vertex detector (VXD3) designed to rectify many of the deficiencies of VXD2 and to enhance the physics potential of SLD. A comparison of VXD2 and VXD3 specifications is shown in Table 1. Two custom-designed CCDs, each with an active area of 1.6 × 8.0 cm and containing 3.2 million pixels of size 20 × 20 μm, are wire-bonded to a beryllium oxide mother card to create a ladder. Electronic readout is done only at the ends of the CCDs. Ladders are arranged into three coaxial layers using a "shingled" geometry with each ladder overlapping its two neighbors (Figure 1). The three layers are placed at nominal radii of 2.84, 3.81, and 4.83 cm giving an average lever arm ratio of 0.7.

In order to minimize multiple scattering, the CCDs are 150 μm thick, the mother cards are thinned to 380 μm, and electronic traces are minimized. Each complete ladder is less than 0.5% of a radiation length thick.

Each CCD has four electronic output nodes simultaneously clocked at a rate of 10 MHz using a two stage output. Signals are read out from both sides of the detector, then shaped and digitized using electronics locally mounted around the beam pipe. Digitized signals are carried by fiber optic cables to Fastbus data aquisition modules for final signal processing.

The impact parameter resolution for VXD3 has been significantly improved over VXD2 by choosing materials with adequate rigidity and long radiation length, and by increasing the lever arm ratio. The resolution is parameterized by $\sigma_b(XY) = 9 \oplus \frac{29}{p \sin^{3/2}\theta}$ and $\sigma_b(RZ) = 14 \oplus \frac{29}{p \sin^{3/2}\theta}$.

Pattern recognition is also enhanced in VXD3 since each track having $|\cos\theta| < 0.85$ has at least 3 CCD hits

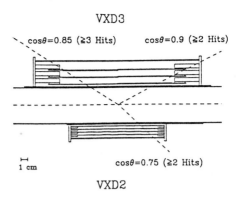

Figure 3. Comparison of VXD2 and VXD3 RZ profiles showing beam pipe, beryllium support structure, ladders, and CCDs.

(Figure 3). This allows independent tracking in both the VXD and the Central Drift Chamber. Monte Carlo Studies indicate that ~99% of all tracks with $p > 0.25$ GeV/c passing through three CCDs are reconstructed by VXD3 alone. Information from these VXD track segments will augment track reconstruction algorithms used in the CDC for tracks with $|\cos\theta| > 0.75$.

5. Physics with VXD3

The SLD collaboration and SLAC plan to produce more than 5×10^5 Z^0 multi-hadronic decays with initial state e^- polarization $P_e > 80\%$ in the next few years. Many measurements made by SLD will benefit from increased solid angle coverage and better impact parameter resolution of VXD3 compared to VXD2. By tagging charged tracks from B hadron decays to identify events containing initial b quarks, a measurement of $R_b = \frac{\Gamma(Z^0 \to b\bar{b})}{\Gamma(Z^0 \to \text{Hadrons})}$ will be made with an accuracy of < 1%. The initial state polarization allows a direct determination of A_b from the forward-backward asymmetry, using $\tilde{A}_{FB}^b = \frac{3}{4}P_e A_b$. The extra solid angle provided by VXD3 is in a region where asymmetries are maximal. Similar methods allow measurement of R_c and A_c. Reconstruction of charm final states will benefit from improved track resolution. Finally, a measurement of the rate of $B_s^0 - \overline{B_s^0}$ mixing could be used as a test of CP violation within the standard model. The B_s meson is expected to have a high oscillation frequency, and any determination of x_s will require measuring the time dependence of the B_s decay. Initial studies indicate that B_s oscillations should be observable for $x_s \lesssim 20$.

References

[1] C.J.S. Damerell *et.al*, Nucl. Inst. Meth. **A288** (1990) 236.
[2] C.J.S. Damerell *et.al*, Proc. XXVI Intern. Conf. on HEP, 1992, p.1862, Ed. J.R. Sanford (AIP 1993); M.G. Strauss, *The Fermilab Meeting DPF 92*, 1992, p.1758, Eds. C.H. Albright *et.al.* (World Scientific 1993).

Parallel Session Pa-18

Top Quark Searches

Convener: C. Quigg (Fermilab)

Scientific secretaries: J. Sloan
                                  P. McCallum (reserve)

*Paper presented at XXVII Int. Conf. on High Energy Physics: Session Pa-18
Glasgow, UK, 20–27 July 1994*

Top Quark Matters

Chris Quigg*

Fermi National Accelerator Laboratory[†], PO Box 500, Batavia, Illinois 60510 USA

Abstract

The top quark's properties test electroweak theory and influence parameters of the everyday world.

The exotic concerns of particle physics—quarks and gluons and Higgs bosons—help us to understand nature on the human scale. We have known since the 1920s that to explain why a table is solid, or why a metal gleams, we must understand the atomic structure of matter, which is ruled not by the customs of everyday life, but by the laws of quantum mechanics. The evidence for the top quark presented in Glasgow makes us think anew about how the microworld influences our surroundings.

It is popular to say that top quarks were created in great numbers in the early moments after the big bang, disintegrated in a fraction of a second, and vanished from the scene until physicists learned to create them in accelerators. That would be reason enough to be interested in top: to learn how it helped sow the seeds for the primordial universe that has evolved into the world of diversity and change we live in. But it is not the whole story; it invests the top quark with a remoteness that hides the immediacy of particle physics. The real wonder is that here and now, every minute of every day, the top quark affects the world around us.

A few numbers determine the dimensions and character of the everyday world, from the size of atoms to the energy output of the sun. Only a generation ago, these parameters of the quotidian—the mass of the proton, the mass of the electron, and the strengths of the fundamental interactions—seemed givens, beyond the reach of science. Today, we have begun to discern links among them. We see how each of them might be understood in principle, or even computed.

Once top is established, the next crucial test of the electroweak theory will come from precise measurements of the top and W masses. If they stand in the predicted relation, we will have new confidence that we understand the weak and electromagnetic interactions—and understand how the top quark influences our world.

A short speculative leap leads to a dramatic example of top's influence on the mundane. In a unified theory, the strengths of the strong, weak, and electromagnetic interactions all are equal at some very high energy. The different strengths we observe arise because the interactions evolve differently with energy. How they evolve depends on the character of the forces themselves and on the spectrum of particles from very high energies down to the energy scale of common experience. Because top stands apart as very much heavier than the other quarks, it has a special influence on running couplings. The mass of the top quark is encoded in the strengths of the forces that rule the everyday world.

But that is not all. The proton is made of up and down quarks bound together by gluons. In a sense we can make reasonably precise in lattice gauge theory, the proton's mass is governed by the QCD scale parameter Λ_{QCD}, which is influenced by the top mass. The top quark is not a constituent of the proton, but if top weighed ten times more or less, the proton mass would shift up or down by about twenty percent. This world—our world—would have a very different character.

While we await definitive news of the top quark, we can savor the realization that to understand one of the most decisive parameters in the everyday world—the proton's mass—we need to know the top's properties. Top matters!

* E-mail: quigg@fnal.gov.
† Operated by Universities Research Association under contract DE-AC02-76CHO300 with the US Department of Energy.

Evidence for Top Quark Production from the CDF Experiment

F. Bedeschi

INFN, Sezione di Pisa
via Livornese 582/a,
S. Piero a Grado, Pisa, ITALY

On behalf of the CDF Collaboration

Abstract

We present the results of a search for the top quark in 19.3 pb^{-1} of $p\bar{p}$ collisions at $\sqrt{s} = 1.8$ TeV. The data were collected at the Fermilab Tevatron Collider using the Collider Detector at Fermilab (CDF) during the 1992/93 data taking period. The analysis assumes Standard Model decays of the top quark; in this framework a rather clean signal is expected in the final states with 2 high p_t leptons (e or μ) and $\not{E}_T$, or one high p_t lepton, $\not{E}_T$ and jets with at least one of the jets identified as a b-quark. Two events are found in the dilepton final state with an estimated background of $0.56^{+0.25}_{-0.13}$. In the lepton plus jet final state, b-quarks are tagged either by identifying a secondary decay vertex, or a lepton (e or μ) consistent with the semileptonic decay of the b-quark or its cascade c-quark. Using the first b-tagging technique six events are found with a background of 2.3 ± 0.3, while using the second we find seven events with a background of 3.1 ± 0.3. We estimate the probability that the combined yield is consistent with a background fluctuation to be 0.26%. While the statistics is still too limited to firmly establish the existence of the top quark, the most natural interpretation is that this excess is due to $t\bar{t}$ production. Very preliminary results based on the first 8 pb^{-1} of data collected this year indicate consistency with the results of the previous run.

1. Introduction

In this paper we shall describe a search for the top quark based on the analysis of 19.3 pb^{-1} of $p\bar{p}$ interaction data collected during the 1992/93 Tevatron Collider run by the CDF Collaboration at Fermilab. We shall assume that the top decays according to the predictions of the Standard Model, that is it decays predominantly to a W boson and a b quark. Previous searches at the Tevatron collider at Fermilab have already placed a lower limit on its mass of 91 GeV/c^2 [1]. More recently the D0 Collaboration has extended this limit to 131 GeV/c^2 [2]. Both results rely on the Standard Model for the decay mode of the top quark and on QCD calculations at next-to-leading order [4, 5] for the production cross section

of $t\bar{t}$ pairs. From the measurement of the width of the W boson the limit $M_{top} > 62 GeV/c^2$ at the 95% CL has been set independently of the top decay mode [3]. The mass of the top quark influences most higher order calculations of electroweak processes. Global fits to the available precision electroweak measurements indicate $M_{top} = 178 \pm 11^{+18}_{-19}$ GeV/c^2, where the second error reflects the uncertainty on the Higgs mass [6].

Since the available lower limit [2] indicates that $M_{top} > M_W + M_b$, the production of top quarks is dominated by $t\bar{t}$ pair production where each top decays into a real W boson and a b-quark. We classify the final states typical of this process according to the decay of the two W's in the event:

i . dilepton mode (BR = 5%): when both W's decay

into a lepton (e or μ) and a ν;

ii . lepton+jet mode (BR = 30%): when one W decays into a lepton (e or μ) and a ν and the other into a quark-antiquark pair, each quark forming hadronic jets;

iii. hadronic mode (BR = 44%): when both W's decay into quark-antiquark pairs.

iv . modes including τ's (BR = 21%): when at least one of the W's decays into a τ and a ν;

Given the small top production cross section expected [5] ($\sim$ 10 pb for $M_{top} = 160 \, \text{GeV}/c^2$) very clean signatures are needed to extract a top signal from the background. For this reason the analysis was focused on the dilepton and lepton+jet mode, where the presence of a high p_t electron or μ, large missing transverse energy from the ν('s), additional jets and the possibility to tag the b content of the jets allow a fairly clean event selection. Analysis of the hadronic [7] and τ modes are currently in progress, but have so far failed to achieve a sufficiently good signal to noise ratio.

The CDF detector is described in detail in [8], but has been significantly improved for the 1992/93 run. An additional 60 cm thick iron filter backed by drift chambers (Central Muon Upgrade) has been added to the muon system in the central region ($|\eta| < 0.6$) to improve the signature for central muons; the coverage in η of the muon system has been extended by the addition of drift chambers in the region $0.6 < |\eta| < 1.0$ (Central Muon Extension). The electron identification has been improved by installing a preradiator between the superconducting solenoid and the central electromagnetic calorimeters, and by upgrading the Central Tracking Chamber (CTC) electronics to allow for dE/dx measurements. Finally a most important improvement to the tracking system has been made by inserting a high resolution silicon microstrip vertex detector (SVX) [9] between the CTC and the beam pipe. This allows the reconstruction of displaced vertices from short lived particles such as b or c hadrons and has played a primary role in the analysis which follows.

2. The dilepton analysis

In the dilepton channel both W's from the $t\bar{t}$ pair decay into an electron or μ and a ν. Given the rather large mass of the W's, both leptons have typically high p_t and the ν's produce a large $\not{E}_T$. For a high mass top ($M_{top} > 120 \, \text{GeV}/c^2$) the b-quarks have enough energy to be detected with good efficiency as hadronic jets in the calorimeters. Background processes which can exibit similar features are: WW, $\gamma/Z \to ee, \mu\mu$ (Drell-Yan), $Z \to \tau\bar{\tau}$, $b\bar{b}$, and lepton misidentification. We now describe the cuts applied to remove the contribution

from such processes.

A $p_t > 20 \, \text{GeV}/c$ cut is applied to each lepton, this is very efficient for top, while suppressing backgrounds from $b\bar{b}$, $Z \to \tau\bar{\tau}$ and lepton misidentification. In addition at least one central lepton ($|\eta| < 1$ for electrons and $|\eta| < 1.2$ for muons) has to pass tight identification cuts including isolation to reduce misidentifications and $b\bar{b}$ contributions. The leptons are also required to have opposite signs. After these cuts there are 5 $e\mu$, 685 ee and 571 $\mu\mu$ events left. For same type dileptons (ee, $\mu\mu$) we remove events where the invariant mass of the leptons is consistent with the Z_0 mass, $75 < M_{ll} < 105 \, \text{GeV}/c^2$. This cut leaves 58 ee and 62 $\mu\mu$ events. At this stage the remaining $e\mu$ events are dominated by the $Z \to \tau\bar{\tau}$ background and the ee, $\mu\mu$ events by Drell-Yan production of lepton pairs. This processes are not expected to have much missing energy so we require that $\not{E}_T > 25 \, \text{GeV}$. In addition we reject events where the azimuthal direction of the $\vec{\not{E}}_T$ is within $20°$ of the direction of either lepton when $\not{E}_T < 50 \, \text{GeV}$, to further suppress semileptonic τ decays. A similar angular cut is applied on the angular separation between the $\vec{\not{E}}_T$ and the jets present in the event with $E_t > 10 \, \text{GeV}$ and $|\eta| < 2.4$ to reject events where the missing energy is the result of mismeasured jet energy. After these cuts only 2 $e\mu$ events and no ee, $\mu\mu$ remain. An additional improvement in signal to noise is obtained by requiring at least 2 jets with $E_t > 10 \, \text{GeV}$ and $|\eta| < 2.4$. Indeed, while two jets are naturally produced in top events by the fragmentation of the b-quarks, for most background sources they have to be produced via higher order processes. This cut reduces the background by approximately a factor 4, while preserving 84% of the signal for $M_{top} = 160 \, \text{GeV}/c^2$. Both $e\mu$ events pass easily the two jet cut, being the E_t's of the two most energetic jets 131 and 61 GeV for the first event, and 85, 26 GeV for the second.

The combined efficiency of the event selection described is a function of the top mass and ranges from 10.0% for $M_{top} = 120 \, \text{GeV}/c^2$ to 17.3% for $M_{top} = 180 \, \text{GeV}/c^2$. We expect to observe 3.7 and 0.7 events respectively for the above top masses, using the production cross section reported in [5].

In the calculation of the expected background a strong effort was put in relying as little as possible on the Montecarlo, using instead real data as far as possible to reduce the systematic error. A detailed description of this calculation is beyond the scope of this paper and we refer the reader to [10] where it is discussed at length. The results of this calculation are shown in table 1.

The total background expected is $0.56^{+0.25}_{-0.13}$ events compared to the 2 events observed. We have checked the background calculation by releasing the $\not{E}_T$ and 2-jet cut and the results agree well with the data as shown in table

		Without $\rlap{/}E_T$ and 2-jet cuts	Without 2-jet cuts	All cuts
$e\mu$	WW	1.1	0.74	0.10±0.04
	$Z \to \tau\bar{\tau}$	3.7	0.22	0.07±0.02
	$b\bar{b}$	1.2	0.10	0.04±0.03
	Fake	1.2	0.19	0.03±0.03
	Total bkg.	7.2	1.25	0.24±0.06
	CDF data	5	2	2
ee, $\mu\mu$	WW	0.6	0.43	0.06±0.02
	$Z \to \tau\bar{\tau}$	3.0	0.20	0.06±0.02
	$b\bar{b}$	1.6	0.12	0.05±0.03
	Fake	1.7	0.25	0.04±0.03
	Drell-Yan	113	0.28	$0.10^{+0.23}_{-0.08}$
	Total bkg.	120	1.28	$0.31^{+0.24}_{-0.10}$
	CDF data	120	0	0

Table 1. Number of background events expected in 19.3 pb^{-1} and the number of events observed in the data

1. In addition if we lower the lepton p_t cut to 15 GeV/c (no $\rlap{/}E_T$ and 2-jet cuts) we expect 25±3 background $e\mu$ events while we observe 18. These checks support our background calculations and, if any, they suggest that we have been somewhat conservative.

Though this analysis shows a small excess of events over the expected background, we can use the data to improve CDF previous lower limit on the top mass. To do this we release the 2-jet cut to gain back sensitivity at the lower top masses and we make the conservative assumption that both events observed are signal events, that is we do not apply any background subtraction. The new lower limit, using the top cross section reported in [5], is 113 GeV/c^2 at the 95% C.L. using 1992-93 data alone. If we apply the same data selection cuts to the old 1988-89 data (3.7 pb^{-1}) no additional events are found. The limit from the combination of the two data sets is 118 GeV/c^2.

3. W+jet analysis

In the W+jet channel only one W decays into an electron or μ and a ν. The signature for this process is then given by a high p_t lepton, missing energy, two hadronic jets from the decay of the second W in the event and two additional jets associated to the b-quarks from the decay of each top. Our event selection starts by requiring a lepton (e or μ) with $p_t > 20$ GeV/c in the central region ($|\eta| < 1.1$ for the electrons and 1.0 for the muons) and $\rlap{/}E_T > 20$ GeV. Z bosons are removed by rejecting events with two oppositely charged leptons (ee or $\mu\mu$) whose invariant mass is in the range 70 to 110 GeV/c^2. A total of 11,949 electron and 7,024 muon events remain after these cuts. This sample is largely dominated by W production; we expect, however, top events to display a significantly higher jet activity. If we define a jet as a calorimeter energy cluster with $E_t >$

15 GeV and $|\eta| < 2.0$, the distribution of the selected events as a function of the number of jets present in the event is shown in figure 1. Overlaid on the same figure are the expectations for $t\bar{t}$ events for two extreme values of the top mass. We observe that applying a cut on the number of jets can greatly improve the signal to noise ratio. We choose to require at least 3 jets. The efficiency of this cut is about 75% for $t\bar{t}$ events at $M_{top} = 160$ GeV/c^2 and less than 0.5% for W events. 52 events remain after applying this cut. However, as figure 1 shows, this is still not sufficient to beat the background. We need an additional handle to improve the signal to noise further. Since $t\bar{t}$ events always contain two b-quarks, while only a few % of W+jet events contain heavy flavours, we can expect a large improvement in the signal to noise ratio by tagging the b content of the jets of the selected events. Two different b-tagging techniques have been used. One searches for displaced vertices consistent with the decay of b-hadrons (SVX), the other looks for soft leptons (e of μ) as a signature of the semileptonic decays of b-hadrons (SLT). These approaches are quite independent from each other, yet they give comparable results as described in the next two sections.

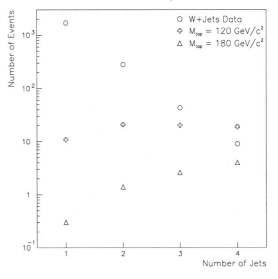

Figure 1. Distribution of the number of observed jets in W+jet data compared to expectations from top Montecarlo

3.1. *SVX b-tagging*

The lifetime of b-hadrons is the order of 10^{-12} sec. If we fold this lifetime with the typical p_t of b-hadrons from top decay, we expect these particles to travel on average a few millimeters in the plane transverse to the beam axis. Their charged decay products are detected in the vertex detector and the central tracker and reconstructed as tracks, whose impact parameter, D, relative to the beam axis, is often significantly different from 0, thanks to the high resolution of the SVX ($\sigma_D \sim$ 15 μm for track $p_t \geq 10$ GeV/c). An efficient and clean selection of large impact parameter tracks requires a good control of the position of the interaction vertex. The luminous region of CDF has a longitudinal width of $\sigma \sim 30$ cm and a transverse width of $\sigma \sim 36$ μm. Its orientation and displacement relative to the detector axis may vary from run to run due to different Tevatron conditions. They are measured every run with an accuracy of ~ 0.4 μm/cm for the slope and ~ 10 μm for the displacement. The logitudinal position of the interaction vertex is measured for each event with an accuracy ~ 1 mm, using the Vertex Time Projection Chambers (VTX). Its transverse position is found event by event by an algorithm which fits to a common vertex all tracks in the event and uses the average beam spot as a constraint. An iterative procedure removes from the fit tracks with large impact parameter relative to the vertex found in the previous iteration. The transverse vertex coordinate resolution of this procedure depends on the number of tracks available for the vertex fit and ranges between 6 μm and the natural transverse beam size.

This analysis has been repeated with three somewhat complementary b-tagging algorithms to make sure that all systematic uncertainties were under control. Having established that the basic results were consistent, the effort to quantify all minor backgrounds and uncertainties and perform various cross-checks was focused on just one of them. We shall refer to this specific algorithm for the remainder of this paper.

This b-tagging algorithm is jet-oriented, that is its goal is to tell whether a given jet contains a b-hadron. It selects all SVX tracks of good quality in the jet, with $p_t > 2$ GeV/c and well separated from the primary vertex ($|D|/\sigma_D > 3.0$). If at least two such tracks are found a common vertex fit is performed and tracks giving too large contribution to the χ^2 are removed iteratively. The final secondary vertex location in the transverse plane, relative to the primary vertex of the event, is then projected onto the jet axis. This quantity is called transverse decay length, L_{xy}. A jet is considered tagged if L_{xy} over its calculated error, $\sigma_{L_{xy}}$, exceeds 3 (positive tag). A negative tag is also defined in the case when $L_{xy}/\sigma_{L_{xy}} < -3$. These tags

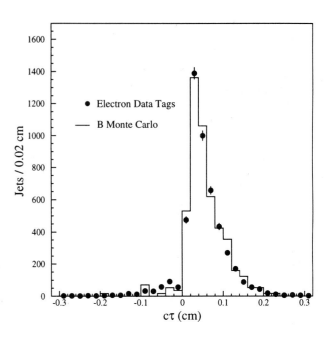

Figure 2. The $c\tau$ distribution for jets with a secondary vertex in the inclusive electron data compared to Montecarlo. Both positive and negative tags are shown

are unphysical since they appear as decays before the interaction vertex and are used later in background calculations.

We have evaluated the performance of the tagging algorithm in a control sample of inclusive electrons with $p_t > 9$ GeV/c and $|\eta| < 1$. This sample has a large component of B semileptonic decays: a b fraction of $37\pm8\%$ has been measured from the yield of muons near the electron compared to the expectations for the cascade decay $B \rightarrow e\mu$ and confirmed with alternate methods. After tagging we expect that in most cases the tracks attached to the secondary vertex come from the decay of a b-hadron. We can test this hypothesis by comparing the distribution of an approximate proper decay length ($c\tau$) of the tagged system with that obtained from $b\bar{b}$ Montecarlo data using the world average inclusive b lifetime. The agreement is quite good as shown in figure 2. The b-tagging efficiency in top events is measured in Montecarlo data. However we check the modeling of the detector by comparing the tagging efficiency calculated in the inclusive electron sample to that of a $b\bar{b}$ Montecarlo. We find that the ratio of the efficiency in the electron sample to that of the Montecarlo is 0.72, independent of jet E_t. To account for the overefficiency of the Montecarlo we degrade the

Source	Background in W+$\geq$ 3 jets
$W b\bar{b}$, $W c\bar{c}$, W+mistags	
Method 1 (default)	1.99±0.26
Method 2 (check)	1.13±0.53
Wc	0.14±0.07
Z→ $\tau\bar{\tau}$, WW, WZ	0.08±0.04
$b\bar{b}$	0.09±0.09
TOTAL	
Method 1 (default)	2.30±0.29
Method 2 (check)	1.44±0.54
Tagged events	6

Table 2. Summary of background calculations in W+multijet events after SVX b-tagging

top efficiency by this ratio and obtain 22±6%, rather independent of the top mass. Using this efficiency and that for the W plus jet selection the expected yield is 7.7±2.5 tagged events for $M_{top} = 120$ GeV/c^2 and 1.4±0.4 events for $M_{top} = 180$ GeV/c^2. We observe 6 W plus 3 or more jet events with an SVX b-tag. To access the significance of this signal we now turn to the calculation of the expected background.

The sources of background in b-tagged W plus multijet events are several: W production in association with heavy quark pairs ($b\bar{b}$, $c\bar{c}$), or with mistags due to tracking errors; $p\bar{p} \rightarrow$ W + charm, $b\bar{b}$ production, WW, WZ and Z→ $\tau\bar{\tau}$. The first two sources are by far the dominant contribution, since we expect them to account for about 80% of all backgrounds. Given the rather large theoretical uncertainties in the currently available W plus jet Montecarlo's, we estimate this major contributions from the data (method 1) and turn to the theoretical estimates (method 2) only as a check and for the calculation of the smaller backgrounds. The first method consists in parametrizing the tagging probability in inclusive jet data, passing our 50 GeV jet trigger, as a function of jet E_t and of the multiplicity of good SVX tracks, and then assuming that, once these dependencies are taken into account, the sum of the tagging probabilities over all jets of our 52 events represents an estimate of the W plus jet background. This method is well justified as long as the heavy flavour fraction in the inclusive jet data is similar to that of W plus jet. Calculations based on HERWIG [11] and VECBOS [12] predict a larger b content in inclusive jets relative to W plus jets; this implies that our estimate of the background, based on this technique, is conservative. A similar procedure, using a parameterization of the negative tags, is applied to calculate the contribution of W plus mistags to be added to the calculation made with method 2. The total background expected with method 1 is 2.30±0.26 events, as shown in table 2 which summarizes all background calculations. We expect 1.44±0.54 with method 2.

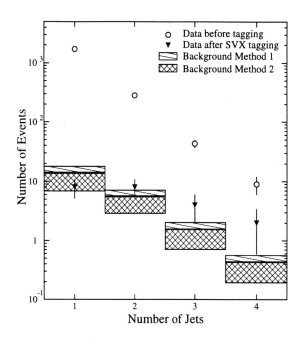

Figure 3. The W + Jet distribution observed in the data compared to background expectations

In figure 3 we show the how the number of tagged events compares with the background expectations as a function of the number of jets. While the number of observed events is consistent with the background in the 1 and 2 jet bin, a slight excess is observed for higher jet multiplicities.

3.2. SLT b-tagging

An alternative way to tag b-quarks is to search for a lepton produced in the decay $b \rightarrow l\nu_l X$ or $b \rightarrow c \rightarrow l\nu_l X$ ($l = e$ or μ). To retain high efficiency for the cascade decay, the lepton p_t threshold is set to 2 GeV/c in this analysis. Since this threshold is rather low, we shall refer to this algorithm as Soft Lepton Tagging (SLT). Identifying electrons and muons with good efficiency and low noise down to this value of p_t in a hadron collider environment is quite a challenge and requires the use of all available detector information.

The search for the electrons is confined to the central electromagnetic calorimeter (CEM) region ($|\eta| < 1.1$). They are defined as CTC tracks which point to a cluster in the strip chambers (CES) located inside the CEM at approximately shower maximum. The CES are proportional chambers which measure both the logitudinal and transverse coordinate of the shower.

The shape and size of these clusters are required to be consistent with the expectations for an electron shower. In addition we require that the ratio of electromagnetic to hadronic energy in the calorimeters is large, consistency between the energy measurement in the calorimeter and the momentum measurement in the CTC ($0.7 < E/p < 1.15$), a signal above 4 minimum-ionizing particles in the the preradiator and a specific ionization (dE/dx) in the CTC consistent with the electron hypothesis.

Muons are identified in the region $|\eta| < 0.6$ by requiring a good match of a CTC track with a segment measured in the muon chambers of the Central Muon system (CMU), located just outside the central calorimers, or in the Central Muon Upgrade (CMP), located behind the CMU after an additional iron absorber. For tracks with $p_t > 3$ GeV/c, which are sufficiently energetic to pass the iron filter between the CMU and the CMP, a good match is also required with the measurement of the CMP chambers, whenever the track extrapolation is within their acceptance. Tracks with $2 < p_t < 3$ GeV/c are too soft to reach the CMP and are looked for in the CMU only. To reduce the punch-through background in the regions not covered by the CMP we apply an additional isolation dependent cut on muon candidates with $p_t > 6$ GeV/c: we require $HAD < 6$ GeV/c$+\sum p$, where HAD is the hadronic energy in the calorimeter tower transversed by the muon and $\sum p$ is the scalar sum of the momenta of all tracks within an $\eta - \phi$ cone of 0.2 around the muon candidate.

A sample of photon conversions selected using only CTC information has been used to evaluate the efficiency for many of the cuts which define the electron selection. For other cuts, like E/p and the electromagnetic to hadronic energy ratio, which depend on the electron isolation, and to determine the geometrical and kinematical acceptances, which depend on the specific process under consideration, a top Montecarlo has been used. For the muon selection, the efficiency for muon stub reconstruction and for the CTC track/muon stub association has been measured from data samples of $J/\psi \to \mu\mu$ and $Z \to \mu\mu$, while a top Montecarlo has been used to evaluate acccceptances and the efficiency of isolation dependent cuts. The overall tagging efficiency for $t\bar{t}$ events has been found to be $\sim$ 16±2.5% roughly independent of the top mass. The expected yield for $M_{top} = 120$ GeV/c^2 is 6.3±1.3 events and 1.1±0.2 events for $M_{top} = 180$ GeV/c^2. We observe 7 SLT tags in the entire 52 W + jet event sample.

The background sources for this analysis are the same which have been described in the SVX tagging case with the addition of a small contribution from Drell-Yan. The calculation of these backgrounds proceeds pretty much as in the previous section: $Wb\bar{b}$, $Wc\bar{c}$, W+mistags are evaluated from direct extrapolation

Source	W + 1 jet	W + 2 jets	W+$\geq$ 3 jets
$Wb\bar{b}$, $Wc\bar{c}$, W+mistags	29.1±2.9	8.8±0.9	2.7±0.27
$b\bar{b}$	1.7±1.2	0.28±0.2	0.05±0.03
WW, WZ, ZZ	0.53±0.25	0.14±0.08	0.04±0.03
$Z \to \tau\bar{\tau}$	0.67±0.24	0.18±0.09	0.14±0.06
Drell-Yan	0.30±0.20	0.05±0.05	0.05±0.05
Wc	0.1.8±0.6	0.42±0.11	0.08±0.03
TOTAL	34.1±3.3	9.9±1.0	3.1±0.3
Tagged events	33	12	7

Table 3. Summary of background calculations in W+multijet events after SLT b-tagging

from the inclusive jet data, while the other smaller backgrounds are estimated primarily via Montecarlo. The technique used for the extrapolation consists in parametrizing the probability to tag a track as an electron or a muon as a function of its p_t and isolation in jet data. These probabilities are then used to scale the expected background in our 52 W + jet events. In table 3 we show a summary of all background calculations: we observe that while there is a good consistency between the background estimate and the number of tagged events for W + 1 and 2 jets, a small excess is present for W + 3 or more jets.

4. Significance of the result

For each of the three top searches we can calculate the significance of the observed signal by taking the Poisson probability that the background fluctuates to the number of observed events or more and folding it with the probability distribution of the background estimate, which we assume to be a gaussian with a width given by the calculated error. The result is 12% for the dilepton analysis, 3.2% for the W plus jet analysis with SVX b-tagging and 3.8% for the SLT b-tagging. All these results are rather marginal, so we attempt to combine together the information of all these analysis to evaluate their combined significance.

Three of the 10 b-tagged events in the W + $\geq$ 3 jet sample are tagged by both b-tagging algorithms. These events are more likely to contain heavy flavour than events with a single tag. To take this information into account in the significance we base our statistical analysis on "counts" rather then events. We define "counts" any of the following: a dilepton event, an SVX tag and an SLT tag in the W plus 3 or more jet sample. Thus a W + 3 jet event with both an SVX tag and an SLT tag would contribute 2 counts, while a dilepton event would contribute only one count even if b-tagged. This approach is conservative, since one of our dilepton events has both an SVX and an SLT tag. We then perform a large number of Montecarlo experiments, as described below, to evaluate the probability to obtain the observed number of "counts" or more. For the W + jet sample we estimate for each background source the mean number of expected events before tagging and the error on the mean. The actual means used for each experiment are extracted from the corresponding Gaussian distributions. Applying Poisson statistics an integer number of events is then extracted for each source. Only the experiments for which the sum of these events is 52 are used in the calculation. Finally tagging efficiencies are applied with binomial statistics to each class of events to determine the total number of tags of each type. Dilepton events are simpler, since the backgrounds can be cumulated and no additional efficiency needs to be applied; so we extract the number of events from a Poisson distribution whose mean is the average background fluctuated by its error. These dilepton "counts" are then added to the SVX/SLT tags for each experiment to get the total number of "counts". In our approach we have assumed that the SVX and SLT tagging are independent, that is in any given data sample the probability for double-tagging is equal to the product of the probabilities for each tag type. This assumption has been verified both in a sample of inclusive jet data and in a top Montecarlo sample.

The result of this study is that the combined probability that our 15 "counts" observed are the result of a background fluctuation is 2.6×10^{-3} using a heavy flavour content consistent with method 1 background estimates. This probability would drop to 2.6×10^{-4} if a W + heavy flavour content consistent with method 2 were used. We have made a similar calculation to estimate the probability that our observed "counts" are consistent with a mixture of top and background. The size of the top component has been determined from the NLO cross section [5]. For $M_{top} = 160$ GeV/c^2 ($\sigma_{t\bar{t}} = 8.2$ pb) we obtain a probability of 20%. This probability tends to grow with lower top masses and to decrease when the top mass is increased, as the result of the fact that our data seems to prefer a higher top cross section [10] than that reported in [5].

5. Conclusions

We conclude that, while the current statistics is still too limited to firmly establish the existence of the top quark, the data has a low probability of being due to background only and is consistent with being a mixture of top and background. It is therefore natural to assume that the observed excess is due to $t\bar{t}$ production.

We have performed many checks and looked for additional evidence. We found many features of the data which support the $t\bar{t}$ hypothesis, but also some which do not. An intriguing observation is the following. We have repeated the b-tagging analysis on the Z + ≥ 3 jet data sample and find 2 tags, while we would expect

0.64. We would not expect a top signal in this channel so the excess of tags can be either due to a fluctuation (the probability is ∼10%) or to an additional source of W/Z + heavy flavour not included in our background estimates. On the other hand higher statistics checks with W/Z + 1 or 2 jets are quite consistent with our background estimates. In addition one dilepton event is tagged by both b-tagging algorithms (we recall that we did not make use of this information in our significance calculation) and both the mass fit and the kinematical analysis of our selected events [10, 13] favour the $t\bar{t}$ hypothesis over the pure background hypothesis.

We have so far collected an additional 10 pb^{-1} this year during the new data taking run (run 1b). 8 pb^{-1} have already been fully analyzed and give us confidence that the CDF detector is performing well. While a full update of the top analysis on the new data sets is not yet available, preliminary results look consistent with the previous run. In particular a new dilepton event $e\mu$ has been observed.

By the end of run 1b we expect almost an order of magnitude increase in statistics over run 1a. This will allow a much more detailed study of the phenomena described in this paper.

References

[1] F. Abe *et al.*, Phys. Rev. Lett. **68** (1992) 447;
   F. Abe *et al.*, Phys. Rev. **D 45** (1992) 3921.

[2] S. Abachi *et al.*, Phys. Rev. Lett. **72** (1994) 2138;
   See also contributions from D0 to the parallel session Pa-18 by S. J. Wimpenny, S. Protopopescu, R. Raja, and the Plenary Session Pl-01 paper by P. D. Grannis in these proceeding.

[3] CDF Collaboration: F. Abe *et al.*, Fermilab preprint: FERMILAB-PUB-94/051-E;
   J. Alitti *et al.*, Phys. Lett. **277B** (1992) 194.

[4] P. Nason, S. Dawson, R. K. Ellis, Nucl. Phys. **B303** (1988) 607; W. Beenakker, H. Kuijf, W. L. van Neerven, J. Smith, Phys. Rev. **D 40** (1989) 54; G. Alterelli, M. Diemoz, G. Martinelli, P. Nason. Nucl. Phys. **B308** (1988) 724.

[5] E. Laenen, J. Smith, W. L. van Neerven, Nucl. Phys. **B369** (1992) 543; E. Laenen, J. Smith, W. L. van Neerven, Phys. Lett. **321B** (1994) 254.

[6] D. Schaile, "Precision Tests of the Electroweak Interaction", Session Pl-02 of this proceedings; Report of the LEP Electroweak Working Group (CERN) LEPEWWG/94-02, July 12, 1994 (unpublished).

[7] CDF Collaboration, "The CDF Top Search In the Multijet Decay Mode", *presented by B. Denby*, Proc. 9th Topical Workshop on Proton-Antiproton Collider Physics, Tsukuba 1993, p. 367; Eds. K. Kondo, S. Kim (Universal Academy Press, Inc. - Tokyo, Japan, 1994).

[8] F. Abe *et al.*, Nucl. Instr. Meth. Phys. Res. **A 271** (1988) 387.

[9] CDF Collaboration: D. Amidei *et al.*, Fermilab preprint: FERMILAB-PUB-94/024-E, submitted to Nucl. Instr. Meth. Phys. Res.

[10] F. Abe *et al.*, Phys. Rev. Lett. **73** (1994) 225;
   CDF Collaboration: F. Abe *et al.*, Fermilab preprint: FERMILAB-PUB-94-097-E (1994) (submitted to Phys. Rev. D).

[11] G. Marchesini, B. R. Webber, Nucl. Phys. **B310** (1988) 461;
   G. Marchesini *et al.*, Computer Phys. Comm. **67** (1992) 465.

[12] F. A. Berends, W. T. Giele, H. Kuijf, B. Tausk, Nucl. Phys.
      B357 (1991) 32.

[13] H. H. Williams, "Top Quark Kinematics and Mass
      Determination", Session Pa-18 of these proceedings.

Top Quark Kinematics and Mass Determination

H.H. Williams

University of Pennsylvania
Department of Physics and Astronomy
Philadelphia, PA 19104

On behalf of the CDF Collaboration

Abstract

An analysis is presented of 10 W $+ \geq 3$ jet events, each with evidence for the presence of a b quark, that were recently observed by the CDF collaboration. Seven of these events include a fourth jet and can be explicitly reconstructed as $t\bar{t}$ production. The best estimate of the top quark mass is $M_t = 174 \pm 10^{+13}_{-12}$ GeV/c^2. A study has also been performed to see if the *kinematical* properties of events with W $+ \geq 3$ jets gives evidence for top production. An excess of events with large jet energies, compared to that expected from direct production of W $+ \geq 3$ jets, is observed. A large fraction of these events also contain a b-quark and a fourth jet.

1. Introduction

In a previous paper [1] and talk presented at this conference [2], evidence for $t\bar{t}$ production from the Collider Detector at Fermilab (CDF) experiment was presented based on the observation of events with two high P_T leptons and missing $E_t (\not{E}_t)$ and W $+ \geq 3$ jet events with a b quark. The presence of the b quark was indicated by the existence of either a secondary vertex or an additional, low P_T lepton. In this paper we present a determination of the top quark mass using the W $+$ jet $+ b$ events which include a fourth jet, and also present additional evidence for top production based on the kinematics of observed W $+$ jet events.

2. Mass Determination

Selecting events with E_t (electron) > 20 GeV (or P_T(muon) > 20 GeV), $\not{E}_t > 20$ GeV, and three jets with $E_t > 15$ GeV, $|\eta| < 2.0$ yields a sample of 52 W $+ \geq 3$ jet events; 10 of these events exhibit a b quark tag, with

three of the events having two tags † The probability that these events, plus the two observed dilepton events, are produced by a background fluctuation is $< 0.26\%$. To investigate whether these events are consistent with being produced by $t\bar{t}$ production and to determine to what extent the value of M_t may be determined, we require the presence of a fourth jet so that a one-to-one correspondence may be made between each jet and one of the partons in the reaction

$$t\bar{t} \rightarrow l\nu\bar{b} + q\bar{q}b \qquad (1)$$

To obtain a higher acceptance, we require the fourth jet to satisfy $E_t > 8$ GeV, $|\eta| < 2.4$; Monte Carlo studies indicate that for $M_t = 170$ GeV 86% of $t\bar{t}$ events which have three jets with $E_t > 15$ GeV, $|\eta| < 2.0$ will also have a fourth jet with $E_t > 8$ GeV, $|\eta| < 2.4$ while only 60% will have a fourth jet with $E_t > 15$ GeV, $|\eta| < 2.0$. Consistent with this expectation 7 of the 10 observed

---

† For the *selection* of this sample of events, which is described in detail in [1], the jet energies and missing transverse energy, $\not{E}_t$, have not been corrected for η and ϕ dependent variations in the calorimetry response or for the energy which is outside the cone size $R = \sqrt{(\Delta\phi)^2 + (\Delta\eta)^2} = 0.4$.

events have a fourth jet. The estimated background in this sample of events is $1.4^{+2.0}_{-1.1}$.

We associate each of the observed jets with one of the final state quarks in the reaction:

$$p\bar{p} \rightarrow t\bar{t}X \rightarrow Wb\,W\bar{b}\,X$$
$$\rightarrow l\nu b\,q\bar{q}\bar{b}\,X \qquad (2)$$

If a jet has a b tag, then it is required to be one of the b quarks. There are then six different possible assignments of the jets to the quarks, and in addition, there are two possible solutions for the longitudinal momentum of the neutrino. The measured energies of each jet are corrected for detector effects and an additional correction is made to estimate the energy of the original parton; a different correction factor is used depending on whether the jet is assigned to a light quark from the W or to a b quark, and on whether the jet has a soft lepton tag or not. The E_t of X is taken to be the total observed transverse energy not associated with the jets or lepton (multiplied by a correction factor of 1.6), but the longitudinal momentum and effective mass of X are left as free parameters. We also require $M_t = M_{\bar{t}}$ and that the decay products of the W's reconstruct to M_W. The resulting fit is overconstrained (2C) so that M_t may be determined. Of the twelve different possible fits for each event, the one with the lowest χ^2 is chosen.

We have tested this procedure by applying it to $t\bar{t}$ events generated with the Herwig program [3] and passed through a simulation of the CDF detector followed by the same reconstruction used for data. The distribution of reconstructed masses for events generated with $M_t = 170$ GeV is shown in Figure 1; the central value is reconstructed at 168 GeV/c^2 and the σ is 23 GeV/c^2.

For comparison, the distribution obtained if one always uses the correct parton-jet assignments is shown by the dashed line. We find that the fitting procedure leads to the correct parton-jet assignments in only 31% of events; however, while for events with incorrect assignments the reconstructed distribution is significantly wider than that shown by the dashed curve, the central value is not significantly altered. In comparison, Figure 2 shows the mass distribution of W $+ \geq 3$ jet events, generated according to the leading order matrix elements [4] and reconstructed as if they were $t\bar{t}$; the distribution is peaked at significantly lower values, approximately 140 GeV.

Monte Carlo studies indicate that 94% of top events should yield a good fit with $\chi^2 < 10$. However, W + jet events also yield a good fit 83% of the time because of the large number of combinations of jet assignments; thus it is not possible to discriminate effectively between $t\bar{t}$ and W + jets on the basis of there existing a good fit.

The masses reconstructed for the 7 data events are shown by the solid line in Figure 3; the distribution

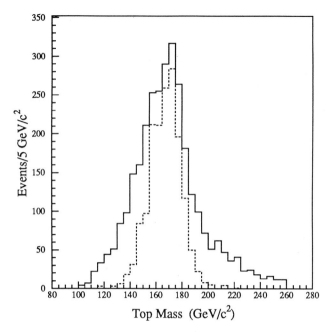

Figure 1. Reconstructed top mass distribution for Monte Carlo events generated with $M_{top} = 170$ GeV/c^2. The full histogram corresponds to the best fit obtained by the fitting program when requiring that one of the b jets is a b in the fit. The dashed histogram refers to the fit with the correct assignment for each of the jets.

bears more resemblance to that expected for top with M_t approximately 170 GeV than it does to the distribution for W + jets.

To determine the best value of the top mass from the seven events, and to check whether the observed distribution is consistent with that expected, we have performed a fit to the seven events using a superposition of the mass distribution, $f_s(m, M_t)$, expected for top (Figure 1) and that expected for the W + jet background, $f_b(m)$, (Figure 2). The likelihood function, L, is defined as

$$L = \frac{1}{\sqrt{2\pi}\sigma_b} e^{-\frac{(n_b - N_b)^2}{2\sigma_b^2}} \cdot \frac{e^{-(n_s+n_b)}.(n_s + n_b)^N}{N!}$$
$$\prod_{i=1}^{N} \frac{(n_b f_b(m_i) + n_s f_s(m_i, M_t))}{(n_b + n_s)} \qquad (3)$$

where n_b and n_s represent the number of background and signal events, N is the number of observed events (7), N_b is the estimated number of background events (1.4), and σ_b is the background uncertainty, set equal to 1.6 for a Gaussian approximation to the asymmetric errors quoted above. This likelihood function is evaluated for several different values of M_t; the results are shown in the insert in Figure 3.

The minimum value of L occurs for $M_t = 174$ GeV, and the statistical error, based on an increase in $\ln L$ of 0.5 and taking into account statistical errors

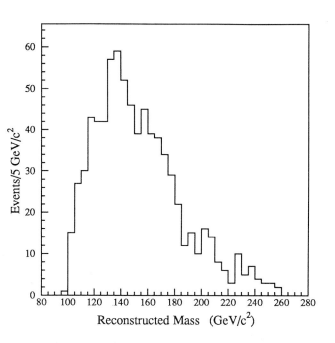

Figure 2. Reconstructed mass distribution for W + multijet Monte Carlo events interpreted as $t\bar{t}$.

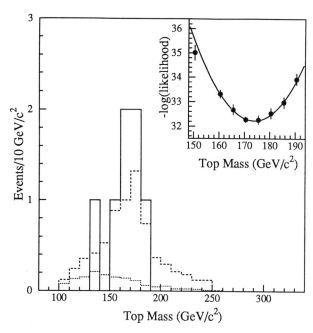

Figure 3. Top mass distribution for the data (solid histogram), the W + jets background (dots), and the sum of background + Monte Carlo $t\bar{t}$ for $M_{top} = 175$ GeV/c^2 (dashed). The background distribution is normalized to the 1.4 background events expected in the mass-fit sample. The inset shows the likelihood of the fit as a function of top mass.

	Systematic uncertainties	(%)
a.	Jet Energy Scale (detector effects)	1.8
b.	Gluon radiation effects on parton energy	4.4
c.	Different backgrounds	$^{+5.3}_{-4.4}$
d.	Effects due to tagging algorithms	1.4
e.	Different likelihood fits	1.1

Table 1. Systematic uncertainties in the top mass measurement.

in the Monte Carlo, is 10 GeV. We have checked whether the value of σ_{M_t} obtained is reasonable by performing a large number of seven event Monte Carlo experiments, each with the number of background events, n_b, generated according to a Poisson distribution with mean 1.4 ± 1.6. The masses, m, of the background events are distributed according to $f_b(m)$ and the 7 - n_b signal events are distributed according to $f_s(m, M_t)$. The most probable error is about 8–12 GeV in good agreement with the value of 10 GeV observed for this experiment. The likelihood observed for the fit to the data is also in good agreement with that expected from the Monte Carlo experiments.

We have studied systematic effects in the determination of M_t including (1) uncertainty in the energy scale of the calorimeter, estimated to range from 10% at 8 GeV to 3% at 100 GeV, (2) uncertainty in the correction for energy outside the cone of the jet, taken to be $\pm$ 10 %, (3) uncertainties in the shape of the background, (4) biases in the jet energies due to the tagging algorithms, and (5) variations due to different fitting procedures. The results are summarized in Table 1, and the uncertainties are added in quadrature to yield a total systematic error on M_t of $^{+13}_{-12}$ GeV/c^2.

Thus our best determination of the top quark mass

from these events is:

$$M_t = 174 \pm 10^{+13}_{-12} \text{GeV}/c^2 \qquad (4)$$

3. Event Kinematics

We have also investigated whether the *kinematic* properties of the events, without requiring a b tag, yield evidence for $t\bar{t}$ production [5]. Alternatively, one may ask what cuts might provide a substantially enriched sample of top events. For this study we correct the jet energies for detector non-uniformities and energy outside the cone of the jets (before final selection of the events) to enable the most accurate comparison with the predicted kinematic distributions for W + jets. We require $\not{E}_t^c > 25$ GeV, where $\not{E}_t^c$ is the missing E_t after the jet energies are corrected, and also add a requirement on the transverse mass of the W, $M_T > 40$ GeV/c^2 to further minimize the background from non-W events.

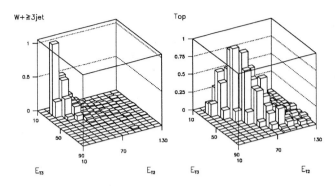

Figure 4. $d\sigma^2/dE_{T2}dE_{T3}$ for QCD $W + \geq 3$ jet and top ($M_{top} = 170$ GeV/c^2) Monte Carlo events.

The jets are required to have $E_t > 20$ GeV and $|\eta| < 2.0$, and we also require a minimum separation between the jets, $|\delta R| > 0.7$, to minimize uncertainties in infra-red divergences in the calculated rates.

We have investigated a number of kinematic variables, including E_{t1}, E_{t2}, E_{t3} (the energies of the jets with the highest, second highest, and third highest energies), $\cos\theta^*$ (the angle of each jet with respect to the beam direction in the center of mass system of the jets + lepton + W), the aplanarity, and the existence and properties of a fourth jet. We find that E_{t2} and E_{t3} are among the most powerful variables for improving the signal-to-noise ratio in a $W + \geq 3$ jet sample of events; this is indicated in Figure 4 which shows the expected distribution of events, as a function of these variables, for both W + jet production and for the production of $t\bar{t}$. The former process has been simulated using the VECBOS program [4], described in more detail below, while the latter process is simulated using HERWIG. Requirement of a fourth jet with transverse energy greater than 10–15 GeV is also a powerful discriminant between W + jet events and $t\bar{t}$ production; however, to maintain the maximum signal size and to minimize systematic errors, we initially do not make this requirement.

Another variable which is useful to improve the signal to background is θ^*, the angle of the jets with respect to the beam direction in the center of momentum frame of the jets and W; as the longitudinal momentum of the neutrino is unknown, we assume it to be zero in computing $\cos\theta^*$. The $\cos\theta^*$ distribution is expected to be significantly more peaked in the forward direction for W + jets than for $t\bar{t}$. We define a "signal" or "top- enriched" sample by requiring $|\cos\theta^*_{max}| \leq 0.7$ and a "control" or "background enriched" sample with $|\cos\theta^*_{max}| > 0.7$; the variable $|\cos\theta^*_{max}|$ is the largest value of $|\cos\theta^*|$ for any of the three jets. The samples contain 15 and 31 events respectively. On an *a priori* basis these two samples are expected to contain approximately equal numbers of top events, but the

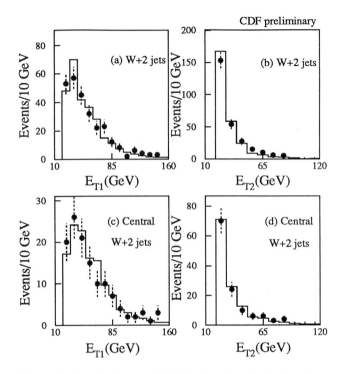

Figure 5. E_T distributions of $W+\geq 2$ jet data (points) and Vecbos $W + \geq 2$ jet events (histograms). (a) leading jet, (b) second to leading jet, (c,d) E_T distributions for events with $|\cos\theta^*_{max}| < 0.7$.

background enriched sample is expected to contain two-three times as many W + jet events.

3.1. *W + jet Events: Predictions and Observations*

A calculation of the properties of W + jet events produced via "standard" QCD interactions has existed for several years at the level of the leading order matrix elements at tree level for production of a W with n final state partons [4]. These matrix elements have been incorporated into the program Vecbos to allow generation of W events with $n = 0, 1, 2, 3, 4$ partons. In order to avoid infrared divergences, cuts are applied in the event generation requiring $P_T(\text{parton}) > 10$ GeV, $|\eta(\text{parton})| < 3.5$, and $|\delta R(\text{parton} - \text{parton})| > 0.4$. Two different fragmentation models, one of which includes simple fragmentation *a la* Field and Feynman [6] and one which includes parton evolution and fragmentation *a la* Herwig, have been utilized; they give very similar results. Numerous previous tests have indicated good agreement between the predictions and experimental observations [7]. Perhaps the best test is provided by the recent CDF $W+ \geq 2$ jet data sample. A comparison of the predicted and observed E_{t1} and E_{t2} distributions, presented in Figure 5, indicates quite good agreement. For this comparison, the Q^2 scale for α_s is chosen to be $< P_t >^2$, the square of the average

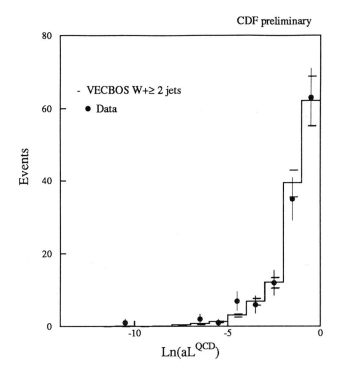

Figure 6. Comparison of the predicted (solid line) and observed (data points) $\ln(aL^{QCD})$ distributions (see text) for $W+ \geq 2$ jet events.

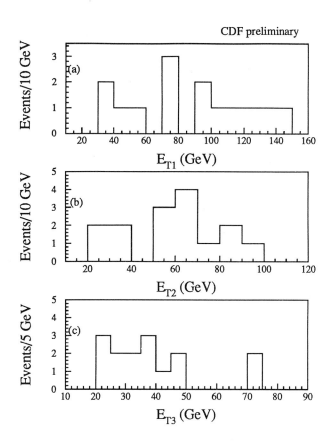

Figure 7. Jet energy distributions for the 15 events passing the signal sample selection cuts. There is one overflow in $E_T(\text{jet}_1)$.

value of the P_t of the outgoing partons; this scale is also used for comparison of the predicted and observed distributions for three jet events. Use of the scale M_W^2 which yields slightly "harder" distributions, gives similar results. A comparison of the predicted and observed energy distributions for jets in $Z+2$ and $Z+3$ jet events also shows good agreement.

Before discussing the $W+3$ jet sample we introduce a variable which conveniently allows representation of the likelihood that an event with a given E_{t1} and E_{t2} is consistent with the expected parent distribution. The *absolute likelihood* is defined as

$$aL = 1/\sigma(d\sigma/dE_{t1}) \times 1/\sigma(d\sigma/dE_{t2}) \qquad (5)$$

We utilize a factorized product of the E_{t1} and E_{t2} distributions for simplicity and have verified that the absence of correlations does not significantly affect the analysis. The predicted and observed distributions of aL are shown in Figure 6. Events with relatively low jet energies, near the peak of the energy distributions, have fairly large likelihoods ($\ln(aL) > -3$ to -2) while events with large energies, on the tail of the energy distributions, have small likelihoods ($\ln(aL) \leq -5$ to -4). Again reasonably good agreement is obtained.

We now compare the observed (Figure 7) and predicted (Figure 8, dashed line) energy distributions for the events in the "signal enriched" sample of $W+ \geq 3$ jet events; it appears that the data has a significantly

larger number of events at high energies than would be expected. The data is consistent with a significant fraction of the events coming from $t\bar{t}$ production with $M_t \approx 170$ GeV; the E_t distributions for this process are also shown in Figure 8 (solid line).

To test quantitatively the consistency of the data with the $W + \geq 3$ jet expectations, combining the information from both E_{t2} and E_{t3}, we define an absolute likelihood for three jet events in an analogous fashion to that for two jet events:

$$aL^{QCD} = 1/\sigma(d\sigma/dE_{t2})1/\sigma(d\sigma/dE_{t3}) \qquad (6)$$

The expected and observed $\ln(aL^{QCD})$ distributions for the $W + \geq 3$ jet enriched sample (control sample) are shown in Figure 9; the data again agrees reasonably well with the expected distribution. However, the observed distribution for the signal or top-enriched sample, where the ratio of top to W + jet events is expected on *a priori* grounds to be between 1:2 and 1:1, does not agree well with the expectations as is shown in Figure 10.

There is a clear excess of events at small likelihood ($aL^{QCD} < -6$). One may ask what the distribution of top events would be in terms of the variable aL^{QCD};

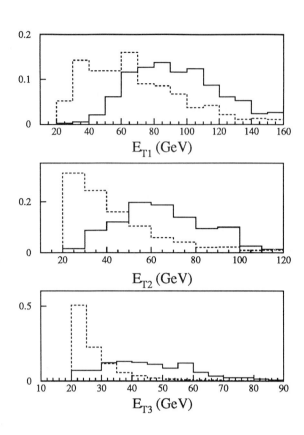

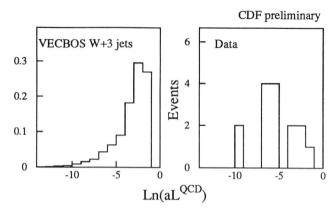

CDF preliminary

Figure 10. Distributions of $\ln(aL^{QCD})$ for $W + \geq 3$ jet events with $|\cos(\theta^*_{max})| < 0.7$ (signal sample); Vecbos Monte Carlo (left) and data (right).

Figure 8. Jet energy distributions for Isajet $t\bar{t}$ (solid line) and Vecbos $W + \geq 3$ jet events (dashed line) passing the signal sample selection cuts.

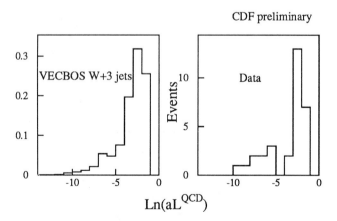

CDF preliminary

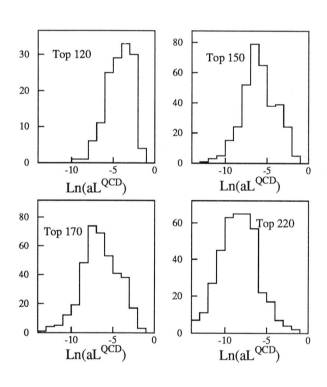

Figure 9. Distributions of $\ln(aL^{QCD})$ for $W + \geq 3$ jet events with $|\cos(\theta^*_{max})| > 0.7$ (control sample); Vecbos Monte Carlo (left) and data (right).

Figure 11. Expected distributions of Isajet $t\bar{t}$ events as a function of $\ln(aL)^{QCD}$, for a number of assumed top masses.

this is shown in Figure 11 for a range of top masses.

A convenient way to represent the *relative likelihood* that an event is from $W + \geq 3$ jets or top production is to define the quantity:

$$rL = aL^{Top}/aL^{QCD} \qquad (7)$$

The variable rL combines information from E_{t2} and E_{t3} and is equivalent to drawing contours in the E_{t2}–E_{t3} plane to select events predominantly from one process or the other (as motivated by Figure 4); in a sample with equal numbers of W and $t\bar{t}$, events with $\ln(rL) > 0$ are most likely to be from $t\bar{t}$ production while those

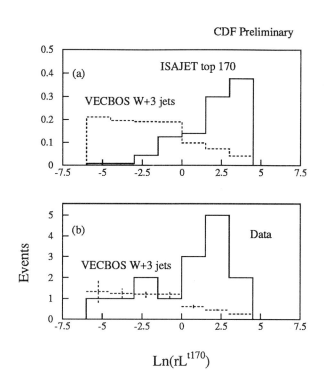

Figure 12. Ln(rL^{t170}) for QCD Vecbos, top Isajet (M$_{top}$ = 170 GeV/c^2) and data events for W+ $\geq$ 3 central jet events (signal enriched sample) (a): W+$\geq$3 jet Vecbos (dotted histogram) and top Isajet (solid histogram), normalized to 1. (b): data (solid histogram) and Vecbos (dotted histogram). Vecbos is normalized to data in the region $ln(rL) < 0$.

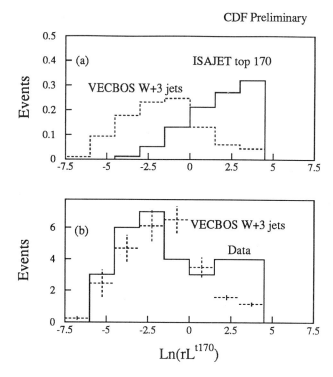

Figure 13. Distributions of $ln(rL)$ for the control sample. (a) Distributions of Vecbos W+3 jet (dotted histogram) and Isajet top events (solid histogram), normalized to 1. (b) 31 data events (solid histogram) versus Vecbos (dotted, with statistical errors). Vecbos has been normalized to data in the region $ln(rL) < 0$.

with $ln(rL) < 0$ are most likely to be from W $+ \geq 3$ jet production. In defining this relative likelihood, it is of course necessary to choose a top mass in order to determine the expected E_{t2}, E_{t3} distributions. As indicated in Figure 11 the results are not very sensitive to the particular mass chosen; we choose $M_t = 170$ GeV in accordance with the results reported in the first half of this paper and the results from studies of electroweak interactions.

Figure 12 (a) shows the expected $ln(rL)$ distributions for W $+ \geq 3$ jet events, and for $t\bar{t}$ production with $M_t = 170$ GeV as generated with the ISAJET program. Figure 12(b) shows the observed distribution; there is a clear excess of events at $ln(rL) > 0$ over what would be expected from W $+ \geq 3$ jets alone.

One may compute the probability that the observed data is a fluctuation of the distribution expected for W $+ \geq 3$ jet events from the binomial probability that a sample of 15 events, distributed according to the dashed curve in Figure 12 (a), yields 10 or more events

with $ln(rL) > 0$; the probability, before consideration of systematic effects, is small. We have tested the sensitivity of the result to various systematic effects— changing the energy scale of the calorimeter by $\pm$ 10% when calculating the expected distributions, assuming different values for the Q^2 scale for α_s in the Vecbos calculation, and using different assumptions for the fragmentation of the outgoing partons. These tests do not yield a significant change in the fraction of QCD produced W + jet events expected with $ln(rL) > 0$. Quantitative evaluation of the probability that the observed distribution is a background fluctuation, including systematic effects and variation in the cuts, will be reported in the near future.

In the control sample, shown in Figure 13, the number of events with $ln(rL) > 0$ is consistent with the presence of $t\bar{t}$ production, but any excess over that expected from W $+ \geq 3$ jets is not statistically significant.

In the next section, we study the presence of b tags to determine whether or not the excess of events at large $ln(rL)$ in the signal sample are most likely due to top production.

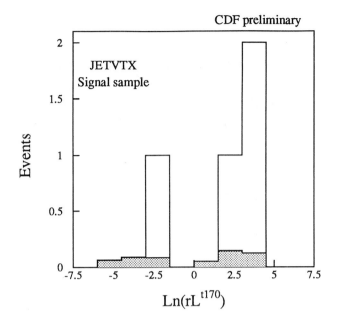

Figure 14. Distribution in ln(rL) of the 4 events of the signal sample tagged by the JETVTX vertexing algorithm. The expected fakes are shown as the shaded histogram.

3.2.   b-tags

As mentioned above and described in [1, 2], evidence for b-quarks in the final state can be provided by the existence of a reconstructed secondary vertex or by the presence of a "soft" lepton in the event. Four of the 15 events in the signal sample have an SVX tag and their distribution as a function of $\ln(rL)$ is shown in Figure 14. The estimated number of tags expected in the absence of top production is shown by the shaded region. Similarly 4 of the 15 events include a soft-lepton tag (SLT) indicating the presence of a b-tag. The expected number of SLT tags in the absence of top production is of order one event.

3.3.   Presence of a 4th jet

If the events with $\ln(rL) > 0)$ are due to $t\bar{t}$, one would also expect a substantial fraction to include a fourth jet: according to the Herwig Monte Carlo approximately 80% of top events will include a fourth jet with $E_t > 15$ GeV (corrected energy) while the expected fraction for W + $\geq$ 3 jet events is much lower, approximately 30% due to the small value of α_s. We find that 7 of the 10 W + $\geq$ 3 jet events with $\ln(rL) > 0$ have a 4th jet while none of the 5 events with $\ln rL < 0$ do. Of these seven events, three have an SVX b-tag and three have a soft lepton tag. A W + 4 jet Monte Carlo, normalized so that it predicts 5 W + $\geq$ 3 jet events with $\ln rL < 0$, predicts of order 1 W + 4 jet event with $\ln rL > 0$. The fact that seven of the 10 W + $\geq$ 3 jet events with $\ln(rL) > 0$ have a fourth jet, and that there

is a total of six b tags among these seven events, is a strong confirmation that these events are indeed from $t\bar{t}$ production.

4.   Conclusion

In a search for the top quark, [1, 2], the CDF experiment has observed 10 W + $\geq$ 3 jet events in which a secondary vertex or low P_T lepton indicates the presence of a b-quark. Three events exhibit two such b-quark tags. The experiment has also observed two events with two high P_T leptons and large missing E_T. The probability that this observation is due to a background fluctuation is < 0.26%. Seven of the ten W+ $\geq$ 3 jet events include a fourth jet, and a detailed fit indicates that each of these events is consistent with coming from $t\bar{t}$ production. The best estimate of the top quark mass, based on these events, is $M_t = 174 \pm 10^{+13}_{-12}$ GeV/c^2.

We have also searched for evidence of top quark production based on the kinematic properties of W+ $\geq$ 3 jet events without requiring a b-tag. For this study we impose slightly different selection criteria using corrected jet energies. We divide the sample into a signal-enriched (top quark) and background enriched (W+ $\geq$ 3 jet) sample and define a relative likelihood (rL) that determines whether a given event fits better the $t\bar{t}$ or W + $\geq$ 3 jet hypothesis. We find that the background-enriched sample and a W + $\geq$ 2 jet sample are consistent with the expectations for W + n jet events, while the signal sample has an excess of events with large jet energies (large relative likelihood for top production). Five of the ten events at large rL contain a b quark tag. Seven of the events also include a fourth jet. The presence of the b quark and the fourth jet provide strong supporting evidence that the excess of events at large rL are indeed from $t\bar{t}$ production. The 5–10 fold increase in data from the present run should allow a more precise determination of the top quark mass and a refinement of the techniques for selecting enriched samples of top quark events.

References

[1] F. Abe et al., Phys. Rev. Lett. **73** (1994) 225; F. Abe et al., Phys. Rev. **D50**, 2966 (1994).

[2] F. Bedeschi, " Evidence for Top Quark Production from the CDF Experiment", this proceedings.

[3] G. Marchesini and B.R. Webber, Nucl. Phys. **B310** (1988) 461; G. Marchesini et al., Comput. Phys. Comm. **67**, (1992) 465.

[4] F.A. Berends, W.T. Giele, H. Kuif, B. Tausk, Fermilab-Pub-90/213-T. W. Giele, Ph.D thesis, unpublished.

[5] A more detailed discussion can be found in M. Cobal, PhD thesis, Univ Pisa, INFN PI/AE/94/004 and M. Cobal, H. Grassman, S. Leone, Il Nuovo Cimento 107A, 75 (1994).

[6] R. Field and R. Feynman, Nucl. Phys. **B136**, (1978) 1.

[7] F. Abe et. al, Phys. Rev. Lett. **70**, 4042 (1993). J. Alitti et al, Phys. Lett. **268B, 145 (1992)**.

Paper presented at XXVII Int. Conf. on High Energy Physics: Session Pa-18
Glasgow, UK, 20–27 July 1994

Top quark cross sections in the standard model

R. K. Ellis

Fermilab
P. O. Box 500, Batavia, IL 60510, USA.

Abstract

Theoretical estimates for the top quark production cross section are reviewed. The top quark cross section is known to about $\pm 30\%$.

CDF has presented results from their top search showing evidence for events above background[1]. Interpreting this data as a signal for top they find $m_t = 174 \pm 10^{+13}_{-12}$ GeV. Using this value of m_t, CDF find that the top quark cross section is $\sigma_{t\bar{t}} = 13.9^{+6.1}_{-4.8}$ pb. The comparison of this result with the central theoretical curve is shown in Fig. 1. The purpose of this contribution is to discuss the reliability in the standard model of the theoretical curve shown in Fig. 1.

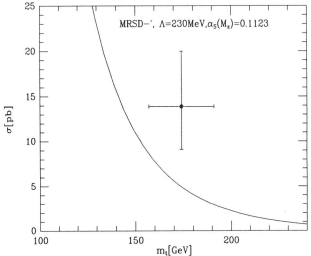

Figure 1. Comparison of the CDF point with the theory.

The top quark cross section is calculable in perturbation theory because $m \gg \Lambda$. This condition is certainly valid for the case of the top quark and

suggests that the top quark cross section should be well determined. The processes which contribute to heavy quark production in order α_S^2 and α_S^3 are,

$$
\begin{aligned}
q + \bar{q} &\to Q + \overline{Q}, & \alpha_S^2, \alpha_S^3 \\
q + \bar{q} &\to Q + \overline{Q} + g, & \alpha_S^3 \\
g + g &\to Q + \overline{Q}, & \alpha_S^2, \alpha_S^3 \\
g + g &\to Q + \overline{Q} + g, & \alpha_S^3 \\
g + q(\bar{q}) &\to Q + \overline{Q} + q(\bar{q}), & \alpha_S^3
\end{aligned}
$$

These processes can be used to calculate the short distance cross section $\hat{\sigma}$. This has been performed in refs. [2, 3]. The hadronic cross section is,

$$
\sigma(S) = \sum_{i,j} \int dx_1 dx_2 \; \hat{\sigma}_{ij}(x_1 x_2 S, m^2) \; F_i^A(x_1, \mu) F_j^B(x_2, \mu)
$$

The expression for short distance cross section can be written as a perturbation series[2],

$$
\hat{\sigma}_{ij}(s, m^2, \mu^2) = \frac{\alpha_S^2(\mu^2)}{m^2} f_{ij}\left(\rho, \frac{\mu^2}{m^2}\right)
$$

$$
f_{ij}\left(\rho, \frac{\mu^2}{m^2}\right) = f_{ij}^{(0)}(\rho) + g^2(\mu^2)\left[f_{ij}^{(1)}(\rho) + \overline{f}_{ij}^{(1)}(\rho) \ln\left(\frac{\mu^2}{m^2}\right)\right]
$$

$$
\rho = \frac{4m^2}{s}, \quad \beta = \sqrt{1 - \rho}.
$$

In order to calculate the f_{ij} in perturbation theory renormalisation and factorisation of mass singularities are performed at mass scale μ. Corrections to the $q\bar{q}$ process are found to be moderate, with the bulk of the correction occurring near threshold. Corrections to the gg process are large, both at threshold and at high energy.

The relative importance of the various kinematic regions is determined by the parton flux, defined as

$$\Phi_{ij}(\tau,\mu) = \tau \int_\tau^1 \frac{dx_1}{x_1} F_i^A(x_1,\mu) F_j^B\left(\frac{\tau}{x_1},\mu\right)$$

where F_i^A is the density of partons of type i in hadron A. In terms of these parton fluxes the hadronic cross-section is given by,

$$\frac{d\sigma(S)}{\ln \tau} = \frac{\alpha_S^2(\mu^2)}{m^2} \sum_{i,j} \Phi_{ij}(\tau,\mu) f_{ij}\left(\frac{\rho^H}{\tau}, \frac{\mu^2}{m^2}\right)$$

Fig. 2 shows that at $\sqrt{S} = 1.8$ TeV, the top quark is produced predominantly by $q\bar{q}$ annihilation, with large corrections near threshold. For $m = 174$ GeV, 89% of the cross section is due to $q\bar{q}$ annihilation.

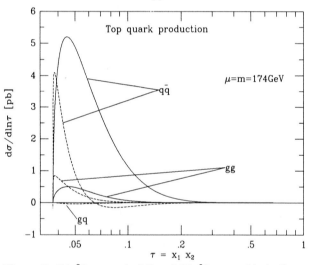

Figure 2. $O(\alpha_S^2)$ curves (solid) and $O(\alpha_S^3)$ curves (dashed)

Near threshold,$(\beta \to 0)$, we have $f_{q\bar{q}}^{(0)}, f_{gq}^{(1)} \to O(\beta)$

$$f_{q\bar{q}}^{(1)} \to \mathcal{N}_{q\bar{q}}\left[-\frac{\pi^2}{6} + \beta\left(\frac{16}{3}\ln^2\left(8\beta^2\right) - \frac{82}{3}\ln(8\beta^2)\right)\right]$$

$$f_{gg}^{(1)} \to \mathcal{N}_{gg}\left[\frac{11\pi^2}{42} + \beta\left(12\ln^2\left(8\beta^2\right) - \frac{366}{7}\ln(8\beta^2)\right)\right]$$

The rapid rise of the cross section near threshold is due to the logarithmic terms shown above. These corrections are larger for smaller top quark mass, when gluon-gluon processes are more important. Attempts have been made to resum these corrections[6]. The resummation is hard to control without treatment of order $1/m$ effects.

The constant behaviour of the cross section near threshold is a consequence of the Coulomb singularity.

This effect is repulsive in the dominant $q\bar{q}$ octet channel. The overall correction due to this effect even after resummation is small (of order a few %), because of cancellation between gg and $q\bar{q}$[7].

We now turn to numerical estimates. Earlier estimates are given in [4, 5]. The sensitivity to the shape of the parton distribution functions is quite small. For the $MRS(D_0')$ distribution the result for $m = 174$ GeV is $\sigma(\mu = m) = 4.93$ pb; the corresponding result for the $MRS(D_-')$ distribution is 4.91 pb. The effect of α_S uncertainty is more important. Increasing α_S by 10%, $\alpha_S(M_Z) \to 0.124$ the cross section changes by 23% to 6.04 pb. This may be an overestimate since it does not take into account the increased shrinkage of the quark distribution functions for larger α_s in the evolution from lower energy. The scale dependence uncertainty is small as shown in Fig. 3. For $m/2 < \mu < 2m$ we find that $5.1 > \sigma > 4.4$ pb for $m = 174$ GeV.

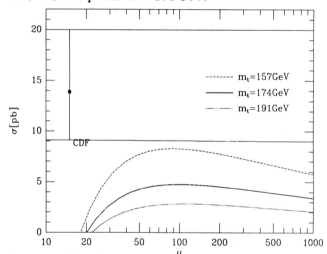

Figure 3. The μ dependence of the theoretical cross section

In conclusion, I find that, at a fixed top mass, the cross section is unlikely to be uncertain by more than 30%. The cross sections quoted above are given in the narrow width approximation. For $m_t = 174$ GeV the top cross section is 35% bigger at $\sqrt{S} = 2$ TeV and more than 100 times bigger at LHC.

References

[1] CDF Collaboration: F. Abe *et al.*, Phys. Rev. **D50** (1994) 2966.

[2] P. Nason, S. Dawson and R. K. Ellis Nucl. Phys. **B303** (1988) 607.

[3] W. Beenakker, H. Kuijf, W. van Neerven, J. Smith, Phys. Rev. **D40** (1989) 54.

[4] R.K. Ellis Phys. Lett. **B259** (1991) 492.

[5] E. Laenen, J. Smith and W. van Neerven, Phys. Lett. **B321** (1994) 254.

[6] E. Laenen, J. Smith and W. van Neerven, Nucl. Phys. **B369** (1992) 543.

[7] V. Fadin, V. Khoze and T. Sjöstrand, Zeit. Phys. **C48** (1990) 613.

Search for the Top Quark in Dilepton Decay Modes at DØ

Stephen J. Wimpenny[†‡]

† Physics Department, University of California, Riverside, CA 92521, USA

For the DØ Collaboration

Abstract

We present preliminary results on the search for the top quark in $p\bar{p}$ collisions at $\sqrt{s} = 1.8$ TeV by the DØ collaboration at the Fermilab Tevatron. The results are based on an integrated luminosity of 13.5 pb^{-1} of data collected by the DØ detector during the 1992-3 Tevatron collider run. We have searched for Standard Model $t\bar{t}$ decays into the dilepton decay modes $ee + X$, $e\mu + X$ and $\mu\mu + X$. No significant signal is observed for top quark production in these channels. We find one candidate event in the $e\mu + X$ channel and no events in the other two channels with an estimated non-top background of 0.76 ± 0.16 events.

1. Introduction

The top quark (t) is one of the few remaining pieces of the Standard Model yet to be experimentally verified. Measurements of the isospin of the b quark [1] and the hadronic width of the Z [2] require the b quark to be the lower mass component of a weak isospin doublet. In the Standard Model its partner the t quark is known, through studies of the decay width of the W boson, to have a mass in excess of 62 GeV/c^2 at 95 % CL [3]. Additional evidence for the large mass of the top quark comes from the analysis of precision electroweak data from LEP and SLC which imply a mass of $m_t = 178 \pm 14^{+18}_{-19}$ GeV/c^2 [2].

Prior to this conference the most stringent results from direct top quark searches come the two $p\bar{p}$ experiments at the Fermilab Tevatron where strong $t\bar{t}$ pair production is believed to be the dominant production mechanism. Each t quark decays via the semiweak transition $t \rightarrow W + b$ and the experimental searches key on the decays of the W bosons. From such studies the DØ collaboration has published an experimental lower bound on the top quark mass of $m_t > 131$ GeV/c^2 at 95 % CL [4] and the CDF collaboration

has shown possible evidence for top quark production at a mass of $174 \pm 10^{+13}_{-12}$ GeV/c^2 [5, 6]. In this and the two following papers [7, 8], we present the results of a new analysis from the DØ collaboration which focuses on the search for the top quark in the mass region $m_t > 130$ GeV/c^2.

This paper concentrates on searches in the three 'dilepton' decay modes: $t\bar{t} \rightarrow ee + \not{E}_T$ +jets, $t\bar{t} \rightarrow e\mu + \not{E}_T$ + jets and $t\bar{t} \rightarrow \mu\mu + \not{E}_T$ + jets. The following paper [7] describes results of searches in the 'lepton+jet' decay modes: $t\bar{t} \rightarrow e\nu$ + jets and $t\bar{t} \rightarrow \mu\nu$ + jets and the third paper [8] describes the result of a search in the decay mode $t\bar{t} \rightarrow e\nu$ + jets in which a soft muon is used to tag possible b quark jets. The third paper also contains the overall analysis summary and a combined estimate of the top quark production cross-section.

2. The DØ Detector

DØ is a second generation multipurpose detector for the study of $p\bar{p}$ interactions at high luminosity. Its hermetic 4π coverage emphasizes good jet, charged lepton and missing energy measurement which are essential for the search for the decay of high mass top quarks. The detector consists of three subsystems:

‡ E-mail: Wimpenny@ucrph0.ucr.edu

a central tracking system for charged track detection; three large uranium liquid argon calorimeters for electromagnetic and hadronic energy measurement; and a muon spectrometer for muon momentum analysis. A detailed description of the detector and data collection systems is given in reference [9]. Here we summarize the features relevent to the top search.

The calorimeter is a uranium liquid argon sampling detector, contained within three cryostats (one central, two forward) which provide coverage out to pseudorapidity $|\eta| = 4.2$. Its fine lateral and longitudinal granularity ($\Delta\phi \times \Delta\eta = 0.1 \times 0.1$ and 0.05×0.05 at shower maximum) are important for electron, muon and jet identification and isolation measurement. The energy resolution, $\sigma/E \approx 15\%/\sqrt{E}$ for electrons, $\approx 50\%/\sqrt{E}$ for single hadrons, and $\approx 80\%/\sqrt{E}$ for jets (where E is in GeV) [9]. For minimum bias events the resolution for either component of the missing transverse energy, $\not{E}_T$, is 1.1 GeV $+ 0.02 \times (\Sigma E_T)$, where ΣE_T is the scalar sum of all the transverse energy in the calorimeter.

The muon system consists of three layers of chambers, with magnetized iron toroids located between the first and second layers. The innermost layer has 4 planes of proportional wire drift tubes and the second and third layers each have 3 planes. The magnetic field in the iron toroid is 1.9 T, providing momentum measurement with a resolution of $\delta(1/p)/(1/p) = 0.20 \oplus 0.01p$ (where p is in GeV/c). The thickness of the calorimeter plus the iron toroids varies from 14-19 λ and minimizes the background from hadronic punchthrough. In-flight π and K decay background is also negligible because of the compact calorimetry and central tracking volume.

DØ was proposed, reviewed, and approved in 1984. The detector was commissioned with $p\bar{p}$ collisions during the summer of 1992 and began its first physics run in August, 1992. This first run was completed in May, 1993 with a total data sample of 13.5 pb^{-1} written to tape. A second collider run began in January 1994 and the total data sample from this second run is expected to be in excess of 100 pb^{-1}.

3.   Particle Identification

The experiment triggers on events with combinations of electron, muon and jet candidates and $\not{E}_T$. The trigger efficiencies are determined from full detector and trigger simulations and vary from 85% to 90% as m_t increases from 140 to 180 GeV/c^2.

Electron candidates are identified as energy clusters in the calorimeter for which more than 90% of the total energy is contained in the electromagnetic section and which have a matching track in the central tracking system. The clusters are also required to have longitudinal and transverse shower profiles consistent

with Monte Carlo calculations and test beam electron measurements [10]. These are further required to be isolated by requiring that the energy deposited in the annular cone $0.2 < \Delta R < 0.4$ about the electron track be less than 10% of the electromagnetic energy contained in the inner cone of radius $\Delta R < 0.2$.

Muons are identified by tracks in the muon spectrometer and are required to be consistent with the reconstructed vertex position. Additional requirements include a matching minimum ionizing energy deposition in the calorimeter and an isolation cut on calorimeter activity near the muon track. Muons which pass through the transition region between the central and end toroids (and thus through an insufficient amount of magnetic field for good momentum measurement) are rejected by requiring a minimum path length in the magnetized iron toroid of $\int Bdl > 1.83$ Tm which corresponds to a p_T kick of 0.55 GeV/c.

Jets are reconstructed using a fixed cone algorithm with cone radius, $\Delta R = 0.5$, where $\Delta R^2 = \Delta\eta^2 + \Delta\phi^2$. The reconstructed jet energies are corrected for non-uniformity of the calorimeter response, out-of-cone leakage, noise, and for the underlying event. The missing transverse energy, as determined from the energy deposited in the calorimeter after all corrections, is denoted by $\not{E}_T^{\text{cal}}$ and same quantity, after correction for muon momentum is denoted $\not{E}_T$.

4.   Dilepton Search

4.1. $t\bar{t} \rightarrow ee + \not{E}_T + jets$

For the ee channel the initial data sample is obtained by requiring two isolated electromagnetic clusters with $E_T > 20$ GeV in the region $|\eta| < 2.5$. After requiring that both clusters match to tracks in the central tracking chamber and that at least one track be consistent with a single minimum ionizing particle, an initial sample of 739 events is obtained. To reduce backgrounds from $Z \rightarrow ee$, a cut is made on the dielectron mass: $|M_{ee} - M_Z| > 12$ GeV/c^2 if $\not{E}_T < 40$ GeV; 111 events remain after this cut. To eliminate background from QCD and the Drell-Yan continuum, an additional cut of $\not{E}_T > 25$ GeV is imposed, leaving 4 events. Finally, to reduce backgrounds from diboson (WW, WZ) events and $Z \rightarrow \tau\tau$ decays, we require two hadronic jets with $E_T > 15$ GeV in the region $|\eta| < 2.5$. No events survive after this cut. To illustrate the basic features of the data, Fig. 1 shows the distribution of $\not{E}_T$ vs. M_{ee} for data and $t\bar{t}$ Monte Carlo ($m_t = 160$ GeV/c^2 after making the initial electron E_T and the final jet cuts.

The acceptance for $t\bar{t} \rightarrow ee$ decays is studied using samples of $m_t = 140$, 160 and 180 GeV/c^2 Monte Carlo events which were generated using ISAJET [11] and put through the full DØ detector simulation and

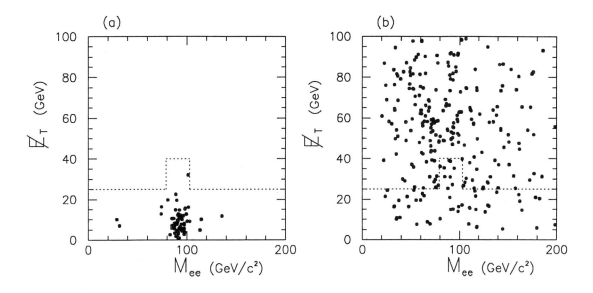

Figure 1. Scatter plots of $\not{E}_T$ vs M_{ee} after all but the $\not{E}_T$ cuts for ee events from (a) data, and (b) $t\bar{t} \to ee$ MC ($m_t = 160$ GeV/c² and $\int \mathcal{L}dt \approx 19$ fb⁻¹).

reconstruction. After making small corrections to the electron efficiencies to account for the differences between simulation and data, the expected top event yields vary from 0.41 ± 0.07 to 0.12 ± 0.02 events as m_t is changed from 140 GeV/c² to 180 GeV/c² for an integrated luminosity of 13.5 pb⁻¹. This is based on the central QCD cross sections of Laenen *et al* to NLO with soft gluon summation [12].

Estimation of non-top background is based on Monte Carlo and data studies. The sources considered include the Drell-Yan continuum, $Z \to ee, Z \to \tau\tau$, $Z \to b\bar{b}$ and $c\bar{c}$, strong production of $b\bar{b}$ and $c\bar{c}$, WW, WZ, W + jets, Z + jets, and fake leptons. The dominant contributions come from $Z \to \tau\tau$ (0.05 events), misidentified electrons (0.05 events) and $Z \to ee$ (0.03 events). Combining all sources gives a total expected background of 0.16 ± 0.07 events.

4.2. $t\bar{t} \to e\mu + \not{E}_T + jets$

The initial $e\mu$ data set is selected by requiring an isolated electron with $E_T > 15$ GeV in the region $|\eta| < 2.5$ and an isolated muon with $p_T > 12$ GeV/c and $|\eta| < 1.7$. For the electron we impose all of the cuts used in the ee analysis except for the single minimum ionizing particle requirement. 12 events satisfy these criteria. Backgrounds from $Z \to \tau\tau$ and QCD/$Z \to b\bar{b}$ and $c\bar{c}$ are suppressed by making a cut on the missing transverse energy: $\not{E}_T > 10$ GeV; 8 events remain after this cut. To eliminate misidentification background from W + jets $\to \mu$ + jets events in which one of the jets fakes an electron, a cut is made on the vector energy

imbalance in the calorimeters, $\not{E}_T^{cal} > 20$ GeV. This cut is particularly useful since for $W \to \mu\nu$ events, $\not{E}_T^{cal}$ is a direct measure of the W transverse momentum. To reject backgrounds due to muon bremsstrahlung (where the outgoing muon radiates a photon which is matched to the muon track in the central tracking chamber), a cut is made on the opening angle, ΔR, between the muon and "electron": $\Delta R^{e\mu} > 0.25$. This leaves 7 events. Lastly, to reduce backgrounds from WW, WZ, and $Z \to \tau\tau$ we imposed the same two jet requirements as were used for the ee channel. One event survives this final cut. Figures 2a and 2b show the distribution of $1/p_T^\mu$ vs E_T^e for the data and $t\bar{t}$ Monte Carlo ($m_t = 170$ GeV/c²) prior to the final jet cuts. The surviving $e\mu$ candidate is marked by a $\star$ in Fig. 2a.

The high mass $t\bar{t} \to e\mu$ acceptance is studied using Monte Carlo event samples generated using ISAJET [11] and put through a full simulation of the DØ detector and trigger system. After folding the resulting acceptances with the Laenen *et al.* production cross section [12] we obtain predicted event yields which vary from 0.72 ± 0.16 to 0.23 ± 0.05 as m_t is varied from 140 GeV/c² to 180 GeV/c².

The corresponding non-top background has been estimated using a combination of Monte Carlo calculations and data measurements. Among the sources investigated are $Z \to \tau\tau$, $b\bar{b}$ and $c\bar{c}$ production in Z decays and QCD multijet events, WW, WZ, and W (or Z) + jet events in which one of the jets fakes a lepton. The dominant contributions come from $Z \to \tau\tau$ (0.18 events), and W + jets $\to \mu$ + jet (fake e) + jets (0.05 events).

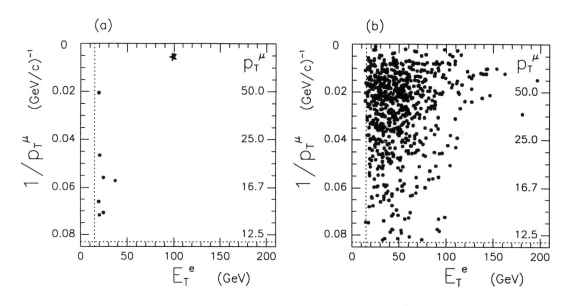

Figure 2. Scatter plots of $1/p_T^\mu$ vs E_T^e prior to final (jet) cut for $e\mu$ events from (a) data, and (b) $t\bar{t} \to e\mu$ MC ($m_t = 170$ GeV/c^2 and $\int \mathcal{L}dt \approx 21$ fb^{-1}).

Combining these with other smaller sources gives a total background of 0.27 ± 0.09 events.

4.3. $t\bar{t} \to \mu\mu + \not{E}_T + jets$

The $\mu\mu$ analysis uses the 9.8 pb^{-1} subset of the full dataset for which the $t\bar{t} \to \mu\mu$ trigger was optimized. The initial event sample was selected by requiring two isolated muons with $p_T > 15$ GeV/c in the region $|\eta| < 1.1$. To remove background from $J/\psi \to \mu\mu$ decays an additional cut on dimuon invariant mass: $M_{\mu\mu} > 10$ GeV/c^2 is imposed, giving an initial sample of 13 events. Similar cuts in the region of the Z mass to exclude $Z \to \mu\mu$ decays are not possible because of the poor momentum resolution at large values of p_T. To exclude these backgrounds we exploit the topological differences between $t\bar{t} \to \mu\mu$ and $Z \to \mu\mu$ decays. Events in which the leading muon is mismeasured leading to fake $\not{E}_T$ are removed by requiring the azimuthal opening angle between the $\not{E}_T$ and leading muon p_T to be < 170°. 10 events survive this cut. Next we exclude events in which one or both muons are significantly mismeasured by requiring that the azimuthal opening angle between the calorimeter energy imbalance ($\not{E}_T^{cal}$) and dimuon transverse momentum vectors be at least 30°. This strongly suppresses mismeasured $Z \to \mu\mu$ decays for which these quantities both measure the p_T of the Z; 5 events remain after this cut. Further background rejection is achieved by requiring a minimum of 40 GeV $\not{E}_T$ for those events in which the azimuthal opening angle between the two muons is > 140°; 2 events remain after this cut. Lastly to reduce backgrounds

from WW, WZ, and ZZ decays we imposed the same two jet requirement as is used for the other two channels. No events survive after this cut. To illustrate the basic features of the data Figs. 3a, 3b and 3c show the distribution of $\Delta\phi^{\mu\mu}$ vs. $\not{E}_T$ for the data and samples of $Z \to \mu\mu$ and $t\bar{t}$ Monte Carlo, respectively.

The acceptance for $t\bar{t} \to \mu\mu$ decays is studied using Monte Carlo event samples generated using ISAJET [11] and put through a full simulation of the DØ detector and trigger system. After folding the resulting acceptances with the Laenen *et al.* production cross section [12] we obtain predicted event yields which vary from 0.24 ± 0.05 to 0.06 ± 0.01 as m_t is varied from 140 GeV/c^2 to 180 GeV/c^2.

The corresponding non-top background has been estimated using a combination of Monte Carlo calculations and data measurements. This is dominated by background from $Z \to \mu\mu$ decays (0.32 events). The contributions from other processes such as WW, WZ, ZZ, and Drell-Yan continuum production are very small. Combining these and other small contributions gives a total background of 0.36 ± 0.06 events.

4.4. Combined Results

Taking the three channels together, we observe one event candidate ($e\mu$ channel) with an estimated non-top background of 0.76 ± 0.16 events. We therefore observe no significant signal for top quark production in the present data. If we interpret the small excess over background to a possible $t\bar{t}$ signal the event yield is consistent with the expectations for a top quark

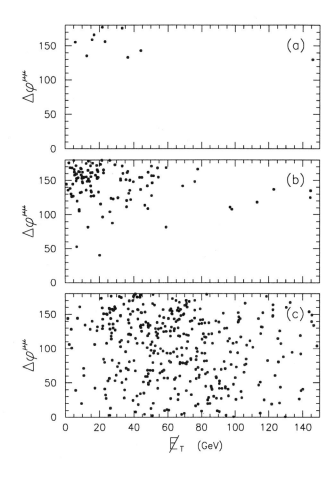

Figure 3. Scatter plots of $\Delta\phi^{\mu\mu}$ vs. $\not{E}_T$ after the initial selection cuts for $\mu\mu$ events from (a) data, (b) $Z \to \mu\mu$ MC ($\int \mathcal{L}dt \approx 110$ pb^{-1}) and (c) $t\bar{t} \to \mu\mu$ MC ($m_t = 160$ GeV/c^2 and $\int \mathcal{L}dt \approx 21$ fb^{-1}).

5. Conclusions

Using the full data sample of the 1992/3 collider run DØ has performed a search dilepton events consistent with the decay of a Standard Model top quark with large mass ($m_t \geq 130$ GeV/c^2). We observe one event in the $e\mu$ channel and no events in either the ee or $\mu\mu$ channels. This is the same $e\mu$ event as was found in the previous top search [4].

For a preliminary analysis of the non-top background and the expectations for $t\bar{t}$ production we observe no significant signal for top quark production. The observed event rate is consistent with a null signal and both the expected event yield for a high mass top quark [12] and the production cross section reported by the CDF collaboration [5].

6. References

References

[1] G. Kane, "Top Quark Physics", UM-TH-91-31, 1991, (unpublished).

[2] D. Schaile, "Precision Tests of the Electroweak Interaction", paper submitted to these proceedings.

[3] Y-K. Kim, "Measurements of the Mass and Width of the W Boson from CDF", Proceedings of XXIXth Rencontres de Moriond, March, 1994. N. Graf, Proceedings of 9th Topical Workshop on $p\bar{p}$ Collider Physics, Tsukuba, 1993.

[4] DØ Collaboration, S. Abachi *et al.*, Phys. Rev. Lett. **72**, 2138, (1994).

[5] CDF Collaboration, F. Abe *et al.*, Phys. Rev. Lett. **73**, 225, (1994).

[6] CDF Collaboration, F. Abe *et al.*, Fermilab Pub-94/097-E, submitted to Phys. Rev. **D**. (1994).

[7] S. Protopopescu, "Search for top in DØ in lepton + jets using a topological tag", paper submitted to these proceedings.

[8] R. Raja, "Search for top in DØ using the electron + jets channel with soft muon tagging", paper submitted to these proceedings.

[9] DØ Collaboration, S. Abachi *et al.*, Nucl. Instrum. Methods **A338**, 185, (1994).

[10] R. Engelmann *et.al.*, Nucl. Instrum. Methods **216**, 45, (1983).

[11] F. Paige and S. Protopopescu, ISAJET V6.49 Users Guide, BNL Report No. BNL38034, (1986), unpublished.

[12] E. Laenen, J. Smith and W. van Neervan, Nucl. Phys. **B369**, 543, (1992), Phys. Lett. **321B**, 254, (1994).

[13] DØ Collaboration, S. Abachi *et al.*, "Search for the Top Quark in $p\bar{p}$ Collisions at $\sqrt{s} = 1.8$ TeV", (to be submitted to Phys. Rev. **D**).

[14] P.D. Grannis, "Search for the Top Quark : Results from the DØ Experiment", paper submitted to these proceedings.

with mass above the present DØ mass limit of 131 GeV/c^2. It is also consistent with the QCD cross section calculations of Laenen *et al.* [12] which give yields of between 1.37 ± 0.24 and 0.41 ± 0.07 events as the m_t is varied between 140 GeV/c^2 and 180 GeV/c^2. The data are also consistent with the yield corresponding to the measured CDF cross section of 13.9 pb [5] which gives a prediction of 1.13 ± 0.49 events.

Further study of the surviving $e\mu$ event shows that it is difficult to explain in terms of the expected non-top backgrounds. Both leptons have transverse momentum well above the selection cuts ($E_T^e \approx 100$ GeV and $p_T^\mu \approx 200$ GeV/c). In addition it has two jets of $E_T = 25$ and 22 GeV, respectively and $\not{E}_T \approx 120$ GeV. The $Z \to \tau\tau$ hypothesis (dominant background) is kinematically excluded and although the lepton transverse momenta are large, the overall likelihood for this event agrees well with expectations for SM top production with a mass of ≈ 150 GeV/c^2 [4, 13, 14].

Search for top in lepton + jets in DØ using a topological tag

Serban Protopopescu

Brookhaven National Laboratory,
Upton, New York 11973, USA

On behalf of the DØ collaboration

Abstract

We have searched for production of $t\bar{t}$ pairs in $p\bar{p}$ interactions at 1.8 TeV center-of-mass energy at the FNAL Tevatron collider. The search assumes standard model decay for top quark into W + b quark. We observe in e + jets and μ + jets final states a small, not statistically significant, excess above the background estimated by two different methods. The results presented are preliminary.

1. Introduction

Assuming the Standard Model decay for top quarks into a W and a b quark, events with $t\bar{t}$ pairs will have one isolated high p_T e or μ accompanied by multiple jets 30% of the time. These channels yield considerably more events than those with 2 isolated leptons in the final state, presented in the preceding contribution to these proceedings by S. Wimpenny [1] , but suffer from larger backgrounds from the channel W+ multi-jets. In this paper we discuss two different methods used to estimate whether a significant $t\bar{t}$ production can be observed in the DØ data over the W + jets background. A previous analysis of these data, searching for top in the mass region 90 to 140 GeV in single and di-lepton final states, has been published [2] and gave a top mass limit of 131 GeV (95% CL). The present analysis is optimized for masses above 130 GeV and should be considered preliminary. The two methods used yield a small, but not statistically significant, excess.

2. Event selection

The DØ detector is described in detail in [3] and in these proceedings by [1], so it will not be discussed here. The events for lepton + jets analysis are obtained with 3 triggers:

- One electromagnetic shower with transverse energy $(E_T) > 15$ GeV, one hadronic jet with $E_T > 10$ GeV and calorimeter missing E_T ($E\!\!\!/_T^{cal}$) > 10 GeV
- One electromagnetic shower with $E_T > 20$ GeV and $E\!\!\!/_T^{cal} > 20$ GeV
- One μ with $p_T > 8$ GeV and one hadronic jet with $E_T > 15$ GeV

Hadronic jets are defined as energy in a cone of $R = \sqrt{\Delta\phi^2 + \Delta\eta^2} = 0.5$ where ϕ is the azimuthal angle in radians and η is the pseudo-rapidity.

After reconstruction the events are selected further by making stricter requirements. For the e+jets sample selection requirements on the electron are based on shower shape, cluster isolation, shower match with a reconstructed track and track ionization cuts to remove conversions. Electrons are required to have $E_T^e > 20$ GeV and $|\eta^e| < 2.0$. Additional requirements on the e + jets sample are $E\!\!\!/_T^{cal} > 25$ GeV, $E_T^{jet} > 15$ GeV and $|\eta_{jet}| < 2.0$. Figure 1a (1b) shows the $E\!\!\!/_T$ distribution for the selected events which pass (fail) the electron cuts. We will refer to the events that satisfied the triggers but failed the offline electron cuts and have $E\!\!\!/_T^{cal} < 25$ GeV as the QCD sample. This sample is used to estimate the non-W background in the e+jets sample and to test the validity of jet multiplicity scaling in section 3.

Selection requirements on the μ are made to remove cosmic rays (by drift chamber timing and no other

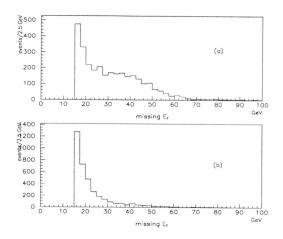

Figure 1. (a) $\not{E}_T^{cal}$ distribution for events satisfying all electron selection criteria, (b) $\not{E}_T^{cal}$ distribution for events satisfying the electron triggers but failing offline selection criteria.

jets	e + jets	non-W bckg.	μ + jets	non-W bckg.
≥ 1	1383	94. $\pm$ 6.	303	48. $\pm$ 8.
≥ 2	243	26 $\pm$ 3.	92	16. $\pm$ 3.
≥ 3	35	5.7 $\pm$ 0.9	22	4.8 $\pm$ 0.8
≥ 4	6	1.1 $\pm$ 0.3	6	1.3 $\pm$ 0.3
≥ 5	2	0.3 $\pm$ 0.1	1	0.3 $\pm$ 0.1

Table 1. Selected e and μ + jets events

jets	Data	non W backg.	calculated W + jets	$t\bar{t}$
≥ 1	1686	142. $\pm$ 20.0	1656 $\pm$ 96	5.7 $\pm$ 10.0
≥ 2	335	50.6 $\pm$ 7.0	278.8 $\pm$ 17	5.6 $\pm$ 9.9
≥ 3	57	10.3 $\pm$ 1.5	42.2 $\pm$ 7.1	4.5 $\pm$ 8.2
≥ 4	12	2.4 $\pm$ 0.4	6.6 $\pm$ 3.8	3.0 $\pm$ 4.6

Table 2. Estimated numbers of W + jets and $t\bar{t}$ events

collinear μ-track), isolation cuts to remove μ's from decays other than W's (minimum separation between μ and jets with $E_T > 8$ GeV of $\Delta R > 0.5$ and core cone isolation energy < 5 GeV in annular cone $0.2 < \Delta R < 0.4$ around μ track) plus calorimeter dE/dx confirmation to reduce accidentals. The μ is required to have $p_T^\mu > 15$ GeV and $|\eta_\mu| < 1.7$. In addition to the μ the μ + jets sample is required to have at least 1 jet with $E_T > 15$ GeV and $|\eta_{jet}| < 2.0$, $\not{E}_T > 20$ GeV, and $\not{E}_T^{cal} > 20$ GeV. The trigger and selection requirements on the μ+jets sample produces a bias for ≤ 2 jets which needs to be corrected when added to e +jets for the jet multiplicity analysis in section 3.

To avoid overlap with the analysis of events in which jets are tagged as containing heavy quarks by the observation of a non-isolated μ, discussed in the contribution to these proceedings by R. Raja [4], μ-tagged events have been excluded from the sample and their loss accounted for in the acceptance calculation.

3. Jet Multiplicity Analysis

The number of events as function of jet multiplicity and the estimated non-W background to e + jets and μ + jets channels are given in table 1. The non-W background for e + jets is mostly from misidentified electrons. In μ+jets events the background comes from two sources: Z + jets where one of the μ is not detected and QCD processes where the μ from a decay other than W satisfies the isolation criteria, the two backgrounds are roughly comparable.

As shown on fig. 3(a) the e + jets data after background subtraction are fit well by a scaling law (as

expected by [5]):

$$W + n\ jets = \frac{[W + (n-1)\ jets] \cdot [W + (n-1)\ jets)]}{[W + (n-2)\ jets)]}$$

This law seems to be satisfied for any E_T^{jet} threshold used for counting jets. The predictions from the VECBOS [6] Montecarlo agree well with the data after ISAJET [7] is used for hadronization and GEANT [8] for simulating the DØ detector. As $t\bar{t}$ events in channels with one isolated lepton are expected to have high multiplicities (2 jets from b's, 2 jets from hadronic W decay plus additional jets from initial and final state radiation) any noticeable $t\bar{t}$ production should appear as an excess of events at high multiplicity, in particular for 4 or more jets and for high E_T threshold. As shown in fig. 2 the 4th jet (ordered in E_T) from high mass top is expected to be considerably more energetic than for W + jets but no significant violation of the scaling law is observed in fig. 3(a). To find how much $t\bar{t}$ production can be accomodated and still satisfy the scaling law we can solve using the number of events with 2,3 and 4 jets for the number of W and top events:

$$N_4 - a_4 \cdot N_t = (N_3 - a_3 \cdot N_t)^2/(N_2 - a_2 \cdot N_t)$$

where N_i is observed number of lepton + jets events with $\geq$i jets, N_t the total number of top events and a_i the corresponding fraction at each multiplicity. The results are given in table 2, of particular interest is the total number of top events $N_t = 5.7 \pm 10.0$. The numbers for ≥ 1 jets are predicted from the numbers obtained using the events with 2,3 and 4 jets.

To check the validity of the scaling law in a case with no $t\bar{t}$ events, we fitted the QCD sample to a simple exponential. In Fig. 3(b) we show the jet multiplicities for that sample (after correcting for

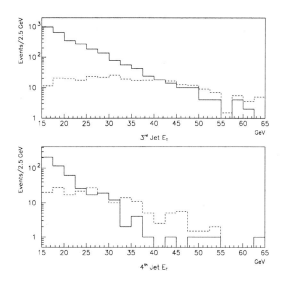

Figure 2. E_T distributions of 3rd and 4th jet from $W + \geq 3$ jets Montecarlo (solid) and $t\bar{t}$ (dotted) with top mass 160 GeV, normalized to 500 pb^{-1}.

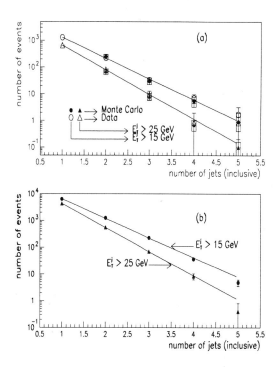

Figure 3. Number of events as function of jet multiplicity (a) e + jets data after non-W background subtraction and VECBOS predictions, boxes indicate uncertainty in prediction, (b) QCD sample after correcting for increased probability for triggering with increasing multiplicity.

the higher probability as a function of increasing multiplicity for having a jet fake an electron). The QCD data is clearly well fitted. We also fitted the predictions of the VECBOS Montecarlo. All the fits give similar values for the ratio of $[W + 3 \text{ jets}]/[W + 2 \text{ jets}]$: .151 ± .020 for the data, .160 ± .013 for VECBOS Montecarlo, .187 ± .004 for the QCD sample. The fit to the VECBOS Montecarlo tends to underestimate the predicted number of 4 or more jet events by 15% while the QCD fit overestimates by the number of 4 jet events by 12%. To account for these deviations we estimate a 20% systematic error in the validity of the scaling law. The fraction (a_i) of top events expected at each multiplicity is obtained from Montecarlo; to estimate the uncertainty in this procedure we compared 2 different Montecarlos (ISAJET and HERWIG [9]). The differences between them were at the level of 10%. There is an additional 15% uncertainty in the top acceptance from the uncertainty in the jet energy scale. From the number of top events and the calculated acceptance times branching ratio we can estimate a cross section for $t\bar{t}$ production:

$$\sigma_{t\bar{t}} = 6.4 \pm 9.8 \text{ (stat.)} \pm 4.0 \text{ (sys.)} \; pb$$

the sytematic error includes a 12% uncertainty in the luminosity.

This cross section is for masses between 160 and 180 GeV. As the acceptance falls moderately below 160 GeV it should be increased by 25% around 140 GeV.

4. $\mathcal{A}$, H_T Analysis

Another method to estimate the number of $t\bar{t}$ and W + jets events in the lepton + jets data is to use event shape information to discriminate between them. As the ratio of signal/background is small for jet multiplicities below 4, this analysis concentrates on events with 4 or more jets. Two parameters found to be useful discriminants are H_T, defined as the scalar E_T sum over jets with $|\eta| < 2.0$, and the aplanarity ($\mathcal{A}$), defined as 3/2 times the smallest eigenvalue of the laboratory 3-momentum tensor of reconstructed objects, normalized to unit trace. Fig. 4 shows the distribution of events in this two variables for the QCD sample, VECBOS Montecarlo, $t\bar{t}$ events with mass 180 GeV and the data. If we divide the $\mathcal{A}$, H_T into 4 quadrants using axes $\mathcal{A} = 0.05$ and $H_T = 140$ GeV we see that the QCD sample and the W + jets Montecarlo sample populate those quadrants more or less equally while the $t\bar{t}$ events are concentrated in the quadrant with $\mathcal{A} > .05$ and $H_T > 140$ GeV. In table 3 we give the expected fractions of W + jets , QCD and $t\bar{t}$ events in each quadrant. To estimate the uncertainties in the W + jets estimation we generated W + jets events in two different ways: one was to use VECBOS to generate $W + 3$ jets events

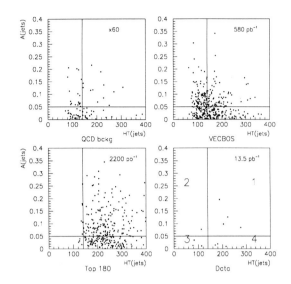

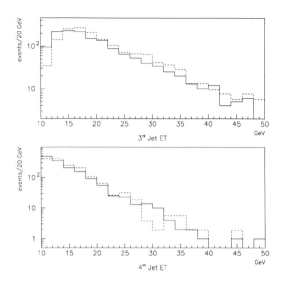

Figure 4. $\mathcal{A}$ vs H_T distributions for events with 4 or more jets: (a) QCD sample, (b) VECBOS Montecarlo, (c) $t\bar{t}$ events, top mass 180 GeV, (d) data, the quadrants used in the fit are numbered, see text.

Figure 5. E_T distributions for 3rd and 4th jet in events with ≥ 4 jets starting from VECBOS with 3 jets (dotted lines) and from VECBOS with 4 jets (solid lines).

(at the parton level) and use ISAJET with those events as input to generate events with 4 or more jets. The other was to use VECBOS to generate $W + 4$ jets and then proceed as in the previous case. One can see from fig. 5 that both sets generate quite similar E_T distributions for the 3rd and 4th jet in events with ≥ 4 jets. As shown in table 3 the fractions estimated with the two different Montecarlo samples differ by less than 20%. The fractions for $t\bar{t}$ were estimated using ISAJET, comparison of ISAJET with HERWIG showed the differences to be less than 10%. Figure 6 illustrates this for $t\bar{t}$ events generated with ISAJET and HERWIG at a top mass of 140 GeV. The number of $t\bar{t}$ events in a given quadrant i $(N_{t\bar{t}}^i)$ is given by

$$N_{t\bar{t}}^i = \epsilon_{t\bar{t}}^i \cdot f_{t\bar{t}} \cdot N$$

where N is the total number of observed events with 4 or more jets, $\epsilon_{t\bar{t}}^i$ is the fraction of $t\bar{t}$ expected in quadrant i and $f_{t\bar{t}}$ is the fraction of N that are $t\bar{t}$ events. The number of expected background events is then:

$$N_{bkg}^i = \epsilon_{bkg}^i \cdot \left(1 - f_{t\bar{t}}\right) \cdot N$$

where N_{bkg}^i is the number of background events in quadrant i and ϵ_{bkg}^i is the expected fraction. Given N and the ϵ's one can fit for $f_{t\bar{t}}$ using Poisson statistics. The results of the fit give $f_{t\bar{t}} = 0.32 \pm 0.30$ events in the sample of data with 4 or more jets. The numbers of observed events (in the 4 quadrants of fig. 4) are 4, 1, 3, 4 while the predicted numbers are 4.1, 2.4, 2.0, 3.5. There is a large systematic error (35%) from

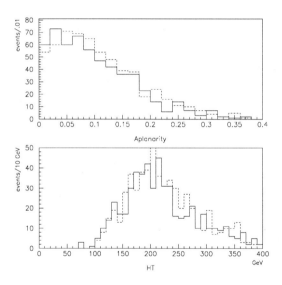

Figure 6. $\mathcal{A}$ and H_T distributions for $t\bar{t}$ events with 4 or more jets for top mass 140 GeV. Events generated by ISAJET are in solid lines, by HERWIG in dotted lines.

the choice of partitioning the $\mathcal{A}$, H_T plane, this error is estimated by moving the axes until one event falls into a different quadrant. An additional 20% systematic error is estimated for the uncertainty in calculating the fractions for each quadrant. The number of $t\bar{t}$ events estimated in the sample with 4 or more jets is thus $N_{t\bar{t}} = 3.8 \pm 3.6(stat.) \pm 1.5(sys.)$ which leads to a $t\bar{t}$ production cross section of

$$\sigma_{t\bar{t}} = 8.1 \pm 6.9(\text{stat.}) \pm 3.8(\text{sys.}) \; pb$$

	ϵ^1	ϵ^2	ϵ^3	ϵ^4
	$\mathcal{A} > .05$	$\mathcal{A} > .05$	$\mathcal{A} < .05$	$\mathcal{A} < .05$
	$H_T > 140$	$H_T < 140$	$H_T < 140$	$H_T > 140$
VECBOS(4)	$0.21 \pm .025$	$0.27 \pm .03$	$0.21 \pm .025$	$0.31 \pm .03$
VECBOS(3)	$0.19 \pm .04$	$0.28 \pm .05$	$0.25 \pm .05$	$0.28 \pm .05$
QCD	$0.19 \pm .04$	$0.25 \pm .05$	$0.28 \pm .05$	$0.28 \pm .05$
$t\bar{t}$ 180	$0.60 \pm .05$	$0.02 \pm .01$	$0.02 \pm .01$	$0.36 \pm .04$

Table 3. Fractions in ≥ 4 jets

additional systematic errors in this estimate are the luminosity (12%), and the $t\bar{t}$ acceptance (20%). This value is in good agreement with that obtained with a totally different method in section 3.

The two methods used to estimate $\sigma_{t\bar{t}}$ can also be used as an estimate of the number of background events after applying cuts of $\mathcal{A} > .05$ and $H_T > 140$ GeV which improve the signal/background ratio by a factor of 3. For method 1 (section 3) we add the fraction of $W + \geq 4$ jets (predicted from the fit) and the fraction non-W events, expected after cuts, to obtain $N_{bckg}(cut) = 1.8 \pm 0.75 \pm 0.40$. From the method used in this section, the background is given by $N_{bckg}(cut) = \epsilon_{bckg}^1 \cdot (1 - f_{t\bar{t}}) \cdot N$ which gives $N_{bckg}(cut) = 1.7 \pm 0.8 \pm 0.5$. The two ways of estimating the background share in common only the fraction expected after $\mathcal{A}$, H_T cuts. The total amount of background to the 4 or more jets channel is estimated in one case by the fit to jet multiplicities, in the other by a fit to the $\mathcal{A}$, H_T plane. It is worth emphasizing that neither method uses the total number of $W + \geq 4$ jet events predicted from Montecarlo. We can compute the $t\bar{t}$ cross section after doing a background subtraction (averaging the background obtained with the 2 methods) to get $\sigma_{t\bar{t}} = 7.3 \pm 7.2 \pm 3.3$ *pb* for $m_{top} = 160 - 180$ GeV. The value should be increased by 25% for $m_{top} = 140$ GeV.

5. Conclusion

Two different ways of analyzing lepton+jets final states lead to a similar estimate of the top production cross section in $p\bar{p}$ interactions at 1.8 TeV center-of-mass energy:

$$\sigma_{t\bar{t}} = 6.4 \pm 9.8 \pm 4.0 \; pb$$

$$\sigma_{t\bar{t}} = 8.1 \pm 6.9 \pm 3.8 \; pb$$

and of the background after $\mathcal{A} > .05$, $H_T > 140$ GeV cuts:

$$1.8 \pm 0.9, \; \text{and} \; 1.7 \pm 0.9$$

with 4 events observed.

The data shows a small excess of events above the expected background but the excess is not statistically significant. The excess above background corresponds to a top cross section of $\sigma_{t\bar{t}} = 7.3 \pm 7.2 \pm 3.3$ *pb*. These results should be considered preliminary.

We thank the Fermilab Accelerator, Computing and Research Divisions, and the support staffs at the collaborating insititutions for their contribution to the success of this experiment. We also acknolwedge the support provided by the U.S. Department of Energy, the U.S. National Science foundation, the Commisariat à L'Energie Atomique in France, the Ministry for Atomic Energy in Russia, CNPq in Brazil, the Department of Atomic Energy in India, Colciencias in Colombia, and CONACyT in Mexico.

References

[1] S. Wimpenny, these proceedings.
[2] S. Abachi et al., Phys. Rev. Letters **72**, 2138 (1994)
[3] DØ collaboration, S. Abachi et al., Nucl. Instr. Meth. A **338**, 185 (1994)
[4] R. Raja, these proceedings
[5] F. A. Berends et al Nucl. Phys. B **357**, 32 (1991).
[6] W. Giele, et al. Report No. Fermilab-Pub 92/230-T, 1992 and Report No. Fermilab-Pub 92/213-T, 1992. B **403**, 633 (1993).
[7] F. Paige and S. Protopopescu, ISAJET v6.49 Users Guide, BNL Report no. BNL38034, 1986 (unpublished).
[8] R. Brun et al, GEANT Users Guide, CERN Program Library (unpublished).
[9] G. Marchesini et al, Comput. Comm. **67**, 465, (1992)

Paper presented at XXVII Int. Conf. on High Energy Physics: Session Pa-18
Glasgow, UK, 20–27 July 1994

Search for top in DØ using the electron + jets channel with soft μ tagging

Rajendran Raja

Fermi National Accelerator Laboratory,
Batavia, Illinois 60510

For the DØ Collaboration

Abstract

We present preliminary results for the search for the top quark in DØ in the electron + jets channel where one of the b quark jets is tagged by means of a soft muon, using 13.5 pb^{-1} of data. Standard model decay modes for the top quark are assumed.

We present the resulting top cross section and error as a function of top mass using this channel combined with the dilepton channel and the untagged lepton + jets channel presented elsewhere in this session. At present, no significant signal for top quark production can be established.

1. Introduction

In the standard model, each top quark decays predominantly to a W boson and a b quark. Each $t\bar{t}$ pair in an event will thus be accompanied by a $b\bar{b}$ pair. If we assume that each b quark decays semi-leptonically ~ 10 % of the time into a muon and likewise for the c quark resulting from the b quark decay, $\sim 44\%$ of the $t\bar{t}$ events will have a soft muon. DØ has a muon detection system [1] that is characterized by nearly 4π in solid angle coverage, containing 12-18 interaction lengths of absorber and a relatively small decay volume in the central tracker. This system is capable of detecting these muons (the average p_t of such muons from a 160 GeV/c^2 top quark is 17 GeV/c)with an efficiency such that $\sim 20\%$ of the $t\bar{t}$ events will have a detected soft muon tag. Because the conventional W + jets background to the lepton + jets channel is expected to be much less rich in b quarks, it is possible to employ looser cuts in event selection as a result of demanding the lepton tag.

The results of top searches employing dilepton channels and lepton + jets channels without tagging the b quark have been reported [2, 3] in this session. We report here the top production cross section and

error combining the results of all these channels. The summary of these three papers is also given in the plenary session [4].

2. Estimation of backgrounds

In order to test our understanding of muon and jet reconstruction efficiencies, we look for soft muons in a QCD dijet sample of events. Figure 1 shows the p_t spectrum of the muons. Also shown are the Monte Carlo [5] calculations of the contributions from muons resulting from π and K decay and b and c quark decay. The sum of these two contributions reproduces the data well for $p_t > 4$ GeV/c . Also shown in the figure is the separation ΔR in $\eta \times \phi$ space of the muon and the nearest jet. The Monte Carlo again reproduces this distribution well.

There are two main sources of background to the channel e+ jets + soft μ tag from $t\bar{t}$ production. The first is from W+Jets production where some of the jets result from the fragmentation of b and c quarks. The second is from QCD multi-jet production containing b or c quarks where one of the jets fakes an electron and the

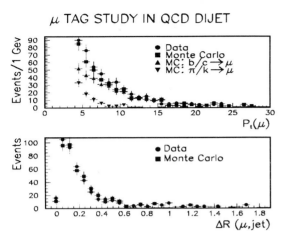

Figure 1. Comparison of data and Monte Carlo predictions for QCD dijet events containing a muon

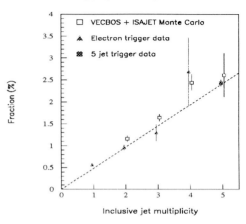

Figure 2. Fraction of events containing muons as a function of the inclusive jet multiplicity

$\not{E}_T$ is produced primarily by detector resolution. In each case we assume that the probability for a jet to emit a detectable muon is independent of the process producing the jet and is a function of the E_T of the jet. The source of the muon may be b or c quark decay, π or K decay or fake μ's due to reconstructing random hits in the muon chambers. We justify this assumption by examining the fraction of events that contain a jet tagged by a muon as a function of the inclusive jet multiplicity (defined as multiplicity $\geq$ a given number of jets) for three different sets of events; for data triggered on a single high E_T ($\geq$ 20 GeV) electron, for QCD 5 jet data and for VECBOS [6] Monte Carlo that describes W+Jets production that has been put through the Isajet [7] shower fragmenter. The results are shown in figure 2. The muon tagging fraction is linearly proportional to the jet multiplicity. The probability for a jet to emit a detectable muon seems to be ~ 0.5 %, justifying the above assumption.

2.1. Definition of the QCD Fake sample

In order to extract the tagging fraction function from data, we first isolate a sample of events which possess a fake electron but which in all other respects resemble the electron + jets event sample under study. Our electron identification algorithm uses a Fisher χ^2 discriminant variable based on 41 quantities describing the energy deposition of the electron in the calorimeter. The χ^2 variable is described as follows.

$$E_{ij} = < x_i x_j > - < x_i > < x_j >$$
$$\chi^2 = \Sigma_{ij} (x_i - < x_i >) H_{ij} (x_j - < x_j >)$$

where the covariance matrix E and its inverse H matrix are defined in terms of the 41 dimensional vector x, which consists of three longitudinal energy fractions, 36 transverse energy fractions at shower maximum,

log(Energy of cluster) and the position of the vertex along the beam direction. The angular brackets $<>$ in the above equations signify averages over events. We employ a different H matrix for each of the 37 towers in pseudo-rapidity for either half of the calorimeter. Figure 3 shows the χ^2 distribution for all electromagnetic clusters with $E_T > 20$ GeV and for those which have $\not{E}_T > 30$ GeV . These latter are dominated by genuine electrons from W's and have a much narrower χ^2 distribution. In defining good electrons, we demand that the χ^2 is less than 100. In addition, we define a track match significance parameter as the error weighted impact parameter between the central detector track and the cluster centroid in the azimuthal and beam directions. We demand a central detector track that passes close to the shower centroid with a track match significance of less than 5 for good electrons. Since we are interested in isolated electrons, we demand the isolation fraction to be less than 0.1. The isolation fraction is defined as

$$\frac{(Total\ Energy\ in\ 0.4\ cone\ -\ EM\ Energy\ in\ 0.2\ cone)}{EM\ energy\ in\ 0.2\ cone}$$

where the cone size is in ΔR space. We define a fake electron as any EM cluster that fails the good electron criteria and the QCD fake sample as those triggers that have electromagnetic clusters with $E_T > 20$ GeV and fail the good electron criteria with no requirement on $\not{E}_T$.

2.2. Determination of tagging fraction function

We now use the QCD fake sample as a source of jets and determine the fraction of jets that have muons as a function of E_T of the jet *and* jet multiplicity. We require muons to have $p_t > 4.0$ GeV/c and $|\eta| <$

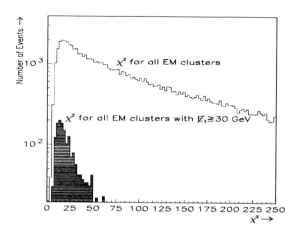

Figure 3. H matrix χ^2 distribution for all EM clusters and for EM clusters with $\not{E}_T > 30$ GeV (shaded)

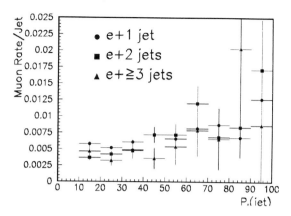

Figure 4. Jet tagging fraction vs E_T of jet for QCD fake events

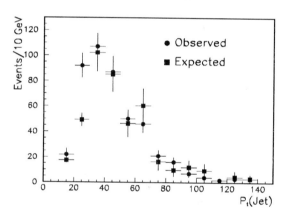

Figure 5. E_T spectrum of of tagged jets in QCD dijets, data and prediction

1.7. We demand that the muon be non-isolated if its p_t is greater than 12 GeV/c . This selection makes this event sample exclusive of the $e\mu$ sample in reference [2]. Figure 4 shows the jet tagging fraction as a function of E_T for the QCD fake sample for jet multiplicities of 1,2 and ≥ 3 jets. We now assume that this tagging function, determined as a function of E_T and multiplicity is universal. As a cross check of this hypothesis, we test this on QCD dijet data. Figure 5 shows the E_T spectrum of jets with tagged muons in QCD dijets and the spectrum that is predicted assuming the above tagging functions. There is seen to be good agreement between prediction and data, which gives us confidence in the hypothesis. As a further cross check, we examine the jet multiplicity distribution of tagged jets in "photon" + jets candidates and QCD multijets. A "photon" is an electromagnetic cluster which passes all the good electron criteria except that it has no central detector track. Figure 6 shows the distribution of jet multiplicity for these two sets of data and the prediction using the tagging fraction function. Again there is seen to be good agreement. In order to calculate the μ tag background in W+jets due to the presence of b and c quarks associated with W production, we apply the tagging fraction functions to the W+ Jets sample.

2.3. Calculation of the W+ jets + μ tag background

Figure 7 shows the $\not{E}_T$ distribution of W+Jet data. The QCD fake background is normalized to the data for $\not{E}_T$ < 15 GeV . We now subtract the QCD fake background from the W+jets data ($\not{E}_T > 20$ GeV) to obtain the total amount of W+Jets production. We apply the tagging fraction function to the amount of signal thus obtained. We handle the QCD fake contribution to tagged events separately, since the QCD fakes are at lower $\not{E}_T$ and

the presence of the muon affects the $\not{E}_T$ distribution sufficiently to warrant a separate calculation.

2.4. Calculation of the QCD fake μ tag background

Since we have normalized the QCD fakes to the W+jets signal for $\not{E}_T$ < 15 GeV , we estimate the QCD fake background by normalizing the tagged muon events in the QCD fake sample with $\not{E}_T > 20$ GeV , by the same factor. We now attempt one further cross check, by comparing the W + 1 Jet data (with $\not{E}_T > 20$ GeV) with the background predictions. Very little top is expected with 1 jet only. Figure 8 shows the comparison of background predictions with data, as a function of E_T of the jet. The agreement between predicted and observed values is good.

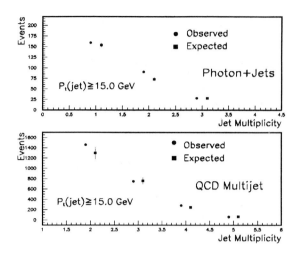

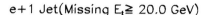

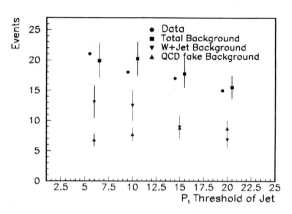

Figure 6. Jet multiplicity distribution of tagged events for "photon" + jets and QCD multijets

Figure 8. Comparison of background predictions and data for electron + 1 jet events with $\not{E}_T > 20$ GeV

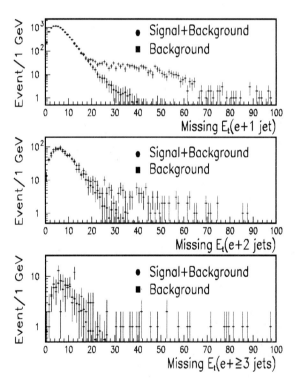

Figure 7. $\not{E}_T$ distribution of W + jet data and QCD fake background normalized to data for different jet multiplicities

Particle type	Cuts
Electron	H-Matrix $\chi^2 < 100$
	Track match signif. < 5.0
	$|\eta| < 2.0$
	$E_T > 20\,GeV$
	dE/dx minimum ionizing
Muon	$|\eta| < 1.7$
	$p_t > 4$ GeV/c
	non-isolated muon or
	$p_t < 12$ GeV/c
$\not{E}_T$	> 20 GeV
	$\Delta\phi(\mu, \not{E}_T) > 25^o$
	if $E_T < 35$ GeV
Jets	≥ 3 jets $E_T > 20$ GeV
Data	Events
	2
Background	Events
W + jets	0.43 ± 0.14
QCD fakes	0.12 ± 0.05
Total	0.55 ± 0.15
Top mass GeV/c^2	Expected events
140	$1.3 \pm .4$
160	$1.0 \pm .2$
180	$0.6 \pm .2$

Table 1. Summary of cuts, data, background and top yields

3. Summary of cuts and the surviving signal and background

Table 1 shows the summary of the cuts used, the surviving number of events and background estimates as well as the expectation from top production at various

masses [8]. The $\Delta\phi(\mu, \not{E}_T)$ cut is introduced to take into account the correlation between $\not{E}_T$ and the muon p_t for QCD fake events. Two events survive the cuts described with a total expected background of 0.55 ± 0.15 events. Figure 9 compares the data and background predictions as a function of inclusive jet multiplicity.

4. Combined top cross section and conclusions

We now combine the results of various DØ top searches [2, 3] reported at this conference with the tagged muon results reported here to obtain a top cross section and

m_t [GeV/c^2]		$e\mu$	ee	$\mu\mu$	e + jets	μ + jets	e + jets(μ)	ALL
140	$\varepsilon \times B(\%)$	$.32 \pm .06$	$.18 \pm .02$	$.11 \pm .02$	1.2 ± 0.3	$.8 \pm 0.2$	0.6 ± 0.2	
	$\langle N \rangle$	$.72 \pm .16$	$.41 \pm .07$	$.24 \pm .05$	2.8 ± 0.7	1.3 ± 0.4	1.3 ± 0.4	6.7 ± 1.2
160	$\varepsilon \times B(\%)$	$.36 \pm .07$	$.20 \pm .03$	$.11 \pm .01$	1.6 ± 0.4	1.1 ± 0.3	0.9 ± 0.2	
	$\langle N \rangle$	$.40 \pm .09$	$.22 \pm .04$	$.12 \pm .02$	1.8 ± 0.5	0.9 ± 0.3	1.0 ± 0.2	4.4 ± 0.7
180	$\varepsilon \times B(\%)$	$.41 \pm .07$	$.21 \pm .03$	$.11 \pm .01$	1.7 ± 0.4	1.2 ± 0.3	1.1 ± 0.2	
	$\langle N \rangle$	$.23 \pm .05$	$.12 \pm .02$	$.06 \pm .01$	1.0 ± 0.2	0.5 ± 0.2	0.6 ± 0.2	2.5 ± 0.4
Background		$.27 \pm .09$	$.16 \pm .07$	$.33 \pm .06$	1.2 ± 0.7	0.6 ± 0.5	0.6 ± 0.2	3.2 ± 1.1
$\int \mathcal{L}dt$ [pb^{-1}]		13.5 ± 1.6	13.5 ± 1.6	9.8 ± 1.2	13.5 ± 1.6	9.8 ± 1.2	13.5 ± 1.6	
Data		1	0	0	2	2	2	7

Table 2. Efficiency × branching fraction ($\varepsilon \times B$), expected number of events ($\langle N \rangle$) for signal and background sources for the observed integrated luminosity ($\int \mathcal{L}dt$), and number of events observed in the data.

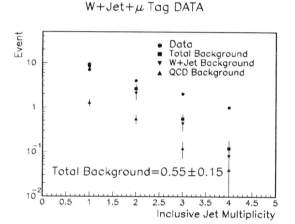

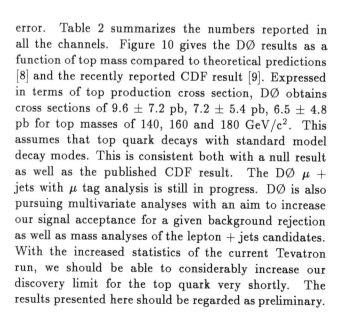

Figure 9. Comparison of background predictions and data as a function of inclusive jet multiplicity.

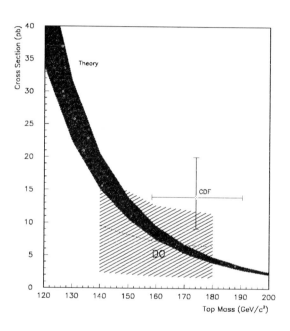

Figure 10. DØ top cross section results compared with theoretical predictions and CDF

error. Table 2 summarizes the numbers reported in all the channels. Figure 10 gives the DØ results as a function of top mass compared to theoretical predictions [8] and the recently reported CDF result [9]. Expressed in terms of top production cross section, DØ obtains cross sections of 9.6 ± 7.2 pb, 7.2 ± 5.4 pb, 6.5 ± 4.8 pb for top masses of 140, 160 and 180 GeV/c^2. This assumes that top quark decays with standard model decay modes. This is consistent both with a null result as well as the published CDF result. The DØ μ + jets with μ tag analysis is still in progress. DØ is also pursuing multivariate analyses with an aim to increase our signal acceptance for a given background rejection as well as mass analyses of the lepton + jets candidates. With the increased statistics of the current Tevatron run, we should be able to considerably increase our discovery limit for the top quark very shortly. The results presented here should be regarded as preliminary.

References

[1] S. Abachi *et al* , Nucl. Instr. Meth. **A338** (1994) 185

[2] S. Wimpenny, these proceedings.

[3] S. Protopopescu, these proceedings.

[4] P. Grannis, these proceedings.

[5] R. Brun *et al* , "GEANT Users Guide", CERN Program Library

[6] W. Giele, E. Glover and D. Kosower, Nucl. Phys. **B403** (1993) 633

[7] F. Paige and S. Protopopescu, ISAJET v6.49 Users Guide, BNL Report no. BNL38034, 1986 (unpublished).

[8] E. Laenen, J. Smith, and W. van Neerven, Phys. Lett. **321B** (1994) 254.

[9] CDF Collaboration: F. Abe *et al.*, Phys. Rev. Lett. **73** (1994) 225, F. Abe *et al.*, Phys. Rev. **D50** (1994) 2966

Top Quark Production and Flavor Physics[†]

Kenneth Lane[‡]

Department of Physics, Boston University,
590 Commonwealth Avenue, Boston, MA 02215, USA

Abstract

Because of the top quark's very large mass, about 175 GeV, it now provides the best window into flavor physics. Thus, pair–production of top quarks at the Tevatron Collider is the most incisive probe of this physics until the Large Hadron Collider turns on in the next century. In this talk I discuss how moments of the $t\bar{t}$ invariant mass distribution can be used to distinguish among standard and alternative mechanisms of $t\bar{t}$ production.

1. Introduction

The CDF collaboration has reported evidence for top–quark production at the Tevatron Collider [1],[2]. According to these papers, the top mass is $m_t = 174 \pm 10 \, ^{+13}_{-12}$ GeV. The data in these papers are based on an integrated luminosity of $19.3 \, \text{pb}^{-1}$. When combined with the detector's efficiencies and acceptances, CDF reports the production cross section $\sigma(p\bar{p} \rightarrow t\bar{t}) = 13.9^{+6.1}_{-4.8}$ pb at $\sqrt{s} = 1800$ GeV. The predicted QCD cross section for $m_t = 174$ GeV, including next–to–leading–log corrections [3] and soft–gluon resummation [4] is $\sigma(t\bar{t}) = 5.10^{+0.73}_{-0.43}$ pb. This is 2.8 times smaller than the central value of the measured cross section. The uncertainty in α_S increases the theoretical error $\sigma(t\bar{t})$ to at most 30% [5].

The error on the CDF cross section is large, but so is the discrepancy with QCD. If it holds up, it heralds the long–awaited collapse of the standard model. In any event, it is clear that the top quark provides a wide-open window into the world of flavor physics. It is the heaviest elementary particle we know and, more to the point, the heaviest elementary fermion by a factor of 40! If the Higgs boson of the minimal one–doublet

† Invited talk given at the 27th International Conference on High Energy Physics, Glasgow, 20–27th July 1994.
‡ email: lane@buphyc.bu.edu

model exists, its coupling to the top quark, renormalized at $m_t = 174$ GeV, is $\Gamma_t = 2^{3/4} G_F^{1/2} m_t = 1.00$. If charged scalars—members of Higgs–boson multiplets or technipions—exist, they couple to top quarks with $O(1)$ strength and they decay as $H^+ \rightarrow t\bar{b}$.

In this talk, we discuss how moments of the $t\bar{t}$ invariant–mass ($\mathcal{M}_{t\bar{t}}$) distribution may be used to distinguish among competing models of top production. We point out that, in QCD, the mean and root–mean-square invariant masses are linear functions of the top-quark mass over the entire interesting range of m_t. Thus, the $\mathcal{M}_{t\bar{t}}$ distribution can provide an *independent* determination of the top quark's mass. We apply this to the existing data [1] and find good consistency with the reported mass. This analysis is made at the simplest theoretical level. The analysis needs to be carefully done by the CDF and DØ collaborations themselves.

The lowest two moments and their variance, $\Delta\mathcal{M}_{t\bar{t}} = \sqrt{\langle \mathcal{M}_{t\bar{t}}^2 \rangle - \langle \mathcal{M}_{t\bar{t}} \rangle^2}$, can provide valuable discrimination among top–production models for limited statistics. Examples of this are given for three models of enhanced $t\bar{t}$–production. The first involves resonant production of a 400–600 GeV color–octet vector meson ("coloron"), V_8, which is associated with electroweak symmetry breaking via top–condensation [6] and which interferes with QCD production via the process $q\bar{q} \rightarrow V_8 \rightarrow t\bar{t}$ [7]. The second example invokes a color–octet pseudoscalar, η_T [8]. In multiscale models of walking technicolor [9],[10], it is produced strongly in gluon–gluon fusion and decays mainly to $t\bar{t}$ [11],[12]. The third model has additional pair–production of an electroweak–*isoscalar*, color–triplet quark, t_s, which is approximately degenerate with the top quark and which, through mass–mixing, decays as $t_s \to W^+b$ [13]. The agreement between the directly measured top–mass and that extracted from the $\mathcal{M}_{t\bar{t}}$ moments does not yet rule out these new mechanisms of top–quark production, but it may do so with data from the current Tevatron run.

For reasons of space, our discussions refer entirely to $t\bar{t}$ production at the Tevatron. The QCD process there is dominated by $q\bar{q}$ annihilation, as is top production in the V_8 model and the isoscalar quark model. As noted, production in the η_T model is dominated by gluon fusion. If the energy of the Tevatron can be increased to 2 TeV, there will be a 35% increase in $\sigma(t\bar{t})$ if the new physics requires $q\bar{q}$ annihilation, but a 65% increase if the η_T is involved[†]. Dramatic differences will occur when LHC energies are reached. The rate in the V_8 model is typically 10–20% higher than the standard QCD rate at the LHC (for $|\eta_t| < 1.5$). The isoscalar quark process remains a few times the standard top–quark rate. However, the rate in the η_T model we consider is 10–15 *times* the standard one, reflecting the importance of gluon fusion for low–x physics. Of course, if there is new physics involved in top–quark production, its origin should be determined at the Tevatron well before the LHC turns on.

A more complete version of the results summarized here was submitted to this conference in Ref. [14] and will appear in Ref. [15]. Also discussed there is the angular distribution of the top quark in $t\bar{t}$ production. Measurements of the angular distributions will require much larger data sets than will be available in the next year or two. Thus, to realize the full potential of the top–quark handle on flavor physics, it is essential that the Tevatron experiments be able to collect samples as large as 1–10 fb^{-1}. Such large data sets may even help our science avoid Mark Twain's characterization of having "such wholesale returns of conjecture for such a trifling investment of fact" [16].

2. Invariant Mass Distributions

We calculated the $\mathcal{M}_{t\bar{t}}$–distribution expected in QCD for the Tevatron Collider and top–quark masses in the interesting range 100–200 GeV and found that it is sharply peaked at $\mathcal{M}_{\max} \simeq 2.1 m_t + 10$ GeV. As a consequence, low moments of the mass distribution, the mean and RMS, are nearly linear functions of the top–

[†] I thank S. Parke for emphasizing this point to me.

quark mass (also see Ref. [18]). We found

$$
\begin{aligned}
\langle \mathcal{M}_{t\bar{t}} \rangle &= 50.0\,\text{GeV} + 2.24\,\text{m}_t \\
\langle \mathcal{M}_{t\bar{t}}^2 \rangle^{1/2} &= 58.4\,\text{GeV} + 2.23\,\text{m}_t\,.
\end{aligned}
\tag{1}
$$

In the range $m_t \simeq 140$–180 GeV, the dispersion in $\mathcal{M}_{t\bar{t}}$ expected for standard QCD production is $\Delta\mathcal{M}_{t\bar{t}} = 70$–$75$ GeV[‡].

In Ref. [1], the top quark mass was determined from a sample of seven $W \to \ell\nu + 4$ jets events by making a constrained best fit to the hypothesis $p\bar{p} \to t\bar{t} + X$ followed by $t \to W^+b$ with one W decaying leptonically and the other hadronically. The CDF paper provides the momentum 4–vectors of all particles in the event. From these, the central values of of the $\mathcal{M}_{t\bar{t}}$ of seven events may be determined. These gave the following mean and RMS invariant masses and the corresponding top–masses:

$$
\begin{aligned}
\langle \mathcal{M}_{t\bar{t}} \rangle &= 439 \pm 11\,\text{GeV} &&\Longrightarrow&& \text{m}_t = 173 \pm 5\,\text{GeV} \\
\langle \mathcal{M}_{t\bar{t}}^2 \rangle^{1/2} &= 443 \pm 11\,\text{GeV} &&\Longrightarrow&& \text{m}_t = 172 \pm 5\,\text{GeV} \\
\Delta\mathcal{M}_{t\bar{t}} &= 59.5\,\text{GeV}\,. && &&
\end{aligned}
\tag{2}
$$

The errors in Eq. (2) are estimated by the "jacknife" method of computing the moments omitting one of the seven events. They are *not* to be interpreted as the true experimental errors. Only the CDF group can provide those.

The results in Eq. (2) give some confidence that the measured central value of the top–quark mass, 174 GeV, is accurate. For example, if $m_t = 160$ GeV (for which Ref.[4] predicts $\sigma(t\bar{t}) = 8.2^{+1.3}_{-0.8}$ pb), we would expect $\langle \mathcal{M}_{t\bar{t}} \rangle = 409$ GeV and $\langle \mathcal{M}_{t\bar{t}}^2 \rangle^{1/2} = 415$ GeV, both well below the values determined above. Thus, if something is going to change in the CDF results from the next large data sample, we expect it will be the cross section—which would need to be 2–3 times smaller to agree with the standard model.

3. Distinguishing Models of Top–Quark Production

In this section we compute the first two moments and dispersion of $\mathcal{M}_{t\bar{t}}$ for various input parameters to

[‡] Our calculations used lowest–order QCD subprocess cross sections and the EHLQ Set 1 parton distribution functions [17]. We believe that our general conclusions will remain true when higher–order corrections are included. Our $t\bar{t}$ cross sections have been multiplied by a factor of 1.6165. This makes our standard QCD rates as a function of m_t agree to within a per cent with the central values quoted in Ref. [4] over the of top masses of interest. The results in Eq. (1) are accurate so long as the higher–order corrections are well–represented by a simple multiplicative factor. Our parton level calculations ignore transverse motion of the $t\bar{t}$ center–of–mass induced, e.g., by initial–state radiation. While this effect is not large, it can and should be taken into account in more detailed simulations.

Model	$\sigma(t\bar{t})$	$\langle\mathcal{M}_{t\bar{t}}\rangle$	$m_t(\langle\mathcal{M}_{t\bar{t}}\rangle)$	$\langle\mathcal{M}_{t\bar{t}}^2\rangle^{1/2}$	$m_t(\langle\mathcal{M}_{t\bar{t}}^2\rangle^{1/2})$	$\Delta\mathcal{M}_{t\bar{t}}$
LO-QCD (EHLQ1)	5.13	440	174	447	174	77
CDF data	13.9	439	173	443	172	60
$M_{V_8^-} = 450$	13.3	431	170	433	168	46
$M_{V_8^+} = 450$	11.0	465	185	469	184	58
$M_{V_8^-} = 475$	14.9	440	174	444	173	53
$M_{V_8^+} = 475$	10.8	482	193	487	192	67
$M_{\eta_T} = 450$	13.5	432	171	435	169	52
$M_{\eta_T} = 475$	11.4	442	175	446	174	55
$t_s(160)\, t(175)$	13.2	421	166	428	166	77
$t_s(165)\, t(190)$	10.0	437	173	444	173	77

Table 1. $p\bar{p} \to t\bar{t}$ total cross sections (in pb) at the Tevatron and their kinematic characteristics for lowest–order QCD, the CDF data [1], and the three nonstandard production models with parameters described in the text.

three nonstandard models of top production [7],[12],[13]. The lowest order QCD subprocess cross sections at parton cm energy $\sqrt{\hat{s}}$ are

$$\frac{d\hat{\sigma}(q\bar{q} \to t\bar{t})}{dz} = \frac{\pi\alpha_S^2\beta}{9\hat{s}}\left(2 - \beta^2 + \beta^2 z^2\right),$$

$$\frac{d\hat{\sigma}(gg \to t\bar{t})}{dz} = \frac{\pi\alpha_S^2\beta}{6\hat{s}}\left\{\frac{1 + \beta^2 z^2}{1 - \beta^2 z^2}\left[1 - \frac{(1-\beta^2)^2}{(1-\beta^2 z^2)}\right]\right.$$
$$+ \frac{1-\beta^2}{1-\beta^2 z^2}\left(1 - \tfrac{1}{8}\beta^2 + \tfrac{3}{8}\beta^2 z^2\right)$$
$$\left. - \frac{9}{16}(1 + \beta^2 z^2)\right\}.$$
$$(3)$$

Here, $z = \cos\theta$ and $\beta = \sqrt{1 - 4m_t^2/\hat{s}}$. For $\hat{s} \gg 4m_t^2$, these cross sections—especially the gluon fusion one—are forward–backward peaked. But, at the modest $\hat{s}$ at which QCD production is large, the cross sections are fairly isotropic.

For the "coloron" bosons of Ref. [7], we adopted a version of the model in which $SU(3)_1 \otimes SU(3)_2$ breaks down to color $SU(3)$, yielding eight massless gluons and equal-mass V_8's. To study also the angular distributions in $t\bar{t}$ production (discussed in [14],[15]), we assumed that the V_8 couples only to left–handed quarks with the amplitude

$$A(V_8^a(p,\lambda) \to q(p_1)\bar{q}(p_2)) =$$
$$g_S\,\xi_q\,\epsilon^\mu(p,\lambda)\,\bar{u}_q(p_1)\frac{\lambda_a}{2}\gamma_\mu\left(\frac{1-\gamma_5}{2}\right)v_q(p_2). \quad (4)$$

Here, g_S is the QCD coupling and, following Ref. [7], we took $\xi_t = \xi_b = \pm 1/\xi_q = \sqrt{40/3}$ ($q = u,d,c,s$). For this chiral coupling, the $q\bar{q} \to t\bar{t}$ angular distribution in Eq. (3) is modified by the addition of

$$\frac{d\hat{\sigma}(q\bar{q} \to V_8 \to t\bar{t})}{dz} = \frac{\pi\alpha_S^2\beta}{36\hat{s}}(1+\beta z)^2$$
$$\times \left\{\left|1 + \xi_q\xi_t\frac{\hat{s}}{\hat{s} - M_{V_8}^2 + i\sqrt{\hat{s}}\,\Gamma(V_8)}\right|^2 - 1\right\}. \quad (5)$$

Ignoring all quark masses except m_t, the V_8 width is

$$\Gamma(V_8) = \frac{\alpha_S M_{V_8}}{12}\left\{4\xi_q^2 + \xi_t^2\left(1 + \beta(1 - m_t^2/M_{V_8}^2)\right)\right\},$$
$$(6)$$

so that $\Gamma(V_8) = 40$ (85) GeV for $M_{V_8} = 450$ (475) GeV. The sign $\xi_q\xi_t$ of the V_8–gluon interference strongly influences the shape of the $t\bar{t}$ mass distribution.

If there exists a relatively narrow η_T decaying predominantly to $t\bar{t}$, it modifies the gluon fusion cross section in Eq. (3) by the addition of the isotropic term [11],[12]

$$\frac{d\hat{\sigma}(gg \to \eta_T \to t\bar{t})}{dz} = \frac{\pi}{4}\frac{\Gamma(\eta_T \to gg)\,\Gamma(\eta_T \to t\bar{t})}{(\hat{s} - M_{\eta_T}^2)^2 + \hat{s}\,\Gamma^2(\eta_T)}. \quad (7)$$

Interference between the η_T and QCD gluon–fusion terms is a small effect and, so, is not displayed here.

So long as the η_T may be treated as a pseudo-Goldstone boson, its decay rates to gluons may be computed from the triangle anomaly [8]. We introduce a model–dependent dimensionless factor C_q in the Yukawa coupling of η_T to $q\bar{q}$ [12]. We expect $|C_q| = O(1)$. Then, the η_T's main decay modes are to two gluons and $t\bar{t}$ and they are given by

$$\Gamma(\eta_T \to gg) = \frac{5\alpha_S^2\,N_{TC}^2\,M_{\eta_T}^3}{384\,\pi^3\,F_Q^2},$$
$$(8)$$

$$\Gamma(\eta_T \to t\bar{t}) = \frac{C_t^2\,m_t^2\,M_{\eta_T}\,\beta_q}{16\pi F_Q^2}.$$

In these expressions, it is assumed that the η_T is composed from a single doublet of techniquarks $Q = (U, D)$ in the $\mathbf{N_{TC}}$ representation of $SU(N_{TC})$; F_Q is the decay constant of technipions in the $\overline{Q}Q$ sector. We took $N_{TC} = 5$, $F_Q = 30\,\mathrm{GeV}$, and $C_t = -\frac{1}{3}$ in calculations. This value of F_Q is typical of the small techniquark decay constant occuring in multiscale technicolor models [9]. Its smallness is crucial to obtaining a large η_T contribution to $t\bar{t}$ production. The η_T width is then 32 GeV for $M_{\eta_T} = 450$ GeV, with branching ratios of $\frac{2}{3}$ and $\frac{1}{3}$ to $t\bar{t}$ and gg, respectively.

The third model of enhanced top–production we considered is one in which an electroweak–isoscalar, charge $\frac{2}{3}$ quark, t_s, is approximately degenerate with the top–quark and mixes with it so they have the same decay mode[13]. If $m_{t_s} = m_t = 174$ GeV (say) the expected rate for the top–quark signal is doubled to 10.2 pb. We illustrate the isoscalar quark model with two cases: $m_{t_s} = 160$ and $m_t = 175$ GeV; $m_{t_s} = 165$ and $m_t = 190$ GeV.

The total $t\bar{t}$ cross sections at the Tevatron and the characteristics extracted from the $\mathcal{M}_{t\bar{t}}$ distributions are displayed in Table 1 for the CDF data (see Eq. (2)) and for the above input parameters to the three nonstandard production models. We stress the following features:

1.) The CDF data is narrower ($\Delta \mathcal{M}_{t\bar{t}} = 60$ GeV) than the QCD expectation (77 GeV). While this $\Delta \mathcal{M}_{t\bar{t}}$ is consistent with the resonant production models, the statistics are so low that we do not consider this significant. It is a feature worth watching for in future data samples.

2.) If $\xi_q \xi_t = -1$ corresponding to the notation V_8^- in the table, the mass distribution is enhanced below the resonance and depressed above it, and vice-versa for $\xi_q \xi_t = +1$ (V_8^+). Thus, for a given M_{V_8}, the extracted value of m_t is somewhat smaller than or *significantly* larger than the directly–measured one, depending on whether $\xi_q \xi_t = -1$ or $+1$.

3.) The η_T does not interfere appreciably with the QCD gluon fusion process. Thus the value of the extracted top mass depends mainly on M_{η_T}. Resonance masses in the range 400–500 GeV return a top mass close to the directly–measured value.

4.) It is easy to double the QCD value of $\sigma(t\bar{t})$ in the isoscalar quark model: just choose $m_{t_s} = m_t$. But, as could be foreseen, it is difficult for the isoscalar quark model to give both a 13.9 pb cross section and an extracted mass close to the directly–measured one. To get a cross section $\sim$ 3 times as large as QCD requires choosing one of the masses significantly lower than 174 GeV, leading to too small an extracted value. This model should be the easiest to eliminate with data from the current Tevatron run.

To sum up: It should be possible to extract valuable information on the mechanism of $t\bar{t}$ production and, possibly, the physics of flavor, from even limited statistics on the $\mathcal{M}_{t\bar{t}}$ distrbution. We urge the CDF and D$\emptyset$ experimenters to keep this possibility in mind. In the end, of course, nothing can make up for large data sets, of $O(1-10)\,\mathrm{fb}^{-1}$. From these one can carry out incisive studies of the detailed shape of the mass distribution and of the $t\bar{t}$ angular distribution. At the same time, one should study subsystem invariant masses to search for alternate mechanisms of top production—and hints of flavor physics. This promises a very exciting physics program for the Tevatron Collider.

I am indebted to Alessandra Caner, Sekhar Chivukula, Estia Eichten, John Huth, Elizabeth Simmons, John Terning and Avi Yagil for many helpful conversations. This research was supported in part by the Department of Energy under Contract No. DE–FG02–91ER40676.

References

[1] F. Abe, et al., The CDF Collaboration, *Evidence for Top-Quark Production in $\bar{p}p$ Collisions at $\sqrt{s}$ = 1.8 TeV*, FERMILAB-PUB-94/097-E (1994), submitted to Physical Review D.

[2] F. Abe, et al., The CDF Collaboration, Phys. Rev. Lett. **73** (1994) 225.

[3] P. Nason, S. Dawson and R.K. Ellis, Nucl. Phys. **B303** (1988) 607; W. Beenakker, H. Kuijf, W.L. van Neerven and J. Smith, Phys. Rev. **D40** (1989) 54.

[4] E. Laenen, J. Smith and W.L. van Neerven, Nucl. Phys. **B369** (1992) 543; FERMILAB-Pub-93/270-T.

[5] K. Ellis, "Top-Quark Production Rates in the Standard Model", invited talk in Session Pa-18 given of the 27th International Conference on High Energy Physics, Glasgow, 20–27th July 1994.

[6] C.T. Hill, Phys. Lett. **266B** (1991) 419; S.P. Martin, Phys. Rev. **D45** (1992) 4283; *ibid.* **D46** (1992) 2197.

[7] C. Hill and S. Parke, Phys. Rev. **D49** (1994) 4454.

[8] E. Farhi and L. Susskind, Phys. Rev. **D20** (1979) 3404; S. Dimopoulos, Nucl. Phys. **B168** (1980) 69; T. Appelquist and G. Triantaphyllou, Phys. Rev. Lett. **69** (1992) 2750; T. Appelquist and J. Terning, Phys. Rev. **D50** (1994) 2116.

[9] K. Lane and E. Eichten, Phys. Lett. **222B** (1989) 274; K. Lane and M.V. Ramana, Phys. Rev. **D44** (1991) 2678.

[10] B. Holdom, Phys. Rev. **D24** (1981) 1441; Phys. Lett. **150B** (1985) 301; T. Appelquist, D. Karabali and L.C.R. Wijewardhana, Phys. Rev. Lett. **57** (1986) 957; K. Yamawaki, M. Bando and K. Matumoto, Phys. Rev. Lett. **56** (1986) 1335; T. Akiba and T. Yanagida, Phys. Lett. **169B** (1986) 432; T. Appelquist and L.C.R. Wijewardhana, Phys. Rev. **D36** (1987) 568.

[11] T. Appelquist and G. Triantaphyllou, Phys. Rev. Lett. **69** (1992) 2750.

[12] E. Eichten and K. Lane, Phys. Lett. **327B** (1994) 129.

[13] V. Barger and R.J.N. Phillips, U. Wisconsin Preprint, MAD/PH/830 (May 1994).

[14] K. Lane, *Top-Quark Production and Flavor Physics*, (Contributed paper gls0379 to the Invited talk given at the 27th International Conference on High Energy Physics, Glasgow, 20–27th July 1994; Boston University Preprint BUHEP-94-11 (1994).

[15] K. Lane, in preparation, to be submitted to The Physical Review.

[16] Mark Twain, *Life On The Mississippi*, Dillon Press, Minneapolis (1967).

[17] E. Eichten, I. Hinchliffe, K. Lane and C. Quigg, Rev. Mod. Phys. **56** (1984) 579.

[18] See, e.g., *GEM Technical Design Report*, Chapter 2; GEM TN-93-262, SSCL-SR-1219; Submitted by the GEM Collaboration to the Superconducting Super Collider Laboratory (April 30, 1993).

Parallel Session Pa-19

Field Theory and String Theory

Conveners: I. Antoniadis (Ecole Polytechnique)
S. Wadia (TATA, Bombay)

Scientific secretaries: P. Page
J. I. Skullerud (reserve)

Paper presented at XXVII Int. Conf. on High Energy Physics: Session Pa-19
Glasgow, UK, 20–27 July 1994

Topological Amplitudes and Recursion Relations in Four Dimensional Strings

Edi Gava

Istituto Nazionale di Fisica Nucleare, sez. di Trieste, Italy,
International Centre for Theoretical Physics, I-34100,Italy.

Abstract

In this talk I review the recently found relation between higher genus F-terms corrections to 4-dimensional superstrings effective actions and the topological field theories obtained by twisting the corresponding internal $N = 2$ theories. Some results contained in a paper in preparation with I. Antoniadis, K.S. Narain, T.R. Taylor and C. Vafa on the recursion relations in the heterotic string are discussed.

1. Introduction

It is well known that F-terms in the tree level, 4-dimensional superstring effective action (e.g. Yukawa couplings) have a topological interpretation within the twisted version of the corresponding internal $N = 2$ sigma model [1]. More recently, it was pointed out [2, 3, 4] that also one-loop corrections to gauge couplings (threshold corrections) [5, 6, 7] admit such an interpretation: they are indeed related to the "new index" $TrF(-)^F$ studied in [4].

The purpose of the following discussion is to indicate how these results generalize to higher genus.

The motivation for exploring this possibility is given by the fact that, usually, topological (string) theories are much simpler objects than ordinary strings. Indeed, the experience gained with two-dimensional gravity and matrix-models tells us that some of the structures that one finds in that context can be better understood realizing their underlying topological nature. In particular one can understand how, due to boundary interactions, recursion relations among correlation functions at different genera arise.

These recursion relations, one the other hand, can be encoded in a master equation, which one might to use as non perturbative definition of the theory.

An example of master equation has been recently

discussed in the context of topological strings obtained after twisting Calabi-Yau sigma models [8]. What we will show in the following is how, at least in some sector, ordinary 4-dimensional supersymmetric strings are intimately related to this kind of topological strings. One might thus hope, exploiting this connection, to get a better understanding of string theory at the quantum level.

2. The type II string

I will review in this section the results obtained in [9, 8] for the type II string. To have a clue on which direction to look for generalizations to higher genus of the tree level and one-loop results mentioned in the introduction, it is useful to recall how ordinary $N = 2$ superconformal field theories, in particular those entering in string compactifications, are turned into a topological field theories by twisting [10].

Let us concentrate on the left moving sector: the $N = 2$ algebra (with $c = 9$) is generated by the stress energy tensor T, by the supercurrents $G^{\pm}$ and by the $U(1)$ current J. The states we are interested in are the the so called chiral (anti-chiral) states with integral $U(1)$ charge, characterized by the relation $h = q/2$ ($h = -q/2$) for chiral (anti-chiral), h and q denoting the conformal dimension and $U(1)$ charge respectively. Unitarity implies $|q| \leq 3$, states with $q = \pm 1$ give rise, in string theory, to 4-dimensional chiral (anti-chiral) supermultiplets. The identity operator ($q = 0$) gives rise to gravitational and gauge multiplets.

The procedure of twisting amounts to modify the stress energy tensor, $T \to T + \frac{1}{2}\partial J$. In this way the dimensions h of fields of charge q is shifted to $h - q/2$: in particular G^+ and G^- become of dimensions 1 and 2 respectively. Moreover, from the $N = 2$ algebra, it is consistent to identify $\oint G^+$ as the BRST charge, Q_{BRST}, of the topological theory. The modified stress energy tensor becomes BRST-exact, $T = \{Q_{BRST}, G^-\}$, and has vanishing central charge.

The $U(1)$ current J becomes anomalous: in genus g there is a background charge $3(g-1)$. This implies that, after twisting also the right moving sector, we have all the elements to couple to gravity our topological field theory, by simply taking as reparametrization b ghosts the G^-'s (similarly for right moving, take $\bar{G}^-$ as $\bar{b}$) to be folded with the appropriate Beltrami differentials μ_a, and we are guarantee, by the topological algebra, to have a consistent measure over moduli space M_g of genus g Riemann surfaces. The topological partition function is indeed given by:

$$F_g = \int_{M_g} \langle \prod_{a=1}^{3g-3} |\mu_a G^-|^2 \rangle, \qquad (1)$$

The physical states are given now by the BRST cohomology i.e. by the chiral primary states of the original $N = 2$ theory. In particular, those with charges $(1,1)$ are in correspondence with the holomorphic $(1,2)$ (complex structure) target space moduli: their two-form version (with $q = \bar{q} = 0$) can be added as marginal perturbation to the action. The anti-holomorphic moduli on the other hand are BRST-exact and should decouple. Cosequently, one expects the correlation functions of the theory to be holomorphic. Actually, as shown in [8], this expectation turns out to be wrong, as a consequence of boundary terms in the integration over M_g. For the genus g topological partition function F_g indeed one gets:

$$\partial_{\bar{i}} F_g = \bar{C}_{\bar{i}\bar{j}\bar{k}} e^{2K} G^{j\bar{j}} G^{k\bar{k}} \left(D_j D_k F_{g-1} + \frac{1}{2} \sum_r D_j F_r \cdot D_k F_{g-r} \right), (2)$$

where $G_{i\bar{i}}$ is the Zamolodchikov metric on the moduli space and K the associated Kähler potential, D is a covariant derivative, the $\bar{C}$'s are topological "Yukawa couplings". Notice that F_g is a section of a holomorphic line bundle: it transforms under Kähler transformations $K \to K + \phi + \bar{\phi}$ as $F_g \to e^{(2g-2)\phi} F_g$ i.e. it has Kähler

weight $2g-2$. This explains the presence of the covariant derivatives†.

I will come back to the derivation of this "holomorphic anomaly equation" when discussing the corresponding equation for the heterotic case. On the other hand, the $(1,1)$(Kähler structure) moduli are also BRST trivial as well as their complex conjugates, and can be shown to be truly decoupled ‡.

Let us now go back to type II strings: we will consider models with $N = 2$ spacetime supersymmetry, and show that there are string amplitudes whose dependence on moduli is precisely governed by the topological partition function F_g discussed above.

To see this, first of all let me notice that we can think of the twisting of T as due to an addition to the action of the untwisted theory of a background charge of amount $\frac{3}{2}(2g - 2)$ in genus g. Assuming the two dimensional curvature to have delta-function support at $2g-2$ points, we have that at each of these points there is a charge $3/2$. Bosonizing the $U(1)$ current in the usual way $J = i\sqrt{3}\partial H$, we see that at each of the $2g - 2$ points we should have an insertion of the operator $e^{-i\frac{\sqrt{3}}{2}H}$, which is just the internal spin field i.e. the internal part of the spacetime SUSY charge in the corresponding string theory. Of course, similar arguments apply to the right moving sector. In the type II string, this corresponds to the insertion of $2g - 2$ (Ramond-Ramond) graviphoton vertex operators (in the $-1/2$ picture).

To see more precisely which amplitude we should compute, recall that the anti-selfdual part of the graviphoton field strength is the lowest component of an $N = 2$ chiral superfield $W_{\mu\nu}^{ij}$, by which we can form the scalar superfield W^2:

$$\begin{aligned} W^2 &\equiv \epsilon_{ij}\epsilon_{kl}W_{\mu\nu}^{ij}W_{\mu\nu}^{kl} \\ &= T_{\mu\nu}T_{\mu\nu} - 2(\epsilon_{ij}\theta^i \sigma_{\mu\nu}\theta^j)R_{\mu\nu\lambda\rho}T_{\lambda\rho} \\ &\quad -(\theta^i)^2(\theta^j)^2 R_{\mu\nu\lambda\rho}R_{\mu\nu\lambda\rho} + \dots \end{aligned} \qquad (3)$$

where $R\mu\nu\lambda\rho$ is the anti-selfdual part of the Riemann tensor.

Then the F-term component of W^{2g} will contribute to an amplitude involving 2 gravitons and $2g - 2$ graviphotons.

This amplitude $A^g = \langle T^{2g-2}R^2 \rangle$, to be computed at genus g, can be worked out starting from the appropriate vertex operators for gravitons and graviphotons. The calculation is factorized and identical in left and right moving parts. Notice also that since we are using graviphoton vertex operators all in the (-1/2)-picture, we need $3g-3$ picture changing operators. Then internal

---

† Derivatives must be also reparametrization covariant when acting on correlation functions.

‡ For simplicity we have restricted the discussion to type B models.

$U(1)$ charge conservation implies that only their $G^{(-)}$, $(\bar{G}^{(-)})$ part contribute. Using bosonization formulae to compute the spacetime part of correlators, the Riemann theta identity to perform the spin structure sum, one can check that the non-zero mode determinants of spacetime fields cancel out, and that moreover their zero mode part cancels precisely the factor $(\det Im\tau)^{-2}$ arising from the integration over the four dimensional spacetime momenta. As a result, at leading order in external momenta, the amplitude becomes proportional to the topological partition function.

Working out the kinematics in detail, one verifies that indeed the amplitude just discussed can be derived from the bosonic part of the effective Lagrangian $F_g W^{2g}|_{F-term}$.

Moreover, arguments involving the coupling of the dilaton in $N = 2$ supergravity, suggest that the amplitude discussed above, $\langle T^{2g-2}R^2\rangle$, does not receive contributions at genus g' different from g.

3. The heterotic string

After the discussion in the previous section, it is not difficult to guess how to proceed for the heterotic string (with $N = 1$ spacetime SUSY) [11]. Indeed we have learned that the effect of twisting is realized by the insertion, at g-th loop level, of $2g-2$ operators involving the internal spin field in the corresponding sector. So, the twisting is intimately linked to spacetime SUSY. In the heterotic string, contrary to the type II with $N = 2$ spacetime SUSY, where the internal SCFT has $(2,2)$ supersymmetry, one has in general $(2,0)$ supersymmetry (and in any case, spacetime SUSY is provided by the left moving sector only). As a result, the fields which play the role of the graviphotons of the previous section are now either guginos, gravitinos or dilatinos: they both involve the internal spin field in the left moving sector. Let us consider gauginos: they sit in a $N = 1$ chiral, spinor, superfield W_α^a, where a is a gauge group index, out of which we can form the scalar superfield $W^2 \equiv W^{a\alpha}W_\alpha^a$:

$$W^2 = -\lambda^a\lambda^a + \cdots + 2i\bar{\lambda}^a\sigma^\mu\mathcal{D}_\mu\lambda^a\theta^2 + \frac{1}{2}F_{\mu\nu}^a F_{\mu\nu}^a\theta^2, \quad (4)$$

where F is actually the anti-selfdual part of the gauge field strength and λ is the gaugino field. We can then consider the F-term component of W^{2g} in the effective action: it will contribute to amplitudes involving $2g-2$ gauginos and 2 gauge fields (at genus g).

The vertex operators for gauginos and gauge fields are:

$$\begin{aligned} V_\lambda &= e^{-\phi/2}S_\alpha e^{-i\frac{\sqrt{3}}{2}H}\bar{J}^a e^{ip\cdot X}, \\ V_A &= (\partial X_\mu + ip\cdot\psi\psi_\mu)\bar{J}^a e^{ip\cdot X}, \end{aligned} \quad (5)$$

where ϕ is the scalar bosonizing superghosts, $\bar{J}$'s are Kac-Moody currents and S_α is the spacetime spin field.

One immediately realizes that, as far as the left-moving sector is concerned, the computation is identical to the type II case. The right-moving sector instead involves the correlator of $2g$ Kac-Moody currents $\bar{J}^a$.

It turns out that the simplest way to arrive at a topological expression is to consider currents along the Cartan generators, and then take appropriate linear combinations of different gauge group correlators, in such a way to eliminate all double poles in the Kac-Moody currents OPE. In this way only the zero modes of the currents, $Q_i^a\bar{\omega}_i$ contribute. $\bar{\omega}_i$ are the g antiholomorphic one-forms, Q_i^a is the a-th charge flowing in the i-th loop. One can then perform the integrals over positions of the vertex operators, and like in the type II case, one gets a factor $(\det Im\tau)^2$. Finally, to second order in the external momenta, one arrives at an expression proportional to:

$$\begin{aligned} A^g &= \int_{M_g}\langle\det Q_k^{b_k}\det Q_j^{c_j} \\ &\quad \prod_{i=1}^{3g-3}(\mu_i G^-)(\bar{\mu}_i\bar{b})\rangle_{top}. \end{aligned} \quad (6)$$

Here b_k and c_j run over partitions of g elements of the $2g$ gauge indices. The subscript "top" means that the correlator is computed in the left- moving topological theory and right-moving ordinary bosonic theory. So, we end up with some kind of "heterotic topological theory" (HTT). Notice however that the above expression, which is not modular invariant, is just one of the terms of a modular invariant linear combination abtained requiring the cancellation of double poles in the currents correlator.

The spectrum of physical states of the HTT so obtained is constituted of all states corresponding to spacetime chiral superfields (including moduli, charged matter, singlets). The unphysical states, which should naively decouple, are those corresponding to the antichiral superfields.

However, similarly to what happens in type II case, this decoupling does not occur, again due to boundary terms in the integration over M_g.

4. Recursion relations

The structure of (2) can be understood by noticing that taking $\partial_{\bar{i}}$ of F_g amounts to compute the one-point function of $\Phi_{\bar{i}} = \{Q_{BRST},\{\bar{Q}_{BRST}\Psi_{\bar{i}}\}\}$, where $\Psi_{\bar{i}}$ is an antichiral field of charges (-1,-1). Doing BRST contour deformation, one obtains $\partial_t\partial_{\bar{i}}$ of the one point function of $\int\Psi_{\bar{i}}$, where t is a coordinate parametrizing a boundary component of M_g ($t = 0$ corresponds to Riemann surfaces with nodes). In either case, dividing or handle pinching, one gets a nonzero contribution if the one-point function goes like $\ln(t\bar{t})$ for small t. This implies that $\Psi_{\bar{\imath}}$ sits at the node. The structure of (2) can then easily obtained by exploiting anomalous $U(1)$ conservation.

In the heterotic case, $\partial_{\bar{\imath}}A^g$ amounts to insert $\Phi_{\bar{\imath}} = \{Q_{BRST}, \Psi_{\bar{\imath}}\}$, where $\Psi_{\bar{\imath}}$ is an antichiral field of left charge and dimension (-1) and 1 respectively. Doing BRST contour deformation, one obtains now ∂_t of the one-point function of $\int \Psi_{\bar{\imath}}$. We have a non zero contribution if the latter behaves as $1/\bar{t}$ for small t, which means that a state of right dimension 1 propagates. In a generic situation we then have that $\Psi_{\bar{\imath}}$ is now distributed over the complement of the node. Consider the case of pinching a dividing geodesic: the Riemann surface Σ_g splits into Σ_{g_1, g_2}, $g_1 + g_2 = g$, with punctures $P_{1,2}$ respectively. Supposing $\Psi_{\bar{\imath}}$ is on Σ_1, then essentially anomalous left $U(1)$ charge conservation tells us that on Σ_2 we have just $D_J A^{g_2}$, D being a Kähler covariant derivative, due to the fact that A^g has Kähler weight $g - 1$, and $\jmath$ stands for any gauge group singlet.

On the other hand, on Σ_1 we have a new object, $A^{g_1}_{\bar{\imath}, \jmath}$. This is the two-point function involving $\Psi_{\bar{\imath}}$ and a charge 2 operator, which can be thought of as $\oint dz \rho(z) \Psi_{\bar{\jmath}} \bar{c}$, where $\bar{c}$ is the reparametrization ghost, ρ is the holomorphic tree form (charge 3 chiral field). This operator has left and right dimensions $(0,0)$. Notice that on Σ_1 we have $3g_1 - 3 + 1$ G^-'s. So, we get an anomaly equation of the form:

$$\partial_{\bar{\imath}} A^g = \sum_{g_1 + g_2 = g} A^{g_1}_{\bar{\imath}, \jmath} G^{\jmath\bar{\jmath}} D_J A^{g_2} + \cdots. \quad (7)$$

Here the dots stand for the handle contribution, for which similar arguments should apply, however we do not understand completely this part at the moment.

The main point of (7) is that, contrary to the type II case (2), it leds us outside the realm of topological correlators: indeed $A^{g_1}_{\bar{\imath}, \jmath}$ involves the unphysical operator $\Psi_{\bar{\imath}}$.

One can proceed by further taking an antiholomorphic derivative $\partial_{\bar{k}}$ of $A^{g_1}_{\bar{\imath}, \jmath}$: after antisymmetrizing $\bar{k}$ and $\bar{\imath}$ one again gets a boundary contribution: repeating the steps indicated before, one is led to introduce an object $A^{g_3}_{\bar{k}\bar{\imath}, \bar{l}\jmath}$, where $\bar{k}$ again refers to a charge (-1) antichiral state end $\bar{l}$ to a charge 2 state as before. Notice the antisymmetry between $\bar{k}\bar{\imath}$ and between $\bar{l}\jmath$. More generally one has amplitudes of the kind $A^g_{\bar{\imath}_1 \cdots \bar{\imath}_n, \bar{\jmath}_1 \cdots \bar{\jmath}_n}$, totally antisymmetric in $\bar{\imath}$'s and $\bar{\jmath}$'s †, with Kähler weight $g - 1 + n$, for which one can write a recursion relation similar to (7), considering $\partial_{\bar{\imath}}$ as an exterior derivative with respect to the $\bar{\imath}$ indices.

Thinking of $A^g_{\bar{\imath}_1 \cdots \bar{\imath}_n, \bar{\jmath}_1 \cdots \bar{\jmath}_n}$ as an n-form in the $\bar{\imath}$

indices, we can say that the recursion relation is a manifestation of of the fact that it fails to be closed.

One can in particular consider tree level amplitudes, i.e. put $g = 0$. One has then only the dividing contribution and it is possible to summarize all the recursion relations in a master equation for the generating function of connected amplitudes, which is reminiscent of a SUSY Ward identity. Indeed introduce Grassman parameters $\theta^{\bar{\imath}}$ and $\eta^{\bar{\jmath}}$, and form the quantity

$$A^0 = \sum \frac{1}{(n!)^2} A^0_{\bar{\imath}_1 \cdots \bar{\imath}_n, \bar{\jmath}_1 \cdots \bar{\jmath}_n} \theta^{\bar{\imath}_1} \cdots \theta^{\bar{\imath}_n} \eta^{\bar{\jmath}_1} \cdots \eta^{\bar{\jmath}_n}. \quad (8)$$

Define also $\delta \equiv \theta^{\bar{\imath}} D_{\bar{\imath}}$. Then the tree level recursion relations are all contained in the master equation:

$$\delta A^0 = \left(\frac{\partial}{\partial \eta^{\bar{\jmath}}} A^0\right) G^{\jmath\bar{\jmath}} D_J A^0. \quad (9)$$

The identity $\delta^2 = 0$ gives a consistency check on (9).

Finally, one can also relate the "topological" amplitudes $A^g_{\bar{\imath}_1 \cdots \bar{\imath}_n, \bar{\jmath}_1 \cdots \bar{\jmath}_n}$ to heterotic string amplitudes: it turns out that they are related to higher weight F-terms, not present in the ordinary supergravity Lagrangian [12].

Indeed given any real function of chiral, antichiral superfields $Z^i, \bar{Z}^i, f(Z, \bar{Z})$, one can perform a chiral projection: $\Pi = (\bar{D})^2 f$, where for simplicity I used the $\bar{D}$ of rigid SUSY. The above $A^0_{\bar{\imath}_1 \cdots \bar{\imath}_n, \bar{\jmath}_1 \cdots \bar{\jmath}_n}$'s correspond, loosely speaking, to F-terms of the kind Π^n. The two different type of "topological" states denoted with $\bar{\imath}$ and $\bar{\jmath}$ indices correspond to the two spacetime spinor indices of the fermion component $\bar{\chi}$ of $\bar{Z}$. In view of this correspondence, (9) has clearly the structure of a SUSY Ward identity‡, if one identifies $(-G^{\jmath\bar{\jmath}} D_J A^0)$ with the auxiliary field of $Z^{\bar{\jmath}}$, $h^{\bar{\jmath}}$.

A similar identification of "topological amplitudes" with string amplitudes involving additional insertions of the W^2 superfield, arise for $g \geq 1$.

5. Effective field theory

From the effective field theory point of view the previous results may sound rather odd: indeed, from the experience in the study of gauge threshold corrections, holomorphic anomalies are believed to be due to the circulation of massless fermions in one-loop diagrams, which give rise to non-localities in the effective action [5, 6, 7]. On the other hand, we have considered in the previous section tree level "anomalies". One has to remember however that we are not dealing with with 1PI amplitudes but with string amplitudes, i.e. amputated,

---

† The antisymmetry follows from the anticommuting nature of the corresponding operators.

‡ Notice however that A^0 is a generating function for connected amplitudes.

connected, on-shell Green functions. The following exercise sheds some light on what is happening: suppose one adds to the ordinary SUGRA Lagrangian an F-term of the type Π^2, i.e.

$$F = e^{-K/2} \bar{\chi}^{\bar{i}} \bar{\chi}^{\bar{j}} \partial_\mu \bar{z}^{\bar{k}} \partial_\mu \bar{z}^{\bar{l}} f^{(1}_{\bar{i}\bar{j}} f^{2)}_{\bar{k}\bar{l}} + \cdots, \qquad (10)$$

where $\bar{z}$ is the lowest component of $\bar{Z}$. This corresponds to a closed form, in the sense of the previous section. However one can now compute amplitudes involving four $\bar{\chi}$'s, two $\bar{z}$'s and quadratic in momenta (a Π^3-type term). In doing this one eliminates auxiliary fields and takes into account reducible contributions of the kind p^2/p^2, where p is some intermediate momentum. One then finds that the complete (connected) amplitude is not closed, but satisfies the appropriate recursion relation which can be read off from (9).

From this example, one is actually led to suspect that the recursion relations have very little dynamical content, perhaps they just reflect spacetime SUSY. Continuing with this idea, higher genus recursion relations could be possibly solved by starting from an effective Lagrangian which includes Π^n terms plus the genuine 1-loop anomaly, after eliminating auxiliary fields and taking into account reducible diagrams as in the tree level example above.

6. Conclusions

The discussion of the last section strongly suggests that the "anomalous" part of the amplitudes we were considering, governed by the recursion relations, contains little dynamical information. If this is so, then the dynamics is precisely encoded in the non-anomalous (holomorphic) part. Although holomorphic forms are usually severely constrained given their modular properties (for orbifolds say), this is not enough: for example, in the type II case for orbifolds, one starts having holomorphic ambiguities from genus 3 and higher, and actually the ambiguity increases with g, since the number of holomorphic modular forms of the appropriate weight increases with g. Clearly some physical input is needed to fix completely the boundary conditions.

References

[1] E. Witten, *Mirror Manifolds and Topological Field Theory*, in *Essays on Mirror Manifolds*, Ed. S.-T. Yau, p.37 (International Press 1992).

[2] I. Antoniadis, E. Gava and K.S. Narain, Nucl. Phys. **B386** (1992) 93.

[3] I. Antoniadis, E. Gava, K.S. Narain and T.R. Taylor, Nucl. Phys. **B407** (1992) 706.

[4] S. Cecotti, P. Fendley, K. Intriligator and C. Vafa, Nucl. Phys. **B386** (1992) 405.

[5] L. Dixon, V.S. Kaplunovsky and J. Louis, Nucl. Phys. **B355** (1991) 649.

[6] J.-P. Derendinger, S. Ferrara, C. Kounnas and F. Zwirner, Nucl. Phys. **B372** (1992) 145.

[7] G.L. Cardoso and B.A. Ovrut, Nucl. Phys. **B369** (1992) 351.

[8] M. Bershadsky, S. Cecotti, H. Ooguri and C. Vafa, Harvard preprint: HUTP-93/A008, hep-th/9302103.

[9] I. Antoniadis, E. Gava, K.S. Narain and T.R. Taylor, Nucl. Phys. **B413** (1994) 162.

[10] E. Witten, Comm. Math. Phys. **118** (1988) 411; T. Eguchi and S.-K. Yang, Mod. Phys. Lett. **A4** (1990) 1653.

[11] I. Antoniadis, E. Gava, K.S. Narain, T.R. Taylor and C. Vafa, in preparation.

[12] I. Antoniadis, E. Gava, K.S. Narain and T.R. Taylor, *Effective μ-term in superstring theory*, to appear in Nucl. Phys. **B**.

Paper presented at XXVII Int. Conf. on High Energy Physics: Session Pa-19
Glasgow, UK, 20–27 July 1994

Two Dimensional QCD, W_∞ Algebra and String Theory

Spenta R. Wadia[†]

Theoretical Physics Group
Tata Institute of Fundamental Research
Homi Bhabha Road, Bombay 400 005, INDIA

Abstract

We review some recent work on the phase space of QCD$_2$ in terms of gauge invariant string like variables. They form a W_∞ algebra with non-linear constraints. The large N master field specifies a co-adjoint orbit of W_∞. We identify the phase space co-ordinates of this orbit. The fluctuation equation is related to 't Hooft's equation for mesons. We comment on the baryons in this model which are the stringy solitons.

1. Introduction

Gauge theories and string theory have a long standing symbiotic relationship [1]. Infact it was the string model that inspired 't Hooft's work on the $\frac{1}{N}$ expansion of non-abelian gauge theories [2]. In this work 't Hooft discovered the deep connection between Feynman diagrams of matrix valued field theories and 2-dim. Riemann surfaces. Subsequently it is this connection that formed the basis of the matrix model formulations of non-perturbative low dimensional string theories. In particular much effort has been devoted to the $c = 1$ matrix model that defines a closed 2-dim. string theory. This theory has an exact representation in terms of 1-dimensional non-relativistic fermions and its phase space is described by the bilocal variables made out of the non-relativistic fermions: $\Phi(x,y) = \psi(x)\psi^+(y)$. These bilocal variables satisfy a W_∞ algebra which is the analogue of the poisson bracket algebra. The W_∞ algebra along with some constraints completely specifies the string theory [3].

In this talk we report on work which applies some of these ideas developed in string theory to 2-dim. gauge theories with fermions [4]. In particular we characterize the gauge invariant "phase space" in terms natural

string-like gauge invariant variables which satisfy a W_∞ algebra. These variables satisfy an infinite set of non-linear constraints.

We present the action principle in this phase space and set up a systematic $\frac{1}{N}$ expansion, where N is the number of colours. The classical solution gives us the large N 'master field' of this model. The spectrum around this master field is given by a fluctuation equation that is related to the 't Hooft equation of 2-dim. QCD. Interactions are in principle exactly calculable in powers of $\frac{1}{N}$. This formulation also enables us to discuss master fields of non-zero baryon number. These are the baryons which were originally discussed by Witten.

2. Hamiltonian formulation of 2-dim. QCD

The model is defined as follows: The gauge group is $SU(N)$ and the corresponding gauge fields are traceless hermitian matrices $A_\mu^{ab}(x), \mu = \pm; a, b = 1, \ldots, N$. The fermions are in the fundamental representation of $SU(N)$ $\psi_\alpha^a(x), \alpha = 1, 2$ is the dirac index and $a = 1, \ldots, N$. The lagrangian is standard,

$$\mathcal{L} = -\frac{1}{4} tr F_{\mu\nu} F^{\mu\nu} + \bar{\psi} i \not{D} \psi + m \bar{\psi} \psi, \tag{1}$$

† E-mail: wadia@theory.tifr.res.in

Since our space-time is the 2-dim. plane we can use the lorentz covariant gauge condition, $A_+ = \frac{1}{2}(A_0 + A_1) = 0$ for all space-time points. Below we summarize the hamiltonian formulation in this gauge, treating x^+ as a "time".

$$H = \int dx^- \left[\frac{1}{8} \, tr \, E^2 - \frac{m}{2} \left(\psi_-^+ \psi_+ + \psi_+^+ \psi_- \right) \right]$$

$$[A_-(x^-, x^+), E(y^-, x^+)] = i\delta(x^- - y^-), \qquad (2)$$

ψ_+ and ψ_- are chiral components of the dirac field. The associated Gauss constraint on the physical states is

$$\partial + E^{ab} + i\frac{g}{\sqrt{N}} \, [A_-, E]^{ab} -$$

$$\frac{2g}{\sqrt{N}} \left(\psi_-^{+b} \psi_-^a - \frac{1}{N} \delta^{ab} \psi_-^{+c} \psi_-^c \right) |\psi\rangle = 0 \qquad (3)$$

In the gauge $A_+ = 0, \psi_+^a$ is determined in terms of ψ_-^a using the dirac equation $2 \left(i\partial_- - \frac{g}{\sqrt{N}} A_- \right) \psi_+ + m\psi_- = 0$.

In the hamiltonian formulation a further reduction of degrees of freedom is possible by choosing the gauge $A_- = 0$ at a fixed x^+. Then solving for the electric field in Gauss's law the hamiltonian can be expressed entirely in terms of the gauge invariant bilocal operator

$$M_{--}(x^-, y^-) = \frac{1}{N} \sum_{a=1}^{N} \psi_-^a(x^-) \psi_-^{a+}(y^-) \equiv M(x^-, y^-)$$

$$\qquad (4)$$

$$H = N \int dx^- dy^- \left[\frac{g^2}{4} \, M(x^-, y^-) |x^- - y^-| M(x^-, y^-) \right.$$

$$- \frac{im^2}{4} \, \text{Sgn} \, (x^-, y^-) \, M(x^-, y^-)$$

$$\left. - \frac{g^2}{4N} \, M(x^-, x^-) |x^- - y^-| M(y^-, y^-) \right]. \qquad (5)$$

Using this fermion anti-commutation rules it is easy to verify that- $M(x, y)$ satisfies a W_∞ algebra

$$[M(x, y), \, M(x', y')] =$$

$$\delta(x - y') \, M(x', y) - \delta(x' - y) \, M(x, y'). \qquad (6)$$

Further using the fact that the physical states are invariant under the residual global gauge transformations one can prove the constraint

$$M^2(x, y)|\psi\rangle = \left(\frac{1}{2} + \frac{B}{N} \right) M(x, y)|\psi\rangle \qquad (7)$$

where $M^2(x, y) \equiv \int M(x, x') \, M(x', y) dx'$ and B is the baryons number given by the formal expression

$$B = Tr(1 - M). \qquad (8)$$

3. The Classical Action

Eqs. (6), (7), (8) define the gauge invariant phase space formulation of the gauge theory. A classical action can be constructed using the method of co-adjoint orbits for W_∞[3]. The constraints (8) specify the co-adjoint orbit. The path integral can also be constructed using the method of W_∞ coherent states [3]. We quote the results:

$$S = N \left[2i \int_\Sigma ds dx^+ Tr \left(M \left[\partial_+ M, \partial_s M \right] \right) \right.$$

$$\left. - \int_{-\infty}^{+\infty} dx^+ Tr \left(\frac{1}{4} im^2 SM + \frac{1}{4} g^2 M\tilde{M} \right) \right]$$

where

$$\tilde{M}(x, y, t) \equiv |x - y| M(x, y, t), \; S(x, y) = \text{Sgn} \, (x - y)$$

In the above $M^2 = M$ and $trM = $ costant and $M(x, y, t)$ is to be regarded as a matrix with indices x and y. The region Σ of (s, x^+) integration is the lower half plane $x^+ \in (-\infty, +\infty), s \in (-\infty, 0]$ and we have the boundary condition that $M(x^+, s = 0) = M(x^+)$ and $M(x^+, s) \to$ a constant $(x^+$-independent) matrix as $s \to -\infty$. The equation of motion can be derived by considering infinitesimal motion on the co-adjoint orbit which preserves the constraints [7, 8]. Such a motion is given by

$$\delta M = i[\epsilon, M]. \qquad (9)$$

Setting $\delta S = 0$, we get

$$i\partial_+ M = (im^2/8)[M, S] + (g^2/4) \left[M, \widetilde{M} \right] \qquad (10)$$

4. Classical Solution

The classical solution in the zero baryon number sector is easily found in terms of the double fourier transforms of $M(k^-, k^{-'}, x^+) = \frac{1}{2\pi} \int dx_- dy'_- M(x^-, y^-, x^+) e^{+ik_-x^- - ik'_-y'^-}$. It is given by (for detail see ref. [4]).

$$M_0(k^-, k^{-'}) = \theta(k^-)\delta(k^- - k^{-'}) \qquad (11)$$

It satisfies the equation of motion (10) and also the constraints. Physically it corresponds to calculating the expectation value of the bilocal operator in a filled fermi sea with fermi level $k^- = k_F^- = 0$. This then is the large N "master field" of this model. It basically labels a classical co-adjoint orbit of W_∞ around which we can develop a systematic perturbation expression. Note that we define the regularized baryon number to be zero for M_0.

5. Perturbation expansion and fluctuation equation

A W_∞ covariant perturbation theory can be set up by parametrizing

$$M = e^{iW/\sqrt{N}} M_0 \, e^{-iW/\sqrt{N}}$$

W is the fluctuation. M satisfies the constraints (7), (8) because M_0 does. Using (12) we have the expansion

$$M^{++}(k, k') = \delta(k - k') -$$

$$(1/N) \int_0^\infty dk'' W^{+-}(k, k'') W^{-+}(k'', k') + o(N^{-3/2})$$

$$M^{+-}(k, k') = -(i/\sqrt{N}) W^{+-}(k, k') + o(N^{-1})$$

$$M^{-+}(k, k') = (i/\sqrt{N}) W^{-+}(k, k') + o(N^{-1})$$

$$M^{--}(k, k') =$$

$$(1/N) \int_0^\infty dk'' W^{-+}(k, k'') W^{+-}(k'', k) \tag{12}$$

where $M^{\pm\pm}(k, k')$ and $W^{\pm\pm}(k, k')$ are defined by $A^{++}(k, k') = A(k, k'), A^{+-}(k, k') = A(k, -k')$, $A^{-+}(k, k') = A(-k', k), A^{--}(k, k') = A(-k, -k')$ for $k, k' > 0$. In this basis the W_∞ algebra (7) becomes

$$[M^{++}, M^{--}] = 0 \tag{13}$$

$$[M^{++}(k, k'), M^{+-}(l, l')] = (1/2N)\delta(k' - l)M^{+-}(k, l')$$

$$[M^{++}(k, k'), M^{-+}(l, l')] = -(1/2N)\delta(k - l')$$

$$M^{-+}(l, k') \tag{14}$$

$$[M^{--}(k, k'), M^{+-}(l, l')] = -(1/2N)\delta(k - l')M^{+-}(l, k')$$

$$[M^{++}(k, k'), M^{-+}(l, l')] = (1/2N)\delta(k' - l)$$

$$M^{-+}(k, l') \tag{15}$$

$$[M^{+-}(k, k'), M^{-+}(l, l')] =$$

$$(1/2N)\big(-\delta(k - l')M^{--}(l, k') +$$

$$\delta(k' - l)M^{++}(k, l') \big)$$

$$[M^{+-}, M^{+-}] = 0 = [M^{-+}, M^{-+}] \tag{16}$$

and implies the commutation relations for the fluctuation $W^{\pm\pm}(k, k')$ to leading order:

$$[W^{+-}(k, k'), W^{-+}(l, l')] = (1/2)\delta(k - l')\delta(k' - l) +$$

$$o(N^{-1/2})$$

$$[W^{+-}, W^{+-}] = [W^{-+}, W^{-+}] = 0 + o(N^{-1/2}) \tag{17}$$

and that

$$[\overline{M}^{++}(k, k'), W^{+-}(l, l')] =$$

$$(1/2)\delta(k' - l)W^{+-}(k, l') + o(N^{-1/2})$$

$$[\overline{M}^{++}(k, k'), W^{-+}(l, l')] =$$

$$-(1/2)\delta(k - l')W^{-+}(l, k') + o(N^{-1/2}) \tag{18}$$

Here $\overline{M}^{++} \equiv NM^{++}$. Similar statements are true for M^{--}. Note that it is the $\overline{M}$'s that in the large N-limit have an N-independent structure constant. Thus, in the limit $N = \infty$ we get a Heisenberg algebra of the W^{+-}, W^{-+} which forms a module of $W_{\infty+} \otimes W_{\infty-}$. Hence W^{+-}, W^{-+} are the phase space co-ordinates and $W_{\infty+} \otimes W_{\infty-}$ are like the canonical transformations acting on the phase space. We remark that the c-number term in (18) denotes the central charge of the Heisenberg algebra and arises as a consequence of the original algebra (6) and an expansion around the background (12).

To develop the perturbation expansion we substitute eq. (13) into the action (9). The N independent term that determines the spectrum turns out to be

$$S^{(1)} = -2 \int dx^+ \int_0^\infty dk \int_0^\infty dk'$$

$$\Big[W^{+-}(k', k; x^+) i\partial_+ W^{-+}(k, k'; x^+)$$

$$-(m^2/4)(1/k + 1/k') W^{+-}(k, k'; x^+) W^{-+}(k', k; x^+)$$

$$+(g^2/8\pi) W^{+-}(k', k; x^+) \int_k^{-k'} (dp/p^2)$$

$$(W^{-+}(k - p, k' + p; x^+) - W^{-+}(k, k'; x^+))$$

$$+(g^2/8\pi) W^{-+}(k', k; x^+) \int_k^{-k'} (dp/p^2)$$

$$(W^{+-}(k' + p, k - p; x^+) - W^{+-}(k', k; x^+)) \Big]$$

$$+0(N^{-1/2}) \tag{19}$$

This gives rise to the linear equation of motion for the fluctuation

$$i\partial_+ W^{-+}(k, k'; x^+) = (m^2/4)(1/k + 1/k') W^{-+}(k, k'; x^+)$$

$$-(g^2/4\pi) \int_k^{-k'} dp(1/p^2) \big[W^{-+}(k - p, k' + p; x^+) -$$

$$W^{-+}(k, k'; x^+) \big] + o(N^{-1/2}) \tag{20}$$

where k and k' are both ≥ 0. Let us now define

$$r_- = k + k'$$
$$x = k'/r_- \tag{21}$$

and also change the variable from p to y in the integral on the r.h.s. of (19), where y is defined by

$$y = \frac{p + k'}{r_-} \tag{22}$$

Clearly both x and y range over the interval $[0, 1]$. Finally, writing

$$W^{-+}(k, k'; x^+) = \int \frac{dr^+}{2\pi} \phi(x; r_-, r_+) e^{ir_+ x^+} \tag{23}$$

we get

$$4r_- r_+ \phi(x) = m^2 (\tfrac{1}{x} + \tfrac{1}{1-x}) \phi(x)$$
$$- \tfrac{g^2}{\pi} \int_0^1 \frac{dy}{(y-x)^2} (\phi(y) - \phi(x)) \tag{24}$$

which is the same as the 'tHooft equation for mesons [5].

Let us briefly discuss the boundary conditions on $\phi(x)$ at $x = 0$ and $x = 1$. From (22) we see that $x = 0$ implies $k' = 0$, and $x = 1$ implies $k' = \infty$. We note that $W^{-+}(k, k' = 0) = 0$ by fermi statistics, because k' = 0 is the fermi-level and it is occupied. $W^{-+}(k, k' = \infty) = 0$ because that corresponds to an infinite energy fermion. Hence $\phi(0) = \phi(1) = 0$. It is well known that (25) with these boundary conditions leads to a infinite tower of mesons. In fact for the high mass states the fermion mass term in (25) can be neglected and the eigenvalue equation can be easily solved:

$$\phi_n(x, r_+, r_-) \sim \sin n\pi x$$
$$r_+ r_- \sim n \tag{25}$$

It is interesting to note that the same spectrum can be obtained from a Nambu string with a correct treatment of the longitudinal (Liouville?) mode[6].

6.   Baryons and String Solitons

Witten had pointed out that baryons are solitons of the large N theory [7]. In the present framework we have to solve the eqn. of motion (11) with $M^2 = M$ and $Tr(1-M) = B$. Their amplitude is proportional to e^{-N}, which is typical of stringy non-perturbative behaviour [8]. We have to hold the regularized baryon number to be non-zero. These non-trivial classical solutions will correspond to different self-consistent Hartree-Fock potentials which arise out of populating quasi-particle wave function above the Dirac sea. The important point here is that these classical solutions are given by a

function $M_{cl}(k^-, k^{-\prime}, t)$ of 2 variables: $k^- \pm k^{-\prime}$. If we call the conjugate variables Y and X, then the fourier transform of M_{cl} is $M_{cl}(Y, X)$. X represents a centre of mass type co-ordinate. The variable Y does not seem to have an analogue in point particle theories. It indicates the possibility that the baryon is itself a stringy states which appears particle-like only at long wave lengths. One wonders whether these remarks on stringy solitons have any bearing to those in [9].

References

[1] *The Large N Expansion in Quantum Field Theory and Statistical Physics: From Spin Systems to 2-Dimensional Gravity*, Eds. E. Brezin and S.R. Wadia (World Scientific 1993).

[2] G. 'tHooft, Nucl. Phys. **B72** (1974) 461.

[3] A. Dhar, G. Mandal and S.R. Wadia, Mod. Phys. Lett. **A7** (1992) 3129; A. Dhar, G. Mandal and S.R. Wadia, Mod. Phys. Lett. **A8** (1993) 3557.

[4] A. Dhar, G. Mandal and S.R. Wadia, Phys. Lett. **B329** (1994) 15.

[5] G. 'tHooft, Nucl. Phys. **B75** (1974) 461.

[6] See W.A. Bardeen, I. Bars, A.J. Hanson and R.D. Peccei, Phys. Rev. **D13** (1975) 2364, where the 'tHooft spectrum is derived starting from an open Nambu-Goto type string whose essential dynamics is at the end-points.

[7] E. Witten, Nucl. Phys. **B160** (1979) 57.

[8] S.H. Shenker, in Proceedings of the Cargese Workshop in *Random Surfaces, Quantum Gravity and Strings 1990*, Eds. O. Alvarez, E. Marinari and P. Windey.

[9] J.P. Gauntlet and J.A. Harvey, EFI–94–36, hep-th/9407111.

Paper presented at XXVII Int. Conf. on High Energy Physics: Session Pa-19
Glasgow, UK, 20–27 July 1994

Anomaly Cancellations and String Symmetries
in the Effective Field Theory

Jean-Pierre Derendinger

Institut de Physique, Université de Neuchâtel,
A. L. Breguet 1, 2000 Neuchâtel, Switzerland

Abstract

This contribution briefly describes some developments of the use of string symmetries and anomaly cancellation mechanisms to include string loop corrections in the construction of the low-energy effective supergravity of superstrings.

1. Effective field theory

The purpose of the effective low-energy field theory is to describe the dynamics of massless string modes in the low-energy domain where string massive states have only virtual effects. This energy range can be characterized by an ultraviolet physical cutoff M_{uv}, which is smaller than the lightest massive mode of the string theory. The effective field theory is specified by a local lagrangian density, a Wilson effective lagrangian $\mathcal{L}_{eff}$. In string perturbation theory which is not expected to lead to spontaneous breaking of supersymmetry[†], the effective low-energy field theory of a superstring will be a $N = 1$ supergravity.

Consider a certain amplitude $\mathcal{A}(p_1, p_2, \ldots)$ for a physical process involving only massless external string modes, computed in string perturbation theory:

$$\mathcal{A}(p_1, p_2, \ldots) = \sum_{L \geq 0} \mathcal{A}^{(L)}(p_1, p_2, \ldots), \qquad (1)$$

where L is the string loop order. Its arguments are external momenta, helicity or internal quantum numbers attached to the external states and also parameters which must be introduced to define string perturbation theory. For instance, the presence of massless modes requires the introduction of an infrared

cutoff Λ to regulate loops. This arbitrary scale parameter may be identified with the ultraviolet cutoff M_{uv} of the effective field theory, but this is not necessary. In the limit where all energies and momenta in (1) are small compared with M_{uv}, it is expected that (1) is reproduced by the same amplitude computed perturbatively in the quantum field theory defined by the effective lagrangian $\mathcal{L}_{eff}$. In correspondance with expansion (1), this effective lagrangian will have a formal expansion in string-loop order:

$$\mathcal{L}_{eff} = \sum_{k \geq 0} \mathcal{L}_{eff}^{(k)}. \qquad (2)$$

At string tree-level in (1) ($L = 0$) and in the low-energy limit, the amplitude $\mathcal{A}^{(0)}(p_1, p_2, \ldots)$ can be obtained using the tree-level effective lagrangian $\mathcal{L}_{eff}^{(0)}$ in which the effect of massive string modes is hidden in non-renormalisable interactions. At this order, $\mathcal{A}^{(0)}$ and $\mathcal{L}_{eff}^{(0)}$ do not depend on Λ and the amplitude $\mathcal{A}^{(0)}(p_1, p_2, \ldots)$ is the sum of all tree diagrams obtained with $\mathcal{L}_{eff}^{(0)}$. The knowledge of string tree amplitudes allows then in principle to construct $\mathcal{L}_{eff}^{(0)}$.

In the low-energy limit, the string one-loop contribution to (1), $\mathcal{A}^{(1)}(p_1, p_2, \ldots)$, corresponds in the effective field theory to two classes of contributions. Firstly, the sum of the relevant one-loop diagrams obtained using $\mathcal{L}_{eff}^{(0)}$ only. Secondly, the new

[†] For a discussion of the status of supersymmetry breaking in superstrings, see the contribution by D. Lüst [1]

interactions described by $\mathcal{L}_{eff}^{(1)}$, which are formally already "string one-loop", lead to a number of tree diagrams generated by $\mathcal{L}_{eff}^{(0)} + \mathcal{L}_{eff}^{(1)}$ and containing one vertex present in $\mathcal{L}_{eff}^{(1)}$. Since $\mathcal{A}^{(1)}$ will depend on the infrared cutoff Λ, the effective lagrangian will also depend on Λ starting with the one-loop term $\mathcal{L}_{eff}^{(1)}$.

In general, a Feynman diagram of the effective lagrangian (2) with ℓ loops will have a "string-loop-order" given by adding to ℓ the orders of all vertices, as defined by the expansion (2). Summing all diagrams up to "string-loop-order" L_{max} will provide the low-energy limit of the amplitude (1) computed up to L_{max} string loops.

2.　String gauge symmetries and anomalies

An important help in the construction of the effective field theory $\mathcal{L}_{eff}$ is provided by string symmetries which leave a physical amplitude like (1) invariant at each order of string perturbation theory. These symmetries strongly constrain the form of the effective lagrangian, even if they are not in general symmetries of $\mathcal{L}_{eff}$, which is not a physical object. At string tree-level, the invariance of $\mathcal{A}^{(0)}$ implies the invariance of $\mathcal{L}_{eff}^{(0)}$. In general however, this symmetry of $\mathcal{L}_{eff}^{(0)}$ can be anomalous: some one-loop diagrams which contribute to the effective description of $\mathcal{A}^{(1)}$ do not respect the symmetry. Then, the invariance of $\mathcal{A}^{(1)}$ imposes that the effective contributions generated by $\mathcal{L}_{eff}^{(1)}$ cancel the one-loop anomaly and restore the string symmetry. Since the knowledge of $\mathcal{L}_{eff}^{(0)}$ is sufficient to compute the one-loop anomalous diagrams, the requirement of anomaly cancellation gives a strong constraint on the form of $\mathcal{L}_{eff}^{(1)}$. In some cases, the anomaly-cancellation condition is strong enough to determine completely the one-loop terms $\mathcal{L}_{eff}^{(1)}$. This procedure can be in principle pursued order by order, except if the existence of non-renormalisation theorems (similar to the Adler-Bardeen theorem) terminates the argument at the one-loop order.

Green and Schwarz [2] found the first example of string symmetries realized in this "anomaly-cancellation mode" in ten-dimensional (heterotic or type I) superstrings, which possess space-time [the Lorentz group $SO(1,9)$] and gauge [$E_8 \times E_8$ or $SO(32)$] symmetries. Both symmetries are anomalous in the tree-level effective lagrangian and their restoration requires specific contributions in $\mathcal{L}_{eff}^{(1)}$. The argument can be summarized as follows, considering for simplicity gauge symmetries only.

1) The theory contains massless fermions, described by Majorana-Weyl spinors, which couple chirally to gauge fields. The effective tree-level lagrangian generates then chiral gauge anomalies through one-loop anomalous diagrams with six external gauge fields. The formal expression of the anomaly factorises for gauge groups $E_8 \times E_8$ and $SO(32)$, a necessary requirement to be able to cancel it.

2) The theory also contains an antisymmetric tensor field $b_{\mu\nu} = -b_{\nu\mu}$. In the tree-level effective lagrangian $\mathcal{L}_{eff}^{(0)}$, this field appears through its gauge invariant curl

$$H_{\mu\nu\rho} = \partial_{[\mu} b_{\nu\rho]} - \frac{\kappa}{\sqrt{2}} \omega_{\mu\nu\rho}, \qquad (3)$$

involving the gauge Chern-Simons form $\omega_{\mu\nu\rho}$ suitably normalised. The tree-level lagrangian contains a term proportional to $H_{\mu\nu\rho} H^{\mu\nu\rho}$, and then an interaction of the form

$$\partial^{\mu} b^{\nu\rho} \omega_{\mu\nu\rho}, \qquad (4)$$

which couples $b_{\mu\nu}$ to two gauge fields.

3) The one-loop contribution $\mathcal{L}_{eff}^{(1)}$ will contain precisely the terms necessary to cancel the gauge anomaly: a coupling of $b_{\mu\nu}$ with four gauge fields, and a contact interaction involving six gauge fields. These terms in $\mathcal{L}_{eff}^{(1)}$ have to be gauge variant, and their variation is specified by the chiral anomaly computed using the tree-level lagrangian. The sum $\mathcal{L}_{eff}^{(0)} + \mathcal{L}_{eff}^{(1)}$ is then gauge non invariant.

In four dimensions, only $U(1)$ gauge symmetries can be realised in the anomaly-cancellation mode: only abelian (or mixed abelian–nonabelian) chiral anomalies factorise. Gauge anomaly cancellation can then only appear in string vacua with gauge groups containing at least a $U(1)$ factor. The cancellation mechanism, described by Dine, Seiberg and Witten [3], is closely analogous to ten-dimensional case mentioned above. The same coupling (4) is present at tree-level. To cancel the gauge anomaly, $\mathcal{L}_{eff}^{(1)}$ contains in particular a gauge-variant term of the form

$$b_{\mu\nu} \partial^{\mu} A^{\nu}$$

(A_{μ} is the abelian gauge field), and the chiral anomaly generated by the triangle diagram is cancelled using the exchange of the antisymmetric tensor. The one-loop contribution $\mathcal{L}_{eff}^{(1)}$ plays the rôle of a Fayet-Iliopoulos term which gives a mass to the abelian vector multiplet removing the anomalous $U(1)$ symmetry from the low-energy symmetry content of the model.

The global supersymmetrization of this anomaly cancellation mechanism is very simply described using a linear multiplet [4, 5], which contains the antisymmetric tensor $b_{\mu\nu}$, a real scalar and a Majorana spinor. The real linear superfield L is defined by the supersymmetric constraints $\mathcal{D}DL = \overline{\mathcal{D}D}L = 0$. A supersymmetric lagrangian generalizing the expressions (3) and (4) is

$$\int d^4\theta \, F(L - \Omega), \qquad (5)$$

omitting the explicit dependence on chiral superfields and superpotential terms. Ω is the supersymmetric generalisation of the Chern-Simons form and the superfield $L - \Omega$ contains (3). Gauge invariance requires

$$\delta L = \delta \Omega. \tag{6}$$

In general, Ω is a fixed linear combination of the Chern-Simons forms of all factors of the gauge group, which is supposed to contain an anomalous $U(1)$ factor [with superfield $\tilde{V}$]. The chiral anomaly can be represented by the non-local expression

$$c \int d^2\theta \, WW \, \mathcal{P}_L \tilde{V} + h.c., \tag{7}$$

where $\mathcal{P}_L$ is the chiral (non-local) projector and W is the chiral gauge curvature superfield. Since $\delta \tilde{V} = \Lambda + \overline{\Lambda}$, its gauge variation is

$$c \int d^2\theta \, WW \Lambda + h.c. = -\frac{c}{4} \int d^4\theta \, (\Lambda + \overline{\Lambda})\Omega,$$

using simple identities. The one-loop contribution to the effective lagrangian which cancels this anomaly is then clearly of the form

$$-\frac{c}{4} \int d^4\theta \, (L - \Omega)\tilde{V}, \tag{8}$$

the introduction of L being necessary to avoid unwanted non-abelian anomalies. This superfield expression contains the required coupling proportional to $b_{\mu\nu}\partial^\mu \tilde{V}^\nu$. The one-loop corrected effective lagrangien is then

$$\mathcal{L}_{eff} = \int d^4\theta \left[F(L - \Omega) - \frac{c}{4}(L - \Omega)\tilde{V} \right], \tag{9}$$

omitting superpotential terms. The supergravity generalisation of this globally supersymmetric lagrangian is, in the superconformal formalism,

$$\mathcal{L}_{eff} = \left[S_0 \overline{S}_0 F \left(\frac{L - \Omega}{S_0 \overline{S}_0} \right) - \frac{c}{4}(L - \Omega)\tilde{V} \right]_D, \tag{10}$$

where S_0 is the chiral compensating multiplet (this is "old minimal supergravity") and $[\ldots]_D$ denotes the real vector density formula of superconformal tensor calculus.

It is well known that the antisymmetric tensor can be transformed into a pseudoscalar with a duality transformation. Its supersymmetric version, which will be discussed in the last section, transforms the linear multiplet into a chiral one.

3. Kähler symmetry

The coupling of a chiral matter–super-Yang-Mills system to supergravity is naturally invariant under Kähler transformations. In the superconformal approach, the lagrangian density is [6]

$$\mathcal{L} = \left[S_0 \overline{S}_0 e^{-\mathcal{K}/3} \right]_D + [S_0^3 \omega + fWW]_F, \tag{11}$$

where the Kähler potential $\mathcal{K}(\Sigma, \overline{\Sigma}e^V)$ is a real function of the chiral multiplets Σ, and the introduction of the gauge vector multiplet V ensures gauge invariance of the theory. W is the gauge curvature chiral multiplet and the function f which appears in the chiral density $[\ldots]_F$ is a holomorphic fonction of Σ. Gauge transformations, with chiral parameter Λ act according to

$$\Sigma \longrightarrow e^{i\Lambda}\Sigma, \qquad \overline{\Sigma} \longrightarrow \overline{\Sigma}e^{-i\overline{\Lambda}}, \qquad e^V \longrightarrow e^{i\overline{\Lambda}}e^V e^{-i\Lambda}, \tag{12}$$

so that $\overline{\Sigma}e^V \Sigma$ is gauge invariant.

The theory (11) is invariant under the Kähler transformation

$$\begin{cases} \omega & \longrightarrow \quad e^{-\varphi(\Sigma)}\omega \\ S_0 & \longrightarrow \quad e^{\varphi(\Sigma)/3}S_0 \\ \mathcal{K} & \longrightarrow \quad \mathcal{K} + \varphi(\Sigma) + \overline{\varphi}(\overline{\Sigma}) \end{cases}, \tag{13}$$

V, W and f being unaffected. This Kähler transformation is a formal symmetry which indicates that the lagrangian (11) only depends on the function

$$\mathcal{G} = \mathcal{K} + \log \omega\overline{\omega} \tag{14}$$

[choose $\varphi = \log \omega$ in (13)]. Notice that the quantity $\overline{S}_0 e^{-\mathcal{K}/3}$, which appears in the lagrangian (13), is analogous to the argument $\overline{\Sigma}e^V$ of $\mathcal{K}$ itself. Also the Kähler invariant combination $S_0 \overline{S}_0 e^{-\mathcal{K}/3}$ is similar to the gauge invariant $\overline{\Sigma}e^V \Sigma$. The function $\mathcal{K}$ is then a Kähler connection in the same way as V is the gauge connection. $\mathcal{K}$ is a composite multiplet which enters algebraically in lagrangian (13). Since the theory (13) is both Kähler and gauge invariant, the composite Kähler connection will appear in fermion covariant derivatives, together with gauge potentials (in V) and also sigma-model covariantization of kinetic terms.

It is then natural to consider potential anomalies of Kähler symmetry, or more generally of sigma-model local symmetries [7, 8]. The supersymmetric formalism sketched in the previous section translates directly to these cases. For instance, a Kähler anomaly would correspond to the chiral F-density

$$c_K \left[WW\mathcal{P}_L K \right]_F \tag{15}$$

(c_K is a numerical coefficient), replacing $\tilde{V}$ in(7) by the Kähler connection $\mathcal{K}$. And the effective lagrangian for the theory with the linear multiplet including the anomaly-cancelling Green-Schwarz one-loop term is [8,

9]:

$$\mathcal{L}_{eff} = \mathcal{L}_{eff}^{(0)} + \mathcal{L}_{eff}^{(1)},$$

$$\mathcal{L}_{eff}^{(0)} = [(L-\Omega)F(X,\ldots)]_D , \quad (16)$$
$$X = (L-\Omega)e^{\mathcal{K}/3}(S_0\overline{S}_0)^{-1}$$

$$\mathcal{L}_{eff}^{(1)} = -\tfrac{1}{4}c_K[(L-\Omega)\mathcal{K}]_D ,$$

omitting again the superpotential. The tree-level lagrangian $\mathcal{L}_{eff}^{(0)}$ is written in a Kähler invariant form: the variable X is invariant and the dots denote a possible dependence on other invariant functions of the chiral multiplets.

Kähler symmetry is a property of supergravity couplings. In the superconformal approach, it is directly related to the chiral internal $U(1)$ part of the conformal superalgebra. Its relation with superstrings has to do with the fact that certain string symmetries act on the massless fields of the effective theory with Kähler transformations. An example is target-space duality in $(2,2)$ orbifolds or Calabi-Yau strings. Considering a idealized model with a unique $(1,1)$ modulus T, the Kähler connection for this modulus would be

$$\mathcal{K}_T = -3\log(T+\overline{T}).$$

Target-space duality acts on T according to

$$T \longrightarrow \frac{aT-ib}{icT+d}, \qquad ad-bc=1.$$

On the connection,

$$\mathcal{K}_T \longrightarrow \mathcal{K}_T + 3\log|icT+d|^2,$$

which is a particular Kähler transformation. A Kähler anomaly would then also be a target-space duality anomaly, and the fact that target-space duality is a quantum string symmetry implies that the effective lagrangian should include anomaly-cancelling terms of the form introduced in (16).

The component expansion of the loop-corrected effective lagrangian (16) contains, besides the anomaly-cancelling terms, corrections to the gauge kinetic terms which depend on the Kähler connection. A string one-loop computation of gauge kinetic terms [i.e. a string amplitude (1) with two external gauge fields and an arbitrary number of moduli] is then able to directly establish the existence of the quantum correction $\mathcal{L}_{eff}^{(1)}$. This calculation of threshold corrections, performed in the context of $(2,2)$ symmetric orbifolds [10] (see also [11, 12]), has in fact been at the origin of the use of Kähler anomaly cancellation for loop-corrected effective supergravities, as developed in ref. [8]. It should however be mentioned that the inclusion of the

complete set of (untwisted) moduli present in generic $(2,2)$ symmetric orbifold, as in [10] and [8], leads to a situation more complicated than the simple example considered here†.

4. Axion–antisymmetric tensor duality

We have up to now discussed anomaly cancellation using the linear multiplet. This is a natural approach since the Chern-Simons form is the crucial object in this mechanism and gauge invariance of the tree-level effective lagrangian associates the Chern-Simons form with the antisymmetric tensor, as in (3). As already mentioned, duality can always be used to transform the antisymmetric tensor into a pseudoscalar or the linear superfield into a chiral one. Suppose for instance that we want to apply duality to lagrangian (5). This theory is equivalent with

$$\int d^4\theta \left[F(U)-(S+\overline{S})(U+\Omega)\right], \quad (17)$$

where U is a real vector superfield and S is chiral. The equation of motion for S indicates that $U+\Omega$ is linear, and hence (17) and (5) are equivalent. Or solving the equation of motion for U,

$$\frac{\partial}{\partial U}F(U) = S+\overline{S}, \quad (18)$$

allows to express U as a function of $S+\overline{S}$ and leads to the equivalent theory

$$\int d^4\theta \left[F(U)-(S+\overline{S})U\right]_{U=U(S+\overline{S})}$$
$$+\tfrac{1}{4}\left(\int d^2\theta\, SWW + h.c.\right) \quad (19)$$
$$\equiv \int d^4\theta\, G(S+\overline{S}) + \frac{1}{4}\left(\int d^2\theta\, SWW + h.c.\right).$$

The comparison of (5) and (9) shows immediately that the addition of the abelian gauge anomaly cancelling term in the one-loop effective lagrangian is equivalent to the substitution

$$G(S+\overline{S}) \longrightarrow G(S+\overline{S}+\tfrac{c}{4}\tilde{V}) \quad (20)$$

in eq. (19), as observed in ref. [3]. The case of Kähler anomaly is similar. The chiral theory dual to $\mathcal{L}_{eff}^{(0)}$ in eq. (16) is

$$[UF(X_U,\ldots)-(S+\overline{S})U]_D + \tfrac{1}{4}[SWW]_D ,$$
$$X_U = Ue^{\mathcal{K}/3}(S_0\overline{S}_0)^{-1}, \quad (21)$$

† See also [13], [14] and [15].

where U is the function of $S + \overline{S}$ such that

$$\frac{\partial}{\partial U} U F(X_U, \ldots) = S + \overline{S}.$$

The loop correction $\mathcal{L}_{eff}^{(1)}$ in (16) corresponds then to the substitution

$$S + \overline{S} \quad \longrightarrow \quad S + \overline{S} + \frac{1}{4} c_K \mathcal{K}. \tag{22}$$

Notice however that the duality transformation does not respect the string loop expansion of the effective Wilson lagrangian. The expansion (2), which has been applied in the linear multiplet formalism, is resummed by the duality transformation of the linear multiplet L into the chiral superfield S. This observation suggests that the formal equivalence of L and S does not necessarily mean that the choice of formulating the effective theory of superstrings either with S or with L is indifferent. Expansion (2) could apply to one version of the theory only, which would then allow for an easier and more natural field theory interpretation of physical quantities computed in string perturbation theory.

The calculations performed in $(2, 2)$ string models suggest that the fields contained in the linear multiplet are in closer relationship to string physical parameters. More precisely, a study of the E_8 sector of some $(2, 2)$ orbifolds [16, 9] shows that the scalar component C of the linear multiplet is directly related to the renormalised, physical E_8 gauge coupling constant g_Γ:

$$\frac{1}{\kappa^2 \langle C \rangle} - \frac{C(E_8)}{16\pi^2} = \frac{1}{g_\Gamma^2} \tag{23}$$

$[C(E_8) = 30$ is the E_8 quadratic Casimir]. On the other hand, the scalar component s of the chiral multiplet S is related to the bare, unphysical gauge coupling constant appearing in the Wilson effective lagrangian $\mathcal{L}_{eff}$, in the term

$$-\frac{1}{4} \frac{1}{g_W^2} F_{\mu\nu}^A F^{A \, \mu\nu}.$$

Then,

$$\frac{1}{2} \langle s + \overline{s} \rangle = \frac{1}{g_W^2}. \tag{24}$$

Duality can then be viewed as a transformation from bare to physical quantities, or as a renormalisation-group transformation from some unified string coupling to a low-energy running coupling.

More realistic theories need however to be considered in order to decide of the choice of the most appropriate set of low-energy fields, which would provide the most natural interpretation of string perturbative calculations. This is also needed to decide whether the linear multiplet is of special interest in the discussion of superstring effective supergravities.

References

[1] D. Lüst, these proceedings.
[2] M.B. Green and J.H. Schwarz, Phys. Lett. **B149** (1984) 117.
[3] M. Dine, N. Seiberg and E. Witten, Nucl. Phys. **B289** (1987) 589.
[4] S. Ferrara, J. Wess and B. Zumino, Phys. Lett. **B51** (1974) 239.
[5] W. Siegel, Phys. Lett. **B85** (1979) 333.
[6] E. Cremmer, S. Ferrara, L. Girardello and A. Van Proeyen, Nucl. Phys. **B212** (19883) 413.
[7] G.L. Cardoso and B.A. Ovrut, Nucl. Phys. **B369** (1992) 351; and Nucl. Phys. **B392** (1993) 315.
[8] J.-P. Derendinger, S. Ferrara, C. Kounnas and F. Zwirner, Nucl. Phys. **B372** (1992) 145.
[9] J.-P. Derendinger, F. Quevedo and M. Quirós, preprint: NEIP–93–007, IEM–FT–83/94 (hepth-9402007); to appear in Nucl. Phys. **B** .
[10] L. Dixon, V.S. Kaplunovsky and J. Louis, Nucl. Phys. **B355** (1991) 649.
[11] I. Antoniadis, K.S. Narain and T.R. Taylor, Phys. Lett. **B267** (1991) 37;
I. Antoniadis, E. Gava and K.S. Narain, Phys. Lett. **B283** (1992) 209; and Nucl. Phys. **B383** (1992) 93;
I. Antoniadis, E. Gava, K.S. Narain and T.R. Taylor, Nucl. Phys. **B413** (1994) 162.
[12] P. Mayr and S. Stieberger, Nucl. Phys. **B407** (1993) 725; and Nucl. Phys. **B412** (1994) 502.
[13] J. Louis, in *Particles, Strings and Cosmology*, p.751; Eds. P. Nath and S. Reucroft (World Scientific 1992).
[14] J.-P. Derendinger, in *Particles, Strings and Cosmology*, p.766; Eds. P. Nath and S. Reucroft, (World Scientific 1992).
[15] D. Lüst and L.E. Ibáñez, Nucl. Phys. **B382** (1992) 305.
[16] J.-P. Derendinger, S. Ferrara, C. Kounnas and F. Zwirner, Phys. Lett. **B271** (1991) 307.

Paper presented at XXVII Int. Conf. on High Energy Physics: Session Pa-19
Glasgow, UK, 20–27 July 1994

Duality Symmetries and Supersymmetry Breaking in String Compactifications*

G. Lopes Cardoso[†], D. Lüst[†] and T. Mohaupt[$]

† Humboldt Universität zu Berlin, Institut für Physik, D-10099 Berlin
$ DESY-IfH Zeuthen, Platanenallee 6, D-15738 Zeuthen

Abstract

We discuss some aspects of spontaneous supersymetry breaking whitin the low-energy effective supergravity action of four-dimensional superstrings

1. Introduction

Based on theoretical motivations, in particular the so-called hierarchy problem, and stimulated by some indirect experimental hints, like coupling constant unification and the top quark mass, the minimal supersymmetric standard model (MSSM) was extensively discussed during the last years. Unfortunately, the necessary violation of supersymmetry has to be put in by hand into the MSSM and is described by the socalled soft supersymmetry breaking parameters (SSBP) like the gaugino masses etc. For reasons of simplicity these SSBP were assumed in most of the phenomenological discussions to be universal for all different gauginos and also for the various matter fields. For some SSBP, a possible deviation from universality is severely constrained by phenomenological requirements like the absence a flavor changing neutral currents [1].

On the other hand, superstring theories are a very promising candidate for a consistent quantization of gravity. For this purpose, the typical string scale has to be identified with the Planck mass M_P of order 10^{19} GeV. Therefore one strongly hopes that superstrings may solve some puzzles concerning quantum physics at M_P. Now for the actual relevance of superstring theories it is of most vital importance to make direct contact to the standard model (SM) or perhaps better to the MSSM. This programm attracted a lot of attention

during the last 10 years, and the results of this research are, at least conceptually, quite successful. Indeed, the low energy effective lagrangian of a large class of four-dimensional heterotic string theories is just given by the standard $N = 1$ supergravity action with gauge group potentially containing the gauge group of the SM and with matter coming very near to the three chiral families of the SM. Deriving the effective string action, it is very important to realize that the low energy spectrum and the low energy effective interactions among the almost massless fields are to some extent controlled by the stringy symmetries which are still reminiscent after integrating out the infinite number of massive modes. A particular nice example of this kind are the well established duality symmetries (for a review see [2]) which proved to provide useful information about the effective string action on general grounds.

A very attractive feature of $N = 1$ supergravity in general is the fact that upon spontaneous supersymmetry breaking in some hidden sector of the theory the SSBP in the observable sector automatically emerge due to gravitational couplings among observable and hidden fields. Thus in string theory the SSBP are, at least in principle, calculable from first principles. However at the moment, the actual mechanism of supersymmetry breaking is far from being completely understood. However recently it was demonstrated [3, 4, 5, 6, 7] that, parametrizing the SSBP without specifying the actual supersymmetry breaking mechanism, some interesting

---

* Talk presented by D. Lüst

generic features of supersymmetry breaking in superstring theories can be derived. In particular it turned out that the SSBP are generically non-universal.

This contribution will be organized as follows: first we will set up the general formalism of supersymmetry breaking in $N = 1$ supergravity with special emphasis on the structure of the SSBP in four-dimensional strings. As more specific examples we will then present some results for Abelian orbifolds.

2. $N = 1$ effective supergravity action for four-dimensional heterotic strings

Let us first specify the string modes with masses small compared to M_P which we assume to appear in the effective action. First there is the $N = 1$ supergravity multiplet containing the graviton field and the spin $\frac{3}{2}$ gravitino. Next, the gauge degrees of freedom are described by $N = 1$ vector multiplets V_a with spin 1 gauge bosons and Spin $\frac{1}{2}$ gauginos λ_a. The gauge index a is assumed to range over the SM gauge group $SU(3) \times SU(2) \times U(1)$ and an unspecified hidden gauge group G_{hid}. Finally we consider chiral matter multiplets Φ^I with complex scalars and spin $\frac{1}{2}$ Weyl fermions. These chiral fields, i.e. the index I, separate into socalled matter fields Q^α which contain the matter of the MSSM, $Q^\alpha_{SM} = (q, l, H_1, H_2)$, and matter which only transforms non-trivilly under G_{hid}, Q^α_{hid}. The second type of chiral fields Φ^I correspond to the socalled moduli fields M^i whose vacuum expextation values (VEV's) are undetermined in perturbation theory since the M^i correspond to the free parameters of the four-dimensional string models. The moduli are assumed to be SM singlets (however note that H_1 and H_2 could be in principle moduli). The duality group Γ acts on the moduli M^i as discrete reparametrizations, $M^i \rightarrow \tilde{M}^i(M^i)$, which leave the underlying four-dimensional string theory invariant. Therefore, the effective action of the massless field must be Γ invariant which provides a link between L_{eff} and the theory of Γ-modular functions [8]. Moreover strong restrictions on the massless spectrum arise [3] due to the required absence of potential duality anomalies.

The effective $N = 1$ supergravity action, up to two space-time derivatives, is specified by three different functions of the chiral fields Φ^I [9]. First, the Kähler potential K is a gauge-invariant real analytic function of the chiral superfields. To compute later on the SSBP it is enough to expand K up to quadratic order in the matter fields:

$$K = K_0(M, \bar{M}) + K_{\alpha\bar{\beta}}(M, \bar{M})Q^\alpha \bar{Q}^{\bar{\beta}} + (\frac{1}{2}H_{\alpha\beta}Q^\alpha Q^\beta + h.c.)$$

$$(1)$$

Note that for SM matter fields the last term in eq.(1) can be non-vanshing only for a mixing term of the two

Higgs fields: $(\frac{1}{2}H_{12}(M, \bar{M})H_1 H_2 + h.c.)$. K_0 is just the Kähler potential of the Kählerian moduli space $\mathcal{K}_0$. Γ-duality transformations act as Kähler transformations on K, $K \rightarrow K + g(M) + \bar{g}(\bar{M})$ ($g(M)$ is a holomorphic function of the moduli), and induce a 'rotation' on the matter fields, $Q^\alpha \rightarrow h_{\alpha\beta}(M)Q^\beta$.

Next we consider the moduli dependent effective gauge couplings $g_a(M, \bar{M})$:

$$g_a^{-2}(M, \bar{M}) = Re\, f_a(M) - \frac{1}{16\pi^2}\Big((C(G_a) - \sum_\alpha T_a(\alpha))$$

$$K_0(M, \bar{M}) + 2\sum_\alpha T_a(\alpha) \log \det K_{\alpha\bar{\beta}}(M, \bar{M}) \Big).$$

$$(2)$$

$C(G_a)$ is the quadratic Casimir of the gauge group G_a and $T_a(\alpha)$ the index of the massless matter representations. The holomorphic gauge kinetic function $f_a(M)$ includes the tree level moduli dependence as well as possible one-loop quantum corrections from massive modes; however beyond one loop the are no perturbative corrections to $f_a(M)$ [10]. The non-holomorphic terms in eq.(2) originate from one-loop corrections involving massless fields. Specifically, these terms describe the presence of Kähler as well as σ-model anomalies [11, 12]. $g_a(M, \bar{M})$ has to be a duality invariant function. Therefore the duality non-invariance of the non-holomorphic anomaly terms has to be cancelled by a non-trivial transformation behaviour of $f_a(M)$: $f_a(M) \rightarrow f_a(M) + \frac{1}{8\pi^2}((C(G_a) - \sum T_a(\alpha))g(M) - \frac{1}{4\pi^2}\sum T_a(\alpha) \log \det h_{\alpha\beta}(M)$.

Third the superpotential will be conveniently split into a SUSY-preserving tree-level part and into a SUSY-breaking piece which does not depend on the matter fields: $W = W_{tree}(Q, M) + W_{SUSY-breaking}(M)$. Duality invariance of the effective action demands that W transforms as $W \rightarrow e^{-g(M)}W$. The structure of W_{tree} is such that it generates the moduli-dependent Yukawa couplings for the matter fields as well as possible moduli-dependent mass terms for some hidden matter fields; the observed matter fields are assumed to stay massless for all values of the moduli fields: $W_{tree} = \frac{1}{3}h_{\alpha\beta\gamma}(M^i)Q^\alpha Q^\beta Q^\gamma + \frac{1}{3}h_{i\alpha\beta}(M^i)Q^\alpha_{hid}Q^\beta_{hid}$. Thus it may happen that at some points in the moduli space, $h_{i\alpha\beta}(M^i) = 0$, there are additional massless hidden matter fields. Very often they go together with additional massless gauge bosons at these points.

Essentially, there are two very promising mechanisms of supersymmetry breaking in the last years' literature. First at tree level by the socalled Scherk-Schwarz mechanism [13]. This can be described in the effective field theory by a tree-level superpotential. Second supersymmetry can be broken due to non-perturbative effects. Unfortunately it is not possible at the moment to caluclate these non-perturbative effects directly in string theory. However, let us assume that non-perturbative field theory effects give a dominant contribution to the spontaneous breaking of supersymmetry. In particular, one can show that non-perturbative gaugino condensation in the hidden gauge sector potentially breaks supersymmetry [14]. Integrating out the dynamical degrees of freedom corresoponding to the gaugino bound states, the duality invariant [15, 16] gaugino condensation can be described by an effective non-perturbative superpotential, which depends holomorphically on the moduli fields: $W_{SUSY-breaking}(M) = e^{\frac{24\pi^2}{b_a}f_a(M)}$ (b_a is the $N = 1$ β-function coefficient). It is remarkable that this expression is in a sense exact since $f_a(M)$ is only renormalized up to one loop. It is this exactness of $W_{SUSY-breaking}$ which provides very strong confidence in the applicability of the used method.

Now let us discuss the form of the SSBP in the effective action which arise after the spontaneous breaking of local supersymmetry. This discussion will not refer to the actual (perturbative or non-perturbative) breaking mechanism; nevertheless some interesting information about these couplings can be obtained at the end. The scalar potential in the low-energy supergravity action has the form [9] $V = |W_{SUSY-breaking}(M)|^2 e^{K_0}(G^i G_i - 3)$. ($e^G = |W|^2 e^K$, $G_I = \frac{\partial G}{\partial \phi_I}$.) Deriving this formula we have assumed that, upon minimization of V, $< G_\alpha >= 0$ and $< Q_\alpha >= 0$ in the matter sector. This assumption, which is satisfied in most realistic scenarios, means that the spontaneous supersymmetry breaking takes places in the moduli sector, i.e. $< G_i > \neq 0$ for at least one of the moduli fields. Then the gravitino mass becomes $m_{3/2} = e^{K_0(M,\bar{M})/2}|W_{SUSY-breaking}(M)|$. $m_{3/2}$ should be of order TeV; thus the smallness of this scale compared to M_P must come either from the Kähler potential and/or from the superpotential. Now we obtain the following SSBP: first the gaugino masses take the form

$$m_a(M\,\bar{M}) = \frac{1}{2}m_{3/2}G^i(M,\bar{M})\partial_i \log g_a^{-2}(M,\bar{M}). \quad (3)$$

The scalar masses (squarks and sleptons) become [4]

$$m^2_{\alpha\bar{\beta}} = m^2_{3/2}[K_{\alpha\bar{\beta}}(M,\bar{M}) - G^i(M,\bar{M})G^{\bar{j}}(M,\bar{M})R_{i\bar{j}\alpha\bar{\beta}}].$$
$$(4)$$

($R_{i\bar{j}\alpha\bar{\beta}} = \partial_i\bar{\partial}_j K_{\alpha\bar{\beta}} - \Gamma^\gamma_{i\alpha}K_{\gamma\bar{\delta}}\bar{\Gamma}^{\bar{\delta}}_{\bar{j}\bar{\beta}}$, $\Gamma^\gamma_{i\alpha} = K^{\gamma\bar{\delta}}\partial_i K_{\alpha\bar{\gamma}}$. These parameters are generically of the order of $m_{3/2}$. Their exact values depend on the details of K, W and the (dynamically fixed) VEV's of the moduli fields. It is quite evident that in general these SSBP are non-universal [3]. The non-universality arises due to the non-universal moduli dependence of the gauge couplings and the matter kinetic energies. Similar expression can be also obtained for the trilinear couplings [17, 4, 5]

Finally let us investigate the possible apperance of a mass mixing term for the two standard model Higgs fields H_1, H_2 which is necesary for the correct radiative breaking of the electro-weak gauge symmetry. Clearly, a tree-level mixing due to a quadratic term in the superpotential, $W_{tree} = \mu H_1 H_2$, would be a desaster, since it will be most likely of the order of M_P. (This is often called the μ-problem.) However, if there exist [18] a possible, holomorphic mixing term H_{12} among H_1 and H_2 in the tree-level Kähler potential (see eq.(1)), then an effective μ-term will be generated after the spontaneous breaking of supersymmetry: $W_{eff} = \hat{\mu}H_1 H_2$, $\hat{\mu} = m_{3/2}[H_{12}(M,\bar{M}) - G^{\bar{i}}\partial_{\bar{i}}H_{12}(M,\bar{M})]$.

3. Abelian orbifolds

In this chapter we want to apply our previous formulas to the case of Abelian orbifold compactifications [19]. Every orbifold of this type has three complex 'planes', and each orbifold twist $\vec{\theta} = \theta_i$ (i=1,2,3) acts either simultaneously on two or all three planes. Generically, for all four-dimensional strings there exist as moduli fields the dilaton (D) – axion (a) chiral multiplet $S = e^D + ia$. Then the tree-level Kähler potential for the S-field has the form $K_0 = -\log(S + \bar{S})$.

Next we consider the internal moduli of the orbifold compactification. We will concentrate on the untwisted moduli fields. For each Abelian orbifold there exist at least three Kähler class moduli T_i each associated to one of the three complex planes. We will call the T_i (2,2) moduli, since they do not destroy a possible (2,2) superconformal structure of the underlying string theory, i.e. their VEV's do not break the (2,2) gauge group $E_6 \times E_8$. Next we consider socalled (0,2) untwisted moduli which are generically present in any orbifold compactification. A non-vanishing VEV for these kind of fields destroys the (2,2) world sheet supersymmetry and breaks $E_6 \times E_8$ to some non-Abelian subgroup. In addition they will generically give mass to some matter fields by a superpotential coupling. Specifically these types of moduli correspond to continuous Wilson line background fields [20] which are again associated to each of the three complex planes. For the case that $\theta_i \neq \pm 1$, there is generically at least one complex Wilson line field A_i (for example a 27 of E_6). The combined T_i, A_i Kähler potential reads [21, 22] $K_0 = -\log(T_i + \bar{T}_i - A_i\bar{A}_i)$ and leads to the Kähler metric of the space $\mathcal{K}_0 = SU(1,2)/SU(2) \times U(1)$. If $\theta_i = \pm 1$ there will be additional moduli fields namely, first, the (2,2) modulus U_i which corresponds to the possible deformations of the complex structure. In addition there will be again some (0,2) moduli, namely generically at least two complex Wilson line moduli B and C [22]. (B and C being, for example, 27 respectively 27 of E_6). Then the Kähler potential for these fields can be determined as follows [22]: $K_0 = -\log[(T_i + \bar{T}_i)(U_i + \bar{U}_i) - \frac{1}{2}(B_i + \bar{C}_i)(\bar{B}_i + C_i)]$. The corresponding Kähler moduli space is given by $\mathcal{K}_0 = SO(2,4)/SO(2) \times SO(4)$. A few remarks are at hand. First note that in the absence of Wilson lines ($B = C = 0$) the Kähler potential splits into the sum $K_0 = K(T,\bar{T}) + K(U,\bar{U})$, which is the well-known Kähler potential for the factorizable coset $SO(2,2)/SO(2) \times SO(2) = SU(1,1)/U(1)_T \otimes SU(1,1)/U(1)_U$. On the other hand, turning on Wilson lines, the moduli space does not factorize anymore into two submanifolds. Thus it is natural to expect that also in a more general situation the moduli space is not anymore factorizable into a space of the Kähler class moduli times a space of the complex structure moduli (as it is true for (2,2) compactifications) as soon as (0,2) moduli are turned on. Also note that the complex Wilson lines give rise to holomorphic BC and antiholomorphic $\bar{B}\bar{C}$ terms in the Kähler potential. This is in principle just what is needed for the solution of the μ-problem; upon identification of H_1 with B and H_2 with C the mass mixing term becomes $H_{12} = \frac{1}{(T+\bar{T})(U+\bar{U})}$ [23, 22]. (This is also true in general if B and C are not moduli but matter fields with tree-level zero VEV's [4, 23].) Thus we learn that holomorphic mixing terms in the Kähler potential can occur if $\theta_i = \pm 1$, i.e. if there exists a complex structure modulus U_i. Consequently, the Higgs fields should be associated to this particular complex plane.

Now let us briefly discuss the duality symmetries. We consider the most interesting case with four complex moduli T, U, B and C. (For more discussion see [22].) In addition we assume that the complex plane corresponds to a two-dimensional subtorus. The duality, i.e. modular group in question is then given by the discrete group $O(2,4,Z)$. The modular group $O(2,4,Z)$ contains an $SO(2,2,Z) = PSL(2,Z)_T \times PSL(2,Z)_U$ subgroup. $PSL(2,Z)_T$ acts in the standard way on the T modulus $T \to \frac{aT-ib}{icT+d}$ ($a,b,c,d \in Z$, $ad - bc = 1$). However U transforms also non-trivially under this transformation as $U \to U - \frac{ic}{2}\frac{BC}{icT+d}$. Thus, in the presence of B and C, T and U get mixed under duality transformations [22, 23] which reflects the non-factorizable structure of the moduli space.

For the discussion of supersymmery breaking one also needs to include one-loop corrections to the moduli Kähler potential. These arise due to a one-loop mixing of the S-field with the internal moduli. This is the socalled Green-Schwarz mixing with mixing coefficient δ_{GS}^i. Specifically one can show that the loop corrected Kähler potential has the following structure [12, 24]: $K_0^{1-loop} = -\log Y + K_0^{tree}(T,U,A,B,C)$, with $Y = S + \bar{S} + \frac{1}{8\pi^2}\sum_{i=1}^3 \delta_{GS}^i K_{0\,i\,tree}(T_i,U_i,A_i,B_i,C_i)$. Furthermore for the computation of the SSBP we need the tree-level Kähler potential of the matter fields. It can be shown to have the following form [25, 3]: $K_{\alpha\bar{\beta}} = \delta_{\alpha\bar{\beta}}\prod_{i=1}^3 (T_i + \bar{T}_i)^{n_\alpha^i}$. (For simplicity we have

included only the generic T_i moduli.) The integers n_α^i are called modular weights of the matter fields, since the Q_α transform under $PSL(2,Z)$ as $Q^\alpha \to Q^\alpha \prod_{i=1}^3 (ic_iT_i+d_i)^{n_\alpha^i}$. (The Wilson line moduli A,B,C have modular weight -1.)

As a final ingredient we have to specify the form of the gauge kinetic function in orbifold compactifications. Including one A-type modulus, the f-function in lowest order in A is given as $f(S,T_i,A)_a = S - \frac{1}{8\pi^2}(b_1 - b_0)\log[h(T_i)A] - \frac{1}{8\pi^2}\sum_{i=1}^3 (b'_a^i - \delta_{GS}^i)\log\eta(T_i)^2$. Here $\eta(T_i)$ is the well-known Dedekind function and reflects the one-loop threshold contributions of momentum and winding states [26]. The A contribution corresponds to the mass thresholds [27, 28] of those fields Q^α which get mass by a superpotential coupling to A: $W \sim h(T_i)AQ^\alpha Q^\beta$. If one assumes that all matter fields, that are charged under G_a, get a A-dependent masses one obtains $b_0 = -3C(G_a)$, $b_1 = -3C(G_a) + \sum_\alpha T_a(\alpha)$. Then $b'_a^i = -C(G_a) + \sum_\alpha T_a(\alpha)(1 + 2n_\alpha^i)$. It is not difficult to verify the correct duality transformation behaviour of f.

Now let us apply these formulas to discuss some specific aspects of supersymmetry breaking in orbifold compactifications. Let us focus on the non-perturbative gaugino condensation in the hidden gauge sector a. The non-perturbative superpotential then reads
$$W_{SUSY-breaking} = \frac{e^{\frac{24\pi^2}{b_0}S}[h(T_i)A]^{3(b_0-b_1)/b_0}}{\prod_{i=1}^3 [\eta(T_i)]^{6(b'_a^i-\delta_{GS}^i)/b_0}}.$$ This leads to the following expression [28] for the scalar potential V using the one-loop corrected Kähler potential but neglecting for simplicity a possible A contribution, i.e. $b_0 = b_1 = 3b'_a^i$ (the inclusion of A can be found in [29, 28]): $V = m_{3/2}^2[|1 - \frac{24\pi^2}{b_0}Y|^2 + \sum_{i=1}^3 \frac{Y}{8\pi^2 Y - \delta_{GS}^i}(1 - 3\frac{\delta_{GS}^i}{b_0})(T_i + \bar{T}_i)^2|\hat{G}_2(T_i)|^2 - 3]$. The minimization of this scalar potential leads to the following results. First note that in case of complete Green-Schwarz cancellation, i.e. $b_0 = 3\delta_{GS}^i$, there is no T_i dependence in the potential (as well as in $m_{3/2}$) and T_i still remains as a undetermined parameter. On the other hand, for $3\delta_{GS}^i \neq b_0$, the modulus T_i gets dynamically fixed. A specific analysis was performed in [15, 17] for the case $\delta_{GS}^i = 0$ with the result that at the minimum $T_i \sim 1.2$ supersymmetry gets spontaneously broken in the T_i sector since at that point $G_{T_i} \neq 0$. However there is an important caveat witin this analysis since it used the assumption that at the minimum $G_S = 0$. In fact, the above potential, triggered by the gaugino condensate, has no stable minimum with respect to S. Therefore the dilaton dynamics has to be modified in order to justify this assumption. One way could be that there are gaugino condensates in more that one hidden gauge sector [30]. Then $G_S = 0$ is rather generic, however several β-function coefficients have to be tuned in a

careful way in order to get $m_{3/2} \sim O(1\text{TeV})$. A different, very interesting possibility is that the non-perturbative dilaton dynamics is governed by the socalled S-duality [31, 32]. This means that the true non-perturbative string partition function is actually $PSL(2, Z)$ invariant resp. covariant with respect to the S-field due to non-perturbative monopol-like configuration in target space. The simplest possibility within this context is that the partition function looks like [31] $Z \sim \frac{1}{(S+\bar{S})|\eta(S)|^4}$. In the effective field theory this could mean that the effective superpotential contains a term $\eta(S)^{-2}$ instead of the 'standard' e^S dependence. Such types of superpotentials possibly lead to $G_S = 0$. Finally one has to remark in this context that the cosmological constant tends to be non-vanshing within the non-perturbative scenario, which is very disturbing but probably reflects our ignorance about the exact supersymmetry breaking dynamics dynamics. (For a recent discussion about the cosmological constant see [6]; in [33] it has been argued that a negative cosmological constant after gaugino condensation might be a desirable feature, for the fully renormalized cosmological constant to vanish.)

Now, we could proceed to calculate the SSBP resulting from this type of superpotentials. For example the squark and slepton masses are obtained as a function of the modular weights n_α [3]. At this stage it is very convenient to parametrize the unknown supersymmetry dynamics by some angle $\tan\theta \sim \frac{G_S}{G_T}$ [5], i.e. the relative strength of the supersymmetry breaking in the S and T sectors. Then the exact form of the (perturbative or non-perturbative) superpotential is parametrized by θ and $m_{3/2}$, and the form of the SSBP depends only on known perturbative quantities like K. Specifically the scalar masses have the form (assuming vanishing cosmological constant, the index i is suppressed now) [5]: $m_\alpha^2 = m_{3/2}^2[1 + n_\alpha(1 - \frac{\delta_{GS}}{24\pi^2 Y})^{-1}\cos^2\theta]$. For arbitrary values of θ these SSBP are non-universal. However for $\theta = \pi/2$, i.e. the dilaton dominated supersymmetry breaking, the SSBP are in fact universal [34]. Finally, for the gaugino masses similar expressions can be derived. Concluding, it would be very interesting to test some of these features in future colliders.

References

[1] Y. Nir and N. Seiberg, Phys. Lett. **309** (1993) 337;
M. Dine, R. Leigh and A. Kagan, Phys. Rev. **D84** (1993) 4269;
A. Lleyda and C. Munoz, Phys. Lett. **B317** (1993) 82;
T. Kobayashi, D. Suematsu and Y. Yamagishi, hep-ph 9403330;
N. Polonsky and A. Pomarol, hep-ph 9406224;
Y. Kawamura, H. Murayama and M. Yamaguchi, hep-ph 9406245;
D. Matalliotakis and H.P. Nilles, hep-ph 9407251;
M. Olechowski and S. Pokorski, hep-ph 9407404;
D. Choudhury, F. Eberlein, A. König, J. Louis and S. Pokorski, hep-ph 9408275.
[2] A. Giveon, M. Porrati and E. Rabinovici, hep-th 9401139.
[3] L.E. Ibáñez and D. Lüst, Nucl. Phys. **B382** (1992) 305.
[4] V. Kaplunovsky and J. Louis, Phys. Lett. **B306** (1993) 269.
[5] A. Brignole, L.E. Ibáñez and C. Munoz, Nucl. Phys. **B422** (1994) 125.
[6] S. Ferrara, C. Kounnas and F. Zwirner, hep-th 9405188.
[7] C. Kounnas, F. Zwirner and I. Pavel, hep-th 9406256.
[8] S. Ferrara, D. Lüst, A. Shapere and S. Theisen, Phys. Lett. **B225** (1989) 363.
[9] E. Cremmer, S. Ferrara, L. Girardello and A. van Proyen, Nucl. Phys. **B212** (1983) 413.
[10] H.P. Nilles, Phys. Lett. **B180** (1986) 240;
V. Kaplunovsky and J. Louis, hep-th 9402005.
[11] J. Louis, in Proc. 2nd Int. Symposium on Particles, Strings and Cosmology, 1991;
G. Lopes Cardoso and B. Ovrut, Nucl. Phys. **B369** (1992) 352; and *ibid.* **B392** (1993) 315.
[12] J.P. Derendinger, S. Ferrara, C. Kounnas and F. Zwirner, Nucl. Phys. **B372** (1992) 145.
[13] C. Kounnas and M. Porrati, Nucl. Phys. **B310** (1988) 355;
S. Ferrara, C. Kounnas, M. Porrati and F. Zwirner, Nucl. Phys. **B318** (1989) 75.
[14] H.P. Nilles, Phys. Lett. **B115** (1982) 193;
S. Ferrara, L. Girardello and H.P. Nilles, Phys. Lett. **B125** (1983) 457;
J.P. Derendinger, L.E. Ibáñez and H.P. Nilles, Phys. Lett. **B155** (1985) 65;
M. Dine, R. Rohm, N. Seiberg and E. Witten, Phys. Lett. **B156** (1985) 55.
[15] A. Font, L.E. Ibáñez, D. Lüst and F. Quevedo, Phys. Lett. **B245** (1990) 401.
[16] S. Ferrara, N. Magnoli, T.R. Taylor and G. Veneziano, Phys. Lett. **B245** (1990) 409;
H.P. Nilles and M. Olechowski, Phys. Lett. **B248** (1990) 268.
[17] M. Cvetic, A. Font, L.E. Ibáñez, D. Lüst and F. Quevedo, Nucl. Phys. **B361** (1991) 194.
[18] G.F. Giudice and A. Masiero, Phys. Lett. **B206** (1988) 480.
[19] L. Dixon, J. Harvey, C. Vafa and E. Witten, Nucl. Phys. **B261** (1985) 678; and *ibid.* **B274** (1986) 285.
[20] L.E. Ibáñez, H.P. Nilles and F. Quevedo, Phys. Lett. **B192** (1987) 332.
[21] S. Ferrara, C. Kounnas and M. Porrati, Phys. Lett. **B181** (1986) 263;
M. Cvetic, J. Louis and B. Ovrut, Phys. Lett. **B206** (1988) 227.
[22] G. Lopes Cardoso, D. Lüst and T. Mohaupt, hep-th 9405002.
[23] I. Antoniadis, E. Gava, K.S. Narain and T.R. Taylor, hep-th 9405024.
[24] I. Antoniadis, E. Gava, K.S. Narain and T.R. Taylor, Nucl. Phys. **B407** (1993) 706.
[25] L. Dixon, J. Louis and V. Kaplunovsky, Nucl. Phys. **B329** (1990) 27;
S. Ferrara, D. Lüst and S. Theisen, Phys. Lett. **B233** (1989) 147.
[26] V. Kaplunovsky, Nucl. Phys. **B307** (1988) 145;
L. Dixon, J. Louis and V. Kaplunovsky, Nucl. Phys. **B355** (1991) 649;
I. Antoniadis, K.S. Narain and T.R. Taylor, Phys. Lett. **B267** (1991) 37.
[27] B. de Carlos, J.A. Casas and C. Munoz, Phys. Lett. **B263** (1991) 248.
[28] D. Lüst and C. Munoz, Phys. Lett. **B279** (1992) 272.
[29] D. Lüst and T.R. Taylor, Phys. Lett. **B253** (1991) 335.
[30] N.V. Krasnikov, Phys. Lett. **B193** (1987) 37;
L. Dixon, in Proc. 15th APS D.P.F. Meeting, 1990;
J.A. Casas, Z. Lalak, C. Munoz and G.G. Ross, Nucl. Phys. **B347** (1990) 243;

T.R. Taylor, Phys. Lett. **B252** (1990) 59.

[31] A. Font, L.E. Ibáñez, D. Lüst and F. Quevedo, Phys. Lett. **B249** (1990) 35.

[32] S.J. Rey, Phys. Rev. **D43** (1991) 256;
A. Sen, Nucl. Phys. **B404** (1993) 109; Phys. Lett. **B303** (1993) 22; and *ibid.* **B329** (1994) 217;
J. Schwarzand A. Sen, Phys. Lett. **B312** (1993) 105; and Nucl. Phys. **B411** (1994) 35;
J. Gaunlett and J. Harvey, hep-th 940232;
C. Vafa and E. Witten, hep-th 9408074;
N. Seiberg and E. Witten, hep-th 9407087; and hep-th 9408099.

[33] K. Choi, J. Kim and H.P. Nilles, hep-ph 9404311.

[34] R. Barbieri, J. Louis and M. Moretti, Phys. Lett. **B312** (1993) 451.

Paper presented at XXVII Int. Conf. on High Energy Physics: Session Pa-19
Glasgow, UK, 20–27 July 1994

String rearrangement of gauge theories

C.S. Lam[†]

Department of Physics, McGill University
3600 University St., Montreal, P.Q., Canada H3A 2T8

Abstract

Feynman diagram expressions in ordinary field theories can be written in a string-like manner. The methods and the advantages for doing so are briefly discussed.

1. Introduction

There are three reasons why one wants to arrange ordinary Feynman diagrams in a string-like manner: it simplifies calculations and it gives new insights into gauge and gravitational theories. Moreover, this is done (graphically) all the time so we might as well find out exactly what that means. For example, The tree diagrams for the process $\pi^+ K^0 \rightarrow \pi^0 K^+$ are given by figures 1(a) and 1(b), but one often shows only the quark diagram figure 1(c), which can be considered also as a string diagram with hadronic strings strung between $q\bar{q}$ pairs. String diagrams are also used for pure QCD in the large-N_c limit as shown in figure 2.

Is it possible then to make the string-like diagrams *quantitative* by writing down for them a set of 'Feynman rules'? When one tries to do that several problems are encountered. For ordinary Feynman diagrams, (i) loop momenta k_a have to be introduced and integrated over; (*ii*) interactions occur at the vertices though particles propagate freely between them. In particular, loop momenta k_a injected at the vertices can change the direction of the combined momentum flow. Similarly, flavour, colour, and spin are altered at the vertices; (*iii*) gauge invariance determines the vertex factor for gauge interactions, for example to be $\epsilon(p) \cdot (q' + q'')$ in scalar QED, where p is the momentum of the external photon and q', q'' are the charged particle momenta; (*iv*) a sum of many Feynman diagrams is needed to describe a process in a given order. In contrast, for

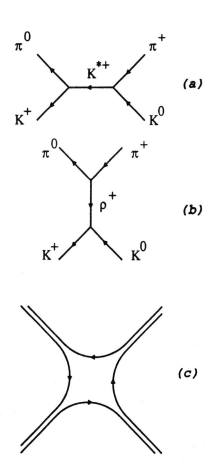

Figure 1. Lowest-order diagrams for $\pi^+ K^0 \rightarrow \pi^0 K^+$.

string diagrams, (*i'*) if we consider only hadronic *ground*

† E-mail: lam@physics.mcgill.ca

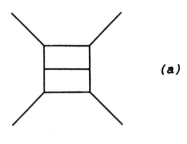

(a)

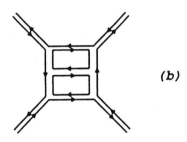

(b)

Figure 2. A pure-gluon QCD process.

states so as to freeze string excitations, the propagation of a string is described only by the 'proper time' parameter τ, so that scattering amplitudes are expressed as integrations over the proper-time parameters τ_m; (ii') the geometrical shape of a string diagram is arbitrary (reparametrization and conformal invariance), so vertices cannot be present and strings propagate freely throughout the diagram. In particular, external momenta can merge and divide inside a diagram but there are no additional loop momenta present to alter their directions. Flavour and colour flow smoothly along the quark lines as given respectively by figure 1(c) and figure 2(b) and similarly for spin as we shall see later; (iii') conformal invariance determines external gauge-interaction vertices, for example to be $\epsilon(p) \cdot [\partial_\tau x(\tau)] \exp[ip \cdot x(\tau)]$ for scalar QED where $x^\mu(\tau)$ is the spacetime (operator) coordiantes of the string at the proper time τ. The vertex factor for this operator is then $\epsilon(p) \cdot [\partial_\tau(-i\partial/\partial p)]$, quite different from the corresponding field-theoretic vertex in (iii); (iv') (Veneziano) duality [1] is valid. The sum of many Feynman diagrams is replaced by one or few string diagrams, as in figure 1.

In the rest of this note, we will show how to rearrange (i)–(iv) to resemble (i')–(iv'). The calculational and conceptual advantages for doing so will also be briefly discussed.

2. Momentum, flavour, colour, and spin flows

To convert (i) to (i'), it is sufficient to introduce a Schwinger parameter α_r for the denominator of every propagator:

$$(-q_r^2 + m_r^2 - i\epsilon)^{-1} = i \int_0^\infty d\alpha_r \exp[-i\alpha_r(m_r^2 - q_r^2)] . \quad (1)$$

Substituting this into the general expression for a T-matrix amplitude

$$T(p) = \int \left(\prod_a d^4 k_a \right) S_0(q, p) \prod_r (-q_r^2 + m_r^2 - i\epsilon)^{-1} , \quad (2)$$

the loop momentum integrations can be explicitly carried out to yield [2]

$$T(p) \sim \int_0^\infty \left(\prod_r d\alpha_r \right) \Delta^{-2}(\alpha) S(q, p) \prod_r \exp[-i\alpha_r(m_r^2 - q_r^2)] . \quad (3)$$

This is the string-like form where momentum flow is described by q_r, a quantity best thought of as the current flowing through the rth line of an electric circuit given by the Feynman diagram, in which the branch resistances are α_s and the external currents are p_i. Explicit rules are available to calculate these currents and other quantities in $T(p)$ directly from the Feynman diagram. If a proper time τ is assigned to each vertex, and if line $r = (ij)$ connects vertices j to i, then α_r can also be interpreted as the proper-time difference $|\tau_i - \tau_j|$.

The factor $S_0(q, p)$ in (2) contains all the vertex factors and numerators of propagators, so it encodes the flows of flavour, colour, and spin and is given by a sum of products of these factors. The quantity $S(q, p)$ in (3) is equal to $S_0 + S_1 + S_2 + \cdots$, and can be obtained from S_0 through momentum contraction [2]. The factors for flavour, colour, and spin flows can all be read off directly from the appropriate quark, or string-like, diagrams, and it is important to note that the quark diagrams are *different for different flows*. The general rules and their derivations are given elsewhere [3], but specific examples can be seen from figures 3 and 4 respectively for colour and spin flows. In each case diagram (a) is the Feynman diagram and diagram (b) is the equivalent string-like diagram from which the factors for S_0 can be read off to be

$$S_0^{(m)colour} = T^a T^b T^c T^d \mathrm{tr}(T^e T^f T^g T^h) , \quad (4)$$

$$S_0^{spin} = [p_2 q_1]\langle q_1 p_3 \rangle \cdot [p_4 p_5] \cdot \langle k_5 q_9 \rangle [q_9 q_3]\langle q_3 p_1 \rangle \cdot \langle p_6 q_6 \rangle [q_6 q_5]\langle q_5 q_8 \rangle [q_8 k_6] . \quad (5)$$

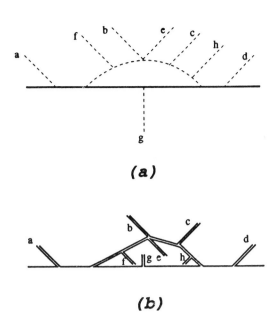

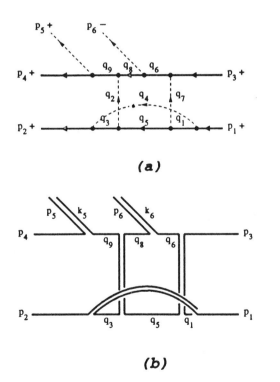

Figure 3. An example to illustrate colour flow. See eq. (4).

Figure 4. An example to illustrate spin flow. See eq. (5).

T^a in (5) are the $(S)U(N)$ generators in the fundamental representation. The superscript (m) indicates that there are many colour factors for figure 3(a) and that in (4) is the one appropriate to figure 3(b). Other colour factors

can be obtained from other string-like diagrams, which in the case of $U(N)$ can be obtained from 3(b) by crossing the quark lines at the vertices. For $SU(N)$ there are other quark diagrams in which some of the internal gluon lines are omitted. The spin-flow (or more correctly helicity-flow) factor S_0^{spin} in (5) is obtained by assuming the fermion masses to be zero. In that case the string-like diagram 4(b) is unique once 4(a) is given, and the direction the fermion lines turn depends on the helicities of the external particles, indicated in the diagram by a + or a − sign. More diagrams will be necessary if the internal particles are massive. The square and angular brackets are the overlap of the massless Dirac wave functions with definite helicities:

$$[p_i p_j] = \bar{u}_+(p_i)u_-(p_j), \quad \langle p_i p_j \rangle = \bar{u}_-(p_i)u_+(p_j), \quad (6)$$

When internal momenta q_r appear in these brackets, it is understood that they should first be expanded in terms of the external massless momenta p_i with only diagonal terms kept. Note that Dirac matrices are completely absent so the usual four-channel problem is reduced to a one-channel expression. This is possible because of helicity and chirality conservations for massless fermions. Note that it would have been impossible to write (5) before the loop momenta were eliminated in going from (2) to (3).

The final factor S_0 is obtained from $S_0^{(m)colour} S_0^{spin} \ldots$ by summing over all m. The main advantage in this string-like arrangement is to be able to use the spinor helicity technique [4], developed originally for *tree* diagrams, now for arbitrary processes with any number of loops. It also allows the gauge-invariant colour subamplitudes to be easily separated.

3. External gauge vertices

The scalar QED vertex (*iii*) can be replaced by the string-like vertex (*iii'*) by using differential circuit identities [3]. The presence of $\partial/\partial\tau$ in the latter expression allows integration-by-parts to be used, to redistribute the gauge-dependent terms among different diagrams in order to minimize their appearance and thereby increase computability. It also makes the Ward-Takahashi identity realized in a different way, and allows the possibility of formulating gauge invariance in another way.

4. Duality

Veneziano duality (*iv'*) can be simulated by formally summing up a number of Feynman diagrams into a single integral expression, at least for QED-like theories [5]. Take for example the sum of the 6!4!3! QED diagrams, obtained from fig. 5 by permuting the photon vertices along each of the three charged lines.

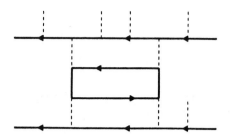

Figure 5. A QED diagram.

In the proper-time representation (3), a proper time $[\tau_i'(1 \leq i \leq 6),\ \tau_j''(1 \leq j \leq 4),\ \tau_k'''(1 \leq k \leq 3)]$ is assigned to each vertex, and each Feynman diagram is given by a fixed ordering of the τ's, τ''s, and τ'''s, so for each diagram the proper-time integration region in (3) is the product of three *hyper-triangular regions*. The 'dual sum' of these 6!4!3! diagrams is obtained by summing all these permutations, and is thus given by a *single* integral over the product of three *hypercube* regions, one each for τ', τ'', and τ'''. Moreover, it is gauge invariant. Unfortunately, it is often impossible to carry out this single integral analytically, but it can be used as a starting point for gauge-invariant approximations. For example, the result for the soft-photon eikonal approximation can be obtained very easily in this way.

It is also worthwhile pointing out an interesting parallel. Each Feynman diagram with n vertices is a sum of $n!$ time-ordered (old-fashioned) diagrams. An individual time-ordered diagram is not Lorentz invariant, but the Feynman diagram is. In our case, the dual sum puts together Feynman diagrams that have different *proper-time* orderings, each of which is not gauge invariant, but the dual sum is.

References

[1] G. Veneziano, Nuovo Cim. **57A** (1968) 190.

[2] C.S. Lam and J.P. Brun Nuovo Cim. **59A** (1969) 397

[3] C.S. Lam Nucl. Phys. **B397** (1993) 143; Phys. Rev. **D48** (1993) 873; and Can.J.Phys. (1994) July-August.

[4] M.L. Mangano and S.J. Parke, Phys. Rep. **200** (1991) 301; R. Gastmans and T.T. Wu, *The Ubiquitous Photon* (Clarendon Press 1990).

[5] Y.J. Feng and C.S. Lam, to be published.

Paper presented at XXVII Int. Conf. on High Energy Physics: Session Pa-19
Glasgow, UK, 20–27 July 1994

Free Field Construction of Chiral $SU(N)$ WZW Models at Level One

Meifang Chu and Peter Goddard

D.A.M.T.P. University of Cambridge, Silver Street, Cambridge CB3 9EW, UK

Abstract

The free field realisation of Frenkel-Kac and Segal is extended to construct the chiral vertex operators in the basic representations of the level-one $SU(N)$ WZW model. These operators are nonlocal and intertwine between physical states in the chiral Hilbert space. The corresponding symmetry algebras in the chiral model are also determined.

In this paper, we explain the free field construction of the chiral $SU(N)_{k=1}$ WZW models based on our recent work [1,2]. Our motivation is to understand the formulation of the chiral conformal field theory, which can be useful in compactifying various superstring models from ten dimensions down to four dimensions. The aim is to formulate the chiral theory with its defining fields, the so called *chiral vertex operators* [3,4]. These are nonlocal chiral primary fields obeying an exchange relation given by a braiding matrix. The chiral Hilbert space is decomposed into irreducible representations of the chiral symmetry algebras and the chiral vertex operators relate states in different representations of this space. Following [5], we study the holomorphic factorisation of the level-one $SU(N)$ Wess-Zumino-Witten (WZW) models on a circle. In particular, we extend the construction of Frenkel-Kac and Segal [6] to obtain the chiral vertex operators explicitly in terms of free scalar fields. The main conclusion is that the finite number of new degrees of freedom thus introduced into the chiral models implement an additional symmetry described by a quantum group. This provides an understanding of the role of quantum groups in quantum field theory.

Let us quickly review some of the known results of the level-one $SU(N)$ WZW model on a circle. The action of this model can be written in terms of a periodic group element $g(\tau, x)$ defined on a cylinder $\mathcal{M}$. This action is conformal invariant at the infra-red fixed point

and it can be written as follows:

$$
\mathcal{A}[g] = -\frac{k}{16\pi}\Big\{ \int_{\mathcal{M}} \mathrm{tr}\left(g^{-1}\partial_\mu g g^{-1}\partial^\mu g\right) d^2x
$$
$$
- \frac{2}{3}\int_{\mathcal{B}} \epsilon^{\lambda\mu\nu}\mathrm{tr}\left(\hat{g}^{-1}\partial_\lambda \hat{g}\hat{g}^{-1}\partial_\mu \hat{g}\hat{g}^{-1}\partial_\nu \hat{g}\right) d^3x\Big\}.
$$

$$(1)$$

The second term is a topological term obtained from integrating over a three-dimensional manifold $\mathcal{B}$, whose boundary is the cylinder $\mathcal{M}$ and $\hat{g}(\tau, x, y) \in SU(N)$ is defined on $\mathcal{B}$ such that it maps to $g(\tau, x)$ at $y = 0$. The level k is set to be one in the following discussion. We shall denote a basis of the generators in $SU(N)$ with $T^a \in \{H^i, E^\alpha\}$. Since we can quantise the two chiral sectors separately, the following discussion will mainly concerns the left-moving sector. According to [1], the chiral vertex operator in the left-moving sector is defined as the chiral group element, $U(x^+)$, factorised from the periodic defining variable $g(\tau, x)$, i.e. $x^\pm \equiv \tau \pm x$ and

$$
g(x^+, x^-) = U(x^+)e^{-iq_\nu \cdot H}V(x^-).
$$

$$(2)$$

In this parameterisation[1], U has a monodromy given by the maximal torus of the group.

$$
U(x^+ + 2\pi) = U(x^+)e^{i2\pi\nu \cdot H}.
$$

$$(3)$$

Upon quantisation in the gauge-fixed approach, the monodromy momentum ν conjugates to q_ν in (2). Under the affine symmetry, U transforms as the *chiral primary fields* of the Kac-Moody algebra,

$$
[J_m^a, U(x^+)] = e^{imx^+}T^a U(x^+),
$$

$$(4)$$

where the $SU(N)_{k=1}$ Kac-Moody algebra can be written in the Cartan-Weyl basis as [6,7]

$$[J_m^i, J_n^j] = m\delta^{ij}\delta_{m,-n} \qquad\qquad i,j = 1,2,..N-1.$$

$$[J_m^i, J_n^\alpha] = \alpha^i J_{m+n}^\alpha$$

$$[J_m^\alpha, J_n^\beta] = \begin{cases} \epsilon(\alpha,\beta)J_{m+n}^{\alpha+\beta} & \text{if } \alpha+\beta \text{ is a root} \\ \sum_{j=1}^{r} \alpha^j J_{m+n}^j + m\delta_{m,-n} & \text{if } \alpha = -\beta \\ 0 & \text{otherwise.} \end{cases}$$

(5)

The structure constants, $\epsilon(\alpha,\beta)$, are normalised to be ± 1.

Moreover, the quantum commutation [1,5,8] of two U's is specified by a braiding matrix $Q(\nu)$; e.g. in the tensor notation: $U_1 \equiv U \otimes \mathcal{I}$ and $U_2 \equiv \mathcal{I} \otimes U$,

$$U_1(x^+)U_2(y^+) = U_2(y^+)U_1(x^+)Q\left(x^+ - y^+, \nu\right). \quad (6)$$

In [1], the braiding matrix Q is solved explicitly in the fundamental representation of $SU(N)$ for all level k. It is written in terms of a parameter $t \equiv e^{i\chi(k)}$ and $\eta(x) \equiv 2[x] + 1$ where $[x]$ denotes the maximal integer less than x.

$$Q(x) = t^{(\frac{N-1}{N})\eta(x)}\left(1 \otimes 1 - \sum_{\alpha \in \Phi} E_\alpha E_{-\alpha} \otimes E_{-\alpha}E_\alpha\right)$$

$$+ t^{-\frac{1}{N}\eta(x)}\sum_{\alpha \in \Phi} \cos\theta(\alpha \cdot \nu)E_\alpha E_{-\alpha} \otimes E_{-\alpha}E_\alpha$$

$$- t^{-\frac{1}{N}\eta(x)}\sum_{\alpha \in \Phi} t^{-\frac{\alpha\nu}{\chi}\eta(x)}\sin\theta(\alpha \cdot \nu)E_\alpha \otimes E_{-\alpha},$$

where $\quad \sin\theta(\alpha \cdot \nu) = \dfrac{1}{[\frac{\alpha \cdot \nu}{\chi}]_t}, \qquad [A]_t \equiv \dfrac{t^A - t^{-A}}{t - t^{-1}}.$

(7)

This braiding matrix can be related to the Racah coefficients [9,10] of $U_t(SL(N))$ and thus implies that $U_t(SL(N))$ is the additional symmetry acting in the chiral theory. In order to understand the implementation of this additional symmetry, we construct the chiral vertex operators in terms of free scalar fields by extending the unitary realisation of the level-one Kac-Moody algebra a la Frenkel-Kac and Segal [6].

Let us introduce $N-1$ left-moving scalar fields $\phi^j(z)$, $j = 1,2,...N-1$, and expand it on a complex plane with $z = e^{ix^+}$,

$$\phi^j(z) = q^j - ip^j \ln z + i\sum_{n\neq 0, \in \mathbb{Z}} \frac{1}{n}\phi_n^j z^{-n},$$

$$\phi_n^{j\dagger} = \phi_{-n}^j, \quad [\phi_m^i, \phi_n^j] = m\delta_{m,-n}\delta^{ij},$$

$$p^{j\dagger} = p^j, \quad [q^i, p^j] = i\hbar\delta^{ij}.$$

(8)

Then, according to [6], the current generators can be

realised as follows.

$$J^\alpha(z) = \mathcal{O}^\alpha(z)e^{-i\alpha \cdot q}\hat{C}_\alpha, \qquad \forall \; \alpha \; \text{is a root,}$$

$$J^j(z) = iz\partial_z\phi^j(z), \qquad\qquad j = 1,2,..N-1,$$

where $\quad \mathcal{O}^\alpha(z) \equiv z^{\alpha^2/2}{}^\times_\times \exp(i\alpha \cdot \phi(z))^\times_\times.$

(9)

Conformal symmetry is ensured by the Virasoro generators which can be obtained from the affine currents according to the Sugawara construction,

$$L(z) = \frac{1}{2(1+N)}{}^\times_\times \sum_{a=1}^{N^2-1} J^a(z)J^a(z)^\times_\times. \quad (10)$$

In (9), we have included a zero-mode operator $\hat{C}_\alpha$ defined on the root lattice, Λ_R. These operators obey the following cocycle condition,

$$\hat{C}_\alpha\hat{C}_\beta = S(\alpha,\beta)\hat{C}_\beta\hat{C}_\alpha = \epsilon(\alpha,\beta)\hat{C}_{\alpha+\beta},$$

$$\text{where} \quad S(\alpha,\beta) = e^{i\pi\alpha \cdot \beta}, \qquad \forall \alpha,\beta \in \Lambda_R.$$

(11)

The structure constant $\epsilon(\alpha,\beta)$ is determined by the symmetry factor $S(\alpha,\beta)$ according to the following consistency requirements,

$$\epsilon(\alpha,\beta)\epsilon(\alpha+\beta,\gamma) = \epsilon(\alpha,\beta+\gamma)\epsilon(\beta,\gamma),$$

$$\epsilon(\alpha,\beta) = S(\alpha,\beta)\epsilon(\beta,\alpha),$$

$$S(\alpha,\beta)S(\gamma,\beta) = S(\alpha+\gamma,\beta),$$

$$S(\alpha,\beta) = S^{-1}(\beta,\alpha).$$

(12)

In order to extend these results to construct the chiral primary fields defined in (4), it is necessary to extend the cocycles to the weight lattice, Λ_W. For example, in the fundamental representation, the chiral primary field is a $N \times N$ matrix labelled by the weights of the representations and its conformal weight is given by $\Delta_N = (N^2 - 1)/2N(1+N)$.

$$\hat{U}_{rs}(z) = {}^\times_\times e^{i\lambda_r \cdot \phi(z)}{}^\times_\times e^{-i\lambda_r \cdot q_\phi}\hat{C}_{rs}. \quad (13)$$

The new cocycle $\hat{C}_{rs}$ is defined on a cross product of two weight lattice $\Lambda_W \times \Lambda_W$. In other words, $\hat{C}$ depends on two sets of zero modes, $[q^i, p^j] = i\hbar\delta^{ij}$ and $[\bar{q}^i, \bar{p}^j] = i\hbar\delta^{ij}$.

$$\hat{C}_{rs} \equiv e^{i(\lambda_r q + \lambda_s \bar{q})}C_{(\lambda_r,\lambda_s)}(p,\bar{p}),$$

$$\forall \; (\lambda_r,\lambda_s) \in \Lambda_W \times \Lambda_W.$$

(14)

The new set of harmonic oscillators commutes with the left-moving Kac-Moody current. They are introduced to replace the zero-modes in the right-moving vertex operator [1] $V(x^-)$ which otherwise would not decouple completely.

The symmetry factors for the new cocycles must satisfy the last two conditions in (12) on the new lattice and we are led to choose:

$$S(\vec{\mu}, \vec{\nu}) = e^{i\pi(\mu \cdot \nu - \overline{\mu} \cdot \overline{\nu})}, \qquad \forall \quad \vec{\mu}, \vec{\nu} \in \Lambda_W \times \Lambda_W. \quad (15)$$

Once the symmetry factor is specified, we can determined $\epsilon(\vec{\mu}, \vec{\nu})$ from $S(\vec{\mu}, \vec{\nu})$ using the first two conditions in (12). This way, we can construct the cocycles as functions of the momentum $\vec{p}$ according to

$$\hat{C}_{\vec{\lambda}} \equiv e^{i\vec{\lambda} \cdot \vec{q}} \epsilon(\vec{\lambda}, \vec{p}), \qquad \forall \quad \vec{p} \in \Lambda_W \times \Lambda_W. \quad (16)$$

This determines the cocycle completely up to the following gauge transformation [7,11],

$$\begin{cases} \hat{C}_{\vec{\mu}} & \longrightarrow \quad t(\vec{\mu})\hat{C}_{\vec{\mu}}; \\ \epsilon(\vec{\mu}, \vec{\nu}) & \longrightarrow \quad \dfrac{t(\vec{\mu})t(\vec{\nu})}{t(\vec{\mu} + \vec{\nu})}\epsilon(\vec{\mu}, \vec{\nu}), \end{cases} \quad (17)$$

where $t(\vec{\mu}) = t(\mu)\bar{t}(\bar{\mu})$ denotes a non-zero scaling constant. Subsequently, the solution for the chiral primary field in (4) is

$$\hat{U}_{rs}(z) = {}^{\times}_{\times} e^{i\lambda_r \cdot \phi(z)} {}^{\times}_{\times} e^{i\lambda_s \cdot \bar{q}} C_{(\lambda_r, \lambda_s)}(p_\phi, \bar{p}). \quad (18)$$

It is straightforward to check that the correlation functions of these chiral primary fields satisfy the level-one Knizhnik-Zamolodchikov equations. One can also examine the local properties of the chiral primary fields directly. They obey the following braiding relation,

$$\hat{U}_1(z)\hat{U}_2(w) = \hat{U}_2(w)\hat{U}_1(z)R(\arg(z/w)), \qquad |z| > |w|,$$
$$R(x) = \exp\left\{ i\pi H_1 \cdot H_2 \eta(x) \right\}. \quad (19)$$

Notice that the R-matrix in (19) is diagonal. For $\eta(x) = 1$, it can be identified as the R-matrix [12] of $U_t(SL(N))$ in the fundamental representation with $t = e^{i\pi}$.

$$R(t) = t^{-\frac{1}{N}} \left\{ t \sum_{r=1}^{N} e_{rr} \otimes e_{rr} + \sum_{r \neq s=1}^{N} e_{rs} \otimes e_{rs} \right.$$
$$\left. + (t - t^{-1}) \sum_{r>s=1}^{N} e_{rs} \otimes e_{sr} \right\}, \quad t = e^{i\pi}. \quad (20)$$

Notice that we have denoted the deformation parameter with $t = q^{\frac{1}{2}}$ rather than with q as in [12]. Since $t = -1 \in \mathbb{R}$, we have also replaced $U_t(SL(N))$ by $U_t(SU(N))$. This braiding parameter agrees with one of the two possible deformation parameters obtained in [1] for $k = 1$.

To complete the construction of the chiral vertex operator defined in (2-6), we can multiply the chiral primary field $\hat{U}(z)$ with a N-dimensional matrix, A,

which commutes with the Kac-Moody current; i.e. in terms of $\hat{A} \equiv e^{iH\bar{q}} A(\bar{p})$,

$$U(z) \equiv e^{i\phi(z)H} e^{-iq_\phi H} \hat{C} e^{-i\bar{q}H} \hat{A}. \quad (21)$$

This new vertex operator, U, will obey the braiding relation in (6) provided that $\hat{A}$ satisfies the following equation,

$$R(t)\hat{A}_1\hat{A}_2 = \hat{A}_2\hat{A}_1 Q(\nu, t). \quad (22)$$

One can easily verify that if (22) holds for $R(x,t)$ and $Q(x, \nu, t)$ when $\eta(x) = 1$, then it will also hold for all x.

Equation (22) relates R-matrix and the braiding (Racah) matrix of $U_t(SL(N))$ and it is also known as the IRF-Vertex transformation [2,3,4,12] where $\hat{A}$ gives the Wigner-matrix of $U_t(SL(N))$. For $U_t(SL(2))$, this operator identity had been realised explicitly for all t in [2]. It is shown that $\hat{A}$ depends on two sets of harmonic oscillators: $(\bar{q}, \bar{p})$ and (q_ν, ν), where ν is the monodromy momentum in the braiding matrix Q. They are independent degrees of freedom in the sense that they commute with the Kac-Moody current. The Wigner operator [2] can be written in the limit of $t = e^{i\pi}$ as follow:

$$\hat{A} = e^{i\frac{\sigma_3}{\sqrt{2}}\bar{q}} \begin{pmatrix} \sqrt{\dfrac{\nu+\bar{p}}{2\nu}} & -\xi^{-1}\sqrt{\dfrac{\nu-\bar{p}}{2\nu}} \\ \xi\sqrt{\dfrac{\nu-\bar{p}}{2\nu}} & \sqrt{\dfrac{\nu+\bar{p}}{2\nu}} \end{pmatrix} e^{i\frac{\sigma_3}{\sqrt{2}}q_\nu}, \quad (23)$$
where $\quad \xi \equiv e^{-i\frac{\pi}{\sqrt{2}}(\nu+\bar{p})}$.

This completes the construction of the chiral vertex operator $U(z)$ in (21). Note that U is unitary because both $\hat{C}$ and $\hat{A}$ are unitary.

In order to implement the $U_{-1}(SU(2))$ symmetry in the chiral model, let us write down the generators in terms of the new sets of harmonic oscillators [2],

$$S^3 \equiv \frac{1}{\sqrt{2}}\bar{p},$$
$$S^\pm \equiv e^{\pm i\sqrt{2}q} t^{\mp \frac{\nu}{\sqrt{2}}} \sqrt{\left(\frac{\nu}{\sqrt{2}}\right)^2 - \left(\frac{\bar{p}}{\sqrt{2}} \pm \frac{1}{2}\right)^2}. \quad (24)$$

Because the deformation parameter is $t = -1$, this algebra is isomorphic to $SU(2)$. Under this algebra, $\hat{A}$ transforms according to

$$t^{S_3}(A_{+b}, A_{-b}) = (A_{+b}, A_{-b}) t^{S_3} t^{\frac{\sigma_3}{2}},$$
$$S^\pm(A_{+b}, A_{-b}) = (A_{+b}, A_{-b})\left(S^\pm t^{\mp\frac{1}{2}\sigma_3} + \sigma_\pm t^{\pm S_3}\right). \quad (25)$$

This transformation can be formulated in a covariant way in terms of the coproducts of $U_{-1}(SU(2))$ as in [2]. Furthermore, its quadratic Casimir operator is given by $\left(\frac{\nu}{\sqrt{2}}\right)^2 - \frac{1}{4}$. Thus, the irreducible representations $\overline{V}_j$ of $U_{-1}(SU(2))$ are labelled by the eigenvalues of of the monodromy momentum, $j = \frac{\nu}{\sqrt{2}} - \frac{1}{2}$, for $j =$

$0, \frac{1}{2}, 1, \ldots$ Like the irreducible representations of $SU(2)$, the dimension of $\overline{V}_j$ is $(2j+1)$. Consequently, U acts on the irreducible representations of $U_{-1}(SU(2))$ like an intertwining (Wigner) operator. Notice that because the quantum group structure is rather trivial in this case, there is no truncation on the spin j. Together with the irreducible representations of the affine current, the Hilbert space for the left-moving $SU(2)_{k=1}$ WZW model is decomposed as

$$\mathcal{H}_L = \left(H_0 \otimes (\oplus_{j=0, \mathbb{Z}_+} \overline{V}_j) \right) \bigoplus \left(H_{\frac{1}{2}} \otimes (\oplus_{j+\frac{1}{2} \in \mathbb{Z}_+} \overline{V}_j) \right). \tag{26}$$

Let us now remark on the monodromy of the chiral vertex operator. From the explicit construction of U in (21), and from the definition of monodromy momentum ν in (3), we find a constraint between the monodromy momentum ν and the free-field momentum p_ϕ,

$$e^{i2\pi p_\phi \cdot \lambda_r} = e^{i2\pi \nu \cdot \lambda_s}, \qquad \forall \lambda_r, \lambda_s = \pm\frac{1}{\sqrt{2}}. \tag{27}$$

This condition is manifestly satisfied for the physical states in the chiral Hilbert space (26).

These results for the chiral vertex operators in the fundamental representation can be generalised to other basic representations of $SU(N)$ for $N \geq 2$. In particular, (21) and (22) still holds and the chiral Hilbert space is decomposed as

$$\mathcal{H}_L = \bigoplus_{\lambda=0, \text{minimal}} H_\lambda \otimes (\oplus_{\mu \in \Lambda_\lambda} \overline{V}_\mu), \tag{28}$$

where H_λ's are the minimal representations of the left-moving $SU(N)_{k=1}$ Kac-Moody algebra and μ's denote all the highest weights of $U_{-1}(SU(N))$ which are in the same weight lattice as λ. The Hilbert space of the right-moving sector can be constructed in a similar way,

$$\mathcal{H}_R = \bigoplus_{\lambda=0, \text{minimal}} (\oplus_{\mu \in \Lambda_\lambda} V_\mu) \otimes \overline{H}_\lambda \tag{29}$$

Since the new degrees of freedom which implements $U_{-1}(SU(N))$ symmetry do not appear in the original Wess-Zumino models, they should be gauged away when we "join" the left-moving and the right-moving sectors together.

$$\mathcal{H}_{\text{WZW}} = \bigoplus_{\lambda=0, \text{minimal}} H_\lambda \otimes \overline{H}_\lambda \tag{30}$$

This gauging process is not at all trivial and one needs to know more precisely in order to describe the chiral model in the Lagrangian formulation.

To conclude, the free field construction of the chiral vertex operators for the $SU(N)_{k=1}$ WZW model described in this paper gives an explicit description of how to factorise the model into two chiral sectors. A finite number of new degrees of freedom is introduced into the chiral sectors. Consequently, the chiral Hilbert space acquires an additional symmetry governed by $U_{-1}(SU(N))$. This factorisation is different from the one proposed in the previous treatments [3,4,13] where the additional symmetry is proposed to be $U_t(SL(N))$ with $t = e^{i\frac{\pi}{1+N}}$. In this latter case, however, an explicit realisation of the chiral vertex operators is still lacking.

Acknowledgments

We would like to thank David Olive for many helpful discussions in the early stages of this work. We are also grateful to Fedor Smirnov for helpful discussions about the IRF-Vertex relation. This work is supported by the Science and Engineering Research Council under the grant GR/H57929.

References

[1] M. Chu, P. Goddard, "Quantisation of the $SU(N)$ WZW Models at Level k", preprint DAMTP-94-42.
[2] M. Chu, P. Goddard, "Quantisation of a particle moving on a group manifold", DAMTP preprint DAMTP-94-41, to appear in Phys. Lett. B.
[3] G. Moore and Yu. Reshetkhin, Nucl. Phys. **B328** (1989) 557.
[4] G. Felder, K. Gawedzki and A. Kupiainen, Nucl. Phys. **B299** (1988) 355; Commun. Math. Phys. **117** (1988) 127.
[5] M. Chu, P. Goddard, I. Halliday, D. Olive, A. Schwimmer, Phys. Lett. **B266** (1991) 71.
[6] I.B. Frenkel, V.G.Kac, Invent. Math. **62** (1980) 23; G. Segal, Commun. Math. Phys. **80** (1981) 301.
[7] P. Goddard, D. Olive, Int. Jour. Mod. Phys. **A1** (1986) 303.
[8] L.D. Faddeev, Commun. Math. Phys. **132** (1990) 131.
[9] A.N. Kirillov, N. Yu. Reshetikhin, "Infinite-dimensional Lie algebras and groups" edited by V. G. Kac, World Scientific, Singapore, (1989) page 285.
[10] F. Pan, Jour. Phys. A. Math. Gen. **26** (1993) 4621.
[11] P. Goddard, W. Nahm, D. Olive, A. Schwimmer, Commun. Math. Phys. **107** (1986) 179.
[12] N. Yu. Reshetikhin, "Quantised Universal Enveloping Algebras, The Yang-Baxter Equation and Invariants of Links, I, II", LOMI preprint LOMI-E-4-87.
[13] Private communication from M. Gaberdiel.

Parallel Session Pa-20

Low Q^2 and Soft Phenomena

Conveners: G. Ingelman (Uppsala University)
W. Kittel (University of Nijmegen)

Scientific secretaries: A. Wilson
M. Utley (reserve)

Paper presented at XXVII Int. Conf. on High Energy Physics: Session Pa-20
Glasgow, UK, 20–27 July 1994

Diffractive scattering in μXe and μD interactions at 490 GeV

K. Kadija[†]

Max-Planck-Institut für Physik, München, Germany

E665 Collaboration

Abstract

From a study of the x_{Bj} dependence of hadron production in μD and μXe scattering, and from consideration of events with a large rapidity gap, evidence is found for a significant contribution of diffractive scattering in the kinematic region where shadowing of the cross section is observed.

The experimental data were obtained with the E665 detector in the μ beam line of the Tevatron at Fermilab. The average μ^+ energy is $\sim$ 490 GeV and the targets relevant for the present analysis are liquid Deuterium and gaseous Xenon. The detector, which includes a streamer chamber as vertex detector, provides 80-90% acceptance for charged particles over the full solid angle for momenta greater than 200 MeV/c. Details about the experiment can be found in [1]. The following kinematic range is considered: $50 < \nu < 400$ GeV, $1 < Q^2 < 20$ GeV^2 and $0.002 < x_{Bj} < 0.2$, where ν is the energy of the virtual photon (γ^*) in the laboratory system, Q^2 is the negative of the four-momentum squared of the virtual photon, and x_{Bj} is the Bjorken-scaling variable. After all cuts the final statistics amount to 6071 events on D and 1999 events on Xe.

We have investigated the possible differences in hadron production in the shadowing ($x_{Bj} < 0.02$), and non-shadowing region ($x_{Bj} > 0.02$) [2, 3]. The average values of those quantities which are most sensitive to nuclear effects in the hadronic system: the total charge of hadronic system, the number of "grey tracks" (protons with laboratory momenta between 200 and 600 MeV/c), and the difference between the backward multiplicities od charged hadrons in μXe and μD scattering, are studied as a function of x_{Bj}. In μXe there is a clear trend, in all three quantities, of increasing

particle production with increasing x_{Bj}. That implies more nuclear effects in the non-shadowing than in the shadowing region of μXe scattering. The enhanced hadron production in the non-shadowing region is in contradiction to [4] where a multiplicity decrease by 20-40% is predicted when passing from the shadowing to non-shadowing region. It has been suggested [4, 5, 6] that a significant contribution to the cross section in the shadowing region comes from diffractive scattering. A study of the diffractive scattering may therefore help to understand the observed unexpected enhancement of hadron production in the non-shadowing region. The diffractive events consist of a quasi-elastic scattering of the target and projectile nucleons. The hadrons coming from dissociation of the projectile are well separated in rapidity from the rest of the hadronic system. Therefore selecting events with a large rapidity gap enhances the diffractive component. In the samples where diffractive events are expected to dominate ($\Delta y^* > 3.5$), we have observed a significantly larger fraction of large rapidity gap (LRG) events in the shadowing than in the non-shadowing region (see Fig. 1). The effect is more pronounced in μXe than in μD scattering. In Fig. 2 the fraction of LRG events ($\Delta y^* > 2$) is plotted as a function of x_{Bj}. While the μD fraction is nearly independent of x_{Bj}, the μXe data exhibit a significant drop with increasing x_{Bj}. All this is consistent with the concept that nuclear shadowing is intimately connected with diffractive scattering ,

† On leave from Rudjer-Boskovic-Institute, Zagreb, Croatia

	shadowing region		non-shadowing region	
	μD	μXe	μD	μXe
$((\text{diffractive}/\text{LRG})_{\min}$	0.44 ± 0.06	0.61 ± 0.07	0.32 ± 0.09	0.49 ± 0.13
$((\text{diffractive}/\text{total})_{\min}$	0.12 ± 0.02	0.18 ± 0.03	0.08 ± 0.03	0.09 ± 0.03

Table 1. Lower limits on the fraction of diffractive events in the LRG and total event sample, in the shadowing and non-shadowing region of μD and μXe scattering.

and that the relative contribution of diffractive events increases with the atomic mass A. These LRG events are further characterized by smaller average effective masses, and by smaller average hadron multiplicities of dissociated system as compared to small-rapidity gap (SRG) events (with $\Delta y^* < 2$), as one expects for diffractive events. In the VENUS Monte Carlo Model

estimated from the data, and shown in Table 1. There

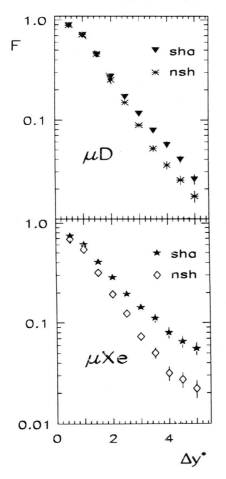

Figure 1. Fraction of events with a large rapidity gap greater than Δy^* as a function of Δy^*, in the shadowing and non-shadowing region, for μXe and μD scattering.

[7] which does not include diffractive processes, and which is supposed to properly describe non-diffractive scattering, no difference is seen between LRG and SRG samples. Lower limits of the fraction of "diffractive events" in shadowing and non-shadowing regions were

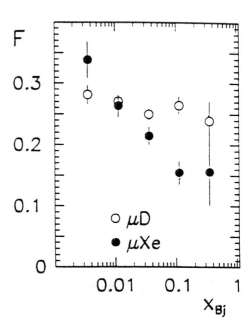

Figure 2. Fraction of LRG events ($\Delta y^* > 2$) as a function of x_{Bj} for μXe and μD scattering. The shadowing and non-shadowing regions are defined by $x_{Bj} < 0.02$ and $x_{Bj} > 0.02$ respectively.

is a strong contribution from diffractive scattering in the low x_{Bj} region (the shadowing region). The fraction of diffractive events is larger in μXe as compared to μD scattering. Recent calculations within the shadowing model are consistent with these findings [8].

References

[1] M.R. Adams et al., Z. Phys. **C61** (1994) 179
[2] M.R. Adams et al., Phys. Rev. Lett. **68** (1992) 3266
[3] M.R. Adams et al., Phys. Lett. **B287** (1992) 375
[4] G.V. Davidenko et al., Nucl. Phys. **B135** (1978) 333
[5] L. Stodolsky, Phys. Rev. Lett. **18** (1967) 135
[6] N.N. Gribov, Sov. Phys. **JETP 29** (1969) 483
[7] K. Werner, Phys. Rep. **232** (1993) 87
[8] N.N. Nikolaev et al., **KFA-IKP(TH) 1994-13**

Photoproduction and Diffraction at HERA

Sampa Bhadra

York University, Department of Physics, 4700 Keele Street, Toronto, Canada, and
Deutsches Elektronen Synchrotron, Notkestrasse 85, 22603 Hamburg, Germany.
(on behalf of the ZEUS and H1 collaborations)

Abstract

Results from photoproduction at HERA are presented, including cross section measurements for ρ^0, ϕ, and J/ψ production. We have found jets which are a signature for hard scattering processes. An analysis of two-jet events allows us to probe the structure of both the photon and the proton. Comparisons are made of di-jet production to predictions from LO QCD, using different structure functions of the proton and photon. We have searched for hard scattering in diffractive events and compared our results to models where the exchanged pomeron is composed of partons.

1. Introduction

The gauge interactions of the electron and photon are well known, but the interaction of the photon with hadrons or photons is less well understood. HERA is an electron (26.7 GeV) - proton (820 GeV) collider. However, the large flux of quasi-real photons ($Q^2 \approx 0$) from the electrons makes it an ideal machine to explore the nature and structure of the photon. The average centre of mass energy $W_{\gamma p} \approx 200$ GeV is a factor of ten higher than in previous experiments. Hence it is interesting to compare our results [1] to theoretical models which are sensitive to the high energy behaviour, since pre-HERA predictions vary widely.

An excellent review by Storrow [2] brings some order to the varied and sometimes confusing classification of photon interactions. The classification is made in terms of the P_t scale, where "low P_t" is the region where the differential cross section is well described by an exponential behaviour in P_t. This soft physics is non-perturbative and not presently calculable in QCD. The subprocesses contributing are elastic, inelastic diffractive, and non-diffractive. The slope in P_t at larger values is more like a power law, and in this region of hard scattering, we can use perturbative QCD to describe the scattering process. The photon interacts directly,

or resolves itself before interacting. One important distinction between photons and hadrons is that photons can interact directly with the partons of the proton, while hadrons only interact through their constituent partons.

The fractional momentum x_γ (x_p) carried by the parton in the photon (proton) can be written as

$$x_\gamma = \frac{E_t^1 e^{-\eta_1} + E_t^2 e^{-\eta_2}}{2E_\gamma}, x_p = \frac{E_t^1 e^{\eta_1} + E_t^2 e^{\eta_2}}{2E_p} \quad (1)$$

where E_γ (E_p) is the photon (proton) energy, E_t^1, E_t^2 refer to the transverse energies, and η_1, η_2 to the pseudorapidities of the outgoing partons. The direct component, where all the energy of the photon enters the reaction, has $x_\gamma = 1$, while the resolved component will result in a value less than 1. We use the variables x_γ and x_p to probe the quark and gluon content of the photon and proton.

2. Cross section measurements of $\rho^0, \phi, J/\psi$

Photoproduction results from the 1992 and 1993 data taking period of HERA have been obtained from about 25 nb^{-1} and 500 nb^{-1} of data, respectively. The photoproduction triggers for ZEUS required calorimetric energy to be deposited in the rear (photon) direction, and were of two types:

a.) "tagged"; requiring the detection of the scattered electron at very small angles, thereby limiting Q^2 to less than 0.02 GeV^2 and

b.) "untagged"; with no requirement on the detection of the scattered electron, but with energy deposition in the rear direction and the detection of at least one charged track. This allows the direct reconstruction of the photoproduced vector mesons decaying into charged track states. The offline requirement of the absence of a detected scattered electron in the main rear calorimeter limits Q^2 to less than 4 GeV^2.

The total "tagged" photoproduction cross sections $\sigma(\gamma p)_{tot}$ at HERA for the 1993 data [3],[4] are shown in Fig 1, for $W_{\gamma p} \approx 200$ GeV. Also shown (solid circles) are lower energy measurements [5]. Global event characteristics are used by ZEUS to obtain the fraction of non-diffractive, inelastic diffractive, and elastic components to be 64.0%, 23.3%, and 12.7% respectively. Assuming that 82% of the elastic cross section is due to ρ^0 production yields an indirect measurement of the elastic cross section $\sigma(\gamma p \to \rho^0 p)$ to be 14.8 ± 5.7 μb, and this is shown in Fig 1.

particles are produced are rejected by requiring that there be less than 200 MeV in any calorimeter cell outside a limited region around the track direction.

Proton diffraction is a serious background, and in the absence of a fully equipped leading proton spectrometer, we require that there be less than 1 GeV in the forward calorimeter (i.e. the proton direction). Demanding $0.55 < m_{\pi\pi} < 1.0$ GeV reduces the contamination from other vector mesons. Finally, we limit the ρ^0 transverse momentum squared to be less than 0.5 (GeV/c)^2 to further reduce the proton diffraction contamination.

The mass spectrum is shown in Fig 2. The deviation from a Breit-Wigner shape for the ρ^0 is well known, and is caused by the interference (dashed-dotted) of the resonant $\pi^+\pi^-$ production (dotted) and a non-resonant background (dashed). A functional form of the three contributions is used to extract the resonant contribution to the cross section. The result is $\sigma(\gamma p \to \rho^0 p) = 12.5 \pm 0.7(stat) \pm 2.8(syst)$ μb, and is shown in Fig 1, where lower energy data (open circles) are also shown for comparison [5].

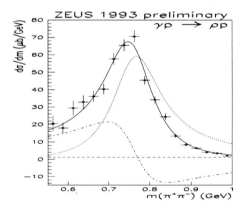

Figure 2. Invariant mass distribution of $\pi^+\pi^-$.

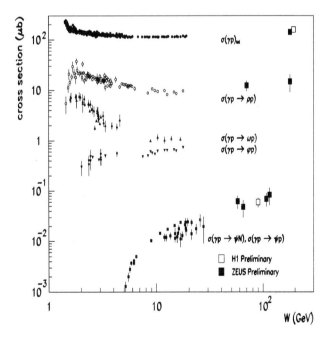

Figure 1. Photoproduction cross section measurements from HERA and lower energy experiments.

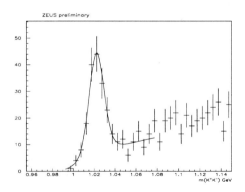

Figure 3. Invariant mass distribution of K^+K^-.

The direct measurement of the ρ^0 elastic cross section has been obtained by ZEUS from the "untagged" trigger at $60 < W_{\gamma p} < 80$ GeV. Two well reconstructed tracks of opposite charge coming from a good vertex are required, and an invariant mass is formed by assuming these two tracks to be pions. Events in which neutral

ZEUS has performed a similar analysis to obtain a

measurement of the elastic ϕ cross section for the decay channel ($\phi \to K^+K^-$). The invariant mass distribution is shown in Fig 3. However, the cut on the ϕ transverse momentum squared is $0.2 < P_t^2 < 1.0$ (GeV/c)^2, as the acceptance drops sharply below 0.2 (GeV/c)^2 due to the geometry of the detector and the trigger. The average acceptance in the selected region is 20%. The elastic cross section $\sigma(\gamma p \to \phi p)$ within this restricted range in $W_{\gamma p}$ and P_t^2 is measured to be $278 \pm 30(stat) \pm 78(syst)$ nb.

The investigation of the photoproduction of heavy quarks is a probe of strong interaction physics in a region characterised by the transition between perturbative QCD and non-perturbative interactions. The photoproduction of J/ψ is an ideal process to explore this regime. A clear signal can be seen from H1 in Fig 4 from the invariant mass distribution of the sum of the electron and muon decay modes of J/ψ. The analysis for the measurement of $\sigma(\gamma p \to (J/\psi)p)$, where $J/\psi \to e^+e^-$ or $\mu^+\mu^-$, is covered elsewhere in these proceedings, but the results are shown in Fig 1 for H1 and ZEUS, along with lower energy data [5].

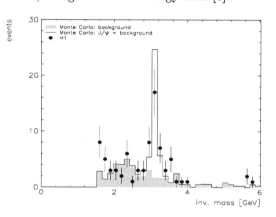

Figure 4. Invariant mass distribution of e^+e^- and $\mu^+\mu^-$.

3. Inclusive transverse momentum distributions

Photon diffractive events are characterised by a gap in rapidity between the leading particle and the photon dissociated system of mass M_x, where the reaction is mediated by the exchange of a pomeron [6] having the quantum numbers of the vacuum. Detectors being installed in the very forward region will tag the recoiling proton for an unambiguous classification of diffractive events. The final implementation of these detectors is still in progress, and hence not used in this analysis.

The tagged data sample has been divided into diffractive and non–diffractive subsets, according to the pseudorapidity † η_{max} of the most forward calorimeter

† $\eta = -log(tan(\theta/2))$, where the polar angle is with respect to

deposit with energy above 400 MeV. We have found that a cut on $\eta_{max} < 2.0$ is very effective in separating the diffractive events from non-diffractive events.

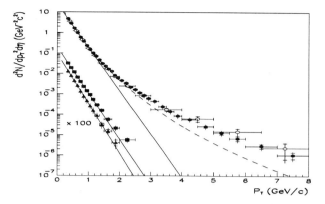

Figure 5. Transverse momentum distribution of charged tracks for photoproduction events.

The spectrum of transverse momenta P_t of tracks satisfying stringent quality criteria in diffractive events is shown in Fig 5, where the data are displayed in two different M_x bins: triangles for $\langle M_X \rangle = 5$ GeV, squares for $\langle M_X \rangle = 10$ GeV. Here M_x is the relevant energy scale for the interaction. Exponential fits (solid lines), normalised to the data points below 1.2 GeV/c, shows that the diffractive data points are consistent with such a fit.

The non-diffractive events are shown in the same figure for H1 (open circles,[7]) and ZEUS (solid circles). The dashed curve is a power law fit to UA1 [8] data for $p\bar{p}$ collisions at a centre of mass energy of 200 GeV. Although is not clear at what energies the comparison should be made, it is clear that the HERA data at similar energies have a harder spectrum. This is hardly surprising since, although the photon exhibits hadron-like properties, the parton distributions in the photon and proton are different, and also because the photon interacts directly.

4. Hard Scattering in Photoproduction

A deviation from the "soft" exponential term in Fig 5 is an indication of hard interactions, and searching for jet structure is the next step, as jets are the observable objects most closely related to the partons. Both H1 and ZEUS have found jets in photoproduction events with transverse energy greater than 5 GeV. The partonic definition of x_γ in Eqn. 1 is redefined to refer to the variables measured from the jets.

Both ZEUS and H1 have evidence for the direct and resolved components in photoproduction through the variable x_γ, as seen from the distribution of x_γ

the proton direction.

from the ZEUS data in Fig 6. Monte Carlo simulations are also shown for the resolved (dashed) and direct (dotted) contributions, and the sum (solid line). The operational definition used for the photon classification is that $x_\gamma < 0.75$ is "resolved" and $x_\gamma > 0.75$ is "direct".

At HERA, events with two observable jets ($E_T^{jet} \gtrsim 6$ GeV, $\eta^{jet} \lesssim 2$) are sensitive to x_p as low as 10^{-3} and x_γ of approximately 10^{-1}. We consider jets at nearly equal pseudorapidities, with an average of $\bar{\eta}$, as the configuration of "same-side" jets allows very small x values of the initial partons to be examined [9].

The differential cross section in $\bar{\eta}$ for $x_\gamma > 0.75$ is dominated by direct photon interactions and so is insensitive to the parton distribution in the photon, but sensitive instead to the gluon distribution in the proton. This is shown in (Fig 7a) (solid circles) and compared to LO QCD calculations using various parton distribution sets for the proton. Low-x effects such as non-zero k_T of the incoming partons may explain why the measured cross section lies below most curves at low $\bar{\eta}$ [10]. However, other higher order or hadronisation corrections have not yet been fully considered.

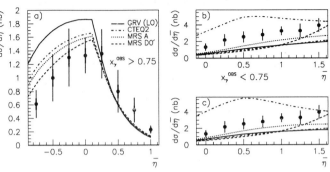

Figure 7. $\bar{\eta}$ distribution for $x_\gamma > 0.75$ is shown in fig a.). GS2 set was used for the photon, and the sets for the parton distribution for the proton were: GRV (solid line), CTEQ2 (dash-dotted line), MRSA (dotted line) and (MRSD0)' (dashed line). In fig b.) and c.), $x_\gamma < 0.75$ and the parton distributions for the photon are LAC3 (high, dash-dotted line), GS2 (dotted line), GRV (solid line), LAC1 (dashed line), and DG (low, dash-dotted line). The parton distribution for the proton was MRSA for fig b.) and GRV (LO) for fig c.).

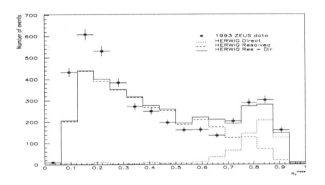

Figure 6. x_γ distribution for data and HERWIG Monte Carlo with direct and resolved components

The region $x_\gamma < 0.75$ is sensitive to the gluon distribution in the photon. As the x_p values probed here are in the region where the parton densities of the proton are well constrained by other measurements, the sensitivity to different parton distribution sets in the proton is small as can be seen from a comparison of MRSA in Fig 7b and GRV (LO) in Fig 7c. However, the sensitivity to different photon parton distribution sets is large as can be seen from the variations in the predictions. Higher order QCD calculations are necessary before strong conclusions can be drawn.

5.   Hard Diffraction in Photoproduction

The observed properties of the diffractive cross section have been described by Regge theory, where the process

proceeds through the exchange of the pomeron. The interplay of Regge theory and perturbative QCD is one motivation for studying hard scattering in diffractive processes [11], since these subjects are mostly without experimental overlap. In one such treatment of this subject [12], Ingelman and Schlein have modelled the pomeron as a hadron having constituent partons. The result of hard interactions is the production of jets, similar to the discussion in section 4. Monte Carlo programs modelling a partonic interaction of the pomeron and based on pQCD now exist, (e.g. POMPYT [13]) and we can confront these with HERA diffractive data.

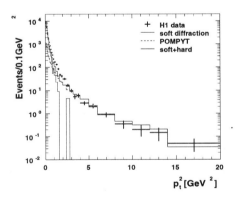

Figure 8. Square of the transverse momentum distribution for photoproduction diffractive events from H1.

Fig 8 shows the transverse momentum squared for diffractive events selected with $\eta_{max} < 1.5$, from H1 data [14]. PYTHIA, which models soft diffraction, cannot account for the high P_t^2 tail, but POMPYT, which models hard diffraction, reproduces this hard tail well, which could be an indication of hard partonic scattering in photon diffraction events.

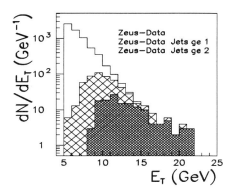

Figure 9. Transverse energy of diffractive events from ZEUS for all events with E_t greater than 5 GeV (solid line), and the subset with at least one jet (crossed) , and greater than one jet (shaded).

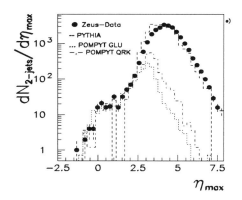

Figure 10. η_{max} for all γp events with two jets from ZEUS.

It is natural to search for jet structure in such diffractive events. Fig 9 shows the transverse energy E_t spectrum for diffractive events with $E_t > 5$ GeV, and we see that 6.5% (2.1%) of the events have at least one (or more) jet(s). Jet production dominates the high E_t region, with jets having E_t as large as 10 GeV being observed.

To verify that this is not the tail of the non-diffractive data, we show in Fig 10 the η_{max} distribution for photoproduction events with two jets in ZEUS. The excess of jets for η_{max} below 1.5 is not reproduced by photoproduction processes as modelled in PYTHIA, which predicts less than 0.1% of events with jets in this region, to be compared to the 0.63% seen. However, POMPYT, with hard interactions from a quarkonic (QRK) or gluonic (GLU) pomeron, gives a reasonable agreement in this region. These observations are consistent with hard partonic scattering in diffractive γp collisions.

The restriction on η_{max} imposes a limit in the

range of phase space available for large masses and large E_t jets which are desirable for more conclusive studies of the hard interactions. We will cleanly identify diffractive events with the final implementation of the Leading Proton Spectrometers and the Forward Neutron Calorimeters in H1 and ZEUS. Already, ZEUS has detected fully measured $\gamma p \rightarrow \rho^0 p$ events. High energy leading neutrons have also been observed for the first time. In addition to the diffractive processes, reactions from a pion exchange with the production of a forward neutron will also be investigated. The study of forward baryonic states will be an important aspect of the future physics programs at HERA.

6. Conclusions

We have reported on a wide range of physics results from photoproduction at HERA, from cross section measurements to detailed studies of the elastic and inelastic diffractive subprocesses. The large centre of mass energy of HERA has allowed the observation of the direct and resolved components of the photon interaction, and jets as evidence for hard scattering. We have found evidence of hard partonic scattering in diffractive γp collisions. With the final implementation of the forward detectors, we will be able to identify and explore the characteristics of high mass diffractive events.

7. Acknowledgements

We thank the DESY directorate for their strong support and encouragement. The remarkable achievements of the HERA machine group were essential and are appreciated. The author appreciates the time and effort invested by several H1 and ZEUS members during the preparation of this talk.

References

[1] Contributed papers to this conference ICHEP Ref 672,682,686,688,690,691,692,693.

[2] J.K. Storrow, J. Phys, G19 (1993) 1641.

[3] H1 Collaboration, Phys Lett. B 299 (1993) 374.

[4] ZEUS Collaboration, Zeit.Phys. C63 (1994) 391.

[5] A. Baldini et. al., Landolt-Bornstein, Group I, Vol 12b, Springer-Verlag, ed. H.Schopper.

[6] K. Goulianos, Phys. Rep. 101 (1983) 169.

[7] H1 collaboration, Phys. Lett.B328 (1994) 176.

[8] C. Albajar et. al., Nucl. Phys. B335 (1990) 261.

[9] J. R. Forshaw and R. G. Roberts, Phys. Lett. B319 (1993) 539.

[10] J. R. Forshaw and R. G. Roberts, Phys. Lett. B335(1994) 494.

[11] E. Berger et. al., Nucl Phys. B286 (1987) 704.

[12] G. Ingelman and P. Schlein, Phys. Lett. B152 (1985) 256.

[13] P. Bruni and G. Ingelman, DESY 93-187.

[14] S. Levonian, Proceedings on the Workshop on Two-Photon Physics at LEP and HERA, Lund, May 1994, 96.

Mini-Jets at HERA
as a Probe of the Perturbative Pomeron

W.J. Stirling

Departments of Mathematical Sciences and Physics, University of Durham, Durham DH1 3LE, England.

Abstract

The photoproduction of minijet pairs with small transverse momentum and large relative rapidity at the HERA electron-proton collider is studied. We examine, in particular, the predictions, of the BFKL 'perturbative pomeron' of QCD. The distribution in the azimuthal angle difference of the jets is shown to be particularly sensitive to the BFKL resummation, and is therefore more likely to provide a distinct signature than the mini-jet cross section itself.

The photoproduction of jets at the HERA ep collider can provide several important tests of QCD. One example is the interface between the 'soft' and 'hard' production regimes, as discussed for example in Ref. [1]. Another concerns the production of jets with modest transverse momentum and sizeable separation in rapidity. Several years ago, Mueller and Navelet [2] showed that the cross section for producing a pair of such 'mini-jets' could be used to probe the the Balitsky-Kuraev-Fadin-Lipatov (BFKL) [3] 'perturbative pomeron'. The cross section is predicted to rise roughly as $e^{\lambda \Delta y}$, where $\lambda \simeq 0.5$, with increasing rapidity difference Δy. This is in exact analogy to the predicted rise $\sim x^{-\lambda}$ at small x of deep inelastic structure functions. In both cases it is the multiple emission of soft gluons which is responsible for the predicted behaviour.

These ideas have recently been applied [4, 5] to jet production at the Tevatron $p\bar{p}$ collider. For fixed collider energy, the dependence of the cross section on the rapidity difference is dominated more by the fall-off of the parton distributions at large x, rather than by the predicted BFKL behaviour of the parton subprocess cross section. Coupled with theoretical uncertainties concerning the choice of scale, sub-leading corrections etc., this makes the observation of BFKL behaviour from the total mini-jet cross section alone

rather difficult. One can instead study the correlations in azimuthal angle difference: jets with a small rapidity difference are dominantly produced back-to-back in $\Delta\phi$, while the correlation weakens as the jets separate in rapidity until in the limit $\Delta y \to \infty$ the distribution in $\Delta\phi$ becomes flat [4, 5]. It is the leading-logarithm contributions to the cross section from this gluon emission which are resummed by the BFKL equation.

Here we extend the analysis to the photoproduction of mini-jet pairs at HERA. For the (small) jet transverse momenta in which we are interested, 'resolved photon' (quark and gluon) contributions to the cross section dominate the 'direct photon' contribution. The formalism is essentially the same as for $p\bar{p}$ collisions, and many of the results of Ref. [5] can be applied directly to the HERA analysis. One important difference is that at the $p\bar{p}$ collider the largest Δy's are obtained by considering large equal and opposite jet rapidities, whereas the beam energy asymmetry at HERA makes it more appropriate to consider one jet produced centrally with another produced at large backward (i.e. proton direction) rapidity.

The 'resolved photon' contribution to the inclusive two-jet cross section at HERA is given in leading order by

$$\frac{d\sigma^{res}}{dy_1 dy_2 dp_T^2} = \frac{1}{16\pi^2 s^2} \sum_{a,b,c,d=q,g} x_e^{-1} f_{a/e}(x_e, \mu^2)$$

$$x_p^{-1} f_{b/p}(x_p, \mu^2) \overline{\sum} |\mathcal{M}(ab \to cd)|^2 \,, \qquad (1)$$

where the jets have equal and opposite transverse momentum $p_T \ll \sqrt{s}$, and rapidities y_1 and y_2. The momentum fractions are fixed by the final state kinematics: $x_e = (p_T/2E_e)\,e^{y_1}\,(1 + e^{-\Delta})$ and $x_p = (p_T/2E_p)\,e^{y_1}\,(1 + e^{\Delta})$, where $\Delta = y_2 - y_1$. At HERA, $E_e \ll E_p$ and so the phase-space limit corresponding to $x_e = 1$ is reached for relatively modest positive jet rapidities. In contrast, for jets with $p_T \ll E_p$ large negative rapidities are accessible. For large Δy, we therefore require one jet to have small positive rapidity, while the other has large negative rapidity. For example, if we take $E_e = 30$ GeV, $E_p = 820$ GeV and $p_T = 5$ GeV/c, then Fig. 1 shows the momentum fractions x_e and x_p for $y_1 = 1$ as a function of Δ. Note that

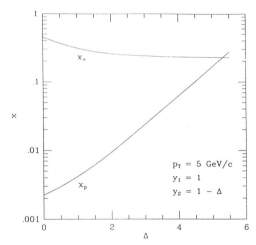

Figure 1. Parton momentum fractions in the proton (x_p) and in the electron (x_e) for the $2 \to 2$ jet cross section.

we are generating a large rapidity difference in a way which corresponds to an approximately constant x_e and a rapidly varying x_p. This means that the poorly known photon structure functions tend to factor out of the cross section, while the proton's structure functions are probed in a region where they are well determined by fixed-target deep inelastic scattering experiments. In the limit $\Delta \to \infty$ we can use the effective subprocess approximation, in which all parton subprocesses are taken into account by using the $gg \to gg$ matrix element and multiplying by the combination $G \equiv g + (4/9)\sum(q + \bar{q})$ of parton distributions.

The subprocess cross section integrated over transverse momenta $p_T > P_T$ exhibits the *scaling* behaviour: $P_T^2 \, \hat{\sigma}(gg \to gg) \simeq \alpha_s C_A \pi/2$. When Δ is so large that $\alpha_s \Delta \sim O(1)$, higher-order contributions proportional to $\alpha_s^2(\alpha_s \Delta)^n$ appear and must be resummed. This is achieved using the BFKL equation, as described for ex-

ample in Ref. [5]. Schematically,

$$\hat{\sigma}_{\rm BFKL} \simeq \frac{\alpha_s^2 C_A^2 \pi}{2P_T^2} \left[1 + \sum_{n \geq 1} a_n \left(\frac{\alpha_s C_A}{\pi} \Delta \right)^n + \dots \right],$$
$$(2)$$

where the $\dots$ on the right-hand side refers to corrections outside the leading logarithm approximation implicit in (2), i.e. terms of order $\alpha_s^n \Delta^{n-1}$, $\alpha_s^n \Delta^{n-2}$, $\dots$ and 'power-correction' terms suppressed by powers of $e^{-\Delta}$. The asymptotic behaviour of $\hat{\sigma}_{\rm BFKL}$ as $\alpha_s \Delta \to \infty$ is [2, 3], with $t = \alpha_s C_A \Delta/\pi$,

$$\hat{\sigma}_{\rm BFKL} \sim \left(\frac{\alpha_s C_A}{\pi} \right)^2 \frac{\pi^2}{4P_T^2} \frac{1}{\sqrt{\frac{1}{2}\pi 7\zeta(3)t}} e^{4\log 2\, t} \,, \qquad (3)$$

Thus $\hat{\sigma}_{\rm BFKL} \sim e^{\lambda\Delta}$, with $\lambda = (\alpha_s/\pi)\,4\,C_A \log 2 \simeq 0.5$. Integrating over $p_T^2 > P_T^2$ then gives [5]

$$\frac{d\sigma^{\rm res}}{dy_1 dy_2}\bigg|_{y_2 = y_1 - \Delta} \simeq \hat{\sigma}_{\rm BFKL}$$
$$\times \int_1^{X^{-2}} \frac{du^2}{u^4} x_e f_{G/e}(uX\rho, \mu^2) x_p f_{G/p}(uX/\rho, \mu^2)(4)$$

with

$$X = \frac{2P_T}{\sqrt{s}} \cosh \frac{\Delta}{2} \,, \qquad \rho = \sqrt{\frac{E_p}{E_e}}\, e^{y_1 - \frac{1}{2}\Delta} \,. \qquad (5)$$

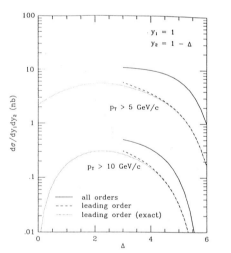

Figure 2. The two-jet inclusive cross section $d\sigma/dy_1 dy_2 (y_1 = 1, \ y_2 = 1 - \Delta)$ at HERA as a function of Δ.

Fig. 2 shows the two-jet inclusive cross section as a function of the rapidity difference Δ, for $P_T = 5, 10$ GeV/c. The three curves correspond to: (i) (dotted line) the exact lowest-order $2 \to 2$ cross section defined in Eq. (1), integrated over $p_T > P_T$, with all the different subprocesses correctly included, (ii) (dashed line) the approximate scaling form of the lowest-order cross section, i.e. Eq. (4) with the subprocess cross section of Eq. (2) without the $n \geq 1$ terms in the series, and (iii) (solid line) Eq. (4) with the all-orders cross section defined in Eq. (2), which incorporates the full BFKL behaviour. We see that at large Δ the lowest-order cross section is indeed well-approximated in shape by the scaling form. The BFKL behaviour of the subprocess cross section is then reflected in an increase in normalization and a slower fall-off in rapidity, as the $e^{\lambda \Delta}$ behaviour partially compensates the decrease in the proton's parton distributions at large x_p. We should emphasize that the BFKL prediction is derived in the leading-logarithm approximation: the size of the sub-leading corrections is as yet unknown.

We turn now to the azimuthal angle difference $\Delta \phi = \phi_1 - \phi_2$ between the two jets.† It is straightforward to extend the BFKL analysis to include the ϕ distribution [5, 4]. The result is

$$\frac{1}{\sigma^{\text{res}}} \frac{d\sigma^{\text{res}}}{d\phi} \simeq F(\phi, \Delta) , \qquad (6)$$

where σ^{res} denotes the cross section of Eq. (4), and

$$F(\phi, \Delta) = \delta(\phi) + \sum_{n \geq 1} f_n(\phi) \left(\frac{\alpha_s C_A}{\pi} \Delta \right)^n . \qquad (7)$$

Expressions for the functions $f_n(\phi)$ can be found in Ref. [5]. Note that in the absence of gluon emission, the two jets are back-to-back as expected. In the limit $\alpha_s \Delta \to \infty$, we have [5]

$$F(\phi, \Delta) \sim \frac{1}{2\pi \sqrt{\frac{1}{2} \pi 7 \zeta(3) t}} e^{4 \log 2 \, t} , \qquad (8)$$

with $t = \alpha_s C_A \Delta / \pi$. Asymptotically, the ϕ distribution becomes *flat*: the emission of an infinite number of soft gluons completely smears out the back-to-back correlation exhibited at leading order.

Fig. 3 shows the ϕ distributions for various Δ. The transition from a distribution strongly peaked at $\phi = 0°$ for small Δ, to a flat distribution at large Δ, is evident. If, as seems possible from Fig. 2, Δ values as high as 4 are accessible at HERA, then this may be large enough to allow the flattening effect to be observed. The average $\langle \cos \phi \rangle$ is shown in Fig. 4 as a function of Δ. Here we have superimposed the result obtained when the perturbation series in Eq. (7) is truncated at next-to-leading order $(n = 1)$, i.e.

$$\langle \cos \phi \rangle_{\text{NLO}} == 1 + \frac{\alpha_s C_A}{\pi} 4(\log 2 - 1) \Delta . \qquad (9)$$

This shows that the higher-order perturbative contributions are already becoming important at $\Delta \approx 3$.

† We define $\phi = \pi - \Delta \phi$, so that $\phi = 0$ corresponds to jets which are back-to-back in the transverse plane

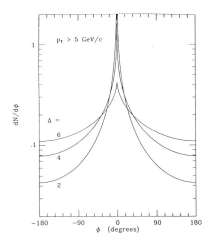

Figure 3. The $\phi = \pi - \Delta \phi$ distributions normalized to unit area, at fixed Δ with $y_1 = 1$, $y_2 = 1 - \Delta$ and $p_T > 5$ GeV/c.

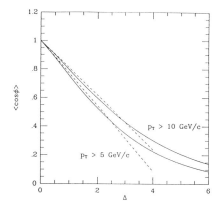

Figure 4. The all-orders BFKL prediction for the average azimuthal angle difference $\langle \cos \phi \rangle$ as a function of Δ. The dashed line is the next-to-leading order approximation.

Note that since $a_1 = \int d\phi f_1(\phi) = 0$ [5], the effects of multigluon emission are felt earlier in the ϕ distribution than in the total ϕ-integrated cross section.

While we have demonstrated that the effects corresponding to the leading behaviour are measureable at the parton level, it will be vitally important to confirm that these survive the inclusion of sub-leading contributions, and also to perform more realistic Monte Carlo simulations to quantify the effects of hadronization, jet reconstruction, and detector effects.

References

[1] A. Donnachie and P.V. Landshoff, Cambridge preprint DAMTP/94/28 submitted to this conference.
[2] A.H. Mueller and H. Navelet, Nucl. Phys. **B282** (1987) 727.
[3] L.N. Lipatov, Sov. J. Nucl. Phys. **23** (1976) 338. E.A. Kuraev, L.N. Lipatov and V.S. Fadin, Sov. Phys. JETP **45** (1977) 199. Ya.Ya. Balitsky and L.N. Lipatov, Sov. J. Nucl. Phys. **28** (1978) 822.
[4] V. Del Duca and C.R. Schmidt, Phys. Rev. **D49** (1994) 4510.
[5] W.J. Stirling, Nucl. Phys. **B 423** (1994) 3751.

Gluon Radiation Patterns in Pomeron Exchange Events

Dieter Zeppenfeld[†]

Department of Physics, University of Wisconsin, Madison, WI 53706, USA

Abstract

Color singlet two gluon exchange provides a perturbative model for the pomeron. This mechanism is thought to explain the production of rapidity gaps in hard dijet events at the Tevatron. It is shown that in qQ scattering via two gluon color singlet exchange the emission of soft gluons follows closely the pattern found for t-channel photon exchange. Gluon emission is strongly suppressed between the two quark jets. After hadronization this leads to a depressed level of hadronic activity between the jets and thus allows the formation of rapidity gaps.

The formation of rapidity gaps, regions in pseudorapidity without hadronic activity, is a well known phenomenon in hadronic collisions. Elastic scattering or single diffractive dissociation are examples of low Q^2 processes with rapidity gaps and they have long been understood in terms of pomeron exchange [1, 2].

A similar phenomenon has recently been observed in *hard* scattering events at the Tevatron [3]. The D0 Collaboration has studied a sample of dijet events with jet transverse energies in excess of 30 GeV. In about 0.5% of all events with widely separated jets no sign of hadronic activity is observed between the two jets. Sampling hadrons between the two jets, a clear break at low multiplicities is seen in the multiplicity distribution. This signals the existence of a qualitatively new source of forward parton scattering. Such events have been predicted [4], at the observed level, in terms of the t-channel exchange of two gluons in a color singlet state which is the Low-Nussinov model for the pomeron [5].

The exchange of a t-channel color singlet object, like the pomeron or a photon, can be seen to lead to rapidity gaps in the color string picture. In such events color is restored by forming a string between the forward scattered partons and their respective beam remnants. Hence, hadrons are predominantly produced in the forward and backward regions, leaving a rapidity

gap between the two scattered partons.

Alternatively, the distribution of hadrons can be understood in terms of the pattern of (typically soft) radiated gluons in the hard scattering event. In the case of γ exchange in forward $qq \rightarrow qq$ scattering, color coherence [6] between initial and final state gluon radiation is known to lead to an exponentially suppressed gluon emission probability into the rapidity region between the two final state quarks [7]. This suppression then leads to the formation of rapidity gaps. The marked difference in the gluon radiation patterns of t-channel photon vs. t-channel gluon exchange is demonstrated in Fig. 1a. Due to its color singlet structure one expects that the same would occur for the t-channel exchange of a pomeron. However, since the Low-Nussinov pomeron is an extended object with colored constituents, the validity of this analogy is not obvious: gluon radiation may resolve the internal color structure of the pomeron. This talk discusses a recent analysis of this problem [8].

It is instructive to first study the process $q_{i_1}Q_{i_3} \rightarrow q_{i_2}Q_{i_4}g^a$, mediated via photon (QED) or single gluon exchange (QCD), at the tree level. The general scattering amplitude for this process can be decomposed into two color singlet and two color octet exchange amplitudes. Here, we only need to consider color singlet exchange as viewed by quark Q which is given by the M_{34} coefficient in the color decomposition of the

† E-mail: dieter@pheno.physics.wisc.edu

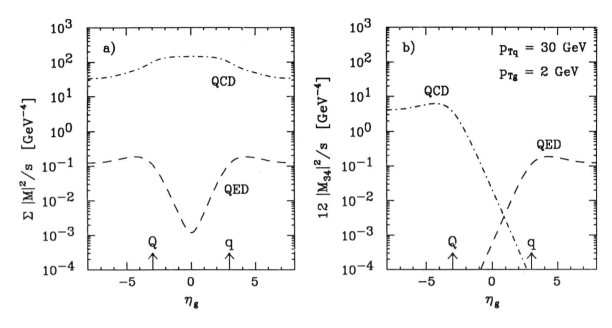

Figure 1. Rapidity distribution of emitted gluons in $qQ \to qQg$ scattering for fixed final state parton transverse momenta of $p_{Tq} = 30$ GeV and $p_{Tg} = 2$ GeV. The quark rapidities are fixed at $\eta_q = \pm 3$ (indicated by the arrows). In part a) results are shown for the sum over all color structures for single gluon and for t-channel photon exchange. The M_{34} terms alone, in part b), demonstrate the difference between the QED and the QCD color singlet exchange terms.

amplitude,

$$M = \frac{\lambda_{i_2 i_1}^a}{2} \, \delta_{i_4 i_3} \, M_{34} + \dots \quad (1)$$

Even for t-channel gluon exchange this color singlet amplitude exists. However, the rapidity distribution of the emitted gluon is markedly different from photon exchange. In the QED case the M_{34} amplitude corresponds to emission of the final state gluon off the quark q. In forward scattering ($\eta_q = +3$ in Fig. 1) the gluon is radiated between the initial and final state q directions. The color i_1 of the initial quark q is thus transferred to a low mass color triplet object which emerges close to the beam direction. At lowest order this is the final state q, at $\mathcal{O}(\alpha_s)$ it is the qg system. The situation is thus stable against gluon emission at even higher order for the QED case and gluon radiation is suppressed in the rapidity range between the two final state quarks.

In the QCD case M_{34} corresponds to emission of the gluon from the quark Q. The gluon is preferentially emitted between the initial Q-beam and the final Q directions (dash-dotted line in Fig. 1b). Thus the color triplet qg system, into which the initial quark q evolves, consists of a widely separated quark and gluon. Higher order corrections will lead to strong gluon radiation into the angular region between the two and thus also into the rapidity range between the two final state quarks.

These typical patterns found for t-channel color singlet and color octet exchange may now be used as a

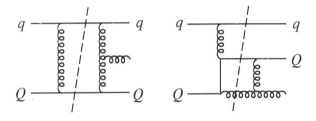

Figure 2. Two of the 31 Feynman graphs contributing to the imaginary part of the color singlet exchange amplitude M_{34}.

gauge for the radiation pattern produced in $qQ \to qQg$ scattering via the exchange of two gluons in a color singlet state. In the lowest order process, $qQ \to qQ$, the color singlet exchange amplitude is dominated by its imaginary part [9]. Hence, we may estimate the radiation pattern by calculating the imaginary part of the gluon emission amplitude M_{34} only. Typical Feynman graphs are shown in Fig. 2. Details of the calculation are given in Ref. [8].

For massless internal gluon propagators the phase space integrals over the qQ, qg, and gQ intermediate states are divergent. They can be regularized by replacing the massless gluon propagator by a version which avoids unphysical gluon propagation over long distances [2]. QCD Pomeron models of this kind have been found to give a good description of available

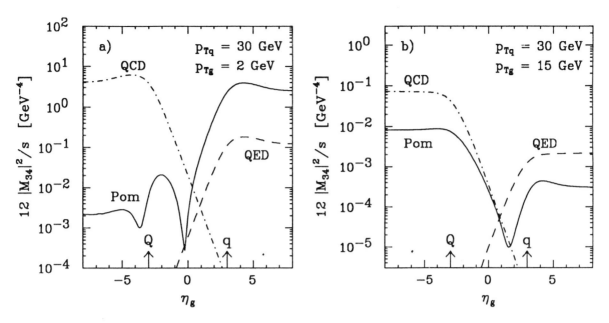

Figure 3. Rapidity distribution of emitted gluons in $uc \to ucg$ scattering via two gluon color singlet exchange as seen by the charm quark. The phase space parameters for the quarks are the same as in Fig. 1 and results are shown for a) the case of a soft gluon ($p_{Tg} = 2$ GeV) and b) a hard gluon ($p_{Tg} = 15$ GeV). For comparison tree level results are shown for gluon (dash-dotted lines) and photon exchange (dashed lines).

data [10]. These refinements can be approximated by using an effective gluon mass of $m_r = 300$ MeV in the calculation.

A second problem arises because some of the contributions to $\mathrm{Im}M_{34}$ correspond to $q \to g$ splitting and subsequent $gQ \to gQ$ scattering via pomeron exchange. These contributions cannot be expected to be suppressed when the gluon is emitted between the q and the Q directions and thus would mask the radiation off pomeron exchange in qQ scattering. These splitting contributions have been subtracted in Ref. [8] to yield the square of the pomeron exchange radiation pattern, $|\mathrm{Im}M_{34}^{\mathrm{pom}}|^2$, which is shown in Fig. 3.

For high transverse momentum of the emitted gluon (of order of the quark momenta, see Fig. 3b) the radiation pattern is quite similar to the one obtained for single gluon exchange. Hard emitted gluons have too short a wavelength to see the screening of the color charge of the harder exchanged gluon by the second, typically very soft, exchanged gluon. The Low-Nussinov pomeron thus reveals itself as an extended object. Hard gluon emission is able to resolve the internal color structure of the Pomeron.

As the transverse momentum of the emitted gluon is decreased, a qualitative transition occurs, as is apparent by comparing the $p_{Tg} = 2$ GeV and 15 GeV cases in Fig. 3. The gluon radiation has too long a wavelength to resolve the internal color structure and hence the pomeron appears as a color singlet object. As a result the emission of a soft gluon ($p_{Tg} \ll p_{Tq}$) follows a

pattern very similar to the one observed for t-channel photon exchange. This pattern is expected to lead to the formation of rapidity gaps. Since the overall gluon emission rate is dominated by the soft region, one concludes that two gluon color singlet exchange in dijet events may indeed lead to the formation of rapidity gap events as observed at the Tevatron [3].

Acknowledgements This research was supported in part by the University of Wisconsin Research Committee with funds granted by the Wisconsin Alumni Research Foundation and by the U. S. Department of Energy under contract No. DE-AC02-76ER00881.

References

[1] See *e.g.* L. V. Gribov, E. M. Levin, and M. G. Ryskin, Phys. Rep. **100C** (1983) 1; Ya. Ya. Balitsky and L. N. Lipatov, Sov. J. Nucl. Phys. **28** (1978) 822; E. M. Levin and M. G. Ryskin, Phys. Rep. **189C** (1990) 267, and references therein.

[2] P. V. Landshoff and O. Nachtmann, Z. Phys. **C35** (1987) 405;

[3] D0 Collaboration, S. Abachi et al., Phys. Rev. Lett. **72** (1994) 2332; A. Brandt, these proceedings.

[4] J. D. Bjorken, Phys. Rev. **D47** (1993) 101.

[5] F. E. Low, Phys. Rev. **D12** (1975) 163; S. Nussinov, Phys. Rev. Lett. **34** (1975) 1286.

[6] Y. L. Dokshitzer et al., Rev. Mod. Phys. **60** (1988) 373, and references therein.

[7] R. S. Fletcher and T. Stelzer, Phys. Rev. **D48** (1993) 5162.

[8] H. Chehime and D. Zeppenfeld, Univ. of Wisconsin preprint MAD/PH/814 (1994).

[9] J. R. Cudell and B. U. Nguyen, Nucl. Phys. **B420** (1994) 669.

[10] F. Halzen, G. I. Krein, and A. A. Natale, Phys. Rev. **D47** (1992) 295; M. B. Gay Ducati, F. Halzen, and A. A. Natale, Phys. Rev. **D48** (1993) 2324.

Paper presented at XXVII Int. Conf. on High Energy Physics: Session Pa-20
Glasgow, UK, 20–27 July 1994

Recent results in photon structure study from DELPHI and TOPAZ collaborations.

Igor Tyapkin, JINR, Dubna.

DELPHI

Abstract

Recent results in experimental study of photon structure from DELPHI and TOPAZ collaborations are presented. For the quasi-real $\gamma\gamma$ collisions data have been compared to Monte Carlo predictions including contributions described by the Vector meson Dominance Model, Quark Parton Model and the perturbative hard scattering of the partonic constituents of the photon (QCD-Resolved Photon Contribution). In the deep-inelastic $e\gamma$ scattering data have been compared with VDM and all order QCD model (FKP) prediction. The data correspond to integrated luminosity of about $60\ pb^{-1}$ for DELPHI and about $113\ pb^{-1}$ for TOPAZ.

1. Introduction.

The kinematics of the process illustrated in Fig.1 and associated processes are shown here as well. Different kinematical regions in the process may be chosen by the requirement, either to detect the scattered $e^{+(-)}$ in the different angular region (ST-Single Tagged mode) or not detect it at all (NT-No Tagged mode). The structure of DELPHI tagging devices is shown in Fig.1.

TOPAZ[1] has a similar structure, providing the measurements starting from $Q^2 \sim 3\text{GeV}^2$. A barrel calorimeter was used to reach very high Q^2 ($\sim 80\ \text{GeV}^2$).

The dual nature of the photon is formalized through a hadron-like part, Fig.1b (VDM) and a point-like part Fig.1c (QPM).

Recently, interest in the structure of the photon has been awakened in the light of results obtained by the TRISTAN[2,3], LEP[4,5] and HERA[6] collaborations, which reported evidence for the production of high transverse momentum jets in quasi-real $\gamma\gamma$ collisions on the e^+e^- colliders and in the γp collisions at HERA. This involves the quark and gluon structure of quasi-real photons through a leading log resolved photons formalism (Fig.1c,d). Through this, interest is

revived in the x and Q^2 behavior of the $\gamma\gamma$ interaction because many parameterizations already obtained by solving inhomogeneous Altarelli-Parisi equations with deep inelastic scattering data at relatively high Q^2 as an input.

In the NT mode gluon density may be probed directly. However, as no clear prediction for the gluon content exists, the NT mode will prove a very interesting field of study.

2. Models.

The VDM model has a lot of uncertainties: A and B parameters in the cross section formula, primary quark angular distribution and fragmentation parameters. All these parameters can be varied to get better agreement with data, but for the moment the values as used in many of previous reports will be explored, to obtain easy comparisons with other experiments.

There are some uncertainties in the QCD-RPC model: these are the parton density functions of the photon, the choice of QCD scale and the cut, which is used to separate the perturbative and non-perturbative regions. In this analysis we use mainly GS2[7] and

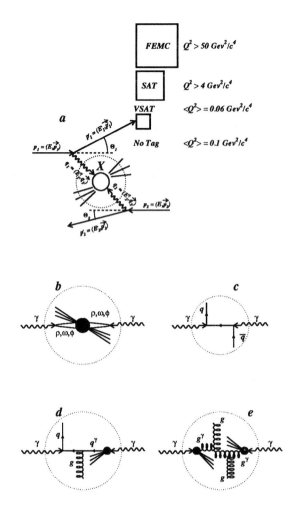

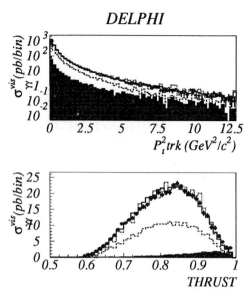

Figure 2. Distributions of event variables in comparison with Monte Carlo predictions. QPM - hatched area, QPM+VDM - dashed line, QPM+VDM+GS2 - full line QPM+VDM+LAC1 - dotted line.

Figure 1. Different contributions to a description of the two photon interaction. VDM (b), QPM (c) and QCD-RPC (d,e) diagrams.

LAC1[8] functions (as being the best from our previous study[4]). As a QCD scale we use p_t of outgoing partons, and the p_t^{min} cut is treated as a free parameter determined from the data. Remnant jets were generated along the direction of the incoming quasi-real photon.

The perturbative calculation for a point-like contribution is available both in the QPM and QCD (FKP formula for example).

The partons produced are then fragmented by the LUND string-fragmentation scheme.

3.   Event selection

Sets of standard criteria[1-5] were used to select NT and ST events. For the DELPHI NT analysis, the Z background is dominant one and its contribution is estimated as 4%. For the DELPHI ST, analysis the main source of background is $\gamma\gamma^* \to \tau\bar{\tau}$, contributed as 3.3 % of the signal.

In the TOPAZ ST analysis, background from

different sources is estimated at about 5 % in the low Q^2 region($\sim$ 5 GeV^2) and up to 40 % in the high Q^2 region($\sim$ 80 GeV^2).

4.   DELPHI no-tag results.

In the previous DELPHI NT analysis we did not succeed in seeing the difference between GS2 and LAC1 models. In this work we reduce the thresholds for the neutral particles and include all the calorimeters in the event analysis but not only in the event selection. For each density function, the parameter p_t^{min} was determined by requirement that the three component model should reproduce the measured cross-section. The results for two different parton density function are:

$p_t^{min}(GS2) = 1.86 \; GeV/c$
$p_t^{min}(LAC1) = 2.28 \; GeV/c$,

which are in good agreement with our previous study[5].

The result of these improvements is the following: Some distributions are not very sensitive to the event topology , they may be fitted quite well by both parameterizations (Fig.2), while the others more sensitive to the event topology and the slight shift between the data and both parameterization can be seen (Fig.3). I want to underline here that the disagreement is not too large essentially for the GS2 parameterization. And if we concentrate our attention on the plot with logarithmic scale we will notice almost the same level of disagreement as in many publications on this subject. It is true that region of low p_t of jets is sensitive to uncertainty from the VDM in this region. But the

DELPHI

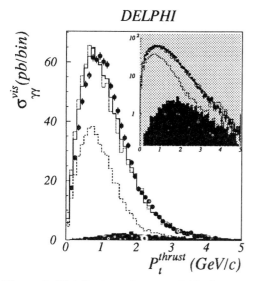

Figure 3. Distributions of event variables in comparison with Monte Carlo predictions. Upper left corner- the same but in log. scale.

DELPHI

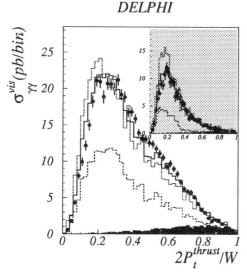

Figure 4. Distributions of event variables in comparison with Monte Carlo predictions. Upper right corner - the same but W> 7GeV.

DELPHI

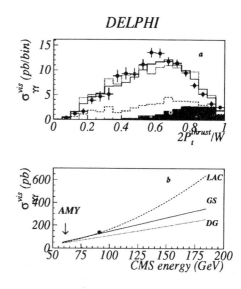

Figure 5. (a)Distribution of $2p_t^{thrust}/W$ for AMY-like selection criteria in comparison with Monte Carlo predictions. (b)- Monte Carlo calculated energy dependency for the three component model prediction.

difference between the GS2 and LAC1 is also maximal here. As we have found, the ratio of $2p_t^{thrust}$ over invariant mass (Fig.4), which is a visible analog of true x, is the most sensitive variable to the parameterization behavior in the region of low x. We made a test, increasing the lower limit for the invariant mass from 4 GeV to 7 GeV we are significantly reduce the VDM contribution in the sample but the disagreement in the $2p_t^{thrust}/W$ distribution is almost the same for GS2 and even higher for LAC1. From this distribution we draw the conclusion that the GS2 parameterization shows better agreement with the data. The LAC1 parameterization indicates a too high gluon density in the region of low x.

By selecting the ST events with VSAT as a tagging device we are dealing with the same NT physics, due to the very small angular region of the VSAT (Fig.1). But the experimental conditions and the background are different for this sample. We consider this analysis as a cross-check of the NT conclusions. Statistical analysis of this data made on the basis of several distributions shows a clear preference for GS2 parameterization among the DO, DG and LAC1. This test confirms our previous conclusions.

The next question we must ask ourselves is whether these results are in agreement with results of other collaborations. To check, we choose the AMY results because a great number of AMY publications are available. The detector acceptance has been modified in accordance with AMY and AMY-like selection criteria were applied. The results are illustrated in Fig.5a We are considering the agreement between data and the model as good, except for the total cross-section. But here we keep the p_t^{min} cut, as determined from our NT data. From Fig.5a we can draw the conclusion: that lower energy, acceptance and selection criteria used by AMY reduced the sensitivity to the details of parameterization in the region of low x. In Fig.5b, the energy dependence of the total visible cross-section of $\gamma\gamma$ interaction with AMY-like cuts and the DELPHI data in these conditions are presented. From this plot, it comes clear that at TRISTAN energy and with AMY selection criteria data, may be fitted by the DG[9], LAC1 and GS2 parameterization, and at the DELPHI energy only by the LAC1 and GS2. At LEP2 energy, the separation between models can be done even at the cross-section level. For us, this test confirms that there is a good

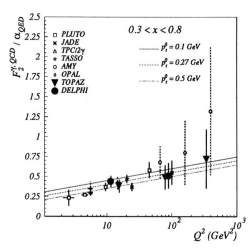

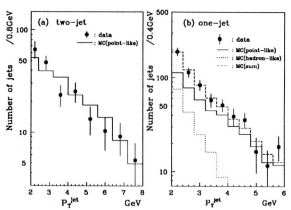

Figure 6. Q^2-dependence of F_2^γ structure function with the results from the previous experiments. The charm quark contribution has been subtracted from data. The theoretical expectation for the FKP+VDM prediction are shown.

consistency between AMY and DELPHI results.

5.   Single tagged analysis.

5.1. F_2^γ measurements

To take into account the effects of detector acceptance and resolution, the Blobel technique was used. The results, in two bins of Q^2 for DELPHI and in three bins for TOPAZ, summarized in Fig.6. On the plot, one can see the results of some previous experiments together with DELPHI and TOPAZ data. The theoretical expectations for the FKP+VDM predictions are shown on the same plot. Both experiments are in agreement here, and show clear increase in F_2^γ with the rise of Q^2, the slope is consistent with $ln(Q^2)$ dependency, which is predicted by QPM and QCD. But the accuracy of measurement is still not high enough to come to conclusion on p_T^0 parameter in the FKP formula.

No rise in the region of low x was observed by the DELPHI group for any Q^2, but TOPAZ reported some for $< Q^2 >= 14 GeV^2$.

5.2.   TOPAZ jet analysis

The last result I want to mention is the jet analysis of ST events made by TOPAZ[1]. This test was done to check the difference in the final state topology for hadron-like and point-like contributions. Jets in the final state were reconstructed with the jet-cone algorithm in azimuth and pseudo-rapidity space. In Fig.7 the transverse momentum of jets for the two-jet and one-jet events is shown versus FKP+VDM models prediction. As expected, two-jet events may be explained by a point-like part only, the hadron-like part should be included to explain the one-jet distribution. A fit of data to a

Figure 7. Transverse momentum of jets for the two-jet(a) and one-jet(b) events in the ST two-photon sample (TOPAZ) $(3.0 < Q^2 < 30 GeV^2)$.

superimposition of Monte Carlo distributions leads to a best-value for the fraction of the hadron-like part to be $44 \pm 8\%$. This result is consistent with the value of 37% for VDM+FKP, then $(P_t^0)=0.5$ GeV is used.

6.   Conclusions

In DELPHI no-tag analysis the GS2 and LAC1 photon density functions describe the majority of event variables.   But in the distributions based on the jet analysis disagreement with model prediction is observed. It is shown that this disagreement is determined not only by uncertainty in VDM prediction but also by the parton density function behavior in the region of low x.   For the first time single tagged analysis in the region of very low Q^2 have been done by DELPHI and confirmed the main conclusions of DELPHI no-tag analysis. DELPHI results are in reasonable agreement with AMY results.

The jet production in deep-inelastic $e\gamma$ scattering was studied for the first time with jet-cone algorithm by the TOPAZ collaboration. The fraction of the hadron-like part was found to be in agreement with model prediction.   The DELPHI and TOPAZ single tagged analyses are in the agreement except for the region of low x.

References

[1] TOPAZ Collaboration, Phys. Lett. **B332** (1994) 477.
[2] AMY Coll., R. Tanaka et al., Phys. Lett. **B277** (1992) 215.
[3] TOPAZ Coll., R. Enomoto et al., KEK-93-107, KEK-93-215;
    H. Hayashii et all., Phys.Lett. **B314** (1993) 149.
[4] ALEPH Coll., D. Buskulic et al., Phys. Lett.**B313** (1993) 509.
[5] DELPHI Coll., P. Abreu et all., CERN-PPE/94-04.
[6] H1 Coll. T. Ahmed et al. DESY-92-160.
    H1 Coll. T. Ahmed et al. Phys. Lett. **B297** (1992) 205.
[7] L. E. Gordon and J.K. Storrow, Z. Phys. **C56** (1992) 307.
[8] H. Abramowicz, K. Charchula and A. Levy, Phys. Lett. **B269** (1991) 458.
[9] M. Drees and R.M. Godbole, Nucl. Phys. **B339** (1990) 355.

Bose-Einstein Correlations

E.A. De Wolf[†]

Physics Department Universitaire Instelling Antwerpen,
Universiteitsplein 1, B 2610 Wilrijk, Belgium

Abstract

A brief review is presented of new Bose-Einstein correlation data submitted to the conference. We report on results from LEP on correlations in $\pi^0\pi^0$ and $K_S^0 K_S^0$-pairs, HERA photoproduction data on like-sign pion pairs and evidence for higher-order Bose-Einstein effects in $\pi^+/K^+ p$ interactions. The relation to intermittency is discussed in the framework of colour-string models.

1. Introduction

Bose-Einstein correlations (BEC) between identical bosons have been investigated in high-energy physics for a long time‡. The production of two identical bosons 1,2 from two particle sources is governed by an amplitude which is symmetrized with respect to interchange of bosons 1,2, resulting in an enhanced probability of emission if the bosons have similar momenta. BE correlations are usually measured in terms of the function

$$R_2 = \sigma \frac{d^2\sigma}{dp_1 dp_1} / \frac{d\sigma}{dp_1} \frac{d\sigma}{dp_2}. \tag{1}$$

Here σ denotes the total cross section, $d\sigma/dp$ the single-particle inclusive cross section, and $d^2\sigma/dp_1 dp_2$ the two-particle cross section. BEC can be an important tool for the study of production dynamics. In particular, it can be argued that (as in the astrophysical study of photon sources), $R_2 - 1$ is directly related to the Fourier transform of the spacetime distribution of particle production points. Thus, R_2 provides a measure of the distribution and lifetime of the boson sources. However, this may be questioned since particle sources in high-energy collisions move relativistically with respect to each other. This is crucial for the proper interpretation of BEC in particle physics. There is also the possibility of coherent production, in which case BEC are absent.

† Senior Research Associate NFWO Belgium.
‡ A list of reviews is given in [1].

In experimental work, a useful parametrization, of BEC is, among many others, the Goldhaber expression

$$R_2 = 1 + \lambda \exp\left(-R_G^2 Q_{12}^2\right), \tag{2}$$

where $Q_{ij}^2 \equiv Q^2 = -(q_1 - q_2)^2$ is (minus) the square of the 4-momentum difference of bosons i, j. In the naive optical picture, the particle source is assumed to have a Gaussian shape in the rest-frame of the pair; R_G then measures the source size and λ the strength of the effect: $0 \le \lambda \le 1$.

For extensive discussion of other parametrizations, their interpretation, the choice of "reference distributions" (to which the measured $d^2\sigma/dp_1 dp_2$ is to be compared), and the many experimental problems involved, we have to refer to the litterature.

In this brief report we describe almost exclusively new results submitted to the conference. We end the paper with a discusion of the connection between BEC, intermittency and their interpretation in colour-string models.

1.1. $\pi^0\pi^0$ correlations

The L3 collaboration studied, for the first time in e^+e^- annihilations, BEC for π^0-pairs, in a sample of 929K events at the Z^0. JETSET 7.3 [2] (without BE) and HERWIG 5.6 [3] is used to obtain the reference background.

The correlation function $R_2(Q)$, corrected for

$f(Q)$ from	λ	R_G (fm)
JETSET	$2.96 \pm 0.26 \pm 0.77$	$0.46 \pm 0.02 \pm 0.08$
HERWIG	$2.09 \pm 0.20 \pm 0.61$	$0.50 \pm 0.04 \pm 0.12$

Table 1. L3: fit-results to $R_r(Q)$ using JETSET or HERWIG.

detector effects (using the same MC's) exhibits a significant enhancement above Monte Carlo expectation for $Q < 0.6$ GeV (figure 1). A fit with expression (2) yields $\lambda = 0.37 \pm 0.03 \pm 0.12$, $R_G = 0.40 \pm 0.03 \pm 0.13$ fm. Here and in the following, the first (second) error is the statistical (systematic) error. In the fit, the interval $0.3 \leq Q \leq 0.5$ GeV is excluded to avoid the influence of η and K_S^0 decays. These fit-values are not incompatible with those for like-charged pion pairs (cfr. table 2).

The correlation function is strongly influenced at small Q by resonance decays (such as $\eta \to \pi^0 \pi^0 \pi^0$, η', $f_0 \to \pi^0 \pi^0$) and other final-state interactions. Also, identical pions from decays of long-lived resonances and heavy-flavour states show a BE-enhancement only at Q-values well below the experimental resolution and are effectively uncorrelated. Under these circumstances, the measured correlation function $R_m(Q)$ can be written as

$$R_m(Q) = f(Q) + (1 - f(Q))\ R_r(Q) \qquad (3)$$

where $R_r(Q)$ is the expected "real" BE-correlation and $f(Q)$ is the fraction of π^0-pairs with at least one π^0 originating from long-lived resonances and heavy-flavour states. The function $f(Q)$, obtained from JETSET and HERWIG varies between $0.9 - 0.6$ for $0 < Q < 1$ GeV and is, unfortunately, quite different in the two Monte Carlo's. Fits to $R_r(Q)$ with eqn. (2) yield values collected in Table 1.

Although R_G remains stable in the correction procedure, λ now takes on very large values. The authors speculate that such a large λ could arise from strong attractive forces among π^0's, not simulated in the models, or from residual correlations in long-lived resonance decays. Clearly, a correct interpretation of BEC in π^0-pairs needs much better understanding of the final-state interactions in small-invariant-mass systems.

Note that, in a string model, pairs of prompt π^0's can be emitted in adjacent string breakups, unlike $\pi^\pm \pi^\pm$-pairs. In momentum space, the BE correlation function might therefore be wider for neutral pions than for charged ones. This effect is not seen in the data.

1.2. $K_S^0 K_S^0$ correlations

Bose-Einstein correlations among charged kaon pairs were observed in hadron-hadron collision experiments [4]. New results on $K_S^0 K_S^0$ interference in $e^+ e^-$-annihilations now exist from DELPHI [5] and OPAL [6]. OPAL presented a (preliminary) update of previous

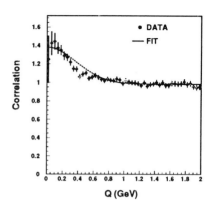

Figure 1. L3: The BE correlation function R_m versus Q for $\pi^0 \pi^0$ pairs. Solid line shows fit result. Dashed line indicates region excluded from the fit.

Experiment	λ	R_G (fm)
$K_S^0 K_S^0$ [6]	$1.17 \pm 0.23 \pm 0.32$	$0.72 \pm 0.10 \pm 0.11$
$K_S^0 K_S^0$ [5]	$1.13 \pm 0.54 \pm 0.23$	$0.90 \pm 0.19 \pm 0.10$
$\pi^\pm \pi^\pm$ [8]	$0.51 \pm 0.04 \pm 0.11$	$0.65 \pm 0.04 \pm 0.16$
$\pi^\pm \pi^\pm$ [9]	$1.06 \pm 0.05 \pm 0.16$	$0.49 \pm 0.01 \pm 0.05$
$\pi^\pm \pi^\pm$ [10]	$1.08 \pm 0.05 \pm 0.14$	$0.93 \pm 0.02 \pm 0.15$

Table 2. Results for λ and R_G from BEC studies at LEP of K_S^0-pairs and $\pi^\pm \pi^\pm$-pairs in the Goldhaber variable Q.

work based on >15K events with ≥ 2 identified K_S^0's. The $K_S^0 K_S^0$ system is interesting since K_S^0's should interfere even if they orginate from a (non-identical) $K^0 \overline{K}^0$ system [7] (see also G. Alexander in ref.[1]).

DELPHI and OPAL use JETSET to obtain a reference background and fit the data to eqn.(2-3), with $f(Q)$ representing the non-interfering background (mainly) from charm and beauty decays. The OPAL data, together with the best-fit curve, are shown in figure 2a. Results of the fit are illustrated in figure 2b in a (R_G, λ) contour-plot, which also shows OPAL $(\pi^\pm \pi^\pm)$ and DELPHI $(K_S^0 K_S^0)$ results. The "radius" parameters for K_S^0-pairs compare well with those measured for pions within large systematic uncertainties (Table 2).

2.   BEC in photoproduction at HERA

First, preliminary results on BEC at HERA were obtained by H1 in a 325K sample of small-angle electron-tagged $e^- p$ collisions. These data effectively correspond to quasi-real photon-proton collisions at a γp c.m.s. energy $160 < \sqrt{s_{\gamma p}} < 250$ GeV ($< \sqrt{s_{\gamma p}} > = 200$ GeV). Charged tracks are reconstructed in two cylindrical drift-chambers and dE/dx information is used to select pions with $p_{\text{lab}} > 250$ MeV/c. H1 uses the $\pi^+ \pi^-$ Q-distribution as a reference background and compares to

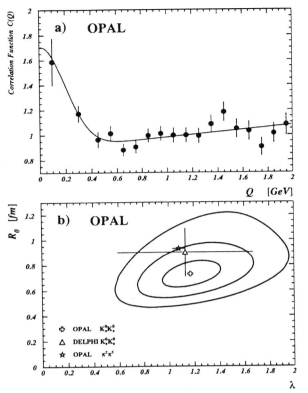

Figure 2. OPAL: (a) The BE correlation function R_m versus Q for $K_S^0 K_S^0$ pairs. Solid line shows fit result;
(b) $R_G - \lambda$ contour-plot (39%, 88% and 99% CL, resp.).

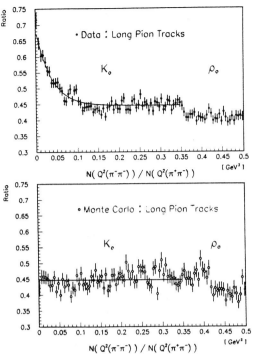

Figure 3. H1: (a) The BE correlation function, not corrected for detector efects, versus Q^2 for $\pi^{\pm}\pi^{\pm}$ pairs with superimposed fit. (b) As in (a) for Monte Carlo events without BEC

Monte Carlo (without BEC) to establish a clear BE-enhancement in like-charge pairs for $Q^2 < 0.1$ GeV^2 (figure 3). A fit with (2) yields $R_G = 1.04 \pm 0.04 \pm 0.1$ fm, $\lambda = 0.54 \pm 0.04 \pm 0.07$. Comparison with the (highest available energy) meson-proton data at ~ 10 times smaller $\sqrt{s}$ does not reveal any significant energy dependence of R_G or λ.

3. Higher-order BEC

Bose-Einstein correlations among groups of three or more like-sign pions have been studied earlier in several hh and e^+e^- experiments (see Table 3 and [11]). Here the interesting question arises whether higher-order BEC contain additional information beyond that derived from 2-particle studies. To answer this question. it is necessary to analyse the "genuine" or "connected" correlation functions. More specifically, for identical particles, the inclusive density $\rho_p(1, 2, \ldots, p)$ can be written as

$$\rho_2(1,2) = C_2(1,2) + \rho_1(1)\rho_1(2),$$
$$\rho_3(1,2,3) = C_3(1,2,3) + \sum_{(3)} \rho_1(1)\rho_2(2,3)$$
$$-2\rho_1(1)\rho_1(2)\rho_1(3). \tag{4}$$

etc, where the summations indicate all possible permutations. The correlation functions $C_p(1,\ldots,p)$ represent the *genuine* p-particle correlations, while the other terms in the expansions are contributions from lower-order densities. It is also convenient to use the normalised inclusive densities and correlations:

$$R_p(1,\ldots,p) = \rho_p(1,\ldots,p)/\rho_1(1)\ldots\rho_1(p), \tag{5}$$

$$K_p(1,\ldots,p) = C_p(1,\ldots,p)/\rho_1(1)\ldots\rho_1(p). \tag{6}$$

The normalised inclusive density for two identical pions is [cfr. (1)]

$$R \equiv R_2(1,2) = 1 + K_2(1,2). \tag{7}$$

Experiments have studied R_p as a function of

$$Q_p^2 = \sum_{i=1}^{p} (q_i)^2 - (p\,m_\pi)^2; \tag{8}$$

and use the empirical parametrisation

$$R_p(Q_p^2) = \gamma_p[1 + \lambda_p \exp(-r_p^2 Q_p^2)](1 + \delta_p Q_p^2), \tag{9}$$

where λ_p characterizes the strength of the interference effects, γ_p is a normalisation coefficient and δ_p is introduced to account for a possible variation of $R_p(Q_p^2)$ outside the interference peak.

NA22 has presented new data on BEC up to 4-th order in a sample of 102K non single-diffractive $\pi^+ p$ and

Gaussian parametrisation in Q			
Expt.	$\sqrt{s}$ (GeV)	r_3 (fm)	r_2 (fm)
NA22 (π^+/K^+p)	22	0.51 ± 0.01	0.83 ± 0.03
NA23 (pp)[12]	26	0.58 ± 0.07	0.99 ± 0.17
AFS (pp)[13]	63	0.41 ± 0.02	0.82 ± 0.05
e^+e^- SPEAR J/Ψ[14]	3.1	$0.53 \pm 0.01 \pm 0.03$	$0.81 \pm 0.02 \pm 0.05$
e^+e^- $\gamma\gamma$[14]	5	$0.55 \pm 0.01 \pm 0.03$	$0.84 \pm 0.06 \pm 0.05$
e^+e^- SPEAR $q\bar{q}$[14]	4-7	$0.45 \pm 0.02 \pm 0.03$	$0.71 \pm 0.03 \pm 0.04$
e^+e^- PEP $q\bar{q}$[14]	29	$0.64 \pm 0.04 \pm 0.04$	$0.84 \pm 0.06 \pm 0.05$
e^+e^- TASSO[15]	29-37	0.52 ± 0.07	0.88 ± 0.09

Table 3. Results on two- and three-particle BEC

K^+p interactions at $\sqrt{s} = 22$ GeV. The denominators in eqn.(5-6) were calculated from a reference sample composed by combining tracks randomly chosen from different events of the same charged particle multiplicity. Their data for R_p ($p = 2, 3, 4$) are displayed in figure 4. Fitted values of r_2 and r_3 using eqn.(9) are compared with other data in Table 3. The various values of r_2 and r_3, respectively, are well consistent with each other. For a completely chaotic source one can derive the bounds $\frac{r_2^2}{3} \leq r_3^2 \leq \frac{r_2^2}{2}$. The data are consistent with these bounds.

The solid lines in Figure 4 are fits to parametrisations derived in the quantum statistics formalism, assuming static and partially coherent radiation sources [16] (see also [11]) and also describe the data quite well.

The NA22 data allow to extract the normalised three-particle correlation function $K_3(Q_3^2)$. The function $K_3(Q_3^2)+1$ is shown in Figure 5, after Coulomb correction. A non-zero K_3 is observed for $Q_{3\pi}^2 < 0.2$ (GeV/c)^2.

In terms of the Q_{ij} variables and for the case of a completely chaotic source (complex-gaussian stochastic process), the normalised three-pion density is [16]

$$R_3(1,2,3) = 1 + |F(Q_{12}^2)|^2 + |F(Q_{13}^2)|^2 + |F(Q_{23}^2)|^2$$
$$+ 2\text{Re}F(Q_{12}^2)F(Q_{13}^2)F(Q_{23}^2); \qquad (10)$$

and

$$K_2(1,2) = |F(Q_{12})|^2, \qquad (11)$$
$$K_3(1,2,3) = 2\text{Re}\{F(Q_{12}^2)F(Q_{13}^2)F(Q_{23}^2)\}. \qquad (12)$$

In general, $K_3(1,2,3)$ is not completely determined by $K_2(i,j)$ but also depends on the phase of the Fourier transform $F(Q)$ of the source. To the extent that such phase factors may be neglected, K_3 is related to K_2 via the expression

$$K_3(Q_3^2) = 2\sqrt{K_2(Q_3^2)} \qquad (13)$$

and the three-particle correlation can be expressed completely in terms of the two-particle correlation

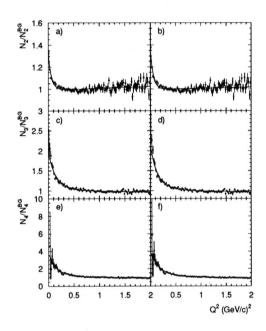

Figure 4. NA22: The normalised two-, three- and four-particle inclusive densities not corrected (a,c,e) and corrected (b,d,f) for Coulomb effects, as a function of Q_p^2. Curves show the result of fitting by expressions for a partially coherent source.

function. The solid line in Figure 5 is obtained under this assumption and agrees with the data.

4. BEC, intermittency and the string model

Some recent experiments have shown that the Gaussian parametrisation of the BEC correlation function does not fit well the data at Q-values below 100 MeV [17]. Indeed, these data indicate that R_2 is steeper than a Gaussian and better represented by an exponential in Q or by a sum of two Gaussians. This could be explained by the fact that resonance decays lead to a larger effective pion source. This interpretation finds some confirmation in a recent E665 (μN interactions) analysis [18]. OPAL [10], on the other hand, attributes

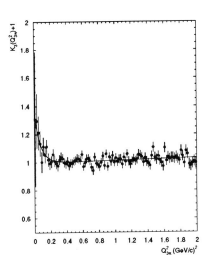

Figure 5. NA22: The function $1 + K_3(Q_3^2)$. The curve is calculated under the assumption that higher-order correlations obey the properties of a Gaussian stochastic process.

the steeper-than-Gaussian dependence to kinematical effects.

The possibility has been advanced† that the BE correlation functions may, in fact, follow a power-law in Q. BEC are now indeed known to be the likely origin of the so-called "intermittency" effect [19], with its characteristic power-law behaviour. Physically this would imply that BE interferometry measures a quasi scale-free hadronisation process wherein the emission regions have (multi-)fractal properties.

A possibly complementary interpretation is offered by the colour-string model. As emphasised by Andersson and Hofmann [20] and Bowler [21], the string hadronisation model contains most of the ingredients for a proper understanding of BEC data in "elementary" processes. The model is stochastic in nature and thus provides the chaoticity necessary for BEC to exist. Particle emission occurs "on the light-cone" and is characterised by a strong correlation between production points in space-time and the momenta of particles. Such a correlation is neglected in almost all pictures of BEC based on optical analogy. It follows that the length-scale relevant for BEC is not the total size of the emission volume, but a local region only of the colour string. Its size is controlled by the string tension. The source size measured in BE interferometry is therefore predicted to be independent of the total interaction energy and of the primary process creating the colour strings. Detailed calculations [20, 21] prove that this model is able to reproduce the data. Most interestingly, the predicted 2-particle correlation function is well approximated by a power-law for small Q.

It is tempting to conclude that the string model, which also links spectroscopy to hadronisation, can not only account for much of the phenomenology of the Bose-Einstein effect, studied since 1959 in particle physics, but also offers a proper framework for our understanding of the much more recent work on intermittency.

References

[1] V.G. Grishin, Sov. Phys. Usp. 22 (1977) 1; A. Giovannini, G.C. Mantovani, S.P. Ratti, Riv. Nuovo Cimento 2 No10 (1979); G. Goldhaber, Proc. Int. Conf. Lisbon, 1981; G. Goldhaber, Proc. 1st Int. Workshop on local equilibrium in Strong Interaction Dynamics, Eds. D.K. Scott& R.M. Weiner, 1986; W. Hoffmann, *A fresh look at Bose-Einstein Correlations*, LBL-report 23108 (1987) and Ann. Rev. Nucl. Part. Sci. 38 (1988) 279. W.A. Zajc, in Hadronic Multiparticle Production, Ed. P. Carruthers World Scientific Singapore 1988, p. 235; M.I. Podgoretskii, Sov. J. Nucl. Phys. 20 (1989) 266;B. Lörstad, Int. J. Mod. Phys. A4 (1989) 2861;D.H. Boal et al., Rev. Mod. Phys. 62 (1990) 553;S. Marcellini, Proc. Joint Lepton-Photon Symp. and EPS Conf. Geneva 1991, p. 750; G. Goldhaber, in Correlations and Multiparticle production, Eds. M.Plümer, S. Raha, R.M. Weiner, World Scientific Singapore 1991; B. De Lotto, Proc. XXVIth Int. Conf. High Energy Physics, Dallas 1992, p. 955; G. Alexander, Int. Conf on Bose and the 20th century physics, Tel-Aviv preprint TAUP-2133 (1994).
[2] T. Sjöstrand, Computer Phys. Comm. 39 (1986) 347,T. Sjöstrand and M. Bengtsson, Computer Phys. Comm. 43 (1992) 47.
[3] G. Marchesini, B. Webber, Nucl. Phys. B310 (1988) 461,I.G. Knowles, Nucl. Phys. B310 (1988) 571;G. Marchesini et al., Computer Phys. Comm. 67 (1992) 465..
[4] T. Åkesson et al., Phys. Lett. B155 (1985) 128;M. Aguilar-Benitez et al., Zeit. Phys. C54 (1992) 21;A.M. Cooper et al., Nucl. Phys. B139 (1978) 45.
[5] P. Abreu et al., Phys. Lett. B323 (1994) 242.
[6] P.D. Acton et al., Phys. Lett. B298 (1993) 456.
[7] H. Lipkin,Phys. Rev. Lett. 69 (1992) 3700;Phys. Lett. B219 (1989) 474;idem Argonne report ANL-HEP-PR-88-66.
[8] D. Decamp et al., Zeit. Phys. C54 (1992) 75.
[9] P. Abreu et al., Zeit. Phys. C63 (1994) 17.
[10] P.D. Acton et al., Phys. Lett. B267 (1991) 143.
[11] N. Neumeister et al.(UA1): Phys. Lett. B275 (1992) 186.
[12] J.L. Bailly et al. (NA23), Zeit. Phys. C43 (1989) 341.
[13] T. Åkesson et al. (AFS), Zeit. Phys. C36 (1987) 517.
[14] I. Juricic et al. (MARK II), Phys. Rev. D39 (1989) 1.
[15] M. Althoff et al. (TASSO), Zeit. Phys. C30 (1986) 355.
[16] V.L. Lyuboshitz, Yad. Fiz. 53 (1991) 823; M. Biyajima et al., Prog. Theor. Phys. 84 (1990) 931.
[17] H. Aihara et al.(TPC), Phys. Rev. D31 (1985) 996; T. Åkesson et al., (AFS), idem Zeit. Phys. C36 (1987) 517;idem Phys. Lett. B187 (1987) 420;idemPhys. Lett. B129 (1983) 269;N. Agababyan et al. (NA22), Zeit. Phys. C59 (1993) 405;A. Bialas, these proceedings.
[18] M.R. Adams et al. (E665) Preprint Max-Planck Munchen MPI-PhE/93-10.
[19] E.A. De Wolf, L.M. Dremin, W. Kittel: *Scaling laws for density correlations and fluctuations in multiparticle dynamics*, to be publ. in Phys. Rep. C.
[20] B. Andersson, W. Hofmann,Phys. Lett. 169B (1986) 364.
[21] M. Bowler, Particle World 2 (1991) 1.

† see A. Bialas, these proceedings.

Multiplicity, correlations, fluctuations

A.Bialas

Institute of Physics, Jagellonian University,
Reymonta 4, Cracow, Poland

Abstract

Recent investigations of multiparticle correlations in e^+e^-, lepton–hadron and hadron–hadron collisions are reported with a particular emphasis on scaling features ("intermittency") of the particle spectra.

1. Introduction

Studying multiparticle correlations is a specific (and very useful) way of looking on multiplicity distributions: correlation parameters measure deviation of the observed multiplicity distribution from the Poisson one (which describes the uncorrelated emission). If the observed fluctuations of multiplicity are larger than those in Poisson distribution (with the same average) the correlations are positive — otherwise they are negative.

Historically we distinguish long-range and short-range correlations in momentum space. Long range correlations describe total multiplicity distribution or distribution in a large part of the available phase space. At not too low energies (to avoid constraints from conservation laws) the observed correlations are positive. This is often interpreted as evidence for a multicomponent nature of high energy collisions. The success of the negative binomial distribution (which can be written as a continuous superposition of Poisson distributions) [1] is a good example of this situation. Another interpretation, advocated by Warsaw group [2] suggests a cascading mechanism. The resulting log-normal distribution describes well the data up to ~ 300 GeV/c incident energy. A thorough discussion of total multiplicity distributions was given by Wróblewski at the Singapore Conference [3].

Multiplicity distributions in restricted domains of phase-space give information on the so-called short-range correlations. Numerous studies in the seventies showed that the data can be described in terms of clusters, i.e. isotropically decaying objects, rather densely packed in the phase space available for soft particles. Surprisingly enough, the data in different rapidity intervals can also be described by the negative binomial distribution [1]. This is explained by the fact that, as emphasized by Giovannini and Van Hove [1, 4], the negative binomial distribution can be written in the form which corresponds to independent emission of clusters.

In the last few years the main focus of research is on correlations of very short range, much shorter than those related to cluster decay. This kinematic region — very difficult experimentally — became accessible by increasing statistics and quality of the data, and by the development of new, sensitive tools. It started with factorial moments [5] which played an important role at the beginning. Significant progress was possible when a novel technique, called "correlation integrals" and "star integrals" was proposed and developed by the Tucson–Vienna collaboration [6]. This turned out to be a great improvement which allowed to measure correlation functions with an unprecedented precision. A recent example of such a measurement is shown in Fig. 1, where the data from NA22 coll., submitted to this conference [7], are plotted. One notices a high-precision measurement of not only two-particle but also three- and four-particle correlations. One also sees that the correlation functions increase with decreasing momentum interval down to about 50 MeV.

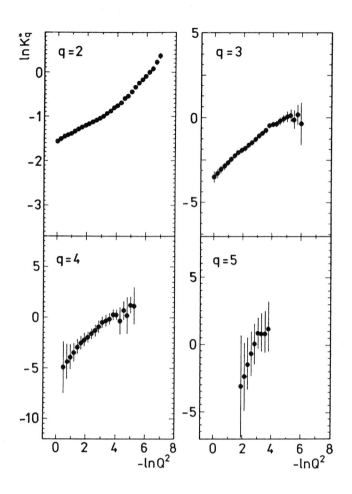

Figure 1. Genuine higher order correlations measured by star integration technique in EHS/NA22 experiment [7].

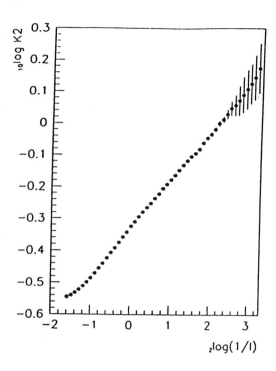

Figure 2. Second cumulant of the charged particles distribution produced in $p\bar{p}$ collisions at 640 GeV/c (UA1 coll. [11]) plotted versus $l = \delta\phi\delta y\delta(\log p_\perp)$.

In two papers submitted to this conference [8] the Alma–Ata group proposed a new method of investigation of correlations in very short rapidity intervals. It amounts to study directly the particle density as function of rapidity interval considered. The method was tested using data on hadronic and nuclear collisions. This may turn out to be an interesting and useful proposal. However, it seems necessary to generalize (and apply) it to multidimensional spectra before one shall be able to assess fully its potential.

2. Scaling of correlation functions

The early observation that the data [9] indicate the presence of very short range correlations led to the suggestion that — perhaps — there exist correlations at all scales [5]. A natural consequence was the idea of scaling, i.e. power law dependence of the factorial moments on the size of the phase-space bin (called "intermittency" in Ref. [5]).

Experimental investigations of factorial moments allowed to confirm existence of intermittency in many reactions [10]. A typical result is shown in Fig. 2, where the second cumulant of the charged particle distribution in 640 GeV $\bar{p}p$ collisions [11] is plotted versus the size of the three-dimensional bin in momentum space. One sees that the data follow rather accurately a straight line which, in this log-log plot, represents the power law

$$C(\delta) \sim \delta^{-f}, \qquad (1)$$

i.e. scaling in the 3-dimensional momentum space.

3. Self-similar cascade

The most natural possibility (although — by far — not the only one [10]) to explain the scaling behaviour of multiparticle densities is the self-similar cascade, which served as a guiding example from the very beginning. In particular, the original suggestion [5] of the scaling phenomenon was modelled as a cascade of a "strongly interacting liquid" in analogy to the turbulent flow in hydrodynamics. This analogy emphasizes the relation of the observed phenomenon to the "chaotic behaviour" of the system in question. In view of the recent work by Müller and collaborators [12] who find a clear signal of chaotic behaviour of the gluon fields, it is not unlikely that this may turn out to be more than just a formal analogy.

The first cascade calculation — using a self-similar cluster model — was performed by Ochs and Wosiek [13]. Calculations in the framework of parton model were started by Konishi, Ukawa and Veneziano [14] and continued extensively by Van Hove and Giovannini [15] and Giovannini and collaborators [16]. They emphasized the general correlation structure of the parton cascade, however, rather than its scaling behaviour. In the paper submitted to this conference [16] a significant progress was reported: the rapidity dependence of clan parameters are now explained by considering clans as independent sources of gluons produced in a Markovian process.

Recently, the analytic calculations of the QCD parton cascade [17] became available. Three groups produced results almost simultaneously [18]. The major ones are (a) the QCD cascade is not actually self-similar because the coupling constant varies along the cascade. Consequently, the scaling is only approximate and the moments tend to saturate at small distances in 3-dimensional phase-space; (b) new observables for testing the predicted behaviour were suggested. They are constructed of angular variables and thus relatively easy to analyze experimentally. In the paper submitted to this conference [19], NA22 collaboration showed first analysis of these new observables.

4. Hadronization

Explanation of scaling in multiparticle spectra in terms of cascade models has one common drawback: they are formulated in terms of partons or other non-observable degrees of freedom rather than in terms of the measured final hadrons. This brings immediately the question why the process of hadronization does not spoil the scaling behaviour. I would like to emphasize that this question is a very serious one: we are talking here about the momentum resolution up to about 40 MeV — significantly below the pion mass — and it is really difficult to understand why the reshuffling of partons into observed hadrons does not affect even such small momentum differences. This puzzled all of us for some time and was — I think — a serious obstacle to the progress.

5. HBT correlations

About two years ago experimental analyzes provided an unambiguous evidence [10] that, as suggested for some time [20], at very small difference of momenta, correlations are dominated by HBT effect, i.e. quantum interference [21]. This is illustrated in Fig. 3 and Fig. 4, where the data from UA1 and DELPHI collaborations

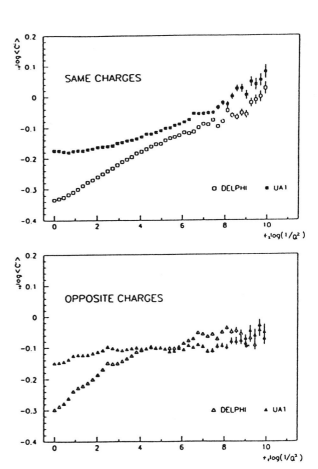

Figure 3. Two-particle correlation integrals for like-sign and opposite-sign particles produced in 640 GeV $p\bar{p}$ collisions and in Z^0 decays. DELPHI and UA1 coll. [22].

[22] and from NA22 collaboration [23] are plotted versus Q^2, the difference of particle four-momenta squared. One clearly sees that at small Q the correlations between like-sign particles are much more peaked than those between unlike-sign ones. Similar effect is seen when the data are analyzed in terms of invariant mass of the pion system [24]. In the simplest interpretation this implies that (a) the production of pions in this kinematic range is, at least to a large extent, incoherent (this is the necessary condition for HBT correlations to be present); (b) the correlations observed at low Q are related to the space-time structure of the system rather than to its structure in momentum space. I would like to emphasize the importance of the conclusion (b): it drastically changes the way of thinking about the problem, as compared to the ideas based on cascade in momentum space described in section 3. What is perhaps even more important, it allows finally to understand why hadronization in not an obstacle for

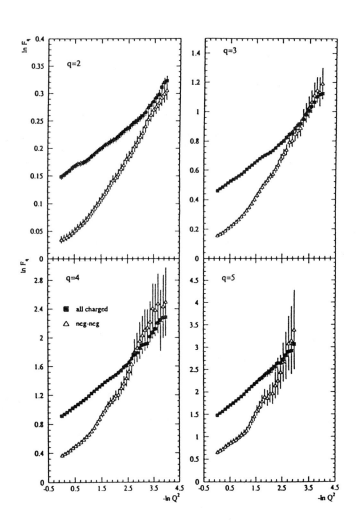

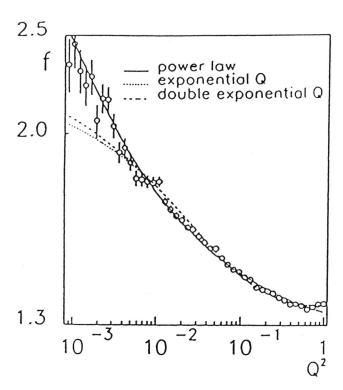

Figure 5. Second factorial moment plotted versus $Q^2 = |(p_1 - p_2)^2|$. UA1 coll. [25].

Figure 4. Factorial moments in 250 GeV/c $\pi/K\,p$ collisions. EHS/NA22 coll. [23].

having strong correlations at low Q. Indeed, since at low Q correlations reflect mostly the space-time structure of the source, they are little sensitive to details of its composition and on momentum distribution of the constituents. That is to say, it does not matter if the source of pions is made of partons, of hadronic fluid, of decaying clusters, or of anything else. Also, the mechanism of formation of the final pions is (almost) irrelevant. What matters is the space-time structure of the source and incoherent character of pion emission.

Thus one annoying problem seems to be solved. Others remain, however.

The first one : how can one justify the scaling law (1) at small Q ? To underline the importance of this question, the UA1 data for like-sign pion correlation function [25] are again shown in Fig. 5 (in different scale). One sees that they do indeed closely follow the power law at small Q. If one takes the point of view

that the scaling law, as seen in Figs. 2–5 is not just a dynamical accident [26], one is led to the idea that the region of pion emission does not have a well-defined radius but rather a long tail decreasing as a power of distance (at large distances from the center) [27]. It remains an open question whether a fractal structure of the source is also necessary to explain the data. This can be eventually decided when precise data on higher order correlations are available [28].

The second question, which I myself find rather fundamental, can be formulated as follows. The comparison of e^+e^- data and the existing QCD cascade models shows that the region of medium Q (0.2 GeV $\leq$ $Q \leq$ few GeV) can possibly be described by the standard quark-gluon cascade followed by hadronization [29]. On the other hand, we have just seen that the very small Q region ($Q \leq 0.2$ Gev) reflects the space-time structure of the system. This — a priori — has nothing to do with the anomalous QCD dimensions and the value of the strong coupling constant which determine the behaviour of the QCD cascade in the medium Q region. How can one thus explain that the shape of the correlation function (Figs. 3–5) does not visibly change when one passes from one region to another? The problem is well illustrated by the difference between correlation functions for like-sign and unlike-sign pions in the data of DELPHI coll. shown in Fig. 3. For unlike pairs there is a clear change of shape at $Q \approx .2$ GeV indicating perhaps the end of the scaling region of the quark-gluon cascade. For like-sign pairs, however, the slope continues essentially unchanged until the smallest Q measured. This indicates surprising connection between the original quark-gluon cascade and the space-time structure of the region of pion emission at the late stage of the collision. Its verification for higher-order correlations, and its theoretical understanding are — in my opinion — the main challenges for the future work.

6. Conclusions

The main points of this report can be summarized as follows:

(*i*) New methods of measurement of the multiparticle correlation functions allowed recently to determine correlation parameters with a rather high precision. First measurement of genuine higher order correlations in very small kinematic regions was presented at this conference by EHS/NA22 collaboration.

(*ii*) Experimental data on e^+e^-, lepton-hadron and hadron-hadron collisions published by several groups are consistent with the idea of scaling of multiparticle spectra. In particular, very accurate measurements of two-particle correlations show scaling in the interval of Q from several GeV down to present experimental accuracy of about 30 MeV.

(*iii*) QCD parton cascade seems a natural candidate for explanation of scaling in the kinematic region down to Q of several hundred MeV. It fails, however, to account for scaling at lower values of Q.

(*iv*) For Q below 200 MeV, the two-particle correlation function is dominated by Hanbury–Brown and Twiss effect. This implies that the scaling in the space-time structure of the volume of particle emission is responsible for scaling in this kinematic region and thus explains why the smearing due to hadronization is of little importance.

(*v*) The apparent similarity of scaling parameters in the two regimes (large Q dominated by QCD cascade and small Q dominated by HBT correlations) suggests a — not yet understood — relation between the two mechanisms. Explanation of this phenomenon remains a subject for further work.

Apologies and Acknowledgements

The limited space given to this report did not allow to treat the subject more completely and thus many important contributions had to be omitted. The reader is invited to consult Ref. [10] for a recent review and a full list of references. For the same reason the results of the papers submitted to this conference could not be described in more detail. I would like to apologize to the authors.

Thanks are due to Wolfram Kittel for arranging my participation in the Conference. This work was supported in part by the KBN grant PB 2009291 01.

References

[1] UA5 coll., G.J. Alner *et al.* Phys. Lett. **B160** (1985) 193; A. Giovannini and L. Van Hove, Z. Phys. **C30** (1986) 391.

[2] R. Szwed, G. Wrochna and A. Wróblewski, Mod. Phys. Lett. **A6** (1991) 245; 981.

[3] A. Wróblewski, Report at the 25-th Int. Conf. on High-Energy Physics, Singapore, 1990.

[4] A. Giovannini an L. Van Hove, Acta Phys. Pol. **B19** (1988) 495.

[5] A. Bialas and R. Peschanski, Nucl. Phys. **B273** (1986) 703; *ibid* **B308** (1988) 847.

[6] P. Lipa, P. Carruthers, H.C. Eggers, and B. Buschbeck, Phys. Lett. **B285** (1992) 300; H.C. Eggers, P. Lipa, P. Carruthers, and B. Buschbeck, Phys. Rev. **D48** (1993) 2040.

[7] EHS/NA22 coll., N.M. Agababyan *et al.*, Phys. Lett. **B332** (1994) 458, paper submitted to this Conference.

[8] E.G. Boos *et al.*, The investigation of pions clusterization mechanism in hadron-nucleon collision; Mutiparticle correlations in nuclear interactions at 4.2 A GeV/c; papers submitted to this Conference.

[9] JACEE coll., T.H. Burnett *et al.*, Phys. Rev. Lett. **50** (1983) 2062.

[10] For a recent review, see E. De Wolf, I. Dremin and W. Kittel, preprint HEN-362 (1993), to be published.

[11] UA1 coll., Y.F. Wu *et al.*, Proc. of the Cracow Workshop on Multiparticle Production 1993, p.22 (World Scientific, Singapore 1994).

[12] B. Muller and A. Trayanov, Phys. Rev. Lett. **68** (1992) 3387 and B. Muller, private communication.

[13] W. Ochs and J. Wosiek, Phys. Lett. **B214** (1988) 617; *ibid* **B232** (1989) 271.

[14] K. Konishi, A. Ukawa and G. Veneziano, Nucl. Phys. **B157** (1979) 45.

[15] L. Van Hove and A. Giovannini, Acta Phys. Pol. **B19** (1988) 917; *ibid* **B19** (1988) 931.

[16] R. Ugoccioni and A. Giovannini, Z. Phys. **C53** (1992) 239; S. Lupia, A. Giovannini and R. Ugoccioni, Z. Phys. **C59** (1993) 427; A. Giovannini, S. Lupia and R. Ugoccioni, Clans as independent intermediate gluon sources, paper submitted to this Conference.

[17] Discussion of numerous Monte Carlo studies are beyond the scope of this report.

[18] W. Ochs and J. Wosiek, Phys. Lett. **B289** (1992) 159; **B304** (1993) 144; Ph. Brax, J.L. Meunier and R. Peschanski, Z. Phys. **C62** (1994) 649; Yu.L. Dokshitzer and I.M. Dremin, Nucl. Phys. **B402** (1993) 139.

[19] EHS/NA22 coll., N.M. Agababyan *et al.*, Phys. Lett. **B328** (1994) 199, paper submitted to this Conference.

[20] P. Carruthers *et al.* Phys. Lett. **B222** (1989) 487; M. Gyulassy, Festschrift L. Van Hove, p.479; Eds. A. Giovannini and W. Kittel (World Scientific, Singapore 1990).

[21] R. Hanbury–Brown and R.Q. Twiss, Nature **177** (1956) 27.

[22] UA1 and DELPHI coll., F. Mandl and B. Buschbeck, Proc. XXII Int. Symp. on Multiparticle Dynamics, Santiago del Compostela 1992, Ed. A. Pajares, (World Scientific 1993).

[23] EHS/NA22 coll., N. Agababyan *et al.,* Z. Phys. **C59** (1993) 405.

[24] EHS/NA22 coll., I.V. Ajinenko *et al.,* Z. Phys. **C61** (1994) 567; DELPHI coll., P. Abreu *et al.,* Z. Phys. **C63** (1994) 17, paper submitted to this conference.

[25] UA1 coll., N. Neumeister *et al* ., Z. Phys. **C60** (1993) 633.

[26] Other point of view was advocated by R Weiner and collaborators, see I.V. Andreev *et al.,* Phys. Lett. **B316** (1993) 583.

[27] A. Bialas, Nucl. Phys. **A525** (1991) 345c; **A545** (1992) 285c; Acta Phys. Pol. **B23** (1992) 561; For early suggestions of scaling in space-time structure of the interaction region see I.M. Dremin, JETP Lett. **45** (1987) 643.

[28] A. Bialas and B. Ziaja, Acta Phys. Pol. **B24** (1993) 1509.

[29] DELPHI coll., P. Abreu *et al.,* Phys. Lett. **B247** (1990) 137; A. De Angelis, Mod. Phys. Lett. **A5** (1990) 2395.

QCD Colour Coherence and String Effects

W. J. Metzger

University of Nijmegen, 6525 ED Nijmegen, Netherlands

Abstract

Conference contributions 406, 553, 627 and 629, which present experimental evidence for QCD colour coherence, are briefly reviewed.

1. Introduction

The hadronization of a quark-antiquark pair is currently thought to proceed via the radiation of gluons from the quarks and subsequent gluons. QCD implies that this parton radiation be coherent. Four papers submitted to this conference report experimental evidence for this coherence. In the first[1] L3 examines angular correlations within quark jets in e^+e^- interactions. The so-called string effect in e^+e^- interactions is studied by L3[2] and OPAL[3]. Finally, CDF has found evidence for coherence in high-E_t jet events from $p\overline{p}$ interactions.[4]

This coherence can be incorporated into Monte Carlo programs as angular ordering whereby successive branchings occur at smaller angles with respect to the parent parton direction.[5] All four papers find agreement of data with Monte Carlo models which incorporate angular ordering and disagreement with models which do not.

2. Colour coherence within a jet

L3 has studied the effects of angular ordering (AO) *within* a jet using hadronic events from e^+e^- interactions at the Z.[1]

The idea of local parton hadron duality (LPHD)[6] suggests that features at the parton level survive the fragmentation process. We can therefore expect that the angular ordering of the parton radiation will be reflected in angular ordering of the observed particles. This suggests using variables based on the angles between particles. Well-known variables are the energy-energy correlation (EEC) and its asymmetry (EECA). These variables have the advantage of being 'infra-red safe', *i.e.*, calculable. However, for the purpose of investigating the extent of angular ordering, they, by virtue of their energy weighting, put undue emphasis on the earliest branchings. Therefore use is made of analogously defined variables, where the energy weighting is removed:

$$
\begin{aligned}
\mathrm{PPC}(\chi) &= \frac{1}{N_{\mathrm{Event}}}\frac{1}{\Delta\chi}\sum_{1}^{N_{\mathrm{Event}}}\sum_{i=1}^{N_{\mathrm{ch}}}\sum_{j=1}^{N_{\mathrm{ch}}}\frac{\delta(\chi_{\mathrm{bin}}-\chi_{ij})}{N_{\mathrm{ch}}^2} \\
\mathrm{PPCA}(\chi) &= \mathrm{PPC}(180°-\chi)-\mathrm{PPC}(\chi)
\end{aligned}
$$

which are called the particle-particle correlation (PPC) and its asymmetry (PPCA).

At $\sqrt{s}=M_{\mathbf{Z}}$, the fraction of two-jet events is very high. Therefore consider for now only two-jet events. Particles in different jets will in general be separated by an angle χ greater than 90°. The PPC for $\chi > 90°$ can therefore serve as an indication of what to expect within a jet ($\chi < 90°$) *in the absence of* angular ordering (or other short-range angular correlatons). By forming the asymmetry, these 'uninteresting' correlations are effectively subtracted. The effects of angular ordering should therefore be more directly observable in the PPCA than in the PPC.

Using events passing the standard L3 hadronic event selection, the PPC is calculated. The resulting PPC distribution is corrected for detector effects, which have been determined using the JETSET, HERWIG, and COJETS Monte Carlo generators and the standard L3 detector simulation. The PPCA distribution is

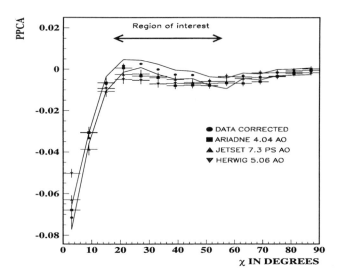

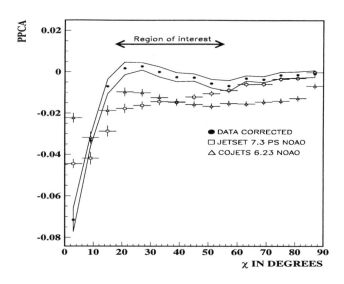

Figure 1. Comparison of the PPCA for L3 data with Monte Carlo models which incorporate angular ordering. The band indicates the uncertainty on the data points, including the systematic uncertainty due to unfolding of detector effects using different Monte Carlo models.

Figure 2. Comparison of the PPCA for L3 data with Monte Carlo models which do not incorporate angular ordering. The band indicates the uncertainty on the data points, including the systematic uncertainty due to unfolding of detector effects using different Monte Carlo models.

calculated from the corrected PPC distribution and compared to Monte Carlo models, all of which have been tuned to reproduce satisfactorily standard one-dimensional distributions.[7] The PPCA distributions for angular ordered models is strikingly different from those of non-angular ordered models, particularly for angles smaller than about 50°, a region comparable to the angular size of a jet. It has been checked that this difference is much larger than variations introduced by uncertainty in various Monte Carlo parameters. Nor can the difference be explained by the Bose-Einstein effect, as was found by varying the appropiate parameters of JETSET. The Bose-Einstein effect is, of course, greatest at small angles where also detector corrections are the least well understood. For these reasons the comparison of data with the models should not be taken too seriously for χ below 10 or 15 degrees.

The comparison with models incorporating angular ordering, namely, JETSET 7.3[8], HERWIG 5.6[9] and ARIADNE 4.4, is shown in figure 1; the comparison with non-angular ordered models, JETSET 7.3 and COJETS 6.23[11], in figure 2.

The PPCA in parton shower models which incorporate colour coherence is strikingly different from that in parton shower models lacking it. Data from the L3 experiment strongly favour the coherent models.

3.   String effect in e^+e^- interactions

It has long been thought that the so-called string effect, first predicted by the LUND string model and later

confirmed by the JADE experiment[12] and others, is due to colour coherence,[13] which causes destructive interference between amplitudes for soft gluon emission in the region between q and $\bar{q}$ jets and constructive interference in the region between quark and gluon jets.

L3[2] and OPAL[3] have performed very similar analyses. They compare the particle flow (L3 also the energy flow) of $q\bar{q}g$ and $q\bar{q}\gamma$ events in the region between the q and $\bar{q}$. The gluon jet is assumed, in first instance, to be the least energetic of the three jets. However, both experiments also used a method of lepton (μ for L3 and μ or e for OPAL) tagging, whereby the presence of a high momentum lepton in one of the two least energetic jets tags that jet as not being a gluon (since leptons arise predominantly from heavy quark decays). This method results in higher purity of the gluon identification at the cost of a large loss in statistics.

Care was taken that the $q\bar{q}$ systems be directly comparable. The event selection is done in such a way that the two samples are kinematically similar, as is shown for L3 in figure 3. The difference in figure 3a is due to better angular resolution for the γ than for the g jet. To compensate for this L3 imposes a cut on this angle of 8° for $q\bar{q}\gamma$ whereas 10° is used for the $q\bar{q}g$ selection. Also the orientation of the events within the detector is similar; this minimizes systematic detector effects in the comparison.

The particle (and energy) flows are compared in figure 4 (L3) and figure 5 (OPAL) as function of the angle in the event plane as measured from the most energetic jet (0°) towards the second quark jet ($\sim 160°$). The

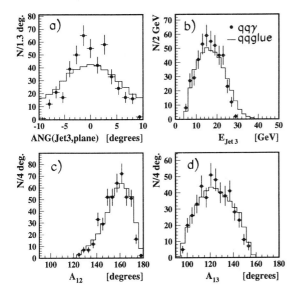

Figure 3. Comparison for L3 of (a) the angle between jet 3 (g or γ) and the plane defined by the q and $\bar{q}$ jets; (b) the energy of jet 3; (c) the angle between the q and $\bar{q}$ jets; (d) the angle between the most energetic jet and jet 3.

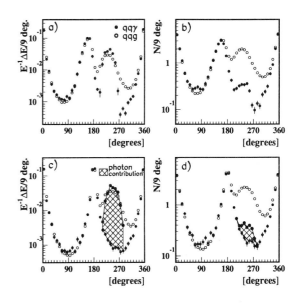

Figure 4. Comparison for L3 of the energy flow (a and c) and particle flow (b and d) in the lab. frame (a and b) and in the centre of mass of the q and $\bar{q}$ jets (c and d).

string effect is seen as a relative depletion of particle (and energy) flow for $q\bar{q}g$ as compared to $q\bar{q}\gamma$ in the region between the two quark jets, in particular around 50-110°. L3 also shows the flows in the $q\bar{q}$ centre of mass and quantifies the effect by the ratio of the integrals of these distributions between 54° and 135° giving $R_N = 0.828 \pm 0.040$ and $R_E = 0.821 \pm 0.053$ for particle and energy flow, respectively. OPAL instead normalizes (per event) the angle by the angle between the q and $\bar{q}$ jets and takes the ratio between 0.3 and 0.7 yielding $R = 0.72 \pm 0.04$. If instead of energy ordering, the lepton tag is used, the values of the ratios decrease: $R_N = 0.757 \pm 0.042$, $R_E = 0.759 \pm 0.056$, and $R = 0.65 \pm 0.06$. The ratio is significantly less than the value 1 in all cases and decreases with higher gluon identification purity in line with expectation. The difference between R_N and R is apparently due to the different methods of the two analyses, since the COJETS Monte Carlo, which is incoherent with independent fragmentation, should produce no string effect but gives $R_N = 1.046 \pm 0.062$ and $R = 0.90 \pm 0.03$.

Both experiments also make comparisons with the coherent Monte Carlo models HERWIG, JETSET, and ARIADNE, which all produce a string effect, as measured by the above ratios, of the same magnitude as found in the data, although L3 notes some small differences in the values of the particle and energy flows themselves. However, OPAL notes that the ERT $O(\alpha^2)$ matrix element[14] as implemented in JETSET with string fragmentation also reproduces the string effect.

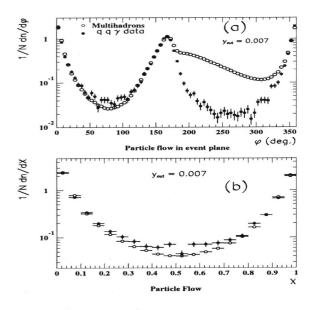

Figure 5. Comparison for OPAL of the particle flow (a) as function of the angle ϕ in the lab. frame and (b) as function of the reduced angle $X = \phi/\Phi$, where Φ is the angle between jets 1 and 2.

4. Coherence effects in p$\bar{\text{p}}$ jets

The CDF collaboration has studied colour coherence effects in p$\bar{\text{p}}$ jet events involving three high-p_t jets.[4] The situation is, of course, more complicated than in e^+e^- interactions. Examples of colour flow diagrams are shown in figure 7 for hard $q\bar{q}$ and qg scattering. In figure 7a the colour flow is comparable to that in

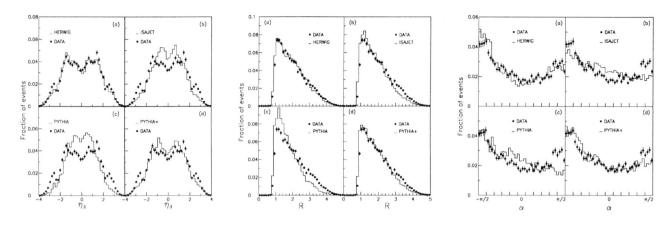

Figure 6. Comparison for CDF of the variables η_3, R, and α with the HERWIG, ISAJET, PYTHIA 5.6, and PYTHIA+ Monte Carlo models.

$e^+e^- \to q\bar{q}g$: the colour system in which interference occurs (thick lines in figure 7) is entirely in the final state and the parton showers are time-like. But in figure 7b the cancellation results from interference between initial and final state and space-like showers are also possible.

The three high-p_t jets are ordered in E_t: $E_{t1} > E_{t2} > E_{t3}$. Jet 3 is then most likely to be the radiated gluon and jet 2 the quark belonging to the colour lines from which the gluon was radiated. Variables sensitive to coherence are the 'distance' between jets 2 and 3 as measured by the difference in pseudorapidity, $\Delta\eta = \eta_3 - \eta_2$, and azimuthal angle, $\Delta\phi = |\phi_3 - \phi_2|$. Instead of $\Delta\eta$ and $\Delta\phi$ CDF prefers to use polar coordinates in (η, ϕ)-space: $R = \sqrt{(\Delta\eta)^2 + (\Delta\phi)^2}$ and $\alpha = \arctan\frac{\text{sign}(\eta_2)\cdot\Delta\eta}{\Delta\phi}$. Also, the η_3 distribution can be expected to be wider as a result of coherence: *e.g.*, for $q\bar{q} \to q\bar{q}g$ the initial q and $\bar{q}$ are along the beam direction. The distributions of η_3, R, and α are compared with four Monte Carlo models in figure 6, respectively. The models are ISAJET 6.25[15], which contains no coherence, HERWIG 3.2, which does, and two versions of PYTHIA[16], version 5.6 containing coherence only for time-like showers and a pre-release of version 5.7 (here called PYTHIA+) in which angular ordering has been incorporated for the first gluon emission from colour lines flowing from initial to final state.

From these comparisons it is clear that colour coherence is needed in the models. HERWIG, which implements coherence for both time- and space-like showers, agrees reasonably well. PYTHIA+ agrees less well. PYTHIA and ISAJET fail to reproduce the data.

5.   Conclusion

These studies all confirm the necessity of colour coherence in parton showers.

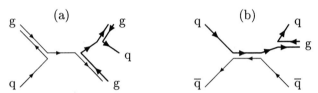

Figure 7. Colour flow in (a) qg and (b) q$\bar{q}$ hard scattering. The thicker lines correspond to the colour system in which cancellation occurs.

References

[1] L3 Collaboration, "Coherence Effects in Perturbative QCD", paper 629.
[2] L3 Collaboration, "A Study of String Effect in Z Hadronic Decays", paper 627.
[3] OPAL Collaboration, "The String Effect Using Final State Photons", paper 553.
[4] CDF Collaboration, "Evidence for Color Coherence in Jet Events", paper 406.
[5] B. I. Ermolaev and V. S. Fadin, JETP Lett. **33** (1981) 269; A. H. Mueller, Phys. Lett. **B104** (1981) 161; A. Bassetto, M. Ciafaloni, G. Marchesini and A. H. Mueller, Nucl. Phys. **B207** (1982) 189; and G. Marchesini and B. R. Webber, Nucl. Phys. **B238** (1984) 1.
[6] Ya. I. Azimov, Yu. L. Dokshitzer, V. A. Khoze and S. I. Troyan, Zeit. Phys. **C27** (1985) 65.
[7] B. Adeva *et al.*, Zeit. Phys. **C55** (1992) 39.
[8] T. Sjöstrand and M. Bengtsson, Computer Phys. Comm. **43** (1987) 367; and T. Sjöstrand, CERN preprint: CERN-TH.6488/92.
[9] G. Marchesini *et al.*, Computer Phys. Comm. **67** (1992) 465.
[10] L. Lönnblad, Computer Phys. Comm. **71** (1992) 15.
[11] R. Odorico, Computer Phys. Comm. **72** (1992) 235.
[12] W. Bartel *et al.*, Phys. Lett. **B101** (1981) 129.
[13] Ya. I. Azimov, Yu. L. Dokshitzer, V. A. Khoze and S. I. Troyan, Phys. Lett. **B165** (1985) 147.
[14] R. K. Ellis, D. A. Ross, and A. E. Terrano, Nucl. Phys. **B178** (1981) 421.
[15] F. E. Page and S. D. Protopopescu, BNL Report No. 38034 (1986).
[16] H.-U. Bengtsson and T. Sjöstrand, Computer Phys. Comm. **46** (1987) 43; and T. Sjöstrand, CERN preprint: CERN-TH.7112/93.

Paper presented at XXVII Int. Conf. on High Energy Physics: Session Pa-20
Glasgow, UK, 20–27 July 1994

Inclusive Particle Production in Z^0 Decays

Richard J Hemingway[‡]

Institute of Particle Physics and Carleton University,
Ottawa, Ontario K1S 5B6, Canada

Abstract

A mini-review is given of the characteristics of inclusive particle production in Z^0 decays. Differential cross sections, inclusive rates, and QCD aspects are discussed. A compilation of all measured inclusive rates is provided.

1. INTRODUCTION

The study of inclusive particle production in Z^0 decays has become almost a cottage industry involving all four LEP experiments. Already the list of well-measured particle species is very impressive. It is hoped that a complete set of measurements will lead to a better understanding of the fragmentation processes which are temporarily calculated via MonteCarlo methods [1, 2]. At the very least, the measurements will allow more realistic tuning of the MonteCarlo generators and thereby improve the experiment simulation packages.

Prior to this conference a number of papers have already been published or reported at previous conferences. They include

- Pseudoscalar Mesons: π^0[28], K^0[18, 34], η[9, 29], $\eta'(958)$[9]
- Vector Mesons: $K^*(892)^0$[19, 37], $K^*(892)^{\pm}$[18, 37], $\rho(770)^0$[19], $\phi(1020)$[37]
- Charm Sector: D^0[20], $D^{\pm}$[20], $D^*(2010)^{\pm}$[7, 20, 33], J/Ψ[30, 35]
- Strange Baryons: Λ[18, 21, 38], Ξ^-[10, 18, 38], $\Sigma(1385)^{\pm}$[38], $\Xi(1530)^0$[38], Ω^-[10, 38]
- L=1 Sector: $f_0(975)$[19], $f_2(1270)$[19], χ_{c1}[30]

At this conference a large number of additional contributions to the subject have been submitted, either as updates to previous work or entirely new data. These are listed below. In most cases the data are preliminary.

‡ E-mail: ryh@physics.carleton.ca

- Aleph new data: K^0, Λ[12], $\pi^{\pm}$, $K^{\pm}$, p[13], $\rho(770)^0$, $K^*(892)^{\pm}$[15], D^0, $D^{\pm}$[11]
- Aleph updated data: η, $\eta'(958)$[14], $D^*(2010)^{\pm}$[11]
- Delphi new data: π^0[25], $K^{\pm}$, p[22], $\Sigma(1385)^{\pm}$, $\Xi(1530)^0$[26], J/Ψ, $\Psi(3685)$, χ_{c1}[23]
- Delphi updated data: Λ[21], Ξ^-[26], K^0, $\rho(770)^0$, $K^*(892)^{\pm}$, $f_0(975)$, $f_2(1270)$[24], D^0, $D^{\pm}$, $D^*(2010)^{\pm}$[27]
- L3 new data: K^0, Λ[31]
- L3 updated data: π^0, η[31]
- OPAL new data: $\pi^{\pm}$, $K^{\pm}$, p[40], $K_2^*(1430)^0$[41], Λ_c^+[43]
- OPAL updated data: $K^*(892)^0$, $\phi(1020)$[41], Λ, Ξ^-, $\Sigma(1385)^{\pm}$, $\Xi(1530)^0$, Ω^-[42], $D^*(2010)^{\pm}$[44]

2. DIFFERENTIAL CROSS SECTIONS

Only selected results are described here. The reader is advised to consult the full list of references to obtain a complete picture.

OPAL [40] has recently published a measurement of the production rates of charged hadrons at the Z^0, using energy loss measurement in the jet chamber to separate the $\pi^{\pm}$, $K^{\pm}$, and p components. ALEPH and DELPHI have contributed results to this conference in basic agreement with the OPAL results. The essential features are given as follows. Figure 1 shows the OPAL differential cross section for $K^{\pm}$ in comparison to the predictions of JETSET/HERWIG. The cross-section has been determined over 3 orders of magnitude and is seen to deviate only slightly, but significantly

Particle	J^P	Experiment	Reference	Rate/event Measured	Rate/event JETSET7.4	Rate/event HERWIG5.5
All charged		MK2,A,D,L,O	[6, 8, 17, 28, 32]	20.92 ± 0.19	20.97	21.49*
π^0	0^-	D,L	[25, 31]	9.26 ± 0.66	9.60	10.20
$\pi^\pm$	0^-	O	[40]	17.05 ± 0.43	16.97	17.66
η	0^-	A,L	[14, 31]	0.91 ± 0.11	1.01	1.26*
$\rho(770)^0$	1^-	A,D	[15, 24]	1.31 ± 0.13	1.51	1.29
$\eta'(958)$	0^-	A	[14]	0.064 ± 0.014 (a)	0.126* (a)	0.104 (a)
$f_0(975)$	0^+	D	[24]	0.098 ± 0.016 (b)		
$\phi(1020)$	1^-	O	[41]	0.100 ± 0.008	0.192*	0.135*
$f_2(1270)$	2^+	D	[24]	0.170 ± 0.043 (c)		
$K^\pm$	0^-	O	[40]	2.42 ± 0.13	2.30	2.46
K^0	0^-	A,D,L,O	[12, 18, 24, 31, 34]	2.047 ± 0.031	2.207*	2.336*
$K^*(892)^\pm$	1^-	A,D,O	[15, 18, 24, 39]	0.724 ± 0.035	1.107*	0.930*
$K^*(892)^0$	1^-	D,O	[19, 41]	0.74 ± 0.04	1.09*	0.87*
$K_2^*(1430)^0$	2^+	O	[41]	0.19 ± 0.07 (d)		
$D^\pm$	0^-	A,D	[11, 27]	0.228 ± 0.022	0.176	0.221
D^0	0^-	A,D	[11, 27]	0.506 ± 0.039	0.488	0.457
$D^*(2010)^\pm$	1^-	A,D,O	[11, 27, 44]	0.189 ± 0.011	0.241*	0.231*
J/Ψ	1^-	D,L,O	[23, 30, 35]	0.0042 ± 0.0004	0.0051	0.0012*
χ_{c1}	1^+	D	[23]	0.007 ± 0.002		
$\Psi(3685)$	1^-	D,L	[23, 30]	0.0016 ± 0.0008		
p	$\frac{1}{2}^+$	O	[40]	0.92 ± 0.11	1.20	0.83
Λ	$\frac{1}{2}^+$	A,D,L,O	[12, 18, 21, 31, 42]	0.370 ± 0.010	0.385	0.353
Ξ^-	$\frac{1}{2}^+$	A,D,O	[10, 18, 26, 42]	0.0250 ± 0.0011	0.0279	0.0378*
$\Sigma(1385)^\pm$	$\frac{3}{2}^+$	D,O	[26, 42]	0.0377 ± 0.0036	0.0744*	0.1203*
$\Xi(1530)^0$	$\frac{3}{2}^+$	D,O	[26, 42]	0.0066 ± 0.0009	0.0055	0.0149*
Ω^-	$\frac{3}{2}^+$	A,O	[10, 42]	0.0016 ± 0.0004	0.0006	0.0041*
Λ_c^+	$\frac{1}{2}^+$	O	[43]	0.075 ± 0.024	0.060	0.047

Table 1. Particle Production rates at 91.2 GeV compared with default versions of JETSET74 and HERWIG55. The experiments are Aleph(A), Delphi(D), L3(L), Opal(O), and MK2. Particle and anti-particle rates are summed and sequential particle decay is activated. (a)kinematic range $x_E > 0.1$ only, (b)kinematic range $x_p > 0.05$ only, (c)kinematic range $x_p > 0.1$ only, (d)kinematic range $x_E < 0.3$ only, * indicates that rate differs from measurement by more than three standard deviations.

(the observed momentum spectrum is harder), from the JETSET prediction. At low momentum the HERWIG predictions are 30-40% too large. Figure 2 shows the ALEPH [13] p cross section and indicates that both JETSET and HERWIG have a harder fragmentation at large x_p than the data. At low momentum, the data stradle the predictions. Both OPAL and ALEPH have a range of momentum where measurements are difficult due to the overlap of energy loss bands, but new data from the DELPHI RICH detector [22] in Figure 3 should help to close the gap.

L3 [31] have exploited the good resolution of their barrel electromagnetic calorimeter and improved their previous measurements of π^0 and η production [28, 29]. The differential cross sections are shown in Figure 4 together with the JETSET prediction. While the π^0 agrees well with JETSET, the η distribution has a slightly softer spectrum and a lower cross section. The limited range of x_p for π^0 has been extended by DELPHI [25] using a combination of converted photons prior to their TPC together with EM showers in the barrel high density projection chamber. Their data,

shown in Figure 5, is consistent with both the L3 measurement and JETSET.

ALEPH [14] have updated their previous measurements [9] of η and $\eta'(958)$ production. Figure 6 shows the η cross section to be in excellent agreement with JETSET (note that the range of x_p is higher than that of L3), whereas Figure 7 shows the $\eta'(958)$ cross section to be significantly lower than JETSET. Bowler [4] has pointed out that the latter result may be due to the wrong pseudoscalar mixing angle in JETSET.

OPAL [41] have updated their previous measurements [37] of vector meson production, $K^*(892)^0$ and $\phi(1020)$. The differential cross sections are shown in Figure 8 and Figure 9 together with the JETSET/HERWIG predictions. Although the spectrum shapes are in reasonable agreement, the predicted rates are significantly higher. ALEPH [15] have contributed new data on $\rho(770)^0$ and $K^*(892)^\pm$ production and the differential cross sections are shown in Figure 10 and Figure 11 respectively. Although the $\rho(770)^0$ distribution looks fine wrt JETSET, the $K^*(892)$ rate is again significantly lower than JETSET.

OPAL [42] have updated their previous measurements [38] of strange baryon production and the differential cross sections for Λ, Ξ^-, $\Sigma(1385)^\pm$, and $\Xi(1530)^0$ are shown in Figure 12 and Figure 13. When compared with the normalised JETSET predictions, the data distributions are seen to have a softer momentum spectrum. This trend is confirmed by updated DELPHI data submitted to this conference [26] and shown in Figure 14 (here the JETSET predictions are not normalised).

A new result on inclusive charm baryon production was submitted to this conference by OPAL [43]. The $pK^-\pi^+$ mass distribution with a prominent Λ_c^+ peak, shown in Figure 15, has enabled a determination of the inclusive rate.

3. SUMMARY OF INCLUSIVE PARTICLE RATES

Table 1 gives a compilation of all measured inclusive particle rates together with the predictions of the default MonteCarlo programs JETSET (version 7.4) and HERWIG (version 5.5). With the exception of η', f_0, f_2, and K_2^*, the particle rates cover the full x_p range. The rates are simple weighted averages and ignore possible common systematic errors. When the expected rate differs by more than 3 standard deviations from the measured rate, it is marked by an asterisk. There are many rates in this category, more in HERWIG than JETSET, and particularly in the strange/charm sector. Missing entries refer to those cases where JETSET has no prediction (predominantly L=1 states). In comparison with rate compilations from lower energy e^+e^- experiments [3], the current LEP rates are competitive and, in many cases, more precise. Better agreement between JETSET/HERWIG and data will be possible after a new, total, tune of the MonteCarlo parameters.

4. QCD ANALYSES

Instead of plotting the cross section as a function of scaled energy/momentum, the data can be compared to QCD-inspired calculations [5] by plotting the cross section as a function of the variable ξ (the logarithm of the inverse of the scaled momentum). Such distributions are expected to show an approximate Gaussian shape whose maximum value, ξ^*, should decrease with increasing particle mass. Figure 16 and Figure 17 show a recent compilation of K^0 and Λ cross sections [12] while Table 2 gives a compilation of the available ξ^* data and does indeed indicate a steady decrease in ξ^* as the meson mass increases. However, there is a definite discontinuity at the baryons. This is seen more clearly in Figure 18 where the mesons are seen to lie higher than the baryons. The arrows on this figure indicate the

Particle	Experiment	Reference	ξ^* value
All charged	D,L,O	[18, 28, 32]	3.61 ± 0.01
π^0	L	[28, 31]	4.01 ± 0.11
$\pi^\pm$	O	[40]	3.81 ± 0.02
$K^\pm$	D,O	[22, 40]	2.64 ± 0.03
K^0	D,L,O	[18, 22, 31, 34]	2.86 ± 0.03
η	L	[31]	2.52 ± 0.10
$K^*(892)^0$	O	[41]	2.40 ± 0.04
$\phi(1020)$	O	[41]	2.29 ± 0.05
p	D,O	[22, 40]	2.99 ± 0.07
Λ	D,L,O	[18, 21, 31, 38]	2.78 ± 0.04
Ξ^-	D,O	[26, 38]	2.58 ± 0.09

Table 2. Values of ξ^* peak positions as measured by the LEP experiments Delphi(D), L3(L), and OPAL(O).

size of correction needed to transform inclusive ξ^* values to those for primary hadrons only [41]. Since these corrections are large, one should be careful in making quantitative conclusions.

5. CONCLUSIONS

Some very careful work by all four LEP experiments has given an impressive range of results covering approximately 30 particle species. The differential cross sections, which now cover 3-4 orders of magnitude over the (almost) entire range of x_p, show no significant disagreement between experiments and have a precision comparable to, and in many cases better than, the lower energy compilations.

When compared to the expectations of the default MonteCarlos one sees

- Minor variations in the shape of fragmentation functions (eg. baryons are too soft and strange mesons are too hard),
- Major problems with inclusive rates, particularly in the strange and baryon sectors,
- Clear evidence for the production of L=1 states (eg. $f_0(975)$, $f_2(1270)$, $K_2^*(1430)$, χ_{c1}, and p-wave charmed mesons,

all of which indicate that a new, total, tune of the MonteCarlos is needed.

When compared to the expectations of 'QCD-inspired' models, there is clearly some difference in the behaviour of mesons and baryons. It has been shown that resonance decay complicates simple interpretation of the data.

For the future we can expect more data with improved precision, new data on other particle species, 2-particle correlation studies, and the measurement of particle production within quark and gluon jets.

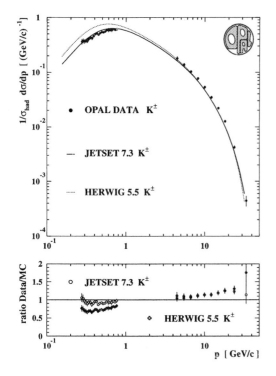

Figure 1. Differential cross section for $K^{\pm}$ as measured by OPAL [40]

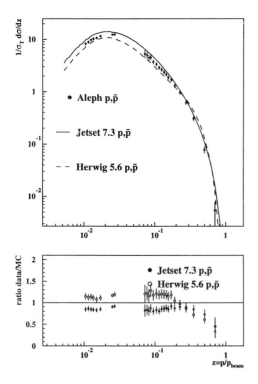

Figure 2. Differential cross section for p as measured by ALEPH [13].

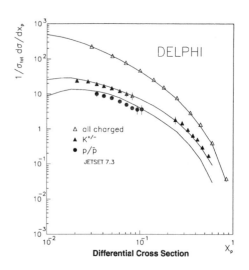

Figure 3. Differential cross sections for total charged, $K^{\pm}$, and p as measured by DELPHI [22].

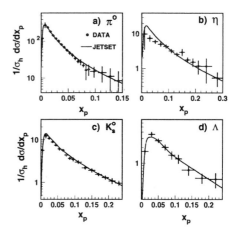

Figure 4. Differential cross sections for π^0, η, K^0, and Λ as measured by L3 [31].

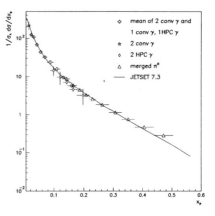

Figure 5. Differential cross section for π^0 as measured by DELPHI [25].

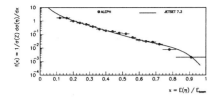

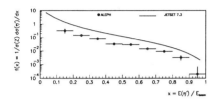

Figure 6. Differential cross section for η as measured by ALEPH [14].

Figure 7. Differential cross section for $\eta'(958)$ as measured by ALEPH [14].

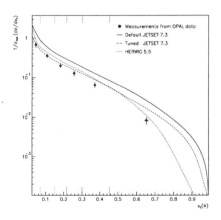

Figure 8. Differential cross section for $\phi(1020)$ as measured by OPAL [41].

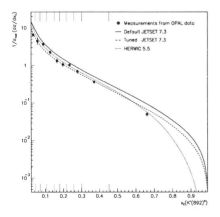

Figure 9. Differential cross section for K*(892)^0 as measured by OPAL [41].

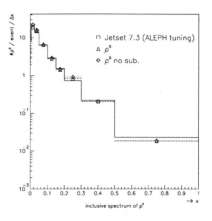

Figure 10. Differential cross section for $\rho(770)^0$ as measured by ALEPH [15].

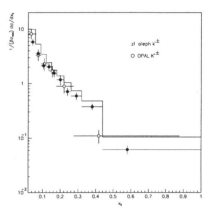

Figure 11. Differential cross section for K*(892)$^\pm$ as measured by ALEPH [15].

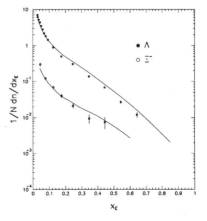

Figure 12. Differential cross sections for Λ and Ξ^- as measured by OPAL [42].

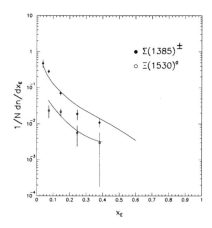

Figure 13. Differential cross sections for $\Sigma(1385)^{\pm}$ and $\Xi(1530)^0$ as measured by OPAL [42].

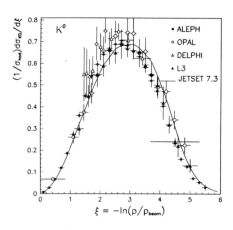

Figure 16. Momentum spectra of K^0 as measured by the four LEP experiments [12, 18, 31, 34].

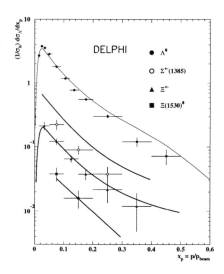

Figure 14. Differential cross sections for Λ, $\Sigma(1385)^{\pm}$, Ξ^- and $\Xi(1530)^0$ as measured by DELPHI [26].

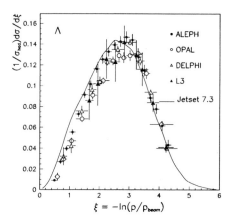

Figure 17. Momentum spectra of Λ as measured by the four LEP experiments [12, 21, 31, 38].

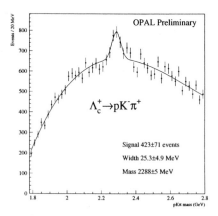

Figure 15. Invariant mass distribution of $pK^-\pi^+$ as measured by OPAL [43].

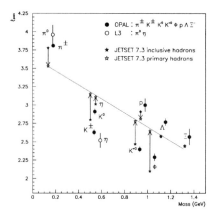

Figure 18. Variation of ξ^* peak with mass for various hadron states. The plot is taken from OPAL [41].

References

[1] T. Sjöstrand, Comp. Phys. Comm. **39** (1986) 347;
T. Sjöstrand and M. Bengtsson, Comp. Phys. Comm. **43** (1987) 367.

[2] G. Marchesini and B.R. Webber, Nucl. Phys. **B310** (1988) 461.

[3] K. Hikasa et al., Phys. Rev. **45D** (1992) III.79.

[4] M. Bowler, Phys. Lett. **180B** (1986) 299.

[5] Y.L. Dokshitzer, V.A. Khoze and S.I. Troyan, J.Phys.G: Nucl.Part.Phys. **17** (1991) 1481;
Y.L. Dokshitzer, V.A. Khoze and S.I. Troyan, Z. Phys. **C55** (1992) 107.

[6] MARK2 Collaboration, G.S. Abrams et al., Phys. Rev. Lett. **64** (1990) 1334.

[7] ALEPH Collaboration, D. Decamp et al., Phys. Lett. **266B** (1991) 218.

[8] ALEPH Collaboration, D. Decamp et al., Phys. Lett. **273B** (1991) 181.

[9] ALEPH Collaboration, D. Buskulic et al., Phys. Lett. **292B** (1992) 210.

[10] ALEPH Collaboration, *Ξ and Ω Production in Z Decays*, preliminary results presented at ICHEP92 Dallas.

[11] ALEPH Collaboration, *Production of Charmed Mesons in Z Decays*, CERN-PPE/93-208, submitted to Z. Phys. C.

[12] ALEPH Collaboration, *Production of K^0 and Λ in hadronic Z Decays*, CERN-PPE/94-74, submitted to Z. Phys. C.

[13] ALEPH Collaboration, *Inclusive $\pi^{\pm}$, $K^{\pm}$ and $(p,\overline{p})$ Cross sections at the Z Resonance*, preliminary results presented at ICHEP94 Glasgow.

[14] ALEPH Collaboration, *Production Rates of η and η' in Hadronic Z Decays*, preliminary results presented at ICHEP94 Glasgow.

[15] ALEPH Collaboration, *Inclusive Production of Light Vector Mesons in Hadronic Z Decays*, preliminary results presented at ICHEP94 Glasgow.

[16] ALEPH Collaboration, *Production of P-Wave Charmed Mesons in Z Decay*, preliminary results presented at ICHEP94 Glasgow.

[17] DELPHI Collaboration, P. Abreu et al., Z. Phys. **C50** (1991) 185.

[18] DELPHI Collaboration, P. Abreu et al., Phys. Lett. **275B** (1992) 231.

[19] DELPHI Collaboration, P. Abreu et al., Phys. Lett. **298B** (1993) 236.

[20] DELPHI Collaboration, P. Abreu et al., Z. Phys. **C59** (1993) 533.

[21] DELPHI Collaboration, P. Abreu et al., Phys. Lett. **318B** (1993) 249.

[22] DELPHI Collaboration, *Inclusive $K^{\pm}$ and $p/\overline{p}$ Production in Z^0 Decays Measured with the Delphi Detector*, preliminary results presented at ICHEP94 Glasgow.

[23] DELPHI Collaboration, *J/Ψ Production in the Hadronic Decays of the Z*, preliminary results presented at ICHEP94 Glasgow.

[24] DELPHI Collaboration, *Production Characteristics of K^0 and Light Meson Resonances in Hadronic Decays of the Z^0*, preliminary results presented at ICHEP94 Glasgow.

[25] DELPHI Collaboration, *Measurement of Inclusive π^0 Production in Z^0 Decays*, preliminary results presented at ICHEP94 Glasgow.

[26] DELPHI Collaboration, *Strange Baryons Production in Z^0 Hadronic Decays*, preliminary results presented at ICHEP94 Glasgow.

[27] DELPHI Collaboration, *Study of D, D*, and D** Production in Z^0 Hadronic Decays*, preliminary results presented at ICHEP94 Glasgow.

[28] L3 Collaboration, B. Adeva et al., Phys. Lett. **259B** (1991) 199.

[29] L3 Collaboration, O. Adriani et al., Phys. Lett. **286B** (1992) 403.

[30] L3 Collaboration, O. Adriani et al., Phys. Lett. **317B** (1993) 467.

[31] L3 Collaboration, *Measurement of Inclusive Production of Neutral Hadrons from Z Decays*, CERN-PPE/94-53, submitted to Physics Letters B.

[32] OPAL Collaboration, M.Z. Akrawy et al., Phys. Lett. **247B** (1990) 617.

[33] OPAL Collaboration, G. Alexander et al., Phys. Lett. **262B** (1991) 341.

[34] OPAL Collaboration, G. Alexander et al., Phys. Lett. **264B** (1991) 467.

[35] OPAL Collaboration, G. Alexander et al., Phys. Lett. **266B** (1991) 485.

[36] OPAL Collaboration, P.D. Acton et al., Z. Phys. **C53** (1992) 539.

[37] OPAL Collaboration, P.D. Acton et al., Z. Phys. **C56** (1992) 521.

[38] OPAL Collaboration, P.D. Acton et al., Phys. Lett. **291B** (1992) 503.

[39] OPAL Collaboration, P.D. Acton et al., Phys. Lett. **305B** (1993) 407.

[40] OPAL Collaboration, *Measurement of the Production Rates of Charged Hadrons in e^+e^- Annihilation at the Z^0*, CERN-PPE/94-49, submitted to Z. Phys. C.

[41] OPAL Collaboration, *Inclusive strange vector and tensor meson production in hadronic Z^0 decays*, preliminary results presented at ICHEP94 Glasgow.

[42] OPAL Collaboration, *Strange Baryon Production and Correlations in Hadronic Z^0 Decays*, preliminary results presented at ICHEP94 Glasgow.

[43] OPAL Collaboration, *A measurement of Λ_c^+ production in Z^0 decays*, preliminary results presented at ICHEP94 Glasgow.

[44] OPAL Collaboration, *A Measurement of the Production of $D^{*\pm}$ Mesons on the Z^0 Resonance*, preliminary results presented at ICHEP94 Glasgow.

Parallel Session Pa-21

Rare Decays

Conveners: A. Masiero (INFN/Padova)
M. Zeller (Yale University)

Scientific secretaries: S. Dorris
G. Jenkins (reserve)

Towards Precise Determinations of the CKM Matrix without Hadronic Uncertainties*

Andrzej J. Buras

Technische Universität München, Physik Department
D-85748 Garching, Germany
Max-Planck-Institut für Physik – Werner-Heisenberg-Institut –
Föhringer Ring 6, D-80805 München, Germany

Abstract

We illustrate how the measurements of the CP asymmetries in $B^0_{d,s}$-decays together with a measurement of $Br(K_L \rightarrow \pi^0 \nu \bar{\nu})$ or $Br(K^+ \rightarrow \pi^+ \nu \bar{\nu})$ and the known value of $\mid V_{us} \mid$ can determine all elements of the Cabibbo-Kobayashi-Maskawa matrix essentially without any hadronic uncertainties. An analysis using the ratio x_d/x_s of $B_d - \bar{B}_d$ to $B_s - \bar{B}_s$ mixings is also presented.

1. Setting the Scene

An important target of particle physics is the determination of the unitary 3×3 Cabibbo-Kobayashi-Maskawa matrix which parametrizes the charged current interactions of quarks:

$$J^{cc}_\mu = (\bar{u}, \bar{c}, \bar{t})_L \gamma_\mu \begin{pmatrix} V_{ud} & V_{us} & V_{ub} \\ V_{cd} & V_{cs} & V_{cb} \\ V_{td} & V_{ts} & V_{tb} \end{pmatrix} \begin{pmatrix} d \\ s \\ b \end{pmatrix}_L \quad (1)$$

It is customery these days to parametrize these matrix by the four Wolfenstein parameters $(\lambda, A, \varrho, \eta)$. In particular one has

$$\mid V_{us} \mid = \lambda \qquad \mid V_{cb} \mid = A\lambda^2 \quad (2)$$

and

$$V_{ub} = A\lambda^3(\varrho - i\eta) \qquad V_{td} = A\lambda^3(1 - \bar{\varrho} - i\bar{\eta}) \quad (3)$$

Here following [1] we have introduced

$$\bar{\varrho} = \varrho(1 - \frac{\lambda^2}{2}) \qquad \bar{\eta} = \eta(1 - \frac{\lambda^2}{2}). \quad (4)$$

which allows to improve the accuracy of the Wolfenstein parametrization.

From tree level K decays sensitive to V_{us} and tree level B decays sensitive to V_{cb} and V_{ub} we have:

$$\lambda = 0.2205 \pm 0.0018 \qquad \mid V_{cb} \mid = 0.039 \pm 0.004 \quad (5)$$

$$R_b \equiv \sqrt{\bar{\varrho}^2 + \bar{\eta}^2} = (1 - \frac{\lambda^2}{2})\frac{1}{\lambda} \left| \frac{V_{ub}}{V_{cb}} \right| = 0.36 \pm 0.14 \quad (6)$$

corresponding to

$$\left| \frac{V_{ub}}{V_{cb}} \right| = 0.08 \pm 0.03 \quad (7)$$

R_b is just the length of one side of the rescaled unitarity triangle in which the length of the side on the $\bar{\varrho}$ axis is equal unity. The length of the third side is governed by $\mid V_{td} \mid$ and is given by

$$R_t \equiv \sqrt{(1 - \bar{\varrho})^2 + \bar{\eta}^2} = \frac{1}{\lambda} \left| \frac{V_{td}}{V_{cb}} \right| \quad (8)$$

In order to find R_t one has to go beyond tree level decays.

As we have seen at this conference a large part in the errors quoted in (5), (6) and (7) results from theoretical (hadronic) uncertainties. Consequently even

* Supported by the German Bundesministerium für Forschung und Technologie under contract 06 TM 732 and by the CEC science project SC1–CT91–0729.

if the data from CLEO II improves in the future, it is difficult to imagine at present that in the tree level B-decays a better accuracy than $\Delta \mid V_{cb} \mid = \pm 2 \cdot 10^{-3}$ and $\Delta \mid V_{ub}/V_{cb} \mid = \pm 0.01$ ($\Delta R_b = \pm 0.04$) could be achieved unless some dramatic improvements in the theory will take place.

The question then arises whether it is possible at all to determine the CKM parameters without any hadronic uncertainties. The aim of this contribution is to demonstrate that this is indeed possible. To this end one has to go to the loop induced decays or transitions governed by short distance physics. We will see that in this manner clean and precise determinations of $\mid V_{cb} \mid$, $\mid V_{ub}/V_{cb} \mid$, $\mid V_{td} \mid$, ϱ and η can be achieved. Since the relevant measurements will take place only in the next decade, what follows is really a 21st century story.

It is known that many loop induced decays contain also hadronic uncertainties [2]. Examples are $B^0 - \bar{B}^0$ mixing, ε_K and ε'/ε. Let us in this connection recall the expectations from a "standard" analysis of the unitarity triangle which is based on ε_K, x_d giving the size of $B^0 - \bar{B}^0$ mixing, $\mid V_{cb} \mid$ and $\mid V_{ub}/V_{cb} \mid$ with the last two extracted from tree level decays. As a recent analysis [1] shows, even with optimistic assumptions about the theoretical and experimental errors it will be difficult to achieve the accuracy better than $\Delta\varrho = \pm 0.15$ and $\Delta\eta = \pm 0.05$ this way. Therefore in what follows we will only discuss the four finalists in the field of weak decays which essentially are free of hadronic uncertainties.

2. Finalists

2.1. CP-Asymmetries in B^0-Decays

The CP-asymmetry in the decay $B_d^0 \to \psi K_S$ allows in the standard model a direct measurement of the angle β in the unitarity triangle without any theoretical uncertainties [3]. Similarly the decay $B_d^0 \to \pi^+\pi^-$ gives the angle α, although in this case strategies involving other channels are necessary in order to remove hadronic uncertainties related to penguin contributions [4]. The determination of the angle γ from CP asymmetries in neutral B-decays is more difficult but not impossible [5]. Also charged B decays could be useful in this respect [6]. We have for instance

$$A_{CP}(\psi K_S) = -\sin(2\beta)\frac{x_d}{1+x_d^2}, \qquad (9)$$

$$A_{CP}(\pi^+\pi^-) = -\sin(2\alpha)\frac{x_d}{1+x_d^2} \qquad (10)$$

where we have neglected QCD penguins in $A_{CP}(\pi^+\pi^-)$. Since in the usual unitarity triangle one side is known, it suffices to measure two angles to determine the triangle completely. This means that the measurements of $\sin 2\alpha$ and $\sin 2\beta$ can determine the parameters ϱ and η. The main virtues of this determination are as follows:

- No hadronic or $\Lambda_{\overline{MS}}$ uncertainties.
- No dependence on m_t and V_{cb} (or A).

2.2. $K_L \to \pi^0\nu\bar{\nu}$

$K_L \to \pi^0\nu\bar{\nu}$ is the theoretically cleanest decay in the field of rare K-decays. $K_L \to \pi^0\nu\bar{\nu}$ is dominated by short distance loop diagrams involving the top quark and proceeds almost entirely through direct CP violation. The last year calculations [7,8] of next-to-leading QCD corrections to this decay considerably reduced the theoretical uncertainty due to the choice of the renormalization scales present in the leading order expression [9]. Typically the uncertainty in $Br(K_L \to \pi^0\nu\bar{\nu})$ of $\pm 10\%$ in the leading order is reduced to $\pm 1\%$. Since the relevant hadronic matrix elements of the weak current $\bar{s}\gamma_\mu(1-\gamma_5)d$ can be measured in the leading decay $K^+ \to \pi^0 e^+\nu$, the resulting theoretical expression for $Br(K_L \to \pi^0\nu\bar{\nu})$ is only a function of the CKM parameters, the QCD scale $\Lambda_{\overline{MS}}$ and m_t. The long distance contributions to $K_L \to \pi^0\nu\bar{\nu}$ are negligible. We have then:

$$Br(K_L \to \pi^0\nu\bar{\nu}) = 1.50 \cdot 10^{-5}\eta^2 \mid V_{cb} \mid^4 x_t^{1.15} \qquad (11)$$

where $x_t = m_t^2/M_W^2$ with $m_t \equiv \bar{m}_t(m_t)$. The main features of this decay are:

- No hadronic uncertainties
- $\Lambda_{\overline{MS}}$ and renormalization scale uncertainties at most $\pm 1\%$.
- Strong dependence on m_t and V_{cb} (or A).

2.3. $K^+ \to \pi^+\nu\bar{\nu}$

$K^+ \to \pi^+\nu\bar{\nu}$ is CP conserving and receives contributions from both internal top and charm exchanges. The last year calculations [7,8,10] of next-to-leading QCD corrections to this decay considerably reduced the theoretical uncertainty due to the choice of the renormalization scales present in the leading order expression [9]. Typically the uncertainty in $Br(K^+ \to \pi^+\nu\bar{\nu})$ of $\pm 20\%$ in the leading order is reduced to $\pm 5\%$. The long distance contributions to $K^+ \to \pi^+\nu\bar{\nu}$ have been considered in [11] and found to be very small: two to three orders of magnitude smaller than the short distance contribution at the level of the branching ratio. $K^+ \to \pi^+\nu\bar{\nu}$ is then the second best decay in the field of rare decays. Compared to $K_L \to \pi^0\nu\bar{\nu}$ it receives additional uncertainties due to m_c and the related renormalization scale. Also its QCD scale dependence is stronger. Explicit expressions can be found in [10,12]. The main features of this decay are:

- Hadronic uncertainties below 1%
- $\Lambda_{\overline{MS}}$, m_c and renormalization scales uncertainties at most $\pm(5-10)\%$.
- Strong dependence on m_t and V_{cb} (or A).

2.4. $B^o - \bar{B}^o$ Mixing

Measurement of $B_d^o - \bar{B}_d^o$ mixing parametrized by x_d together with $B_s^o - \bar{B}_s^o$ mixing parametrized by x_s allows to determine R_t:

$$R_t = \frac{1}{\sqrt{R_{ds}}} \sqrt{\frac{x_d}{x_s}} \frac{1}{\lambda} \qquad (12)$$

with $R_{d,s}$ summarizing SU(3)–flavour breaking effects. Note that m_t and V_{cb} dependences have been eliminated this way and R_{ds} contains much smaller theoretical uncertainties than the hadronic matrix elements in x_d and x_s separately. Provided x_d/x_s has been accurately measured a determination of R_t within $\pm 10\%$ should be possible. The main features of x_d/x_s are:

- No $\Lambda_{\overline{MS}}$, m_t and V_{cb} dependence.
- Hadronic uncertainty in SU(3)–flavour breaking effects of roughly $\pm 10\%$.

Because of the last feature, x_d/x_s cannot fully compete in the clean determination of CKM parameters with CP asymmetries in B-decays and with $K_L \to \pi^0 \nu \bar{\nu}$. Although $K^+ \to \pi^+ \nu \bar{\nu}$ has smaller hadronic uncertainties than x_d/x_s, its dependence on $\Lambda_{\overline{MS}}$ and m_c puts it in the same class as x_d/x_s [2].

3. $\sin 2\beta$ from $K \to \pi \nu \bar{\nu}$

It has been pointed out in [13] that measurements of $Br(K^+ \to \pi^+ \nu \bar{\nu})$ and $Br(K_L \to \pi^0 \nu \bar{\nu})$ could determine the unitarity triangle completely provided m_t and V_{cb} are known. In view of the strong dependence of these branching ratios on m_t and V_{cb} this determination is not precise however [12]. On the other hand it has been noticed recently [12] that the m_t and V_{cb} dependences drop out in the evaluation of $\sin(2\beta)$. Introducing the "reduced" branching ratios

$$B_+ = \frac{Br(K^+ \to \pi^+ \nu \bar{\nu})}{4.64 \cdot 10^{-11}} \qquad B_L = \frac{Br(K_L \to \pi^0 \nu \bar{\nu})}{1.94 \cdot 10^{-10}} \qquad (13)$$

one finds

$$\sin(2\beta) = \frac{2 r_s(B_+, B_L)}{1 + r_s^2(B_+, B_L)} \qquad (14)$$

where

$$r_s(B_+, B_L) = \frac{\sqrt{(B_+ - B_L)} - P_0(K^+)}{\sqrt{B_L}} \qquad (15)$$

so that $\sin(2\beta)$ does not depend on m_t and V_{cb}. Here $P_0(K^+) = 0.40 \pm 0.09$ [10,12] is a function of m_c and $\Lambda_{\overline{MS}}$ and includes the residual uncertainty due to the renormalization scale μ. Consequently $K^+ \to \pi^+ \nu \bar{\nu}$ and $K_L \to \pi^0 \nu \bar{\nu}$ offer a clean determination of $\sin(2\beta)$ which can be confronted with the one possible in $B^0 \to \psi K_S$ discussed above. Any difference in these two

determinations would signal new physics. Choosing $Br(K^+ \to \pi^+ \nu \bar{\nu}) = (1.0 \pm 0.1) \cdot 10^{-10}$ and $Br(K_L \to \pi^0 \nu \bar{\nu}) = (2.5 \pm 0.25) \cdot 10^{-11}$, one finds [12]

$$\sin(2\beta) = 0.60 \pm 0.06 \pm 0.03 \pm 0.02 \qquad (16)$$

where the first error is "experimental", the second represents the uncertainty in m_c and $\Lambda_{\overline{MS}}$ and the last is due to the residual renormalization scale uncertainties. This determination of $\sin(2\beta)$ is competitive with the one expected at the B-factories at the beginning of the next decade.

4. Precise Determinations of the CKM Matrix

Using the first two finalists and $\lambda = 0.2205 \pm 0.0018$ [14] it is possible to determine all the parameters of the CKM matrix without any hadronic uncertainties [15]. With $a \equiv \sin(2\alpha)$, $b \equiv \sin(2\beta)$ and $Br(K_L) \equiv Br(K_L \to \pi^0 \nu \bar{\nu})$ one determines ϱ, η and $| V_{cb} |$ as follows [15]:

$$\bar{\varrho} = 1 - \bar{\eta} r_+(b) \quad , \quad \bar{\eta} = \frac{r_-(a) + r_+(b)}{1 + r_+^2(b)} \qquad (17)$$

$$| V_{cb} | = 0.039 \sqrt{\frac{0.39}{\eta}} \left[\frac{170 \, GeV}{m_t} \right]^{0.575} \left[\frac{Br(K_L)}{3 \cdot 10^{-11}} \right]^{1/4} \qquad (18)$$

where

$$r_\pm(z) = \frac{1}{z} (1 \pm \sqrt{1 - z^2}) \qquad z = a, b \qquad (19)$$

We note that the weak dependence of $| V_{cb} |$ on $Br(K_L \to \pi^0 \nu \bar{\nu})$ allows to achieve high accuracy for this CKM element even when $Br(K_L \to \pi^0 \nu \bar{\nu})$ is not measured precisely.

As illustrative examples we consider in table 1 three scenarios. The first four rows give the assumed input parameters and their experimental errors. The remaining rows give the results for selected parameters. Further results can be found in [15]. The accuracy in the scenario I should be achieved at B-factories, HERA-B, at KAMI and at KEK. Scenarios II and III correspond to B-physics at Fermilab during the Main Injector era and at LHC respectively. At that time an improved measurement of $Br(K_L \to \pi^0 \nu \bar{\nu})$ should be aimed for. Table 1 shows very clearly the potential of CP asymmetries in B-decays and of $K_L \to \pi^0 \nu \bar{\nu}$ in the determination of CKM parameters. It should be stressed that this high accuracy is not only achieved because of our assumptions about future experimental errors in the scenarios considered, but also because $\sin(2\alpha)$ is a very sensitive function of ϱ and η [1], $Br(K_L \to \pi^0 \nu \bar{\nu})$ depends strongly on $| V_{cb} |$ and most importantly because of the clean character of the quantities considered.

	Central	I	II	III
$\sin(2\alpha)$	0.40	±0.08	±0.04	±0.02
$\sin(2\beta)$	0.70	±0.06	±0.02	±0.01
m_t	170	±5	±3	±3
$10^{11}Br(K_L)$	3	±0.30	±0.15	±0.15
ϱ	0.072	±0.040	±0.016	±0.008
η	0.389	±0.044	±0.016	±0.008
$\|V_{ub}/V_{cb}\|$	0.087	±0.010	±0.003	±0.002
$\|V_{cb}\|/10^{-3}$	39.2	±3.9	±1.7	±1.3
$\|V_{td}\|/10^{-3}$	8.7	±0.9	±0.4	±0.3
$\|V_{cb}\|/10^{-3}$	41.2	±4.3	±3.0	±2.8
$\|V_{td}\|/10^{-3}$	9.1	±0.9	±0.6	±0.6

Table 1. Determinations of various parameters in scenarios I-III

	Central	I	II	III
R_t	1.00	±0.10	±0.05	±0.03
$\sin(2\beta)$	0.70	±0.06	±0.02	±0.01
m_t	170	±5	±3	±3
$10^{11}Br(K_L)$	3	±0.30	±0.15	±0.15
ϱ	0.076	±0.111	±0.053	±0.031
η	0.388	±0.079	±0.033	±0.019
$\|V_{ub}/V_{cb}\|$	0.087	±0.014	±0.005	±0.003
$\|V_{cb}\|/10^{-3}$	39.3	±5.7	±2.6	±1.8
$\|V_{td}\|/10^{-3}$	8.7	±1.2	±0.6	±0.4
$\|V_{cb}\|/10^{-3}$	41.3	±5.8	±3.7	±3.3
$\|V_{td}\|/10^{-3}$	9.1	±1.3	±0.8	±0.7

Table 2. As in table 1 but with $\sin(2\alpha)$ replaced by R_t.

It is instructive to investigate whether the use of $K^+ \to \pi^+\nu\bar{\nu}$ instead of $K_L \to \pi^0\nu\bar{\nu}$ would also give interesting results for V_{cb} and V_{td}. We again consider scenarios I-III with $Br(K^+ \to \pi^+\nu\bar{\nu}) = (1.0\pm0.1)\cdot10^{-10}$ for the scenario I and $Br(K^+ \to \pi^+\nu\bar{\nu}) = (1.0 \pm 0.05) \cdot 10^{-10}$ for scenarios II and III in place of $Br(K_L \to \pi^0\nu\bar{\nu})$ with all other input parameters unchanged. An analytic formula for $|V_{cb}|$ can be found in [15]. The results for ϱ, η, and $|V_{ub}/V_{cb}|$ remain of course unchanged. In the last two rows of table 1 we show the results for $|V_{cb}|$ and $|V_{td}|$. We observe that due to the uncertainties present in the charm contribution to $K^+ \to \pi^+\nu\bar{\nu}$, which was absent in $K_L \to \pi^0\nu\bar{\nu}$, the determinations of $|V_{cb}|$ and $|V_{td}|$ are less accurate. If the uncertainties due to the charm mass and $\Lambda_{\overline{MS}}$ are removed one day this analysis will be improved [15].

An alternative strategy is to use the measured value of R_t instead of $\sin(2\alpha)$. Then (17) is replaced by

$$\bar{\varrho} = 1 - \bar{\eta}r_+(b) \quad , \quad \bar{\eta} = \frac{R_t}{\sqrt{2}}\sqrt{br_-(b)} \qquad (20)$$

The result of this exercise is shown in table 2. We observe that even with rather optimistic assumptions on the accuracy of R_t, this determination of CKM parameters cannot fully compete with the previous one. Again the last two rows give the results when $K_L \to \pi^0\nu\bar{\nu}$ is replaced by $K^+ \to \pi^+\nu\bar{\nu}$.

5.   Final Remarks

- Precise measurements of all CKM parameters without hadronic uncertainties are possible.
- Such measurements are essential for the tests of the standard model. Of particular interest will be the comparison of $|V_{cb}|$ determined as suggested here with the value of this CKM element extracted from tree level semi-leptonic B-decays. Since in contrast to $K_L \to \pi^0\nu\bar{\nu}$ and $K^+ \to \pi^+\nu\bar{\nu}$, the tree-level decays are to an excellent approximation insensitive to any new physics contributions from very high energy scales, the comparison of these two determinations of $|V_{cb}|$ would be a good test of the standard model and of a possible physics beyond it.

Precise determinations of all CKM parameters without hadronic uncertainties along the lines presented here can only be realized if the measurements of CP asymmetries in B-decays and the measurements of $Br(K_L \to \pi^0\nu\bar{\nu})$, $Br(K^+ \to \pi^+\nu\bar{\nu})$ and x_d/x_s can reach the desired accuracy. All efforts should be made to achieve this goal.

References

[1] A.J. Buras, M.E. Lautenbacher and G. Ostermaier, *Phys. Rev.* **D** (1994) hep-ph 9403384.
[2] A.J. Buras, "CP Violation: Present and Future" TUM-T31-64/94, hep-ph 9406272.
[3] Y. Nir and H.R. Quinn in " B Decays ", ed S. Stone (World Scientific, 1992), p. 362; I. Dunietz, ibid p.393 and refs. therein.
[4] M. Gronau and D. London, *Phys. Rev. Lett.* **65** (1990) 3381, *Phys. Lett.* **B 253** (1991) 483; Y. Nir and H. Quinn, *Phys. Rev.* **D 42** (1990) 1473, *Phys. Rev. Lett.* **67** (1991) 541; R. Aleksan, I. Dunietz, B. Kayser and F. Le Diberder, *Nucl. Phys.* **B 361** (1991) 141.
[5] M. Gronau, J.L. Rosner and D. London, *Phys. Rev. Lett.* **73** (1994) 21 and refs. therein; R. Fleischer, *Phys. Lett.* **B 332** (1994) 419.
[6] M. Gronau and D. Wyler, *Phys. Lett.* **B 265** (1991) 172.
[7] G. Buchalla and A.J. Buras, *Nucl. Phys.* **B 398** (1993) 285.
[8] G. Buchalla and A.J. Buras, *Nucl. Phys.* **B 400** (1993) 225.
[9] C.O. Dib, I. Dunietz and F.J. Gilman, *Mod. Phys. Lett.* **A 6** (1991) 3573.
[10] G. Buchalla and A.J. Buras, *Nucl. Phys.* **B 412** (1994) 106.
[11] D. Rein and L.M. Sehgal, *Phys. Rev.* **D 39** (1989) 3325; J.S. Hagelin and L.S. Littenberg, *Prog. Part. Nucl. Phys.* **23** (1989) 1; M. Lu and M.B. Wise, *Phys. Lett.* **B 324** (1994) 461.
[12] G. Buchalla and A.J. Buras, *Phys. Lett.* **B 333** (1994) 221.
[13] A.J. Buras and M.K. Harlander, A Top Quark Story, *in* Heavy Flavors, eds. A.J. Buras and M. Lindner, World Scientific (1992), p.58.
[14] H. Leutwyler and M. Roos, *Zeitschr. f. Physik* **C25** (1984) 91; J.F. Donoghue, B.R. Holstein and S.W. Klimt, *Phys. Rev.* **D 35** (1987) 934.
[15] A.J. Buras, *Phys. Lett.* **B 333** (1994) 476.

Penguin B deacys $b \to sl^+l^-$ and $b \to sg^*$

N G Deshpande[†] and Xiao-Gang He[‡]

Institute of Theoretical Science, University of Oregon,
Eugene, OR 97403-5203, USA

Abstract

The penguin mediated processes $b \to sg$ and $b \to sl^+l^-$ are studied. In the Standard Model, for the leptonic modes improvement in experimental limits will put strigient bounds on the top mass, where the present limit from $b \to s\mu^+\mu^-$ is 390 GeV. For hadronic penguin processes, although the gluonic penguin dominates, we find the electroweak contribution are around 30% for the upper range allowed top mass. The branching ratio for $B \to X_s\phi$ is predicted to be in the range $(0.6 \sim 2) \times 10^{-4}$. Effects of the charged Higgs in two Higgs doublet models are discussed.

Rare B decays, particularly pure penguin decays, have been subject of considerable theoretical and experimental interest recently[1]. The photonic penguin induced process $B \to K^*\gamma$ has been observed by CLEO collaboration[2] and is consistent with the Standard Model (SM) prediction[3]. In this talk we will concentrate on two other classes of penguin decays, $b \to sl^+l^-$ and $b \to sg$.

1. Process $b \to sl^+l^-$

The process $b \to sl^+l^-$ is sensitive to top mass unlike $b \to s\gamma$, and improvement in the experimental bound should greatly improve the top quark mass upper limit which is at present at ~ 390 GeV from $b \to s\mu^+\mu^-$[4]. This process for large top mass has dominant contribution from Z exchange and the box diagram[5].

The effective Hamiltonian density relevant for $b \to sl^+l^-$ decay is:

$$H_{eff} \cong \frac{4G_F}{\sqrt{2}} \left(V_{cb}V_{cs}^*\right) \sum \tilde{c}_j(m)\tilde{O}_j(m) \ . \quad (1)$$

The important operators for us are:

$$
\begin{aligned}
\tilde{O}_7 &= \left(e/16\pi^2\right) m_b \left(\overline{s}_L \sigma_{\mu\nu} b_R\right) F^{\mu\nu} \quad , \\
\tilde{O}_9 &= \left(e^2/16\pi^2\right) \left(\overline{s}_L \gamma_\mu b_L\right) \overline{\ell}\gamma^\mu\ell \quad , \\
\tilde{O}_{10} &= \left(e^2/16\pi^2\right) \left(\overline{s}_L \gamma_\mu b_L\right) \overline{\ell}\gamma^\mu\gamma_5\ell \ .
\end{aligned}
\quad (2)
$$

Here $F_{\mu\nu}$ is the electromagnetic interaction field strength tensor.

The QCD-renomalized coefficients $\tilde{c}_j(m)$ are calculated in Ref. [6], and their implications are discussed in Ref.[4]. The branching ratio of $b \to sl^+l^-$ can be written after normalizing the rate to $BR(b \to ce\overline{\nu}) \approx 0.108$, [6, 7]:

$$
BR(b \to sl^+l^-) =
K[F_1(|\tilde{c}_9|^2 + |\tilde{c}_{10}|^2) + F_3\tilde{c}_9\tilde{c}_7 + F_2|\tilde{c}_7|^2] \ , \quad (3)
$$

where

$$K = (\alpha/4\pi)^2 \left(2/\lambda\widetilde{\rho}\right) BR\left(b \to ce\overline{\nu}\right) = 1.6 \cdot 10^{-7} \quad (4)$$

and α is fine structure constant. The phase space factor $\widetilde{\rho}$ and the QCD correction factor λ for the semileptonic process are well known [8]. We have used $\widetilde{\rho} = 0.5$ and $\lambda = 0.889$. The phase space integration from $min = (2m_\ell/m_b)^2$ to $max = (1 - m_s/m_b)^2$ give the following values [9] for the constants F_i:

$$F_1 = 1, \quad F_3 = 8, \quad \text{for} \quad min \cong 0, \quad max \cong 1 \quad , \quad (5)$$

* Work supported in part by the Department of Energy Grant No. DE-FG06-85ER40224.
† E-mail: desh@oregon.uoregon.edu.
‡ E-mail: he@quark.uoregon.edu

$$F_2 = 32\left[\ln\left(m_b/2m_\ell\right)\right]; \quad \text{for} \quad max \cong 1; \quad \ell = e, \mu. \quad (6)$$

We plot in Fig. 1 the branching ratios for $b \to sl^+l^-$ as a function of the top mass for the standard model. In the SM the process $b \to se^+e^-$ is enhanced over $b \to s\mu^+\mu^-$ by $\sim 60\%$ for $m_t = 150$ GeV due to the small electron mass [9]. As noted, the decay rate is highly dependent on m_t and improvement on this limit should improve bounds on m_t significantly.

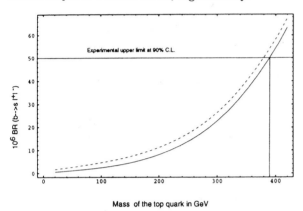

Figure 1. Branching ratios for $b \to se^+e^-$ (dashed line) and $b \to s\mu^+\mu^-$ (solid line) as a function of the top mass.

In Ref.[4] the implications of additional Higgs doublet on $b \to sl^+l^-$ is discussed. The conclusions are:

1) In two-Higgs doublet model II, where couplings are like the minimal supersymmetric model, constraints are possible for all values of $\tan\beta = v_2/v_1$ for smaller Higgs masses; although the experimental bounds will have to be improved to draw useful conclusions.

2) In the two-Higgs doublet model I, the constraints on Higgs masses are similar to $b \to s\gamma$, and tight constraints can be derived on Higgs masses only for small values of $\tan\beta = v_2/v_1$.

2. Process $b \to sg$

The gluonic penguin induced B decays are expected to be observed very soon. A large number of gluonic penguin induced B decay channels were studied in Ref.[10] using $\Delta B = 1$ effective Hamiltonian $H_{\Delta B=1}$ in the lowest nonvanishing order. In Ref.[11] the next-to-leading order QCD corrected pure gluonic penguin $H_{\Delta B=1}$ was used with top quark mass m_t fixed at 150 GeV. In this talk we present a study of the next-to-leading order QCD corrected Hamiltonian $H_{\Delta B=1}$ in the SM and in two Higgs doublet models, taking particular care to *include the full electroweak contributions* and find the dependence on m_t and α_s. The cleanest signature of hadronic penguin processes are: $B \to X_s\phi$, $B \to K\phi(K^*\phi)$, and $B_s \to \phi\phi$. The process $B \to X_s\phi$ is

m_t(GeV)	c_1	c_2	c_3	c_4	c_5
130	-0.313	1.150	0.017	-0.037	0.010
174	-0.313	1.150	0.017	-0.037	0.010
210	-0.313	1.150	0.018	-0.038	0.010
m_t(GeV)	c_6	c_7/α_{em}	c_8/α_{em}	c_9/α_{em}	c_{10}/α_{em}
130	-0.045	-0.061	0.029	-0.978	0.191
174	-0.046	-0.001	0.049	-1.321	0.267
210	-0.046	0.060	0.069	-1.626	0.334

Table 1. The Wilson coefficients for $\Delta B = 1$ at $m_b = 5\ GeV$ with $\alpha_s(m_Z) = 0.118$.

particularly recommended because it is free from form factor uncertainties. We find not only that the QCD correction in next-to-leading order are large, but also inclusion of the full electroweak contributions have significant effect on the branching ratio which could reduce the pure gluonic penguin contribution by 30% at the upper range of allowed top quark mass. Our results which have been derived independently[12], agree with Fleischer[13]. The electroweak corrections alter the isospin structure of penguins, and have a major impact on the analysis of certain B decays. This will be presented in a forthcoming publication[14].

The QCD corrected $H_{\Delta B=1}$ relevant to us can be written as follows[15]:

$$H_{\Delta B=1} = \frac{G_F}{\sqrt{2}}[V_{ub}V_{us}^*(c_1O_1^u + c_2O_2^u)$$
$$+V_{cb}V_{cs}^*(c_1O_1^c + c_2O_2^c) - V_{tb}V_{ts}^*\sum c_iO_i] + H.C.\,, \quad (7)$$

where the Wilson coefficients (WCs) c_i are defined at the scale of $\mu \approx m_b$; and O_i are defined as

$$
\begin{aligned}
O_1^q &= \bar{s}_\alpha\gamma_\mu(1-\gamma_5)q_\beta\bar{q}_\beta\gamma^\mu(1-\gamma_5)b_\alpha\,, \\
O_2^q &= \bar{s}\gamma_\mu(1-\gamma_5)q\bar{q}\gamma^\mu(1-\gamma_5)b\,, \\
O_3 &= \bar{s}\gamma_\mu(1-\gamma_5)b\bar{q}'\gamma_\mu(1-\gamma_5)q'\,, \\
Q_4 &= \bar{s}_\alpha\gamma_\mu(1-\gamma_5)b_\beta\bar{q}'_\beta\gamma_\mu(1-\gamma_5)q'_\alpha\,, \quad (8) \\
O_5 &= \bar{s}\gamma_\mu(1-\gamma_5)b\bar{q}'\gamma^\mu(1+\gamma_5)q'\,, \\
Q_6 &= \bar{s}_\alpha\gamma_\mu(1-\gamma_5)b_\beta\bar{q}'_\beta\gamma_\mu(1+\gamma_5)q'_\alpha\,, \\
O_7 &= \frac{3}{2}\bar{s}\gamma_\mu(1-\gamma_5)be_{q'}\bar{q}'\gamma^\mu(1+\gamma_5)q'\,, \\
Q_8 &= \frac{3}{2}\bar{s}_\alpha\gamma_\mu(1-\gamma_5)b_\beta e_{q'}\bar{q}'_\beta\gamma_\mu(1+\gamma_5)q'_\alpha\,, \\
O_9 &= \frac{3}{2}\bar{s}\gamma_\mu(1-\gamma_5)be_{q'}\bar{q}'\gamma^\mu(1-\gamma_5)q'\,, \\
Q_{10} &= \frac{3}{2}\bar{s}_\alpha\gamma_\mu(1-\gamma_5)b_\beta e_{q'}\bar{q}'_\beta\gamma_\mu(1-\gamma_5)q'_\alpha\,.
\end{aligned}
$$

Here q' is summed over u, d, and s.

We work with renormalization scheme independent WCs c_i as discussed in Ref.[15]. In Table 1, we show some sample values of c_i for some values of m_t with the central value $\alpha_s(m_Z) = 0.118$ and $\mu = m_b$[12].

We also need to treat the matrix elements to one-loop level for consistency. These one-loop matrix elements can be rewritten in terms of the tree-level matrix elements $< O_j >^t$ of the effective operators, and one finds [13, 16] $< c_i Q_i >$ to be equal to

$$c_i[\delta_{ij} + \frac{\alpha_s}{4\pi}m^s_{ij} + \frac{\alpha_{em}}{4\pi}m^e_{ij}] < O_j >^t \equiv c^{eff}_i < O_i >^t . \tag{9}$$

We have worked out the full matrices $m^{s,e}$. For the processes we are considering only c_{3-10} contribute. These are given by,

$$\begin{aligned} c^{eff}_3 &= c_3 - P_s/3 , & c^{eff}_4 &= c_4 + P_s , \\ c^{eff}_5 &= c_5 - P_s/3 , & c^{eff}_6 &= c_6 + P_s , \\ c^{eff}_7 &= c_7 + P_e , & c^{eff}_8 &= c_8 , \\ c^{eff}_9 &= c_9 + P_e , & c^{eff}_{10} &= c_{10} . \end{aligned} \tag{10}$$

The leading contributions to $P_{s,e}$ are given by: $P_s = (\alpha_s/8\pi)c_2(10/9 + G(m_c, \mu, q^2))$ and $P_e = (\alpha_{em}/9\pi)(3c_1 + c_2)(10/9 + G(m_c, \mu, q^2))$. Here m_c is the charm quark mass which we take to be 1.35 GeV. The function $G(m, \mu, q^2)$ is give by

$$G(m, \mu, q^2) = 4 \int_0^1 x(1-x)dx \ln\frac{m^2 - x(1-x)q^2}{\mu^2} . \tag{11}$$

In the numerical calculation, we will use $q^2 = m_b^2/2$ which represents the average value.

We obtain the decay amplitude for $B \to X_s\phi$

$$\begin{aligned} A(B \to X_s\phi) &\approx A(b \to s\phi) = \\ &-\frac{g_\phi G_F}{\sqrt{2}} V_{tb}V^*_{ts}\epsilon^\mu C\bar{s}\gamma_\mu(1-\gamma_5)b , \end{aligned} \tag{12}$$

where ϵ^μ is the polarization of the ϕ particle; $C = c^{eff}_3 + c^{eff}_4 + c^{eff}_5 + \xi(c^{eff}_3 + c^{eff}_4 + c^{eff}_6) - (c^{eff}_7 + c^{eff}_9 + c^{eff}_{10} + \xi(c^{eff}_8 + c^{eff}_9 + c^{eff}_{10}))/2$ with $\xi = 1/N_c$, where N_c is the number of colors. The coupling constant g_ϕ is defined by $< \phi|\bar{s}\gamma^\mu s|0 >= ig_\phi\epsilon^\mu$. From the experimental value for $Br(\phi \to e^+e^-)$, we obtain $g_\phi^2 = 0.0586\,GeV^4$.

The decay rate is, then, given by

$$\begin{aligned} \Gamma(B \to X_s\phi) &= \frac{G_F^2 g_\phi^2 m_b^3}{16\pi m_\phi^2}|V_{tb}V^*_{ts}|^2|C|^2\lambda_{s\phi}^{3/2} \\ &\times[1 + \frac{3}{\lambda_{s\phi}}\frac{m_\phi^2}{m_b^2}(1 - \frac{m_\phi^2}{m_b^2} + \frac{m_s^2}{m_b^2})] , \end{aligned} \tag{13}$$

where $\lambda_{ij} = (1 - m_j^2/m_b^2 - m_i^2/m_b^2)^2 - 4m_i^2m_j^2/m_b^4$.

We normalize the branching ratio to the semileptonic decay of $B \to X_c e\bar{\nu}_e$. We have

$$\begin{aligned} Br(B \to X_s\phi) &= Br(B \to X_c e\bar{\nu}_e)\frac{|V_{tb}V^*_{ts}|^2}{|V_{cb}|^2} \\ &\times\frac{12\pi^2 g_\phi^2\lambda_{s\phi}^{3/2}}{m_\phi^2 m_b^2\lambda_{\hat{\rho}}}|C|^2[1 + \frac{3}{\lambda_{s\phi}}\frac{m_\phi^2}{m_b^2}(1 - \frac{m_\phi^2}{m_b^2} + \frac{m_s^2}{m_b^2})] . \end{aligned} \tag{14}$$

We show in, Fuigure 2 and 3 the predictions for the branching ratio $Br(B \to X_s\phi)$ in the SM as a function of top quark mass m_t and the strong coupling constant

$\alpha_s(m_Z)$ with and without electroweak corrections, and for $N_c = 2$ and 3.

The dominant contribuitons are from the gluonic penguin. There is a very small m_t dependence for the branching ratio calculated without the inclusion of the electroweak penguin contributions. The inclusion of the full electroweak contribuitons have sizeable effects which reduce the branching ratios by about 20% to 30% for the central value of α_s with m_t varying from 100 GeV to 200 GeV. It is clear from Figure 2 and 3 that the full contribution has a large m_t dependence. There may be corrections to the branching ratios predicted by the factorization method. It is a common practice to parameterize the possible new contributions by treating ξ as a free parameter[17, 18, 19]. Using experimental values from non-leptonic B decays, it is found that[18], $a_1 = c_2 + \xi c_1$ and $a_2 = c_1 + \xi c_2$ have the same signs, and $|a_2| \approx 0.27$ and $|a_1| \approx 1.0$. The branching ratios for $N_c = 2$ are about 2 times those for $N_c = 3$.

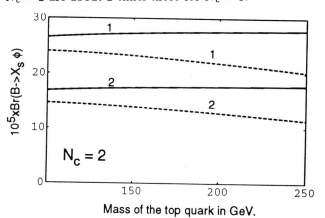

Figure 2. $Br(B \to X_s\phi)$ as a function of top mass with $N_c = 2$, and $\alpha_s(m_Z) = 0.125$ (curves 1) and $\alpha(m_Z) = 0.111$ (curves 2). The dashed and solid lines are for the branching ratios with the full strong and electroweak penguin contributions, and without the electroweak contributions, respectively.

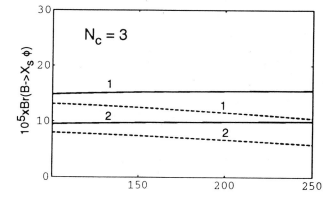

Figure 3. The same as above but with $N_c = 3$.

For the central value of $\alpha_s(m_Z)$ and the central value of $m_t = 174$ GeV reported by CDF[20], the value for

$Br(B \to X_s\phi)$ is about 1.7×10^{-4} for $N_c = 2$.

Using form factors from Refs.[17, 18], we also calculated the exclusive decay rates for $B \to K\phi$, $B \to K^*\phi$, and $B_s \to \phi\phi$. The exclusive branching ratios $B \to K\phi$ and $B \to K^*\phi$ are about the same which are 1×10^{-5} if the form factors from Ref.[17] are used. If the form factors from Ref.[18] are used, one obtains $Br(B \to K\phi) \approx 1.7 \times 10^{-5}$, $Br(B \to K^*\phi) \approx 0.5 \times 10^{-5}$, and $Br(B_s \to \phi\phi) \approx 0.4 \times 10^{-5}$.

We have also looked at $b \to sg$ in two-Higgs doublet model[12]. Both models I and II give the same results. The ratio of decay rates of the SM predictions to the two-Higgs doublet model predictions weakly depends on N_c. We find that the effects of the charged Higgs boson contributions are small for $cot\beta < 1$. When increasing $cot\beta$, the charged Higgs contributions become important and the effect is to cancel the SM contributions. When $cot\beta$ becomes very large the charged Higgs boson contributions become the dominant ones. However, using the information from $B \to X_s\gamma$, it is found that for small $m_H \sim 100$ GeV and $m_t \sim 174$ GeV, $cot\beta$ is constrained to be less than 1[21]. For these values, the charged Higgs boson effects on the processes discussed in this paper are less than 10%. For $m_H \sim 500$ GeV, the charged Higgs boson effects can reduce the hadronic penguin B decays by 40% because the range of $cot\beta$ allowed from $b \to s\gamma$ is now larger[21]. The effects become smaller for larger m_H.

3. $B \to K\pi/\pi\pi$ modes

We now present a summary of contribution by Hayashi, Joshi, Matsuda and Tanimoto[22] to this conference. They focus on gluonic effects in the exclusive channels $B \to K\pi$ and $B \to \pi\pi$. These channels have contrbutions from both the tree operastors $O_{1,2}$ and the penguin operators. their Hamiltonian includes leading order QCD correction, but not the Z,γ penguin and W box contributions to the penguin diagrams. Effect of charm loop is included in the same manor as discussed by us where c_i^{eff} are introduced. The value of q^2 is taken as $m_b^2/2$ in P_s. The factorization hypothesis is employed, with further assumption that $N_c = 3$, which might lead to incorrect estimates.

The amplitude for $B^0 \to K^+\pi^-$ and $B^0 \to \pi^+\pi^-$ can both be expressed in terms of a universal form factor $F_0^{B\pi}(q^2)$ if B annihilation terms are neglected

$$q^\mu < \pi^-|\bar{u}\gamma_\mu b|B_d^0 > = (m_B^2 - m_\pi^2)F_0^{B\pi}(q^2) . \quad (15)$$

This form factor drops out when ratios of $B^0 \to K^+\pi^-$ to $B^0 \to \pi^+\pi^-$ decay rates are taken. This ratio is, however, sensitive to $|V_{ub}/V_{cb}|$ and the phase of $V_{ub} = |V_{ub}|e^{-i\phi}$. The authors find $R_B = \Gamma(B_b^0 \to K^-\pi^+)/\Gamma(B_d^0 \to \pi^+\pi^-)$ can range from 0.4 to 7.0. They also calculated the relative contribution of penguin and

tree contributions to $B \to K\pi$ and $B \to \pi\pi$ processes. Their results for ratio of amplitudes for $\phi = 90^0$ are

$$\frac{A(penguin)}{A(tree)} = \begin{cases} 4.22\frac{0.08}{|V_{ub}/V_{cb}|} , & \text{for } B \to K\pi \\ 0.22\frac{0.08}{|V_{ub}/V_{cb}|} , & \text{for } B \to \pi\pi \end{cases} \quad (16)$$

The present CLEO observation of $BR(B \to K^+\pi^- + \pi^+\pi^-) = (2.4^{+0.8}_{-0.7} \pm 0.2) \times 10^{-5}$ imposes the limit $F_0^{B\pi}(0) = 0.26$ to 0.55 which is consistent with BSW model $F_0^{B\pi}(0) = 0.33$.

The authors have also considered CP asymmetry in $B \to \pi^+\pi^-$ decay arising from the phase of V_{ub} as well as the imaginary part c^{eff}. The asymmetry can be as large as 30%.

References

[1] For a review see: *B Decays*, edited by S. Stone, World Scientific, 1992.

[2] CLEO Collaboration, Phys. Rev. Lett. **71**, 674(1993).

[3] N.G. Deshpande et. al., Phys. Rev. Lett. **59**, 183(1987); S. Bertolini, F. Borzumati and A. Masiero, *ibid*, 180(1987); N.G. Deshpande, P. Lo and J. Trampetic, Z. Phys.**C40**, 369(1988); C. Dominguez, N. Paver and Riazuddin, Phys. Lett. **B214**, 459(1988); A. Ovchinnikov and V. Slobodenyuk, Phys. Lett. **B237**, 569(1990); P.J. O'Donnel and H.K.K. Tung, Phys. Rev.**D44**, 741(1991); R. Casalbuoni et. al., Phys. Lett. **B312**, 315(1993).

[4] N.G. Deshpande, K. Panose and J. Trampetic, Phys. Lett. **B308**, 322(1993).

[5] W.S. Hou, R.I. Willey and A. Soni, Phys. Rev. Lett. **58**, 1608(1987).

[6] B. Grinstein, M. J. Savage and M. Wise, Nucl. Phys. **B339**, 271(1990); B. Grinstein, R. springer and M. Wise, Nucl. Phys. **B339**, 269(1990); M. Misiak, Nucl. Phys. **393**, 23(1993).

[7] N.G. Deshpande and J. Trampetic, Phys. Rev. Lett. **60**, 2583(1988).

[8] V. Barger, M. Berger and R. Phillips, Phys. Rev. Lett. **70**, 1368(1993).

[9] N. G. Deshpande, J. Trampetic and K. Panose, Phys. Rev. **D39**, 1461(1989).

[10] N.G. Deshpande and J. Trampetic, Phys. Rev. **D41**, 895(1990).

[11] A. Deandrea, et. al., Phys. Lett. **B320**, 170(1993).

[12] N. G. Deshpande and Xiao-Gang He, Preprint, OITS-538, (1994) (Phys. Lett. B. in press).

[13] R. Fleischer, Preprint, TUM-T31-40/93 (Z. Phys. in press).

[14] N. G. Deshpande and Xiao-Gang He, Preprint, OITS-553.

[15] A. Buras, M. Jamin, M. Lautenbacher and P. Weisz, Nucl. Phys. **B400**, 37(1993); A. Buras, M. Jamin and M. Lautenbacher, ibid, 75(1993); M. Ciuchini, E. Franco, G. Martinelli and L. Reina, Nucl. Phys. **B415**, 403(1994).

[16] R. Fleischer, Z. Phys. **C58**, 483(1993); G. Kramer, W. Palmer and H. Simma, Preprint, DESY-93-192.

[17] M. Bauer, B. Stech and M. Wirbel, Z. Phys. **C34**, 103(1087).

[18] A. Deandrea, N. Di Bartolomeo, R. Gatto and G. Nardulli, Phys. Lett. **B318**, 549(1993).

[19] N.G. Deshpande, M. Gronau and D. Sutherland, Phys. Lett. **B90**, 431(1980).

[20] F. Abe, et al., CDF Collaboration, Preprint, FERMILAB-PUB-94/097-E, CDF/PUB /TOP/PUBLIC/2561.

[21] J.L. Hewett, Phys. Rev. Lett. **70**, 1045(1993); V. Barger, M. Berger, R. Phillips, *ibid*, 1368(1993).

[22] T. Hayashi, G. Joshi, M. Matsuda and M. Tanimoto, Contribution to this conference, gls0101.

Paper presented at XXVII Int. Conf. on High Energy Physics: Session Pa-21
Glasgow, UK, 20–27 July 1994

$B \to X_s \gamma$ and $B \to K^* \gamma$ in the standard and 2H models

Marco Ciuchini[†]

INFN, Sezione Sanità,
V.le Regina Elena 299, 00161 Roma, Italy

Abstract

Theoretical predictions for the branching ratios of the $B \to X_s \gamma$ and $B \to K^* \gamma$ decays are calculated in the Standard Model and in the (type II) two-Higgs-doublet model. Both the complete leading and the partially known next-to-leading order QCD corrections are included. The uncertainties due to the regularization scheme dependence introduced by the incomplete NLO terms are discussed. The results are compared with the recent CLEO II measurements and a new lower limit on the charged Higgs boson mass, $M_{H^\pm} > \sim 200$ GeV, is obtained.

We calculate the theoretical predictions of the branching ratios for the decay $B \to X_s \gamma$ and $B \to K^* \gamma$ in the Standard Model and the type II two-Higgs-doublet model [1]. It is well known that the leading order (LO) QCD corrections are important [2], almost doubling the amplitudes of these decays. We include QCD correction using the results of ref. [3] to compute the relevant Wilson coefficient, $C_7^{eff}(\mu)$. We also include those next-to-leading (NLO) corrections which are already known [4, 5], as explained in ref. [6]. This results in a significant reduction of the dependence of $C_7^{eff}(\mu)$ on the renormalization scale μ, which is the main source of theoretical uncertainty in the leading order calculation [7], see figure 1. However this procedure is not consistent theoretically and, in fact, an unphysical regularization scheme dependence is introduced in the physical predictions in this way. We try to cope with this problem by considering two different cases, the $\overline{\text{MS}}$ 't Hooft-Veltman (HV) and naive dimensional (NDR) regularization/renormalization schemes, taking, for each prediction, the mean value over the two schemes as the physical result. Moreover, the difference between them is assumed as a systematic error associated to our ignorance of the full next-to-leading corrections. This

† E-mail: ciuchini@vaxsan.iss.infn.it.

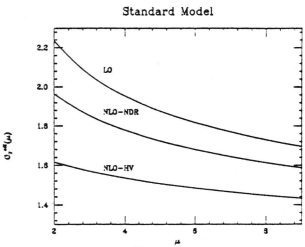

Standard Model

Figure 1. LO and NLO C_7^{eff} as a function of μ.

error is presented along with the usual one, due to the variation of the relevant parameters, Λ_{QCD} and m_t.

The relevant formulae to calculate the branching ratios we are interested in are

$$BR(B \to X_s \gamma) = \left[\frac{\Gamma(B \to X_s \gamma)}{\Gamma(B \to X l \nu_l)} \right] BR(B \to X l \nu_l),$$

$$\left[\frac{\Gamma(B \to X_s \gamma)}{\Gamma(B \to X l \nu_l)} \right] = \frac{|V_{ts}^* V_{tb}|^2}{|V_{cb}|^2} \frac{\alpha_e}{6\pi g(m_c/m_b)} F |C_7^{eff}(\mu)|^2,$$

$$g(z) = 1 - 8z^2 + 8z^6 - z^8 - 24z^4 \ln(z), \quad F = \frac{K(m_t/M_W, \mu)}{\Omega(m_c/m_b, \mu)}.$$

Parameter	Value
$|V_{ts}^* V_{tb}|^2 / |V_{cb}|^2$	0.95 ± 0.04
m_c/m_b	0.316 ± 0.013
m_t (GeV)	174 ± 17
λ_1 (GeV^2)	-0.15 ± 0.15
λ_2 (GeV^2)	0.12 ± 0.01
$m_b(\mu = m_b)$ (GeV)	4.65 ± 0.15
$F_1(0)$	0.35 ± 0.05
$BR(B \to X l \nu_l)$	0.107 ± 0.005
$\Lambda_{QCD}^{n_f = 4}$ (MeV)	330 ± 100
μ	$m_b/2 - 2m_b$

Table 1. Values of the parameters used to predict the radiative B decay rates.

$$BR(B \to K^*\gamma) = \left[\frac{\Gamma(B \to K^*\gamma)}{\Gamma(B \to X_s\gamma)}\right] \left[\frac{\Gamma(B \to X_s\gamma)}{\Gamma(B \to X l \nu_l)}\right] BR(B \to X l \nu_l)$$

$$\left[\frac{\Gamma(B \to K^*\gamma)}{\Gamma(B \to X_s\gamma)}\right] = \left(\frac{M_b}{m_b}\right)^3 \left(1 - \frac{M_{K^*}^2}{M_B^2}\right)^3 \frac{|F_1(0)|^2}{1 + (\lambda_1 - 9\lambda_2)/(2m_b^2)}$$

$BR(B \to X_s\gamma)$ includes also the known next-to-leading corrections to the matrix element, while non-perturbative $1/m_b^2$ corrections are included in $BR(B \to K^*\gamma)$. The numerical values of the different quantities appearing in these expressions are given in table 1. For more details on their choice, see ref. [6].

Using the previous formulae, we calculate the branching ratios in table 2. The errors shown in this table are due to the uncertainties on Λ_{QCD} and m_t. Combining the NLO results in HV and NDR for different values of μ, we obtain our final predictions in the Standard Model

$$BR(B \to K^*\gamma) = (4.3 \pm 0.9^{+1.4}_{-1.0}) \times 10^{-5}$$
$$BR(B \to X_s\gamma) = (1.9 \pm 0.2 \pm 0.5) \times 10^{-4}$$
$$\frac{\Gamma(B \to K^*\gamma)}{\Gamma(B \to X_s\gamma)} = 0.23 \pm 0.09,$$

Comparing them with the recent measurements [8, 9]

$$BR(B \to K^*\gamma) = (4.5 \pm 1.5 \pm 0.9) \times 10^{-5}$$
$$BR(B \to X_s\gamma) = (2.32 \pm 0.51 \pm 0.29 \pm 0.32) \times 10^{-4},$$

	$BR(B \to X_s\gamma) \times 10^4$		
μ (GeV)	LO	NLO$_{HV}$	NLO$_{NDR}$
$m_b/2$	3.81 ± 0.47	1.92 ± 0.19	2.77 ± 0.32
m_b	2.93 ± 0.33	1.71 ± 0.18	2.25 ± 0.25
$2m_b$	2.30 ± 0.26	1.56 ± 0.17	1.91 ± 0.21
	$BR(B \to K^*\gamma) \times 10^5$		
μ(GeV)	LO	NLO$_{HV}$	NLO$_{NDR}$
$m_b/2$	6.9 ± 1.5	4.4 ± 0.8	6.4 ± 1.3
m_b	5.3 ± 1.1	3.8 ± 0.8	5.0 ± 1.0
$2m_b$	4.2 ± 0.9	3.3 ± 0.7	4.1 ± 0.8

Table 2. Theoretical predictions of the radiative branching ratios.

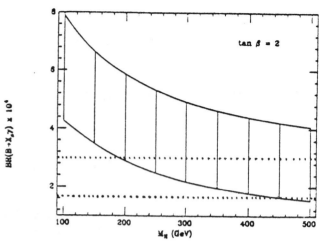

Figure 2. Predictions for $BR(B \to X_s\gamma)$ in the 2H model with $\tan\beta = 2$ are given as a function of $M_{H\pm}$. The experimental band is delimited by the dotted lines.

a very good agreement is found. Notice, however, that the estimate of the exclusive branching ratio strongly depends on the value assumed for the form factor $F_1(0)$.

Finally, let us consider the two-Higgs-doublet model known in the literature as Model II [1]. Two more free parameters are present in this model, $M_{H\pm}$ and $\tan\beta$. The charged Higgs boson exchange only modifies the initial conditions of the Wilson coefficients. Moreover, for $\tan\beta > 1.5-2$, these become practically independent of $\tan\beta$. In figure 2, the $BR(B \to X_s\gamma)$ is reported as a function of $M_{H\pm}$ for $\tan\beta = 2$. The band accounts for the theoretical uncertainties. The comparison with the experimental result gives a limit on $M_{H\pm} > \sim 200$ GeV.

Acknowledgments

It is a pleasure to acknowledge the friendly collaboration of E. Franco, G. Martinelli, L. Reina and L. Silvestrini.

References

[1] S. Glashow and S. Weinberg, Phys. Rev. **D15** (1977) 1958; L.F. Abbott, P. Sikivie and M.B. Wise, Phys. Rev. **D21** (1980) 1393.

[2] B. Grinstein, R. Springer and M.B. Wise, Phys. Lett. **B202** (1988) 138.

[3] M. Ciuchini et al., Phys. Lett. **B316** (1993) 127; M.Ciuchini et al., Nucl. Phys. **B421** (1994) 41.

[4] A.J. Buras et al., Nucl. Phys. **B400** (1993) 37; *ibid.* **B400** (1993) 75.

[5] M. Ciuchini et al., Nucl. Phys. **B415** (1994) 403.

[6] M. Ciuchini et al., Phys. Lett. **B334** (1994) 137.

[7] A.J. Buras et al., MPI-Ph/93-77, TUM-T31-50/93.

[8] R. Ammar et al. (CLEO Collaboration), Phys. Rev. Lett. **71** (1993) 674.

[9] E.H. Thorndike (CLEO Collaboration), these proceedings.

Paper presented at XXVII Int. Conf. on High Energy Physics: Session Pa-21
Glasgow, UK, 20–27 July 1994

The decay $b \to s\gamma$ in SUSY extensions of the standard model

Pran Nath[†‡§] and R. Arnowitt[||]

† Theoretical Physics Division, CERN, CH-1211 Geneva 23, Switzerland
|| Center for Theoretical Physics, Department of Physics, Texas A & M University, College Station, TX 77843, USA

Abstract

A brief review is given of the decay $b \to s\gamma$ in SUSY extensions of the Standard Model. It is found that the recent CLEO results put strong constraints on the parameter space of minimal N=1 Supergravity unified theory. Dark Matter analyses are also strongly constrained for $\mu > 0$.

1. Introduction

Recently, the experimental situation on the measurement of $b \to s\gamma$ branching ratio has improved dramatically. Last year the CLEO Collaboration [1] found an upper bound of $B(b \to s\gamma) < 5.4 \times 10^{-4}$ at 95% CL. This result is now superseded by the first actual measurement of this process reported at this conference. Thus CLEO gives [2]

$$B(b \to s\gamma) = (2.32 \pm 0.51 \pm 0.29 \pm 0.32) \times 10^{-4} \quad (1)$$

where the first error is statistical, the second error is systematic arising from uncertainty in yield, and the third error is also systematic arising from uncertainty in efficiency. In this paper we discuss the implications of these results for supersymmetric extensions of the Standard Model which depend very much on the value of the branching ratio predicted by the SM. Thus we begin by reviewing briefly the current status of the SM prediction for the $b \to s\gamma$ decay.

To leading QCD order $B(b \to s\gamma)$ is given by [3]

$$\frac{B(b \to s\gamma)}{B(b \to ce\bar{\nu})} = \frac{6\alpha_{em}}{\pi\rho\lambda} \frac{|V_{ts}^{\star} V_{tb}|^2}{|V_{cb}|^2} |\bar{c}_7(m_b)|^2 \quad (2a)$$

where ρ is a phase-space factor, λ is a QCD correction factor, V_{ts} etc. are KM matrix elements and $\bar{c}_7(m_b)$ is

‡ Permanent address: Department of Physics, Northeastern University, Boston, MA 02115, USA
§ Speaker at the Conference

the effective Wilson co-efficient of the photonic magnetic penguin at scale the m_b, i.e.,

$$\bar{c}_7(m_b) = \eta^{\frac{16}{23}} c_7(M_W) + \frac{8}{3}\left(\eta^{\frac{14}{23}} - \eta^{\frac{16}{23}}\right) c_8(M_W) + c_2 \quad (2b)$$

Where $\eta = \alpha_s(M_W)/\alpha_s(m_b)$, $c_7(c_8)$ are the Wilson co-efficients for the photonic (gluonic) magnetic penguins at scale M_W and c_2 is an operator mixing co-efficient. In the SM, $c_7(c_8)$ receive contributions from W-exchange. The evaluation of c_2 depends on the computation to $\mathcal{O}(g^2)$ of an 8×8 anomalous dimension matrix. The previous $\mathcal{O}(1)\%$ ambiguities in this computation have now been resolved as reported by Ciuchini here [4]. The analysis of $B(b \to s\gamma)$ in the SM using equation (2) suffers from many uncertainties. These include experimental uncertainties in the quark masses, in α_s, and in the KM matrix elements. However, the largest uncertainty arises due to the possible next-to-leading order QCD corrections. These could be in the vicinity of $\mathcal{O}(30)\%$ or more [5]. Recently Ciuchini et al. have obtained an upgraded theoretical evaluation for $B(b \to s\gamma)$ in SM using all the known (but incomplete) next to leading order (NLO) corrections [4]. They give a value of

$$B(b \to s\gamma) = (1.9 \pm 0.2 \pm 0.5) \times 10^{-4} \quad (4)$$

However, equation (3) is a mean of two significantly different evaluations; one which uses the t' Hooft-Veltman regularization and the second one which uses the naive dimensional reduction regularization. In view of this many workers prefer to use only the leading order (LO) prediction of SM, pending the full NLO evaluation in SM. For example the CLEO Collaboration uses a mean LO SM value of

$$B(b \to s\gamma) = (2.75 \pm 0.8) \times 10^{-4} \qquad (5)$$

for comparison of their experimental results with theory. In our analysis we shall choose the range given by equations (3) and (4). The reason for enumerating the uncertainties in the evaluation of $B(b \to s\gamma)$ in the SM is that many of these uncertainties are generic and similar uncertainties appear when one computes the branching ratio in models based on extensions of SM.

There are several ways in which one can carry out a SUSY extension of the Standard Model. These include the minimal extension, and the non-minimal extensions where either there is extra matter, or the gauge group is larger (such as L-R symmetric models) and variations there of [6]. Here we shall discuss only the minimal extension. The minimal SUSY extension (MSSM) consists of adjoining SUSY multiplets to the $SU(3)_c \otimes SU(2)_L \otimes U(1)_Y$ quark-lepton multiplets of the SM and introducing a pair of Higgs doublets and their SUSY partners. Thus in addition to quarks and leptons the additional states consist of 32 SUSY particles (these are 12 squarks, 9 sleptons, 2 charginos, 4 neutralinos, 1 gluino and 4 Higgs). In the MSSM there are additional contributions to $B(b \to s\gamma)$ arising from the exchange of the charged Higgs, the charginos, the neutralinos, the gluino, and the squarks [7]. In all twenty new (supersymmetric) states enter in the analysis. The physics of $b \to s\gamma$ decay is controlled by the mechanism of supersymmetry breaking. This can be understood from the fact that one has a cancellation of c_7 and c_8 in the exact SUSY limit [8]. Thus the parameters that characterize SUSY breaking are central to the computation of c_7 and c_8. Unfortunately the MSSM, does not accommodate a phenomenologically viable way of breaking supersymmetry spontaneously. To generate a viable phenomenology one must add soft SUSY breaking terms by hand to the MSSM. However, the number of allowed possibilities is enormous. One can add up to 137 different soft SUSY breaking terms to the theory. A sharp reduction in the number of soft SUSY breaking parameters occurs within the framework of N=1 supergravity grand unification [9]. Coupled with radiative breaking of the electro-weak symmetry the parameter space of the theory becomes 4 dimensional. The conventional choice of the residual parameters is [10] m_0, $m_{1/2}$, A_0 and $\tan\beta$ where m_0 is the universal scalar mass, $m_{1/2}$ is the universal gaugino mass and A_0 is the trilinear coupling in the potential that breaks supersymmetry softly. The analysis of Ref. [11] chooses a different residual set of parameters than the ones above. In that analysis A_0 is replaced by B_0 where

B_0 the co-efficeint of the Higgs mixing term in the soft SUSY breaking potential.

We give now a brief description of the $b \to s\gamma$ branching ratio in supergravity grand unification. Many analyses of this decay have appeared recently [12-15, 11]. First the contributions of neutralino and gluino exchange are found to be typically small and we neglect these in our analysis. Charged Higgs make contributions which are always constructive relative to the W-exchange [12]. However, the chargino exchange contributions are very model dependent and can be either constructive or destructive [13-15]. An interesting phenomenon that surfaces is that $B(b \to s\gamma)$ can become very small even away from the exact SUSY limit due to cancellations among the W, charged Higgs and chargino exchange [14-15]. In general the $b \to s\gamma$ experiment constrains the parameter space of N=1 minimal supergravity [14-15]. An important effect relates to the sensitivity of the $b \to s\gamma$ rate in the region when one is close to the Landau pole [14-16]. In this domain small variations in the input parameters such as m_t, α_G and $\tan\beta$ can lead to large variations in the output quantites [14-16].

Another interesting phenomenon relates to the effect of the $b \to s\gamma$ experiment on dark matter analyses. The effect of the experimental constraints of CLEO 93 results on $b \to s\gamma$ on analyses of dark matter were investigated in references [15-17]. It was found that the CLEO 93 results put very strong constraints on dark matter for $\mu > 0$. Here $\mathcal{O}(2/3)$ of the parameter space which satisfies dark matter constraints implied by the COBE constraint [18] is eliminated. For $\mu < 0$, the constraints were less stringent in that only $\mathcal{O}(1/5)$ of the parameter space was eliminated. Similar conclusions hold for the CLEO 94 results of equation (1). However, analysis of reference (16) shows that the CLEO 93 bounds do not constrain the minimal $SU(5)$ model very much. A similar results holds for the CLEO 94 result of equation (1).

One convenient way to quantify SUSY effects is via the parameter defined by

$$r_{SUSY} = \frac{B(b \to s\gamma)_{SUSY}}{B(b \to s\gamma)_{SM}} \qquad (6)$$

To leading QCD order and ignoring SUSY threshold effects equation (2) also holds for the minimal N=1 supergravity extension with the only difference that $c_7(c_8)$ in equation (2) are modified to include the charged Higgs and superparticle exchanges. In this approximation r_{SUSY} is given by the ratio of $\bar{c}_7(m_b)$ for the SUSY and the SM cases and is thus relatively free of the ambiguities of the outside factors in equation (2a). Setting $B(b \to s\gamma)_{SUSY}$ to the experimental value of equation (1), and using the range of SM values given by equations (3) and (4), we find the following range for

r_{SUSY}:

$$r_{SUSY} = (0.46 - 2.2) \qquad (7)$$

which has an average value of $r_{SUSY} = 1.33$. An interesting phenomenon is related to the implication of equation (6) for the SUSY spectrum. Figure 1 exhibits the maximum and the minimum values of the low lying SUSY particles (the light Higgs, the light chargino and the light stop) as a function of r_{max} where r_{SUSY} is allowed to vary in the interval $(0.46-r_{max})$ and r_{max} lies in the range given by equation (6). One finds that SUSY mass bands exhibit a significant narrowing as r_{SUSY} falls below 1. This phenomenon arises due to the constraint that one needs a light SUSY spectrum to cancel the effect of the W and charged Higgs exchange and move r_{SUSY} below the canonical SM value of 1.

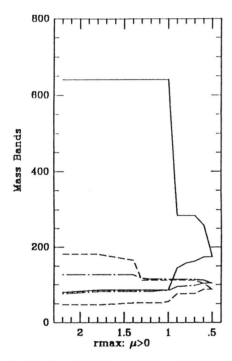

Figure 1. Mass bands for the light Higgs (dash-dot), chargino (dashed) and the light stop (solid) as a function of r_{max} when $\mu > 0$, $m_t = 168$ GeV and all other parameters are integrated out.

In conclusion, the CLEO results on $b \rightarrow s\gamma$ put severe constraints on the parameter space of minimal supergravity and also significantly affect SUSY dark matter analyses. Specifically it is found that the neutralino relic density analysis for the case $\mu > 0$ is significantly affected. Also the maximum event rates for the detection of neutralinos in dark matter detectors are reduced for the $\mu > 0$ case. However, discovery of supergravity via $b \rightarrow s\gamma$ decay would require the full analysis of NLO corrections in supergravity theory including threshold corrections in the evolution of Wilson co-efficients due to different SUSY [19]

thresholds, as well as significant further improvement in experiment.

References

[1] R. Ammar *et al.*, Phys. Rev. Lett. **71** (1993) 674; E. Thorndike *et al.* Bull. Am. Phys. Soc. **38** (1993) 993.

[2] E.H. Thorndike, thee proceedings.

[3] S. Bertolini, F. Borzumati and A. Masiero, Phys. Rev. Lett. **59** (1987) 180; N. Deshpande *et al.*, Phys. Rev. Lett. **59** (1987) 183; B. Grinstein *et al.*, Phys. Lett. **B202** (1988) 138.

[4] M. Ciuchini, these proceedings; see also M. Ciuchini *et al.*, CERN preprint: CERN-TH 7283/94.

[5] A.J. Buras *et al.*, Max-Planck Preprint: MPI-Ph/93; A. Ali and C. Greub, Zeit. Phys. **C60** (1993) 433.

[6] For a review of some of these see: J. Hewett, "Top Ten Models Constrained by $b \rightarrow s\gamma$", Lectures at the 21st SLAC Summer Institute, hep-ph/9406302.

[7] S. Bertolini, F. Borzumati, A. Masiero and G. Ridolfi, Nucl. Phys. **B353** (1991) 591; R. Barbieri and G. Giudice, Phys. Lett. **B309** (1993) 86.

[8] S. Ferrara and E. Remiddi, Phys. Lett. **B53** (1974) 347.

[9] A.H. Chamseddine, R. Arnowitt and P. Nath, Phys. Rev. Lett. **29** (1982) 970. For reviews see: P. Nath, R. Arnowitt and A.H. Chamseddine, "Applied N=1 Supergravity", (World Scientific, 1984); H.P. Nilles, Phys. Rep. **110** (1984) 1.

[10] For a review see: P. Nath and R. Arnowitt, these proceedings; also: P. Nath and R. Arnowitt, in "From Superstrings to the Real Superworld" Ed. A. Zichichi (World Scientific, 1992); R. Arnowitt and P. Nath, Swieca Summer School Lectures, Campos do Jordao, Brazil 1993, (World Scientific).

[11] S. Bertolini and F. Vissani, SISSA 40/94/EP.

[12] J. Hewett, Phys. Rev. Lett. **70** (1993) 1045; V. Barger, M. Berger and M.A. Phillips, Phys. Rev. Lett. **70** (1993) 1368.

[13] R. Barbieri and G. Giudice, Phys. Lett. **B309** (1993) 8; N. Oshima, Nucl. Phys. **B304** (1993) 20; R. Garisto and J.N. Ng, Phys. Lett. **B339** (1993) 372; Y. Okada, Phys. Lett. **B315** (1993) 119; M.A. Diaz, Phys. Lett. **B322** (1994) 207; F.M. Borzumati, DESY preprint: Desy 93-090 (1993); J. Lopez, D. Nanopoulos, and G. Park, Phys. Rev. **D48** (1993) 974; G. Kane, C. Kolda, L. Roszkowski and J.D. Wells, UM-TH-93-24 (1993); G. Bhattacharyya and A. Raychaudhuri, CERN preprint: CERN-TH-7245/94; P. Nath and R. Arnowitt, Talk at the Conf. "Unified Symmetry in the Small and in the Large", at Coral Gables, CERN preprint: CERN-TH-7167/94; V. Barger, M. Berger, P. Ohmann and R. Phillips, Madison preprint: MAD-PH-842 (1994); M. Carena and C.E.M. Wagner, CERN-TH-7393/94.

[14] J. Wu, R. Arnowitt and P. Nath, CERN-TH-7316/94, CTP-TAMU-03/94, NUB-TH-3092/94.

[15] P. Nath and R. Arnowitt, CERN-TH-7214/94, NUB-TH-3093/94, CTP-TAMU-32/94, to appear in Phys. Lett. **B**.

[16] P. Nath, J. Wu and R. Arnowitt, in preparation; P. Nath and R. Arnowitt, Talk at Recontres de Moriond "Electroweak Interactions and Unified Theories", Meribel, France, 1994; CERN preprint: CERN-TH-7288/94.

[17] F. Borzumati, M. Drees and M. Nojiri, DESY preprint: DESY/94-096.

[18] See P. Nath and R. Arnowitt, these propceedings; and CERN-TH-7363/94, NUB-TH-3099/94, CTP-TAMU-38/94.

[19] H. Anlauf, SLAC preprint: SLAC-PUB-62 (1994).

Towards a Model Independent Analysis of Rare B Decays

Ahmed Ali[‡¶] , Gian Giudice[§†] and Thomas Mannel[||]

Theory Division, CERN, CH-1211 Geneva 23, Switzerland.

Abstract

We propose to undertake a model-independent analysis of the inclusive decay rates and distributions in the processes $B \to X_s \gamma$ and $B \to X_s\ \ell^+\ell^-$ ($B = B^\pm$ or B_d^0). We show how measurements of the decay rates and distributions in these processes would allow us to extract the magnitude and sign of the dominant Wilson coefficients of the magnetic moment operator $m_b \bar{s}_L \sigma_{\mu\nu} b_R F^{\mu\nu}$ and the four-fermion operators $(\bar{s}_L \gamma_\mu b_L)(\bar{\ell}\gamma^\mu \ell)$ and $(\bar{s}_L \gamma_\mu b_L)(\bar{\ell}\gamma^\mu \gamma^5 \ell)$.

1. The Decay $B \to X_s \gamma$ in SM and Experiment

The measurements of the decay mode $B \to K^*\gamma$, reported last year by the CLEO collaboration [1], having a branching ratio $\mathcal{B}(B \to K^*\gamma) = (4.5 \pm 1.0 \pm 0.9) \times 10^{-5}$, and the inclusive decay $B \to X_s\gamma$, reported at this conference [2] with a branching ratio $\mathcal{B}(B \to X_s\gamma) = (2.32 \pm 0.51 \pm 0.32 \pm 0.20) \times 10^{-4}$, have put the physics of the electromagnetic penguins on an experimental footing. In the standard model (SM), these transitions are dominated by the short-distance contributions and provide valuable information about the top quark mass and the Cabibbo-Kobayashi-Maskawa (CKM) weak mixing matrix elements $V_{ts} V_{tb}$ [3]. The rapport between the SM and experiment may be quantified in terms of the CKM matrix element ratio [4]:

$$0.62 \leq \left| \frac{V_{ts}}{V_{cb}} \right| \leq 1.1 \ , \tag{1}$$

which is consistent with unity, resulting from the unitarity constraints. Alternatively, one can set $V_{ts}/V_{cb} = 1$ to obtain from the CLEO measurement bounds on the Wilson coefficient $C_7(m_b)$ of the effective

magnetic moment operator. Using $\mathcal{B}(B \to X_s\gamma)$ from [2], one obtains

$$0.22 \leq |C_7(m_b)| \leq 0.30. \tag{2}$$

Using, however, the 90%-confidence-level range from the CLEO measurement $\mathcal{B}(B \to X_s\gamma) = (2.31 \pm 1.1) \times 10^{-4}$ and the theoretical calculation for $\mathcal{B}(B \to X_s\gamma)$ from [4] we obtain

$$0.19 \leq |C_7(m_b)| \leq 0.32. \tag{3}$$

We also remark that the photon energy and hadron mass spectra measured by CLEO are in good agreement with the SM-based calculations in [5]. The bound (2) can be used to constrain the non-SM contribution to the decay rate $\mathcal{B}(B \to X_s\gamma)$ as discussed in these proceedings [6, 7].

2. Motivation for a Model Independent Analysis of Rare B Decays

The determination of $|C_7(m_b)|$ from the inclusive branching ratio $\mathcal{B}(B \to X_s\gamma)$ is a prototype of the kind of analysis that we would like to propose here to be carried out for the rare B decays in general and for the semileptonic decays $B \to X_s\ \ell^+\ell^-$, in particular. First steps towards a model-independent analysis of the FCNC electroweak rare B decays involving these decay modes have recently been proposed in [8], to which we

‡ e-mail: alia@cernvm.cern.ch
¶ On leave of absence from DESY, Hamburg, FRG.
§ e-mail: giudice@vxcern.cern.ch
† On leave of absence from INFN, Sezione de Padova, Italy.
|| e-mail: mannel@cernvm.cern.ch

refer for details and references to other related work. Here, we summarize the main assumptions and results.

The main interest in rare B decays is to measure the effective FCNC vertices in order to test the SM and search for new physics. We have argued that with some plausible assumptions these vertices can be parametrized through a limited number of effective parameters, which govern the rates and shapes (differential distributions) in rare B decays $B \rightarrow X_s\gamma$, $B \rightarrow X_s \ell^+\ell^-$ and $B_s \rightarrow \ell^+\ell^-$. The search for physics beyond the SM in these decays can be carried out in terms of three effective parameters, $C_7(\mu)$, $C_9(\mu)$ and $C_{10}(\mu)$, characterizing the strength of the magnetic moment and two four-fermion operators $(\bar{s}_L\gamma_\mu b_L)(\bar{\ell}\gamma^\mu\ell)$ and $(\bar{s}_L\gamma_\mu b_L)(\bar{\ell}\gamma^\mu\gamma^5\ell)$. This can then be interpreted in a large class of models. The presence of non-SM physics may manifest itself by distorting the differential distributions in $B \rightarrow X_s \ell^+\ell^-$. Some possible examples of such distortions have been worked out in [8]. Here we present profiles of the Wilson coefficients in the best-motivated extensions of the SM, namely the Minimal Supersymmetric Standard Model (MSSM).

Our analysis is based on an effective Hamiltonian of the form

$$\mathcal{H}_{eff}(b \rightarrow sX) = -\frac{4G_F}{\sqrt{2}}\lambda_t \sum_{i=1}^{10} C_i(\mu)\mathcal{O}_i(\mu) \ . \quad (4)$$

where X stands for $q\bar{q}$, γ, gluon and $\ell^+\ell^-$ and $\lambda_t = V_{ts}^*V_{tb}$. The operator basis $\mathcal{O}_{1\ldots10}$ is given in [8] and is the same as in the SM, thereby restricting our analysis to cases, in which the effective Hamiltonian may be written as (4).

3. Analysis of the Decays $B \rightarrow X_s\gamma$ and $B \rightarrow X_s\ell^+\ell^-$

The experimental quantities we consider in this paper are the following: **(i) Inclusive radiative rare decay branching ratio $\mathcal{B}(B \rightarrow X_s\gamma)$; (ii) Invariant dilepton mass distributions in $B \rightarrow X_s\ell^+\ell^-$; (iii) Forward-backward (FB) charge asymmetry $\mathcal{A}(s)$ in $B \rightarrow X_s\ell^+\ell^-$.**

The FB asymmetry $\mathcal{A}(\hat{s})$ is defined with respect to the angular variable $z \equiv \cos\theta$, where θ is the angle of the ℓ^+ with respect to the b-quark direction in the centre-of-mass system of the dilepton pair. It is obtained by integrating the doubly differential distribution $d^2\mathcal{B}/(dz\,d\hat{s})(B \rightarrow X_s \ell^+\ell^-)$ [9]:

$$\mathcal{A}(\hat{s}) \equiv \int_0^1 dz \frac{d^2\mathcal{B}}{dz\,d\hat{s}} - \int_{-1}^0 dz \frac{d^2\mathcal{B}}{dz\,d\hat{s}}, \quad (5)$$

where $\hat{s} = (p_1 + p_2)^2/m_b^2$ and p_1 and p_2 denote, respectively, the momenta of the ℓ^+ and ℓ^-.

We remark that the decay rate $\mathcal{B}(B \rightarrow X_s\gamma)$ puts a bound on the absolute value of the coefficient $C_7(\mu)$. However, the radiative B decay rate by itself is not able to distinguish between the solutions $C_7(\mu) > 0$ (holding in the SM) and the solutions $C_7(\mu) < 0$, which, for example, are also allowed in the MSSM as one scans over the allowed parameter space. We recall that the invariant dilepton mass distribution and the forward-backward asymmetry in $B \rightarrow X_s \ell^+\ell^-$ are sensitive to the sign and magnitude of $C_7(\mu)$ [9]. Using $\mathcal{H}_{eff}$ given in (4), one obtains for the dilepton invariant mass distribution

$$\frac{d\mathcal{B}}{d\hat{s}} = \mathcal{B}_{sl}\frac{\alpha^2}{4\pi^2}\left|\frac{\lambda_t}{V_{cb}}\right|^2 \frac{\hat{w}(\hat{s})}{f(m_c/m_b)} \quad (6)$$

$$\times \left[\left(|C_9 + Y(\hat{s})|^2 + C_{10}^2\right)\alpha_1(\hat{s},\hat{m}_s) \right.$$
$$\left. + \frac{4}{\hat{s}}C_7^2\alpha_2(\hat{s},\hat{m}_s) + 12\alpha_3(\hat{s},\hat{m}_s)C_7(C_9 + \text{Re }Y(s)) \right],$$

where the auxiliary functions α_i depend only on the kinematic variables and $Y(\hat{s})$ depends on the coefficients $C_1, \cdots, C_6$ of the four quark operators (see [8]).

The corresponding differential asymmetry as defined in (5) is

$$\mathcal{A}(\hat{s}) = -\mathcal{B}_{sl}\frac{3\alpha^2}{8\pi^2}\frac{1}{f(m_c/m_b)}\hat{w}^2(\hat{s})C_{10} \quad (7)$$
$$\times \left[\hat{s}(C_9 + \text{Re }Y(\hat{s})) + 4C_7(1 + \hat{m}_s^2)\right].$$

We first present the partial branching ratio $\mathcal{B}(\Delta s)$ and partial FB asymmetry $\mathcal{A}(\Delta s)$, where Δs defines an interval in the dilepton invariant mass. In order to minimize long-distance effects we shall consider the kinematic regime for s below the J/ψ mass (low invariant mass) and for s above the mass of the ψ' (high invariant mass). Integrating (7) over these regions for the invariant mass one finds

$$\mathcal{B}(\Delta s) = A(\Delta s)\left(C_9^2 + C_{10}^2\right) + B(\Delta s)C_9 + C(\Delta s), \quad (8)$$

where A, B and C are fixed in terms of the Wilson coefficients $C_1 \cdots C_6$ and C_7. For the numerical analysis we use $m_b = 4.7$ GeV, $m_c = 1.5$ GeV, $m_s = 0.5$ GeV. The resulting coefficients A, B, and C are listed in Table 1 for the decays $B \rightarrow X_s e^+e^-$ and $B \rightarrow X_s\mu^+\mu^-$.

For a measured branching fraction $\mathcal{B}(\Delta s)$, one can solve the above equation for $\mathcal{B}(\Delta s)$, obtaining a circle in the C_9-C_{10} plane, with centre lying at $C_9^* = B(\Delta s)/(2A(\Delta s))$ and $C_{10}^* = 0$. The radius of this circle is proportional to $\sqrt{\mathcal{B}(\Delta s) - \mathcal{B}_{min}(\Delta s)}$, where the minimum branching fraction

$$\mathcal{B}_{min}(\Delta s) = C(\Delta s) - \frac{B^2(\Delta s)}{4A(\Delta s)} \quad (9)$$

Δs	C_7	$A(\Delta s)$	$B(\Delta s)$	$C(\Delta s)$ $\ell = e$	$C(\Delta s)$ $\ell = \mu$
$4m_\ell^2 < s < m_{J/\psi}^2$	+0.3	2.86	−5.76	84.1	76.6
$4m_\ell^2 < s < m_{J/\psi}^2$	−0.3	2.86	−20.8	124	116
$m_{\psi'}^2 < s < (1 - m_s^2)$	+0.3	0.224	−0.715	0.654	0.654
$m_{\psi'}^2 < s < (1 - m_s^2)$	−0.3	0.224	−1.34	2.32	2.32

Table 1. Values for the coefficients $A(\Delta s)$, $B(\Delta s)$ and $C(\Delta s)$ (in units of 10^{-8}) for the decay $B \to X_s \ell^+ \ell^-$.

Δs	C_7	$\alpha(\Delta s)$	$\beta(\Delta s)$
$4m_\ell^2 < s < m_{J/\psi}^2$	+0.3	−6.08	−24.0
$4m_\ell^2 < s < m_{J/\psi}^2$	−0.3	−6.08	55.4
$m_{\psi'}^2 < s < (1 - m_s^2)$	+0.3	−0.391	0.276
$m_{\psi'}^2 < s < (1 - m_s^2)$	−0.3	−0.391	1.37

Table 2. Values for the coefficients $\alpha(\Delta s)$ and $\beta(\Delta s)$ (in units of 10^{-9}).

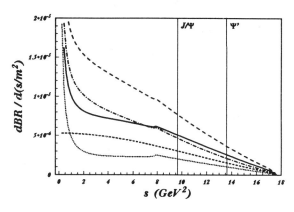

Figure 1. The dependence of the invariant-mass spectrum on the Wilson coefficients. Solid line: SM. Long-dashed line: $C_7 \to -C_7$, with other coefficients retaining their SM values. Short-dashed line: The contribution of C_{10} only. Dotted line: $C_{10} = 0$, with other coefficients retaining their SM values. Dash-dotted line: same as for the dotted one, but with $C_7 = -0.3$. The vertical lines indicate the location of the J/Ψ and Ψ' resonances.

is determined mainly by the present data on $B \to X_s \gamma$, i.e. by $|C_7|$.

To further pin down the Wilson coefficients, one could perform a measurement of the forward-backward asymmetry $\mathcal{A}$. Integrating (5) over a range (Δs) yields

$$\mathcal{A}(\Delta s) = C_{10} \left(\alpha(\Delta s) C_9 + \beta(\Delta s) \right). \tag{10}$$

For a fixed value of $\mathcal{A}(\Delta s)$, one obtains hyperbolic curves in the C_9-C_{10} plane; like the coefficients A, B and C, the parameters α and β are given in terms of the Wilson coefficients $C_1 \cdots C_6$, C_7 and Δs; their values are presented in Table 2.

Given the two experimental inputs, the branching fraction $\mathcal{B}(\Delta s)$ and the corresponding asymmetry $\mathcal{A}(\Delta s)$, one obtains a fourth-order equation for the Wilson coefficients C_9 and C_{10}, which admits in general four solutions, which can be plotted as contours for a fixed value for the branching fraction $\mathcal{B}(\Delta s)$ and the FB asymmetry $\mathcal{A}(\Delta s)$. The possible solutions for C_9 and C_{10} are given by the intersections of the circle corresponding to the measured branching fraction and the hyperbola, corresponding to the measured asymmetry. Details can be seen in [8].

We stress that the spectrum itself is very sensitive to the values of the Wilson coefficients and to the sign of C_7. In fig. 1 we plot the various contributions to the spectrum, for positive and for negative C_7.

In a similar way, it may become possible to measure also the differential asymmetry (5); the various contributions to $\mathcal{A}(s)$ are shown in fig. 2.

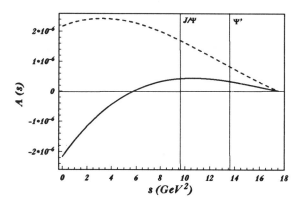

Figure 2. The dependence of the differential FB asymmetry on the Wilson coefficients. Solid line: SM. Long-dashed line: $C_7 \to -C_7$, with the other parameters retaining their SM values. The vertical lines indicate the location of the J/Ψ and Ψ' resonances.

4. Model Predictions for the Wilson Coefficients

As an illustrative example we shall consider here the MSSM; we shall show, how the predictions for the Wilson coefficients C_7, C_9, and C_{10} are altered in this model.

Once the gluino contributions (as well as the analogous ones from neutralino exchange) are neglected, the flavour violation in the supersymmetric models is completely specified by the familiar CKM matrix. The one-loop supersymmetric corrections to the Wilson coefficients C_7, C_9, and C_{10} are given by two classes of diagrams: charged-Higgs exchange and chargino exchange [10].

The charged-Higgs contribution is specified by two input parameters: the charged-Higgs mass (m_{H+}) and the ratio of Higgs vacuum expectation values ($v_2/v_1 \equiv \tan\beta$). This contribution alone corresponds to the two-Higgs doublet model which has also been considered in [8].

In addition to the diagrams with charged-Higgs exchange, the MSSM leads also to chargino-mediated diagrams. The chargino contribution is specified by six parameters. Three of them enter the 2×2 chargino mass matrix:

$$m_{\chi^+} = \begin{pmatrix} M & m_W \sqrt{2} \sin\beta \\ m_W \sqrt{2} \cos\beta & \mu \end{pmatrix}. \qquad (11)$$

Following standard notations, we call $\tan\beta$ the ratio of vacuum expectation values, the same that appears also in the charged-Higgs sector, and M, μ the gaugino and higgsino mass parameters, subject to the constraint that the lightest chargino mass satisfies the LEP bound, $m_{\chi}^+ > 45$ GeV. The squark masses

$$m_{\tilde{q}^2_{\pm}}^2 = \tilde{m}^2 + m_q^2 \pm A\tilde{m}m_q \qquad (12)$$

contain two additional free parameters besides the known mass of the corresponding quark m_q: a common supersymmetry-breaking mass $\tilde{m}$ and the coefficient A. The last parameter included in our analysis is a common mass $m_{\tilde{l}}$ for sleptons, all taken to be degenerate in mass, with the constraint $m_{\tilde{l}} > 45$ GeV. Therefore the version of the MSSM we are considering is defined in terms of seven free parameters.

We have computed the Wilson coefficients in the MSSM and then varied the seven above-defined parameters in the experimentally allowed region. The results of our analysis are presented in fig. 3, which shows the regions of the C_9–C_{10} plane allowed by possible choices of the MSSM parameters. The upper plot of fig. 3 corresponds to parameters which give rise to positive (same sign as in the SM) values of C_7, consistent with experimental results on $b \to s\gamma$ ($0.19 < C_7 < 0.32$), while the lower plot corresponds to values of C_7 with opposite sign ($-0.32 < C_7 < -0.19$). We also show how our results are affected by an improvement in the experimental limits on supersymmetric particle masses, as can be expected from the Tevatron and LEP 200. Fig. 3 also shows the $C_9 - C_{10}$ regions allowed by the MSSM if the further constraints $m_{H+} > 150$ GeV, $m_{\tilde{i}}$, m_{χ^+}, $m_{\tilde{l}} > 100$ GeV are imposed.

The regions shown in fig. 3 illustrate the typical trend of the supersymmetric corrections. If supersymmetric particles exist at low energies, we can expect larger values of C_{10} and smaller (negative) values of C_9 than those predicted by the SM. This is the general feature, although the exact boundaries of the allowed regions depend on the particular model-dependent assumptions one prefers to use. However, the most interesting feature of supersymmetry is that solutions with

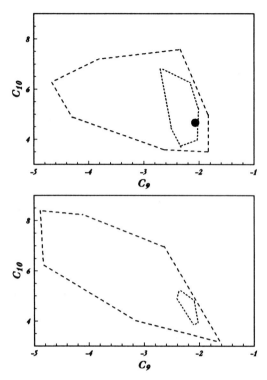

Figure 3. The region in the C_9-C_{10} plane obtained by varying the MSSM parameters. The upper (lower) plot corresponds to solutions that satisfy the $b \to s\gamma$ experimental constraint with positive (negative) C_7 given in eq.(2) and the present bounds ($m_{H+} > 80$ GeV, $\tilde{m}_t, m_{\chi^+}, \tilde{m}_\ell > 45$ GeV). The smaller areas limited by the short-dashed line correspond to the region of the MSSM parameter space that will survive an unsuccessful search for supersymmetry at the Tevatron and LEP 200 ($m_{H+} > 150$ GeV, $m_{\tilde{i}}$, m_{χ^+}, $m_{\tilde{l}} > 100$ GeV).

negative values of C_7 are possible and are still consistent with present data. Moreover, values of the other two coefficients C_9 and C_{10} sufficiently different from the SM are allowed, leading to measurable differences in the decay rates and distributions of $B \to X_s \ell^+ \ell^-$ and $B_s \to \ell^+ \ell^-$.

References

1 R. Ammar et al. (CLEO Collaboration), Phys. Rev. Lett. **71** (1993) 674.
2 E. Thorndike (CLEO Collaboration), these proceedings.
3 N. Cabibbo, Phys. Rev. Lett. **10** (1963) 531; M. Kobayashi and T. Maskawa, Prog. Theor. Phys. **49** (1973) 652.
4 A. Ali and C. Greub, Z. Phys. **C60** (1993) 433.
5 A. Ali and C. Greub, Z. Phys. **C49** (1991) 431; Phys. Lett. **259B** (1991) 182.
6 N. G. Deshpande, these proceedings.
7 P. Nath, these proceedings.
8 A. Ali, G. Giudice and T. Mannel, CERN-TH.7346/94.
9 A. Ali, T. Mannel and T. Morozumi, Phys. Lett. **B273** (1991) 505; B. Grinstein, M.J. Savage and M.B. Wise, Nucl. Phys. **B319** (1989) 271; W. Jaus and D. Wyler, Phys. Rev. **D41** (1990) 3405; D. Wyler (private communication).
10 S. Bertolini, F. Borzumati, A. Masiero, and G. Ridolfi, Nucl. Phys. **B353** (1991) 591.

*Paper presented at XXVII Int. Conf. on High Energy Physics: Session Pa-21
Glasgow, UK, 20–27 July 1994*

Quark off-shell contributions
to $K, B \rightarrow \gamma\gamma$ decays*

J. O. Eeg[†‡] and I. Picek[§||]

† Department of Physics, University of Oslo, Box 1048 Blindern,
N-0316 Oslo, Norway
§ Department of Physics, Faculty of Science, University of Zagreb, POB 162,
HR-41000 Zagreb, Croatia

Abstract

We demonstrate the importance of effective Lagrangians, which vanish on the quark mass shell. After presenting these effects on the $K_L \rightarrow \gamma\gamma$ decay in two different approaches (the low-energy QCD chiral quark model, and a bound-state approach), we show the viability of the same effect in the heavy-light quark system decay, such as $B_s \rightarrow \gamma\gamma$.

Introduction. The purpose of this presentation is to turn ones attention to the role of the off-shellness of quarks in mesons. Within the standard treatment of non-leptonic and weak radiative decays, one omits operators containing $(i\gamma \cdot D - m_q)$, by appealing to the equations of motion (EOM) for quark fields [1, 2]:

$$(i\gamma \cdot D - m_q) \rightarrow 0 \, , \qquad (1)$$

where D_μ is the covariant derivative containing the gluon and the photon fields. This procedure corresponds to going on-shell with external quarks in quark operators. Certainly, quarks are not exactly on-shell in hadrons, especially not in the pseudoscalar mesons π, K, η. We will see that the naive use of (1) is not correct in general. In demonstrating this we choose simple processes, the hadronic matrix elements of which can be related to the meson decay constants. We start by recalling that practically the entire $\pi^0 \rightarrow \gamma\gamma$ decay amplitude is of the off-shell origin. Then we observe that a significant part of the $K_L \rightarrow \gamma\gamma$ amplitude originates in the off-shellness. Finally we show that $B_s \rightarrow \gamma\gamma$ decay contains nonnegligible off-shell contributions.

* Presentation by I. Picek, supported in part by the EU contract CI1*–CT91–0893 (HSMU).
‡ E-mail: eeg@vuoep6.uio.no
|| E-mail: picek@phy.hr

Off-shellness in the $K_L \rightarrow \gamma\gamma$ amplitude. It was tempting for us to relate the off-shellness in the process $K_L \rightarrow \gamma\gamma$ to the well-known electromagnetic $\pi^0 \rightarrow \gamma\gamma$ decay governed by the axial anomaly: The term $\mathcal{A} = \frac{\alpha}{4\pi}\varepsilon_{\mu\nu\alpha\beta}F^{\mu\nu}F^{\alpha\beta}$ is missing on the r.h.s. of the divergence of the axial current, $\partial^\mu(\bar{q}\gamma_\mu\gamma_5 q) = 2m_q\bar{q}\gamma_5 q$, resulting from an inadequate application of EOM on the off-shell quark-field circulating in the triangle loop.

An effective field theory that enables one to handle off-shell quarks is the chiral quark model advocated by many authors [3]. The chiral quark model starts with the ordinary QCD lagrangian and adds a term $\mathcal{L}_\chi$ that takes care of chiral-symmetry breaking,

$$\mathcal{L}_\chi = -M(\bar{q}_R U q_L + \bar{q}_L U^\dagger q_R) \, , \qquad (2)$$

where $\bar{q} = (\bar{u}, \bar{d}, \bar{s})$ and the 3×3 matrix U contains in the exponent the pseudoscalar octet mesons. The $\mathcal{L}_\chi$ term, proportional to the constituent quark mass $M \sim 300$ MeV, includes the Goldstone meson octet in a chiral-invariant way, and provides a meson-quark coupling that makes it possible to calculate matrix elements of quark operators as loop diagrams. Notably, the quark triangle evaluation with the quark-meson coupling defined in eq. (2) reproduces the required anomalous π^0 decay!

Let us now recall the appearance of the off-shellness

[4, 5] in $K_L \to \gamma\gamma$. The evaluation of the loop diagrams without going to the mass shell, results in an effective Lagrangian [4]

$$\mathcal{L}(s \to d)_\gamma = B\, \epsilon^{\mu\nu\lambda\rho} F_{\mu\nu} (\bar{d}_L\, i\, \overleftrightarrow{D}_\lambda\, \gamma_\rho s_L)\,, \qquad (3)$$

where $B \sim eG_F\lambda_{KM}$ depends on the loop integration, and the quarks are interacting fields with respect to QCD. It is convenient to rewrite (3) as a sum of the off-shell $(\mathcal{L}_F)$ term and the magnetic-moment $(\mathcal{L}_\sigma)$ term

$$\begin{aligned}
\mathcal{L}_F &= B_F\, \bar{d}[(i\gamma \cdot D - m_d)\,\sigma_{\mu\nu} F^{\mu\nu} L \\
&\quad + \sigma_{\mu\nu} F^{\mu\nu} R (i\gamma \cdot D - m_s)]s\,, \\
\mathcal{L}_\sigma &= B_\sigma\, \bar{d}(m_s\sigma_{\mu\nu} F^{\mu\nu} R + m_d\sigma_{\mu\nu} F^{\mu\nu} L)\, s\,.
\end{aligned} \qquad (4)$$

Here we anticipate that the coefficients B_F and B_σ, being equal at the W-scale, evolve differently down to the scale ~ 1 GeV. It has been shown that $\mathcal{L}_F$ does *not* contribute to $s \to d\gamma\gamma$ when the external quarks are on-shell: The irreducible $s \to d\gamma\gamma$ part, with $iD_\mu \to e_{s(d)}A_\mu$, is exactly cancelled by reducible diagrams [6]. By explicit calculation within the chiral quark model, we found a non-zero contribution to $\overline{K^0} \to \gamma\gamma$ from $\mathcal{L}_F$. Although formally suppressed by M^2/m_0^2, $m_0 = 2\pi f_\pi\sqrt{6/N_c}$ being the chiral symmetry-breaking scale, its coefficient is sizeable, yielding a significant amplitude, both in the CP-conserving [5] and CP-violating case [4]. Thus we disagree with some authors [7] who claim that this effect is unimportant.

The $\overline{K^0} \to \gamma\gamma$ transition amplitude [5] is $\sim eB_F\frac{1}{f_\pi}\frac{M^2}{m_0^2}\epsilon_{\mu\nu\rho\sigma}A^\nu F^{\rho\sigma}\partial^\mu \overline{K^0}$, which can easily be brought to the $F\tilde{F}$ anomaly form. Thus, besides the $K_L \to \pi^+\pi^-\gamma$ decay, which can be read off in refs. [9], we offer the decay $K_L \to \gamma\gamma$ as a new candidate representing the *direct* anomalous neutral kaon decays. This result was recently confirmed in the bound-state calculation [10].

The quark-loop $B_s \to \gamma\gamma$ amplitude. The pseudoscalar character of the heavy B-meson allows us to parametrize the quark-meson vertex in a simple way, replacing the $\mathcal{L}_\chi$ term in (2) by

$$iG_B\, \bar{s}\gamma_5 b B_s\,. \qquad (5)$$

Thereby, as usually done [4], we trade the (in general non-local) meson-quark coupling G_B in favour of the meson-decay constant f_B. In calculating the contributions from $\mathcal{L}_F$ and $\mathcal{L}_\sigma$ in (4) (with the obvious replacements $s \to b$ and $d \to s$), we obtained [11] an amplitude of the following form

$$\begin{aligned}
M(B_s \to \gamma\gamma) &= e_D\, f_B[A_{(+)} F_{\mu\nu} F^{\mu\nu} + iA_{(-)} F_{\mu\nu}\tilde{F}^{\mu\nu}]\,, \\
A_{(\pm)} &= \tau_F^{(\pm)} B_F + B_\sigma \tau_\sigma^{(\pm)}\,,
\end{aligned} \qquad (6)$$

where $\frac{B_F}{B_\sigma} \simeq \frac{4}{3}$ at the $\mu = m_b$ scale. The quantities $\tau_{F,\sigma}^{(\pm)}$ are dimensionless, of order one, and depend on the bound-state dynamics, giving a branching ratio

$$\mathrm{Br}(B_s \to 2\gamma) \simeq 10^{-8} - 10^{-7}\,.$$

This result is not far from that given in [12]. We find that the genuine off-shell term $\mathcal{L}_F$ increases the rate by a factor of ~ 1.5 to 3.

In calculating the contribution from the off-shell operator $\mathcal{L}_F$, we have arrived at an important observation: The off-shellness of the light quark is characterized by the heavy-quark mass, whereas the off-shellness of the heavy quark is characterized by the light-quark mass. However, if the light-quark momenta are damped as in [13], we have two competing effects, and the effect for the light quark will be less pronounced. Thus, the off-shell effects of both the heavy and light quarks are important.

Conclusions. We have demonstrated that the naive use of the (perturbative) EOM (1) is not applicable in general. This should be no surprise because, in general, one has to supplement the EOM's by the appropriate boundary conditions. In this sense the bound-state interactions within mesons might be understood as a change of the equations of motion.

The genuine off-shell effects are formally suppressed in a certain limit by $1/M_b$ for $B \to \gamma\gamma$ and by $(M/m_0)^2$ for $K \to \gamma\gamma$. The fact that the off-shell contributions are substantial in these processes warns us that the corresponding effects should be explored in the important process $B \to K^*\gamma$, in order to be able to set the constraints on the extensions of the standard model.

References

[1] J. Collins: *Renormalization* (Cambridge 1984).
[2] H. Politzer, Nucl. Phys. **B172** (1980) 349;
    H. Simma, Z. Phys. **C61** (1994) 67.
[3] A. Manohar and H. Georgi, Nucl. Phys. **B234** (1984) 189;
    J. Bijnens, Nucl. Phys.**B367** (1991) 709;
    A. Pich and E. de Rafael, Nucl. Phys. **B358** (1991) 311;
    S. Weinberg, Phys. Rev. Lett. **67** (1991) 3473.
[4] J.O. Eeg and I. Picek, Phys. Lett. **B301**(1993) 423.
[5] J.O. Eeg and I. Picek, Phys.Lett.**B323**(1994) 193.
[6] G.J. Lin et al., Phys. Rev. Lett. **61** (1990) 1498;
    H. Simma and D. Wyler, Nucl. Phys. **B344** (1990) 283.
    S. Herrlich and J. Kalinowski, Nucl. Phys. **B381** (1992) 501 .
[7] J. Liu, 1992, quoted in B. Winstein and L. Wolfenstein, Rev. Mod. Phys. **65** (1993) 1113.
[8] J. Wess and B. Zumino, Phys. Lett. **B37** (1971) 95;
    E. Witten, Nucl. Phys. **B233** (1983) 422.
[9] G. Ecker, H. Neufeld and A. Pich, Phys. Lett **B278** (1992) 337, and CERN-TH.6920/93; J. Bijnens, G. Ecker and A. Pich, Phys. Lett. **B286** (1992) 341.
[10] D. Kekez, D. Klabučar, K. Kumerički and I. Picek, Bielefeld preprint BI-TP 94/21 and Zagreb preprint ZTF-94/05.
[11] J.O. Eeg and I. Picek, CERN-TH.7278/94 and ZTF - 94/06, to appear in Phys. Lett. B.
[12] G. Lin, J. Liu and Y. Yao, Phys. Rev. **D42** (1990) 2314;
    T.M. Aliev and G. Turan, Phys. Rev. **D48** (1994) 1176;
    P. Singer, Phys. Rev. **D49** (1994) R7.
[13] B. Holdom and M. Sutherland, Phys. Rev. **D49** (1994) 2356.

Rare B deacys from CLEO, with emphasis on $b \to s\gamma$

Edward H. Thorndike

Department of Physics and Astronomy
University of Rochester
Rochester, New York 14627, USA

On behalf of the CLEO Collaboration

Abstract

A CLEO search for the decay $B^{\pm} \to \tau^{\pm}\nu$ yields the upper limit $Br(B \to \tau\nu) < 2.2 \times 10^{-3}$ at 90% c.l. Searches for exclusive, charmless, hadronic B decays yield several new or improved upper limits. An update on the $\pi^-\pi^+/K^-\pi^+$ study gives $Br(\bar{B}^0 \to \pi^-\pi^+) < 2.2 \times 10^{-5}$, $Br(\bar{B}^0 \to K^-\pi^+) < 1.9 \times 10^{-5}$, at 90% c.l., and $Br(\bar{B}^0 \to K^-\pi^+) + Br(\bar{B}^0 \to \pi^-\pi^+) = \left(1.8 \pm {}^{0.6}_{0.5}\right) \times 10^{-5}$. A search for $B \to K^{(*)}\ell^+\ell^-$ gives upper limits on branching ratios $\sim 10^{-5}$. A search for examples of $b \to d\gamma$ decays gives an upper limit $\Gamma(B \to \rho/\omega\gamma)/\Gamma(B \to K^*\gamma) < 0.34$ at 90% c.l., suggesting $|V_{td}/V_{ts}| < 0.7$. The inclusive $b \to s\gamma$ branching ratio is measured to be $(2.32 \pm 0.51 \pm 0.29 \pm 0.32) \times 10^{-4}$, where the first error is statistical, the second error is the additive systematic error from uncertainty in yield, and the third error is the multiplicative systematic error from uncertainty in efficiency. Upper and lower limits on the branching ratio, at 95% c.l., are $1 \times 10^{-4} < Br(b \to s\gamma) < 4 \times 10^{-4}$. The upper limit implies a lower limit on the mass of a charged Higgs with Model II coupling of 260 GeV. The upper and lower limits on the branching ratio restrict the allowed region of the $\Delta\kappa - \lambda$ space describing anomalous $WW\gamma$ couplings, eliminating half of the area allowed by $\bar{p}p \to W\gamma X$ measurements.

1. Introduction

I will present CLEO results from five recent analyses. My main emphasis is on a measurement of the inclusive rate for $b \to s\gamma$. The data sample for all analyses is $2fb^{-1}$ at the $\Upsilon(4S)$, 2 million $B\bar{B}$ events, 6 million continuum background events. The continuum is a major background for 4 of the 5 analyses. We have $1fb^{-1}$ of data taken just below the resonance, to use for subtractions.

2. $B^{\pm} \to \tau^{\pm}\nu$

We have searched for $B^{\pm} \to \tau^{\pm}\nu$. In the Standard Model, this decay proceeds via annihilation to $W^{\pm}$, has a rate proportional to $f_B^2|V_{ub}|^2$, and a branching

ratio $\sim 5 \times 10^{-5}$. Our search has nowhere near that sensitivity, and so is a search for non-standard-model physics, in particular a charged Higgs with a large $\tan\beta$. We search for $B \to \tau\nu$ by looking for the leptonic decay of the τ. In such events, all detectable particles except the lepton are from the other B. We compute the mass and energy of this collection of particles, and look for a peak in the $M - E$ plane. The signal would have such a peak, the background not. We find no evidence for signal and obtain a 90% c.l. upper limit of 2.2×10^{-3} for the branching ratio, implying M_{Higgs} (in GeV) must be greater than $1.5 \times \tan\beta$.

3.   Exclusive, charmless, hadronic B decays

The second analysis is a search for exclusive, charmless, hadronic B decays. These will proceed either via a $b \to u$ spectator diagram, a $b \to s$ or $b \to d$ penguin diagram, or a combination of the two. Some of these decays (e.g. $B \to \pi^+\pi^-$) are candidates for CP violation measurements via $B^0 - \bar{B}^0$ mixing, some (e.g. $B \to K^-\pi$) for direct CP violation searches, some for understanding "penguin pollution" backgrounds to $B \to \pi\pi$ or hadronic phases in $B \to K\pi$. Some (e.g. $B \to K^{(*)}\phi$) are examples of pure penguins. Our search uses the conventional B reconstruction method, augmented by a powerful continuum suppression technique. For channels other than $K^-\pi^+$ and $\pi^-\pi^+$, we have no strong evidence for a signal. Upper limits, and an update to our result[1] on $K^-\pi^+$ and $\pi^-\pi^+$ are given in Table 1. Improvements over previous upper limits[2] are typically a factor of 5. In several cases we are close to theoretical predictions.

4. $B \to K^{(*)}\ell^+\ell^-$

The third analysis is a search for $B \to K^{(*)}\ell^+\ell^-$, examples of the parton level process $b \to s\ell^+\ell^-$. This process happens in the Standard Model, with small QCD corrections and a very small rate, so it is a good place to look for non-standard-model effects such as a tree-level violation of the GIM mechanism. As a matter of course, one simultaneously searches for the lepton-number-violating decays $b \to s\mu e$ along with $b \to se^+e^-$ and $b \to s\mu^+\mu^-$. In our search, we suppress the continuum background with event-shape cuts, suppress $B \to K^{(*)}\psi$, $\psi \to \ell^+\ell^-$ with a dilepton mass cut, and use conventional B reconstruction techniques. We see no evidence for signal, and give upper limits in Table 1.

5. $B \to \rho/\omega\gamma$

The fourth analysis is a search for examples of $b \to d\gamma$ decays, in particular $B^0 \to \rho^0\gamma$, $B^0 \to \omega\gamma$, and $B^\pm \to \rho^\pm\gamma$. One expects that the ratio of widths for $b \to d\gamma$ and $b \to s\gamma$ will equal $|V_{td}/V_{ts}|^2$, although concerns have been expressed that non-perturbative QCD corrections and long range effects may complicate this simple picture. In our search, there is a background from the continuum, which we suppress using event-shape cuts. There is a background to $B^0 \to \rho^0\gamma$ from $B^0 \to K^{*0}\gamma$, $K^{*0} \to K^+\pi^-$, illustrating the rule that last year's discovery[3] is this year's background. Using kinematic variables, we devise a cut that keeps 50% of the signal and 5% of the background. Our search yields no evidence for $B \to \rho^0\gamma$, $\omega\gamma$, or $\rho^\pm\gamma$. We find $\Gamma(B \to \rho/\omega\gamma)/\Gamma(B \to K^*\gamma) < 0.34$, at 90% c.l. Allowing for SU(3) breaking, but otherwise throwing theoretical

Mode	Upper Limit on $BR(10^{-5})$	Previous UL (10^{-5})	Theory (10^{-5})
$\pi^0\pi^0$	1.0	–	0.03-0.10
$\pi^\pm\rho^\mp$	9.5	52	1.9-8.8
$\pi^0\rho^0$	2.9	40	0.07-0.23
$\pi^+\pi^0$	2.3	24	0.6-2.1
$\pi^+\rho^0$	4.1	15	0.0-1.4
$K^0\pi^+$	6.3	–	0.5-0.8
$K^{*+}\pi^-$	23.8	38	0.1-1.9
$K^{*0}\pi^0$	3.5	–	0.3-0.5
$K^+\rho^-$	4.3	–	0.0-0.2
$K^0\phi$	10.7	42	0.1-1.3
$K^{*0}\phi$	3.9	32	0.0-3.1
$\phi\phi$	4.8	–	–
$K^+\pi^0$	3.2	–	0.3-1.3
$K^0\pi^+$	6.8	10	1.1-1.2
$K^{*0}\pi^+$	6.0	15	0.6-0.9
$K^+\rho^0$	2.6	8	0.01-0.06
$K^+\phi$	1.4	9	0.1-1.5
$K^{*+}\phi$	9.0	130	0.0-3.1
$\pi^+\pi^-$	2.2	2.9	1.0-2.6
$K^+\pi^-$	1.9	2.6	1.0-2.0
K^+K^-	0.7	0.7	–
$\pi^+\pi^- + K^+\pi^-$	$(1.8^{+0.6}_{-0.5})$	$(2.4^{+0.8}_{-0.7})$[1]	
$K^-e^+e^-$	1.2	6	0.06
$\bar{K}^{*0}e^+e^-$	1.6	29	0.6
$K^-\mu^+\mu^-$	0.9	17	0.06
$\bar{K}^{*0}\mu^+\mu^-$	3.1	2.3	0.3
$K^-e^\pm\mu^\mp$	1.2	2×640	0
$\bar{K}^{*0}e^\pm\mu^\mp$	2.7	–	0

Table 1. Upper limits on (measurements of) the branching ratios, previous upper limits (measurements) and theoretical predictions. Upper limits are at the 90% confidence level. Previous limits are taken from reference [2].

cautions to the winds, we obtain $|V_{td}/V_{ts}| < 0.64 - 0.76$, depending on SU(3)-breaking parameter. This limit is less restrictive than that from unitarity.

6. $b \to s\gamma$

The final, and principal analysis that I will present is a measurement of the branching ratio for the inclusive process $b \to s\gamma$. Theoretical interest in this process began in 1982[4]. Thereafter, it was recognized that there were large QCD corrections to the basic penguin diagram, and progressively more complete calculations, based on the method of renormalization-group-improved perturbation theory, were applied to the problem[5]. There is now general agreement among theorists on the full leading log calculation[6], and some, but not all, of the next-to-leading logarithmic QCD correctons have been calculated[7]. The QCD corrections increase the rate a factor of 2-3 over the basic penguin diagram. The Standard Model branching ratio for a leading-log calculation is $(2.75 \pm 0.80) \times 10^{-4}$[8], where the error is dominated by the uncertainty in the renormalization scale $m_b/2 < \mu < 2m_b$. If those next-to-leading log terms that have been calculated are included, the branching ratio falls to 1.9×10^{-4}[9]. The branching ratio is sensitive to non-standard-model physics, such as charged Higgs[10], anomalous $WW\gamma$ coupling[11], and many others[12].

Last year CLEO observed the decay $B \to K^*(892)\gamma$[3], a hadron-level example of the parton-level process $b \to s\gamma$. This was the first conclusive observation of a penguin, and established the existence of penguins generally and $b \to s\gamma$ in particular. However, there are large theoretical uncertainties in the hadronization process, and so $\Gamma(B \to K^*\gamma)$ gives only a very rough indication of $\Gamma(b \to s\gamma)$, the quantity of theoretical interest.

Our signature for the inclusive $b \to s\gamma$ process is a photon from B meson decay with energy between 2.2 and 2.7 GeV. There are small, calculable backgrounds from other B decay processes. There are *large* backgrounds from the continuum, both from the initial state radiation (ISR) process $e^+e^- \to q\bar{q}\gamma$, and from the normal $(q\bar{q})$ continuum reaction $e^+e^- \to q\bar{q}$, with the high energy photon arising from the hadronic debris $(\pi^0, \eta, \omega \to \pi^0\gamma$, etc). We suppress the continuum, two ways, and then subtract what is left, using data taken at E_{cm} just below the $\Upsilon(4S)$ resonance.

In the first method for suppressing the continuum, we take 8 carefully chosen event-shape variables: R_2, $S_\perp$, R'_2, $\cos\theta'$ as defined in Ref[3], and the energies in $20°$ and $30°$ cones, parallel and antiparallel to the high energy photon direction. We combine the 8 variables into a single variable r which tends towards $+1$ for $b \to s\gamma$ and tends towards -1 for ISR and $q\bar{q}$, using a neural network. Distributions in r are shown in Fig. 1, for MC signal, MC background, and off-resonance data. There is substantial discrimination between signal and background, and good agreement between MC background and off-resonance data. Given r, we perform a weighted sum of candidate high energy photon events, with an r-dependent weighting, large near $r = +1$, small near $r = -1$, optimized based on Monte Carlo samples of signal and background. This weighting procedure is equivalent to performing a 1-parameter fit to the r distribution.

In the second method for suppressing the continuum, we search each event containing a high energy γ for combinations of particles which fit the $B \to X_s\gamma$ decay hypothesis. We use: the γ; $K^\pm$ or $K_s^0 \to \pi^+\pi^-$; 1-4 π's, which may include 0 or 1 π^0. We do not concern ourselves with cross-feed, combinatoric

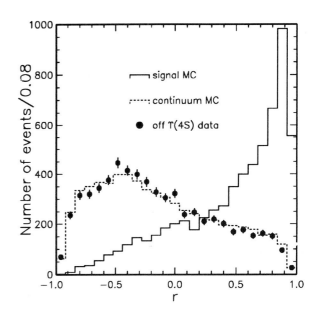

Figure 1. Distributions in the neural net variable r, for Monte Carlo samples of $b \to s\gamma$ signal (solid histogram) and continuum background (dashed histogram), and for the off-resonance data sample (points).

background, or reconstruction ambiguities, as we are using reconstruction to suppress the continuum, and *not attempting a mode-by-mode B reconstruction analysis*. In each event, we pick the best combination of particles, and for that combination consider

$$\chi_B^2 = \left(\frac{M_B - 5.279}{\sigma_M}\right)^2 + \left(\frac{E_B - E_{beam}}{\sigma_E}\right)^2. \quad (1)$$

We also calculate $\cos\theta_{tt}$, where θ_{tt} is the angle between the thrust axis of the candidate B and the thrust axis of the rest of the event. Both χ_B^2 and $\cos\theta_{tt}$ give good discrimination between signal and background. We make cuts $|\cos\theta_{tt}| < 0.6$ and $\chi_B^2 < 6.0$.

There are backgrounds from B decay processes other than $b \to s\gamma$, in particular from $b \to cW^-$, $b \to uW^-$, and $b \to sg$. As a first approximation, we take these from Monte Carlo. We then correct for any difference between the π^0 momentum spectra from data and Monte Carlo, and similarly for the η momentum spectra. Thus, in a very real sense, these backgrounds are determined from data. It is only for those small B-decay backgrounds *not* from π^0 or η that we rely on Monte Carlo.

The photon energy spectra from the event-shape

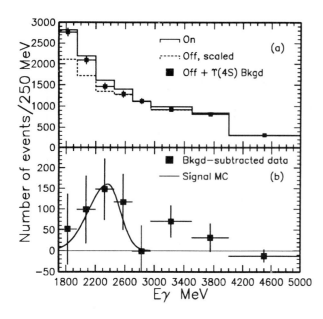

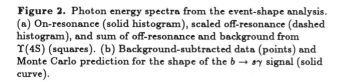

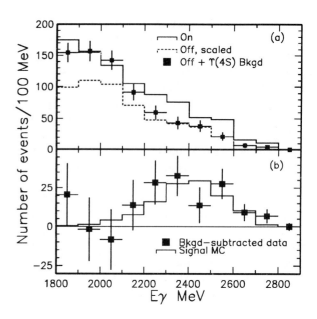

Figure 2. Photon energy spectra from the event-shape analysis. (a) On-resonance (solid histogram), scaled off-resonance (dashed histogram), and sum of off-resonance and background from $\Upsilon(4S)$ (squares). (b) Background-subtracted data (points) and Monte Carlo prediction for the shape of the $b \to s\gamma$ signal (solid curve).

Figure 3. Photon energy spectra from the B reconstruction analysis. (a) On-resonance (solid histogram), scaled off-resonance (dashed histogram), and sum of off-resonance and background from $\Upsilon(4S)$ (squares). (b) Background-subtracted data (points) and Monte Carlo prediction for the shape of the $b \to s\gamma$ signal (solid curve).

analysis are shown in Fig. 2a, while those from the B reconstruction analysis are shown in Fig. 3a. In both cases, the on-resonance spectrum exceeds the sum of off-resonance plus $\Upsilon(4S)$ backgrounds in the energy interval 2.2 - 2.7 GeV, demonstrating the presence of $b \to s\gamma$. The subtracted spectra are shown in Figs. 2b and 3b, along with a Monte Carlo prediction of the shape of the $b \to s\gamma$ photon spectrum. A signal of the expected shape is apparent. Yields between 2.2 and 2.7 GeV for the two analysis procedures are given in Table 2.

To calculate the detection efficiency, we model $b \to s\gamma$ with the spectator model of Ali and Greub[13], which includes gluon bremsstrahlung and higher order radiative effects. It gives us the X_s mass distribution. We hadronize X_s with conventional models of quark hadronization. In the Ali-Greub model, we vary P_F and $m_{spectator}$ simultaneously such that the b quark average mass $< m_b >$ is constant at 4.87 ± 0.10 GeV, a value suggested by recent theoretical work[14]. We take $P_F = 270 \pm 40$ MeV/c, based on fits to our $B \to X\ell\nu$ data with the same $< m_b >$.

We find $Br(b \to s\gamma) = (1.88 \pm 0.67) \times 10^{-4}$ with the event-shape analysis, and $(2.75 \pm 0.63) \times 10^{-4}$ with the

	Event Shape	B Reconstruction
On	3013 ± 59	281 ± 17
Off(scaled)	2618 ± 73	155 ± 18
$\Upsilon(4S)$ background		
$b \to c$	50.7 ± 5.1	12 ± 2
$b \to u$	11.9 ± 4.0	2 ± 1
π^0 correction	50.2 ± 27.7	-0.7 ± 2.3
η correction	16.5 ± 33.7	2.0 ± 8.5
Non-$B\bar{B}$	2.3	
$\Upsilon(4S)$ total	132 ± 44	15 ± 9
On$-$Off$-\Upsilon(4S)$	263 ± 94	110 ± 25
	± 49	± 10

Table 2. Yields of events with 2.2 - 2.7 GeV photons, for the two $b \to s\gamma$ analysis procedures.

B reconstruction analysis. Allowing for correlations, the difference is $1.1\,\sigma$. We combine the two results, allowing for correlations, obtaining

$$Br(b \to s\gamma) = (2.32 \pm 0.51 \pm 0.29 \pm 0.32) \times 10^{-4}, \quad (2)$$

where the first error is statistical, the second error is the additive systematic error from uncertainty in yield,

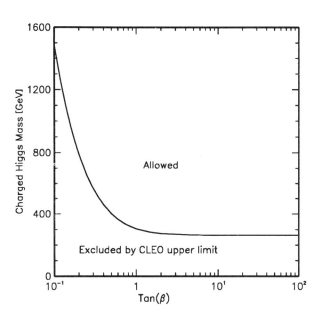

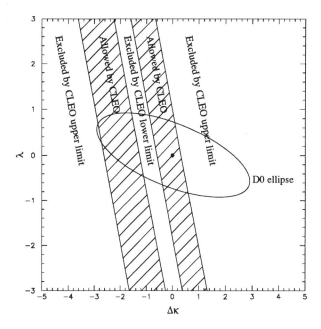

Figure 4. Lower limit on Two-Higgs-Doublet-Model-II Higgs mass as a function of $\tan(\beta)$. The region below the curve is ruled out by the upper limit on the $b \to s\gamma$ branching ratio reported here.

Figure 5. Limits on anomalous $WW\gamma$ coupling parameters λ and $\Delta\kappa$. The shaded regions are consistent with the $b \to s\gamma$ branching ratio reported here. The space between the shaded regions is ruled out by CLEO's lower limit, while the spaces outside the shaded regions are ruled out by CLEO's upper limit. D0's yield of $p\bar{p} \to W\gamma X$ limits the allowed range to the interior of the ellipse (the CDF $p\bar{p} \to W\gamma X$ limit gives a similar ellipse)[15]. The Standard Model value is shown as the dot at $\Delta\kappa = \lambda = 0$.

and the third error is the multiplicative systematic error from uncertainty in efficiency, including model dependence. We further obtain 95% c.l. lower and upper limits on the branching ratio

$$1 \times 10^{-4} < Br(b \to s\gamma) < 4 \times 10^{-4}. \tag{3}$$

Our measurement, $(2.3 \pm 0.7) \times 10^{-4}$ is in good agreement with the Standard Model expectation $(2.8 \pm 0.8) \times 10^{-4}$. (For theory, we use $m_t = 175$ GeV, leading log terms only, and a renormalization scale $m_b/2 < \mu < 2m_b$. We assume a 10% theoretical uncertainty in addition to the renormalization scale uncertainty.) We illustrate the implications of our result for non-standard models with two examples.

A charged Higgs, with Model II coupling, would increase the $b \to s\gamma$ branching ratio, and by larger amounts for lower Higgs masses[10], so our upper limit on $b \to s\gamma$ provides a lower limit on charged Higgs mass. This limit is shown in Fig. 4. (With additional SUSY particles, this limit can be circumvented.)

Anomalous $WW\gamma$ couplings could either increase or decrease the $b \to s\gamma$ branching ratio[11], and so both our upper and lower limits rule out portions of the $\Delta\kappa - \lambda$ space that describes these anomalous couplings. In Fig.

5 we show the regions of the $\Delta\kappa - \lambda$ plane allowed and excluded by our limits, and also the regions allowed and excluded by $\bar{p}p \to W\gamma X$ measurements[15]. One notes a complementarity of the two types of measurements. The Standard Model gives $\Delta\kappa = \lambda = 0$.

7. Conclusion

I have presented five searches for rare B decays by CLEO. Upper limits on hadronic charmless decays are approaching Standard Model predictions. The measurement of branching ratio for $b \to s\gamma$ is in good agreement with Standard Model predictions, and places constraints on non-standard models. Further progress here requires completion of a next-to-leading log calculation, to reduce the theoretical uncertainty from renormalization scale.

Acknowledgement

I thank Ahmed Ali and Christoph Greub for performing several spectator model calculations for us, and for many interesting conversations. JoAnne Hewett and Tom Rizzo have helped me understand the implications of $b \to s\gamma$ for non-standard models. I thank Jesse Ernst and Peter Kim for help in preparing this paper, and for many interesting discussions. This work was supported by the National Science Foundation, the U.S. Dept. of Energy, the Heisenberg Foundation, the SSC Fellowship program of TNRLC, Natural Sciences and Engineering Research Council of Canada, and the A.P. Sloan Foundation.

References

[1] M. Battle *et al.* (CLEO Collaboration), Phys. Rev. Lett. **71**, 3922 (1993).

[2] M. Aguilar-Benitez *et al.* (Particle Data Group), Phys. Rev. **D50**, 1173 (1994).

[3] R. Ammar *et al.* (CLEO Collaboration), Phys. Rev. Lett. **71**, 674 (1993).

[4] B.A. Campbell and P.J. O'Donnell, Phys. Rev. D **25**, 1989 (1982).

[5] S. Bertolini *et al.*, Phys. Rev. Lett. **59**, 180 (1987); N. Deshpande *et al.*, Phys. Rev. Lett. **59**, 183 (1987); B. Grinstein *et al.*, Phys. Lett. **B202**,138 (1988); R. Grigjanis *et al.*, Phys. Lett. **B213**, 335 (1988); G. Cella *et al.*, Phys. Lett. **B248**, 181 (1990); M. Misiak, Phys. Lett. **B269**, 161 (1991).

[6] M. Ciuchini *et al.*, Phys. Lett. **B316**, 127 (1993); M. Misiak, Phys. Lett. **B321**, 113 (1994); G. Cella *et al.*, Phys. Lett. **B325**, 227 (1994).

[7] A. Ali and C. Greub, Phys. Lett. **B259**, 182 (1991); Z. Phys. **C60**, 433 (1993); A.J. Buras *et al.*, Nucl. Phys. **B370**, 69 (1992); **B375**, 501 (1992); **B400**, 37 (1993); 75 (1993); M. Ciuchini *et al.*, Phys. Lett. **B301**, 263 (1993); Nucl. Phys. **B415**, 403 (1994).

[8] A.J. Buras *et al.*, Max Planck Institute preprint MPI-Ph/93-77.

[9] M. Ciuchini *et al.*, preprint CERN-TH.7283/94 (June 1994).

[10] R.G. Ellis *et al.*, Phys. Lett. **B179**, 119 (1986); T. G. Rizzo, Phys Rev. **D38**, 820 (1988); W.-S. Hou and R.S. Wiley, Phys Lett. **B202**, 591 (1988); C.Q.Geng and J.N. Ng, Phys Rev. **D38**, 2858 (1988); V. Barger, J.L. Hewett, and R.J.N. Phillips, Phys. Rev. **D41**, 3421 (1990); J.L. Hewett, Phys. Rev. Lett. **70**, 1045 (1993); V. Barger, M. Berger, and R.J.N. Phillips, Phys. Rev. Lett. **70**, 1368 (1993).

[11] S.-P. Chia, Phys. Lett. **B240**, 465 (1990); K.A. Peterson, Phys. Lett. **B282**, 207 (1992); T.G. Rizzo, Phys. Lett. **B315**, 471 (1993); U. Baur, in Proceedings of the *Summer Workshop on B Physics*, Snowmass, CO, 1993; X.-G. He and B. McKellar, Phys. Lett. **B320**, 165 (1994).

[12] For a recent review of implications of $b \to s\gamma$ for non-Standard models, see J.L. Hewett, SLAC-PUB-6521 (May 1994).

[13] A. Ali and C. Greub, Phys. Lett. **B259**, 182 (1991).

[14] M. Voloshin and Y. Zaitsev, Sov. Phys. Usp. **30**, 553 (1987); C.T.H. Davies *et al.*, preprint SCRI-94-39.

[15] "Electroweak Boson Pair Production at CDF", The CDF Collaboration, Contribution to this conference GLS0357; D0 Collaboration measurement of $W\gamma X$ rates, proceedings of 1993 Moriond conference.

Paper presented at XXVII Int. Conf. on High Energy Physics: Session Pa-21
Glasgow, UK, 20–27 July 1994

New Results on Rare Beauty Decays

A. M. Litke†

Santa Cruz Institute for Particle Physics
University of California, Santa Cruz, CA 95064, USA

Abstract

We summarize new results on rare beauty decays from experiments at DORIS, LEP, and the Tevatron Collider. Charmless hadronic decays are observed at the 3.1 σ level by ARGUS, and at the 3.5 σ level by ALEPH, but no specific decay mode has been unambiguously identified. Upper limits on charmless hadronic decays of B_d, $B^{\pm}$, B_s, and Λ_b are given, as well as new limits on $B_s \to \phi\gamma$, $\Lambda_b \to \Lambda\gamma$, and $B^{\pm} \to \mu^+\mu^- K^{\pm}$.

1. Introduction

Beauty hadrons decay most of the time via the dominant $b \to cW^*$ quark transition. A great deal of experimental and theoretical work has been devoted to these decays, including, as an example, $B \to \bar{D}^*\ell\nu$. Much less is known experimentally about decay modes due to other, comparatively infrequent, quark transitions. These rare transitions (and some corresponding decay channels) include:‡

- $b \to uW^*$ ($b \to u$ transition; $B_d \to \pi^+\pi^-$; $B_s \to K^-\pi^+$; $\Lambda_b \to p\pi^-$)
- $b \to s\,gluon$ (hadronic "penguin" transition; $B_d \to K^+\pi^-$; $B_s \to K^+K^-$; $\Lambda_b \to pK^-$)
- $b \to d\,gluon$ (CKM-suppressed hadronic "penguin" transition; $B_d \to \pi^+\pi^-$; $B_s \to K^-\pi^+$; $\Lambda_b \to p\pi^-$)
- $b \to s\gamma$ (electromagnetic "penguin" transition; $B_s \to \phi\gamma$; $\Lambda_b \to \Lambda\gamma$)
- $b \to d\gamma$ (CKM-suppressed electromagnetic "penguin" transition; $B_s \to K^*\gamma$)
- $b \to s\ell^+\ell^-$ (flavor-changing neutral current transition; $B^+ \to \mu^+\mu^- K^+$)
- $b \to d\ell^+\ell^-$ (CKM-suppressed FCNC transition; $B^+ \to \mu^+\mu^-\pi^+$)

$\dagger$ e-mail: LITKE@CERNVM.CERN.CH
$\ddagger$ Throughout this report, charge-conjugate modes are also implied.

In this report, we will summarize some recent experimental results on most of the above-listed processes, as submitted to this conference by the ARGUS, ALEPH, DELPHI, OPAL, L3, and CDF Collaborations.

2. Charmless Hadronic Beauty Decays

Charmless hadronic B decays were first observed by the CLEO Collaboration [1]. They measured the branching ratio $BR(B_d \to \pi^+\pi^-, K^+\pi^-) = (2.4^{+0.8}_{-0.7} \pm 0.2) \times 10^{-5}$, but were unable to obtain statistically significant signals in the individual modes. New searches for charmless hadronic beauty decays at DORIS and LEP are reported in this section.

2.1. Search for $b \to s\,gluon$ (ARGUS) [2]

ARGUS has searched for charmless B decays that can arise from $b \to s\,gluon$ transitions. Their strategy was to use fully-reconstructed $\Upsilon(4S) \to B\bar{B}$ events.

The search was conducted in the channels $B \to (K^{\pm}, K^0_s)n\pi^{\pm}$, with $1 \le n \le 7$ (this B is called the "tagged" B). The decays considered for the second B in the event (the "tagging" B) were the semi-leptonic modes $B \to D^{(*)}\ell^-\bar{\nu}$, and the hadronic modes $B \to D^{(*)}\pi^-$, $D^{(*)}\rho^-$, and $D^{(*)}a_1^-$.

In a data sample of 209K $\Upsilon(4S)$ decays, 7 candidate

events were found in the signal region. In five of these events, the decay products of the tagged B include a D or a ψ', consistent with a $b \to cW^*$ transition. In the remaining two candidate events, no charm or charmonium state was found in the decay products of the tagged B.

The continuum background, evaluated from data collected below the $\Upsilon(4S)$ resonance, is 0.03 ± 0.02 events. The probability for this background to fluctuate to the two observed events is 8×10^{-4}. The combinatorial background from $\Upsilon(4S)$ decays is less than 0.01 events. The overall background probability is therefore $\leq 9 \times 10^{-4}$, a $\approx 3.1\sigma$ effect.

One of the candidate events includes a decay consistent with the mode $B_d \to K^+\pi^-$. However, this decay is also consistent with the decay hypothesis $B_d \to \pi^+\pi^-$, with a probability of 8% relative to the $K^+\pi^-$ hypothesis. The second candidate event contains a possible decay $B^- \to K^-4\pi^\pm$, but, with approximately the same probability, this decay is also consistent with $B^- \to 5\pi^\pm$. We conclude that there is evidence, at the 3.1σ level, for charmless hadronic B decays. However, there is no significant separation between modes arising from $b \to s\,gluon$ transitions compared to $b \to d\,gluon$ or $b \to uW^*$ transitions.

This difficulty to unambiguously identify specific decay modes was already mentioned in connection with the original CLEO observation, and will arise again with the ALEPH results. However, particle identification in DELPHI (see section 2.2.2) illustrates a possible solution.

2.2. *Results from LEP*

All four LEP experiments have searched for charmless hadronic beauty decays, with B_d, B_u, B_s, and Λ_b all produced in $Z^0 \to b\bar{b}$ events. The number of charmless decays expected is limited: taking the CLEO branching ratio of 2.4×10^{-5} [1] for $BR(B_d \to \pi^+\pi^-, K^+K^-)$, the present LEP data sample of $\approx 1.6M$ $Z^0 \to hadrons$ events, and a typical reconstruction efficiency of 28%, we expect ~ 7 $B \to \pi^+\pi^-, K^+K^-$ decays produced with ~ 2 detected. Nonetheless, a number of features of the events at LEP make the search worthwhile, in ways which are complementary to the work at CLEO and ARGUS:

- The data from LEP can provide new information on B_s and Λ_b decays.
- The large boost of the b hadron in $Z^0 \to b\bar{b}$ events, combined with the precision measurement capability of silicon vertex detectors, provides the possibility for observing separated, well-identified decay vertices.
- In the events at LEP, there is very little overlap between the tracks from the *b* hadron decay and

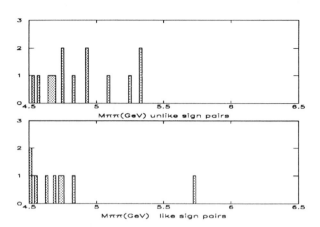

Figure 1. Invariant mass distribution for $B \to h^+h^-$ candidates in ALEPH, with each particle assigned the $\pi^\pm$ mass. Also shown is the corresponding distribution for like-sign pairs.

those from the $\bar{b}$ hadron decay.
- Particle id, particularly with the ring imaging Cherenkov detector (RICH) of the DELPHI experiment, will potentially allow unambiguous determination of the decay modes.

All these points will be illustrated below.

2.2.1. Results from ALEPH [3] ALEPH searched for charmless hadronic beauty decays in the channel with two oppositely-charged hadrons, h^+h^-. Particular use is made of the silicon vertex detector.

Background with one or two tracks originating from the primary vertex is suppressed by vertexing and momentum requirements. The background whereby the two tracks originate from a b hadron decay which includes charm is suppressed by demanding that the h^+h^- invariant mass be significantly above the kinematic limit for $b \to c$ decays (4.8 GeV/c^2 for b meson decays and 5.0 GeV/c^2 for b baryon decays, taking each hadron to have the $\pi^\pm$ mass).

In a data sample of 1.6M $Z^0 \to hadrons$ events, three $B \to h^+h^-$ candidates in the signal region are found, as shown in figure 1. Also shown is the corresponding distribution for like-sign pairs, with one candidate found. The efficiency for this search is about 28%, and the mass resolution is ≈ 40 MeV/c^2.

From Monte Carlo studies, we expect 0.07 ± 0.04 background events to populate the h^+h^- signal region. The corresponding binomial probability to observe three or more background events in the data is 1.8×10^{-4}. We conclude that charmless hadronic beauty decays have been observed in ALEPH with a statistical significance of 3.5σ.

One of these events is shown in figure 2. The h^+h^- has a $\pi^+\pi^-$ mass of 5.34 ± 0.05 GeV/c^2, a momentum of 40 GeV/c, and a decay length of 0.95 cm, with a decay length significance of 73σ.

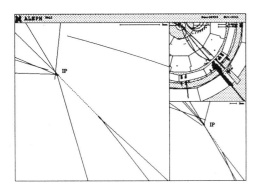

Figure 2. A $B \to h^+ h^-$ candidate decay in ALEPH. Two magnified orthogonal views, close to the interaction point (IP), are shown, along with a partial $r - \phi$ view of the event.

	Upper Limits	
Decay Mode	DELPHI [10^{-5}]	PDG94 [4] [10^{-5}]
$B_d \to K^+ a_1$	51	
$B_d \to \pi^+ \pi^+ \pi^- \pi^-$	28	67
$B_d \to K^+ \pi^+ \pi^- \pi^-$	27	
$B^- \to \rho^0 \pi^-$	26	15
$B^- \to K^{*0} \pi^-$	48	15
$B^- \to K^- \rho^0$	19	8
$B^- \to K^- \phi$	44	9
$B^- \to \pi^+ \pi^- \pi^-$	22	19
$B^- \to K^- \pi^+ \pi^-$	40	19
$B^- \to K^+ K^- K^-$	31	35
$B_s \to K^+ a_1$	169	
$B_s \to K^+ \pi^+ \pi^- \pi^-$	91	

Table 2. Branching ratio upper limits (90% C.L.) from DELPHI on two, three, and four-body charmless hadronic B decays.

	Upper Limits				
Decay Mode	ALEPH [10^{-5}]	DELPHI [10^{-5}]	OPAL [10^{-5}]	L3 [10^{-5}]	PDG94 [10^{-5}]
$B_d \to \pi^+ \pi^-$	7.5	5.5	4.7		2.9
$B_d \to K^+ \pi^-$	7.5	12	8.1		2.6
$B_d \to K^+ K^-$	3.2	16			0.7
$B_d \to p\bar{p}$	3.2				3.4
$B_d \to \eta \pi^0$				84	180
$B_d \to \eta \eta$				210	
$B_s \to \pi^+ \pi^-$	25				
$B_s \to K^- \pi^+$	25	39	26		
$B_s \to K^+ K^-$	11	52	14		
$B_s \to p\bar{p}$	11				
$\Lambda_b \to p\pi^-$	16				
$\Lambda_b \to pK^-$	16				

Table 1. Branching ratio upper limits (90% C.L.) for two-body charmless hadronic decays of B_d, B_s, and Λ_b. PDG94 refers to [4].

To try to identify the specific decay channels for the candidate decays, a χ^2 probability P_{χ^2}, based on the $h^+ h^-$ invariant mass, the dE/dx for each track, and the corresponding resolutions, is used. Unfortunately, each of the three candidate decays satisfies two or more decay hypotheses, with $P_{\chi^2} > 0.1$, so there is no unambiguous identification of a decay channel. For example, the decay illustrated in figure 2 is consistent with the channels $B_d \to K\pi$, $B_s \to \pi\pi$, and $B_s \to K\pi$. Therefore, we set branching ratio upper limits for specific decay modes, as given in Table 1. For comparison, the limits compiled in the "Review of Particle Properties" [4] are also shown.

2.2.2. Results from DELPHI [5] DELPHI has searched for charmless hadronic B decays in the channels $B \to n_1\pi^{\pm}$, $n_2 K^{\pm}$, and $K^{\pm} m\pi^{\pm}$, with $2 \le n_1 \le 4$, $2 \le n_2 \le 3$, and $1 \le m \le 3$. They have used both their silicon vertex detector and RICH for this analysis, which is based on a data sample of 1.7M $Z^0 \to hadrons$ events.

In the two-body modes (which include the two-prong channels $\pi\pi$, $K\pi$, and KK, as well as the three

and four-prong channels $\pi\rho$, $K\rho$, Ka_1, πK^* and $K\phi$), three candidate decays are found with a background, estimated from Monte Carlo, of 0.34 ± 0.08 decays. The corresponding statistical significance for a possible combined signal is at the 2.5σ level. No individual decay channel is observed with a significant signal. Also, in the three and four-body modes, no signal is observed above background. Consequently, branching ratio upper limits are reported in Table 1 (for two-prong modes) and Table 2 (for three and four-prong modes).

One of the two-body candidate decays, in the mode $B^- \to \pi^- K^{*0}(892)$, with $K^{*0}(892) \to K^- \pi^+$, is of interest as it illustrates the power of the RICH for particle identification. The RICH data for this decay, as well as the dE/dx data, is shown in figure 3. The RICH allows for the unambiguous identification of the three particles.

2.2.3. Results from OPAL [6] In a data sample of 1.9M multihadronic Z^0 decays, OPAL has searched for the decays $B_d \to \pi^+ \pi^-$, $B_d \to K^+ \pi^-$, $B_s \to K^- \pi^+$, and $B_s \to K^+ K^-$. Mass resolutions are 137 to 152 MeV/c^2, and the efficiencies range from 20 to 24%. The background is estimated from a fit to the invariant mass distribution outside of the signal region. No signal is observed above the estimated background in any of the four channels. The upper limits on the corresponding branching ratios are given in Table 1.

2.2.4. Results from L3 [7] Taking advantage of its BGO electromagnetic calorimeter, L3 has searched for charmless hadronic B decays into the all-photon final states $B_d \to \eta\eta$ and $\eta\pi^0$, with $\eta \to \gamma\gamma$ and $\pi^0 \to \gamma\gamma$. In a data sample of 1.2M hadronic Z^0 decays, with B mass resolutions of ~ 112 MeV/c^2, and efficiencies of $\sim 3.5\%$ (not including $BR(\eta \to \gamma\gamma)$), no candidates are found in the signal region for either channel. The corresponding

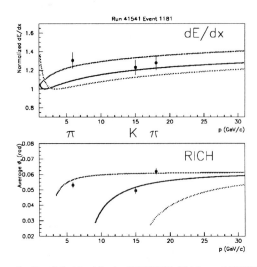

Figure 3. Particle id with the DELPHI dE/dx and RICH systems. The curves give the expected values for π, K, and p, as a function of momentum. The data points correspond to the three particles in the candidate decay $B^- \to \pi^- \bar{K}^{*0}$, with $\bar{K}^{*0} \to K^- \pi^+$.

Decay Mode	Upper Limits	
	ALEPH [10^{-5}]	PDG94 [4] [10^{-5}]
$B_s \to \phi\gamma$	29	–
$\Lambda_b \to \Lambda\gamma$	56	–

Table 3. Branching ratio upper limits (90% C.L.) on $b \to s\gamma$ decay modes from ALEPH.

branching ratio upper limits are listed in Table 1.

3. Searches for $b \to s\gamma$ transitions in B_s and Λ_B decays (ALEPH) [8]

A search in ALEPH has been conducted for electromagnetic penguin transitions via the decays $B_s \to \phi\gamma$ (with $\phi \to K^+K^-$), and $\Lambda_b \to \Lambda\gamma$ (with $\Lambda \to p\pi^-$). In a data sample of 1.8M hadronic Z^0 decays, no candidates have been found in either channel. The search efficiencies were 17% and 10%, respectively (not including $BR(\phi \to K^+K^-)$ or $BR(\Lambda \to p\pi^-)$), with mass resolutions $\sim 140\, MeV/c^2$. The derived branching ratio upper limits are given in Table 3.

4. Searches for $B^\pm \to \mu^+\mu^- K^\pm$ (CDF) [9]

The CDF Collaboration has looked for evidence for the flavor-changing neutral current transition $b \to s\ell^+\ell^-$ by searching for $B^\pm \to \mu^+\mu^- K^\pm$ decays at the Tevatron Collider. A silicon vertex detector is used to identify the displaced B decay vertex and thereby substantially reduce the combinatorial background.

$B^\pm$ decays to $J/\psi K^\pm$, with $J/\psi \to \mu^+\mu^-$, are

used for normalization. These decays are identified by restricting the $\mu^+\mu^-$ invariant mass $M_{\mu\mu}$ to the J/ψ region $3.017 \leq M_{\mu\mu} \leq 3.177\, GeV/c^2$. 50.3 ± 9.4 such decays are observed above background.

When $M_{\mu\mu}$ is in one of two non-ψ regions, $3.3 \leq M_{\mu\mu} \leq 3.6\, GeV/c^2$ or $3.8 \leq M_{\mu\mu} \leq 4.5\, GeV/c^2$, the $\mu^+\mu^- K^\pm$ invariant mass distribution shows no significant B signal above background. Hence it is found that $BR(B^\pm \to \mu^+\mu^- K^\pm, partial) < 7.4 \times 10^{-6}$ at the 90% confidence level, where "partial" refers to the sum of the two non-ψ $M_{\mu\mu}$ regions given above. A theoretical calculation [10], based on heavy quark effective theory, is used to extrapolate this "partial" result to the full allowed region in $M_{\mu\mu}$. Then $BR(B^\pm \to \mu^+\mu^- K^\pm) < 3.2 \times 10^{-5}$, again at the 90% confidence level. This is a factor of 5.3 below the PDG94 limit [4] of 17×10^{-5}.

5. Conclusions

Following the first observation by CLEO, there have been "sightings" of charmless hadronic beauty decays by ARGUS at DORIS (3.1σ effect) and ALEPH at LEP (3.5σ effect). However, there has been no unambiguous determination of a specific decay mode. The particle id result from DELPHI's RICH shows promise in this area. The expected factor of two increase in the LEP data sample this year will clearly help the LEP efforts.

Many new branching ratio upper limits for charmless hadronic beauty decays have been established at LEP, particularly in the realm of B_s and Λ_b decays. However, these limits are still far above the values expected by theory, in the absence of new physics.

New branching ratio upper limits have been set for decays mediated by flavor-changing neutral currents: $B^\pm \to \mu^+\mu^- K^\pm$ by CDF; $B_s \to \phi\gamma$ and $\Lambda_b \to \Lambda\gamma$ by ALEPH. In the absence of new physics, these limits are above the expected values.

References

[1] CLEO Collaboration, M. Battle *et al.*, Phys. Rev. Lett. **71** (1993) 3922.
[2] ARGUS Collaboration, contribution #199 to ICHEP 94 Conference, Glasgow (1994).
[3] ALEPH Collaboration, contribution #583 to ICHEP 94 Conference, Glasgow (1994).
[4] Particle Data Group, Phys. Rev. **D50** (1994) 1173.
[5] DELPHI Collaboration, internal note #94-105 (1994).
[6] OPAL Collaboration, R. Akers *et al.*, CERN preprint: CERN-PPE/94-98 (1994).
[7] L3 Collaboration, internal note #1604 (1994).
[8] ALEPH Collaboration, contribution to ICHEP 94 Conference, Glasgow (1994).
[9] CDF Collaboration, contribution #128 to ICHEP 94 Conference, Glasgow (1994).
[10] G. Baillie, Zeit. Phys. **C61** (1994) 667.

Paper presented at XXVII Int. Conf. on High Energy Physics: Session Pa-21
Glasgow, UK, 20–27 July 1994

Recent Experimental Results on Rare Charm Decays

Kwong Lau

Physics Department, University of Houston, Houston, Texas 77204-5506

Abstract

Preliminary results on rare charm decays from fixed-target experiments E771, E791, and WA92 are reviewed. E771 and WA92 have searched for the charm changing neutral current (CCNC) decay $D0 \rightarrow \mu^+\mu^-$, and found no evidence. They have obtained upper limits which are comparable to the present limit of 1.1×10^{-5}. E791 has searched for the CCNC decay $D^\pm \rightarrow \mu^+\mu^-\pi^\pm$, and found 5 events which are consistent with misidentified $D^\pm \rightarrow \pi^+\pi^-\pi^\pm$ decays. The resulting upper limit of 4.3×10^{-5} is almost two orders of magnitude better than the current limit. These preliminary results are expected to be improved in the near future by increasing statistics. E771 expects to have a more significant improvement by also including vertex information from the silicon vertex detector.

1. Introduction

The rare charm decays, $D0 \rightarrow \mu^+\mu^-$ (1) and $D^\pm \rightarrow \mu^+\mu^-\pi^\pm$ (2), are sensitive probes to the charm sector of flavor changing neutral currents (FCNCs). The best published upper limit for (1) is 1.1×10^{-5} [1], obtained almost a decade ago in a fixed-target experiment[2]. The current upper limit for $D^\pm \rightarrow \mu^+\mu^-\pi^\pm$ (2.9×10^{-3}) was obtained by the CLEO collaboration in e^+e^- interactions[3]. The decay rates for (1) and (2) are suppressed by the GIM mechanism[4] in the standard model (SM). (1) is more severely suppressed in the SM due the zero spin of the $D0$. At the quark level the decay rate for (1) is given by [5]

$$\Gamma(D \rightarrow \mu\mu) = \frac{G_F^2 m_c^5}{192\pi^3}(\frac{f_D}{m_D})^2(\frac{m_\mu}{m_D})^2|\sum V_{ui}V_{ci}^*C(x_i)|^2,$$

where most of the notations are standard, and the sum is over the three quark generations. The function $C(x_i)$ has been evaluated[6], and found to be proportional to $x_i = m_i/m_W$ when $x_i \ll 1$; m_i is the quark mass. Unlike analogous FCNC decays for strange and beauty hadrons, which have either been mesured ($BR(K_L \rightarrow \mu\mu = 7.3 \pm 0.4 \times 10^{-9}$)[1] or is expected to have a BR of about 10^{-9}[7], the expected branching ratio (BR) for (1) is miserably small, of the order of 10^{-19}[5]. Even though long-distance effects may enhance the BR by several orders of magnitude, (1) induced by the SM has no chance of being detected in the near future. Therefore, decay (1) is a clean searching ground for physics beyond the SM. Most extensions of the SM possess FCNC, causing (1) to proceed at a typical BR

of 10^{-10}[8]. While this tiny contribution to the strange and beauty FCNC decays may be obscured by the SM rate, the observation of FCNC for charm hadrons at this level is an unambiguous signal for new physics. Dedicated fixed-target experiments in the near future can achieve this level of sensitivity for (1). Decay (2) is also mediated by CCNC. The SM prediction of the BR for (2) is considerably larger, about 10^{-10}[9], as a result of the dominance of the photon propagator in the decay process and the absence of helicity suppression.

Heavy flavor fixed-target experiments at the Tevatron and the SPS are prolific sources of hadrons of heavy quarks. For example, as many as 10^9 charm hadrons were produced in one month of running in E771. This charm sample is sizable, even after taking into account modest acceptance and efficiency losses. These large samples provide sensitive searches for decays (1) and (2), at the level of 10^{-6} to 10^{-7}. Two experiments, E771[10] and WA92[11], have conducted searches for (1) based on about half of their 91-92 data. E791 has performed a search for (2)[12]. This mini-review summarizes their preliminary findings.

2. $D0 \rightarrow \mu^+\mu^-$

2.1. E771

E771 is a fixed-target experiment at FNAL, primarily designed to study beauty hadron production in 800 GeV proton-nucleus interactions by searching for beauty hadrons decaying to J/ψ's which decay to muons. The detector is a large aperture magnetic spectrometer equipped with conventional wire chambers and a 12-plane precision silicon vertex detector. The pitch of the silicon planes ranges from 25 to 50 μm, providing impact parameter resolution of about 25 μm. The experiment was conducted with a specialized trigger of requiring either two muons in the final state, or one high transverse momentum muon, $p_t \geq 1.5$ GeV. During the 1992 runs, the experiment recorded about 127 M dimuon triggers and 62 M single muon triggers, corresponding to about 6.6×10^{11} interactions.

The candidates for decay (1) were selected by requiring a fully-reconstructed muon pair in the event. To reduce K/π decay background, one muon is required to have at least 1 GeV p_t and the other muon has to have a $p_t \geq 0.4$ GeV. The muon pair is required to originate from the target region; for this preliminary analysis the vertex information is based on the wire tracking chambers. The invariant mass spectra for opposite-sign (solid histogram) and same-sign (dotted histogram) dimuons are shown in fig. 1. The resonances for the well-known vector mesons : J/ψ, ϕ, and ρ/ω are clearly visible in the opposite-sign spectrum, but not in the same-sign dimuons.

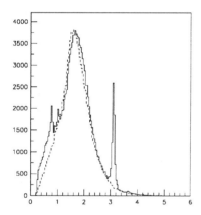

Figure 1. Dimuon mass spectra for same (dotted) and opposite (solid) sign dimuons (E771).

The search region for a $D0$ signal is shown in fig. 2, where no obvious enhancement is seen. The mass spectrum is well-described by a 4th-order polynomial. To arrive at an upper limit for the BR, the spectrum is fitted to a Gaussian function at the $D0$ mass, superimposed on the 4th-order polynomial. The width of the Gaussian is the mass resolution at $D0$, which was determined by interpolating the observed resolutions at ϕ and J/ψ. The fit which allows the maximum number of $D0$s in the data, obtained by increasing the $D0$ signal until the fit reaches 10% probability, is shown as a solid line in fig. 2. Normalizing the upper limit on the $D0$ yield (95.4) to the observed number of J/ψ muon pairs (6258), an upper limit of 1.3×10^{-5} at 90% confidence level (CL) was obtained.

The E771 result is clearly limited by the background arising from double K/π decays. Such muons are expected to originate from the primary interaction point, which can be removed by vertex information. Due to the finite lifetime of $D0$, muons from $D0$ decays are expected to form a secondary vertex downstream of the interaction point, and the muons should have significant(≥ 50 μm) impact parameter. By using tracking information from the vertex detector, these signatures could be incorporated in the analysis, allowing further rejection of the decay background. Analysis along this direction is currently underway.

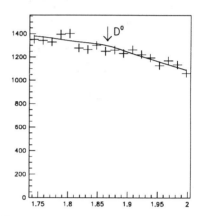

Figure 2. Mass spectrum near the $D0$ region. The solid line is the fit described in the text(E771).

2.2. WA92

WA92 is a fixed-target heavy quark experiment based on the OMEGA spectrometer at CERN. The incident beam is 350 GeV π^-s, derived from the SPS. The heart of the experiment is a vertex detector which consists of 17 planes of 10 μm pitch silicon detectors with analog readout. The analog readout allows the rejection of secondary interactions in the silicon detector. The experiment has collected 2.7×10^9 interactions in 1992 with Cu and W targets. The total number of opposite-sign muon pairs observed in the spectrometer is 125154. The mass spectra for the same- and opposite-sign dimuons are shown in fig. 3. As one can see, the low-mass vector mesons are also clearly visible in the opposite-sign sample. The number of events in the search region (1.78 to 1.92 GeV) is reduced to 143 by applying cuts to the vertex topology based on information from the silicon detector. The 143 events are scanned visually. None of the 143 candidates met the criteria for decay (1). Similar criteria, when applied to Monte Carlo events, recovered about 60 % of the decays. Using an upper limit of 2.3 events for zero candidate (at 90% CL), and normalizing to the J/ψ yield, an upper limit of 1.4×10^{-5} is obtained for the BR.

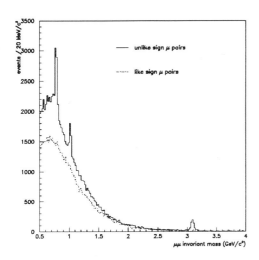

Figure 3. Invariant mass distributions for opposite-sign (solid histogram) and same-sign (dotted histogram) dimuons (WA92).

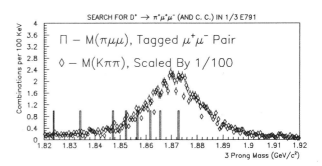

Figure 4. Mass distribution of 3-prong $K\pi\pi$ and $\pi\mu\mu$ events with a detached vertex (E791).

3. $D^{\pm} \to \pi^{+}\pi^{-}\pi^{\pm}$

3.1. E791

A search for the CCNC decay (2) was performed by E791, a fixed-target charm experiment at FNAL. E791 was conducted with an open trigger with huge data throughput. The detector features good vertex detection and particle identification. The search was based on a sample of 9693 3-prong events with a detached vertex. Details of the selection is described elsewhere[12]. The mass distribution for the $K\pi\pi$ events is shown in fig. 4. The D signal in the $K\pi\pi$ channel (open diamonds) is clearly visble. The mass distribution for the $\pi\mu\mu$ events is shown also in fig. 4 as open histogram. Five $\pi\mu\mu$ events satisfied the D selection criteria. These 5 events are consistent with a background source due to the misidentification of two of the three pions in the $D \to \pi\pi\pi$ decay. This background was estimated to be 4.6 events. Using a 90% CL upper limit of 5.4 events for the D signal, an upper limit of 4.3 x 10^{-5} was obtained for the BR. This is an improvement of almost two orders of magnitude over the current limit in the PDG.

4. Summary and Future Prospects

Recent heavy quark fixed-target experiments at the Tevatron and SPS have proved to be prolific sources of hadrons of heavy quarks, especially charm hadrons. The use of vertex information from silicon strip detectors in these experiments provided sensitive searches for charm hadrons decaying to rare final states. Among them are CCNC decays with a muon pair in the final state. These final states are easy to recognize, and are almost free of background from known physics processes. The search for these rare decays provides nontrivial tests of the SM. No evidence for these decays was found at the present level of sensitivity. Preliminary upper limits on BRs of the order of 10^{-5} were obtained by E771, WA92, and E791. Improvements in the limits are expected in the near future.

Acknowledgement

The author thanks G. Mo, A. Nguyen, and G. Penso for discussions of the results from E771, E791, and WA92, respectively. He is indebted to J. Appel, S. Conetti, B. Cox, B. Osculati, L. Rossi, and M. Zeller for useful discussions. K.L. is supported by a grant from the Texas Advanced Research Program.

References

[1] Review of Particle Properties, Particle Data Group, Phys. Rev. D **45**, 1 (1992).

[2] W. C. Louis *et al.*, Phys. Rev. Lett. **56** (1986) 1027.

[3] P. Haas *et al.*, (CLEO Collaboration), Phys. Rev. Lett. **60** (1988) 1614.

[4] S. L. Glashow, J. Iliopoulos, and L. Maiani, Phys. Rev. D2, 1285 (1970).

[5] S. Pakvasa, talk presented at Charm 2000, to be published in the proceedings.

[6] T. Inami and C. S. Lim, Prog. Theor. Phys. 65(1981)297 (E:1772) and references therein.

[7] See, e.g., M. Savage, Phys. Lett. B266, (1991)135.

[8] For a recent review, see J. L. Hewett, talk presented at the *XXI SLAC summer institute*, 1993, Stanford, CA.

[9] K. S. Babu, X-G. He, Xue-Qian Li, and Sandip Pakavasa, Phys. Lett. B205, (1988)540.

[10] T. Alexopoulos *et al.*, (E771 Collaboration), paper submitted to the 27th Int. Conf. on High Energy Physics, Glasgow, Scotland (GLS0422), FERMILAB-Conf-94/170-E and UHIBPD-HEP-94-003, June 1994.

[11] M. Adamovich *et al.*, (WA92 Collaboration), abstract submitted to the 27th Int. Conf. on High Energy Physics, Glasgow, Scotland (GLS0333), June 1994.

[12] A. Nguyen *et al.*, (E791 Collaboration), paper submitted to the 27th Int. Conf. on High Energy Physics, Glasgow, Scotland (GLS0665), June 1994.

A search for the strangeness changing neutral current $K^+ \rightarrow \pi^+\mu^+\mu^-$

John S. Haggerty

Brookhaven National Laboratory,
Upton, New York 11973-5000, USA

On behalf of the Brookhaven E787 Collaboration[1]

Abstract

Preliminary results of a search for the rare decay $K^+ \rightarrow \pi^+\mu^+\mu^-$ using the E787 detector at Brookhaven are presented.

1. Introduction

Experiment 787 at the Brookhaven AGS is designed to be primarily a sensitive search for the strangeness changing neutral current $K^+ \rightarrow \pi^+\nu\bar{\nu}$. This extremely rare decay, expected to occur in the Standard Model with a branching ratio of about 2×10^{-10}, is particularly interesting because it is a second order weak decay which is not subject to large QCD corrections or non-perturbative effects. The current experimental limits on this process from E787 are still more than an order of magnitude away from the Standard Model prediction, but the E787 spectrometer can be used to search for many other rare and radiative decays. This report will discuss the preliminary results of a search for the rare decay $K^+ \rightarrow \pi^+\mu^+\mu^-$.

2. Expectations for $K^+ \rightarrow \pi^+\mu^+\mu^-$

The decay $K^+ \rightarrow \pi^+\mu^+\mu^-$ cannot be calculated in the Standard Model as cleanly as $K^+ \rightarrow \pi^+\nu\bar{\nu}$ because of the long distance effects which result from the coupling of the charged particles to intermediate photons. However, the closely related process $K^+ \rightarrow \pi^+e^+e^-$ has been measured to have a branching ratio of $(2.74 \pm 0.23) \times 10^{-7}$ in another Brookhaven experiment[2] from about 500 observed decays. Chiral Perturbation Theory[3] has been used to calculate both these decays within a single theoretical framework and

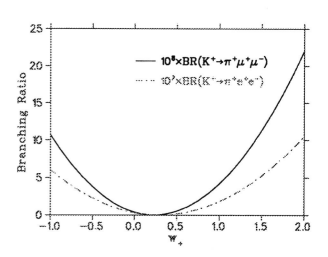

Figure 1. Expected branching ratio of $K^+ \rightarrow \pi^+\mu^+\mu^-$ and $K^+ \rightarrow \pi^+e^+e^-$ as a function of the Chiral Perturbation Theory parameter w_+.

to predict both decays as a function of one undetermined parameter, called w_+. Figure 1 shows the predicted branching ratio as a function of w_+ for these two decays. The measured spectrum of e^+e^- masses from $K^+ \rightarrow \pi^+e^+e^-$ has been used to break the quadratic ambiguity and results in a value of $w_+ = 0.89^{+0.24}_{-0.14}$. This value of w_+ results in a predicted branching ratio for $K^+ \rightarrow \pi^+\mu^+\mu^-$ of $(1.9 - 5.6) \times 10^{-8}$. The previous limit on $K^+ \rightarrow \pi^+\mu^+\mu^-$ was set by E787[4] to be less than 2.3×10^{-7} at the 90% confidence level.

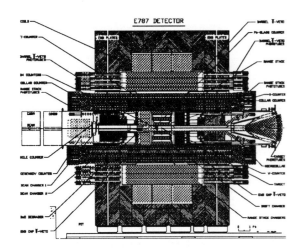

Figure 2. The E787 detector.

3. The E787 Detector

The E787 detector is shown in Figure 2. This detector is designed around an 800 MeV/c stopping K^+ beam with an intensity of about $3 \times 10^5 K^+$ per 3 sec spill. The K^+ beam is tagged by a Čerenkov counter, slowed by a BeO degrader, and stopped in a scintillating fiber target read out by 379 photomultiplier tubes. The target is surrounded by a hexagonal array of scintillation counters referred to as I counters used for triggering and particle identification.

The detector is designed for precision measurements of the range, energy, and momentum of the decay π^+ in $K^+ \to \pi^+ \nu \bar{\nu}$. The momentum of charged particles is measured by the central drift chamber in a 1 T magnetic field. The chamber consists of five superlayers, each of which has six sense wires in a jet cell configuration. The central chamber is surrounded by a range stack, consisting of 21 layers of scintillator read out at both ends, and instrumented with 500 MHz transient digitizers, which can record activity over many microseconds. The inner layers of the range stack are ganged together, so that after an initial 0.6 cm thick trigger layer, there are layers which are 7.6, 5.7, and 3.8 cm thick, followed by 11 1.9 cm thick layers.

The entire detector is surrounded by photon veto calorimeters consisting of layers of lead and scintillator. For π^0 from $K^+ \to \pi^+ \pi^0$ decay, the measured π^0 inefficiency is on the order of 2×10^{-6}.

The trigger for $K^+ \to \pi^+ \mu^+ \mu^-$ requires that there be two or three tracks which penetrate at least to the second layer of the range stack, at least 20 target elements hit, and two or more non-adjacent hit I counters. The trigger constrains $K^+ \to \pi^+ \mu^+ \mu^-$ decays quite strongly, since a particle must have a momentum of at least 60 MeV/c to reach the range stack and the total kinetic energy available to the reaction is only 143 MeV/c². Events are vetoed if they have energy outside

the first few layers of the range stack or in the photon vetoes. About 10% of all $K^+ \to \pi^+ \mu^+ \mu^-$ decays satisfy the trigger requirements.

4. Preliminary Requirements

The philosophy of the analysis is to begin by making a pass through the data making cuts which are consistent with the trigger requirements using calibrated offline data. These requirements use the veto system to reject events with photons, apply simple topological cuts consistent with the trigger, and limit the momentum of any particle to below kinematic limit of $K^+ \to \pi^+ \mu^+ \mu^-$ (172 MeV/c).

Most of the kaon decays which remain as background to $K^+ \to \pi^+ \mu^+ \mu^-$ have one or more $e^{\pm}$ from a π^0 which Dalitz decays or where one of the photons converts. Therefore, after the initial pass through the data, events with $e^{\pm}$ are rejected using particle identification techniques developed for this analysis. Finally, the kinematics of the remaining events are examined, and the mass and missing momentum are reconstructed. Successful candidates will conserve momentum and reconstruct to the kaon mass.

In more detail, events are required to have:

- Two range stack tracks which connect to drift chamber tracks.
- The range stack and drift chamber tracks have the following properties:
  - Measured times in the range stack within ±10 ns to reject accidentals,
  - Small number of range stack counters on each track at decay time, which rejects rejects $e^{\pm}$ which start to shower,
  - Momentum less than 172 MeV (rejects $K^+ \to \pi^+ \pi^0$),
  - Energy in the first four layers of the range stack less than 150 MeV
- Less than 1 MeV photon energy visible outside the first four layers of the range stack, or in the photon vetoes in $\sim 1-3$ ns time window around decay time, and less than 10 MeV photon energy outside the tracks in the range stack.
- Another track in the drift chamber to at least superlayer 3, which requires a momentum of about 30 MeV/c.

In order to bring the full power of the detector to bear on the background, events are required to have both positively charged tracks reaching the range stack. This forces the e^+ in the most serious background ($K^+ \to \pi^+ \pi^- e^+ \nu$) into the range stack, where it can be eliminated using the particle identification techniques described below. Finally, events are required to have one negative and two positive tracks, and the target

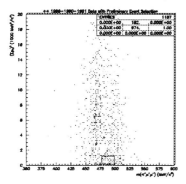

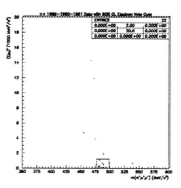

Figure 3. Kinematics of events after requiring that both positive tracks reach the range stack. The horizontal axis is the reconstructed kaon mass, the vertical axis is the magnitude of the vector sum of the transverse momentum.

Figure 4. Kinematics of events after using the likelihood analysis to reject 90% of events with electrons or positrons.

vertex must be within 1.8 cm of the K^+ stop position. The events which remain are shown in Figure 3, where the mass combination with the minimum value of the magnitude of the vector sum of the transverse momentum is chosen.

5. Selection of the Final Sample

Samples of reference data were used to obtain the expected dE/dx and time of flight distributions. Data from the $\pi^+\mu^+\mu^-$ trigger was used so the event topology is similar to the final sample of events. Electrons from π^0 Dalitz or conversions were identified by a high momentum track consistent with $K_{\pi 2}$ with opposite charged tracks having opening angle less than 20°. Pions were identified by their decay $\pi \to \mu$ by the 500 MHz transient digitizers. Electrons and pions that make a complete orbit in the drift chamber were distinguished by time of flight from I counter to I counter.

Using these reference samples, likelihood functions for drift chamber dE/dx, dE/dx in the first layer of the range stack, and time of flight from I counter to the range stack were constructed in momentum bins. I counter dE/dx was also calibrated, though it was not used directly in the likelihood, but was instead used as a check on the contamination of the final sample with $e^\pm$.

The data that was used corresponds to about 2.5×10^{11} stopped kaons taken in 1989, 1990, and 1991. Although the detector had several major upgrades in this period, for the purpose of this analysis the detector was quite stable; the exceptions were additional Level 1 trigger requirements and improved timing in 1990 and 1991, which were taken into account. The final sample of candidate events is shown in Figure 4, where 90% of events with $e^\pm$ were rejected by the likelihood analysis.

A total of 13 events remain in the signal box.

Backgrounds were estimated by use of a full detector Monte Carlo with all kaon decay modes, an estimate from the data itself in nearby kinematic background regions, and an estimate from I counter dE/dx of electron contamination. The most serious background was $K^+ \to \pi^+\pi^-e^+\nu$ (K_{e4}) which trigger and analysis forced to peak in and around the signal region. Estimates agree on a background level of about 2 ± 1 events in the signal box. The decay $K^+ \to \pi^+\pi^+\pi^-$, which could be a serious background, has so little kinetic energy available (75 MeV), that it is suppressed strongly in the trigger and by later kinematic requirements.

Measurement of the acceptance depends on the Monte Carlo of the signal, checked in many ways with data and given an overall check by measurement of the K_{e4} branching ratio in a parallel analysis which resulted in about 500 candidates. The final analysis of the acceptance is still in progress, but the observed branching ratio is estimated to be in the region of 10^{-8}.

References

[1] The E787 collaboration consists of Brookhaven National Laboratory: S. Adler, M.S. Atiya, I-H. Chiang, J.S. Frank, J.S. Haggerty, T.F. Kycia, K.K. Li, L.S. Littenberg, A. Sambamurti, A. Stevens, R.C. Strand and C. Witzig; Los Alamos National Laboratory: W.C. Louis; Princeton University: D.S. Akerib, M. Ardebili, M. Convery, M.M. Ito, D.R. Marlow, R. McPherson, P.D. Meyers, M.A. Selen, F.C. Shoemaker, and A.J.S. Smith; and TRIUMF: E.W. Blackmore, D.A. Bryman, L. Felawka, P. Kitching, A. Konaka, Y. Kuno, J.A. Macdonald, T. Numao, P. Padley, J.-M. Poutissou, R. Poutissou, J. Roy, R. Soluk, and A.S. Turcot.

[2] C. Alliegro *et al., Phys. Rev. Lett.* **68**, 278 (1992).

[3] G. Ecker, A. Pich, and E. de Rafael, *Nucl. Phys.* **B291**, 692 (1987).

[4] M.S. Atiya et al., *Phys. Rev. Lett.* **63**, 2177 (1989); Mats Selen, *Hunting for the Rare Decay* $K^+ \to \pi^+\mu^+\mu^-$, DOE/ER/3072-49, Princeton University thesis (unpublished), (1989).

Paper presented at XXVII Int. Conf. on High Energy Physics: Session Pa-21
Glasgow, UK, 20–27 July 1994

Search for Rare Z Decays at LEP

Sergey Shevchenko

Lauritsen Laboratory
California Institute of Technology
Pasadena, CA 91125, USA

L3 Collaboration

Abstract

We discuss preliminary results of the LEP experiments on rare or forbidden Z decays. The present sensitivity to the branching ratios is about $10^{-5} - 10^{-6}$. Results on searches for lepton flavor violation and decays with photons in the final state are presented here.

1. Introduction

In this note we consider Z decays that are either forbidden or have expected branching ratios that are very small in the framework of the Standard Model [1]. In many models involving new physics such rare decays can be enhanced, and become observable at LEP, when one takes into account new couplings. Therefore, their observation can be interpreted as the manifestation of new physics.

In the following section we review the search for lepton flavor violation and decays with the photons in the final state.

2. Lepton flavor violating decays

In the Standard Model lepton flavor is conserved. However, there is no gauge principle requiring this conservation. Different models, beyond the Standard Model, allow processes which violate lepton flavor conservation. In theories where such violation arises through mixing with new particles [2], the branching ratios for processes, e.g. $Z \to \mu\tau$, have been calculated to be as large as 10^{-4} in certain models. All four LEP experiments have searched [3] for $Z \to e\tau$, $Z \to \mu\tau$. Here, recent L3 results, including 1993 data, are reported.

The expected experimental signature is an electron or a muon with an energy close to the beam energy recoiling against a different type of lepton or hadrons from tau decay. Background arises from Standard Model leptonic final states and can be divided into two classes : (i) incorrectly reconstructed e^+e^- and $\mu^+\mu^-$ events; (ii) $\tau^+\tau^-$ events with one or both of the taus decaying into an electron or a muon which carries almost all the energy of the tau. Good electron and muon energy resolution is essential to reduce the latter background while retaining a high detection efficiency. This is demonstrated in figure 1 from the L3 experiment showing the muon energy for data, background and expected signal, normalised to the beam energy. The limits on the branching ratios were obtained with a maximum likelihood fit. The normalised energy distribution for data was fitted by the sum of the background prediction plus signal contribution and the following bounds at the 95% confidence level were obtained :

$$Br(Z \to e\tau) \; < \; 8.7 \times 10^{-6}$$

$$Br(Z \to \mu\tau) \; < \; 11 \times 10^{-6}$$

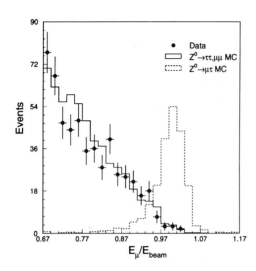

Figure 1. The L3 distribution of the normalised muon energy for the data, background and signal Monte Carlo $Z \to \mu\tau$. The signal normalisation is arbitrary.

3.   Search for Z decays into a photon plus a meson

Within the context of the Standard Model, Z decays to a single photon plus either a single pseudoscalar or a single vector meson are expected to be rare. However, the magnitudes of the branching ratios for such Z decays are theoretically disputed and estimates range over many orders of magnitude, $10^{-4} - 10^{-11}$. Hence, experimental results will aid clarification of this dispute. If observable, such Z decays would yield useful information regarding strong interaction dynamics and quite possibly imply new physics.

Two methods can be used for the above searches : one can look for the charged decay modes of a meson or for the neutral ones. For the first case the experimental signature is the following one : an isolated photon, with an energy close to the beam energy, in one hemisphere of the detector associated with a narrow jet along the opposite direction. For Z decays into pure neutral final states one can look for a possible deviation of the measured $e^+e^- \to \gamma\gamma(\gamma)$ cross section from the QED prediction at Z energies, which can be interpreted as evidence for rare or forbidden Z decays, such as $Z \to \gamma\gamma(\gamma)$, $\gamma\pi^0$, $\gamma\eta$, $\gamma\omega$, all of which have a similar experimental signature since the neutral decay of a high energy meson is not distinguished from the passage of a single photon. This possibility was tested by analyzing the dependence of the total $e^+e^- \to \gamma\gamma(\gamma)$ cross section on the cente-of-mass energy. To obtain the upper limits on such rare decays the cross section was fitted to the sum of the QED prediction plus a Z decay contribution,

decay mode	L3 limit	search mode	DELPHI limit	search mode
$Z \to \gamma\gamma$	5.2		5.5	
$Z \to \gamma\pi^0$	5.2		5.5	
$Z \to \gamma\eta$	4.0	charged	8.0	neutral
$Z \to \gamma\eta'$	1.7	charged		
$Z \to \gamma J/\psi$	1.9	charged		
$Z \to \gamma\omega$			65.	neutral
$Z \to \gamma\gamma\gamma$	0.8		1.7	

Table 1. 95% confidence level upper limits on rare Z decays in units of 10^{-5}.

given by a Breit-Wigner line shape.

The updated L3 (with 1993 statistics) and DELPHI (with 1992 statistics) results are shown in table 1.

4. $Z \to \gamma\gamma\gamma$

In the Standard Model the branching ratio of $Z \to \gamma\gamma\gamma$ is of the order of 10^{-9}. However, if Z is composite it can couple to photons and gluons through its charged and coloured constituents. In some models [5] the decay $Z \to \gamma\gamma\gamma$ can have a branching ratio as high as 10^{-4}. The main background for this search comes from the QED radiative process $e^+e^- \to \gamma\gamma\gamma$. Figure 2 shows the distribution of the least energetic photon for data, signal and QED background (the 10 GeV cut was applied) from the L3 experiment. The obtained 95% confidence level limit is

$$Br(Z \to \gamma\gamma\gamma) \; < \; 8.1 \times 10^{-6}$$

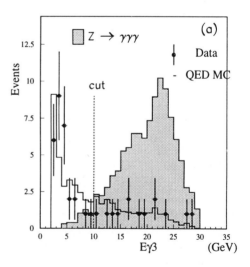

Figure 2. Energy of the least energetic photon for data, QED background and composite signal $Z \to \gamma\gamma\gamma$. The signal normalisation is arbitrary.

The $\gamma\gamma\gamma$ final state can be also used for the search for anomalous production of high mass photon pairs in $e^+e^- \rightarrow \gamma\gamma\gamma$ events. This search is motivated by the L3 collaboration's observation of four events of the type $e^+e^- \rightarrow \ell^+\ell^-\gamma\gamma$ with an invariant mass of the two photons clustering around 60 GeV [6]. If a new resonance X were produced in assosiation with a virtual photon, which could explain the $\ell^+\ell^-$ in the $e^+e^- \rightarrow \ell^+\ell^-\gamma\gamma$ events of L3 collaboration and the absence of $\nu\nu\gamma\gamma$ events, then it may also be produced in association with a real photon leading to a final state with three photons. The main background to this search is the QED process $e^+e^- \rightarrow \gamma\gamma\gamma$. The L3 collaboration has updated the results on this search with 1993 statistics (totall 65 pb^{-1}). The results are presented in figure 3. No significant structure was observed in the distribution of invariant mass of the two photons. The probability of the four events, shown in the upper left corner, to originate from QED process is about 4%.

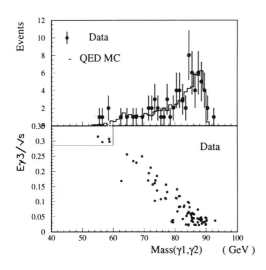

Figure 3. Upper picture : the distribution of invariant mass of the two photons for data and QED background. Down picture : The distribution of invariant mass of the two photons versus the energy of the least energetic photon for data.

Large couplings of magnetic monopoles to Z's and γ's were predicted in [7]. Therefore, one can search for virtual-monopole effects in the $\gamma\gamma\gamma$ final state. The characteristic features of the photons produced through the monopole loop are the following : (i) all 3 photons are energetic; (ii) they are not peaked in the forward region, as in the case of QED process. Using the theoretical predictions [7], the L3 95% confidence level upper limit

$$Br(Z \rightarrow \gamma\gamma\gamma) \ < \ 8.1 \times 10^{-6}$$

can be translated into the mass limit of magnetic monopole

Mass of magnetic monopole $> 0.51\ Tev$

Acknowledgement

I am indebted to T. Coan, H. Jannsen, V. Shoutko and J. Ulbricht for providing me with preliminary data.

References

[1] S. Weinberg, Phys. Rev. Lett. **19** (1967) 1264;
S.L. Glashow, J. Iliopoulos and L. Maiani, Phys. Rev. **D2** (1970) 1285.

[2] T.K. Kuo and N. Nakagawa, Phys. Rev. **D32** (1985) 306;
G. Eilam and T.G. Rizzo, Phys. Lett. **B188** (1987) 91.

[3] ALEPH Collaboration: D. Decamp *et al.*, Phys. Rep. **216** (1992) 253;
DELPHI Collaboration: P. Abreu *et al.*, Phys. Lett. **B298** (1992) 247;
L3 Collaboration: O. Adriani *et al.*, Phys. Lett. **B316** (1993) 427;
OPAL Collaboration: M.Z. Akrawy *at al.*, Phys. Lett. **B254** (1991) 293.

[4] B. Guberina *et al.*, Nucl. Phys. **B174** (1980) 317;
L. Arnellos *et al.*, Nucl. Phys. **B196** (1982) 378;
N.N Achasov, Novosibirsk preprint : T.Ph. No. 2 (194) 1992;
M. Jacob and T.T. Wu, Phys. Lett. **B232** (1989) 529;
D. Chatterjee and S. Ghosh, Mod. Phys. Lett. **A5** (1989) 1493;
G. West, Mod. Phys. Lett. **A5** (1990) 2281;
D. Chatterjee and S. Ghash, Z. Phys. **C50** (1991) 103;
C.H. Chang it et al., Beijing preprint : AS-ITP-88-049.

[5] F. Boudjema and F.M. Renard, Z Physics at LEP, CERN 89-08, Vol. 2, 1989, 185.

[6] L3 Collaboration: O. Adriani *et al.* Phys. Lett. **B295** (1992) 337.

[7] A. De Rujula, CERN preprint : CERN-TH.7273/94.

Searches for lepton flavour violating processes

Ch. Findeisen[||]

Physics department, University of Zurich, Switzerland

Representing SINDRUM II

Abstract

The two experiments MEGA and SINDRUM II are searching for lepton flavor violating processes of the muon. MEGA looks for the decay $\mu^+ \rightarrow e^+\gamma$ and SINDRUM II for the coherent $\mu^- - e^-$ conversion in the presence of a nucleus. The SINDRUM II search yields a preliminary limit of $B(\mu^- - e^-) < 1.0 \cdot 10^{-12}$ (90% CL) on titanium. The status and prospects of both experiments are discussed.

1. Introduction

In the framework of the standard model (SM) the leptons are arranged in three families. So far lepton flavor ¶ changing processes are not observed and this fact is put into the SM "by hand". Any observation of a leptonic flavor changing process points at physics beyond the SM.

There are many models predicting such lepton flavor changing processes. Figure 1 gives an example with additional neutral Higgs bosons. A recent review on forbidden muon decays can be found in [1].

The search for lepton flavor changing processes is probing masses of the exchanged particles in the TeV region (table 1). Which process is the most sensitive is model dependent. Limits on the branching ratio B translate into limits on the mass m_x of the exchanged particle through

$$B \propto \frac{1}{m_x^4}. \tag{1}$$

2. The Experiments MEGA and SINDRUM II

The MEGA and SINDRUM II experiments are located at the meson factories LAMPF (Los Alamos) and PSI (Switzerland), respectively.

|| E-mail: findeisen@cvax.psi.ch
¶ in the literature also known as lepton family

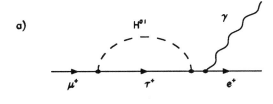

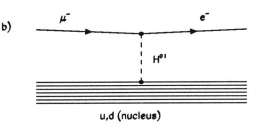

Figure 1. Additional neutral Higgs bosons H^{0I} permitting lepton flavor changing processes: (a) $\mu^+ \rightarrow e^+\gamma$; (b) coherent $\mu^- - e^-$ conversion in the presence of a nucleus (Z,A).

MEGA [7] searches for the decay $\mu^+ \rightarrow e^+\gamma$ at rest. The experimental signature is one e^+ and one γ (52.8 MeV each), which are back-to-back, in time coincidence ($\Delta t = 0$ ns), and originate from a common vertex in the target. The μ^+ are stopped in a thin CH_2 target in the centre of the MEGA spectrometer (Figure 2).

Process	B(90% CL)	Horizontal gauge boson [5] M_X TeV	Higgs scalar [6] M_X TeV
$\mu^+ \to e^+\gamma$	$< 4.9 \cdot 10^{-11}$[2]	> 15	> 0.3
$\mu^+ \to e^+e^+e^-$	$< 1.0 \cdot 10^{-12}$[3]	> 82	> 2
$\mu^- Ti \to$ $e^- Ti^{g.s.}$	$< 4.3 \cdot 10^{-11}$[4]	> 203	> 24

Table 1. The rescaled lower limits of the mass m_x of the exchanged particles as predicted by two models (cf. eq. 1).

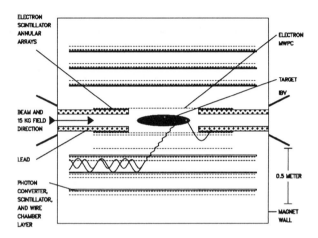

Figure 2. View of the MEGA detector with a simulated $\mu^+ \to e^+\gamma$ event superimposed. The magnetic field of 1.5 T is parallel to the detector axis.

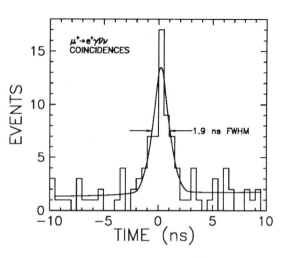

Figure 3. Preliminary MEGA result: the e^+ - γ time difference spectrum. The peak at $\Delta t = 0$ ns is due to radiative muon decays ($\mu^+ \to e^+\gamma\bar{\nu}\nu$).

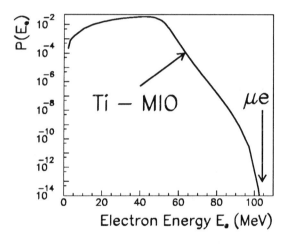

Figure 4. The theoretical electron energy spectrum from muon decay in orbit (Ti - MIO, from [12]). The μe conversion signal is situated at the kinematical endpoint. The detector accepts only electrons with $E_e > 70$ MeV.

The e^+ trajectory is measured with low mass MWPCs [8] and the time of arrival with segmented plastic scintillator hodoscope rings located at both ends. The γ energy, direction and time are measured with a set of three concentric pair spectrometers [9] with an expected total efficiency of 6%. These detectors consist of lead converters, scintillator hodoscopes and wire chambers. The trigger selects γ's with large transverse energy. The main background source is a random coincidence between e^+ and γ. The design resolutions are 0.7% for E_e, 3.2% for E_γ and 0.8 ns for Δt (FWHM). An example of the detector response is shown in Figure 3.

SINDRUM II [10] searches for the coherent conversion in the presence of a titanium nucleus: $\mu^- Ti \to e^- Ti^{g.s.}$. The signature is a monoenergetic electron with $E_{e^-} \approx 104.3$ MeV. The muonic Ti - atoms have a lifetime of 329 ns. Decays proceed via muon decay in orbit MIO ($e^- \bar{\nu}_e \nu_\mu Ti$, 15%) and nuclear capture ($\nu_\mu Sc^*$, 85%). The electron energy spectrum

of MIO extends up to the kinematical endpoint of 104.3 MeV (Figure 4). The background from MIO is less than 10^{-14} for a detector energy resolution below 2 MeV (FWHM).

The SINDRUM II detector consists of the following concentric components (Figure 5): a Ti target in the center, a plastic scintillator barrel hodoscope for triggering and timing information † , two radially projecting drift chambers [11] for the 3-dim reconstruction of the particle trajectories and Čerenkov rings at both ends

---

† An additional plastic scintillator barrel hodoscope (not shown in Figure 5) just around the target is also used for triggering and timing information.

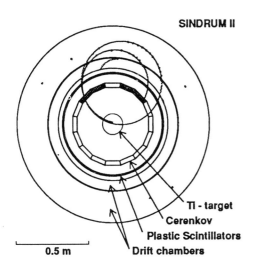

Figure 5. Front view of the SINDRUM II detector. A measured electron trajectory is superimposed. The magnetic field of 1.2 T is parallel to the detector axis.

of the detector for triggering. The momentum resolution at the kinematical endpoint of 2.1 MeV (FWHM) is dominated by the energy loss in the target.

3. Status and Outlook

Presently, both experiments are analyzing data taken in 1993. SINDRUM II observes no candidate for $\mu^- \, Ti \to e^- \, Ti^{g.s.}$ (Figure 6) and gives a preliminary upper limit for the branching ratio:

$$B(\mu^- - e^-) \; < 1.0 \cdot 10^{-12} \; (90\% \, CL, preliminary) \quad (2)$$

which is a factor 4 below the present upper limit [4].

The search sensitivities (90% CL) for both experiments are summarized in table 2.

Acknowledgments

I like to thank Richard E. Mischke (MEGA collaboration) for his help in preparing the talk and this report.

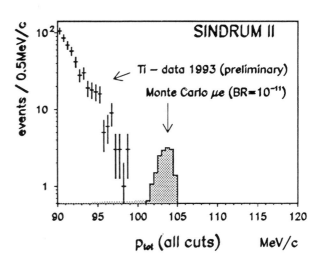

Figure 6. Measured electron momentum spectrum for the data taken in 1993. A Monte Carlo simulation of the $\mu - e$ signal is superimposed with an assumed branching ratio of B = 10^{-11}.

Process	Experiment	sensitivity (90% CL)
$\mu^+ \to e^+ \gamma$	MEGA 1993 data MEGA 1994+95 data	$3.3 \cdot 10^{-12}$ $7 \cdot 10^{-13}$
$\mu^- Ti \to$ $e^- Ti^{g.s.}$	SINDRUM II + new beamline (πE5) and new pion-muon converter [13] starting in 1995	$2 \cdot 10^{-14}$

Table 2. Extected sensitivities (90% CL) of MEGA and SINDRUM II.

References

[1] A. van der Schaaf, in Prog. Part. Nucl. Phys. **31** p.1; Ed. A. Faessler (Pergamon, 1993)
[2] R.D. Bolton *et al.*, Phys. Rev. **D38** (1988) 2077
[3] U. Bellgardt *et al.*, Nucl. Phys. **B299** (1988) 1
[4] C. Dohmen *et al.*, Phys. Lett. **B317** (1993) 631
[5] R.N. Cahn and H. Harari, Nucl. Phys. **B176** (1980) 135
[6] O.Shanker, Phys. Rev. **D20** (1979) 1608
[7] M. Cooper *et al.*, LAMPF Proposal No. 969 (1985)
[8] V. Armijo *et al.*, Nucl. Inst. Meth. **A303** (1991) 293
[9] M. Barakat *et al.*, Nucl. Inst. Meth. (to be published)
[10] A. Badertscher *et al.*, SIN Proposal No. R 87-03.1 (1986)
[11] M. Grossmann-Handschin *et al.*, Nucl. Inst. Meth. **A327** (1993) 378
[12] M. Grossmann-Handschin, PhD thesis, University of Zurich, 1991, unpublished.
[13] C. Niebuhr *et al.*, SINDRUM II Note 16 (1993), unpublished.

Parallel Session Pa-22

New Detectors and their Physics Aims

Conveners: A. Astbury (University of Victoria)
M. Breidenbach (SLAC)

Scientific secretaries: M. Stavrianakou
S. Gowdy (reserve)

Paper presented at XXVII Int. Conf. on High Energy Physics: Session Pa-22
Glasgow, UK, 20–27 July 1994

HERA-B: An experiment to study CP violation in decays of B-mesons using an internal target at the HERA proton ring

W. Hofmann

Max-Planck-Institut für Kernphysik, Heidelberg

for the HERA-B collaboration

Abstract

HERA-B is a fixed-target experiment using a halo target in the HERA proton ring to generate B mesons in 820 GeV proton-nucleus interactions. The experiment is aimed primarily at the detection of CP violation in B decays. After a conditional approval, full approval is expected for early 1995, and the detector should start data taking in 1998. In this paper, the HERA-B detector and its physics reach is reviewed.

One of the fundamental features of the standard model is the violation of CP symmetry, as observed in the kaon system. Neutral B mesons provide one of the few other systems in nature where CP violation might be observable, allowing stringent tests of the consistency of the standard model description of the mechanisms of CP violation. Basic goal of the HERA-B experiment is the detection of CP violation in the "gold plated" $B^o \to J/\psi K_s$ decay mode, using a dedicated detector triggered on lepton pairs from J/ψ decays. The B mesons are generated in hadronic interactions of protons stored in the HERA storage ring with an internal target. Emphasis is on the $J/\psi K_s$ decay mode as a) this mode ist best accessible experimentally, and b) it provides a very clean and model-independent test of standard model predictions. The CP asymmetry

$$A = \frac{\Gamma(B^o \to J/\psi K_s) - \Gamma(\overline{B}^o \to J/\psi K_s)}{\Gamma(B^o \to J/\psi K_s) + \Gamma(\overline{B}^o \to J/\psi K_s)} = \sin 2\beta \sin xt$$

is generated by the interference between the direct decay of a B^o and its decay through mixing, and depends only on CKM matrix elements and on the strength $x \approx 0.7$ of $B^o - \overline{B}^o$ mixing.

The HERA-B experiment [1, 2] was presented first in 1992 in its letter of intent, followed by a progress report in 1993 and the proposal in 1994. The experiment has received a conditional approval, with the final approval depending on the availablitity of sufficient resources and funding.

HERA-B will be located in the West Hall of the HERA storage ring. The experiment relies on an internal halo target - 8 thin wires positioned in the halo of the stored proton beam - to provide hadronic interactions, without significantly disturbing the ep luminosity operation of the machine. The wire target provides production vertices which are well localized in two dimensions; at the same time, multiple interactions can take place during one bunch crossing, with the event vertices well separated in the remaining dimension (along the wires). The operation of the target has been demonstrated in a series of test measurements over two years, and is described in a contribution to these proceedings [3].

In interactions of protons with target nuclei, b particles are produced together with other fast tracks and a number of low-energy nuclear fragments. At a beam energies of 820 GeV, a B meson will have a median momentum of about 120 GeV, and a flight path of about 7 mm. For decays into $J/\psi K_s$, with $J/\psi \to e^+e^-, \mu^+\mu^-$, the leptons have a median momentum around 25 GeV, and typical transverse

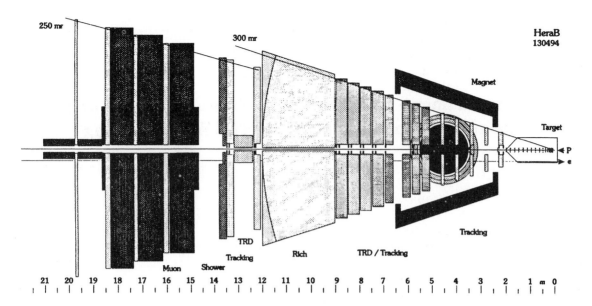

Figure 1. The HERA-*B* detector (top view)

momenta around 1.5 GeV. The high-*p*, high-$p_\perp$ leptons as well as the separated *B* decay vertex provide a clean signature of the events, which is exploited in the trigger. As the CP-asymmetry *A* is modulated with a term $\sin xt$, events where the *B* meson decays after less than one mean lifetime do not contribute significantly to the CP violation measurement. Therefore, rather stringent cuts on vertex separation can be used without increasing the statistical error in the measurement of $\sin 2\beta$.

Since the decay mode $B^o \to J/\psi K_s$ leads to a CP eigenstate, one cannot tell from the final state whether one is observing a B^o or $\overline{B}^o$ decay. For the measurement of a CP asymmetry, the initial flavor of the decaying *B* has to be tagged by other means. For the proposed experiment, we studied tagging based on either the charge of leptons from the semileptonic decay of the second *B* in the event, or on the charge of kaons from the decay of this second *B*, or on the sum of charges of secondary-vertex tracks.

The actually observed (time-integrated) CP asymmetry is smaller than $\sin 2\beta$: $a_{obs} = D_{Tag} D_{CP} \sin 2\beta$. The dilution factor $D_{Tag} \approx 0.4$ accounts for imperfect flavor tagging, sometimes also caused by mixing of the tagging *B*; $D_{CP} \approx 0.6$ describes the averaging over the time-dependent asymmetry, and the influence of the vertex cut. The statistical error in the determination of the CP asymmetry $\sin 2\beta$ is then given by $\Delta \sin 2\beta \approx 1/D_{Tag} D_{CP} \sqrt{N}$, where *N* is the number of tagged events.

To achieve a statistical error $\Delta \sin 2\beta \approx 0.1$ (compared with expected values ranging from 0.3 to 0.9), one needs roughly 1000 events. To relate this number of tagged *B* decays to the total number of

interactions required, we need to account for the ratio of the $b\bar{b}$ cross section to the total cross section ($\approx 5 \cdot 10^{-7}$ for a nuclear target), for the probability to generate a B^o or $\overline{B}^o$ in a $b\bar{b}$ event (≈ 0.8), for the B^o branching ratio to $J/\psi K_s$ ($\approx 5 \cdot 10^{-5}$), for the leptonic J/ψ branching ratio (≈ 0.12) and for the $K_s \to \pi^+\pi^-$ branching ratio (0.69), resulting in roughly 10^{-11} decays per interaction. Trigger, reconstruction, and tagging efficiencies reduce the rate by about another order of magnitude. Alltogether, we find that the search for CP violation requires about 10^{15} interactions, achievable, e.g., by running the experiment for 3 years at interaction rates of 30 MHz. The natural rate of proton diffusion into the beam halo in HERA will be about a factor 2 higher (for 100 h beam lifetime), hence a sufficient number of protons is available for interaction with the wire target. Given that the bunch crossing rate at HERA is only 10 MHz, a 30 MHz rate implies that the detector has to be able to handle and sort out multiple events in each bunch crossing.

The requirements on the detector can be summarized as follows:

- Reconstruction of multiple events with as many as 100 tracks per bunch crossing at 10 MHz bunch crossing rate with high efficiency
- Reconstruction of *B* decay vertices
- Identification of leptons and charged kaons
- Fast and highly selective trigger on J/ψ
- Radiation-hard detector elements.

The design of the detector is shown in Fig. 1. With an aperture of 300 mrad in the bending view and 160 mrad in the non-bending view, the detector covers about 90%

of the solid angle in the center-of-mass of the reaction, providing high detection efficiencies for multi-body B decays. A 2 m long vertex detector system is followed by the analysis magnet, tracking chambers inside and after the magnet, an imaging Cerenkov counter for kaon identification, chambers for tracking and triggering, a small TRD to assist lepton identification in the very forward region, the electromagnetic calorimeter and the muon system. Note that the HERA electron ring has to go through the detector near the pole face of the magnet, about 90 cm below the proton beam.

The high density of tracks places serious restrictions on the choice of detectors; requirements there are similar to those at LHC. As a result, many detector concepts are "borrowed" from LHC R&D, including e.g. the radiation-hard silicon detectors of the vertex detection system, the microstrip gaseous counters of the inner tracking system, the honeycomb and/or straw chambers of the outer tracker and the TRD, and the "shashlik" calorimeter. Also readout electronics and DAQ system profit from LHC R&D, as evidenced in the VLSI front-end electronics with its data pipelines, the general DAQ architecture, the multi-level triggering scheme and the fast data links connecting DAQ and trigger components. For quite a few of the LHC R&D projects, HERA-B will provide a first real field-test.

Already early in the process of detector design, fully functional pattern recognition and track fitting packages were developed and were used to provide feedback concerning the detector layout and in particular concerning the number, segmentation and granularity of the tracker planes. At the present stage, the four decay products of a $B^o \to J/\psi K_s \to \mu^+\mu^-\pi^+\pi^-$ decay are reconstructed in the main tracking system with 90% efficiency (not including the purely geometrical efficiency). The lepton pair and its decay vertex is reconstructed in the vertex detector with 98% probability, and the K_s decay vertex is found for 97% of all K_s. Prototyping of many detector components has started; particularly noteworthy is a RICH design using TMAE-based proportional wire cells to detect photons, which proved to be quite stable and reliable.

The expected performance of the experiment is summarized in Fig. 2, which shows the CP triangle in its presently preferred geometry, together with the 1-σ and 2-σ confidence regions for the position (ρ, η) of the tip of the triangle [4]. Shaded are the regions where HERA-B would provide a 4-σ detection of CP violation after one, two, and four years of running. Almost the entire 1-σ range of the tip is covered after two years. The ranges given in Fig. 2 assume a $b\bar{b}$ cross section of 12 nb, based on QCD calculations [5]. Recent experimental data [6] suggest a somewhat lower cross section, which might require a doubling of the running time to four years in order to cover the parameter space presently allowed by

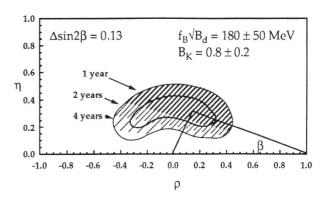

Figure 2. Unitarity triangle in the (ρ, η) plane, showing the uncertainty in the position of the tip [4] and the regions covered by the experiment after 1, 2, and 4 years of running.

the standard model.

Apart from CP violation, a wide range of topics in B physics and beyond are accessible to the experiment. The trigger decisions are based on lepton tracks reconstructed in the first trigger level and — besides the basic J/ψ trigger — include a dilepton trigger, where the mass cut is replaced by $p_\perp$ cuts on the individual leptons, a single-lepton trigger and possibly a di-hadron trigger. A B decay to $J/\psi X$ will be triggered with about 50% probability, an event where both B decay semileptonically with 30%, and single semileptonic decays with about 4%, resulting in samples of about 20k fully reconstructed B decays per year and several millions of inclusive semileptonic B decays and also of charm decays.

In June 1994, the experiment has been given conditional approval by DESY. A final decision is anticipated for early 1995. Already in the 1995/96 HERA shutdown, we hope to install the spectrometer magnet and first detector prototypes in the West Hall of HERA. Completion of the detector system should occur in 1997/98, with the commissioning and running in of the detector during 1998.

References

[1] H. Albrecht et al., "An Experiment to Study CP Violation in the B System Using an Internal Target at the HERA Proton Ring", Letter of Intent, DESY-PRC 92/04 (1992); Progress Report, DESY-PRC 93/04 (1993); Proposal, DESY-PRC 94/02 (1992).
[2] W. Hofmann, Nucl. Instr. Meth. **A 333** (1993) 153.
[3] K. Ehret, these proceedings.
[4] A. Ali, **CERN-TH-7123/93** (1993).
[5] P. Nason, S. Dawson and R.K. Ellis, Nucl. Phys. **B303** (1988) 607, **B327** (1989) 49, **B335** (1990) 260.
[6] M. Schub, Talk at the 28th Rencontre de Moriond, Les Arcs (1994).

Paper presented at XXVII Int. Conf. on High Energy Physics: Session Pa-22
Glasgow, UK, 20–27 July 1994

Progress report on the NA48 CP violation experiment at CERN

Pascal Debu

CEA, DSM/DAPNIA, CE-Saclay, F-91191 Gif-sur-Yvette Cedex, France

Abstract

After recalling the physics aim of the NA48 experiment, the principle of the measurement is briefly explained. The experimental setup is described ; it is followed by a status report on the beams operation, the tagging sytem, the electromagnetic calorimeter and the spectrometer. The schedule for running the experiment is given.

1. Introduction

The main aim of the NA48 experiment at CERN is to measure the direct CP violation parameter ϵ'/ϵ with a precision better than $2\ 10^{-4}$ [1]. This quantity is related to the ratio of the CP violating amplitudes $A(K_L \to \pi\pi)$ to the CP conserving ones $A(K_S \to \pi\pi)$:

$$\frac{A(K_L \to \pi^+\pi^-)}{A(K_S \to \pi^+\pi^-)} \equiv \eta^{+-} \simeq \epsilon + \epsilon' \qquad (1)$$

$$\frac{A(K_L \to \pi^0\pi^0)}{A(K_S \to \pi^0\pi^0)} \equiv \eta^{00} \simeq \epsilon - 2\epsilon' \qquad (2)$$

The two most precise measurements of ϵ'/ϵ are $(7.4 \pm 5.2 \pm 2.9)10^{-4}$ [2] from E731 at FNAL and $(2.3 \pm .65)10^{-3}$ [3] from NA31 at CERN. They are not in good agreement. It is desirable to clarify the experimental situation in view of trying to establish direct CP violation with better significance.

2. Principle of the measurement

The measurement of the ratio R of the rates of K_L and K_S decays to two charged and two neutral pions gives access to ϵ'/ϵ :

$$R = \frac{\Gamma(K_L \to \pi^0\pi^0)}{\Gamma(K_S \to \pi^0\pi^0)} \bigg/ \frac{\Gamma(K_L \to \pi^+\pi^-)}{\Gamma(K_S \to \pi^+\pi^-)} \simeq 1 - 6Re(\epsilon'/\epsilon) \qquad (3)$$

NA48 aims at measuring R with a precision of $1\ 10^{-3}$. In order to minimize the systematic uncertainties, the following strategy has been adopted :

- the four decay modes $K_{L,S} \to \pi^+\pi^-, \pi^0\pi^0$ are measured concurrently. This reduces the sensitivity of the measurement to time variations of the detector efficiencies and to losses of good events due to accidental activity in the detector.

- two nearly collinear K_L and K_S beams converging at the detector position are produced. Also, the decay fiducial region is the same for all modes. In this way, corrections for acceptance and detector resolution are very small. To further reduce them, K_L events are weighted with a factor $\exp(z/\Lambda_L - z/\Lambda_S)$ where z is the vertex position along the beam direction and $\Lambda_{S,L}$ are the decay lengths of the $K_{L,S}$.

- the assignment of an event to the K_S beam relies upon tagging the protons diverted towards the K_S target : an event is called K_S decay if the time of its detection is in a window of 5 ns around the proton detection time after correction for the time of flight.

In order to achieve the desired precision for the measurement of R, not only a high statistics is needed (about $3\ 10^6$ $K_L \to \pi^0\pi^0$ decays should be detected), but also a high resolution detector is essential to reduce background levels to a few 10^{-3} in both charged and neutral decays of the K_L.

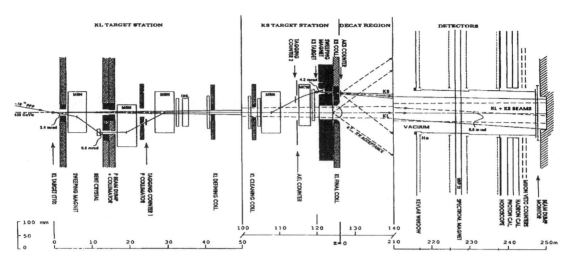

Figure 1. NA48 experimental setup

3.   Experimental setup and beams operation

The layout of the experimental setup is shown in fig. 1.

The 450 GeV/c proton beam of the CERN SPS impinges on a beryllium target at 2.4 mrad angle to produce the K_L beam. Most of the protons are then dumped but a small fraction (about $2\ 10^{-5}$) is used to produce K_S with a target located 120 m downstream. These protons are diverted by channelling through a silicon bent crystal. On their way, they encounter the proton tagging detector described in the following section. The extracted fraction of the beam is chosen so that the K_S over K_L detected decay ratio is close to 3.

Beams have been operated to about one third of the nominal intensity (1.5 10^{12} protons per pulse) to allow fast access to the experimental area during the tests. The particle fluxes measured appear to be close to what is expected from extrapolations of NA31 operation and detailed simulations of the beam transport.

The second part of the experimental setup is the decay region starting about 2 m downstream of the K_S target, after the K_S anticounter system. This element allows the definition of the K_S decay region with very high geometrical precision. It is followed by a 100 m evacuated zone : a large vacuum tube instrumented with anticounter rings to detect escaping γ rays from $3\pi^0$ K_L decays. A kevlar window ends the large vacuum tube.

A helium tank made of stainless steel follows, which encloses the charged particle spectrometer. It is closed by an aluminium window. Further downstream are two hodoscopes planes for triggering on charged decays, the liquid krypton electromagnetic calorimeter, the hadron calorimeter and the muon veto system, a set of three hodoscopes planes separated by iron walls. A vacuum pipe of about 10 cm radius goes through all the detector elements to let the neutral beam through.

4.   The proton tagging detector

The tagging system allows a precise measurement of the arrival time of protons producing the K_S beam. It is an essential part of the apparatus since the assignment of an event as K_S decay relies upon the delayed coincidence of its detection with that of a proton in the tagging system. A thorough description of the system and the results obtained during the 1993 test period have been published elsewhere [4]. We make a brief summary here.

Two rows, one horizontal, one vertical, of 12 small scintillator pieces are precisely fixed on a carbon fiber structure so that each counter intercepts about one tenth of the beam. A slight overlap of a few μm ensures a fully efficient detection. The counters are instrumented with photomultipliers. More than 400 photoelectrons are produced when a proton goes through a counter. During the test, the signals were digitized by 6 bit 450 MHz FADC's. By tilting the whole set to align two counters with the beam, one could measure the time resolution to be better than 110 ps per counter. In addition, the double pulse separation is below three sampling units. This indicates that the dead time of the proton detection will be of the order or less than about .5 % with the 1 GHz sampling rate that is planned for the final setup. This in turn translates into a .5 % probability to misidentify a K_S decay as a K_L decay, but since it is independant of the decay mode, this only results in a dilution of ϵ'/ϵ. Moreover, it can be measured with charged decays for which the beam origin of the decaying kaon can be assigned with no ambiguity.

5.   The electromagnetic calorimeter

The requirements for the electromagnetic calorimeter of NA48 are an excellent energy resolution (close to 1 %

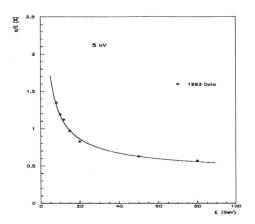

Figure 2. Energy resolution of the calorimeter prototype.

at 10 GeV), a good position resolution (1 mm) and a high granularity to allow a powerful rejection of 3 π^0 K_L decays. In addition, the readout has to be fast because of the high rate of particles illuminating the detector. The time resolution should be below 1 ns to allow the identification of K_S decays with the tagging system. The design properties can be summarized as follows.

It is a quasi-homogeneous liquid krypton calorimeter with 2×2 cm^2 tower structure, 2.4 m diameter acceptance and 1.25 m (or 27 radiation lengths) active length. It contains about 23 t of krypton. The 13000 cells are readout with cold preamplifiers. Signals are shaped to have a short rise time (about 40 ns) and last about 160 ns. One cell consists in 3 thin (40 μm) Cu-Be ribbons 1.8 cm wide and separated by 1 cm.The central ribbon is set to high positive voltage. Electrons from electromagnetic showers drift towards this ribbon.

In order to ensure a 100 μm precision positioning of the ribbons, those are pulled through five stesalit spacers with accurately machined slots. A 47 mrad zig-zag angle from one spacer to the next is imposed to soften the non-uniformity of the response of the calorimeter as a function of the impact position of the incoming particle across the cell.

A prototype of 184 cells has been built and tested in autumn 1993. A detailed description of the experimental setup will appear in a forthcoming publication. Preliminary results obtained with electrons are shown in figure 2. The relative energy resolution is well described by the formula :

$$\sigma/E = 3.5\%/\sqrt{E} \oplus .42\% \oplus .04/E (GeV) \qquad (4)$$

The transverse position resolution is 1 mm at 25 GeV.

To conclude, the prototype has shown performances of the required quality to proceed with the construction of the full size calorimeter.

6. The spectrometer

The charged particle spectrometer consists in a 2.45 $\times$ 2.4 m^2 aperture dipole magnet and a set of 4 drift chambers.

The maximal magnetic field is 3.7 kG and the transverse momentum kick is about 250 MeV/c. The field map has been measured by using a set of 12 Hall probes mounted on a moving arm. In total, the three components of the field have been measured at 50000 different points in a $2.4 \times 2.4 \times 16$ m^3 volume.

Each drift chamber has four views to measure coordinates of the charged particles with redundancy. Each view consists in two staggered sets of three wire planes : one sense wire plane at 1 cm spacing plus two potential wire planes 3 mm away on each side. Sense wires have 20 μm diameter and are made of golden plated Re-W and connected to ground through the preamplifiers. Potential wires are 120 μm Ti-Cu wires at about -2400 V.

The geometrical acceptance of the chambers is a 2.4 m wide octagon, and the total number of equipped channels is about 7000. Chambers have a hole to insert the vacuum tube.

Two small prototype chambers (16×16 cm^2) with 2 views each have been operated with Argon-Isobutane 70-30. The resolution is about 70 μm per view. This matches the desired precision.

7. Schedule

Many elements of the apparatus - anticounter rings, charged hodoscopes, muon veto counters, hadron calorimeter - are now being tested with beam. In addition, the performances obtained with the beams, the tagging system, the prototype chambers and the prototype calorimeter are at the required level of quality.

The drift chambers are being constructed. Three of them should be in opration in summer 1995. The fourth chamber should be installed at the end of 1995.

The construction of the large liquid krypton calorimeter has been launched early this year. It should be calibrated in autumn 1996.

The data taking for the ϵ'/ϵ measurement should start end of 1996.

References

[1] G.D. Barr *et al.*, CERN/SPSC/90-22/P253.
[2] L.K. Gibbons *et al.*, Phys. Rev. Lett. **70** (1993) 1203.
[3] G.D. Barr *et al.*, Phys. Lett. **B317** (1993) 233.
[4] P. Grafström *et al.*, Nucl. Instr. and Meth. **A344** (1994) 487.

Superconducting Toroidal Spectrometer for Precision Studies of Muon Deep Inelastic Scattering at CERN and Serpukhov UNK

A A Feschenko, V G Krivokhizhin, L A Merkulov, <u>I A Savin</u>[†]
Yu A Shishov, G I Smirnov, Z U Usubov

Joint Institute for Nuclear Research,
Dubna, 141980, Russia

Abstract

Construction of the muon beam and specialized experimental facility at Serpukhov UNK – a Superconducting Toroidal Spectrometer (STORS) – will provide good opportunities to continue the Deep Inelastic Scattering (DIS) studies in the energy region 100-400 Gev. Beam characteristics, properties of STORS and DIS programme are reviewed.

1. Introduction

As it is well known, the structure of nucleons, free or bound in nucleus, or the structure of the whole nucleus, is probed [1] in inclusive Deep Inelastic Scattering (DIS).

Major discoveries on the quark structure of nucleons at the distances up to $10^{-15} - 10^{-16} cm$ have been made in few generations of the electron, muon and neutrino experiments on DIS at SLAC, FNAL and CERN. Further investigations of the matter structure at the frontier distances require extention of the kinematical regions in x and Q^2 and improvement of the apparatus. These are the subjects of the new proposal [2].

2. Layout of the experiment

2.1. Muon beams

Presently, there are two muon beams which partially meet the requirements of this experiment. They are located at CERN and Fermilab. The experiments could be started there and continued at UNK.

At the first stage of the UNK project (UNK-600) the protons will be accelerated up to 600 GeV with designed intensity up to $6 \cdot 10^{14}$ protons per 120 s cycle and the extracted beam spill length up to 20 s. The main properties of the proposed muon beam [3] at UNK-600 are summarized as follows: muon momentum range 100-400 GeV; beam size, $\sigma_{x,y}=10$ mm; at 100 Gev/c the muon intensity per proton is $3.1 \cdot 10^{-5}$ and $1.1 \cdot 10^{-5}$ for μ^+ and μ^-, respectively; at 400 GeV/c the intensities are $2.5 \cdot 10^{-6}$ and $5.9 \cdot 10^{-7}$. At the last stage of the UNK the muon energy could be extended to 2000 GeV. These beams are adequate to the requirements of the new experiments.

2.2. Schematic layout of the experiment (see Fig.1)

STORS consists of a field free FORV part, 2-3 modules of the toroidal magnetic spectrometer TORS, each 12 m long and 5.5 m in diameter, and muon identification systems MUSL, MUSS.

Eight superconducting coils (frames) located in radial planes around the beam axis, create a roughly toroidal field[4]. In the material free space between the coils (the octants), a set of proportional and/or minidrift chambers samples the trajectories of the scattered muons. Six to eight TARGet sections, 5.0 m long each, could be placed in the beam.

[†] E-mail: ISAVIN@cernvm.cern.ch

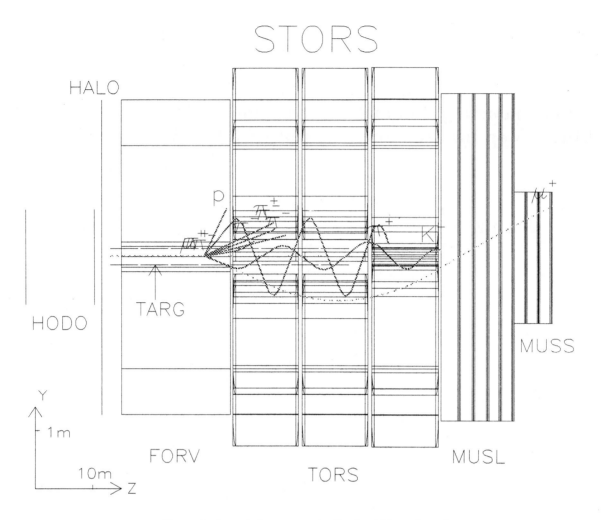

Figure 1. Layout of a superconducting toroidal spectrometer

2.3. Muon recognition, acceptance and resolutions

The hadronic shower produced in DIS can create problems for the recognition of the scattered muon tracks. This effect has been estimated using a GEANT based Monte-Carlo program [5] which simulates the experiment. This study has shown that the scattered muon track can always be easily reconstructed.

The acceptance in the variables (x, Q^2) has been also calculated using the Monte-Carlo program. Combining the target sections and the incident energies one can get the flat top 100% acceptance curves, ranging from $x \approx 0.01$ to $x \geq 1$ and from $Q^2 \approx 1 GeV^2$ to $Q^2 \approx 700 GeV^2$.

With such an air spectrometer the resolutions on x and Q^2 better than 1% can be achieved everywhere in the measured kinematical domain [6].

2.4. Systematic errors

Main systematic errors of DIS measurements come from: resolutions, calibration of the incident and scattered energy, normalization of incident beam, detectors

efficiencies, muon energy losses. They are evaluated and taken into account as contributions to the systematic errors in F_2 and the scale parameter $\Lambda_{\overline{MS}}$. The total error in $\Lambda_{\overline{MS}}$ will be less than 10 MeV.

3.   Summary of physics goals

We summarize here the main physics goals of the proposed experiment.

3.1. Hydrogen and deuterium targets

−High precision measurement of the nucleon structure functions $F_2^{p,n}(x, Q^2)$. The F_2^p expected from the proposed experiment in two realistic years of running (i.e. 50% efficient) with a hydrogen target is shown in Figure 2 together with the measurement expected from HERA in two "ideal" (i.e. 100% efficient) years of running ($200 pb^{-1}$). These simulated data are based on the "QCD-inspired" phenomenological fit [2]. The errors on the expected data points are purely statistical

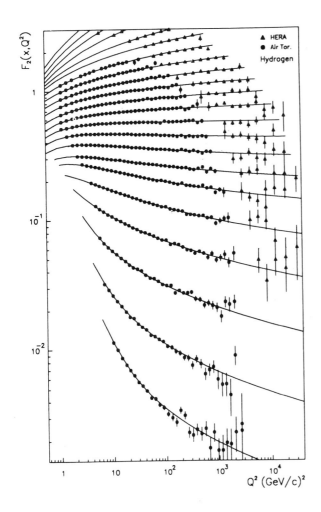

Figure 2. STORS expected precision on proton structure functions

in-depth study of nuclear effects in a wide kinematical region, including F_2^A measurements at large $x(x > 0.80)$. Due to experimental difficulties and small effect, F_2^A at large x and Q^2, is poorly measured [7]. With STORS F_2^A can be measured precisely up to $x \approx 2$.

3.3. Polarized targets

–A measurement of polarized structure functions $g_{1,2}(x,Q^2)$ at $Q^2 > 10$ GeV^2 and $x > 0.01$.

4. Reference

[1] See J. Feltesse talk at the Pl-4 session of this Conference.
[2] A. Feschenko et.al., JINR Communication E1-04-232, Dubna, 1994 and references there.
[3] V. Kotov, Report at the workshop on UNK-600 physics programme, Protvino, July 1993, Unpublished.
[4] S. Andreev et.al., JINR preprint, E1-93-384, Dubna, 1993.
[5] P. Akishin et al., JINR Communication, P1-92-167, Dubna, 1992.
[6] A. Bonjushkina, JINR Communication, P10-92-370, Dubna, 1992.
[7] BCDMS: A.C. Benvenuti et al., JINR preprint E1-93-133, Dubna, 1993. Zeitshr. fur Phys.C 63, (1994)29.

but the foreseen systematic errors are almost everywhere smaller than the statistical ones.

–A precise test of perturbative QCD including determination of gluon distributions and $\Lambda_{\overline{MS}}$ from global fits, x-dependence of log slopes, Q^2-variation of α_s and x- and Q^2-dependence of $R = \sigma_L/\sigma_T$. The expected accuracy of the data will allow to determine α_s with a precision $\approx 1\%$ and demonstrate the Q^2-variation of α_s to more than 12 standard deviations compared with the hypothesis of constant α_s.

–A study of higher-twist effects in structure functions.

–A study of various exclusive reactions.

3.2. Nuclear targets

–All topics involving tests of QCD (see 3.1).
–The simultaneous measurement of F_2^A and F_2^D and

Design and Performance of the CHORUS Detector

T. Patzak[†‡]

† Institute of Elementary Particle Physics, Humboldt University Berlin,
Unter den Linden 6, 10099 Berlin, Germany

On behalf of the CHORUS Collaboration

Abstract

A new search for ν_μ - ν_τ oscillation has recently started at CERN by the CHORUS Collaboration.

In order to explore the domain of small mixing angles down to $\sin^2 2\Theta_{\mu\nu} \sim 3 \times 10^{-4}$ for mass parameters $\Delta m^2 > 1eV^2$ a new modular detector was built. The CHORUS detector is designed to detect the occurence of the inclusive reaction $\nu_\tau N \rightarrow \tau^- X$ in a background of ν_μ induced charged (CC) and neutral current (NC) events. This detection is based on the observation of the characteristic decay topology of the short lived τ lepton.

Nuclear emulsions with a resolution of $\sim 1\mu m$ are used as a target. In order to select and reconstruct events compatible with τ decay, an electronic detector composed of large arrays of scintillating fibers, a magnetic spectrometer, a high resolution calorimeter and a muon spectrometer are used. Selected events which fulfil the kinematical constraints will be scanned in the emulsion using computer assisted microscopes. The tracks of the events are reconstructed and extrapolated back to the exit point of the emulsion to guide the microscopes.

This event selection is a very effective method for achieving the sensitivity we are aiming for.

1. Introduction

Recent results from the solar neutrino experiments confirm the existence of the solar neutrino problem. A consistent description by a MSW solution seems to be a possible explanation for the neutrino deficit. The COBE-IRAS data seem to prefer a mixed dark matter scenario with $m_{\nu_\tau} \sim 7$ eV.

All these results motivated a new search for ν_μ - ν_τ oscillation in the domain of mass parameters $\Delta m^2 > 1eV^2$. The CHORUS detector was designed to increase the sensitivity with respect to previous experiments by a factor of ~ 20, it is taking data since May 1994.

‡ E-mail: patzakt@cernvm.cern.ch
Address: CERN/PPE, CH-1211 Geneve 23

2. Experimental Concept

The CHORUS experiment searches for the appearance of ν_τ neutrinos in a beam of ν_μ, by detecting the occurrence of the inclusive reaction $\nu_\tau N \rightarrow \tau^- X$ in a background of ν_μ induced charged and neutral current events. The detection of the tau lepton is based on its short life time ($(0.305 \pm 0.006) \times 10^{-12}s$) [1] and on the characteristic decay topology due to the invisible neutrinos. 800 kg of nuclear emulsions are used as a target. The spacial resolution which can be achieved is about $1\mu m$. Within 2×200 days runing time of the experiment approximately 5×10^5 ν_μ induced charged current events will be accumulated. To search for ν_τ interactions in such a large sample of events it is necessary to reduce the number of events to be scanned in the emulsion. Events are selected based on kinematical constraints, leading a reduction to a

EMULSION TARGET

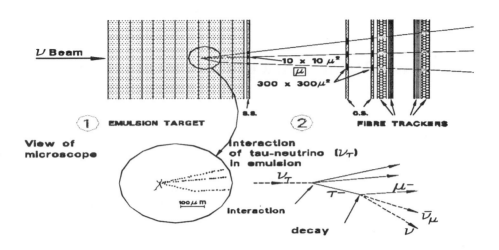

Figure 1. target region and fiber tracker

sample of ∼ 40,000 events. An electronic detector composed of arrays of 10^6 scintillating fibers, a magnetic spectrometer, a high resolution hadron calorimeter and a muon spectrometer, is used to select events with a negative muon or pion and missing p_T. Tracks of such selected events are reconstructed and extrapolated to the exit point at the emulsion [fig. 1] [2].

2.1. *Principle of the Kinematical Event Selection*

The kinematical selection criteria are based on the unbalanced p_T in the ν_τ interaction. An example is given in fig.2 and fig.3 for the ν_τ reaction and the corresponding background reaction.

3. Procedure for Event Analysis

As shown in fig.1 the emulsion targets are followed by scintillating fiber trackers. Two emulsion stacks, separated by a pair of special emulsion layers, are followed by a drift space in which three scintillating fiber trackers are positioned. The special emulsion layers serve as an interface between the electronic detector and the emulsions. The interfaces are exchanged every 3 weeks in order to keep the background small.

With the help of the fibers track predictions are made on the surface of the interface-emulsions. The precision is $300 \times 300 \mu m^2$. Computer assisted microscopes equipped with CCD cameras, starting from these predictions perform a fully automatic scanning of the emulsion [3] [4]. From the measured tracks a new prediction is made in an area of $10 \times 10 \mu m^2$ at the surface of the bulk emulsion. The final result inside the bulk emulsion will

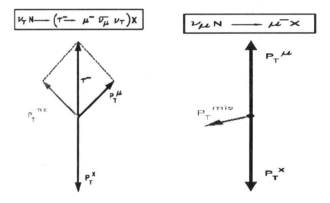

Figure 2. $P_T^{mis} > 0.4 \text{GeV}/c$; lower mean muon momentum; P_T^{mis} opposite to P_T^X

Figure 3. small P_T^{mis}; isotropic distribution; higher mean muon momentum

be an event analysis with a precision of ∼ 1 μm. The principle is shown in fig.1.

3.1. *Scintillating Fiber Tracker*

The fiber trackers are composed of plastic scintillating fibers with 500μm diameter. Each fiber tracker provides a measurement in 4-projections y,z,y',z'(y' and z' are rotated with respect to y and z by 8°) to determine an unambiguous space track. A good two track resolution of about 540μm allows the handling of large particle densities close to the interaction vertex. Fig.4 shows the achieved resolution. The fibers are read out with an optoelectronic chain composed of 4 image intensifiers followed by a CCD camera [5].

The target section is followed by an air core magnet

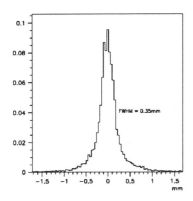

Figure 4. track residual per hit in the fiber tracker $\sigma_{track-residual} \approx 350\mu m$ at FWHM

decay mode	br	$\epsilon \cdot$ br	N_τ	background
$\mu^- \bar{\nu}_\mu \nu_\tau$	0.178	0.098	23	0.27
$h^-(n\pi^0)\nu_\tau$	0.503	0.046	29	0.72
$\pi^+\pi^-\pi^-(n\pi^0)\nu_\tau$	0.138	0.065	12	0.71
total		0.049	64	1.70 (0.4)

Table 1. Expected number of tau events and the background contamination in the three decay channels normalized to 5×10^5 charged current events

to determine the charge and the momentum of particles before they enter the calorimeter. The coordinates are also measured with scintillating fiber arrays which are adapted to the hexagonal shape of the magnet.

3.2. High Resolution Calorimeter

For the event selection it is necessary to determine the hadron shower energy and direction with high precision. A calorimeter was built for this purpose. The CHORUS calorimeter is the first large scale application of the SPACAL technique using scintillating fibers in a matrix of lead [6]. The calorimeter consists of three sectors with decreasing granularity, called EM, HAD1 and HAD2. The first sector measures the electromagnetic component of the hadronic shower, while the other two sectors are completing the measurement of the hadronic component. The volume ratio between lead and scintillator is 4:1 in order to achieve compensation. All sections are interleaved with streamer tube planes to perform tracking inside the calorimeter. The energy flow vector of the hadron final state is determined by measuring the center of gravity and connecting it to the vertex position measured by the fiber tracker. The resolution obtained in recent calibration runs is $\left[\frac{\sigma(E)}{E}\right]_{e^-} = \frac{(13.8+0.4)\%}{\sqrt{E}} + (0.1 \pm 0.1)\%$ and $\left[\frac{\sigma(E)}{E}\right]_{\pi^-} = \frac{(29.4+1.8)\%}{\sqrt{E}} + (2.4 \pm 0.6)\%$ [7].

3.3. Muon Spectrometer *

The muon spectrometer consists of six circularly magnetised iron modules and seven tracking gaps - one in front, five between and one behind the magnets. Each of these new tracking sections consist of one drift chamber and eight streamer tube planes. Each drift chamber contains three planes with sense wires

oriented at $0°$ and $\pm 60°$. The streamer tube planes are equipped with digital, analog and drift time readout. With the help of these three independent coordinate measurements one can prove the self consistency of the spectrometer measurements. The combination of the data determine a space vector behind the modules for each track. From the fit of these space vectors through the whole spectrometer the charge and the momentum of the muon is obtained. These tracking sections improve the sensitivity to muons with low momenta. The achieved resolution is $\sigma=800\mu m$ at FWHM and $\left[\frac{\Delta p}{p}\right]_{meas} = 12\%$ at 5Gev.

4. Conclusion

If oscillations would occur at the present limit ($sin^2 2\Theta_{\mu\tau} = 5 \times 10^{-3}, \Delta m^2 > 50eV^2$) we would observe 64 ν_τ events in a background of 1.7 events. Owing to the capability of the experiment to scan the primary vertecies in the emulsions the statistical significance can be further improved and the background can be reduced to 0.4 events. In case that there is no candidate for ν_μ - ν_τ oscillation we are able to improve the limit for large Δm^2 to $sin^2 2\Theta_{\mu\tau} = 3.1 \times 10^{-4}$.

The detected signal modes and there contribution to the number of events expected is shown in table 1.

References

[1] Particle Data Group;Phys. Rev. D45,Part2(June 1992).
[2] M. de Jong et al.;CHORUS Collaboration, CERN - PPE/93-134(1993).
[3] N. Ushida et al.;Phys. Rev. Lett. 57(1986) 2897.
[4] N. Ushida et al.;Nucl.Instr.Methods 224(1984) 50.
[5] S.Aoki et al.;Nucl.Instr.Methods A344(1994) 143.
[6] M.D.Acosta et al.;Nucl.Instr.Methods A294 (1990)193.
[7] S.Buontempo et al.;CERN - PPE/94-19(1994).
[8] M.Holder et al.;Nucl.Instr.Methods 148(1978)235.

* Major parts of the muon spectrometer have kindly been lend us by the CDHS Collaboration. It is described in detail elsewhere [8].

Paper presented at XXVII Int. Conf. on High Energy Physics: Session Pa-22
Glasgow, UK, 20–27 July 1994

Physics Capabilities of the DØ Upgrade Detector

John Ellison[†‡]

† Physics Department, University of California, Riverside, CA 92521, USA

For the DØ Collaboration

Abstract

The DØ detector at Fermilab is being upgraded to meet the demands imposed by high luminosity Tevatron running planned to begin in 1998. The central tracking detectors will be replaced with silicon and scintillating fiber tracking systems inside a solenoidal magnetic field and a preshower detector will be added to aid in electron identification. The design and performance of these systems are described and detailed simulations of the physics capabilities of the upgraded detector are presented. In particular we focus on the study of electroweak boson properties and top quark physics and briefly describe the b-physics capabilities.

1. Introduction

The future physics program at Fermilab will be greatly enhanced by the Tevatron upgrade which will result in an increase in luminosity by a factor of about 10-20. For the run planned to start in the Fall of 1998 (after installation of the Main Injector) the luminosity will be $\approx 10^{32}$ cm^{-2} s^{-1}. This upgrade will be accompanied by a decrease in the bunch crossing time from the current value of 3.5 μs to 396 ns and finally to 132 ns as the number of bunches is increased in stages.

To take full advantage of the new physics opportunities and to contend with the much higher radiation environment and shorter bunch crossing times, an extensive ugprade of the DØ detector is being undertaken[1].

The existing tracking systems and TRD are based on gaseous detectors and will be significantly degraded by radiation damage at 10^{32} cm^{-2} s^{-1} luminosity. Also, the typical drift time is ≈ 1 μs which will prevent operation with the short bunch crossing times. These considerations require completely replacing all the existing tracking detectors.

The upgraded tracking system has been designed to meet several goals: momentum measurement by the introduction of a solenoidal field; good electron identification and e/π rejection (to compensate for the loss of the TRD); tracking over a large range in pseudorapidity ($\eta \approx \pm 3$); secondary vertex measurement for identification of b-jets from top and for b-physics; first level tracking trigger; fast detector response to enable operation with a bunch crossing time of 132 ns; and radiation hardness. The design chosen to meet these requirements consists of an inner silicon tracking system and an outer scintillating fiber tracker enclosed within a 2 T superconducting solenoid. A preshower detector based on scintillating strips with fiber readout will be placed outside the solenoid. Fig. 1 shows an $r - z$ view of the DØ upgrade.

Other parts of the DØ detector will also be upgraded: a cosmic ray scintillator shield will be added and upgrades to readout electronics, trigger and data acquisition systems will be implemented.

2. Silicon Tracking

The silicon tracking system[2] is based on 50 μm pitch silicon microstrip detectors providing a spatial resolution of approximately 10 μm in $r\phi$. The high resolution is important to obtain good momentum measurement and vertex reconstruction. The detector consists of a system of barrels and interleaved disks designed to provide good coverage out to $\eta \approx 3$ for all tracks emerging from the interaction region, which is distributed along the beam direction with $\sigma_z \approx 25$ cm.

The barrel has 7 sections, each 12 cm long and containing 4 layers. The first and third layers are made of single-sided detectors with axial strips and the second and fourth layers are made from double-sided detectors with axial and 2° stereo strips. The small angle stereo design provides good pattern recognition with a resolution in $r - z$ at the vertex of 0.5-1.0 mm, allowing separation of primary vertices from multiple interactions.

The detectors are ac-coupled – each strip has an integrated coupling capacitor and polysilicon bias resistor. This technology has been shown to be sufficiently radiation hard[3]. The front end readout

‡ E-mail: ellison@ucrph0.ucr.edu

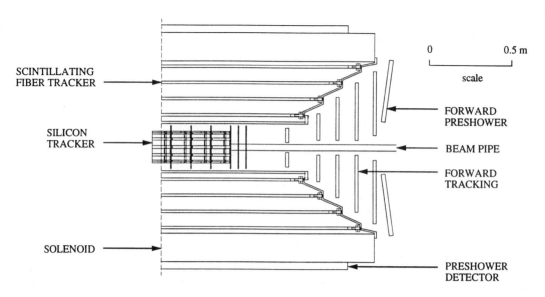

Figure 1. Schematic $r - z$ view of the DØ upgrade tracking systems and preshower detector.

chip (SVX II) has been prototyped in CMOS technology. It contains 128 channels, each channel comprising a double-correlated sampling amplifier, a 32-cell analog pipeline, and an analog-to-digital converter. The chip also contains sparse readout circuitry to limit the total readout time. The SVX II chips are mounted on a kapton high density circuit which is glued to the surface of the silicon detector. The detectors are mounted on beryllium bulkheads which serve as a support and provide cooling via water flow through beryllium tubes integrated into the bulkheads. The silicon tracker has a total of 837,000 channels.

3.   Scintillating Fiber Tracker

The outer tracking in the central region is based on scintillating fiber (SciFi) technology with visible light photon counter (VLPC) readout[4]. The SciFi tracker consists of 4 superlayers, each containing 4 fiber doublets in an $xuvx$ configuration (x = axial fibers and u, v = ± small angle stereo fibers). Each doublet consists of two layers of 830 μm diameter fibers with 870 μm spacing, offset by half the fiber spacing. The inner axial doublet is separated from the other doublets by a 1.5 cm thick carbon fiber support cylinder. This configuration provides very good efficiency and pattern recognition and a position resolution of $\approx$ 120 μm in $r\phi$.

The fibers are up to 2.5 m long and the light is piped out by 8 m clear fibers to the VLPC's outside the tracking volume. The VLPC's are solid state devices with a pixel size (1 mm) matched to the fiber diameter. The fast risetime, high gain and excellent quantum efficiency of these devices makes them ideally suited to our application.

The SciFi tracking system has a total of about 81,000 channels. Since this technology is rather novel we have done extensive testing. This includes the characterization of over 4,000 channels of VLPC's and the setup of a cosmic ray test stand consisting of 3 superlayers with over 3,000 fully instrumented fibers. The measured photoelectron yield, a critical measure of the system performance, was found to be 19 photoelectrons per doublet. This is well above the requirement of 5 photoelectrons needed for fully efficient tracking based on detailed GEANT simulations. The tracking efficiency measured with the cosmic ray stand is shown in Fig. 2 – for a fiber doublet it is above 98%. Also shown is a histogram of the track residuals in the SciFi superlayers for the 3-superlayer setup. The rms residual is 170 μm giving a resolution per superlayer of 139 μm, close to the predicted value of 120 μm.

4.   Detector Performance and Physics Capabilities

The momentum resolution of the proposed upgrade tracker is shown in Fig. 3. At $\eta = 0$ the resolution is approximately $\delta p_T/p_T = 17\%$ for $p_T = 100$ GeV. With this resolution the upgrade tracking will enable E/p matching for electron identification, improve the muon momentum resolution, provide charge sign determination for charged particles and help in calorimeter calibration.

Another important use of the tracking will be the tagging of displaced secondary vertices for $t\bar{t}$ physics and b-physics. Fig. 4 shows the resolution of the 2-dimensional impact parameter b as a function of pseudorapidity. The resolution is less than 20 μm

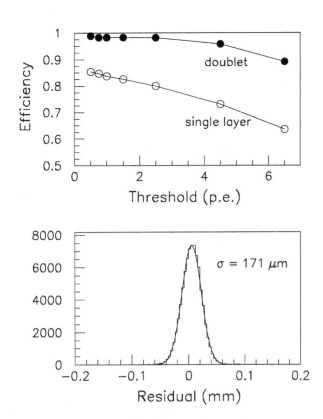

Figure 2. Measured SciFi efficiency and resolution.

for tracks with $p_T < 1$ GeV over the approximate range $\eta \leq 2$, which is the region of interest for tagging b-jets from top decays. A detailed study was carried out to determine the efficiency per event for tagging top events in the lepton plus jets decay channel using the impact parameter measurement. Events were generated and processed through a GEANT upgrade detector simulation and the signed impact parameter $b_{\pm}$ was obtained for tracks within jets in each event. A minimum of 3 tracks was required to be within a jet. Fig. 5 shows the tagging efficiency per event as a function of the $b_{\pm}$ significance cut. Also shown is the tagging efficiency for W + jets events. A signed impact parameter significance cut of 3 results in tagging 50% of the $t\bar{t}$ events and only 2% of the W + jets background.

One of the primary goals of the DØ upgrade physics program is the measurement of the top quark mass. This can be achieved using events in the lepton plus jets channel where the b-jets are tagged using the silicon tracker. The invariant mass of the $W + b$ can then be obtained. Studies have shown that the expected precision from this method is about $\delta m_t = 5$ GeV and with sufficient statistics $\delta m_t = 3$ GeV may be possible.

Another important goal is the measurement of the W mass. With the large data samples expected (> 1 fb^{-1}) the level of statistical precision will be of order 10 MeV and systematic errors in the measurement and model will dominate. We estimate that the overall error

will be approximately $\delta m_W = 50$ MeV.

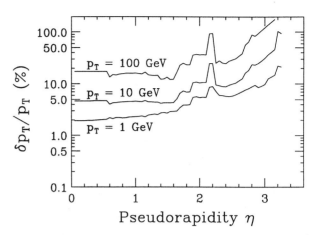

Figure 3. Transverse momentum resolution vs. pseudorapidity.

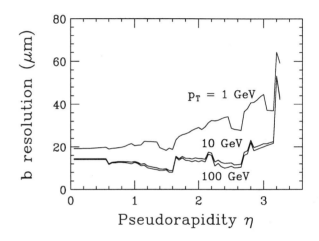

Figure 4. 2d impact parameter resolution vs. pseudorapidity.

The measurement of the forward-backward asymmetry (A_{FB}) will be possible in DØ utilizing $Z \rightarrow \ell^+\ell^-$ events. A preliminary study has shown that an estimated error on $\sin^2\theta_W$ of ≤ 0.001 is achievable using events on the Z pole only. We can improve this measurement by exploiting the variation of A_{FB} with the e^+e^- invariant mass due to $\gamma - Z$ interference. Studies are in progress to determine the ultimate sensitivity of this method and we expect that the error on $\sin^2\theta_W$ will be competitive with the LEP measurements.

The parameters m_t, m_W and A_{FB} are all linked through the Standard Model and it will be important to use the very precise measurements of these quantities from DØ to overconstrain the SM and search for new physics. This is shown in Fig. 6, where we used $m_t = 130$ GeV and a Higgs mass of $m_H = 1$ TeV. The region of overlap is small, indicating that DØ can make a sensitive search for physics beyond the SM.

Using the measured Z mass from LEP we may relate m_t and m_W for a given m_H as shown in Fig. 7 (solid curves). The DØ measurements of m_t and m_W (dashed lines) may yield valuable information on the Higgs mass, as illustrated in the plot.

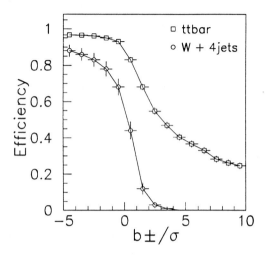

Figure 5. Tagging efficiency per event vs. signed impact parameter significance cut for $t\bar{t}$ events (squares) and $W + 4$ jet events (circles).

Some other important topics in the high p_T physics program include: measurement of the trilinear gauge boson couplings via the production of di-boson pairs; search for a charged Higgs via $t \to H^+ b$; search for the Higgs via $H^0 \to b\bar{b}$; and the search for non-SM particles e.g. supersymmetric particles.

For an integrated luminosity of 1 fb^{-1} at the Tevatron approximately 5×10^{10} b-quark pairs will be produced. Therefore, a wide range of b-physics studies will be possible. These include b-quark cross sections, rare B decays, B_s mixing and CP violation in the $B\bar{B}^0$ system. In contrast to high p_T physics, B mesons are produced at relatively high η and low p_T. Therefore, tracking and vertexing out to $\eta \approx 3$ is important for b-physics studies. Simulations using 1 fb^{-1} indicate that B_s mixing could be detected for values of the mixing parameter x_s up to 20 and that CP violation could be accessible with an error on $\sin(2\beta)$ of about 0.24.

5. Summary

The upgrade of the DØ detector is well underway and is planned to be complete by mid 1998. Conceptual designs for all the subsystems have been completed and construction of some components has already begun. The upgrade will considerably extend the physics reach of DØ. With ≥ 1 fb^{-1} of data, we expect to measure the top mass to within 5 GeV and the W mass to within 50 MeV.

I thank my colleagues for their help and useful discussions. In particular I thank R. Brock, A. Bross, S. Errede, R. Lipton Y.M. Park, J. Solomon, M. Tuts and M. Wayne.

References

[1] DØ Collaboration, "The DØ Upgrade", 18 October 1990; DØ Collaboration "E823 (DØ Upgrade) – Step I and Beyond", DØ Note 1421, May 1992; DØ Collaboration "E823 (DØ Upgrade) – DØ$_\beta$", DØ Note 1733, May 1993.

[2] DØ Collaboration, "DØ Silicon Tracker Technical Design Report", DØ Note 2169, July 1994.

[3] D. Pitzl et al., Nucl. Phys. B (Proc. Suppl.) **23A** (1991) 340; H.J. Ziock et al., IEEE Trans. Nucl. Sci. **NS-38** (1991) 269.

[4] M.D. Petroff and M.G. Staplebroek, IEEE Trans. Nucl. Sci., **36**, No. 1 (1989) 158; M.D. Petroff and M. Attac, IEEE Trans. Nucl. Sci., **36**, No. 1 (1989) 163.

[5] F. Halzen and B.A. Kniehl, Nucl. Phys. **B353** (1991) 567; S. Errede, private commumnication.

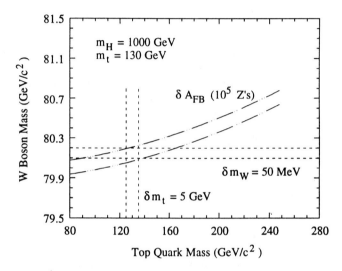

Figure 6. Plot of m_t vs. m_W showing the expected errors on the masses and the constraint from the A_{FB} measurement.

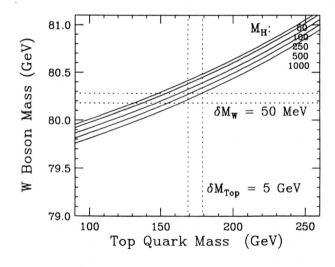

Figure 7. Plot of m_t vs. m_W showing the expected errors and the SM curves for different m_H using the Z mass from LEP. The curves are from ref. 5.

CMS - A Compact Solenoidal Detector for LHC

R M Brown

Rutherford Appleton Laboratory, Chilton, Didcot, OXON, OX11 0QX, UK

On behalf of the CMS Collaboration

Abstract

The CMS Collaboration has designed a general purpose detector able to run at the highest luminosity at LHC. It will permit studies of a wide range of possible new physics both within and beyond the Standard Model. Emphasis has been placed on the identification and high precision measurement of muons, photons and electrons. The energy resolution for these particles will be better than 1% at 100 GeV. The experimental design is centred on a large, 4T superconducting solenoid. The strong magnetic field allows the muon spectrometer to be made relatively compact without compromising its momentum resolution.

1. Introduction

Proton collisions at the LHC will open a window on parton parton interactions in the TeV energy range, where very general theoretical considerations predict that the Standard Model (SM) must break down. Various scenarios have been proposed in which there are one or more Higgs bosons, a spectrum of supersymmetric particles or observable effects arising from strong interactions between pairs of intermediate vector bosons.

Signatures for these different possibilities would appear in final states containing high p_T charged leptons or photons. The CMS detector has therefore been designed to measure these particles with high precision, in order to be sensitive to a wide range of electroweak symmetry breaking mechanisms, and to search for Higgs bosons in the mass range from 90 GeV to 1 TeV.

The design of CMS is well advanced but it is not yet completed. In the following we describe some of the main features of the detector as it is conceived at present, however, changes may be expected before the details are finally frozen. The available space does not permit a description of all parts of the detector here. Among the important omissions are the hadron calorimeter, the very forward calorimeters and the first level trigger. A much more detailed description of CMS can be found in the references listed under [1].

2. Design Overview

The basic design objectives can be simply summarised as:
1) To have an excellent muon detection system with built in redundancy to ensure robustness.
2) To have the best possible electromagnetic calorimeter consistent with 1.
3) To have a central tracking system able to reconstruct all high p_T muons and isolated electrons.
4) To ensure that the total cost does not exceed the resources available to the collaboration.

These considerations have led to the arrangement shown in figure 1. At the heart of the design is the superconducting solenoid which is 14 m long, with an inner radius of 2.9 m and a field of 4 Tesla. This long solenoid allows efficient muon detection and measurement up to a pseudo-rapidity (η) of ± 2.5, without additional forward toroids. The first muon measurement outside the central tracking volume is made immediately after the coil where the bend angle is greatest. This is made possible by having the ECAL and the HCAL inside the coil. The inner tracker extends out to a radius of 1.3m where the occupancy is reduced by the high magnetic field. (At small radii the occupancy is increased because of curling tracks). Forward calorimeters ensure hermetic detector coverage to $|\eta| = 4.7$. We now consider some of the elements of CMS in more detail.

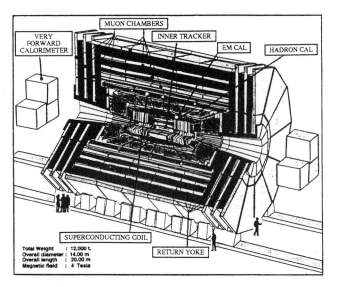

Fig. 1 Three dimensional view of the CMS Detector.

3. The Magnet

A solenoidal configuration has been chosen for the magnet because the bending of charged particle trajectories starts at the beam axis and this minimises the detector size for a given bending power. Combined with the very strong magnet field, this has enabled a relatively compact design to be achieved without compromising the momentum resolution. (CMS is only half as long and 2/3 of the diameter of ATLAS). Furthermore, with this arrangement, the bending is in the plane transverse to the beam and in this plane the primary vertex is given by the beam size to within 20 μm, which facilitates muon triggers based on vertex pointing.

The coil is wound in four layers and the total thickness, including the cryostat, is 70 cm (1.1λ). The magnet yoke contains 12000 tons of steel. The barrel section is 1.8 m (10λ) thick (excluding spaces for muon chambers) and it is fully saturated by the return field of the solenoid.

4. The Muon System

Three almost independent measurements of the muon momentum are made: inside the central tracker, immediately after the coil, and in the iron return yoke. The two measurements outside the coil are guaranteed, even at high luminosity.

The arrangement of muon chambers in the barrel region is shown in figure 2. There are four stations, each consisting of three groups of four planes of drift tubes. Two groups measure the (r - φ) coordinate and one group measures z. Each station measures a muon vector with 100 μm precision in position and better than 1 mrad in direction in the bend plane. Mean timer electronics identifies the bunch crossing and produces a signal for the muon trigger. Planes of resistive plate chambers before and

after the drift tubes provide independent trigger information and beam crossing identification.

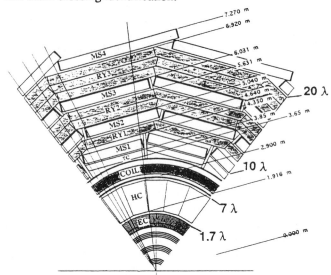

Fig. 2 A transverse slice through the barrel section of CMS, showing the disposition of the four muon stations, MS1 to MS4.

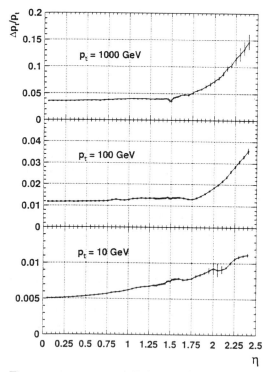

Fig. 3 The muon momentum resolution as a function of rapidity.

The end cap region is instrumented with cathode strip chambers since these devices are able to operate in a high magnetic field and can handle high rates.

The bending power of the solenoid is 16 T.m in the central region and decreases with rapidity above |η| = 1.5, to a value of 6 T.m at |η| = 2.5. The muon momentum resolution is shown as a function of η in figure 3.

5. The Central Tracker

The physics process in which a putative intermediate mass Higgs boson decays into 4 leptons via a real Z^0 and a virtual Z^0 is particularly challenging experimentally and can be used to set the design goals for the central tracker.

In order to achieve a good signal to background ratio in this channel, the lepton acceptance should extend out to 2.5 in $|\eta|$ and down to 5 GeV/c in p_T. The momentum resolution should be better than 1% at 100 GeV/c. Efficient pattern recognition is needed to allow all high p_T tracks to be found and reconstructed and for isolation criteria to be established. This requires small cell sizes and a very large number of channels.

The performance objectives are achieved in a tracker design which employs just two technologies: silicon microstrip detectors and microstrip gas chambers (MSGCs). Figure 4 shows how the two types of detector are arranged within a cylindrical volume 7 m long and 2.6 m in diameter.

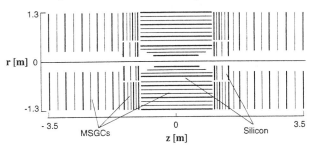

Fig. 4 The arrangement of detectors in the central tracker. Thick lines denote layers with rϕ and stereo readout.

In the barrel region, tracks with $p_T > 5$ GeV/c pass through four planes of silicon detectors (125 mm long strips at 50 μm pitch) followed by eight planes of MSGCs (125 or 250 mm long strips at 200 μm pitch). Half of the measurements have z information obtained from stereo strips at an angle of 100 mrad.

In the forward region the detectors are configured in discs. At each end of the tracking volume there are ten discs composed of MSGC detectors alone. A further six inner discs at each end have both silicon detectors and MSGCs. Half the planes provide stereo information. On average about 14 points are measured per track.

Type of Track	$\|\eta\| \leq 0.5$		$1.5 \leq \|\eta\| \leq 2.5$		Total: $\|\eta\| \leq 2.5$	
	Eff. (%)	Ghosts/ Track	Eff. (%)	Ghosts/ Track	Eff. (%)	Ghosts/ Track
Isolated Tracks	99	0.01	98	0.01	98	0.02
Tracks in Jets, E_t=100 GeV	95	0.06	93	0.02	94	0.11
Tracks in Jets, E_t=500 GeV	90	0.07	90	0.02	90	0.13

Table 1: The track finding efficiency and probability for a ghost for tracks with $p_t \geq 2$ GeV (summed over 2 crossings, $L = 10^{34}$ cm^{-2}s^{-1})

Table 1 summarises the track finding efficiencies and ghost track probabilities obtained from a full simulation of the tracker performance at a luminosity of 10^{34} cm^{-2} s^{-1}.

6. The Electromagnetic Calorimeter

The performance goals of the ECAL have been set by requiring that it be capable of detecting the signal from a Higgs boson (SM or MSSM) decaying into two photons. For a mass in the range from 90 to 130 GeV/c^2, measurement of the two photon final state may offer the only possibility for discovering such a particle.

The observed width of such a state would be dominated by the detector resolution with contributions from both the energy measurement and the determination of the opening angle between the two photons. At high luminosity there are multiple collisions at each beam crossing and the interaction vertex cannot be used to constrain the photon trajectories. The photon directions must therefore be measured within the calorimeter, the required precision being of the order of 60 mrad/√E.

Two classes of electromagnetic calorimeter are under consideration for CMS, a lead/scintillator sampling device ('Shashlik') and a system based on a homogenous detection medium (crystals or glass).

The current "base-line option" is the Shashlik design. In this scheme 34000 towers, each subtending an element of solid angle $\Delta\eta \times \Delta\phi = 0.03 \times 0.03$, are arranged in a projective geometry covering the region $|\eta| < 2.6$. A typical tower consists of 75 layers of 2 mm thick lead plates interleaved with 3 mm thick plastic scintillator. The scintillation light is collected and concentrated on to a single silicon photo-diode via 36 wavelength shifter fibres threaded longitudinally through the tower.

Immediately in front of the main calorimeter there is a preshower detector. This consists of 2X$_0$ of lead, followed by silicon detectors with strips at 2 mm intervals measuring the φ-coordinate, followed by 1X$_0$ of lead, followed by a second plane of silicon with orthogonal strips. Photon directions are determined by comparing the shower centroid measured in the presampler with that measured in the main calorimeter. Information from the pre-shower detector is also used to enhance γ/π^0 discrimination.

Extensive test beam studies have been made on Shashlik prototypes in order to establish the energy resolution and photon pointing accuracy that can be achieved. Some results are shown in figure 5.

A crystal calorimeter would give an important improvement in the energy resolution relative to Shashlik, increasing sensitivity to the channel H → γγ to the point where a discovery might be possible during the first two years of LHC operation. Studies have concentrated on two scintillating crystals which meet the CMS requirements (cerium fluoride and lead tungstenate) and intensive efforts are being made to bring the costs down to an affordable level.

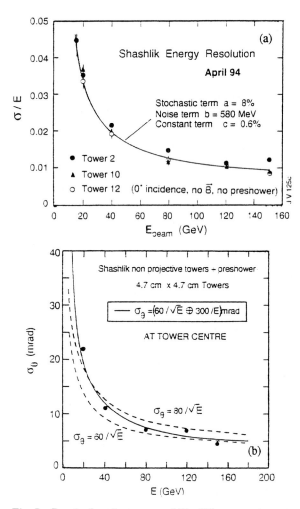

Fig. 5 Results from beam tests of Shashlik prototypes
(a) Energy resolution as a function of energy
(b) Angular resolution as a function of energy.

Property		CeF$_3$	PbWO$_4$	Hf$_4$ Glass	Shashlik
Radiation length	cm	1.7	0.85	1.6	1.7
Moliere radius	cm	2.6	2.0	2.8	3.4
Density	g/cm^3	6.2	8.3	6.0	4.5
Light Yield (LY)	γ/MeV	1500	100	100	13
τ (short)	ns	9	≤ 10	8	≤ 10 ns
(long)	ns	32	36	25	-
% Light in 25 ns		50	85	50	≈ 100
Peak wavelength	nm	325	480	325	500
T dependence of LY	%/° C	0.15	1.6	-0.39	-
Radiation Hardness	Mrad	≈ 10	≈ 10	?	1
Volume for 25 χ$_0$	m^3	26.3	12.5	24.5	26.3

Table 2: A comparison of the properties of crystals, glasses and Shashlik

An interesting alternative is to use a dense scintillating glass, since this would avoid the expensive operation of growing large, ultra pure crystals. Encouraging results have been obtained with fluoro-hafnate glass doped with CeF$_3$.

Some properties of the various CMS ECAL options are summarised in table 2.

7. Data Acquisition

The data acquisition system consists of four distinct parts: the front-end electronics, the first level trigger processors, the read-out network and the on-line event filter. The front-end electronics and the level 1 trigger are synchronous and pipe-lined whereas the readout and event filter are asynchronous.

Of particular note is the absence of a second level trigger implemented in dedicated hardware. The philosophy adopted instead is to perform on-line filtering with software running on a powerful farm of proprietary RISC processors (10^6 -10^7 Mips), fed through a high bandwidth (500 Gbit/s) readout network using standard protocols and telecommunication industry components. Based on an extrapolation of recent trends, it is confidently predicted that networking and processing elements with the necessary performance will become available at an affordable price by the time they are required.

An important advantage of this approach is that the readout network and event filter are scalable in bandwidth and computing power, and can readily benefit from further advances in technology.

8. Summary

A brief overview has been given of the CMS proposal as it stands in mid-1994. The design of the experiment is well advanced and the general performance characteristics have been established. Further evolution of the design is expected as prototyping continues.

9. Acknowledgements

This paper is based on the CMS letter of intent, 'milestone documents' produced for the LHCC, and various CMS Technical Notes. It is a distillation of the results of an enormous amount of work undertaken by many people. I thank all of my colleagues who have contributed to the creation of the CMS concept.

References

[1] CMS Letter of Intent, CERN/LHCC 92-3, LHCC/I1, 1 October, 1992.
Staging of the CMS Detector, CERN/LHCC 93-22, LHCC/I1 Add. 1, 19 March 1993.
CMS Status Report and Milestones, CERN/LHCC 93-48, 15 October 1993.
CMS Status Report and Milestones, CERN/LHCC 94-20, 24 May 1994.
CMS A General Purpose Detector for the LHC, CMS TN/94-133, 5 January 1994. Paper GLS0934, submitted to this conference.

Paper presented at XXVII Int. Conf. on High Energy Physics: Session Pa-22
Glasgow, UK, 20–27 July 1994

Physics with KLOE at DAΦNE

Paolo Franzini

Dipartimento di Fisica dell'Università e Sezione INFN, Roma I, "La Sapienza"
P.le A. Moro, I–00185, Roma, Italy

On behalf of the KLOE Collaboration

Abstract

Experimental measurements which can be done at DAΦNE, the ϕ-factory under construction at the Laboratori Nazionali di Frascati dell'INFN, are presented. We also describe the KLOE detector, optimized for performing these measurements.

1. Introduction

The Frascati ϕ–factory, DAΦNE,[1] is a bright source of neutral K's in a pure quantum state, of charged K pairs and also of ρ's, η's and η''s. ϕ radiative decays are also observable. Unique to DAΦNE is the possibility of studying *kaon interferometry*, which allows accurate determinations of the parameters of the neutral kaons. These studies will be performed with the KLOE detector proposed by the KLOE collaboration and under construction at present.[2] At full DAΦNE luminosity, KLOE can collect some 10^{11} events per year. KLOE is "self-calibrating" via numerous K decay channels and Bhabha scattering. An absolute normalization of the K_S, K_L fluxes is also available.

2. *CP* and *CPT* at DAΦNE

The KLOE program at DAΦNE is aimed at measuring CP and possible CPT violation in neutral K decays, with a sensitivity comparable to that of the next generation fixed target experiments $(\delta\Re(\epsilon'/\epsilon)\sim 10^{-4})$, both by using pure K_S, K_L beams and from observing interference effects due to the coherence of the K_S, K_L state. The quantities $\Re(\epsilon'/\epsilon)$, $\Im(\epsilon'/\epsilon)$, Δm, $|\eta_{\pi\pi}|$, $\phi_{\pi\pi}$, can be measured with improved accuracy.[3] Assuming CPT and defining the usual amplitude ratios and epsilon parameters $\eta_{+-} = \epsilon + \epsilon'$ and $\eta_{00} = \epsilon - 2\epsilon'$ where η's and ϵ's are all complex, experimental

observation of $\epsilon' \neq 0$ would be proof that CP is violated in the decay amplitude. The standard model, in the context of the CKM quark mixing mechanism, predicts $\Re(\epsilon'/\epsilon)\sim 10^{-3}$ with large uncertainties and possible cancellations.[4,5] The relationships between $\eta_\pm$, η_{00} and ϵ, ϵ', when one allows for CPT violation, remain as above but both ϵ, ϵ' each acquire terms which violate CP and CPT separately.[3]

At DAΦNE neutral K-pairs are produced in a C-odd state. Defining $\eta_i = \langle f_i | K_L \rangle / \langle f_i | K_S \rangle$, $\Delta t = t_1 - t_2$, $t = t_1 + t_2$, $\Delta\mathcal{M} = \mathcal{M}_L - \mathcal{M}_S$ and $\mathcal{M} = \mathcal{M}_L + \mathcal{M}_S$, the decay intensity $I(f_1, f_2, \Delta t = t_1 - t_2)$ to final states f_1 and f_2 is :

$$I(f_1,\ f_2;\ \Delta t) = \frac{1}{2}\int\limits_{\Delta t}^{\infty} |A(f_1, t_1;\ f_2, t_2)|^2 \mathrm{d}t =$$

$$\frac{1}{2\Gamma}|\langle f_1 | K_S \rangle\langle f_2 | K_S \rangle|^2 \times \Big(|\eta_1|^2 e^{-\Gamma_L \Delta t} + |\eta_2|^2 e^{-\Gamma_S \Delta t}$$
$$- 2|\eta_1||\eta_2|e^{-\Gamma\Delta t/2}\cos(\Delta m\Delta t + \phi_1 - \phi_2)\Big),$$

with $\eta_i = A(K_L \rightarrow f_i)/A(K_S \rightarrow f_i) = |\eta_i|e^{i\phi_i}$, exhibiting interference terms sensitive to phase differences. We can perform "kaon-interferometry" by using the decay intensity of the previous equation with appropriate choices of the final states f_1, f_2.

1). f_1=f_2: we can measure Γ_S, Γ_L and Δm, since all the phases disappear. Rates can be measured to $\times 10$

improvement in accuracy and Δm to $\times 2$.

2), $f_1 \neq f_2$: a). with $f_1 = \pi^+ \pi^-$, $f_2 = \pi^0 \pi^0$, we can measure $\Re(\epsilon'/\epsilon)$, and $\Im(\epsilon'/\epsilon)$. The former by concentrating on large time differences, the latter for $|\Delta t| \leq 5\tau_s$. b). with $f_1 = \pi^+ \ell^- \nu$ and $f_2 = \pi^- \ell^+ \nu$, we can measure the CPT-violation parameter δ_K, the real part by concentrating on large time difference regions; and the imaginary part for $|\Delta t| \leq 10\tau_s$, fig. 1. c). If $f_1 = 2\pi$, $f_2 = K_{\ell 3}$, this leads to measurements of CP and CPT violation parameters at large time differences, since we measure the asymmetry in K_L semileptonic decays. At small time differences, we obtain Δm, $|\eta_{\pi\pi}|$ and $\phi_{\pi\pi}$, figs. 2, 3. Choosing appropriate f_1 and f_2 channels one can perform 16 independent measurements in neutral K decays. If the validity of the $\Delta S = \Delta Q$ rule is assumed there are only 13 paramaters to determined. Experiments at DAΦNE can thus test CPT invariance, in addition to studying CP violation. If the $\Delta S = \Delta Q$ rule does not hold (it is violated to $\sim 1/10^7$ in the SM), there are in fact 17 independent parameters,[5] therefore we need to also use strangeness tagged K^0 obtained from charge exchange of K^+ mesons, in turn tagged by observation of a K^- meson, from $\phi \rightarrow K^\pm$ decays.

3. Measuring $\mathcal{R}^\pm / \mathcal{R}^0$

In addition, we can also use the classical method of the double ratio $\mathcal{R}^\pm / \mathcal{R}^0 = 1 + 6 \times \Re(\epsilon'/\epsilon)$, and other ways of measuring $\Re(\epsilon'/\epsilon)$ from selected final states. Very different systematics are involved, thus allowing a self check of the results.

4. Other CP Violations at DAΦNE

So far CP violation has been observed only in the K_L system. Observation of $K_S \rightarrow 3\pi^0$ would constitute a new proof of CP violation. One can collect ~ 30 events in one year, with zero background. At DAΦNE one can also easily measure the difference in rates between $(K_S \rightarrow \pi^\pm \ell^\mp \nu)$ to 4×10^{-4}.

Evidence for direct CP violation can be also be obtained from the decays of charged kaons which are copiously produced at DAΦNE. CP requires equality of the partial rates for $K^\pm \rightarrow \pi^\pm \pi^+ \pi^-$ $(\tau^\pm)$ and for $K^\pm \rightarrow \pi^\pm \pi^0 \pi^0$ $(\tau'^\pm)$. One can improve the present rate asymmetry by two orders of magnitude. One can also observe differences in the Dalitz plot distributions for K^+ and K^- decays in both the τ and τ' modes; at DAΦNE one could reach sensitivities of $\sim 10^{-4}$. Rate differences in the radiative decays $K^\pm \rightarrow \pi^\pm \pi^0 \gamma$, are also proof of direct CP violation. The reachable sensitivity is $\sim 1.4 \times 10^{-3}$.

5. Chiral Perturbation Theory

In the last decade chiral perturbation theory (CHP-T) has been extended to the next order terms in the

chiral expansion ($\mathcal{O}(m^4)$, $\mathcal{O}(p^4)$, $\mathcal{O}(m^2 p^2)$). Many new amplitudes can then be predicted.

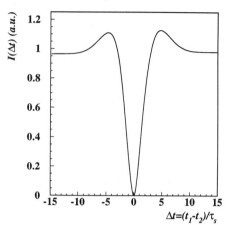

Fig. 1 Interference for $f_1 = \pi^+ \pi^-$, $f_2 = \pi^0 \pi^0$

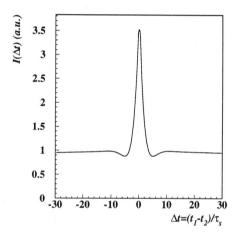

Fig. 2 Interference for $f_1 = \ell^+$, $f_2 = \ell^-$

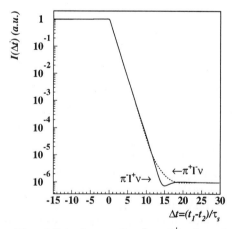

Fig. 3 Interference for $f_1 = \ell^\pm$, $f_2 = 2\pi$

At lowest order the CHPT relation predicts the slope of the scalar form factor, λ_0. There is at present disagreement from experiment with the CHPT prediction, 0.017 ± 0.004: one can measure λ_0 for K_L to an accuracy of 1.4×10^{-5}. Similar accuracy are obtained for $K^\pm$ and for λ_+. There is only one measurement of the relevant

$K_{\ell 4}$ form factors. These decays also provide another opportunity for the determination of the $\pi\pi$ phase shifts. The amplitudes for $K_{\ell 2,\gamma}$, $K_{\ell 2,e+e-}$ and $K_{\ell 3,\gamma}$ depend on the K charge radius.

The rate for $K^{\pm}\to\pi^{\pm}\gamma\gamma$ and the $\gamma\gamma$ distributions are uniquely predicted by the chiral lagrangian approach. Dalitz type decays of K mesons and two photon production of pions are also of great interest. At DAΦNE one can improve vastly on all these topics.

6. Radiative ϕ Decays

The study of light meson spectroscopy, rare radiative decays are possible at DAΦNE. The unique, lightest scalar meson state $f_0(975)$ is poorly described by current models, one can easily contribute to solving the puzzle.[6]

7. KLOE

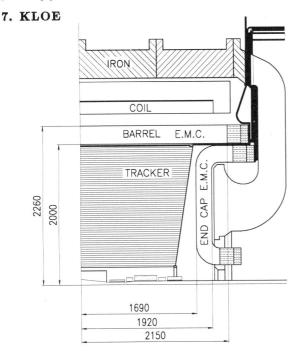

Fig. 4 KLOE cross section along the beam axis.

The KLOE Collaboration[7] has designed[8] and begun construction of the KLOE detector whose main mission is to study CP violation with a sensitivity of $\mathcal{O}(10^{-4})$ and is fully capable of investigating a whole range of other physics described above. The scale of KLOE is driven by a fundamental parameter, the mean decay path length of the long lived K^0-meson $L(K_L)$. At DAΦNE, $\beta(K)$=0.216 and $L(K_L)=\gamma\beta c\tau=3.44$ m. Which is a large number indeed! Economical reasons and technical problems as well lead to a choice of a 2 m drift space for the K_L decays.

The experimental apparatus must be able to track charged particles of momenta between 50 and 250 MeV/c. It must also detect with very high efficiency γ's with energy as low as 20 MeV, measure their en-

ergies with a resolution $\delta E_\gamma/E_\gamma \sim 15\%$ at 100 MeV and provide the space coordinates of the photon conversion point. Thus while the general features of the KLOE detector are similar to those of a *typical* general purpose collider's apparatus: a cylindrical structure surrounding the beam pipe, consisting of a highly efficient, large tracking device for detecting the charged K^0 decay products, an electromagnetic calorimeter with exceptional timing ability, which also provides some particle identification, enclosed in a solenoidal field. A cross section view of KLOE is shown in fig. 4.

8. Detector Performance.

Some parameters of the detector are given in table 1.

Calorimeter	
δ(Shower Apex)	=1 cm
$\delta E/E$	= 5%/$\sqrt{E\ (\mathrm{GeV})}$
δt	= 66 ps/$\sqrt{E\ (\mathrm{GeV})}$
Drift Chamber	
δpoint	= 200 μm, r and ϕ
	= 2 mm, z
δp_t	= 0.5%×p_t
$\delta(\tan(\theta))$	= $(3.5\oplus2.5)\times10^{-4}$

Table 1. DAΦNE Detector Performance.

References

1. G. Vignola, *Proc. of the Workshop on Physics and Detectors for DAΦNE*, G. Pancheri Ed., Frascati, 1991, p. 1.
2. *KLOE, a General Purpose Detector for DAΦNE*, the KLOE Collaboration, LNF Report LNF-92/019, 1992.
3. C. Buchanan *et al.*, Phys. Rev. **D45**, 4088 (1992).
4. P. J. Franzini, *Les Rencontres de Physique de la Vallée d'Aoste*, La Thuile, Italy, March 3-9 1991, M. Greco Ed., p. 257.
5. L. Maiani, "CP and CPT Violation in Neutral Kaon Decays", *DAΦNE Physics Handbook*, L. Maiani *et al.* ed., LNF, Frascati.
6. J. Lee-Franzini, W. Kim, and P. J. Franzini, Phys. Lett. **B287**, 259 (1992).
7. Università and Sezione INFN, Bari; IHEP, Chinese Academy of Science, Beijing; Ben-Gurion University; Laboratori Nazionali di Frascati dell'INFN, Frascati; Institut für Experimentelle Kernphysik, Universität Karlsruhe; Università and Sezione INFN, Lecce; Università and Sezione INFN, Napoli; Columbia University, New York; Università and Sezione INFN, Pisa; Università and Sezione INFN, Roma I; Università and Sezione INFN, Roma II; ISS and Sezione INFN, ISS, Roma; SUNY at Stony Brook; Tel-Aviv University; Università and Sezione INFN, Trieste/Udine.
8. *The KLOE Detector Technical Proposal*, the KLOE Collaboration, LNF Report LNF-93/002, 1993.

Paper presented at XXVII Int. Conf. on High Energy Physics: Session Pa-22
Glasgow, UK, 20–27 July 1994

The CLEO III detector upgrade and physics goals

David H Miller[†]

Purdue University
Physics Dept W. Lafayette IN 47907-1396, USA

Representing the CLEO collaboration

Abstract

The CLEO III upgrade and physics plans are reviewed. Currently the CLEO II detector has accumulated over 4 fb^{-1} on the $\Upsilon(4S)$ with instantaneous luminosities as high as 2.5×10^{32} cm^{-2}sec-1. The planned upgrade will include a new drift chamber ,a four layer silicon vertex detector, and particle identification. In parallel the accelerator, CESR, will be upgraded with superconducting RF with a goal of reaching luminosities of 3.0×10^{33}.

1. CLEO-III DETECTOR UPGRADE

The CLEO collaboration has been the acknowledged leader in *b*-quark physics since it discovered the *B* meson in 1980 [1]. The CLEO-II detector was the first to achieve better than 2% resolution simultaneously in charged particle momentum and electronic shower energy for GeV particles.

In January 1995 there will be an upgrade of the CLEO detector to replace the present inner five-layer straw-tube drift chamber by a three-layer silicon drift chamber.

For Phase III a much more extensive upgrade of the detector is required. The detailed plan for the CLEO-III upgrade is contained in a design report issued in late 1993 [2] and a separate document on the CESR/CLEO upgrade plans [3]. The existing superconducting coil (B= 1.5 T, r = 1.5m , l = 3m), the magnet iron, the muon detection system, and the 7800 CsI calorimeter will be kept. The tracking system will be replaced with one of equal performance to the current chamber but allowing 20 cm of radial space for the installation of advanced particle identification devices for good K/π separation up to 2.8 GeV/c, the highest momentum possible in decays of *B* mesons produced at the $\Upsilon(4S)$

† E-mail: DHM@LNS62.LNS.CORNELL.EDU

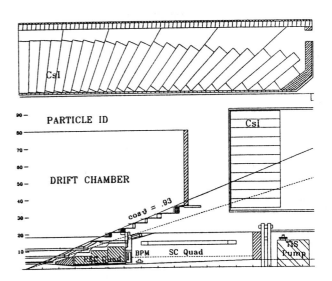

Figure 1. Quarter section view of the CLEO-III detector. The outer portions of the iron flux return and the muon chambers are not shown.

resonance. This system will consist of a four layer silicon vertex detector with layers at 2.5, 3.75, 7.5, and 10.0cm, comprised of 452 identical double sided pieces followed by a drift chamber to a radius of 80cm. A particle identification system will be installed in the 20cm of free space with two technologies being considered. The first is a fast RICH where beam tests have been completed at CERN and a full scale prototype is under construction. The second is high pressure tubes with a single threshold and these are also in the prototype stage. In addition as with the current detector dE/dx with an r.m.s of about 6 % will be used in the drift chamber. A quarter section of the CLEO-III detector is shown in Fig. 1. Angular coverage is defined by the interaction region quadrupole stay-clear line at $\theta = 300$ mrad. The active volume of the tracking system extends down to $\theta = 330$ mrad (93% of 4π steradians) with the remaining volume for cables and mechanical support.

2. PHYSICS GOALS

2.1. Luminosity Expectations

The peak luminosity goals for Phase II and Phase III of the CESR upgrade are shown in the table.

Phase	II	III	∞
Installation date	1994	1997	2000?
Peak luminosity, 10^{32} cm^{-2}s^{-1}	6	10	30
Average luminosity, fb^{-1}/yr	6	10	30

The last column shows what might optimistically be the asymptotic performance several years after the Phase III upgrade installation, when extensive experience with the new operating conditions will have enabled us to get the maximum out of the upgrade. In the other columns the Phase II and Phase III luminosity figures probably apply about a year after the corresponding installation date.

CESR now delivers between 1.2 and 1.5 fb^{-1} of integrated luminosity per year. In discussing the future physics potential it is useful to think of the integrated luminosity in units of 10 fb^{-1}. We can hope that by late 1998, as a result of the Phase II and III luminosity upgrades, CESR will have delivered two 10 fb^{-1} units and will be running at a rate of one unit per year. The goal for the PEP-II B Factory is 3 units per year. Ultimately, that rate may be possible also with the upgraded CESR.

2.2. Rare B Decays

Since its partner t quark is heavier, the b quark can decay only through mixing of quark families. The amplitudes are proportional to off-diagonal elements, V_{cb} and V_{ub}, of the Kobayashi-Maskawa matrix [6] that governs the flavor changing weak decays. Since V_{cb} is about 0.04, rare decays can compete and are a sensitive probe for new physics beyond the Standard Model.

2.2.1. b to u decays
Lowest order tree diagram decays of the b quark occur through two possible W emission graphs, $b \rightarrow cW$ and $b \rightarrow uW$. The charmless amplitude is suppressed relative to the charmed decay amplitude by the factor

$$|V_{ub}/V_{cb}| = \lambda|\rho - i\eta| = 0.08 \pm 0.02,$$

where λ, ρ, and η are three of the four Wolfenstein parameters [7] in terms of which the nine KM matrix elements can be expressed. Hence, in spite of the relative phase space advantage of the charmless final states, the b to u modes are rare, with an inclusive branching ratio of about 2%.

The b to u decay is of special interest, because

- the amplitude involves V_{ub}, a basic constant of the Standard Model,
- the particular combination of CKM parameters, $\sqrt{\rho^2 + \eta^2}$, is not accessible in any other measurement,
- the measurement fixes the length of one side of the unitarity triangle, whose area determines the degree of CP violation in B meson decay,
- CP violating asymmetries are expected to be measurably large in exclusive hadronic b to u decay modes, such as $B \rightarrow \pi^+\pi^-$.

Our present information on $|V_{ub}/V_{cb}|$ comes from the observation of semileptonic B decays with lepton momenta beyond the end point for $B \rightarrow D\ell\nu$ [8]. Independent checks on $|V_{ub}/V_{cb}|$ can come from the measurement of branching ratios for exclusive charmless hadronic decay channels. A first observation of such decays has already been reported by CLEO [9]. The present CLEO detector can distinguish individual $B \rightarrow \pi^+\pi^-$ events from $B \rightarrow K^+\pi^-$ only at the 2.5 standard deviation level, by combining dE/dx (1.8 s.d. K/π separation) and kinematics (1.7 s.d. shift in reconstructed m_B). So the sum of the two branching ratios,

$$\mathcal{B}(B \rightarrow K^+\pi^-) + \mathcal{B}(B \rightarrow \pi^+\pi^-) = (2.4 \pm 0.8) \times 10^5,$$

is better measured than the $\pi^+\pi^-$ branching ratio, $(1.3 \pm 0.8) \times 10^{-5}$. The number of events will increase with the upgraded CESR luminosity and the reliability of the signal will improve with the new CLEO particle identification. We can expect $\pi^+\pi^-$ and other hadronic b to u decay modes to show up at the level of a hundred or more detected events per 10 fb^{-1} unit of integrated luminosity. A study of the pattern of branching ratios in the various modes will be necessary for the detailed understanding of the mechanisms responsible for these decays, which in turn will be essential for the interpretation of CP violating asymmetries.

We can construct loop diagrams for processes $b \rightarrow s\gamma$ or $b \rightarrow sg$, called "penguin" modes. The intermediate loop contains a W boson and either a u, c, or t quark, with the heaviest particle dominating the amplitude. Although the theoretical predictions [10] for the inclusive radiative decays,

$$\mathcal{B}(b \to s\gamma) = 4 \times 10^{-4} \left| \frac{V_{ts}}{0.046} \right|^2 \left(\frac{m_t}{150 \text{ GeV}} \right)^{0.5},$$

are subject to large QCD corrections, they are considered reliable, within $\pm 10\%$ uncertainties coming from Λ_{QCD}. CLEO has detected $b \to s\gamma$ in the exclusive channels $\overline{B} \to K^{*0}\gamma$ and $B^- \to K^{*-}\gamma$, the first experimental observation of penguin decays. The measured average branching ratio is $(4.5 \pm 1.5 \pm 0.9) \times 10^{-5}$ [11]. The inclusive rate has now been measured [12] and is $(2.32 \pm 0.51 \pm 0.2 \pm 0.32) \times 10^{-4}$. As an indication of the importance of these modes this measurement sets a limit on the Higgs mass in the two Higgs doublet model.

2.2.2. Other B Physics

With data samples of tens of fb^{-1} a wide variety of unique physics can be probed some of these are:

- Purely leptonic decays such as $B \to \tau\nu$.
- B decay to baryons and the detailed decay mechanisms.
- Forbidden dilepton decays such as $B \to \mu e$.
- Precision measurements of semileptonic decays and form factors.
- Precision measurements of CKM elements such as V_{ub} and V_{cb}.
- Measurement of exclusive $b \to u$ semileptonic decays.
- Using events with one fully reconstructed B decay to study in detail the decay of the other B and to separate cleanly B^0 from B^- decays.

2.3. CP Asymmetries in B Decays without Tagging

In 1964 we learned that CP symmetry is violated in about 0.2% of the weak decays of neutral kaons [14]. The phenomenon of CP violation may be the basis for the striking asymmetry in the occurrence of matter and antimatter in the universe. In 1973, before the discovery of the charmed quark, Kobayashi and Maskawa [6] realized that the most general 3×3 quark doublet rotation matrix for six quarks can contain an imaginary piece (the $i\eta$ in the Wolfenstein parametrization [7]) that can give rise to CP violation at the level observed in kaon decay.

CP violation effects in B decays [15] are accessible to experiments carried out at a symmetric-energy e^+e^- collider operating near the $b\bar{b}$ threshold and in general require measuring rate differences.

A particular example is the decay $B^\mp \to K^\mp\pi^0$ since the decay $B^- \to K^-\pi^0$ can proceed through either the spectator diagram, with $b \to u + s\bar{u}$ or through the penguin loop process with $b \to s + u\bar{u}$.

Starting with a sample of equal numbers of B^+ and B^-, one looks for an asymmetry in the occurrence of $K^+\pi^0$ and $K^-\pi^0$ final states. In terms of the Wolfenstein parameters, the asymmetry is

$$A = \frac{\Gamma - \overline{\Gamma}}{\Gamma + \overline{\Gamma}} = \frac{2sp\eta \sin(\delta_s - \delta_p)}{s^2\lambda^2(\rho^2 + \eta^2) + p^2\lambda^{-2} + 2spp\cos(\delta_s - \delta_p)}.$$

There are many such possible decay modes that can be used and these searches can be carried out in any experiment in which B and $\overline{B}$ are produced in equal numbers. One simply compares the total numbers of observed B and $\overline{B}$ decays to the chosen CP-conjugate modes. Tagging and decay length measurements are not needed. Many of the favorable modes are charmless modes which do not suffer from the low detection efficiencies typical of charmed final states.

The total number of produced $B\overline{B}$ pairs required to get an asymmetry A with significance s standard deviations is $N(B\overline{B}) = s^2/\mathcal{B}A^2\epsilon$. Provided that there is at least one mode or summable set of modes with branching ratio times efficiency $\mathcal{B}\epsilon > 10^{-5}$ and asymmetry $A > 10\%$, then 1.6×10^8 events would be sufficient to establish CP violation to 4 standard deviations. That would correspond to a run of 150 fb^{-1} integrated luminosity.

Gronau and Wyler [17] have pointed out a class of decay modes that could in principle be used to extract the angle ϕ_s in the unitarity triangle, and for which the asymmetry is independent of hadronic matrix elements. The decays that they consider are $B^- \to D^0K^-$, $B^- \to \overline{D}^0K^-$, $B^- \to D^0_{CP}K^-$, and their charge conjugates. (Both the K^- and the D^0 can be replaced by similar final state particles of the same quark content, for example K^{*-} or D^{*0}.) Interference can occur between the first two amplitudes if the D^0 decay is into a non-flavor-specific final state such as K^+K^-. CP violation may be observable in these modes if the branching ratio for $B^- \to D^{(*)0}K^{(*)-}$, summed over modes, is greater than 5.4×10^{-6} [18]. Otherwise, the background may swamp the signal.

2.4. Non-B Physics

Our normal pattern of running yields the following numbers of events per fb^{-1} of integrated luminosity.

$b\bar{b}$	650,000
$c\bar{c}$	1,000,000
$\tau^+\tau^-$	800,000

CESR will in fact be a "Tau-Charm Factory". Also, running at the $\Upsilon(3S)$ resonance one gets 4 million $\Upsilon(3S)$ decays per fb^{-1}, including a wealth of transitions to lower $b\bar{b}$ bound states: $\Upsilon(2S)$, $\Upsilon(1S)$, $\chi_b(2P_{0,1,2})$, $\chi_b(1P_{0,1,2})$, $\eta_b(1^1S_0)$, $\eta_b(1^1S_0)$, $h_b(2^1P_1)$, $h_b(1^1P_1)$, $\Upsilon(1D)$, *inter alia*.

CLEO has already demonstrated its capabilities in these fields. A survey of the publication record (up to the end of 1993) reveals the following numbers of non-B published papers.

Charmed mesons	29
Charmed baryons	9
Tau decays	14
Photon-photon physics	3
Upsilon bound states	28

Besides increasing the data sample size by at least an order of magnitude, the upgrade will improve our ability to identify charm and tau decays, by isolating the decay vertices and by separating secondary kaons and pions. There are a number of interesting topics for which the number of events now available is not sufficient for definitive study. Some examples are

- pushing down the upper limit on the tau neutrino mass, now about 30 MeV, or making a measurement if m_{ν_τ} is nonzero,

- second-class current decays of the tau, such as $\tau^- \to \pi^- \eta \nu_\tau$, expected at the level of 10^{-5} in the Standard Model,

- the search for forbidden tau decays, like $\tau^- \to e^- e^+ e^-$, $\tau^- \to \mu^- e^+ e^-$, $\tau^- \to e^- K^0$, and $\tau^- \to \mu^- \rho^0$,

- rare decays of the charmed mesons, D^+, D^0, D_s, particularly the rare and forbidden modes $D \to \mu e$ and $D \to X \ell^+ \ell^-$,

- $D^0 - \overline{D^0}$ mixing, expected in the Standard Model at the level of 10^{-4},

- the decay modes of the charmed baryons, Λ_c^+, Σ_c^0, Σ_c^+, Σ_c^{++}, Ξ_c^0, Ξ_c^+, Ω_c^0,

- the spectroscopy of charmed mesons, D^{**} and D_s^{**}, and baryons, Λ_c^*, Σ_c^*, Ξ_c^*, and Ω_c^*,

- the spectroscopy of the $b\bar{b}$ bound states, especially, the so far undiscovered η_b and h_b singlet states and the $\Upsilon(D)$'s,

- the search for new glueballs, $q\bar{q}g$ hybrids, 4-quark $q\bar{q}q\bar{q}$ states, and $C = +1$ $c\bar{c}$ states in two-photon processes.

As the statistical errors decrease with larger and larger data samples and as rarer and rarer processes become accessible, many incisive tests of the Standard Model become possible, increasing the likelihood of finding new physics beyond the Standard Model. A more detailed survey of the possibilities is given in reference [13], chapters 7-10.

3. CONCLUSIONS

The Standard Model of six quarks and six leptons interacting through the unified electroweak interaction and quantum chromodynamics is consistent with all

we know from experiment but there are still many unanswered questions.

The CLEO III detector together with the upgraded CESR accelerator will clearly probe new regions that may contain answers to some of these questions and will be a major step forward in our understanding of quarks and leptons and the fundamental interactions. The sensitivity we will reach in rare B decays certainly opens a new window to observe physics beyond the standard model. This coupled with high precision measurements on b, c, and τ decays and the possibility of measuring CP violation will keep the experiment at the very forefront of discovery for the next decade and beyond.

4. References

References

[1] C. Bebek et al., Phys. Rev. Lett. **46**, 84 (1981).

[2] H. Kagan et al., "The CLEO III Detector", Feb, 1994; CLNS 94/1277.

[3] K. Berkelman et al., "The CESR/CLEO upgrade project", CLNS 93/1265.

[4] M. Bauer, B. Stech, and M. Wirbel, Z. Phys. **C34** 103 (1987).

[5] D. Du and Z. Xing, Phys. Rev. **D48**, 4155 (1993).

[6] M. Kobayashi and T. Maskawa, Prog. Theor. Phys. **35**, 252 (1977).

[7] L. Wolfenstein, Phys. Rev. Lett. **51**, 1945 (1984).

[8] R. Fulton et al., Phys. Rev. Lett. **64**, 16 (1990); H. Albrecht et al., Phys. Lett. **B234**, 409 (1990).

[9] M. Battle et al., CLEO preprint CLNS 93/1235.

[10] R. Grigjanis, H. Navelet, M. Sutherland, and P. O'Donnell, Phys. Lett. **B213**, 355 (1988); A. Ali, C. Greub, preprint DESY 90-102 (1990); N.G. Despande and J. Trampetic, Phys. Rev. Lett. **61**, 2583 (1988);

[11] R. Ammar et al., Phys. Rev. Lett. **71**, 674 (1993).

[12] E. H. Thorndike This proceedings of the ICHEP conference.

[13] *Physics Rationale for a B Factory*, Cornell, June, 1993.

[14] J.H. Christenson, J.W. Cronin, V.L. Fitch, and R. Turlay, Phys. Rev. Lett. **13**, 138 (1964).

[15] Much of the theory of CP violation in B decays was first developed by I. Bigi and A. Sanda. Their work is summarized in I. Bigi, V.A. Khoze, N.G. Uraltsev, and A. Sanda in "CP Violation", ed. C. Jarlskog, World Scientific, Singapore, 1988, and preprint SLAC-PUB-4476 (1987). These include references to earlier work.

[16] M.B. Gavela et al., Phys. Lett. **B154**, 425 (1985); L.-L. Chau and H.Y. Cheng, Phys. Rev. Lett. **53**, 1037 (1984) and Phys. Lett. **B165**, 429 (1986); J.M. Gerard and W.S. Hou, Phys. Rev. **D43**, 2909 (1991); H. Simma, D. Wyler, and G. Eilam, Nuc. Phys. **B352**, 367 (1991); L. Wolfenstein, Phys. Rev. **D43**, 151 (1991); G. Kramer and R. Palmer, Phys. Rev. **D45**, 193 (1992) and Phys. Lett. **B279**, 181 (1992).

[17] M. Gronau and D. Wyler, Phys. Lett. **B265**, 172 (1991).

[18] S. Stone, "Possible Ways of Observing CP Violation at a Symmetric e^+e^- B Factory," Syracuse University preprint HEPSY 92-2 (1992).

[19] S. Stone, Modern Physics Letters **A3**, 541 (1988); see also D.S. Akerib et al., Phys. Rev. Lett. **67**, 1692 (1991).

Paper presented at XXVII Int. Conf. on High Energy Physics: Session Pa-22
Glasgow, UK, 20–27 July 1994

The MILAGRO VHE Gamma Ray Observatory

C.Y. Chang,[1] H.S. Ahulwalia,[9] S. Barwick,[2] D. Bauer,[6] D. Berley, [11] S.D. Biller,[2] D. Caldwell,[6] M. Cavalli-Sforza,[4] M.L.Chen,[1] P. Chumney,[2] D.G. Coyne,[4] B.L. Dingus,[12] C.L. Dion,[1] D.E. Dorfan,[4] R.W. Ellsworth,[5] S.J. Freedman,[10] B.K. Fujikawa,[10] J.A. Goodman,[1] T.J. Haines,[3] C.M. Hoffman,[3] L.A. Kelley,[4] S. Klein,[4] A. Lu,[6] A.I. Mincer,[8] D.E. Nagle,[3] P. Nemethy,[8] T.J. O'Neill,[7] V.D. Sandberg,[3] G. Sanders,[3] S. Schaller,[3] D.M. Schmidt,[3] A. Shoup,[2] C. Sinnis,[3] O.T. Tumer,[7] D.H. White,[3] D.A. Williams,[4] T. Yang,[4] S. Yellenin,[6] G.B. Yodh,[2] and A. Zych[7]

[1] The University of Maryland, College Park, [2] The University of California, Irvine, [3] Los Alamos National Laboratory, Los Alamos, New Mexico, [4] University of California, Santa Cruz, [5] George Mason University, Fairfax, Virginia, [6] University of California, Santa Barbara, [7] University of California, Riverside, [8] New York University, New York, [9] University of New Mexico, Albuquerque, [10] University of California, Berkeley, [11] US National Science Foundation, Virginia, [12] Goddard Space Flight Center, Greenbelt, Maryland

Abstract

Milagro is a water-Čerenkov detector designed to observe EAS in a large, unexplored energy gap between existing VHE and UHE gamma ray detectors. It extends the all-sky, continuous operation attributes of the EAS array to energies as low as serval hundred GeV.

1. The Milagro Observatory

Milagro is a water-Čerenkov detector designed to observe extensive air showers (EAS) in the large, unexplored energy gap between existing Very High Energy (VHE) and Ultra High Energy (UHE) gamma ray detectors. It is jointly funded by the US National Science Foundation and the US Department of Energy, and is being built with an existing reservoir located in the Hot Dry Rock Geothermal project area of the Los Alamos National Laboratory. The area is known as the Fenton Hill in the Jemez mountains, about 35 miles west of the town of Los Alamos in New Mexico.

The reservoir, which measured 60m x 80m x 8m deep is located at longitude $106°47.5'$ W, and latitude $35°52.5'$ N at an elevation of 8700'(2650 m) above sea level. The 8700' elevation suggests a low detection energy threshold of about 250 GeV (VHE region) for the primary cosmic particles. Unlike conventional air shower detectors, which sample less than 1% of the particles which reach detector level, Milagro will be totally sensitive to the electrons, photons, hadrons, and muons in the air shower. In particular, the water-Čerenkov technique is extremely efficient for registering photons via pair production in the first 0.5 m or so of water; photons are the most aboundant shower secondary particles reaching the ground. Milagro is operational 24 hours a day in all weather conditions.

Milagro utilizes 8" PMTs with excellent timing and charge resolution. The PMTs will be deployed in 3 layers, as shown in Figure 1, in the light-tight pond filled with 5 million gallons of purified water. The PMT pinouts and bases will be encapsulated to prevent water from reaching this area. The first layer of 450 tubes (facing up), viewing the 2.0 m of water below the surface area of 5,000 m^2, will be used to measure the time of arrival of an air-shower wave front as it induces Čerenkov light in the water. Based on the 'test beam' results with five swimming-pool water-Čerenkov detectors in conjunction with the CYGNUS EAS array located at Los Alamos, we have estimated the preformance of Milagro with a Monte Carlo simulation.

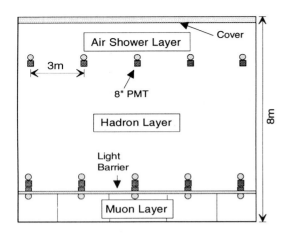

Figure 1. Schematic diagram of Milagro

The pools are arranged in roughly a cross shape with 60 m arms. Each pool is 7.5 m in diameter and $\sim$ 3 m deep, containing 7 fast 10" Burle PMTs. A comparison between the pools and the CYGNUS EAS array yields a measurement of the primary shower axis with an angular accuracy better than .5°[1]. The second layer of 170 PMTs will will view the top 6 m of water and will detect particles which penetrate the top 2 m of water. The third and final layer will consist of 170 PMTs (facing down) located about 7 m deep and will be optically isolated from the above water. This layer will be viewing the 1500 m^2 area of the bottom 1.0 m of the pond to detect penetrating muons.

2.   Physics Aim

The low energy threshold coupled with its large aperture and high duty factor give Milagro a high sensitivity for detecting transient astrophysical sources such as gamma-ray bursters (GRB) seen by BATSE[2], and high energy (from MeV to GeV) emissions from Active Galactic Nuclei (AGN), such as Markarian 421 seen by EGRET[3]. The observed spatial distributions of the GRB sources are isotropic and nonuniform suggesting that they are consistent either with sources in an extended galactic halo, or with sources at cosmological distances. If they are located at such a large cosmological distance from the earth (e.g. Markarian 421 is more than 100 Mpc away), then they are extremely liminous and compact. Since gamma ray flux falls rapidly with energy, especially for γ ray with energy above 100 TeV, they will be severally attenuated by the 2.7 K cosmic microwave background remnant(CMBR) from the Big Bang via the $\gamma\gamma \rightarrow e^+e^-$ interactions. Furthermore, γ rays between TeV and 100 TeV originated from sources at large distances

may suffer the galactic infrared absorption which makes the intergalactic space opaque to them. However, the distances from the sources can not be determined by those instruments aboarding the Compton Gamma Ray Observatory satellite. Milagro should be able to extend these studies to higher energies and reaching at larger distances with much larger acceptance and sensitivity, hence provides a clue to the distance from earth to these sourves.

Air-Čerenkov telescopes have shown that the steady emission from at lease some of the sources detected by EGRET (most notably the Crab and Markarian 421) extends up to several TeV. They have derived from their observed data on Markarian 421 from 400 GeV to 5 TeV. The spectrum follows $1.04 \times 10^{-11}E^{-2.25}photonscm^{-2}s^{-1}TeV^{-1}$ and shows no sign of cut off at the high energy end of their observed spectrum[4]. Milagro , with low energy threshold and high sensitivity, can certainly measure the energy spectrum of these sources to see if the episodic emission see by EGRET also extends to higher energies. Such an information is of most important in understanding the mechanism of the acceleration of cosmic rays.

On the UHE side, there were claims of detected emission above 100 TeV from x-Ray binaries such as Cygnus X-3 and Hercules X-1, etc. However, observations with current, more sensitive arrays have not revealed any further evidence. Although this does not necessary mean the earlier observations were wrong, Milagro should be able to fill up the gap and clarify the enigmatic situation.

Milagro will offer a highly sensitive search for evaporating primordial black holes, an all-sky map in the 1-TeV region. Milagro is also interested in solar physics studies including the first determination of the axial solar magnetic field and the first determination of the short-time behaviour of energetic solar flares.

3.   Summary

To conclude, Milagro with a four-year construction schedule is envisioned its completion and data taking in 1998. Its unique capabilities will allow an observation of the unexplored energy gap between existing VHE and UHE gamma ray detectors and provide us an unprcedented view of the heavens.

References

[1] D. E. Alexanreas, *et al.* 1993, **Proc. 23rd ICRC, OG 4.1.8**
[2] C.A. Meegan, *et al*, **Nature 355**, (1992) 143.
[3] Y.C. Lin, *et al*, **Apj, 401,L61.** (1992).
[4] G. Mohanty, *et al.* 1993, **Proc. 23rd ICRC, OG 4.6.10**

Status of the VIRGO experiment

Michel Yvert

Laboratoire d'Annecy de Physique des Particules
BP110, 74941 Annecy-le-Vieux CEDEX, France

On behalf of the VIRGO Collaboration

Abstract

The VIRGO experiment has been approved in September 1993. The goal of the French-Italian collaboration is to detect Gravitational Waves using a 3km arm-length Michelson interferometer. The construction of the detector, which will be installed near Pisa, is under way. The experiment is planned to take data with nominal sensitivity of h=3.10^{-23} at the begining of year 2000. The motivations, main sources of noise and status of the experiment are presented.

1. Introduction

Gravitational waves are emitted when a massive system with non-zero quadrupolar moment undergoes an acceleration[1]. They were predicted to exist by Einstein[2] already in 1916-1918 and have still not been directly detected. Thanks to the work of Taylor[3] interpreted by Damour and Deruelle[4] on the evolution of the pulsar PRS1913+16, we have now solid "indirect" evidence for their existence . The discovery of gravitational waves will not be only a test of General Relativity , it will also give a better understanding of the gravitational force. Since gravitational waves are real gravitons, their detection will be a first step towards the evidence of the gravitational force intermediate boson. Astrophysicists share also another motivation for the direct detection of gravitational waves. Their arguments are that:

-1) unlike electromagnetic waves, gravitational waves are not absorbed by matter,

-2) all our knowledge about the universe is based on information carried by E.M. waves (except a few ν events),

-3) gravitational waves are expected to be emitted from places where the density of matter is large (places from where electromagnetic waves cannot escape).

Therefore the detection of gravitational waves will give us a completely new picture of the universe.

The first goal of the VIRGO experiment is to detect gravitational waves. The next step will be to perform, in conjunction with other similar detectors, more precise measurements (i.e. the mass and helicity state of the graviton) and start gravitational wave astrophysical observations.

2. Generalities

We recall here a few relevant features of the gravitation theory, more details can be found in reference[1] . When a gravitational wave propagates through space, the metric is perturbed. In the case of weak field, we have:

$$g_{\mu\nu} = \eta_{\mu\nu} + h_{\mu\nu} \quad with \quad h_{\mu\nu} \ll 1$$

where $h_{\mu\nu}$ is the gravitational perturbation to the flat space-time Minkowski metric $\eta_{\mu\nu}$. This translates into a change $\frac{\Delta L}{L}$ of the distance L between two free masses. When the gravitational wavelength is small compared to L one has $\Delta L = \frac{hL}{2}$. When a massive system emits an amount of energy E_g as gravitational waves, the corresponding order of magnitude of the h value at a distance r is given by[5] :

$h \approx \frac{R_s}{r}$ with R_s =Schwarzschild radius corresponding to E_g : where $R_s = \frac{2GM}{c^2}, M = \frac{E_g}{c^2}$ and G is the Newtonian gravitational constant. Like electromagnetic waves, gravitational waves are predicted to have two states of polarisation: $h+$ and $h\times$, the angle between the two states being 45^0 (instead of 90^0 in the electromagnetic case). In the frame of the theory of General Relativity gravitational waves propagate only in an helicity state of 2.

3. Sources of gravitational waves

With today's technologies, it seems hopeless to achieve an Hertz-like experiment (emission and reception in the laboratory) because any conceivable Earth-based apparatus cannot radiate enough power to produce detectable gravitational waves. Astrophysical processes, which involve large masses suffering large accelerations, are the expected sources of detectable gravitational radiation. Three main types of sources are considered:

1) explosion-like phenomena: supernovae or black holes formation. These events are expected to produce very short bursts of gravitational radiation, whose amplitude and time evolution are very poorly known[6]. These poor predictions are a direct image of our ignorance about the degree of asymmetry of the collapse (a perfectly symmetric collapse does not radiate) and about the physical processes involved. Some predictions gave a typical value of $h \approx 10^{-21}$ for a supernova exploding at the centre of the Virgo cluster (1000 galaxies): the VIRGO experiment aims at a sensitivity good enough to detect such events, hence its name. A few such events are expected per year.

2) Periodic sources: slightly asymmetric pulsars are also expected to radiate gravitational waves. Their amplitude is predicted to be small because the radiated power tends to symmetrize the pulsar rotation. A few pulsars are predicted to emit gravitational waves in the frequency range 10 to 100Hz (double of the optical frequency). A typical prediction for the Crab pulsar emission gives values ranging from $h \approx 10^{-24}$ to $h \approx 10^{-28}$.

3) Semi-periodic sources: they are the final state of the coalescence of a binary system[7]. From the observed properties of the 1913+16 pulsar and of some other binary systems, one can infer that coalescences, within the VIRGO sensitivity, occur a few times per year, emitting bursts of gravitational radiation whose amplitude and frequency behaviour are completely predictable.

4. Virgo, interferometric detection

The full description of the VIRGO detector has been given elsewhere[8], here only the main features, improvements with respect to the proposal or new status

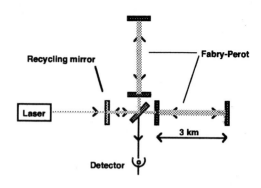

Figure 1.   Principle of the VIRGO interferometer

of key points will be discussed.

The principle of the detector is sketched on Figure 1. A 3km arm-length Michelson interferometer, with suspended mirrors (test masses), is used. The phase difference $\Delta\varphi$ between its two arms is "magnified" using a Fabry-Perot cavity of finesse $\mathcal{F} = 50 \cdot$ in the arms. Aiming for detection sensitivity of $h \approx 3.10^{-23}/\sqrt{Hz}$, VIRGO is a very delicate experimental challenge because of the competition between various sources of noise and the very small expected signal. The interferometer being tuned on the "dark fringe", the signal to noise ratio is mainly limited, in our range of sensitivity, by:
- the photon counting noise (shot noise)
- the refractive index fluctuations in the interferometer arms
- the fluctuations of the input laser amplitude and frequency
- the vibrations of the critical optical components

4.1. Photon counting

The shot noise corresponds to the Poisson statistical fluctuations of the photons number in the light beam, its relative effect decreases like $\frac{1}{\sqrt{P}}$ where P is the beam power. This noise can be decreased by using high efficiency photo detectors and by increasing the laser light power. Unfortunately, the light power cannot be increased at will, mainly for two reasons:

1) the stabilisation of a very high power laser becomes unmanageable. A practical limit in our Nd:YAG laser case is 20W. To overcome this difficulty, we will "recycle" the light which is reflected from the interferometer. This is performed by a semi-transparent recycling mirror see Figure 1 which is carefully kept in position such as to be in-phase with the incoming light beam.

2) The energy which can be stored in the Fabry-Perot cavities is limited due to the absorption in the

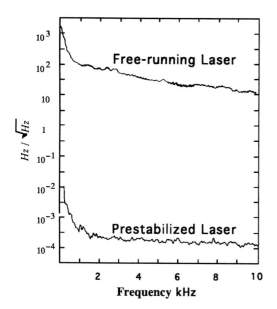

Figure 2.   Frequency stabilization of the input laser

mirrors. The very high quality mirrors required for this interferometer are now only available in very small dimension. A special R&D program is undertaken in Lyon to reach their ultimate specifications which have been optimised, on the basis of complete cavities simulation, using a specially developed method[9].

Once these two conditions are fulfilled, the photon counting noise will limit the signal to noise ratio for frequencies above a few hundred hertz.

4.2. Index fluctuations

The 3km arms of the interferometer will be kept under vacuum. A fluctuation of residual gas density will create a fluctuation in the light propagation velocity. Being not correlated between the two arms, these velocity fluctuations will produce a fluctuating phase difference between the arms and thus a signal. The tubes are planned to be kept under a very good vacuum of 10^{-8} mbar in order to ensure the signal to noise ratio not to be limited by this effect.

4.3. Laser fluctuations

Due to the small asymmetries between the two arms, a fluctuation in the laser frequency will produce a noise signal. It is therefore important to use a very stable laser. The scheme which will be used in VIRGO is based on the use of a high power laser (20W) which is the slave by injection-locking of an ultra-stable low power (1W) laser.

On Figure 2 are shown the results of the R&D which are currently made towards this direction[10]. The performance of the frequency stabilisation servosystem is already sufficient to deal with an asymmetry of 1%.

4.4. Mirror vibrations

The mirror position fluctuations caused by non gravitational waves effect produce a noise signal, which must be carefully kept at the lowest possible level. In this context, the critical sources of noise are:

1) the seismic noise which corresponds to the vibrations transmitted via the ground to the mirrors. In order to minimise this effect, the mirrors are suspended at a seven stage blade attenuator. This system is new with respect to the initial proposal in which a gas spring attenuator device was envisaged. The blade springs system produces the same attenuation but is much easier to stabilise. On Figure 3 is shown the global attenuation of this new system. This result is based on measurements performed on a prototype. We see that the seismic noise is very well attenuated down to very low frequencies. At 4 Hz it gives an equivalent sensitivity of $h \approx 10^{-22}/\sqrt{Hz}$, well below the contribution of the thermal noise.

2) the thermal noise which corresponds to the excitation of the suspension+mirror assembly by the thermal forces. It is the main limitation in sensitivity at frequencies up to a few hundred hertz. The different contributions of these noises are sketched on Figure 4. These calculations are based on the Fluctuation-Dissipation theorem and on its experimental tests[11]. An R&D program, both theoretical and experimental, is underway in order to find ways to decrease further this source of noise.

5. Global sensitivity

On Figure 4 the overall sensitivity is shown. Below 10Hz the graph uses the conservative estimation of the seismic noise contribution and does not take into account the preliminary result obtained on the new

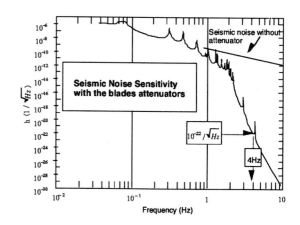

Figure 3.   Seismic attenuation with the blades attenuators

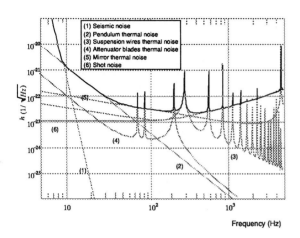

Figure 4.   The VIRGO expected sensitivity

super-attenuators which is shown on Figure 3. The dominant limiting effects are thus the seismic noise below 10Hz, the thermal noise of the suspension system and of the mirrors themselves up to about 300Hz. At frequencies greater than 500Hz the dominant source of noise becomes the photon counting noise. The best sensitivity lies in the range 100-200Hz at a value of $h \approx 3.10^{-23}/\sqrt{Hz}$.

6.   Simulation and Data treatment

Simulation: In order to describe the full behaviour of the VIRGO interferometer, we have developed a simulation program[12] which allows to take into account all sources of noise. This simulation, which is still under development, is an essential tool for the commissioning of the detector and for the running in of data analysis. It helps in finalising parts of the interferometer design, as for instance its global feedback control system.

Data acquisition: The total rate of data to be recorded is expected to be of the order of 600kbytes/s. When recorded continuously over long periods, their amount equals the order of magnitude registered near the large detectors used in high energy physics and calls for a safely organised data management. A Data Acquisition System is being set up[13]. It includes a notion of "trigger" on potentially interesting events[14]. This triggering scheme is optimised using the above simulation tools.

Data analysis: For all events involving a burst of gravitational radiation, we will analyse the data in coincidences with other similar detectors, like the LIGO project, but also the large arrays of cosmic ray showers detectors, the neutrino detectors and the gamma ray sensitive satellites. The idea behind these coincidences

is to find possible correlation between gravitational wave emissions and unexplained phenomena, like the recently observed gamma-ray bursts.

7.   Status of the experiment

The experiment was approved by both the French and Italian authorities in September 1993. This approval includes the funding time-table. The foreseen planning is to start in such a way that we will have a "small interferometer" installed on the final site in 1997, with the final equipment. This "small interferometer" will have the VIRGO specifications except for the quality of the optical components and the length of the arms. This organisation will allow us to test and optimise most of the delicate parts of the experiment (laser, input optics, detection, feed back system) while the optics are realised with their quoted quality (R&D are needed and a special coating machine has to be built for this purpose) and while the 3km vacuum tube is assembled. According to the plans, we expect to take data with nominal sensitivity at the beginning of year 2000.

References

[1] C.W. Misner, K.S. Thorne, J.A. Wheeler . Gravitation . W.H. Freeman and Company San Francisco (1973).

[2] A. Einstein: "Naherungweise Integration der Feldgleichungen der Gravitation" Konog Preuss, Akad der Wissenschaften Litr., Erster Band (1916) 688; "Uber Gravitationswellen", ibidem Erster Band (1918) 154.

[3] J.H. Taylor and J.M. Weisberg , Astrophys. J. 345(1989)434.

[4] T. Damour and N. Deruelle Ann. Inst. H. Poincar (Phys. Thor.) 44(1986)263.
J.H. Taylor et al Nature 355(1992)132

[5] K.S. Thorne Rev. Mod. Phys. 52(1980)285

[6] Three hundred years of gravitation. Chapter 9: Gravitational radiation by K.S. Thorne Edited by S.W. Hawking and W. Israel Cambridge University Press (1987).

[7] B.F. Schutz. Nature 323(1986)310

[8] Virgo: Proposal for the construction of a large interferometric detector of Gravitational waves (1989) Virgo: Final Conceptual Design Documents available on request

[9] A high accuracy method for the simulation of non-ideal optical cavities J.-Y. Vinet, P. Hello, C. N. Man, A. Brillet, J. Phys. I France 2(1992)1287

[10] Virgo project: The stabilized laser source C. N. Man, E. Durand, F. Cleva,P. Fritschel, L. Latrach. Presented at the 7th Marcel Grossman Meeting San Francisco July 1994.

[11] H.B. Callen and T.A. Welton, Phys. Rev.. 83(1951)34 H.B. Callen and R.F. Greene, Phys.Rev.86(1952)702 P.R. Saulson, Phys.Rev. D11(1990)2347

[12] B. Caron, A. Dominjon, R. Flaminio,F. Marion,L. Massonnet, R. Morand, B. Mours, D. Verkindt, M. Yvert. A simulation program for the VIRGO experiment. Presented at "Frontier Detectors for Frontier Physics" La Biodola 22-28 May 1994. Pre-print LAPP-EXP-94-13

[13] B. Caron, A. Dominjon, R. Flaminio,F. Marion,L. Massonnet, R. Morand, B. Mours, D. Verkindt, M. Yvert. Preparation for the signal search in the VIRGO data. Presented at the 7th Marcel Grossman Meeting San Francisco July 1994. Pre-print LAPP-EXP-94-14

[14] D. Verkindt, Thesis May 1993 Université de Savoie

Parallel Session Pa-23

Light Quark and Gluonium Spectroscopy

Conveners: F. Close (RAL)
                Yu Prokoshkin (IHEP, Protvino)

Scientific secretaries: I. Fleck
                        P. Page (reserve)

Meson Spectroscopy: Are gluon-rich states found?

F. E. Close

Rutherford Appleton Laboratory,
Chilton Didcot, Oxon OX11 0QX, Great Britain

Abstract

There is now clear evidence that meson states exist additional to the traditional $q\bar{q}$ states. I show how it is possible to test whether some of these states are gluon-rich. The possibility that new metastable charmonium states are responsible for the anomalous production of ψ' at CDF is raised

At the previous conference in Dallas I noted that the light quark spectroscopy was at last beginning to become complete [1]. The 0^+ sector was particularly important in that this is where the lightest glueball is predicted and there are already more 0^+ states than the $q\bar{q}$ model allows. This has sharpened with the improving data from both Crystal Barrel and WA91, presented here [2, 3]. We also have new data from VES [4] on $0^{-+}, 2^{-+}$ at 1.8 - 2 GeV in diffractive production: these may be radial excitations of $q\bar{q}$ but they have some tantalising properties of hybrid (gluon rich $q\bar{q}$) states. Together with the recent possible 1^{-+} in the 1.9 GeV region [5], these could complete a hybrid supermultiplet.

I begin with the 0^{++} states. The f_0 (975) and a_0 (980) clearly exist and their nature may become clear when DAFNE turns on [7]. In any event there is now an overpopulation of 0^{++} states as far as $q\bar{q}$ interpretation is concerned. The a_0 (1450) seems rather clear now [2] and it fits conveniently with the f_0 (1370) into a 0^{++} nonet whose strange member is the well established K (1430). Beyond this, the situation becomes confused. Lets take two regions — below 1500 MeV and above. Note that the new PDG [6] have continued to misassign the f_0 (1450) of the WA collaboration as a $\rho(1450)$: this **narrow** f_0 may or may not be the same as the Crystal Barrel f_0 (1370) or f_0 (1520). Furthermore the PDG [6] note a broad **elastic** f_0 (1300) which appears to be distinct from the **inelastic** f_0 (1370) and/or f_0 (1450). The most conservative solution is to assume a single f_0 inelastic state (call it f_0 (1370)) and leave its relation

to the elastic f_0 (1300) for future analysis. Above 1500 MeV I believe an interesting picture is developing.

The scenario that I favour is that the ninth member of the $q\bar{q}$ nonet (the f_0 (1590?)) **and** a gluon-rich state (f_0 (1520)) may be distinct and revealed. The f_0 (1520) seems not to couple strongly to $K\bar{K}$ which argues against its $s\bar{s}$ constituency (so $p\bar{p} \to K\bar{K}\pi$ data will be pivotal in future). Furthermore the similarity in mass spectrum of $p\bar{p} \to \pi\eta\eta$ from E760 [9] and $\psi \to \gamma(4\pi)$ argues against the 0^- interpretation of the 1500 bump in the latter (since $0^- \to \eta\eta$ is forbidden in the former). It is plausible that a strong singal for gluon-rich 0^+ is already seen in $\psi \to \gamma(4\pi)$ [10]. A major question will be to decide if the f_0 (1520) seen by Crystal Barrel in $\pi\pi$ and $\eta\eta, \eta\eta'$ channels is the same as f_0 (1590) seen by GAMS [8], or if the latter is $s\bar{s}$ [10].

In view of the impending studies of η and η' final states by WA91 in collaboration with GAMS. I recall a test that any glueball must pass which involves comparison of $\eta\eta$ and $K\bar{K}$ decay branching ratio.

1.   A gluonic anti-selection rule [11]

In searching for gluonic hadrons, there are three particular topics of concern: How do you produce gluonic states, what is their spectroscopy expected to be, and how do they decay? There is agreement on the first question: $\psi \to \gamma(4\pi)$ and central production in the WA experiments are consistent with this. There is qualitative consensus on the second, in particular that

0^{++} is the lightest glueball and that it should be in the 1.5 GeV mass region, which is also consistent with the emerging candidate(s). However, predictions for decays are so varied that they give little or no useful guide. There is however, one rather sharp test that can be made when data on both η and K decays are available. This will become very relevant in the next year or two as the data from CERN accumulates. In view of its potential importance I shall describe this in some detail.

A naive first orientation has been to argue that as gluons are flavourless, they produce all flavours with equal facility, and hence have flavour-symmetric decays. However, we know from QCD-inspired fits to hadron spectroscopy that single-gluon exchange can exhibit dependence on the mass of the quarks to which it couples (the m^{-1} familiar in magnetic coupling), so one should expect that the coupling of time-like gluons to strange quarks, say, will differ from that to up or down.

What I intend to do here is allow $g \to s\bar{s}$ to differ from $g \to u\bar{u}$ and $d\bar{d}$ without specifying whether it is enhanced or suppressed. Interesting selection rules still obtain and, insofar as they do not depend on the relative size or sign of the $s\bar{s}/d\bar{d}$ coupling, may be hoped to have validity more general than any particular model.

Consider a $C = +$ glueball — in particular, a two-gluon state where I label the gluons a and b to distinguish them. There are two amplitudes to consider: A is where $g_a \to s\bar{s}, g_b \to n\bar{n}$ and B is where $g_b \to s\bar{s}, g_a \to n\bar{n}$, ($n\bar{n}$ = nonstrange isoscalar $q\bar{q}$).

Depending on the G parity of the meson final state, one adds ($G = +$) or subtracts ($G = -$) the two amplitudes. Thus

$$G \to 0^-0^- \sim A + B \tag{1}$$

$$G \to 0^-1^- \sim A - B. \tag{2}$$

If the amplitudes for

$$g_a \to q\bar{q} \equiv g_b \to q\bar{q} \tag{3}$$

then $A \equiv B$ and the 0^-1^- decays will be forbidden. This is the standard G parity selection rule.

Now relax the constraint (Eq. (3)) in the case of strange quarks and write for the amplitudes

$$\frac{g_{a,b} \to s\bar{s}}{g_{a,b} \to d\bar{d} \text{ or } u\bar{u}} = s_{a,b} \tag{4}$$

Thus the branching ratios (apart from phase space effects) are

$$\frac{G \to K^+K^-}{G \to \pi^+\pi^-} = \left(\frac{s_a + s_b}{2}\right)^2 \tag{5}$$

$$\frac{G \to KK^*}{G \to K\bar{K}} = \left(\frac{s_a - s_b}{s_a + s_b}\right)^2 \tag{6}$$

Final states involving η and/or η' are not well studied, and there is the possibility that our failure to find glueballs is because they have a propensity to decay into these channels. I will work in the approximation that η and η' contain equal amounts of strange and nonstrange quarks $n\bar{n} \equiv \frac{1}{\sqrt{2}}(u\bar{u} + d\bar{d})$

$$\eta = \frac{1}{\sqrt{2}}(n\bar{n} - s\bar{s})$$

$$\eta' = \frac{1}{\sqrt{2}}(n\bar{n} + s\bar{s}) \tag{7}$$

(A realistic mixing angle modifies the result only slightly.) In this approximation final states consisting of $K\bar{K}, \eta\eta, \eta'\eta'$ or $\eta\eta'$ each are 50:50 mixtures of strange and non-strange quarks; the flavours are merely distributed among the hadrons differently. So any symmetry breaking effects associated with the strange/non-strange quark production will be common to all, and rather general conclusions may be anticipated.

Specialising to the case when $s_a \equiv s_b = s$, we have for the rates

$$\frac{G \to \eta\eta'}{G \to \eta\eta + \eta'\eta'} = \left(\frac{1 - s^2}{1 + s^2}\right)^2 \tag{8}$$

$$\frac{G \to \eta\eta}{G \to K^+K^-} = \frac{1}{8}\left(\frac{1}{s^2} + 2 + s^2\right) \tag{9}$$

which in the symmetry limit $s = 1$ recover the familiar results

$$\eta\eta' \neq 0 \; ; \; \eta\eta = \frac{1}{2}K^+K^- = \frac{1}{4}K\bar{K} \tag{10}$$

Notice that the results are invariant under $s \leftrightarrow 1/s$ and so are true whether strange $q\bar{q}$ are suppressed or enhanced relative to non-strange. Notice also that symmetry breaking always enhances $\eta\eta$ relative to $K\bar{K}$. This is because one of the $q\bar{q}$ productions is disfavoured relative to the other (suppose it is $s\bar{s}$). The $\eta\eta$ production can be fed by the "easy" route ($n\bar{n}$ in this case), whereas the KK necessarily involves both pairs to be present — hence paying a penalty for the disfavoured contribution.

If there is intrinsic glue in η and η', this will reinforce the rule. One can extend the analysis to more realistic mixing angles and one finds a natural fit to the f_0 (1520) branching ratios [12]. The gluon-rich nature of f_0 (1520) begins to be tantalisingly suggestive. It is now critical to compare $\eta\eta$ with $K\bar{K}$ to see if f_0 (1590) is distinct and the $s\bar{s}$ nonet member.

2.   Hybrid states

If 0^+ glueballs are being found in the 1.5 GeV region, this reinforces model expectations for their spectroscopy.

It also supports belief that hybrid states should exist in the 1.5 - 2 GeV region and that the lightest such states will include $0^{-+}1^{-+}2^{-+}$ [13]. Furthermore they are expected to decay dominantly into $S + P$ wave $q\bar{q}$ [14].

This year a BNL experiment [5] has a possible signal for the exotic 1^{-+} at 1.9 ± 0.3 GeV decaying to $\pi + f_1$ (1285) in accord with the $S + P$ rule. At this conference VES are reporting 0^{-+} (1.8 GeV) and 2^{-+} (2.2 GeV) with unusual decay modes, notably $\pi f_0, KK_0$ but **not** $\pi\rho$ and KK^*.

These too are tantalisingly hybrid-like.

The immediate test will be the improved statistics from BNL who have yet to show whether the 1^{-+} is a resonant structure.

If these signals are indeed light quark hybrids, they will reinforce the predictions that hybrid charmonium will occur just above the $D\bar{D}$ threshold. Models, QCD Sum Rules and Lattice QCD all focus on the 4.2 ± 0.2 GeV mass region for the lightest states [15]. Moreover, models predict that such states may be metastable if they lie below $DD^{**}(D^{**} = 0^+1^+2^+)$ threshold. A dedicated study of e^+e^- at a Tau-Charm Factory could prove useful. However there is the tantalising possibility that such states may be responsible, in part, for the enhanced ψ' production reported at this conference [16].

The production of charmonium, in particular $\psi\psi'$, at the Tevatron is dominated by gluon fragmentation. Gluon distributions in the proton are rather well determined and so rates for ψ production are predictably reliable. However the observed rate for the ψ appears to be enhanced by a factor of 2 or 3, while that of the ψ' is a factor of 30-50 larger than theoretical expectation. This is too large a discrepancy to be accommodated by tinkering with parameters in the theory and suggestive of a source additional to those so far included in the calculations. Three main candidates occur for metastable charmonium more massive than the ψ', and whose production and decay could enhance the ψ' and ψ signals.

(i) conventional charmonium states $2^{-+}, 2^{--}$, predicted at 3.81 to 3.85 GeV and thereby metastable (parity forbids the $D\bar{D}$ decay),

(ii) the radial excitation $2^3P_1(\approx 3.9$ GeV) whose decay $\to DD^*$ is near threshold where radial wavefunctions can suppress widths and its partner $2^3P_2(\approx 3.9$ - 4.0 GeV) whose decays into $D\bar{D}, D\bar{D}^*$ are similarly suppressed by $D-$wave phase space and dynamical effects,

(iii) hybrid charmonium states where the gluonic degrees of freedom are dynamically excited in the presence of charmed quarks. Some of these states are predicted to be metastable if their mass is below DD^{**} threshold (≈ 4.3 GeV).

It is possible that the $2^3P_{1,2}$ widths are small enough, and hence the radiative Branching Ratio to

ψ' large enough to be the full source of the extra ψ'. However, if gluon-rich charmonium exists in Nature, then its production in a gluon favoured environment, such as at the Tevatron, is rather natural. If these states are below DD^{**} threshold and thereby metastable there is the exciting possibility that they may be awaiting discovery in the ψ' data at Fermilab. Invariant mass plots involving ψ' with $\gamma, \pi\pi, \eta$ may reveal a source of the ψ' and reveal new charmonium states, in particular the long sought evidence for gluon rich or hybrid states.

While each of the candidates — glueballs at 1.6 GeV, light hybrids at 1.8-2.0 GeV and charmonium hybrids at or near DD threshold is still tenuous, the picture is suggestive and the future path for exploration is clear.

References

[1] F.E. Close, Proc. of 26 Int. Conf. on HEP, Dallas (1992), p. 543 and p. 562.
[2] N.P. Hessey, Crystal Barrel, this session.
[3] O. Villalobos Bailie, WA91, this session.
[4] A. Zaitsev, VES, this session.
[5] J.H. Lee et al., Phys. Lett. **B323** (1994) 227.
[6] Particle Data Group, Phys. Rev. **D50** (1994).
[7] J. Lee-Franzini et al., "In pursuit of the f_0, contribution 0215 to this session.
[8] F. Binon et al., Nuovo Cimento **78** (1983) 313; **80** (1984) 363 D. Alde et al., Nucl. Phys. **B269** (1986) 485.
[9] T. Armstrong et al., Phys. Lett. **B307** (1993) 399.
[10] D. Bugg, Proc. of EPS Conf. on HEP, Marseille (1993) p. 717.
[11] F.E. Close, Rep. Prog. Phys. **S1** (1988) 833.
[12] C. Amsler, Plenary talk, these proceedings.
[13] T. Barnes, F.E. Close and F. de Viron, Phys. Lett. **116B** (1982) 365; Nucl. Phys. **B224** (1983) 241 M. Chanowitz and S. Sharpe, Nucl. Phys. **B222** (1983) 211 N. Isgur and J. Paton, Phys. Rev. **D31** (1985) 2910.
[14] F.E. Close and H.J. Lipkin, Phys. Lett. **196B** (1987) 245 F. Idder et al., Phys. Lett. **B205** (1988) 564 N. Isgur et al., Phys. Rev. Lett. **54** (1985) 869.
[15] F.E. Close, RAL-94-093, hep-9409203, Phys. Lett. (in press).
[16] M. Mangano, CDF Collaboration, these proceedings.

Paper presented at XXVII Int. Conf. on High Energy Physics: Session Pa-23
Glasgow, UK, 20–27 July 1994

Recent results in light meson spectroscopy from low-energy $p\bar{p}$ annihilations

N.P. Hessey

Universität München, D-85748 München, Germany

The Crystal Barrel Collaboration*

Abstract

The Crystal Barrel Detector at LEAR has accumulated large data sets on low energy antiproton annihilation for meson spectroscopy. In particular, the analysis of 3-pseudoscalar final states $(3\pi^0, 2\pi^0\eta, 2\eta\pi^0, \pi^0\eta\eta')$ shows three new scalar resonances with $J^{PC} = 0^{++}$: two isoscalars $f_0(1400)$ and $f_0(1500)$, and one isovector $a_0(1450)$. Their decay branching ratios into various final states have been determined. The $\pi^0\eta\eta'$ data is well fitted by the hypothesis that it is dominated by $f_0(1500) \to \eta\eta'$. With this assumption, the $f_0(1500)$ shows an interesting decay pattern into $\pi^0\pi^0$, $\eta\eta$, and $\eta\eta'$.

1. Introduction

The Crystal Barrel Spectrometer [1] is a 4π detector for charged and neutral particles. It has a 1.5 Tesla solenoid magnet, inside which are 1380 CsI crystals arranged in a centre pointing (barrel) geometry which are used for photon energy and position measurement (resolution 2.5% at 1 GeV and 20 mrad). Inside this barrel is a cylindrical drift-chamber for measuring charged tracks. At the centre of the detector there is a liquid hydrogen or deuterium target, surrounded by two wire chambers used for triggering on charge multiplicity. The detector has been used at LEAR with low energy

* University of California, LBL, Berkeley, CA 94720, USA, Universität Bochum, D-44788 Bochum, Germany, Universität Bonn, D-53115 Bonn, Germany, Academy of Science, H-1525 Budapest, Hungary, Rutherford Appleton Laboratory, Chilton, Didcot OX11 0QX, UK, CERN, CH-1211 Genève, Switzerland, Universität Hamburg, D-22761 Hamburg, Germany, Universität Karlsruhe, D-76344 Karlsruhe, Germany, Queen Mary and Westfield College, London E1 4NS, UK, University of California, Los Angeles, CA 90024, USA, Universität Mainz, D-55099 Mainz, Germany, Universität München, D-85748 München, Germany, Carnegie Mellon University, Pittsburgh, PA, USA, Centre de Recherches Nucléaires, F-67037 Strasbourg, France, Universität Zürich, CH-8001 Zürich, Switzerland,

antiproton – nucleon annihilations to study the light meson spectrum, especially by searching for exotic (non $q\bar{q}$) states.

This paper concentrates on recent developments in the three pseudo-scalar final states, describing new results based on the whole all-neutral data sample and on a set of data taken with a special trigger to enhance the $2\eta\pi^0$ and $\pi^0\eta\eta'$ final states. This trigger selected events with six photons which could be paired to give invariant masses consistent with the $2\eta\pi^0$ or $\pi^0\eta\eta'$ final state.

2. Data Reduction

We have taken 16.8 M $p\bar{p}$ events with an all-neutral trigger, i.e. requiring no hits in the wire chambers. From this data set we selected events with 6 photons above 20 MeV and subjected them to a 4C kinematic fit requiring energy and momentum conservation. 1.4 M events survived, which we subjected to higher constraint fits, combining the photons into all possible final states involving π^0, η, η', and ω mesons. Events were selected for the respective Dalitz plots based on the fit probabilities and the branching ratios for the final states.

The $3\pi^0$, $2\pi^0\eta$, $2\eta\pi^0$, and $\pi^0\eta\eta'$ Dalitz plots from all-neutral triggers contain 712 k, 187 k, 31 k and 158 events respectively. The special trigger data set gives a further 160 k $2\eta\pi^0$ events and 819 $\pi^0\eta\eta'$ events. The data sets are essentially background free except for $\pi^0\eta\eta'$ which contains about 20% background. In all cases, the detection efficiency is flat (less than 5% variation).

3. Dalitz Plot Analysis

We have carried out several analyses of the data. Early work [2] [3] took the Au-Morgan-Pennington [4] amplitudes (AMP) without modification for the $\pi\pi$ S-wave and added further resonances using Breit-Wigner forms. A small subset of the $3\pi^0$ data was fitted with this method and gave a good fit with the introduction of a 2^{++} state, "Ax(1520)", arising largely from atomic P-states. The large P-state contribution in the fit was surprising since most $p\bar{p}$ annihilation in liquid takes place from S-states.

There are two main problems with this approach: firstly, the AMP amplitude applies to $\pi\pi \rightarrow \pi\pi$ scattering – production effects can modify the amplitude in $p\bar{p}$ annihilation; secondly, the addition of two or more Breit Wigners in the same channel can in principle lead to a violation of unitarity – the K-matrix formalism is preferable.

In the first of the new analyses, the first problem is overcome with the N/D method [5][6] for the $\pi\pi$ S-wave below 1.1 GeV. We add further Breit-Wigners where needed above this mass in the expectation that the second problem is small. The parameters for the denominator D are fixed by fitting $\pi\pi \rightarrow \pi\pi$ data. The numerator is parameterised with 4 complex free parameters to take account of the production effects when fitting to $p\bar{p}$ annihilation data. This analysis gives good fits to the data with only contributions from the $^1S_0$ atomic state. Consistency between the three main channels is ensured by fitting the $3\pi^0$, $2\pi^0\eta$, and $2\eta\pi^0$ Dalitz plots simultaneously.

In the second new analysis, both problems are tackled by using the P-vector approach [7], which is a modification of the K-matrix formalism in which free parameters are introduced to account for production effects. To avoid too many free parameters, we restrict ourselves to two channels, $\pi\pi$ and $K\bar{K}$. Good fits are achieved to individual Dalitz plots, either restricting the initial state to $^1S_0$ or allowing P-states as well.

Both new analyses agree in the important conclusions: the necessary introduction of two isoscalar-scalar resonances $f_0(1400)$ and $f_0(1500)$, and an isovector-scalar $a_0(1450)$ [8].

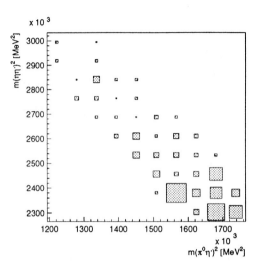

Figure 1. $\pi^0\eta\eta'$ Dalitz plot, showing the enhancement at low $\eta\eta'$ masses.

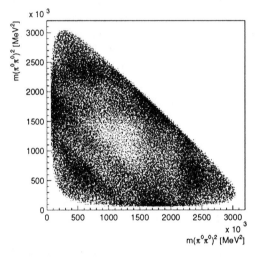

Figure 2. $3\pi^0$ Dalitz plot. The band at 2.25 GeV^2 is due to the $f_0(1500)$.

4. Results

The combined $\pi^0\eta\eta'$ data (figure 1) show a clear enhancement at low $\eta\eta'$ masses. This is what one expects from $p\bar{p} \rightarrow f_0\pi$, $f_0 \rightarrow \eta\eta'$, with an f_0 mass below but close to the $\eta\eta'$ threshold. The Dalitz plot is well fitted by a flat background plus a Breit-Wigner 0^{++} state, $\chi^2/\text{d.o.f.} \approx 1.2$. The optimum mass and width in this simple fit are 1545 ± 25 MeV and 100 ± 40 MeV, with 681 events from the Breit Wigner. We obtain the branching ratio

$$\text{BR}(p\bar{p} \rightarrow \pi^0\eta\eta') = (2.5 \pm 0.5) \times 10^{-4}.$$

For the $3\pi^0$ data (figure 2), the P-vector analysis is nearing completion. It confirms the earlier results,

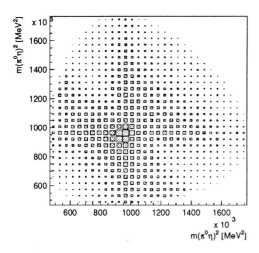

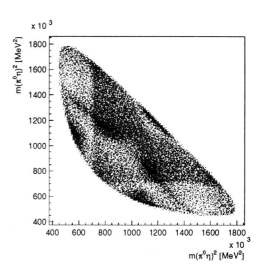

Figure 3. $2\eta\pi^0$ Dalitz plot. The lower diagonal band is due to the $f_0(1500)$.

Figure 4. $2\pi^0\eta$ Dalitz plot. The $a_0(1450)$ is obscured by strong interferences and the angular structure of the $a_2(1320)$.

that the data show contributions from the intermediate states $\pi\pi$ S-wave (containing $f_0(975)$, $f_0(1400)$ and $f_0(1500)$), $f_2(1270)$ and $f_2(1520)$. The mass of the $f_0(1500)$ appears somewhat lower than before, at 1500 MeV. The $f_2(1520)$ contribution is very dependant on the assumptions made for the initial atomic state. It is observed through its interference with the low energy $\pi\pi$ S-wave, and may reflect imperfect parametrisation of this. We do not attribute a resonance interpretation to it yet. The $f_0(1400)$ is highly inelastic, unlike the Particle Data Group state at 1400 MeV; indeed, we find its 4π decay is almost 5 times its 2π decay.

The analysis of the full statistics for $2\eta\pi^0$ (figure 3), including the special triggered data, is continuing. So far, it confirms the previous result that the data show $f_0(1400)$ and $f_0(1500)$ decaying to $\eta\eta$.

Both the new analyses of $2\pi^0\eta$ data (figure 4) show the existence of an isovector 0^{++} state at 1450 MeV. Without it, the χ^2 of the fits almost double. However, it is obscured on the Dalitz plot by strong interferences and the strong angular structure of the $a_2(1320)$. The data also show a small but definite $\eta\pi$ P-wave (which has the exotic quantum numbers 1^{-+}). However it appears to be non-resonant. The data exclude the presence of a 1^{-+} resonance with the parameters reported by GAMS for $\hat{\rho}(1405)$ [9].

5. Conclusions

The $a_0(1450)$ and $f_0(1400)$ have masses close to the well established $K_0^*(1430)$ and fit well into the expected 0^{++} nonet. They could replace the states previously assigned to this nonet, $a_0(980)$ and $f_0(975)$, leaving them free to other interpretations.

We see the $f_0(1500)$ decaying to $\pi^0\pi^0$, $\eta\eta$, and $\eta\eta'$. Under the likely assumption that the $\pi^0\eta\eta'$ final state is dominated by this intermediate state, we obtain the following approximate decay ratios:

$$f_0(1500) \rightarrow \begin{array}{cccc} \pi\pi : & \eta\eta : & \eta\eta' : & K\bar{K} \\ 5.1 : & 0.7 : & 1.0 : & < 0.6 \end{array}$$

where the upper limit on $K\bar{K}$ is derived from bubble chamber data [10].

The $K\bar{K}$ decay is smaller (by at least an order of magnitude) than one would expect for an $s\bar{s}$ state, so it seems unlikely to be the ninth member of a nonet. The presence of this extra 0^{++} state leaves the possibility that it is a glueball, strongly mixed with $q\bar{q}$ to explain the decay ratios.

References

[1] E. Aker *et al.*, Nucl. Instrum. Methods **A321** 69 (1992)
[2] E. Aker *et al.*, Phys. Lett. **B260** 249 (1991)
[3] C. Amsler *et al.*, Phys. Lett. **B291** 347 (1992)
[4] K.L. Au *et al.*, Phys. Rev. **D35** 1633 (1987)
[5] D.V. Bugg *et al.*, Submittted to Phys. Rev. D (1994)
[6] V. V. Anisovitch *et al.*, Phys. Lett. **B323** 233 (1994)
[7] S.U. Chung *et al.*, Submitted to Z. Phys. C (1994)
[8] C. Amsler *et al.*, Accepted for publication in Phys. Lett. (1994)
[9] M. Boutemeur and M. Poulet, Hadron 89, ed. F. Binon, J.M. Frère, J.P Peigneux (Ed. Frontiérs 1989) p. 119
[10] L. Gray *et al.*, Phys. Rev. **D27** 307 (1983)

Observation of new states in the reaction
$pp \rightarrow p_f(\pi^+\pi^-\pi^+\pi^-)p_s$ at 300 and 450 GeV/c

F Antinori[||], D Barberis[||], R P Barnes[§], A Bayes[§], W Beusch[||], J N Carney[§], S Clewer[§],
J P Davies[§], D Di Bari[‡], C J Doddenhoff[§], D Elia[‡], D Evans[||], R Fini[‡], B R French[||],
B Ghidini[‡], A Jacholkowski[‡], J B Kinson[§], A Kirk[||], Y Kulchitsky[¶], V Lenti[‡],
R A Loconsole[‡], S Maljukov[¶], V Manzari[‡], P Martinengo[||], I Minashvili[¶], F Navach[‡],
K Norman[§], E Quercigh[||], V Romanovsky[¶], N Russakovich[¶], A Semenov[¶], M Sené[||],
R Sené[||], A Solovjev[¶], G Tchlatchidze[¶], G Vassiliadis[†], I Vichou[†], O Villalobos Baillie[§],
and M F Votruba[§]

†. Athens University, Nuclear Physics Department, Athens, Greece
‡. Dipartimento di Fisica dell'Università and Sezione INFN, Bari, Italy
§. University of Birmingham, Physics Department, Birmingham, U K
||. CERN, European Organization for Nuclear Research, Geneva, Switzerland
¶. JINR, Dubna, Russia.

Presented by O. Villalobos Baillie[††]

Abstract

The reaction $pp \rightarrow p_f(\pi^+\pi^-\pi^+\pi^-)p_s$ has been studied at 300 and 450 GeV/c. In addition to the $f_1(1285)$, the $\pi^+\pi^-\pi^+\pi^-$ mass spectrum shows evidence for two states previously observed only by the WA76 experiment, the X(1450) and the X(1900). A spin parity analysis performed on both data sets leads to the assignment $I(J^{PC}) = 0(0^{++})$ for the X(1450), which decays to $\rho^0\pi^+\pi^-$, and $I(J^{PC}) = 0(2^{++})$ for the X(1900) which decays to $f_2(1270)\pi^+\pi^-$ and $a_2(1320)\pi$.

1. Introduction

The WA91 experiment, performed at the CERN Omega Spectrometer, aims to study centrally produced mesons. Production is believed to be dominated by Double Pomeron Exchange (DPE)[1], and as such has been suggested as a source of gluonic states [2]. In this paper we present results on the reaction

$$pp \rightarrow p_f(\pi^+\pi^-\pi^+\pi^-)p_s \qquad (1)$$

with a 450 GeV/c incident proton beam. The subscripts f and s refer to the fastest and slowest particles in the

††E-mail: ovb@i.ph.bham.ac.uk

laboratory frame respectively. The reaction has already been studied at 300 GeV/c incident momentum by the WA76 collaboration [3], who reported the observation of two new states, the X(1450) and the X(1900). One of the principal aims of the WA91 experiment [4], which is a continuation of the WA76 experiment, is to confirm the existence of these states and determine their quantum numbers.

2. Data Sample

Reaction (1) has been isolated from the sample of events having six outgoing tracks by imposing cuts on the

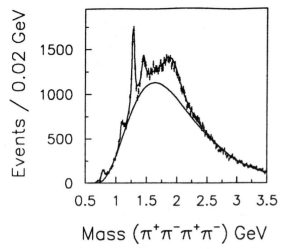

Figure 1. $\pi^+\pi^-\pi^+\pi^-$ effective mass spectrum.

components of missing momentum: $|missing P_x| < 14.0$ GeV/c, $|missing P_y| < 0.16$ GeV/c, $|missing P_z| < 0.08$ GeV/c, where the x axis is along the beam direction. The slow particle is identified as a proton using the correlation of momentum and pulse height obtained in a system of scintillation counters. The $\pi^+\pi^-\pi^+\pi^-$ central system is selected by computing the quantity

$$\Delta = MM^2(p_f p_s) - M^2(\pi^+\pi^-\pi^+\pi^-) \qquad (2)$$

and applying a cut $|\Delta| < 3.0$ (GeV)^2. An additional requirement $M(p_f\pi^+) > 1.3$ GeV is made to remove forward $\Delta^{++}(1232)$ contribution, leaving 98860 centrally produced events.

3. $\pi^+\pi^-\pi^+\pi^-$ Effective Mass Spectrum

Figure 1 shows the $\pi^+\pi^-\pi^+\pi^-$ effective mass spectrum. The spectrum has been fitted using three relativistic Breit-Wigner functions to represent the $f_1(1285)$, the X(1450) and the X(1900), plus a background of the form $a(m - m_{th})^b \exp(-cm - dm^2)$. m is the $\pi^+\pi^-\pi^+\pi^-$ effective mass, m_{th} the threshold mass, and a, b, c and d are fit parameters. In addition, reflections from the $\eta\pi^+\pi^-$ decay of the η' and the $f_1(1285)$ can be seen at 0.8 GeV and 1.1 GeV, where the π^0 from the η decay is undetected. The $\pi^+\pi^-\pi^+\pi^-$ spectrum for events where there was no activity in the electromagnetic calorimeter shows X(1450) and X(1900) signals enhanced relative to background, indicating that they are not themselves reflections of resonances involving a π^0. In addition, the $\pi^+\pi^-\pi^+\pi^-$ mass spectrum has been studied in two intervals for t, the four-momentum transfer at each vertex, namely for $|t| \leq 0.15$ GeV^2 and for $|t| > 0.15$ GeV^2. It is found that both the X(1450) and X(1900) are produced predominantly at low t.

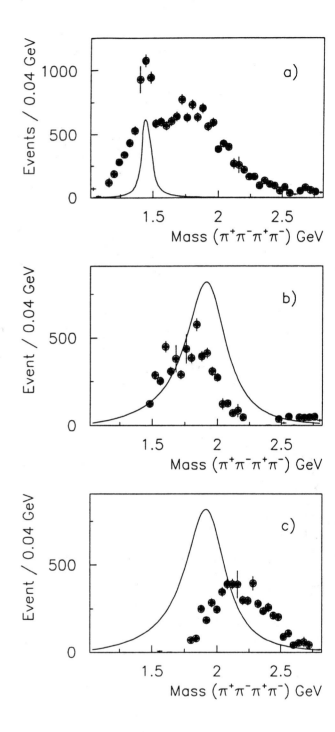

Figure 2. (a) $J^P = 0+\rho(\pi\pi)_{Pwave}$ contribution,
(b) $J^P = 2^+a_2(1320)\pi$ contribution, and
(c) $J^P = 2^+f_2(1270)(\pi\pi)_{Swave}$ contribution, 450 GeV/c data.

4. X(1450) and X(1900) Decays

The decays of the X(1450) and X(1900) have been studied by performing a channel likelihood fit[5] using a modified version of CHAFIT[6]. The method is

	Mass (MeV)	Width (MeV)	Observed decay mode	$I(J^{PC})$	Mass and Width from ref. [3]. (MeV)
$f_1(1285)$	1280 ± 2	40 ± 5	$\rho\pi\pi$	$0(1^{++})$	M 1281 ± 1 Γ 31 ± 5
$X(1450)$	1446 ± 5	56 ± 12	$\rho\pi\pi$	$0(0^{++})$	M 1449 ± 4 Γ 78 ± 18
$X(1900)$	1926 ± 12	370 ± 70	$a_2(1320)\pi$ $f_2(1270)\pi\pi$	$0(2^{++})$	M 1901 ± 13 Γ 312 ± 61

Table 1. Parameters of resonances in the fit to the $\pi^+\pi^-\pi^+\pi^-$ mass spectrum.

described in reference [7]. The principal results are:-

1 The X(1450) decays dominantly to $\rho^0\pi^+\pi^-$.

2 The X(1900) decays almost equally to $f_2(1270)\pi^+\pi^-$ and $a_2(1320)\pi$.

Note also that the $\rho^0\rho^0$ channel, which opens in the region of the X(1450), has a low intensity in this region and does not appear to be associated with X(1450) production.

A spin-parity analysis of the $\pi^+\pi^-\pi^+\pi^-$ system has been performed, using an isobar model. Only angular momenta up to two are considered, using the amplitudes for the decay modes $\rho^0\rho^0$, $\rho^0(\pi^+\pi^-)_{Swave}$, $\rho^0(\pi^+\pi^-)_{Pwave}$, $\rho^0(\pi^+\pi-)_{Dwave}$, $a_1(1260)\pi$, $a_2(1320)\pi$, $f_2(1270)(\pi^+\pi^-)_{Swave}$, $f_2(1270)(\pi^+\pi^-)_{Pwave}$ and $f_2(1270)(\pi^+\pi^-)_{Dwave}$. The angular distributions have been fitted in 40 MeV bins in the $\pi^+\pi^-\pi^+\pi^-$ effective mass, using a logarithmic likelihood function describing an incoherent sum of decay amplitudes. The method is described in reference [7]. Figure 2a shows the $J^P = 0^+\rho(\pi\pi)_{Pwave}$ contribution, in which a peak at the X(1450) can be clearly seen. Figs 2b and 2c show the $J^P = 2^+a_2(1320)\pi$ and $J^P = 2^+f_2(1270)(\pi\pi)_{Swave}$ contributions, which show enhancements in the X(1900) region. Although neither contribution describes the X(1900) alone, their sum accounts for the resonance in both shape and intensity.

The same method has been applied in a re-analysis of the 300 GeV/c data. The results of the analysis are very similar, and in particular the spin assignments for the X(1450) and the X(1900) are the same. As both X(1450) and X(1900) have positive G-parity this allows the isospin to be determined. The results of the analysis are summarized in table 1.

5. Summary

In summary the WA91 experiment confirms the existence of the X(1450) and the X(1900). A spin parity analysis determines the quantum numbers of the X(1450) to be $I^G(J^{PC}) = 0^+(0^{++})$ decaying to $\rho\pi\pi$, and the X(1900) to be $I^G(J^{PC}) = 0^+(2^{++})$ decaying to $f_2(1270)\pi\pi$ and $a_2(1320)\pi$. A re-analysis of the 300 GeV/c data confirms this assignment.

References

[1] D.M Chew and G.F. Chew, Phys. Lett. **53B** (1974) 191.
[2] D. Robson Nucl. Phys. **B130** (1977) 328.
[3] T.A. Armstrong et al. Phys. Lett. **B328** (1989) 536.
[4] S. Abatzis et al., CERN/SPSC 90-2 SPSC/P 249 (1990)
[5] P.E. Condon and P. Cowell, Phys. Rev. **D9** (1974) 2268.
[6] Ph. Gavillet and J.C. Marin, CHAFIT, CERN/D.Ph. II/PROG 75-2 (1975).
[7] S. Abatzis et al. Phys. Lett. **B324** (1994) 509.

Paper presented at XXVII Int. Conf. on High Energy Physics: Session Pa-23
Glasgow, UK, 20–27 July 1994

Experimental study of the S-wave in the $\pi^0\pi^0$-system

A.A. Kondashov, Yu.D. Prokoshkin and S.A. Sadovsky

Institute for High energy Physics, Protvino, Russia

Representing the GAMS Collaboration

Abstract

A study of the $\pi^0\pi^0$-system produced in the $\pi^-p \to \pi^0\pi^0 n$ reaction at 38 GeV/c is carried out at IHEP with the GAMS-2000 multiphoton spectrometer. Partial-wave analysis which includes S and D waves is performed in the $|t|$-range up to 1 (GeV/c)^2. The $S^*/f_o(980)$ resonance is seen as a dip in the S-wave amplitude at small $|t|$. A distinct peak of a 997 ± 5 MeV mass and a 48 ± 10 MeV width is observed in the S-wave at $|t| > 0.3$ (GeV/c)^2. The production cross sections are measured.

In this work* the GAMS collaboration continues the study of the $\pi^0\pi^0$-system produced in a charge-exchange reaction

$$\pi^-p \to \pi^0\pi^0 n \qquad (1)$$
$$\qquad \hookrightarrow 4\gamma$$

at 38 GeV/c π^- beam momentum. The previous studies of this reaction [1, 2] were limited to a low momentum transfer region in order to intensify the one-pion exchange contribution. In the present work a partial-wave analysis (PWA) of the $\pi^0\pi^0$-system was carried out in the 4-momentum transfer range extended up to 1 (GeV/c)^2. Our goal was to study the t-behaviour of the S-wave at the $\pi^0\pi^0$ mass of about 1 GeV, the region being very interesting due to a presence of the $S^*/f_o(980)$, the lightest scalar meson ($J^{PC}I^G = 0^{++}0^+$), which has been a puzzle since the 1970's [4].

The measurements have been performed at the IHEP 70 GeV proton accelerator with he multiphoton hodoscope spectrometer GAMS-2000 [5]. A total of $2 \cdot 10^6$ $\pi^0\pi^0$-events were collected during the two one-month runs (1982 and 1984). The accumulated statistics in the second run was four times larger than in the first one. Event selection procedures and cuts used to reject physical and instrumental backgrounds were analogous to those described in [2]. The stronger selection criteria were used in the 1982 run, for which the instrumental background is somewhat larger. The final $\pi^0\pi^0$ sample is virtually background-free.

The low momentum transfer region shows, along with the dominating $f_2(1270)$-meson, a dip below 1 GeV [2]. The dip disappears with $|t|$ increase, and a clear peak appears in the same mass region (fig. 1a). Its mass and width equal to 995 ± 10 MeV, and to

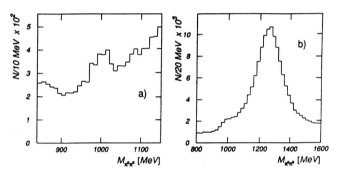

Figure 1. Mass spectrum of the $\pi^0\pi^0$ events after 3C-fit, not corrected for efficiency, $|t| > 0.2$ (GeV/c)^2. a) high-resolution data, b) low-resolution data.

50 ± 10 MeV, with the spectrometer mass resolution taken into account. A shoulder, instead of the peak, is observed in the 1984 low-resolution data (fig. 1b).

To study this structure in detail and to determine its quantum numbers, a PWA of the 1984 run data was performed. The detection efficiency was calculated as described in [2]. The PWA includes S, D_o, D_-, and D_+ waves‡ (the contribution of higher waves is negligible in the mass range under study). The PWA was carried out in several $|t|$-intervals, up to 1 (GeV/c)^2, using the maximum likelihood method.

The S-wave in both low-$|t|$ and high-$|t|$ regions is shown in fig. 2 for the physical and unphysical solutions (the latter one is characterized by unphysically large D-waves near the threshold). At low momentum transfer, $|t| < 0.2$ (GeV/c)^2, both solutions are in a good agreement with the previous results [1]. The physical solution exhibits a dip below 1 GeV (fig. 2a), the result of the $S^*/f_o(980)$ destructive interference with

* Reported by Yu.D. Prokoshkin

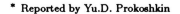

‡ Here and below the notations [3] for the waves and amplitudes are used.

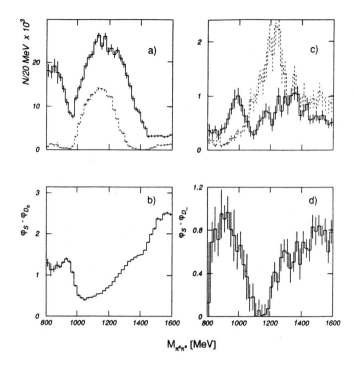

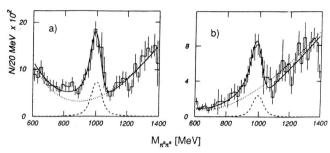

Figure 3. $|S|^2$ at large momentum transfer. $|t|_{min}$: a) 0.30 $(\text{GeV}/c)^2$, and b) 0.45 $(\text{GeV}/c)^2$; the upper $|t|$-limit is 1 $(\text{GeV}/c)^2$. Solid lines show the result of the fit with a B.-W. curve and a polynomial background, interference being taken into account. Dotted lines show the background, dashed curves correspond to the B.-W. resonances.

Figure 2. $|S|^2$, of the physical solution (solid histogram) and of the unphysical one (dashed histogram): a) $|t| < 0.2$ $(\text{GeV}/c)^2$, c) $0.4 < |t| < 1.0$ $(\text{GeV}/c)^2$. b) a relative phase of the S and D_o waves, physical solution, $|t| < 0.2$ $(\text{GeV}/c)^2$; d) a relative phase of the S and D_- waves, physical solution, $|t| > 0.4$ $(\text{GeV}/c)^2$.

the background. A rapid variation of the relative phase of the S and D_o waves confirms the presence of the $S^*/f_o(980)$ resonance (fig. 2b). A wide structure is observed at 1.2 GeV with a width of about 300 MeV, which is naturally associated with the $\epsilon/f_o(1300)$-meson [4]. Its mass agrees with the mass of the S-wave resonance seen both in the $\eta\eta$-system [6] and in previous studies of the $\pi^o\pi^o$-system [1, 7].

The S-wave changes significantly at large momentum transfer, $|t| > 0.4$ $(\text{GeV}/c)^2$ (fig. 2c). The physical solution exhibits a distinct peak at 1 GeV. The S-wave phase measured relative to that of the D_--wave (the $|D_o|^2$ is almost zero here) drops in the peak region (fig. 2d) showing a typical resonance behaviour. The narrow $0^{++}0^+$ state observed in the S-wave at large $|t|$ survives, when the lower edge of the t-interval, $|t|_{min}$, is varied from 0.3 $(\text{GeV}/c)^2$ to 0.5 $(\text{GeV}/c)^2$ with the upper edge being fixed at 1 $(\text{GeV}/c)^2$ (fig. 3). The peak disappears at $|t|_{min} < 0.3$ $(\text{GeV}/c)^2$.

A relativistic B.-W. resonance with the energy dependent width, interfering with a polynomial background, was used to fit the S-wave amplitude squared (fig. 3). The B.-W. curve was convoluted with a Gaussian representing the mass resolution of the GAMS-2000 spectrometer ($\sigma_M/M \approx 2\%$ at 1 GeV). The mass and the width of the S-wave resonance observed at large $|t|$

are found to be

$$M = 997 \pm 5 \text{ MeV}, \ \Gamma = 48 \pm 10 \text{ MeV}. \quad (2)$$

The production cross section of this resonance is equal to 6.1 ± 0.8 nb at $|t| > 0.3$ $(\text{GeV}/c)^2$, and 1.6 ± 0.4 nb at $|t| > 0.5$ $(\text{GeV}/c)^2$. The cross section becomes twice as large if the interference between the resonance and the background is not taken into account.

The mass of 960 ± 10 MeV and the width of 95 ± 20 MeV were obtained for the $f_o(980)$, $|t| < 0.2$ $(\text{GeV}/c)^2$. The production cross section of the $f_o(980)$ is found to be 64 ± 8 nb ($|t| < 0.2$ $(\text{GeV}/c)^2$), this corresponds to $\sigma \cdot \text{BR} = 75 \pm 10$ nb for the whole t-range taking into account the OPE t-dependence of the cross section. The OPE dependence $\sigma \sim \int t \exp bt/(t - m_\pi^2)^2 dt$, $b = 4.7$ $(\text{GeV}/c)^{-2}$, fits well the cross sections measured both at low $|t|$ and high $|t|$.

It should be noted that the parameters of $S^*/f_o(980)$ given in [4] were obtained through the analysis of complicated interference pictures with many channels involved, its width remained uncertain (40 MeV to 400 MeV). Contrary to this, the parameters (2) of the scalar meson, observed in the present work at large $|t|$, are defined in a model-independent way. The narrow resonance peak is pronounced directly in the measured mass spectra (figs. 1-3).

References

[1] S.A. Sadovsky, Proc. 3rd Intern. Workshop on Light Quark Spectroscopy, p. 87, KEK 92-8, Tsukuba, 1992.
[2] A.A. Kondashov, Yu.D. Prokoshkin, Proc. 5th Intern. Conf. on Hadron Spectroscopy HADRON'93, Como, Italy, 1993.
[3] G. Costa *et al.*, Nucl. Phys. **B175** (1980) 402.
[4] Rev. Particle Properties, Phys. Rev. **D50** (1994) 1173.
[5] F.G. Binon *et al.*, Nucl. Instr. Meth. **A248** (1986) 86.
[6] D. Alde *et al.*, Nucl. Phys. **B269** (1986) 485.
[7] W.D. Apel *et al.*, Nucl. Phys. **B201** (1982) 197; Yad. Fiz. **41** (1985) 347.

Study of resonance production in $\pi^- N$ diffractive reactions at $P_{\pi^-} = 37$ GeV/c

D. Amelin[†], E. Berdnikov[†], S. Bityukov[†], G. Borisov[†], Yu. Gouz[†], Yu. Ivanyushenkov[†],
I. Kachaev[†], A. Karyukhin[†], Yu. Khokhlov[†], G. Klyuchnikov[†], V. Konstantinov[†], S. Kopikov[†],
M. Kostrikov[†], V. Kostyukhin[†], A. Kriushin[†], T. Lomtadze[§], V. Matveev[†], A. Ostankov[†],
D. Ryabchikov[†], G. Sehniaidze[§], O. Solovianov[†], E. Starchenko[†], E. Tskhadadze[§] E. Vlasov[†],
A. Zaitsev[†]

† IHEP, Protvino.   § IPh, Tbilisi.

Presented by A. Zaitsev on behalf of the VES collaboration

1. Introduction

The VErtex Spectrometer (VES) setup [1, 2] is a large aperture magnetic spectrometer including a system of proportional and drift chambers, a multichannel threshold Čerenkov counter, lead-glass γ-detector and Be target. The setup runs on the negative charge beam with the momentum 37 GeV/c of 70 GeV proton accelerator. In this report we present the results on the reactions $\pi^- N \to \pi^+ \pi^- \pi^- N$ and $\pi^- N \to K^+ K^- \pi^- N$.

2. Reaction $\pi^- N \to \pi^+ \pi^- \pi^- N$

The results presented here are based upon the statistics of about $2 \cdot 10^6$ events with $|t'| < 0.06$ GeV^2. The PWA [3] of the system $\pi^+ \pi^- \pi^-$ has been performed in the 0.7–2.6 GeV mass region in 10 MeV bins. The set of partial waves included into the analysis is given below:

0^- $(S0 + \epsilon\, D0 + f_2)\, S0 + f_0\, P0 + \rho$
1^+ $(S0 + \rho\, D0 + \rho\, P0 + f_2)\, P0 + \epsilon P0 + f_0\, S1 + \rho$
1^- $P1 + \rho$
2^- $(S0 + f_2\, P0 + \rho\, D0 + \epsilon\, D0 + f_0\, D0 + f_2)$
        $S1 + f_2\, P1 + \rho$
2^+ $D1 + \rho$

3^+ $(S0 + \rho_3\, P0 + f_2\, D0 + \rho)$
4^- $(P0 + \rho_3\, D0 + f_2\, F0 + \rho)$

The notations of the waves are given in the form of $J^P LM \eta$ *isobar*. The FLAT "wave" which is constant over all variables and non-interfering with other waves was also introduced. The states in brackets are assumed to be coherent in order to decrease the number of parameters in the ρ-matrix. The isobars $\rho(770)$, $f_2(1270)$, $\rho_3(1690)$ have been described by relativistic Breit-Wigner functions with the standard parameters. The S-wave in the channel $\pi^+ \pi^-$ has been parameterized by two different states:

f_0 – the "narrow" resonance with the $f_0(975)$ parameters;

ϵ – the "broad" wave which is the AMP M-solution [4] with $f_0(975)$ removed.

$J^{PC} = 0^{-+}$ In the wave $0^- \epsilon$ there is a broad maximum at $M \approx 1.3$ GeV. In the waves $\epsilon\pi$ and $f_0\pi$ a clear resonance-like peak is observed at $M \approx 1.8$ GeV figure 1(a,b). There is no such structure in the $\rho\pi$ channel figure 1(c). The parameters of the resonance in the $\epsilon\pi$ and $f_0\pi$ channels are:

$\epsilon:$ $M = 1786 \pm 7(stat) \pm 30(syst)$ MeV,
        $\Gamma = 192 \pm 20(stat) \pm 30(syst)$ MeV;

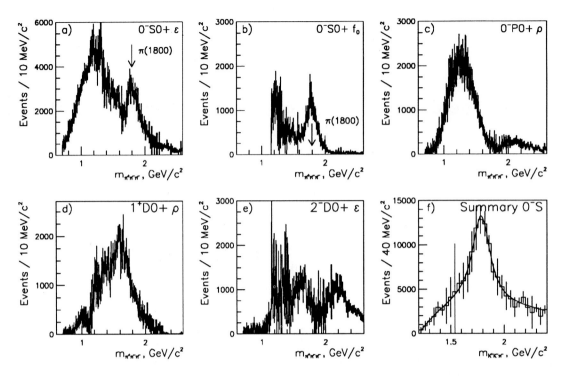

Figure 1. Some wave intensities in $\pi^+\pi^-\pi^-$ (a-e) and $K^+K^-\pi^-$ (f) systems.

$$f_0: \quad M = 1782 \pm 5(stat) \pm 5(syst) \text{ MeV},$$
$$\Gamma = 151 \pm 15(stat) \pm 10(syst) \text{ MeV}$$

The relative probability of the decay $\pi(1800)$ into $f_0\pi$ and $\epsilon\pi$ is equal to

$$\frac{\Gamma(\pi^-(1800) \to f_0(\pi^+\pi^-)\pi^-)}{\Gamma(\pi^-(1800) \to \epsilon(\pi^+\pi^-)\pi^-)} = 0.9 \pm 0.1$$

$$\frac{\Gamma(\pi(1800) \to \rho^0\pi^-)}{\Gamma(\pi(1800) \to f_0(\pi^+\pi^-)\pi^-)} < 0.3 \text{ at } 95\% \text{ C.L.}$$

The natural classification of $\pi(1800)$ can be the second radial excitation of π-meson. Nevertheless features of this object noted above point to its possibly exotic (hybrid-like) nature.

$J^{PC} = 1^{++}$ In the wave $1^+S0+\rho$ the a_1 signal is seen at $M \approx 1.2$ GeV and some shoulder at $M \approx 1.7$ GeV. Significant excess of the $1^+S0+\rho$ wave over Deck effect [5] together with the structures in $1^+P0+\epsilon$, $1^+D0+\rho$ figure 1(d) waves can be considered as an indication on the existance of an object with $J^{PC} = 1^{++}$, $M \approx 1.7$ GeV, which decays into all those channels with comparable probabilities.

$J^{PC} = 2^{-+}$ In the wave 2^-S0+f_2 a clear signal from $\pi_2(1670)$ resonance is seen. In the $2^-D0+\epsilon$ wave one can observe the structure with two maxima at $M \approx 1.7$ GeV and $M \approx 2.2$ GeV Figure 1(e). The first one can be identified as $\pi_2(1670)$, the second is probably a new object [6].

3. Reaction $\pi^-N \to K^+K^-\pi^-N$

The PWA of the system $K^+K^-\pi^-$ has been performed in the 1.2–2.4 GeV mass region divided into 30 mass bins, each 40 MeV wide.

0^-	$S0 + \kappa K^-$ $S0 + f_0\pi^-$ $P0 + K^*K^-$
1^+	$S0 + K^*K^-$ $P0 + \kappa K^-$ $P0 + f_0\pi^-$ $D0 + K^*K^-$
2^-	$S0 + K_2K^-$ $S0 + f_2\pi^-$ $P0 + K^*K^-$ $D0 + \kappa K^-$
3^+	$D0 + K^*K^-$

Two waves 0^-S κK^- and 0^-S $f_0\pi^-$ dominate in the 0^- state. The sum of the two waves figure 1(f) shows a structure with parameters: $M = 1.79 \pm 0.02$ GeV, $\Gamma = 0.20 \pm 0.05$ GeV. The resonance is not seen in the $0^-P0 + K^*K^-$ channel. $BR(\pi(1800) \to K^*(K^+\pi^-)K^-)/BR(\pi(1800) \to K^+K^-\pi^-(S \text{ wave})) < 0.1$ at 95% C.L.

References

[1] S.I. Bityukov *et al.*, Phys. Lett. **B268** (1991) 137.
[2] E.B. Berdnikov *et al.*, Phys. Lett. **B313** (1993) 276.
[3] J.D. Hansen *et al.*, Nucl. Phys. **B81** (1974) 403.
[4] K.L. Au, D. Morgan, M.R. Pennington, Phys. Rev. **D35** (1987) 1633.
[5] G. Ascoli *et al.*, Phys. Rev. **D8** (1973) 3894.
[6] C. Daum *et al.*, Phys. Lett. **B89** (1980) 285.

Results from the $\bar{p}p \to \phi\phi$ reaction by the JETSET experiment[+]

H. Wirth[*]

Fakultät für Physik, Universität Freiburg, D–79104 Freiburg, Germany

representing the JETSET collaboration

Abstract

The JETSET (PS202) internal H_2 cluster-jet target experiment at CERN–LEAR has as a main objective the study of the OZI suppressed reaction $\bar{p}p \to \phi\phi$ via the subsequent $\phi\phi \to K^+K^-K^+K^-$ decay. Measurements were performed over the whole accessible centre-of-mass energy region from near threshold to the LEAR maximum, corresponding to beam momenta between 1.0 and 2.0 GeV/c. A strong $\phi\phi$ signal was found, but yet no clear evidence for resonant behaviour.

The experimental confirmation or the proof of non-existence of exotic states would be a fundamental discovery [1]. So far, the experimental work has been focused on the hadronic spectrum in the mass range $1 \ldots 2$ GeV/c^2. There is, however, a significant lack of information around and above 2 GeV/c^2, where all but the lowest-lying gluonic states are expected [1, 2].

The new form of hadronic matter may show up experimentally as intermediate states. Particularly interesting are those reaction channels with different valence-quark flavours in the initial and final states. In $\bar{p}p$ annihilations the production of hidden or open strangeness in the form of ϕ or K mesons has been chosen by the PS202 (JETSET) experiment at CERN–LEAR, which physics programme [3] is focused on the investigation of the reaction $\bar{p}p \to \phi\phi$, where $\phi \to K^+K^-$ is the detected decay channel.

The experiment is installed in the LEAR machine and uses an internal hydrogen-cluster jet target [4]. The interaction region is surrounded by a compact detector arrangement. A detailed description of the tracking

detector can be found in reference [5] as well as a list of references for the other components.

The first-level on-line trigger is based on a charged particle multiplicity of four, the rejection of photons and pions, and on the specific event topologies. After a multi-step reduction, about four percent of the events that produced a first-level 'four-kaon' trigger have survived the selection criteria.

Four-particle kinematics yields up to two real solutions for the momenta. A small violation of the energy conservation is accepted, taking into account the finite detector resolution. The solutions are tested for compatibility with the Cherenkov and the silicon $\mathrm{d}E/\mathrm{d}x$ information. Less than one percent of those event candidates that remained after the reduction finally passed this check of consistency.

The selected four-kaon event candidates are shown in figure 1 as a Goldhaber plot for data taken at 1.4 GeV/c incident $\bar{p}$ momentum. The charge of the kaons not being measured, all three possible mass combinations of the kaon pairs are entered. An enhancement in the $\phi\phi$ region is clearly observable. The accumulation on the upper diagonal is the combinatoric reflection of the $\phi\phi$ peak. Figure 2 shows the effective mass distribution of kaon pair combinations, where the effective mass of the opposite pair falls into the ϕ mass region $(1.00$ GeV/$c^2 \leq m(KK) \leq 1.04$ GeV/$c^2)$. A clean ϕ sig-

[+] supported partly by CERN, the German Bundesministerium für Forschung und Technologie, the Italian Istituto Nazionale di Fisica Nucleare, the Swedish Natural Science Research Council, and the United States National Science Foundation.
[*] Present address: PPE Division, CERN, CH-1211 Genève 23, Switzerland.
E-Mail: harald@cernvm.cern.ch

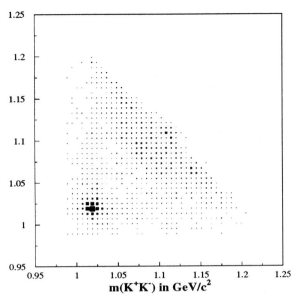

Figure 1. Goldhaber plot of $m(K_3 K_4)$ vs. $m(K_1 K_2)$ at 1.4 GeV/c incident $\bar{p}$ momentum.

nal with little background can be seen. A Breit-Wigner fit to the ϕ region gives $m = (1019.4 \pm 0.4)$ MeV/c^2 and $\Gamma = (14.6 \pm 1.1)$ MeV/c^2, in excellent agreement with the PDG mass [6]. The reconstructed width is dominated by the experimental resolution and is well reproduced in Monte-Carlo simulations.

The determination of the $\phi\phi$ *signal* is done using the channel-likelihood technique [7]. Three channels are considered in the fit: $\phi\phi$, ϕKK, and 4K phase space. Events from background reactions, when reconstructed

under the four-kaon mass hypothesis, form a broad continuum in the mass plot. Hence the background is undistinguished from the four-kaon phase space by the channel-likelihood fit. As a test of the quality of the fit, we show in figure 2, as shaded histogram, the KK mass distribution which is found by the fit to belong to phase space. The *acceptance* is obtained by generating Monte-Carlo events and simulating the detector response using GEANT. A smooth momentum-dependent trigger acceptance of the order of 15 % is obtained. Passing the generated events through the whole analysis chain, the final reconstruction efficiency turned out to be about 3 %. The *luminosity* is determined using elastic $\bar{p}p$ scattering.

In conclusion, we have studied the four-charged-kaon final states produced in $\bar{p}p$ annihilations at LEAR over the whole accessible centre-of-mass energy region 2.04 GeV$/c \leq \sqrt{s} \leq 2.43$ GeV/c. A strong $\phi\phi$ signal relative to the uncorrelated 4K or ϕKK channel can be seen at all measured momenta. During preliminary evaluations [8] no clear evidence for resonant behaviour has yet been found. The analysis for the data at 1.4 GeV/c incident $\bar{p}$ beam momentum has been completed and cross sections for the $\bar{p}p \rightarrow \phi\phi$ and the $\bar{p}p \rightarrow K^+K^-K^+K^-$ reaction at this energy will be reported [9]. At higher energies, a smaller contribution of the $\phi\phi$ signal relative to the non-resonant 4K 'background' can be noticed, e.g. comparing the data at 1.8 GeV/c^2 to that at 1.4 GeV/c^2. This might be partly caused by a larger contribution of the ϕKK channel to the 4K final state. A detailed analysis of the full data sample using refined off-line particle identification techniques, which will give 'cleaner' data with less background, is in progress [9].

References

[1] K. Königsmann, *Proc. XI International Conference "Physics in Collisions"*, Colmar, 1991, p. 355; T.H. Burnett and S.R. Sharpe, Ann. Rev. Nucl. Part. Sci. **40** (1990) 327; K. Peters, Nucl. Phys. **A558** (1993) 93c.

[2] F. Close, Rep. Prog. Phys. **51** (1988) 833; G.S. Bali *et al*, Phys. Lett. **B 309** (1993) 378.

[3] N. Hamann *et al*, *Proc. International School on Physics with Low-Energy Antiprotons (4th Course: Medium-Energy Antiprotons and the Quark–Gluon Structure of Hadrons)*, Erice, 1990, eds. R. Landua, J.-M. Richard and R. Klapisch (Plenum Press, New York, 1991), p. 165.

[4] C. Evangelista *et al*, CERN/SPSLC 92-42, SPSLC M501 (1992).

[5] N.H. Hamann *et al*, Nucl. Instr. Meth. **A 346** (1994) 57.

[6] K. Hikasa *et al* (*Particle Data Group*), *Review of Particle Properties*, Phys. Rev. **D 45** (1992) .

[7] P.E. Condon and P. Cowell, Phys. Rev. **D 9** (1974) 2558.

[8] O. Steinkamp, Dissertation, Universität Bonn (1993), Jül 2877, Forschungszentrum Jülich (1994).

[9] L. Bertolotto *et al*, to be submitted to Phys. Lett. B; R. Jones, invited contribution to the *3rd Biennial Conf. on Low-Energy Antiproton Physics*, Bled, Slovenia, 1994; S. Passagio, *ibid.*

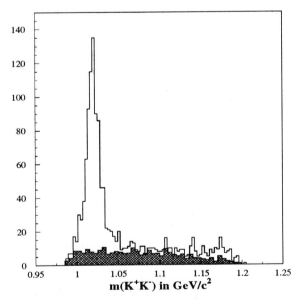

Figure 2. Effective mass distribution of kaon pair combinations where the effective mass of the opposite pair falls into the ϕ band. The shaded histogram represents the portion of the data which is allocated to phase space by the channel likelihood fit.

Paper presented at XXVII Int. Conf. on High Energy Physics: Session Pa-23
Glasgow, UK, 20–27 July 1994

Two-Photon Physics at ARGUS

Ervin Križnič [‡]

Jožef Stefan Institute,
Jamova 39, Ljubljana, Slovenia, SI 61000

On behalf of the ARGUS Collaboration

Abstract

In the reaction $\gamma\gamma \to \omega\rho^0$, a partial wave analysis that was performed on the five-pion final state, showed a dominance of the wave with spin and parity $(J^P, J_z) = (2^+, 2)$. The cross section and angular distributions of the reaction $\gamma\gamma \to \phi\rho^0 \to K^+K^-\pi^+\pi^-$ were measured for the first time. The production of the vector-meson pair $\phi\omega$ is observed in two-photon interaction $\gamma\gamma \to K^+K^-\pi^+\pi^0\pi^-$.

1. Introduction

Two photon productions of $\pi^+\pi^+\pi^0\pi^-\pi^-$, $K^+K^-\pi^+\pi^-$, and $K^+K^-\pi^+\pi^0\pi^-$ have been studied using the ARGUS detector at the e^+e^- storage ring DORIS II at DESY. The data correspond to an integrated luminosity of 456 pb^{-1} collected at beam energies between 4.7 and 5.3 GeV. The ARGUS detector, its trigger and its particle identification system are described elsewhere [1]. A detail description of event selections for all three reactions is found in [2].

2. Reaction $\gamma\gamma \to \omega\rho^0 \to \pi^+\pi^+\pi^0\pi^-\pi^-$

After imposing the selection criteria, 2717 events remained. Most of the events are concentrated in the $W_{\gamma\gamma}$ region between 1.3 and 2.5 GeV/c^2. In this region a thorough *partial–wave analysis* was performed that included 6 $\omega\rho$ waves with different spin-parities and sum of vector-meson spins j: $(J^P, J_z) =$ $(0^+, 0)$, $(0^-, 0)$, $(2^+, \pm 2)$, $(2^+, 0)$, $(2^-, 0)_{j=1}$, $(2^-, 0)_{j=2}$ and 3 isotropic channels: $\omega\pi^+\pi^-$, $\rho^0\pi^+\pi^-$ and $\pi^+\pi^+\pi^0\pi^-\pi^-$. For $\omega\rho^0$ partial waves the background is not subtracted since in general its angular distribution is unknown. It is found that the $(J^P, J_z) = (2^+, 2)$

‡ E-mail: Ervin.Kriznic@ijs.si.

wave dominates (fig. 1) and that the helicity 0 component of $J^P = 2^+$ is suppressed over the helicity 2 component. The contributions of negative parity states are also small. It was found that the inclusion of interference terms has a negligible effect on the results of the analysis.

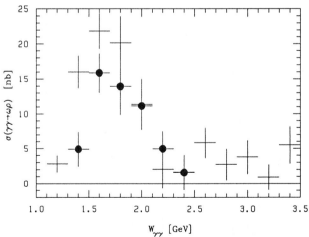

Figure 1. Cross section for $\omega\rho^0$ partial wave with spin and parity $(J^P, J_z) = (2^+, 2)$ and a sum of all $\omega\rho^0$ cross sections.

The remaining statistically less significant regions ($W_{\gamma\gamma} < 1.3$ GeV/c^2 and $W_{\gamma\gamma} > 2.5$ GeV/c^2) were treated in a simplified manner by *mass likelihood fit.* At $W_{\gamma\gamma} > 2.5$ GeV/c^2 the contributions of $\omega\rho^0$, $\omega\pi^+\pi^-$, $\rho^0\pi^+\pi^0\pi^-$ and $\pi^+\pi^+\pi^0\pi^-\pi^-$ were treated isotropically. At two–photon invariant masses well below the $\omega\rho^0$ threshold ($W_{\gamma\gamma} < 1.3$ GeV/c^2) $\gamma\gamma \to \omega\pi^+\pi^-$ and $\gamma\gamma \to \omega\rho$ as well as $\gamma\gamma \to \rho^0\pi^+\pi^0\pi^-$ and $\gamma\gamma \to \pi^+\pi^+\pi^0\pi^-\pi^-$ are indistinguishable. The fit procedure, therefore, included only reactions $\gamma\gamma \to \omega\rho$ and $\gamma\gamma \to \pi^+\pi^+\pi^0\pi^-\pi^-$ in this region.

The background events obtained from simulation of other two-photon reactions, tau pair production and reactions $e^+e^- \to$ hadrons were subject to the same *mass likelihood fit* as the measured data. It was found that 76 % of all 638 background events migrates into $\gamma\gamma \to \pi^+\pi^+\pi^0\pi^-\pi^-$ and only 7% in $\gamma\gamma \to \omega\rho^0$. A sum of all $\omega\rho^0$ cross sections subtracted for the background are shown in fig. 1. The systematic error equals to 11% for $(2^+, 2)$ wave and 8.5% for the sum of all $\omega\rho^0$ partial waves.

3.   Reaction $\gamma\gamma \to \phi\rho^0 \to K^+K^-\pi^+\pi^-$

For the selected $\gamma\gamma \to K^+K^-\pi^+\pi^-$ events an enhancement is seen in the $\phi\rho$ region of the scatter plot of K^+K^- versus $\pi^+\pi^-$ invariant masses [2]. The ϕ mesons were identified by requiring their invariant mass to differ from the nominal one by less then 12 MeV/c^2. Since ρ^0 is a broad resonance, its mass distribution depends on the invariant mass of the $\phi\rho$ system $W_{\gamma\gamma}$. This dependence is determined by the simulation of the reaction $\gamma\gamma \to \phi\rho^0$ and applied to define a cut on two-pion invariant mass [2].

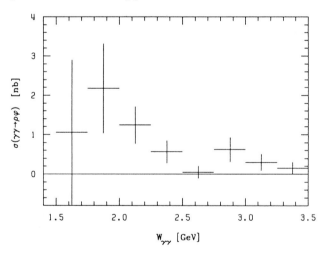

Figure 2. Cross section of the reaction $\gamma\gamma \to \phi\rho^0$.

The total number of measured events that fulfil the selection criteria for $\gamma\gamma \to \phi\rho^0$ is 33 [2]. As found by simulation, 5.3±1.0 of these come from non $\gamma\gamma \to \phi\rho^0$ processes. By subtracting the corresponding $W_{\gamma\gamma}$ distributions from each other and accounting for

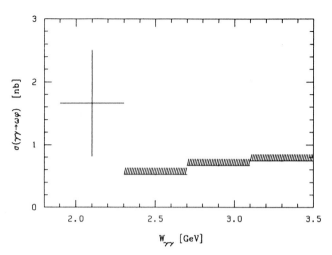

Figure 3. Cross section and upper limits at 95% confidence level for the reaction $\gamma\gamma \to \phi\omega$.

the acceptance and the $\phi \to K^+K^-$ branching ratio, a cross section for $\gamma\gamma \to \phi\rho^0$ is obtained (fig. 2a). The overall systematical error is 12%.

An attempt was made to compare the measured angular distributions to Monte Carlo expectations for pure partial waves with spin, parity: $(J^P, J_z) = (0^+, 0)$, $(0^-, 0)$, $(2^+, 2)$, $(2^+, 0)$, $(2^-, 0)$. The Monte Carlo expectations include the same $W_{\gamma\gamma}$ distributions as determined from the measured data. Of the above mentioned pure spin-parity assignments it is only $(2^-, 0)$ that is not in conflict with the data.

4.   Reaction $\gamma\gamma \to \phi\omega \to K^+K^-\pi^+\pi^0\pi^-$

An attempt was made to extract the $\gamma\gamma \to \phi\omega$ cross section from the sample of selected $\pi^+\pi^-\pi^0 K^+K^-$ events. Restricting the K^+K^- invariant masses to values that differ less than 12 MeV/c^2 from the nominal ϕ mass, we obtain an enhancement in the ω region of the $\pi^+\pi^-\pi^0$ invariant mass spectrum. Of the total 9 events, 4 have invariant masses that lie closer to the nominal ω mass than 50 MeV/c^2. The non $\phi\omega$ contribution to the selected events was estimated by Monte Carlo simulation. An upper limit of 0.6 events (95% confidence level) was found. After accounting for acceptance and branching ratios for $\phi \to K^+K^-$ and $\omega \to \pi^+\pi^0\pi^-$, the cross section for $\gamma\gamma \to \phi\omega$ is found (fig. 3). Since no events were observed in the $W_{\gamma\gamma}$ region above 2.3 GeV/c^2, only an upper limit was set to the cross section.

References

[1] ARGUS Coll., H. Albrecht *et al.*, Nucl. Instr. Meth. **A275** (1989) 1.

[2] E. Križnič *Production of $\omega\rho^0$, $\rho^0\phi$ and $\omega\phi$ in Two-Photon Interactions at the ARGUS Spectrometer*, Ph.D. thesis, University of Ljubljana (Ljubljana 1993).

Parallel Session Pa-24

Future Accelerators

Conveners: R. Siemann (SLAC)
              Y. Kimura (KEK)
Chairman: J. M. Paterson (SLAC)

Scientific secretaries: S. Thorn
                          M. Smith (reserve)

Paper presented at XXVII Int. Conf. on High Energy Physics: Session Pa-24
Glasgow, UK, 20–27 July 1994

The LHC Project Status and Plans

Lyndon R. Evans

CERN, CH - 1211 Geneva 23

Abstract

The Large Hadron Collider (LHC) project is based on a pair of superconducting storage rings to be installed in the LEP tunnel. The primary objective of the machine is to provide proton-proton collisions with a centre of mass energy of 14 TeV and an unprecedented luminosity of 10^{34} cm^{-2} s^{-1}. It will also provide colliding beams of Pb ions and a number of proposals are under study for B-physics experiments, either with colliding beams or in fixed-target mode. In a second phase, e-p collisions could be provided if desired by colliding the proton beam in one of the rings with LEP. The most critical elements of the LHC are the superconducting magnet system operating at a bending field of 8.65 Tesla and its associated cryogenic system. In order to reach this high field, the magnets must be cooled to below 2 degrees Kelvin over more than 24 km of its circumference. In addition, space limitations in the tunnel as well as cost considerations dictate a novel two-in-one magnet design where the two rings are incorporated into the same cryostat. An overview of the project status is given and the main technological and accelerator physics problems are discussed.

1. Introduction

The CERN Large Hadron Collider will provide proton-proton collisions with a centre of mass energy up to 14 TeV with a nominal luminosity of 10^{34} cm^{-2} s^{-1} and heavy ion (Pb-Pb) collisions with a luminosity of up to 10^{27} cm^{-2} s^{-1}. The reference design of the LHC has been presented at several conferences and two design reports exist [1, 2, and 3]. The main parameters of the machine for proton-proton operation are given in Table 1.

The basic layout of the LHC mirrors that of LEP, with eight long straight sections available for experimental detectors or utilities (Figure 1). The present experimental programme envisages two high luminosity proton-proton experiments (ATLAS and CMS), one heavy ion experiment (ALICE) and a possible B-physics initiative to be chosen from a number of proposals. Two major utilities, the beam cleaning and dump insertions also require long straight sections. The existing LEP experimental caverns at the even numbered points will be modified and reused as much as possible but the size and shape of the major proton-proton detectors, in particular ATLAS makes it economically sensible to open up a new experimental area at Point 1 of the machine.

Table 1. LHC main parameters

Energy	(TeV)	7.0
Dipole field	(T)	8.65
Luminosity	(cm^{-2} s^{-1})	10^{34}
Beam-beam parameter		0.0032
Injection energy	(GeV)	450
Circulating current/beam	(A)	0.53
Bunch spacing	(ns)	25
Particles per bunch		1×10^{11}
Stored beam energy	(MJ)	332
Normalized transverse emittance	(μm)	3.75
R.m.s. bunch length	(m)	0.075
Beta values at I.P.	(m)	0.5
Crossing angle	(μrad)	200
Beam lifetime	(h)	22
Luminosity lifetime	(h)	10
Energy loss per turn	(keV)	6.9
Critical photon energy	(eV)	45.6
Total radiated power per beam	(kW)	3.7

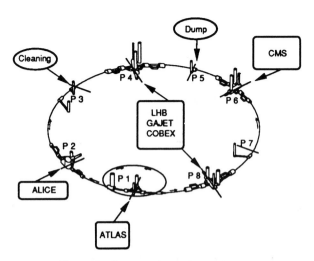

Figure 1.   Layout of experimental areas.

In view of the fact that the machine will be installed in the existing 27 km circumference LEP tunnel, considerable technological innovation is needed to achieve the high magnetic field required to fit the two rings into the existing tunnel cross section whilst leaving enough space for an eventual lepton ring based on existing LEP components for possible future ep operation. In this report, design features of the major systems are reviewed with particular emphasis on the technological developments required to achieve the performance goals.

2.   Injectors

The existing accelerator chain (Linac/Booster/PS/SPS) will be used for LHC injection. The achievement of the small transverse emittance, high bunch intensity and bunch spacing shown in Table 1 requires substantial modifications in the PS and Booster.   In the Booster a new harmonic h=1 system will be needed for acceleration with a superimposed h=2 system for bunch shaping in order to minimize the space charge effects. In addition, in order to reduce the Laslett detuning in the PS at injection, the booster energy must be upgraded from 1 GeV to 1.4 GeV (kinetic).

In the PS the main hardware addition will be a harmonic 84 (40 MHz) RF system for rebunching the protons to give the time structure finally required for the LHC.

Recently, machine experiments where one of the Booster rings was modified to give the necessary beam parameters have succeeded in producing bunches at PS extraction (26 GeV) of the nominal emittance and intensity for the LHC.

3.   Magnets

The magnet system [4] contains many innovative features in order to reduce cost and to fit the two rings into the constrained geometry of the LEP tunnel. The basic structure of both dipoles and quadrupoles are the two-in one design, where the two beam channels are incorporated into a single iron yoke and cryostat (Figure 2) and operating in superfluid helium to achieve the very high guide field required. In order to retain the very large bursting force of more than 500 tons per meter the coils must be very firmly clamped in a rigid mechanical structure. Combined aluminium collars have been chosen instead of the alternative separate stainless steel collars in order to minimise the pre-stress required at room tempera-ture and to ensure the best possible parallelism between the dipole fields in the two channels.

Each fifty one meter long lattice half-period contains three dipoles with a nominal field of 8.65 Tesla each 13.14 meters in magnetic length and a short straight section containing a 3.05 meter long quadrupole with a gradient of 220 T/m together with correction elements, quench protec-tion diodes, beam instrumentation and a cryogenic service unit in which the primary superfluid helium is fabricated. The dipole, octupole and sextupole correction elements adjacent to each quadrupole are not of the 2-in-1 construc-tion in order to completely decouple the two rings as far as the correction packages are concerned.

The main characteristics of the dipole magnet are given in Table 2. The regular lattice will require 1280 dipoles and 384 quadrupoles as well as the specialised elements in the disper-sion suppressors and insertions.

In order to achieve the unprecedented value for an accelera-tor magnet of 8.65 Tesla in the dipoles, the magnets must be cooled to 1.9 K below the lambda point of helium. The magnet cryostat must therefore be of an advanced design in order to limit the heat influx to the 1.9 K cold mass. This requires two layers of thermal insulation (Figure 2) to intercept the radiated heat at temperature levels of 50 K and 4.5 K as well as a careful design of the cold mass support structure. The cryostat also serves to carry the considerable amount of cryogenic piping, thus obviating the need for a separate line.

The quench protection [5] system is based on the so-called "cold diode" concept. The diodes will be installed in the He-II cryostat of the short straight section of a half cell where they could be exposed to a radiation dose of up to 50 kGy and a total neutron flux of 10^{15} n/cm^2 over 10 years. Test results obtained by irradiating diodes at liquid nitrogen temperature in an SPS beam line have shown that only the thin base epitaxial diodes are really radiation resistant and that annealing by carrier injection and occasional warm-up to room temperature can extend the service life of irradiated diodes considerably.

The large stored energy (500 kJ/m) of the magnets make it necessary to detect quickly a developing quench and fire strip heaters which spread the quench over the full volume of the magnet. Since the quench protection diodes operate at the level of the half cell, these heaters must be fired not only in the quenching magnet but also in its neighbours

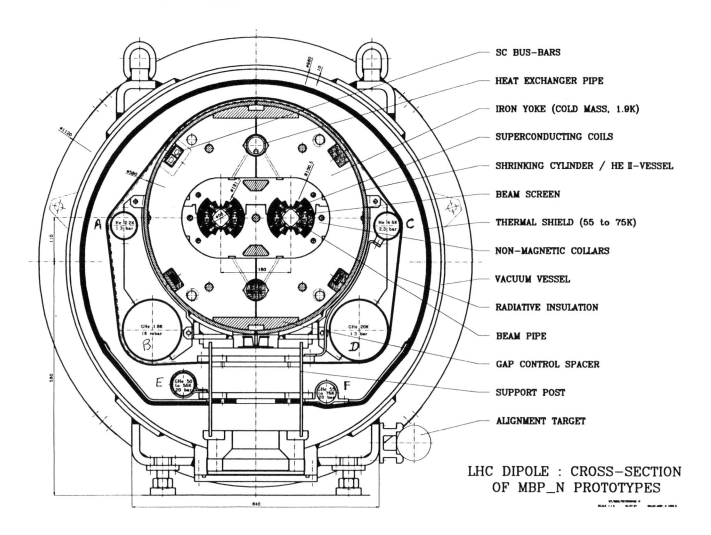

SC BUS-BARS

HEAT EXCHANGER PIPE

IRON YOKE (COLD MASS, 1.9K)

SUPERCONDUCTING COILS

SHRINKING CYLINDER / HE II-VESSEL

BEAM SCREEN

THERMAL SHIELD (55 to 75K)

NON-MAGNETIC COLLARS

VACUUM VESSEL

RADIATIVE INSULATION

BEAM PIPE

GAP CONTROL SPACER

SUPPORT POST

ALIGNMENT TARGET

LHC DIPOLE : CROSS-SECTION
OF MBP_N PROTOTYPES

Figure 2. Cross section of the dipole magnet.

Table 2. Dipole Parameters

Operational field	(T)	8.65
Coil aperture	(mm)	56
Magnetic length	(m)	13.145
Operating current	(A)	12000
Operating temperature	(K)	1.9
Coil turns per beam channel:		
inner shell		30
outer shell		52
Distance between aperture axes	(mm)	180
Outer diameter of cold mass	(mm)	560
Overall length of cold mass	(mm)	14085
Outer diameter of cryostat	(mm)	980
Overall mass of cryomagnet	(t)	29
Stored energy for both channels	(MJ)	7.2
Self-inductance for both channels	(mH)	110

A considerable amount of development work on the main dipole and quadrupole design has already been done. Ten 1.3 m long dipole models have been constructed and tested. Detailed results of these tests have been reported elsewhere [6]. Generally these models have behaved in a very similar way, achieving short sample field with little or no training at 4.2 K and showing some training behaviour at 1.8 K. All models have exceeded 9 T, with the best reaching 10.5 T. The great majority of quenches are observed to occur in the magnet ends.

Seven 10-meter long prototypes have been ordered in industry and the first two have arrived at CERN (Figure 3). The first of these has been fully tested. It reached 8.67 T on the first quench and 9 T after two more quenches. Measurements of field quality have shown that the multipole coefficients are close to the values expected. The other five prototypes will arrive at CERN before the end of the year. Three of these, together with a short straight section will be mounted in a "string" test facility

Figure 3.   The first long dipole prototype.

simulating the basic half-cell, cryogenically cooled, powered and protected in an identical way to the real machine. The string will be mounted on a slope of 1.4%, the maximum slope of the LEP tunnel in order to simulate the cooling of the magnets under the least favourable conditions.

Two full-size quadrupoles of 56 mm aperture and 3 meters length have been designed and constructed under a CERN-CEN/Saclay collaboration agreement [7]. Both magnets have been tested and have reached their design field with very few training quenches. The quadrupoles will be mounted into short straight sections (Figure 4) which also contain the beam pick-up monitor, dipole, sextupole and octupole correction elements and the quench protection diodes. The precise alignment of this ensemble is very important. The straight section also contains a vacuum barrier of advanced composite material to segment the insulation vacuum and the cryogenic service unit from which the primary superfluid is derived.

Models of the main correction elements have also been successfully built [8]. Prototypes of the tuning quadrupole (120 T/m, 0.8m length) and octupole corrector (10^5 T/m^3) have been built in industry. A prototype combined dipole/sextupole corrector (1.5 T, 8000 T/m^2) has been built and tested at 4.5 K at RAL and at 1.8 K at CERN. A single aperture enlarged quadrupole for the low-beta insertions is being built in collaboration with industry (250 T/m, 70 mm bore) [9]. An important feature of this quadrupole is the very large heat flux (up to 40 W) it must absorb due to irradiation by particles from the interaction point.

The LHC magnet system will involve one of the most massive applications of superconductivity ever undertaken. About 1200 tons of conductor will be needed of which more than 400 tons will be Nb/Ti alloy. A large amount of research and development on the superconducting cable has been required to achieve the required performance. More than 70 km of cable satisfying all the main requirements have been produced by five European manufacturers to date.

The two-layer coil uses graded cable with different conduc-tors in the inner and outer layer. The main characteristics of the wire and cable are given in Table 3.

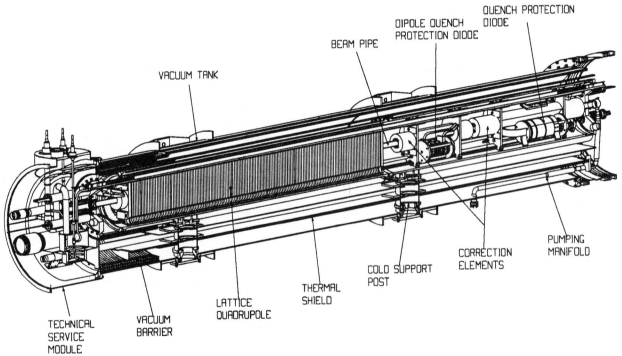

Figure 4.   Short straight section.

Table 3. Cable parameters

		Inner layer	Outer layer
Strand			
Diameter	(mm)	1.065	0.825
Cu/Sc ratio		1.6	1.9
Filament size	(mm)	7	6
Number of filaments		8900	6520
Twist pitch	(mm)	25	25
Critical current (A) 10 T, 1.9 K / 9T, 1.9 K		≥ 510	≥ 370
Cable			
Number of strands		28	36
Cable dimension: thin edge	(mm)	1.72	1.34
thick edge	(mm)	2.06	1.60
Transposition pitch	(mm)	110	100
Critical current (A) 10 T,1.9 K/9 T,1.9 K		≥ 13750	≥ 12960

To reduce persistent and eddy current effects during ramping of the magnets the filaments must be very fine, 6/7 microns diameter. The finished cable must also have very tight dimensional tolerances (6 microns in the 1.47 mm mid-plane thickness) in order to achieve the required field quality in the finished magnets.

One particular problem to be overcome is that of current sharing in the conductors distorting the magnetic field during ramping. In order to minimise this effect an inter strand resistance of at least 10 μΩ is needed. A number of coating materials for the cable strands are under investigation. These include Ni, AgSn and "poisoned" Sn coatings.

4. Cryogenics

Cooling the 30000 tons of material in the LHC magnets poses a particular challenge [10]. The elementary LHC cooling loop matches the periodicity of the machine lattice and corresponds to the half-cell of 51m length (Figure 5). Static superfluid helium pressurised at 1 bar permeating the magnet laminations is cooled by heat exchange with saturated superfluid helium flowing through a tube running through the magnet chain over the whole length of the half-cell. Sub-cooled helium (2.2K) is tapped from line A, expanded to saturation through a Joule-Thomson valve and sent to the end of the loop from where it returns, gradually vapourising as it gathers heat in the heat exchanger tube. The whole loop including heat exchanger tube and phase separator is maintained at saturation pressure by line B, through which cold helium vapour is pumped back to the cryoplant.

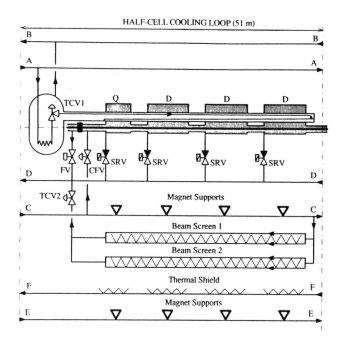

Figure 5.   The elementary cryogenics loop.

An important advantage of using the latent heat of vapourisation is that the temperature of each magnet is independent of its distance from the cryoplant. A key technology for the attainment of large capacity refrigeration in this temperature range is the development of cold sub-atmospheric helium compressors. The design of these units builds on previous experience at the Tore Supra tokamak and at CEBAF. In view of the importance of this technology, CERN has launched in collaboration with CEA (Grenoble) a comprehensive development programme on the design, construction and testing of a prototype LHC multistage cold compressor box.

The four existing LEP cryoplants, each of 12 kW capacity at 4.5K will be boosted to 18 kW and supplemented by a further four units of the same capacity. The eight cryogenic units will be concentrated at the four even LEP pits where adequate infrastructure including compressor buildings and cooling towers already exist. Consequently, the whole octant, 3.4 km in length must be supplied with liquid helium from the even points.

The cryogenic infrastructure for LEP already uses a two stage cold box in order to avoid large hydrostatic pressure. The upper cold box on the surface cools helium gas to 20 K whereas the lower cold box at tunnel level performs the final liquefaction. The lower cold box will be supplemented by a cold compressor box responsible for further cooling of the liquid to just above the lambda point and for the production ofthe 16 mb pressure in the low pressure line. In order to avoid a too large pipe diameter the lower cold compressor box is split into two, one at each end of the octant.

5. Vacuum

The LHC beam vacuum poses particular problems [11]. Due to the synchrotron radiation emitted by the protons (4 kW per ring at 7 TeV) and the heating due to the image currents in the wall of the vacuum chamber, the magnet cold bore at 1.8 K must be shielded from the beam, otherwise the required cryogenic power would become excessive. (1 Watt at 2K needs approximately 1 kW at room temperature.) An inner liner cooled to around 20 K through tubes carrying high pressure gas will therefore be installed inside the cold bore.

Synchrotron radiation impinging on this liner will cause gas to be desorbed from the bulk material which will in turn be cryopumped to the surface of the liner. This is particularly undesirable especially for hydrogen. Once a surface layer of this gas builds up the pressure will rise to that of the vapour pressure of hydrogen at the temperature of the liner, more than two orders of magnitude higher than required for an adequate beam lifetime. In order to avoid this, slots must be cut in the liner so that hydrogen can be cryopumped by the cold bore surface at much lower temperature.

The inner wall of the liner must be copper plated in order to reduce the growth rate of the transverse resistive wall instability to a tolerable value but at the same time it must be able to withstand the strong forced due to eddy currents during a quench.

6. Beam dump

In order to remove the beams from the machine in a safe and efficient manner at the end of a physics run or in case of equipment malfunction, two beam dumps are required. Each beam dump must be able to absorb the stored energy of more than 300 MJ per beam and will be built from a graphite core surrounded by aluminium and iron, with a total weight of close to 1000 tons.

The kickers needed to extract the beam must have a rise time of 3 μs with a flat top length of 89 μs and must operate at a very high field of up to 0.85 T. Such field levels are beyond the capability of ferrite magnets. Instead, a construc-tion based on tape-wound cores made from 0.05 mm thick silicon steel is envisaged. A prototype kicker based on this design has been built and first results are encouraging.

The kicker pulse generators require fast high power switches (35 kV, 30 kA, 6 μs) of very low repetition rate and high reliability. Alternative solutions based on both pseudo-spark switches employing ferro-electric triggers [12] and alternative solid state devices [13] are being developed in collaboration with industry.

7. Conclusions

The considerable amount of R&D accomplished over the past few years has validated the main technical choices for the construction of the LHC. In particular, the two-in-one magnetic structure operating at high field in helium II has proved to be a cost effective and viable solution for obtaining the required performance.

8. Acknowledgements

It is a pleasure to acknowledge the outstanding contribution of Giorgio Brianti, who has guided this project from its conception.

9. References

[1]   The LHC Study Group, Design Study of the Large Hadron Collider, CERN 91-03 (1991).

[2]   The LHC Study Group, The Large Hadron Collider Accelerator Project, CERN/AC/93-03 (LHC) (1993).

[3]   G. Brianti, LHC Progress and Status, Proc. 1993 Particle Accelerator Conference, Washington, 3917 (1993).

[4]   R. Perin, J. Vlogaert, Magnets for the Large Hadron Collider, Proc. European Conference on Applied Superconductivity, Göttingen, Germany (1993).

[5]   L. Coull et al., LHC Magnet Quench Projection System [1].

[6]   R. Perin, Status of the Large Hadron Collider Magnet Development [1].

[7]   J.M. Rifflet et al., Status of the Fabrication and Test of the Prototype LHC Lattice Quadrupole Magnets [1].

[8]   D.E. Baynham et al., Design of Superconducting Corrector Magnets for LHC [1].

[9]   R. Ostojic et al., Design and Construction of a One-Meter Model of the 70 mm Aperture Quadrupole for the LHC Low-Beta Insertions [1].

[10]   J. Casas et al., Design concept and first experimental validation of the superfluid helium system for the LHC project at CERN, Proc. ICEC 14, Cryogenics Vol. 32, ICEC Supplement, Butterworth-Heinemann (1992).

[11]   A. Mathewson, Vacuum Technology for Superconducting Colliders, Proc. 1993 Particle Accelerator Conference, Washington, 3828 (1993).

[12]   L. Ducimetière et al., Pseudo-Spark Switch Development for the LHC Beam Dumping System [2].

[13]   J. Bonthond et al., High Current, High DI/DT Switching with Optimised GTO Thyristors [2].

---

[1]   Proc. 13th Int. Conf. on Magnet Technology, Victoria, Canada (1993).

[2]   Proc. 21st. Int. Power Modulator Symposium, Los Angeles (1994).

Scientific Contributions

During the preparations for the Conference the Scientific Organizing Committee received 950 submitted abstracts and a subsequent 613 full papers. The majority of abstracts were received electronically with papers arriving as hard copy. This facilitated the use of a database which automatically acknowledged receipt of abstracts and electronically forwarded them to the 46 parallel session conveners and 22 plenary rapporteurs. It also assisted in the creation of libraries of submitted abstracts and, with the help of Dr. M. Draper and the other members of the Document Handling Group, A.S. Division, CERN, scanned versions of the papers. From the time of the Conference these databases were made publicly available to the whole community via the Internet and World Wide Web, together with all the transparencies from the plenary talks.

On the subsequent pages all the full papers are listed according to the Glasgow reference number, giving title and lead author (alphabetical). First, several graphs are presented which indicate he origin of the contributions and the sessions to which they were sent.

There were 24 parallel and 22 plenary sessions; plenary session 22 being the conference summary received all submissions. Figure 1 shows the numbers of abstracts and full papers sent to each of these sessions. Due to the inevitable overlap between subject areas many submissions were sent to more than one session.

It is also possible to try to divide the 950 abstracts according to their subject matter, this shows that: 500 (53%) dealt with experimental results; 393 (41%) with theoretical developments; and 57 (6%) with experimental techniques. Repeating this classification for the 613 full papers shows that: 292 (48%) dealt with experimental results; 284 (46%) with theoretical developments; and 37 (6%) with experimental techniques. Figures 2 and 3 show the distribution of full papers in these three groups for the parallel and plenary sessions.

Finally the experimental abstracts and papers can be broken down by Collaboration which is done in figures 4 and 5. Only the larger Collaborations, as defined by number of submissions, are shown. Smaller Collaborations are collected together under the CERN/Fermilab fixed target programmes or under Other experiments. Experimental techniques, as distinct from results, are treated separately. Note that the 393 abstracts and 284 papers submitted by theorists are not shown.

Parallel and Plenary Session Contributions

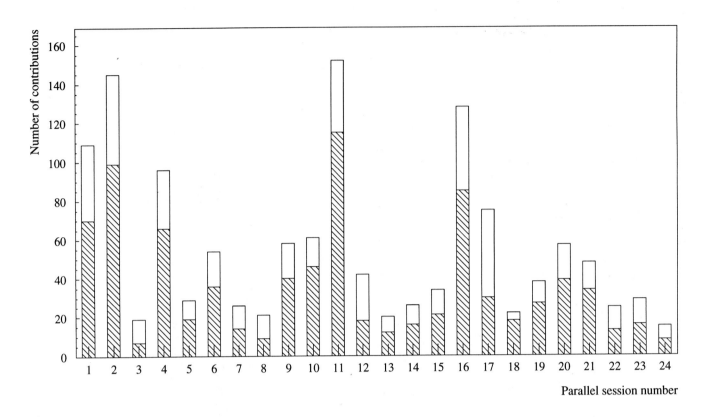

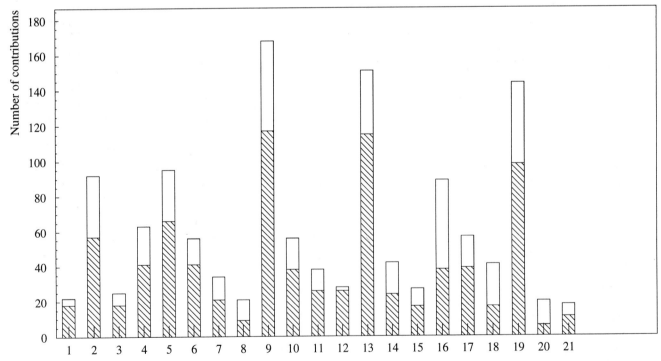

Figure 1 The number of abstracts (white) and papers (hatched) sent to each parallel (top) and plenary (bottom) session; note that many submissions were sent to more than one session. Keys to the session numbers accompany the next two graphs.

Parallel Session Papers According to Subject

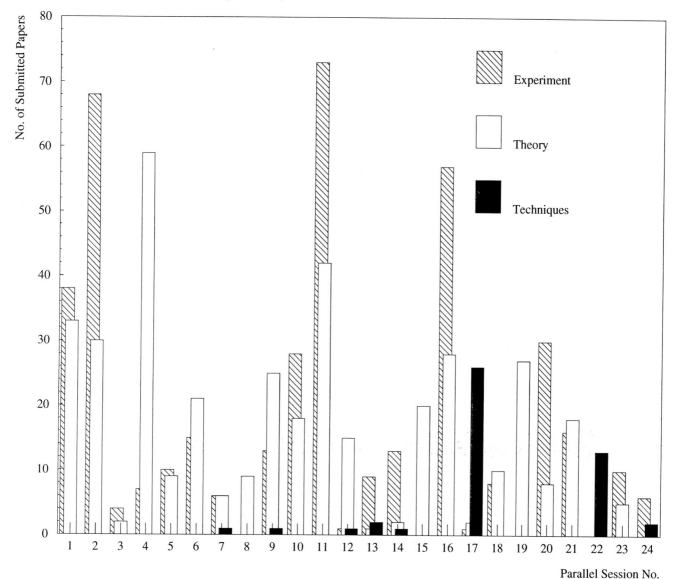

Figure 2 The number of full papers submitted to each parallel session classified as experimental results (hatched), theory (white) and experimental techniques (black). The parallel session numbers are listed below.

Pa-1   Electroweak Interactions
Pa-2   Heavy Quark Physics
Pa-3   Heavy Ion Collisions
Pa-4   Beyond the Standard Model
Pa-5   Low x Physics
Pa-6   Deep Inelastic Scattering and Structure Functions
Pa-7   Neutrino Masses, Mixing and Oscillations
Pa-8   Lattice Gauge Theory
Pa-9   CP Violation and $B\bar{B}$ Mixing
Pa-10 Searches for New Particles
Pa-11 QCD and Jet Physics
Pa-12 Particle Astrophysics and Cosmology

Pa-13 Non-Accelerator Experiments
Pa-14 Flavour Production on Hadronic Targets
Pa-15 Non-Perturbative Methods
Pa-16 Weak Decays
Pa-17 Experimental Techniques
Pa-18 Top Quark Searches
Pa-19 Field Theory and String Theory
Pa-20 Low Q^2 and Soft Phenomena
Pa-21 Rare Decays
Pa-22 New Detectors and their Physics Aims
Pa-23 Light Quark and Gluonium Spectroscopy
Pa-24 Future Accelerators

Plenary Session Papers according to Subject

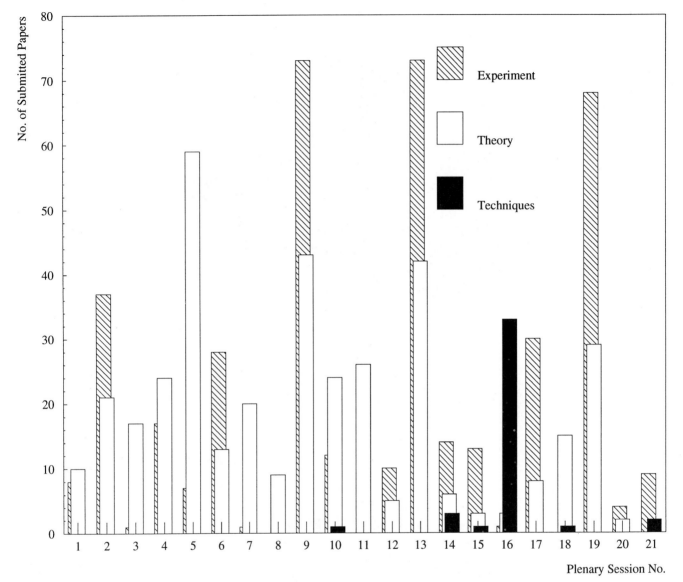

Figure 3 The number of full papers submitted to each plenary session classified as experimental results (hatched), theory (white) and experimental techniques (black). The plenary session numbers are listed below.

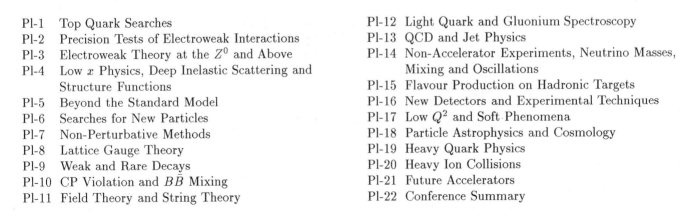

Pl-1   Top Quark Searches
Pl-2   Precision Tests of Electroweak Interactions
Pl-3   Electroweak Theory at the Z^0 and Above
Pl-4   Low x Physics, Deep Inelastic Scattering and
        Structure Functions
Pl-5   Beyond the Standard Model
Pl-6   Searches for New Particles
Pl-7   Non-Perturbative Methods
Pl-8   Lattice Gauge Theory
Pl-9   Weak and Rare Decays
Pl-10   CP Violation and $B\bar{B}$ Mixing
Pl-11   Field Theory and String Theory

Pl-12   Light Quark and Gluonium Spectroscopy
Pl-13   QCD and Jet Physics
Pl-14   Non-Accelerator Experiments, Neutrino Masses,
        Mixing and Oscillations
Pl-15   Flavour Production on Hadronic Targets
Pl-16   New Detectors and Experimental Techniques
Pl-17   Low Q^2 and Soft Phenomena
Pl-18   Particle Astrophysics and Cosmology
Pl-19   Heavy Quark Physics
Pl-20   Heavy Ion Collisions
Pl-21   Future Accelerators
Pl-22   Conference Summary

Abstracts Submitted by Experiments

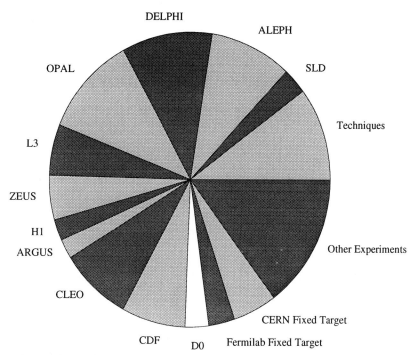

Figure 4 The 557 experimental results and techniques abstracts submitted, broken down according to the major experiments; 393 theoretical abstracts are not shown.

Full Papers Submitted by Experiments

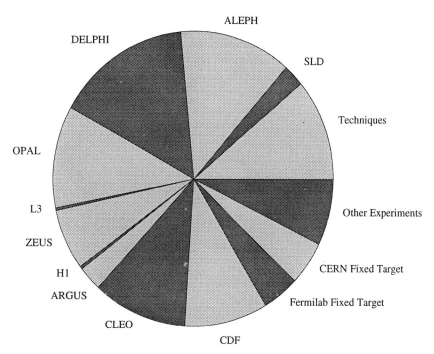

Figure 5 The 329 experimental results and techniques full papers submitted, broken down according to the major experiments; 284 theoretical papers are not shown.

No.	Author(s)	Title
001	U. Baur *et al.*	Rapidity correlations in $W^{\pm}\gamma$ production at hadron colliders
002	U. Baur *et al.*	Amplitude zeros in $W^{\pm}Z^0$ production
008	H. Gao *et al.*	Some features of blown-up nonlinear sigma models
009	B. Gavela *et al.*	Standard model CP-violation and baryon asymmetry
011	J. Bijnens *et al.*	Two-and three-point functions in the extended NJL model
013	K. Choi *et al.*	Effects of cosmological constant on soft terms in supergravity
015	A. Kondashov	Experimental study of S-wave in the $\pi^0\pi^0$ system
016	H. Albrecht *et al.*	Two-photon physics at ARGUS
017	A. Schwarz *et al.*	HERA-B: an experiment to study CP-violation in the B system using an internal target at the HERA proton ring
018	J. Spengler *et al.*	A test of internal halo targets for heavy flavour hadro-production at the HERA proton ring
019	A. Alessandrello *et al.*	The Milano-Gran Sasso experiment on neutrinoless double beta decay using a thermal detector
021	M. Campbell *et al.*	A hybrid pixel detector for the readout of scintillating fibres
023	K. Kadija	Diffractive scattering and low momentum protons in μXe and μD interactions at 490 GeV
024	K. Kadija	Strangeness enhancement and space-time characteristics of pion production in ultra-relativistic nucleus-nucleus collisions from the NA35 experiment
025	J. Kim *et al.*	Effects of neutrino degeneracy on the primodial abundances of ^{9}Be and ^{11}B
026	M. Mekhfi	Homotopic loops, their mutual interactions and the effective winding number
027	M. Braun *et al.*	Nuclear structure functions and particle production in the cumulative region in the parton model
029	E. Boos *et al.*	The investigation of pions clusterisation mechanism in hadron-nucleon collisions
031	D. Ebert *et al.*	Effective heavy meson Lagrangians from quark flavor dynamics
032	F. Gareev	Systematic investigation of mass distributions of hadronic resonances and predictions for new resonance regions
033	V. Kuvshinov	On existence of gluon squeezed states in QCD jets
034	E. Boos *et al.*	On the nature of the "knee" in observed high energy cosmic rays spectra
035	M. Jamin *et al.*	QCD corrections to inclusive $\Delta S = 1, 2$ transitions at next-to-leading order
037	C. Dohmen *et al.*	Search for $\mu \to e^+e^-$ conversion
040	C. Jin *et al.*	Inclusive semileptonic decays of B mesons in a parton model
041	B. Allanach *et al.*	The next-to-minimal supersymmetric standard model
042	E. Laenen *et al.*	Anomalous dimension of high twist operators in QCD at $n \to 1$ and large Q^2
043	R. Arnowitt *et al.*	$b \to s + \gamma$ decay in supergravity grand unification
044	R. Arnowitt *et al.*	Testing supergravity grand unification at future accelerator and underground experiments
046	R. Werding	Charmed hadrons in the WA89 hyperon beam experiment
047	T. Elliott *et al.*	Unification constraints on the minimal and next-to-minimal supersymmetric models
048	G. Bocquet *et al.*	Inclusive production of charged paticles and minijets in proton antiproton collisions at $\sqrt{S} = 630$ GeV
049	D. Kazakov *et al.*	Complete α_s correction to the J/ψ photoproduction cross-section
050	D. Kazakov	On a possible explanation of the origin of the quark mass spectrum
053	A. Giovannini *et al.*	Clans as independent intermediate gluon sources
054	J. Edwards *et al.*	On the kinematical effects of Bose-Einstein correlations in jets
055	N. Maksimenko *et al.*	The determination of the effective action for interaction of electromagnetic field with two-particle bound system
060	V. Baier	Integral characteristics of radiation in QED in external field at high energies
062	E. Boos *et al.*	Multiparticle correlations in nuclear interactions at 4.2A GeV/c
063	B. Arbuzov	On consequences of a symmetry breaking in the t-quark electromagnetic vertex for t-production in Tevatron collider experiments
064	A. Arkhipov	Quark-quark forces in QCD
065	E. Boos *et al.*	Properties of the reactions $e^+e^- \to b\bar{b}$, l^+l^- $(\nu\bar\nu)$ and the Higgs signal at LEP 200 and NLC

066	J. Gracey	Large N_f QCD and deep inelastic scattering
067	D. Choudhury *et al.*	Two-loop neutrino masses and the solar neutrino problem
070	Y. Prokoshkin *et al.*	Analysis of D-wave in $\pi^- p \to a_2(1320)n$ reaction
071	P. Silvestrov	On the instanton induced asymptotics of perturbation theory expansion in QCD
072	D. Adams *et al.*	Measurement of the spin-dependent structure function $g_1(x)$ of the proton
073	G. D'Ambrosio *et al.*	Strong rescattering in $K \to 3\pi$ and low-energy meson dynamics
075	CDF Collaboration	Measurement of the b quark and B meson cross-sections in proton-antiproton collisions at 1.8 TeV using fully reconstructed decays
076	Y. Feng *et al.*	String organization of field theories: duality and gauge invariance
077	M. Duetsch *et al.*	Causal construction of nonabelian gauge theories
078	M. Faber *et al.*	Monopole currents and the confinement mechanism in compact QED
079	M. Faber *et al.*	Chiral symmetry breaking and the meson cloud in lattice QCD
082	I. Ali *et al.*	The ZEUS calorimeter first level trigger
083	S. Dasu *et al.*	The CMS first level trigger
084	M. Kawamura *et al.*	The swimming of microorganism and the string- and membrane-like algebra
085	Y. Novozhilov *et al.*	Gluon condensate as a source of diquark mass
088	A. Denisov *et al.*	New measurements of negative K meson and Σ hyperon masses
089	H. Jeremie *et al.*	Comparison of models describing 4-jet angular correlations arising from $q\bar{q}q\bar{q}$ configurations of hadronic decays of the Z^0
090	R. Kenna	Triviality of the $O(n)$ ϕ^4-theory
092	CDF Collaboration	Measurment of the B cross-section at CDF via B semileptonic decays
096	F. Ould Saada	Search for a new light gauge boson in decays of π^0, η and η'
099	C. Nelson	CP violation tests for top/tau processes
100	M. Kim *et al.*	Tests for leptonic CP violation in tau decays
101	M. Matsuda *et al.*	Consistent approach for penguin effects in $B \to K\pi$, $\pi\pi$ and $D \to KK$, $\pi\pi$ Decays
102	T. Hayashi *et al.*	Neutron electric dipole moment and related topics in two-Higgs-doublet model
104	R. Aleksan *et al.*	Determination of the quark mixing matrix from CP-violating asymmetries
105	V. Kartvelishvili *et al.*	Υ production at high p_T: a new way of determining α_s
106	R. Imlay	Early results from the LSND neutrino experiment
109	G. Hou *et al.*	Experimental and theoretical implications of new sequential leptons
110	G. Hou *et al.*	Weak scale radiative lepton mass
111	CDF Collaboration	Measurement of the B^+ and B^0 meson lifetimes
115	M. Ciuchini *et al.*	Leading order QCD corrections to $b \to s\gamma$ and $b \to sg$ decays in three regularization schemes
116	J. Bahr *et al.*	Beam tests of prototype fiber detectors for the H1 forward proton spectrometer
117	Z. Aydin *et al.*	TeV energy γp colliders: luminosity and physics
118	K. Ciftci *et al.*	Some consequences of a model with lepton charge dynamics
119	Z. Aydin *et al.*	Linac-ring type ep colliders: luminosity and physics
120	S. Sultansoy	Linac-ring type $c - \tau$ factory: luminosity and physics
121	G. Hou	Is the top quark really heavier than the $W^\pm$ boson?
122	CDF Collaboration	Measurement of correlated b quark cross-sections at CDF
123	Z. Aydin *et al.*	CKM mixings in various extensions of the standard model
124	A. Alan *et al.*	SUSY at TeV energy γp - colliders
125	S. Atag *et al.*	Measurement of gluon polarization in polarized γN collisions
126	S. Atag *et al.*	Compositeness at TeV energy γp colliders
128	C. Anway Wiese	New limits on the rare decays $B \to \mu\mu K^{0*}$ and $B \to \mu\mu K^\pm$ from CDF
129	NA22 Collaboration	Transverse momentum compensation in $\pi^+ p$ interactions at 250 GeV/c
130	NA22 Collaboration	Coherent interactions of π^+ and K^+ mesons on Al and Au nuclei at 250 GeV/c
131	NA22 Collaboration	Angular dependence of factorial moments in $\pi^+/K^+ p$ interactions at 250 GeV/c
132	NA22 Collaboration	Genuine higher-order correlations in $\pi^+ p$ and $K^+ p$ collisions at 250 GeV/c
135	NA22 Collaboration	Higher-order Bose-Einstein correlations in $\pi^+ p$ and $K^+ p$ collisions at 250 GeV/c
136	NA22 Collaboration	Angular dependence of Bose-Einstein correlations in interactions of π^+ and K^+ mesons with protons and nuclei at 250 GeV/c
137	NA22 Collaboration	Backward proton production in integration of π^+/K^+ mesons with Al and Au nuclei at 250 GeV/c

140	P. Ermolov *et al.*	Microstrip gas chambers for tracking systems
141	P. Abreu *et al.*	Invariant mass dependence of particle correlations in hadronic final states from the decay of the Z^0
142	P. Abreu *et al.*	Interference of neutral kaons in the hadronic decays of the Z^0
143	P. Kuzhir *et al.*	Quarks' flavors and spin structure functions in the deep inelastic scattering of (anti)neutrino on polarized target
144	CLEO Collaboration	A study of the $B \to D^* l\nu$ semileptonic decay form factors
145	E. Eichten *et al.*	Properties of orbitally excited heavy-light mesons
148	E. Eichten *et al.*	Mesons with beauty and charm: spectroscopy
156	CLEO Collaboration	$\pi - \pi$ energy correlation in τ pair events
157	J. Busto *et al.*	A detector for the study of neutrino-electron scattering at a nuclear reactor
158	A. Lidsey *et al.*	A lattice study of the charmonium spectrum
159	CLEO Collaboration	A constraint on V_{td}/V_{ts} from $B \to \rho(\omega)\gamma/B \to K^*\gamma$
160	CLEO Collaboration	A Search for $B \to \tau\nu$
161	P. Abreu *et al.*	The DELPHI silicon strip microvertex detector with double sided readout
162	P. Abreu *et al.*	An updated measurement of beauty baryon production and lifetime in Z^0 hadronic decays
163	P. Abreu *et al.*	Search for charmless beauty decays with the DELPHI detector at LEP
164	P. Abreu *et al.*	Study of fully reconstructed decays of beauty particles with the DELPHI detector at LEP
165	P. Abreu *et al.*	A topological measurement of charged and neutral B hadron lifetimes
166	P. Abreu *et al.*	Evidence for strange beauty baryons in hadronic Z^0 decays
167	G. Gollin *etal.*	New measurements of CP violation parameters in K meson decay
168	CLEO Collaboration	A study of jet production rates in four flavor continuum and a test of QCD
170	P. Abreu *et al.*	Study of hard scattering processes in multihadron production from $\gamma\gamma$ collisions at LEP
171	P. Abreu *et al.*	Studies of time dependent $B\bar{B}$ mixing
172	P. Abreu *et al.*	A measurement of the B_s^0 meson mass
173	P. Abreu *et al.*	A precision measurement of the average lifetime of B hadrons
174	P. Abreu *et al.*	Improved measurements of cross-sections and asymmetries at the Z^0 resonance
175	P. Abreu *et al.*	Measurement of the $e^+e^- \to \gamma\gamma(\gamma)$ cross-section at LEP energies
176	P. Abreu *et al.*	Charged kaon production in tau decays at LEP
177	P. Abreu *et al.*	Search for the standard model Higgs boson in Z^0 decays
179	P. Abreu *et al.*	Final state photon radiation in hadronic events with the DELPHI experiment at LEP
180	P. Abreu *et al.*	Evidence for the triple-gluon-vertex from 4-jet-events at LEP
181	P. Abreu *et al.*	How well are hadronic distributions described by fragmentation models?
182	P. Abreu *et al.*	Inclusive $K^\pm$ and $p\bar{p}$ spectra measured with the DELPHI detector at LEP
183	P. Abreu *et al.*	Strange baryon production in Z^0 hadronic decays
184	P. Abreu *et al.*	Measurement of the mean charged multiplicity in $Z^0 \to b\bar{b}$ events
185	P. Abreu *et al.*	Study of D, D^* and D^{**} production in Z^0 hadronic decays
186	P. Abreu *et al.*	A search for the Z^0 decay into a Higgs boson and a photon with the DELPHI detector
187	P. Abreu *et al.*	Differences between quark and gluon jets
188	P. Abreu *et al.*	Analysis techniques for the DELPHI ring imaging cerenkov counters
189	H. Albrecht *et al.*	The first measurement of the Michel parameter η in τ decays
190	H. Albrecht *et al.*	Determination of the structure of τ decays in the reaction $e^+e^- \to \tau^+\tau^- \to \rho^+\bar{\nu}_\tau\rho^-\nu_\tau$ and precision measurement of the τ neutrino helicity
192	H. Albrecht *et al.*	Measurement of the decay fractions of D^* mesons
194	H. Albrecht *et al.*	Observation of polarization effects in Λ_c^+ semileptonic decay
195	H. Albrecht *et al.*	Study of D^0 and D^+ decays into final states with two or three kaons
196	H. Albrecht *et al.*	Measurement of the absolute branching fractions for D^0 decays into $K^-\pi^+$, $K^-\pi^+\pi^+\pi^-$, $\bar{K}^0\pi^+\pi^-$
198	H. Albrecht	Reconstruction of the decay $B^- \to D_1^0(2414)\pi^-$
199	H. Albrecht *et al.*	Search for $b \to s$ "*gluon*" decays
200	L. Leistam *et al.*	Preparing the LHC environment for experiments
201	P. Allport *et al.*	Charge division issues with LHC silicon microstrip detectors

202	R. Ball	Double asymptotic scaling at HERA
203	M. Poljsak *et al.*	Regularization of infrared divergences of QCD by temporarily introducing appropriate Higgs fields
205	P. Abreu *et al.*	Inclusive J/ψ production in Z^0 hadronic decays
206	P. Abreu *et al.*	Experience with the ring imaging cherenkov detector of DELPHI
207	P. Abreu *et al.*	Measurements of the τ polarisation in Z^0 decays
208	CDF Collaboration	Study of production mechanisms of J/ψ and $\psi(2S)$
210	M. Shafranov	Muon detector to measure cross-section charm production at 70 Gev proton-proton interactions
211	C. Morningstar *et al.*	CORE – a new method for solving Hamiltonian lattice systems
213	A. Alioio *et al.*	Physics with KLOE
214	A. Antonelli *et al.*	The KLOE electromagnetic calorimeter
215	P. Franzini *et al.*	Solving the f_0 puzzle at DAPHNE
218	W. Blum *et al.*	Development of an optical alignment monitoring system for the ATLAS muon spectrometer
220	J. Donoghue *et al.*	Anatomy of a weak matrix element
221	J. Donoghue *et al.*	The Weinberg sum rules and their phenomenology
222	J. Donoghue	General relativity as a quantum effective field theory: the leading quantum corrections
224	A. Duff *et al.*	Heavy Higgs boson production in association with three jets at hadron supercolliders
225	H. Chehime *et al.*	Evidence for a hard pomeron in perturbative QCD
227	CDF Collaboration	Polarization in the decay $B^0 \to \psi K^{0*}$ in collisions at $\sqrt{S} = 1.8$ TeV
229	P. Abreu *et al.*	Measurement of $\Gamma_{b\bar{b}}/\Gamma_{had}$ using lifetime tagging techniques
230	P. Abreu *et al.*	The forward-backward asymmetry of $b\bar{b}$ and $c\bar{c}$ using prompt leptons
231	P. Abreu *et al.*	Measurement of the forward-backward asymmetry of charm and bottom quarks at the Z^0 pole using $D^{*\pm}$ mesons
232	P. Abreu *et al.*	First measurement of the strange quark asymmetry at the Z^0 pole
233	P. Abreu *et al.*	Lifetime and production rate of the B_s^0 meson
234	P. Abreu *et al.*	Measurements of exclusive τ decay branching fractions from Z^0 events
235	P. Abreu *et al.*	First evidence of hard scattering processes in single tagged $\gamma\gamma$ collisions
237	P. Abreu *et al.*	An update of the study of Z^0 decays to two leptons and a charged particle-antiparticle pair
238	P. Abreu *et al.*	Preliminary results of the search for $ll\gamma\gamma$ events
239	P. Abreu *et al.*	Study of the production of radiative τ pair events with the DELPHI detector
240	CLEO Collaboration	Beam induced detector backgrounds for CESR and CLEO
242	CLEO Collaboration	Determination of $B(\tau^- \to \nu_\tau K^- K^0)$
243	CLEO Collaboration	Evidence for exclusive B decays to final states containing a charmed baryon
245	CLEO Collaboration	First observation of $\Xi_c \to \Xi e \nu$
246	CLEO Collaboration	Inclusive and exclusive $B \to D_s X$ measurements from CLEO
248	CLEO Collaboration	Inclusive decays of B mesons to charmonium
249	CLEO Collaboration	Measurement of $B(\tau^+ \to h^+ h^- h^+ \nu_\tau)$
250	CLEO Collaboration	Measurement of form factor ratios R_2 and R_v in $D_s^+ \to \phi l \nu$ decays
253	CLEO Collaboration	Measurement of the form factor ratio, $R = f_2/f_1$, in $\Lambda_c \to \Lambda l \nu$ decays
254	G. Cowan *et al.*	Measurement of α_s in $e^+ e^-$ annihilation at $E_{cm} = 29$ GeV
255	A. Martin *et al.*	MRS(1994): parton densities of the proton obtained from a global analysis incorporating new data
257	F. Csikor *et al.*	Numerical simulations and the strength of the electroweak phase transition
258	M. Seymour	Matrix-element corrections to parton shower simulation of deep inelastic scattering
259	N. Deshpande *et al.*	Gluon dipole penguin contributions to ϵ'/ϵ and CP violtion in hyperon decays in the standard model
260	N. Deshpande *et al.*	CP violation in a multi-Higgs doublet model with flavor changing neutral current
261	N. Deshpande *et al.*	Gluonic penguin B decays in standard and two Higgs doublet models
262	N. Deshpande *et al.*	Predictive fermion mass matrix ansatze in non-supersymmetric SO(10) grand unification
264	E. Chun *et al.*	Dark matter in axino–gravitino cosmology
267	A. Sandacz *et al.*	Exclusive ρ^0 and ϕ muonproduction at large Q^2

362	CHARM II Collab.	Precision measurement of electroweak parameters from the scattering of muon-neutrinos on electrons
363	CHARM II Collab.	Flavour universality of neutrino couplings with the Z^0
364	T. Ferbel	Inclusive production of direct photons, π^0's, η's and ω's in π^- collisions with Be and Cu Nuclei at 515 GeV/c
365	B. Kim *et al.*	Upper bound on lightest Higgs mass in nonminimal supersymmetric model
366	A. Dobado *et al.*	The applicability of the equivalence theorem in χPT
367	A. Bizzeti	Present status of R&D on parallel plate chambers for LHC experiments
368	CDF Collaboration	Inclusive and double differential jet cross-sections at CDF
371	J. Gunion *et al.*	Unification and the minimal SUSY model: is a fourth generation allowed?
372	J. Gunion *et al.*	Standard model Higgs physics at a 4 TeV upgraded Tevatron
373	J. Dai *et al.*	LHC detection of neutral MSSM Higgs bosons via $gg \to b\bar{b}h \to b\bar{b}b\bar{b}$ and $gg \to t\bar{t}h \to t\bar{t}b\bar{b}$
374	J. Gunion *et al.*	Determining the CP-eigenvalues of the neutral Higgs bosons of the minimal supersymmetric model in $\gamma\gamma$ collisions
375	H. Baer *et al.*	Tevatron probes of string-motivated supergravity models
376	J. Gunion *et al.*	Exploring the Yukawa unified minimal supergravity model at the TEVATRON, LEP II and the LHC
378	K. Golec-Biernat *et al.*	Identification of BFKL dynamics at small x
379	K. Lane	Top–quark production and flavor physics
380	L. Orr *et al.*	Soft jets and top mass measurement at the Tevatron
381	CLEO Collaboration	Measurement of the ratios $B(D_s^+ \to \eta l\nu)/B(D_s^+ \to \phi l\nu)$ and $B(D_s^+ \to \eta' l\nu)/B(D_s^+ \to \phi l\nu)$
382	CLEO Collaboration	Measurement of the tauonic branching ratio of the $\Upsilon(1S)$
383	CLEO Collaboration	Measurement of spectral moments in hadronic decays of the τ and tests of QCD
385	CLEO Collaboration	Measurement of the $B \to D^* l\nu$ branching fractions and V_{cb}
386	CLEO Collaboration	Observation of $D_1(2430)^+$ and $D_2^*(2470)^+$
387	CLEO Collaboration	Precision measurement of the τ lepton lifetime
389	CLEO Collaboration	Search for $b \to s l^+ l^-$ decays
390	CLEO Collaboration	Search for CP violation in D^0 decay
391	CLEO Collaboration	Search for exclusive charmless hadronic B decay modes
392	CLEO Collaboration	Studies of $b \to s\gamma$
393	CLEO Collaboration	Study of $B \to \psi\pi$ decays
394	CLEO Collaboration	Study of inclusive $B \to \eta X$ decays
396	CLEO Collaboration	The CLEO III detector and physics aims
397	CLEO Collaboration	The high luminosity upgrade plans for CESR
399	K. Byrum *et al.*	Improvement in the CDF level-2 inclusive electron trigger
400	V. Barger *et al.*	Multilepton SUSY signals from R-parity violation at the Tevatron
401	V. Barger *et al.*	Singlet quarks beyond the top at the Tevatron?
402	E. Kovacs	Measurement of the SS-OS dijet cross-section ratio
406	M. Dell'Orso *et al.*	Evidence for color coherence in jet events
410	S. Kopp	Measurement of the ratio $\sigma B(W \to e\nu)/\sigma B(Z^0 \to e^+e^-)$ in $\bar{p}p$ collisions at $\sqrt{S} = 1.8$ TeV
411	CDF Collaboration	Search for new, right handed gauge bosons W' in proton-antiproton collisions at $\sqrt{S} = 1.8$ TeV
413	F. Abe *et al.*	Observation of events with rapidity gaps in $\bar{p}p$ collisions at $\sqrt{S} = 1.8$ TeV
414	CDF Collaboration	The measurement of the $W^\pm$ boson mass from CDF
415	CDF Collaboration	Tests of structure functions using leptons at CDF
417	J. Wang	Search for the top quark decaying to a charged Higgs in proton-antiproton collisions at $\sqrt{S} = 1.8$ TeV
418	C. Hawk	A study of parton distribution functions using photon + jet events
419	R. Drucker *et al.*	$W^\pm$ and Z^0 boson production with QCD jets in 1.8 TeV $p\bar{p}$ collisions
422	K. Lau *et al.*	High resolution (50 μm) cathode strip detector using Iarocci-type PVC chambers and printed circuit board strips
424	CDF Collaboration	Results from the CDF top search in the dilepton channel

425	CDF Collaboration	The CDF top search using secondary-vertex b-quark tagging in lepton + jet events
426	CDF Collaboration	The CDF top SEarch using low P_T lepton b-quark tagging in lepton + jet events
427	CDF Collaboration	Discussion of results of the CDF top searches
428	CDF Collaboration	Kinematic properties of lepton plus multijet events at CDF
429	CDF Collaboration	Fitting the top mass from CDF data
430	CDF Collaboration	Search for top in the multijet channel at CDF
431	V. Barger *et al.*	Implications of supersymmetric grand unification
432	S. Kuhlman	Precision measurement of the prompt photon cross-section in proton-antiproton collisions at $\sqrt{S} = 1.8$ TeV
433	R. Abhiraman *et al.*	On abelian bosonization of free Fermi fields with internal coordinates
434	CDF Collaboration	A search for a heavy neutral gauge boson decaying into dielectrons in $p\bar{p}$ collisions at $\sqrt{S} = 1.8$ TeV
435	K. Arisaka *et al.*	Search for CP-violating rare kaon decays at FNAL
437	SLD Collaboration	Measurement of A_b at the Z^0 resonance using a jet-charge technique
439	J. Dowell *et al.*	Analogue optical links for detector front-ends at the LHC
440	J. Abdurashitov *et al.*	Results from SAGE
441	A. Kempf	New regularisation methods from quantum group techniques
442	PEP-II Detector Coll.	A new detector optimized for the study of CP-violation in B^0 decay at PEP-II, the SLAC asymmetric B factory
443	T. Akesson *et al.*	Straw proportional tubes for a transition radiation tracker at the LHC
444	T. Akesson *et al.*	Tracking performance of a straw transition radiation tracker prototype
445	SLD Collaboration	Precise measurement of the left-right cross-section asymmetry in Z^0 boson production by e^+e^- collisions
447	M. Baek *et al.*	Exclusive heavy meson pair production at large recoil
448	H. Kastrup *et al.*	Exact solution of the quantum constraints for spherically symmetric gravity
451	H. Hayashii *et al.*	Measurement of the photon structure function F_2^γ and jet production at TRISTAN
452	M. Bilenky *et al.*	The potential of a new linear collider for the measurement of the trilinear couplings among the electroweak vector bosons
453	E. Eichten *et al.*	Flavor asymmetry in the light-quark sea of the nucleon
454	E. Eichten *et al.*	Flavor asymmetry of the nucleon sea: consequences for dilepton production
455	CLEO Collaboration	Observation of tau decays with two neutral kaons
456	V. Andrianov *et al.*	Vacuum fine tuning and masses of top-quark and Higgs boson
457	V. Andrianov *et al.*	Polycritical quark models
458	CLEO Collaboration	Search for $D^0 \rightarrow K^+ \pi^- \pi^0$
459	CLEO Collaboration	Search for lepton flavor violating decays of the tau lepton
460	CLEO Collaboration	Study of the decays $\tau^- \rightarrow K_S^0 h^- (\pi^0) \nu_\tau$
461	T. Gehrmann *et al.*	Spin-dependent parton distributions from polarized structure function data
463	W. Vogelsang	Next-to-leading order prompt photon production
470	T. Alexopoulos *et al.*	High mass dimuon production in 800 Gev/c pN interactions
471	T. Alexopoulos *et al.*	Search for the flavor changing neutral current decay $D^0 \rightarrow \mu^+ \mu^-$ in 800 GeV/c proton-silicon interactions
476	J. Bernabeu *et al.*	New results in neutrino-electron scattering
479	M. Chu *et al.*	Free field construction of chiral $SU(N)_{k=1}$ WZW models
482	C. Greub *et al.*	Branching ratio and CP-violating asymmetry in the rare decay $B \rightarrow K^* \gamma$
484	R. Akers *et al.*	Update on $K_S^0 K_S^0$ Bose-Einstein correlations
485	R. Akers *et al.*	Measurement of the production rates of charged hadrons in e^+e^- annihilation at the Z^0
486	R. Akers *et al.*	Search for a scalar top quark using the OPAL detector
487	R. Akers *et al.*	Search for low multiplicity events with anomalous event topologies using the OPAL detector at LEP
488	R. Akers *et al.*	Search for neutral Higgs bosons in the minimal supersymmetric extension of the standard model
489	R. Akers *et al.*	Search for the standard model Higgs boson

Conference Participants

The following statement was issued by the International Union of Pure and Applied Physics.

To secure IUPAP sponsorship, the organisers have provided assurances that the XXVII International Conference on High Energy Physics, Glasgow 1994, will be conducted in accordance with IUPAP principles as stated in the ICSU-Document "Universality of Science" (sixth edition, 1989) regarding the free circulation of scientists for international purposes. In particular, no *bone fide* scientist will be excluded from participation on the grounds of national origin, nationality, or political considerations unrelated to science.

A number of bursaries were made available to assist delegates to participate in the Conference. This was made possible by the generosity of:
the British Council
the European Union
the Institute of Physics
the International Science Foundation
the Royal Society
the Soros Foundation.

List of Participants

A Abada	Orsay	L A Barbaro-Galtieri	LBL Berkeley
A A Abouelsaood	Cairo	E B Barberis	UC Santa Cruz
H Abramowicz	Tel Aviv	I M Barbour	Glasgow
D E Acosta	Ohio SU	V D Barger	Univ. Wisconsin Madison
M Aguilar-Benitez	CIEMAT Madrid	B C Barish	Caltech
S Aïd	DESY	T Barker	Colorado
H Aihara	LBL Berkeley	K J Barnes	Southampton
T Åkesson	Lund	R M Barnett	LBL Berkeley
H Albrecht	DESY	F Barreiro	Univ. Autón. Madrid
J W Alcock	Bristol	O Bärring	CERN
R Aleksan	Saclay	M B Baubillier	Univ. Paris VI et VII
R A Alemany	Orsay	J Baur	Florida SU
A A Alessandrello	Milan	A Bay	Geneva
G Alexander	Tel Aviv	C M Becchi	Genova
A Ali	CERN	F Bedeschi	Pisa
T Aliev	Middle E. Tech. Univ. Ankara	G Bella	Tel Aviv
W Alles	Bologna	G Bellini	Milan
P P Allport	Liverpool	E Bellotti	Milan
G Alves	CBPF Rio de Janeiro	A-M Bencheikh	Marseille
M A Alviggi	Naples	F A Berends	Leiden
C Amsler	Zurich	J Bernabéu	Valencia
A A Anselm	St. Petersburg Nucl. Phys. Inst.	W Bernreuther	Aachen
A Antillon	Morelos	S Bertolini	INFN Trieste
F Antinori	CERN	G Bertrand-Coremans	Brussels
I Antoniadis	Ecole Polytechnique	S Bhadra	DESY
J A Appel	Fermilab	G Bhattacharyya	CERN
K Arisaka	UC Los Angeles	A Białas	Kraków
A Arkhipov	Protvino	P D Biddulph	Manchester
Arnold	CRN Strasbourg	J K Bienlein	DESY
C Arpesella	Lab. Naz. Gran Sasso	J Bijnens	Copenhagen
H Asatryan	Yerevan	P Billoir	Univ. Paris VI et VII
B Asman	Fys. Univ. Stockholm	A Bizzeti	Florence
A Astbury	TRIUMF Vancouver	R Blaes	CRN Strasbourg
J-J Aubert	Marseille	G A Blair	RHNBC London
J-E Augustin	CERN	G J Bobbink	CERN
M A Avila	Morelos	F Bobisut	Padova
Z Aydin	Ankara	P Bock	Heidelberg
S K Badyal	Jammu	J Böhm	Czech Acad. Sci.
J Bähr	DESY-Zeuthen	M Bonesini	Milan
V N Baier	Novosibirsk	R Bonino	Geneva
D Bailin	Univ. Sussex Brighton	G Bonvicini	CERN
P H Baillon	CERN	E E Boos	Moscow SU
A M Baldin	JINR Dubna	E G Boos	HEP Inst. Kazakhstan
P Ball	Garching	C N Booth	Sheffield
J Balog	KFKI Budapest	H Böttcher	DESY-Zeuthen
A Bamberger	Freiburg	D Boutigny	CERN
S Banerjee	Tata Inst. Bombay	T Bowcock	Liverpool
G B Barbagli	Florence	C K Bowdery	Lancaster
		V Branchina	Catania

A G Brandt	Fermilab	J S R Chisholm	Canterbury
G Branson	UC La Jolla	J L Chkareuli	Tbilisi
J E Brau	Oregon	J Chrin	CERN
M A Braun	Santiago de Compostela	N Christ	Columbia U
J-C Brient	Ecole Polytechnique	M Chu	Cambridge
V Brisson	Orsay	S Chung	MIT
D I Britton	McGill U	J Chýla	Prague
D J Broadhurst	Open Univ. Milton Keynes	M Ciuchini	Rome
J-M Brom	CRN Strasbourg	R Clare	MIT
N H Brook	Glasgow	F E Close	Rutherford Appleton Lab.
T E Browder	Hawaii	C Coca	Bucharest
L S Brown	Seattle	A Cocco	Naples
R M Brown	Rutherford Appleton Lab.	J Cohen	Tel Aviv
S G Brown	American Phys. Soc.	J Colas	LAPP Annecy
J M Brunet	Coll. de France Paris	P Colas	Saclay
J Brunner	CERN	N Colino	CERN
D Buckholz	Northwestern U	R Collina	Genova
E J Buckley-Geer	Fermilab	S Conetti	Virginia
H Budd	Rochester	G Conforto	Urbino
W M Bugg	Tennessee	C Conta	Pavia
A Buijs	Utrecht	A P Contogouris	Athens
A Buras	Garching	S Cooper	MPI Munich
G Buschhorn	MPI Munich	I F Corbett	PPARC Swindon
P J Bussey	Glasgow	F Cornet	Granada
J I Busto	Neuchâtel	F Corriveau	McGill U
C M Buttar	Sheffield	S R Cotanch	N. Carolina SU
I Butterworth	Imperial Coll. London	W N Cottingham	Bristol
A A Buys	CERN	G D Cowan	Siegen
K L Byrum	Argonne	G Cozzika	Saclay
M L Caccia	Milan	R L Crawford	Glasgow
M Caffo	Bologna	G Crosetti	Genova
D O Caldwell	UC Santa Barbara	J P Cumalat	Colorado
M Campbell	CERN	M Danilov	ITEP Moscow
T Camporesi	CERN	P Darriulat	CERN
G Capon	Frascati	A Datta	Jadavpur U
A Capone	Rome	D P Datta	ICTP Trieste
R K Carnegie	Ottawa	C Daum	CERN
M Carpinelli	Pisa	S D'Auria	Glasgow
R Casalbuoni	Florence	C Da Via	CERN
R J Cashmore	Oxford	A T Davies	Glasgow
A Castro	Padova	C T H Davies	Glasgow
D Cavalli Cantore	Milan	R E Davis	Kansas
V Cavasinni	Pisa	S Dawson	Brookhaven
F Cervelli	Pisa	K De	Univ. Texas Arlington
H M Chan	Rutherford Appleton Lab.	H De Boeck	Antwerp
C Chang	Maryland	W de Boer	Karlsruhe
D Chang	Hsinchu	P Debu	Saclay
J W Chapman	Univ. Michigan	D Decamp	LAPP Annecy
P C Checchia	Padova	A R M Deckmyn	Leuven
M Chemtob	Saclay	A Degré	Juvigny
H Chen	IHEP Beijing	M de Jong	NIKHEF Amsterdam
H Y Cheng	Taipei	F DeJongh	Fermilab
M B Chertok	CERN	A de Lesquen	Saclay
I-H Chiang	Brookhaven	J-P Derendinger	Neuchâtel
G Chiefari	Naples	N G Deshpande	Oregon

C Détraz	Paris
E A De Wolf	Antwerp
D Diakonov	St. Petersburg Nucl. Phys. Inst.
H D Dibon	Vienna
M J Diesburg	Fermilab
A Di Giacomo	Pisa
H B Dijkstra	CERN
S Dimopoulos	CERN
L Dirabito	Lyon
G D Dissertori	Innsbruck
M Dittmar	ETH Zurich
A Dobado	Univ. Complutense Madrid
C A Dominguez	Cape Town
A Donnachie	Manchester
J F Donoghue	Univ. Mass. Amherst
J Dorfan	SLAC
P Dornan	Imperial Coll. London
M Doser	CERN
J D Dowell	Birmingham
A T Doyle	Glasgow
J Drees	CERN
Y Ducros	Saclay
E D Dudas	Orsay
M J Duff	Texas A & M
L Duflot	Orsay
Y D Dufour	CERN
C Dullemond	Nijmegen
W M Dunwoodie	SLAC
M Düren	Erlangen
F Dydak	CERN
D Ebert	Humboldt Univ. Berlin
G Eckerlin	DESY
K Edwards	Ottawa
A V Efremov	JINR Dubna
K Eggert	CERN
K E Ehret	MPI Heidelburg
F Eisele	Heidelburg
T J C Ekelof	Uppsala
N N Ellis	CERN
R K Ellis	Fermilab
J A Ellison	UC Riverside
R P Ely	NSF Arlington
J P Engel	CRN Strasbourg
K Enqvist	Helsinki
M Erdmann	Heidelberg
J K Erdmenger	Cambridge
P F Ermolov	Moscow SU
S M Errede	Illinois
B Esposito	Frascati
L R Evans	CERN
N J Evans	Swansea
C W Fabjan	CERN
M F Fabre	PSI Villigen
H Fanchiotti	La Plata
S H Fanchiotti	CERN
E Farhi	MIT
M T Feindt	CERN
J Feltesse	Saclay
T Ferbel	Rochester
T A Ferguson	Carnegie Mellon U
M J Fero	SLAC
E Ferrari	Rome
F Feruglio	Padova
A T Filippov	JINR Dubna
C Findeisen	Zurich
A Firestone	Iowa SU
W Fischler	Univ. Texas Austin
H E Fisk	Fermilab
A J Flavell	Glasgow
J I Fleck	Glasgow
G Flügge	Aachen
Z Fodor	DESY
J R Forshaw	Rutherford Appleton Lab.
R W Forty	CERN
B Foster	Bristol
E C Fowler	US Dept. of Energy
P H Frampton	Univ. N. Carolina
A Franz	CERN
P Franzini	Rome
G M Fraser	CERN
K Freudenreich	ETH Zurich
A G Frodesen	Bergen
C D Froggatt	Glasgow
Y Fujii	KEK
W Funk	CERN
K J F Gaemers	NIKHEF Amsterdam
R J Gaitskell	Oxford
S N Ganguli	Tata Inst. Bombay
C-S Gao	Peking Univ. Beijing
H Gao	Freiburg
C Garcia Canal	La Plata
A Garfinkel	Purdue U
E G Gava	ICTP Trieste
M B Gavela	CERN
V N Gavrin	Russian Acad. Sci. Moscow
U Gensch	DESY-Zeuthen
V Georgalas	Athens
G Giacomelli	Bologna
M Giammarchi	Milan
V Gibson	Cambridge
G Gidal	LBL Berkeley
M Gilchriese	LBL Berkeley
A J Gill	Imperial Coll. London
F J Gilman	SSCL Dallas
A Giovannini	Torino
L Goerlich	Kraków
M Goldberg	Syracuse
D Gollin	Urbana
M A Gomshi Nobary	Razi Kermanshah
G Gonzalez-Sprinberg	Valencia

P Gorodetzky	CERN
A T G Goshaw	Duke U
E A Gotsman	Tel Aviv
B Govorkov	Lebedev Inst.
C Grab	Zurich
H J Grabosch	DESY-Zeuthen
J A Gracey	Liverpool
P L G Grafström	CERN
P D Grannis	SUNY Stony Brook
F Grard	Mons
H Grässler	Aachen
S W Gray	Cornell
M B Green	Cambridge
T J Greenshaw	Liverpool
P Grosse-Wiesmann	CERN
A G Grozin	Open Univ. Milton Keynes
M W Grünewald	CERN
J A Guida	SUNY Stony Brook
J F Gunion	UC Davis
H E Haber	UC Santa Cruz
N J Hadley	Maryland
J Haggerty	Brookhaven
S L Hagopian	Florida SU
V Hagopian	Florida SU
I G Halliday	Swansea
K Hamacher	Wuppertal
J D Hansen	Copenhagen
J R H Hansen	Copenhagen
N Harnew	Oxford
F Harris	Hawaii
J C Hart	Rutherford Appleton Lab.
F Hautmann	Cambridge
C M Hawkes	CERN
M Hayashi	Tokyo
T H Hayashi	Kogakkan U
H Hayashii	Nara Women's U
M He	Shandong
T Hebbeker	Humboldt Univ. Berlin
J V L Hedberg	CERN
D Hedin	N. Illinois U
R J Hemingway	Ottawa
A W Hendry	Bloomington
A B Henriques	IST Lisbon
M Herrero	Univ. Autón. Madrid
N P Hessey	Munich
R D Heuer	CERN
K Hidaka	Tokyo Gakugei U
S J Hillier	CERN
I Hinchliffe	LBL Berkeley
Z H Hioki	Tokushima
K Hirata	KEK
D Hitlin	Caltech
J Hladký	Czech Acad. Sci.
P R Hobson	Brunel Univ. Uxbridge
W Hofmann	MPI Heidelberg
H Högassen	Oslo
K Honscheid	Ohio SU
J Horejsi	Charles Univ. Prague
A Hörtnagl	Innsbruck
J Hošek	Řež
J Y Hostachy	ISN Grenoble
W S Hou	Taipei
T Huang	IHEP Beijing
H Hufnagel	Heidelburg
E Hughes	SLAC
I S Hughes	Glasgow
K Hultqvist	Stockholm
P Q Hung	Univ. Virginia
T Hurth	Zurich
G Iaselli	Bari
K I Igi	Kanagawa
G J Igo	CERN
B I Ille	Lyon
R L Imlay	Louisiana SU
M Imoto	Nihon U
D C Imrie	Brunel Univ. Uxbridge
J R Incandela	Fermilab
G Ingelman	Uppsala
Q Ingram	PSI Villigen
A M Irwin	THES London
M M Islam	Connecticut
J M Izen	Univ. Texas Dallas
B Jacak	Los Alamos
R G Jacobsen	CERN
G L B Jarlskog	Lund
F Jegerlehner	PSI Villigen
H B Jensen	Fermilab
M Jeżabek	Kraków
C H Jin	Dortmund
A I Jipa	Bucharest
K Jones	Elsevier Amsterdam
R W L Jones	CERN
T W Jones	Univ. Coll. London
W G Jones	Imperial Coll. London
J Jousset	Clermont-Ferrand
C K Jung	SUNY Stony Brook
P K Kabir	Univ. Virginia
E M Kabuß	Mainz
K Kadija	MPI Munich
V G Kadyshevsky	JINR Dubna
R K Kajikawa	Nagoya
G E Kalmus	Rutherford Appleton Lab.
P I P Kalmus	QMWC London
K Kamimura	Toho U
K Kan	Nihon U
K Kang	Brown U RI
H Kapitza	DESY
H Kaplan	Oklahoma
V G Kartvelishvili	Tbilisi
M Kasemann	DESY

H A Kastrup	Aachen	A Kovalenko	JINR Dubna
A L Kataev	CERN	W D Kretschmer	Erlangen
N K Katayama	Cornell	E Križnič	Ljubljana
K Kato	Kogakuin Univ. Tokyo	H Kroha	MPI Munich
M Kaur	Chandigarh	J Krolikowski	Warsaw
H Kawahara	SLAC	I Kronkvist	Lund
E K Kawai	Matsuyama	P Kubinec	Comenius Univ. Bratislava
B J Kayser	NSF Arlington	J H Kühn	Karlsruhe
D I Kazakov	JINR Dubna	S Kullander	Uppsala
V Kazakov	Ecole Normale Super.	A B Kurepin	INR Moscow
R K Keeler	Victoria	M Kuroda	Yokohama
V Kekelidze	JINR Dubna	V K Kurshetsov	Protvino
A Kempf	Cambridge	R K Kutschke	UC Santa Barbara
R Kenna	Liverpool	V I Kuvshinov	Minsk
D C Kennedy	Univ. Florida Gainesville	M Kuze	Tokyo
G Kernel	Ljubljana	P Kyberd	QMWC London
B Khazin	Novosibirsk	P Lacock	Liverpool
V V Khoze	SLAC	G D Lafferty	Manchester
M N Kienzle-Focacci	Geneva	A B Lahanas	Athens
C M Kiesling	MPI Munich	I Laktineh	Lyon
W Kilian	Darmstadt	H Lalla	Lab. Naz. Gran Sasso
B R Kim	Aachen	H C S Lam	McGill U
C S Kim	Seoul	B Lampe	MPI Munich
J E Kim	Seoul	M Lancaster	Oxford
J K Kim	Taejon	J B Lane	Univ. Coll. London
B T King	Liverpool	K D Lane	Boston
S F King	Southampton	A J Lankford	UC Irvine
K Kinoshita	Virginia Tech. Inst.	D C Lanske	Aachen
L E Kirsch	Brandeis U	K H Lau	Houston
E W Kittel	Nijmegen	J Lauber	CERN
N J Kjaer	CERN	M E Lautenbacher	Garching
R Klanner	DESY	J Layssac	Montpellier
C Kleinwort	Univ. Hamburg	I Lazzizzera	Univ. Trento
F R Klinkhamer	Karlsruhe	T J Lecompte	Fermilab
W Kluge	Karlsruhe	K H Lee	Seoul
J L Kneur	Montpellier	S-C Lee	Taipei
G Knies	DESY	J Lee-Franzini	Frascati
T Knöpfle	MPI Heidelberg	J Lefrançois	Orsay
I G Knowles	Glasgow	D Leith	SLAC
M J Kobel	CERN	R Leitner	Charles Univ. Prague
M Koca	Cukurova U	J Lemonne	Brussels
W Koch	DESY	E Lendvai	Budapest
B K S Koene	NIKHEF Amsterdam	E Levin	CBPF Rio de Janeiro
T Köhler	Aachen	A Levy	Tel Aviv
H Kolanoski	Dortmund	J L Li	IHEP Beijing
R Kolb	Fermilab	R Lietava	Birmingham
H J Kölsch	Springer-Verlag Heidelberg	D Liko	Austrian Acad. Sci.
S Komamiya	Tokyo	J-N Lim	McGill U
A A Kondashov	Protvino	S Limentani	Padova
S Kopp	Chicago	Y-C Lin	NCU Taiwan
M Koratzinos	CERN	J Linnemann	Michigan SU
J G Körner	Mainz	L N Lipatov	St. Petersburg Nucl. Phys. Inst.
I Korolko	ITEP Moscow	T Lippert	Wuppertal
C P Korthals Altes	Marseille	T M Liss	Univ. Illinois Urbana
P Kostka	DESY-Zeuthen	A M Litke	UC Santa Cruz

K F Liu	Kentucky
C H Llewellyn Smith	CERN
V M Lobashev	Moscow SU
F Lobkowicz	Rochester
P Loch	Orsay
M Loewe	Univ. Catolica Santiago
E C Loh	Salt Lake City
T Lohse	MPI Heidelberg
L L Lo Monaco	Catania
K R Long	Imperial Coll. London
E Longo	Rome
B G Lörstad	Lund
S T Love	Purdue U
D I Lowenstein	Brookhaven
H Lubatti	Seattle
J B Ludwig	Freiburg
B Lund-Jensen	Stockholm
M Lusignoli	Rome
D Lüst	Humboldt Univ. Berlin
J G Lynch	Glasgow
T J J Maalampi	Helsinki
J S McCarthy	Univ. Virginia
M L McCubbin	Liverpool
N A McCubbin	Rutherford Appleton Lab.
J G McEwen	Southampton
D B MacFarlane	SLAC
I R McLaren	CERN
T J McMahon	Rutherford Appleton Lab.
J M McPherson	Iowa
N M I Madansky	Johns Hopkins U
D T Madigozhin	HEP Inst. Kazakhstan
G Mandelbaum	Fürth
M L Mangano	Pisa
N Mankoč-Borštnik	Ljubljana
S L Manly	Yale U
N S Manton	Cambridge
F Marion	LAPP Annecy
C M Mariotti	Rome
F G Markopoulou	Imperial Coll. London
L A Markosky	Univ. Arizona Tucson
P Markov	Sofia
R Marshall	Manchester
V P Martemyanov	Kurchatov Inst. Moscow
A Martin	CERN
A D Martin	Durham
D J Martin	Glasgow
J F Martin	Toronto
R Maschuw	Bonn
M Masera	Torino
T Mashimo	Tokyo
A Masiero	Padova
H Masuda	SLAC
M Matsuda	Aichi
S Maxfield	Liverpool
M Mekhfi	Univ. Oran

H Melanson	Fermilab
T-C Meng	Berlin
P Méry	Marseille
W J Metzger	Nijmegen
D G Michael	Caltech
A M Migliori	Ecole Polytechnique
G Mikenberg	Weizmann Inst.
S Mikocki	Kraków
R Milburn	Tufts U
D H Miller	Purdue U
D H Miller	Northwestern U
D J Miller	Univ. Coll. London
R E Mischke	Los Alamos
G Mitselmakher	Fermilab
A Miyamoto	KEK
H Miyazawa	Kanagawa U
R Mkrtchyan	Yerevan
J Mnich	CERN
L W Mo	Virginia
K C Moffeit	CERN
R Møller	CERN
B Møllerud	Copenhagen
L Moneta	Imperial Coll. London
K Mönig	CERN
F M Montanet	Marseille
R G Moorhouse	Glasgow
M Moreno	IFUNAM Mexico
D Morgan	Rutherford Appleton Lab.
M Morii	Tokyo
K J Mork	Trondheim
C J Morningstar	Edinburgh
D R O Morrison	CERN
O Morton	The Economist London
W T Morton	Glasgow
M Moshe	Technion Haifa
G Mourier	TTE France
D J Munday	Cambridge
R Munoz-Tapia	Durham
W J Murray	Rutherford Appleton Lab.
G Myatt	Oxford
E Nagy	Marseille
T N Nakada	PSI Villigen
M Nakahata	Tokyo
Y Nakano	Kinki U
N Nandi	Oklahoma SU
A Nappi	INFN Cagliari
V S Narisimham	Tata Inst. Bombay
J Nash	Imperial Coll. London
J P Nassalski	Soltan Inst. Warsaw
P Nath	CERN
Y Ne'eman	Tel Aviv
P J Negus	Glasgow
C A Nelson	SUNY Binghamton
S Nemeček	Czech Acad. Sci. Prague
M Neubert	CERN

J S T Ng	DESY		M L Perl	SLAC
R Nickerson	Oxford		G Perrotta	CERN
J Nico	Los Alamos		J P Perroud	Lausanne
B Nicolescu	Orsay		J Pestieau	Univ. Cath. Louvain
C N Niebuhr	DESY		S P Petrera	Lecce
B S Nielsen	Copenhagen		P Petroff	Orsay
H B Nielsen	Copenhagen		T N Pham	Ecole Polytechnique
N K Nielsen	Odense		K K Phua	Singapore
J M Nieves	Southampton		I Picek	Zagreb
S N Noguchi	Nara Women's U		A Pich	Valencia
G Nolte	Oldenburg		M Pieri	Florence
V A Novikov	ITEP Moscow		A Pilaftsis	Rutherford Appleton Lab.
P J O'Donnell	Toronto		G Piredda	Rome
J R O'Fallon	US Dept. of Energy		N Piskunov	JINR Dubna
B Y Oh	Penn SU		D E Plane	CERN
S K Oh	Seoul		M Pohl	ETH Zurich
T Ohl	Darmstadt		Yu E Pokrovsky	Kurchatov Inst. Moscow
H A Olsen	Trondheim		M Poljsak	Ljubljana
J E Olsson	DESY		L G Pondrom	Univ. Wisconsin Madison
L H Orr	Rochester		Y Pons	Univ. Paris VI et VII
B Osculati-Becchi	Genova		J P Portoles	Durham
V O'Shea	Glasgow		K M Potter	CERN
N Oshimo	GTAE/CFIF Lisbon		R Prepost	Univ. Wisconsin Madison
P Osland	Bergen		C Y Prescott	SLAC
F Ould-Saada	Zurich		L E Price	Argonne
A Ouraou	Saclay		M Primavera	Lecce
H Paar	UC San Diego		N Produit	Geneva
M L Paciello	Rome		Yu Prokoshkin	IHEP Moscow
O P Palamara	Lecce		G M Prosperi	Milan
D Pallin	Clermont-Ferrand		S D Protopopescu	Brookhaven
Y-B Pan	Univ. Wisconsin Madison		M V Purohit	Princeton
G Pancheri	Frascati		J Pyrlik	Houston
V S Panin	Novosibirsk		C Quigg	Fermilab
E Papageorgiu	Orsay		G Rädel	DESY
E Papantonopoulos	Athens		C Raine	Glasgow
M A Parker	Cambridge		R Raja	Fermilab
C Parrinello	Edinburgh		R Ramachandran	Madras
G Passarino	Torino		P N Ratoff	Lancaster
F P Pastore	Pavia		S P Ratti	Pavia
J M P Paterson	SLAC		A Raychaudhuri	Calcutta
S Patricelli	Naples		M N Rebelo	Vienna
J R Patterson	Cornell		P Reeves	Glasgow
T Patzak	Humboldt Univ. Berlin		J J Reidy	Univ. Mississipi
M Pauluzzi	Perugia		B Renk	Mainz
N Pavel	Univ. Hamburg		J-P Repellin	IN2P3 Paris
N Paver	Univ. Trieste		S Reucroft	Northeastern U
K J Peach	Edinburgh		J A Revill	IOP Publishing
P G Pelfer	Florence		F Richard	Orsay
J A Penarrocha	Valencia		D G Richards	Edinburgh
B Pendleton	Edinburgh		B Richter	SLAC
O Pène	Orsay		R Rickendach	Basel
J Peoples	Fermilab		V Riech	Univ. Hamburg
M A Perez	Cinvestav		J Riedlberger	Zurich
S Peris	CERN		S Riemann	DESY-Zeuthen
D H Perkins	Oxford		T Riemann	DESY-Zeuthen

S Riess	Univ. Hamburg	B Seligman	QMWC London
M Rijssenbeek	SUNY Stony Brook	I P Selinov	Russian Acad. Sci.
J K Riles	Univ. Michigan	I Sellevaag	Bergen
J L Ritchie	Univ. Texas Austin	A V Semenov	ITEP Moscow
J P Riunaud	CERN	Y K Semertzidis	CERN
B L Roberts	Boston	P Serra	Bologna
R Rodenberg	Aachen	K K Seth	Northwestern U
J P Rodin	CERN	M H Seymour	Lund
B P Roe	Univ. Michigan	Q Shafi	Delaware
J C Romão	Lisbon	M D Shafranov	JINR Dubna
E Ros	CERN	M Shapiro	LBL Berkeley
S P Rosen	Univ. Texas Arlington	M E Shaposhnikov	CERN
J A Rosiek	Valencia	V A Sharma	CERN
G Ross	Oxford	B Shen	UC Riverside
L Rosselet	Geneva	C H Shepherd-Themistocleous	Ottawa
P Rosselet	Lausanne	P Sherwood	Univ. Coll. London
L R Rossi	Geneva	S Shevchenko	Caltech
P R Roudeau	Orsay	M A Shifman	Minneapolis
P Roy	Tata Inst. Bombay	J Shigemitsu	Ohio SU
A Rubbia	MIT	I Shipsey	Purdue U
R Rubinstein	Fermilab	D V Shirkov	JINR Dubna
W Ruckstuhl	NIKHEF Amsterdam	S M Shotkin	CERN
T Ruf	CERN	N M Shumeiko	Minsk
N A Russakovich	JINR Dubna	K Sibold	MPI Munich
J L F Sacton	Brussels	D S Sillou	CERN
K Šafařík	CERN	H Simma	DESY
G Sajot	Grenoble	E Simopoulou	Demokritos
J Salt	Valencia	V Singh	Tata Inst. Bombay
A Sandacz	Warsaw	Y S Sirois	Ecole Polytechnique
T C Sangster	Lawrence Livermore Lab.	A N Sissakian	JINR Dubna
A F Santoro	CBPF Rio de Janeiro	I O Skillicorn	Glasgow
P Santroni	Genova	T Skwarnicki	Southern Methodist
I Savin	JINR Dubna	J Sloan	Florida SU
D H Saxon	Glasgow	T Sloan	Lancaster
J M Scarr	Glasgow	H Smid	Amsterdam
D S Schaile	CERN	A V Smilga	ITEP Moscow
P G Schiavon	INFN Trieste	A Yu Smirnov	ICTP Trieste
G Schierholz	DESY	A J S Smith	Princeton
D Schildknecht	Bielefeld	J Smith	SUNY Stony Brook
W D Schlatter	CERN	K M Smith	Glasgow
P E Schlein	CERN	L Smolik	Siegen
S Schlenstedt	DESY-Zeuthen	J M Soares	TRIUMF Vancouver
M P Schmidt	Yale U	R J Sobie	Victoria
D J Schotanus	Nijmegen	P Söding	DESY-Zeuthen
H Schröder	DESY	V Soergel	Heidelberg
K R Schubert	Dresden	S Söldner-Rembold	Freiburg
J Schukraft	CERN	C M Sommerfield	Yale U
J Schultz	UC Irvine	D Son	Taegu
A S Schwarz	DESY	H S Song	Seoul
R F Schwitters	Univ. Texas Austin	A S Soni	Brookhaven
I J Scott	CERN	C Soo	
W G Scott	Rutherford Appleton Lab.	A Sopczak	CERN
J K Sedgbeer	Imperial Coll. London	R H Sosnowski	Warsaw
J Segura	Valencia	M Spiro	Saclay
A Seiden	UC Santa Cruz	Y N Srivastava	Perugia

A Stahl	Bonn	Z Trocsanyi	Debrecen
K Stanfield	Fermilab	C Troncon	Milan
R Starosta	Aachen	H D Trottier	Simon Fraser U BC
A Staude	Munich	T L Trueman	Brookhaven
M Stavrianakou	Glasgow	P Truöl	Zurich
P Steffen	DESY	J K Tuominiemi	Helsinki
H J G Steger	Freiburg	M Turała	Kraków
B R Stell	Rome	R M Turnbull	Glasgow
P W Stephenson	Swansea	M Tuts	Columbia U
W J Stirling	Durham	I Tyapkin	JINR Dubna
P Stopa	Kraków	D E Tzamarias	Liverpool
J K Storrow	Manchester	F Uchiyama	Tsukuba
P B Straub	Columbia U	T S Ullrich	Heidelberg
U D Straumann	Zurich	T Vachaspati	Cambridge
M G S Strauss	Univ. Mass. Amherst	M Valdata-Nappi	CERN
U Strohbusch	Univ. Hamburg	G Valencia	Iowa SU
J A Strong	RHBNC London	E V Valente	Rome
R Stroynowski	Southern Methodist U	A Valkarova	Prague
A Sugamoto	Ochanomizu U	E S Vallazza	CERN
H S Sugawara	KEK	J W F Valle	Valencia
S Sultansov	Ankara	M W van der Heijden	NIKHEF Amsterdam
P Suranyi	Swansea	R van Kooten	Bloomington
J P Sutton	Birmingham	C Vannini	Pisa
A Suzuki	Tohoku	R van Woudenberg	NIKHEF Amsterdam
S Suzuki	Nagoya	F Vazeille	Clermont-Ferrand
M Szczekowski	Warsaw	V Vechernin	St Petersburg
D Tadić	Zagreb	A Venturi	Pisa
S F Takach	Cambridge	J Vidal	Valencia
K Tanaka	Ohio SU	R V Vidal	Fermilab
T Tanimori	Tokyo Inst. Tech.	I P Vilja	Turku
R J Tapper	Bristol	O Villalobos Baillie	Birmingham
P Taras	Univ. Montreal	M Virchaux	Saclay
R Tarrach	Barcelona	W Vogelsang	Dortmund
L T G Tauscher	CERN	R R Volkas	Melbourne
S P K Tavernier	Brussels	M B Voloshin	Minneapolis
G N Taylor	CERN	I I Vorobiev	CERN
R Teh	Selangor	J Vrlakova	Košice
S W Teige	Bloomington	M Vysotsky	ITEP Moscow
D V Thomas	Glasgow	S Wadia	Tata Inst. Bombay
A S Thompson	Glasgow	A Wagner	DESY
J Thompson	Rutherford Appleton Lab.	S R Wagner	SLAC
G Thomson	Rutgers U	H Wahl	CERN
M A Thomson	Univ. Coll. London	K C Wali	Syracuse
E H Thorndike	Rochester	M Salter	DESY-Zeuthen
R Thorne	Rutherford Appleton Lab.	B F L Ward	Tennessee
R Thun	Univ. Michigan	S Wasserbaech	Seattle
M Tigner	Cornell	S J Watts	Brunel U
J Timmermans	NIKHEF Amsterdam	T Watts	Rutgers U
K Tittel	Heidelberg	B R Webber	Cambridge
L Tortora	Rome	D Wegener	Dortmund
F T Toyoda	Kinki U	A R Weidberg	Oxford
J T Trampetić	Zagreb	T Weiße	Dortmund
G Triantaphyllou	Toronto	R E Welsh	Williamsburg
F A Triantis	Ionnina	L J Wenham	Imperial Coll. London
R A Tripiccione	Pisa	R Werding	MPI Heidelberg

M Werlen	CERN
M Whalley	Durham
P L White	Southampton
W Wiedenmann	CERN
B H Wiik	DESY
R S Willey	Pittsburgh
H H Williams	Pennsylvania U
P K Williams	US Dept. of Energy
J G Williamson	Glasgow
S Willis	N. Illinois U
G W Wilson	UC Riverside
R J Wilson	Colorado SU
S J Wimpenny	UC Riverside
K Winter	CERN
H Wirth	Freiburg
S G Wojcicki	Stanford
G Wolf	DESY
J Wolinski	Texas A & M
R M Woloshyn	TRIUMF Vancouver
A K Wróblewski	Warsaw
G Wrochina	CERN
S L Wu	CERN
M Wunsch	Heidelberg
T Z Xu	IHEP Beijing
S Yamada	Tokyo
K Y Yamagishi	Tokuyama U
Y Yamaguchi	Tokyo
H Yamamoto	Harvard U
C Yanagisawa	SUNY Stony Brook
A J Yates	Imperial Coll. London
T P Yiou	Univ. Paris VI et VII
K Yu Yokoya	KEK
G P Yost	SSCL Dallas
C Youngman	DESY
M Yvert	LAPP Annecy
O A Zaimidoroga	Milan
A M Zaitsev	Protvino
Yu Zaitzev	ITEP Moscow
W A Zajc	Columbia U
D Zavrtanik	Ljubljana
O Zeldovich	ITEP Moscow
M Zeller	Yale U
D Zeppenfeld	Univ. Wisconson Madison
P M Zerwas	DESY
M T Zeyrek	Middle E. Tech. Univ. Ankara
C C Zhang	IHEP Beijing
G D Zhao	Peking Univ. Beijing
Z Zheng	IHEP Beijing
V Zhilich	Novosibirsk
G Zoupanos	Nat. Tech. Univ. Athens
M Zrałek	Katowice
K Zuber	Heidelberg